ARTISTES & AGENTS

Incorporating The Corporate Events Organiser

Editor: Spencer Block

Artistes & Agents is published by

Richmond House Publishing Company Ltd,
70-76 Bell Street, Marylebone, London NW1 6SP
Tel: 020 7224 9666 Fax: 020 7224 9688
Email: sales@artistesandagents.co.uk
Website: www.artistesandagents.co.uk

ISBN 9781870323567
ISSN 0143-8131

Contents

Contents

The Agents' Association (GB) Members

13 Artists Charles Myatt
01273 601355
charlie.myatt@13artists.com
www.13artists.co.uk

1st Call Entertainment Ltd Julian Franks
0117 923 9299
julian@firstcallentertainment.com
www.1stcallentertainment.co.uk

A I R Ltd Colin Pearson
01388 814632
info@airagency.comwww.airagency.com

A T C Live LLP Alex Bruford
020 7580 7773
alex@atc-live.comwww.atc-live.com

Actastic Entertainments Ltd Paula Bolton
01704 880894info@actastic.co.uk
www.actastic.co.uk

After Dinner World Ltd Jared Mark Davis
0845 475 8866
mark@afterdinnerworld.co.uk
www.afterdinnerworld.co.uk

Alan Field Associates Alan Field
020 8441 1137
alan@alanfield.com

Alan Wood Agency Alan Wood
0114 258 0338
alanwoodagency@aol.com
www.alanwoodagency.co.uk

Andi Mac Associates Ltd Andi Mac
07958 264824
andi@andimacassociates.co.uk
www.andimacassociates.co.uk

Anfield Agency Sandra Johnson
07803 576871
info@anfieldagency.co.uk
www.anfieldagency.co.uk

Angle Entertainments Ltd John Stvan
01709 869613
angleents@btconnect.com
www.angleentertainments.com

Anglia Artistes (UK) Ltd Graham J Colthorpe
01394 283159
info@angliaartistes.com
www.angliaartistes.com

Ann Zahl Personal Management Ann Zahl
020 7724 3684
annz@freenetname.co.uk

Arena Entertainment Organisation Martin Nazaruk
0113 239 2222
stars@arenaentertainments.co.uk
www.arenaentertainments.co.uk

Arlington Enterprises Ltd Annie Sweetbaum
020 7580 0702
annie@arlington-enterprises.co.uk
www.arlingtonenterprises.co.uk

Art and Industry Ltd Mick Griffiths
020 3422 1000
info@artandindustry.co.uk
www.artandindustry.co.uk

Artsworld International Management Ltd
Bob James
01406 330099

Asgard Promotions Ltd Paul Fenn
020 7387 5090
info@asgard-uk.com
www.asgard-uk.com

Ashley Wheelhouse Ents & Ricky Graham LeisureHarry Haywood Ashley Wheelhouse
01977 673500
ashley@ashleywheelhouse.co.uk

Autistic Superstars Terry Snowden MBE
0161 872 8787
info@heroesproject.org.uk
www.heroesproject.org.uk

B & Z Entertainments William Chambers
0116 277 0058
bz_ent@hotmail.com
www.bz-ents.com

B C M Entertainments Ltd Ray Martin
01795 8906132
ray@bcmentertainments.co.uk
www.bcmentertainments.co.uk

B P A Live Bob Paterson
01395 230357
bp@bpa-live.com
www.bpa-live.com

Barry Collings Entertainments Barry Collings
01582 792666
Barry-Collings@btconnect.com
www.barrycollings.co.uk

Barry Dye Entertainments Barry Dye
01473 744287
barrydye@aol.com
www.barrydye.co.uk

Beverley Artistes Agency Ltd Beverley Reeve
0191 385 4163
info@beverleyartistes.com
www.beverleyartistes.com

Big Bang Management Ltd Steven Markbride
01253 595960
agents@bigbang.co.uk
www.bigbang.co.uk

Big Star Entertainments Ltd Richard Hill
0115 972 4849
dick@bigstarentertainments.co.uk
www.bigstarentertainments.co.uk

Big Time Agency Ltd Lee Camm
01332 224366
lee@bigtime.agency
www.bigtime.agency

Blackburn International UK Ltd Jonathan Blackburn 01276 686661
Jonathan.Blackburn@Blackburninternational.com www.blackburninternational.com

Bob Potter Entertainments Ltd Bob Potter O.B.E. 01252 836464

Boogie Management Limited Simon Skinner 020 8390 8634
info@boogiemanagement.co.uk
www.boogiemanagement.co.uk

Busy Bee Promotions Linda Wooder
01942 274666
info@busybee.co.uk
www.busybee.co.uk

Caledonian Music Agency Eddie Buggy
01501 820999
eddie@caledonianmusic.co.uk
www.caledonianmusic.co.uk

Camscott Leisure Cameron Scott
01253 893999
enquiries@camscottleisure.co.uk
www.camscottleisure.co.uk

Caroline Rose Management Ltd Caroline Rose 0845 055 8990
info@caroline-rose.co.uk
www.caroline-rose.co.uk

Catface Talent Management Charlotte Austin 020 7559 3611
charlotte@catfacetalent.com
www.catfacetalent.com

Chambers Management Ltd Hannah Chambers
020 7796 3588
hannah@chambersmgt.co.uk
sophie@chambersmgt.co.uk
www.chambersmgt.com

Champions (UK) PLC Alan Warner
0845 331 3031
awarner@championsukplc.com
www.champions-speakers.com

Chance Entertainment Ltd Andrew Chance 020 7376 5995
info@chanceorganisation.co.uk
www.chanceorganisation.co.uk

Chord Theatrical & Corporate Jeanne C Gray 0151 420 3191
jeannegray@talktalk.net
www.chordtheatrical.com

Cloud9 Management Ltd Andrew Wilson
020 7637 2903
andrew@cloud9management.co.uk
www.cloud9management.co.uk

Coda Agency Ltd Phil Banfield
020 7017 2500
phil@codaagency.com
www.codaagency.com

Comedy Store Management Donald Ward
020 7930 2949
charlotte@thecomedystore.co.uk
www.thecomedystore.co.uk

Comicus Ltd Matthew Willetts
0844 800 0058
matt@comicus.co.uk
www.comicus.co.uk

Costello Entertainments Mike Costello
0161 703 8737
mike@costelloentertainments.co.uk
www.costelloentertainments.co.uk

Creation Worldwide Ltd Andy Rudge
01656 818918
enquiries@creationworldwide.com
www.creationworldwide.com

Creative Artists Agency UK Ltd Emma Banks 020 8846 3000
emma.banks@caa.com
www.caa.com

Creeme Entertainments Ltd Anthony Ivers
01204 305110
anthony@creeme.co.uk
www.creeme.co.uk

Cross Channel Connections Ltd Brian Murphy +44 7725 515611
brian@crosscc.co.uk
www.crosschannelconnections.com

D F O International Music Agency Debra Franks 01759 388900
debra@dfo.org.uk www.derekfranks.co.uk

D J Entertainments Joan Hodgson
01900 64971
djents@btinternet.com

D M F Music Ltd David Farrow
01392 437733
info@dmfmusic.co.uk
www.dmfmusic.co.uk

Danny Lowry Entertainment Ltd Danny Lowry 0161 915 5433
danny@dannylowry.co.uk

Daubney Variety & Gala Agency Margot Wilding 0800 160 1918
info@daubneyagency.co.uk
www.daubneyagency.co.uk

Dave Andrews Entertainments Andrew Prigmore 01234 708618
andrew@daveandrews.co.uk
www.daveandrews.co.uk

Dave Carr Management David Johnston
01388 817755
davecarrman@yahoo.co.uk
www.davecarrmanagement.com

Dave Chumbley David Chumbley
020 7226 4366
dave@primary.uk.com

Dave Winslett Associates David Winslett
020 8668 0531
info@davewinslett.com
www.davewinslett.com

David Anthony Promotions David M Warwick 01925 632496
dave@davewarwick.co.uk
www.davewarwick.co.uk

David Hull Promotions Ltd David Hull
02890 240 360 david@davidhullpromotions.com www.davidhullpromotions.com

Dawson Breed Music Debra Downes
020 7733 0508
debra@dawsonbreedmusic.com
www.dawsonbreedmusic.com

Derek Block Concerts Ltd Derek Block
020 7724 2101
derek@derekblock.co.uk

Dick Horsey Management Ltd Roger De Courcey 01923 710614
roger@dhmlimited.co.uk
www.dhmlimited.co.uk

Dings Entertainment Ian Davis
01234 851166
ding@dings.com
www.dings.com

Direct Music Management Ltd Keith Evans
0121 585 6796
info@directmusicman.com
www.directmusicman.com

Double Act Lydia Wolfson
020 8381 0151l
wolfson@talk21.com
www.double-act.co.uk

Dukeries Entertainments Tanya Walker
01623 635327
tanya@dukeries.com
www.dukeries.com

Edge Entertainment Consultants Ltd Alan Garner 01945 465566
info@theedge-uk.com
www.theedge-uk.com

Elaine Avon Artiste Management Cindy Thompson 01883 622317
cindy@elaineavon.com
www.elaineavon.com

Elastic Artists Agency Ltd Jonathan Slade
020 7239 9000
info@elasticartists.net

Elcock Entertainments Ltd Julie Crane
01902 672972
enquiries@elcock-entertainments.co.uk
www.elcock-entertainments.co.uk

Electric Talent Corrie McGuire
020 7202 2300
corrie@electrictalent.co.uk
www.electrictalent.co.uk

Elevation Entertainments David Reeve
01254 878096 davehazelmere@aol.com
www.rbentertainments.co.uk

Emkay Entertainments Tom Solley
01506 855 555
tom@emkayentertainments.co.uk
www.emkaylothian.co.uk

Entertainment Ideas Keith Donaghy
02871 277997
sales@entertainmentideas.com
www.entertainmentideas.com

Entertainment Services Keith Hall
0845 257 5868
admin@showbizuk.com
www.showbizuk.com

Epic Creative Productions Ltd Jack Applebaum 020 8954 3311
info@ecpl.co.uk
www.ecpl.co.uk

Ernest Swift Ernest Swift
01257 369948
ernieswift@uwclub.net

Essex Entertainment Agency Richard Smith 01206 734164
richard@essexents.com
www.essexents.com

Eva Clarance Enterprises Eva Clarance
01260 274196 artists@evaclarance.com
www.evaclarance.co.uk

Event Production Services Ltd Fran Blackburn 020 8342 9061
info@eventprods.co.uk

Extreme Music Agency Dave Clough
01924 438295
dave@extrememusicagency.com
www.extrememusicagency.com

F3 Entertainments Ltd Tracey Peacock
0141 887 9858
info@f3entertainments.co.uk
www.f3entertainments.co.uk

Factory Music Management & Agency Ltd Sharon Richardson 01303 274189
sharon@factorymusic.co.uk

Flair Theatrical Agency Michael Hainsworth 01924 404818
enquiry@flairentertainments.co.uk
www.flairentertainments.co.uk

Foremost Entertainment Agency Limited Keith A Bestwick 01773 717692
info@foremostentertainments.co.uk
www.foremostentertainments.co.uk

Forrest Entertainment Kenneth W Goodhind 01924 409043
forrestent@btinternet.com
www.forrestentertainments.co.uk

Freak Music James Feeney
0131 467 2539
jay@freakmusic.co.uk
www.freakmusic.co.uk

Fred Butlin Show Bookers UK Fred Butlin
01543 898342
fred@fredbutlin.com
www.fredbutlin.com

Function Junction Ltd Paul Johnstone
01869 320360
info@functionjunction.co.uk
www.functionjunction.co.uk

G T Artistes Tony Littley
01622 675893
tonylittley@btinternet.com
www.gtartistes.biz

Gag Reflex Comedy Management Lee Martin 0161 205 8739
info@gagreflex.co.uk
www.gagreflex.co.uk

Garston Entertainments Ltd Neil Cullen
0845 071 0988
info@garston-entertainment.co.uk
www.garston-entertainment.co.uk

Gem Productions John Landon
01792 646278

Geoff Barber Entertainment Agency
Susan Wood 01274 674928
gbentertainments@btconnect.com

Gordon Kellett Entertainments Gordon Kellett 0113 270 8562
gordon@gordonkellett.co.uk
www.gordonkellett.co.uk

Graham Platts Management Graham Platts 01226 766709
grahamplatts@btconnect.com

Guvnor Management Frank Webb
01792 862905
info@guvnormanagement.co.uk
www.guvnormanagement.co.uk

Hal Carter Organisation Abbie Carter-Burrows 01908 567388
artistes@halcarterorg.com
www.halcarterorg.com

Hawthorn Entertainment Ltd Neville Williams 01656 662835
neville@hawthorn-ents.com
www.hawthorn-ents.com

Henderson Management Mark Henderson
0116 242 9900
agents@henderson-management.co.uk
www.henderson-management.co.uk

Hireaband Ltd Del Cotton
0845 226 0494
del@hireaband.co.uk
www.hireaband.co.uk

Holten Creative Helen Millard
0844 840 8420
info@holtencreative.co.uk
www.holtencreative.co.uk

I AM EPIC Gemma Stoddard
0870 426 3742
info@iamepic.co.uk
www.iamepic.co.uk

I T B Agency Ltd Barry Dickins
020 7637 6979
mail@itb.co.uk
www.itb.co.uk

I. A. M. Luc Chaudhary
020 7709 2041
luc@internationalartistsmanagement.co.uk
www.internationalartistsmanagement.co.uk

Incredible Artists Ltd Anita Watson
07795 466661
anita@incredibleartists.co.uk
www.incredibleartists.co.uk

Industrial Strength Media Ltd Steve Galeazzi 01942 321435
steve@industrial-strength-media.co.uk
www.industrial-strength-media.co.uk

Industry Music Group Ltd Andrew Pountain 020 3080 0023
a.pountain@chooseindustry.com
www.chooseindustry.com

International Circus Stardust Entertainment Shaun Hull 07896 815182
shaun@circusstardust.com
www.circusstardust.com

International Management & Agency Ltd
Norman L Thewlis 01924 299993
lizmarston@im-agency.com
www.im-agency.com

J K Entertainment Jackie O`Shea
0121 313 0504
info@jkentertainmentagency.co.uk
www.jkentertainmentagency.co.uk

J L A Jeremy Lee
020 7907 2800
talk@jla.co.uk
www.jla.co.uk

Jacque Evans Management Ltd Jacque Evans 020 8699 1202
jacque@jacqueevans.com
www.jacqueevans.com

Jef Hanlon Promotions Ltd Jef Hanlon
01444 456717
jef.jhanlon@agents-uk.com

Jerkin Crocus Promotions Ltd Michael Brown 07802 290864
mick.jerkincrocus@googlemail.com
www.jcplmusic.com

Jillie Bushell Associates Ltd Jillie Bushell
020 7582 3048
info@jilliebushell.com
www.jilliebushell.com

Jimmy Retford's Agency Babs Retford
01424 716669

John Bedford Entertainments Ltd Ben Bedford 01489 578777
ben@johnbedford.biz
www.johnbedford.co.uk

John Howe Presentations Ltd John Howe
01903 249912
johnhowe@btconnect.com
www.johnhowepresentations.co.uk

K2 Agency Ltd John Jackson
020 7736 4948
janemiller@k2ours.com

Keith Harrison Entertainments Keith Harrison 01254 677936
info@keithharrisonents.com
www.keithharrisonents.com

Kennedy Street Enterprises Ltd Danny Betesh 0161 941 5151
kse@kennedystreet.com

Kenneth Earle Personal Management
Kenneth Earle 020 7274 1219
kennethearle@agents-uk.com
www.kennethearlepersonalmanagement.com

Kim Holmes Show Business Entertainment Agency Kim Holmes
0115 930 5088
kimholmesshowbiz@hotmail.co.uk
www.kimholmes.co.uk

Kingfisher Entertainments Vickee Lester
01274 976594 lester@kingfisherents.com
www.kingfisherents.com

Kinsella Associates Kevin Kinsella
01625 469988
kevinkinsellasnr@outlook.com

Langford Productions Heather Kerr
Zena Simmons 01934 852822
heather@langfordproductions.co.uk
www.langfordproductions.co.uk

Legends Live Limited Trevor and Brenda Chance 01772 321160
info@legendschance.com
www.legendschance.com

Lincoln Management (UK) Ltd Joanne Makepeace 01522 508355
entertainment@lmg.uk.com
www.lmg-entertainments.co.uk

Live Business Grosvenor Productions Peter Chittenden 020 7384 2050 info@livebusiness.co.uk www.livebusiness.co.uk

Live Music Management Tim Sponder 08454 900515 tim@lmmuk.comwww.lmmuk.com

Live Nation (Music) UK Limited Barry Clayman OBE 020 7009 3333 barry.clayman@livenation.co.uk www.livenation.co.uk

Louise Gubbay Associates Ltd Louise Gubbay 01959 573080 louise@louisegubbay.com www.louisegubbay.com

Lucas Management Barrie S Lucas 01253 851444 info@lucasmanagement.co.uk www.lucasmanagement.co.uk

M P C Entertainment Michael P Cohen 020 7624 1184 mpc@mpce.com www.mpce.com

Mainstream Entertainments Ltd Barry Herbert 02476 319786 barry@mainstream-mgt.co.uk www.mainstream-mgt.co.uk

Mandy Ward Artist Managment Ltd Mandy Ward 020 7434 3569 mandy@mwartistmanagement.com www.mandywardartistmanagement.com

Manhattan Music Ltd Toby Cruse 0845 459 7161 toby:decideworldwide.com www.mml-global.com

Marshall Arts Ltd Barrie Marshall 020 7586 3831 barrie@marshall-arts.co.uk www.marshall-arts.com

Metal Music Bookings & Management Ltd Denise Dale 07891 858 743 denise@metalmusicbookings.com www.metalmusicbookings.com

Michael Vine Associates Michael Vine 020 8347 2580 michael@michaelvineassociates.com www.michaelvineassociates.com

Midland Entertainment & Management Agency Ltd Chrissy Price 02476 715544 chrissy@midland-entertainment.com www.midland-entertainment.com

Midnight Mango Ltd Matthew Bartlett 01458 211117 matt@midnightmango.co.uk www.midnightmango.co.uk

Mike Constantia Artiste Management Ltd Michael Constantinou 01925 810979 showbiz@mikeconstantia.com www.mikeconstantia.com

Mike Hughes Entertainments Michael Hughes 020 7937 9199 mikehughesent@hotmail.co.uk

Mike Malley Entertainments Mike Malley 020 8346 4109 mikemall@globalnet.co.uk www.ukstars.co.uk

Miracle Artists Steve Parker 020 7935 9222 info@miracle-artists.com www.miracle-artists.com

MN2S Sharron Elkabas 020 7378 7321 info@mn2s.com http://mn2s.com/

Music Business Management Phil Barrett 01706 524425 info@mbmcorporate.co.uk www.mbmcorporate.co.uk

Neil Drover - The Agency Neil M Drover 0141 357 3377 neil@neildrover.comwww.neildrover.com

Nice People Productions Ltd Paul Wortley 01603 426009 nicepeopleproductions@hotmail.com www.nicepeopleproductions.com

Norman Phillips Organisation Limited Lianne Phillips 01827 284466 info@normanphillips.co.uk www.normanphillips.co.uk

Northern Music Ltd t/a NMC Live Haydn Britland 01274 306361 haydn@northernmusic.co.uk www.northernmusic.co.uk

Norwich Artistes Brian Russell 01603 407101 info@norwichartistes.co.uk norwichartistes@agents-uk.com www.norwichartistes.co.uk

Ocean Leisure Entertainment Agency David Hirst 01226 720732 daveoceanleisure@aol.com www.oceanleisureagency.co.uk

Omega Promotions Gary Marriott 01704 505222 info@omega-promotions.com www.omega-promotions.com

PAL Entertainments Paul Wilkins 07791 576917 info@pal-entertainments.co.uk www.pal-entertainments.co.uk

Panmedia UK Limited Lili Panagi 020 8446 9662enquiries@panmediauk.co.uk www.panmediauk.co.uk

Paramount Productions Michelle Lord 0121 293 6481 michellelord001@btinternet.com

Parker Entertainments Ltd Colin Parker 01442 248987 office@parker-entertainments.com www.parker-entertainments.com

Partnership Entertainment Events Ltd t/a PEEL Alan Cutler 01756 796176 alan@peelcruise.com www.peelcruise.com

Paul Bridson Productions Paul Bridson 01244 571708 paul@paulbridson.co.uk www.paulbridson.co.uk

Peller Artistes Ltd Barry Peller 0114 247 2365 agent@pellerartistes.com www.pellerartistes.com

Performing Acts Robert Stevenson 0115 939 0251 rs@performingacts.co.uk www.performingacts.co.uk

Performing Artistes Stanley Jackson 020 3740 3640 ask@performingartistes.co.uk www.performingartistes.co.uk

Personal Management (Chesterfield) Peter H Sadler 01246 237221 pmanagement1234@btconnect.com www.personal-management.co.uk

Personality Artistes Ltd Mal Ford 01253 899988 info@personalityartistes.com www.personalityartistes.com

Peter Johnson Entertainments Ltd Mandy O'Nion 01580 754822 enquiries@peterjohnson.co.uk www.peterjohnson.co.uk

Plum Promotions (South Wales) Ltd John Landon 01792 646278

Primary Talent International Ltd Peter Maloney 020 7400 4500 peterm@primarytalent.com www.primarytalent.com

Ralph Phillips Ralph Phillips ralphphillips@hotmail.co.uk

Red Canyon Management Sarah Howkins 07939 365578 info@redcanyon.co.uk www.redcanyon.co.uk

Red Orange Miguel Santos 01727 568716 miguel.santos@redorange.org.uk www.redorange.org.uk

Redroofs Agency June Rose
01628 822982
junemrose@me.com
www.redroofs.co.uk

Regent Music Phil Simpson
01539 528808
info@regentmusic.com
www.regentmusic.com

Riva Media Ltd Harry Gibson
07702 822384
harry.gibson@rivamedia.co.uk
www.rivamedia.co.uk

RKC Promotions Robert Craig
01302 364221
rkcpromotions@aol.co.uk
www.rkcpromotions.co.uk

ROAR Global Jonathan Shalit OBE
020 7462 9060
jonathan@roarglobal.com
www.roarglobal.com

Rumour Entertainments Wayne Williams
0845 901 1520
enquiries@rumour-entertainments.co.uk
www.rumour-entertainments.co.uk

S M C Entertainment Paul A Minney
0845 465 0300
info@smcentertainment.co.uk
www.smcentertainment.co.uk

S O L O Agency Ltd John Giddings
020 7384 6644
soloreception@solo.uk.com
www.solo.uk.com

S W A (Stageworks Agency) Yvette Curtin
01480 812626
agency@stageworksstudio.co.uk

Scott Mackenzie Associates Scott Mackenzie 01643 863330
scottmackenzie4u@hotmail.com
www.scottmackenzie.co.uk

Select Entertainments Grace Walsh
01333 353200
selectentertainments@sky.com

Simon Quarmby Presents Simon Quarmby 03333 442959
simon@sqpresents.com
www.sqpresents.com

Speakers Corner Nick Gold
020 7607 7070
info@speakerscorner.co.uk
www.speakerscorner.co.uk

Speakout Celebrities & Presenters Ltd
Kenny Donaldson 0131 440 9226
info@speakoutuk.com
www.speakoutuk.com

Speaks Volumes Joanne Martin
01352 840911
jomartinltd@gmail.com
www.speaksvolumes.co.uk

Sproule Entertainments Will Sproule
01727 854084
willsproule@yahoo.co.uk

Stagecoach Agency UK Tarquin Shaw-Young 0845 4082468
tarquin@stagecoachagency.co.uk
www.stagecoachagency.co.uk

Stagepalm Entertainments Elaine Hunt
01405 818823
info@stagepalm.net
www.stagepalm.net

Stageworks Management Agency (Blackpool) Amanda Thompson
01253 342426/7
kelly.willars@stageworkswwp.com
www.stageworkswwp.com

Stanley Dallas Stanley Dallas
0116 241 6063
standal@sky.com

Steve Allen Entertainments Steve Allen
01733 569589
steve@sallenent.co.uk
www.sallenent.co.uk

Steve Draper Entertainments Steve Draper 01254 679005
steve@stevedraperents.fsbusiness.co.uk
www.stevedraperentertainments.co.uk

Sue Rider Management Ltd Sue Rider
020 3432 7790
www.sueridermanagement.co.uk

Susan Scott Lookalikes Ltd Susan Scott
020 7281 8029
susan@lookalikes.info
www.lookalikes.info

Susi Earnshaw Management Susi Earnshaw 020 8441 5010
casting@susiearnshaw.co.u
kwww.susiearnshaw.co.uk

TAG - Talent Artistic Group Ltd Debbie King 0203 5070 169
debbie@taglimited.co.uk
www.taglimited.co.uk

Terry Parker Entertainments Terence W Parker 0113 257 2637
tpents@talktalk.net

The Agency Group Ltd Neil Warnock 020 7278 3331
neilwarnock@theagencygroup.com
www.theagencygroup.com

The Business Creative Ltd Ben O'Hara
01273 704888
info@thebusiness.uk.com
www.thebusiness.uk.com

The Crossland Agency Al Crossland 0113 234 1545
RACrossland@hotmail.com
www.crosslandagency.co.uk

The Elfin Network LLP t/a First Contact Agency Adam Elfin 020 3290 0115
info@firstcontactagency.com
www.firstcontactagency.com

The Entertainers Agency Douglas Gillespie 01738 815995
douglas@entertainersagency.com
www.entertainersagency.com

The Entertainment Department (UK) Ltd
Steve Leatham 01582 488888
steve.leatham@tedgroup.com
www.tedtalent.com

The Fraser Lawson Agency Greg Lawson
02920 755020
info@fraserlawson.co.uk
www.fraserlawson.co.uk

The John Boddy Agency John G Boddy
020 8892 0133
jba@johnboddyagency.co.uk
www.johnboddyagency.co.uk

The Mark Lewis Agency Mark Lewis
01670 360036l
ewisagency@dsl.pipex.com

The Mcleod Agency Ltd Liz Hugill
01482 565444
info@mcleodagency.co.uk
www.mcleodagency.co.uk

The Production Suite Ltd Beverley Williams 020 8407 2911
agency@productionsuite.co.uk
www.productionsuite.co.uk

Tim Raffles Entertainments Timothy Raffles 01933 741855
info@timrafflesentertainments.co.uk
www.timrafflesentertainments.co.uk

Tom & Lynne Ivers Entertainments (Creeme) Tom Ivers 01204 796003
tomandlynneivers@btinternet.com

Tony Billingham Music Tony Billingham
0121 550 1272
admin@lapalhouse.co.uk
www.europajazz.co.uk

Tony Clayman Promotions Ltd Tony Clayman 020 7368 3336
tony@tonyclayman.com
www.tonyclayman.com

Trading Faces Ltd Michelle Fowler
020 7287 0866
info@tradingfaces.co.uk
www.tradingfaces.co.uk

Trends Entertainment Ltd Antony Johns
01253 396534
info@trendsentertainment.com
www.trendsentertainment.com

Trevor George Entertainments Ltd Anne George 01803 615600
anne@trevorgeorge.co.uk
www.trevorgeorge.co.uk

Tribute Acts Management Ltd Matthew Hall 0845 094 2569
info@tributeactsmanagement.com
www.tributeactsmanagement.com

Twizzle Parties & Events Peter Robertson 020 8392 0860
party@twizzle.co.uk
www.twizzle.co.uk

Unique Gravity Mark Anstey
01246 567712
mark@uniquegravity.co.uk
www.uniquegravity.co.uk

Unit One Entertainment Steven Sayle
0161 788 8444
steve@unitoneentertainment.co.uk
www.unitoneentertainment.co.uk

Upfront Entertainment Agency Ltd Daryl Preece Tom Faulkes 01562 69433
brianupfront@aol.com
www.upfrontentertainments.com

Value Added Talent Agency (VAT) Dan Silver 020 7704 9720
dan@vathq.co.uk
www.vathq.co.uk

Veritas Entertainment Ltd Mark Halliday
07771 517784
info@veritasentertainment.co.uk
www.veritasentertainment.co.uk

Vern Allen Entertainments Agency Ltd (Inc) Hartbeat Entertainments Paul Winteridge 0870 383 1988
paul@vernallen.co.uk
www.vernallen.co.uk

Virgo Consultancy Services Ltd Hilary Brown 01446 749330
reception@virgoconsultancy.org
www.virgoconsultancy.org

W M Pro Consultancy Wassef Massaad
07984 401460
wass@wm-pro.com
www.wm-pro.com

Was/Is Management & The Act Store Ltd
Neil Tomlinson 0114 281 9475
info@theactstore.com
www.theactstore.com

We, Like Music Ltd Simon Melhuish
020 7346 3920
mel@welike-music.com
www.welike-music.com

West End Theatrical Agency John Thompson 0191 268 4617
info@westendagency.biz

Whatever Artists Management Ltd Jenny Dunster 020 8349 0920
info@wamshow.biz
www.wamshow.biz

William Morris Endeavor Entertainment (UK) Ltd Solomon Parker 020 8929 8400
sparker_asst@wmeentertainment.com
www.wmeentertainment.com

Willow Personal Management Peter Burroughs 01733 240392
office@willowmanagement.co.uk
www.willowmanagement.co.uk

World Dance Management Marina Blore
0203 291 2808
info@worlddancemanagement.com
www.worlddancemanagement.com

X-Ray Touring LLP Chloe Sideris
020 7749 3500
info@xraytouring.com
www.xraytouring.com

XS Promotions Ean Jones
01224 595969
info@xsp.co.uk
www.xsp.co.uk

Yorkshire Entertainment Duncan Wood
01482 441190
info@yorkshireentertainment.co.uk
www.yorkshireentertainment.co.uk

Zisys Events Danny Anderson
01294 238918
danny@zisysavmn.co.uk
www.zisysavmn.co.uk

Agents & Personal Managers

Please note that it is possible to search for a particular Artiste`s Agent(s) by referring to the Artistes' Index at the back of this directory in order to find out who represents them. Artistes represented by more than one agency have all of their representation listed.

1 STOP EVENT MANAGEMENT LTD

25 Juniper Birch Hill Bracknell, Berkshire
RG12 7ZG
Tel: 01344 222700 Fax: 01344 222772
Email: blanche@1stop-events.co.uk
Web Site: www.1stop-events.co.uk
Contact: Blanche Zaph

13 ARTISTS

11-14 Kensington Street, Brighton
BN1 4AJ
Tel: 01273 601 355 Fax: 01273 626 854
Email: charlie@13artists.com
Web Site: www.13artists.com
Agents: Charlie Myatt, Angus Baskerville, Jason Edwards
13 Artists is an independent booking agency established in 1999.

ARTISTES REPRESENTED:

Michael A Grammar
Paul Banks
The Duckworth Lewis Method
The Hot Rats
The Jezabels
Miles Kane
Michael Kiwanuka
The Lake Poets
The Last Shadow Puppets
Stephen Malkmus
Steve Mason
Josh Record
The Ropes
Philip Selway
The Spinto Band
The Stone Roses
The Strypes
The Wytches
22-20's
Brett Anderson
Arctic Monkeys
Athlete
Atoms For Peace
Autre Ne Veut
Balam Acab
Band of Skulls
BEAK
Big Deal
Bloc Party
Blood Orange
Blood Red Shoes
Ian Brown
Bill Callahan
Carly Connor
Casablanca
Alex Clare
Clock Opera
Gaz Coombes
Crime and the City Solution
Dante
Cathy Davey
Delphic
Deptford Goth
Dirty Projectors
Doldrums
Drenge
Ducktails
Duffy
Dutch Uncles
Errors
George Ezra
Factory Floor
Folks
Foxygen
Stephen Fretwell
Gardens And Villa
Grimes
Lisa Hannigan
Ed Harcourt
Health
Hey Sholay
High Highs
How To Dress Well
iamamiwhoami
Interpol
Japandroids
Josephine
Kai Fish
Kele Okereke
Kooks
Kula Shaker
Little Boots
LULS
Clare Maguire
Majical Cloudz
Matt and Kim
Aidan Moffat
Mystery Jets
Kate Nash
Paolo Nutini
Oh Land
Fred Page
Peace
Portishead
Pure X
Radiohead
Damien Rice
S O H N
Salem
Say Lou Lou
Sea Of Bees
Secret Machines
Alabama Shakes
Shed Seven
Simple Minds
Sivu
Skin
Skunk Anansie
Spector
Splashh
Stubborn Heart
Suede
Supergrass
Tame Impala
Temples
The Divine Comedy
The Maccabees
The Magic Numbers
Theme Park
These New Puritans
Thirteen Senses
TOPS
Ultraista
Washington
Weird Dreams
Why?
Wolf People
Youth Lagoon

19 ENTERTAINMENT

Unit 33, Ransomes Dock,
35-37 Parkgate Road, London
SW11 4NP
Tel: 020 7801 1919 Fax: 020 7801 1920
Email: reception@xixentertainment.com
Web Site: www.xixentertainment.com
Senior Personnel: Simon Fuller
Agent: Clare Cook

ARTISTES REPRESENTED:

Rubens Barrichello
David Beckham
Victoria Beckham
Emma Bunton
Jenson Button
Nicki Chapman
Kelly Clarkson
Cathy Dennis
England Football Squad
Simon Fuller
Gareth Gates
Annie Lennox
Sam Nixon
Mark Rhodes
Claudia Schiffer
Rachel Stevens
Ruben Studdard
Amy Studt
Carrie Underwood
Sarah Whatmore
Will Young

1984 PERSONAL MANAGEMENT LTD

Suite 508, Davina House,
137 Goswell Road, London EC1V 7ET
Tel: 020 7251 8046 Fax: 020 7250 3031
Email: info@1984pm.com
Web Site: www.1984pm.com
Senior Personnel: Susan McGoun, Robin Browne

ARTISTES REPRESENTED:

Jim Barclay
Clare Barrett
Becky Barry
Neil Bromley
Robin Browne

Daniel Copeland
Steev Cornwall
Bronya Deutsch
Lucy Ellinson
Jeremy Killick
Amelia Kirk
Adam Lilley
Joseph Macnab
Corinna Marlowe
Susan McGoun
David Meyer
Simon Norbury
Amanda Osborne
Jennifer Pick
Peter Rogan
Clare Scott
Tessa Slack
Nuala Walsh
Joe Woolmer
Selina Zaza

1ST CALL ENTERTAINMENT
Redland Office Centre,
157 Redland Road, Bristol BS6 6YE
Tel: 01179 239 299
Email: julian@firstcallentertainment.com
Web: www.1stcallentertainment.co.uk
Contact: Julian Franks

1ST CHOICE SPEAKERS UK LTD
52 Bois Moor Road Chesham,
Buckinghamshire HP5 1SN
Tel/Fax: 01494 773 020 Mobile: 07821 131 510
Email: enquiries@1stchoicespeakers.co.uk
Web Site: www.1stchoicespeakers.com
Managing Director: Pushpa Kasinather
Specialising in Celebrity Speakers for Cruise Ships, Conferences and Personal Appearances.
Speakers for After Dinner, Sports/Golf, Business, Keynote, Comedians and Product Launches.

ARTISTES REPRESENTED:
After Dinner Speakers:
Bob Champion MBE
Roger Cook
Ann Daniels
Clarrisa Dickson Wright
Paul Fletcher
Bob Flowerdew
Ken Hames
Dr Phil Hammond
Miles Hilton Barber
Lord Michael Howard
John Humphrys
John Regis
Dr Hilary Jones
Lord Digby Jones
Lady Lucinda Lambton
Duncan MacKenzie
David Martin
Tony Mason
Wilf McGuiness
Lawrie McMenemy
Michelle Mone
Tiff Needell
Sir Richard Needham
Andrew Neil
Flt. Lt. John Nichol
Steve Norris
Rosie Swale-Pope MBE
Dan Snow
Peter Snow
Ian St John
Helen Young

1ST CLASS ENTERTAINMENT AGENCY
2 Scotts Way, Riverhead, Sevenoaks, Kent TN13 2DG
Tel: 0870 755 6446 Fax: 08707 55 6471
Mobile: 07850 603 500
Email: email@1stclassentertainment.co.uk
Web: www.1stclassentertainment.co.uk
Senior Personnel: Brenda Pope, Alan Pope
Outdoor Event Specialists, Bands, Groups, Cabaret, Children's Entertainment, Disco, Toastmasters, Pipers, Complete Shows, Corporate Entertainment, Event Management + loads more.
Speciality acts include aerial displays, car stunts, dog displays, donkey derbies, It's A Knockout and many more.

2MA
Springvale, Tutland Road,
North Baddesley, Hants Southampton SO52 9FL
Tel: 023 8074 1354 Fax: 023 8074 1355
Mobile: 07730 662236
Email: mo.matthews@2ma.co.uk
Web Site: www.2ma.co.uk
Senior Personnel: Magee Matthews, Mo Matthews
Suppliers of gymnasts, acrobats and sports artistes. Martial arts, stunt men.

4.A.D.
17-19 Alma Road, London SW18 1AA
Tel: 020 8870 9724 Fax: 020 8874 6600
Email: 4ad@4ad.com
Web Site: www.4ad.com
Senior Personnel: Ann Wilson

ARTISTES REPRESENTED:
Breeders
Tanya Donelly
Lisa Gerrard
Kristin Hersh
His Name is Alive
Magnétophone
Vincent Miller
Mojave 3
Brendan Perry
Piano Magic

A & B ENTERTAINMENT PLUS
PO Box 515 Wigan, Lancashire WN1 9AN
Tel: 01942 323636 Fax: 01942 242600
Email: steve@abplus.co.uk
Web Site: www.abplus.co.uk
Contact: Stephen Dawber

A & J MANAGEMENT
242a The Ridgeway, Botany Bay, Enfield, Middlesex EN2 8AP
Tel: 020 8342 0542
Email: info@ajmanagement.co.uk
Web Site: www.ajmanagement.co.uk
Senior Personnel: Joanne Mclintock
Jamie Nichols
Specialising in Actors/Actresses/Children.

ARTISTES REPRESENTED:
Elizabeth Earl
Joanne McIntosh

A BETTER CLASS OF ACT
Star House, 4 Sparrow Way, Oxford OX4 7GE
Tel/Fax: 01865 776 678 Mobile: 07952 667182
Senior Personnel: Mike Harris

ARTISTES REPRESENTED:
Scott Brothers

A T W ENTERPRISES
PO Box 382 Bicester, Oxfordshire OX26 9FZ
Tel: 01869 350572
Email: andrew@atwenterprises.co.uk
Web Site: www.atwenterprises.co.uk
Contact: Andrew Wilson

A1 DISCOS LTD
PO Box 4242, Goring, Berkshire RG8 9WD
Tel: 0800 801228 (freephone) General
Tel: 01491 871 999 Fax: 01491 871 777
Email: post@a1discos.com
Web Site: www.a1discos.com
Managing Director: Tony Mitchell
Operations Manager: Sue Busch
Supplier of professional discos for corporate and private functions throughout Southern England. We are renowned for our personal service and attention to detail.

A1 INTERNATIONAL ENTERTAINMENTS
19 Holland Park, Belfast, County Antrim BT5 6HB Northern Ireland
Tel: 028 9065 1059 Fax: 028 9266 7989
Email: david.holland3@ntlworld.com
Web Site: www.a1internationalentertainments.com
Owner: David T Holland

THE A6 AGENCY
Willow Moorings Kegworth DE74 2EY
Mobile: 07889 745594
Email: michaelhobson2012@yahoo.co.uk
Web: www.snapshotproductions.co.uk
Senior Personnel: Michael Hobson
Specialising in outdoor and promotional attractions, jazz bands and silouette and origami artistes

ARTISTES REPRESENTED:
Arena Acts & Theatre:
The Amazing Magnus

Balloonologist:
Norman Tinsel
Caricaturist:
Glyn Edwards
David Moss
Jim Naylor
John Roberts
Chris Ryder
Ihor Tymchak
Costume Characters:
Bob the Builder
Postman Pat
Rugrats
Comedy Acts:
The Charleys
Chitty Chitty Bang Bang, the Original Car
Dingle Fingle
What a Palaver
Clowns & Jesters:
Bobo & Zizi
Stuart Fell
Snapshot
Sylvester the Jester
Adrian Wilson
Face Painter:
Cases Faces
Funk It
Giggles
Fire-Eaters & Sword-Swallowers:
Tim Byrom
Nick Putz
Jugglers:
Steve Pike
Shoestring Circus
Scott Tomlinson
Magicians & Illusionists:
Robin Martin
Shaun McCree
Dave Moylan
Bruce Munton
Carl Royle
Mime:
Artizani
Stuart Luis
Mimbo
Frank Terry (Charlie Chaplin)
Mix & Mingle / Street Theatre:
The Aliens
Musicians:
Brasshoppers
Caught on the Hop
Willie Cochrane
Colonel Custard (one man band)
Vic Ellis (one man band)
French Quarter (Jazz)
Harmony Hounds
Ged Hone's Dixie Boys
Peascod
Pink Champagne
Tame Valley (Brass)
Tapestry of Music
Bruce Thompson
Tyneside Pipers
Terry Wadkin
Palmist:
Sue Osborne
Angela Welsh
Plate-Spinners:
Johnnie Ley
Punch & Judy:
Tony James
Snapshot
Silhouettists:
Chris Bright
Stiltwalkers & Unicyclists:
Mr Jellyspoon
Tattooists:
Lisa Lyon
Ventriloquists:
John Piper

AAA (TRIPLE A)

Also Armstrong Academy Agency (Triple A)
The Maidstone Studios New Cut Road
Vinters Park Maidstone, Kent ME14 5NZ
Tel: 01622 691111
Email: scott@triple-a.uk.com
Web Site: www.triple-a.uk.com
Head of Artist Management: Terry Armstrong
Talent Scout: Scott Armstrong
Alternative contact: Kim Armstrong

ARTISTES REPRESENTED:

Felon
Hussey
Kate Sullivan

AARDVARK PRODUCTIONS LIMITED

PO Box 128, Edenbridge, Kent TN8 5WR
Tel: 0800 328 5766
Email: info@aardvarkproductions.biz
Web Site: www.aardvarkproductions.biz
Contacts: Dave Youngs
Specialising in providing high quality entertainment for any event. From supplying individual acts to creating and managing entire corporate events. We provide a complete service.

ABBA GOLD

1 Kingfisher Street, London E6 5JZ
Mob: 07771 801243 02036 590746
Email: info@abbagold.uk.com
Web Site: www.abbagold.uk.com / www.myspace.com/originalabbagold
Contact: Karen Graham

ARTISTES REPRESENTED:

Abba Gold

ABC DIRECT ENTERTAINMENTS

49 Ashgrove Steeple Claydon
Buckingham MK18 2LW
Tel: 01296 738020 / 01296 733292
Email: info@abcdirectentertainments.co.uk
Web: www.abcdirectentertainments.co.uk
Senior Personnel: Len Illing
Consultants for and suppliers of quality entertainments/personnel for corporate, government or private events. Cabaret acts, comedians, bands - any type, including pop, steel etc, dancers, hypnotists, act/look/sing/soundalikes, magicians, models, musicians/singers - classical/pop or mix, pipers, speciality acts.

ARTISTES REPRESENTED:

Bands, Orchestra, Concert & Event:
Alpha Connection
Baby Go Boom
Bulldog
Dance On
Daniel Smith Blues Band
Five Star Swing
James Goff Orchestra
Madison Heights
Todd Miller And The Joe Loss Orchestra & Singers
Musik Express
Quill
The Rivieras
Dance Band Of H.M. Royal Marines
Dance Band Of Scots Guards
Mike Smith Orchestra & Singers
Formal, Classical & Non-Classical Mix:
Pipes & Drums Of Royal Artillery
Marching Band Of H.M. Royal Marines
Band Of the Scots Guards
Pipes & Drums Of 1st Battalion Scots Guards
Instrumental/Vocal - Non-Classical:
The Rhythm Makers (Steel Band)
Instrumental - Classical:
The Becker Ensemble
Divertimento Trio
Stuart Findlay (Pianist)
Michael Georgiades (Classical Guitarist)
Vocal - Non-Classical:
Emer McParland
Conductors/Music Arrangers:
David Arch
Snake Davis (Saxophonist/Arranger)
John Perkins (Classical)
Specialist Artistes:
Ajay (Comedienne / Singer)
Michèle (Magician/Fire eater/Belly dancer)
Jez Rose
Tribute Acts:
Joanne Copeman (Dame Shirley Bassey)
Martin Fox (Elvis)
Carolyn Rowe (Dame Shirley Bassey)

ABCADS

49 Ashgrove, Steeple Claydon,
Buckingham MK18 2LW
Tel: 01296 738 020
Email: info@abcdirectentertainments.co.uk
Web: www.abcdirectentertainments.co.uk
Senior Personnel: Len Illing, Catherine Brandon, Elise Illing, Charlotte Illing, William Illing

ABDC ENTERTAINMENTS

La Loma, 18 Halls Farm Close,
Winchester, Hampshire SO22 6RE
Tel: 01962 885 628 Fax: 0845 3344981
YAK: 07092 035070
Email: anyact@abdc.co.uk
Web Site: www.abdc.co.uk
Senior Personnel: Henry Garfath, Barbara Hall
Entertainment agents offering a comprehensive one-stop service from single acts to complete events - everything from Acrobats to Zydeco - Specialists in Barn/Square Dances, Ceilidhs, Hoedowns & Line Dancing.

ARTISTES REPRESENTED:

007 Casinos & Race Nights
Aces High

Acoustic Jass
Alan Yn Y Fan Twmpath Band
Bob Anderson
Automated Country Disco
Banish Misfortune Barn Dance Band
Barnstorm
Best of Both Disco
Bluegrass Experience
The Blues Brother
Bon Accord Ceilidh Band
Bosun's Call (Sea Shanties)
Cork's Crew
The Crawfish Scrapers
Ronald Crisp (Toastmaster)
D'Accord
Das Orchester Bavarian Band
Garold de Wyndham & Lady Pat
Denver Spur
Easy Rider
Happy the Clown
Just Magic
Ken Morgan Band with Carla Hendriks
La Musette
A K Lee
London Chinese Acrobats
Murder Mystery Southern
Jim Naylor
Parisian Swing
The Purple Puppets
Quicksilver
Reeltime
Rhythm Method
S W Storm & Island Fury
Shanty Jack
Shepherds Hey
Sidewinders
Skinners Rats
Solent Bootskooters
Patricia Spero (Harpist)
Stars & Bars Line Dance Disco
Swags to Riches Bush Band
The Grainger String Quartet
The Light Brigade Ceilidh Band
Ticklish Allsorts
Tziganka - Russian Cossack Music & Dance Spectacular
Chris Walker Swingtet
Shep Woolley
Wraggle Taggle Ceilidh Band

ABLAZE MUSIC MANAGEMENT

Please see Ablaze PR listing for more info
Tel: 0208 533 9899
Email: nadia@ablazepr.com
Agents: Nadia Khan

ARTISTES REPRESENTED:

Fire Camp
Lethal Bizzle (V2 Music)
Moorish Delta 7

ABOVE ALL ENTERTAINMENT

(In Association With Mick Urry Orchestras)
15 Eastport Lane, Lewes, East Sussex BN7 1TL
Tel: 01273 486 622 / 472 931 (3 Lines)
Fax: 01273 486 633
Email: mjurry@msn.com
Web: www.aboveallentertainment.com
Senior Personnel: Mick Urry, Brenda Urry
Specialising in all types of indoor and outdoor entertainment.

ABS AGENCY

PO Box 932A Surbiton KT1 9QR
Tel/Fax: 020 8399 3474
Email: info@absagency.co.uk
Web Site: www.absagency.co.uk
Senior Personnel: Nigel Kerr

ARTISTES REPRESENTED:

Amsterdam
Canned Heat
Cinderella
Dead Kennedys
Dr Feelgood
Dave Edmunds
Howe Gelb
Giant Sand
Marconi Union
Misty in Roots
O.P.8.
The Pirates
Poison
Pretty Things
Max Romeo
[Spunge]
John Squire
The Stranglers
Sultans Of Ping
Sweet
Taxi To The Ocean
John Watts (Fischer-Z)
Zakk Wylde's Black Label Society
The Yardbirds

ACADEMY ARTISTES LTD

57 Rosebank Street, Leek, Staffordshire Staffordshire ST13 6AG
Tel: 01782 519 268 Fax: 01538 388 223
Managing Agency, Contacts Simon Harris & Mr Durber

ARTISTES REPRESENTED:

QEII (Queen tribute)

ACE ENTERTAINMENT LTD

Unit 19 Redwood Avenue Sheffield, South Yorkshire S21 1GH
Tel: 0800 3891715 Tel: 0114 251 3587
Email: sales@aceentertainments.co.uk
Web Site: www.aceentertainments.co.uk
Managing Director: Ms R C Steel
Specialising in bands, casinos and theme nights for the military and corporate markets.

ACE ENTERTAINMENTS (NORTH WEST)

40 Marina Village Preston Brook Runcorn, Cheshire WA7 3BQ
Tel: 01928 790700 Tel: 01928 710 900
Email: aceentertainments@talktalk.net
Web Site: www.ace-entertainments.co.uk
Contact: Yvonne Chadwick

ACE MUSIC ENTERTAINMENTS

103 Roman Road, Salisbury, Wiltshire SP2 9BZ
Tel: 01722 328 755 Fax: 01722 414 513
Email: tony@acemusic.f9.co.uk
Web Site: www.acemusic.f9.co.uk
Senior Personnel: Anthony Reynolds
Moreton

ARTISTES REPRESENTED:

Liaison

ACORN ENTERTAINMENTS

PO Box 64, Cirencester, Gloucestershire GL7 5YD
Tel: 01285 644 622 Fax: 01285 642 291
Email: drussell@acornents.co.uk
Web Site: www.acornents.co.uk
Senior Personnel: Dudley Russell

ARTISTES REPRESENTED:

Pam Ayres
Rodney Bewes "Three Men In A Boat"
Pluck

ACROBAT PRODUCTIONS LTD

2 The Grove Chipperfield Kings Langley Hertfordshire WD4 9JF
Tel: 01923 518989 Mob: 07771 907030
Email: roger@acrobatproductions.com
Web Site: www.acrobatproductions.com
Contact: Roger Robinson

ACTION TALENT INTERNATIONAL

23-31 Great Titchfield Street, London W1W 7PA
Tel: 020 7927 6233 Fax: 020 7927 6223
Email: kim@actiontalent.co.uk
Web Site: www.actiontalent.co.uk
Senior Personnel: Becky Thompson, Kim Farmer, Adam Jones, Matt Wynter.

ARTISTES REPRESENTED:

Ace & Invisible
Agent X
Angel City
The Bar Wizards
Angellica Bell
Calum Best
Big Brother Housemates
The Original Bucks Fizz
The Original Bucks Fizz
Rita Campbell
Dick & Dom
DJ Sammy
Dolly Rockers
Richie Don
Duke
Rick Edwards
Steve Edwards
Clare Evers
Fake Rapper
Filly
Gina G
Genius Cru
GLC Soundsystem
Gramma Funk
Natasha Hamilton
Chanelle Hayes
Matt Home
Hunter
Jeremy Jackson
Duncan James
Bimbo Jones
Journey South
Kavana
Kelly Llorenna
Ralf Little

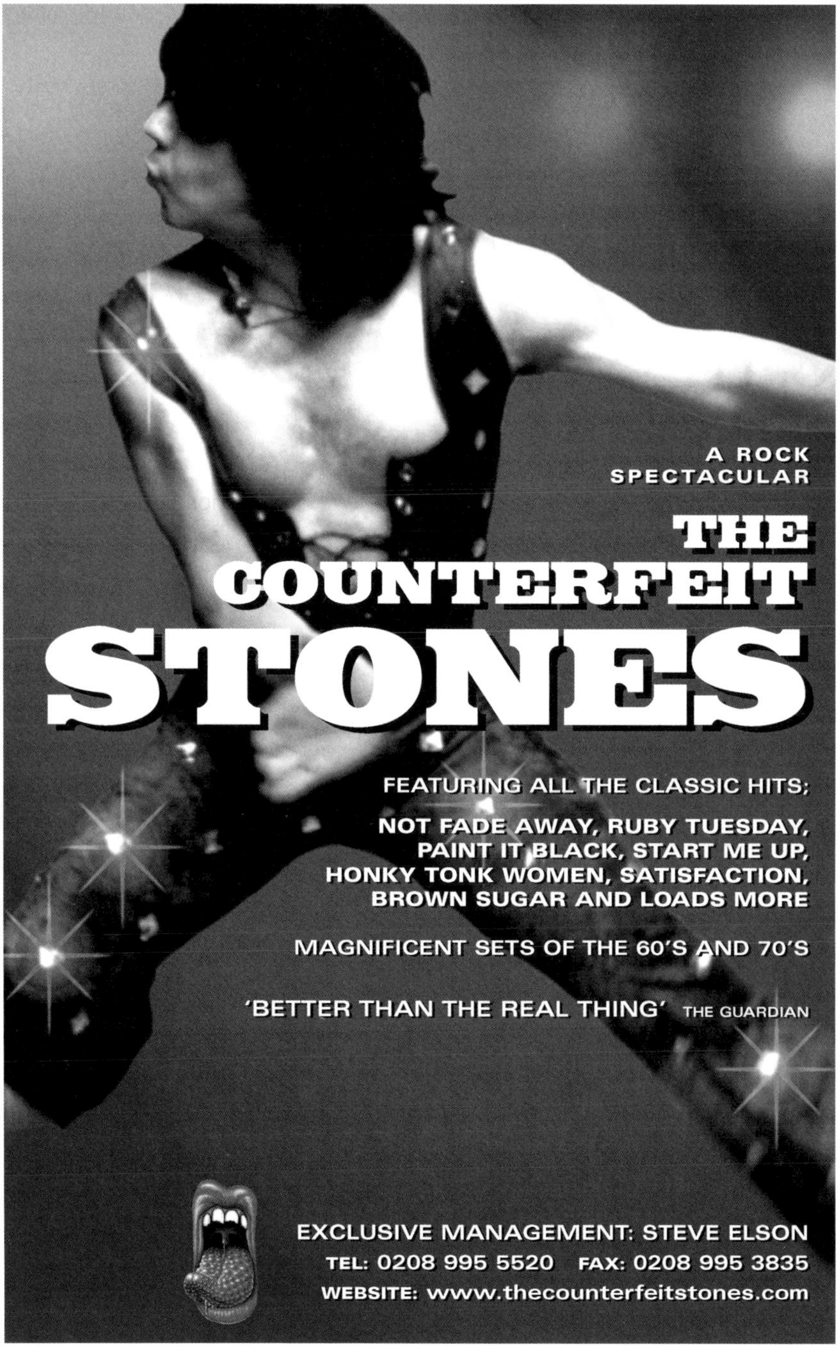

Livin' Joy
Danielle Lloyd
Lolly
Louisa Lytton
Rachel Macfarlane
Bradley Macintosh
Max and OB
Sophia May
Jesse Metcalfe
Ben Mills
Natalia
N-Trance
Out of Office
Roxanne Pallett (Jo, Emmerdale)
Red Blooded Woman
Robbie Craig
Scott Robinson
Rozalla
Lee Ryan
S CLUB Party
Sabrina
Shipwrecked Characters
Shysite
Skins
Stonefoxx
Stush
Supafly Inc
T2
The Wideboys
Ricky Tomlinson
Ultrabeat
Urban Cookie Collective
Matt Willis
Marcella Woods
Sharon Woolf

ACTORS ALLIANCE
Disney Place House,
14 Marshalsea Road, London SE1 1HL
Tel/Fax: 020 7407 6028
Email: actors@actorsalliance.co.uk
Web Site: www.actorsalliance.co.uk
Contact: Rachel Donovan
Co-operative Agency.

ARTISTES REPRESENTED:
Amanda Bellamy
Noa Bodner
Madeleine Bowyer
Orlando Brooke
Denton Chikura
Josie Daxter
Rachel Donovan
Elizabeth Hill
Kieron Jecchinis
Richard Mansfield
Shaun McKee
Rhiannon Meades
Chris Newland
Darragh O'Leary
Donald Pelmear
Robert Stuart
Christopher Terry
Jane Thorne
Joyce Veheary
Matthew Wynn

THE ACTORS FILE
Spitfire Studios, 63-71 Collier Street,
London N1 9BE
Tel: 020 7278 0087 Fax: 020 7278 0364
Email: mail@theactorsfile.co.uk
Web Site: www.theactorsfile.co.uk
Contact: Tania
Co-operative Personal Management.
The Actors File Co-operative Personal Management was created 21 years ago. As one of the first waves of co-operatives in Britain it was at the forefront of the changing face of representation. We do our utmost to stay there, remaining competitive and accessible.
Started by 5 actors (3 of whom are still with us) we now represent around 25 actors covering a wide rage of types and skills.
Many producers, directors and casting directors are keen to deal and work with Co-operatives. We are often more pro-active and committed to performers and have a wide understanding of the way the industry works.

ARTISTES REPRESENTED:
Helen Barford
Jeremy Bennett
Ruth Calkin
Simon Carroll-Jones
Caroline Garland
Gemma Harvey
Alex Humes
Amy Humphreys
Daniel Jennings
Stephen Ley
Gwilym Lloyd
Richard Marshall
T'Nia Miller
Vivienne Moore
Isabel Scott-Plummer
Rajneet Sidhu
Jill Stanford
Matt Warman

THE ACTORS GROUP
(TAG)
21-31 Oldham Street, Manchester
M1 1JG
Tel: 0161 834 4466 Fax: 0161 834 5588
Email: enquiries@theactorsgroup.co.uk
Web Site: www.theactorsgroup.co.uk
Contact: Hazel Cadman

ACTORS IRELAND
Crescent Arts Centre,
2-4 University Road, Belfast,
County Antrim BT7 1NH Northern Ireland
Tel/Fax: 028 9024 8861 Mobile: 077 66033 504
Email: actorsireland@aol.com
Web Site: www.actorsireland.com
Senior Personnel: Geraldine O'Dwyer

ACTORS NETWORK AGENCY (ANA)
See ANA Listing

ACTORUM
2nd floor 9 Bourlet Close London
W1W 7BP
Tel: 020 7636 6978 Fax: 020 7636 6975
Mob: 07916 320700
Email: info@actorum.com
Web Site: www.actorum.com
Contact: Joanna Hole
Application by letter only, enc. CV & photography and showreel if available.
Actorum is the world's original co-operative actors agency, with members since 1973 having included Julie Walters, Pete Postlethwaite, Pam Ferris, Tom Watt, Denise Black, Harry Landis, Vicky Ireland.
All applicants should be aware they will be expected to commit 4 days per month in the office when not employed as actors, as well as to attend theatre & film performances by colleagues.

ARTISTES REPRESENTED:
Ben Adams
Andrew Ashford
David Barnaby
Hannah Boyde
Alice Brickwood
Maurice Byrne
Dominic Cazenove
Lucy Conway
David Broughton Davies
Sarah Fletcher
Eva Fontaine
Oliver Gilbert
Tracy Green
Joyce Greenaway
Andrew Harrison
Joanna Hole
Emil Lager
Peter Landi
Gareth Llewelyn
Amy Loughton
Sarah Maguire
Lucia Mcanespie
Vanessa Morley
Harry Napier
Ben Nathan
Judy Norman
Monserrat Roig De Puig
Beatrice Rose
Paul Sandys
Wolf Sawyerr
Mike Sengelow
Kate Spiro
Carolyn Tomkinson
Mario Vernazza
Roger Walker
Anita Wright
Simon Yadoo

ACTS & ATTRACTIONS
The Coach House 1a Dicconson Terrace,
Wigan, Lancashire WN1 2AA
Tel: 01942 491057 Fax: 01942 821722
Email: info@actsandattractions.co.uk
Web Site: www.actsandattractions.co.uk
Contact: William Clarke

ADASTRA
The Stables,Westwood House
Main Street North Dalton, Driffield,
East Yorkshire YO25 9XA
Tel: 01377 217 662 Fax: 01377 217 754
Email: adastra@adastra-music.co.uk
Web Site: www.adastra-music.co.uk

Senior Personnel: Chris Wade

ARTISTES REPRESENTED:

Adrian Edmondson & The Bad Shepherds (Festivals and Non-UK only)
Andy Irvine & Donal Lunny's Mozaik
Aly Bain & Phil Cunningham
Black Umfolosi (Zimbabwe)
Kevin Burke
Celtic Fiddle Festival (Ireland, Scotland, Brittany)
Chumbawamba
The Coal Porters
Coope, Boyes & Simpson
Brendan Croker
Danú
Barbara Dickson
Dogan Mehmet & the Deerhunters
Uncle Earl
East of Ealing
Hassan Erraji + Oriental Craze (Morocco)
Four Men & A Dog
Frank Yamma
Lennie Gallant (Canada)
Grada
Timothy O'Grady & 'I Could Read The Sky' (Ireland)
Huun - Huur - Tu (Tuva)
Paul Johnston
Si Kahn
Kanda Bongo Man (Congo)
Kasai Masai (Africa)
Klezmer Festival Band
Koshka (Russia/Scotland)
La Bottine Souriante (Quebec)
Le Vent Du Nord
Lonnie Donegan Band feat. Peter Donegan
Lunasa
Claire Lynch Band
Majorstuen
Mambo Jambo
Juan Martin (solo & with dance group)
Rory Motion
Narasirato
New Rope String Band
Osibisa
Pete Brown & Phil Ryan with Psoulchedelia
Steve Phillips
Peter Rowan
Marta Sebestyen
Solas
Patrick Street
Swill & The Swaggerband
Martin Taylor
Sean Taylor
Te Vaka (Pacific Isles/New Zealand)
The Men They Couldn't Hang
The Unusual Suspects

ADVANCED ENTERTAINMENT

Haddef Kingsland Road Holyhead,
Isles of Anglesey LL65 2SP
Tel: 01407 762 727 Mob: 07944 736158
Email: info@2ae.co.uk
Web Site: www.2ae.co.uk
Contact: Tracey Gray

ARTISTES REPRESENTED:

Bands:
45rpm
American Pie
Bavarian Strollers Oompah Band
Big Gunz
Black Ice
The Blues Project
Cat scratch fever
Charm
Contour
Dangerous age
Disco Disciples
Face 4 Radio
Gaz and the Groovers
High time
HOZZ
Kiskadee
Lawnmower blues
Legacy
Love Train
Maria Vincent and the Millionaires
Now Live
Pheena
Platform Soul
Pop of Ages
Poptease
The Professionals
Ratz alley
Red Alert (Shakin' Stevens)
Red Hot and Blue
Respect
Rumble Band
Sahara
The Sharp Cuts
Some Like It Hot
Soul Patrol
Soul Shakers
Soul Solution
Soul Trade
Space Boogie
Storm
The beehives
The Chancers
The Funsters
The Mob
The receders
The Riverbrew
The Stylites
Trinity
Uncle Funk
Young gunz

Big Bands:
Memphis Belle Orchestra
Norman Roy Orchestra
Nick Ross
Chris Smith and the String of Pearls

Tributes:
10 Commitments
Abba Babes
Abba Forever
Abba Now
Abba solutely
Abba Vision
Al Robbins rock n roll show
Ali (Kylie, Shania Twain)
Amanda Clare Poll (Shakira)
American Legends show
Andrew Oliver (Elton John)
Andy McGowan (Robbie Williams)
Paul Barrie (Barry Manilow)
Alan Beck (Buddy Holly & Dean Martin)
Jenny Bonita (Gloria Estafen)
Born Jovi (Bon Jovi Tribute)
Caged soul (Sting)
Catherine Michelle Carter (Cher)
Claptonite (Eric Clapton Tribute)
Conmitments (Commitments Tribute)
Danny Owen (Tom Jones)
Dean Taylor (Ali G, Austin Powers)
Dean Torkington (Meatloaf)
Rob Dee (Tribute to Billy Fury Solo or with Band)
Diane Shaw (Diana Ross Tribute)
Divas Live
Double Diamond blues brothers
Earth Wind For Hire
John Finch (Marti Pellow)
For your eyes only (007 music tribute)
Phil Fryer as Frank Sinatra
Georgie Star (Sinatra, Dean Martin + more)
Tony Grant (Freddie Mercury tribute)
Heart Of Glass (Blondie tribute)
Carmel Hunter (Tina Turner)
Jamie Reeves (Robbie Williams)
John Lewis (Elton John)
Kids (Kylie & Robbie)
Kings Of Queen (Queen tribute)
Kingsativa (Bob Marley)
Robert Lamberti (George Michael)
Robert Leslie (Neil Diamond)
Marade
Marshall Star (Tina Turner, Shirley Bassey)
Micheal King (Elvis)
Mick the Knife (Sinatra)
Money For Nothing (Dire Straits Tribute)
Sally Moore as Celine Dion, Madonna
Mop Top Beatles
Nadie (Kylie)
Navi As Michael Jackson
Nerys Jones (Victoria Beckham)
Nico & the band (Elvis)
Rachel Parga (Sophie Ellis Bextor)
Sarah Jane (Kylie)
Ian Scott as Tom jones
Tracey Shields (Celine Dion)
Silly Connely
Slyde (Slade)
Spy candy
Star Spangled Express (tributes to Buddy Holly, Roy Orbison & The Everley Brothers)
Teresa McGinley (Louise Redknapp)
The Beach boys Inc
Top Secret Beatles
U2 Pop (U2)
UK Beach Boys (Beach Boys Tribute)
US4 (U2 tribute)
What's going on (Marvin Gaye tribute)

Speciality:
Alchemy magic
Ant-e-static
Arbie the Robot
Gordon Bennett
John Birchall
Dance reality
Dark side stilts
Tony Rae
Scalextrix Roadshow
Straight Jacket circus
Veena + Neena (bellytwins)

AFRICAN, CARIBBEAN ASIAN ARTISTS AGENCY

Stars Building, 10 Silverhill Close,
Nottingham NG8 6QL

Tel: 0115 951 9864 Mobile: 07966 945 663 Mobile: 07944 432649
Email: acts@african-caribbean-ents.com
Web: www.african-caribbean-ents.org.uk
Senior Personnel: Mr Kwabena, King Samuel
Supply Bands including: Hilife, Steel, Zouk, Calipso and Reggae Bands. Also, Theatre Groups, African Jazz Bands, Cultural Drummers & Dancers, Asian Bands, Drum workshops, etc. Club DJs, Models, Dancers, Steel Band. Zulu Drummers & Dancers, Bongo Players, Percussionist, Workshop teachers, Acrobat, Asian Acts.

AFTER DINNER SPEAKERS & COMEDIANS LIMITED

Chippings 2 The Old Saw Mills
Ripponden Halifax, West Yorkshire
HX6 4EN
Tel: 0845 4758866 Fax: 01422 884 494
Email: office@comedians.co.uk
Web Site: www.comedians.co.uk
Senior Personnel: Roger Davis, J. Mark Davis

ARTISTES REPRESENTED:

Comedians/After Dinner/Cabaret:
Billy Bean
Duggie Brown
Johnnie Casson
Christine Coles
Al Conway
Josh Daniels
Martin Gold
Paddy Greene
Charlie Hale
Lee Roy James
Mike Kelly
Mike Maguire
Gary Marshall
Chris McGlade
Mike McGuire
Mick Monroe
Lea Roberts
Simon Sands
Brian Sharpe
Seth Shildon
Gary Skyner
Zak Stevens
Steve Tandy
Johnny Wager
Barry York
Dusty Young
Comedy Shows/Double Acts:
Shaun Sweet

AFTER DINNER WORLD LIMITED

Chippings 2 The Old Saw Mills
Ripponden Halifax, West Yorkshire
HX6 4EN
Tel: 0845 388 1966
Email: mark@afterdinnerworld.co.uk
Web Site: www.afterdinnerworld.co.uk
Senior Personnel: Jared Davis

ARTISTES REPRESENTED:

Football:
Gordon Banks OBE
Dave Bassett
Jack Charlton OBE
Allan Clarke
Tommy Docherty
David Fairclough
Paul Fletcher
Jimmy Greaves
Norman Hunter
Alan Kennedy
Steve Kindon
Duncan MacKenzie
Wilf McGuiness
Paul Merson
Jan Molby
Lee Sharpe
Tommy Smith MBE
Ian St John
Alex Stepney
Nobby Stiles MBE
Mike Summerbee
Norman Whiteside
Frank Worthington
Ron Yeats
Cricket:
Mike Cowan
Chris Cowdrey
Graham Gooch OBE
Geoff Miller
Pat Murphy
Derek Randall
Gladstone Small
Mike Watkinson
Boxing:
John Conteh
Adam Fogerty
Barry McGuigan MBE
Nicky Piper
Ernie Shavers
John H Stracey
Rugby:
Phil Bennett OBE
John Bentley
Gareth Chilcott
Terry Crystal
Ray French
Neil Holding
Malcolm Lord
Willie John McBride
Barrie McDermott
Alex Murphy
Terry O'Connor
Jeff Probyn
David Trick
Rory Underwood MBE
David Watkins MBE
Horse Racing:
Bob Champion MBE
Snooker:
Ian McCulloch
John Parrott MBE
Dennis Taylor
John Virgo
General:
Billy Bean
Bob "The Cat" Bevan MBE
Duggie Brown
Norman Collier
Sid Dennis
Harry Gration
David Gunson
Christine Hamilton
Neil Hamilton
Eric Jones
Dr Kevin Jones
David Kendall ACIB
Norman Prince
Ian Richards
Garry Richardson
Lea Roberts
Rod Taylor
Graham (Grumbleweed) Walker
Barry Williams
Steve Womack
Dusty Young

THE AGENCY GROUP

361-373 City Road, Islington, London
EC1V 1PQ
Tel: 020 7278 3331 Fax: 020 7837 4672
Email: neilwarnock@theagencygroup.com
Web Site: www.theagencygroup.com
Director: Geoff Meall
Senior Personnel: Neil Warnock (MD), Derek Kemp, Russell Warby, Paul Buck, Paul Ryan
Agent: Ross Warnock
Specialising in: Rock & Pop

ARTISTES REPRESENTED:

18 Visions
3 Doors Down
A-HA
Arch Enemy
Atreyu
The Australian Pink Floyd Show
Barenaked Ladies
Bayside
Beduoin Soundclash
George Benson
Billy Talent
Blackfield
Blood Has Been Shed
Michael Bolton
Boys Night Out
British Sea Power
Sam Brown
Buck 65
Bullet For My Valentine
The Cat Empire
Catch 22
Alice Cooper
Cornershop
Culture Club
Death Cab For Cutie
Deep Purple
Dexy's Midnight Runners
Diamond Nights
Bruce Dickinson
Dimmu Borgir
Beth Ditto
Donovan
Doves
Dresden Dolls
The Duke Spirit
Europe
Evanescence
The Everly Brothers
Every Move A Picture
Every Time I Die
Bryan Ferry
Funeral For A Friend
Art Garfunkel
David Gilmour
Goldfinger
The Gravelly Hillbillies

Luke Haines
Hawthorne Heights
Bruce Hornsby
Idlewild
Inxs
Katherine Jenkins
Jewel
Juliette and the Licks
Katatonia
Keane
Kenny G
Lacuna Coil
Linda Lewis
Lynyrd Skynyrd
Magnum
Matisyahu
Matt Goss
MC Lars
Members Of The Public
Men, Women and Children
Metro Riots
Motorhead
My Chemical Romance
Bill Nelson
Nickelback
Nightmare Of You
Gary Numan
Dolly Parton
Pink Floyd
The Pogues
Razorlight
Reel Big Fish
Fionn Regan
Reuben
Ripchord
Roddy Frame
Roxy Music
Runrig
Rush
Sepultura
Shinedown
Sikth
The Silent League
Snowfight In The City Centre
The Spill Canvas
Lisa Stansfield
A Static Lullaby
Status Quo
Story Of The Year
Sum 41
Super Furry Animals
The Undertones
Thin Lizzy
Glenn Tilbrook
Van Halen
White Rose Movement
Brian Wilson
The Zutons

AGENCY K-BIS

Clermont Hall, Cumberland Road,
Brighton, East Sussex BN1 6SL
Tel/Fax: 01273 566739
Email: k-bis@live.co.uk
Web Site: www.kbistheatreschool.co.uk
Senior Personnel: Marcia King, Robert Andrews
We are a theatrical agency mainly dealing with young people from 18 months to 22 years. We also represent adults in theatre, TV, film, voice overs, videos, radio, modelling and presenting.

ARTISTES REPRESENTED:

Mark Adel-Hunt
Abbie Alexander
Charlotte Alexander
Megan Allen
Katie Andrews
Leela Andrews
Russell Ashdown
Stephan Ashdown
Paul Aspinall
Michael Attwood
Charlotte Backhouse
Camilla Barrett
Joanna Barrett
Katie Beves
Michael Bithell
Angie Buggy
Laura Callaghan
Allan Cardew
Rebecca Chandler
Sean Chandler
Vic Charles
Daniel Cooke
Christine Corser
Antony Daley
Cathy Dalton
David Daniels
Rachel Denyer
Zoe Edgar
Sarah El-Hini
Rebecca Elsip
Helene Enahoro
Toni Enahoro
Tamara Fernandez
Stephanie Firmin
Dominique Fullerton-Macintyre
Isabelle Gaff
Philip Gardner
Katie Goldfinch
Katy Graham
Cathy Grantham
Kelly Groves
David Hayler
Sally Hayler
Tyla Head
Lisa Heeley
Kristy Hobden
Peter Holt
Joseph Hufton
Kimberley Jones
Laura Jupp
Merve Kalgidim
Sarah Kavanagh-Jones
Zachary Kenton
Nadia Khiavi
Lucy King
Sarah Maile
Anna Maxim
Jenny Maxim
Erin McHugh
Miles Mlambo
Edward Monks
Melanie Moorcraft
Kelly Murdoch
Laura Murdoch
Ceri Osborn
Karen Overton
Jocelyn Oxlade
Jenna Rix
Justin Rock
Roxanna Rock
Saskia Roddick
Natalie Rose
Edward Ross
Michael Ross
Gerard Sassu
Louis Siadatan
Paula Siadatan
Stephanie Siadatan
Samantha Simson
Nathaniel Smith-Layne
Ben Stacey
Adam Steyning-Williams
Alison Stonier
Jasmine Talbot
Roxanne Tanner
Benjamin Thornton
Camilla Trench
Alicia Turrell
Anastasia Ushakova-Carter
Ben Warren
Sarah Wayne
Charlotte Weston

A.I.B. ENTERTAINMENTS

Newhouse Business Park,
Newhouse Road, Grangemouth,
Stirlingshire FK3 8LL Scotland
Tel: 01324 664 111
Email: enquiries@aib-discos.co.uk
Web Site: www.aib-discos.co.uk
Senior Personnel: Alan Burt
Professional mobile discos for corporate events.

AIM (ASSOCIATED INTERNATIONAL MANAGEMENT)

Inc J. Redway & Associates
4th Floor 6-7 Hatton Garden London
EC1N 8AD
Tel: 020 7831 9709 Fax: 020 7242 0810
Email: email@aimagents.com
Web Site: www.aimagents.com
Senior Personnel: Derek Webster, Stephen Gittins

ARTISTES REPRESENTED:

Actors:
Jim Alexander
Linda Armstrong
Amanda Barrie
Emma Barton
Alexandra Bastedo
Susie Benton
Jennifer Biddall
Lionel Blair
Brian Blessed
Rosalind Blessed
Simon Bowman
Alan Bradshaw
Johnny Briggs MBE
Richard Brimblecombe
June Brown
Clare Buckfield
Todd Carty
Paul Curran
Mark Curry
Sandra Dickinson
Lauren Drummond
Nicky Evans (Shane, Shamless)
Frankie Fitzgerald

Jessica Fox
Helen George
Richie Gibson
Jeremy Gittins
Melanie Harris
Adam Paul Harvey
Craig Henderson
Ginny Holder
Emma Hopkins
Michael Howe
Roy Hudd OBE
Sally Hughes
Barrie Ingham
Jean Johansson
Rhydian Jones
Martin Kemp
Terry Kiely
Brooks Livermore
Shane Lynch
Joanna Macleod
Zak Maguire
Christian Malcolm
Jane March
Stephen McGann
Garfield Morgan
Patrick Myles
Hildegard Neil
Jo-Anne Nighy
Philip Olivier
Paul Opacic
David Paisley
Polly Perkins
Robert Purdy
Alex Roe
Julia Sawalha
Nadim Sawalha
Ebe Sievwright
Susan Skipper
Shirley Stelfox
Lolly Susi
Clare Swinburne
Adam Thomas
Dylan Turner
Anthony Valentine
Ramon Vaughan-Williams
Mark Wallington
Dennis Waterman
Colin Wells
Sarah White

Actresses:

Alexandra Bastedo
Susie Benton
Rosalind Blessed
Jean Boht
June Brown
Victoria Bush
Natalie Cassidy
Juliette Caton
Nicola Cowper
Joanne Farrell
Alex Fletcher
Jessica Fox
Kathryn George
Samatha Giles
Helen Gill
Karianne Henderson
Carly Hillman
Barbara King
Katy Lamont
Jane March
Lisa Maxwell
Heather McHale
Tiffany Mulheron
Hildegard Neil
April Olrich
Elaine Paige
Polly Perkins
Wendy Richard
Coralie Rose
Nadia Sawalha
Stephanie Schonfield
Susan Skipper
Shirley Stelfox
Clare Swinburne
Emily Symons
Romla Walker
Sarah White

AIR

G9 Shepherds Building West
Rockley Road Shepherds Bush London
W14 0DA
Tel: 020 7386 1600
Email: info@airmtm.com
Web Site: www.airmtm.com
Managing Director: Marc Connor

ARTISTES REPRESENTED:

Herb Alpert
Jamie Cullum
Placido Domingo
Kyle Eastwood

A.I.R. LIMITED

AIR House, Spennymoor, County Durham
DL16 7SE
Tel: 01388 814 632 Fax: 01388 812 445
Email: info@airagency.com
Web Site: www.airagency.com
Directors: Colin Pearson, John Wray

ARTISTES REPRESENTED:

Sole Agent/Manager:

Clive Baldwin
Balletto Di Milano
Dash
Suzette Dorsey
Ian Fraser
Give My Regards To Jolson
Laura Grace
Karen Western Dancers
Moscow Ballet - La Classique
Moscow By Night

THE AKABUSI COMPANY

14 Doolittle Mill Froghall Road Ampthill
Bedfordshire MK45 2ND
Tel: 0870 444 1975 Fax: 0870 444 1976
Email: info@akabusi.com
Web Site: www.akabusi.com
Proprietor: Kriss Akabusi
Contact: Jane
Media Consultancy. Conference & Motivational Peak Performance Speaker.

ARTISTES REPRESENTED:

Kriss Akabusi MBE MA

ALAN ROBINSON MANAGEMENT (ARM)

9 School Road Twyford Hampshire
SO21 1QQ
Tel: 01962 712123
Email: arm@manhatonrecords.com
Web Site: www.manhatonrecords.com
Senior Personnel: Alan Robinson

ALBERT ALCHEMY ENTERTAINMENT

77 Queen Street Filey North Yorkshire
YO14 9HE
Tel: 01723 515252 Mob: 07799 450643
Email: albert@albertalchemy.com
Web Site: www.albertalchemy.com
Contact: Albert Alchemy
Providing various acts, from Escapologists to Stiltwalkers.

ARTISTES REPRESENTED:

A.K. & Mule
Albert Alchemy
Amazing Magnus
Babu Zukini
Andy Baloney
Kevin Burke
Captain Splash
Celtarabia
Gary Churton
Curious Eyebrow
Norris Egg
Robin Ellwood
Flaming Frank
Tom Fool the Jester
Anthony Freeman
Ginger Beard Circus
Grinnigogs
Stuart Hill
Kracatoa
Mr Lobster
Nigel the Clown
Shoestring Circus
Brett Sirrell
Sloe Gin
Blair Thompson

SEAN ALEXANDER

32 Dunnock Drive Costessey Norwich
NR8 5FF
Tel: 01603 746706 Mob: 07765 881894
Email: sean@seanalexandermagic.com
Web Site: www.seanalexandermagic.com
Contact: Sean Alexander
Please see full page ad within the Magicians & Illusionists section

ARTISTES REPRESENTED:

Sean Alexander

ALL ELECTRIC PRODUCTIONS & DAVID FOSTER MANAGEMENT

40 Lidgate Street Poundbury Dorchester
Dorset DT1 3SJ
Tel: 01305 259605
Email: info@allelectricproductions.co.uk
Web Site: www.allelectricproductions.co.uk
Contact: David Foster
Agent / Personal Manager / Producer specialising in Theatre shows, Musical shows, Concert & Jazz, Speakers & Presenters.

ARTISTES REPRESENTED:

Cabaret, Popular Music:

Rosemary Ashe
Cantabile
Charleston Chasers
Tony Jacobs
Rosemary Squires
Classical Music/Music:
English Serenata
Mediaeval Baebes
John Suchet
Caledon/Scottish Tenors
Opera:
London Festival Opera
Radio, TV & Theatre:
George Baker
The Bloomsbury Boys
Adrian Cale
Bill Giles
David Jacobs CBE DL
Eric Knowles
Sue Monroe
Mark O'Shea
Bill Oddie
Chris Packham
Henry Sandon
John Suchet
Roger Tabor
Hugo Vickers
Rock, Pop & Contemporary Music:
Fab Beatles
Theatre Shows:
The Bloomsbury Boys
Comedy:
Barry Cryer
Nicholas Parsons
Newsreaders:
Helen Fospero

ALL STAR SPEAKERS
23 Tynemouth Street, London SW6 2PS
Tel: 020 7371 7512 Fax: 01892 750 089
Email: laura@allstarspeakers.co.uk
Senior Personnel: Laura Collins
Specialising in After Dinner Speakers, Comedians, Presenters, Sports Personalities and Celebrity Voice Overs.
ARTISTES REPRESENTED:
Bob "The Cat" Bevan MBE
Ian Thomas

ALL STAR WRESTLING PROMOTIONS
81 Fountain Street, Birkenhead, Merseyside CH42 7JD
Tel: 0151 652 6507 (5 lines) Fax: 0151 652 3090 Mobile: 07944 052 367
Email: brian@bigtimewrestlinguk.com
Web Site: www.bigtimewrestlinguk.com
Contact: Brian Dixon (for all wrestling enquiries)
All Star American Wrestling Spectaculars. Top USA wrestling personalities face Best of British in 2 hour family sporting entertainment. As seen on TV. All star superstar live events.

ALLEN DAVID INTERNATIONAL ENTERTAINMENTS
114 Felpham Way Bognor Regis
West Sussex PO22 8QW
Tel/Fax: 01243 582860
Email: allen.david.felpham@gmail.com
Proprietor: Dave Allen
Children & Adult Discos - Acts - Shows - Karaoke - Celebrities - Bands - Etc.

GWENAEL ALLAN PRODUCTIONS LTD
GAAP Ltd, 15 Bunhill Row London EC1Y 8LP
Email: gwenael.allan@gmail.com
Web Site: www.slavasnowshow.com
Senior Personnel: Gwenael Allan
ARTISTES REPRESENTED:
Slava

NICK ALLEN MANAGEMENT
7 Forewoods Common, Holt, Trowbridge, Wiltshire BA14 6PJ
Tel/Fax: 01225 782 281
Email: namanage@aol.com
Web Site: www.namrecording.com
Senior Personnel: Nick Allen
ARTISTES REPRESENTED:
Ben Gunstone
Kaytu

STEVE ALLEN ENTERTAINMENTS
60 Broadway, Peterborough, Cambridgeshire PE1 1SU
Tel: 01733 569 589 Fax: 01733 561 854
Email: steve@sallenent.co.uk
Web Site: www.sallenent.co.uk
Senior Personnel: Steve Allen FEAA
ARTISTES REPRESENTED:
Steve Allen Discotheques
Steve Allen
Boogie Wonderband
Caribbean Harmonics
Caribbean Sounds
The Catch
Crazy Ape
Die Apfelschnapps
Electric Avenue
Fat Chantz
Fever Band
Fully Funktional
George
The Havana Boys
George Henry
Aaron James
Dave Johnson Duo/Trio
Kind Of Jazz
Gary Knights
Luisa Calvo
Madison Square
The Mesh Band
The Motivators
New Simba Steelband
Jed Pascoe
Phil Perry (Magician)
Mad Mark Peters
Platinum Gold
Red Hot and Blue
Red Hot Chillies
Ian Richards
Sahara
Savoir Faire
John Shearer
So Excited!
Stak It Up
Kyle Summers
Superstition
Tennessee Tooters
Uno Hoo
V.I.P.
Vision
Zanzara

VERN ALLEN ENTERTAINMENTS LIMITED
Suite 19, Basepoint Business Centre, Yeoford Way,
Marsh Barton Trading Estate, Exeter EX2 8LB
Tel: 0870 383 1988 (2 lines) Fax: 01392 426 421
Email: paul@vernallen.co.uk
Web Site: www.vernallen.co.uk
Senior Personnel: Paul Winteridge
ARTISTES REPRESENTED:
Fab Beatles
Jakson Lee
Mel Mellers
Puppets From Off The Planet
Rob Reynolds (Elvis Reborn)
Sean Scannell
Tank Sherman
Soap Productions
Ruby Washington

MICHAEL ALLISON ASSOCIATES
Unit 3, The Apollo Building,
18 All Saints Road, London W11 1HH
Tel: 020 7221 2275
Email: mike@acm-records.co.uk
Web Site: www.acm-records.co.uk
Senior Personnel: Michael Allison

THE ALLOTT AGENCY
8 Melbourne Avenue,
Dronfield Woodhouse, Dronfield,
Derbyshire S18 8YW
Tel: 01246 412 365 Fax: 01246 290 338
Mobile: 07733 481005
Email: allottagency@btinternet.com
Web Site: www.allottagency.com
Contact: C M Allott
Various Corporate and Speciality Acts.

ALMOST ELTON
258 St. Johns Road, Yeovil, Somerset BA21 5QP
Tel: 07970 216 459
Email: matthewrock@almostelton.co.uk
Web Site: www.almosteltonjohn.com
Contact: Matthew Rock
A brilliant Elton John Tribute.
ARTISTES REPRESENTED:
Almost Elton

ALPHA PERSONAL MANAGEMENT
Suite B4, 3 Bradbury Street, London

N16 8JN
Tel: 020 7241 0077 Fax: 020 7241 2410
Email: alpha@alphaactors.com
Web Site: www.alphaactors.com
Alpha is an Actors' Co-operative.

ARTISTES REPRESENTED:

Actors:
Alex Bartram
Jonathan Evans
Tim Goodman
Alastair Hudson
Elliot James
Angus Kennedy
Les Kenny-Green
Tom Lynam
Andrew Mitchell
Johnny Myers
Drew Rhys-Williams
Actresses:
Sue Broberg
Frances Millar
Emma Humphries
Samantha Lawson
Rebecca Livermore
Sonia Marceau
Annika Murfitt
Julie Neubert
Elizabeth Ross
Anah Ruddin
Rebecca Semark
Rachel Sternberg

JONATHAN ALTARAS ASSOCIATES (JAA)

11 Garrick Street, London WC2E 9AR
Tel: 020 7836 8722 Fax: 020 7836 6066
Email: info@jaalondon.com
Senior Personnel: Wim Hance, Helen Filmer

ARTISTES REPRESENTED:

Actors:
Mark Aiken
George Anton
Peter Barkworth
Patrick Barlow
Liam Barr
Stephen Beresford
Benedick Blythe
Pierce Brosnan
Ameet Chana
Keith Clifford
Martin Cole
Sir Tom Courtenay
Graham Crowden
Tim Curry
Fuman Dar
Adam Rhys Dee
Reece Dinsdale
Alan Drake
Adrian Edmondson
Lawrence Elman
Tim Evans
Brett Fancy
James Faulkner
Wayne Foskett
Christopher Fox
David Gillespie
Seán Gleeson
Andy Henderson
Richard How
Danny John-Jules
Toby Jones
Kieran Lagan
Mark Lambert
Scott Maslen
Joe McGann
James McKenna
Paul J Medford
Jimi Mistry
Simon O'Brien
Steven O'Donnell
Richard O'Brien
Peter McNeil O'Conor
Carl Pizzie
Q (Kwabena Manso)
John Ramm
Jeff Rawle
Adam Rayner
Martin Rea
Peter Sallis
John Shrapnel
Barry Stanton
Tim Steed
Christopher Stewart
Derek Thompson
William Travis
Zubin Varla
Gary Waldhorn
Peter Wingfield
Mo Zainal
Actresses:
Linda Bassett
Brid Brennan
Sarah Cattle
Rachel Davies
Lesley Dunlop (Brenda, Emmerdale)
Christine Entwisle
Elena Ferrari
Nina Fog
Jenny Foulds
Kemi-Anne Groarke
Claire Hackett
Diana Hardcastle
Elizabeth Hurran
Ganiat Kasumu
Gillian Kearney
Sara Kestelman
Ruth Lass
Sophie Linfield
Hilary Maclean
Julia Mallam
Sian Martin
Emily Morgan
Flora Newbigin
Cecilia Noble
Anna Nygh
Patricia Quinn
Liz Robertson
Zita Sattar
Georgina Sowerby
Lucy Speed
Maggie Steed
Jessica Stevenson
Jessica Turner
Julie T Wallace
Hannah Watkins
Beth Winslet
Choreographers:
Paul J Medford
Quinny Sacks
Anthony Van Laast MBE
Presenters:
John Eccleston

ALW ASSOCIATES

1 Grafton Chambers, Grafton Place, London NW1 1LN
Tel: 020 7388 7018 Fax: 020 7813 1398
Email: alweurope@onetel.com
Web Site: www.alwassociates.co.uk
Senior Personnel: Carol Paul

AMAZING EVENTS

Sunshine Cottage Burton Row Brent Knoll
Somerset TA9 4BY
Tel: 0844 332 0129 Mob: 07791 157719
Email: robbie@amazingevents.co.uk
Web Site: www.amazingevents.co.uk
Managing Director: Robbie Burns
Corporate Hospitality and Event Management specialists working nation-wide, providing; themed parties, murder mysteries, team building, conference support and entertainers including celebrities and after-dinner speakers.

AMBER PERSONAL MANAGEMENT LTD

Planetree House 21-31 Oldham Street
Manchester M1 1JG
Tel: 0161 228 0236
Email: info@amberltd.co.uk
Web Site: www.amberltd.co.uk
Agents: Sally Sheridan, Jasmine Parris, Estelle Jenkins
London Address Tel: 020 7734 7887

ARTISTES REPRESENTED:

Actors:
Daniel Abelson
Michael Atkinson
Nicky Bell
Dennis Blanch
Tony Burgess
John Burke
Nicholas Camm
Tom Cantrell
John Catterall
Stephen Chapman
Craig Cheetham
Christopher Chilton
Carl Cieka
David Crellin
Vincent Davies
John Elkington
Dominic Gately
Nathan Gladwell
Andrew Grose
James Hedley
Kaleem Janjua
Gordon Kane
Glenn Lamont
Dan Li
Peter Lorenzelli
Paul Mallon
Joseph Marsden
John Middleton
Josh Moran
Wayne Perrey
Phil Rowson
Peter Rylands
Liam Shannon
Harmage Singh-Kalirai
Darren Southworth
Graeme Hawley (John, Coronation Street)

Adam Sunderland
Simeon Truby
Nick Underwood
John Webb
Actresses:
Lindsay Allen
Ann Aris
Katrina Beckford
Charis Berry
Janine Birkett
Basienka Blake
Elianne Byrne
Gilian Cally
Sophie Cartman
Beverley Denim
Maria Gough
Amanda Healer
Jane Hogarth
Cherylee Houston
Poppy Jhakra
Rae Kelly
Vanessa Jayne Kerfoot
Anna Kirke
Lorna Laidlaw
Anne Orwin
Barbara Peirson
Laura Richmond
Julie Riley
Maggie Tagney
Ella Vale
Genevieve Walsh
Gillian Waugh
Ruth Westley
Charlotte West-Oram
Gloria Williams
Anna Woodside
Sophie Wright

ANA (ACTORS NETWORK AGENCY)

55 Lambeth Walk, London SE11 6DX
Tel: 020 7735 0999 Fax: 020 7735 8177
Email: info@ana-actors.co.uk
Web Site: www.ana-actors.co.uk
Senior Personnel: Sandie Bakker

ARTISTES REPRESENTED:

Actors:
Peter Barnes
Tim Bruce
Joseph Carole
Tim Charrington
Alastair Cording
John Dibble
Jonathan Emmett
Henry Everett
John Forbes-Robertson
Gareth Jon-Clarke
Richard Klvac
Benedict Martin
Inam Mirza
Steve Nealon
Simon Poland
Peter Quince
Joseph Raisbrook
Sidney Sloane
Simon Thorp
Rory James Wilson
Actresses:
Amanda Van Annan
Daisy Ashford
Amie Bakker
Cristina Barreiro
Yasmin Bodalbhai
Meg Faragher
Clare Fraenkel
Lorraine Hilton
Holli Hoffman
Katherine Judkins
Justine Koos
Caroline Mann
Marianne March
Fiz Marcus
Katie McLean
Willow Nash
Philippa Robson
Jean Trend
Daryl Webster
Clarissa Young
Lana Young

NITA ANDERSON ENTERTAINMENT

165 Wolverhampton Road, Sedgley, Dudley, West Midlands DY3 1QR
Tel: 01902 882 211 / 681 224 Fax: 01902 883 356
Email: nitaandersonagency@hotmail.com
Web Site: www.nitaanderson.co.uk
Senior Personnel: Nita Anderson
Suppliers of Corporate Entertainment and After Dinner Speakers.

ANDERSSENS

4 Rothmans Avenue, Chelmsford, Essex CM2 9UE
Tel/Fax: 01245 476 187 Mob: 07850 589029
Email: john@cockneypride.co.uk
Web: www.pearlykingandqueen.co.uk
Senior Personnel: John Anderssen

ARTISTES REPRESENTED:

Cockney Pride
Peter Pathfinders 1940s Show
Pearly King & Queen

ANDREW MANSON PERSONAL MANAGEMENT

288 Munster Road, London SW6 6BQ
Tel: 020 7386 9158 Fax: 020 7381 8874
Email: post@andrewmanson.com
Web Site: www.talentroom.com / www.andrewmanson.com
Specialising in Actors.

AMANDA ANDREWS AGENCY

30 Caverswall Road, Blythe Bridge, Stoke-on-Trent Staffordshire ST11 9BG
Tel/Fax: 01782 393 889
Email: amanda.andrews.agency@tesco.net
Web: www.amandaandrewsagency.org.uk
Senior Personnel: Amanda Andrews, David Montrose

DAVE ANDREWS ENTERTAINMENTS

24 College Drive, Riseley, Bedford MK44 1DZ
Tel: 01234 708 618 Fax: 01234 709 091
Email: andrew@daveandrews.co.uk
Web Site: www.daveandrews.co.uk
Senior Personnel: Andrew Prigmore

ARTISTES REPRESENTED:

Dave Andrews
Mark Andrews
Finneus Fogg
Front Cover
Indulgence Chocolate Fountain
Midnight Express
Oblivious Brothers
Phil Perry (Magician)
Prestige Fun Casino
Steve Richardson

ANFIELD AGENCY

PO Box 48 Carnforth Lancashire LA6 2UZ
Tel: 07803 576871
Email: info@anfieldagency.co.uk
Web Site: www.anfieldagency.co.uk
Contact: Kevin O'Brien
Specialises in After Dinner Speakers, Cabaret, Corporate and Summer Seasons

SUSAN ANGEL & KEVIN FRANCIS LTD

1st Floor, 12 D'Arblay Street, London W1F 8DU
Tel: 020 7439 3086 Fax: 020 7437 1712
Email: agents@angelandfrancis.co.uk
Web Site: www.angelandfrancis.co.uk
Senior Personnel: Susan Angel, Kevin Francis, Abby Meckin

ARTISTES REPRESENTED:

Actors:
Micah Balfour
Peter Bankole
Matthew Barry
Tom Bennett
Nigel Betts
Philip Bird
John Branwell
William Buckhurst
Timothy Carlton
Daniel Casey
George Chakiris
Jack Chissick
Neil Conrich
Nigel Cooke
Edward Davenport
Andrew Falvey
Sean Francis
Jeremy Gittins
James Greene
Stewart Harwood
David Henry
Neil Henry
Gary Hollywood
Grant Ibbs
William Ilkley
Barry Jackson
Oscar James
Alton Letto
Tony Marshall
Charles Millham
Karl F. Morgan
Samuel Oatley
Arnold Oceng

James Phelps
Oliver Phelps
Tony Pitts
Paul Raffield
David Roper
David Ross
Mark Springer
Chris Sunley
Giles Taylor
Tom Tyler
Gary Whitaker
Actresses:
Jodi Albert
Eva Alexander
Ellie Beaven
Ruby Bentall
Nicola Bland
Meredith Braun
Janet Brown
Lorna Brown
Polly Brunt
Teresa Churcher
Francesca Cundy
Jackie Downey
Janine Duvitski
Nicole Faraday
Elaine Glover
Vicky Hall
Lisa Hammond
Katherine Heath
Zoe Henry
Joanna Horton
Laura Howard
Leila Joyce
Tonya Kerins
Maggie Lloyd-Williams
Alexandra Milman
Tara Moran
Francine Morgan
Eleanor Moriarty
Jackie Morrison
Sereena Parris
Sheila Reid
Veronica Roberts
Linda Spurrier
Sophie Stuckey
Emily Wachter
Fiona Wade
Simone Waller
Victoria Wicks
Casting Directors (Rep by Kevin Francis):
Sarah Hughes
Marilyn Johnson
Andy Pryor
Suzanne M Smith

ANGLE ENTERTAINMENTS LTD
Orchard Place Doncaster Road, Conisbrough, Doncaster, South Yorkshire DN12 3AT
Tel: 01709 869 613 Fax: 01709 869 614
Email: angleents@btconnect.com
Web Site: www.angleentertainments.com
Senior Personnel: Shaun Angell, John Stvan
ARTISTES REPRESENTED:
Dean Andrews
Carol Angel
Aztec
Back 2 the Future
Boyzaloud
David Broadley
Barry Cheese
Damion
DaVinci
Ian Davis
Lydia Evans
The Followers
Elliot Frisby
The Funtime Frankies (Party)
Robin Good
Vicky Jackson
Adam James
Jeepster
Melody Lane
Memphis King
Ian Moor
Davey Nicholls
Kathy Parr
Shane Perkins
Siobhan Phillips
PJ Devlin
Alistair Raines
Richie Taylor Tribute Show
Analicia Ryan
Rachel Saunders
Skillmasters
Soulcity
The Inflations
Valissa Wallace
Tony Walsh
Chrissie White
Jo Wright
Production/Tribute Shows:
Back 2 The 80's
Back to the Future
DaVinci
PJ Devlin (Elton John)
Harris & Day and the Rat Pack Orchestra
Steve Littlewood (Freddie Mercury)
Tracey Shields (Celine Dion)
the Sweet Soul Music Band

ANGLIA ARTISTES (UK) LTD
PO Box 78, Trimley St Mary, Felixstowe, Suffolk IP11 0QW
Tel: 01394 283 159 Fax: 01394 276 162
Email: info@angliaartistes.com
Web Site: www.angliaartistes.com
Senior Personnel: Graham Colthorpe
ARTISTES REPRESENTED:
Sean Carpenter
Dain Cordean (Comedian)
Jokers Wild
John Love
Kate McCabe
David Oakley
Pea Green Philharmonic Pullover Set (Duo)
The Pretentious Juggler
Rock Magic (Chris North and Belinda - Illusion)
Trickstars
Saxon Tylney
Steve Zebs (Comedy/Magic)

ANGRY CAT PROMOTIONS
19a Leicester Road, Blaby, Leicester LE8 4GR
Tel: 0844 879 4783
Email: info@angrycat.co.uk
Web Site: www.angrycat.co.uk
Contact: Angela Thomas

ANIMAL AMBASSADORS
Old Forest, Hampstead Norreys Road, Hermitage, Berkshire RG18 9SA
Tel/Fax: 01635 200 900 Mob: 07831 558 594
Email: info@animalambassadors.co.uk
Web: www.animalambassadors.co.uk
Senior Personnel: Kay Weston
Specialises in the Supply and Training of Animals for Film and Television.

ANIMAL WORLD
Member of Animal Welfare Filming Federation
28 Greaves Road, High Wycombe, Buckinghamshire HP13 7JU
Mobile: 07956 564715
Email: animalswork1@yahoo.co.uk
Web Site: www.animalswork.co.uk
Senior Personnel: Trevor Smith (07956 564715)
Established in1973. Specialising in providing animals to the entertainment industry, while ensuring their safety and protection from harm. Famous Animals who star on TV and in Films.
ARTISTES REPRESENTED:
Clients & Credits:
Esso Tiger
Desmond (Nat West Peacock)
Joa the Cockatoo (Sky TV)
The Secret Garden
Timotei
Jeeves & Wooster
Kit-E-Kat
Pedigree Chum
Andrex
Whistle Down the Wind

ANITA ALRAUN REPRESENTATION
1A Queensway Blackpool Lancashire FY4 2DG
Tel: 01253 343784
Sole Agent: Anita Alraun
Represents various Actors/Actresses. Further details on the majority of artists listed can be found on the Spotlight Directory website. Otherwise, CVs and photos are available on request from our office. Submissions for representation from actors acceptable only by post with headshot, CV & SAE for reply. No emails.
ARTISTES REPRESENTED:
Actors:
Cymon Allen
Vass Anderson
Aidan Barry
James Benson
Jamie Chapman
Anthony Colby
Cyril Cross
Mark Delaney
Matt Devereaux
Harry Dickman
Lynden Edwards

Warwick Evans
Glen Fox
Andrew Francis
Sydney Golder
Ashley Gunstock
Colin Haigh
Christopher Harvey
Marcus Heath
Glenn Holderness
Alan Igbon
Kenneth Jay
Karl Jenkinson
Christopher Key
Tim Kirby
George Leggat
Eddy Lemar
Clive Marlowe
Simon Masterton-Smith
Richard McDougall
Tony McMahon
Gino Melvazzi
Fidel Nanton
Martin Nelson
Arthur Nightingale
Vernon Nurse
David Oakley
Tim Parker
Michael Parkhouse
Luis Pinilla
Michael Poole
Christopher Reeks
Ben Roddy
Malcolm Rogers
Sandeep Sharma
Stuart Sherwin
Julian Tait
Trond Teigen
Ash Varrez
Petar Vidovic
Matt Wing
Nigel Wong
Gary Yershon
Actresses:
Takako Akashi
Natasha Alderslade
Li-Leng Au
Jennifer Brook
Deborah Bundy
Pam Cole
Virginia Courtney
Hal Dyer
Sharon Eckman
Jane Garda
Georgia Gibson
Barbara Grant
Sandra Hale
katie Hebb
Sara Highlands
Joan Hooley
Patricia Kane
Christine Kimberley
June Lewis
Sharon Lloyd
Joy Merriman
Gaynor Miles
Pauline Miller
Audrey Palmer
Elaine Redwood
Helen Rochelle
Mary Rose
Helen Watson

DAVID ANTHONY PROMOTIONS

PO Box 286, Warrington, Cheshire
WA2 8GA
Tel: 01925 632 496 Fax: 01925 416 589
Mob: 07836 752 195
Email: dave@davewarwick.co.uk
Web Site: www.davewarwick.co.uk
Senior Personnel: Dave Warwick
Specialising in Presenters.

ARTISTES REPRESENTED:

Male:
John Amabile
James Balme
Bryan Burnett
Gordon Burns
Mark Evans
Bob Greaves
"Handy" Andy Kane
Tony Livesey
Rob McLoughlin
Fred Talbot
Carl Zealand
Female:
Sophie Clayton-Spinola
Wendy Dignan
Nichola Dixon
Julie Hanson
Laura McCree
Suzie McGuire
Amanda Protheroe-Thomas
Ranvir Singh
Carol Smillie
Claire Smith
Christine Walkden
Denise Waterman
Kate Weston

APM ASSOCIATES

Elstree Studios Shenley Road
Borehamwood Hertfordshire WD6 1JG
Tel: 020 8953 7377 Fax: 020 8953 7385
Email: apm@apmassociates.net
Web Site: www.apmassociates.net
Senior Personnel: Linda French

ARTISTES REPRESENTED:

Ladies:
Lisa Baird
Sarah Baxter
Amanda Bell
Susanna Bishop
Emmy Bradbury
Lisa Burrows
Cressida Carre
Marzia Dal Fabbro
Anita Elilas
Hannah Epps
Fiona Evans
Sarah Gale
Effie Gilmore
Sarah Harvey
Elise Hockley
Sara Jayne
Kate Kelland
Faye Michel
Lisa Quibell
Katie Roddy
Isobel Suttie
Helen Tennison
Gentlemen:
Saikat Ahamed
Kevin Baker
Kit Benjamin
Barry Callan
Richard Campbell
Peter Connell
Gavin Dando
Patrick Duggan
Richard Fletcher
Andy Francesco
Martin Garfield
Kieron Harris
Matt Harvey
John Harwood
Geoff Hennesey
Roy Jackson
Lincoln James
Peter Jamieson
Tom Jude
Joshua Levine
Francis Maston
Ciaron McConville
Ian Needle
Guy Picot
Daniel Robinson
Carl Ryan
Michael Shallard
Benjamin Stanley
Mathew Stirling
Ronnie Toms
Alex Verrey
Ben Woolrych
Miltos Yerolemou

APPLE COUNTY

4 Phillips Close, Bridgwater, Somerset
TA6 7AR
Tel: 01278 452 500 Fax: 01278 434 019
Mob: 07717 327071
Email: sara@applecounty.co.uk
Web Site: www.applecounty.co.uk
Partners: Sara & Don Evans
Entertainment agents and consultants, celebrating 18 years of supplying quality entertainment to all kinds of venues and events. Live music, discos, cabaret, children's shows, fund-raising, star names, theme events, outdoor attractions, corporate functions etc.

ARTISTES REPRESENTED:

Bands/Music:
Bavarian Schunklers (Bavarian)
Canny Band
Cardinal Jazz
Pete Cooke (Irish)
Firebirds (R'n'R)
Frampton Footwarmers (traditional jazz)
Phil Hobbis (vocal)
KJ Band (functions)
Man from Funkle (70s)
New Hurricane Force (steel band)
Popmania (vocal & dance)
Les Spear (country & western)
Spectrum (soul & party band)
The Secret's Out (party band)
Trion Con Brio (classical)
Vanity Fare (ex-chart band)
Westend to Broadway
Tribute Acts:
Bewley Brothers (Blues Brothers)
Michelle Cordelli (Dusty Springfield)
Gidea Park (Beach Boys tribute)
Jeni Jaye (Britney Spears, Geri Haliwell)

Laurence Bolwell (David Bowie)
Los Palmas Six (Madness tribute)
Mangles Wurzels
Taste of Honey (Bee Gees Tribute)
Comedians:
Micky John Bull
Teddi Munro
Maxwell Plum
Tank Sherman
Slim Pickins
Martin Smith
Steve Stevens
Johnny Tait
Tony Was
Bob Webb

BILLY F ARATA

1 Vernon Avenue, Birmingham B20 1DB
Tel: 0121 554 4078 Fax: 0121 523 4603
Email: info@billy-smarts-circus.co.uk
Senior Personnel: Billy Arata
Specialises in Circuses & Variety Acts

ARENA ENTERTAINMENT CONSULTANTS

Regents Court, 39 Harrogate Road,
Leeds, West Yorkshire LS7 3PD
Tel: 0113 239 2222 Fax: 0113 239 2016
Email: stars@arenaentertainments.co.uk
Web: www.arenaentertainments.co.uk
Senior Personnel: Barry McManus, Martin Nazaruk,
Hayley Germain.
MAIL FORWARDED BY ARRANGEMENT ONLY.

ARTISTES REPRESENTED:

Abbalike
Amazing Bavarian Stompers
Tony Ball MBE
The Bandit Beatles
Sir John Banham
Big Mick
Dickie Bird MBE
Sir Chris Bonington CBE
Frank Carson KSG
Casa Latina
The Cavern Beatles
Champagne
Jack Charlton OBE
City Lights
Mike Cowan
Mike Craig
Graham Davies
Sharron Davies MBE
Elizabeth Dawn MBE
Tommy Docherty
Dragonsfire
Vince Earl
Frances Edmonds
Sir Ranulph Fiennes Bt OBE
Michael Fish MBE DSc
Frisco Crabbe (Soul & Funk)
Bill Giles
Robbie Glen
Graham Gooch OBE
Duncan Goodhew MBE
Harry Gration
The Grimethorpe Colliery Band
David Gunson
Stuart Hall
Gavin Hastings OBE
Robert Heller
Simon Hoggart
John Hotowka
John Humphrys
Graham P Jolley
Dr Kevin Jones
Ian Keable
David Kendall ACIB
Miles Kington
Kylie Tribute - Faye
Let Me Entertain You (Robbie Williams)
Mazeppa Cossacks
Ian McCaskill
Shaun McCree
David Mellor
Mirage
Adrian Moorhouse MBE
Ken Morley
Andrew Neil
Richard Noble OBE
The Real Abba Gold
Nigel Rees
Dermot Reeve OBE
Barry Roberts
Jeffrey Robinson
Michael Rodd
John Simonett
Soul Rights
Sounds of The Blues Brothers
Ian St John
John Stalker
Stax of Soul
Mike Sterling
T-Rextasy
William Tarmey
Prof Laurie Taylor
Dave Lee Travis
Terry Venables
John Virgo
Captain Brian Walpole OBE
John Welch
Barry Williams
Bob Wilson
Dave Wolfe
Prof Heinz Wolff

ARENA PERSONAL MANAGEMENT

Room e11, Panther House,
38 Mount Pleasant, London WC1X 0AN
Tel/Fax: 020 7278 1661
Email: arenapmltd@aol.com
Web Site: www.arenapmltd.co.uk
Co-operative Agency.

ARTISTES REPRESENTED:

David Hedges
Hayward Elliot
Olivia Fox
Katherine Hart
Michelle Lobo
Steve O'Halloran
Sonya Raymono
Ben Richardson
Susan Scott
Laura Sheppard
Andy Snowball
Richard Talbot
Emma Thornett
Susannah van den Berg
Sara Wakefield

ARG MANAGEMENT

4 Great Portland Street London
W1W 8PA
Tel: 020 7436 6400 Fax: 020 7436 6700
Email: argall@argtalent.com
Web Site: www.argtalent.com
MD: Sue Latimer
Agents: Claire Comiskey, Lizzie Barroll Brown

ARTISTES REPRESENTED:

Robert Bathurst
Helen Baxendale
Lynda Bellingham
Jim Carter
Julie Christie
Sacha Baron Cohen
Michelle Collins
Brian Conley
Susannah Constantine
Heather Craney
Liam Cunningham
Niamh Cusack
Sinead Cusack
Alan Davies
Phil Davis
Amanda Donohoe
John Duigan
Chris Evans
Alice Eve
Lisa Faulkner
Jerome Flynn
Laurence Fox
Mariella Frostrup
Romola Garai
Henry Goodman
John Hannah
Naomie Harris
Ian Hart
Bernard Hill
Amanda Holden
Jonathan Hyde
Ross Kemp
Rebecca Lacey
Adrian Lester
Janet McTeer
Jason Merrels
Oliver Milburn
Jaime Murray
Parminder Nagra
James Nesbitt
Hermione Norris
Clive Owen
Sarah Parish
Billie Piper
Pauline Quirke
Daniel Radcliffe
Dame Diana Rigg
Colin Salmon
Julian Sands
Julia Sawalha
Andrew Scott
Tony Slattery
Victoria Smurfit
Geraldine Somerville
Hugo Speer
Imelda Staunton
Ken Stott
Neil Stuke
Jeremy Swift
Jamie Theakston
Marsha Thomason
John Thomson

Honeysuckle Weeks
Perdita Weeks
Rollo Weeks
Trinny Woodall

ARGYLE ASSOCIATES
43 Clappers Lane Fulking West Sussex BN5 9ND
Mob: 07905 293319
Email: argyle.associates@me.com
Senior Personnel: Richard Linford, Geraldine Pryor
Personal Management

ARTISTES REPRESENTED:

Male:
Greg Barnett
Roy Boutcher
Stefan Butler
Ray Charman
John Coates
Ravi Kothakota
Thor Kristinsson
Trevor Littledale
Greg Phillips
Sean Rees
Matt Robinson
Mark Siddall
Henry Stephen
Dominic Wilson
Jeremy Worsnip
Mark Wynter
Female:
Winnie Clarke
Carol Cleveland
Jenny Husey
Cameron Leigh
Vicki Randall
Virginia Stride
Sian Todd
Giselle Wright

ARLINGTON ENTERPRISES LTD
1-3 Charlotte Street London W1T 1RD
Tel: 020 7580 0702 Fax: 020 7580 4994
Email: annie@arlington-enterprises.co.uk
Web Site: www.arlingtonenterprises.co.uk
Agent: Hilary Murray

ARTISTES REPRESENTED:

Marc Abraham
Trish Adudu
Lucy Alexander
Sofie Allsop
Kirstie Allsopp
Jamie Anley
Claire Barratt
Nikki Bedi
Jonny Benarr
Jason Bradbury
Dr David Bull
Vicki Butler-Henderson
Nicki Chapman
Michael Collie
Jaspar Corbett
Alison Cork
Rachel De Thame
Charlie Dimmock
Bill Dod
Tessa Dunlop
Nick Ferrari
Cassie Fitzpatrick
Ben Fogle
Pippa Greenwood
Deborah Hall
Ellie Harrison
Jules Hudson
Anjana Khatwa
Katie Knapman
Dominic Littlewood
James May
Alex McKie
Phil Nutley
Tris Payne
Jonathan Phang
Melissa Porter
Jenny Powell
Sophie Raworth
Anna Ryder Richardson
David Riley
Dr Alice Roberts
Hannah Scott Joynt
Philip Serrell
Joanna Sinnott
Jonny Smith
Phil Spencer
Joe Swift
Alan Titchmarsh
Beverley Turner
Bernadette Tynan
Tommy Walsh
Charlene White
James Wong
Kim Woodburn

ARM (ALAN ROBINSON MANAGEMENT)
PO Box 491 Winchester SO23 3BW
Tel: 01962 712123
Email: arm@manhatonrecords.com
Web Site: www.manhatonrecords.com
See Alan Robinson Management Listing

ARMSTRONG ACADEMY AGENCY (TRIPLE A)
Also AAA (Triple A)
GMC Studio, Hollingbourne, Maidstone, Kent ME17 1UQ
Tel: 01622 205839
Email: terry@triple-a.uk.com
Web Site: www.triple-a.uk.com
Managing Director: Terry Armstrong

ARTISTES REPRESENTED:

Felon
Hussey
Danny Litchfield
Kate Sullivan

ALAN ARNISON ENTERTAINMENT CONSULTANTS
PO Box 194, Stockport, Cheshire SK2 5FL
Tel/Fax: 0161 419 9930
Email: mike@alanarnisonentertainments.com
Web: www.alanarnisonentertainments.com
Senior Personnel: Alan Arnison
A wide range of music styles. Speakers including Sports Personalities; Cabaret; Speciality Acts; Disc Jockeys & Discos; Jazz; Comedians.

ART AND INDUSTRY LTD
35 Britannia Row London N1 8QH
Tel: 020 7226 7481
Email: info@artandindustry.co.uk
Web Site: www.artandindustry.co.uk
Mick Griffiths

ARTFIELD
5 Grosvenor Square, London W1K 4AF
Tel: 020 7499 9941
Email: bb@bbcooper.com
Web Site: www.bbcooper.com
Senior Personnel: BB Cooper, Brian Cooper

ARTIMIS MODELS & PROMOTIONS LTD
4 Bills Lane Shirley Solihull, West Midlands B90 2NP
Tel: 0845 468 0333
Email: info@artimis.co.uk
Web Site: www.artimis.co.uk
Contact: Helen Priestley

ARTISTE & MUSICAL (UK)
95 Napier Street, Nelson, Lancashire BB9 0RF
Tel: 01282 611 944 Mobile: 07903749188
Email: wallyday@hotmail.co.uk
Contact: Mr Wally Day
All types of entertainment.

ARTISTES REPRESENTED:

Andy Keith
Carl Schofield

ARTISTE INTERNATIONAL ENTERTAINMENTS AGENCY
50 Lon- y -Mes, Abergele, Clwyd LL22 7JG
Tel: 01745 832561 Fax: 01745 832542
Email: jo@artistesint.fsnet.co.uk
Web Site: www.artistesinternational.co.uk
Contact: Jo Stephens

ARTISTS 2 EVENTS
Unit 11, Betws Business Park Ammanford, Dyfed SA18 2ET
Tel: 01269 597 118 Fax: 01269 596056
Email: mike@artists2events.co.uk
Web Site: www.artists2events.co.uk
Music Management.

ARTS MANAGEMENT (REDROOFS ASSOCIATES)
Agency Office, Littlewick Green Maidenhead, Berkshire SL6 3QY
Tel: 01628 822982 Fax: 01628 882461
Email: junemrose@me.com
Web Site: www.redroofs.co.uk
Contact: June Rose
Specialising in: Children and younger actors

ARTS, SOUND AND LEISURE LTD

Stephenson House, Stephenson Avenue, Gonerby Hill Foot, Grantham, Lincolnshire NG31 8QB
Tel: 01476 516 300 Fax: 01476 516 301
Email: info@asandl.co.uk
Web Site: www.asandl.co.uk
Senior Personnel: John R Smith, Jane A Smith
Specialising in military and corporate entertainment. Providing a range of entertainment, including bands, after dinner speakers, clowns and magicians, theme evening and funfairs. Fun Casino Specialists.

ARTSWORLD INTERNATIONAL MANAGEMENT LTD

Hankins House, 1 Farrow Road, Whaplode Drove, Nr Spalding, Lincolnshire PE12 0TS
Tel: 01406 330 099 Fax: 01406 331 147
Email: bobjamesfeaa@hotmail.co.uk
Senior Personnel: Bob James, Wendy James

ARTISTES REPRESENTED:

Nigel Ellery
Michael Fish MBE DSc
Jilly Jackson
Andy Mann
Sounds of the Supremes
Jeff Stevenson

ASGARD

125 Parkway, London NW1 7PS
Tel: 020 7387 5090 Fax: 020 7387 8740
Email: info@asgard-uk.com
Web Site: www.asgard-uk.com
Senior Personnel: Paul Fenn, Paul Charles, Mick Griffiths

ARTISTES REPRESENTED:

Alison Krauss & Union Station
Joan Baez
Eric Bibb
The Blasters
Deacon Blue
The Blue Nile
BR549
Paul Brady
Effi Briest
Pieta Brown
Jackson Browne
Paul Buchanan
Paul Burch
Camille
Laura Cantrell
Hayes Carll
Kasey Chambers
Mary Chapin Carpenter
Guy Clark
Slaid Cleaves
Julian Cope
Rodney Crowell
Catie Curtis
Ray Davies
Iris DeMent
Justin Townes Earle
Steve Earle & The Dukes
Lisa Ekdahl
Jace Everett
Mary Gauthier
Jimmie Dale Gilmore
Thea Gilmore
The Go! Team
Emmy The Great
Patty Griffin
Emmylou Harris
Nona Hendryx
Joe Henry
Jolie Holland
Hothouse Flowers
Janis Ian
Diana Jones
The Kinks
K.D. Lang
The House of Love
Andy Fairweather Low
Nick Lowe
Ry Cooder & Nick Lowe
Raul Malo
Scott Matthews
Erin McKeown
Don McLean
David Mead
Tift Merritt
Buddy Miller
Mogwai
Christy Moore
Allison Moorer
Joanna Newsom
Jeb Loy Nichols
Beth Nielsen Chapman
Ocean Colour Scene
Mary Margaret O'Hara
Gilbert O'Sullivan
Planxty
Tristan Prettyman
Gerry Rafferty
Robert Randolph & The Family Band
McIntosh Ross
Josh Rouse
Darden Smith
Mindy Smith
Stuart Staples
Th' Legendary Shack*Shackers
The Chieftains
Richard Thompson
Tindersticks
The Waifs
Loudon Wainwright III
Tom Waits
The Waterboys
Lori White
Lucinda Williams
Trisha Yearwood

SHARRON ASHCROFT MANAGEMENT

Dean Clough Halifax, West Yorkshire HX3 5AX
Tel: 01422 883090 Fax: 01422 343417
Email: info@sharronashcroft.com
Web Site: www.sharronashcroft.com
Senior Personnel: Sharron Ashcroft

ASHLEY WHEELHOUSE ENTERTAINMENTS

Kellingley Social Club Marine Villa Road Knottingley WF11 8ER
Tel: 01977 673500
Email: info@rickygrahamleisure.co.uk
Web Site: www.rickygrahamleisure.co.uk
Contact: Ashley Wheelhouse

ASKONAS HOLT LTD

Lincoln House 300 High Holborn London WC1V 7JH
Tel: 020 7400 1700 Fax: 020 7400 1799
Email: info@askonasholt.co.uk
Web Site: www.askonasholt.co.uk
Chief Executives: Martin Campbell-White, Robert Rattray
Specialising in: Classical Music.

ARTISTES REPRESENTED:

Conductors:
Claudio Abbado
Yves Abel
Alexander Anissimov
David Atherton
Daniel Barenboim
Rudolf Barshai
George Benjamin
Harry Bicket
Alexander Briger
Frans Brüggen
Rafael Frühbeck de Burgos
Paul Goodwin
Bernard Haitink
Daniel Harding
Graeme Jenkins
Emmanuel Krivine
Sir Charles Mackerras
Ion Marin
Wayne Marshall
Zubin Mehta
Tadaaki Otaka
Trevor Pinnock
Sir Simon Rattle
Leonard Slatkin
Toughan Sokhiev
Robert Tear
Piano:
Piotr Anderszewski
Emanuel Ax
Daniel Barenboim
Peter Donohoe
Evgeny Kissin
John Lill
Wayne Marshall
Murray Perahia
Lars Vogt
Harpsichord:
Trevor Pinnock
Organ:
Wayne Marshall
Violin:
Augustin Dumay
Sergei Khachatrian
Jaime Laredo
Tasmin Little
Viktoria Mullova
Cello:
Natalie Clein
Yo-Yo Ma
Jian Wang
Guitar:
John Williams
Flute:
Emmanuel Pahud
Ensembles:
Kalichstein/Laredo/Robinson Piano Trio

The Mullova Ensemble
Soprano:
June Anderson
Nancy Argenta
Emma Bell
Christine Brewer
Sophie Daneman
Nuccia Focile
Barbara Frittoli
Susannah Glanville
Susan Gritton
Maria Guleghina
Rosemary Joshua
Yvonne Kenny
Dame Felicity Lott
Geraldine McGreevy
Lisa Milne
Rebecca Nash
Dorothea Röschmann
Janice Watson
Mezzo-Soprano:
Sarah Connolly
Michelle DeYoung
Jane Henschel
Magdelena Kozená
Ann Murray
Randi Stene
Louise Winter
Catherine Wyn-Rogers
Counter-Tenor:
Brian Asawa
David Daniels
Tenor:
John Mark Ainsley
Ian Bostridge
William Burden
Paul Charles Clarke
Greg Fedderly
Jean-Paul Fouchécourt
Vsevolod Grivnov
Robin Leggate
Ilya Levinsky
Chris Merritt
Daniel Norman
Christoph Prégardien
Timothy Robinson
Daniil Shtoda
Toby Spence
Robert Tear
Baritone/Bass-Baritone:
Sir Thomas Allen
Vladimir Chernov
Neal Davies
William Dazeley
Dale Duesing
Vassily Gerello
Rodney Gilfry
Alan Held
Dmitri Hvorostovsky
Simon Keenlyside
Sergei Leiferkus
Christopher Maltman
Hanno Müller-Brachmann
Earle Patriarco
Nikolai Putilin
Teddy Tahn Rhodes
Bass:
Graeme Broadbent
Paata Burchuladze
Sergey Khachatryan
Robert Lloyd
Ayk Martirossian
Tim Mirfin
John Relyea
Peter Rose
Richard Van Allen
Alexander Vinogradov
Accompanists:
Larissa Gergieva
Graham Johnson
Malcolm Martineau
Producers:
John Cox
Martin Duncan
Nicholas Hytner
Stephen Lawless
Mikael Melbye
Deborah Warner

ASQUITH & HORNER PERSONAL MANAGEMENT

The Studio, 14 College Road, Bromley, Kent BR1 3NS
Tel: 020 8466 5580 Fax: 020 8313 0443
Web Site: www.spotlightagent.info/ (Agents PIN 9858-0919-0728)
Senior Personnel: Anthony van der Elst, Helen Melville
Specialising in all types of performers and entertainment.
E-mail on application. Distinguished list of European and Eastern European artists available. For complete client list, please see website: www.spotlightagent.info (Agents PIN 9858-0919-0728).

ASSOCIATED ARTS

8 Shrewsbury Lane, London SE18 3JF
Tel: 020 8856 4958 Fax: 020 8856 8189
Email: karen@associated-arts.co.uk
Web Site: www.associated-arts.co.uk
Senior Personnel: Karen Baker
Specialises in Designers, Lighting Designers and Directors.

ARTISTES REPRESENTED:

Designers:
Keith Baker
Lilja Blumenfeld
Norman Coates
Sue Condie
Dinah England
Peter Ruthven Hall
Michael Holt
Pip Leckenby
Georgia Lowe
Alex Marker
Nancy Surman
Lighting Designers:
Adrian Barnes
Vince Herbert
Peter Higton
Mark Howland
Gerry Jenkinson
Michael Odam
Lennie Tucker
Tom White
Colin Wood
Directors:
James Robert Carson
Chris Garner
Ade Morris

ASSOCIATED SPEAKERS

24a Park Road, Hayes, Middlesex
UB4 8JN
Tel: 020 8848 9048
Senior Personnel: E.A. Davis, P.A. Davis, D.M. Wood, K.A. Davis
Specialising in After Dinner & Multi National Corporation Speakers from Show-Business, Sport & the Media, plus Top TV & Theatre Celebrities for all Personal Appearances.

ATC MANAGEMENT

166-168 Camden Street London
NW1 9BT
Tel: 020 7580 7773 Fax: 020 7580 7776
Email: miriam@atcmanagement.com
Web Site: www.atcmanagement.com
Agent: Miriam Kaufman

ATHOLE STILL INTERNATIONAL LTD

Foresters Hall, 25-27 Westow Street, London SE19 3RY
Tel: 020 8771 5271 Fax: 020 771 8172
Email: enquiries@atholestill.co.uk
Web Site: www.atholestill.com
Contact: Athole Still & Roxanne Still.
Agency specialises in sport opera & modern music.
Opera: Chris Broom, Lucy Brown, Scott Cooper, Barbara Zuckriegl
Sport: Roxanne Still
Football: Eliot Van Til
Music: Jason Still, Mark Titcombe

ARTISTES REPRESENTED:

Baritones:
Tom Erik Lie
Anthony Marber
Carlos Marin
Louis Otey
Stephen Owen
Malcolm Rivers
Russell Smythe
Markus Werba
Basses:
Mark Beesley
Eric Garrett
Manfred Hemm
Jyrki Korhonen
Frode Olsen
Tómas Tómasson
Daniel Lewis Williams
Conductors:
Ivan Anguelov
Noel Davies
Andrew Greenwood
Hilary Griffiths
Günter Neuhold
Football:
Ron Atkinson
John Barnes MBE
George Burley
Barry Davies
Sven Goran Eriksson
John Gregory
Eidur Gudjohnsen
Gerard Houllier
Jim Jeffries
Richard Keys

Steve Maclaren
Mark McGhee
Alex McLeish
Harry Redknapp
Peter Reid
Sir Bobby Robson CBE
Joe Royle
Gordon Strachan
Mauricio Taricco
Gianluca Vialli
Arsene Wenger
Horse Racing:
Willie Carson OBE
Richard Dunwoody MBE
John Francome MBE
Music Artists:
Atlantico
Box Saga
Custom Blue
Junior Delgado
Dorp
Charles Kriel
Sian Martin
Mogul
Mogul
Nextmen
Rodney P
Spacek
Stan Francisco
Storm/Ritchie
Stylus
Tutto Matto
Rowing:
Miriam Battan
Tim Foster MBE
Garry Herbert MBE
Gillian Lindsay
Sir Steven Redgrave CBE
Rugby:
Roger Uttley OBE
Skiing:
Franz Klammer
Sopranos:
Rebecca Caine
Jessica Comeau
Inessa Galante
Cornelia Götz
Cynthia Haymon
Rebecca Langhurst
Cynthia Makris
Sue Patchell
Gail Pearson
Nina Rautio
Anna Ryberg
Michal Shamir
Caroline Stein
Mezzo Sopranos:
Allison Cook
Cornelia Helfricht
Laura Nykänen
Susannah Self
Nora Sowouzian
Cécile Van De Sant
Anne Wilkens
Stage Directors:
Mike Ashman
Tim Coleman
John Lloyd Davies
Dieter Kaegi
Stefanos Lazaridis
Stephen Medcalf
Swimming:
Sharron Davies MBE
Duncan Goodhew MBE
Mark Spitz
Tenors:
Terje Andersen
Bülent Bezdüz
Evan Bowers
Benjamin Butterfield
Francis Egerton
Bruce Ford
Louis Gentile
Lord Michael Howard
Stuart Kale
Jon Ketilsson
Justin Lavender
Colin Lee
Shalva Mukeria
Iain Paton
Bernard Richter
Yorg Schneider
Jorma Silvasti
Ian Thompson
Bradley Williams
Joseph Wolverton
Alan Woodrow

ATHOLE STILL MUSIC

Foresters Hall, 25-27 Westow Street,
London SE19 3RY
Tel: 020 8771 5271 Fax: 020 8771 8172
Email: jason@atholestill-music.co.uk
Web Site: www.atholestill.com
Contacts: Jason Still, John Cracknell,
Mark Titcombe

ARTISTES REPRESENTED:

A.M.P.
Charles Ariel
Box Saga
Custom Blue
Sian Martin
Nextmen
Rodney P
Graham Skinner
Spacek
Stormm

ATLANTIC ENTERTAINMENTS

PO Box 4465, Bournemouth
Bournemouth BH7 7WD
Tel: 01202 417 285 Fax: 01202 417 346
Email: atlantic.entertainments@virgin.net
contacts: Bridie Reid. Also deals with corporate management or Don Jones

AURORA'S CARNIVAL

23 Sunningdale Avenue Marlpool Heanor
Derbyshire DE75 7BS
Tel: 01773 530093 Mob: 07710 788 671
Email: enquiries@aurorascarnival.co.uk
Web Site: www.aurorascarnival.co.uk
Contact: Chris Ehrenzeller
General entertainment agency.

AUTONOMOUS TALENT BOOKING

PO Box 7, Ware, Hertfordshire
SG12 9UD
Tel: 01920 467 780 Fax: 01920 466 077
Email: hincdom@aol.com
Senior Personnel: Mike Hinc

ARTISTES REPRESENTED:

The Godfathers
Little Annie Anxiety
Morrissey
Rizwaan Muazzam Qawwali
Sigue Sigue Sputnik
Neil Sparkes And The Last Tribe
Temple of Sound

AVALON MANAGEMENT

4a Exmoor Street, London W10 6BD
Tel: 020 7598 8000 Fax: 020 7598 7300
Email: management@avalonuk.com
Web Site: www.avalonuk.com
Senior Personnel: Richard Allen-Turner,
Jon Thoday, Rob Aslett, James Taylor

ARTISTES REPRESENTED:

UK Comedians and Comediennes:
Chris Addison
Dan Antopolski
Dan Atkinson
David Baddiel
Greg Behrendt
Tom Bell
Simon Bird
Kurt Braunohler
Jen Brister
Simon Brodkin
Craig Campbell
Alun Cochrane
Fergus Craig
Greg Davies
Tom Deacon
Rob Deering
Rob Delaney
Adam DeVine
Jenny Eclair
Brian Keith Etheridge
Ed Gamble
Brenda Gilhooly
Dave Gorman
Steve Hall
Sadie Hasler
Richard Herring
Harry Hill
Alex Horne
Colin Hoult
Russell Howard
Emily Watson Howes
Aron Kader
Russell Kane
Jen Kirkman
We Are Klang
Lisa Landry
Marek Larwood
Lawry Levin
Nat Luurtsema
Lee Mack
Jimmy McGhie
Dave McNeill
Karl Minns
Stephen Morrison
Fran Moulds
Simon Munnery
Al Murray - The Pub Landlord
Jason Nash
Joanna Neary
Dave Nystrom
Helen O'Brien

John Oliver
Naz Osmanoglu
Ray Peacock
Ed Petrie
Janice Phayre
Ruth Pickett
Rob Pue
Chris Ramsey
Gareth Richards
John Roy
Kristen Schaal
Ahir Shah
Iliza Shlesinger
Frank Skinner
Laura Solon
Stan Stanley
Isy Suttie
Jim Tavare
Karen Taylor
Hayley Terris
Chris Tisdall
Paul F Tompkins
Brendon Walsh
Danielle Ward
Joe Wilkinson
Rosie Wilkinson
Ben Willbond
Steve Williams
Katy Wix
Andy Zaltzman
Presenters:
Fiona Bruce
Adrian Chiles
Victoria Derbyshire
Roann Ghosh
Ed Petrie

AVALON PROMOTIONS LTD
4a Exmoor Street, London W10 6BD
Tel: 020 7598 7333 Fax: 020 7598 7223
Email: info@avalonuk.com
Web Site: www.avalonuk.com
Head of Marketing: Mark Jackson
Avalon Promotions specialises in live artist bookings. Please see listing for 'Avalon Management' to refer to artists available for bookings.

AVENUE ARTISTES LTD
PO Box 1573 Southampton,
Hampshire SO16 3XS
Tel: 02380 760930 Fax: 02380 760930
Email: info@avenueartistes.com
Web Site: www.avenueartistes.com
Senior Personnel: Terry Rolph
ARTISTES REPRESENTED:
Mike Bishop
Mike Christy
Mike Dundas
Johnny Dymond
Harbour Lites Steel Band
Mark McCormack
Paul Mico
Steve Phillips
Malcolm Williams

ELAINE AVON ARTISTES MANAGEMENT/CRUISE CONSULTANT
Montage, 127 Westhall Road,
Warlingham, Surrey CR6 9HJ
Tel: 01883 622 317 Fax: 01883 627 478
Email: elaineavon@btinternet.com
Web Site: www.elaineavon.com
Contact: Elaine Avon
ARTISTES REPRESENTED:
Concert Pianist:
Naki Ataman
Multi-Instrumentalist:
Jay J Downs
Comedian:
Ron Dale

AXM
308 Panther House 30 Mount Pleasant
London WC1X 0AN
Tel: 020 7837 3304
Email: info@axmgt.com
Web Site: www.axmgt.com
Contact: Carrie Jones
Co-operative Agency
PMA Member
ARTISTES REPRESENTED:
David Alcock
Emily Bruce
Emma Carroll
Jack Corcoran
Mac Elsey
William Kempsel
Alexis Leighton
Adam Tabraham

AZA ARTISTES
652 Finchley Road, London NW11 7NT
Tel: 020 8458 7288
Contact: Morris Aza

B & Z ENTERTAINMENT
5 Bradshaw Avenue, Glenparva,
Leicester LE2 9PD
Tel/Fax: 0116 277 0058
Email: bz_ent@hotmail.com
Web Site: www.bz-ent.com
Contacts: Bill Chambers.

B A ENTERTAINMENTS
PO Box 1283 Blackpool FY1 9GF
Tel: 01253 532000
Email: info@baentertainments.com
Web Site: www.beentertainments.com
Steve Lewis

B P A LIVE
One Flint Cottage Kiln Lane Stowlangtoft
Bury St Edmunds IP31 3JZ
Tel: 01395 230357
Email: bp@bpa-live.com
Web Site: www.bpa-live.com
Bob Paterson

PAUL BAILEY AGENCY
32 Hampton Court Crescent,
Graburn Way East Molesey,
Surrey KT8 9BA
Tel: 020 8941 2034 Fax: 020 8941 6304
Email: paul@pbagency.co.uk
Senior Personnel: Paul Baylis
ARTISTES REPRESENTED:
Dance Bands:
E2
Fantasia
Madison Square
Phil Phillips Band
Soul Intention
Jazz Bands:
Scott Baylis Band
Ray Terry Band
Solo Pianists:
Scott Baylis
Carol Lesley
Eugene Porter
John Watson

YVONNE BAKER ASSOCIATES
8 Temple Fortune Lane,
London NW11 7UD
Tel: 020 8455 8687 Fax: 020 8458 3143
Email: y.baker@ukonline.co.uk
Senior Personnel: Yvonne Baker
Representing small scale full length stage shows, drama and children's shows.
ARTISTES REPRESENTED:
Bodger and Badger (Andy Cunningham)
Flanders and Swann "Drop Another Hat"

B.A.M. ASSOCIATES LTD
Benets Cottage, Dolberrow, Churchill,
Bristol, Avon BS25 5NT
Tel: 01934 852 942
Email: casting@ebam.tv
Web Site: www.ebam.tv
Senior Personnel: Louise Alexander, Jude Ferguson
Email: lou@ebam.tv ; jude@ebam.tv
ARTISTES REPRESENTED:
Males:
Peter Bygott
Terence Dauncey
Geoff Gibbons
Joe Hall
Brian Knight
Chris McCalphy
Andrew McGillan
Stuart Powell
Tim Prior
Marco Rossi
Females:
Pameli Benham
Sara Brooks
Natasha Godfrey
Chloe Lucas
Samantha Lynch
Elizabeth Revill
Fiona Stansbury
Bethan Thomas
Meg Whelan-Lyons
Jordon Whyte

BANCHORY MANAGEMENT
Argyle Studios, 24-27 Argyle Court,
1103 Argyle Street, Glasgow G3 8ND

Tel: 0141 204 2269 Fax: 0141 226 3181
Email: fiona@banchory.net
Agent: Fiona Morrison

ARTISTES REPRESENTED:
Belle & Sebastian

JOE BANGAY ENTERPRISES

River House, Riverwood Drive, Marlow, Buckinghamshire SL7 1QX
Tel: 01628 486 193 Fax: 01628 890 239
Mobile: 07860 812529 .
Email: william.b@btconnect.com
Web Site: www.joebangay.com
Senior Personnel: William Bangay, Gerald Edwards, Joe Bangay
Management of Film, TV and music artistes.

ARTISTES REPRESENTED:
Marissa Dunlop

AUSTIN BAPTISTE ENTERTAINMENT AGENCY LIMITED

Austin Baptiste Coral Reef Steelband
29 Court House Gardens, Finchley, London N3 1PU
Tel: 020 8346 3984 Fax: 020 8922 3770
Email: steelbands@aol.com
Web Site: www.steelbands.uk.com
Senior Personnel: Austin Baptiste
Specialises in Cabaret and Steelbands, Jazzbands and Piano Players.

ARTISTES REPRESENTED:
Steel Bands:
Austin Baptiste Steel Band
Clowns:
Mr Doo (clown & juggler)
Groups:
Ken Mackintosh & His Orchestra
The Select Syncopators Jazz Ensemble
Music & Dance:
Shade of Black (Caribbean Dancers)
Warriors from Zeigon
Jazz:
Harry Beckett

GEOFF BARBER ENTERTAINMENT AGENCY

Low Fold Farm, Back Heights Road, Thornton, Bradford, West Yorkshire BD13 3RP
Tel: 01274 835 210 Fax: 01274 834 769
Email: gbentertainments@btconnect.com
Contact: Geoff Barber

GAVIN BARKER ASSOCIATES

2d Wimpole Street, London W1G 0EB
Tel: 020 7499 4777 Fax: 020 7499 3777
Email: gavin@gavinbarkerassociates.co.uk
Web: www.gavinbarkerassociates.co.uk
Senior Personnel: Gavin Barker, Michelle Burke

ARTISTES REPRESENTED:
Actors:
Roy Barraclough
John Barrowman
Gerard Carey
Bernard Cribbins
Charles Daish
Simon Green
Giles Havergal
Jack Jefferson
Matthew Malthouse
Paul J Medford
William Oxborrow
Dominic Rickhards
John Stacey
Will Thorp
Malcolm Tierney
Rudolph Walker
Timothy West
Actresses:
Adele Anderson
Susie Blake
Laura Checkley
Louise Gold
Helen Grace
Kate Graham
Helen Harper
Helen Hobson
Nicola Hughes
Dillie Keane
Nora-Jane Noone
Carli Norris
Jodie Prenger
Vanessa Redgrave
Gwen Taylor
Carryl Thomas
Harriet Thorpe
Lucy Tregear
Lauren Ward
Kate Williams
Jennifer Wiltsie
Creatives:
Larry Blank (Arranger/Conductor/Orchestrator)
Matthew Brind (Orchestrator/Arranger)
Michael Corder (Choreographer)
Geoffrey Garratt (Choreographer)
Simon Green
Giles Havergal
Craig Revel Horwood (Director/Choreographer)
Lisa Kent (Director/Choreographer)
Tim Lusscombe (Writer/Director)
Spencer Soloman (Choreographer)
Nick Winston (Director/Choreopgrapher)
TV Talent:
John Barrowman
Mark Foster
Craig Revel Horwood (Director/Choreographer)
Ben James-Ellis
Jodie Prenger

BARN DANCE LINE DANCE AGENCY

20 Shirley Avenue, Old Coulsdon, Surrey CR5 1QU
Tel: 020 8668 5714 Fax: 020 8645 6923
Email: info@barn-dance.co.uk
Web Site: www.barn-dance.co.uk
Senior Personnel: Derek Jones, Pamela Jones

ARTISTES REPRESENTED:
Accord
The Ald Brickham Barn Dance Band
Alf Alpha & Wild Oats
All Hands Around
Allsorts
Amarillis
Paul Amor
Ancillary
Angels of the North
Apes & Japes
Ashdown Forest Ceildh Band
Backroom Boys
Kate Badrick
Bandwise
Barn Dance Experience
Bedcote Ceilidh
Black Earth Band
Blackberry Quadrille
Blackthorn Band
Bograt
John Bolton
Richard Bowman
Brookfield Band
Bushes & Briars
Cafe' Sol Band
Canny Band
Captain Adequate
Cats Claw
Cats Whiskers Barn Dance Band
Celtic Sounds
Chameleons
Chaos
Bernie Clarke
Clutching at Straws
Contraband
Cottage Industry
Phillip Courtney
Crannog
Crewneck Ceilidh
Dancing Bear
Def Shepherd
Donnybrook Fair
Dropping Clangers
Drops of Brandy
Dual Roles
Easy Street
Easy Weasel
Eilidhs Ceilidh
Terry Elvins
Geoff Elwell
Malcolm Eva
Dave Evans
Joe Fahy
Fast Parts
Alan Ferguson
Fiery Clock Face
Finality Jack
Five Bar Gait
Flat Cap Band
Flowers of Thorn
Footloose
The Footnotes
Foxes Bark
Frayed Knott
Gaberlunzies
Gallimurphy
Gander Band
The Geckoes
Gingerbeer Shindig
Arnold Gray
Keith Harrup
Haylayers
George Hearnden
Heart of England
Hedgehog Pie
High Jinks

Highly Strung
Hired Hands
Hodges Dump
Hogs Head
Hookey Band
Hoolie
Hop Till You Drop
Hopping Mad
Hot Punch
Hurry The Jug
Reg Hutchings
Isle Of Oxney Band
Janices Band
Jiggery Pokery
Kurley Kale
Tony Kelly
Kellys Eye
Kelly's Heroes
Dee Kemp
Kesh Band
Last Man Jack
Brian Laws
Ralph Liddell
Liquid Engineering
The Little Band
Lonesome Bones
Lorika
Malthouse
Masons Apron
Alan May
Peter Merton
Metric Foot
Moonshine
Mothers Ruin
Moves A Foot
The Muckers
Mums Porridge
Murphys Law
Nellie Belle
Odd Sox
O'Djangle
The Old Hog Ceilidh Band
Old School Band
On The Fiddle
On Yer Feet
Organ Grinders
Pass The Buck
Hetty Peglars Tump
Pierrot
Pitchfork
Plain Brown Wrapper
Pogleswood
Pugwash
Pump Action
Geoff Quaife
Rags & Tatters
The Ramblers
Random Jig
Rattle the Boards
Red Herrings
Red River Band
Redwing
Reeltime
Brae Riach Ceilidh Band
Ring O'Bells
Ripchord
David & Penny Rolfe
Rufus Returns
Running on Empty
John Scholey
Mick Scott
Shake a Leg
Shepherds Hey
Sherrifs Rangers
Shin Jig
Rob Sibthorpe (Sibby)
Skinners Rats
Small Town Romance
Some Like It Hot
Speckled Hen
Spring Greens
Square Roots
St George & The Trombone
Sticks Band
Striding Edge
Summerhill Folly
Tanglefoot
Brian Taylor
Temperance Be Damned
Thingumajig
Thirsty Work
Tight Squeeze
Time of Your LIfe
Tranters Folly
Triumph Band
Turktown Troupers
Chris Turner
Two Left Feet
Tykes
Uncle Bernard`s Band
Mike Venables
Bill Warder
Bob Weddell
West Kirby
Wheezle
Whirligig
Wild Silk
Steve Woodcock
Woodsiders

HARRY BARNES ENTERTAINMENTS

5 Braemar Lane, Worsley,
Manchester M28 1HD
Tel: 0161 799 2684 Mob: 07984 803 193
Fax: 0161 799 5678
Email: harold.barnes@ntlworld.com
Senior Personnel: Harry Barnes

PAUL BARRETT ROCK 'N' ROLL ENTERPRISES

21 Grove Terrace, Penarth,
Vale Glamorgan CF64 2NG Wales
Tel: 01222 704279 Fax: 01222 709989
Email: barrettrocknroll@ntlworld.com
Web Site: www.rockabillyhall.com
Senior Personnel: Paul Barrett
Specialist booking agent for rock'n'roll style acts. Able to book any international act in this category from local heroes to living legends. Any and all 50s and early 60s acts available.

ARTISTES REPRESENTED:

Non-exclusive Representation of::
Mike Berry
Big Bad Shakin'
Big Boy Bloater & His Southside Stompers
Sonny Burgess
Ray Campi
The Class of `58
Crazy Cavan & The Rhythm Rockers
Mac Curtis
Fabian
The Flames
Flying Saucers
Frankie Ford
Good Rockin' Tonight
Wee Willie Harris
Heartbreakers
Darrel Higham
Chas Hodges Rock 'N' Roll Trio
The Jets
Jive Romeros
Johnny and the Roccos
Juke Box Jive
Sid & Billy King
The Lennerockers
Janis Martin
Matchbox
Chas McDevitt
Johnny Preston
Razzle Dazzle
Reservoir Cats
Billy Lee Riley
Rock Back the Clock
Rockin' The Joint
Jack Scott
Sky Rockers
Sugar Creek Trio
Gene Summers
Billy Swan
Jean Vincent
Wild Katz

Exclusive Representation::
The Class of `58
Chas Hodges Rock 'N' Roll Trio
Johnny and The Jailbirds
Matchbox
Oo bop sh-bam
Razzle Dazzle
The Reservoir Cats
The Stargazers
The Strollers
Jean Vincent

Booking from the USA::
The Blue Caps
Sonny Burgess
Ray Campi
Mac Curtis
Frankie Ford
Charlie Gracie
Sid & Billy King
Linda Gail Lewis
Janis Martin
Johnny Preston
Billy Lee Riley
Jack Scott
Gene Summers

BEN BARRETTO ENTERTAINMENTS AGENCY

2 Oakham Road, Somerby,
Melton Mowbray, Leicestershire
LE14 2QF
Tel: 01664 454 888
Email: benbarreto@onetel.com
Web Site: www.ourworld.compuserve.co m.homepages/benbarretto
Senior Personnel: Ben Barretto

BARRIE HAWKINS LEISURE SERVICES

13 Jacksons Way, Fowlmere, Royston, Hertfordshire SG8 7TN
Tel/Fax: 01763 208 755
Email: b-hawkins@btconnect.com
Web Site: www.bhls.co.uk
Contact: Barrie Hawkins

ARTISTES REPRESENTED:

Abba Gold
Ashley Dean (hypnotist)
The Anna Reay Band
The PPS Band
Bavarian Strollers Oompah Band
Darius (close up magician)
Mark Goddard's Tribute to Elvis
English Rose String Quartet
Mikki Jay (Michael Jackson)
Kenneth Baker (Caricatures)
Terry Lightfoot & His Band
Littler Britain
Madonna (By Debbie Nunn)
Mario Basilisco (flamenco guitar)
Max Cherry and the Cherrypickers Steel Band
Boney M-featuring Liz Mitchell
Patricia Ford as HM Queen Elizabeth II
The James Taylor Quartet
Silent Disco
Soul Survivors
Soul Traders
Patricia Spero (Harpist)

BARRON KNIGHTS

Rose Cottage, South End, Milton Bryan, Bedfordshire MK17 9HS
Tel: 01525 210 071 Fax: 01525 210 989
Mobile: 07860 635593
Email: plangbk@aol.com
Web Site: www.barronknights.com
Senior Personnel: Pete Langford

ARTISTES REPRESENTED:

The Barron Knights

B.A.S.I.C./J.D. AGENCY/PANTO PEOPLE

3 Rushden House, Tatlow Road, Glenfield, Leicester LE3 8ND
Tel/Fax: 0116 287 9594
Email: jonny.dallas@ntlworld.com
Senior Personnel: Johnny Dallas, John Ross, Jodie Ennis

ARTISTES REPRESENTED:

Actors:
Graham Ashe
James Cross
Johnny Dallas
Alan England
Fairy Tale Theatre
William Fitzgerald
Dan Hogarth
Darren James
Guy James
Steve Jay (Jensen)
Pete Lindup
Rob Maskell
Luke Nugent
Robert Paul
James Powell
Luke Redford
James Robinson
John Ross
Dave Short
Craig Squance
Stan Stennett
David Wainwright
Actresses:
Maxine Daniels
Jill Fletcher
Sylvia Foxall
Barbara Jackson
Alison Philbrick

BCM PROMOTIONS LTD

The Offices, Lower Floor, 6 Park Drive Ilkeston, Derbyshire DE7 5NR
Tel: 0115 932 8615 Fax: 0115 930 2303
Email: ray@bcmpromotions.com
Web Site: www.bcmpromotions.com
Senior Personnel: Ray Martin
All round entertainment agency, for any occasion. Please visit our website for further details. Promotional video and brochure also available.

ARTISTES REPRESENTED:

Audley Anderson
Ballroom Glitz
John Leyton & Band
The Barron Knights
Beatles Experience (Beatles Tribute)
Cliff Bennett and the Rebel Rousers
Dave Berry & The Cruisers
Birthday (Beatle's trribute, 60's and 70's)
Dain Cordean (Comedian)
The Cufflinks
Clem Curtis & the Foundations
The Dakotas
Delorian
Dozy Beaky Mick & Tich
The Dreamers
Easybeats
The Electrix
The Fortunes
The Fourmost
Christopher Gee (1st class impressionist)
Gerry & The Pacemakers
Jaki Graham
Phil Haley & His Comments
Herman's Hermits
The Ivy League
Junior
Jason King (international male vocalist)
Simon King (Freddie Starr tribute)
Kokomo (tribute to Beach Boys)
Love Affair
Marmalade
Middle Of The Road
Midnight Dynamos
New Amen Corner
Next Move (4 piece party band)
Bruce Parker
Freddie Lee Peterkin
Poison Ivy 60's & 70's Show
Brian Poole & Electrix
P.J. Proby
Pure Liberty
Robert L Hughes
Sound of the Four Tops
Sounds of The Drifters
The Swinging Blue Jeans
The Soul Funksters
The Temple Brothers Play Everly
The Tornados
Union Gap
Vanity Fare (ex-chart band)
Voices with Soul

B.D.A. (BRIAN DURKIN ASSOCIATES)

Bryson House, Chiltern Road, Culcheth, Warrington, Cheshire WA3 4LL
Tel: 01925 766 655 Fax: 01925 765 577
Email: briandurkin@btconnect.com
Web Site: www.bdaltd.co.uk
Senior Personnel: Brian Durkin

ARTISTES REPRESENTED:

Jack Berry
The Bogtrotters
Celebration
Detours
Vince Earl
Fivepenny Piece
Finbar Furey
Gary & Vera
Johnny Leeze
Johnny McEvoy
Oldham Tinkers
Henry Sandon
The Senators
Brendan Shine
Sounds Like Sinatra
Elton Welsby
Bernard Wrigley

ANDREW BEAUCHAMP MANAGEMENT

Oaklands Business Centre, 64-68 Elm Grove, Worthing, West Sussex BN11 5LH
Tel: 07737 415 534
Email: abeauchampmgt@aol.com
Proprietor: Andrew Beauchamp

ARTISTES REPRESENTED:

Exclusive Representation:
American Dream
A-Tease
The Big Cheese Sandwich
The Big Cheese
Bowie Experience
Caledonia Dreamin'
Celtic Pride
Celtic Upstarts
Charley's Angels
Cover Story
Cred Zeppelin
Decadence
The Dogs
Elvisly Yours
Flower Power Daze
Get Down On It (Kool & The Gang Tribute)
Glam Stars
Greased (Greece show tribute)
Like Father Like Son
Little Wonder (David Bowie Tribute)
Lochs, Jocks & Two Guiness Barrells
Bet Lynch Experience
Miss Moneypenny
The New Originals
Norali Jones Tribute - Come Away With

Me
Ooze
Ram
Rocky Horrible Show
Rod's Highlights (Rod Stewart tribute)
Rogues
Shocky Horror Show
Slayed (Slade tribute)
Solstice
Soul Man
Spanking Gorgeous
Starskey & Hutch
Stereoironics
Stipe (REM Tribute)
Superstition
Tacky Horror Show
Tartan Craic
Travissing
Trendspotting
Vogue (Madonna tribute)
Whamarama
What's Next
Wonder Women
XFM
Xsive (INXS tribute)

Tribute Acts/Artistes:

Abbaland
Abbamax
Alexis (Cher)
Alliance
Andalus (Gypsy Kings)
Are You Experienced? (Jimi Hendrix)
Artemis Manias (Gloria Estefan tribute)
Bad Manners
Beachboys Inc
The 'B'Eagles (The Eagles tribute)
Ronnie Beharry (Michael Jackson)
Joanna Berns (Cher)
The Blox (Ian Dury - The Blockheads Tribute)
Bog Rolling Stones
The Bohemians (Queen tribute)
Bon Giovi
Boney M
Born To Bruce (Bruce Springsteen tribute)
Jim Bowen
Briefcase Blues Brothers
Britney Back To School
Nova Casper as Tina Turner
Cheeky Monkees
Crowdies House
Deadringer (Meatloaf tribute)
Definitely Might Be (Oasis tribute)
Gwen Dickey (solo)
Disco Inferno
Doctor & the Medics
Foundations
Girls from Abbaland
In4XS
Jingo (Santana tribute)
Louise Kenny (Shania Twain)
La Doors
Robert Lamberti (George Michael)
Limehouse Lizzy (Thin Lizzy tribute)
Little Wonder (David Bowie Tribute)
Livewire (AC/DC tribute)
Los Palmas Six (Madness tribute)
Anelia Manova (Sheryl Crow)
Mentallica
Monster (REM tribute)
More-Alanis-Set
Not Fade Away (Rolling Stones tribute)
Pink Fraud
Pretend Pretenders
Purple Haze
QEII (Queen tribute)
Queen B (Queen tribute)
R We Them (REM tribute)
Resurrection feat John Altman
Tracey Shields (Celine Dion)
Sister Act
TJ Slater as Tom Jones
Chris Smith and the String of Pearls
Stairway to Zeppelin
T-Rextasy
Think Floyd
Tribute To Joe Cocker
UU2
Venus
Veri Geri (Geri Halliwell tribute)
Wonderwall (Oasis tribute)
Worm

JOHN BEDFORD ENTERTAINMENTS LTD

19 Hemingway Gardens, Whiteley, Fareham, Hampshire PO15 7EY
Tel: 01489 578 777 Fax: 01489 575 291
Email: ben@johnbedford.biz
Web Site: www.johnbedford.co.uk
Senior Personnel: John Bedford, Ben Bedford, Sadie Bedford

ARTISTES REPRESENTED:

Bog Rolling Stones
Bogus Quo
Martin David
Glenn M. Ford
Glamrus
Phoney Beatles
Portia
The Queens
Martin Russell

BEES KNEES ENTERTAINMENTS AGENCY

50 Stamford Avenue, Blackpool FY4 2BJ
Tel: 01253 400 000 Mob: 07990 500 040
Mob: 07786 551 701
Email: fiona400000@hotmail.com
Web Site: www.beeskneesent.com
Senior Personnel: Fiona Hall-Shaw

ARTISTES REPRESENTED:

Alpha Karaoke
Charlie Brown
Shania Cain (Shania Twain Tribute)
Danielle
In The Red (Boy Girl Duo)
Nicole James (X Factor Vocalist)
Jayce ('Stars In Their Eyes' - Dolly Parton)
Joe Black
Just Bono (U2 & Bono Tribute)
Nicole Marie
Miss T
Michelle Montuori
Michael Rock
Carlo Sax
Souled As Seen
Mark Yates

JULIAN BELFRAGE ASSOCIATES

46 Albemarle Street, London W1S 4DF
Tel: 020 7287 8544 Fax: 020 7493 5460
Email: email@julianbelfrage.co.uk
Senior Personnel: Victoria Belfrage

ARTISTES REPRESENTED:

Actors:

Xander Berkeley
Billy Connolly
Georges Corroface
Michael Culkin
Daniel Day-Lewis
Richard Durden
Karl Geary
Nicholas Hewetson
Alan Howard
John Hurt
Jude Law
Francis Maguire
Jonathan Pryce
Pearce Quigley
Rufus Sewell
Steven Waddington
David Warner

Actresses:

Ann Bell
Clara Bellar
Abigail Cruttenden
Dame Judi Dench
Rebecca Hall
Sarah Jane Holm
Geraldine James
Finty Williams

BELLTOWER ENTERPRISES

9 Hillside Road, Ashtead, Surrey KT21 1RZ
Tel: 01372 277 703 Fax: 01372 278 406
Mobile: 07850 486 466
Email: music@dragonsfire.uk.com
Web Site: www.dragonsfire.uk.com
Senior Personnel: Nigel & Hilary Perona-Wright

ARTISTES REPRESENTED:

Belltower Medieval Banquet
Bustles & Beaux
Dragonsfire

AUDREY BENJAMIN AGENCY

278A Elgin Avenue, Maida Vale, London W9 1JR
Tel: 020 7289 7180 Fax: 020 7266 5480
Email: aud@elginavenue.fsbusiness.co.uk

ARTISTES REPRESENTED:

Actors:

Kristian Adehola
Rex Allen
Richard Aloi
Sam Banks
Jonathan Brook
Marlan Bulger
Julian Lee Cohen
Mark Colleano
Kevin Connealy
Donal Cox
Mansel David
Ray Edwards
Robert J Francis
John Golightly

Richard Goodwin
Barry Grantham
Andy Grubbs
Robbin John
Mark Jowett
Roy Kean
Kenneth Kennedy
Tim Leon
Nathaniel A. Lloyd
Sam Mancuso
Nicky Margolis
Rupert Mason
Adrian Ross-Jones
David Roth
Godfrey Salter
John Samson
Terence Singleton
Mark Stanway
Brent Stewart
Derek Tobias
Stephen Webber
Alistair Wilkinson
Actresses:
Jaimie Allison
Barbara Atkinson
Maureen Ann Bryan
Sally-Ann Burnett
Rebecca Chapman
Tricia Clarke
Sheila Collings
Christine Collins
Moyna Cope
Victoria Davies
Alison Edmonds
Deliane Forget
Ann Gabrielle
Kathryn Hamilton-Hall
Karen Henson
Shabana Hussain
Vera Jakob
Elizabeth Jordan
Gemma Keeling
Anne Kent
Carmen Knight
Patricia Leach
Virginia Lester
Belinda Low
Greta Lyons
Carla Maclean
Camille Meskill
Mary Monro
Janet Moran
Audrey Nicholson
Tanya Nicole
Saskia Portway
Louisa Riddell
Suzanne Rigden
Gillian Roe
Jacqui Scarborough
Maggie Taylor
Charlotte Winner
Yvonne Worth
Kate Wyvill

TONY BENNELL ENTERTAINMENTS

10 Manor Way, Kidlington, Oxfordshire OX5 2BD
Tel/Fax: 01865 372 645
Mobile: 07885 204274
Email: tonybennell@hotmail.com
Web Site: www.tonybennell.co.uk
Senior Personnel: Tony Bennell

ARTISTES REPRESENTED:
5th Avenue
7 In Bar Barbershop Quartet
Ace High Band
After Dark
Alpha Connection
Bak 2 Bak
Bathsheba's Wedding
Maria Beattie
Bejazzled
Boogie Street
Brandy Wine Bridge
Bright Lights Disco
Brilliant Disguise
Adger Brown
Bustin' Loose
Lee Carroll
Casino Royale Steel Band
Catch 22
Celebration
Champagne Disco
Chord Fiesta Barbershop Quartet
Clarendon String Quartet
Cloud Nine
The Co-Stars
Cocktail
Colinski
Convertibles
Cool Waters Steel Band
The Corsairs
Robert Cox
Dancin' Easy
Darwin's Wish
Dave Wolfe
Don Leather Duo
Electric Avenue
Espree
Evening Star
Fastlane
Trixi Field
Fiona Ann Bennett Jazz Trio
Focus
Tony Gerrard
Peter Gill Jazz Band
Harlequin Disco
Heart and Soul
Hogs Head
Hotline
Imagination
Inflatables
Isis String Quartet
The Mike James Sound
Jazz Nutzz
Limousine
Debbie Miles
Mixolydian Steel Band
Munich Bier Keller Men
New Dorne Valley
Tad Newton's Jazz Friends
Orpheus Greek Band
Over The Hill
Over The Top
Oxford Classic Jazz Band
Panache
Perfect Alibi
Platinum
Portrayal Of A Legend
Prestige
Pump Action
Reel McCoy
The Retros
The Rivieras
Route 66
Alvin Roy Jazzband
Sahara
Scooby Don't
Tony Shepherd's Jazz band
Shooter
Silhouette
Silver Stars Steel Band
Some Like It Hot
Spectra Disco
Strings Attached
Sugar & Spice
Sunblaze Steel Band
Sunfly
Jimmy Tamley
Stan Taylor
The First Class
Tropical Heatwave
Tumbledown Dick
Uncle Wiggy
Unit Six
Wild Honey
Xenons

BENTLEY'S ENTERTAINMENTS

7 Square Rigger Row, London SW11 3TZ
Tel: 020 7223 7900 Fax: 020 7978 4062
Email: charlotte@bentleys.net
Web Site: www.bentleys.net
Contact: Charlotte Jenkinson
Specialising in Party Organisation.

BETTY STUART AGENCY

17 The Square, Hale Barns, Altrincham, Cheshire WA15 8ST
Tel: 0161 904 0462 Fax: 0161 903 9008
Agent: Betty Stuart

ARTISTES REPRESENTED:
Sir Bobby Charlton CBE

BEVERLEY ARTISTES LTD

Beverley House, 14 Beatrice Terrace
Shiney Row Houghton-Le-Spring
Tyne & Wear DH4 4QW
Tel: 0191 3854163
Email: info@beverleyartistes.com
Web Site: www.beverleyartistes.com
Contact: Paul Taylor

BEYOND ENTERTAINMENT

16 High Street, Gainsborough, Lincolnshire DN21 1BH
Tel/Fax: 01427 811150
Email: info@beyondentertainment.co.uk
Web Site: www.beyondentertainment.co.uk
Contact General Manager: Mia Kruger-Munton
Specialises in a variety of acts, magicians, caricutures and mix & mingles.

B.F.P ENTERTAINMENTS

3 Queens Road, Corfe Mullen, Wimborne, Dorset BH21 3NE
Tel: 0845 6441951 Mob: 07778 809968
Email: bfpentertainment@yahoo.co.uk

Web Site: www.thebfpagency.co.uk
Contact: Mike Banting

ARTISTES REPRESENTED:

Wings Banned
Bianca (Vocalist)
Drew Cameron
Emalissa
Kayley
Lady Go Go
Salamander
Magic V
Dave Whitmore

BIG BANG MANAGEMENT LTD

Martins Bank Chambers,
313 Dickson Road, Blackpool, Lancashire
FY1 2JL
Tel: 01253 595 960 Fax: 01253 594 030
Email: agents@bigbang.co.uk
Web Site: www.bigbang.co.uk
Contacts: Steve Markbride Yusef Mohammed, Steve Markbride, Liz Morley
5 times award winning agency of the year - supplying quality entertainment to the nightclub and leisure industry.

ARTISTES REPRESENTED:

Music Acts:
Clem Curtis & the Foundations
Jaki Graham
New Drifters
Kenny Thomas
Revue Shows:
Bad Boys (Wham)
Stallions
The X-Men
UK Storm
Emmerdale Celebrities:
Tony Audenshaw
Matthew Bose
Chris Chittell
Jenna Coleman
Jane Cox
Andy Devine
Joseph Gilgun
Steve Halliwell
Charlie Hardwick (Val, Emmerdale)
Matt Healy
Clive Hornby
Meg Johnson
Tom Lister (Carl, Emmerdale)
Peter Martin
Kat McGregor
Nick Miles
Roxanne Pallett (Jo, Emmerdale)
Verity Rushworth
Hayley Tamaddon
Paula Tilbrook
Matt Wolfenden
Hollyoaks Celebrities:
Devon Anderson
Gemma Bissix
Guy Burnet
Claire Cooper
Ashley Davies
Ashley Taylor Dawson
Sam Derbyshire
Nathalie Emmanuel
Sonny Flood
Leah Hackett
Tony Hurst
Matt Littler
Jamie Lomas
Roxanne McKee
Jimmy McKenna
Gemma Merna (Carmel, Hollyoaks)
Jennifer Metcalfe (Mercedes, Hollyoaks)
Anthony Quinlan
Emma Rigby (Hannah, Hollyoaks)
Kevin Sacre
Carley Stenson (Steph, Hollyoaks)
James Sutton
Eastenders Celebrities:
Emma Barton
Tiana Benjamin
Laurie Brett
Perry Fenwick
Ricky Groves
Charlie G Hawkins
Rob Kazinsky
Kellie Shirley
David Spinx
Joe Swash
Kara Tointon
Lacey Turner
Jake Wood
Tributes:
The Backbeat Beatles
Miss Minogue
Navi As Michael Jackson
Rob Lamberti (George Michael Tribute)
Mark Wright as Elvis
Fake Bee Gees
Personalities:
Fran Cosgrave
Paul Danan
Richard Fleeshman
Leon Lopez
Gary Lucy
Will Mellor
Richard Newman
Stars from the Gladiators
Lea Walker
Coronation Street Celebrities:
Antony Cotton
Eileen Derbyshire
Vicky Entwistle
Sean Gallagher
Alan Halsall (Tyrone, Coronation Street)
Malcom Hebden
Rob James-Collier
Anne Kirkbride
Kym Ryder
Samia Smith

BIG BEAR MUSIC

PO BOX 944, Edgbaston, Birmingham
B16 8UT
Tel: 0121 454 7020
Email: admin@bigbearmusic.com/ tim@bigbearmusic.com
Web Site: www.bigbearmusic.com
Senior Personnel: Tim Jennings, Jim Simpson
Big Bear Music promote jazz, blues and swing through concert and club tours, UK and European festivals, the Starbucks Birmingham International Jazz Festival and Marbella Jazz Festival (Spain).

ARTISTES REPRESENTED:

Bruce Adams/Alan Barnes Quintet
Beiderbecke...and all that jazz
Dr Teeth Big Band
King Pleasure & the Biscuit Boys
Lady Sings The Blues
The Lazy Jumpers (Spain)
Tipitina
Chick Willis (USA)

BIG FOOT EVENTS LTD

321 Red Bank Road, Blackpool FY2 0HJ
Tel: 0871 855 2920 Fax: 0871 855 2922
Email: erica@bigfootevents.co.uk
Web Site: www.bigfootevents.co.uk
Directors: Erica Crompton, Kerry McLeod
Member of Agents' Association (GB)
Suppliers of Name Recording Artists, PAs, Live Bands, Tributes, Comedy, Casino Nights, Themed Events and all categories of entertainment.

BIG LIFE MANAGEMENT

67-69 Chalton Street, London NW1 1HY
Tel: 020 7554 2100 Fax: 020 7554 2154
Email: tony@biglifemanagement.com
Web Site: www.biglifemanagement.com
Agent: Tony Beard

ARTISTES REPRESENTED:

Badly Drawn Boy
Freelance Hellraiser
Gang of Four
Klaxons
Gabriela Montero
Performance
Shitdisco
Snow Patrol
The Futureheads
Vega 4
Wasted Youth Orchestra

BIG MANAGEMENT (UK) LTD (LONDON)

4th Floor 5 Dean Street London
W1D 3RQ
Tel: 020 7287 9949 Fax: 020 7287 9934
Email: camilla@bigmanagementuk.com
Web Site: www.bigmanagementuk.com
Agent: Camilla Storey

ARTISTES REPRESENTED:

Faith Brown
Kelle Bryan
Katie Edwards
Michelle Gayle
Tamer Hassan
Jilly Johnson
Duncan Pow
Chucky Venice
Daniella Westbrook

BIG SISTER PROMOTIONS

Studio 3, 3a Brackenbury Road, London
W6 0BE
Tel: 020 8740 0100
Email: nina@bigsisteruk.com / karen@big-sisteruk.com
Contact: Nina Watson
Agent: Karen Williams

ARTISTES REPRESENTED:

Adem
Amp Fiddler
Ampop

Iain Archer
Archie Bronson Outfit
Arctic Monkeys
Ash
Lou Barlow
Beautiful Newborn Children
Bonnie Prince Billy
Blackbud
Bloc Party
Blueskins
Bright Eyes
British Whale
Kaiser Chiefs
Clap Your Hands Say Yeah
Clayhill
Clearlake
Clinic
Computerman
Cord
Cosmic Rough Riders
The Cribs
DJ Format
The Donnas
Duels
Embrace
Engineers
Feable Weiner
Franz Ferdinand
Fields
Fire Engines
Forward Russia
Four Tet
Funeral For A Friend
Rodrigo Y Gabriela
Gossip
Charlotte Hatherley
The Kills
Klaxons
Seth Lakeman
Ray Lamontagne
Lostprophets
Mattafix
Maximo Park
Millionaire
The Music
Nightmare Of You
Noisettes
Oasis
Palace Fires
Pavement
Peter Bjorn and John
Pigeon Detectives
Psapp
Pull Tiger Tall
Punish The Atom
Shack
Shy FX & T Power
Simple Plan
Skin
Sons & Daughters
Stellastar
Ben Taylor
Teenage Fan Club
Test-Icicles
The Automatic
The Beat Up
The Bronx
The Ivories
The Ordinary Boys
The Perishers
The Race
(The Real) Tuesday Weld
The Rifles
The Sound Explosion
The Sunshine Underground
The Television Personalities
Tiga
Travis
KT Tunstall
Unkle Bob
Vitalic
Saul Williams
Yes Boss
James Yorkston

BIG TALENT GROUP

3rd Floor 207 Regent Street London
W1B 3HH
Tel: 020 7856 0207
Email: terry@bigtalentgroup.co.uk
Web Site: www.bigtalentgroup.co.uk
Director: Terry Mills

ARTISTES REPRESENTED:

911
Blazin Squad
Cheeky Girls
Chico
Darius
Friday Hill
Greg James
Journey South
Kenzie
Michelle McManus
Scott Mills
Kirsten O'Brian
Lee Ryan

BIG TIME ARTISTES LTD

PO Box 6818 Derby DE22 2WZ
Tel: 01332 224 366 Fax: 01332 820 372
Email: bigtimeartistes@hotmail.com
Web Site: www.bigtimeartistes.biz
Senior Personnel: Lee Camm
Specialising in pop/modern cabaret.

BIG WHEEL ENTERTAINMENTS LTD

Redding House, 2 Yeoman Street,
Leicester LE1 1UT
Tel: 0845 373 3578
Email: info@bigwheelentertainments.co.uk
Web Site: www.bigwheelentertainments.co.uk
Contact: Mr Houston, Sarah Barker
Entertainments we provide: Casino Tables; Chocolate Fountains; Magicians; Rodeo Bull; Bungee Run; Sumo Wrestling; Tribute & Party Bands & Theme Nights.

ARTISTES REPRESENTED:

Popular Acts:
Planet Pop
Stax of Soul

BIGSTAR ENTERTAINMENTS

37 Dovedale Avenue, Long Eaton,
Nottingham NG10 3HP
Tel: 0115 972 4849 Fax: 0115 973 3003
Email: dick@bigstarentertainments.co.uk
Web: www.bigstarentertainments.co.uk
Contact: Dick Hill
Specialises in club and corprate entertainment.

BIGWIGS ENTERTAINMENTS

The Yard Rodney Street
Ashton-Under-Lyme OL6 9PY
Tel: 0161 830 0700
Email: trish@bigwigagents.com
Web Site: www.blockbookers.com
Contact: Mr Laughton, Mrs Laughton

BILLBOARD PERSONAL MANAGEMENT

11 Mowll Street, London SW9 6BG
Tel: 020 7735 9956 / 2953 Fax: 020 7793 0426
Email: billboardpm@btconnect.com
Web Site: www.billboardpm.com
Contact: Daniel Tasker

ARTISTES REPRESENTED:

Actors:
Lovelace Akpojaro
Michael Ballard
Jack Bence
Michael Burgess
Rob Carroll
Sean Cook
Daniel Fearn
Jody Halse
Kieron Harris
Joshua Hemmings
Myles Horgan
Shawn Kan
Dean Kelly
Geoffrey Lang
Ian Mayhew
Greg Mcfarnon
Alan Park
James Pearse
Andrew Piper
Peter G Reed
Rod Silvers
Glynne Steele
Daniel Tatarsky
Tony Verner
Actresses:
Julia G Addison
Marva Alexander
Claire Askam
Kath Burlinson
Carol Bush
Lisa Devlin
Sara Dylan
Viss Elliot
Karina Fernandez
Gillie Gratham
Emily Jewell
Laura Kearsey
Lyndsey Lennon
Beverley Limbrick
Louise Mai Newberry
Sally Okafor
Amelia Saberwal
Jacqueline Wood

TONY BILLINGHAM MUSIC

Lapal House, Lapal Lane South,

Halesowen, West Midlands B62 0ES
Tel: 0121 550 1272 / 503 0326
Fax: 0121 550 1562
Email: admin@lapalhouse.co.uk
Web Site: www.europajazz.co.uk
Contact: Tony Billingham

MICHAEL BLACK PERSONAL MANAGEMENT LTD
5 The Ridgeway, Radlett,
Hertfordshire WD7 8PZ
Tel: 01923 856 555 Fax: 01923 859 871
Mobile: 07798 525253
Email: michael@themichaelblack.co.uk
Web Site: www.michaelblack.co.uk
Senior Personnel: Michael Black
Specialising in All Corporate Work, Bands, Discos, After Dinner Speakers.

BLACKBURN INTERNATIONAL UK LTD
Firdt Floor East Marlin 459 London Road
Camberley, Surrey GU15 3JA
Tel: 01276 686661 Fax: 01276 681415
Email: jonathan.blackburn@blackburninternational.com
Web: www.blackburninternational.com
Contact: Jonathan Blackburn

ARTISTES REPRESENTED:
Brooks Aehron
Ralph Heid
Beni Mason
Renato Pagiari
David Reid
Cass Taylor
Leo Ward
Pingxin Xu

BLACKBURN SACHS ASSOCIATES
Argyll House 1a All Saints Passage
London SW18 1EP
Tel: 020 7292 7555
Email: presenters@blackburnsachs.com
Web Site: www.blackburnsachsassociates.com
Senior Personnel: Anthony Blackburn, John Sachs

ARTISTES REPRESENTED:
Presenters:
Tom Abbott
Peter Alliss
Neil Bentley
Gary Bloom
Lorna Dunkley
Jane Farnham
Phil Gayle
Petrie Hosken
Jake Humphrey
Chris Jarvis
David Jensen
Russ Kane
Phil Kennedy
Jessie Klass
Karen Krizanovich
Lisa Marie Long
Dean Martin
David Mercer
Tiff Needell
Jonathan Pearce
Steve Rider
Chris Rogers
Sonia
Anna Williamson

BLACKPOOL'S MIDAS ENTERTAINMENTS
23 Ledbury Road, Blackpool, Lancashire
FY3 7SR
Tel: 01253 395 062 No fax number
Web Site: www.blackpoolmidas.com
Represent Artistes, Groups, Duo's, Magicians. Also Disco/Karaoke P.A. Equipment Hire.

ARTISTES REPRESENTED:
Blackpool's Midas Karaoke/Disco Roadshow

BLAZERS ENTERTAINMENT GROUP
PO Box 52, Marlow, Buckinghamshire
SL7 2YB
Tel/Fax: 01491 579 214
Email: blazersentertain@aol.com
Web: www.blazersentertainment.co.uk
Contact: Leon Fisk

DEREK BLOCK CONCERTS LTD
Suite D, 4-6 Canfield Place, London
NW6 3BT
Tel: 020 7724 2101
Email: dbc@derekblock.co.uk
Web Site: www.derekblock.co.uk
Senior Personnel: Derek Block, Scott Miller, Paul Scarbrow

ARTISTES REPRESENTED:
That'll Be The Day - Touring Review
The Illegal Eagles
Let's Hang On
The Chicago Blues Brothers

BLOCKBOOKERS LTD
The Maltings Old Malton Road, Staxton, Scarborough, North Yorkshire YO12 4SB
Tel: 01944 711755 Fax: 01944 711755
Email: blockbookersltd@btinternet.com
Web Site: www.blockbookers.com
Contact@ Ken Webster

REBECCA BLOND ASSOCIATES
69A Kings Road, London SW3 4NX
Tel: 020 7351 4100 Fax: 020 7351 4600
Email: info@rebeccablondeassociates.com
Senior Personnel: Rebecca Blond

BLOWOUT SAX
South Lodge, North Parade, Bath,
B.A.N.E.S. BA2 4EU
Tel: 01225 339 007
Mobile: 07773 737 880
Email: markarcher@blowoutsax.com
Web Site: www.blowoutsax.com
School Director: Mark Archer
School, shop and musicians.

ARTISTES REPRESENTED:
Mark Archer
The Big Blowout Band

BLUE WAND MANAGEMENT LTD
2nd Floor, 12 Weltje Road,
Hammersmith, London W6 9TG
Tel/Fax: 020 8741 2038 Mobile: 07885 528 743
Email: bluewandproltd@btinternet.com
Senior Personnel: Lino Omoboni

BLUEPRINT MANAGEMENT
PO Box 593, Woking, Surrey GU23 7YF
Tel: 01483 715 336 / 7 Fax: 01483 757 490
Email: blueprint@lineone.net
Senior Personnel: John Glover, Matt Glover

ARTISTES REPRESENTED:
Beverley Craven
Richard Drummie
Go West including Peter Cox
Tony Hadley
Alison Limerick
Martin Fry Of ABC

BLUJAY MANAGEMENT LTD
20b Chancellors Street, London W6 9RN
Tel: 020 8222 7222
Email: info@blujay.co.uk
Web Site: www.blujay.co.uk
Contacts: Steve Tannett, Carly Martin

ARTISTES REPRESENTED:
John Green
Anna Krantz
Mama's Gun

BO PRODUCTIONS LTD
PO Box 201, Macclesfield, Cheshire
SK11 7BS
Tel/Fax: 01189 403 516
Mob: 07710 499 818
Email: bookings@mrmethane.com
Web Site: www.mrmethane.com
Senior Personnel: Barrie Barlow, Paul Oldfield

ARTISTES REPRESENTED:
Mr Methane

BOB PATERSON AGENCY (BPA)
PO Box 670 Ipswich Suffolk IP9 9AU
Tel: 01473 749556 Fax: 01473 749556
Email: bp@bpa-live.com
Web Site: www.bpa-live.com
Contact: Bob Paterson

THE JOHN BODDY AGENCY
10 Southfield Gardens, Twickenham,
Middlesex TW1 4SZ
Tel: 020 8892 0133 / 8891 3809 Fax: 020 8287 0798
Email: jba@johnboddyagency.co.uk
Web Site: www.johnboddyagency.co.uk

Senior Personnel: John Boddy and Jonathan Boddy
Member of Agents Association (GB)

ARTISTES REPRESENTED:

Jazz:
Alan Gresty / Brian White Ragtimers
Kenny Ball & His Jazzmen
John Bayley & Five Go Jiving
Acker Bilk & His Paramount Jazzband
Bruce Boardman's New York Cafe
Brian Dee Group
Dixieland All-Stars
Georgie Fame
The Humphrey Lyttelton Band
Laurie Holloway Trio
The Mardi Gras Joymakers Parade Band
New York Cafe Band
James Taylor Quartet
The Dixie Four
Stan Tracey
Jazz Vocalists:
Jacqui Dankworth
Elaine Delmar And Her Quartet
Stacey Kent
Cleo Laine
Tina May
Clare Teal
Big Bands / Swing:
9.20 Deluxe Swing Band
BBC Big Band
Echoes of Ellington Jazz Orchestra
The Syd Lawrence Orchestra
Glenn Miller Orchestra (UK) directed by Ray McVay
John Miller & His Orchestra "The Glenn Miller Connection"
The National Youth Jazz Orchestra (NYJO)
Salute To The Rat Pack
1920s / 1930s:
The Cotton Club Jazz Orchestra
The Pasadena Roof Orchestra
The Piccadilly Dance Orchestra
Harry Strutter's Hot Rhythm Orchestra
The Temperance Seven
Soul & R&B:
The Empire State Band
Geno Washington & The Ram Jam Band
Party & Function Bands:
Alpha Connection
Candide
Empire State Band
The Empire State Band
Classical:
Angelique String Quartet
Celli Babies
The Covent Garden String Quartet
Rhodri Davies (Harpist)
Divertimento Trio
Jeanette Gondry (Harpist)
Nia Jenkins (Harpist)
The Monaco String Quartet
Opera Box
The Phoenix String Quartet
Royal Philharmonic Concert Orchestra
Southern Concert Brass
Sheila Watts (Harpist)
Catherine White (Harpist)
The Windwood Trio
Tribute Shows:
The Bandit Beatles
The Blues Brothers Experience
Edith Piaf - A celebration of a Legend
He's the One - Robbie Williams Show
The Magic Of Abba
Queen B (Queen tribute)
The Strolling Bones
The World of the Bee Gees
T.Rextacy
Utter Madness
World Music:
Paul Aguilera - Flamenco
Claudio Allodi Italian Ensemble
Candela
Cherry Pickers Steel Band
Edith Piaf - A celebration of a Legend
Jacques Cafe Band
Miguel's All Star Steel Band
Orquesta Caché
Osibisa
Roberto Pla & His Latin Orchestra
Russian Tornado
Taiko Drummers
Tziganka - Russian Cossack Music & Dance Spectacular
Pop & Rock Recording Artistes:
The Searchers
The Swinging Blue Jeans
The Bruvvers
The Tremeloes
Miscellaneous:
~After Dinner Speakers~
~Caricaturists~
~Casinos~
~Discotheques & DJs~
~Magicians~ (Cabaret & Close-Up)
~Military Bands~
Special Concert Presentations:
Edith Piaf - A celebration of a Legend
Georgie Fame
Cleo Laine
A Night of Romantic Opera
Remembering Humph
Swinging at the Cotton Club
The Three Bs - Ball, Barbra & Bilk
Tziganka - Russian Cossack Music & Dance Spectacular
Production Services:
Sound & Lighting Engineers
Sound-Systems
Stage-Lighting
Staging

BODEN AGENCY

99 East Barnet Road, New Barnet, Hertfordshire EN4 8RF
Agency Tel: 020 8447 0909 Fax: 020 8449 5212
Email: Bodens2692@aol.com
Web Site: www.bodenstudios.com
Contact: Mo Boden

BODEN STUDIOS

99 East Barnet Road, New Barnet, Hertfordshire EN4 8RF
Studio Tel: 020 8447 0909 Fax: 020 8449 5212
Email: Bodens2692@aol.com
Web Site: www.bodenstudios.com
Contact: Mo Boden

BODO AGENCY

186 Ashley Road (side door), Hale, Altrincham, Cheshire WA15 9SF
Mobile: 07939 521465
Email: fgarcia777@hotmail.com
Senior Personnel: F L Marshall

ARTISTES REPRESENTED:

Sabbamangalang
François Garcia

BOLDEAN PRODUCTIONS

42 Church Lane, Heacham, King's Lynn, Norfolk PE31 7HN
Tel: 01485 572 347
Email: roger.dean15@btinternet.com
Web Site: www.roger-dean.com
Contact: Roger Dean

ARTISTES REPRESENTED:

Roger Dean Sings Johnny Cash

THE BOLLYWOOD BOOKING AGENCY

53 Newquay Road, Walsall WS5 3EL
Tel:07710 040 183
Email: info@bollywoodbookingagency.com
Web Site: www.bollywoodbookinga-gency.com
Contact: Shin Kang
Specialising in: Corporate Events, Dancers, Bands and Musicians.

BOO BOO'S ENTERTAINMENTS

Pambola Ltd, 170 Watling Street, Grendon, Near Atherstone, Warwickshire CV9 2PH
Tel: 01827 715 011 Fax: 01827 715 665
Email: info@clownsareus.co.uk
Web Site: www.clownsareus.co.uk
Director: John T Jeremy

ARTISTES REPRESENTED:

Gameo Arena
Jay Chaldean
Circus Whiz
Circus Workshop
The Great Tymoni
J Clown Esq
Pandora Face-Painter
The Whiz Jugglers

BOO-BOO THE CLOWN'S ENTERTAINMENTS & PROMOTIONS

170 Watling Street, Grendon, Atherstone, Warwickshire CV9 2PH
Tel: 01827 715 011 Fax: 01827 715 665
Email: info@clownsareus.co.uk
Web Site: www.clownsareus.co.uk
Senior Personnel: David Cooper
Various forms of Corporate and Speciality entertainment. Nation-wide agency for every type of corporate, adult, family and childrens event.

ARTISTES REPRESENTED:

Boo-Boo The Clown

BOOGIE MANAGEMENT

Suite 8, 2nd Floor, Claremont House,

22-24 Claremont Road, Surbiton, Surrey
KT6 4QU
Tel: 020 8390 8634
Email: info@boogiemanagement.co.uk
Web: www.boogiemanagement.co.uk
Creative Director: Simon Skinner

ARTISTES REPRESENTED:

Acts:
Flyin Hi
Artists:
Sarah Louise Broom
Richard Cadell
Duncan Heather
Mark Jones
Sean Smith
Natalie Waters

BOOK A BAND

Ledston Engine Cottages, Ridge Road,
Kippax, Leeds LS1 6DG
Tel: 08707 430 601 Fax: 08707 430 602
Email: bands@book-a-band.co.uk
Web Site: www.book-a-band.co.uk
Senior Personnel: Lenny Phillip
Party bands, wedding bands and function bands available.

ARTISTES REPRESENTED:

The Abba Experience
Abba Vision
Above Average Weight Band
All Souled Out
Alpha Connection
A-Team
Duke Baysee
Brahms & Liszt
The Caribbeans
The Casablanca Steps
Chicago Joe and the Soul Divas
Colonel Custard (one man band)
Crazy Ape
Jimmy Cricket
Dancing Fly
Descarga
The Dizzy Club
Dogs Body
DPA4
Eso-Es
Fat Larry's Soul Band
Frisco Crabbe (Soul & Funk)
Fully Funktional
Gershwin Gang
Get Down On It
Goosehorns
Harlem Gem
Harmony Hounds
Roy G Hemmings
Huge
Jewels
Juke Box Jive
Kopy Katz
The LA Session Band
The "Legendary" Drifters
Les Girls Can-Can Dancers
Loose Covers
Metropolis
The Mighty Juke Box Band
Mixed Feelings
Morris and the Minors
The New Originals
O.K.T.C.
The Party Kings
Private Invitation
The Real Macaws
Rhythm Chaps
Samara
The Savages
The Screaming Beavers
Sean Finch & The Street Band
The Sharp Cuts
Shin Jig
Showstoppers Worldwide
The Six Elements
Society Swing
Soul Function
Soul Rights
Barrie St John
Station
Sun Sea and Sand Band
The Sweat Band
Three Men and a Bass (Rock & Pop)
Upside Down
Van Morisson Tribute Band
V.I.P.
Whirlijig
Steve Womack
Zaccardelli
Paul Zerdin

BOOK OF DREAMS MUSIC

73 Couchmore, Esher, Surrey KT10 9AX
Tel: 020 8398 0255
Email: hpatonevans@bookofdreamsmusic.com
Web Site: www.bookofdreamsmusic.com
Senior Personnel: Harry Paton Evans, David Barnes

BOOKEM DANNO

2 Glastonbury Close, Spennymoor,
County Durham DL16 6XP
Tel: 01388 810 143 Fax: 01388 813 389
Email: sales@bookemdanno.com
Web Site: www.bookemdanno.com
Contact: Sue & Phil Armstrong
Independant concert tours or theatre tour arrangement

THE BOOTLEG BEATLES

Cliveden House 19-22 Victoria Villas
Richmond, Surrey TW9 2JX
Tel: 020 8948 8308 Fax: 020 8332 7183
Email: info@bootlegbeatles.com
Web Site: www.bootlegbeatles.com
Contact: Raj Patel
Bootleg Beatles management and promoters.

ARTISTES REPRESENTED:

Bootleg Beatles

BORDER LEISURE

Top Floor, Richmond Place,
69/71 Edgar Street, Hereford,
Herefordshire HR4 9JR
Tel: 01432 270 470 Fax: 01432 353 867
Email: agents@borderleisure.co.uk
Senior Personnel: Keith Dodd, Ken Sheperd

ARTISTES REPRESENTED:

The 3 Hartbeats
Dan Anderson
Bianco
Paul Christie
Paul Dazeley
Paul Detheridge
Kenny Smiles
The Banderas
Trilogy
Ultima

DEREK BOULTON PRODUCTIONS

PO Box 1123, London SW1V 1HB
Tel: 020 7828 6533 Fax: 020 7828 1271
Email: derekboulton99@yahoo.com
Senior Personnel: Derek Boulton

ARTISTES REPRESENTED:

Ricci Benson
Derek Cox
Simon Dee
Jose Maria Gererro
Millgo Heff
Jonathan Idiagbonya
Jennifer James
Bert Kaempfert Orchestra
Malcolm Laycock
Listen To My Music Show With Chris Dean Big Band
Sheila Southern

BOURNE ENTERTAINMENTS

1 Park Lane, Hemel Hempstead,
Hertfordshire HP2 4YL
Tel: 01442 230 300 Fax: 01442 266 126
Email: simon.daniels@bourne-leisure.co.uk
Web Site: www.bourne-leisure.co.uk
Senior Personnel: Dave Arnold, Peter Allen
Booking Agency for the Bourne Estate.

SANDRA BOYCE MANAGEMENT

1 Kingsway House, Albion Road, London
N16 0TA
Tel: 020 7923 0606 Fax: 020 7241 2313
Email: info@sandraboyce.com
Web Site: www.sandraboyce.com
Contact: Sandra Boyce

ARTISTES REPRESENTED:

Kofi Amankwah
Kenny Aro
Damian Asher
Alexander Blyth
Yvonne Brewster
Claire Callaghan
Emma Cater
Sharon D Clarke
Sylvano Clarke
Paul Collard
Sean Connolly
Richard De Sousa
Rufus Dean
Norma Dixit
Kate Doherty
Derek Elroy
Victor Romero Evans
Glenna Forster-Jones
Andrew Fraser
Malcolm Frederick

Tom George
Everick Golding
Kumall Grewal
Kasia Haddad
Lindsay Haines
Lilian Hammond
Tricia Harrison
Lindsey Haynes
Russ Haynes
Duncan Henderson
Danielle Henry
Judy Hepburn
Brett Hicks-Maitland
Majid Iqbal
Jenny Jay
Ashwin Juneja
Janet Kay
Natasha Kellett
Craig Kerrigan
Debbie Killingback
Joanne King
Peter Landi
Aletta Lawson
Anthony Lennon
Beresford LeRoy
Dominic Letts
Jennifer MacDonald-Anderson
David McCaffrey
Lee McDonald
Dominique Moore
Harsh Nayyar
Kieri Noddings
Nicholas Oscar-Lavelle
Sid Owen
Anthony Oxford
Hazel Palmer
Medhavi Patel
William Penny
Lisa Davina Phillip
Marisa Phillips
Robert D. Phillips
Jackie Robinson-Brown
Alex Sabga
Hari Sajjan
Narinder Samra
Jeff Shankley
Carla Simpson
Michelle Stephenson
Lise Stuart
Liz Sutherland
Andrew Sykes
Blondell Taylor
Cherie Taylor-Battiste
Nicola Tully
Simon Turner
Will Vanderpuye
Joe Vera
Paven Virk
Blanche Williams
Cameron Wilshere
Angela Wynter

BPR PRODUCTIONS

36 Como Street Romford Essex
RM7 7DR
Tel: 01708 725 330 Fax: 01708 725 322
Email: bprmusic@compuserve.com
Web Site: www.bprmusic.com
Musical Director: Brian Theobald

MICHELLE BRAIDMAN ASSOCIATES

3rd Floor Suite, 169 Grange Road,
London SE1 3BN
Tel: 020 7237 3523 Fax: 020 7231 4634
Email: info@braidman.com
Agent: Michelle Braid

ARTISTES REPRESENTED:

Rodney Bewes "Three Men In A Boat"
Dominic Brunt
Sophie Dix
Bryan Ferry
David Groves
James Hooton
Howard Saddler

THE JAMES BRANDON COMPANY

Cherry Tree House, 1 Cherry Tree Street,,
Elsecar, South Yorkshire S74 8DG
Tel: 01226 742 886
Email: info@jamesbrandon.co.uk
Web Site: www.jamesbrandon.co.uk
Managing Director: James Brandon
Production and agency specialising in pantomime, tribute and variety shows, illusion, design and special effects. Radio, Media and road shows. Specialist in corporate events and one-off bespoke entertainments.

PAUL BRIDSON PRODUCTIONS

Motte House, Marford Hill, Marford,
Wrexham, LL12 8SW Wales
Tel: 01244 571 708 / 709 Fax: 01244 571 722
Email: paul@paulbridson.co.uk
Web Site: www.paulbridson.co.uk
Contact: Paul Bridson
Artistes available via my office by arrangement with their respective management; Ken Dodd, Frank Carson, Jim Bowen, Stan Boardman, Jimmy Cricket. Other than those identified here, other circus, magical and speciality acts are available.

ARTISTES REPRESENTED:

Variety Artistes:
Stan Boardman
Jim Bowen
Frank Carson KSG
Norman Collier
Jimmy Cricket
Barry Cryer
Paul Daniels
Ken Dodd OBE
Berni Flint
Jenny Jones
Powys & Jones
Roy Walker
Sound of the 60's:
Dave Berry & The Cruisers
Joe Brown
Wayne Fontana and the Mindbenders
The Fortunes
The Fourmost
Gerry & The Pacemakers
Herman's Hermits
Marmalade
Merseybeats
The Rockin' Berries
The Tremeloes
Vanity Fare (ex-chart band)
Comedy Musical:
The Barron Knights
Black Onyx
Candlewick Green
Chimes Two
Grumbleweeds
Ivy League
Brother Lees
Schooner
Sounds of the 70's:
Black Lace
Brotherhood of Man
Jimmy James & The Vagabonds
Mungo Jerry
Paper Lace
Suzi Quatro
Real Thing
Showaddywaddy
Sports Attractions:
Eric Bristow MBE
Geoff Capes
Bob Champion MBE
Jack Charlton OBE
John Conteh
Sir Henry Cooper OBE KSG
Sharron Davies MBE
Tommy Docherty
Clare Francis
Graham Gooch OBE
Alan Minter
John Parrott MBE
Ray Reardon
Tessa Sanderson CBE
Willie Thorne
John Virgo
David Wilkie MBE
TV Personalities:
Gordon Burns
Barry Cryer
Sir Ranulph Fiennes Bt OBE
Eric Knowles
Ian McCaskill
John Stalker
Ricky Tomlinson
Childrens Shows:
Bananas In Pyjamas
Care Bears Magic Show
Henry's Cat Show
Humpty Dumpty Show
Carol Lee Scott (Grotbags)
National Festival Circus
Otis The Aardvark
Rupert Bear Show
The Troggs

BRITISH & EUROPEAN SPORTS TALENT

13 Montagu Mews South, London
W1H 7ER
Tel: 0871 250 1234
Email: richard@celebrity.co.uk
Web Site: www.celebrity.co.uk/best
Agent: Richard Johnson
Sports personalities for advertising, endorsements and corporate events.

BRITISH SPEAKER BUREAU

A Celebrity Group Company

BSB House, 12 Nottingham Place,
London W1U 5NB
Freephone: 0808 0001 001 Tel: 08712 501 234 Fax: 020 7224 6060
Email: info@bsb.co.uk
Web Site: www.bsb.co.uk
Contact: Simona Gambini, Ron Mowlam

BROADLAND ENTERTAINMENTS
43 Henry Blogg Road Cromer
Norfolk NR27
Tel: 01263 513142 Fax: 01263 515715
Email: broadlandents@hotmail.com
Web: www.uk-entertainment-agency.com
Senior Personnel: Mark Buller
Banquet and corperate entertainment.

THE BROADLEY ENTERTAINMENT GROUP LTD
48 Broadley Terrace, London NW1 6LG
Tel: 020 7258 0324 Fax: 020 7724 2361
Email: manny@broadley-group.demon.co.uk
Contact: Mark French

BROADWATER ENTERTAINMENTS ASSOCIATES
Whittemere, Worcester Road,
Hanley Castle, Worcester WR8 0AA
Tel: 01684 311 467 Fax: 01684 311 462
Mobile: 07768 551 766 (Maraidh)
Email: maraidh@aol.com / info@broadwater-ents.co.uk
Web Site: www.broadwater-ents.co.uk
Owner: Maraidh Clark
ARTISTES REPRESENTED:
Abba Ice
Cher by Marade
Marc Drew (Lee)
Sophie Hardy
Indigo
Adam Lacey
Jackie Lee
Meatloaf Experience
Mel Day
Nicki
Asa Payne
Poison Ivy
John H Stracey
Andy Wilkins
Jo Wright

BRONIA BUCHANAN ASSOCIATES LTD
Nederlander House
7 Great Russell Street, London
WC1B 3NH
Tel: 020 7631 2004 Fax: 020 7631 2034
Email: info@buchanan-associates.co.uk
Web: www.buchanan-associates.co.uk
Contact: Bronia Buchanan
ARTISTES REPRESENTED:
Richard Grieve
Sherrie Hewson
Sylvester McCoy

DOLLY BROOK CASTING
PO Box 5436, Dunmow, Essex
CM6 1WW
Tel: 01371 879 775 Fax: 01371 875 996
Email: dollybrookcasting@btinternet.com
Senior Personnel: Dolly Brook
Casting agency specialising in extras and supporting artistes.

BILL BROOKMAN PRODUCTIONS LTD
101 Ashby Road, Loughborough,
Leicestershire LE11 3AB
Tel: 01509 236 175 Fax: 01509 219 873
Email: office@billbrookman.co.uk
Web Site: www.billbrookman.co.uk
Manager: Bill Brookman
Specialising in Street Performance.
A large developed experienced street theatre company combining street music, street gypsy dancing, fire, stiltwalking, puppetry. Large sets. Celebratory theatre.
ARTISTES REPRESENTED:
The 101 Dance Group
Bill Brookman - One Man Band
The Charnwood Juggling Club

CLAUDE BROOKS ENTERTAINMENTS
19 Sussex Place, Slough, Berks SL1 1NH
Tel: 01753 520 717 Fax: 01753 520 424
Senior Personnel: Claude Brooks

BROTHERHOOD OF MAN MANAGEMENT
Westfield, 75 Burkes Road, Beaconsfield,
Buckinghamshire HP9 1PP
Tel: 01494 673 073 Fax: 01494 680 920
Email: bomagency@aol.com
Web Site: www.brotherhoodofman.co.uk
Contact: Lee Sheriden
ARTISTES REPRESENTED:
Brotherhood of Man

GARRY BROWN ASSOCIATES (INT) LTD
27 Downs Side, Cheam, Sutton,
Surrey SM2 7EH
Tel: 020 8643 3991 Fax: 020 8770 7241
Email: gbaltd@btconnect.com
Senior Personnel: Garry Brown, Helen Machell, Brenda Capper, Denise Webb
Specialising in: Entertainment for Major Shipping Lines and Hotels Worldwide providing a range of artistes, particularly dance teams.
ARTISTES REPRESENTED:
Lorna Dallas

BROWN & SIMCOCKS
Flat 1, 1 Bridgehouse Court,
109 Blackfriar's Road, London SE1 8HW
Tel: 020 7928 1229 Fax: 020 7928 1909
Email: mail@brownandsimcocks.co.uk
Web Site: www.brownandsimcocks.co.uk
Senior Personnel: Carrie Simcocks, Peter Walmsley

ARTISTES REPRESENTED:
Martin Ball
John Bardon
Ian Bleasdale
Eamon Boland
Jeremy Bulloch
Peter Gunn
Billy Hartman
Charles Lawson
Philip Middlemiss
Sue Nicholls
Ben Onwukwe
Tony Osoba
Sylvia Syms

J & S BROWNHUT ENTERTAINMENT PROMOTIONS
(With SG Brownhut Promotions)
22 Kings Road, Bramhope, Leeds,
West Yorkshire LS16 9JN
Tel: 0113 267 5127 Fax: 0113 261 2813
Mobile: 07774 816942
Email: brownhut@tiscali.co.uk
Senior Personnel: Jeff Brownhut
Specialising in Personalities, Stunt Performers, Clowns, Stiltwalkers, Lookalikes etc. Please do not contact for autograph & photograph requests.

DEREK BRUCE ENTERTAINMENTS
2nd Floor, 107 High Street, Evesham,
Worcestershire WR11 4EB
Tel: 01386 442819 / 443456 Fax: 01386 443456 Emergency & Night Tel: 07766 075076
Email: derek@derekbruceents.fsnet.co.uk
Member of NEAC
Senior Personnel: Derek Wells, Imogen Williams
ARTISTES REPRESENTED:
Bavarian Bands:
Frankfurter Schunkle Band
Munich Bier Keller Men
Barry Schmidt Bavarian Band
Bierkeller Schunklers
Brass, Concert or Marching Bands:
Alcester Victoria Silver Band 'Avonbank Band'
Band of West Mercia Constabulary
Bell Inn Band
Bream Silver Band
Bretforton Silver Band
Celebration Reed & Brass Band
Chalford Brass Band
Cinderford Band
Cirencester Band
City of Birmingham Band
City of Coventry Band
Forest of Dean Brass Band
Gloucester Excelsior Band
Gloucester Police Band
Halesowen Brass Band
Highley Band
Malvern Hills District Brass Band
Muller Cleobury Mortimer Band
Shipston Town Band
Shirley Band
St Andrews Pipe Band

Stourport on Severn Brass Band
Tewkesbury Town Band
Triumph Motors RBL Pipe Band
West Mercia Police Band
Wolverhampton Pipe Band
Worcester Concert Brass
Caricaturists:
Glynn Edwards
Children's Entertainers:
Tom Arnold
Captain Spanner
Andy Clay
Fiz & Wiz
Daniel Goodwin
Lindsay Hart
Prof Guy Higgins
Paul Kybert
Stew Martin
Mr Doo (clown & juggler)
Tombo the Clown
Steve White
Comedians:
Phil Anthony
Stew Barker
Rod Beech
Phil Chase
Dave & Amos
Adam Daye
Fred The Ted
Gaffer & Willis
Mike Gold
J.P. James
Mike King
Johnny Moon
Maxwell Plum
Jimmie Quinn
Tommy Quinn
Meadowlark Smith
David St John
Steve Tandy
Patrick Tansey
Bruce Thompson
Country & Western Duos:
Just Crazy
Norman Stevens
Country & Western Bands:
Steve Raymond Band
Discos:
Sam Boulter
Crank It Up
Dooby Doo Disco
Guy Gisbourne
Phil and Simon Hailes
Mayfair
No Limits
Northern Lights
Party Animal Disco
Rhythm of the Night
Unicorn Disco
Comedy Showbands:
Best of British
Black Onyx
Mart Connor and the Carrott Crunchers
Life And Soul
Big Bands:
Derek Bruce Big Band
The Syd Lawrence Orchestra
Mike Smith Orchestra & Singers
Duos:
Amber
Cadenza
Countdown
Dave & Danny
Heartbeat
Inside Out
J & S Duo
Jimmy Mac Duo
Karisma
Kin
Don & Cindy Leather
Limousine
One Way Street
Orbit
Passion
Select Company
Shooting Stars
Sibling Rivalry
Steve & Aska
Tandem
Two Hearts
Tony Whittaker
Exotic Female Dancers/Models:
Annabelle
Jo Carthey
Cee C
Danni
Tina
Exotic Male Dancers/Models:
Hardcore
Jaguar
King Shaft
Female Vocalists:
Kate Ashby
Charlotte Costello
Diana Dee
Nessi Dee
Dawn Diamonds
Debby Gee
Clare Inskip
Dee D James
Louise James
Emma Jenson
Clare Jordan
Jane Kelly
Clare Kindon
Marade
Maria
Debbie Miles
Milli Munro (Shirley Bassey, Tina Turner, Whitney Houston)
Sarah Nicholson
Kate Richards
Roxanne
Samantha Starr
Barni Scott
Lee Ann Solo
Folk Acts:
Pat Brennan
Guitar Vocalists:
Martyn Addis
Dave Beale
Jack Black
Mark Brannelly
Gary Charman
Brian Chriss
Cody
Pete Cresswell
John Dale
Tony Mac
Steve Marsden
Graham Morris
Hypnotists:
Eddie Burke
Julian Caruso
Jed Fortune
Michael Sutherland
Comedy Impressionists:
Mike Gold
David St John
Steve Tandy
Instrumental Acts:
Ian Anderson
Arthur Bancroft
Bellini String Quartet
Broadway Ensemble
Dorian Collins
Contrasts Chamber Ensemble
Cotswolds String Quartet
Audrey Douglas
The Horn Belles
Marie France Riboulet
Kerry Quiney
Pat Rose
Barry Smith
Strauss Quartet
Katherine Thomas
Jugglers/Stilt Walkers:
Andy Clay
Lindsay Hart
Mr Doo (clown & juggler)
Michael Taylor
Steve White
Keyboard Vocalists:
John Harrison
Jess Hope
Jolly Roger
Kate Lennox
Tony Minchella
Eunice Rhymes
Tony Roberts
Jazz Bands:
Avon Jazz Band
Jack Daniels Band
Electric Fred
Elite Jazz Band
Eureeka Jazz Quartet
Jazz Express
Roy Kirby's Paragon Jazz
Dutch Lewis
Perdido Street
Sauce City Jazz
Latin American Acts:
Caliche
Old Time Music Hall:
The Midlands Artists Variety Music Hall Show
Male Vocalists:
Ritchie Brookes
Stephen Charles
Van Greaves
Just Dave
Kristian Knight
Stewart Lea
Andy Leonard
Garry Slade
John Southern
Magicians & Illusionists:
Daniel Goodwin
Paul Kybert
Julie Llusion
Medieval Entertainers:
The Harvesters (Medieval Folk Music)
James Prince
Sylvester the Jester
Musical Comedy:
Micky John Bull

Phil Chase
Gaffer & Willis
J.P. James
Billy Kettle
Fred Wedlock
M.O.R./Pop Groups:
Ballroom Glitz
Big Sur
Breeze
Cats Eyes
Disciples
Facta 3
Hold Tight
Chris Kern & Siam
Kick Back
Merlyn
Move-it
No Exit
Please
Red Hunter
The Rubble
S.A.E
Triangle
Showbands:
Derek Bruce
Carl Dominic Band
Billy Davis
K.J. Music Zone
Square/Barn Dance Bands:
Big Deal
DeKelten
Hodges Dump
Star Attractions:
Dave Berry
Brotherhood of Man
Don MacLean MBE
Marmalade
Todd Miller And The Joe Loss Orchestra & Singers
Showaddywaddy
Vanity Fare (ex-chart band)
Steel Bands:
Caribbean Harmonics
Tropical Islanders Steel Band
Toastmasters:
Alan Myatt
Roger Scott
David Tilt
Traditional Pipers:
John Conroy
Brendan Ryan
Ventriloquists:
Paul Levent
Ken Wood

BRUCE JAMES PRODUCTIONS LTD

68 St George's Park Avenue, Westcliffe-on-Sea, Essex SS0 9UD
Tel/Fax: 01702 335 970 Mobile: 07850 369 018 (Bruce James)
Email: info@brucejamesproductions.co.uk
Web: www.brucejamesproductions.co.uk
Contact: Bruce James, Martin Roddy
We produce all types of top quality theatre from play tours to musicals to repertory seasons (thrillers, comedies, dramas) to children's shows. You name it - we do it!

BRUNSKILL MANAGEMENT LTD (LONDON)

Suite 8a, 169 Queen's Gate, London SW7 5HE
Tel: 020 7581 3388 Fax: 020 7581 3389
Email: contact@brunskill.com
Agents: Geoff Stanton, Roger Davidson
Contact: Candice Stanton

ARTISTES REPRESENTED:

Represented by Roger Davidson::
Claire Adams
Hannah Barrie
Abigail Bond
Abigail Davies
Emma Dewhurst
David Hayler
Cathleen McCarron
Kevin Murphy
Jeremy Nicholas
Eve Pearce
Clifford Samuel
Sean Scanlan
Robert Weatherby
Chinna Wodu
Represented by Geoff Stanton::
David Acton
David Ames
Daniel Barry
Brodie Bass
Tim Birkett
Mark Cameron
Rachel Clarke
Craig Crosbie
Charlie Dore
Julie Dray
John Dulieu
Helen Franklin
Tom Frederic
Lucia Giannecchini
Sammy Glenn
Sarah Harper
Martin Herdman
Tony Hirst
Lucy Ann Holmes
Tara Hugo
Kimberly Jaraj
Stephen Jenn
David Kernan
Aicha Kossoko
Pascal Laurent
Lucy Marriot
Maria Victoria Di Pace
Ellie Piercy
Jim Pyke
Alice Selwyn
Sophie Thursfield
Amanda Waldy
Jane Whittenshaw

BRUNSKILL MANAGEMENT LTD (PENRITH)

The Courtyard, Edenhall, Penrith, Cumbria CA11 8ST
Tel: 01768 881430 Fax: 01768 881850
Email: admin@brunskill.com
Senior Personnel: Aude Powell, Geoff Stanton

ARTISTES REPRESENTED:

Males:
Terry Alexander
Vijay Amritraj
Pepe Balderrama
Jamie Ballard
William Barlow
Thane Bettany
Billy Boyd
Stephen Brennan
Paul Brown
William Chubb
Nicholas Claxton
Kenny Clayton
Scott Cohen
Matt Cullum
Timothy Deenihan
Paul Dinnen
Trystan Gravelle
Piers Harrisson
Stuart Hickey
B J Hogg
Rahul Khanna
Julian Littman
Marcello Magni
Antonio Gil Martinez
Rik Mayall
Gerard McArthur
Tom McDonald
Patrick Moy
Milo O'Shea
Soni Razdan
Lee Reynolds
Adam Rust
James Schlesinger
Tim Scott Walker
Roshan Seth
David Shelley
Bob Tomson
Stephen Yardley
Females:
Shabana Azmi
Sarah Brennan
Hayley Carmichael
Jessica Claridge
Pandora Clifford
Nandita Das
Simone Dillon
Blythe Duff
Elaine Mackenzie Ellis
Polly Findlay
Tanya Franks
Jan Harvey
Catherine Holman
Catherine Holman
Kathryn Hunter
Jennifer Kidd
Veronica Leer
Matilda Leyser
Rosaleen Linehan
Maeve McGrath
Virginia Mckenna
Sarah McNeale
Rupinder Nagra
Kathryn Nutbeem
Louie Ramsay
Lisa Ray
Soni Razdan
Jasmine Russell
Katie Ryder Richardson
Laura Dos Santos
Tara Sharma
Carole Shelley
Maya Sondhi
Diana Stewart

Michelle Terry
Lily Travers
Gabriel Vick
Judith Williams

BTM MANAGEMENT & AGENCY

PO Box 6003, Birmingham B45 0AR
Tel: 0121 477 9553 Fax: 0121 693 2954
Skype: gothan.records
Email: barry@gotham-records.com
Web Site: www.gotham-records.com / www.barrytomesmediagroup.com
Senior Personnel: Barry Tomes, Mac Goatcher, Tara Tomes
Representing artists of all genres of music from rock bands, steel bands to pop.

ARTISTES REPRESENTED:

Rick Brown
Amanda Greenwood
Khaliq
Norma Lewis
Sleepyhead

BTWS (ENTERTAINMENTS) LTD

60 Granshaw Close, Kings Norton, Birmingham B38 8RA
Tel: 0121 458 2462 Fax: 0121 628 2622
Email: KSmart2569@aol.com
Senior Personnel: Keith Smart

ARTISTES REPRESENTED:

The Rockin' Berries

BUBBLEGUM MODEL AGENCY

Pinewood Studios, Pinewood Road
Iver Heath, Buckinghamshire SL0 0NH
Tel: 01753 632 867 Fax: 01753 652 521
Email: kids@bubblegummodels.com
Web Site: www.bubblegumodels.com
Senior Personnel: Penny Hobson, Nicola Barwell
Children and teenagers from newborn to 18 years.

RICHARD BUCKNALL MANAGEMENT (RBM)

3rd Floor, 168 Victoria Street, London SW1E 5LB
Tel: 0207 630 7733 Fax: 0207 630 6549
Email: info@rbmcomedy.com
Web Site: www.rbmcomedy.com
Senior Personnel: Richard Bucknall, Rob Sandy

ARTISTES REPRESENTED:

Brian Appleton
Geoff Boyz
Andy Bull
Rebecca Carrington
Julian Dutton
Graham Fellows
Alan Francis
Laurence Howarth
Miles Jupp
Sarah Kennedy
Stefano Paolini
Guy Pratt
John Shuttleworth
Writers:
Alan Francis
Laurence Howarth
Ben Keaton
Polly Kelly
Matt Owen
Live Work Only:
Mitch Benn
Rhona Cameron
Dominic Holland
The Lost And Lonely Rebels
Mel And Sue
Sue Perkins
Punt and Dennis

BUCKS FIZZ AGENCY

Also See Listing for: Alan Clayton Concerts Ltd
Alcaston Barn, Alcaston, Church Stretton, Shropshire SY6 6RP
Tel: 01694 781 689 Fax: 01694 781 692
Email: alan_clayton@btconnect.com
Contact Agent: Alan Clayton

STEPHEN BUDD MANAGEMENT

Zeppelin Building,
59-61 Farringdon Road, London EC1M 3JB
Tel: 020 7916 3303 Fax: 020 7916 3302
Email: simondix@record-producers.com
Web Site: www.record-producers.com
Senior Personnel: Stephen Budd
Senior Project Manager: Simon Dix

ARTISTES REPRESENTED:

Afreex
Arthur Baker
Colin Emmanuel
Simon Gogerly
Ian Grimble
Greg Haver
Stephen Hayes
Steve Hilton
Tore Johansson
Jon Kelly
Kenisha
KK
Carsten Kroeyer
James Lewis
Steve Lironi
Steve Lyon
Teo Miller
Rick Nowels
Jay Reynolds
Richard Robson
Valgeir Sigurdsson
Rik Simpson
Martijn ten Velden (Audio Drive)
Mark Wallis

BULLET MANAGEMENT LIMITED

PO Box 359, Manchester M28 2UY
Tel: 0161 661 7261 Fax: 0161 661 7262
Email: bullet.man@virgin.net
Web Site: www.bulletmanagement.co.uk
Contact: Diccon Hubbard, Phil Watts
Specialising in festivals, corporate events, production and tour management.

ARTISTES REPRESENTED:

Animals and Friends
Bad Manners
Cliff Bennett and the Rebel Rousers
Dave Berry & The Cruisers
Mike Berry
Brotherhood of Man
Errol Brown
Joe Brown
Bucks Fizz
Paul Carrack
Petula Clark
Class of 64 (Chip Hawkes etc)
Climax Blues Band
Clem Curtis & the Foundations
The Dakotas
Dave Dee, Dozy, Beaky, Mich & Tich
Steve Ellis' Love Affair
Emperors of Rhythm
The Fortunes
Gerry & The Pacemakers
Glitter Band
Go West including Peter Cox
Tony Hadley
Heaven 17
Hot Chocolate
Human League
The Ivy League
Kid Creole & the Coconuts
Johnny Logan
The Manfreds
Marmalade
Martin Fry Of ABC
Les McKeowns Bay City Rollers
The Merseybeats
Modern Romance
Peter Noone
Mike Pender's Searchers
Brian Poole & Electrix
Suzi Quatro
The Rubettes
The Salford Jets
Showaddywaddy
Slade
Smokie
Melanie Stace
Alvin Stardust
Sweet
Swinging Blue Jeans
The Tremeloes
The Troggs
The Undertakers
Union Gap
John Walker
Dionne Warwick
Mary Wilde & The Wildcats
Roy Wood
Paul Young
Radio Presenters:
Mike Read
Mike Sweeney
Dave Lee Travis
Soul, Mowtown & Disco:
Atlantic Soul Band
Boney M featuring Maizie Williams
The Commitments
Gwen Dickeys Rose Royce
The Drifters
Gloria Gaynor
Heatwave
Imagination
Jimmy James & The Vagabonds
George McCrae
Odyssey
Sister Sledge

Souled As Seen
Stax of Soul
Tavares
The Real Thing
Geno Washington & The Ram Jam Band
Womack & Womack
Tribute Acts:
Abba 2000
Abba Gold
Bandit Beatles
Bjorn Again
Bleach (Blondie Tribute)
Bootleg Beatles
Bootleg Buddy (Buddy Holly & The Crickets tribute)
Boyzonly
Britney Baby
Car Wash
Cheatles
Counterfeit Bee Gees
FABBA
The Illegal Eagles
Jean Genie (David Bowie tribute)
Love Machine
Ludwig Beatles
Magic
Paul Metcalfe (Rod Stewart)
Pat Myers (Freddie Mercury)
Probably Robbie
QEII (Queen tribute)
Queen B (Queen tribute)
Queen on Fire (Queen tribute)
Ricky Martin Show
The Royal Family
Rumours Of Fleetwood Mac
So 80's
Sounds of The Blues Brothers
Status Clone (Status Quo Tribute)
A Taste of Honey
Tom The Voice
Village Boyz (Village People tribute)
Wham Duran
Who's Who

BULRUSH MANAGEMENT

Unit 5, Mart Road, Minehead, Somerset TA24 5BJ
Tel: 01643 707 277 Mobile: 07773 238 073 Mobile: 07891 944 304
Email: info@bulrushstudios.co.uk / bulrush.studios@virgin.net
Web Site: www.bulrushstudios.co.uk
Senior Personnel: Roger Cawsey

ARTISTES REPRESENTED:

Joan Armatrading Tribute Band
The Artistes
Macy Gray Tribute Band
The Gloria Lawrence Band
The Vision

BURNETT GRANGER ASSOCIATES

3 Clifford Street London W1S 2LF
Tel: 0207 437 8008 Fax; 0207 287 3239
Email: associates@burnettgranger.co.uk
Web Site: www.burnettgranger.co.uk
Senior Personnel: Barry Burnett, Lindsay Granger
Theatrical agents.

ARTISTES REPRESENTED:

Ladies:
Alice Arnold
Marcia Ashton
Ruth Augilera
Rae Baker
Amanda Barrie
Annalene Beechey
Dora Bryan OBE
Sheila Burrell
Victoria Bush
Anne Charleston
Freya Copeland
Helen Cotterill
Leila Crerar
Emma Davies
Anita Dobson
Liz Edmiston
Elizabeth Estensen
Eva Fontaine
Kate Gillespie
Tiffany Graves
Elspet Gray
Natasha Gray
Shobna Gulati
Linzi Hateley
Sarah Head
Jean Heywood
Sue Holderness
Nerys Hughes
Jacqueline Kington
Jenny Fitzpatrick
Katie Rowley Jones
Miriam Karlin OBE
Penelope Keith OBE
Shona Lindsay
Eliza Lumley
Claire Marlowe
Diana May
Lynette McMorrough
Katharine Monaghan
Penny Morrell
Deirdra Morris
Caroline Mortimer
Anjali Myachadna
Claire Oberman
Ellen O'Grady
Sally Oliver
Lucy Pargeter (Chasity, Emmerdale)
Lyn Paul
Angela Ridgeon
Liz Robertson
Anne Rogers
Naomi Ryan
Louise Shuttleworth
Jean Simmons OBE
Angela Sims
Sue Lloyd
Sophia Thierens
Sally Ann Triplett
Denise Welch
Sheila White
Bayla Whitten
Barbara Windsor MBE
Anna Wing
Gillian Wright
Men:
kwaku Ankomah
Damian Arnold
Danny Bage
Edward Baker Duly
Robert Beck
Paul Bentley
Andrew Bicknell
Stuart Boother
Billy Boyle
Ian Burford
Richard Calkin
Ayden Callaghan
John-James Cawood
John Challis
Patrick Clancy
Nicolas Colicos
John Conroy
Geoffrey Davies
Andrew Derbyshire
John Diedrich
Julius D'Silva
David Durham
Phillip Edgerley
Mark Van Eeuwen
Dafydd Emyr
Tim Flavin
Grahame Fox
Pete Gallagher
Howard Gossington
Fenton Gray
Brian Greene
Linal Haft
Andrew Halliday
Richard Hansell
Graham James
Ben Joiner
Willie Jonah
Robert Kazinsky
Kevin Kennedy
Adam Lake
Gavin Lee
Gareth Marks
Michael McCarthy
Mark McKerracher
Ian McLarnon
Richard Meek
Max Milner
Ryan Molloy
Nathaniel Morrison
Robert Mountford
Patrick Mower
Lucas Nicoll
Mark Oxtoby
Donald Pickering
Nicholas Pound
Duncan Preston
Richard Reynard
Yo Santhaveesuk
Michael Sharvell-Martin
Guy Siner
Corey Skaggs
Victor Spinetti
Malcolm Stoddard
Ian Talbot
Richard Vincent
Paddy Ward
Ewan Wardrop
Derek Waring
Nick Waring
Jay Webb
Lee White
Nick Wilton
David Wood OBE

MEL BUSH ORGANISATION

26 Albany Business Park, Cabot Lane,

Poole, Dorset BH17 7BX
Tel: 01202 691 891 Fax: 01202 691 896
Email: info@melbush.com
Senior Personnel: Mel Bush

ARTISTES REPRESENTED:

David Essex
Maksim Mrvica (pianist)

JILLIE BUSHELL ASSOCIATES

15 Claylands Place, The Oval,
London SW8 1NL
Tel: 020 7582 3048 Fax: 020 7793 8658
Mob: 07831 330 340
Email: info@jilliebushell.com
Web Site: www.jilliebushell.com
Senior Personnel: Jillie Bushell
Book entertainment, speakers/motivational speakers, presenters and Jazz & Blues for corporate functions.

ARTISTES REPRESENTED:

Darren Bennet (Strictly Come Dancing)
Lilia Copylova (Strictly Come Dancing)
Caroline Hamilton
Zig Zag
Chicago - The Musical
ZooNation

BUSINESS EVENT MANAGEMENT

Moulton Park Business Centre,
Redhouse Road, Moulton Park,
Northampton NN3 6AQ
Tel: 01604 497 770 Fax: 01604 670 446
Email: enquiries@businessevent.co.uk
Web Site: www.businessevent.co.uk
Senior Personnel: Geoff Morgan
Specialising in all types of bespoke corporate entertainment/hospitality.

ARTISTES REPRESENTED:

Mika Hakkinen (Lookalike)
Michael Schumacher (Lookalike)

BUSINESS SPEAKERS BUREAU

13 Montagu Mews South, London
W1H 7ER
Tel: 0871 250 1234
Email: elizabeth@bsb.co.uk
Web Site: www.bsb.co.uk
Agent: Elizabeth Van Cleef
Guest Speakers, Celebrities & Entertainers for Corporate events.

BUSY BEE PROMOTIONS

216 Church Road, Haydock, St Helens,
Merseyside WA11 0LE
Tel: 01942 274 666 Fax: 01942 718 803
Email: info@busybee.co.uk
Web Site: www.busybee.co.uk
Senior Personnel: Linda Wooder
Specialise in children's entertainment.

BUZZ COMEDY CONSULTANCY

The Buzz in Chorlton closed in 2003
Apple Cottage, Carr Lane, Dunswell,
East Yorkshire HU6 0AT
Tel: 01482 806 001
Email: johnmarshall@buzzcomedy.co.uk
Web Site: www.buzzcomedy.co.uk
www.buzzcomedy.co.uk has details of current comedy shows.

BY INVITATION ONLY

Cotswold House, Netherstreet, Bromham,
Chippenham, Wiltshire SN15 2DW
Tel: 01380 859 255 Fax: 01380 850 453
Email: enquiries@by-invitation-only.co.uk
Web Site: www.by-invitation-only.co.uk
Contact: Rosemary English

ARTISTES REPRESENTED:

Magicians:
Roy Heath
Paul Macleavy
Jack Stephens

C.A. ARTISTES MANAGEMENT

26-28 Hammersmith Grove, London
W6 7BA
Tel: 020 8834 1608 Fax: 020 8834 1144
Email: casting@caartistes.com
Web Site: www.caartistes.com
Senior Personnal: Laila Debs

CABAL MANAGEMENT

9-10 Regent Square, London WC1H 8HZ
Tel/Fax: 020 7837 9648
Email: mikosapanin@hotmail.com
Contact: Michael Osapanin
Representing Jazz and Funk artists.

ARTISTES REPRESENTED:

Afronauts
Jazz Afrique Int.
Kabbala

CALEDONIAN MUSIC AGENCY

Caledonian Suite, 1 Bridge Place, Shotts,
Lanarkshire ML7 5JE
Tel: 01501 820 999 Fax: 01501 820 751
Email: eddie@caledonianmusic.co.uk
Web Site: www.caledonianmusic.co.uk
Senior Personnel: Eddie Buggy

ARTISTES REPRESENTED:

Diane Barry
Mandy Cowan
Stevie Scott
Too Special
Susan Weir

CALYPSO VOICES

25-26 Poland Street, London W1F 8QN
Tel: 020 7734 6415 Fax: 020 7437 0410
Email: calypso@calypsovoices.com
Web Site: www.calypsovoices.com
Senior Personnel: Jane Savage
Voice Over Agency - call for details.

CAM LONDON

55-59 Shaftesbury Avenue, London
W1D 6LD
Tel: 020 7292 0600 Fax: 020 7734 3205
Email: ld@cam.co.uk
Web Site: www.cam.co.uk
Senior Personnel: Michael Wiggs, Peter Brooks, Dawn Green, Lucy Doyle

ARTISTES REPRESENTED:

Jan Anderson
Nicole Appleton
Michelle Austin
Sarah Barrand
Lucy Benjamin
Chris Bisson
Natalie Casey
Jason Connery
Lindsey Coulson
Letitia Dean
Martin Delaney
Gaynor Faye
Connie Fisher
Martin Freeman
Adam Garcia
Claire Goose
Samantha Janus
Jonathan Kerrigan
Brooke Kinsella
Petra Letang
Gary Lucy
Cherie Lunghi
Michael McKell
Will Mellor
Siwan Morris
Laila Morse
Alison Newman
Tracy-Ann Oberman
Maggie O'Neill
Ray Panthaki
Heather Peace
Duncan Pow
Michael Praed
James Redmond
Georgia Reece
Ben Richards
Adam Rickitt
Samantha Robson
Laila Rouass
Jack Ryder
Cristian Solimeno
Dalip Tahil
Simon Thomas
Cathy Tyson
Paula Wilcox
Tam Williams
Jaime Winstone
Lois Winstone
Ray Winstone
Leigh Zimmerman

CAMBRIAN

24 Titan Court, Laporte Way, Luton,
Bedfordshire LU4 8EF
General Tel: 01582 488 888 Bookings
Tel: 0870 200 5000 Fax: 01582 488877
Email: dean@cambrian.tv
Web Site: www.cambrian.tv
Senior Personnel: Robin Breese-Davies
Executive Bookers: Dean Spain, Rob Malone
Entertainment Agency for live artists.

ALISON CAMPBELL MODEL AGENCY

381 Beersbridge Road, Belfast,
County Antrim BT5 5DT Northern Ireland
Tel: 028 9080 9809 Fax: 028 9080 9808
Email: info@alisoncampbellmodels.com

Web: www.alisoncampbellmodels.com
Senior Personnel: Alison Campbell
Various artistes for corporate & promotional events., inc Miss Northern Ireland

ARTISTES REPRESENTED:

Miss Northern Ireland

CANDLE

44 Southern Row, London W10 5AN
Tel: 020 8960 0111
Mobile: 07860 912192
Email: tony@candle.org.uk
Web Site: www.candle.org.uk
Managing Director: Tony Satchell
Creative Director: Charlie Spencer
Original composition for TV, Radio and Film.

ARTISTES REPRESENTED:

Charlie Spencer
Ian Ritchie
John Thomas
Philip Thurston

ALEXANDRA CANN REPRESENTATION

52 Beauchamp Place, London SW3 1NY
Tel: 020 7584 9047
Email: mail@alexandracann.co.uk
Senior Personnel: Alexandra Cann

ARTISTES REPRESENTED:

Writers:
Adrian Bailey
Ian Curteis
Colin Dann
Barbara Derkow
Keith Dewhurst
Disselbeck
Jamie Facer
Sean Hardie
Charlie Higson
Paul Laverty
Jeremy Lloyd
Gina Moxley
Tom Murphy
Philip Myall
Brendan O'Casey
Stewart Parker Estate
Alan Plater
Johnny Speight Estate
Paul Whitehouse
Directors:
Simon Cox
Michael Cumming
William Gaskill
Clive Gordon
Sean Hardie
Charlie Higson
Roxana Silbert
Sarah Wooley
Producers:
Sean Hardie
Charlie Higson
Paul Whitehouse

CANTABILE ARTISTS AGENCY

Gydar Ty Du Road, Glan Conwy, Colwyn Bay, Clwyd LL28 5NW
Tel: 01492 580202 Fax: 08700 516 248
Mobile: 07768 025 440
Email: haydn@cantabileartistsagency.co.uk
Web: www.cantabileartistsagency.co.uk
Agent: Haydn Jones
Cantabile Artists Agency are agents for outstanding young opera singers whose details can be found on the website.
In addition to their operatic work they are available for concerts, opera galas, oratorio and corporate entertainment.
Voice samples can be heard by visiting the shows page on the website.

CAPEL & LAND

29 Wardour Street London W1D 6PS
Tel: 020 7734 2414 Fax: 020 7734 8101
Email: anita@capelland.co.uk
Web Site: www.capelland.com
Director: Anita Land
Corporate: Joscelyn Evans

ARTISTES REPRESENTED:

Richard Arnold
Mark Austin
Nicky Campbell
Flora Fraser (Dramatic Rights)
Tristram Hunt
Aled Jones
Colleen McCullogh
Sir Trevor McDonald
Jonathan Meades
Vince Cable MP
Adam Nicolson
Jeremy Paxman
Stella Rimington
Andrew Roberts
Ian Sansom
Simon Sebag-Montefiore
John Sergeant
Alastair Stewart OBE
Louis Theroux
Fay Weldon

CAPITAL ARTS THEATRICAL AGENCY

Wyllyotts Centre, Wyllyotts Place, Darkes Lane, Potters Bar, Hertfordshire EN6 2HN
Tel/Fax: 020 8449 2342
Mobile: 07885 232414
Email: capitalarts@btconnect.com
Senior Personnel: Kathleen Shanks
Specialising in Award Winning Children's Choir, Show Choir.

CARDIFF CASTING

Actors Co-operative Management
Chapter Arts Centre, Market Road, Canton, Cardiff, South Glamorgan CF5 1QE Wales
Tel: 029 2023 3321 Fax: 029 2023 3380
Email: admin@cardiffcasting.co.uk
Web Site: www.cardiffcasting.co.uk
Co-operative agency working from Cardiff, representing Welsh and English actors for theatre, TV and film, to work in Wales and internationally.

ARTISTES REPRESENTED:

Madeline Adams
Sara Beer
Agnieska Blonska
Caroline Bunce
Kate Carter
Gareth Wyn Griffiths
Julie Gibbs
Aled Herbert
Llinos Mai
Naomi Martell
Bethan Morgan
Chris Morgan
Jared Morgan
Philip North
John Norton
Gareth Potter
Lizzie Rogan
Alastair Sill
Gerri Smith
Terry Victor
Nick Wayland Evans
Catherine Wilde

ROGER CAREY ASSOCIATES

Suite 909, The Old House, Shepperton Film Studios, Studios Road, Shepperton, Middlesex TW17 0QD
Tel: 01932 582 892 Fax: 01932 569 602
Email: info@rogercarey.f2s.com
Senior Personnel: Roger Carey, Primi Carey
Specialising in Actors, Producers, Directors and Packaging

ARTISTES REPRESENTED:

Christien Anholt
Carol Cleveland
Gerry Cowper
Linda Gray
Jane Seymour

CARNIVAL BAND SECRETARIES LEAGUE

15 Brendon Way, Long Eaton, Nottinghamshire, NG10 4JS
Tel: 0115 9725282 Mobile: 07790759571
Email: bands@cbsl.org.uk
Web Site: www.cbsl.org.uk
Senior Personnel: Mr B Cook
5 Bands in Senior Membership, Contests of 3-5 Bands organised consisting of 15 minutes each of intricate figure marching with live instruments. Alternatively, individual bands provided for engagements.

CAROL HAYES MANAGEMENT

5-6 Underhill Street London NW1 7HS
Tel: 020 7482 1555 Fax: 020 7482 3666
Email: carol@carolhayesmanagement.co.uk
Web: www.carolhayesmanagement.co.uk
Senior personnel: Carol Hayes

ARTISTES REPRESENTED:

Gok Wan

CAROUSEL EVENTS LLP

Incentive House 23 Castle Street
High Wycombe GP13 6RU
Tel: 01494 511266 Fax: 01494 511501
Email: alex@carouselevents.co.uk
Web Site: www.carouselevents.co.uk
Senior Personnel: Carole Fraser
Booking Agency and Event Management.

Specialising in corporate entertainment and themed events.

CAROUSEL PROMOTIONS

12 Hawks Way, Cuckoo Lane, Ashford, Kent TN23 5UN
Tel/Fax: 01233 620 120 Mobile: 07881 781517
Email: mikitravis@ntlworld.com
Web Site: www.carouselpromotions.co.uk
Sole Proprietor: Miki Travis

CAROUSELWINDSOR

7 Lawn Close, Datchet, Berkshire SL3 9JZ
Tel: 01753 546 374 Fax: 01753 546 370
Email: info@carouselwindsor.com
Web Site: www.carouselwindsor.com
Senior Personnel: R Gates, J Ponting
Specialising in business entertainment for conferences, exhibitions and team building.

NORRIE CARR AGENCY

Holborn Studios, 49 Eagle Wharf Road, London, N1 7ED
Tel: 020 7253 1771 Fax: 020 7253 1772
Email: info@norriecarr.com
Web Site: www.norriecarr.com
Contact: Sally Peters. Kate Blakey
Specialising in: Kids, babies & Adults up to 80 years old.

FRANK CARSON

118 Newton Drive, Blackpool FY3 8JA
Tel: 01253 391 361
Email: aidancarson@hotmail.com

ARTISTES REPRESENTED:

Frank Carson KSG

HAL CARTER ORGANISATION

41 Horsefair Green, Stony Stratford, Milton Keynes MK11 1JP
Tel: 01908 567388 Fax: 01707 657822
Mob: 07958 252906
Email: artistes@halcarterorg.com
Web Site: www.halcarterorg.com
Managing Director: Abbie Carter-Burrows

ARTISTES REPRESENTED:

Sole Representation:
The Carpenters Story
The Illegal Eagles
Eden Kane
Mud II ft. members of Les Grays Mud
Oh Boy! It's Rock 'n' Roll feat. The Vernon Girls, John Leyton & Rockin' Horse
Slade
Non-Exclusive Representation:
Dave Dee, Dozy, Beaky, Mich & Tich
The New Seekers
The Rubettes
Rumours Of Fleetwood Mac
The Swinging Blue Jeans
The Tremeloes
The Troggs
Marty Wilde & The Wildcats

CARTEUR'S THEATRICAL AGENCY

170a Church Road, Hove, East Sussex BN3 2DJ
Tel: 01273 770 445 Fax: 01273 770 444
Email: dianacarteur@stonelandsschool.co.uk
Web Site: www.stonelandsschool.co.uk
Contacts: Diana Cateur
Specialising in management of Children.

CASAROTTO RAMSAY & ASSOCIATES LTD

Waverley House, 7-12 Noel Street, London W1F 8GQ
Tel: 020 7287 4450 Fax: 020 7287 9128
Email: agents@casarotto.co.uk, info@casarotto.co.uk
Web Site: www.casarotto.co.uk
ADMINISTRATION:
Film and television department: Jeenne Casarotto
Theatrical Department: Tom Erhardt and Mel Kenyon
One of the UK's leading creative agencies, representing writers, directors, directors of photography, production designers, costume designers and editors.

ARTISTES REPRESENTED:

Writers: Film & Television:
John Arden
JG Ballard
John Barton
Smita Bhide
Adam Bostock-Smith
Howard Brenton (German)
Simon Brett
Irena Brignull
John Byrne
Simon Callow
Bob Carlton
Daragh Carville (French)
Caryl Churchill
Boyd Clack
Lucy Clarke
Rob Colley
Sean Conway
Ben Cooper
Paul Copley
Nancy Crane
David Cregan
Sarah Daniels
April De Angelis
Brian Dooley
Frank Dunlop
Chris Durlacher
Richard Easter
Chris Fewtrell
Emma Forrest
Paul Fraser
Dan Freeman
Jeremy Front
Dan Gaster
Peter Gill
Roger Goldby
Mark Grant
Chris Green
Heidi Greensmith
David Greig
Tony Grisoni
Roger Hall
Christopher Hampton (French/German)
Mike Harding
Sir David Hare
Zinnie Harris
David Harrower
Vaclav Havel
Jane Hawksley
Phil Hughes
Angela Huth
Will Ing
Helen Jacey
Stephen Jeffreys
Ann Jellicoe
Amy Jenkins
Lisa Jewell
Genevieve Jolliffe
Laura Jones
Sadie Jones
Terry Jones (Southport Weekender)
Neil Jordan
Sarah Kennedy
Raymond Khoury
Hardeep Singh-Kohli
Larry Kramer
Karen Laws
Pete Lawson
David Leland
Matthew Leys
Don Macpherson
Melanie Martinez
Paul Mayhew-Archer
Frank McGuinness
John McKay
Shane Meadows
Andrew Meehan
Menno Meyjes
Dominic Minghella
Chloe Moss
Susan Nickson
Phil Nodding
Sam North
Gary Parker
Ged Parsons
Paul Powell
Adam Preston
Peter Prince
Neal Purvis & Robert Wade
Mark Ravenhill
Yasmina Reza
Gillian Richmond
Aileen Ritchie
Tony Roche
Nicholas Rohl
Amy Rosenthal
David Rudkin
Howard Schuman
Wallace Shawn
Ariane Sherine
Martin Sherman
Ned Sherrin
Ben Silburn
Vaughan Sivell
Shawn Slovo
Will Smith & Roger Drew
Neville Smith
Simon Stephens
Jessica Stevenson
Kay Stonham
Peter Straughan
Martin Trenaman
Arabella Weir
Timberlake Wertenbaker (French/Italian/Greek)

Philip Whitchurch
Ted Whitehead
David Wood OBE
Kfir Yefet
Writers: Playwrights:
Kate Atkinson
Sir Alan Ayckbourn
Edward Bond
Howard Brenton (German)
Caryl Churchill
David Cregan
Ben Elton
David Hare
David Harrower
Stephen Jeffreys
Ben Musgrave
Phyllis Nagy (French)
Moses Raine
David Rudkin
Willy Russell
Writers/Directors:
Lexi Alexander
Saul Dibb
Roger Goldby
Heidi Greensmith
Tony Grisoni
Duane Hopkins
Neil Hunter
Neil Jordan
Sam Leifer
Sergio Muchado
Translators:
Howard Brenton (German)
Daragh Carville (French)
Christopher Hampton (French/German)
Meredith Oakes (German)
Timberlake Wertenbaker (French/Italian/Greek)
Estates:
Peter Barnes
Debbie Barnham (Estate)
Robert Bolt (Estate)
Jeremy Brooks (Estate)
Roald Dahl (Estate)
John Hawkesworth
Aldous Huxley (Estate)
Sarah Kane (Estate)
Frank Marcus (Estate)
John McGrath (Estate)
David Mercer
Michael Meyer (Estate)
Bill Naughton (Estate)
Joe Orton (Estate)
Manuel Puig (Estate)
Jean Rhys (Estate)
Jack Rosenthal
James Saunders
HG Wells (Estate)
Tennessee Williams (Estate)
Dame Muriel Spark (Estate)
Directors:
Carine Adler
Lexi Alexander
Stephen Burke
Bob Carlton
Tom Carty
Vesna Cudic
Hattie Dalton
Jasmin Dizdar
Ciaran Donnelly
Chris Durlacher
David Evans
Brian Farnham
Sheree Folkson
Stephen Frears
Sarah Gavron
Terry Gilliam
Roger Goldby
Karl Golden
Piers Haggard
Peter Hewitt
Enda Hughes
Tom Hunsinger
Genevieve Jolliffe
Terry Jones (Southport Weekender)
Neil Jordan
Liam Kam & Grant Hodgson
David Kerr
David Leland
Richard Loncraine
Fraser MacDonald
Toby Macdonald
John Madden
John McKay
Shane Meadows
Chris Menges
Menno Meyjes
Marc Munden
Mark Mylod
Billy O'Brien
Damien O'Donnell
Angela Pope
Tristram Powell
Udayan Prasad
Jamie Rafn
Aileen Ritchie
Bernard Rose
Miguel Sapochnik
Philip Saville
Tristram Shapeero
Robin Sheppard
Iain Softley
Rachel Talalay
Julien Temple
Joachim Trier
Mat Wakeham
Dearbhla Walsh
Paul Weiland
Tim Whitby
Andy Wilson
Claire Winyard
Stephen Woolley
David Yates
Kfir Yefet

CASTCALL CASTING SERVICES

106 Wilsden Avenue, Luton, Bedfordshire LU1 5HR
Tel: 01582 456 213 Fax: 01582 480 736
Email: info@castcall.co.uk
Web Site: www.castcall.co.uk
Senior Personnel: Ron O'Brien

THE CASTING COUCH

213 Trowbridge Road, Bradford-on-Avon, Wiltshire BA15 1EU
Tel: 07932 785 807 Fax: 01225 869 029
Email: moiratownsend@yahoo.co.uk
Contact: Moira Townsend

THE CASTING STUDIO

The Burnside Centre, 38 Burnside Crescent, Middleton, Manchester M24 5NN
Tel/Fax: 0161 643 6266
Email: info@thecastingstudio.co.uk
Web Site: www.thecastingstudio.co.uk
Senior Personnel: Jonathan Burns
Accounts Manager: Stacey Ward

THE CASTING NETWORK

2nd Floor, 10 Claremont Road, Surbiton, Surrey KT6 4QU
Tel: 020 8339 9090 Fax: 020 8390 0605
Email: lesleycastingnetwork@talk21.com
Web Site: www.thecastingnetwork.co.uk
Agency owner Lesley Reid is the most experienced crowd casting specialist in the country, and has trained and worked in this field for twenty five years. Established in 1999 The Casting Network insists that all the artists we represent are experienced professionals, preferably with some kind of formal training. We actively reject applications from people wanting to be on television as a hobby.

CASTME UK

Talgarth House 15 Crosby Road South, Liverpool L22 1RG
Tel: 07840 435235
Email: michelle@michellebillington.co.uk
Web Site: www.castmeuk.com
Contact: Michelle Billington

THE CBS GROUP

The Old School House, Blendworth, Waterlooville, Hampshire PO8 0AB
Tel: 023 9257 0001 Fax: 023 9257 0002
Mobile: 07850 305631 / 2
Email: info@cbsgroup.co.uk
Web Site: www.cbsgroup.co.uk
Senior Personnel: Steve Cook, Russ Brewster, Nigel Smith
The UK's leading band management company - providing bands and entertainers for corporate, charity and private parties and events.

ARTISTES REPRESENTED:

Exclusive Representation:
Star
Mixed Feelings
Scaramouch
China Grove
Souled Out
Co-Stars
Twilight Zone Disco
Vice Versa
La Tour
The Mix
All That's Jazz
Gary Marshall Roadshow
Represented:
Alpha Connection
Caprice
Cuff Billet Jazz Band
Fred Dinenage
James Duke Band
Gentlemen & Players
Intrigue
Ian Irving (Comedian)

Jambalaya
Liaison
Madison Square
Mr Sketchum's Caricatures
Musik Express
Tommy Quinn
Slap & Tickle
The Spotlites
Top Hat 'N Tales
Westway
Zig Zag

CCA MANAGEMENT

Garden Level, 32 Charlwood Street, London SW1V 2DY
Tel: 020 7630 6303 Fax: 020 7630 7376
Email: dulcie@ccamanagement.co.uk
Proprietor & Technician's Agent: Dulcie Huston
Actor's Agent: Patrick Hambleton
CCA has been an Agency for over 40 years and is a member of the PMA (Personal Managers Association). CCA represents actors, actresses, directors of photography, production designers, editors, directors and make-up & hair designers. Please call either Dulcie or Patrick for further information.

CCM (CHANCERY CO-OPERATIVE MANAGEMENT)

Panther House, 38 Mount Pleasant, London WC1X 0AP
Tel: 020 7278 0507 Fax: 020 7813 3103
Email: casting@ccmactors.com
Web Site: www.ccmactors.com
We are an actor's co-operative agency seeking professional employment in film, television and theatre.

ARTISTES REPRESENTED:

Actors:
Martin Bendel
Michael Esswood
Actresses:
Isabel Barbuk
Lesley Cook
Elaine Postil

CDA (CAROLINE DAWSON ASSOCIATES)

125 Gloucester Road, London SW7 4TE
Tel: 020 7373 3323 Fax: 020 7373 1110
Email: cda@cdalondon.com
Senior Personnel: Caroline Dawson, Belinda Wright, Laura Gibbons

ARTISTES REPRESENTED:

Robbie Coltrane

C.D.E.C.

108 Old Yarmouth Road, Effingham (West), Bungay, Suffolk NR35 3PG
Tel: 01508 518 247
Senior Personnel: Clive Dee

ARTISTES REPRESENTED:

AMERICAN
The Classics
East Coast West
Honeycombs2
Mirror & Dee
The Sixties Supergroup
Sound As A Pound

CEC MANAGEMENT

65-69 White Lion Street, London N1 9PP
Tel: 020 7837 2517 Fax: 020 7287 5915
Email: michelle@cecmanagement.com
Contact: Michelle Heaven
Agent: Nathan McGough
Artiste Managers: Phil Morais, Garry Boorman, Matt Willis

ARTISTES REPRESENTED:

Absentee
Dee Adams
Chungking
Luke Haines
Hafdis Huld
KTP
Members Of The Public
Opera House
Ben Parker
Pets for Pilots
The Rakes
Screaming Ballerinas
The Be Be See
The Eighties Matchbox B-Line Disaster
The On Offs
The Others
The Switches
The Zico Chain
Untitled Music Project
Vile Imbeciles

CEEBEE VARIETY AGENCY

4a Queens Road, Sheffield S2 4DG
Tel: 0114 275 3909 / 4507 Fax: 0114 272 8091
Email: info@ceebeevariety.com
Web Site: www.ceebeevariety.com
Contact: Keith Chapman

ARTISTES REPRESENTED:

Comedy:
Jimmy Carol
Duos:
Awesome Duesome
Super Kings
The Truth
Special Show:
Stars of the Future, Produced by Stephanie King
Male Vocalists:
Robbi 'H'
Ethan Leigh
Wayne Marcus
Lenny Michaels
Gary Philips
Female Vocalists:
Kerry Anne
Bev Brookes
Gemma Jay
Jessica Jay
Kadi Kane
Stephanie King
Jade McKenzie
Kitty Michelle
Rachel Raynor
Sarah Lee Scott

CELEBRATION ENTERTAINMENTS MANAGEMENT & AGENCY

PO Box 238, Lord Street, Southport, Merseyside PR8 6GQ
Tel: 08707 567 345 Fax: 08707 063 322
Email: info@celebrations-entertainments.uk.com
Web: www.celebrations-entertainments.uk.com
Senior Personnel: Glynis Blackburn, David Chadwick

ARTISTES REPRESENTED:

The Beetles - UK
Paula Delaney
Mandi Gibbons
Sharron Knight
The Spice of Life Variety Show
Zenika

CELEBRATION MODEL MANAGEMENT

PO Box 91, Neston, Cheshire CH64 6LX
Mobile: 07776 236 367
Email: agents@celebration-manag.co.uk
Web Site: www.celebration-manag.co.uk
Senior Personnel: Dave Bradshaw, Tom Bradshaw
Model Agency representing glamour and fashion models to the model industry, corporate functions, page 3, nightclubs, promotions, company promotions.

ARTISTES REPRESENTED:

Tanya Arnold
Nicole Binney
Mellissa Blake
Jackie Brown
Debi Bryan
Debbie Clarke
Lisa Clarke
Sarah Craven
Debbie Cross
Lisa Marie Curtain
Annette Davies
Helen Edgar
Lorna Edgar
Lorna Edgar
Michelle Evans
Roxy Gregory
Louise Horn
Lucy Hunter
Joanie
Terri Jones
Claire Keirnan
Nathan Kenshaw
Karolina Ksiazek
Gemma Lamonby
Heather Latona
Lisanne Meadowcroft
Julia Moorley
Sue Morgan
Louise Noble
Cassie Northwood
Viki Pearson
Tracey Platt
Lisa Roberts
Viet Roberts
Sonya Roseman
Shinobie
Michelle Trainer

THE CELEBRITY GROUP
13 Montagu Mews South, London
W1H 7ER
Tel: 0871 250 1234
Email: brad@celebrity.co.uk
Web Site: www.celebrity.co.uk
Agent: Brad Cohen
Celebrities for Advertising, Endorsements and Corporate Events.

CELEBRITY MANAGEMENT LTD
A Celebrity Group Company
12 Nottingham Place, London W1U 5NE
Freephone: 080 800 808 808 Bookings: 020 7224 5050 Fax: 020 7224 6060
Email: info@celebrity.co.uk
Web Site: www.celebrity.co.uk
Contact: Simona Gambimi

CSA - CELEBRITY SPEAKERS LTD
90 High Street, Burnham, Berkshire
SL1 7JT
Tel: 01628 601 400 Fax: 01628 601 4101
Email: csa@speakers.co.uk
Web Site: www.speakers.co.uk
Senior Personnel: Alex Krywald

CENTRAL ENTERTAINMENTS
105 Blake Road, Corby,
Northamptonshire NN18 9LW
Tel: 01536 398 275 Fax: 01536 398 468
Email: centralact@ntlworld.com
Senior Personnel: Brian Spooner

ARTISTES REPRESENTED:
Cory Gray

CENTRAL EVENTS UK LTD
The Barn Fifield Farm Marlston Road
Marlston Nr Hermitage Berkshire
RG18 9UN
Tel: 01235 760 342 Fax: 01635 202 088
Email: heidi.smith@s-l-v.co.uk
Web Site: www.central-production.co.uk
Senior Personnel: Jim Williams
Specialise in production of rigging, staging, lighting, PA, theming, power distribution, marquees and catering for corporate and private parties.
At Central Events UK, we pride ourselves in being a full service events management company whcih gives us the freedom to offer the very best in service, product and price to our customers.

ARTISTES REPRESENTED:
Simon Curry Jazz Band
Fingle String Quartet

CENTRAL LINE CO-OPERATIVE PERSONAL MANAGEMENT
11 East Circus Street, Nottingham
NG1 5AF
Tel: 0115 941 2937 Fax: 0115 950 8087 - on request only
Email: centralline@btconnect.com
Web Site: www.the-central-line.co.uk

ARTISTES REPRESENTED:
Julia Binns
Aaron Bixley
Matt Brown
Orde Browne
Hayley Considine
Julia Damassa
Richard Ely
Steve Finch
Kim Gillespie
Diana Johnson
Glen Kinch
Rebecca Mahon
Sophia Ortiz
Amanda-Leigh Owen
Nick Paley
Sally Siner
Karon Spragg
Lou Webb

CHAMBERS MANAGEMENT LTD
39-41 Parker Street London WC2B 5PQ
Tel: 020 7796 3588 Fax: 020 7796 3676
Email: hannah@chambersmgt.co.uk/sophie@chabersmgt.co.uk
Web Site: www.chambersmgt.co.uk
Contact: Hannah Chambers
A management agency specialising in stand up comedians, comedian actors and presenters. Artists currently include 2 Perrier award winners and 2 Perrier nominees. We are also booking agents for a number of International Comedy Festivals.

ARTISTES REPRESENTED:
Ninia Benjamin
Frankie Boyle
Jimmy Carr
Pippa Evans
Flight Of The Conchords
Josh Howie
Andrew Lawrence
Demetri Martin
Sarah Millican
David O'Doherty
Jack Whitehall
Jack Whitehall
Jason Wood

CHAMPIONS (UK) PLC
Barrington House Leake Road, Costock, Loughborough, Leicestershire LE12 6XA
Tel: 08453 313 031 Fax: 08453 313 032
Mob: 07976 170576
Email: owillson@championsukplc.com
Web Site: www.championsukplc.com
Contact: Oliver Willson (Celebrity Manager)
Sporting event management services for winners,

ARTISTES REPRESENTED:
Sole Managed:
Andy Abraham
Dennis Amiss MBE
Liz Bennett
David Bryon
Tony Jacklin CBE
Brian Close CBE
Tony Currie
Stuart Davis
Phillip Defreitas
Big Joe Egan
Emma Jesson
Tony Knowles
Gary Wolstenholme MBE
Alan Mullery MBE
Henry Olonga
Craig Phillips
Peter Shilton MBE OBE
Graeme Storm
John H Stracey
Dennis Taylor
Willie Thorne
Chris Walker
William Roache MBE
Rod Woodward
Sporting Speakers:
Nicola Adams
Ade Adepitan
Rebecca Adlington OBE
Ben Ainslie
Kriss Akabusi MBE MA
Gary Alliss
Peter Alliss
John Amaechi
Bob Anderson
Lizzie Armistead
Lance Armstrong
Clare Balding
Sue Barker OBE
Martin Bayfield
Bill Beaumont OBE
Boris Becker
Graham Bell
Phil Bennett OBE
Dickie Bird MBE
Roger Black MBE
James Blake
Henry Blofeld OBE
Annabelle Bond
Peter Bowler
Bradley Wiggins
Alan Brazil
Paul Broadhurst
Sir Trevor Brooking CBE
Alistair and Jonathan Brownlee
Frank Bruno MBE
Katy Bullock
Joe Calzaghe
Steve Caridge
Will Carling OBE
Pat Cash
Andrew Castle
Mike Catt
Tony Jacklin CBE
Dwain Chambers
Bob Champion MBE
Gareth Chilcott
Jeremy Clarkson
Brian Close CBE
Lord Sebastian Coe
Pierluigi Collina
Steve Collins
Jimmy Conors
John Conteh
David Coulthard
James Cracknell OBE
Steve Cram MBE
Annabel Croft
Steve Daking
Tom Daley
Jonathan Davies MBE
Steve Davis

Frankie Dettori
Lee Dixon
Luke Donald MBE
Richard Dunwoody MBE
Charlotte Durjardin
Jonathan Edwards CBE
Big Joe Egan
Gail Emms
Jessica Ennis
Chris Eubanh
John Famworth
Mo Farah
Mick Fitzgerald
Andrew Flintoff MBE
Andy Fordham
Brendon Foster CBE
Chris Froome
Bobby George
Graham Gooch OBE
Darren Gough
Andy Gray
Will Greenwood MBE
Sally Gunnell OBE
Jeremy Guscott
Pen Haddow
Alan Hansen
John Hartson
David Haye
Austin Healey
Tim Henman
Johnny Herbert
Damon Hill OBE
Matthew Hoggard
Dame Kelly Holmes
Jahe Humphrey
Dan Hunt
Nasser Hussain OBE MA
Eddie Irvine
Colin Jackson CBE
Mark James
Martin Johnson CBE
Michael Johnson
Jade Jones
Anthony Joshua
Kevin Keagan
Jason Kenny
Amir Khan
Bernhard Langer OBE
Sugar Ray Leonard
Denise Lewis
Lennox Lewis
Gary Lineker OBE
Carl Llewellyn
John Lowe
Sandy Lyle
Dean Macey
Dean Macey
Penny Mallory
Nigel Mansell OBE
Matt Dawson MBE
Gary Wolstenholme MBE
Gary McAllister
Perry McCarthy
John McEnroe
Barry McGuigan MBE
Rory McIlroy
Alan McInally
Ed McKeever
Paul Merson
Geoff Miller
Colin Montgomerie
Andy Murray
Rafael Nadal
Gary Neville
Henry Olonga
Michael Owen
Ray Parlour
John Parrott MBE
Matthew Pinsent
Gary Player
Mike Procter
Sir Steven Redgrave CBE
Derek Redmond
Mark Regan MBE
Dean Richards
Jason Robinson MBE
Laura Robson
Neil Ruddock
Greg Rutherford
Tessa Sanderson CBE
Goldie Sayers
Peter Schmeichel MBE
David Seaman
Lee Sharpe
Alan Shearer
Peter Shilton MBE OBE
Sir Chris Hoy
Louis Smith
Sir Garfield Sobers
Jeff Stelling
Alec Stewart
Graeme Storm
John H Stracey
Andrew Strauss
Ronnie O'Sullivan
Dennis Taylor
Phil Taylor
Iwan Thomas
Derek Thompson
Daley Thopmson CBE
Willie Thorne
Sam Torrance
Laura Trott
Phil Tufnell
Mike Tyson
Michael Vaughan OBE
Victoria Pendleton
John Virgo
Murray Walker OBE
Doddie Weir
Lee Westwood
Jonny Wilkinson
Amy Williams
Peter Wilson
Ian Woosnam

Entertainers & Comedians:
Chris Addison
Bruce Airhead
Jon Allen
Stephen K Amos
Beardyman
Anton Du Beke and Erin Boag
Jo Brand
Gyles Brandreth
Roy Bremner
Kevin Bridges
Adger Brown
Derren Brown
Alan Carr
Jimmy Carr
Jeremy Clarkson
Kevin Connelly
Steve Daking
Paul Daniels
Jim Davidson OBE
Graham Davies
Greg Davies
Bobby Davro
Angus Deayton
Hugh Dennis
Omid Djalili
Dynamo
Simon Evans
Micky Flanagan
Stephen Fry
Tony Hawks
Brendan Healy
Rufus Hound
Aaron James
Graham P Jolley
Milton Jones
James & Ola Jordan
Russell Kane
Sean Lock
Laura London
Gary Marshall
Alistair McGowan
Michael McIntyre
Sarah Millican
Tim Minchin
Patrick Monahan
Alfie Moore
Al Murray - The Pub Landlord
Kev Orkian
Andy Parsons
Piff the Magic Dragon
Fay Presto
David Redfearn
Jon Richardson
Ted Robbins
Mark Rough
Martin Semple
Jamie Sutherland
Sean Walsh
Jack Whitehall
Spencer Wood
Dom Woodward
Rod Woodward

Music Acts:
Clive Abbot
Andy Abraham
Peter Andre
Campbell Bass
Beardyman
Anton Du Beke and Erin Boag
Buble Fever
Marcus Collins
Fearne Cotton
Diversity
Escala
Stavros Flatley
Flight Of The Conchords
Lesley Garrett
Gareth Gates
Groove Nation
Calvin Harris
Katherine Jenkins
Jessie J
Danyl Johnson
James & Ola Jordan
Amelia Lilly
Johann Lippowitz
Ruth Lorenzo
Mango Acoustic
MIB Band
Olly Murs

Platinum
Rang-a-Tang
Rawless
Schwing
Signature
Shaun Smith
Spellbound
The Boys Next Door
The Krystalettes
The Risk
The RPJ Band
The Saturdays
The Tootsie Rollers
The Upbeat Beatles
Ione Thomas
Tulisa Contostavlos
Shayne Ward
Laura White
John Wilding

Event Hosts:
Peter Alliss
John Amaechi
Ant & Dec
Sue Barker OBE
Anton Du Beke and Erin Boag
Graham Bell
Jeff Brazier
Michael Buerk
Jim Davidson OBE
Hugh Dennis
Nadine Dereza
Ben Fogle
Stephen Fry
Ainsley Harriott
Colin Jackson CBE
Bernard Langer OBE
Gary Lineker OBE
Gabby Logan BA
Gary Wolstenholme MBE
Davina McCall
Alistair McGowan
Dermot O'Leary
Craig Phillips
Sir Steven Redgrave CBE
Charlie Ross
Jonathan Ross
John Sergeant
Peter Shilton MBE OBE
Jeff Stelling
Lord Alan Sugar
Willie Thorne
William Roache MBE
Professor Lord Robert Winston

TV Personalities:
Chris Addison
Ant & Dec
Mike Baker
Sue Barker OBE
Boris Becker
Anton du Beke
Graham Bell
Karren Brady
Jeff Brazier
Derren Brown
James Buckley
Michael Buerk
Jimmy Carr
Andrew Castle
Jeremy Clarkson
Suzanne Collins
Brian Cox
Steve Cram MBE
Annabel Croft
Paul Daniels
Jim Davidson OBE
Greg Davies
Angus Deayton
Beverley Denim
Nadine Dereza
Omid Djalili
Paddy Doherty
Leon Doyle
Dynamo
Chris Ellison
Ben Fogle
Brendon Foster CBE
Stephen Fry
Jeremy Guscott
Miranda Hart
Austin Healey
Nick Hewer
Sherrie Hewson
Rufus Hound
Jake Humphrey
Colin Jackson CBE
Emma Jesson
Russell Kane
Jamie Laing
Nigella Lawson
Gary Lineker OBE
Sean Lock
Gabby Logan BA
Penny Mallory
Matt Dawson MBE
Davina McCall
Perry McCarthy
John McEnroe
Ewan McGregor
Michael McIntyre
Colin Murray
Andrew Neil
Dermot O'Leary
Craig Phillips
Ted Robbins
Jonathan Ross
John Sergeant
Alan Shearer
Lord Alan Sugar
The Only Way Is Essex
Willie Thorne
Matt le Tissier
Tulisa Contostavlos
Greg Wallace
Jack Whitehall
William Roache MBE
Professor Lord Robert Winston
Anthony Worrall Thompson
Mark Wright

Auctioneers:
Michael Buerk
Andrew Castle
Tony Jacklin CBE
Jeremy Clarkson
Chris Eubanh
Stephen Fry
Gary Lineker OBE
Sir Steven Redgrave CBE
Charlie Ross
John Sergeant
Peter Shilton MBE OBE
Jeff Stelling
Dennis Taylor
Willie Thorne
Phil Tufnell

Business and Motivational Speakers:
Lord Andrew Adonis PC
Kriss Akabusi MBE MA
James Alexander
John Amaechi
Lance Armstrong
Lord Paddy Ashdown
Mike Baker
Duncan Bannatyne OBE
James Bellini
Sir Tim Bernes-Lee
Jasmine Birtles
Lord Ian Blair
David Blunkett
Annabelle Bond
Philippe Bourguignon
Major David Bradley
Karen Brady
Sir Richard Branson
David Bryon
Paul Burrell
William Butler-Adams
James Caan
Alistair Campbell
Tim Campbell MBE
Rene Carayol MBE
Barbara Cassani
Peter Cochrane
Pete Cohen
Colonel Tim Collins
Charles Van Commence
Martin Corry MBE
Brian Cox
BJ Cunningham
David Davis
Frankie Dettori
Leon Doyle
Richard Dunwoody MBE
Wilfred Emmanuel-Jones
Josephine Fairley
Adrian Fawcett
Sir Ranulph Fiennes Bt OBE
Ben Fogle
Kevin Fong
Rupert Gavin
PY Gerbeau
Jacqueline Gold
Craig Goldblatt
Bear Grylls
Sir Stuart Hampson
Andy Hanselman
Mike Harris
Sahar Hashemi
Wayne Hemingway MBE
Nick Hewer
Anthony Hilton
Brent Hoberman
Matthew Hoggard
Christer Holloman
Chris Huhme
Alex Hunter
Baron Douglas Hurd CH CBE PC
Lord Digby Jones
Andy Kirkpatrick
Lord Norman Lamont
Jim Lawless
Terry Leahy
Ken Livingstone
Dr Pippa Malmgren
Martin Glenn
Gary Wolstenholme MBE
Martin McCourt

Andrew McMillan
Deborah Meaden
David Milliband MP
Michelle Mone
Colin Montgomerie
Chris Moon
Andrew Neil
Richard Park
John Pienaar
Matthew Pinsent
Mary Portas
Michael Portillo
Lord John Prescott
Shaf Rasul
Gerald Ratner
Sir Steven Redgrave CBE
Richard Reed
Mark Regan MBE
Doug Richard
Jeremy Rifkin
Levi Roots
Goldie Sayers
John Sergeant
Lee Sharpe
Peter Shilton MBE OBE
Elaine Sihera
David Smith
Jayne Storey
Lord Alan Sugar
Simon Weston OBE
Ann Widdecombe
Amy Williams
Professor Lord Robert Winston
Sharon Wright

Celebrity Chefs:

Tom Aikens
Ed Baines
Mary Berry
Raymond Blanc
Gino D'Acampo
Sara la Fountain
Ainsley Harriott
Paul Hollywood
Rachel Khoo
James Martin
Jean Christophe Novelli
Jamie Oliver
Gordon Ramsay
Simon Rimmer
Levi Roots
Michael Roux Jr
Rick Stein OBE
James Tanner
The Fabulous Baker Brothers
John Torode
Brian Turner
Marco Pierre White
Aldo Zilli

CHANCE ENTERTAINMENT

321 Fulham Road, London SW10 9QL
Tel: 020 7376 5995 Fax: 0207 376 3598
Email: info@chanceorganisation.co.uk
Web Site: www.chanceorganisation.co.uk
Contacts: Andrew Chance & Jeremy Anderson

CHANCE PROMOTIONS

The Nook, Bee Lane, Penwortham, Preston PR1 9TU
Tel: 01772 321 160
Email: info@legendschance.com
Web Site: www.legendschance.com
Managing Directors: Trevor Chance, Brenda Chance
Creative Musical director: Richard Chance
Choreographer: Wendy Holland
Company Production Manager: Tony Harvey
Specialising in Look/Sound Alike Shows & Tributes.

ARTISTES REPRESENTED:

Tribute Artists:

Maxine Barrie (Shirley Bassey)
Hamilton Brown (Lionel Richie)
Matt Byrne (Robbie Williams)
Vinette Cawan (Tina Turner & Diana Ross)
Jack Danson (Rod Stewart)
Great Legends of Rock
Jonathan Kane (Elton John)
Billy Lee as Tom Jones
Legends
Tony Lewis (Robbie Williams)
Clayton Mark (Elvis)
Nick McCullock (Neil Diamond)
Kerry Miller (Kylie Minogue)
Waterloo (Abba tribute)

DAVID CHARLES AGENCY

2 Betjeman Way, Hemel Hempstead, Hertfordshire HP1 3HH
Tel: 01442 264 402 Mobile: 07767 813 231
Email: david@davidcharlesent.co.uk
Web Site: www.davidcharlesent.co.uk
Senior Personnel: David Charles, Penny Charles
Specialising in adult entertainment, bands and groups.

ARTISTES REPRESENTED:

007' seventies
Abba-Dabba-Do
Bad Boys (Wham)
Jazz Beans
Bees Knees (Bee Gees tribute)
Belt & Braces
Ben Dover
Boogielicious
Crazy 'K' Barn Dance
Eclipse The Band
Elvis Shmelvis (Ind Art)
Extreme Force
Glam & Glitz
Louise Hodges
Hot & Horny
Frankie Jakeman
Martin Jenner
Sammy Jessop
Ky-Lee (Kylie Minogue)
Mandrake
Johnny McGee
Linsey Dawn McKenzie
Men in Black
Funk Monkeys
Nite Vibes Disco
Not The "Blues Brothers"
Planet Funk
Raggle Taggle Cielidh
Savoir Faire
Second Time Around
Neith Snake
Phil Steed (Tom Jones)
Sassy Stryker
Tequilaville
Triple 'X' Showgirls
Wet Tarts

PETER CHARLESWORTH & ASSOCIATES

2nd Floor, 68 Old Brompton Road, London SW7 3LQ
Tel: 020 7581 2478 Fax: 020 7589 2922
Email: info@petercharlesworth.co.uk
Senior Personnel: Peter Charlesworth, Sharry Clark

ARTISTES REPRESENTED:

Actors:

Nick Bateman
Lionel Blair
Donnie Burns & Gaynor Fairweather
Marcus Clarke
Peter Donegan
Clive Dunn
James Ellis
Mikey Graham
Kenneth Haigh
Melvyn Hayes
Fred Housego
Barry Howard
Harry Landis
Mike McStat
Michael Offei
Lee Ormsby
Anthony Parker
Dean Read
Pat Roach
Howard Samuels
George Sewell
George Shane
Andrew Swift
Vernon Thompson
Brian Tipping
Giles Watling
Colin Welland
Sean Wilton

Actresses:

Avril Angers
Liz Banks
Colette Bibby
Angela Bull
Zalie Burrow
Katherine Cameron
Karen Mayo Chandler
Suzie Chard
Lorraine Chase
Jennifer Clulow
Joan Collins
Britt Elland
Liz Fraser
Hollie Garrett
Emma Gilmour
Susan Hanson
Susan Hanson
Anita Harris
Jeannie Harris
Emma Hibbert
Samantha Hughes
Katy Manning
Corinne Martin
Kate O'Sullivan
Mandy Perryment
Shani Phillips

Jennifer Reischel
Jennifer Reischel
Rachel Victoria Roberts
Julie Rogers
Chrystal Rose
Tracy Shaw
Jemma Shepherd
Annemette Klinkby Silver
Kathy Sorley
Lynda Steadman
Laurie Veale
Shani Wallis
Shani Wallis
Valerie Walsh
Sally Ann Webster

CHASE PERSONAL MANAGEMENT
Modelplan's Celebrity & Presenter Division
Tel: 0161 819 1180
Email: sue@sammon.fsnet.co.uk
Agents: Sue Sammon, Michelle Davenport
ARTISTES REPRESENTED:
TV Presenters:
Franchesca Robinson
Sarah Whitefoot

CHATTO & LINNIT LTD
123a Kings Road, London SW3 4PL
Tel: 020 7352 7722 Fax: 020 7352 3450
Email: rchatto@chattolinnit.com
Web Site: www.chattolinnit.com
Senior Personnel: Rosalind Chatto, Lucy Robinson
ARTISTES REPRESENTED:
Ronnie Barker
Keith Baxter
Tom Bell
Alan Bennett
Dr John Bird OBE
Bryan Brown
Jasper Conran
Judy Davis
Susan Hampshire
Robert Hardy
Ursula Howells
Paul Jones
Felicity Kendal
Moira Lister
Nicholas Lyndhurst
Sarah Miles
Hayley Mills
Franco Nero
Nanette Newman
Isobil Nisbet
Neil Nisbet
Paul Scofield
Johnny Shannon
Dinah Sheridan
Donald Sinden
David Threlfall
Rachel Ward
Kara Wilson

CHERRY PARKER MANAGEMENT
Also see listing for Richard Starnowski Management
Tel: 01702 522 647
Email: info@cherryparkermanagement.com
Web: www.cherryparkermanagement.com / www.rsm.uk.net
Agent: Cherry Parker
ARTISTES REPRESENTED:
Gary Hailes
Jayne Kitt
Jonathan Leonard
Katya Mirza
Albert Moses
Susie Verrico

CHESTER ALTERNATIVE ARTS
1 City Walls, Chester, Cheshire CH1 2JG
Tel/Fax: 01244 400 414
Email: pt@alexandersjazz.com
Web Site: www.alexandersjazz.com
Contact: Ms Thompson
Comedy Promoter and Agency

CHESTER BENSON PRODUCTIONS
PO Box 4227, Worthing, West Sussex BN11 5ST
Tel: 01903 248 258 Fax: 01903 700 389
Email: dave@davebensonphillips.co.uk
Web Site: www.davebensonphillips.co.uk
Proprietor: Dave Benson Phillips
A small company that's big on creating live shows and interactive experiences for children and adults. Over 20 years in the business, video & television! Producing "The all new Dave Benson Phillips Show", "Benson's Jumparound Activity Centres" and "Get Your Own Back". All shows are perfect for indoor/outdoor events.
ARTISTES REPRESENTED:
Dave's Get Up & Go Show

CHILDSPLAY EVENT SERVICES
Briar House, Caldbec Hill, Battle, East Sussex TN33 0JR
Tel/Fax: 01424 775 450 Mobile: 07850 311202
Email: info@kidsco.co.uk
Web Site: www.kidsco.co.uk
Senior Personnel: Nick Bryant
Specialising in Childrens Event Organisation & Management. Agents for children's entertainers.

CHILDSPLAY MODELS LLP
114 Avenue Road, Beckenham, Kent BR3 4SA
Tel: 020 8659 9860 Fax: 020 8778 2672
Email: info@childsplaymodels.co.uk
Web Site: www.childsplaymodels.co.uk
Partner: Wendy Lee
We cater from babies right up to adults.

CHIMES INTERNATIONAL ENTERTAINMENTS LTD
P.O. Box 26312 Clarkston, Glasgow, G76 7WX Scotland
Tel: 0141 577 7798 Fax: 0141 577 9991
Email: roychimes@aol.com
Web Site: www.chimesinternational.com
Senior Personnel: Robert Pratt, Mary Connell
ARTISTES REPRESENTED:
Rita Coolidge
Suzette Dorsey
Foster & Allen
Crystal Gayle
Gerry & The Pacemakers
Jack Jones
Dominic Kirwan
Matt Munro Jnr.
Peking Opera
The Platters
Red Army Chorus & Dance Ensemble
Russian Classical Ballet
Stiltskin
The Crystals
BJ Thomas
Ultimate Psychic Experience ft. Shaun Dennis and Alan Bates
Don Williams
Ray Wilson MBE

CHOICE PROMOTIONS
574-578 Mansfield Road, Nottingham NG5 2FS
Tel: 0115 960 3758 Fax: 0115 969 2024
Contact: Robert Stevenson

CHOKOLATE LTD
Unit B - Second Floor 326 Kensal Road, London W10 5BZ
Tel: 020 8960 9993
Email: caroline@chokolate.tv
Web Site: www.chokolate.tv
Contact: Caroline Khouri

CHORALE MUSIC PRODUCTIONS LTD
211 Piccadilly, London W1J 9HF
Tel: 020 7917 9542
Email: office@childrenscompany.com
Senior Personnel: Robert Howes

CHORD THEATRICAL & CORPORATE
PO Box 163, Widnes Delivery Office, Widnes, Cheshire WA8 5DP
Tel: 0151 420 3191 Fax: 0151 423 1869
Mob: 07764 770232
Email: jeannegray@talktalk.net
Web Site: www.chordtheatrical.com
Senior Personnel: Jeanne Gray
ARTISTES REPRESENTED:
Tributes Acts:
David Kidd (Tom Jones)
Ga Ga (Queen tribute)
Rik Stevens (David Bowie tribute)
Vocal Entertainers:
Freeway
David Kidd
Pastorale Duo
Polaris

CHRIS CREW ENTERPRISES
2 Glan Rhos Bungalows, Maes Madyn,

Amlwch Anglesey, Gwynedd LL68 9EP
North Wales
Tel: 01407 830 992
Mobile: 079 7738 1608
Email: myfirstcar1@tiscali.co.uk
Contact: Chris Crewe
Record Breakers, Look-a-Likes, Songwriters, Comics & Artists Agency.

CHRIS DAVIS MANAGEMENT

St. Martin's House, 2nd floor
80-81 St. Martin's Lane, London
WC2N 4AA
Tel: 020 7240 2116 Fax: 01584 819 076
Email: info@cdm-ltd.com
Web Site: www.cdm-ltd.com
Senior Personnel: Chris Davis

ARTISTES REPRESENTED:

Martin Daniels
Paul Daniels
Peter Duncan
Anita Harris
Mark Little
Debbie McGee
Ken Morley
Billy Pearce
Jane Rossington
Tony Christie

C.I.A. (CALAVEROCK INTERNATIONAL AGENCY)

25 Sycamore Close, Biggleswade,
Bedfordshire SG18 0HY
Tel: 01767 318 518
Email: info@cia-ents.co.uk
Web Site: www.cia-ents.co.uk
Senior Personnel: D.J. Maxwell
Specialising in bands and tributes plus all forms of entertainment for functions.

CINEL GABRAN MANAGEMENT

P.O. Box 5163, Cardiff CF5 9BJ
Tel: 0845 0666 605 Fax: 0845 0666 601
Mobile: 07958 583718
Email: info@cinelgabran.co.uk
Web Site: www.cinelgabran.co.uk
Senior Personnel: David A Chance
Representing actors, singers, songwriters, composers, writers, directors, cabaret and voice-overs in film, television and theatre. 70% of client list is Cardiff-based, and 30% London-based. Specialising in Welsh language film and television.

CIRCUIT PERSONAL MANAGEMENT LTD

Suite 71, S.E.C, Bedford Street, Shelton,
Stoke-on-Trent, Staffordshire ST1 4PZ
Tel: 01782 285 388 Fax: 01782 206 821
Email: mail@circuitpm.co.uk
Web Site: www.circuitpm.co.uk
Contact: David Bowen

ARTISTES REPRESENTED:

Leo Atkin
James Atkinson
David Bowen
Rebecca Bridle
Liz Fitzgerald-Taylor
Victoria Fleming
Martin Harris
Martin Harris
Phil Hemming
Stuart Horobin
Margaret Jackman
Holly King
Darren Langford
Alex Nikitas
Lisa O'Hannon
Jacqueline Redgewell
Abby Sheldon
Tracy Sheldon
Cathy Shiel
Robin Sims
Adam Speers
Zoe Thomas
Daniel Wallace
Susi Wrenshaw

CIRCUS PRODUCTIONS

Also see 'Cody's Wild West' listing
Black Horse Lodge, Wolverton Road,
Great Linford, Milton Keynes,
Buckinghamshire MK14 5AL
Tel/Fax: 01908 605 938
Email: toddcody@yahoo.co.uk
Contact: Tod Cody

CIRCUS PROMOTIONS

36 St Luke's Road, Tunbridge Wells, Kent
TN4 9JH
Tel: 01892 537 964 Fax: 01892 683 401
Mobile: 07973 512845
Email: info@heyprestoentertainments.co.uk
Web: www.heyprestonentertainments.co.uk
Senior Personnel: Michael Alan Bonfield

CITY ACTORS MANAGEMENT

Oval House 52-54 Kennington Oval,
London SE11 5SW
Tel: 020 7793 9888 Fax: 020 7793 8282
Email: info@city-actors.freeserve.co.uk
Web: www.city-actors.freeserve.co.uk

ARTISTES REPRESENTED:

Christopher Brooklyn
Christina Catalina
Gareth Clarke
Hugo Cox
Olayinka Giwa
Maria Golledge
Abigail Hood
Victoria John
Beryl King
Anna Kirke
Michael Lovatt
Tom Marshall
Jon Mcdiarmid
Catherine McDonough
Oliver Naylor
Bee Peak
Denis Quilligan
Nicholas J Rose
Mary Sheen
Mandy Vernon-Smith

CITYPLAY LTD

PO Box 50978 London E4 9ZA
Tel: 07766 660394
Email: info@cityplay.co.uk
Web Site: www.cityplay.co.uk
Contact: Keith Lazarus

CKK ENTERTAINMENT

PO Box 24550, London E17 9FG
Tel: 020 7531 6300 Fax: 020 7515 6373
Email: ckk.entertainment@virgin.net
Contact: Caroline Gannon
CKK Provide artists for corporate events, conferences, exhibitions, product launches, etc. Also supply specialist skills for commercials, film and television productions.

ARTISTES REPRESENTED:

Acro-Balance:
Circle of Two
Nicholas Daines
Dr Southall
Duel Impact
Fizziks
Heir of Insanity - aerial, hand balance, artistic stilts
London Chinese Acrobats
Dan Thomas
Tuyo
UK Chinese Acrobatic Company
Aerial:
Aerial Roots
Bernie Bennett
Cirq-U
Electrix
Entwine (female duo)
Lucy Francis
Legendary Lynn
Kirsty Little
Melissa Merran
Viva
Caricaturists:
Sarah Bailey
Sheba Cassini
Simon Cassini
Steven Garner
Picasso Griffiths
The Hit Man
Jeff Morgan
Jim Naylor
Ian Parratt
Jed Pascoe
John Roberts
Rog
Children's Entertainment:
Balloonatic
Natalie Davey
Clare Evans
Fizzie Lizzie
Indigo Moon
Just George
Marjin Entertainment
Strawberry the Clown
Clowns & Circus:
Big Grey
Dingle Fingle
Helena Hatstand
Potts
Sticks and Stones
Swamp Circus Theatre
Tweedy & Alexis
Contortion:
Yvette Du Sol
Louise Gibb

Kathryn Halliwell
Desiree Kingerod
Rubber Ritchie
Dance:
Amira
Paul Crook (from 'Strictly Dance Fever)
Felipe De Algeciras Flamenco Dance Co
Funki Feathers
Natasha Hall (from 'Strictly Dance Fever)
Maria Louisa
Melek
Liza Samari
Samsara
Snakey Sue
Vashti
Juggling:
Tim Bat
Stuart Clark
Tony De La Fou
Flux
Junction Jugglers
Sam I Am
Slap & Tickle
Thomas Trilby
Magic & Illusion:
Chris Dugdale
Guy Hollingworth
Phil Jay
Adam Keisner
Paul Kieve
Magic Matt
Richard McDougall
Peter Mehtab
Bruce Munton
Hugh Nightingale
David Penn
Chris Priest
Safire
Martin Sanderson
Tensai
Michael Vincent
Mime/Visual Comedy:
Melvyn Altwarg
Michael Blackledge
Donimo
Emile Epstein
Richard Knight
Stuart Luis
Jason Maverick
David Sant
Joelle Simpson
Andy Sinclair - mime
Pamela Sinclair
Brendan Stapleton
Unclassified Mime
Music:
Band of Two
The Bikini Beach Band
Cantabile
The Casablanca Steps
Clatteratti
Dante Ferrara
James Duke Band
Fantazia
The Graffiti Classics
Miniscule Of Sound
The Oberon String Quartet
The Picasso Players
Lindsay Scandrett
Shir
Status Cymbal
Tenors Incognito
Tenors Unlimited
The Very Big Penguin Band
Origami & Silhouettes:
Rick Beech
Paper Magic
The Roving Artist & Co
Robots:
Arbie the Robot
Borg Stiff
Electra
Hammerstein
Junior
Primo
Robo Max 2000
Zios
Speciality Acts:
Tommy Baker
Nikki Berwick
Keith Charnley
The Dreamweaver
Cecily Fay
Althea Finch
Fluke
Rainer Hersch
The Invisible Men
Pamela Kempthorne
Miss Behave
Paul Morocco
Catherine Selford
Lee Thompson
Wendy Abrahams with Colin The Dodo
Wink Taylor
The Wizard
Statues:
Anonymous
Petronella Carter
Joseph Gatt
Incarnation
Mechanical Fracture
Still Living Statues
Stiltwalking:
Jules Baker
Circo Rum Ba Ba
Cirque Bijou
Creature Features
Curious Company
Divine Act
The Grand Theatre of Lemmings
High Rise Rubber
Larkin' About
Los Kaos
Nutkhut
Pearshape
Poles Apart
Rin Tin Tin
Scarabeus
Mark Tate
Virtigo
Voodoo Dolls
Walkabout Characters:
Artizani
Attention Seekers
Comic Character Creations Co
The Complimentary Compliments Service
Dotcomedy
The Giant Penguins
Allin Kempthorne
Lady Christobel & Her Butler
Mark Mark Productions
Original Mixture
Pik'n'Mix
Random Acts Of Jazz
The Ugs
The Weathermen

CLAIRE SIBLEY MANAGEMENT

15 Tweedale Wharf, Madeley, Telford,
Shropshire TF7 4EW
Tel: 01952 588 951
Email: claire@clairesibleymanagement.co.uk
Web: www.clairesibleymanagement.co.uk
Contact: Claire Sibley

EVA CLARANCE ENTERPRISES

Belgrave Apartments, 3 Wharf Mill,
Congleton, Cheshire CW12 3GQ
Tel/Fax: 01260 274 196
Email: artists@evaclarance.com
Web Site: www.evaclarance.com
Senior Personnel: Eva Clarance
International booking agent specialising in Five Star Hotels abroad.

CLARENDON LAURENCE-EVOY

P.O. Box 551, Cliffe, Rochester, Kent
ME3 7WY
Tel: 01634 220 077 Fax: 01634 404436
Email:
clarendon.entertainments@btinternet.com
Web: www.clarendonentertainments.co.uk
Senior Personnel: Stuart Tranter
Entertainment consultants and suppliers.

CLARION/SEVEN MUSES

47 Whitehall Park, London N19 3TW
Tel: 020 7272 4413 / 5125 / 8448 Fax:
020 7281 9687
Email: admin@c7m.co.uk
Web Site: www.c7m.co.uk
Partners: Caroline Oakes, Nicholas Curry

ARTISTES REPRESENTED:

Conductors:
Christopher Austin
Matthew Halls
Vernon Handley CBE
Nicolae Moldoveanu
Benjamin Pope
Andrea Quinn
Matthew Rowe
John Wilson
String Soloists:
Gautier Capucon (Cello)
Monica Huggett (Violin)
Chantal Juillet (violin)
Marisa Robles (harp)
Elizabeth Wallfisch (Baroque & Classical Violins)
String Quartets:
Vogler Quartet
Piano Trio:
Gould Piano Trio
Pianists:
Rolf Hind
Leon McCawley
Pascal Rogé
Singers:
Phillipe Jaroussky (Countertenor)
Gary Williams
Wind Soloists:
David Pyatt (Horn)
Special Attractions:

An Evening with Queen Victoria (with Prunella Scales)
Richard Rodney Bennett and Claire Martin In Cabaret
Ensembles:
L'Arpeggiata
Sonnerie
Baroque Orchestra:
Tafelmusik

CLASS ACTS PROMOTIONS IRELAND LTD
Wellington House, 39 Wellington Park, Belfast, County Antrim BT9 6DN
Northern Ireland
Tel: 028 9068 1041 Fax: 028 9038 7453
Mobile: 07850 818859
Email: info@classactspromotions.com
Web Site: www.classactspromotions.com
Senior Personnel: Trevor McClintock, Susan Brookes
Providing high quality entertainment for events on any scale.

CLASSIQUE PROMOTIONS
8 Skelcher Road, Shirley, Solihull, West Midlands B90 2EZ
Tel: 0121 745 1920 Fax: 0121 745 1905
Email: enquiries@classiquepromotions.com
Web Site: www.classiquepromotions.com
Senior Personnel: Nicky Plant, Mac Plant
General entertainment agency.

TONY CLAYMAN PROMOTIONS
Vicarage House,
60 Kensington Church Street, London W8 4DB
Tel: 020 7368 3336 Fax: 020 7368 3338
Mobile: 07831 312 993
Email: tony@tonyclayman.com
Web Site: www.tonyclayman.com
Contact: Tony Clayman
ARTISTES REPRESENTED:
Tterry Alderton
Keedie Babb
Jessica Bailey-Woodward
Cheryl Baker
Georgea Blakey
Elkie Brooks
Garry Bushell
Hanieh Chehrehnegary
Matthew Crane
Rachael Downie
Lorna Fitzgerald
Steve Guttenberg
Jane Hartley
Michael Heath
Peter Howarth
Aled Jones
Amy Kaur
Kezia
Debbie King
Roger Kitter
Marina Laslo
Chris Lawrence
Ute Lemper
Francine Lewis
Linda Lewis
Joe Longthorne
Sophie Mackaill
Jjarone Macklin-Page
Maria McCaul
Clare McGlinn
Sue Moxley
Heidi Mumford
Matt Munro Jnr.
Tanya Nicole
Lucy Noble
Jane Omorogbe
Barry Robinson
Gemma Scott
Simone Simmons
Melanie Stace
Debra Stephenson
Alexis Strum
Tucker
John Walker
Bradley Walsh
James Whale
Fiona Wight
Mari Wilson
Sharon Wright

CLAYPOLE MANAGEMENT
PO Box 123, Darlington, County Durham DL3 7WA
Tel: 0845 650 1777 Fax: 0870 133 4784
Email: info@claypolemanagement.co.uk
Web: www.claypolemanagement.co.uk
Contact: Sam Claypole
Actors for Theatre/Film/TV. Dancers, Choreographers, Singers.

CLIC AGENCY
Rhostryfan, Rhosisaf, Caernarfon, Gwynedd LL54 7NF
Tel: 01286 831001
Email: enquiries@clicagency.co.uk
Web Site: www.clicagency.co.uk
Agent: Helen Pritchard
ARTISTES REPRESENTED:
TV Presenters:
Laura Louis
Actors:
Greg Drysdale
Owen Frost
Actresses:
Emma Burn
Rachel Jackson
Circus Acts:
Tom Dawson
Singers:
Ceri Bostock
Nesta Hanks
Iago McGuire

CLUBLAND ENTERTAINMENTS LTD
PO Box 5 Carnforth, Lancashire LA5 9WT
Tel: 01524 733310 Fax: 01524 733155
Email: clubland@tiscali.co.uk
Web: www.clublandentertainments.co.uk
Contact: Lester Simpson

CLUBLINE PROMOTIONS
56 Rowner Lane, Gosport, Hampshire PO13 0DT
Tel: 01329 317 280 Fax: 01329 317 285
Email: clubline1@aol.com
Senior Personnel: Derek Cole
ARTISTES REPRESENTED:
Bacardi II Disco
Ian Christie Roadshow
James Duke Band
Malibu Roadshow
Miami International Roadshow
The Shack

CMO MANAGEMENT (INTERNATIONAL) LTD
Studio 2.6, Shepherds Building, Richmond Way, London W14 0DQ
Tel: 020 7316 6969 Fax: 020 7316 6970
Email: becky@cmomanagement.co.uk
Web Site: www.cmomanagement.co.uk
Managing Director: Chris Morrison
Office Manager: Becky Hamilton
Band Manager: Brendan Coyle
ARTISTES REPRESENTED:
Matty Benbrook
Blur
Capricorn 2
Graham Coxon
Siobhan Donaghy
Justine Frischmann
GBQ
Gorillaz
Alex James
Morcheeba
Shlomo
Skye
Pauline Taylor
The Ailerons
The Rushes
Turin Brakes

COACH HOUSE ENTERTAINMENT
The Coach House, Kings Lane, Yelvertoft, Northamptonshire NN6 6LX
Tel: 01788 822 336 Fax: 01788 824 354
Mobile: 07725 790 185
Email: susan@coachhouseentertainment.co.uk
Web: www.coachhouseentertainment.co.uk
Senior Personnel: Susan Keyes
Specialising in Themed Events
ARTISTES REPRESENTED:
GB Characters
Hugo and the Hugonotes
Miscilly Music
David Penn

CODA MUSIC AGENCY LTD
229 Shoreditch Hight Street London E1 6PJ
Tel: 020 7456 8888
Email: phil@codaagency.com
Web Site: www.codaagency.com
Phil Banfield
Agent: Alex Hardee
ARTISTES REPRESENTED:
Live Roster:
Adem
Banco De Gaia
Beachbuggy
Jeff Beck

Black Car
Bonobo
Boy George
Billy Bragg
Calexico
Terry Edwards
Fingathing
Floetry
The Freestylers
Ian Gillan
The Handsome Family
Hem
Jazz Jamaica Allstars
Kelly Joe Phelps
Kid Koala
King Sunny Ade
Kings of Convenience
Kosheen
Lagbaja
Lambchop
London Elektricity
Los de Abajo
Mika Bomb
Mylo
Nina Nastasia
Oh Susanna
Oysterband
Maceo Parker
Portishead
Gruff Rhys
Scissor Sisters
Emma Shapplin
Si Begg (Live)
St Germain (UK/Asia/Aus)
Supertramp
Surreal Madrid
Amon Tobin
Trans Am
Yat-Kha
Yo La Tengo
The Young Gods
Zucchero
DJ Roster:
808 State
Bonobo
Matt Cantor
Capoeira Twins (DJ)
Die
DJ Food
DJ Krush
DJ Marky
DJ Patife
DJ Zinc
DK
Dynamo Productions
Herbaliser DJs
High Contrast
David Holmes
Jacques Lu Cont
Kid Koala
Kruder & Dorfmeister
Krust
Lee Combs
London Elektricity
Meat Katie
Mekon
Mr Scruff (DJ)
Mike Paradinas
Peter Parker
Plump Dj's
Plus One
Prime Cuts
Rich Thair
Scratch Perverts
Shakedown
Si Begg (Live)
Tim Simenon
Roni Size
Stanton Warriors
Tayo
Teebee
The Freelance Hellraiser
Tony Vegas
Luke Vibert

CODY'S WILD WEST

Also see 'Circus Productions' listing
Black Horse Lodge, Wolverton Road, Great Linford, Milton Keynes, Buckinghamshire MK14 5AL
Tel/Fax: 01908 605 938
Email: toddcody@yahoo.co.uk
Senior Personnel: Todd Cody

COFFEE ARTISTS

5 Weyhill Close, Maidstone, Kent ME14 5SQ
Tel: 01622 222 222 Fax: 01622 222 223
Email: gelli@coffeeartists.com
Web Site: www.coffeeartists.com
Head of Artists: Gelli Graham
Artist Management: Steve Piper
Coffee Artists UK DJ and musicians booking agency representing a select rosta of dj's and musicians and arranging tours for the clubbing industry promoters, club owners and party goers across the world.

ARTISTES REPRESENTED:

DJ's:
Dirty Bug
Mister Ed
Fingz
Miss Jools
Lucci
Dave Mills
Retronym
Jonathan Schippers
Tang
Musicians:
JJ Appleton
Annie Minogue
Pete and J
Jake Stigers
TGK
Trik Turner

COLCLOUGH ENTERTAINMENT & EVENTS

Newton House, 1 Newton Drive, Blackpool, Lancashire FY3 8BT
Tel: 01253 302262 Mobile: 07711 473 874 Fax: 01253 300 072
Email: laurayne@colclough-entertainment.co.uk
Web: www.colclough-entertainment.co.uk
Senior Personnel: Laurayne Colclough

ARTISTES REPRESENTED:

Billy Bedlam
Cameo
Gaynor Connor
Mike Craig
Vince Earl
John Martin
Safire
The Senators
Tony Stevens
Van Buren & Company

GRAHAM COLE MANAGEMENT

51 Grove Avenue, Weymouth, Dorset DT4 7RJ
Tel: 01305 777 253 Fax: 01305 788 853
Mob: 07767 872 157
Email: grahamcole@hotmail.co.uk
Senior Personnel: Derick Graham Cole

ARTISTES REPRESENTED:

Alexander
Mike Berry
The Brew Band
The Dolmen
Craig Douglas
Edison Lighthouse
English Baroque Ensemble
Flip the Lid
The Four Pennies
The Glitter Band
The Honeycombs
Ice
Irish Folk Rock Show
Jigsaw
The Tornados
Fred Wedlock
The Yetties
Tribute Bands:
The Abba Tribute
Bryan Adams Tribute Show
David Bowie Tribute Band
The Bristol Baroque Ensemble
Fab Beatles
Fat Lizzy (Thin Lizzy tribute)
Mark Mason is Robbie Williams
Paddy Millner (Little Richard tribute)
The Silver Beatles (Beatles tribute)
Sounds of The Four Tops
Ricky Storm (Billy Fury/Elvis tributes)
Tamla Motown Experience
Tribute to the Supremes
Tina Turner Tribute Band
Ben Waters (Jerry Lee Lewis tribute)
Freddy Zapp (Gary Glitter)

COLE KITCHENN PERSONAL MANAGEMENT

ROAR House 46 Charlotte Street London W1T 2GS
Tel: 0207 427 5680 / 427 5681 Fax: 0207 353 9639
Email: info@colekitchenn.com
Web Site: www.colekitchenn.com
Personal Management:
Managing Director/Agent: Stuart Piper
Contact:stuart@colekitchenn.com
Senior Agent: Oliver Thomson
Contact: oliver@colekitchenn.com
Agent: Alex Segal
Contact: alex@colekitchenn.com
Associate Agents: Jo Fell and Ashley Vallance
Contact:
jo@colekitchenn.com,ashley@colek-

itchenn.com
Talent Manager: Lucy Marriott
Contact: lucy@colekitchenn.com
Chairman: Jonathan Shalit
Contact: jonathan@roarglobal.com
Director: Guy Kitchenn
Contact: guy@colekitchenn.com
Agents for Actors and Creatives.

ARTISTES REPRESENTED:

Jonathan Ansell
Marc Baylis
David Bedella
Christopher Biggins
Vicky Binns
Kelly Brook
Michelle Collins
Louis Emerick
Lisa Greenwood
Dani Harmer
Sherrie Hewson
Javine Hylton
Louise Jameson
Vinnie Jones
Stephen Marcus
Mark Moraghan
Sid Owen
Roxanne Pallett (Jo, Emmerdale)
Deena Payne (Viv, Emmerdale)
Frances Ruffelle
Adele Silva
Cat Simmons
George Takei
Tulisa Contostavlos
Ian H Watkins
Denise Welch

DAVID COLEMAN

13 Barra Drive, Davyhulme, Manchester
Lancashire M41 7EU
Tel: 0161 748 7791 Fax: 0161 747 2954
Web Site: www.agentsassociation.co.uk
Senior Personnel: David Coleman

ARTISTES REPRESENTED:

The New Squadronaires Orchestra
Roll Out The Barrel
Shades of Shearing
The Best of Joyce Grenfell
The Dolly Parton Story
The Glenn Miller Tribute Orchestra
The Snow Queen
The Vox Lirika Opera Company
There Only Make Believe
Three Tenors In Concert - Tenorissimo
Unforgetable - The Nat King Cole Story

COLLECTIVE DANCE & DRAMA / ARAENA ENT

The Studio, Rectory Lane,
Rickmansworth, Hertfordshire WD3 2AD
Tel/Fax: 020 8428 0037
Email: info@collectivedance.co.uk
Web Site: www.collectivedance.co.uk
Propietor: Debra Hemmings
Specialising in: Children, teenagers and adults for film, theatre, modelling, television & commercials.

MAX COLLIE RHYTHM ACES

26 Wendover Road, Bromley, Kent
BR2 9JX
Tel: 020 8460 1139 Fax: 020 8466 7005
Email: max@maxcollie.fsnet.co.uk
Web Site: www.maxcollie.co.uk
Senior Personnel: Max Collie
Specialising in Traditional and New Orleans Jazz

ARTISTES REPRESENTED:

The High Society Show
New Orleans Mardi Gras

BARRY COLLINGS ENTERTAINMENTS

PO Box 1151 St Albans AL1 9WB
Tel: 01702 201880 Fax: 01702 201880
Email: barry-Collings@btconnect.com
Web Site: www.barrycollings.co.uk
Senior Personnel: Barry Collings, Lorraine Collings
All artistes available by arrangement with their respective managements.

ARTISTES REPRESENTED:

Animals
Aswad
Bad Manners
Kenny Ball & His Jazzmen
Cliff Bennett and the Rebel Rousers
Dave Berry & The Cruisers
Boney M featuring Maizie Williams
Brotherhood of Man
Bucks Fizz
Chas 'n' Dave
Chesney Hawkes
Chicory Tip
C'Mon Everybody (Rock n Roll Show)
Darts
Hazel Dean
Gwen Dickey (solo)
Doctor Feelgood
Edison Lighthouse
Steve Ellis' Love Affair
Eruption feat Precious Wilson
The Fortunes
The Foundations Featuring Clem Curtis
Gerry & The Pacemakers
Gidea Park (Beach Boys tribute)
Junior Giscombe
Go West including Peter Cox
Tony Hadley
Tommy Hunt (northern soul legend)
Abba Illusion
Imagination feat Leee John
Jimmy James & The Vagabonds
Martin Jarvis As Tom Jones
Mungo Jerry
Howard Jones
Junior
Katrina (from Katrina & the Waves)
Korgis
Robert Lamberti (George Michael)
Limahl
London Beat ft. Jimmy Helms
Marmalade
George McCrae
Middle Of The Road
Modern Romance
Dean Parrish
The Pasadenas
Pinkertons Assorterd Colours
Suzi Quatro
Queen B (Queen tribute)
Racey
Real Thing
The Rockin' Berries
Rose Royce featuring Gwen Dickey
The Rubettes featuring Bill Hurd
Sailor
Peter Sarstedt
Showaddywaddy
Lorraine Silver (northern soul legend)
Alvin Stardust
Sweet
The Swinging Blue Jeans
Kenny Thomas
Three Degrees
The Tremeloes
Vanity Fare (ex-chart band)
Village Boyz (Village People tribute)
Geno Washington & The Ram Jam Band
Marty Wilde
Paul Young

SHANE COLLINS ASSOCIATES

Garden Studios, 11-15 Betterton Street, London WC2H 9BP
Tel: 020 7470 8864 Fax: 0870 460 1983
Email: info@shanecollins.co.uk
Web Site: www.shanecollins.co.uk
Specialising in Actors & Actresses. Please phone for details of roster.

COMBINED SERVICES ENTERTAINMENT/SSVC

Chalfont Grove, Narcot Lane,
Gerrards Cross, Buckinghamshire
SL9 8TN
Tel: 01494 878 361 / 237
Fax: 01494 878 007
Email: angie.avlianos@ssvc.com
Web Site: www.ssvc.com
Entertainment Manager: Angie Avlianos
Providing live entertainment shows for British operational troops worldwide

COMEDY STORE MANAGEMENT

1a Oxendon Street, London SW1Y 4EE
Tel: 020 7839 1862 / 2949 Fax: 020 7930 2951
Email: charlotte@thecomedystore.co.uk
Web Site: www.comedystoremanagement.co.uk
Senior Personnel: Don Ward, Charlotte Smith

ARTISTES REPRESENTED:

Andy Askins
Mick Ferry
Rhod Gilbert
Mike Gunn
Steve Hughes
Roger Monkhouse
Tom Stade
Paul Tonkinson
Tom Wrigglesworth

COMICUS LTD.

The Studio 12, The Village Barn,
Patcham, Brighton BN1 8YU
Tel: 0844 800 0058

Email: matt@comicus.co.uk
Web Site: www.comicus.co.uk
Contact: Matthew Willetts

THE COMMERCIAL AGENCY

7 Cornwall Crescent, London W11 1PH
Tel: 020 7233 8100 Fax: 020 7373 4783
Email: anne@thecommercialagency.co.uk
Web: www.thecomemrcialagency.co.uk
Agent: Anne Shore

ARTISTES REPRESENTED:

TV Presenters:
Ant & Dec
Fearne Cotton
Simon Cowell
David Furnish
Kerry Katona
Jayne Middlemiss
Richard & Judy
Margherita Taylor
Holly Willoughby
Music:
Martin Fry
Dannii Minogue
Richie Neville
Sister Sledge
Actors:
Alexandra Aitken
Jane Asher
Nicholas Ball

COMMERCIAL CASTING

12 Colas Mews, London NW6 4LH
Tel: 0207 372 0009 Fax: 0207 372 3141
Email: info@commercialcasting.com
Web Site: www.commercialcasting.com
Senior Personnel: Charles Benenson
Specialists in providing Celebrities for corporate events.

COMPACT MANAGEMENT & ENTERTAINMENT AGENCY

98 Shellards Road, Longwell Green, Bristol, South Gloucestershire BS30 9DT
Tel: 0117 932 4344 Fax: 0117 932 6006
Mobile: 07831 446958
Email: paul@compactents.co.uk
Web Site: www.compactents.co.uk
Senior Personnel: Paul Wolf

ARTISTES REPRESENTED:

Bands:
The Alligators
Ballroom Glitz
Big Mac Soul Band
Brotherhood of Man
Chain Gang
Diamond Dogz
Doreen Doreen
Dozy Beaky Mick & Tich
The Fabulous Doughboys
Firebirds (R'n'R)
The Fortunes
Herman's Hermits
Love Affair
Madassa
The Manfreds
Marmalade
The New Ivyleague
Paper Lace
Mike Pender's Searchers
The Rockin' Berries
The Rubettes
Showaddywaddy
Spectrum (soul & party band)
The Tremeloes
Vanity Fare (ex-chart band)
Comedians/Comedy Acts:
Best of British
Bonkers
Micky John Bull
Chris Bylett & Co
Copy Katz
Jimmy Cricket
Dave & Amos
El Loco
Tony Gerrard
Glam & Glitz
Glen Fiddich
J.P. James
Karena Marie
Allan King
Johnny Laff
Paul Lavent
Looney Toons
Terri Martell
Johnny Moon
Gill Morris
Ben Murphy
Oddballs
Simon Sands
Tank Sherman
Matt Slack
Martin Smith
Sweeney
Jimmy Tamlin
Bob Taylor
Tina Turn
David Valentine
Bob Webb
Young at Heart
Tribute Acts:
Absolute Abba
Beachboys Inc
The Bohemians (Queen tribute)
Bootleg Buddy (Buddy Holly & The Crickets tribute)
Cheeky Monkees
The Counterfeit Beatles
Fat Lizzy (Thin Lizzy tribute)
Ricky Ford (Roy Orbison)
Gerry Grant (Roy Orbison)
Mikki Jay (Michael Jackson)
Jean Genie (David Bowie tribute)
Jimmy Jemain as Cliff Richard
Kinky (Kinks tribute)
Paul Leegan (Lonnie Donegan)
Like A Rolling Stone
Ludwig Beatles
Johnny Mack (Rod Stewart)
Maximum Who
Moondog Beatles
Queen B (Queen tribute)
Rats In The Kitchen (UB40 Tribute)
Marc Robinson (Buddy Holly)
The Rolling Clones
Status Go
Stayin' Alive (Bee Gees tribute)
Russ Stewart & The Fake Faces
Stoned Again

COMPLETE ENTERTAINMENT SERVICES LTD

PO Box 112, Seaford, East Sussex BN25 2DQ
Tel: 0870 755 7610 Fax: 0870 755 7613
Email: info@completeentertainment.co.uk
Web: www.completeentertainment.co.uk
Senior Personnel: Chris Bray, Emalee Welsh

ARTISTES REPRESENTED:

Chris Bylett & Co
Eazy Street
Fabulous Jazz Caverners
Brendan Grant
Hair Of The Dog
One + One
John Romero
Smartie
Ray Sparks
Kevin Stokes
Chris Wheeler
Danny King
Caché
Bob Smartie & The Failures
Jose Leon
Malachi S
Get Down On It
Tropical Heatwave
Amber Rae
Strawberry Strings
Flute Flutters
Glamtastic
Jon's Elton (Elton John)
Once More Into the Bleach (Blondie)
Ian Scott as Tom jones
Mike McCabe
Richard Bowen
Follies
Poles Apart
Brighton Jive Dancers
Art Deco Murders
Martin Russell
Tensai
Andy Sinclair - mime
Helena Hatstand
Hui Ling Zhu
Dark Angel
Adger Brown
Adam Night
David Bryne as Del Boy
Los Albertos

CONNECTIONS

The Meadlands, 11 Oakleigh Road, Hatch End, Pinner, Middlesex HA5 4HB
Tel: 020 8420 1444 Fax: 020 8428 5836
Email: mail@connectionsuk.com
Web Site: www.connectionsuk.com
Senior Personnel: Martin & Barbara Roberts
Specialising in technicians for the film and TV industry. Personal diary service/agents for film and video technicians.

CONNEXTIONS ENTERTAINMENT LTD

114 Westleigh Avenue, Putney, SW15 6UZ
Tel: 020 8789 6645 Fax: 020 8785 3533
Email: info@connextions.co.uk

Web Site: www.connextions.co.uk
Contact: Duncan Storer
Dancefloor hire and corporate entertainment.

MIKE CONSTANTIA ARTISTE MANAGEMENT LTD

41 Manchester Road, Woolston,
Warrington, Cheshire WA1 4AE
Tel: 01925 810 979 Fax: 01925 850 777
Email: showbiz@mikeconstantia.com
Web Site: www.mikeconstantia.com
Senior Personnel: Michael Constantinou

ARTISTES REPRESENTED:

Alpha Connection
Citizen
Sean Hourihan
Sara Langton
The Lomax Brothers
Freddie Mensah
Oh Boy 'Show'
One Night Stand
Overdub
Platinum High
The Pop Tarts
Red Hot & Blue Orchestra
Respect
Tom Scott
The Screaming Beavers
Turning Point
Vicus

CONTINENTAL DRIFTS

8 Hilton Grove, Hatherley Mews,
Walthamstow, London E17 4QP
Tel: 020 8509 3353 Fax: 020 8509 9531
Email: info@continentaldrifts.co.uk
Web Site: www.continentaldrifts.co.uk
Senior Personnel: Mel Wilds, Chris Meikan
Event Production and Performance Specialists.
The finest in event entertainment and production, whether a single stilt walker or a fully choreographed show. Continental Drifts artists range from the bizarre to the beautiful and we have an in-house creative team to formulate ideas and realise your vision. Full technical production is available, along with fully trained event crews. Continental Drifts take a client-centred approach are are more than happy to meet with you to discuss your event requirements in full detail.

ARTISTES REPRESENTED:

24 Seven
Alice
Alien Babies
Anatomik
Arnold's Flea Circus
The Baghdaddies
Baraka
Bedlam Oz
Big Beat Percussion Workshop
Big Bug
Big Fun
The Bollywood Brass Band
Boneshaker
Bound To Bounce
Bread & Butter Theatre Company
Carnival Collective
Carnival On De Road
Chameleon
Circo Rum Ba Ba
Circus Akwaba
Circus Hazzrd
Cirq-U
Claire De Loon
Clown Berts
Creature Features
Curious
Cyberstein Creations (Robotics)
Debate With Gravity
Dept Of Correction
Dhol
DJ Workshops
Dotcomedy
Eclipse
ELXT90
Entwine Acrobatic Silk Show
Eriksonlaver
Fair Play
Fairly Famous
Feeding the Fish
Fezheads
Fizziks
Flamin Gorgeous
Fling
Florence
The Flying Dudes
Freaks
Freedom Of Movement
Funding Pending
The Giant Penguins
Glam R Us
Groovy Movie
Helena Hatstand & Big Grey
Heir of Insanity - aerial, hand balance, artistic stilts
High Rise Rubber
Higher Motion
Hybrid
Incandescence
Innersense
The Invisible Men
Jeepers
Kwabana
Layla
Le La Les
Lucifire
Lucy
Lynn
MAD
Mahoney
Martinez and Fabrigez
Max
Maynard Flip Flap
Mechanical Fracture
Mimbre
Mimeworks
Miniscule
Mischief La Bas
Miss Behave
Mouth and Trousers
Mr Fizzbangs
Mr Green and Mr Orange
Neighbourhood Watch
No Strings
Organ Zola
Other Half
Paka
Dr Palfi Clown
Jo Peacock
Pearshape
Planet Plastic
Plastique
Poles Apart
Pomegranate
Primo
Pronghorn
Quilombo
Red Dragon
Rin Tin Tin
Risky
Roma Rad
John Row
Rumpelstiltskin
Les Rustines
Sawdid
Scarlet Fusion
Several Stories High
Nikita Shannon
Sid and Nancy
Skitzo
Still Living Statues
The Strangelings
Stretch
Superfly
Swamp
Tatty and Scruffy
Theatre Of Adventure
Turbozone
Uber and Alice
Viva
Weapons of Sound
The Wizard
Wrong Size
Wynnie
Zambra

CLIVE CONWAY PRODUCTIONS

32 Grove Street, Oxford OX2 7JT
Tel: 01865 514 830 Fax: 01865 514 409
Email: info@celebrityproductions.org
Web: www.cliveconwayproductions.com
Managing Director: Clive Conway
Producing celebrity entertainments featuring Britain's leading actors, writers, musicians and politicians.

CONWAY VAN GELDER GRANT

8/12 Broadwick Street London W1F 8HW
Tel: 020 7287 0077 Fax: 020 7287 1940
Email: info@conwayvg.co.uk
Web Site: www.conwayvg.co.uk
Senior personel: Nicola Van Gelder, John Grant

ARTISTES REPRESENTED:

Denise Black
Claire Bloom
Samantha Bond
Helena Bonham Carter
Peter Bowles
Jim Broadbent
Jim Carter
Brian Cox
Peter Davison
Lindsay Duncan
Harry Enfield
Michael Gambon
Tristan Gemmill
Julian Glover

Hannah Gordon
Sarah Greene
Ruthie Henshall
Eddie Izzard
Louise Jameson
Dervia Kerwan
Denis Lawson
Maureen Lipman CBE
Joanna Lumley OBE
Helen McCrory
Samantha Morton
Hermione Norris
Tamzin Outhwaite
Geoffrey Palmer
Judy Parfitt
Steve Pemberton
Rupert Penry-Jones
Clarke Peters
Jemma Redgrave
Siobhan Redmond
Anne Reid
Miranda Richardson
Gaby Roslin
Greta Scacchi
Prunella Scales
David Schneider
Josette Simon
Liz Smith
Imelda Staunton
Harriet Walker
Zoe Wannamaker
Richard Wilson

COOL BADGE PROMOTIONS

40 Dunford Road, London N7 6EL
Tel: 020 7609 5115 Fax: 020 7609 5225
Email: russell@coolbadge.com
Agent: Russell Yates

CLIVE CORNER ASSOCIATES

3 Bainbridge Close, Ham, Richmond, Surrey TW10 5JJ
Tel: 020 8332 1910
Mobile: 07946 894 870
Email: cornerassociates@aol.com
Web Site: www.cornerassociates.cwc.net
Senior Personnel: Clive Corner, Duncan Stratton
Specialising in: character actors for film TV and theatre together with singers and actor/musicians for West-End musicals. Also a large section of actors and character models for photographic advertising and TV commercials.

COSMIC COMEDY MANAGEMENT & CONSULTANCY

34 Cannon Court Road, Maidenhead, Berkshire SL6 7QN
Tel/Fax: 01628 415 683
Email: joss@cosmiccomedy.co.uk
Web Site: www.cosmiccomedy.co.uk
Senior Personnel: Joss Jones
Comedy artiste representation and consultancy with over 15 years experience, promoting comedy venues and management.

ARTISTES REPRESENTED:

Paul B Edwards
Danny James
John Mann
Brendan Riley
Jovanka Steele

COSMOS AGENCY & PROMOTIONS

26a Bellevue Crescent, Edinburgh, Mid Lothian EH3 6NF Scotland
Tel: 0131 558 3146 Fax: 0131 557 8511
Email: georgeduffin@yahoo.com
Senior Personnel: George Duffin

ARTISTES REPRESENTED:

The Abba Experience
Abba Forever
Absolute Abba
Absolute Britney
Beatles Beat
Big Vern and the Shootahs
Blues'n'Trouble
The Cuban Brothers
Deaf Heights Cajun Aces
Fools Gold (Stone Roses tribute)
Instant Replay
Midas Touch
Millenium 2000 (Robbie Williams tribute)
S Steps Club 7
Scottish Blues Brothers
Soul Kings
Soul Sisters
That Swing Thang

COSTELLO ENTERTAINMENTS

6 Lightwood, Worsley, Manchester M28 1ZL
Tel: 0161 703 8737
Email: mike@costelloentertainments.co.uk
Web: www.costelloentertainments.co.uk
Contact: Mike Costello

ALAN COTTAM AGENCY

19 Charles Street, Wigan, Lancashire WN1 2BP
Tel: 01942 321435 Mob: 07703 574 756
Email: alan@alancottamagency.com
Web Site: www.alancottamagency.com
General Manager: Alan Cottam
Tour Manager: Steve Galeazzi
Consultant: William Leyland
Entertainment agent and consultant to clubs and corporate buyers.

ARTISTES REPRESENTED:

Exclusive Representation:
Spencer Davis Group
Lights Out By Nine
Logan
Nazareth
Redhouse
Non-exclusive Representation:
Budgie
China Crisis
Dr Hook
Paul D'Ianno and Killer (from Iron Maiden)
Oliver Dawson Saxon
Ten Years After
Thunderclap Newman
Tygers of Pan Tang

CRAWFORDS

po box 44 394 London SW20 0YP
Tel: 020 8947 9999 Fax: 020 8879 1437
Email: nick@crawfords.tv
Web Site: www.crawfords.tv
Senior Personnel: Nicholas Young
Specialises in TV Commercials and Modelling

CREATION WORLDWIDE

Suite 105, Wyndham Wyndham Street Bridgend CF31 1EF
Tel: 01656 818918
Email: enquiries@creationworldwide.com
Web Site: www.creationworldwide.com
Andy Rudge

CREATIVE ARTISTES AGENCY

4th floor,Space One 1 Beadon Road, London W6 0EA
Tel: 020 8846 3000 Fax: 020 8846 3090

ARTISTES REPRESENTED:

Guy Ritchie

CREATIVE ARTISTS AGENCY UK LTD

4th Floor, Space One 1 Beadon Road, London W6 0EA
Tel: 020 8846 3000 Fax: 020 8846 3090
Email: ebanks@caa.com
Web Site: www.caa.com
Contact: Emma Banks

CREATIVE MAIN EVENT MANAGEMENT

1a The Courtyard, Henham, Bishop's Stortford, Hertfordshire CM22 6BJ
Tel: 08707 601 311 Fax: 01279 850 732
Email: andy@creative-mainevent.com
Web Site: www.creative-mainevent.com
Senior Personnel: Andy Philippou

CREATIVE PRODUCTIONS

14 Tithe Farm Avenue, Harrow HA2 9AE
Tel: 0208 422 7180
Mobile: 07956 275 216
Email: creativerom007@aol.com
Web Site: www.modern-romance.com
Lead Singer: Andy Kyriacou
Exclusive Management for Modern Romance, 80's Salsa Pop Sensations.

ARTISTES REPRESENTED:

Modern Romance

CREEME ENTERTAINMENTS

First Floor 293 Darwen Road Bromley Cross Bolton, Lancashire BL7 9BT
Tel: 01204 30511
Email: anthony@creeme.co.uk
Web Site: www.creeme.co.uk
Senior Personnel: Tom Ivers, Anthony Ivers, Lynne Ivers
Specialising in Booking Social & Cabaret Venues.

ARTISTES REPRESENTED:
All Mouth & Trousers
Angie Allen
Dave Baron
Jean Barrow
Dave Buck
Maggie Cole
Terry Cotta
Ivor Davies
Samantha Elka
Donna Elson
Gasp
Sam Homer
Morgan Lee James
Elisha Jayne
Annie Lawrence
Ricky Livid
Frank Patterson
Colin Paul and the Persuaders
Ronnie Ravey
Don Reid
Replica
Roxanne
Sunny Daye
Ven Tracey
Vince Williams
Mark Williamson

CRESCENT MANAGEMENT
10 Barley Mow Passage, Chiswick, London W4 4PH
Tel: 020 8987 0191 Fax: 020 8987 0207
Email: mail@crescentmanagement.co.uk
Web: www.crescentmanagement.co.uk
Senior Personnel: Jenny Benson
ARTISTES REPRESENTED:
Males:
John Ashton
Daniel Beckitt
James Bolt
Graham Bowe
John Cooper-Day
Chris Courtenay
Martin Durrant
Jonathan Ellen
Ben De Halpert
John JK Harty
Graham Hornsby
Robert Linden
Charles Neville
Females:
Lara Agar-Stoby
Lorna Doyle
Anne Etchells
Nichola Evans
Nicola Fisher
Kate Glover
Sara Kewly
Luanna Priestman
Ami Sayers
Jane Scott
Caterina Sforza

CROMWELL MANAGEMENT
20 Drayhorse Road, Ramsey, Huntingdon, Cambridgeshire PE26 1SD
Tel: 01487 815 063 Fax: 01487 711 896
Email: tricvic@lineone.net
Web Site: www.jazzmanagement.ic24.net
Senior Personnel: V Gibbons, P A Gibbons
ARTISTES REPRESENTED:
100 Club All Stars
The Cotton Club Jazz Orchestra
Katie Gibbons & Take 6
Gerard Kenny
Paul Leegan (Lonnie Donegan)
Terry Lightfoot & His Band
The London Ragtime Orchestra
Alan Price
John Slaughters Blues Band

CROSS CHANNEL CONNECTIONS LTD
7 Clarendon Place King Strret Miadstone ME14 1BQ
Tel: 01233 812223
Email: brian@crosscc.co.uk
Web Site: www.crosschannelconnections.com
Contact: Brian Murphy

AL CROSSLAND ENTERTAINMENTS
16 Toronto Place, Chapel Allerton, Leeds, West Yorkshire, LS7 4LJ
Tel: 0113 294 0824
Tel/Fax: 0113 294 0825
Email: racrossland@hotmail.com
Senior Personnel: Al Crossland, Richard Crossland
With over 20 years experience in the entertainment industry, we have established ourselves as one of the the leading agencies in our field. Specialising in the supplying of quality entertainment to club, pub, cabaret & corporate venues both home and abroad.

SARA CROUCH MANAGEMENT
Suite 1, Ground Floor, 1 Duchess Street, London W1W 6AN
Tel: 020 8894 7978 Fax: 020 7436 4627
Email: saracrouch@btinternet.com
Contact: Sara Crouch
ARTISTES REPRESENTED:
Men:
Jonathan Adams
Patrick Allen
John Banks
Richard Bates
Julian Battersby
Nigel Bowden
Barrie Cookson
Toby Davies
David Garfield
John Gillett
Steven Law
Dewi Morris
Miles Petit
Gary Pillai
Andrew Ramsay
Gordon Rennie
Roger Stephens
Guy Stevens
Jams Thomas
Orlando Vitorini
William Wilde
Griff Williams (Anthony Hopkins)
Matthew Wolf
Women:
Sorcha Brooks
Anna Clarkson
Jo Crawford
Kay D'Arcy
Jeni Ireland
Margaret John
Julia Johnston
Emma Kilbey
Damaris Lockwood
Jo Martell
Sally Nesbitt
Victoria Newlyn
Leigh Outram
Timna Rose
Rosemary Smith
Shelley Thompson
Sally Wallis
Heather Williams

CROWD PULLERS (STREET PERFORMERS AND BANDS)
14 Somerset Gardens, London SE13 7SY
Tel: 020 8469 3900 Fax: 020 8469 2147
Mobile: 07831 150170
Email: jhole@crowdpullers.co.uk
Web Site: www.crowdpullers.co.uk
Senior Personnel: John Hole
ARTISTES REPRESENTED:
Mark Abbott
Franco Bassetti
The Brass Hoppers
Circo Rum Ba Ba
Doolally
Electra
Fishy Business
Fluke
Heir of Insanity - aerial, hand balance, artistic stilts
The Jelly Rollers
Kovari
Ralph Leslie
Lococo Face Painters
Maria Louisa
Jason Maverick
Original Mixture
The Panasonic Steel Band
Steve Rawlings
Mat Ricardo
Still Life
Stretch People
Baron Von Grindle - Vampire

CROWN ENTERTAINMENTS
103 Bromley Common, Bromley, Kent BR2 9RN
Tel: 020 8464 0454
Email: dave@crownentertainments.co.uk
Web: www.crownentertainments.co.uk
Senior Personnel: Dave Nash
ARTISTES REPRESENTED:
Function Groups:
Bronx
Caprice
Charade
Eazy Street
Escada
Mixed Feelings
Night Music

Phoenix
Riviera Breeze
Six Till Midnite
Spice
The Spotlites
Tuxedo Class Disco
String Quartets:
Angelique String Quartet
The Monaco String Quartet
Strawberry Strings
German Bands:
Papa Schnitzel's Bavarian Dance Band
Jazz Bands:
The 4 Busketeers
Steel Bands:
The Tony Charles Steel Band

CRUICKSHANK CAZENOVE LTD

97 Old South Lambeth Road,
London SW8 1XU
Tel: 020 7735 2933 Fax: 020 7582 6405
Email: office@cruickshankcazenove.com
Senior Personnel: Harriet Cruickshank, Sky Macaskill
Specialising in Directors, Designers & Choreographers. Does NOT deal with actors.

CRUISIN' MUSIC

P.O. Box 3187, Radstock BA3 5WD
Tel: 01373 834 161 Fax: 01373 834 164
Email: sil@cruisin.co.uk
Web Site: www.cruisin.co.uk
Contact: Sil Wilcox

ARTISTES REPRESENTED:

Amsterdam
Tina Cousins
Saturday Morning Pictures
The Stranglers
The Bluetones
The Wurzels

CS ENTERTAINMENTS

31 Sherwood Road, Winnersh,
Wokingham, Berkshire RG41 5NH
Tel: 0118 978 5989 Fax: 0709 237 5151
Mobile: 07831 428068
Email: info@csents.co.uk
Web Site: www.csents.co.uk
Senior Pesonnel: Chris Skeet
Specialiing in: Live music, Discos, Cabaret and General entertainment for private and corporate functions.

ARTISTES REPRESENTED:

The 007-ties
Abacus
After Dark
The Ald Brickham Barn Dance Band
All Wrapped Up
Alpha Connection
Aurora Harp-Flute Duo
Barons of Bavaria
The Bavarian Strollers
Adrienne Black
The Blues Project
The Boogie Nights Band
Anji Britton
Burgundy Wine
Siempre Caliente
Cambiata
Capriccio String Quartet
Carribbean Sunrise
Champagne Disco
Charm
Chemistry
The Chosen Few Big Band
The Club Quintet
Sue Coppard
Robert Cox
Crawford String Quartet
Ian Cruishank's Gypsy Jazz
Simon Currie Jazz Quartet
Simon Curry Jazz Band
Tony Dancer
Darktown
The Dixieland Swing Kings
Dragonsfire
The Dynamos Sixties Band
The Terry Ede Quartet
Essence
Steve Finn
Fiona Ann Bennett Jazz Trio
Five Star Swing
Flashback
Foxy
Eric Gilchrist Jazz and Blues Quintet
Groove Central Grand
The Groove Company
David Hawkins
Robert A. Hooper
Jamie & The First Class
Latin Fiesta
Denise Lawrence & Her Band
The Leonardo String Quartet
Les Compagnons Du Bal
Jane Lister
The Local Yokels
Los Charros
Lucy and The Celebrities
Masquerade
Nuages
Pentagon
Danielle Perrett
Platform Soul
Rio
Satu Salo
George Saunders
Savoir Faire
The School Disco Band
The Shakin' Chefs
Tim Shoesmith
Short People
Ian Simmons
The Slacks
Slim Pickins
Ron Smiley
Kate Smith
Alex Soames
Solid Steel
Something Scarlet
Soultown
The Sound Experiment
The Sounds Of Swing Orchestra
Patricia Spero (Harpist)
Staccato
Richard Stamper
Status Cymbal String Quartet
Sterling String Quartet
Straight Eight
Cavatina Strings
Mike Taylor (Solo Sax)
Too Hot to Handle
Tournament
Tropical Heat
Tropical Sound
Tropicalia Band
Viva Flamenco
Peter Westlake
Whittakers Patent Remedy

CT ENTERTAINMENTS

PO Box 52, Newtownards, County Down
BT23 3FX Northern Ireland
Tel: 028 9042 8800 Fax: 028 9042 3999
Email: ctentertainment@ukgateway.net
Web Site: www.theuntouchables.info
Senior Personnel: Cecil Thompson
Comedians & DJ's also available

ARTISTES REPRESENTED:

This Way Up
The Bizz
D.Y.C.
E-Male
Free Spirit
Pop Fiction
Rio
Sunshine
The Untouchables

CUNNINGHAM MANAGEMENT LTD

Suite 50, London House, 271 King Street,
London W6 9LZ
Tel: 020 8233 2824 / 2820
Email: info@cunningham-management.co.uk
Web: www.cunningham-management.co.uk
Senior Personnel: Chloe Cunningham
Contact: Simon Fairclough
Manages TV presenters and speakers. Specialises in inspirational people of achievement.

ARTISTES REPRESENTED:

Graham Bell
Frank Bordoni
Geoff Burch
Vivien Creegor
Lynsey de Paul
Glenn Ferguson
Lorraine Gabriel
Culver Greenridge
Bear Grylls
Ken Hames
Cat Hartley
Francesca Kimpton
Dr David Lewis
Penny Mallory
Ian Maxwell
Jake Meyer
Ben Saunders
Dr Mike Stroud OBE
Crispin Swayne

CURTIS BROWN GROUP

5th Floor, Haymarket House,
28-29 Haymarket, London SW1Y 4SP
Tel: 020 7393 4400 Fax: 020 7393 4401
Email: jonathan@curtisbrown.co.uk
Web Site: www.curtisbrown.co.uk
Senior Personnel: Nick Marston
Agent: Jonathan Lloyd

Today, with over one hundred years of experience and more than twenty agents within our Book, Media, Actors and Presenters Divisions we represent many of the world's most popular and successful writers, directors, actors, playwrights and celebrities.

ARTISTES REPRESENTED:

David Aaronovitch
Fiona Allen
Ben Anderson
Clive Anderson
Duncan Bannatyne OBE
Francesca Beauman
Richie Benaud
Ravinder Bhogal
Angela Buttolph
Matthew Cain
Artem Chigvintsev
Alexis Conran
Stewart Copeland
Gary Crowley
Les Dennis
Grace Dent
Stacey Dooley
Kerr Drummond
Yvette Fielding
Johnnie Fiori
Amanda Foreman
Sisco Gomez
Jodie Harsh
Matt Hayes
Matt James
Jason Gardiner (Queer Eye for a Straight Guy)
Kate Jenkins
Spencer Kelly
Carol Klein
Alexis Knox
David Muniz and David Lesniak
Ollie Locke
Sheena Macdonald
Stewart MacKay
Gareth Malone
JO Malone
Tim Marlow
Rory McGrath
Bill McGuire
Danille Meagher
Louise Mensch
Xanthe Milton
Drummond Money-Coutts
Annie Nightingale
Simon O'Brien
Oonagh O'Hagan
Polly Parsons
Tony Parsons
Grayson Perry
Philippa Perry
Gavin Pretor Pinney
Alex Polizzi
Jay Rayner
Noelle Reno
James Richardson
David Schneider
Ivor Setterfield
Laury Smith
Olly Smith
Sam Stern
Edward Stourton
ash Stymest
Philippa Tuttiett
Holly Valance
Sasha Wilkins
Bryn Williams
David Wilson

D F O INTERNATIONAL MUSIC AGENCY

PO Box 627 York YO1 0FL
Tel: 01759 388900
Email: debra@dfo.org.uk
Web Site: www.derekfranks.co.uk
Drebra Franks

JUDY DAISH ASSOCIATES

2 St Charles Place, London W10 6EG
Tel: 020 8964 8811 Fax: 020 8964 8966
Email: judy@judydaish.com
Web Site: www.judydaish.com
ADMINISTRATION:
Senior Personnel: Judy Daish, Tracey Elliston, Howard Gooding
Representing writers, directors, designers and choreographers for theatre, film, television, radio and opera.

ARTISTES REPRESENTED:

Writers:
Jim Allen (Estate)
Amma Asante
Howard Barker
Sudha Bhuchar
Stephen Bill
Tilly Black
Keith Blackler
Charlie Boucher
Peter Bradshaw (Dramatic Rights)
Jez Butterworth
Annette Carducci
Ruth Carter
Nazrin Choudhury
Brian Clark
Stephen Clark
Tom Clarke (Estate)
Shane Connaughton
Helen Cooper
Kerry Crabbe
Martin Crimp
Frank Delaney (Dramatic Rights)
Richard Eyre
Antonia Fraser (Dramatic Rights)
Flora Fraser (Dramatic Rights)
Julian Garner
Caroline Gawn
Liewella Gideon
Faye Gilbert
Bob Goody
Gawn Grainger
Simon Gray
Ann Guedes
Tamantha Hammerschlag
Ronald Harwood
Daniel Hill
Max Hillman
Ron Hutchinson
Kazuo Ishiguro (Dramatic Rights)
Peter Jukes
Frank Keating
Shaheen Khan
Tania Kindersley (Dramatic Rights)
David Lan
Gareth Lewis
Stephen Lowe
Philip Mackie (Estate)
Susannah MacMillan
Patrick Marber
Rosemary Mason
Sean Mathias
Mustapha Matura
Anthony Minghella
Daniel Mornin
Caryl Phillips
Tom Pickard
Harold Pinter
Stephen Poliakoff
Dennis Potter (Estate)
Marcus Romer
Vassily Sigarev
Helen Slavin
Sara Sugarman
The Presnyakov Brothers
Drew Thomas
Michael West
Hugh Whitemore
Hugh R B Williams
Nigel Williams
Kevin Wong
Nick Wright
Directors:
Jon Amiel
Kevin Billington
Jez Butterworth
Annette Carducci
Robert Carson
Richard Eyre
Caroline Gawn
Faye Gilbert
Charlie Hanson
Pedr James
David Jones
Richard Jones
Jonathan Kent
David Lan
Kristine Landon-Smith
Gareth Lewis
Ken Loach
Sean Mathias
Anthony Minghella
Annilese Miskimmon
Tom Pickard
Stephen Poliakoff
Ian Rickson
Daniel Slater
Sara Sugarman
Delyth Thomas
David Wheatley
Nicholas Wright
Peter Yates
Designers:
Maria Bjornson (Estate)
Sue Blane
The Brothers Quay
Lez Brotherston
Giles Cadle
Peter J Davison
William Dudley
Jonathan Fensom
Tim Hatley
Rob Howell
Richard Hudson
Jean Kalman
Stewart Laing
Michael Levine
Ian MacNeil

Huntley Muir
Tania Spooner
Choreographers:
Amir Hosseinpour
Jonathan Lunn
Composers:
Alexandra Harwood
Producers:
Carolyn Choa
Charlie Hanson

DALY PEARSON ASSOCIATES

586A Kings Road, Fulham, London
SW6 2DX
Tel: 020 7384 1036 Fax: 020 7610 9512
Email: agents@dalypearson.co.uk
Senior Personnel: David Daly

ARTISTES REPRESENTED:

Actors:
Charlie Adams
CJ Allen
Johnny Amobi
Peter Amory
John Arthur
Gary Bakewell
Trevor Bannister
Sean Barrett
Rolan Bell
Adam C Booth
Terence Booth
Robert Cawsey
Christopher Chittell
Vince Earl
Martyn Ellis
John Gill - Retired
Jon Glover
Christopher Godwin
Tom Godwin
Murray Head
Matt Hebden
Richard Lloyd King
Eugene McCoy
Sean McGinley
Graeme Mearns
Kenneth Price
Steve Ramsden
James Smillie
Frank Thornton
Richard Thorp
John Turner -Retired
Mike Walling
Timothy Watson
Actresses:
Karen Ascoe
Gaynor Barrett
Margot Boyd - Retired
Barbara Brennan
Lucinda Curtis
Angela Darcy
Sarah Edwardson
Fionnuala Ellwood
Abigail Fisher
Sabina Franklyn
Lindsay Fraser
Carly Harris-Sutcliffe
Julie Hewlett
Amanda Humphrey
Claire King
Mary Larkin
Sallyanne Law
Kirsty Lee-Turner
Rula Lenska
Lesley McGuire
Lesley Meade
Sophie Millett
Lesley Nicol
Emma Noble
Alicia Patrick
Helen Pearson
Georgina Redhead
Heather Robbins
Elizabeth Segojame
Alison Skilbeck
Ursula Smith
Claire Thurgood
Evelyn Turner
Sally Watts
Sara Weymouth
Nicola Wheeler
Alice Wilson
Judy Wilson
Directors:
Gill Wilkinson

DALZELL & BERESFORD LTD

26 Astwood Mews, London SW7 4DE
Tel: 020 7341 9411 Fax: 020 7341 9412
Email: mail@dbltd.co.uk
Senior Personnel: Simon Beresford

DANCE CRAZY MANAGEMENT

294-296 Nether Street, Finchley Central,
London N3 1RJ
Tel: 020 8343 0848 Fax: 020 8343 0747
Email: dancecm@aol.com
Web Site: www.dancecrazy.co.uk
Contacts: Kelly Isaacs
Specialises in reording arts, pa management & promotion, touring american artistes, clowns and corprate entertainment. Also includes artistes covering 70's up to present day music.

DANCE FUNKI FEATHERS AGENCY

Sycamore House, 8 Sycamore Road,
Bearwood, Birmingham B66 4NL
Tel/Fax: 0121 420 4396 Mobile: 07958 945701 / 2
Email: funkifeathers@telco4u.net
Web: www.dance-funkifeathers.8k.com
Contact: Julie Anne Phillips, Simon Bisel
Supplying: Dancers and fully choreographed shows and spectacular costumes

ARTISTES REPRESENTED:

Andre Armstrong
Sarah Birch
Kerry Bladen
Lucia Brady
Emma Brookes
Kerry Clarke
Sophie Clarke
Vicky Collier
Tina Dancer
Sarah Farmer
Victoria Gregson
Sara Jaye
Sarah Jayne
Lee Lauren
Antoni Le Faux
Gemma Linsey
Kerry Long
Mary Mangan
Sarah McGrath
Lorrian O'Leary
Rachel Piggot
Susan Priest
Jane Pye
Vicky Richards
Viviane Segade
Simone Spiterie
Katy Watson
Susan Watts
Cally Wills
Joy Worsley
Francis Young

DANCERS AGENCY

1 Charlotte Street, London W1T 1RD
Tel: 020 7637 1487 Fax: 020 7636 1657
Email: info@features.co.uk
Web Site: www.features.co.uk
Senior Personnel: Roy Clark

PAUL DANIELS

c/o International Artistes Lapley Hall,
Lapley, Staffordshire ST19 9JR
Tel: 01785 841 991 Fax: 01785 841 992
Email: cdavis@intart.co.uk
Web Site: www.pauldaniels.co.uk
Contact: Chris Davis

ARTISTES REPRESENTED:

Paul Daniels

DANSATAK

Worth House, 15 Worth Street, Carlton,
Nottingham NG4 1RX
Tel: 0844 888 7722 Fax: 08707 444 556
Email: info@dansatak.com
Web Site: www.dansatak.com
Senior Personnel: Scott Peters, Tony Sherwood

ARTISTES REPRESENTED:

Bootleg Blues Brothers
The Commitments
Factor X (Boyband Tribute)
Fake That
Dave Finnegans Commitments
Flesh For Fantasy
Freddie - The Show Must Go On!
John & Paul (Beatles Tribute)
Kylie Fever
McFli
The Merseybeats
Millennium (Robbie Williams Tribute)
Mr Swing
Mike Pender's Searchers
Pure Abba
Rob Idol
Take This
The Curvettes
The Flirts
West Like
Westlives

DARK BLUES MANAGEMENT

Puddephat's, Markyate, Hertfordshire

AL3 8AZ
Tel: 01582 842 226 Fax: 01582 840 010
Email: info@darkblues.co.uk
Web Site: www.darkblues.co.uk
Senior Personnel: Fiona Hewetson

ARTISTES REPRESENTED:

The Dark Blues
The Wallace Collection
The Dark Blues Discotheque
Jazz Nights

THE DAUBNEY VARIETY & GALA AGENCY LTD

1 Bent Lane, Staveley, Chesterfield, Derbyshire S43 3UG
Tel: 01246 477677
Email: info@daubneyagency.co.uk
Web Site: www.daubneyagency.co.uk
Contact: Margot Wilding
Fixers and finders for all outdoor requirements

ARTISTES REPRESENTED:

Super Jumper

DAUBNEY VARIETY AND GALA AGENCY

1 Bent Lane Stavely S43 3UG
Tel: 01246 477677
Email: info@daubneyagency.co.uk
Web Site: www.daubneyagency.co.uk
Margot Wilding

DAVE ANTHONY ENTERTAINMENTS

Cragdene, 41 Lumby Hill, Monk Fryston, Leeds LS25 5EB
Tel: 01977 681935 Fax: 01977 683572
Email: dave@daveanthony.co.uk
Web Site: www.daveanthony.co.uk
Senior Personnel: Dave Anthony

DAVE CARR MANAGEMENT

PO Box 102 Spennymoor DL16 9BF
Tel: 01388 817755
Email: davecarrman@yahoo.co.uk
Web: www.davecarmanagement.com
David Johnston

DAVE CHUMBLEY

31 Aberdeen Park, London N5 2AR
Tel: 020 7226 4366 Fax: 020 7226 4346
Email: dave@primary.uk.com
Contact: David Chumbley

DAVE DEE ENTERTAINMENTS & DISCOTHEQUES

14 Redstone Manor, Redhill RH1 4BS
Tel: 01737 765279 Tel: 01737 779014
Fax: 01737 767699
Contact: David Wool

THE DAVID AGENCY

26-28 Hammersmith Grove, London W6 7BA
Tel: 020 7967 7001
Email: casting@davidagency.net
Web Site: www.davidagency.net
Contact: Leila Debs
Specialist in crowd and supporting artists.

DAVID DICKINSON PRODUCTIONS LTD

High Barn, Cocksheadhey Road, Bollington, Macclesfield, Cheshire SK10 5QZ
Tel/Fax: 01625 560 821
Mobile: 07836 601 278

ARTISTES REPRESENTED:

David Dickinson

DAVID REES MANAGEMENT

Highridge, Bath Road, Farmborough, Bath North Somerset BA2 0BG
Tel: 07050 277 053 Tel: 01761 471 089
Mob: 07968 434 570
Email: davidrees@poportunity.co.uk
Senior Personnel: David Rees

ARTISTES REPRESENTED:

David Legend - The Music of Legend

LENA DAVIS/JOHN BISHOP ASSOCIATES

Cottons Farmhouse, Whiston Road, Cogenhoe, Northants NN7 1NL
Tel: 01604 891 487
Email: admin@cottonsfarmhouse.freeserve.com.uk
Senior Personnel: Lena Davis, John Bishop

ARTISTES REPRESENTED:

Tim Arnold
Lena Davis
Ian Noble
Polly Perkins
Dee Quemby
Caroline Scattergood
Toby Tobias
Robert Valentine

DAWSON BREED MUSIC LTD

Spencer House London SE24 0NR
Tel: 020 7733 0508 Fax: 020 7733 0508
Email: debra@dawsonbreedmusic.com
Web Site: www.dawsonbreedmusic.com
Contact: Ms Debra Downes

DBA SPEAKERS

58 Station Avenue, Walton-on-Thames, Surrey KT12 1NQ
Tel: 01932 228 544 Fax: 01932 224 961
Email: diana@dbaspeakers.com
Web Site: www.dbaspeakers.com
Senior Personnel: Diana Boulter, Sarah Hobbs
We provide leading business speakers & entertainers, including e-business, economy, finance, sport, motivation, future business, vision strategy and political commentators.

ARTISTES REPRESENTED:

Brian Alexander
Ian Angell
Tony Ball MBE
Sir John Banham
Tony Benn
Roger Black MBE
Jennie Bond
Lady (Betty) Boothroyd
Geoff Burch
Adrian Cooper
Major General Patrick Cordingley DSO
Frances Edmonds
Gareth Edwards
Sir Ranulph Fiennes Bt OBE
Elizabeth Filkin
Louise Goodman
Andy Green (world landspeed record)
Sally Gunnell OBE
Pen Haddow
Christine Hamilton
Judith Hann
Ian Irving (Comedian)
Michael Johnson
Charles Kennedy
Kevin Money
Chris Moon
Robin Oakley
Allan Pease
Dame Mary Peters
Michael Portillo
John Potter
Dame Stella Rimington DCB MA
Rebecca Stephens MBE
Justin Urquhart Stewart
Terry Waite CBE
Simon Weston
Nicholas Witchell
Christopher Wood
Sir Clive Woodward

DCM (DAVE CARR MANAGEMENT)

PO Box 102 Spennymoor, County Durham DL16 9BF
Tel: 01388 817755
Email: seancarragent@yahoo.co.uk
Contacts: Sean Carr, David Johnston

PETER DE RANCE

74 Ormonde Crescent, Netherlee, Glasgow, G44 3SW Scotland
Tel/Fax: 0141 637 3308
Senior Personnel: Peter de Rance

ARTISTES REPRESENTED:

Andy Cameron
Kenneth McKeller
Magical Comedian:
John Shearer
Multi-Instrumental:
Geoff Graham
After Dinner Speaker:
Robbie Glen

THE DEANS OF MAGIC

Suite 33, 10 Barley Mow Passage, London W4 4PH
Tel: 07733 106540
Email: info@thedeansofmagic.biz
Web Site: www.thedeansofmagic.com
Contact: Carl Dean & Claudine (The Deans Of Magic)

Illusionists of international acclaim. Carl Dean has over 25 years experience in the world of Magic working worldwide. They now specialise in spectacular shows for the corporate market for both grand and intimate events.

ARTISTES REPRESENTED:

Carl Dean & Claudine
The Deans of Magic

DEBI ALLEN ASSOCIATES

22 Torrington Place London WC1E 7HP
Tel: 020 7255 6123
Email: info@debiallenassociates.com
Web Site: www.debiallenassociates.com
Senior Personel: Debi Allen, Michael Ford, Craig Latto, Charlene McManus

ARTISTES REPRESENTED:

Presenters:
Carol McGriffin

DELUXXE MANAGEMENT

PO Box 373, Teddington, Middlesex TW11 8QZ
Tel: 020 8755 3630 Fax: 020 8404 7771
Email: diane@deluxxe.co.uk
Web Site: www.deluxxe.co.uk
Agent: Diane Wagg

ARTISTES REPRESENTED:

Singers:
Lily Fraser
Hip Hop:
Electrolux
Lockdown Project
Touriste

IVOR DEMBINA

Email: dembonet@aol.com
Web Site: www.thinkbeforeyoulaugh.com
London based Jewish writer, stand-up comedian and resident host of the Hampstead Comedy Club.

ARTISTES REPRESENTED:

Ivor Dembina

ALAN DENI ENTERTAINMENTS

38 Rosedale Avenue, Crosby, Liverpool, Merseyside L23 0UQ
Tel: 0151 924 8589
Email: fullpenny@blueyonder.co.uk
Senior Personnel: A. Fairley
Booking Agents

DENMARK STREET MANAGEMENT

Packington Bridge Workspace
1b Packington Square, London N1 7UA
Tel: 020 7354 8555 Fax: 020 7354 8558
Email: mail@denmarkstreet.net
Web Site: www.denmarkstreet.net
Co-operative actors agency.

ARTISTES REPRESENTED:

Anna Brook
Peter Cadden
Mark Carlisle
Liz Carney
Sam Chapman
Adam Dunseath
Rebecca Gross
Lynn Robertson Hay
Glen Hill
Kathryn Hodges
Libby Liburd
Susanna Northern
Sarah O'Leary
Lenny Peters
Tom Underwood
John Walters
Stephen Weller

TONY DENTON PROMOTIONS

Charter House, 157 - 159 High Street, London N14 6BP
Tel: 020 8447 9411 Fax: 020 3232 0085
Email: info@tdpromo.com
Web Site: www.tdpromo.com
Director: Tony Denton, Peter Apps, Bennie Edwards

ARTISTES REPRESENTED:

3T
911
Abba Gold
ABC
Marc Almond
Altered Images
Adam Ant
Apache Indian
Rick Astley
Aswad
Baccara
Bananarama
Bay City Rollers
The Best Disco In Town Live
Best of British Variety
Big Brovaz
The Blockheads
Blondie
Boney M
Brenda
Elkie Brooks
Steve Brookstein
Angie Brown
Errol Brown
Bucks Fizz
Belinda Carlisle
Dina Carroll
David Cassidy
Chaka Khan
Chas 'n' Dave
Chesney Hawkes
Chic
China Crisis
Rita Coolidge
Antony Costa
Randy Crawford
Culture Club
Curiosity Killed The Cat
Cutting Crew
Dead Men Walking
Dead or Alive
Kiki Dee and Carmelo Luggeri
Dr & The Medics
The Drifters
Former members of Electric Light Orchestra PTII
Emotions
David Essex
Gabrielle
Stephen Gately
Michelle Gayle
The Go-Go's
Deborah Harry
Heaven 17
Here & Now Tour
Nick Heyward
Jennifer Holliday
Honeyz
Hot Chocolate
Human League
Imagination
La Toya Jackson
Jamelia
Javine
Grace Jones
Howard Jones
Jonny Hates Jazz
Kavana
KC & The Sunshine Band
Nik Kershaw
Kid Creole & the Coconuts
Evelyn Champagne King
Kool & The Gang
Amanda Lear
Limahl
Alison Limerick
Living In A Box
Glen Matlock ex Sex Pistols
Kym Mazelle
George McCrae
Dannii Minogue
The New Seekers
Billy Ocean
Odyssey
Once In A Lifetime Tour
Alexander O'Neal
Jimmy Osmond
Merrill Osmond
The Osmonds
Billy Paul
Daniel Pearce
Pointer Sisters
Suzi Quatro
Martha Reeves And The Vandellas
Rose Royce
Rozalla
Jennifer Rush
Leo Sayer
Shalamar
Showaddywaddy
Sinitta
Sister Sledge
Soft Cell
Jimmy Sommerville
Candi Staton
The Stylistics
The Supremes
Sybil
Tavares
The Real Thing
Kenny Thomas
Three Degrees
Toyah
T'Pau
Trammps
Ultra Nate
Midge Ure
Village People
Visage
Voices with Soul
The Von Trapp Children

Dionne Warwick
Weather Girls
Kim Wilde
Bill Wyman & The Rhythm Kings
X Factor Stars
Paul Young

DEREK REDMOND

Verry House, Chine Crescent Road,
Bournemouth BH2 5LQ
Tel 01202 242 434 Fax 01202 242 428
Email: info@derekredmond.com
Web Site: www.derekredmond.com
Contact: Derek Redmond
Former 400m athlete: Won Gold in the 4X400m with Black, Akabusi & Regis and his semi-final race in the Barcelona Olympics, has since become one of the most famous sporting images of modern times. Inspirational Speaker. Sports Commentator.

ARTISTES REPRESENTED:

Derek Redmond

DEREK'S HANDS & BODY PARTS

26-28 Hammersmith Grove,
London W6 7BA
Tel: 020 8834 1609 Fax: 020 8834 1144
Email: casting@derekshands.com
Web Site: www.derekshands.com
Director: Laila Debs
Specialist Hands & Body parts Agency.

DERI PROMOTIONS

9 Templars Close, Bognor Regis,
West Sussex PO22 6RU
Tel/Fax: 01243 585 545
Email: deripromotions@btopenworld.com
Web Site: www.deripromotions.org.uk
Senior Personnel: Roy Cooper
Specialising in Country & Western.

ARTISTES REPRESENTED:

The Allen James Band
Carroll Baker
Philomena Begley
Ann Brean
Tommy Cash
Charlie
Circuit Judge
Skeeter Davis
The Dean Brothers
Sydney Devine
Dirty Hat Band
Joe Dolan
Lonnie Donegan
Mary Duff
Narvel Felts
Freddie Fender
Raymond Froggatt
Jim Glaser
George Hamilton IV
Steve Hanks Band
The Heros
Jan Howard
Roger Humphries
Kenny Johnson and Northwind
Sarah Jory
Kris Kelly
Dominic Kirwan
Scooter Lee
Jimmy C Newman & His Cajun Band
Amanda Normansell (Patsy Cline)
Stu Page
Stella Parton
Johnny Paycheck
Ronnie Prophet
Puttin' on the Ritz
Johnny Russell
Jeannie Selly
Sharon "13"
Jean Shepard
Brendan Shine
Skiff A Billy
Billie Jo Spears
Cathie Stewart
Billy Walker
Dez Walters

MALCOLM DERRICK THEATRICAL ENTERPRISES

Poolbank House, 266 Longbridge Lane,
Northfield, Birmingham B31 4RJ
Tel: 0121 475 8759 Mob: 0788 618 179
Senior Personnel: Malcolm Derrick
Specialists in After Dinner Speakers

ARTISTES REPRESENTED:

Johnny Carroll
Tracie Hughes
Pat Wayne

DESERET ENTERTAINMENTS

2a Fern Court Drakefell Road London
SE14 5SN
Tel: 020 7635 8928
Email: just.william1@yahoo.co.uk
Contact: William Joines

DEVIL MANAGEMENT

PO Box 23, Spennymoor,
County Durham DL16 7YZ
Tel: 01388 818 888 Fax: 01388 811 222
Email: steve@devilmanagement.com
Web Site: www.devilmanagement.com
Contact: Steve Dodds, Paul Carr

ARTISTES REPRESENTED:

Duos:
2 Way Street
Angel Eyes
Attic Jam
Black Mist
Fatal Attraction
Inseparable
Passion
Powder Blue
Pulse
Spellbound
Time Slip
Illusion/Speciality:
Christian
John Danbury
Naughty NIgel Harvey
Tony Junior
Debi Lawrence
Steve Lucock
Magic Mike
Professor Nincompoop
Lawrence Sinclair
Mister Topper
Comedy Entertainers:
Aiden Jay
Jeff Alvey
Ray Banks
Brenda Collins
Peter La Scalla
Steven J Riley
Justin Sane
Vocal Entertainers:
Mark Allen
Robbie Allen
Amanda
Laurie Bennett
Charlene
Jayne Curry
Suzanne Gayle
Robin Good
Robbie Jacks
Mark Langley
Mikki Lawton
Sadie Lee
Liza McKenzie
Davey Nicholls
Claire Page
Chris Ritchie
Anita Ryan
Amanda Scala
Dixon J Scott
Carrie Steele
Dean Stewart
Steve Walls
Joe White
Helen Whitney
Van Williams
Jo Wright
Maggie Young
Groups/Trios:
Deadringer (Meatloaf tribute)
Kay Ward's Baker Street
Meat The Blues
Revolutionaires
Shelley Stevens Explosion
The Gangsters Of Ska
X-Factor

DG ENTERPRISES

20 Dale Road, Spondon,
Derby DE21 7DF
Tel: 01332 544 600 Fax: 01332 677 005
Email: annie.caple1@btopenworld.com
Senior Personnel: Annie Caple
Established 30 years, supplying entertainment to the Midlands, South Yorkshire and further afield.

ARTISTES REPRESENTED:

2 Groove
Al
Alter Egos
Brothers in Soul
Natasha Fox
Impromtu

DHM LIMITED

Suite One, Cottingham House,
Chorleywood Road, Rickmansworth,
Hertfordshire WD3 4EP
Tel: 01923 710614 Fax: 01923 710888
Email: roger@dhmlimited.co.uk
Web Site: www.dhmlimited.co.uk

Contact: Roger De Courcey

ARTISTES REPRESENTED:

Roger De Courcey
Rick Wakeman

DIAMOND MANAGEMENT

31 Percy Street, London W1T 2DD
Tel: 020 7631 0400 Fax: 020 7631 0500
Email: ld@diman.co.uk
Agent: Lesley Duff

ARTISTES REPRESENTED:

Actors:
Kelly Adams
Christopher Biggins
Shirley Eaton
Lisa Maxwell
Sir Roger Moore
Charlotte Rampling
Ian Richardson

DICK HORSEY MANAGEMENT

Suite 1 Cottingham House,
Chorley Wood Road, Rickmansworth,
WD3 4EP
Tel: 01923 710614 Fax: 01923 710614
Email: roger@dhmlimited.co.uk
Web Site: www.dhmlimited.co.uk
Contact: Roger De Courcey

DINGS ENTERTAINMENT

From 1st Dec 2012
Suite 1 106A Bedford Road Wootton
Bedford MK43 9JB
Tel: 01234 851 166 Fax: 01234 840 383
Email: ding@dings.com
Web Site: www.dings.com
Senior Personnel: Ian Davis FEAA

ARTISTES REPRESENTED:

Centre Of Attraction
Infantasia
Mike Jerome
The Mad Hatters
Triple Cream
Russ Williams

DINOSAUR PROMOTIONS/DINOSAUR MUSIC

5 Heyburn Crescent, Westport Gardens,
Stoke-on-Trent ST6 4DL
Tel: 01782 824 051 Fax: 01782 761 752
Email: agency@dinoprom.com
Web Site: www.dinoprom.com
Senior Personnel: Alan Dutton, Karen Bradbury
Specialising in all types of acts, management and sole representation. Music Publishing. (MCPS & PRS Registered)

ARTISTES REPRESENTED:

3.27
Alan Avon
DJ Cotton
Seamus Fitzsimmons
Groups & Duos:
3.27
Cool Wave
Hedgehoppers Anonymous
Hollywood Nites
Krys
QEII (Queen tribute)
Vice Versa
Female Vocalists:
Karen Andesson
Deeva
Claire Kennedy
D.D. King
Tracy King
Samantha Powers
Sonya
Joanne Thompson
Male Vocalists:
Leigh Anthony
John Buchanan
Elmo
Seamus Fitzsimmons
John Flint
Connor O'Niel
Chestor Riggon
Kenny Stevens
David Wainwright
Gary Wells
Dodgie Williams
Mark Yates

DIRECT MUSIC MANAGEMENT

11 Witly Avenue, Halesowen,
West Midlands B63 4DN
Tel: 0121 585 6796 Fax: 0121 602 3337
Email: info@directmusicman.com
Web Site: www.directmusicman.com
Senior Personnel: Keith Evans

ARTISTES REPRESENTED:

A-Tom-Ic Jones & The Explosive Reload Orchestra
The Classic Soul Show
The Disco Disciples
Jaki Graham
Not Chocolate
Quill
The Soul Survivors
The New Amen Corner
The Summer Of Love

DIRECT PERSONAL MANAGEMENT

Park House, 62 Lidgett Lane, Leeds,
West Yorkshire LS8 1PL
Tel/Fax: 0113 266 4036 London Office:
St John's House, 16 St John's Vale,
London SE8 4EN Tel/Fax: 020 8694 1788
Email: daphne.franks@directpm.co.uk
Web Site: www.directpm.co.uk
Senior Personnel: Daphne Franks

ARTISTES REPRESENTED:

Rachel Jane Allen
Stephen Anderson
Dan Armour
Gillian Baskeyfield
Sonia Beck
Ron Blass
Alastair Chisholm
Ashley Christmas
Ruth Curtis
Peter Dawson
Steve Evets
Julian Finnigan
Leigh Gardner
Alex Hall
Rebekah Hughes
Susan Louise Jinks
Kathleen Jordan
Muzz Khan
Martina McClements
Byron McGuiness
Jill Myers
Richard Povall
David Robertson
Shireen Sarkhoy
Jean Stevens
Alan Strangeway
Tony Xu
Robert Took
David Toole
Lauren Tritton
Mark Wadsworth
Caroline Woodruff
Andy Selby Worthington

DIVA ENTERTAINMENTS AGENCY

50-54 Farnham Road, Seven Kings, Ilford,
Essex IG3 8QD
Tel: 020 8590 8050 Fax: 020 8590 8099
Email: honeykalaria@divaentertainments.com
Web Site: www.divaentertainments.com
Contact: Honey Kalaria
Specialising in Bollywood/Asian acts

THE DIXON AGENCY

58 Hedley Street, Gosforth,
Newcastle-upon-Tyne, Tyne and Wear
NE3 1DL
Tel: 0870 438 8888 Fax: 0870 438 7777
Email: bill@dixonagency.com
Web Site: www.dixonagency.com
Agent: Bill Dixon

ARTISTES REPRESENTED:

5 Steps 2 Abba
Abba Express
Abba Mia
Alexander's Palace
Andrew Kerry Association
Ant Hill Mob
Baha Beach Boys
Bernadette Wilde Band
Big City
Blue Notes
Bon Jordi
Boyz
Lorraine Crosby Band
Dee Dowling Band
Dexter & The Revelations
Dionne Andre's Absolute 80's
Disco Knights
Dream Machine
Envy
The Flying Emperors
Foxx
Great Glam Mothers
Groovy Movie
Harlene Evans Band
Jade
Leroy Johnson & The Flicks
Male Order
Men in Black
Power & Soul
Revolution

Robbie Williams Experience
Sister Sarah
Sk8er Boys
Sounds Of The Suburbs
Sounds Of The Suburbs
Stardust Experience
Two Out Of Three

DJ ENTERTAINMENTS

22 Alexander Close, Ashfield Park
Workington, Cumbria CA14 3HQ
Tel/Fax: 01900 64971
Email: djents@btinternet.com
Contact: Joan Hodgson

DMF MUSIC LTD.

51 Queen Street Exeter EX4 3SR
Tel: 01392 437733
Email: info@dmfmusic.co.uk
Web Site: www.dmfmusic.co.uk
Contact: David Farrow

DON WORLDWIDE ENTERTAINMENTS

133 Brown Royd Avenue, Huddersfield
HD5 9QB
Tel: 01484 512103 Fax: 01484 512103
Email: donlevitt@ntlworld.com
Web: www.donentertainment.blogspot.com
Contact: Don Levitt

THE PETER DONEGAN BAND

21 Belsay Grove, Bedlington,
Northumberland NE22 5YU
Mob: 07563 379 245
Email: peter-donegan@hotmail.com
Web Site: www.peterdonegan.com
Contact: Peter Donegan

ARTISTES REPRESENTED:

Peter Donegan

DOUB7E SEVEN EVENTS LTD

Authorised House 4 Endowood Road
Sheffield, S7 2LZ
Tel: 0114 2362 874 Mob: 07966 060777
Email: roop@77events.co.uk
Web Site: www.77events.co.uk
Contact: Roop Mullins
We supply entertainment for private and corporate events, ranging from celebrities, bands, speakers to magicians and walkabout entertainment.

ARTISTES REPRESENTED:

Background Music:
Lois Alexander (Cocktail Vocals)
Rod Coope (Pianist)
Dixie De Luxe
Hot Club (Jazz & Swing)
Kendall String Quartet
Quintessential Swing Band
Saudade (Salsa)
Interactive & Walkabout Entertainment:
Belly Dancer On Stilts
Christmas Trees (Interactive)
Kelly Cox (Caricaturist)
Elvis on Stilts
Gold Fingers (Magician & Caricaturist)
Halloween Horror Frenzy
Human Statues
Pirates & The Skeleton Army
Darren Robson (Magician)
Tequila Slammers
The 007 Performers
The Members Of The Spoof Paparazzi
The Oscar Performers
Barnaby Wild (Kids Fun)
Peter Zenner (Hypnotist)
Lookalikes:
Suzie Kennedy as Marilyn Monroe
Miltra as Foxy Cleopatra
Luke De Silva as Ali G & Borat
The Bond Girls
Party Bands:
Big J & the Piccolo Chickens
Frisco Crabbe (Soul & Funk)
The Funtime Frankies (Party)
Jules (Ecclectic)
Soul Rights
The Bluetones
The Bootleggers (covers)
The Upside Down Band (Ecclectic)
Three Men and a Bass (Rock & Pop)
Tributes:
Beatlemania
Phil Fryer as Frank Sinatra
Sally Moore (Madonna)
John E Prescott as Elvis
The Frank and Dean Show
Speakers:
Herol Bomber Graham (Boxing)
Gervaise Phinn (School Governor)
Steve Smith MBE (Lawyer & Author)
Leon Taylor

DOUBLE ACT

PO Box 25574 London NW7 3GB
Tel: 020 8381 0151 Fax: 020 8201 1795
Email: info@double-act.co.uk
Web Site: www.double-act.co.uk
Contact: Lydia Wolfson

DOWNES PRESENTERS AGENCY

96 Broadway, Bexleyheath, Kent
DA6 7DE
Tel: 020 8304 0541
Email: downes@presentersagency.com
Web Site: www.presentersagency.com
Senior Personnel: Wendy Downes, Lee Downes, Cheryl Downes

ARTISTES REPRESENTED:

Male:
David Ashford
Johnny Ball
Sean Brickell
Doc Cox
Ross Edmonds
John Edmunds
Steve Le Fevre
Neil Francis
Derek Gibbons
Simon Groom
Paddy Haycocks
Russell Hurn
Frankie McPolin
Adrian Mills
John Noakes
Derek Partridge
Lance Percival
Richard Phillips
Peter Purves
Phil Sayer
Jonathan Wheatley
Female:
Patricia Driscoll
Sue Edelson
Sally James
Yiolanda Koppell
Trish Lynch
Sarah Parnell
Ali Paton
Anna Perry
Elise Raynor
Jean Rogers
Debbie Shore

STEVE DRAPER ENTERTAINMENTS

2 The Coppice, Beardwood Manor,
Blackburn, Lancashire BB2 7BQ
Tel/Fax: 01254 679 005
Email:
steve@stevedraperents.fsbusiness.co.uk
Web: www.stevedraperentertainments.co.uk
Senior Personnel: Steve Draper, Tracey Kendall
Administrator: Jacky Draper

ARTISTES REPRESENTED:

Amy G
David Lee Andrews
Badboys (Male Revue Team)
Pete Chariot
Dolly Dee
The Elvis Experience
Kelly Fox
Maria Jordon
Male / Female Strippers
Miss Van Dyke
Emma Nicholls
Max Pressure
Strippagrams

DREAMS INTERNATIONAL MODEL & CASTING AGENCY

Empire House, 175 Piccadilly, Mayfair,
London W1J 9TB
Tel: 020 7359 4786 Fax: 020 7688 0771
Mobile: 07949 548904
Senior Personnel: Deborah Hillaire

BRYAN DREW LTD

Quadrant House, 80/82 Regent Street,
London W1B 5AU
Tel: 020 7437 2293 Fax: 020 7437 0561
Email: bryan@bryandrewltd.com
Web Site: www.bryandrewltd.com
Senior Personnel: Bryan Drew, Mina Parmar
Specialising in Actors, Actresses, Writers, Directors, Voice Overs

NEIL DROVER - THE AGENCY

Event House, 437 Crow Road, Glasgow,
Strathclyde G11 7DZ Scotland
Tel: 0845 062 3377 Fax: 0141 334 4796

Email: neil@neildrover.com
Web Site: www.neildrover.com
Senior Personnel: Neil Drover, Angela Prentice, Julie Hume
Specialising in a variety of entertainment and corporate hospitality.

D&S ARTISTES

19 Reffley Lane, King's Lynn, Norfolk PE30 3EF
Tel/Fax: 01553 671 693 Mobile: 07904 524 051
Email: info@dandsartistes.co.uk
Web Site: www.dandsartistes.co.uk
Senior Personnel: Alan Johnston, Mark Pearman
Specialising in groups, cabaret, children's entertainers, discos and celebrity appearances.

DSA THEATRICAL AGENCY

23 Hartswood Road, London W12 9NE
Tel: 020 8740 8120 Fax: 020 8743 7017
Email: laura@dsaproductions.co.uk
Web Site: www.dsaproductions.co.uk
Senior Personnel: Svend Johannsen

PAUL DUDDRIDGE MANAGEMENT

32 Rathbone Place, London W1T 1JD
Tel: 020 7580 3580 Fax: 020 7580 3480
Email: paul@paulduddridge.com
Web Site: www.paulduddridge.com
Agents: Paul Duddridge, Mike Leigh

ARTISTES REPRESENTED:

Presenters:
Nana Akua
Brandon Block
Steve Brody
Jono Coleman
Chris Corcoran
Dominik Diamond
Elle Dible
Buddy Dolphin
Milo McCabe
Bob Mills
Normski
Paul Ross
Rav Singh
Dave Wellman
Comedians:
Lenny Beige
Ruth Bratt
Steve Brody
Rob Brydon
Chris Corcoran
Phil Cornwell
doktor cocacolamcdonalds
Steve Furst
Dominic Holland
Mark Hurst
Marianne Levy
Milo McCabe
Jimmy McGhie
Bob Mills
Thomas Nelstrop
Kirsten O'Brien
Curtis Walker
Wendy Wason
Actors:
Tamzin Aitken
Camilla Beeput
John Biddle
Ruth Bratt
Steve Brody
Rob Brydon
Jennifer Castle
Chris Corcoran
Matthew Crompton
Lucy Cudden
Trevor Cuthbertson
Chas Early
Steve Furst
Will Garthwaite
Robin Goodchild
Christopher Haydon
John Holden-White
Dominic Holland
Stephanie Jory
Pia de Keyser
Julie Marie-Taylor
Milo McCabe
Charlotte Melen
Alec Nicholls
Kirsten O'Brien
Richard Saade
Paul Sadler
Claudia Sermbezis
Katherine Templar
Victoria Temple-Morris
Anna Victoria
Matt Warman
Wendy Wason
David Whitney
Sam Woodward
Farris Wren

DUKERIES ENTERTAINMENTS

The Edis Building, 3 The Broadway, Mansfield, Nottinghamshire NG18 2RL
Tel: 01623 635 327 Fax: 01623 635887
Email: tanya@dukeries.com
Web Site: www.dukeries.com
Senior Personnel: Tanya Walker

ARTISTES REPRESENTED:

2 to Go
Decade
Craig Deegan
James Hart
Denise Johnson
Chris Lafferty
The New Chevrons
Ruth Stanford
Tony Wallace
Y'can't Touch This

BRIAN DURKIN ASSOCIATES

Bryson House Chiltern Road, Culcheth, Warrington WA3 4LL
Tel: 01925 766655 Fax: 01925 765577
Email: briandurkin@btconnect.com
Web Site: www.bdaltd.co.uk
See B.D.A. Listing

DUROC MEDIA LTD

Riverside House, 10-12 Victoria Road, Uxbridge, Middlesex UB8 2TW
Tel: 01895 810 831 Fax: 01895 231 499
Email: persha@durocmedia.com
Web Site: www.durocmedia.com
Contacts: Simon Porter, Persha Sethi

ARTISTES REPRESENTED:

Uriah Heep
Status Quo

BARRY DYE ENTERTAINMENTS

PO Box 888, Ipswich, Suffolk IP1 6BU
Tel: 01473 744 287 Fax: 01473 745 442
Mobile: 07831 700799
Email: barrydye@aol.com
Web Site: www.barrydye.co.uk
Barry Dye

ARTISTES REPRESENTED:

Jon Bell
Olly Day
Hayley Dye
Graham P Jolley
Micky Zany
Greg Monaghan
Graham Powell
Rock Magic (Chris North and Belinda - Illusion)
Leo Shavers
Alan Wallace
Richard Wymark

KENNETH EARLE PERSONAL MANAGEMENT

214 Brixton Road, Brixton, London SW9 6AP
Tel: 020 7274 1219 Fax: 020 7274 9529
Email: kennethearle@agents-uk.com
Web Site: www.entertainment-kennethearle.co.uk
Senior Personnel: Kenneth Earle FEAA

ARTISTES REPRESENTED:

Stuart Allen
Sarah Beauvoisin
Nick Charles
Carrie Clark
Rochelle Cole
Michael Cule
Peter J Elliott
Jez Foster
Harry Fowler
Melissa Franklyn
Jonnie Hurn
Preece Killick
Royston Mayoh
Georgina Moon
Peter Osborne
Doyle Richards
Rebecca Richardson
Chrissy Rock
Susan Roquette
Sally Tomsett
Chris Williams
Claudette Williams
Maria Wilson
Kytsun Wolfe

SUSI EARNSHAW MANAGEMENT

Susi Earnshaw Theatre School,
68 High Street, Barnet, Hertfordshire EN5 5SJ
Tel: 020 8441 5010 Fax: 020 8364 9618

Email: casting@susiearnshaw.co.uk
Web Site: www.susiearnshaw.co.uk
Senior Personnel: Susi Earnshaw, Fran Proctor-Gibbs

EAST ANGLIAN ENTERTAINMENTS

Ashdown House, Livermere Road, Great Barton, Bury St Edmunds, Suffolk IP31 2RZ
Tel/Fax: 01284 787 494
Email: john.ranson@eastanglianents.co.uk
Web Site: www.eastanglianents.co.uk
Senior Personnel: John Ranson
Representing the best in bands, cabarets, discos, magic, corporate events. Individual packages to suit all budgets and occasions.

EC1 MUSIC AGENCY

1 Cowcross Street, London EC1M 6DR
Tel: 020 7490 8990 Fax: 020 7490 8987
Email: jack@ec1music.com
Senior Personnel: Alex Nightingale, Jack Notman

ARTISTES REPRESENTED:

African Headcharge
Dot Allison
Anjali
Battant
Chemical Brothers
Death In Vegas
Delphian Complex
Electrelane
Electric Six
Jan Wobble & The Invaders of the Heart
The Orb
Adrian Sherwood
Soulsavers
South
St Etienne
The Concretes
The Pioneers

EDDIE LOCK

2, The Old Parish Hall The Square
Lenham Kent ME17 2PQ
Tel: 01622 858300 Mob: 07710 772207
Email: info@eddielock.com
Web Site: www.eddielock.co.uk / www.goldie.co.uk
Contact: Eddie Lock
Exclusive Worldwide Management & Agent of Goldie

ARTISTES REPRESENTED:

Goldie

EDGE ENTERTAINMENT CONSULTANTS LTD

Woodgate House, Hollycroft Road, Emnet, Cambridgeshire PE14 8BD
Tel: 0800 781 3343 Fax: 08707 557 643
Email: info@theedge-uk.com
Web Site: www.theedge-uk.com
Senior Personnel: Andy Harvey, Alan Garner, S Kerrigan, M Brown

ARTISTES REPRESENTED:

The 70's Sensations
The Cash Cube
Alan G
Giant Games
Andy Nick
The Speciality Troop
The Amusing Sister Ruth!

E.K.A MODEL & ACTOR MANAGEMENT

The Warehouse Studios, Glaziers Lane, Culcheth, Warrington WA3 4AQ
Tel: 0871 222 7470 Fax: 0871 222 7471
Email: info@eka-agency.com
Web Site: www.eka-agency.com
Company Director: Debbie Ikin
Senior TV & Film Casting Agent: Rebecca Keeley
Actor Management: Kate Sinclair
Agents to talented and experienced models and actors 18 to 80 yrs of all nationalities. Photographic, Television Commercials and Programmes, Films. Main & Supporting Artistes. We are a large agency covering the North West, Midlands and all UK. 20 Staff. Casting and Photographic Studios available. Friendly and efficient service.
E.K.A Management and Eurokids & Adults Agency is part of Eurokids Ltd.

ELAINE MURPHY ASSOCIATES

Suite 1, 50 High Street Wanstead, London E11 2RJ
Tel: 020 8989 4122 Fax: 020 8989 1400
Email: elaine@elainemurphy.co.uk
Web Site: www.elainemurphy.co.uk
Senior Personnel: Elaine Murphy

ELCOCK ENTERTAINMENTS LTD

41 Strathmore Crescent, Wombourne, Wolverhampton WV5 9AR
Tel: 01902 672972 Tel: 01902 884301
Fax: 01902 881060
Email: enquiries@elcock-entertainments.co.uk
Web: www.elcock-entertainments.co.uk
Contact: Jake Elcock

ELEVATION ENTERTAINMENTS

Hazelmere Preston Road Ribchester
PRESTON PR3 3XL
Tel: 01254 878096
Email: davidhazelmere@aol.com
Web Site: www.rbentertainments.co.uk
David Reeve

ELEVENTH HOUR MANAGEMENT LTD

7/11 Minerva Road, Park Royal, London NW10 6HJ
Tel/Fax: 020 8575 9024
Mobile: 07712 980 210
Email: eleventh_hour@btinternet.com
Contact: John Cooke
Specialising in celebrity booking and music management.

ARTISTES REPRESENTED:

Cameo
Tito Jackson
Cleo Rocos
The Gap Band

ELINOR HILTON ASSOCIATES

BAC, Lavender Hill, London SW11 5TF
Tel: 020 7738 9574 Fax: 020 7924 4636
Email: info@elinorhilton.co.uk
Web Site: www.elinorhilton.co.uk
Con

ARTISTES REPRESENTED:

Males:
Daniel Alexander
Ali Amadi
Dermot Canavan
Derek Carlyle
Alan Corser
Richard Da Costa
Jeremy David
Guy Fearon
Jim Fish
Kenneth Gilbert
Jon-Sel Gourkan
Imran Mirza
Laurence Inman
Tim Kane
Richard Latham
Edward Law
Adrian Lewis Morgan
Matt Odell
Chris Pickles
Colin Rote
Barry Shannon
Paul Stephenson
Mark Stevenson
Martin Trent
Peter Winnal
Females:
Francesca Anderson
Alice Barclay
Betty Benjamin
Jilly Bond
Jennifer Burgess
Lorraine Coady
Sara Coward
Carole Dance
Ellie Darvill
Elise Davison
Carol Fitzpatrick
Sonia Fraser
Tanya Hossick
Jo Howard
Helen Hurd
Sheen Irving
Susan Jeffrey
Joanna Eliot
Sayan Kent
Angela Kumari
Sarah Lawn
Penelope McDonald
Gwynne McElveen
Sunny Ormonde
Samantha Parry
Marianne Sheehan
Nadia Silva
Julia Taudevin
Rebecca Vaughan
Louise Winstone

ELITE & CHILDREN'S PARTY ENTERTAINMENT LTD
8 The Hillway, Fareham, Hampshire
PO16 8BL
Tel: 02392 379597 Tel: 02392 788868
Fax: 02392 788868
Email: acts@childrenspartyents.co.uk
Web Site: www.childrenspartyents.co.uk
Contact: Nicola Stapleford

ELITE CELEBRITY MANAGEMENT LTD
Gwerneinon House
224 Derwem Fawr Road SWANSEA
SA2 8EA
Tel: 01792 536120
Email: sheila@welshstars.co.uk
Web Site: www.welshstars.co.uk
Sheila Willicombe

ELITE ENTERTAINMENT (MANCHESTER) LTD
PO Box 113, Newton-le-Willows
WA3 2FU
Tel: 0845 260 1106
Email: info@eliteentertainments.co.uk
Web Site: www.eliteentertainments.co.uk
Contact: Duane Thornborough

ELITE PROMOTIONS
1A Thistle Place, Aberdeen AB10 1UZ
Scotland
Tel: 01224 636 363 Fax: 01224 652 980
Email: info@elitepromotions.net
Web Site: www.elitepromotions.net
Senior Personnel: John Anderson, Kathleen Anderson
Wedding Co-ordinator: Susan Moultrie
Entertainment Consultants and Booking Agents - Supplying all entertainment sectors and corporate hospitality packages.

ARTISTES REPRESENTED:
Stan Boardman
John Conteh
Stuart Coull
Iron Broo (Ceilidh Band)
KFS
Jim Leishman
Lily & The Boys
Patrice
Steve Ransome Band
Slinky
Splash
The Big Deal
Jim Watt MBE
Celebrity Chefs:

STEVE ELSON
11 Ernest Gardens, London W4 3QU
Tel: 020 8995 5520 Fax: 020 8995 3835
Mobile: 07976 276 375
Email: steve@counterfeitstone.demon.co.uk
Web Site: www.thecounterfeitstones.net
Senior Personnel: Steve Elson
Production and management of The Counterfeit Stones - "A Rolling Stones Tribute Show".

ARTISTES REPRESENTED:
The Counterfeit Stones

ELSPETH COCHRANE PERSONAL MANAGEMENT
16 Old Town, Clapham, London
SW4 0JY
Tel: 020 7819 6256 Fax: 020 7819 4297
Email: elspeth@elspethcochrane.co.uk
Senior Personnel: Elspeth Cochrane

EMKAY LOTHIAN ENTERTAINMENTS
The Sutherland Suite
Cooper Buisness Park Buchan Lane,
Broxburn, West Lothian EH52 5QD
Tel: 01506 845 555 Fax: 01506 856751
Email: tom@emkayentertainments.co.uk
Web Site: www.emkaylothian.co.uk
Senior Personnel: Tom Solley, Alex Smith, Glyn Davies & Susan Davies
Specialising in variety (light entertainment), corporate, military and leisure.

ARTISTES REPRESENTED:
See website for roster:

EMPTAGE HALLETT LTD
14 Rathbone Place London W1T 1HT
Tel: 020 7436 0425 Fax: 020 7580 2748
Email: mail@emptagehallett.co.uk
Web Site: www.emptagehallett.co.uk
Contacts: Michael Emptage, Michael Hallett
Commercials/Voice-Overs: Denise Ramkissoon

ARTISTES REPRESENTED:
Roger Alborough
Lucy Arkhurst
David Ashton
Holly Atkins
Charlotte Avery
Steven Berkoff
Vas Blackwood
Richard Bremmer
David Brooks
James Callis
Kathy Kiera Clarke
Kathy Kiera Clarke
Sam Crane
Phil Daniels
Matthew Devitt
Jack Doolan
Fish
Benjamin Fisher
Hadley Fraser
Laura Fraser
Rafi Gavron
Gabrielle Glaister
Constantine Gregory
Roger Griffiths
Brian Hibbard
Arbel Jones
Antonie Kamerling
Simon Kunz
Eleanor Lawrence
Valerie Lilley
Eugene Lipinski
Caroline Loncq
Amelia Lowdell
Philip Madoc
Rory McCann
Colin McFarlane
Steven Meo
Izabella Miko
Richard Moore
Naoko Mori
Gavan O'Herlihy
Rob Ostlere
Lisa Palfrey
Rhys Parry Jones
Meghan Popiel
Robert Pugh
Ieuan Rhys
Josha Richards
Shane Rimmer
David Robb
Natalie Roles
Kevin Rooney
Carol Royle
Amber Sainsbury
Amy Shiels
Steve Speirs
Denise Stephenson
Shane Taylor
Gareth Thomas
Matt Wait
Phoebe Waller-Bridge
Ed Westwick
Toyah Wilcox
Shaun Williamson (Barry, Eastenders)
Tom Wisdom

DOREEN ENGLISH 95
4 Selsey Avenue, Bognor Regis,
West Sussex PO21 2QZ
Tel/Fax: 01243 825 968
Senior Personnel: Gerry Kinner
Specialising in Children.

THE ENTERTAINERS AGENCY
49A Comyn Drive, Wallacestone, Falkirk,
Stirlingshire FK2 0YR Scotland
Tel: 01738 815995 Mob: 07831 845 250
Email: douglas@entertainersagency.com
Web Site: www.entertainers-agency.co.uk
Contact: Douglas Gillespie
Scottish entertainment specialists.
Corporate and conference consultants.

ENTERTAINERS COMPANY LTD
The UK's No.1 Entertainment Agency
200 London Road, Hadleigh, Benfleet,
Essex SS7 2PD
Tel: 01702 427 100 / 0870 233 0836
Fax: 01702 427 109 Mob: 07850 111616
Email: enquiries@entertainers.co.uk
Web Site: www.entertainers.co.uk / www.easytheatres.co.uk
Director: Michael Taylor (michael@entertainers.co.uk)
Senior Personnel: Ben Hatton
The one stop shop for entertainment.

ARTISTES REPRESENTED:
Please see Complete Talent Agency Ltd:

ENTERTAINERS MANAGEMENT LTD

200 London Road, Hadleigh, Benfleet, Essex SS7 2PD
Tel: 01702 427 100 Fax: 01702 427 109
Mob: 07850 111616
Email: enquiries@entertainers.co.uk
Web Site: www.easytheatres.com
Senior Personnel: Ben Hatton
Director: Michael Taylor
Contact: michael@entertainers.co.uk
The UK's no 1 entertainment agency.

ARTISTES REPRESENTED:

Stage Shows:
70's Soul Train
An American Trilogy
Back To Back
The Magic Of Motown
Magical Night With The Stars
The Rat Pack Live
The Roaring 20's
Rock'n'Roll Magic
Thank You For The Music
They Will Rock You
Yankee Blues Brothers
Tribute Bands:
Abba Inferno
Abba Magic
Abba Max
Baby Boney M
Bee Gees Magic
Bootleg Beatles
Fort Brothers as Everly Brothers
Gidea Park (Beach Boys tribute)
New Recruits
Oasisn`t (Oasis Tribute)
Other Beatles
Stoned Again
Trenchtown Experience (Bob Marley & The Wailers tribute)
Tribute To The Tops
U2 Magic
Ultimate Madness (Madness Tribute)
Upbeat Beatles
Yesterday Once More
General Bands:
Glambusters
The Grimleys
Threepenny Bit
Solo Tribute Acts:
James Alexander (Lionel Richie)
Maxine Barrie (Shirley Bassey)
Harry Cambridge as Luther Vandross
Jacquii Cann as Alison Moyet
Richard Carter (George Michael)
Nova Casper as Tina Turner
Shenton Dixon as Stevie Wonder
Enrique Experience
Rebecca Eve (Celine Dion/Shania Twain)
Kevin Fitzsimmons (Sinatra)
Keith George (as Boy George)
Lee Griffiths As Bobby Darin
Hitz Of The Blitz
Max Hutton (Robbie Williams)
Sammy J (Kylie)
Alan James as Chris de Burgh
Jani Jaye (B. Spears)
Jimmy Jemain as Cliff Richard
Natalie Lane (Shania Twain)
Greg Lawrence as Fats Domino
Glen Leon as Tom Jones
Chris Martyn as Robbie Williams, Mick Hucknall
Maxine Mazumder as Lulu, Dusty
Sally Moore as Celine Dion, Madonna
Milli Munro (Shirley Bassey)
Terry Nash (Meatloaf)
Patti (as Kylie)
John Rickard (Neil Diamond)
Rob By Nature (Robbie Williams)
Anne Shirley (Diana Ross)
Kenny Simon (Errol Brown)
Gerry Trew (Rod Stewart)
Barry Wide (Barry White)
Andy Wood (Ricky Martin)
Comedy Bands:
The Barron Knights
The Black Abbots
The Brother Lees
The Original Ivy League
The Rockin' Berries
Star Bands & Singers:
Boney M
Brotherhood of Man
Joe Brown
Bucks Fizz
Chas 'n' Dave
Clem Curtis & the Foundations
Gwen Dickey (solo)
Edison Lighthouse
The Fortunes
The Fourmost
Gerry & The Pacemakers
Heatwave
Herman's Hermits
The Hollies
Hot Chocolate
Jimmy James & The Vagabonds
Mungo Jerry
Ben E King
The Manfreds
Marmalade
George McCrae
The Pasadenas
Mike Pender's Searchers
Brian Poole & Electrix
Suzi Quatro
The Rubettes
Jimmy Ruffin
The Searchers
Showaddywaddy
Slade II
Smokie
The Tremeloes
The Troggs
Wet Wet Wet

THE ENTERTAINING BUSINESS

19 Rush Hill Road, Uppermill, Saddleworth OL3 6JD
Tel: 01457 877 700 Fax: 01457 877 600
Email: info@entsbiz.com
Web Site: www.entsbiz.com
Contact: Miss Adele Mitchison
We specialise in corporate entertainment and speciality acts.

THE ENTERTAINMENT COMPANY LTD

Elizabeth House, Royal Elizabeth Yard, Dalmeny, Edinburgh, Mid Lothian EH29 9EN Scotland
Tel: 0131 331 3400 Fax: 0131 331 3468
Email: gavin@entertainmentcompany.com
Web: www.entertainmentcompany.com
25 years experience in providing the highest quality events & entertainment.

ENTERTAINMENT DIRECT

Harry Margolis Entertainment Organisation
14 Heathside Road, Giffnock, Glasgow, Strathclyde G46 6HL Scotland
Tel: 0141 638 0724 Fax: 0141 620 0799
Mobile: 07949 166054
Email: musicdirct@aol.com
Web Site: www.musicdirct.co.uk
Senior Personnel: Harry Margolis

ARTISTES REPRESENTED:

Harry Margolis & His Big Band 'Glenn Miller' Sound

ENTERTAINMENT FX

Suppliers of Entertainment Throughout Europe (5 Star)
PO Box 190 Exeter EX2 6ED Devon
Tel: 0800 015 1017 Fax: 0845 300 4560
Email: info@entertainmentfx.co.uk
Web Site: www.entertainmentfx.co.uk
Contact: Terry Mills

ARTISTES REPRESENTED:

Cheeky Girls
Chris Collman
Nicholas Dorsett (X Factor)
Fab Beatles
Griff Griffiths
Jonnie Hawkins (X Factor)
Phillip Magee (X Factor)
Marc D (Pop Idol)
Marc Dillon (Pop Idol 2004)
Pop of Ages
Rick Waller (Pop Idol 2003)
Roxanne (Pop Idol 2004)
Tarrot Lee (Radio DJ)
Terry Mills (Radio / Compare / DJ)
Un-Used Toys

ENTERTAINMENT SERVICES

PO Box 237 Plymouth PL5 1WW
Tel: 0845 257 5868
Email: admin@showbizuk.com
Web Site: www.showbizuk.com
Contact: Keith Hall

ENTERTAINMENT SHOP

223 Argyle Avenue, Hounslow TW3 2LR
Tel: 020 8755 2551
Email: info@entertainmentshop.biz
Web Site: www.entertainmentshop.biz
Senior Personnel: Mr Cobbing

ENTERTAINMENTS INCORPORATED

14 The Drive, Marple, Stockport, Cheshire SK6 6DR
Tel: 0161 427 7307 Fax: 0161 221 0457
Leyland Office (2 Offices) 61A Hough Lane, Leyland, Preston PR25 2SA Tel: 01772-422388 Contact: Jack Wood
Contact for Leyland is Jack Lane.

ENTERTAINMENTS UNLIMITED
4 Greenford Road, Southport, Merseyside PR8 3JT
Tel/Fax: 01704 574 732
Email: info@ents-unltd.com
Web Site: www.ents-unltd.com
Senior Personnel: R E Palmer

ENTIRE OCCASIONS
Sundays Hill Cottage, Sundays Hill Lane, Falfields, Gloucestershire GL12 8DQ
Tel: 0800 011 2434 Mobile: 07768 170617
Email: hardy@entireoccasions.com
Web Site: www.entireoccasions.com
Senior Personnel: Malcolm Hardy
Specialising in weddings, pre-match entertainment, corporate events and parties.

EPIC CREATIVE PRODUCTIONS
The Studio 38 Acacia Close STANMORE HA7 3JR
Tel: 020 8954 3311
Email: info@ecpl.co.uk
Web Site: www.ecpl.co.uk
Jack Applebaum

JUNE EPSTEIN ASSOCIATES
62 Compayne Gardens, London NW6 3RY
Tel: 020 7328 0864 / 7372 1928
Fax: 020 7328 0684
Email: june@june-epstein-associates.co.uk
Agent: June Epstein

EQUATOR MUSIC
17 Hereford Mansions, Hereford Road, London W2 5BA
Tel: 020 7727 5858 Fax: 020 7229 5934
Email: mail@equatormusic.com
Web Site: www.equatormusic.com
Senior Personnel: Ralph Baker

ARTISTES REPRESENTED:
Jeff Beck
Tony Iommi
De Luca

ERNEST SWIFT FEAA
3 Naylor Farm Avenue Shevington WN6 8EQ
Tel: 01704 892357
Email: ernieswift@uwclub.net
Contact: Ernest Swift FEAA

ES PROMOTIONS
Unit 24, Larkwood, Larkwood Close, Kettering, Northamptonshire NN16 9NQ
Tel: 01536 310 520 Fax 01536 358 113
Email: sales@es-promotions.com
Web Site: www.es-promotions.com
Financial Director: Dave Turner
The Agency supplies circus performers, children's entertainment, street entertainers, arena and aerial acts.
Outdoor event specialists, entertainment agency, team events, themed events, fun casino. Inflatables and unusual games for hire. Balloons, balloon gas, balloon releases and balloon decorating.

ESSANAY
PO Box 44394 London SW20 0YP
Tel: 020 8879 7076 Fax: 0203 258 5037
Email: info@essanay.co.uk
Senior Personnel: Nicholas Young

ESSENTIAL ENTERTAINMENT
The Conservatory,
48 Hawkesworth Drive, Bagshot, Surrey GU19 5QZ
Tel: 01276 477 292 Fax: 01276 451 956
Mobile: 07860 732919
Email: enquiries@essential-entertainment.com
Web: www.essential-entertainment.com
Senior Personnel: Tracy Jacobs
We supply artistes to the corporate industry.

ARTISTES REPRESENTED:
Da Vinci's Seasons (Jersey Boys - Four Seasons Tribute)
The Hot Dogs
Lewis Dixon (Michael Buble tribute)
The Overtures (60's Band)
The Slaves

ESSEX ENTERTAINMENT AGENCY
78 High Road, Layer-de-la-Haye, Colchester, Essex CO2 0DT
Tel: 01206 734 164 Fax: 01206 734 165
Email: richard@essexents.com
Web Site: www.essexents.com
Senior Personnel: Richard Smith

ARTISTES REPRESENTED:
David Alacey (Frank Sinatra Tribute)

Angel Street
Beeline Roadshow Disco
Casino Royale (Casino)
Champagne String Quartet
Keith "The Thief" Charnley
Steve Garner
Marc Jacobs
Octavius Steel Band
Vince Rayner (Comedy)
Ian Richards
Super Troopers

ETM LTD

Mosley House,
122 Mosley Common Road, Worsley,
Manchester M28 1AN
Tel: 0161 790 4640 / 799 7605
Fax: 0161 703 8521
Email: csmbooker@aol.com
Web Site: www.artistsuk.com
Senior Personnel: Roy Hastings

ARTISTES REPRESENTED:

Derek Acorah
Mick Miller
Peter Reeves
James Whale
Gary White

ETS EVENTS

P.O. Box 844, Crawley, West Sussex
RH10 0YU
Tel: 0845 838 7437
Email: info@etsevents.co.uk
Web Site: www.etsevents.co.uk
Senior Personnel: Eddie Smith
Many more Artistes represented, but to name a few.

EUROKIDS & ADULTS INTERNATIONAL CASTING & MODEL AGENCY

The Warehouse Studios, Glaziers Lane,
Culcheth, Warrington, Cheshire WA3 4AQ
Tel: 0871 222 7470 Fax: 0871 222 7471
Email: info@eka-agency.com
Web Site: www.eka-agency.com
Contact: Debbie Ikin
Agents to talented models and actors. Birth to 80 years of all nationalities. Photographic, television commercials & programmes, films. Main & supporting artistes. Extras for background work. We are a large agency covering the North West and Midlands. 20 staff. Casting & photographic studios available. Friendly & efficient service. Eurokids &adults agency is part of EuroKids Ltd

EUROPEAN ARTISTES MANAGEMENT

PO Box 9, Rochdale, Lancashire
OL16 4JU
Tel: 01706 299 880 Fax: 01706 844 719
Proprietor: Tony Hayes

ARTISTES REPRESENTED:

Backbeat Beatles
Barton & Paige
Tony Grant (Freddie Mercury tribute)
Pulp Culture
Souled As Seen
Stax of Soul
Turn It Loose

EVANS & REISS

100 Fawe Park Road, London SW15 2EA
Tel: 020 8877 3755 Fax: 020 8877 0307
Email: marcia@evansandreiss.co.uk
Senior Personnel: Jan Evans, Wendy Padbury

JACQUE EVANS MANAGEMENT LTD

Suite 1 14 Holmesley Road, London
SE23 1PJ
Tel: 020 8699 1202 Fax: 020 8699 5192
Email: jacque@jemltd.demon.co.uk
Web Site: www.jacqueevansltd.com
Senior Personnel: Jacque Evans
Specialising in Journalists, Broadcasters & Presenters.

ARTISTES REPRESENTED:

Loulla Astin
Juliet Bawden
Dougie Brimson
Dave Cash
Granville Danny Clarke
Dave Dayes
David Domoney
Dr Kristina Downing-Orr
David Emanuel
Liza Evans
Nino Firetto
Caroline Froggatt
Christina Gorna
Henrietta Green
David Gyimah
Kevin Horkin
Paul Jacobs
Kieran Kelly
Teri King
Michele Knight
Elaine Lipworth
Maddie McGowan
Trude Mostue
Sophie Parkin
Anna Rajan
Dr Gillian Rice
Susan Roche
Bridget Rowe
Katie Scott
Leo Stevenson
Jane Struthers
Jimmy Young

EVENT PRODUCTION SERVICES

4 Great North Road, London N6 4LX
Tel: 020 8341 3387 Tel: 020 8374 6467
Fax: 020 8374 6273
Email: info@eventprods.co.uk
Contact: Fran Blackburn

F3 ENTERTAINMENTS LTD

95 Fisher Drive Paisley PA1 2TP
Tel: 0141 8879858
Email: info@f3entertainments.co.uk
Web Site: www.f3entertainments.co.uk
Tracey Peacock

FAB PRODUCTIONS

Yew Tree Farm, Oglet Lane, Hale Village,
Liverpool, Merseyside L24 5RJ
Tel: 0151 425 5070
Email: info@fabproductions.co.uk
Web Site: www.fabproductions.co.uk
Proprietor: Richard Blasbery

ARTISTES REPRESENTED:

Abbamax
Bryan Adams Experience
The Cavern Beatles
Elevation (tribute to U2)
Experienced
Into the Bleach (Blondie tribute)
Led Zed
The Overtures (60's Band)
Police Force (Police tribute)
Robbing Williams
T-Rextasy
Vogue (Madonna tribute)

FACTORY MUSIC MANAGEMENT & AGENCY LTD

216 Cheriton High Street, Folkestone,
Kent CT19 4HS
Tel: 01303 274189
Email: sharon@factorymusic.co.uk
Contact: Sharon Richardson

FAIRPLAY ENTERTAINMENTS

46 College Road, Alsager,
Stoke-on-Trent, Staffordshire ST7 2ST
Tel: 01270 873 848 / 876 054 Fax: 01270 873 848
Senior Personnel: George Morris, B Mason

ARTISTES REPRESENTED:

Always ABBA
Aphrodite
Backbeat
Carl Brent
Bubblegum
Double Jay
Hollywood Nites
International Wrestling
Intrigue
Brad James
Sarah Jane
Josh
Kennedy & Brent
Koo-Ka-Choo
Krys
Lenny Lee
Bernard Manning Show
Shelley Marie
Meatloaf II
Midnight Group
Night & Day
Pink Cadillac
Poison Ivy
Shooter

FAMOUS ENTERTAINMENT GROUP

795 Heiningen Bergen op Zoom 4623 TV

The Netherlands
Tel: 00 31 164249603
Email: info@famousentertainmentgroup.eu
Web: www.famousentertainmentgroup.eu
Managing Director: Klaas Beekvelt

FAMOUS FACES
PO Box 69, Kingsbridge, Devon
TQ7 4WZ
Tel: 01548 559 165 Fax: 01548 559 165
Louise EspigTel: 08452
Email: ideas@famousfaces.co.uk
Web Site: www.famousfaces.co.uk
Contact: Jeremy Harmer
Famous Faces provide speakers, celebrities and cabaret artistes for promotional activities, conference and corporate entertainment, catering for all occasions and audiences.

FANFARE 3000
Gibbs House Kennel Ride, Ascot,
Berkshire SL5 7NT
Tel: 01344 883894 Tel: 0844 800 6824
Fax: 01344 883895 / 0844 800 6825
Email: entertainment@fanfare.co.uk
Web Site: www.fanfare.co.uk
Senior Personnel: Peter Richardson, Paul Baxter
ARTISTES REPRESENTED:
Absolute Strings
Angelique String Quartet
Havana
Richard Linton Discoteque
Mixed Feelings
Phoenix
Rolla Coaster
Star
The Three Waiters

FBI AGENCY LTD
PO Box 250, Leeds LS1 2AZ
Tel: 07050 222 747
Email: casting@fbi-agency.ltd.uk
Web Site: www.fbi-agency.ltd.uk
Film, Television & Photographic casting agency.

FEATURES
1 Charlotte Street, London W1P 1DH
Tel: 020 7636 1876 Fax: 020 7636 1657
Email: info@features.co.uk
Web Site: www.features.co.uk
Managing Director: Margot Clarke
Specialising in Actors & Actresses for theatre & TV.

FRANK FEENEY ENTERTAINMENT AGENCY
9a High Street, Normanby,
Middlesbrough, Cleveland TS6 0NQ
Tel: 01642 455366 Fax: 01642 455 532
Senior Personnel: Frank Feeney

MALCOLM FELD AGENCY
Malina House, Sandforth Road,
Sandfield Park, Liverpool, Merseyside
L12 1JY
Tel: 0151 259 6565
Email: malcolm@malcolmfeld.co.uk
Web Site: www.malcolmfeld.co.uk
Senior Personnel: Malcolm Feld
ARTISTES REPRESENTED:
Gloria Gaynor
Kid Creole & the Coconuts
Night Games
Billie Jo Spears

FELIX DE WOLFE
103 Kingsway, London WC2B 6QX
Tel: 020 7242 5066 Fax: 020 7242 8119
Email: info@felixdewolfe.com
Agent: Caroline De Wolfe

COLETTE FENLON PERSONAL MANAGEMENT
2a Eaton Road, West Derby, Liverpool,
Merseyside R12 7JJ
Tel: 07824 556 135 Tel: 0151 7077703
Email: collettefenlon@hotmail.com
Agent: Colette Fenlon
Colette Fenlon places many young actors and actresses of the highest standard in many television and theatre productions known for efficiency - a theatrical agency with a theatrical background.
ARTISTES REPRESENTED:
Liam Byatt
Paul Byatt
Stephen Molden
Ashley Morgan
Raymond Quinn

FI STEPS AGENCY
107 Merryfield Drive, Horsham,
West Sussex RH12 2AU
Tel: 01403 888 182
Email: fiona@fisteps.com
Web Site: www.fisteps.com
Senior Personnel: Fiona Whyte
Specialising in Commercials, Theatre, Film, TV & Radio Roadshows, Dances, Choreographers and Children.
Also, a part-time theatrical school for children, specialising in song and dance.

FICTION RECORDS
364-366 Kensington High Street, London
W14 8NS
Tel: 020 7471 5352 / 07779 294 412
Fax: 020 7471 5344
Email: fictionrecords@umusic.com
Web Site: www.fictionrecords.co.uk
Contact: Natalie Nissim
ARTISTES REPRESENTED:
Ian Brown (music)
Kate Nash

ALAN FIELD ASSOCIATES
3 The Spinney, Bakers Hill,
Hadley Common, Barnet EN5 5QJ
Tel: 020 8441 1137 Fax: 020 8447 0657
Mobile: 07836 555300
Email: alanfielduk@aol.com
Senior Personnel: Alan Field
ARTISTES REPRESENTED:
Declan Galbraith
Kenny Lynch
The Searchers

FIGHTING TALK PROMOTIONS
30 Peterborough Way, Fellgate, Jarrow,
Tyne and Wear NE32 4XD
Tel: 0191 422 3816 Fax: 0191 422 3816
Mobile: 0775 251 5280
Email: md@boxingcelebrities.co.uk
Web Site: www.boxingcelebrities.co.uk
Contact: Martyn Devlin
Featuring and providing boxing celebrities for after dinner speaking, talk-ins and appearances at events. Specialising in artist booking, both direct and in collaboration with their agents.
ARTISTES REPRESENTED:
Nigel Benn
Ken Buchanan
Steve Collins
John Conteh
Jane Couch
John Coyle
Ian Darke
Roberto Duran
Reg Gutteridge OBE
Colin Hart
Ricky Hatton
Lloyd Honeyghan
Terry Marsh
Glenn McCrory
Barry McGuigan MBE
Brian Meadows
Alan Minter
Spencer Oliver
Nicky Piper
Earnie Shavers
John H Stracey
Michelle Sutcliffe
Jim Watt MBE

RICHARD FILLINGHAM AGENCY
22 Williamwood Park West, Netherlee,
Glasgow, Strathclyde G44 3TE Scotland
Tel: 0141 633 2298 Fax: 0141 633 1100
Email: r.fillingham@tiscali.co.uk
Web Site: www.richardfillingham.com
Senior Personnel: Richard Fillingham

FILM RIGHTS LTD
Mezzanine, Quadrant House,
80-82 Regent Street, London W1B 5AU
Tel: 020 7734 9911 Fax: 020 7734 0044
Email: brendan@filmrights.ltd.uk
Web Site: www.filmrights.ltd.uk
Contact: Brendan Davis

FIREFLY PRODUCTIONS
Craig Cottage, Crask of Aigas, By Beauly,
Inverness-shire Scotland IV4 7AD
Tel: 01463 783 032
Web Site: www.firefly-productions.co.uk
Director: Donna Cunningham
Project Manager: Lindsay Dunbar

Music agency and Management, Music Business Management, Music Business Training Courses, Festival Management, Arts Project Management, Fine Art, Graphic & Web Design, CD Artwork.

ARTISTES REPRESENTED:
Musicians:
Aly Bain & Phil Cunningham
Duncan Chisholm & Ivan Drever
Carol Laula
Ishbel MacAskill
Tejedor
Voces Del Sur
Audio/Visual Shows:
Christine Hanson - The Cremation of Sam McGee
Kin

FIRST ARTIST CORPORATION PLC
First Artist House, 87 Wembley Hill Road, Wembley, Middlesex HA9 8BU
Tel: 020 8900 1818 Fax: 020 8903 2964
Email: reception@firstartist.com
Web Site: www.firstartist.com
Chief Executive: Jon Smith
Contact: Corrinne Goodall
First Artist are one of the leading international sporting agencies looking after a myriad of football players and media personalities.

FIRST ARTIST MANAGEMENT
3 Tenterden Street, London W1S 1TD
Tel: 020 7096 9999 Fax: 020 3205 2140
Email: info@firstartist.co.uk
Web Site: www.firstartist.co.uk
Managing Director: Nicola Ibison
Executive Assistant & Artist Manager: Courtneay Yeates
ARTISTES REPRESENTED:
Kaye Adams
Janet Ellis
Emma Forbes
Charlotte Hawkins
Ruthie Henshall
Eamonn Holmes
Jenni Trent Hughes
Ruth Langsford
Gillian McKeith
Andrea McLean
Sally Meen
Anjula Mutanda
Julie Peasgood
Natalie Pinkham
Lorne Spicer
Ingrid Tarrant
Merryn Somerset Webb

FIRST CLASS PROMOTIONS & MANAGEMENT
PO Box 172 Widnes, Cheshire WA8 7WX
Tel: 0151 420 3779 Fax: 0870 136 0271
Email: firstclassprom@aol.com
Contact: Barry Monaghan
Established since 1979

FIRST CONTACT AGENCY
Top Floor 206 Chalk Farm Road, London NW1 8AB
Tel: 020 7485 0999 Fax: 020 7691 1589
Email: info@firstcontactagency.com
Web Site: www.firstcontactagency.com
Contact: Adam Elfin

FIRST TIME MANAGEMENT
Sovereign House, 12 Trewartha Road, Praa Sands, Penzance, Cornwall TR20 9ST
Tel: 01736 762 826 Fax: 01736 763 328
Email: panamus@aol.com
Web Site: www.songwriters-guild.co.uk / www.panamamusic.co.uk
Senior Personnel: Roderick G Jones

ARTISTES REPRESENTED:
21st Century Clown
Pete Arnold
A Band Called Frank
Colin Eade
Panama Music Library
Willow

ROGER FISHER MUSIC SERVICES
64 Whitley Court Road, Quinton, Birmingham B32 1EY
Tel: 0121 422 8590 Mobile: 07941 089218
Email: roger@rfms.org.uk
Web Site: www.rfms.org.uk
Contact: Roger Fisher
Entertainment agency offering professional musicians and high quality music from swing to the subtle rhythms of Latin America and many more.

FLAIR THEATRICAL AGENCY
28 Cornmill Lane, Liversedge, West Yorkshire WF15 7DZ
Tel: 01924 404 818 Fax: 01924 406 624
Email: enquiry@flairentertainments.co.uk
Web Site: www.flairentertainments.co.uk
Senior Personnel: Mike Hainsworth

FLAT CAT BARN DANCE BAND
Oakleigh, Chitcombe Road, Broad Oak, Rye, East Sussex TN31 6EU
Tel/Fax: 01424 882 046
Email: flatcatlangley@supanet.com
Web Site: www.flatcatband.com
Contact: Denis Langley
The Flat Cat Barn Dance Band, based in Hastings, are a well-established and accommodating band with a line-up comprising fiddle, concertina and guitars. An accordionist is also available if required. Their repertoire includes jigs, polkas, hornpipes and waltzes. A fun evening for all ages is guaranteed.

ARTISTES REPRESENTED:
Barn Dance Band
Flat Cat Barn Dance Band

GRAHAM FLETCHER PROMOTIONS
42 Sycamore Close, Fulwood, Preston, Lancashire PR2 9NA
Tel: 01772 791 087 Fax: 01772 703 068

THE FLYING MUSIC COMPANY
PO Box 1959, London W11 2LY
Tel: 020 7221 7799 Fax: 020 7221 5016
Email: info@flyingmusic.co.uk
Web Site: www.flyingmusic.com
Directors: Derek Nicol and Paul Walden
General Manager: Mark Strange
Production Manager: Andy Sharrocks
Head of Marketing: Ginette Sinnott
ARTISTES REPRESENTED:
The All American Solid Gold Rock 'n Roll Show
Dancing in the Streets
Frank, Sammy + Dean - The Rat Pack
Gaelforce Dance
Glitz Blitz & 70's Hits
Hollywood & Broadway the Musicals
In The Mood - Tribute to Glenn Miller with the Herb Miller Orchestra
The Magic of Sinatra
The Magic of the Musicals
Magical World of the Musicals
Maximum Rhythm 'n' Blues
Rumours Of Fleetwood Mac
Solid Gold Rock 'n' Roll Show
The Solid Silver 60's Show
The Solid Silver 70's Show
Tango Passion
Trash
What A Feeling - The Rock 'n' Pop - Musicals in Concert

FOLK ENTERTAINMENTS LTD
20 Shirley Avenue, Old Coulsdon, Surrey CR5 1QU
Tel: 020 8668 5714 Fax: 020 8645 6923
Mobile: 07802 688 072
Email: americanthemeevents@btinternet.com
Web Site: www.american-theme.com
ARTISTES REPRESENTED:
Dave Evans & Barnstorm
Greta & The Stray Shots
Jacksonville
Luke & Floyd Country Duo
Phil Partridge
Liz Scholey
Struck It Rich Country Band

FOOL'S PARADISE
9 Colleton Crescent, Exeter, Devon EX2 4DG
Tel: 01392 454 160 Fax: 01392 848 384
Email: fools@foolsparadise.co.uk
Web Site: www.foolsparadise.co.uk
Senior Personnel: Jo Burgess, Nicki Street
Specialising in Acrobats, Circus, Comedians, Magicians, Mime, Outdoor, Puppets, Speciality Acts, Street Theatre.
ARTISTES REPRESENTED:
Matt Barnard
Bash Street Theatre

Bernie Bennett
The Black Eagles
Rex Boyd
The Chipolatas
Circo Rum Ba Ba
The Desperate Men
The Dream Engine
Gandini Juggling Project
The Grand Theatre of Lemmings
The Half Human Video Show
Heir of Insanity - aerial, hand balance, artistic stilts
The Invisible Men
Bob & Bob Jobbins
Lady Christobel & Her Butler
Jason Maverick
Mimbre
Parachute Theatre Co
Physical Jerks
Skate Naked
The Sneakers
The Splott Brothers
Stickleback Plasticus
Weapons of Sound

JUNE FORD-CRUSH

PO Box 57948 London W4 2UJ
Tel: 0208 742 7724 Mob: 07711 764160
Email: info@junefordcrush.com
Web Site: www.junefordcrush.com
Personal Management and Representation: June Ford-Crush

ARTISTES REPRESENTED:

Clients:
Jasmine Birtles
Sally Boazman
Dr David Bull
Dr Ian Campbell MBE
Colonel Bob Stewart DSO
Anna Ford
Bob Harris
Paul Heiney
Joe Inglis
Libby Purves OBE
Diana Madill
Adrian Mills
Marc Koska OBE
Suzi Digby OBE
Nicholas Owen
Richard Randall
Sean Bolger
Julia Stephenson
Mark Worthington

FOREMOST ENTERTAINMENT AGENCY LTD

19 Ray Street, Heanor, Derbyshire DE75 7GE
Tel: 01773 717 692 Fax: 01773 764 998
Email: info@foremostentertainments.co.uk
Web: www.foremostentertainments.co.uk
Senior Personnel: Mr Keith Bestwick

FORM TALENT

Tel: 020 8704 0772
Email: info@formtalent.com
Web Site: http://formtalent.com

ARTISTES REPRESENTED:

Presenters:
Lucy Arrowsmith
OJ Borg
Rachel Brady
Chris Collins
Lee Dainton
Femme Fatale (Radio 1 Extra)
Michael Gibson
Michael Holmes
Tim Kash
Ewen MacIntosh
Pamella B
Sarah Rees
Steve Toms
Mike Weeks
Sven Wombwell
Chefs:
Danny Boome

FORREST ENTERTAINMENTS

64 Church Street, Heckmondwike, West Yorkshire WF16 0AZ
Tel: 01924 409 043/ 01924 468712 Fax: 01924 412738 Mobile: 07976 285 550
Email: forrestent@btinternet.com
Web: www.forrestentertainments.co.uk
Contact: Kenneth W Goodhind
Specialising in clubland, theatrical and representation.

DAVID FORSHAW ENTERPRISES

Incorporating Tops Discotheques
PO Box 39, Seaforth, Liverpool, Merseyside L21 5WZ
Tel: 0151 928 7660 Fax: 0151 920 5688
Email: davidforshawent@hotmail.com
Contact: David Forshaw
Established over 35 years, specialising in Discotheques, Karaokes, Musicians and Dance Bands.

ARTISTES REPRESENTED:

Discotheques:
Boogie Nights Disco
Campari Disco
Disco's Here
Lawros Disco
Magnum Disco
Mike's Disco
Music & Motion Disco
Phoenix Disco
Revelution Disco
Rhythm & Lites Disco
Shining Star Disco
Steve's Disco
Top Tunes Disco
Traveling Lite Disco
Karaoke and Disco:
A1 Karaoke Disco
Billy's Karaoke Disco
Disco Madness Karaoke Disco
Harlequin Karaoke and Disco
KooL Karaoke Disco
Mad Petes Karaoke Disco
Dave Roberts Karaoke Disco
Terry's Karaoke Disco
Dance Bands:
Kenny Clark Sound
Jazz Bands:
Matthew Street Ragtime Jazz Band
Organists:
Dave Antrobus
Ken Clark
Sammy Howard
Ian McDonald
Ron Neild
Gary Reece
Alan Vincent
Drummers:
Mike Easthope
Ken Folksman
Tommy Limb
Terry McCuster
Colin Woodruff
Artistes:
Freddie Lloyd
The Maddisons
Ron Neild
Lyn Rose
The Tivoli String Trio / Quartet
Gus Travis
Tom Western
John Williamson
Chris Wilson

JILL FOSTER LTD

1 Lyric Square, London W6 0NB
Tel: 020 3178 4409
Email: agents@jflagency.com
Web Site: www.jflagency.com
ADMINISTRATION:
Senior Personnel: Jill Foster, Alison Finch, Simon Williamson, Dominic Lord, Gary Wild
Founded in 1976, Jill Foster Ltd represents writers working in film, television, radio and theatre

ARTISTES REPRESENTED:

Bennett Arron
Colin Bostock-Smith
Paul Brodrick
Tim Brooke-Taylor
Ian Brown
Grant Buchanan Marshall
Grant Cathro
Linda Cotterill
Mark Daydy
Nick Doughty
Jan Etherington & Gavin Petrie
David Firth
Phil Ford
Nev Fountain
Rob Gittins
Timandra Harkness
Wayne Jackman
Tom Jamieson
Julia Jones
Terry Kyan
David Lane
Jenny Lecoat
Wendy Lee
Bernard McKenna
Guy Meredith
Tony Millan & Mike Walling
Stephen Mollett
Jim Pullin
Jackie Robb
Geoff Rowley
Keiron Self
David Semple
Pete Sinclair
Paul Smith (writer)

Fraser Steele
Berny Stringel
Peter Tilbury
Susan Wilkins
Roger Williams
Pamela Woods

FOUR STAR WRESTLING PROMOTIONS
66 Bartram Avenue, Braintree, Essex
CM7 3RB
Tel/Fax: 01376 327 963
Email: nvans@fourstarwrestling.co.uk
Senior Personnel: Neil Evans
Specialising in: American Style Wrestling, Top UK Wrestlers. Complete Package Shows.
ARTISTES REPRESENTED:
Four Star Wrestling Promotions

FOX ARTIST MANAGEMENT
Concorde House,
101 Shepherds Bush Road, London
W6 7LP
Tel: 020 7602 8822 Fax: 020 7603 2352
Email: fox.artist@btinternet.com
Web Site: www.foxartistmanagement.tv
Senior Personnel: Tony Fox
ARTISTES REPRESENTED:
Benedict Allen
Nick Bateman
Monica Bhaskar
Bruno Brookes
Keith Chegwin
Matt Chilton
Nino Firetto
Matt Foister
Valentina Harris
Limahl
Kate McIntyre
Phillipa Mole
P.J. Ellis
Mike Read
Ricardo
Jason Roberts
Terri Seymour
Ray Shah
Helen Sharman OBE
Spencer Smith
Rebecca Stephens MBE
Carryl Varley
Kate Weston

FOXROE ARTIST MANAGEMENT
103 Nottingham Road New Basford
Nottingham NG7 7AJ
Tel: 0115 847 8719 Fax: 0115 847 8719
Email: dawn@foxroe.com
Web Site: www.foxroe.com

FRANK WHITE AGENCY
52 Broadwick Street, London W1F 7AH
Tel: 020 7434 7385 Fax: 020 7434 7383
Email: adam@frankwhite.co.uk
Web Site: www.frankwhite.co.uk
Agent: Adam Sutherland

KAYE FRANKLAND ENTERTAINMENT AGENCY
155/157 Cinderhill Road, Bulwell,
Nottingham NG6 8RQ
Tel/Fax: 0115 927 1319
Email: kayefrankland@ntlworld.com
Web Site: www.kayefrankland.com
Director: Kaye Frankland
ARTISTES REPRESENTED:
Danielle Body Art (Temporary Tatoos & Face Painting)
Simon Hickling
Barbara Jones
Laurel & Hardy (Lookalikes)
Paul Levent
Pete Lucas
Mission Blue (Tamla Motown tribute)
Mosaic (Band)
Tino Navas (Juggler)
Out to Play
Palm Quartet
Lisa Preston
Sounds Interesting Quartet
Charmaine Ward

DEREK FRANKS ORGANISATION
Kexby Lodge, Kexby, York YO41 5LA
Tel: 01759 388 900 Fax: 01759 380 674
Email: debra@dfo.org.uk
Web Site: www.derekfranks.co.uk
Contact: Debra Franks
ARTISTES REPRESENTED:
The Manfreds
'ReelinandaRockin'
The Troggs
Al Martino
Vince Hill

JEM FRAZER LIMITED
6 Shancara Court, Tingley, Wakefield,
West Yorkshire WF3 1JP
Tel: 01132 529 062 Mob: 07870 666 840
Email: jem@jemfrazer.co.uk
Web Site: www.jemfrazer.co.uk
Contact : Jem Frazer
Please see ads : Haurel and Lardy, Ziddler, Funderbirds, Jem Frazer Characters, Hogwarts characters
ARTISTES REPRESENTED:
Jem Frazer

FREAK MUSIC
111 George Street Edinburgh EH2 4JN
Tel: 0131 467 2539 Fax: 0870 762 1865
Email: jay@freakmusic.co.uk, general_info @freakmusic.co.uk
Web Site: www.freakmusic.co.uk
Contact: James Feeney

FREE TRADE AGENCY
20-22 Curtain Road, London EC2A 3NF
Tel: 020 7655 6900 Fax: 020 7655 6909
Email: info@freetradeagency.co.uk
Web Site: www.freetradeagency.co.uk
Director: Paul Boswell
Senior Personnel: Michael Brown, James Alderman, Claire Courtney, Roxy Mehta
ARTISTES REPRESENTED:
Aberfeldy
Aberfeldy
Absentee
Aereogramme
Annuals
Archie Bronson Outfit
Average White Band
Beastie Boys
Howie Beck
Brendan Benson
Big Star
James Blunt
Tracy Bonham
Buzzcocks
Caesars
Cake
Carbon / Silicon
Vic Chesnutt
Lloyd Cole
Lloyd Cole & The Commotions
Cowboy Junkies
Damien Dempsey
Dirty Three
Dr John
Eighteenth Day Of May
Engineers
Envy & Other Sins
Catherine Feeny
The Flaming Lips
Fun Lovin` Criminals
Futon
Garbage
Get Cape Wear Cape Fly
Good Shoes
Grand Drive
Hayseed Dixie
The Human League
I Am Kloot
Killing Joke
Just Jack
Kubichek!
Little Feat
Mary Lorson
Low
Baaba Maal
Mates of State
Mercury Rev
Mew
Midlake
Milk Kan
Bob Mould
The National
New Pornographers
Nizlopi
Heather Nova
Ok Go
Courtney Pine
The Posies
Racine
The Rakes
Regurgitator
Robyn Hitchcock and The Venus 3
Nile Rogers & Chic
Henry Rollins
Steel Pulse
Ken Stringfellow
Ben Taylor
Teddybears
Terrorvision
The Boy Least Likely To
The Bright Space

The Broken Family Band
The Decemberists
The Frames
The Little Ones
The The
They Might Be Giants
Claire Toomey
Tunde
Two Gallants
Violent Femmes
The Webb Brothers
Wheat
Bertine Zetlitz

FREEDOM MANAGEMENT

4 Canalot Studios, 222 Kensal Road, London W10 5BN
Tel: 020 8960 4443 Fax: 020 8960 9889
Email: martyn@frdm.co.uk / freedom@frdm.co.uk
Web Site: www.frdm.co.uk
Agent: Martyn Barter

ARTISTES REPRESENTED:

Milburn
The Future Sound of London
The Guild

FREQUENCY MEDIA GROUP

Suite 115, The Greenhouse
Custard Factory 2 Gibb Street
Birmingham B9 4AA
Tel: 0121 224 7450 Fax: 0121 224 7451
Email: margaret@fmguk.com
Web Site: www.fmguk.com
Agent: Margaret Murray

ARTISTES REPRESENTED:

Simon Le Bon
Yasmin Le Bon
Duran Duran
Ocean Colour Scene
Nick Rhodes
Andy Taylor
John Taylor
Roger Taylor

FRESH PARTNERS

1 Hardwicks Square London SW18 4AW
Tel: 020 7198 8478
Email: hello@fresh-partners.com
Web Site: www.fresh-partners.com
Debbie Catchpole

ARTISTES REPRESENTED:

Laurence Llewelyn-Bowen
Matt Skinner

FREUD COMMUNICATIONS

19-21 Mortimer Street, London W1T 3DX
Tel: 020 7580 2626 Fax: 020 7637 2626
Email: juliana.love@freud.com
Web Site: www.freud.com
Agent: Mark Freud, Juliana Love

ARTISTES REPRESENTED:

Natalie & Nicole Appleton
BBMak
Martine McCutcheon
Toploader

FRONTLINE MANAGEMENT LTD

Colombo Centre, 34-68 Colombo Street, London SE1 8DP
Tel/Fax: 020 7261 9466
Email: agents@frontlinemanagement.org
Web Site: www.frontlinemanagement.org
Contact: Philip Wolff

ARTISTES REPRESENTED:

Females:
Sarah Alborn
Ceri Ashcroft
Cara Chase
Chandrika Chevli
Jackie Drew
Sophie Hobson
Rebecca Kenyon
Tracey-Anne Liles
Brittan Maassen
Kitty Martin
Josephine Myddleton
Lola Remi
Kathryn Sharratt
Clare Wallis
Males:
Jon Campling
Stuart Crossman
Tom Edden
Barry Fitzgerald
James Folan
Edward Grace
Antony C. Hyde
Michael Irving
Robert Lightfoot
Richard Matthews
Jacob Dylan Thomas
Philip Wolff

FULL HOUSE PRODUCTIONS

High Tree Cottage, Prince Hold Road, Lower Way, Thatcham, Berkshire RG19 3TH
Tel: 01635 862 822
Email: foreverin.bluejeans@sky.com
Web Site: www.foreverinbluejeans.uk.com
Senior Personnel: Carol & Bob Newman
Agents and Producing Managements for "Forever In Blue Jeans", and Voice of the Heart "Karen Carpenter"

ARTISTES REPRESENTED:

Forever In Blue Jeans

MIKE FULWOOD MANAGEMENT

14 Naseby Close, Heathfield, Sherwood, Nottingham NG5 1NU
Tel: 0115 962 3777 Fax: 0115 969 3553
Email: mike@mfm-management.co.uk
Web Site: www.mfm-management.co.uk
Contact: Mike Fulwood

FUNCTION JUNCTION LTD

7 Market Square, Bicester, Oxfordshire OX26 6AA
Tel: 01869 320360 / 0800 034 3232 Fax: 01869 248771
Email: info@functionjunction.co.uk
Web Site: www.functionjunction.co.uk
Contact: Paul Johnstone
Specialising in wedding, private & corprate functions.

FUNHOUSE PRODUCTIONS LTD

91 Regent Court, North Promenade, Blackpool, Lancashire FY1 1RT
Tel: 01274 619 832 / 01253 297945 Fax: 01274 610 569 Mobile: 07860 662 948
Email: funhouse.productions@virgin.net
Web Site: www.funhouseproductions.net
Senior Personnel: Garth Cawood, Stuart Reynolds

ARTISTES REPRESENTED:

80's Affair
Abbadream
Bryan Adams Experience
Dave Adams
Andy Nolan as Ronan Keating
Carl Ashington
Auf Weiderseh'n Set
Bad Boys (Wham)
Lee Baker (Freddie Mercury)
Paul Barrie (Barry Manilow)
Dave Berry & The Cruisers
Big Wolfe Oompah Band
Birmingham Blues Brothers
Blackpool Brass Band
Blue Barons Oompah Band
Bootleg Bee Gees
Bootleg Blondie
Brass Routes
Brian T Strollers
Hamilton Brown (Lionel Richie)
Cactus
Johnny Caesar
Garth Cawood
Centurions
James Chadwick (Frank Sinatra)
Champagne Super Nova (Oasis)
Chancer
Christie
The Cingalees
Jess Conrad
Clem Curtis & the Foundations
Deadringers
Diamonds
Dino (Dean Martin)
Diva Diva
Don't You Want Me 80's
Dynamics Steel Band
John Ellis (Elton John)
The Fab Four (The Beatles)
Jamie Forth
David & Ian Fortt (Everleys)
Funtime Frankies
Good Rockin' Tonight
Roy G. Hemmings
Roy G Hemmings & The Dictionary Of Soul
Ian Houghton (Gene Pitney)
Rob Hughes (David Bowie)
John Hylton is Neil Diamond
Mikki Jay (Michael Jackson)
Jeni Jaye (Britney Spears)
Jimmy Jemain as Cliff Richard
Joe Public
Juke Box Jive
Ned Kelly
Al Kilvinston & The Aces
Bobby Knutt
Krystalettes
Chris Lee
Kylie Likely
Barry McQueen
Sally Moore (Madonna)

Ian Moorhouse
Gary Mullen (Freddie Mercury)
Milli Munro (Shirley Bassey)
Nicky Newsome
Tina Oberman (Dusty Springfield)
Planet Abba
Planet Soul
Brian Poole & Electrix
Proffessionals
Chris Quinten
Red Alert (Shakin' Stevens)
Right Stuff
Darren Rivers (Elvis)
Marc Robinson (Buddy Holly)
Rock Back the Clock
Rosanna Hart American Diva's Show
The Rubettes
Rob Russell
Scarlet Heights
Harvey Seager
Shiraz
The Solicitors
Stars & Stripes Show (Elvis & Tina Turner)
Status Clone (Status Quo Tribute)
Stayin' Alive (Bee Gees tribute)
Straight Up
Supreme (Robbie Williams)
Paul Sutton (Ronan Keating)
Dean Taylor (Little Britain)
Total Beach Boys
Gerry Trew (Rod Stewart)
Blakeston Tyler
V.I.P.
Terry Webster
Andy Wood (Ricky Martin)

FUNKY BEETROOT CELEBRITY MANAGEMENT LTD

PO Box 143, Faversham, Kent ME13 9LP
Tel: 01227 751549 Fax: 01227 752300
Mobile: 07814 010691
Email: melanie@funky-beetroot.com
Web Site: www.funky-beetroot.com
Director: Melanie Sacre
Supply actors for Film, TV including: Advertisements, Game/Panel Shows & Chat Shows, Theatre including: Pantomime & musicals.

ARTISTES REPRESENTED:

Actors:
Suzanne Collins
Angela Lonsdale
Leon Lopez
Toyah Wilcox
Singers:
Cheryl Baker
Ben Steel
Entertainers:
Kevin Hudson
Wayne Sleep
Brian Wheeler
Shaun Williamson (Barry, Eastenders)
Performers:
Louis Emerick

FUSHION PUKKA BOSH

27 Old Gloucester Street, London WC1N 3XX
Tel: 08700 111 100 (6 lines) Fax: 08700 111 020 (2 lines) New York Office: Fushion, #28, 1328 Broadway, Suite 524, New York 10001
Email: mark@fushion-uk.com
Contact Director: Mark Binmore
Exclusive and established London & New York agency offering personal, sole and exclusive representation. Professional artistes only.

ARTISTES REPRESENTED:

Male:
Desmond Backhouse
Mark Binmore
Joe Booth
Andrew Brazier
Brendon Byrnes
Marvin Campbell
Danny Clark
Edward Colverson
Cyril Davey
Shaun Dovacton
Neil E Dunne
Jon Durbridge
Nick Fawcett
Jon Fox
Gary Georgiou
Darren Gayle
Junior Henry
Ben Humble
James Graham
Ali Jehangit
Lee McCann
Matt McDowall
John McHugh
Carl Medland
David Nielson
Simon Paul
Christopher Pritchard
Raymond Reece
Paul Revere
Mark Terry
Simon Westbrook
Bryan Wilson
Female:
Lola Abodo
Shira Alfandai
Blondie
Reeta Bryant
Caron Bosler
Beth Cohen
Emma Crook
Marisa De Andrade
Kym Dixon
Chloe Field
Rebecca Fowler
Bella Gomez
Fay Greenhalgh
Bryony Growden
Manthe Harrap
Lucie Holmes
Emma Jean
Lucy Klein
Diane Montgomery
Sarah Richmond
Louisa Ross
Rachel Sanders
Themoula
Jo Vandervlist
Hanifah Waite
Ceri Wetherill
Andrea Williamson

FX ENTERTAINMENTS

39 Green Leach Lane, St Helens, Merseyside WA11 9LU
Tel: 01744 733 705 Mobile: 07973 402 224
Email: kieron.pickavance@blueyonder.co.uk
Contact; Kieron Pickavance
Specialising in entertainment for sports events e.g club football games and sports events.

G ENTERTAINING

16 Coney Green, Abbotts Barton, Winchester SO23 7JB
Tel: 08456 016 285
Email: enquiries@g-entertaining.co.uk
Web Site: www.g-entertaining.co.uk
Contact: P Nouwens

ARTISTES REPRESENTED:

Bands:
Amethyst
Ballroom Glitz
Big Macs Wholly Soul Band
Broad St
Déjà Vu
Intrigue
Jubilee
K.J. Music Zone
Nightride
Shooting Stars
Terrain
Cabaret:
Adger Brown
Micky John Bull
Dave & Amos
Jet Harris
Aaron James
Karizma
Paul Levent
Phil Lowen (Tom Jones)
Pete Lucas
Barry Moon
Maxwell Plum
Mal Rich
Ian Richards
Matt Slack
Jimmy Tamley
Jerry Thomas
Bob Webb
Tributes:
Abba Inferno
Anne-Marie (Tina Turner)
Alan Beck (Buddy Holly & Dean Martin)
Fab Beatles
Jeni Jaye (Britney Spears, Geri Haliwell)
Billy Lee as Tom Jones
Debbie Nunn (Madonna)
John E Prescott
Rats In The Kitchen (UB40 Tribute)
Rolling Clones (Rolling Stones Tribute)
Eva Royle (Celine Dion, Lisa Stansfield)
Taste of Honey (Bee Gees Tribute)
Walk Right Back !

G.A.A. (GOLD ARTIST AGENCY)

16 Princedale Road, London W11 4NJ
Tel: 020 7221 1864 Fax: 020 7221 1606
Email: bob@goldartists.co.uk
Agent: Paul Wilson

ARTISTES REPRESENTED:
Del Amitri
Eurythmics
Feeder
Chris Rea
R.E.M.
Roachford
S Club
Alexei Sayle
Roger Taylor
Wilco

GABLES AND TTH MANAGEMENT
321 Leigham Court Road, London SW16 2RX
Tel: 020 8769 7411 Mob: 07957 496 034
Senior Personnel: Adrian Watt, Ivor Cohen
ARTISTES REPRESENTED:
Jona Lewie
Terry Dactyl and the Dinosaurs

GAG REFLEX COMEDY MANAGEMENT
34 Northbank Gardens Manchester M19 1BE
Tel: 0161 432 9836
Email: info@gagreflex.co.uk
Web Site: www.gagreflex.co.uk
Contact: Lee Martin

HILARY GAGAN ASSOCIATES
187 Drury Lane, London WC2B 5QD
Tel: 020 7404 8794 Fax: 020 7430 1869
Email: hilary@hgassoc.freeserve.co.uk
Contact: Hilary Gagan
ARTISTES REPRESENTED:
Actors:
David Arneil
David Ashley
Stefan Bednarczyk
Kevin Curtin
Toby Dale
Nolan Frederick
Samuel Gough
Gordon Griffin
Ian Lavender
Roger Moss
Jerome Pradon
Gavin Stewart
Michael Strassen
Nathan Taylor
Bryan Torfeh
Martin Wimbush
Actresses:
Rosemary Ashe
Rebecca Blake
Vanessa Bray
Cathy Breeze
Elizabeth Chambers
Lesley Coleman
Anna Farnworth
Isabelle George
Leda Hodgson
Abigail Hopkins
Carolyn Jordan
Brenda Longman
Judith Paris
Caron Pascoe
Helen Weir

GAILFORCE MANAGEMENT LTD
55 Fulham High Street, London SW6 3JJ
Tel: 020 7384 8989 Fax: 020 7384 8988
Email: gail@gailforcemanagement.co.uk
Senior Personnel: Gail Colson
ARTISTES REPRESENTED:
Mike Edwards
Peter Hammill
Chrissie Hynde
The Pretenders
Stephen Street
The Subways

GALAXY EVENTS
Galaxy House, Mian Yard,
86 Wallis Road, London E9 5LN
Tel: 0208 1330 558
Email: info@galaxy-events.co.uk
Web Site: www.galaxy-events.co.uk
Senior Personnel: Mel Harvey
Artist Management and Event Coordination.
ARTISTES REPRESENTED:
The Care Bears
Jazz Bands
The Mad Hatter`s Tea Party
Mel's Magic
Old MacDonald's Farm
Presto the Magic Rabbit
Punch & Judy
Spotty The Clown
The Trolls
The Wacky Wizard Show
Wizz About The Wizard

GALLOWAYS ONE
15 Lexham Mews, Kensington, London W8 6JW
Tel: 020 7376 2288 Fax: 020 7376 2416
Email: hugh@gallowaysone.com
Web Site: www.gallowaysone.com
Senior Personnel: Hugh Galloway
Specialising in: Actors appearing in commercials & corporate / training films.

BRIAN GANNON MANAGEMENT
St James House, Kiln Lane, Milnrow, Rochdale, Lancashire OL16 3JF
Tel: 01706 374 411 Fax:01706 377 303
Email: nospambrian@briangannon.co.uk
Web Site: www.briangannon.co.uk
Senior Personnel: Brian Gannon
ARTISTES REPRESENTED:
5000 Volts
The Animals
Bay City Rollers
Belushi (Brothers Of The Blues)
Cliff Bennett and the Rebel Rousers
Dave Berry & The Cruisers
Pete Best Band
Brotherhood of Man
Polly Brown`s Picketty Witch
Bucks Fizz
The Byrds
The Casuals
Chicory Tip
China Crisis
Commodores
Clem Curtis & the Foundations
The Dakotas
Spencer Davis Group
Donovan
Dozy Beaky Mick & Tich
Dr Hook featuring Ray (Eye Patch) Sawyer
The Drifters
Easybeats
Edison Lighthouse
Equals
Wayne Fontana and the Mindbenders
The Fourmost
Gibson Brothers
Gidea Park (Beach Boys tribute)
The Glitter Band
Guys n' Dolls
Hawkwind
Eric Haydock Band
Herman's Hermits
Katrina & The Waves
Kenny
Kool & The Gang
Denny Laine Band
Ray Lewis
Little River Band
Love Affair
Marmalade
Merseybeats
Middle Of The Road
The Mindbenders
Sam Moore & Friends
Mud
Nashville Teens
New Amen Corner
Paper Lace
Mike Pender's Searchers
Lieutenant Pigeon
Pinkertons Colours
Brian Poole & Electrix
Racey
The Rubettes
Captain Sensible
Showaddywaddy
Sister Sledge
Percy Sledge
Stars from the Commitments
The Supremes
Survivor
The Sweet
T Rex
Tavares
Temptations Review With Dennis Edwards
Three Degrees
T'Pau
The Tremeloes
Tribute To The Carpenters
The Troggs
The Ultimate British Invasion
Unit 4 Plus 2
Ricky Valance
Vanity Fare (ex-chart band)
White Plains
Roy Wood Big Band
The Yardbirds

GARDNER HERRITY LTD

Douglas House, 16-18 Douglas Street, London SW1P 4PB
Tel: 020 7388 0088 Fax: 020 7388 0688
Email: info@gardnerherrity.co.uk
Senior Personnel: Andy Herrity

ARTISTES REPRESENTED:

Actresses:
Marion Bailey
Celia Bannerman
Lavinia Bertram
Tilly Blackwood
Susan Bovell
Amanda Boxer
Mona Bruce
Penny Bunton
Constance Chapman
Charlotte Christie
Sandra Dickinson
Gabrielle Drake
Liz Ewing
Susannah Fellows
Sarah Find
Janette Foggo
Clare Francis
Sophie Franklin
Laura Girling
Sally Grey
Camilla Heaney
Samantha Holland
Eliza Hunt
Mamta Kash
Susan Kyd
Alexandra Lilley
Kate Lock
Nancy Mansfield
Maggie McCarthy
Annette McLaughlin
Annie Miles
Georgia Moffett
Fiona Mollison
Libby Morris
Maggie Norris
Paula O'Grady
Suzanne Packer
Sherri Parker Lee
Stephanie Putson
Tanya Ronder
Amy Ryan
Gemma Saunders
Marlene Sidaway
Siobhan Stanley
Stephanie Turner
Susie Ann Watkins
Sharon White
Sara Williams
Kate Wilton
Sarah-Louise Young
Actors:
Robert Austins
Angus Barnett
Ron Berglas
Cameron Blakely
Tom Bowles
Stephen Boxer
Liam Brennan
Jasper Britton
Tyler Butterworth
Silas Carson
David Collings
David Delve
Gary Dunnington
Jonathan Elsom
Andrew Fallaize
David Fielder
John Gorrie
Frank Grimes
Andrew Hall
Andrew Hallett
Tom Hodgkins
Robin Hooper
Will Huggins
Christopher Hunter
Jack James
Richard Kane
Christopher Kelham
Teddy Kempner
Edward Kingham
Junior Lanigan
Christian McKay
Liam McKenna
Robert Meadmore
David Michaels
Christopher Mills
Michael Mueller
Ben Nealon
Eddie O'Connell
Derrick O'Connor
Martin Parr
Simon Roberts
James Rochfort
Christopher Rowe
John Rowe
Christopher Ryan
Toby Salaman
Darren Saul
Rob Sheridan
James Simmons
Vaughan Sivell
Roger Sloman
Robin Soans
Colin Stinton
Nick Stringer
Howard Teale
Patrick Toomey
Martin Turner
Milo Twomey
Andrew C Wadsworth
Terence Wilton

GARRICKS

Angel House, 76 Mallinson Road, London SW11 1BN
Tel: 020 7738 1600 Fax: 020 7738 1881
Email: info@garricks.net
Senior Personnel: Megan Willis

GARSTON ENTERTAINMENTS LTD

Po Box 755 Altrincham Cheshire WA15 5DY
Tel: 0845 071 0988 Fax: 01925 425 976
Email: info@garston-entertainment.co.uk
Web: www.garston-entertainment.co.uk
Senior Personnel: Neil Cullen

ARTISTES REPRESENTED:

4th Dimension
Connexion
Simon Dorey
The Easybeats
Foxed Up
Simon J
Matt Johnson
Derek Jones
Paul Knight
Kate Michaels
Rip Rock Brothers
Shaw Sounds
SOS
The Soulsonics
Marty Stone
Sweet Escape
...and others:

PATRICK GARVEY MANAGEMENT

PO Box 54, Filey, North Yorkshire YO14 0WT
Tel: 01723 516 613 Fax: 01723 514 678
Email: patrick@patrickgarvey.com
Web Site: www.patrickgarvey.com
Managing Director: Patrick Garvey
Director: Andrea McDermott
Specialising in classical artistes, principally conductors.

ARTISTES REPRESENTED:

Conductors:
David Angus
Moshe Atzmon
Tomasz Bugaj
Andrew Constantine
Anthony Halstead
Dirk Joeres
Ole Schmidt
Tuomas Ollila
David Porcelijn
Leif Segerstam
Michel Tabachnik
Jan Wagner
Niklas Willen
Takuo Yuasa
Composer:
Pablo González
Jonathan Harvey
Violinists:
Nicola Loud
Pianists:
John Browning
Philip Fowke
Cellist:
Arto Noras
Horn:
Michael Thompson
Ensemble:
Michael Thompson Wind Quartet
Organist:
Thomas Trotter

GB PROMOTIONS AND ENTERTAINMENT AGENCY

Point West, 27 Countess Wear Road, Exeter, Devon EX2 6LR
Tel: 01392 411 194 Fax: 01392 278 860
Email: info@gb-promotions.co.uk
Web Site: www.gb-promotions.co.uk
Senior Personnel: Gordon & Diane Bess

ARTISTES REPRESENTED:

AJ's Big Band
AJ's Caravan Band
Limited Company

GEM PRODUCTIONS
35 Finsbury Terrace, Brynmill, Swansea, West Glamorgan, SA2 0AH South Wales
Tel: 01792 646 278 Fax: 01792 475 109
Senior Personnel: Mr & Mrs Landon
ARTISTES REPRESENTED:
Karina
Wayne Richmond
Jonny Lee Sage
Tanya

GENRE ENTERTAINMENTS
4 Cumberland Avenue Aigburth Liverpool L17 2AQ
Tel: 07521 370099
Email: dtgreaves@btinternet.com
Web: www.genre-entertainment.co.uk
David Greaves

TREVOR GEORGE ENTERTAINMENTS LTD
PO Box 135, Torquay, Devon TQ1 3ZW
Tel: 01803 615 600 / 700 Fax: 01803 615 888 Mobile: 07502 042 995
Email: anne@trevorgeorge.co.uk
Web Site: www.trevorgeorge.co.uk
Senior Personnel: Anne George, Beverley Korman
ARTISTES REPRESENTED:
Herbie Adams
Andre's Magical Madness
Anthony Batey
Zac Bauman
Chris Cross
Adam Daye
Paul Eastwood
Debbie Farrell
Cheryl Hadley
Damien James
Jason Steele & Joanne
Midnight Affair
Bruce Parker
Tony Rudd
Mike Samuels
Spencer & Lee
Paul Sylvester (Mr Soulman)
A Taste Of Tina

GERRY KING ENTERPRISES
9 Limes Close, Staincross, Barnsley, South Yorkshire S75 6JS
Tel: 01226 382924 Fax: 01226 384633
Email: gerryeking@aol.com
Contact: Gerry King

GET INVOLVED LTD
Park House, 206-208 Latimer Road, London W10 6QY
Tel: 020 8962 8040 Fax: 0870 420 4392
Email: keith@getinvolvedltd.com
Agents: Clare Woodcock, Keith Howison
Founding partner and co-organiser of Bestival.
ARTISTES REPRESENTED:
Ali B
The Cuban Brothers
Different Strokes
Dub Pistols
Eclectic Method
Annie Mac
Phat Phil Cooper
Sean Rowley
Yeti

G.F. MANAGEMENT LTD
No 3, Pont Park, Berwick Hill, Ponteland, Newcastle-upon-Tyne, Tyne and Wear NE20 0JX
Tel: 01661 855 444 Fax: 01661 820 589
Mobile: 07802 213862
ISDN: 01661 820014
Email: michael@gfmanagement.co.uk
Senior Personnel: Michael Forster

ERIC GLASS LTD
25 Ladbroke Crescent, London W11 1PS
Tel: 020 7229 9500 Fax: 020 7229 6220
Email: eglassltd@aol.com
Senior Personnel: Janet Glass
ARTISTES REPRESENTED:
Jim Dale
Roy Dotrice
Ron Moody
Edward Woodward

GLASSHOUSE PRODUCTIONS LIMITED
Democracy Records
Upper York Street, (Private Road East), Earlsdon, Coventry, Warwickshire CV1 3GQ
Tel: 024 7622 3892 Fax: 024 7622 9341
Email: admin@glasshouseproductions.co.uk
Web: www.glasshouseproductions.co.uk
Senior Personnel: Amos Anderson, Maria Faser
ARTISTES REPRESENTED:
Alpha Connection
Charley Anderson (Ex Selecter)
Century Steel Band
Cyrus & Denver
Danger
Dion (Rap, Hip Hop)
DJ Vice (House, Garage, Dance)
Loving Jahband (Roots, Rock, Reggae)
Magenkyo (Taiko Drummers)
Mikey Dread - Channel One (Roots Reggae) Sound System
The New Royals (Covers - Rock, Soul, Pop)
No Abode (Irish Duet, Folk)
Phase One Steelband
The Mighty Quinn
The Sessions (Soft Rock)
Shizell (Soul, R&B, Gospel, Reggae)
Will Stepper (Reggae)
Two Tone Collective (By Arrangement)
The Voices of Ujima (Roots, Rock, Reggae)
Wander Brass (Pop, Rock, Soul, Funk)

GLOBAL ARTISTS
Formerly known as Michael Garrett Associates Ltd
23 Haymarket, London SW1Y 4DG
Tel: 020 7839 4888 Fax: 020 7839 4555
Email: info@globalartists.co.uk
Web Site: www.globalartists.co.uk
Company Director: Michael Garrett
Agents: Simon Bashford, Niki Winterson

GLOBAL ENTERTAINMENT AGENCY
6 Digby Street, Ilkstone, Derbyshire DE7 5TG
Tel: 0115 917 2767 Fax: 0115 917 4458
Mob: 07836 614 203
Email: tony@global-ents.co.uk
Web Site: www.globalents.com
Contact: Tony Barry
Booking, Tribute Acts, Bands, Chart Acts, Wedding Entertainment, Magicians, Look-a-Likes, everything in entertainment.
ARTISTES REPRESENTED:
Abba Babes
ABBA Party Girls
Ray Allen
Baverian Brassumpah
BC Sweet
Bogus Brothers
Boney M
Bootleg Bee Gees
Brothers in Soul
Carwash
Complete Madness
Geoff Crapes
Dolonos Funk
Dr & The Medics
Electrix
Fab 4 (Beatles Tribute)
Foundations
Foxy Angels
Gentle Jazzmen
Gillettes
Simon Hickling (magician)
Jazz Function
Pete Johnson Jazz
Lexicon Corperation
Primo
Queen B (Queen tribute)
Soul Train (Soul Band)
Sounds of The Blues Brothers
Tamla Motion
The Bootleg Shadows
Jefflee Walker

GLOBAL TALENT MANAGEMENT
2nd Floor, 53 Frith Street, London W1D 4SN
Tel: 0207 292 9675 Fax: 0207 292 9611
Email: jobrock@globaltalentgroup.com
Web Site: www.globaltalentgroup.com
Contact: Jo Brock
ARTISTES REPRESENTED:
Andy Abraham
Chico
Nicholas Dorsett (X Factor)
G4
Maria Lawson
Shayne Ward

GM ENTERTAINMENTS
32 Veronica Road, Crestwood Park, Kingswinford, West Midlands DY6 8SN

Tel: 01384 265 742 Mobile: 07971 745595
Senior Personnel: Gwendolyn May

ARTISTES REPRESENTED:

Simon Abbotts as Tom Jones
Paul Hopkins (tribute to Roy Orbison)
Dolly James (Tina Turner Tribute)
Pete James
Jimmy Jemain as Cliff Richard
Just Fred
Chris Knott as David Essex
Marrie Lloyd (Cher Tribute)
Meat Loef
Pete McCray (UB40 Tribute)
Peter Mylet
Our Fred
Gary Pearce (Rod Stuart Tribute)
Joe Priestley as Elvis Presley
Wayne Rivers as Garth Brooks
Tracey Shields as Celine Dion
Steve Woodley is The Great Pretender
Freddi Mercury

GO ENTERTAINMENTS

The Arts Exchange, Dane Mill Congleton, Cheshire CW12 1LA
Tel: 01260 276 627 Fax: 01260 270 777
Email: info@arts-exchange.com
Web Site: www.arts-exchange.com
Contact: Phillip or Carol Gandey
Big tops up to 5000 people worldwide supply.

ARTISTES REPRESENTED:

Bolshoi Circus
Cirque Surreal
Fist Of The Dragon
Ice Fantasia
Kremlin Ballet
Lady Boys of Bangkok
Monster Truck Show
Spirit of the Horse

GOLD STAR ENTERTAINMENTS

PO Box 35, West Derby, Liverpool L12 0RB
Tel: 0151 549 2004 Welsh Office: Somerset House, 30 Wynnstay Road, Colwyn Bay, Clwyd LL29 8NB Wales
Email: lynn@goldstarents.freeserve.co.uk
Contact: Jim West

GOLD STAR PR

PO Box 130, Ross-on-Wye, Herefordshire HR9 6WY
Tel: 01989 770 105
Email: nita@goldstarpr.com
Web Site: www.goldstarpr.com
Agent: Nita Patel

ARTISTES REPRESENTED:

A-frames
Aggrolites
Bad Religion
Death by Stereo
Lisa Germano
Kultur Shock
Matchbook Romance
Megan Reilly
The Exploders
Wolf Eyes
Young Widows

GOLDSTAR ENTERTAINMENT UK

Homefield, Rotherham Road, Middlecliffe, Barnsley, South Yorkshire S72 0HA
Tel: 01226 340 011 Fax: 01226 751 011
Email: lynn@goldstarents.freeserve.co.uk
Web: www.goldstarentertainment-uk.com
Senior Personnel: Lynn Winks

ARTISTES REPRESENTED:

$heer
The Buzztones
Café
The Consultants
Glamtastic
Goodison Avenue
The Incredibles
Junction 6
Mad Manners
Rock Legacy
Charlie Rox
Teaser
Vertego

GORDON & FRENCH

12-13 Poland Street, London W1V 8QB
tel: 020 7734 4818 Fax: 020 7734 4832
Email: mail@gordonandfrench.net
Agent: Donna French

ARTISTES REPRESENTED:

Gael Garcia Bernal
Hugh Bonneville
Kellie Bright
Christopher Colquhoun
Anne-Marie Duff
Jimmi Harkishin
Anthony Head
Ralph Ineson
Martina Laird
Chris O'Dowd
Indira Varma

CHRIS GORDON THEATRICAL AGENCY LTD

29 Well Garth, Well Head, Halifax, West Yorkshire HX1 2BJ
Tel/Fax: 01422 355 339 Mobile: 07974 962210
Email: chris@chrisgordontheatricalagency.co.uk
Web: www.chrisgordontheatricalagency.co.uk
Contact: Chris Gordon Hopkinson

ARTISTES REPRESENTED:

Steve Brown
Richie Cullen
Dean Farrar
Flint Duo
Rachel Hooton
Sharon Horton
Julieanna
Jason Lee
Joe Thomas
Kim Valentine
Larry White

GERALD GOSS LIMITED

19 Gloucester Street London SW1V 2DB
Tel: 020 7592 9202
Email: info@geraldgoss.co.uk
Contact: Gerald Goss

ARTISTES REPRESENTED:

Russ Abbott
Louise Doherty
Bella Emberg
Lisa George
Gary Lovini
Joanna Maddison
Graham McLusky
Christopher Short
John Virgo
Roy Walker

GOWN & GAUNTLET PROMOTIONS

1 Court Lawns, Tylers Green, Penn, Buckinghamshire HP10 8DH
Tel/Fax: 01494 814 587
Email: gownandgauntlet@yahoo.co.uk
Web Site: www.coolsoundz.co.uk
Included in Client List: Corporate and Masonic Clubs, Military Bases, Shopping Centres, Seaside Resorts, Clubs, Bars and Discos. We have international recording artistes and bands for corporate functions and parties.

ARTISTES REPRESENTED:

Alastair Black (caricaturist)
Alan J Bowman (singer/songwriter)
Terry Cole (world stunt record holder)
Rob Cox (close-up)
Jane Elizabeth (actress, singer, presenter)
Golden Eagle Archery Display (minstrels troup)
Thelma L'Estrange (soprano)
Paul Lehmann (actor, mimic)
Lawrence Simmons (magician)
Russell C Writer (Producer/songwriter)

THE GRAFFITI CLASSICS

37 Twickenham Road, Leytonstone, London E11 4BN
Tel/Fax: 020 8556 5949 Mob: 07956 909981
Email: info@graffiticlassics.com
Web Site: www.graffiticlassics.com
The Group's unique character and style has developed a refreshing insight into the world of classical music, the principal aim being to entertain, educate and bring an interactive involvement to all audiences of all ages and abilities.

ARTISTES REPRESENTED:

The Graffiti Classics

LEA GRAHAM ENTERTAINMENT

Hillcrest House, 84 Valebridge Road, Burgess Hill, West Sussex RH15 0RP
Tel: 01444 235 475 Fax: 01444 871 577
Email: susan@leagraham.com
Web Site: www.leagraham.com
Senior Personnel: Susan Fleet, Deborah Hammond
Specialising in entertainment for parties, weddings, corporate functions etc.

GRAHAM LEEDHAM PROMOTIONS
Po Box 92, Ellesmere Port, Cheshire
CH65 7WD
Tel: 0151 356 4640
Mobile: 07903 664 581
Email: graham.leedham@ntlworld.com
Web Site: www.glpromotions.org.uk
Contact: Graham Leedham

JAMES GRANT MANAGEMENT
94 Strand On The Green Chiswick
London W4 3NN
Tel: 020 8742 4950 Fax: 020 8742 4951
Email: enquiries@jamesgrant.co.uk
Web Site: www.jamesgrant.co.uk
Contacts: Paul Worsley, George Ashton, Alison Astall, John Knight, Anne-Marie Corbett
ARTISTES REPRESENTED:
Ant & Dec
Fearne Cotton
Simon Cowell
Jenni Falconer
Judy Finnigan
Richard Madeley
Jayne Middlemiss
Stephen Mulhern
Andi Peters
Phillip Schofield
Ben Shephard
Margherita Taylor
Anna Walker
Jonathan Wilkes
Holly Willoughby
Reggie Yates

GRANTHAM-HAZELDINE
5 Blenheim Street, New Bond Street,
London W1S 1LD
Tel: 020 7038 3737 Fax: 020 7495 3370
Email: agents@granthamhazeldine.com

DARREN GRAY MANAGEMENT
2 Marston Lane, Portsmouth, Hampshire
PO3 5TW
Tel: 023 9269 9973 Fax: 023 9267 7227
Mobile: 07798 662 889
Email: darren.gray1@virgin.net
Web: www.darrengraymanagement.co.uk
Senior Personnel: Darren Gray
Only theatrical agent in the UK to specifically represent Australian actors, presenters, writers, producers, directors and playwrights whilst they are working in England. The Agency has been in operation for 15 years.
ARTISTES REPRESENTED:
Paige Alcock
Chantelle Barry
Gemma Bishop
Chelsea Blake
Antoinette Byron
Elena Carapetis
Josephine Clark
Alan Coleman
Lara Cox
Dimitri
Zac Drayson
Amy Felman
Sean Freebairn
Kate Garven
Caroline Gillmer
Kate Gorman
Reg Gorman
Mark Hollis
Inga Hornstra
Queenie Hover
Roy Hover
Anna Hruby
Lyn James
Vernon Johnson
Catherine Kelly
Val Lehman
Jeannie Lightbrown
Robin Littlewood
Sue Manger
Yvonne Matthew
Angela McGrath
Brendan McKensey
Doug Moody
Ada Nicodemou
Judy Nunn
Roy Pack
Karen Petersen
Gwen Powers
David Price
Chris Quinten
Esther Rappaport
Ian Rawlings
Jaime Robbie Reyne
Tom Richards
Andrew Robb
Judith Roberts
Brooke Satchwell
John Scholes
Victoria Scott
Krista Vendy
Kristy Wright

GRAYS MANAGEMENT & ASSOCIATES LTD
Panther House, 38 Mount Pleasant,
London WC1X 0AP
Tel: 020 7278 1054 Fax: 020 7278 1091
Email: e-mail@graysmanagement.idps.co.uk
Web Site: www.graysman.com
Agents: Mary Elliot Nelson, Mark Frankum
ARTISTES REPRESENTED:
Rosie Armstrong
Sally Armstrong
Charles Aston
Anthony Austin
Tracy Bargate
Carolyn Bazely
Paul Beech
Michelle Boucher
Oliver Bradshaw
Apple Brook
Connor Brown
Melody Brown
Vic Bryson
Neil Bull
Natalia Campbell
Nicholas Chambers
Danny Charles
John Cormack
Zoe Cotty
Jules Craig
John Davitt
Paul Dodds
Richard Ede
Osaze Ehibor
Justin Ellery
Katie Fabel
Kyle Fabel
Lynn Fairbairn
Simon Firth
Peter Foley
Marc Frankum
Robert French
Chad Gomez
Maggie Guess
Christopher Hampson
Bryone Harding
Lara Harvey
Mark Hayden
Ted Heath
Elaine Heathfield
Denise Hoey
Valerie Holliman
David Horne
Mark Huckett
Shirley Keane
Sean Kearney
Basil King
Patrick Knox
Senya Koroma
Keith Lancaster
Sarah Lawrie
Adrian Lloyd-James
Jan Lower
Sarah Mahony
Sidney Malin
Kate Marlais
David Martin
Rosanna Mason
David Matthews
William Mickleborough
Anne Micklethwaite
Paul Milton
Antonietta Mirto
Juliet Moore
Ric Morgan
Adrian Morris
Delmozene Morris
Natalie Moss
Mary Elliott Nelson
Katarina Olsson
Grant Orbiss
Darren Palmer
Thomas Power
Juliet Prague
Bryonie Pritchard
Paul Rattee
David Redgrave
Natasha Redmond
Jack Reid
Liz Richardson
Yvonne Riley
Cerianne Roberts
Mae Louis Robinson
Jarka Rudavska
Michael Sherwin
Angie Smith
Peter Sowerbutts
Andrew St Clair James
Michael Strobel
Alan Suri
Anstey Thomas
Annabel Thrower
Paul Townsend

Lisa Tramontin
Jay Venn
Kathrine Vernez
Gilbert Vernon
Carla Voller
Greg Wagland
Jason Webb
Roy Weskin
Natalie Wilcox
Edmund Wood
Emily Wood
John Samuel Worsey

GREASEPAINT MAKE-UP PLACEMENT AGENCY
143 Northfield Avenue, Ealing, London W13 9QT
Tel: 020 8840 6000 Fax: 020 8840 3983
Email: agency@greasepaint.co.uk
Web Site: www.greasepaint.co.uk
Senior Personnel: Julia & Hannah Cruttenden
Greasepaint offers two interlinked services as a school and Agency. The Agency specialises in allocating highly skilled make-up and hair designers to TV, film, theatre and fashion productions at competitive rates. The School offers 14-week TV, Film and Theatre (make-up, prosthetics & hair) courses three times a year, and 4-week Fashion (make-up & hair) courses four times a year.

GREAT WESTERN ENTERTAINMENT AGENCY
46 Critchill Road, Frome, Somerset BA11 4HF
Tel: 01373 461 666
Mobile: 07774 694316
Senior Personnel: Graham Wilkin
Specialising in all types of entertainment.

GREEN AND UNDERWOOD
PO Box 44394, London SW20 0YP
Tel: 020 8879 1775 Fax: 020 3258 5037
Email: info@greenandunderwood.com
Senior Personnel: Nicholas Young

STAN GREEN MANAGEMENT
PO Box 4, Dartmouth, Devon TQ6 0YD
Tel: 01803 770 046 Fax: 01803 770 075
Email: tv@stangreen.co.uk
Web Site: www.stangreen.co.uk
Senior Personnel: Stan Green
Production Manager: Adrian Worsley
ARTISTES REPRESENTED:
Ana Ann
Keith Floyd
Reg Presley
The Troggs

CARL GRESHAM PRESENTATIONS
Part of the Carl Gresham Group
PO Box 3, Bradford, West Yorkshire BD1 4QN
Tel: 01274 735 880 Fax: 01274 827 161
Mobile: 07932 750512
Email: gresh@carlgresham.com
Web Site: www.carlgresham.com
Senior Personnel: Carl Gresham

SANDRA GRIFFIN MANAGEMENT
6 Ryde Place, Richmond Road, Twickenham, Middlesex TW1 2EH
Tel: 020 8891 5676 Fax: 020 8744 1812
Email: office@sandragriffin.com
Senior Personnel: Sandra Griffin, Howard Roberts
ARTISTES REPRESENTED:
Madge Hindle
Sally Knyvette

GT ARTISTES
4 Maple Avenue Allington Maidestone ME16 0DD
Tel: 01622 675 893 Mob: 07778 288 634
Email: tony.littley@btinternet.com
Web Site: www.gtartistes.com
Contact: Tony Littley

GT MANAGEMENT PROMOTIONS
99 Gnoll Park Road, Neath, West Glamorgan SA11 3BU
Tel: 01639 643555 Fax: 01639 641643
Email: gareth@gtmp.co.uk / gtdeliver12@tiscali.co.uk
Contact: Gareth Thomas

GTA MUSIC CONSULTANTS AND AGENCY
14 Glamorgan Road Hampton Wick, Kingston-upon-Thames, Surrey KT1 4HP
Tel: 020 8943 9113 / 020 8412 0096
Fax: 020 8943 9112
Email: info@gtamusic.co.uk
Web Site: www.gtamusic.co.uk
Senior Personnel: Gilly Tarrant, David Kelly
ARTISTES REPRESENTED:
Maggie Bell
The Blues Band
Dana Gillespie
Paul Jones & Dave Kelly
Dave Kelly & The Blues Call
Dave Kelly
Michael Roach

GUILD OF INTERNATIONAL PROFESSIONAL TOASTMASTERS
12 Little Bornes, Dulwich, London SE21 8SE
Tel: 020 8670 5585 Fax: 020 8670 0055
Web Site: www.ivorspencer.com
Life President: Ivor Spencer
The Guild Members officiate at functions all over the United Kingdom and undertake engagements abroad. They are expert organisers who arrange authentic British Banquets with the traditional ceremonies (Loving Cup, Baron of Beef, etc.) anywhere in the world. The Guild Toastmasters are experts at officiating on Royal occasions.
Conferences and Banquets from 12 to 10,000 guests organised.

JO GURNETT PERSONAL MANAGEMENT LTD
12 Newburgh Street, London W1F 7RP
Tel: 020 7400 1850 Fax: 020 7287 9642
Email: mail@jgpm.co.uk
Web Site: www.jgpm.co.uk
Directors: Mark Wogan, Alan Wogan
Senior Personnel: Jo Gurnett
ARTISTES REPRESENTED:
Ken Bruce
Richard Corrigan
Christopher Edwards
Dr Jonathan Foyle
Paul Heiney
Libby Purves OBE
Leigh Miles
Oliver Paton
Arkin Salih
Ed Stewart
Terry Wogan
Steve Wright

GUVNOR MANAGEMENT
PO Box 553 Swansea SA8 4WQ
Tel: 01792 862905
Email: info@govnormanagement.co.uk
Web: www.guvnormanagement.co.uk
Frank Webb

H & MARCEL ENTERPRISES
282 Staniforth Road, Sheffield, South Yorkshire S9 3FT
Tel/Fax: 0114 444052
Senior Personnel: Albert Hall

CINDY HACKER ASSOCIATES
24 Cavendish Buildings, Gilbert Street, London W1K 5HJ
Tel: 020 7629 2998 Fax: 020 7355 3510
Email: cindy@parrotprods.co.uk
Web Site: www.ronniescotts.co.uk/parrot
ARTISTES REPRESENTED:
Robin Jones King Salsa
Robin Jones Latin Jazz Sextet

YVETTE HALES AGENCY
203 The Chart House, Burrells Wharf, London E14 3TN
Tel: 020 7538 4736 Fax: 020 7538 4778
Email: yvette.hales@dsl.pipex.com
Contact: Yvette Hales
ARTISTES REPRESENTED:
Linda Nolan

TONY HALL GROUP OF COMPANIES
16-17 Grafton House,
2-3 Golden Square, London W1F 9HR
Tel: 020 7434 7286 Fax: 020 7437 3852
Senior Personnel: Tony Hall

ARTISTES REPRESENTED:
Paul Buckmaster (Europe)
Lynden David Hall
Real Thing

HAMILTON HODELL LTD
Fifth Floor, 66-68 Margaret Street,
London W1W 8SR
Tel: 020 7636 1221 Fax: 020 7636 1226
Email: christian@hamiltonhodell.co.uk
Web Site: www.hamiltonhodell.co.uk
Senior Personnel: Lorraine Hamilton,
Christian Hodell
ARTISTES REPRESENTED:
Damien O'hare
Jack Davenport
Christopher Eccleston
Shaun Evans
Pam Ferris
Stephen Fry
Jane Gurnett
Ashley Jensen
Robert Lindsay
Lloyd Owen
Tilda Swinton
Emma Thompson
Gabriel Thomson
Polly Walker
Emily Woof

HAMPSONS THEATRICAL AGENCY
136 Hamstead Road, Handsworth,
Birmingham B20 2QR
Tel: 0121 554 2191 Fax: 0121 686 9220
Email: vham105193@aol.com
Senior Personnel: Vidya Hampson
Specialising in: All types of Variety & Circus Acts.

ROGER HANCOCK LTD
7 Broadbent Close, London N6 5JW
Tel: 020 8341 7243
Email: info@rogerhancock.com
ADMINISTRATION:
Contacts: Tim Hancock
Specializing in mainly comedy writers for film and television.

HANDE CASTING ADVERTISING AGENCY
Epping Film Studio
Brickfield Business Centre Epping, Essex
CM16 6TH
Tel: 01992 570662 Fax: 01992 570601
Email: caa@hande.org
Web Site: www.hande-caa.co.uk
Contact: Justine Maynard

HANDSHAKE LTD
2 Holly House, Mill Street, Uppermill,
Saddleworth, Lancashire OL3 6LZ
Tel: 01457 819 350 Fax: 01457 810 052
Email: info@handshakegroup.com
Web Site: www.handshakegroup.com
Managing Director: Stuart Littlewood
Promoters / Producers / Managers of Live Entertainment. Handshake Ltd is a member of the Concert Promoters Association (CPA).
ARTISTES REPRESENTED:
Max Boyce MBE
Roy "Chubby" Brown
Lisa Williams
Shows::
Abba Mania
That's Amore
Jake & Elwood The Best Blues Brothers Show In The World ...... EVER!!!
Letz Zep
Live At
Oh! What A Night
One Night Of Elvis
One Night Of Queen

JEF HANLON PROMOTIONS
Orchard House, 23 Lewes Road,
Haywards Heath, West Sussex
RH17 7SP
Tel: 01444 456717
Email: jef.hanlon@agents-uk.com
Contact: Jef Hanlon FEAA

ALISON HARGREAVES MANAGEMENT
27 Hamilton Road, London NW10 1NS
Tel: 020 8438 0112
Email: agent@alisonhargreaves.co.uk
Web Site: www.alisonhargreaves.co.uk
Senior Personnel: Alison Hargreaves
Theatre agency representing theatre designers, lighting designers and directors.

KEITH HARRISON ENTERTAINMENTS
364 Whalley New Road, Blackburn,
Lancashire BB1 9SL
T/F: 01254 677 936
Mobile: 07944 887 467
Email: info@keithharrisonents.com
Web Site: www.keithharrisonents.com
Senior Personnel: Keith Harrison
Specialising in Disco and Piano Vocalists.

HARRY MARGOLIS ENTERTAINMENT ORGANISATION
14 Heathside Road, Giffnock, Glasgow,
Strathclyde G46 6HL Scotland
Tel: 0141 638 0724 Fax: 0141 620 0799
Mob: 07949 166054
Email: musicdirect@aol.com
Web: www.yell.co.uk/sites/harrymargolis
Contacts: Harry Margolis FEAA

LES HART (SOUTHAMPTON) ENTERTAINMENTS
6 Crookhorn Lane, Purbrook,
Waterlooville, Hampshire PO7 5QE
Tel: 023 9225 8373 Fax: 023 9225 8369
Email: rod@leshart.co.uk
Web Site: www.leshart.co.uk
Contact: Rod Watts
ARTISTES REPRESENTED:
Non-exclusive Representation::
3's Company
Alphabet
"Angels"
Big Brother Soul
Caprice
Emmarald
Audrey Cameron Finnemore
Fourth Element
Tania Holland
Hurricane Force
Steve Kingsley
Mission Blue (Tamla Motown tribute)
Phoenix Discotheque
James Prince
Q-Tones
Raw Deal
Relative Strangers
Sounds Familiar
Swing 39
Tapestry
Gill Tolliday
Exclusive Representation::
Chuckles
Ian James
Joker
Midnight Express
Kevin Peters
Jan Schmidt Oompah Band
Society Swing
Dean Stuart

HARTBEAT ENTERTAINMENTS LTD
Suite 12 Basepoint Business Centre
Yeoford Way
Marsh Barton Trading Estate, Exeter
EX2 8LB
Tel: 01752 881 155 Fax: 01752 880 133
Email: hartbeat@lineone.net
Web Site: www.hartbeat.co.uk
Senior Personnel: Robbie Hart, Liz Hart
ARTISTES REPRESENTED:
Armada Jazzband
Caterpillar Roadshow
James Christopher
Drake Fun casino
The Fab
Firebird Show
General Confusion
Generation Gap
Geoff Gillett
Dave Hawkes Hot Stuff
Chris james Hypnotic Entertainment Ltd
Leonora
Roger Marks Society Band
David Merlin (Magician)
Midnight Showband
Newclear Waste
Plymouth Barracudas
Rhythm Machine
Yorkie

HARVEY VOICES LTD
4th Floor, 54-55 Margaret Street, London
W1W 8SH
Tel: 020 7952 4361
Email: info@harveyvoices.co.uk
Web Site: www.harveyvoices.co.uk

Contact: Emma Harvey
Also represent children of all ages and Foreign Artistes

ARTISTES REPRESENTED:

Male:
Russ Abbott
Steve Ackerman
Tom Adams
Richard Attlee
Harry Capehorn
Mark Caven
Norman Chancer
Nick Coady
Daniel Craig
Andy Davies
Ben Davies
Alex Donald
Electric Forecast
Richard Elis
Nick Ellsworth
Christopher Finney
Bruce Forsyth CBE
Rolf Harris AM CBE
Dominic Holland
Nicky Horne
Howard Hughes
Ronny Jhutti
Dave Kelly
Dean Kelly
Paul Leyshon
Liam McKenna
David Michaels
Jeremy Nicholas
Scott Palmer
Redd Pepper
Howard Ritchie
Graham Skidmore
Nathan Taylor
Peter Temple
Addy Van Der Borgh
Dale Winton
Female:
Amber Agar
Lysette Anthony
Charlotte Avery
Kelly Beckett
Ninia Benjamin
Caroline Crier
Magenta De Vine
Louise Fullerton
Jaye Griffiths
Sara Griffiths
Fran Guy
Ayesha Hazarika
Rachael Hopper
Melissa Johnson
Shauna Lowry
Anouschka Menzies
Daniela Nardini
Julie Richmond
Lynda Steadman
Tina Stewart
Rachael Stirling
Mary Stockley
Miriam Stoppard
Lizzie Tear
Suki Webster

HATSTAND CIRCUS

Unusual Entertainment for Events Stilt Characters/Whips/Fire/Juggling/Sparks
Westferry Studios, 2nd Floor, Unit 98, 98 Milligan Street, London E14 8AS
Tel: 020 7538 3368 Mob: 07748 005 839
Email: helenahatstand@btconnect.com
Web Site: www.hatstandcircus.co.uk
Contact: Helena Hatstand
Bright and colourful and themed stilt characters, unique and unusual shows, juggling, UV show/blackout glo show, fire shows with fire eating and manipulation of fire props including fire whips. Meet and greet and mix and mingle.

HATTON MCEWAN LTD

P O Box 37385, London N1 7XF
Tel: 020 7253 4770 Fax: 020 7251 9081
Email: info@thetalent.biz
Web Site: www.thetalent.biz
Senior Personnel: Stephen Hatton, Aileen McEwan

ARTISTES REPRESENTED:

Matt Bardock
Kathy Burke
Kevin R McNally
Mark Monero
Nicholas Palliser
Lucy Speed

JACK HAWKINS ORCHESTRA

Ferndale, 157 Portsmouth Road, Horndean, Waterlooville, Hampshire PO8 9LG
Tel/Fax: 023 9259 6721
Email: jackhawkinsband@talk21.com
Senior Personnel: Jack Hawkins
Specialising in: Music & Entertainment for all occasions.

HAWTHORN ENTERTAINMENT

1st Floor, Nathaniel House, David Street, Bridgend Industrial Estate, Bridgend, Mid Glamorgan CF31 3SA Wales
Tel: 01656 662 835 / 0870 444 5894
Fax: 01656 661872
Email: neville@hawthorn-ents.com
Web Site: www.hawthorn-ents.com
Senior Personnel: Neville Williams

ARTISTES REPRESENTED:

Second 2 Everleys
Second 2 None
Jeff Alvey
BZRK
Paul Christie
In-Fusion
Wendy Kane
Life of Riley
Rachel Parsons
Andy Rudge
Steve Saint
Undecided
Andrew York

HAZARD CHASE LTD

Hazard Chase Ltd, 25 City Road, Cambridge CB1 1DP
Tel: 01223 312 400 Fax: 01223 460 827
Email: info@hazardchase.co.uk
Web Site: www.hazardchase.co.uk
Chairman: John Willan
Assistant Artist Manager: Alice Murray
Senior Personnel: James Brown, Sue Nicholls

ARTISTES REPRESENTED:

Conductors:
Petr Altrichter
Douglas Bostock
Stephen Cleobury
Christian Curnyn
Junichi Hirokami
Dwain Arwel Hughes
Emma Johnson
Stephen Layton
Adrian Leaper
Jahja Ling
Grant Llewellyn
Director/Soloists:
Emma Johnson
Martin Roscoe
Andrew Watkinson
Stage Director:
John Copley
Singers:
Giselle Allen
Marie Arnet
Simon Baker
Finnur Bjarnason
Mark Le Brocq
Jeremy Carpenter
Charles Daniels
Michael Druiett
Andrew Foster-Williams
Alexandra Gibson
James Gilchrist
Carla Huhtanen
Natasha Jouhl
Emma Kirkby
Miriam Murphy
Robert Murray
Anne-Marie Owens
Christopher Purves
Mark Wilde
Violin:
Isabelle Faust
Matthew Trusler
Andrew Watkinson
Cello:
Richard Harwood
Guitar:
Julian Bream
Harp:
Catrin Finch
Clarinet:
Emma Johnson
Piano:
Harry
Noriko Ogawa
Martin Roscoe
Piano Duo:
Martin Roscoe & Peter Donohoe
Kathryn Stott & Noriko Ogawa
String Quartets:
Endellion String Quaretet
RTE Vanbrugh Quartet
Vocal Duo:
Operababes
Vocal Ensembles:
The Choir of The Temple Church
The Hilliard Ensemble
Polyphony
The Tallis Scholars

Instrumental Ensembles:
Bang On a Can All-Stars
Conchord
Ensemble Bash
Guildhall Strings
Emma Johnson & Friends
Steve Martland Band
Michael Nyman Band
Jocelyn Pook Ensemble

HAZEMEAD LTD

Camellia House, 38 Orchid Road,
Sundridge Park, Bromley, Kent BR1 2PS
Tel: 0870 240 2082 Fax: 020 8460 5830
Email: magnolia87@msn.com
Senior Personnel: Anne Chudleigh, Adrian Leggett

ARTISTES REPRESENTED:

The Acquah Brothers
Amethyst
Beechy Colclough
Dana
Kevin Hubbard (Associate Producer)
Maurice Leonard
Nina Myskow
Hal Nolan
Russell Norman (Director)
Andy Rumble

HCA

(Also Howard Cooke Associates)
19 Coulson Street, London SW3 3NA
Tel: 020 7591 0144 Fax: 020 7591 0155
Email: mail@hc1.co.uk
Senior Personnel: Howard Cooke, Bronwyn Sanders

HEAD ON MANAGEMENT

88 Lewisham Way, New Cross, London
SE14 6NY
Tel/Fax: 020 8469 2576
Mobile: 07796 447 302
Email: headonman@yahoo.co.uk
Web Site: www.headonmanagement.com
Senior Personnel: Nick Wren, Chloe Wren
Personal Band Management.
Live Event promotions, Euphoria-Live, DJ Events, Live 3D Graphics.

ARTISTES REPRESENTED:

Dance Artists:
Euphoria Albums Tour
Mr. Praganza
Euphoria Live
I Spatticus
Shadow Red
DJs/VJs:
Ross Assenhiem (DJ)
Stuart Cooke (DJ)
Darren James (DJ)
Meskalin
Moose (P.F. Project) (DJ)
Marc Mynard (DJ)
Robert Van Ryn (DJ)
VJ Freedom
VJ Voyeur
Simon Webdale (DJ)
Adam White
Tribute Acts:
Abba Dream
AB/CD
Achtung Baby (U2)
"Angels"
Bad Obsession (Guns + Roses)
The 'B'Eagles (The Eagles tribute)
The Beatels
B.Gees Fever
Bi Jovi
Black Celebration (Depeche Mode)
Bootleg Abba
The Briefcase Blues Brothers
Clone Roses
Deepest Purple
D-Ran D-Ran
The Fab Four (The Beatles)
Face Value (Phil Collins)
Fleetwood Back
Forgotten Sons (Marillion)
Fragile (Yes Tribute)
Gene Genie
Glory Days (Bruce Springstein)
In The Cage (Genesis)
Into the Bleach (Blondie tribute)
Ironically Maiden
The Jamm
Limehouse Lizzy (Thin Lizzy tribute)
Louie Rockerfella And The Dixie Mafia Band (Elvis)
The Ludwig Beatles
One Step Behind (Madness tribute)
Other Smiths
Piledriver (Status Quo)
QEII (Queen tribute)
Really Hot Chilli Peppers
Rip Off The Machine
Robbing Williams
Sisters Of Murphy
State Of Quo
Stax Atlantic
Stax of Soul
Stereotonics
Sus-Sex Pistols
Talon (Eagles)
The Likeness
The Paul Weller Experience
Think Floyd
Travesty
T.Rextacy
UB4T & The Allska's
Unknown Pleasures (Joy Division)
UU2
Vogue
Who's Who
Wonderwall (Oasis tribute)
Bands:
Ballroom Glitz (70's show)
Carwash
Hampsters
Kick Up The 80s
The Ladybirds
The Ladykillers
Louie Rockerfella And The Dixie Mafia Band (Elvis)
John Ottway
The Pop Tarts
Screaming Beavers
Sister Act
Superbad
Tarantinos

DENNIS HEANEY PROMOTIONS

Whitehall, 8 Ashgrove Road, Newry,
County Down BT34 1QN Northern Ireland
Tel: 028 3026 8658 Fax: 028 3026 6673
Mobile: 07860 377 414
Email: dennis_heaney@hotmail.com
Web Site: www.susanmccann.com
Senior Personnel: Dennis Heaney

ARTISTES REPRESENTED:

Susan McCann

HEART OF ENGLAND PROMOTIONS LTD

Old Hall, Wall Hill Road, Fillongley,
Coventry, Warwickshire CV7 8DX
Tel: 01676 540 333 Fax: 01676 540 365
Email: sales@heartofengland.co.uk
Web Site: www.heartofengland.co.uk
Senior Personnel: Stephen Hammon
Specialising in DJs, Comperes and Children's Entertainment

ARTISTES REPRESENTED:

Disc Jockeys:
Mark Cooper
Steve Hammon
Adrian Hobson

HELTER SKELTER AGENCY LTD

Bond House
347-353 Chiswick High Road, London
W4 4HS
Tel: 020 8742 5500 Fax: 020 8742 5611
Email: peten@helterskelter.co.uk
Web Site: www.helterskelter.co.uk
Senior Personnel: , Emma Banks, Paul Bolton, Jeff Craft, Mike Greek, Ian Huffman, Peter Nash, Steve Strange, Paul Franklin, Adam Saunders, Nigel Haffler

ARTISTES REPRESENTED:

1 Giant Leap
Afro Celts
Apocalyptica
B52's
Battle
Belle & Sebastian
Beulah
Bilal
Bjorn Again
Bootleg Beatles
Bowling for Soup
The Brand New Heavies
Kaiser Chiefs
Charlotte Church
Cradle of Filth
The Datsuns
Craig David
Dido
Ani Difranco
Dixie Chicks
DragonForce
Duels
Sophie Ellis-Bextor
Faithless
Fightstar
Michael Franti and Spearhead
Hell is for Heroes
Hundred Reasons
Natalie Imbruglia
INME
Alicia Keys

Avril Lavigne
Linchpin
Machine Head
Serena Maneesh
Loreena McKennitt
Sarah McLachlan
Dannii Minogue
Mandy Moore
Alison Moyet
Ms Dynamite
Paradise Lost
Mica Paris
Pet Shop Boys
Planet Funk
Robert Post
Powderfinger
Reef
Roadstar
The Roots
Xavier Rudd
Safri Duo
Say Anything
Scritti Politti
Shinedown
Shiny Toy Guns
Simple Plan
Sirens
SixNationState
Sons of Dork
Sons of Jim
Sugababes
Richard Swift
Taking Back Sunday
The Perishers
The Soho Dolls
Therapy?
Sandi Thom
The Tragically Hip
Travis
Underoath
Amy Winehouse

HEMMINGS LEISURE ENTERTAINMENT AGENCY (MIDLANDS)

124 Waterside Heights, Waterside, Dickens Heath, Solihull, West Midlands B90 1UD
Tel: 0121 744 3338
Email: live@hemmingsleisure.co.uk
Web Site: www.hemmingsleisure.co.uk

HENDERSON MANAGEMENT

89-91 Charles Street, Leicester LE1 1FA
Tel: 0116 242 9900 Fax: 0116 262 1214
Email: agents@henderson-management.co.uk
Web: www.henderson-management.co.uk
Senior Personnel: Mark Henderson
Specialising in live bands.

ARTISTES REPRESENTED:

Abba Dream
Abba Forever
Abbadabbadoo
Abbasolutely Live
Atlantic Soul Machine
Backbeat
The Backbeat Beatles
Bad Manners
Bad Manners featuring Buster
Bloodvessel
Ballroom Glitz
Beachboys Inc
Dave Berry & The Cruisers
Big J & the Piccolo Chickens
Big Macs Wholly Soul Band
Big Wolfe Oompah Band
Bleach (Blondie Tribute)
Bon Giovi
Boogie Wonderband
The Booze Brothers
Brotherhood of Man
Cavern Beatles
The Cheatles (The Beatles)
Cheeky Monkees
Chesney Hawkes
Clem Curtis & the Foundations
Dakotas
Dave Dee, Dozy, Beaky, Mich & Tich
Dirrty (Christina Augilera)
Dr & The Medics
Duppy Conquerors (Bob Marley tribute)
Earth Wind For Hire
Fakin' Stevens
Fearless Brothers
Steve Ferringo Band
Firebirds (R'n'R)
Fools Gold (Stone Roses tribute)
Fortunes
Four Pennies
Frisco Crabbe & The Atlantic Frantics
Lewis Gates Elvis Experience
Gidea Park (Beach Boys tribute)
The Girl from Nutbush
Good Rockin' Tonite
Greased Lightning
Keith Harris with Orville & Cuddles
Herman's Hermits
Hooper
Into the Bleach (Blondie tribute)
Ivy League
Jimmy James & The Vagabonds
The Jamm
Jean Genie (David Bowie tribute)
Jumpin'
Mark Keeley's Elvis Show
Kinky (Kinks tribute)
Koo-Ka-Choo
Krankies
Ladies and Gentlemen (George Michael tribute)
Latino Heat (Ricky Martin tribute)
Marlo
Marmalade
Sally Moore as Celine Dion, Madonna
Milli Munro (Shirley Bassey, Tina Turner, Whitney Houston)
Now 80's
Oasisn't (Oasis Tribute)
One Step Behind (Madness tribute)
Pink Fraud
QEII (Queen tribute)
Queen B (Queen tribute)
Rats In The Kitchen (UB40 Tribute)
Marc Robinson as Buddy Holly & The Counterfeit Crickets
The Screaming Beavers
Secret Police (Police tribute)
The Senators
The Sharp Cuts
Ska Wars
Splash
Steve Steinman's Meatloaf 2
T-Rextasy
Taste of Honey (Bee Gees Tribute)
Kenny Thomas
Del Boy Trotter
US4 (U2 tribute)
Geno Washington & The Ram Jam Band
Marty Wilde & The Wildcats
Andy Wood (Ricky Martin, Tom Jones, Michael Bolton)
Good Vibrations
Just Korrs
Kelly Marie
Rob Lamberti (George Michael Tribute)
Steve Preston (As Elvis Presley)
Stoned Again
Swinging Blue Jeans
Tremeloes
Hazel Dean
Jay Tee (Justin Timberlake Tribute)
Jeni Jaye (Britney Spears)
Jets
Madonna (By Debbie Nunn)
Mersey Beatles
Michael Jackson (By Navi)
Troggs
Ultimate Madness (Madness Tribute)
Wayne Fontana
Xerox
Monarchy (Queen Tribute)
Overtures
Police Force

JOHN HESSENTHALER ENTERTAINMENTS

6 Constable Court, Barn Street, Lavenham, Sudbury, Suffolk CO10 9RB
Tel: 01787 247 838 Fax: 01787 247 898
Email: john.hessenthaler@btinternet.com
Senior Personnel: John Hessenthaler
Stage PA & Lighting Systems, Stages, Disco Show. Act representation and Concert tours.

ARTISTES REPRESENTED:

Abba Gold
Amen Corner
The Animals
Bachelors
BC Sweet
Dave Berry & The Cruisers
The Blues Band
Blues Brothers Tribute
Colin Blunstone and Rod Argent
Can You Feel The Force Tour
Chas 'n' Dave
Country Gold Tour
Mike Diabo & His Mighty Quintet
Doctor Feelgood
Craig Douglas
Dozy Beaky Mick & Tich
Elvis Presley Museum On Tour
Raymond Froggatt
Gerry & The Pacemakers
The Glitter Band
Groovejuice
The Hamsters (Jimi Hendrix Tribute)
Heatwave
Herman's Hermits
Imagination
Wilko Johnson
Paul Jones & Dave Kelly

Dennis Lecoriere - Voice of Dr Hook
Love Affair
M People Experience
The Manfreds
Merry Xmas Every Body Tale
Merseybeats
Miller Magic
Naughty Rhythms
Oasisn`t (Oasis Tribute)
Brian Poole
Suzi Quatro
Scream Concerts Tour
Showaddywaddy
The Soul Commitments
Spicey Girls
T-Rextasy
Mick Taylor Blues Band
Thin Lizzy
The Tornados
Steve Travis
Tribute To The Carpenters
Roy Wood
The Yardbirds

HEY PRESTO ENTERTAINMENTS AGENCY
36 St Luke's Road, Tunbridge Wells, Kent TN4 9JH
Tel: 01892 537 964 Fax: 01892 683 401
Mobile: 07973 512845
Email: info@heyprestoentertainments.co.uk
Web: www.heyprestoentertainments.co.uk
Senior Personnel: Michael Alan Bonfield

JEREMY HICKS ASSOCIATES
3 Richmond Buildings, London W1D 3HE
Tel: 0207 734 7957 Fax: 0207 734 6302
Email: julie@jeremyhicks.com
Web Site: www.jeremyhicks.com
Contact: Jeremy Hicks, Sarah Dalkin, Julie Dalkin or Emma Jayne Williams
ARTISTES REPRESENTED:
Angela Boggiano
Arnold Brown
Carl Cooper
Gino D'Acampo
Frances Donovan
Richard Fairbrass
Fork
Silvana Franco
Jilly Goolden
Sandy Gort
Roopa Gulati
Pen Haddow
Ainsley Harriott
Nina Hobson
Kenneth Kendall
Roddy Kohn
John Langdon
Andrew McCaldon
John McCarthy
Toby Musgrave
Nice Mum
Merrilees Parker
Paul Sampson
Tony Robinson
Hermione Ross
Nick Swift
Rhodri Williams

HIGHFIELD ARTISTES / HIGHFIELD PRODUCTIONS
PO Box 180, Cirencester GL7 1WL
Tel: 01285 644 200 Fax: 01285 644 480
Email: info@highfieldproductions.com
Web Site: www.highfieldproductions.com
Senior Personnel: Steven Hutt, Susie Skinner
ARTISTES REPRESENTED:
Jasper Carrott OBE
Phil Cool

HIGHFIELD MANAGEMENT & PROMOTIONS
7 Foundry Close, Cottenham, Cambridge CB24 8TU
Tel/Fax: 01954 251 900
Email: info@highfieldmanagement.com
Web: www.highfieldmanagement.com
Proprietor: Shirley Roberts
ARTISTES REPRESENTED:
Function Bands:
Alpha Connection
Avalon
Boogie Nights
China Grove
Julie Cooper Band
Escada
Freestyle
Madison Square
MInd The Gap
Mixed Feelings
Night Music
Star
Vice Versa
Jazz Bands:
Cambridge Jazz Company
The Usual Suspects
Barn Dance Bands:
Alien Ceilidh Company
Fen Blow Ceilidh Band
Parsons Nose Band
Country & Western Bands:
Circuit Judge
Country Law
Jackson Queen
Classical Music Ensembles:
Elaine Pamphilon (Harpist)
Sensky String Trio
Patricia Spero (Harpist)
Comedians:
Al Benson
John Cassidy
Keith "The Thief" Charnley
Mike Dowling
Tony Gerrard
Ian Irving (Comedian)
Steve Lee
Micky Zany
Ian Richards
Alan Wallace
Illusionists:
Rock Magic (Chris North and Belinda - Illusion)
Discos:
Argentum Roadshow
Boogie Nights Roadshow
Coast to Coast Roadshow
DJ's Disco
G Force Roadshow
Mayhem Roadshow
Original Sin Roadshow
The U.A. Roadshow
Solos/Duos:
Crowjane
Essence
Evergreen
Now And Then
Derek Pendred

LOUISE HILLMAN & KATIE THRELFALL
33 Brookfield, Highgate West Hill, London N6 6AT
Tel: 020 8341 2207 Fax: 020 8340 9309
Email: info@hillmanthrelfall.net
Senior Personnel: Louise Hillman, Katie Threlfall
ARTISTES REPRESENTED:
Men:
Nicholas Asbury
Martin Bayfield
Philip Bond
Daniel Bowers
Martin Brett
Joe Bright
Philip Brook
Gareth Bryn
Adam Burton
Tony Coote
Brian Cowan
Leon Davies
Sean De Vrind
Antony Edridge
Stuart Christian Evans
Kieron Forsyth
Ben Freeman
Tom Graham
Chris Harper
Simon Hepworth
Michael Imerson
Paul Ireland
Hosh Kane
Jon Laurimore
Steve Lennon
Tommy Luther
Breffni McKenna
Lawrence Mullin
Jeremy Nicholas
William Oliver
Edward Peel
David Pullan
Nick Raggett
Dale Rapley
Daniel Roberts
Jason Rush
Ian Saynor
Michael Shaw
Richard Simons
Charlie Simpson
Paul Simpson
Anthony Smee
Rob Storr
Jeremy Turner-Welch
Christopher Villiers
James Wells
Tim Wylton
Women:
Anna Acton
Mina Anwar
Julie Atherton

Rachel Atkins
June Barrie
Anita Carey
Brenda Cavendish
Bethan Cecil
Nichola Clackson
Marty Cruickshank
Alice Dooley
Claudia Elmhirst
Emily Bowker
Michelle Esclapez
Elizabeth Estensen
Tammi Gwyn
Stacy Hart
Zoe Hart
Louise Hickson
Kathy Hipperson
Carmel Howard
Sally Hurst
Maggie Jones
Jo Joyner
Harriet Kemsley
Sara Lloyd
Michelle Luther
Sharon Maiden
Kate McGregor
Briony McRoberts
Annie Miles
Sasha Mitchell
Caryl Morgan
Victoria Newlyn
Phillipa Peak
Kerry Peers
Samantha Power
Isobel Raine
Sian Reese-Williams
Alison Reid
Katherine Rogers
Paula Stockbridge
Louise Yates

HIRE-A-BAND ENTERTAINMENT AGENCY

35 Trent Road, Ipswich, Suffolk IP3 0QL
Tel: 01473 712 624
Email: hab@ourservice2u.co.uk
Senior Personnel: Colin Gilbert, Mim Gilbert

ARTISTES REPRESENTED:

'56 Cadillac
Ace High Country Band
The Basement Band
The Beanies
Clive Betts (classical guitarist)
The Blues Agents
Boogie
Booze & Blues
Caribbean Steel Band
Dave Cass
Champagne String Quartet
Charlie Cheesecake The Children's Entertainer
Classical Cream
Clementine String Quartet
Colini the Magician
Tom Collins Jazz Band
Cupid's Stunts Glam Rock Band
Diversions Classical Trio
Dixie Jazz Bandits
East Coast Blues
Fiddlers Elbow
First Set
Funk Foundation
Funtazia Disco
Gordon & His Organ
Greenwood
Halebopp Jazz Duo
Harley Street
John Hogger Big Band
Xenia Horne the Harpist
Java Function Band
Jug City
Klowns Karaoke
Krackers
The Management
The Marques Brothers
Masquerade
Misterfield Magic Show
The Muck Spreaders Barn Dance Band
Pale Moon 17 Piece Big Band
Prohibition
Reeds & Keys With Gina
Riski Bizniz
Rush Hour
Keith Ryder Solo Act
Sapphire
Savoir Faire
Shaboogamoo Shufflers
Skiphire Ceilidh Band
South of the Border
Steel Street Blues
Steel'n'Lace
Andrew Sterling
Strangeways
Strate Linze
Suffolk Punch Country Duo
Trunkles Ceilidh Band
Vinko Solo Act
Tim Williams

HIREABAND LTD

The RBS Building 1 Manse Road,
West Kilbride, Ayrshire KA23 9AT
Tel: 01294 470820 Fax: 01294 470820
Email: del@hireaband.co.uk
Web Site: www.hireaband.co.uk
Contact: Del Cotton, Lisa Cotton, Janice Kelly, Nicola Bell, Heather Stuart, Mandy Blythe,

ARTISTES REPRESENTED:

Abbamania
Robert Allen (X-factor contestant)
Ayr Pipe Band
Bahookie Ceilidh Band
Bakerloo Line
Big Brother
Big Rory
Big Vern and the Shootahs
Carwash
Counselled Out
Stewart Duff
Dunno The Clown
Elton Experience
The Elvis Cleaning Company
Glamo
Jazz Collective
Last Tram Tae Auchenshuggle
Le Jazz Hot
Jim McMail
Craig McMurdo & That Swing Thang
Midas Touch
Ceilidh Minogue
Mischief Labas
Monaco
Gary Mullen (Freddie Mercury)
Nikita (X-factor contestant)
Northern Star
Real Easy
Red Hot Poker Band
The Right Thing
The Scottish Blues Brothers
Supreme (Robbie Williams)
The Fabs
The Macdonald Brothers (X-factor contestants)
The Soul Kings
Thistle Dubh Ceilidh Band
US4 (U2 tribute)
Vivid

HIRED HANDS

12 Cressy Road, London NW3 2LY
Tel: 020 7267 9212 Fax: 020 7267 1030
Email: hirehandsagency@aol.com
Web Site: www.hiredhandsmodels.com
Senior Personnel: Steve Barker

HOBSON'S ACTORS

62 Chiswick High Road, London W4 1SY
Agency Tel: 020 8995 3628 Fax: 020 8996 5350
Email: actors@hobsons-international.com
Web: www.hobsons-international.com
Agency Contacts: Linda Sacks, Christina Beyer

DAVE HOLLY ARTS MEDIA SERVICES

The Annexe, 23 Eastwood Gardens,
Felling, Tyne and Wear NE10 0AH
Tel: 0191 438 2711 Fax: 0191 438 2722
Web Site: www.daveholly.co.uk
Senior Personnel: Dave Holly

HOLT MANAGEMENT

Whitehall Arts Centre Rayleigh Road,
Leigh-on-Sea, Essex SS9 5UU
Tel: 01702 529299 Tel: 07775 967334
Fax: 01702 512181
Contact: Daniel Holt

HOPE MANAGEMENT

Unit 4.16 The Paintworks, Bath Road,
Bristol BS4 3EH
Tel: 0117 971 2397 Fax: 0117 972 8981
Email: luke@hopemanagement.co.uk
Web Site: www.hopemanagement.co.uk
Director: Leon Alexander
Artist Managers: Luke Allen, Matt Richard

ARTISTES REPRESENTED:

Alan Bremner
Adam Freeland
Hyper
JoKate
Locodice
Martin Buttrich
General Midi
Omi
D Ramirez

Saturation Point
Nick Warren
Way Out West
Jody Wisternoff

SALLY HOPE ASSOCIATES

108 Leonard Street, London EC2A 4XS
Tel: 020 7613 5353 Fax: 020 7613 4848
Email: casting@sallyhope.biz
Web Site: www.sallyhope.biz
Senior Personnel: Sally Hope

ARTISTES REPRESENTED:

Simon Callow
Michael Crawford
Julie Graham
Tamsin Greig

THE HORNE CONCERT AGENCY

44 Linton Road, Castle Gresley, Swadlincote, Derbyshire DE11 9HS
Tel: 01283 218 335 Mobile: 07906 288 450
Senior Personnel: Janet M Love, John Love

ARTISTES REPRESENTED:

Gerry Aidan
Alf Alpha & Wild Oats
The Armpit Jug Band
Aynuk
Sarah Bailey
Sean Carpenter
Centenary Barbershop
Doctors of Jazz
The Roger Fisher Band
The Harvesters Duo
Laurie Hornsby
Ian Irving (Comedian)
The Jagermeisters Umpah Band
David Jay Disco
Johnny Kennedy
Suzanne Kern
Don & Cindy Leather
John Love
Roy Lowe Trio
Don MacLean MBE
Natasha Marie
Catherine Mason
John Minton
Nicky Moran
David Oakley
Maggie O'Hara
Christina Paterson
The Poor Boys Rock Band
Ron Popple
Prof "P" Punch & Judy
Ronaldo the Third
Guy Rowland
The Salon String Quartet
Barry Schmidt Bavarian Band
Roger Scott
Terry Seabrooke
Dave Sealey
Pete Smith & John Buckley
Malcolm Stent
Gary Stevens
Patrick Tansey
Sid Tate
Alan Towers
Leo Turner
Saxon Tylney
Dorothy "Dottie"Wayne
Fred Wedlock
Les Wilson
Shep Woolley

HOUSE OF LORDS

Westminster, London SW1A 0PW
Tel: 020 7219 3000 (Parliamentary Switchboard) Tel: 020 7219 3107 (House of Lords Info. Office) Fax: 020 7219 0620
Email: hcio@parliament.co.uk
Web Site: www.parliament.co.uk

ARTISTES REPRESENTED:

Baroness Thatcher

AMANDA HOWARD ASSOCIATES LTD

21 Berwick Street, London W1F 0PZ
Tel: 020 7287 9277 Fax: 020 7287 7785
Email: mail@amandahowardassociates.co.uk
Web: www.amandahowardassociates.co.uk
ADMINISTRATION:
Senior Personnel: Amanda Fitzalan Howard, Mark Price, Kirsten Wright, Darren Rugg, Kevin Brady, Chloe Brayfield.
Amanda Howard Associates are leading talent and literary agents representing actors, presenters, producers, directors, designers, composers, voice-overs and writers of comedy, entertainment and drama. Our clients work across all forms of media, including television, radio, theatre and film productions.

ARTISTES REPRESENTED:

Darren Boyd
Ann Bryson
Clare Buckfield
Brian Cant
Andrew Collins
Stephen Frost
Siobhan Hayes
Stuart Maconie
Gigi Morley
Cliff Parisi
David Quantick
Caroline Quentin
Jan Ravens
Suggs

HOWARD OLSON PROMOTIONS

16 Penn Avenue, Chesham, Buckinghamshire HP5 2HS
Tel: 01494 785 873 Fax: 01494 784 760
Email: helson1029@aol.com
Senior Personnel: Howard Elson, Antony Bishop.

ARTISTES REPRESENTED:

Don Fardon
Roger Whittaker

JOHN HOWE PRESENTATIONS LIMITED

2 Meadow Way, Ferring, Worthing, West Sussex BN12 5LD
Tel: 01903 249 912 Tel: 01903 503271
Fax: 01903 507698
Email: johnhowe@btconnect.com
Web: www.johnhowepresentations.moonfruit.com
Senior Personnel: John Howe FEAA

HUGHES ENTERTAINMENTS

PO Box 1AS, London W1A 1AS
Tel: 020 7224 9666 Fax: 020 7224 9688
Contact: Charlie Hughes
Agency for all types of street entertainers, from statues to stilt-walkers, jugglers to jesters.

JANE HUGHES MANAGEMENT

4 Dundrennan Close, Poynton, Stockport, Cheshire SK12 1SQ
Tel: 01625 858 556 Mob: 07766 130 604
Email: gill@jhm.co.uk
We are a Management Company providing Presenters for TV/Radio and corporate work. We also producers/directors for all media.

ARTISTES REPRESENTED:

Khalid Aziz
Tanya Beckett
Peter Crawford
Suzanne Dando
Jules de Jongh
Robin Galloway
Debbie Greenwood
Stuart Hall
Jilly Halliday
Kate Harding
Michael Jordan
Lisa B
Alex Lush
Elisa Portelli
Nina Sebastiane
Lis Speight
Cris St Valery
Kathy Tayler
Anna Walker
Patricia Yorston

OWEN HUGHES ENTERTAINMENTS

87 Holly Road, Aspull, Wigan, Lancashire WN2 1RY
Tel: 01942 832 806 / 832022
Fax: 01942 510 758
Email: owenhughes1@btconnect.com
Web Site: www.owenhughesentertainments.co.uk
Senior Personnel: Owen Hughes

ARTISTES REPRESENTED:

ABBA Again
Josh Addams
Aphrodite
Cats Pyjamas
Crawford and Brown
Dave Decks and The Love Thing
Destiny
Forbidden
Garry Freeman
Heatwave
Hollywood Flairz
JBO
Joseph
Last Chance

Loaded
Loaded
Makerfield
Makin Trax
Mates
Phil Richmond
She Bop
Slingback
Snapshot
Soul Suspects
Sweet Dreams
Undisputed
Wonder Years
Wyte Lyze

DAVID HULL PROMOTIONS LTD
46 University Street, Belfast, BT7 1HB
Northern Ireland
Tel: 028 9024 0360 Fax: 028 9024 7919
Email: info@dhpromotions.com/david@davidhullpromotions.com
Web Site: www.davidhullpromotions.com
Managing Director: David Hull
General Manager: Tony Brown
UK and Irish Celebrity and Personality Agency. UK and Ireland Tour Bookers. Representing the best in Irish Entertainment.
ARTISTES REPRESENTED:
Gerry Anderson
William Caulfield
Sean Crummey
Dana
Johnny Day
Hugo Duncan
Gene Fitzpatrick
Characters from Give My Head Peace
Flash Harry
Hole In The Wall Gang
Eamonn Holmes
Irelands Showbands Do You Come Here Often?
George Jones
Gerry Kelly
Patrick Kielty
Ruth Langsford
John Linehan
Gerard McCarthy
May McFettridge
Nuala McKeever
Rose-Marie
Zoe Salmon
Lawrie Sanchez
Julian Simmons

BERNARD HUNTER ASSOCIATES
13 Spencer Gardens, London SW14 7AH
Tel: 020 8878 6308
Agent: Bernard Hunter
ARTISTES REPRESENTED:
Directors/Producers:
Michael Blakemore
Patrick Garland
Ken Riddington
Actors:
Ballard Berkely (Estate)
Avis Bonnage (Estate)
David Conville
Colin Douglas (Estate)
Philippa Gail
David Griffin
Arthur Lowe (Estate)
Fulton Mackay (Estate)
Aubrey Morris (Estate)
Denis Quilley (Estate)

HURRICANE PRODUCTIONS LTD
Freepost EDO 5910, London SW15 6BR
Enquiries Tel: 0208 878 6622 Bookings Tel: 0800 731 2677 Fax: 0208 878 1771
Email: hurricanetheatre@aol.com
Web: www.hurricaneproductions.co.uk
Contact: Maria O'Hara

HYPER AGENCY
PO Box 2222 Reading RG1 4WH
Tel: 0844 991 8888 Fax: 0844 991 8889
Email: info@hyperagency.co.uk
Web Site: www.hyperagency.co.uk
Senior Personnel: Guy Robinson
ARTISTES REPRESENTED:
DJs:
Toby Anstis
Martin Archer
Dave Berry
Gemma Cairney
Kaz Carter
Cut Up Boys
Chappers & Dave
Headphone Disco
Dave & Dom
Fabio
Mark Goodier
Paul Hayes
Ronnie Herel (Radio 1)
Leo 'The Lion' Ihenacho
Greg James
JK & Joel
Aled Haydn Jones
James King
Rickie & Melvin
Scott Mills
Dave Pearce
Joshua Roberts
Sean Scott
Pat Sharp
Slipmatt
Huw Stephens
Matt Wilkinson
Celebrities:
Dirk Benedict
Bodger and Badger (Andy Cunningham)
Jeff Brazier
Chesney Hawkes
Antony Costa
Ashley Taylor Dawson
Dustin Diamond
Peter Dickson
Jeremy Edwards
Alan Fletcher (UK only)
Ron Jeremy
Michelle Keegan (Tina, Coronation Street)
Rodrigo Lopes
Ewen MacIntosh
Timmy Mallett
Jennifer Metcalfe (Mercedes, Hollyoaks)
Ryan Moloney
Andrew Moss
Dave Benson Phillips
Kieran Richardson
Emma Rigby (Hannah, Hollyoaks)
Suzanne Shaw
Carley Stenson (Steph, Hollyoaks)
Verne Troyer
Stephen Uppal
Roy Walker
Glen Wallace
Ricky Whittle (PC Calvin Valentine, Hollyoaks)
Emma Willis

I. A. M.
Tower Bridge
Suite 210, 46-48 East Smithfield LONDON E1W 1AW
Tel: 020 7709 2041
Email: luc@internationalartistsmanagement.co.uk
Web Site: www.internationalartistsmanagement.co.uk
Luc Chaudhary

I AM EPIC
79 Wollaston Way
Burnt Mills Industrial Estate BASILDON SS13 1DJ
Tel: 0870 426 3742
Email: info@iamepic.co.uk
Web Site: www.iamepic.co.uk
Gemma Stoddard

IAN AND FRIENDS
35 Hibernia Point, Wolvercote Road, London SE2 9TL
Tel/Fax: 020 8310 4376 Mobile: 07860 183471
Email: info@ianandfriends.co.uk
Web Site: www.gingernutt.com
Contact: Ian Thom
Speciality Act. Puppets and characters including Gingernutt the Clown, Tofi-Stilt Clown and Bigwig the Ten Foot Magician.
ARTISTES REPRESENTED:
Big Wig the Wizard
Gingernutt the Clown
Ian and Friends
The Rabbit Redford Show
Tofi The Clown

ICON ACTORS MANAGEMENT
Tanzaro House, Ardwick Green North, Manchester M12 6FZ
Tel: 0161 273 3344 Fax: 0161 273 4567
Email: nancy@iconactors.net
Web Site: www.iconactors.net
Contact: Rhian Salmon
Agent Director: Nancy Morris-Long
Represent actors for work in all areas of the industry. Casting suite available to hire.
ARTISTES REPRESENTED:
Actors:
John Afzal
Dicken Ashworth
Kevin Brannagan
Emanuel Brierley
David Brown

Andy Burke
Des Cummings
Ben Curley
Mark Folan Deasy
Marvyn Dickinson
Nick Dutton
James Foster
Chris Grahamson
Karl Greenwood
Edward Harrison
Chris Hollinshead
Jonathan Howard
Chris Jack
Darren Kuppan
Paul Lemming
Richard Lily
Paul McGreevy
Andy Moore
James Morley
Miles Moss
Richard Nutter
Leyland O'Brien
Joe O'Byrne
Chris Perry-Metcalf
Carl Rice
Ben Sutherland
Martin Tomms
Justyn Towler
Everal Walsh
Guy Warburton
Anthony Wingate
Mike Woodhead
Actresses:
Brittany Ashworth
Marilyn Bar-Ilan
Tracey Briggs
Maxine Burth
Michelle Butt
Jessica Clement
Mary Ann Coburn
Melanie Dagg
Gilly Daniels
Raine Davison
Ebony Feare
Alison George
Julie Glover
Sue Kimberley
Janet Maher
Victoria May
Bibi Nerheim
Gemma North
Sophie Osbourne
Angeline Plummer
Erica Rogers
Elizabeth Rose
Annie Sawle
Gail Marie Shapter
Karen Shaw
Chloe Singer
Jemma Thompson
Paula Wharton
Helen Wilding

IDENTITY ONE MANAGEMENT
90-96 Brewery Road, London N7 9NT
Tel: 0871 717 5860 Fax: 07092 863 762
Email: jonathan@identityone.co.uk
Web Site: www.identityone.co.uk
Agent: Jonathan Lipman
ARTISTES REPRESENTED:
Females:
Caprice
Lucy Clarkson
Hayley Dixon
Michelle Gayle
Charlie Murray
Alex Slater
Michelle Thorne
Males:
Julian Bennett
Richard Biedul
Dave Courtney
Kenzie
Lee Latchford-Evans

IE MUSIC
111 Frithville Gardens, London W12 7JQ
Tel: 020 8600 3400 Fax: 020 8600 3401
Mob: 07792 706 801
Email: alison@iemusic.co.uk
Web Site: www.iemusic.co.uk
Senior Personnel: Tim Clark, David Enthoven
ARTISTES REPRESENTED:
Archive
Craig Armstrong
Passenger
Sia
Robbie Williams

IFOREVENTS LTD
Studio 4H, Beehive Mill Jesrsey Street
Manchester M4 6JG
Tel: 0161 341 0064
Email: phin@iforgroup.co.uk
Web Site: www.ifortalent.co.uk
Phin Mackness

IGNITION MANAGEMENT
54 Linhope Street, London NW1 6HL
Tel: 020 7298 6000 Fax: 020 7258 0962
Email: mail@ignitionman.co.uk
Agent: Marcus Russell
ARTISTES REPRESENTED:
Oasis

IMG ARTISTS
The Lightbox 111 Power Road
London W4 5PY
Tel: 020 7957 5800 Fax: 020 7957 5801
Email: artistseurope@imgartists.com
Web Site: www.imgartists.com
Senior Vice President & Managing Director: Claire Dacam, Marketing & Publicity Agent: Tristen Hennigs
IMG Artists is recognised as one of the world's leading classical music management and touring companies. It is a worldwide organisation which has its main European office in London, sister offices in North America, France and Malaysia, and affiliated branches in Italy, Japan and Singapore.
IMG Artists also organise tours and appearances for orchestras and ensembles. Please call for further details.
ARTISTES REPRESENTED:
Conductors:
Kees Bakels
Mattlas Bamert
Giordano Bellincampi
Jiri Belohlavek
Justin Brown
Alan Buribayev
Jean-Claude Casadesus
Michael Christie
Jonathan Darlington
Thomas Dausgaard
Stéphane Denève
Barry Douglas
Sachio Fujioka
János Fürst
Alan Gilbert
Leonid Grin
Emmanuelle Haim
Manfred Honeck
Jakub Hrusa
Pieta Inkinen
Vladimir Jurowski
Zoltán Kocsis
Nicola Luisotti
John Nelson
Paolo Olmi
Kazushi Ono
Eiji Oue
Antonio Pappano
Itzhak Perlman
Libor Pesek
Vasily Petrenko
En Shao
David Stern
Muhai Tang
Yuri Temirkanov
Yan Pascal Tortelier
Bramwell Tovey
Jaap Van Zweden
Benjamin Wallfisch
Franz Welser-Most
Barry Wordsworth
Long Yu
Pianists:
Dmitri Alexeev
Leif Ove Andsnes
Michel Dalberto
Barry Douglas
Derek Han
Freddy Kempf
Zoltán Kocsis
Elizabeth Leonskaya
Alexander Melnikov
Natasha Paremski
Simon Trpceski
Ayako Uehara
Violinists:
Joshua Bell
Nicola Benedetti
Sarah Chang
Pamela Frank
Ilya Gringolts
Hilary Hahn
Henning Kraggerud
Itzhak Perlman
Vadim Repin
Charles Siem
Kyoko Takezawa
Nikolaj Znaider
Cellists:
Guy Johnston
Li-Wei
Julian Lloyd Webber
Johannes Moser

Double Bass:
Edgar Meyer
Clarinet:
Julian Bliss
David Shifrin
Chamber Music:
Emerson String Quartet
Eroica Trio
Perlman/Schmidt/Bailey
Spole to USA Chamber Music
Zephyr
Special Ensembles:
Monteiro Piano Duo
The Five Browns
Charles Wadsworth
Accompanists:
Julius Drake

IMG WORLD

Pier House Strand On The Green London W4 3NN
Tel: 020 8233 5000 Fax: 020 8233 5001
Web Site: www.imgworld.com

ARTISTES REPRESENTED:

Tim Henman

IMWP (UK) LTD

3 the Raven, 140 Westbridge Road, London SW11 3PF
Tel: 020 7223 7112 Fax: 020 7223 7414
Email: imwpuk@aol.com
Web Site: www.imwpuk.com
Agent: Ian Wilson

ARTISTES REPRESENTED:

TV Presenters:
Bruce Forsyth CBE
Sean Meo
Amanda Ursell
Comedians:
Graham Anthony
Carl Barron
Hal Cruttenden

INCREDIBLE ARTISTS LTD

PO Box 545, Wigan WN1 9BZ
Tel: 07795 466 661 Fax: 01942 680 608
Email: info@incredibleartists.co.uk
Web Site: www.incredibleartists.co.uk
Directors: Anita Watson

INDEPENDENT MANAGEMENT LTD

The White House,
52-54 Kennington Oval, London
SE11 5SW
Tel/Fax: 020 7587 1080
Email: iml.london@btconnect.com
Web Site: www.iml.org.uk
Co-operative agency.

ARTISTES REPRESENTED:

Actresses:
Catherine Bellamy
Holly Berry
Lil Binham
Anne Bird
Rhian Jayne Bull
Nicola Delaney
Mira Dovreni
Elizabeth Holland
Rebecca Kennedy
Carys Lewis
Lucy Middleweek
Amanda Reed
Amy Rockson
Carmen Rodriguez
Actors:
Donal Cox
Leandro D'andrea
Ross Finbow
Ozzie Gardner
Steven George
Christopher Knott
Peter Leafe
Ben Marks
Samuel Metcalf
Philippe Spall
Matt Stacy
Ian Street
Patrick Taggart

INDEPENDENT TALENT GROUP

Oxford House, 76 Oxford Street, London W1D 1BS
Tel: 020 7636 6565 Fax: 020 7323 0101
Web Site: www.independenttalent.com/presenters
Contact: Laura Hill, Jessica Stone

ARTISTES REPRESENTED:

Imran Ahmed
Saffron Aldridge
Sarah Beeny
Seb Bishop
James Brown
Lisa Butcher
Amanda Byram
Cambridge Jazz Company
Alexa Chung
Brendan Coogan
Francesco Da Mosto
Michael Daunt
Angus Deayton
Hugh Dennis
Dr Cecilia d'Felice
Alesha Dixon
Kate Edmondson
Matt Edmondson
Huw Edwards
Lisa Eldridge
Rosie Fellner
Colin Firth
Emma Forbes
Tom Fortes Mayer
Kevin Fortune
Neil Fox (aka "Foxy")
Bay Garnett
Mel Giedroyc
Richard E Grant
David Green
Philippa Gregory
Guy Grieve
Dr Mark Hamilton
Richard Hammond
Nick Hancock
Tony Hawks
Jonty Hearnden
Dan Hopwood
Duncan James
Richard Johnson
Camilla Johnson-Hill
Kira Jolliffe
Steve Jones
Jacqui Joseph
Lauren Laverne
Pearl Lowe
Emily Maitlis
Steve Marsh
Zara Martin
Miquita Oliver
Gwyneth Paltrow
Adil Ray
Martin Roberts
John Scott
Owen Sheers
Dr Basil Singer
Tania Strecker
Alice Sykes
Alexandra Tolstoy
Johnny Vaughan
John Weir
Matthew Wilson
Dan Wright
Toby Young

INDUSTRY MUSIC GROUP LTD

Genesis Centre 18 Innovation Way
Stoke-on-Trent ST6 4BF
Tel: 01782 213140 Fax: 01782 213150
Email: a.pountain@chooseindustry.com
Web Site: www.chooseindustry.com
Managing Director: Andy Pountain

ARTISTES REPRESENTED:

Diversity
Ruth Lorenzo
Laura White

INGPEN & WILLIAMS LTD

7 St George's Court,
131 Putney Bridge Road, London
SW15 2PA
Tel: 020 8874 3222 Fax: 020 8877 3113
Email: ds@ingpen.co.uk / hh@ingpen.co.uk
Web Site: www.ingpen.co.uk
Director: David Sigall
Artist Managers: Helen Hogh, Lulu Chivers
Senior Personnel: Thomas Hull, Jonathan Groves
Specialising in Opera and Classical Music

ARTISTES REPRESENTED:

Conductors:
Martin André
Richard Armstrong CBE
Ivor Bolton
Richard Bonynge
Pierre Boulez
Douglas Boyd
Paul Daniel CBE
Johannes Debus
Sir Edward Downes CBE
Sian Edwards
Mark Elder CBE
Richard Farnes
Michael Gielen
William Lacey
Diego Masson
Alexander Polianichko
Michael Schonwandt
Markus Stenz
Garry Walker
Bruno Weil

Sopranos:
Laura Aikin
Valdine Anderson
Hope Briggs
Emma Gane
Kathryn Harries
Barbara Hendricks
Claire Ormshaw
Alison Roddy
Joan Rodgers CBE
Claire Weston
Mezzo-Sopranos:
Jane Irwin
Katarina Karnéus
Serena Kay
Susan Parry
Arlene Rolph
Victoria Simmonds
Anna Stephany
Hilary Summers
Ann Taylor
Wendy Dawn Thompson
Male Soprano:
Jacek Laszczkowski
Counter-Tenor:
Michael Chance
Tenors:
Peter Auty
Graham Clark
Poul Elming
John Hudson
Jeffrey Lloyd- Roberts
Ed Lyon
Paul Nilon
Dennis O'Neill CBE
Nigel Robson
Ronald Samm
Peter Wedd
Baritones & Basses:
Nathan Gunn
Robert Hayward
Robert Holl
Gwynne Howell CBE
Darren Jeffery
Franz Mazura
Alastair Miles
Wolfgang Schöne
Andrew Shore
Daniel Sumegi
Henry Waddington
Nathaniel Webster
Opera Directors:
Andrea Breth
Tim Carroll
Graham Vick
Pianists:
Alfred Brendel
Till Fellner
Janina Fialkowska
Paul Lewis
Joanna MacGregor
Peter Serkin
Accompanist:
Roger Vignoles
Cellist:
Adrian Brendel
Ralph Kirshbaum
Oboists:
Heinz Holliger
Clarinettist:
Andrew Marriner
French Horn:
Radovan Vlatkovic
String Trio:
Leopold String Trio
String Quartets:
Elias String Quartet
Goldner String Quartet
Guarneri Quartet
Orchestra:
Chicago Symphony Orchestra
West-Eastern Divan Orchestra (D. Barenboim)
Master Classes:
Phyllis Bryn Julson
Dame Anne Evans
Christa Ludwig
Sherrill Milnes
Special Projects:
Nash Ensemble of London
Violin:
Peter Cropper
Jack Liebeck
Marianne Thorsen
Viola:
Lawrence Power

INITIATIVE UNLIMITED

13 Brook Business Park,
Cowley Mill Road, Uxbridge, Middlesex
UB8 2FX
Tel: 01895 234313 Fax: 01895 236651
Email: david@dmlmarketing.co.uk
Web Site: www.initiativeunlimited.co.uk
Senior Personnel: Adam Hayes
Specialises in actor management and representation. Our corporate events not only help improve employee motivation and productivity, they also help colleagues get to know each other better in a relaxed environment. Team building games can also help you achieve work-related objectives in an entertaining way. Who says its all work and no play?

INSANITY ARTISTS

5 Little Portland Street London W1W 7JD
Tel: 020 7927 6222 Fax: 020 7927 6223
Email: hello@insanitygroup.com
Web Site: www.insanityartists.co.uk
Insanity Artists was established in 2003, and has grown during that time to become the UKs largest live agency exclusively representing DJ and PA talent from the areas of music, television and radio.
CEO: Andy Varley
Managing Director: Kirsty Williams

ARTISTES REPRESENTED:

DJ Contacts:
Ace & Invisible
Alfie Allen
CJ Beatz
Melanie Blatt
Bloc Party
Blue
Benji Boko
Mike Fielding (The Mighty Boosh)
Francis Boulle
Edith Bowman
VV Brown
Keisha Buchanan
James Buckley
Gemma Cairney
Mary Charteris
Alexa Chung
Gabriella Cilmi
Phil Clifton
Fearne Cotton
Sarah Cox
Tom Crane
Daisy Dares You
Sebastian De Souza
Adam Deacon
Darwin Deez
Dick & Dom
DJ Swerve
Eliza Doolittle
Danny Dyer
Rick Edwards
Sophie Ellis-Bextor
Paloma Faith
Caroline Flack
Gareth Gates
Pixie Geldof
Good Shoes
Ellie Goulding
Her Majesty & The Wolves
Henry Holland
Mathew Horne
Jade Jagger
Nathan Stewart Jarrett
Danny Jones (McFly)
Just Jack
Eddie Kadi
La Roux
George Lamb
Lostprophets
Daisy Lowe
Merveille Lukeba
Bradley Macintosh
Greg McHugh
Midnight Beast
Mr Hudson
Mutya, Keisha, Siobhan
Noisettes
Jack O'Connell
Patsy Palmer
Luke Pasqualino
Pritchard vs Dainton
Nicola Roberts
Samuel Robertson
Stooshe
Sean Teale
The Alias
The Big Pink
The Maccabees
The Rumble Strips
The Wombats
Thepetebox
Tim Burgess
Diana Vickers
Jo Whiley
Vanessa White
Kimberley Wyatt
Alex Zane
PA Clients:
Big Brother
Francis Boulle
Jessica Clement
Paddy Doherty
Trevor Donovan
Gabriella Ellis
Binky Felstead

Fredrik Ferrier
Joseph Gilgun
Girls Roc
Cheska Hull
Laya Lewis
Ollie Locke
Merveille Lukeba
Millie MacKintosh
Liz McClarnon
Luke Pasqualino
Megan Prescott
Priscilla, Queen of the Desert
Pritchard vs Dainton
Samuel Robertson
Kristina & Karissa Shannon
Steve John Shepard
Skins Cast
Lauren Socha
Hugo Taylor
The Only Way Is Essex
Music Clients:
A1
Basshunter
Jenny Berggrenn
Big Brovaz
Booty Luv
Damage
Diva Fever
Five
Gareth Gates
Gracious K
Howie D
Let Loose
Lil Chris
Stacey McClean
N-Trance
S Club 3
Scooch
Strictly Come Dancing Band
The Cameleonz
The Mend
Sam Tsui
Untouched
Julia Volkova
Shayne Ward
Shaun Williamson (Barry, Eastenders)

INSANITY TALENT MANAGEMENT

Moray House
23-31 Great Titchfield Street London
W1W 7PA
Tel: 020 7927 6222 Fax: 020 7927 6223
Email: agents@insanitygroup.com
Web Site: www.itmlondon.com

ARTISTES REPRESENTED:

Sean Maguire
Martine McCutcheon

INSPIRATION MANAGEMENT

Room 227, The Aberdeen Centre,
22-24 Highbury Grove, London N5 2EA
Tel: 020 7704 0440 Fax: 020 7704 8497
Email: mail@inspirationmanagement.org.uk
Web: www.inspirationmanagement.org.uk
Actors Co-operative. Established since 1985. General agency handling work in all areas; Theatre, Film, Television, Audio and New Media. Pleasea apply by letter with photo and resumé.

ARTISTES REPRESENTED:

Nikki Brown
Colin Chapman
Heather Coombs
Laura Curnick
David Dobson
Richard Foster
Dominique Gerrard
Adam Henshaw
Madeleine Hutchins
Patrick Hyde
Michelle Jamieson
Pat Kelman
Juanita Margerison
Jerry Marwood
Margaret Moore
Aidan O'Neill
Christopher Oxford
Jonathan Reason
Jenna Shaw
Hannah Smith
Lesley Stone
Ed Taylor-Gooby
Patrick Thornton

INSPIRATIONAL ARTISTE BOOKING

Suite D, 4-6 Canfield Place, London
NW6 3BT
Contact by post only.
Senior Personnel: Hadleigh Scott

ARTISTES REPRESENTED:

Christopher Biggins
Honor Blackman
Richard Blackwood
Nicky Campbell
Freddy Cannon
Sacha Baron Cohen
Steve Coogan
Letitia Dean
Cat Deeley
Anne Diamond
Michael Grade
Nigel Havers
Lesley Joseph
Lord Lawson
Nigella Lawson
Laurence Llewelyn-Bowen
Kerry McFadden
Van Morrison
Paul Nicholas
Sian Phillips
Billie Piper
Katie Puckrik
Caroline Quentin
John Sessions
Janet Street-Porter
Melanie Sykes
David Walliams
Anthony Worrall Thompson

INTERNATIONAL ARTISTES LTD

4th Floor, Holborn Hall,
193-197 High Holborn, London
WC1V 7BD
Tel: 020 7025 0600 Fax: 020 7404 9865
Email: reception@internationalartistes.com
Web Site: www.internationalartistes.com
Senior Personnel: Robert Voice, Michele Milburn, Phil Dale, Mandy Ward
Financial Directors: Paul Parnaby

ARTISTES REPRESENTED:

Ray Alan
Hils Barker
Caroline Berry
Katy Brand
Gyles Brandreth
Cannon & Ball
Scott Capurro
Crocodile Casting
Nathan Caton
Chuckle Brothers
Julian Clary
Ronnie Corbett OBE
Jim Davidson OBE
Windsor Davies
Ken Dodd OBE
Mike Doyle
Toby Hull & Emu
Jo Enright
Tara Flynn
Antonio Forcione
Alan Gilchrist
Janey Godley
Tom Grren
Grumbleweeds
Grumbleweeds
Guizer Scottish Music
Hale & Pace
Mike Hayley
John Hopkins
Reginald D. Hunter
John Inman
Eddie Large
George Logan
Paul Merton
David Mitchell
John Moloney
Joe Pasquale
Peter Piper
Greg Proops
Ian Royce
Rob Schneider
Shed Simove
Matt Slack
Jimmy Tarbuck OBE
Ray Tizzard
Robert Webb
Mike Yarwood
Paul Zerdin

INTERNATIONAL CIRCUS STARDUST ENTERTAINMENT

Two Elms Brickhouse Road
Tolleshunt Major MALDON CM9 8JZ
Tel: 07896 815182
Email: shaun@circusstardust.com
Web Site: www.circusstardust.com
Shaun Hull

INTERNATIONAL CLASSICAL ARTISTS

The Tower Building, 11 York Road,
London SE1 7NX
Tel: 020 7902 0520 Fax: 020 7902 0530
Email: info@icartists.co.uk
Web Site: www.icartists.co.uk
Chairman/ Head of Artist Management: Stephen Wright
Senior Artist Manager: Cathy Carson

ARTISTES REPRESENTED:
Conductors:
Roland Böer
Semyon Bychkov
Sylvain Cambreling
Kristjan Järvi
Stephen Kovacevich
Rory MacDonald
Olli Mustonen
Kent Nagano
Matthias Pintscher
Esa-Pekka Salonen
Yasuo Shinozaki
Michael Tilson Thomas
Ilan Volkov
Hugh Wolff
Piano:
François-Frédéric Guy
Stephen Kovacevich
Olli Mustonen
Violin:
Viviane Hagner
Viola:
Yuri Bashmet
Chamber Ensembles:
Borodin String Quartet
Soprano:
Ingela Bohlin
Ha Young Lee
Mezzo-Soprano:
Karen Cargill
Tove Dahlberg
Tenor:
Edgaras Montvidas
Andrew Tortise
Thomas Walker
Baritone/Bass Baritone:
Stephan Loges
Roderick Williams
Opera Director:
Laurent Pelly
Composers:
Matthias Pintscher
Esa-Pekka Salonen
Mark-Anthony Turnage
Kevin Volans
Counter-Tenor:
Lestyn Davies

INTERNATIONAL MANAGEMENT & AGENCY LTD
2 Bond Terrace, Rishworth Street,
Wakefield, West Yorkshire WF1 2HW
Tel: 01924 299 993 Fax: 01924 200 750
Email: lizmarston@im-agency.com
Web Site: www.im-agency.com
Senior Personnel: Norman Thewlis FEAA,
Barry Marshall

ARTISTES REPRESENTED:
Aces
Beat Street International
Boyz Limited
B-Yond
Detroit Soul
Diva
Emaculate
Groovies Ghost
Hero (Enrique Tribute)
Hey Jude
Housequake
Jimmy James & The Vagabonds
Jazmine
Limit
Manhattans
Mens Club
Northern Xposure
Popkorn
Rhythm Nation
Simply Untouchable
Swing Kings
Tabu
Tamla Motion
Taylor Made
Three, The Real McKoy
Touch & Go
Ultimate Madness (Madness Tribute)

INTERNATIONAL TALENT BOOKING LTD (ITB)
1st Floor, Ariel House
74a Charlotte Street London W1T 4QJ
Tel: 020 7637 6979
Email: mail@itb.co.uk
Web Site: www.itb.co.uk
Barry Dickens

INTERNATIONAL THEATRE & MUSIC LTD
Garden Studios, 11 - 15 Betterton Street,
Covent Garden, London WC2H 9BP
Tel: 020 7470 8786 Fax: 020 7379 0801
Email: info@it-m.co.uk
Web Site: www.it-m.co.uk
Managing Director: Piers Chater Robinson
Management Executive: Claire Lloyd

ISIS AGENTS LTD
Crusader House 145-157 St John Street
London EC1V 4PW
Tel: 0203 150 0552
Email: andi@isisagents.co.uk
Web Site: www.isisagents.co.uk
Andi Mac

ITALIA CONTI AGENCY LTD
Italia Conti House, 23 Goswell Road,
London EC1M 7AJ
Tel: 020 7608 7500 Fax: 020 7253 1430
Email: agency@italiaconti.co.uk
Senior Personnel: Carrie Newton

ITB (INTERNATIONAL TALENT BOOKING)
1st Floor, Ariel House,
74a Charlotte Street, London W1T 4QJ
Tel: 020 7637 6979 Fax: 020 7637 6978
Email: mail@itb.co.uk
Web Site: www.itb.co.uk
Agents: Rod MacSween, Barry Dickins,
David Levy, Martin Horne, Mike Dewdney,
Scott Thomas, Maria Hutt.

ARTISTES REPRESENTED:
Aerosmith
Christina Aguilera
Tori Amos
Fiona Apple
Audioslave
Ashley Beedle
Bell X1
Ben Christophers
Black Rebel Motor Cycle Club
Black Sabbath
Jerry Cantrell
Hernan Cattaneo
Kelly Clarkson
Biffy Clyro
The Cooper Temple Clause
Chris Cornell
Cosmic Rough Riders
Nikka Costa
Counting Crows
D'Angelo
Def Leppard
Deftones
Doobie Brothers
Bob Dylan
Eels
The End
Eve 6
Fleetwood Mac
Adam Freeland
New Found Glory
Godsmack
David Guetta
Darren Hayes
Hootie & The Blowfish
Howie B
Billy Idol
Julio Iglesias
Chris Isaak
Jamiroquai
Jem
Judas Priest
Gary Jules
Kasabian
Kiss
Jeff Klein
Frankie Knuckles
Korn
Lenny Kravitz
K's Choice
Layo & Bushwacka
Limp Bizkit
The Living End
Lostprophets
Madness
Jesse Malin
Maroon 5
Dave Matthews Band
John Mayall & The Bluesbreakers
John Mayer
Tom Mcrae
Medicine8
Midtown
Minus
Joni Mitchell
Moloko
Gary Moore
David Morales
Mr C
Randy Newman
Paul Oakenfold
Oceansize
Joan Osborne
Kelly Osbourne
Ozzy Osbourne
Jimmy Page & Robert Plant
Pearl Jam
A Perfect Circle
Tom Petty And The Heartbreakers

Puddle of Mudd
Puressence
The Raveonettes
Zack De La Rocha
Rocky and Diesel
Diana Ross
Satoshie Tomiie
Boz Scaggs
Scorpions
Seal
Seether
Shakira
Paul Simon
Something Coporate
Soulfly
Soulwax
Steely Dan
Sufjan Stevens
The Tea Party
The Fratelli's
The View
The Thorns
Tool
Towers Of London
Train
Matchbox Twenty
UB40
Velvet Revolver
Vendetta Red
Whitesnake
The Who
X-Press 2
Neil Young
Zap Mama
ZZ Top

J K ENTERTAINMENT
1 Church Lane, Wishaw, Sutton Coldfield, West Midlands B76 9QH
Tel: 0121 313 0504 Mob: 07977 041 628
Email: info@jkentertainmentagency.co.uk
Web: www.jkentertainmentagency.co.uk
Contact: Jackie O' Shea

JABBERWOCKY AGENCY
Glassenbury Hill Farm,
Glassenbury Road, Cranbrook, Kent
TN17 2QF
Tel: 01580 714306 Fax: 01580 714346
Email: info@jabberwockyagency.com
Web Site: www.jabberwockyagency.com
Senior Personnel: Christina Yates
Casting Agents: Jessica Francis, Nicky Milford
Children's theatrical agency for artists from birth to 18 years.

JACLYN AGENCY
52 Bessemer Road, Norwich, Norfolk
NR4 6DQ
Tel: 01603 622 027 Fax: 01603 612 532
Email: info@jaclyn2000.co.uk
Web Site: www.jaclyn2000.co.uk
Senior Personnel: Julian Sandiford, Henrietta Cassidy
Specialising in: Supporting Artistes for TV & Film Companies. Covers East Anglia, E. Midlands, N. London. Over one thousand professional artistes available.

JADE ENTERTAINMENTS
10 Denston Close, Northampton
NN4 0DD
Tel: 01604 661 668 Fax: 01604 661 949
Email: adrian@jadeentertainments.co.uk
Contacts: Adrian Sawford

JAFFREY MANAGEMENT LTD.
The Double Lodge, Pinewood Studios, Pinewood Road, Iver Heath, Bucks
SL0 0NH
Tel: 01753 785162 Fax: 01753 785163
Email: jennifer@jaffreyactors.co.uk
Web Site: www.jaffreyactors.co.uk
Senior Personnel: Jennifer Jaffrey
Formerly Magnolia Management & Tim Kent Associates

JOHNNY JALLAND ENTERPRISES
8 Manners Road, Balderton, Newark, Nottinghamshire NG24 3HW
Tel/Fax: 01636 701 710
Senior Personnel: Johnny Jalland

JAM HOT PRODUCTIONS
38 Surbiton Hill Park, Surbiton, Surrey
KT5 8ES
Tel: 020 8390 2275 Fax: 020 8390 2275
Mob: 07889 431 004
Email: bazmoran@btinternet.com
Contact: Barry Moran

ANDREW JAMES
Tel: 07880 557 428
Email: andrew.rafferty@ntlworld.com
Web Site: www.easy-lover.co.uk / www.illinoisbluesbrothers.com
Contact: Andew James

ARTISTES REPRESENTED:
Easy Lover - Phil Collins Tribute
Illinois Blues Brothers

LEE JAMES ASSOCIATES LTD
PO Box 61, York YO61 1WD
Tel: 01347 821121 Fax: 01347 824 499
Mobile: 07739 227 687
Email: leejamesltd@btconnect.com
Web Site: www.leejamesltd.com
Senior Personnel: Lee James, Gail James, Scott James

ARTISTES REPRESENTED:
Country Legends
Mercury (Queen)
Tamala Motown Gold
The Chicago Blues Brothers
The Curvettes
Voulez Vous (Abba Tribute Show)

JOY JAMESON LTD
2.19 The Plaza, 535 Kings Road, London
SW10 0SZ
Tel: 020 7221 990 Fax: 020 7352 1744
Executives: Joy Jameson, Jane Hearsey
Agents for Actors & Actresses.

ALEX JAY PERSONAL MANAGEMENT
8 Higher Newmarket Road, Newmarket, Nailsworth, Gloucestershire GL6 0RP
Tel/Fax: 01453 834 783
Email: alexjay@alex-jay-pm.freeserve.co.uk
Senior Personnel: Alex Jay
Specialising in artistes for film, television, theatre, commercials and TV & radio presenters.

ARTISTES REPRESENTED:
Dominic Cazenove
Paul Chan
Charlie McArdle (TV Presenter)
Wayne Sleep
Alex Tanner
Anne White
Leonard Whiting
Giselle Wolf

JAY BEE PROMOTIONS
200 Shetcliffe Lane, Bradford BD4 6QJ
Tel: 01274 683 564
Email: info@kissogrambradford.co.uk
Web Site: www.kissogrambradford.co.uk
Contact: Jeant Brogden
Male/female striptease abd stripograms, comedians, drag, male & female review shows. All forms of adult entertainment.

JAYCO ENTERTAINMENTS
53A Comber Road, Dundonald, Belfast, County Antrim BT16 2AA Northern Ireland
Tel/Fax: 028 9048 1783 Mobile: 07831 677912 (Jimmy Johnston)
Email: jaycokane@aol.com
Senior Personnel: Jimmy Johnston, Trevor Kane

JAZZABLE
41 Mount Pleasant Road, London
N17 6TR
Tel/Fax: 020 8808 1415 Mobile: 07939 252 241
Senior Personnel: Susan Jameson
Professional musicians available.
Specialising in duos.

JAZZCO
Formerly Dankworth Management
Ten Acre Farm, Stonehill Road, Ottershaw, Chertsey, Surrey KT16 0AQ
Tel: 08450 008 007 / 01932455904
Email: les@jazzco.co.uk
Web Site: www..jazzco.co.uk

ARTISTES REPRESENTED:
Kenny Ball & His Jazzmen
Best of British Jazz
Beverley Sisters
The Cotton Club Jazz Orchestra
Jacqui Dankworth & Her Musicians
The John Dankworth Quintet
Elaine Delmar And Her Quartet
"Ellingtonia"
Digby Fairweather's Half Dozen
The Ella Fitzgerald Songbook
The Giants Of Jazz
The Great British Jazz Band

Barb Junga & Her Musicians
Cleo Laine & John Dankworth
Terry Lightfoot & His Jazzmen
Don Lusher Big Band
The Humphrey Lyttelton Band
Remembers Humph & celebrates his music
Tina May & Her Musicians
George Melly with Digby Fairweather's Half-Dozen
The National Youth Jazz Orchestra (NYJO)
Pasadena Roof Orchestra
Courtney Pine
The Dave Shepherd Quintet
The Temperance Seven
Stan Tracey Quartet
Stan Tracey Octet

JB AGENCY ONLINE CASTING

Chelsea Business Centre,
73-77 Britannia Road, London SW6 2JR
Tel/Fax: 020 7751 0910
Email: info@jb-agency.com / darrel@ukast.co.uk
Web Site: www.jb-agency.com
Contacts: Darrel Mington, Christian Fletcher
Deals with featured players, walk-ons and extras for Film and TV. Commercials &d Photographic.

JB ASSOCIATES

4th Floor, Manchester House,
84-86 Princess Street, Manchester
M1 6NG
Tel: 0161 237 1808 Fax: 0161 237 1809
Email: info@j-b-a.net
Web Site: www.j-b-a.net
Senior Personnel: John Basham
Representing actors and actresses.

JB ENTERTAINMENTS

44 Beaumont Avenue, Southwell, Notts
NG25 0BB
Tel/Fax: 0115 923 5747 + 01636 812 369
Email: jbents.richard@tiscali.co.uk / jbentertainments@ntlworld.com
Senior Personnel: Richard Barratt / Jason Barratt / Nicola Barratt

ARTISTES REPRESENTED:

After Dark
Al Sinclair (Guitar Vocal)
Richard Comfort (Award-Winning Vocalist)
Decade
Robbie Dixon
Paul Friday
Dawn Fury
Girl Ambition
Karl Howard
Inez
Martin Lee Jordan
Katrice
Kellie Leish
Tony Rutherford
Sazzu
Terry Woodpecker

JEFFREY & WHITE

9-15 Neal Street, London WC2H 9PW
Tel: 020 7240 7000 Fax: 020 7240 0007
Email: jeffite@hotmail.com
Senior Personnel: Jeremy White, Judith Jeffrey

ARTISTES REPRESENTED:

Actresses:
Carolyn Allen
Eileen Battye
Helen Brampton
Karen Clegg
Janie Dee
Jacqueline Dutoit
Susan Fay
Jackie Fielding
Josefina Gabrielle
Rachel Hale
Frankie Jordan
Marjorie Keys
Jacqueline King
Ruby King
Beverly Klein
Vicki Lee Taylor
Illona Linthwaite
Sarah Manton
Gloria Onitin
Jo Powell
Roisin Rae
Nicola Sloane
Christine St John
Sin Svegler
Nicola Wainwright
Deborah Winckles
Rachel Wooding
Actors:
Paul Ansdell
Tony Boncza
John Burton
Bill Champion
Anthony Cozens
Ali Craig
Scott Cripps
Howard Crossley
Teddy Green
Leon Greene
Randal Herley
Adam Hills
James Hornsby
Bryan Kennedy
Colm Kirwen
David Lyms
Tam Mutu
Lloyd Notice
Morris Perry
Jack Power
Philip Ralph
Dudley Rogers
Paul Spicer
Marcello Walton
Nigel Williams
Peter Yapp

JERKIN CROCUS PROMOTIONS

87 Roedale Road, East Sussex Brighton
BN1 7GD
Tel: 020 8123 1794 Fax: 01273 883 974
Mob: 07802 290 864
Email: mick.jerkincrocus@googlemail.com
Web Site: www.jcplmusic.com
Contact: Michael Brown

JESSICA CARNEY ASSOCIATES

Fourth Floor, 23 Golden Square,
London W1F 9JP
Tel: 020 7434 4143 Fax: 020 7434 4173
Email: info@jcarneyassociates.co.uk
Web: www.jessicacarneyassociates.co.uk
Senior Personnel: J Carney
Represent Actors, Film and Television Technicians: DoPs, Editors, Designers and Associate Producers. CV in first instance. No unsolicited showreels please. If you are an actor, please only write if we can see your work in theatre in London, unless you have a substantial TV CV.

ARTISTES REPRESENTED:

Actors include::
John Burgess
Kathleen Byron
Geff Francis
Andrew Mackintosh
Jake Nightingale

JGM

15 Lexham Mews, London W8 6JW
Tel: 020 7376 2414 Fax: 020 7376 2416
Email: mail@jgmtalent.com
Web Site: www.jgmtalent.com
Senior Personnel: Jilly Moore, Hugh Galloway, Isabelle Desrochers

J.H. PROMOTIONS LTD

61 Crystal Avenue, Hornchurch, Essex
RM12 6SJ
Tel: 08707 557 667 Fax: 08707 557 677
Email: enquiries@jhpromotions.com
Web Site: www.jhprom.com
Events Director: Julie Howsego
Established in 1992, we offer a wide range of entertainment services for adults and children alike, on a nation-wide basis. From a Mix & Mingle magician to a full fun fair!

JILL MASSEY MANAGEMENT

2 Sydenham Cottages, Marvels Lane,
London SE12 9PQ
Tel: 020 8851 3386 Fax: 020 8851 1862
Email: jmhome@lycos.co.uk
Contact: Jill Massey

ARTISTES REPRESENTED:

Brenda Cochrane
Maz Polladino

JIM SANDWELL ENTERTAINMENTS LTD

2 Kent Avenue, Thornton-Cleveleys,
Lancashire FY5 2PS
Tel/ Fax: 01253 822442
Email: jseents@btinternet.com
Web: www.jimsandwellentertainments.co.uk
Contact: Derek & Julie Montgomery

JIMMY RETFORD'S AGENCY

9 St Leonards Maze Hill
St Leonard's on Sea TN38 0HN
Tel: 01424 716 669
Babs Retford

JIVE ENTERTAINMENT
PO Box 5865, Corby, Northamptonshire
NN18 9WY
Tel: 01536 743 366
Email: hoJive@aol.com
Senior Personnel: Dave Bartram
Secretary: Sue Carr
ARTISTES REPRESENTED:
Suzi Quatro
Showaddywaddy

JLA (JEREMY LEE ASSOCIATES LTD)
80 Great Portland Street London
W1W 7NW
Tel: 020 7907 2800 Fax: 020 7907 2801
Email: talk@jla.co.uk
Web Site: www.jla.co.uk
Senior Personnel: Jeremy Lee
ARTISTES REPRESENTED:
Lisa Aziz
Chris Barrie
David Bodanis
Guy Browning
Clive Bull
René Carayol
William Hague MP
Ian Hislop
Lee Hurst
Jiving Lindy Hoppers
John Lenahan
Hans Liberg
James Naughtie
John Pienaar
Jeff Stelling
Adrian Webster

JLM PERSONAL MANAGEMENT
4th Floor, Holburn Hall,
193-197 High Holborn, London
WC1V 7BD
Tel: 020 7025 0630 Fax: 020 7404 9865
Email: info@jlmpm.co.uk
Senior Personnel: Janet Malone, Sharon Henry, Sarah Lee
ARTISTES REPRESENTED:
Freema Agyeman
Antony Audenshaw
Donnaleigh Bailey
Sarah Baxendale
Tupele Dorgu
Rupert Hill
Derek Martin
Fay Masterson

JO SARSBY PR LTD
58 St Johns Road, Clifton Bristol
BS8 2HG
Tel: 0117 973 8589 Mob: 0778 810 8182
Email: jo@josarsby.com
Web Site: www.josarsby.com
Agent: Jo Sarsby
Specialising in factual broadcasters including some of the UK's most recognised presenters in their field.
ARTISTES REPRESENTED:
Benedict Allen
Steve Backshall
Lloyd Buck
Saba Douglas-Hamilton
Ellie Harrison
Miranda Krestovnikoff
Monty
Frank Pope
Mary Rhodes
Junior Saunders
Michaela Strachan

JOHN FIELD - THEATRE AND PUPPETRY
1 Grange House,
229 Stoke Newington Church Street,
London N16 9HL
Tel: 020 7690 7449
Email: johnfield.theatreandpuppetry@btinternet.com
The only agency in the UK dealing with puppetry and all its aspects. "If It Waggles - We Cover It". Ideal for indoor/outdoor corporate events.
ARTISTES REPRESENTED:
Puppeteers and Makers:
Sue Beattie
Sue Dacre
Geoff Felix
Ken Haines
Janet Knechtel
Nick Mercer
Sally Preisig
Melvyn Rawlinson
Ian Thom
Puppet Companies:
E.F. Productions
Geoff Felix Complete Punch & Judy Show
Ian and Friends
Jacolly Puppets
Jactito Theatre Co
Myths & Legwarmers
On The Other Hand Puppet Theatre Co
Parachute Theatre Co
Presto Puppets
Professor Popup
Prof John Styles
Rowan Wylie
Storytellers:
Dave Arthur's Storybox
Children's Theatre Co's:
Krazy Kat Theatre
Magic Mirror Theatre Co
Clowns & Mime:
Tim Bat Trick Show
Gingernutt the Clown
Dr Palfi Clown
Brendan Stapleton's Amazing Animates
Workshop Leaders:
Ken Haines
Melvyn Rawlinson
Adult & Family Entertainment:
Ken Haines' Moving Tales

JOHN OLIVER ORGANISATION
Catsash House, Catsash Road, Newport, Gwent NP18 1JQ
Tel: 01633 423 234 Fax: 01633 423 252
Email: john@johnoliverlive.com
Web Site: www.johnoliverlive.com
Contact: John Oliver.
Manages 'John Oliver Live' a 11 piece band does corprate and other function events. Also Manages String Mania (String quartet) - classical and pop. Bond Girl Tribute act.
ARTISTES REPRESENTED:
John Oliver Band and Singers
String mania

JOHN RATCLIFF
High Jarmany Farm Jarmany Hill,
Barton St. David, Somerton, Somerset
TA11 6DA
Tel: 01458 851187 Fax: 10458 851029
Email: johnratcliff@mac.com
Contact: John Ratcliff

PETER JOHNSON ENTERTAINMENTS LTD
Hastings Road, Hawkhurst, Kent
TN18 4RT
Tel: 01580 754 822 Fax: 01580 754 808
Email: enquiries@peterjohnson.co.uk
Web Site: www.peterjohnson.co.uk
Senior Personnel: Peter Johnson, Mandy O'Nion
Specialising in all forms of Outdoor Entertainments. Arena Entertainments, Mix 'n' Mingle,Corporate Participation Attractions and Music and Dance Groups.

JOKER ENTERTAINMENTS
Dwyfach Farm, Glanwyfach,
Garndolbenmaen, Gwynedd LL51 9LJ
Wales
Tel: 01766 530 726
Email: thejoker@btinternet.com
Web Site: www.thejoker.btinternet.co.uk
Contact: Susan Rayner
ARTISTES REPRESENTED:
Clown Bubbles (comedy act)
Los Ricardos (Knife Thrower/Fire Eater)
Miss Jemella (Exotic Python Act)
Baron Samedi (Lookalike)
Richard St John (Escapologist/Illusionist)

JON FOWLER MANAGEMENT LTD
JFM Ltd, 60a Highgate High Street,
London N6 5HX
Tel: 020 8348 1122Tel: 020 8340 9990
Mobile: 07789 000484
Email: jon@jonfowlermanagement.com
Agent: Jon Fowler
ARTISTES REPRESENTED:
Kelly Brook
Keeley Hazell
Holly Valance
TV Presenters:
Charlie Webster

JON HOLMES MEDIA LTD
Formerly Known as SFX Sports Group (Europe) Ltd
5th Floor, Holborn Gate,
26 Southampton Buildings, London
WC2A 1PQ
Tel: 020 7861 2550 Fax: 020 7861 3067
Email: dominic@jonholmesmedia.com
Web Site: www.jonholmesmedia.com

Senior Personnel: Jon Holmes, Diana Van Bunnens
Client Manager: Dominic Van Bunnens
Email Address for specific contact person: firstname@jonholmesmedia.com

ARTISTES REPRESENTED:
Broadcasters:
Jonathan Agnew
Mike Atherton OBE MA
Simon Brotherton
Peter Drury
David Gower OBE
Lesley Graham
Alan Hansen
Miles Harrison
Nasser Hussain OBE MA
Richard Keys
Gary Lineker OBE
Gabby Logan BA
Rebecca Lowe
Chloe Marshall
John Motson OBE
Guy Mowbray
Rishi Persad
Jim Rosenthal
Brough Scott MA
Rugby:
John Beattie
Kyran Bracken MBE LLB
Geoff Cooke OBE
Lawrence Dallaglio
Sean Fitzpatrick
Martin Johnson CBE
Kenny Logan
Geoff Miller
Brian Moore
Dewi Morris
Dean Richards
Victor Ubogo Bsc
Rory Underwood MBE
Tony Underwood BSc BA
JPR Williams
Yachting/Sailing:
Ben Ainslie
Tracy Edwards MBE
Cricket:
Dickie Bird MBE
Mike Brearley OBE
Chris Broad
Chris Cowdrey
Duncan Fletcher
Horse Racing:
Richard Dunwoody MBE
John Francome MBE
Jenny Pitman OBE
Walter Swinburn
Athletics:
Steve Backley MBE OBE
Roger Black MBE
Steph Cook MBE BM Bch MA
Lynn Davies MBE
Liz McColgan
Swimming:
Nick Gillingham MBE
Mountaineering:
Matt Dickinson
Golf:
Diane Barnard
Howard Clark
Polar Explorer:
Ann Daniels
Football:
Alan Ball MBE
John Barnes MBE
Peter Beardsley
Peter Beardsley
Jack Charlton OBE
Jimmy Hill OBE
Lawrie McMenemy
Peter Reid
Ian St John
Chris Waddle
Business:
Jon Holmes
Martin Glenn
Hamish McRae

LARRY JONES
Castle House 86 Teehey Lane, Wirral, Merseyside CH63 8QU
Tel: 0151 608 8503 Mob: 07851 023695
Email: handl.jones@btconnect.com
Contact: Larry Jones

ARTISTES REPRESENTED:
Larry Jones

JONGLEURS
20b Chancellors Street, Hammersmith, London W6 9RN
Tel: 0870 011 1205 Tel: 08700 111 890
Fax: 0870 011 1970
Email: dan.foley@jongleurs.com, info@jongleurs.com
Web Site: www.jongleurs.com
Senior Personnel: Maria Kempinska
Contact: Dan Foley
Representing Comedians.

ARTISTES REPRESENTED:
Blind Venetians
Paul Bloxham
Eddy Brimson
Crystal
Keith Fields
Dominic Frisby
Brian Higgins
Anthony King
Jamie Mathieson
Men in Coats
The Raymond and Mr Timpkins Revue
Rev Obadiah Steppenwolfe III

JS ENTERTAINMENTS
April Rise, Llanover Road, Blaenavon, Gwent NP4 9JQ Wales
Tel/Fax: 01495 790 619
Mobile: 07811 687850
Email: johnsmallmanents@aol.com
Senior Personnel: John Smallman

DAWN JUDD ENTERTAINMENTS
(Incorporating Jolly Roger Entertainments)
19 Ashness Gardens, Greenford, Middlesex UB6 0RL
Tel: 020 8902 3373 / 8903 5533 Fax: 020 8902 9538
Web Site: www.dawnjuddentertainments.co.uk
Senior Personnel: Dawn Judd

JUKES PRODUCTIONS LTD
PO Box 13995, London W9 2FL
Tel: 020 7286 9532 Fax: 020 7286 4739
Email: jukes@easynet.co.uk
Web Site: www.jukesproductions.co.uk
Senior Personnel: Geoff Jukes

ARTISTES REPRESENTED:
Kate Bush
Sir Bob Geldof
Jeanette Obstoj
Underworld

JUNCTION 2 MUSIC
28 Gaskarth Road London SW12 9NL
Tel: 020 8675 2501
Email: info@junction2music.com
Web Site: www.junction2music.com
Florence Arpin

K2 AGENCY LTD
4 Courtyard House Lensbury Avenue, London SW6 2TR
Tel: 020 7736 4948 Fax: 020 7471 4949
Email: janemiller@k2ours.com
Web Site: www.sanctuarygroup.com
Contact: John Jackson

KAL MANAGEMENT
95 Gloucester Road, Hampton, Middlesex TW12 2UW
Tel: 020 8783 0039 Fax: 020 8979 6487
Email: kaplan222@aol.com
Web Site: www.kaplan-kaye.co.uk
Senior Personnel: Kaplan Kaye, Beryl Kaye, Al Lampert

ARTISTES REPRESENTED:
Female:
Dawn Charatan
Sarah Cowan
Bryany Joan Elliot
Claire Harding
Jacqueline Joyce
Melody Kaye
Penny Lane
Catherine McCulloch
Kelly Philpott
Terri Scoble
Male:
Matt Berry
Martin Buchanan
Larry Dann
Peter Dean
Jonas3
Christopher Lafferty
Jeremy Milnes
Steve O'Toole
Timothy Page
Lex Van Delden
Geno Washington & The Ram Jam Band
Nigel Wild

KALEIDOSCOPE
75 Fernhurst Road, Portsmouth, Hampshire PO4 8AA
Tel: 0800 298 5499 Fax: 023 9229 7210
Email: info@kmusic.co.uk
Web Site: www.kmusic.co.uk
Contact: Andrew Mcvittie

ARTISTES REPRESENTED:
Mr Sketchum's Caricatures

ROBERTA KANAL AGENCY
82 Constance Road, Twickenham, Middlesex TW2 7JA
Tel: 020 8894 2277 Fax: 020 8894 7952
Senior Personnel: Roberta Kanal
ARTISTES REPRESENTED:
Madeleine Smith
Ursula Smith
Matt Zimmerman

KARUSHI MANAGEMENT
Unit 10, 7 Wenlock Road, London N1 7SL
Tel: 0845 900 5511 Fax: 0845 900 5522
Email: lisa@karushi.com
Web Site: www.karushi.com
Contact: Lisa Thomas, Victoria Lepper, Nathalie Laurent-Marke, Emily Saunders.
ARTISTES REPRESENTED:
Danny Bhoy
John Bishop
Jason Byrne
Mackenzie Crook
Richard Glover
Iain Lee
Adam Longworth
Jason Manford
Tom Price
Paul Tonkinson
Danny Wallace
Mark Watson

KBJ MANAGEMENT
5 Soho Square London W1D 3QA
Tel: 020 7434 6767 Fax: 020 7287 1191
Email: general@kbjmgt.co.uk
Web Site: www.kbjmgt.co.uk
Agent: Joanna Kaye
Corporate Booking Agent: Candida Alderson
ARTISTES REPRESENTED:
TV Presenters:
Simon Amstell
Alfie Brown
Dallas Campbell
Noami Clever
Millie Clode
Mark Durden-Smith
Emma Freud
Charles Hazlewood
Mishal Husain - Presenter
Natasha Kaplinsky
Martha Kearney
Charlie Luxton
Kevin McCloud
Dermot Murnaghan
Alex Proud
Danielle Proud
Rachel Riley
Helen Skelton
Michelle De Swarte
Marcel Theroux
Kirsty Wark
Claudia Winkleman
Kirsty Young

PAT KEELING MODEL AGENCY
38 Northgate Street, Leicester LE3 5BY
Tel: 0116 262 2540 Fax: 0116 253 7712
Email: pat@patkeelingagency.freeserve.co.uk
Web: www.patkeelingagency.freeserve.co.uk
Senior Personnel: Pat Keeling
Specialising in Modeling for Male, Female & Children. Fashion Shows, Photographic Promotions. TV & Video Work.

GORDON KELLETT ENTERTAINMENTS
Garden Cottage 4 Moor Flatts Road, Middleton, Leeds, West Yorkshire LS10 3SW
Tel: 0113 270 8562 / 2301
Fax: 0113 277 3267
Email: gordon@gordonkellett.co.uk
Web Site: www.gordonkellett.co.uk
Senior Personnel: Gordon & Joan Kellett
ARTISTES REPRESENTED:
5th Avenue
Larry Anderson
Carl Ashington
Baby Grande
Brad Bowers
Trisha Bright
Jonathan Carroll
Crazy Diamond
Bruce Deane
Paul Franks
Mick Gale
Kenny James
Sammie Jay
Tony Jordan
Phil Lawrence
Sasha Lawrence
Carol Lee
Joe Lloyd
Laura McCormick
Barbara Michaels
N-Joy
Ritchie Penrose
Diane Peters
Peter Phillips
Platonic
Mark Ritchie
Kathie Ryan
Shirley Ann Scott
Sister Sister
Rob Stevens
Paul Stewart
Maddie Storm
Debby Wyte

ROBERT C KELLY LTD
PO Box 5597 Glasgow, Strathclyde G77 9DH Scotland
Tel: 0141 533 5856
Email: robert@robertckelly.co.uk
Web Site: www.robertckelly.co.uk
Senior Personnel: Robert C Kelly
ARTISTES REPRESENTED:
Dean Park

KELLY'S KIND
Dance & Casting Agency
3rd Floor, 17-18 Margaret Street, London W1W 8RP
Tel: 020 7323 1489 Fax: 020 7323 4038
Email: info@kellyskind.co.uk
Web Site: www.kellyskind.co.uk
Senior Personnel: Kelly Colman, Angela Barnes
Suppliers of models, dancers and choreographers with special skills. Specialising in all kinds of shows from lingerie to swimwear to sport shows to hair shows.

THE KENNY BALL MANAGEMENT
Ten Acre Farm, Stonehill Road, Ottershaw, Woking, Surrey KT16 0AQ
Tel: 08707 544 544 Fax: 08707 545 545
Email: les@jazzco.co.uk
Web Site: www.jazzco.co.uk

KERNOW ENTERTAINMENTS
Aqua House 23 Tregoinggie Estate Falmouth Cornwall TR11 4SN
Tel: 01326 377 500/ 08454583311 Fax: 01326 377100
Email: enquiries@kernowentertainments.co.uk
Web: www.kernowentertainments.co.uk
Senior Personnel: Stephen K Gilbert, Graham M Bradshaw
ARTISTES REPRESENTED:
Bash Street Circus
Cyberstein Creations (Robotics)
Jazz Foundation
Kernow Pyrotechnics
Tony King
Platinum II
Vincent & Lee

JOHN KETTLEY
Television/Radio Weather Presenter
Weatherview House, 50 Beaumont Way, Hazlemere, High Wycombe, Buckinghamshire HP15 7BE
Tel: 01494 715 115 Fax: 01494 715 115
Email: kettley@britishweatherservices.co.uk
Web: www.britishweatherservices.co.uk
Contact: Jim Dale

KEY ENTERTAINMENT SERVICES
18 Heathwood Road, Bournemouth BH9 2JX
Tel: 01202 528135
Email: info@keyents.co.uk
Senior Personell: Jeremy Fearom

KIM HOLMES SHOW BUSINESS AGENCY
8 Charles Close, Ilkeston, Derbyshire DE7 5AF
Tel: 0115 930 5088 Fax: 0115 930 9636
Mobile: 07896 286 316
Email: kimholmesshowbiz@googlemail.com
Web Site: www.kimholmes.co.uk
Contact: Kim Holmes

ADRIAN KING ASSOCIATES

33, Marlborough Mansions, Cannon Hill, London NW6 1JS
Tel: 020 7435 4600 / 4700
Fax: 020 7435 4100
Email: akassocs@aol.com
Contact: Adrian King, Caroline Funnell
Acting Agency. We also represent a select number of Directors and Voice Over Artists - further details available on request.

ARTISTES REPRESENTED:

Female:
Julie Armstrong
Helena Blackman
Charon Bourke
Pamela Buchner
Karen Davies
Marissa Dunlop
Georgina Field
Jenny Galloway
Hannah Grover
Jennifer Guy
Sally Hunt
Melissa Jacques
Amanda-Jane Manning
Kathryn Pemberton
Helen Phelps
Pui Fan Lee
Pippa Sparkes
Anna Stranack
Martha Swann
Male:
Robert Archibald
David Baker
Simon Bishop
Andrew Branch
Mark Christopher
David Conville
Richard Costello
Matthew Lloyd Davies
Adrian Dixon
Toafique Folarin
Anthony Glennon
Abdi Gouhad
Gary Hailes
Jeffrey Harmer
Andrew Harrison
Gareth Heesom
Anthony Hunt
Andrew Hutchings
Nick Ingram
Kieran Jae
Benedict James
Nicholas Jordan
Richard Kent
Duncan Law
Simon McCoy
Jack McKenzie
Anthony Monjaro
Michael Neilson
Craig Perry
Stan Pretty
Paul Shelford
Peter Shorey
Ashley Stanton
Neal Swettenham
James Templeton
David Terence
Charlie Tighe
Tim Welton

KEVIN KING MANAGEMENT

16 Limetrees, Llangattock, Crickhowell, Powys NP8 1LB Wales
Tel: 01873 810 142
Email: kevinkinggb@aol.com
Web Site: www.silverword.co.uk
Senior Personnel: Kevin Holland King

ARTISTES REPRESENTED:

Jordan Adams
Ashmore
Kenneth Benson
Spike Breakwell
Kate Chapman
Crystalle
Carl Dean & Claudine
Michael Dimitri
Clive Edwards
Fausto Franco
Robert Garnay
Mike Gold
Guys n' Dolls
Jeff Hooper
Huron
Chris James
Jekyll & Hyde
Kevin King
Chris McGlade
Modern Romance
David Paramor
Peter Prince
Rockin Ron
Jerry Senfluk
The Southlanders
Lawrie Thompson

KING STREET GROUP PLC

Sheperds Building G12 Sheperds Studio, Rockley Road London W14 0DA
Tel: 0207 751 1155
Email: andy@kingstreetmedia.com
Contact: Andrew Wilkinson

KINGFISHER ENTERTAINMENTS

5 Maresfield Road PRESTON PR1 8ER
Tel: 01772 490 509
Email: lester@kingfisherentertainments.co.uk
Web: www.kingfisherentertainments.co.uk
Vickee Lester

KINSELLA ASSOCIATES

Victoria House Ack Lane East Bramhall SK7 2BE
Tel: 0800 999 9980
Email: kev@kinsellatax.co.uk
Contacts: Norma Kinsella, Kevin Kinsella FEAA, Kate Doherty

ARTISTES REPRESENTED:

Base Rate
Sara Brace
Frank Sidebottom
Snafu

KITCHENWARE MANAGEMENT

St Thomas Street Stables,
St Thomas Street, Newcastle-upon-Tyne, Tyne and Wear NE1 4LE
Tel: 0191 230 1970 Fax: 0191 232 0262
Email: info@kitchenwarerecords.com
Web Site: www.kitchenwarerecords.com
Manager: Keith Armstrong

ARTISTES REPRESENTED:

Kid;Coda
Lighthouse Family
Prefab Sprout
Sirens
The Motorettes

KM ENTERTAINMENTS

21 Bury Road, Gosport, Hampshire PO12 3UE
Tel: 023 9234 4444 Fax: 023 9234 4445
Email: acts@kmentertainments.co.uk
Contact: Mark Allen

ARTISTES REPRESENTED:

DJ Mark Chinnery
Chubby the Clown
Expresso
DJ Dave Hurst
Mr Sketchum's Caricatures
DJ Ashley Riggs
Scooter the Clown
DJ Andy Tullett

KNIGHT AYTON MANAGEMENT

114 St Martin's Lane, London WC2N 4BE
Tel: 020 7836 5333 Fax: 020 7836 8333
Email: info@knightayton.co.uk
Web Site: www.knightayton.co.uk
Agents: Sue Knight, Sue Ayton

ARTISTES REPRESENTED:

Male:
Peter Allen
Steve Allen
Matthew Bannister
Professor Brian Bates
Rob Bonnet
Michael Brunson
Michael Buerk
Paul Burden
Adrian Chiles
Huw Edwards
Mike Embley
Dr Niall Ferguson
David Fitzgerald
Sandy Gall
Adrian Goldberg
Liam Halligan
Allan King
James King
Nigel Leck
Dr. Armand Leroi
Martin Lewis
Colin McAllister
Sir Trevor McDonald
Lawrence McGinty
Dr. Scott Miller
Sir David Nicholas CBE
Nicholas Owen
Nick Owen
Julian Richards
Graham Rogers
Justin Ryan
Tim Sebastian
Adam Shaw
Peter Sissons
Jon Snow
Sir Roy Strong

Alex Thomson
Justin Webb
Female:
Samira Ahmed
Fiona Armstrong
Zeinab Badawi
Joan Bakewell
Carol Barnes
Jennie Bond
Rosie Boycott
Fiona Bruce
Prof Margaret Cox
Victoria Derbyshire
Maya Even
Jane Garvey
Prof Susan Greenfield
Nina Hossein
Mishal Husain - Presenter
Judi James
Sue MacGregor
Tessa Mayes
Rosie Millard
Susan Osman
Helena Frith Powell
Angela Rippon
Selina Scott
Mary Ann Sieghart
Catrina Skepper
Shelley Von Struckel
Moira Stuart
Tamzin Sylvester
Manisha Tank

RAY KNIGHT CASTING

21a Lambolle Place, Belsize Park, London NW3 4PG
Tel: 020 7722 1551 Fax: 020 7722 2322
Email: tony@rayknight.co.uk
Web Site: www.rayknight.co.uk
Senior Personnel: Tony Gerrard, Rachel Adamson, John Whelan, Judy Szucs

KNIGHTS ENTERTAINMENT LIMITED

121 London Road, Sawbridgeworth, Hertfordshire CM21 9JJ
Tel: 01279 725 862 Mobile: 07957 600873
Email: knightsentertainment@ntlworld.com
Web Site: www.knightsentertainment.com
Senior Personnel: John Robert Knight, Lorraine Knight
Agents for Bands, Duo Cabaret, Disco/Karaoke and Specialist Entertainment.

KRUGER COWNE LIMITED

Unit 18G Chelsea Wharf, 15 Lots Road, London SW10 0QJ
Tel: 020 7352 2277 Fax: 020 7900 6545
Email: info@krugercowne.com
Web Site: www.krugercowne.com
Director: Gina Nelthorpe-Cowne
Chief Executive Officer: Mark Cowne
Kruger Cowne represent the 'creme de la creme' of after dinner and public speakers, presenters, hosts or entertainers including Bob Geldof KBE, John Simpson CBE, Jamie Oliver, Sarah Duchess of York, Princess Michael of Kent, Uri Geller, Ruby Wax, Jerry Hall, Ranulph Fiennes KBE, OBE, Dr Jane Goodall DBE, John Sergeant, Martin Bell OBE and other top personalities.
Many of the people that we represent are also available for voice-over work for radio and television commercials, audio visual presentations and general narration.

ARTISTES REPRESENTED:

Martin Bell OBE
Ben Brown
Mariella Frostrup
Sir Bob Geldof
Harvey Goldsmith CBE
HRH Princess Michael of Kent
John Humphrys
Fergal Keane OBE
Sue Lawley OBE
Jamie Oliver
Sarah Duchess of York
John Simpson CBE
Ruby Wax

THE KRUGER ORGANISATION - TKO

PO Box 130, Hove, East Sussex BN3 6QU
Tel: 01273 550 088 Fax: 01273 540 969
Email: h.kruger@tkogroup.com
Web Site: www.tkogroup.com
Senior Personnel: Drn Jeffrey Kruger MBE, Howard Kruger
Specialising in Concert & Event Promotions and Management.

ARTISTES REPRESENTED:

Glen Campbell
Vic Damone
Zsa Zsa Gabor
Lanie Kazan
Marcy Lafferty
Al Martino
James Oliverio

KRYSTINA VARIETY AGENCY

251 Shinfield Road, Shinfield, Reading, Berkshire RG2 8HF
Tel: 0118 986 4135 / 0831 635 662 Fax: 0118 931 1219
Email: info@krystina.co.uk
Web Site: www.krystina.co.uk
Specialising in all types of Entertainment and Corporate Hospitality. Please call for further details.

MICHAEL LA ROCHE MANAGEMENT

PO Box 35, Bexhill, East Sussex TN40 2WA
Tel: 01424 216 400 Fax: 01424 223644
Email: mlr@michaellaroche.com
Web Site: www.michaellaroche.com
Providing tribute and revival shows, call for further details.

ARTISTES REPRESENTED:

Stan Boardman
Frank Carson KSG
The George Michael Band
Jimmy Jones
Bernard Manning
T-Rextasy
Taste of Honey (Bee Gees Tribute)
Utter Madness

BETTY LAINE MANAGEMENT

The Studios, East Street, Epsom, Surrey KT17 1HH
Tel/Fax: 01372 721 815
Email: enquiries@betty-laine-management.co.uk
Senior Personnel: Betty Laine, Rolph Patterson
Specialising in Dancers, Singers, Actors 16-45 Years.

LAINE MANAGEMENT LIMITED

Laine House, 131 Victoria Road, Hope, Salford, Lancashire M6 8LF
Tel: 0161 789 7775 Fax: 0161 787 7572
Email: elaine@lainemanagement.co.uk
Web Site: www.lainemanagement.co.uk
Senior Personnel: Elaine Greeley

ARTISTES REPRESENTED:

Alex Carter
Jo Gilgun
Rebecca Ryan (Shamless)

LANGFORD ASSOCIATES

17 Westfields Avenue, London SW13 0AT
Tel: 020 8878 7148 Fax: 020 8878 7078
Email: barry.langford@btconnect.com
Senior Personnel: Barry Langford

ARTISTES REPRESENTED:

Male:
Michael Tudor Barnes
Alexander Ellis
John Enthoven
Simon Gregson
Raji James
Michael Kazirakos
Sam Lathem
Tristan Oppenheimer
Oliver Oxley
Brendan Price
Clive Robertson
Doug Rollins
John Rose
Michael T Ross
Craig Russell
Daniel Schutzmann
Andy Steed
Mark Straker
Louis Tamone
Sam Vincenti
David Warwick
Simon Weybridge
Ross White
Female:
Amanda Brewster
Chrissie Cotterill
Jaq Croft
Ann Davies
Lynsey de Paul
Fenella Fielding
Felicity Finch
Juliette Kaplan
Helen Lederer
Aimie Macdonald

Zienia Merton
Jeanne Mockford
Brett O'Brien
Hazel O'Connor
Jane Partridge
Jacki Piper
Ingrid Pitt
Myra Sands
Alison Senior
Carolyn Seymour
Suzanne Sinclair
Mary Tamm
Sarah Thomas

LANGFORD PRODUCTIONS

Pentoby 8 Ladymead Lane, Langford, Bristol BS40 5EG
Tel: 01934 852822 Fax: 01934 853173
Email: heather@langfordproductions.co.uk
Web: www.langfordproductions.co.uk
Contact: Heather Kerr, Zena Simmons

LATIN ARTS SERVICES (LAS) MUSIC

PO Box 57817, London SE23 3PT
Tel/Fax: 020 8291 9236 Mobile: 07956 446342
Email: info@latinartsgroup.com
Web Site: www.latinartsgroup.com
Senior Personnel: Hector Rosquete
Latin entertainment promoters. Our new show is The Mambo Boyz Salsa Show.

ARTISTES REPRESENTED:

Afro Bloc
Afromambo Cuban Ensemble
Maricachi Aztlan
Brazil Tropical
Casa Latina
Conexion Latina
Conjuto Sabrosa
Oscar D'Leon
Espiritu Negro Drummers & Dancer Folk
Fiesta Latina
Flamenco Express
Guitarras Latinas
Gupo Azteca Mexican Mariachi
Gypsy Ensemble
Victor Hugo Latin Quartet
Victor Hugo's Salsa Show with the Picante Dancers
Kariba
King Salsa
La Clave
Latin Fiesta
Los Charros
Los Latinos
Los Soneros
Made in Brazil
The Mambo Boys
Ricky Martin
Palenque
Roberyto Pla Latin Jazz Band
Snowboy & the Latin Section
Spanish Classical Guitar
Tango Experience
Tropicalisimo (Latin Show)
Viramundo
Viva Flamenco
Viva Peru
Winyaya-pipes of the Andes
Yurupari Latin Dance Team

LATIN-TOUCH ENTERTAINMENTS

Fatima Community Centre, Commonwealth Avenue, London W12 7QR
Tel: 020 8740 9020 Fax: 020 8749 8903
Email: sales@latintouch.com
Web Site: www.latintouch.com
Senior Personnel: Rincon P Orlando

ARTISTES REPRESENTED:

Andes Music:
Amaru III
Antara
Duende
Katary
Mexican Folk Music:
Mariachi Chapala
Cuarteto Azteca
Los Charros
Mariachi Azteca
Paraguayan Folk Music:
Martin Chapman
Los Madrigales
Flamenco - Gypsy Kings Music:
Andalus (Gypsy Kings)
Gypsy Kingdom
Los Chicos
Brazilian Music:
Made in Brazil
Sarabanda
Zumbida
Hot-Salsa/Latin Jazz:
Casa Latina
Chiva Riva
Chocolate on Ice Cream
Conjuto Sabrosa
La Clave
Sexteto Cafe

TESSA LE BARS MANAGEMENT

54 Birchwood Road, Petts Wood, Orpington, Kent BR5 1NZ
Tel/Fax: 01689 837 084
Mob Tel: 07860 287 255
Email: tessa.lebars@ntlworld.com
Web Site: www.galtonandsimpson.com
Specialising in Mainly Comedy Writers. Member of Personal Managers Association. Existing Clients Only.

ARTISTES REPRESENTED:

John Antrobus
Ray Galton
Joe McGrath
Kjartan Poskitt
Barrie Shore
Alan Simpson

LEE NETWORK INTERNATIONAL LLP

Top Floor 206 Chalk Farm Road, Camden Lock Place London NW1 8AG
Tel: 020 7485 1001 Fax: 020 7485 1112
Email: ae@theleenetwork.com
Web Site: www.theleenetwork.com
Contact: Adam Elfin

WENDY LEE MANAGEMENT

Fourth Floor Suite, 40 Langham Street, London W1W 7AS
Tel: 020 7580 4800 Fax: 020 7580 8700
Email: wendy-lee@btconnect.com
Managing Director: Wendy Lee

ARTISTES REPRESENTED:

Ladies:
Marianne Adams
Julia G Addison
Rachael Atherton
Paula Coughtrie
Natasha Dunn
Kerry Enright
Damaris Fowler
Chloe Hughes
Tracy Kearney
Victoria Leigh
Natasha Lewis
Roma Malik
Lisa McDonald
Charlotte McKay
Hannah Murphy
Lisa Raynsford
Tata Real
Helen Reynolds
Lisa Roberts
Naomi Slater
Lucy Victory
Laura Yates
Gentlemen:
Alex Andrea
Paul Barrass
Terry Burns
Jamie Capewell
James Cowdery
Jose Cuenco Junior
Brett Goldstein
Mark Lawson
Lee Mead
Karl Moffatt
Stephen Pierre
Damian Pinder
Steven Rathman
Alex Scott-Fairley
Paul Symington

LEE'S PEOPLE

16 Manette Street, London W1D 4AR
Tel: 020 7734 5775 Fax: 020 7734 3033
Mobile: 07970 527252 / 527152
Email: lee@lees-people.co.uk
Web Site: www.lees-people.co.uk
Senior Personnel: Lee Towsey

JANE LEHRER ASSOCIATES

100A Chalk Farm Road, London NW1 8EH
Tel: 020 7482 4898 Fax: 020 7482 4899
Email: janelehrer@aol.com
Web Site: www.janelehrer.com
Senior Personnel: Jane Lehrer, Caz Swinfield

ARTISTES REPRESENTED:

Russell Floyd
Daren Elliot Holmes
Martino Lazzeri
Christine Mackie
Tony Selby
Sheridan Smith

LEIGH MANAGEMENT
14 St Davids Drive, Edgware, Middlesex HA8 6JH
Tel/Fax: 020 8951 4449
Email: leighmanagement@aol.com
Senior Personnel: Nathan Leigh, Michelle Leigh

LEIGHTON-POPE ORGANISATION
8 Glenthorne Mews
115a Glenthorne Road, London W6 0LJ
Tel: 020 8741 4453 Fax: 020 8741 4289
Email: andrew@l-po.com
Web Site: www.l-po.com
Contact: Carl Leighton-Pope, Andrew Leighton-Pope
ARTISTES REPRESENTED:
Sir Bob Geldof

THE LEIGHTON-POPE ORGANISATION
8 Glenthorne Mews,
115A Glenthorne Road, Hammersmith, London W6 0LJ
Tel: 020 8741 4453 Fax: 020 8741 4289
Email: carl@l-po.com / info@l-po.com
Web Site: www.l-po.com
Senior Personnel: Carl Leighton-Pope
ARTISTES REPRESENTED:
Bryan Adams
Chris Botti
Magic Of The Dance
Michael Bublé
Bonnie Tyler
Keith Urban

LEISURE MANAGEMENT
PO Box 48, Spennymoor,
County Durham DL16 7YL
Tel: 01388 420 050 Fax: 01388 420 037
Email: info@lmpresents.com
Web Site: www.lmpresents.com
Senior Personnel: Alan Leightell
ARTISTES REPRESENTED:
Production Shows/Concerts:
At the Hop!
Leah Bell's - Rock ' Roll ' Remember !
The Classic Soul Show
The Imposters - Ultimate 60's show
Magic - A Kind Of Queen
Rocky Meats The Blues
Show Groups:
The Booze Brothers
Juke Box Jive
L'Abba D'Abba
Piggies Show

LEMON TREE ENTERTAINMENT
Hamilton House, 8 Hamilton Close,
Prestwich, Manchester M25 9JS
Tel: 0161 773 1600 Fax: 0161 773 0508
Email: mail@lemontreeband.co.uk
Web: www.lemontreeentertainment.co.uk
Contact: Brian Warner, Maxine Warner.

LEO MANAGEMENT & AGENCY
PO Box 381, Wigan WN6 7WB
Tel: 01942 701 942 Fax: 01942 519091
Mob: 07951 051 814
Email: info@leomanagement.co.uk
Web Site: www.leomanagement.co.uk
Senior Personnel: John Baxendale FEAA, Steve Brennan
ARTISTES REPRESENTED:
Paul Abbot
Azure
Dante Ferrara
Mickey Gunn
Tom Jackson
Brendon McCormack
Damon Noone
Andy Prior & His Orchestra
Harry Robson
Schooner
Spanner in the Works
Streetlevel
Mike Summers Band
X-Etra

COLIN LEWIN MANAGEMENT
PO Box 891, Gerrards Cross,
Buckinghamshire SL9 0BS
Tel/Fax: 01494 874 326
Email: clm@enterprise.net
Web Site: www.andycollins.biz
Senior Personnel: Colin Lewin
ARTISTES REPRESENTED:
Andy Collins
Ian Royce

LEY ENTERTAINMENT PRODUCTIONS
14 Stanshaw Close, Frenchay, Bristol,
Avon BS16 1JY
Tel/Fax: 0117 956 5599
Web Site: www.tumblairs.com.uk
Senior Personnel: John Ley
ARTISTES REPRESENTED:
Ace Fun Trampolines
Jon "Lofty" Ley
Barbara Ley's Circus Trampoline Time
Rudolpho & His Amazing Bouncing Bed
The Wacky Tumblairs Comedy Trampoline Act

LIBERTY ENTERTAINMENTS
2 Burnleigh Gdns, New Milton, Hampshire BH25 5RE
Tel: 01425 621 682
Mobile: 07759 345 755
Email: libertyents@yahoo.co.uk
Senior Personnel: E Daniels.
All Types of Artistes for all occasion and venues.
ARTISTES REPRESENTED:
Dynamix Sound Entertainments
The Purple Puppets

LIME ACTORS AGENCY AND MANAGEMENT LTD
Nemesis House, 1 Oxford Court,
Manchester M2 3WQ
Tel: 0161 236 0827 Fax: 0161 228 6727
Email: georgina@limemanagement.co.uk
Contact: Georgina Andrew
The company specialises in the representation and management of leading actors.
ARTISTES REPRESENTED:
Male:
Akeel Ahmed
Armand Beasley
Steve Bell
Mike Burns
Justin Burrows
Les Caffrey
Simon Cassidy
Adam Colclough
Glen Cunningham
Paul Darby
Chris Finch
Mark Foutain
Liam Fox
Keith French
Matthew Ganley
Steve Garti
Trevor Hancock
Chris Hargreaves
Paul Hine
Ellis Hollins
Adil Mohammed Javed
Anthony Kavanagh
Christian Knott
Adam Lowe
Garth Maunders
Kevin McGowan
Anthony Merna
Greg Milburn
Ali Natkiel
Alan Neal
Rob Norbury
Rodney Paulden
Martin Potter
Kieron Richardson (Hollyoaks actor)
Mark Rigby
Darrell Scott
Peter Sheath
Leslie Simpson
Matt Southall
Joe Standerline
Pierce Starre
Steve Swift
Danny Thornton
Sam Townend
Tom Vaughan
Mark Whiteley
Alex Yates
Adam Zane
Female:
Melanie Ash
Randeep Assi
Nicole Barber-Lane (Myra, Hollyoaks)
Jade Bishop
Lucy Bowen
Hollie Bowes
Christine Brennan
Kayleigh Brown
Sarah Jane Buckley
Catherine Calloway
Tiffany Chapman
Robyn Charlesworth
Nikki Cohen
Lynsey Coleman
Sarah Jane Cottrell
Elisa Cowley
Amanda Crossley

Tara Daniels
Kate Deakin
Jacqueline Dillon
Enid Dunn
Daryl Fishwick
Julie Fountain
Vicky Gates
Nicola Gossip
Suzanne Hall
Gemma Harvey
Debbie Howard
Jacquelyn Hynes
Faye Jenelle
Chantelle Joseph
Caroline Kennedy
Gina Lamb
Clare Lever
Janet Marsh
Katie Matthews
Kate McCann
Faye McLaughlin
Gemma Merna (Carmel, Hollyoaks)
Nina De Mitri
Samantha Montgomery
Sonya Louis Morris
Laura Oldham
Amy O'Neil
Monica Patel
Gabriella Peeters
Karen Rosario
Katie Ross
Debbie Rush
Poppy Rush
Sarah Totty
Emma Vaudry
Joanne Venet
Amy Walsh
Karen West
Lisa Whiteside
Stacey Winfield

LIMELIGHT MANAGEMENT

33 Newman Street, London W1T 1PY
Tel: 020 7637 2529 Fax: 020 7637 2538
Email: linda.limelightmanagement@virgin.net
Web: www.limelightmanagement.com
Senior Personnel: Fiona Lindsay, Linda Shanks
Celebrity Management company and Literary Agency.

ARTISTES REPRESENTED:

Julie Arkell
Helen Atkinson Wood
Ed Baines
Mary Berry
Ginny Blom
John Bly
Steve Bradley
Tessa Bramley
Barbara Griggs
Salvatore Calabrese
Adam Caplin
Pat Chapman
Oz Clarke
Nigel Colborn
Ursula Ferrigno
Sue Fisher
Paul Gayler
Bill Giles
Mary Gilliatt
Jo Glanville Blackburn
Jerry Harpur
Paul Hayes
Alastair Hendy
Dr Rob Hicks
David Joyce
Fiona Kennedy
Noel Kingsbury
Kisen
Louise Lear
Madeleine Marsh
Arne Maynard
Penny Meadmore
Stephanie Meadows
Sally Morgan
Jim Murray
Paula Pryke
Paul Rankin
Val Sampson
James Alexander Sinclair
David Stevens
Sonia Stevenson
Anne Swithinbank
James & Chris Tanner
Michael Van Straten
Lesley Waters
Antony Worrall Thompson
Aldo Zilli

LINCOLN MANAGEMENT (UK) LTD

LMG Building 2 Tritton Road, Lincoln LN6 5LN
Tel: 01522 508355 Fax: 01522 689984
Email: entertainment@lmg.uk.com
Web Site: www.lmg-entertainments.co.uk
Contacts: Joanne Makepeace, Karen Hays, Marian Bryans

LINE MUSIC PROMOTIONS

19 Captains Close, Sutton Valence, Kent ME17 3BA
Tel: 01233 333 435
Mobile: 07711 166 817
Email: linemusic2k@aol.com
Director: Jon Keys
Specialising in: Country Music Acts

ARTISTES REPRESENTED:

Pinto Bennett
Roger Humphries and Bite the Bullet
Glenn Rogers Experience
Joe Sun

LINE-UP PMC

10 Matthew Close, Newcastle upon Tyne NE6 1XD
Tel / Fax: 0191 275 9745
Mob: 07808 300 906
Email: chrismurtagh@line-up.co.uk
Web Site: www.line-up.co.uk
Senior Personnel: Chris Murtagh

ARTISTES REPRESENTED:

Adisa
After Eden
Apu
The Baghdaddies
Big Fun Club
Black Voices
Coco Vega Y Latinos Salsa Band
Merry-May Gill
Macumba
The Mugenkyo Taiko Drummers
Urgent Live Turkeys
Bobby Valentino
Hank Wangford & The Lost Cowboys

LINKS MANAGEMENT

34-68 Colombo Street, London SE1 8DP
Tel/Fax: 020 7928 0806
Email: agent@links-management.co.uk / Links@eidosnet.co.uk
Web Site: www.links-management.co.uk
Contact: John Hollaway

ARTISTES REPRESENTED:

Actors:
Andrew Barron
Rafe Beckley
Michael Grinter
Antony Jardine
John Paton
Actresses:
Vivienna Garnett
Adanna Oji
Alicia Swordes
Sarah Waddell

LINKSIDE AGENCY

21 Poplar Road, Leatherhead, Surrey KT22 8SF
Tel: 01372 802 374 / 378 398
Email: linksideagency@yahoo.co.uk
Senior Personnel: Eileen Wellings, Fiona Fisher-Greene

ARTISTES REPRESENTED:

Women:
Maria Bergman
Tatyana Colombo
Clare Day
Ellen Holden
Alannah Davis Kelly
Catherine Lake
Samantha Lee
Lulu Miller
Krysha O'Sullivan
Jennifer Page
Helen Pritchard
Annette Ross
Samantha Waddilove
Cassie Wadsworth
Pauline Walker
Amy Westgarth
Maureen Younger
Men:
Dominic Fowler
Nicholas John
Alistair Kelly
Mark Lambourne
Barry Rocard
Tim Rowland
Graham Sandry
Alex Surguy

LINTON MANAGEMENT

3 The Rock, Bury, Lancashire BL9 0JP
Tel: 0161 761 2020 Fax: 0161 761 1999
Email: carol@linton.tv
Senior Personnel/Agent: Carol Godby
Represents adult actors, child actors and background artists.

ARTISTES REPRESENTED:
Sam Aston (Chesney, Coronation Street)
Liz Avis
Jessica Baglow
Rebecca Bellamy
Liam Boyle
Nichola Burley
Katy Clayton
Rico Dixon
Lauren Drummond
Helen Flanagan
Gerogia Foote
Chris Fountain (Justin, Hollyoaks)
Jazmine Franks
Nicola Headley
Amber Hodgkiss
Paul Holowaty
Oliver Hudson
Casey Lee Jolleys
Junaid Khan
Lucien Laviscount
Maria Mescki
Katy Ross
Nikki Sanderson
Ben Thompson
Elliot Tittensor
Luke Tittensor
Lee Worswick

LIP SERVICE CASTING LIMITED
60-66 Wardour Street, London W1F 0TA
Tel: 020 7734 3393 Fax: 020 7734 3373
Email: bookings@lipservice.co.uk
Web Site: www.lipservice.co.uk
Also a roster of Foreign Artistes. Call for further details.

ARTISTES REPRESENTED:
Male:
Mark Arden
Nick Ball
Quint Boa
Steve Brody
Peter Capaldi
Charlie Condou
Paul Danan
Hugh Dennis
James Dreyfus
Neil Dudgeon
Paul Mark Elliott
Jack Fortune
Iain Fraser
Dan Freeman
Steve Frost
Aden Gillett
Nicholas Gleaves
Demetri Goritsas
John Hannah
Andy Harrison
Lloyd Hutchinson
Richard Huw
Paterson Joseph
Hugh Laurie
Eric Loren
Dominic Mafham
John Pickard
Alexei Sayle
Simon Schatzberger
Liam Shannon
Michael Smee
David Soul
Ray Stevenson
Colin Stinton
Jamie Theakston
Paul Viragh
Julian Wadham
Female:
Amanda Abbington
Holly Best
Rob Carroll
Julienne Davis
Janet Dibley
Susannah Doyle
Emma Ferguson
Pam Ferris
Judy Flynn
Christopher Fulford
Louise Gold
Beverley Hills
Gillian Kirkpatrick
Doon Mackichan
Dan Morgan
Helen Parkinson
Amanda Redman
Alex Reeves
Joanna Roth
Sue Scott-Davison
Sheila Steafel
Amanda Symonds
Frances Tomelty
Jo Unwin
Paul Viragh
Arabella Weir
Tessa Wojtczak

LITTLE TONE PROMOTIONS
Unit 1, Perfecta Works, Bordesley Street, Birmingham B5 5PG
Tel/Fax: 0845 124 9758 Mobile: 07976 916 208
Email: info@littletone.co.uk
Web Site: www.littletone.co.uk
Contact: Tony Diponio
Sports and entertainment promotions company.

LIVE BUSINESS GROSVENOR PRODUCTIONS
136-144 New Kings Road Fulham
London SW6 4LZ
Tel: 020 7384 2050
Email: jobs@livebusiness.co.uk
Web Site: www.livebusiness.co.uk
Contact: Peter Chittenden, Blain Fairman, Mark Dixon
Supplying entertainment of all kinds to the leisure industry and corporate clients as well as to individual private events.

LIVE MUSIC MANAGEMENT LTD
Meden Cottage TopRow, Pleasley Vale
Nottingham NG19 8RN
Tel: 08454 900515 Fax: 08454 900514
Email: tim@lmmuk.com
Web Site: www.lmmuk.com
Contact: Tim Sponder

LIVE PROMOTIONS LTD
Riverside Quay, Double Street, Spalding, Lincolnshire PE11 2AB
Tel: 01775 768 661 Fax: 01775 768 665
Email: enquiries@livepromotions.co.uk
Web Site: www.truckfest.co.uk
Managing Director: Colin Ward
Specialising in: Outdoor Entertainment & Celebrities. The UK's leading automotive event specialists.

ARTISTES REPRESENTED:
Geoff Capes

LIZ HOBBS GROUP LIMITED
65 London Road, Newark,
Nottinghamshire NG24 1RZ
Tel: 08700 702 702 Fax: 08703 337 009
Email: casting@lizhobbsgroup.com
Web Site: www.lizhobbsgroup.com
Chief Executive: Liz Hobbs
Assistant: Cherrie Rollerson
Artist Management: Harriet Robson
Exclusive management and agency for actors, presenters & entertainers. Events - concerts, hospitality events, themed events. Producers - theatrical productions, corporate videos.

ARTISTES REPRESENTED:
Cheryl Baker
Justin Barley
Luke Baxter
Emma Bentley
Paul Burnham
Danielle Campbell-Scott
Colin Carmichael
Vicki Carr
Debbie Chapman
Darren Clewlow
Gary Croome
Paul Darby
Jack Edwards
Lucinda Gill
Lesley Graham
Murray Grant
Sheree Headington
Frazer Hines
Liz Hobbs MBE
Matt Hodgson
Lionel Jeffries
Gary Jordan
Hayley Longhurst
Francis Lunn
Chris McDonnell
Verity Anne Meldrum
Louise Michelle
Vicki Michelle
Anj Mukerji
Sean Oliver
Stephen Paget
Amanda Redington
Kathryn Rooney
Sanjay Sag
Anna Southgate
Mark Taylor
Derek Thompson
Daniel Woodhouse

LJ ENTERTAINMENTS
1 Lincoln Road, Blackpool Lancashire
FY1 4HA
Tel/Fax: 01253 292543
Email: ljents@hotmail.co.uk
Proprietor: Shaun McGilloway

ARTISTES REPRESENTED:
Lisa Cassidy
Deuce Duo
Georgia & The McSmiths
Becky Jay
Rob Johnstone
Michael Kane
Johnny Mac
Sean MacRae
Lee Roberts
Dave Surman
Paul Topham
Ronnie West
Stephanie Young

LM2 ENTERTAINMENT
P.O. Box 57619, London NW7 0BX
Tel/Fax: 020 8349 1933
Email: info@lm2.co.uk
Web Site: www.lm2.co.uk
Contact: Brad Lazarus
ARTISTES REPRESENTED:
Ray Gelato
The Leo Green Experience
Dominic Halpin & The Honey B's
Shwing
The Jazz Canons

L.O.E. ENTERTAINMENT LTD
L.O.E. House 159 Broadhurst Gardens,
London NW6 3AU
Tel: 020 7328 6100 Fax: 020 7624 6384
Email: kato@loe.uk.net
Web Site: www.loe.uk.net
Senior Personnel: Hidoto Watanabe

LONDON MUSIC AGENCY
7 Rosewood Drive, Orchard Heights
Ashford, Kent TN25 4QF
Tel: 01233 623 623 Mob: 07885 032 132
Email: enquiries@londonmusicagency.co.uk
Web: www.londonmusicagency.co.uk
Proprietor: Jenny Braby
Everything in entertainment for Private and Corporate functions, e.g. Jazz, String Quartets and all types of band, music and the unusual.
ARTISTES REPRESENTED:
Academy
Claudio Allodi Italian Ensemble
Andalus (Gypsy Kings)
Anna & José León
Bob Ash
Balalaika
Barrel Organ
Maria Beattie
Big Al's Jazzers
Boogie Nights Band
Danny Bravo
Matthew Brown
Cameo Dancers
Carlin Discotheques
Keith "The Thief" Charnley
David Cheney
Jonny Clarke
Cockney Pride
Rick Colman
Ray Cooper (Close Up Magic)
Corazon Flamenco
Keith Cross
Nick Crown
Andy Cunningham
Gabrielle Dall-Olio
Gavin Davey
Andy Davy
Debbie Boyd Band
Diamond Fun Casinos
Dragonsfire
Hayley Dredge
Ray Durrant
Gary Edwards
Simon Ellinas
Richard Elmes
Alan Evans
Jennie Fitzgerald
Five Go Jiving
Robert Freeman
Frog Island Jazz Band
Gaelic Hat
Joe Goodman
Emma Granger
Glen Grant
Gwalia Welsh Male Voice Choir
Highlife
Hula Bluebirds
International Fun Casinos
David Jackson
Jambalaya
Mike James Band/Sound
Jan Steele Latin Jazz Band
Jazz Chill
Jump Jive
Kaiso
Kemistry Duo
Bob Kerr's Whoopee Band (Jazz & Comedy)
Steve Lane's Southern Stompers
Roger Limb
Louis Lintz Jelly Roll Jazz Band
Locarno Big Band
Luton Male Voice Choir
Terry Machin
Mariachi Azteca
Marrakesh Express
Anthony Mason
Mazaika
Midnight Oasis
Minstrels Gallery
Roger Montgomery
Mr Toots
New Digswell Banjo Band
Original Blend
The Pasadena Roof Orchestra
Jed Pascoe
Danielle Perrett
The Piccadilly Dance Orchestra
Russ Pinder
Polished Brass
Malcolm Povah
David Price
David Price Hot Jazz Trio/Quartet
Emma Ramsdale
Rebound
Reduced Brass Band Company
John Richard
Peter Rudeforth Ensemble
Steve Russell
Sahara
Shaky Jake
Oliver Sheen
Slimline Tonic Discos
Solid Steel
Jonathan Stevens
Strings Attached
Harry Strutter's Hot Rhythm Orchestra
The O'Reely's
Keziah Thomas
Stanley Toohey
Tziganka - Russian Cossack Music & Dance Spectacular
Versatile Vocab
Jonathan Vinten
Viva Flamenco
Welwyn Garden City Male Voice Choir
Welwyn Harmony
David Wood OBE
Wraggle Taggle Ceilidh Band
Richard Wymark
Peter York Trio

LONDON MUSICIANS LTD
Cedar House, Vine Lane, Hillingdon,
Uxbridge, Middlesex UB10 0BX
Tel: 01895 252 555 Fax: 01872 863 557
Email: mail@londonmusicians.co.uk
Senior Personnel: Naomi Furihata
Musicians for film, recording and theatre.

THE LONDON SPEAKER BUREAU
Elsinore House, 77 Fulham Palace Road,
London W6 8JA
Tel: 020 8748 9595 Fax: 020 8741 8723
Email: tom@londonspeakerbureau.co.uk
Web: www.londonspeakerbureau.co.uk
Senior Personnel: Tom Kenyon-Slaney, Brendan O'Connor, Lucinda Swan
Specialising in Business and Political Speakers.
ARTISTES REPRESENTED:
Sir Christopher Bland
Joe DiVanna
Anna Ford
Bear Grylls
Ken Hames
Charles Leadbeater
Ben Saunders
Sir Gerry Robinson
Robert Swan OBE
Sir Alan West
Dr Linda Yueh
Dr Mohammad Yunus

LONGRUNARTISTS
Marylebone Dance Studios
12 Lisson Grove, London NW1 6TS
Tel: 0207 258 0767 Fax: 0207 258 1868
Email: producer@ukfd.co.uk
Web Site: www.longrunartistes.co.uk
Contact: Gina Long, Irene Wernli

LOOK WHO`S TALKING
PO Box 3257 Ufton, Leamington Spa,
Warwickshire CV33 9YZ
Tel: 01926 614443 Fax: 01926 614156
Email: ian@look-whos-talking.co.uk
Web Site: www.lookwhostalking.net
Contact: Ian Holroyd

JOE LOSS LTD
89 North Gate, Prince Albert Road, London NW8 7EJ
Tel/Fax: 01932 858 246
Senior Personnel: Mildred B Loss
Provides all kinds of music.
ARTISTES REPRESENTED:
Todd Miller And The Joe Loss Orchestra & Singers
The Joe Loss Ambassadors
The Phil Allen Sound

LOU COULSON ASSOCIATES
1st Floor, 37 Berwick Street, London W1F 8RS
Tel: 020 7734 9633 Fax: 020 7439 7569
Email: lou@loucoulson.co.uk
Agent: Lou Coulson
ARTISTES REPRESENTED:
Gary Beadle
Sanjeev Bhaskar
Deborra-Lee Furness
Julie Hesmondhalgh
Scarlett Johnson
Alex Kingston
John McArdle
Victor McGuire
Gretchen Mol
Alfred Molina
Cillian Murphy
Jim Norton
Andy Serkis
Carol Starks
Joanne Whalley
Tom Wilkinson

LOUISE DYSAN AT VISABLE PEOPLE - DISABLED ARTISTS
P.O. Box 80 Droitwich, WR9 0ZE
Tel: 01386 555 170
Email: louise@visablepeople.com
Web Site: www.visablepeople.com
Contact: Louise Dyson
VisABLE is the UK's first professional agency representing only actors and models with disabilities.

LOUISE GUBBAY ASSOCIATES
26 Westmore Road, Tatsfield, Westerham, Kent TN16 2AX
Tel: 01959 573080
Email: louise@louisegubbay.com
Web Site: www.louisegubbay.com
Managing Director: Louise Gubbay

LOVETT LOGAN ASSOCIATES
5 Union Street, Edinburgh EH1 3LT Scotland
Tel: 0131 478 7878 Fax: 0131 478 7070
London Address: 40 Margaret Street London W1G 0JH Tel: 020 7495 6400 Fax: 020 7495 6411
Email: london@lovettlogan.com
Email: edinburgh@lovettlogan.com
Web Site: www.lovettlogan.com
Senior Personnel: Pat Lovett, Dolina Logan

LRO ARTIST MANAGEMENT
PO Box 492, Weston-super-Mare, Avon BS23 9BU
Tel: 01934 521 222 / 01934 417 806
Fax: 01934 521 333
Email: lrowsm@btconnect.com
Web Site: www.lroents.com
Senior Personnel: Gary Gratton
ARTISTES REPRESENTED:
Bryan Adams Tribute Show
Rob Angelo
Beauty & The Beast
Cocktail Trio
Cody
Mike Cox
Kimberley Dayle (Britney Spears & Christina Aguilera Tribute)
Tribute to Buddy Holly (Ind Art)
Jacqueline
Jerusha
Kenny K
Kerry's Gold
Kickback Band
Steve Lawrence
Legend
Manhatten Nights
Natasha
Pete Le Feet
Rudy The Soul Man
Souled Out
The Two Beatles
Ryan Turner

LUCAS MANAGEMENT
14 Promenade North, Thornton Cleveleys, Blackpool, Lancashire FY5 1DB
Tel: 01253 851 444 Fax: 01253 851 777
Email: info@lucasmanagement.co.uk
Web Site: www.lucasmanagement.co.uk
Senior Personnel: Barrie Lucas, Vicci Lucas
ARTISTES REPRESENTED:
The American Drifters
The Flirtations
Ricky Lee
Rob Malone
Soul Satisfaction Four Tops Show

LULU LE VAY
Mobile Tel: 07956 945 847
Email: lulu@lululevay.com
Web Site: www.lululevay.com
Agent: Lulu Levay
ARTISTES REPRESENTED:
Louie Austen
George Demure
Spektrum

MARK LUNDQUIST MANAGEMENT & CONCERT PROMOTIONS
5 Tuckey Grove, Send Marsh, Ripley, Surrey GU23 6JG
Tel: 01483 224 118 Mobile: 07971 401510 Fax: 01483 479 417
Email: mark@marklundquist.com
Web Site: www.marklundquist.com
Contact: Mark Lundquist
Press And Marketing Officer: Canada Hepp
Established in 1990. Mark Lundquist specialises in personal representation of major recording artistes and bookings for Theatres, Art Centres, Festivals, Clubs, Corporate & Private Functions WORLD-WIDE.
ARTISTES REPRESENTED:
Bev Bevans
Billie Holiday - Strange Fruit
The Cavern Beatles
The Commitments
The Drifters
Hot Chocolate
John Miller and his Orchestra
Los Pacaminos
Mercury - The Queen Tribute
Motown Show
One Step Behind (Madness tribute)
The Real Abba Gold
Rockin' On Heaven's Door
T Rextasy
The Jones Gang
Vogue-Experience Madonna

THE LUXFACTOR GROUP (UK)
Fleet Place, Nelson Drive, Petersfield, Hampshire GU31 4SJ
Tel: 0845 370 0589 Fax: 0845 370 0588
Email: info@luxfactor.co.uk
Web Site: www.luxfactor.co.uk
Managing Director & Agent: Michael D. Finch
Primarily representing Lighting, Sound, Video, Set, Costume and Scenic Designers, LUXFactor picks up where others are left bewildered. With clients on four continents we truly are an international agency. LUXFactor Client Management operates on a flexible international timeline status and during "theatre' hours too!

DENNIS LYNE AGENCY
108 Leonard Street, London EC2A 4RH
Tel: 020 7739 6200 Fax: 020 7739 4101
Email: info@dennislyne.com
Senior Personnel: Dennis Lyne
ARTISTES REPRESENTED:
Actresses:
Pauline Black
Julia Dalkin
Josephine Melville
Rynagh O'Grady
Gwyneth Powell
Kate Rawson
Judith Sharp
Maggie Wells
Actors:
Richard Attlee
Chris Barnes
Patrick Brennan
Carl Chase
Gareth Cooper
Darren Greer
Paul Hampton
Clive Hayward
J.D. Kelleher
John Labanowski
Peter Lindford

David Maccreedy
Simon Nock
Danny Nutt
Michael Starke
Antony Strachan
Simon Tcherniak
Bill Wallis
Fergus Webster
Lighting Cameraman:
Stephen Macmillan
Costume Designer:
Clare Mitchell
Theatre Directors:
Michael Elwyn
Richard Georgeson
Wyn Jones
Judith Sharp
Simon Usher
Steven Wrentmore
Theatre Designers:
Sarah Blenkinsop
Kate Burnett
Angela Davies
Annabel Lee
Francis O`Connor
Alice Purcell
Caroline Scott
Libby Watson
Lighting Designers:
Tanya Burns
Rick Fisher
Peter Higton
Paul Russell
Production Designers:
Frank Conway
Angela Davies

M C S ENTERTAINMENTS
Beckford Business
Unit 10, Beckford Street HAMILTON
ML3 0BT
Tel: 01698 401 310
Email: john@mcsentertainments.co.uk
JOhn Cummiskey

M F MANAGEMENT LTD
55 Newman Street London W1T 3EB
Tel: 020 3291 2929 Fax: 020 3291 2925
Email: mfmall@mfmanagement.com
Web Site: www.mfmanagement.com
ARTISTES REPRESENTED:
Alexander Armstrong
Alan Davies
Laurence Fox
Celia Imrie
Patrick Kielty
Michael Kitchen
Janet McTeer
Parminder Nagra
Sam Neill
Jeremy Northam
Billie Piper
Anna Richardson
Jenny Seagrove
Stellan Skarsgard
Ken Stott

M G ENTERTAINMENTS
11 Kirkless Villas Cale Lane WIGAN
WN2 1HQ
Tel: 01942 494 757
Email: wendymgents@btinternet.com
Wendy Sweeney

M W MANAGEMENT
11 Old School Court Drapers Road
London N17 6PZ
Tel: 020 8376 2025 / 020 8376 5358
Email: pm015d6080@blueyonder.co.uk
Contact: Peter McCulloch
ARTISTES REPRESENTED:
Men:
David Antrobus
Shane Attwooll
Rick Bland
David Bluestone
Ian Brooker
H Ben Campbell
Carl Coleman
Michael Conrad
Marc Danbury
Peter Dineen
John Dorney
Paul Downing
Michael Dylan
Peter Edbrook
John Fleming
Michael Geary
John Gower
Jeffrey Harmer
Basil Hoskins
Sidney Kean
Russell Kilmister
Duncan Law
Mark Lingwood
Peter McMichael
Tim Meats
Terry Molloy
David Monico
John Moraitis
Andi Jon Narsi
Stephen Pallister
Maurey Richards
Sanjit Sil
Howard Southern
Andrew James Spooner
Roman Stefanski
Mark Trotman
Adam Warren
Ron Welling
Women:
Holly Ashton
Lois Burgess
Harriet Cater
Julia Chapman
Elizabeth-Ann Conlon
Sara Coward
Kareena Dainty
Nicola Delaney
Sue Freebury
Joyce Gibbs
Rhian Grice
Allison Harding
Clarke Hayes
Beth Hayward
Alexandra Hogg
Barbara Horne
Rebekah Janes
Sunna Jarman
Theresa Kartell
Anne Kavanagh
Victoria Little
Melanie MacHugh
Joanna Mackie
Sarah Nash
Sunny Ormonde
Janet Pate
Drina Pavlovic
Donna Pickup
Katrina Ramsay
Penelope Rawlins
Jenny-Ann Topham
Ellen Wilkinson
Joyce Windsor
Rachel Woolrich

M.A.P. AGENCY
Ashfield House, 50 Sutton Lane, Byram,
Knottingley, West Yorkshire WF11 9DP
Tel: 01977 675 052 Fax: 01977 675 053
Email: map.agency@sky.com
Senior Personnel: William Bastow

M.B.M. CORPORATE LIMITED
Labrican Healey Dell Nature Reserve
Rochdale, Lancashire OL12 6BG
Tel: 01706 524425
Email: info@mbmcorporate.co.uk
Web Site: www.mbmcorporate.co.uk
Contact: Anne Barrett

M.S. ENTERTAINMENT GROUP
160 Bybrook Road, Kennington, Ashford,
Kent TN24 9JG
Tel/Fax: 01227 367 310 Tel: 01233 610
023
Email: m.sentertainment@amserve.com
Web Site: www.msentertainment.com
Senior Personnel: Mr Malcolm Sprawling
ARTISTES REPRESENTED:
Abba 2000
Apache
Al Benson
Barry Bethell
Chairman Mal
Edison Lighthouse
Extreme Force
Kelly Marie
Myles McKoy
Brian Poole
Gary Scott
Soul Man
Wellington Bootles
George Williams

MACFARLANE CHARD TALENT AGENCY
33 Percy Street, London W1T
Tel: 020 7636 7750 Fax: 020 7636 7751
Email: theresa@macfarlane-chard.co.uk
Web Site: www.macfarlane-chard.co.uk
Agent: Theresa Hickey
ARTISTES REPRESENTED:
Actors:
William Armstrong
Roger Barclay
Naomi Bentley
Suzanne Burden

Kirsty Bushell
Jake Canuzo
Claudia Carroll
Niall Cleary
Tony O'Callaghan

SCOTT MACKENZIE ASSOCIATES

The Gatehouse, Porlock, Minehead, Somerset TA24 8ES
Tel: 01643 863 330 / 02
Fax: 01643 863 341
Email: scottmackenzie4u@hotmail.com
Web Site: www.scottmackenzie.co.uk
Senior Personnel: Scott Mackenzie

ARTISTES REPRESENTED:

The 80's Experience
Bjorn Smackee "Abba the Show"
Boys Next Door
Tony Carnagie - Divas In Concert
Tony Carnagie's Pop Goes The 80's
Curious Potion
Let Me Entertain You (Robbie Williams)
Smackee - "The Musicals"
The Swains
Barry Walker`s Smackee

MAD ENTERTAINMENTS AGENCY

56 New Croft, Weedon, Northampton NN7 4RJ
Tel: 01327 349 938
Mobile: 07788 570 747
Email: dd.colonel@btopenworld.com
Senior Personnel: David Dickens
Corporate Events & Product Launches catered for. Any type of Entertaiment catered for. Any Budget. Management for the Billy Fury Band & Darren H. (Elvis Presley Tribute). Agents for 60s, 70s & 80s Tribute Bands and Morris Dancers.

ARTISTES REPRESENTED:

Clem Curtis & the Foundations
The Flying Pickets

MAD MANAGEMENT LTD

7 The Chase, Rayleigh, Essex SS6 8QL
Tel: 01268 771 113 Fax: 01268 774 192
Email: madmanagementltd@aol.com
Contact: Alex Rose

ARTISTES REPRESENTED:

Barclay James Harvest

PAUL MADELEY

17 Valley Road, Bredbury, Stockport, Cheshire SK6 2EA
Tel/Fax: 0161 430 5380 Mobile: 07929 199 969
Email: celebrities@amserve.com
Specialising in: Publicity Consultancy/Representation.

ARTISTES REPRESENTED:

Jim Bowen
Paul Daniels
Bella Emberg
Michael Fish MBE DSc
Uri Geller
Tony Green
Chris Greener
John McCririck
Debbie McGee
Sir Patrick Moore
Ken Morley
Nicholas Parsons
Cynthia Payne
David Vine
Wincey Willis

MAGIC JUNIOR LIMITED

187 Goulden House, Bullen Street, London SW11 3HG
Tel: 0845 166 2169 Tel: 020 7801 0201
Fax: 020 7801 0272
Email: mj@magicjunior.com
Web Site: www.magicjunior.com
Contact: Magic Junior

ARTISTES REPRESENTED:

Magic Junior

MAGICK EYE RECORDS

PO Box 3037, Wokingham, Berkshire RG40 4GR
Tel: 0118 932 8320 Fax: 0118 932 8237
Email: chris@magickeye.com
Web Site: www.magickeye.com
Contact Chris Hillman

ARTISTES REPRESENTED:

Another Green World
Astralasia
Children of Dub
Cybernaut
Magic Mushroom Band
SYT
Under The Honeytunnel
UVX

MICHAEL MAGILL ENTERTAINMENTS

"Chez Nous", Burren Road, Warrenpoint, Newry, County Down BT34 3SA
Northern Ireland
Tel: 028 4177 3618 / 4175 2229 Fax: 028 4175 2020
Email: info@michaelmagillentertainments.com
Senior Personnel: Michael Magill

MAINSTAGE ARTISTS

Unit B 11 Bell Yard Mews,
175 Bermondsay Street London SE1 3TN
Tel: 020 7407 4466 Fax: 020 7407 9719
Email: guy@mainstageartists.com
Web Site: www.mainstageartists.com
Contact: Guy Ornadel

MAINSTREAM ENTERTAINMENTS LTD

11a Kingsway Kings Street BEDWORTH CV12 8HY
Tel: 024 7631 9786
Email: barry@mainstream-mgt.co.uk
Web Site: www.mainstream-mgt.co.uk
Contact: Barry Herbert

MAINSTREAM EVENTS

5 The Mews, 6 Putney Common, Putney SW15 1HL
Tel: 020 8788 2669 Fax: 020 8788 0073
Email: info@mainstreamleisure.co.uk
Web Site: www.mainstreamleisure.co.uk
Senior Personnel: Nigel Scandrett
Own and operate eight riverboats in London and the Maidenhead area. Have Party Planning services in London and the Home Counties. Original venues a speciality. Represent a wide variety of artistes.

ARTISTES REPRESENTED:

Caricaturists:
Jeff Morgan
Magicians:
Richard Jones
Musicians:
Jim Barry
Burlington String Quartet
Casino Roadshow
Flaming Limbo Show
London All Stars Steel Band
Lush Life Blues Duo
Original Jubilee Jazz Band
The Prefects
Premier Cru Dance Band
Silversounds Disco Roadshow
Stephen Strickland Jazz Trio
Psychics:
Anna Ellis

MAITLAND MUSIC (INC. CAPITAL VOICES)

Brook House, 8 Rythe Road, Claygate, Esher, Surrey KT10 9DF
Tel: 01372 466 228 Fax: 01372 466 229
Email: capvox@aol.com
Web Site: www.capitalvoices.com
Senior Personnel: Anne Skates
Session Fixers. All vocal styles covered by young, attractive singers.

MAJOR ENTERTAINMENT AGENCY

6c Standbridge Lane, Sandal, Wakefield, West Yorkshire WF2 7DY
Tel: 01924 254 350 Fax: 01924 259 414
Senior Personnel: Mr Toby Major

ARTISTES REPRESENTED:

Mark Atkinson
John Cotton
Electrix
Jagged
Sneezewort
Soul Sisters
T-Rex

MIKE MALLEY ENTERTAINMENTS

10 Holly Park Gardens, Finchley, London N3 3NJ
Tel: 020 8346 4109 / 4293 Fax: 020 8346 1104 Mobile: 07785 375661 / 2
Email: mikemall@globalnet.co.uk
Web Site: www.ukstars.co.uk
Senior Personnel: Mike Malley

ARTISTES REPRESENTED:
Gary Ambrose
Coco Express
Kevin Coffey
Dampness
Lesley Guinness (Edina from Ab Fab)
Tony Lee
Queen B (Queen tribute)
Queen on Fire (Queen tribute)
The Rat Pack
Red Hot Silli Feckers
Sister Act
Stevie Starr
Michael Sutherland
The Collective
Utter Madness
Nikki Williams

MANDY WARD ARTIST MANAGEMENT LTD
4th Floor 73-74 Berwick Street London W1F 8TE
Tel: 020 7434 3569
Email: mandy@mwartistmanagement.com
Web: www.mandywardartistmanagement.com
Contact: Mandy Ward

JOHNNY MANS PRODUCTIONS LIMITED
Incorporating 'Real Publicity' & 'Encore Magazine'
PO Box 196, Hoddesdon, Hertfordshire EN10 7WG
Tel: 0845 467 0792
Email: johnnymansagent@aol.com, encoremags@aol.com
Web: www.johnnymansproductions.co.uk www.encoremagazine.org.uk
ADMINISTRATION:
Managing Director: Johnny Mans
Administration: Philip Crowe, Elliot Mans, David Perry.
ARTISTES REPRESENTED:
Esteban Antonio
Kenny Baker
Bernard Bale
Beverley Sisters
Elliott Brooks
Julia Burnett
Anthony Bygraves
Max Bygraves OBE
Jess Conrad
Daniel Dean
Sara Dee
Joanne Diaz
Feverking
Glenn Ford
Gerry George
Peter Goodwright
William Hall
Derek Hatton
Squire Ronnie Hayward
Vince Hill
Bill Holden
Carol Lee Scott (Grotbags)
Lucy Mans
Ernest Maxin
Rowan O'Duffy
Dave Prowse
Joan Regan
Caroline Rippin
The Rolling Clones
Roxy Magic
Terry Seabrooke
Sara Jayne Silverton
Charlie Smithers
Songbook Orchestra & Singers
Jeremy Spake
Isla St Clair
Thoughts of Chairman Alf (Warren Mitchell)
Jeff Wayne
Bert Weedon
Lol Williams Band
Sir Norman Wisdom OBE
Victoria Yellop

MARIA FRANZONI
The London Speaker Bureau
153 Stoughton Road, Guildford, Surrey GU1 1LQ
Tel: 01483 576228 Fax: 01483 526443
Email: maria@londonspeakerbureau.co.uk
Web: www.londonspeakerbureau.co.uk
Contact: Maria Franzoni

MARIE-LOUISE HOGAN
Tel: 020 7371 8474
ARTISTES REPRESENTED:
Arthur Mathews

THE MARK LEWIS AGENCY
76A Waterloo Road, Blyth, Northumberland NE24 1DG
Tel: 01670 360 036 Fax: 01670 355 203
Mobile: 07703 128449
Email: lewisagency@dsl.pipex.com
Senior Personnel: Mark Lewis

MARK SUMMERS CASTING
(Mark Summers Casting Director)
137 Freston Road, London W10 6TH
Tel: 020 7229 8413 Fax: 020 7243 1987
Email: mark@marksummers.com / info@marksummers.com
Web Site: www.marksummers.com
Senior Personnel: Mark Summers
Specialising in casting for commercials, film and TV in the UK and worldwide. UK/US passports.

MARKHAM & FROGGATT LTD
Julian House, 4 Windmill Street, London W1T 2HZ
Tel: 020 7636 4412 Fax: 020 7637 5233
Email: millie@markhamfroggatt.co.uk
Web Site: www.markhamfroggatt.com
Senior Personnel: Pippa Markham
ARTISTES REPRESENTED:
Frances Albery
Sam Alexanders
Naveen Andrews
Alun Armstrong
Patricia Arquette
Kate Atkinson
Joe Don Baker
Fairuza Balk
Edoardo Ballerini
Lara Belmont
John Benfield
Sia Berkeley
Kieran Bew
Stephen Billington
Rachael Blake
Marco Bonini
Betsy Brantley
Emily Bruni
Brian Capron
Ruaidhri Conroy
Dominic Cooper
Julie Cox
Peter Coyote
Kenneth Cranham
James Cromwell
Tony Curtis
Ben Daniels
James D'Arcy
Emma Darwell-Smith
Eleanor David
Jacqueline Defferary
Julie Delpy
Bryan Dick
Michael Dixon
Adrian Dunbar
Joel Edgerton
Chiwetel Ejiofor
Maria Ellingsen
Kate Fahy
Christopher Fairbank
Adam Farr
Nicholas Farrell
Ray Fearon
Deborah Findlay
Jonathan Firth
Bridget Fonda
Peter Fonda
Rupert Frazer
Sarah Michelle Gellar
Patrick Godfrey
Glen Goei
Stella Gonet
Rachel Griffiths
Haydn Gwynne
Krystof Hadek
Daisy Haggard
Amanda Hale
Marina Hands
Emma Handy
Scott Handy
Claudia Harrison
David Hayman
Barbara Hershey
Melanie Hill
David Hollett
Sir Ian Holm
William Houston
Timothy Hutton
Philip Jackson
Sarah Kants
Gorden Kaye
Gerard Kelly
Edward Kelsey
Yasmin Kerr
Julian Kerridge
Patricia Kerrigan
Melanie Kilburn
Rory Kinnear
Leon
Lydia Leonard

Damian Lewis
Andrew Lincoln
Thomas Lockyer
John Lynch
Cal MacAnineh
Niall Macgregor
Michael Maloney
Joseph Marcell
Caroline Martin
Anna Massey
Malcolm McDowell
Ian Mcniece
Ben Meyjes
Elsa Mollien
Stephen Moore
Peter Mullan
William Nadylam
Luke Neal
Alec Newman
Bill Nighy
Mary Nighy
Frances O'Connor
Sophie Okonedo
Martha Plimpton
Amanda Plummer
Christopher Plummer
Pete Postlethwaite
Ben Pullen
Emily Raymond
Ian Redford
Nick Reding
Saskia Reeves
Paul Rhys
Rachel Rice
Clifford Rose
Tim Roth
Amanda Ryan
Georgina Rylance
Mark Rylance
David Schwimmer
John Sessions
John Shea
Jack Shepherd
Alexander Siddig
Alexander Skarsgard
Claire Skinner
Christian Slater
Renee Soutendijk
Rafe Spall
Timothy Spall
Terence Stamp
Geoffrey Steatfeild
Theo Fraser Steele
Juliet Stevenson
Sting
Mark Strong
Kirsty Stuart
Kiefer Sutherland
Magda Szabanski
Owen Teale
Sylvestra Le Touzel
David Troughton
Sam Troughton
Margaret Tyzack
Adriano Vilanova
Zoe Waites
Polly Walker
Naomi Watts
Danny Webb
Robert Whitclock
Jeffry Wickham
Heathcote Williams
Scott Wilson
John Wood

BILLY MARSH ASSOCIATES LTD

76a Grove End Road, St John's Wood
London NW8 9ND
Tel: 020 7449 6930 Fax: 020 7449 6933
Email: jan@billymarsh.co.uk
Agent: Jan Kennedy

ARTISTES REPRESENTED:

Peter Cook (Estate)
Jon Culshaw
David Dickinson
Sacha Distel (Estate)
Rosemarie Ford
Bruce Forsyth CBE
Bianca Gascoigne
Sheryl Gascoigne
Rolf Harris AM CBE
David Jacobs CBE DL
Bonnie Langford
Morecambe & Wise (Estate)
Fiona Phillips
Esther Rantzen CBE
Mark Speight
Claire Sweeney
Charlotte Uhlenbroek
Dale Winton
Chris Young

BILLY MARSH DRAMA LIMITED

(Actors/Actresses)
11 Henrietta Street, London WC2E 8PY
Tel: 020 7379 4800 Fax: 020 7379 7272
Email: info@billymarshdrama.co.uk
Senior Personnel: Linda Kremer

ARTISTES REPRESENTED:

Bethan Bevan
Frazer Hines
Paul Shane
Marti Webb

MARSHALL ARTS LTD

Uint 6, Utopia Village, 7 Chalcot Road,
London NW1 8LH
Tel: 020 7586 3831 Fax: 020 7586 1422
Email: info@marshall-arts.co.uk / barrie@marshall-arts.co.uk
Web Site: www.marshall-arts.co.uk
Managing Director: Barrie Marshall
Director: Doris Dixon
Agent: Ben Martin
Production Manager: Mike Stewart
International concert presentations.

ARTISTES REPRESENTED:

Joe Cocker
Al Jarreau
Sir Elton John
Sir Paul McCartney
Katie Melua
Mohair
Pink
Lionel Richie
David Sanborn
Tony Joe White

BRIAN MARSHALL MANAGEMENT

Unicorn Street, Bloxham, Banbury,
Oxfordshire OX15 4QA
Tel: 01295 812 288 Fax: 01295 720 811
Email: marshall_brian@btconnect.com
Senior Personnel: Brian Marshall

ARTISTES REPRESENTED:

Leanna Bridges (Sooty)
Nick Cochrane (Coronation Street)
Sheila Ferguson (Soul Train, Victoria Palace)
Alan Fletcher (UK only)
Lynne-Marie Haslam
AJ Lewis
Melanie Marshall (Soul Train)
McGee & Mooney (Children's ITV)
Otter
Tucker

SCOTT MARSHALL PARTNERS LTD

2nd floor 15 Little Portland Street London
W1W 8BW
Tel: 020 7637 4623 Fax: 020 7636 9728
Email: smpm@scottmarshall.co.uk
Web Site: www. scottmarshall.co.uk
Senior Personnel: Amanda Evans, Suzy Kenway, Manon Palmer.

ARTISTES REPRESENTED:

Jill Halfpenny

MARTIN ENTERTAINMENTS

2 Conifer Drive, Stockton-on-Tees,
Cleveland TS19 0UL
Tel: 01642 616 710 Fax: 01642 615 737
Email: martinents@hotmail.co.uk
Web: www.martinentertainments.co.uk
Senior Personnel: Martin Taylor

ARTISTES REPRESENTED:

Trios:
Beggarmans Lane
Buster
Step It Up
Duos:
Backbeat
Born Slippy
Robson Day
Second Nature
Shine
Sound Academy
Male Vocal:
Terry Adams
Phil Alexander
Steve Birley
Gary Brown
Tony Brown
DJ Richie
Gilly
Colin Peters
Paul Robinson
Dixon J Scott
Martin Scott
PA Wood
Female Vocal:
Becky
Nicki Dee
Sarah Judd
Amber Louise

Louise Miller
Emily Reef
Viv Sheldon
Clare Weaver

RICHARD MARTIN AGENCY

Fast Helicopter Building Hangar 4, Shoreham Airport, Shoreham-By-Sea, West Sussex BN43 5FF
Tel: 01273 446 484 / 0845 4600 333
Fax: 01273 44 6494 Mob Richard Martin: 07860 722255
Email: ric@ricmartinagency.com
Web Site: www.ricmartinagency.com
Contact: Richard Martin & Anita Cave

ARTISTES REPRESENTED:

Spencer Davis Group
Hot Chocolate

RON MARTIN MANAGEMENT

Dorset House, Church Street Wimborne, Dorset BH21 1JH
Tel/Fax: 01202 881 247 (4 Lines)
Email: enquiries@ronmartin.co.uk
Web Site: www.ronmartin.co.uk
Senior Personnel: Ron Martin, Adam Thompson
General Enquiries: Lindsay Wilkinson

ARTISTES REPRESENTED:

TV Presenters:
Gina Akers
Opal Bonfante
Gary Bushell
Fayon Cottrell
Adam Freeman
Rachel Hopkins
Raychel Howard-Jones (Vocalist/Presenter)
Gareth James (Comedy Vocalist)
Rob Lamar
Helen McDermott
Paul Metcalfe (Rod Stewart)
Steven Milne
Peter Simon
TV Personality:
Tony Bullimore
Rikki Jay (International Comedy)
Denise Nolan
Nicholas Parsons
Peter Simon
Nikki Stevens
Ed Stewart
Rik Waller
International Artists:
Jr Walker's All Stars
Kaaren Ragland's The Supremes
Ollie Williams "Temptations"
Richard Street's The Temptations
The Temptations
Light Entertainment:
Alex Lodge (Magician)
Atmosfear (illusion)
Bianca (Vocalist)
Brotherhood of Man
C.O.D.E (Female Trio)
Desire (Female Trio)
Entwine (female duo)
Footlight Dance Academy (Dance Troop)
Gareth James (Comedy Vocalist)
Rikki Jay (International Comedy)
Kinda Magic (Illusionists)
Cassie Lawrence (Female Vocalist)
Martin James (Comedy Illusion)
Palma Nova Puppets (UV Comedy Magic Show)
Martin Steele (Male Vocalist)

NIGEL MARTIN-SMITH MANAGEMENT LTD

Nemesis House, 1 Oxford Court, Bishopsgate, Manchester M2 3WQ
Tel: 0161 228 6465 Fax: 0161 228 6727
Email: liz@nmsmanagement.co.uk
Web Site: www.nemesisagency.co.uk
Senior Personnel: Nigel Martin-Smith, Liz Beeley

MATCHROOM SPORT LTD

Mascalls, Mascalls Lane, Brentwood, Essex CM14 5LJ
Tel: 01277 359 900 Fax: 01277 359 935
Email: john.wischhusen@matchroom.com
Web Site: www.matchroomsport.com
For Boxing enquiries, contact: John Wischhusen

ARTISTES REPRESENTED:

Keith Arthur
Steve Davis
Barry Hearn
Jesse May
Greg Owen
Phil Taylor

MATTERS MUSICAL

The Loft, Rear of 8 West Street, Dorking, Surrey RH4 1BL
Tel: 01306 741 007 Fax: 01306 741 008
Email: info@mattersmusical.com
Web Site: www.mattersmusical.com
Senior Personnel: Frank Warren
Plus Dance Instruction/Demonstration for all the styles listed below.

ARTISTES REPRESENTED:

African & Arabic:
Simbas Acrobats
Farid Adjazairi
Amabutho
Harir Band
Baraka
Berakah
Ngoma Drum & Dance
El-Andalus
Zubop Gambia
Harare
Nizar Al Issa
Kadialy Kouyate
Mamadou
Nzinga
Abdelkader Saadoun
Takaleed
Uthingo
Americana:
Alan Tyler and the Lost Sons of Littlefield
Arcadians
The Bearcat Cajun Playboys
Beckett/Brokovich
The Slowdown Boys
R Cajun & the Zydeco Brothers
The Coal Porters
Foghorn Leghorn
Petite Et La Gross
The Hackney Ramblers
Hootenanny 3
Los Pistoleros
Trailer Trash Orchestra
Z-Funk
Asian & Even Further East:
4x4 Bhangra Dance Troupe
Kuljit Bhamra Band
Bollywood Brass Band
Bollywood Dreams Dancers
Crishna & Camilita
Ministry of Dhol
Sekar Enggal
UK Chinese Ensemble
Joji Hirota
Japanesque
Tomono Kawamura
Bhangra Latina
Jonathan Mayer
Metalworks (Gamelan Orchestra)
The Mugenkyo Taiko Drummers
Bombay Gold Orchestra
The Ku-Da-Mix Orchestra
The Teak Project
Vasda Punjab
Rhythmworks
Sanju Sahai
Sangeeta
Kotono Sato
Baluji Shrivastav/Jazz Orient
Kiranpal Singh
Taala
Taiko Meantime
Taiko to Tabla
UK Chinese Acrobatic Company
Wei Li Chinese Orchestra
Cheng Yu
Guo Yue
Blues,Soul,Swing & Rock 'n' Roll:
9.20 Deluxe Swing Band
Art Deco Swing Quartet
Backstreet Soul
Chris Beck & the Valentine Vagabonds
Robin Bibi Band
Blue Harlem
The Bogus Blues Brothers
Swing Confidential
Funk Federation
The Fugitives
The Ray Gelato Giants
Good Rockin' Tonight
The James Hunter Band
Little Big Band
Ola Onabule
Kit Packham's One Jump Ahead
The Val Kelly Jazz Quartet
The Red Stripe Band
Ronnie & The Rex
OTB Soul
Gary Williams
Caribbean:
Alexander D Great and the Great Band
Fimber Bravo
Ska Cubano
Ebony Steel Band
Hike
We Be Jammin'!
Kaiso
Kaniki
Pan Pioneers

Shades of Black
Solid Steel Ambassadors
Jeanette Springer
Tropical Storm
Tim Hain & Jamside Up!

Classical:

Arion Duo
John Cadman
Chameleon Brass
Chi 2
The Covent Garden String Quartet
Cumuli Wind Quintet
Divas Incongnito
Aurora Duo
Eclipse Strings
Graffiti Classics
Bethan (Harp)
Camilla (Harp)
Fiona Harrison
Hatstand Opera
Kate (harpist)
Tomono Kawamura
London Concertante
The London Pops Orchestra
Manchester String Quartet
Monaco String Quartet
Jamie Moore
No Strings Attached
Omega Brass Quintet
Urban Soul Orchestra
Oyster Opera
Premier Brass
Jennifer Raven
Opera On The Run
Kotono Sato
Emma (Soprano)
Imogen (Soprano)
Stringfever
Peacock Strings
S Strings
Sapphire Strings
Z Strings
Ensemble Suavis
Bradley (Tenor)
Tenors Incognito
Tenors Unlimited
London Trio
Trumpeters of London
Travelling By Tuba

Covers/Function Bands:

The Chris Barton Band
Peter Bennett
Bop Asylum
Carwash
China Grove
Back In The Day
Dual Control
End Of The Century
The Eighties Experience
Freespirit
Tom Butterworth / Fretless
Funkology
Black & Gold
Groovejuice
Grouper
Hussey
Lost In Music
Objayda
Blame The Parents
PartyDown
Mark Pearson
Claire Phoenix
Andy Robinson
Sera Golding & The Men In Black
The Pretend Pretenders
Too Darn Hot
Trenchtown Experience (Bob Marley & The Wailers tribute)
The Goldrush (Crosby, Stills & Nash tribute)
Tuxedo Class Disco
Space UK
Visage

DJs & Discos:

Firebird Entertainment
Starsound Entertainment
Surround Sounds Entertainment
Tuxedo Class Disco

Eastern European/Russian/Klezmer Bands:

Balalaika Orchestra
Beskydy
Bohdan Chomenko/Zvuk Bazaar
Club Tabou
Bibs Ekkel's Tziganka
Gypsy Jazz
K Groove
Dunajska Kapelye
Klezmania
The Kremlinaires
Mukka
Sergei Pachnine
Yuri Stepanov / Russian Passion
Russian Tornado
Szapora
Tziganarama
The Volkovtski Cossacks
Zig
Zum

Global Fusion:

Diego Brown & the Good Fairy
Café Aman
Mike Edwards
Fantazia
Fiddling Around The World
Finality Jack
Hoover the Dog
Horace X
The Jones Project
Kangeroo Moon
Elliet Mackrell/Didgeridoo

Gospel:

Citizen K
Kingdom Choir
Visual Ministry Choir

Irish/Celtic Bands:

Ceilidh Allstars
Band of Two
Beckett
Blackthorn Band
Paul Brennan/Carrig
Carmina
Cats Whiskers Barn Dance Band
Celtic Feet Irish Dance Company
Ceolsha
Damhsa
Beckett Irish Dancers
Finality Jack
Joe Giltrap
Highland Swing
Irish Mist
Kelly's Heroes
Paul Kerr
Gina Mackey
Newfolks
The Long Notes
Orchestrad
Ben Paley & Tab Hunter
The Polkaholics
Quicksilver
Scottish Ceilidh Bands
The Marsh Town Stompers
Thingumajig
Truss & Bucket Band
Uillean Pipers
Willie Cochrane/The Balmoral Highlanders
Wraggle Taggle Ceilidh Band

Jazz - Contemporary:

Acoustica!
Luke Annersley Quartet
Badooba
Bakehouse
JJ Vinten Band
The Stirling Austin Swing Band
Clanidade
Philip Clouts Trio
Club Tabou
Simon Curry Jazz Band
Shamus Dark
Clare Foster
The Jazz Functionaires
Gary Grace
The Johnny Hillard Trio
Russell Jarret
The Jazz Dynamos
Anita Kelsey
Dave Martin
Emma Munro-Wilson
Victoria Newton/Katmandhu
Jonathan Nickoll
Nicolinda
Caroline Nin
Nuages
Gary Parkes
Gentlemen Prefer
Nigel Price
The Val Kelly Jazz Quartet
Quintette
Razzle Dazzle
Neville Skelly
Russell Jarret & Simon Taylor
Trebeka
Bobby Valentino
Jonathan Vinten
Dave Warren Quartet
Nigel Price & Matt Wates
Zubop

Jazz - Traditional:

78 rpm Jazz Band
Colin Anthony
Mardi Gras Jazz Band
The BBC Big Band
Dr Bone & The Rhythm Boys
Andrew D Brewis
The Casablanca Steps
Simon Curry Jazz Band
Funky Butt Swing & Dance Ensemble
The Gambit Jazzmen
In The Mood
Tony Jacobs
Jambalaya
Ashley Knight
The London Ragtime Orchestra
Jamie Moore
Ooh Baby Ooh
Piccadilly Dance Orchestra

Original Blend
Rockin' In Rhythm
Latin Styles:
America
Choro Bandido
Bloco Do Sul
Casa Latina Allstars/Bugalu/Conjunto
Salsanito
Coco Express
Como No
Cubanito
Viramundo Dancers
Sambossa Duo
El Equipo/Soneando
Latin Fiesta
Factor Latino
Lido 66
London School of Samba
Los Soneros
Merengada
Orquesta Caché
Orquesta Huracan
Otra Vez
Pa'Gozar Salsa Band
La Cuba Ritmo
Tango Select
Tango Siempre/Subitango!
Los Tapatios
Viramundo
Vivo Latino
Medieval/Renaissance:
John Cadman
Dante Ferrara
Dragonsfire
Grinnigogs
Trevor James
Martin + Thornbury
Medieval Minstrels
Null Nomine Daunce
Sautrie
Stromenti
Princes In The Tower
Yair
Mexican/Spanish/Pan Pipes:
Paul Aguilera - Flamenco
Amaru III
Andalus (Gypsy Kings)
Apu
Bamboleo
Guillermo & Juan Carlos
Corazon Flamenco
Amor Flamenco
Katari Group
José Leon/Sol Y Sombra
Los Charros
Mariachi Lajara
Mariachi Tequila
Soléa
Mariachi Tapatio
Viva Flamenco
Miscellaneous:
Voyager 2
Have A Banana One-Man Band
Woody's One-Man Band
Broadway UK
Stephen & Charlotte
The Cosmic Sausages
Daily Planet
Drum'n'Didg/Mark Walker's Talking Drums
Edwardian Soirée
Noise Ensemble
The Hula Bluebirds
The Incredibly Strange Film Band
Jane Bom-Bane
Barb Junga & Her Musicians
Keta
Khalisha
Lei Aloha
Urban Strawberry Lunch
Manaia
Mandolin Express
Showstopper! The Improvised Musical
The New English Mandolin Orchestra/The Fretful Federation
Ngati Ranana
Ooh Baby Ooh
Original Blend
John Otway
Holly Penfield
Poles Apart
Polished Brass
Premier Brass
Mia Serra
Shaken Not Stirred
The Sugarfoot Stompers
Ukulele Orchestra of Great Britain
Verona Chard Cockney Show
Vox Angelica
Drum Waiters
Warriors from Zeigon
Western European:
The Claudio Allodi Band
Alpengold Blaskapelle Bavarian Band
Asteria
Café du Monde
Chris Haigh
Alan Dunn
Maguin
Mandelino
Troia Nova
Odysseus
Fleur De Paris
Paris Moon
Papa Schnitzel's Bavarian Dance Band
The Spartans
Zephyros

MAGEE MATTHEWS ASSOCIATES (2MA)

Springvale, Tutland Road,
North Baddesley, Southampton,
Hampshire SO52 9FL
Tel: 023 8074 1354
Mob: 07730 66 22 36
Email: info@2ma.co.uk
Web Site: www.2ma.co.uk
Sports, Stunt and Circus Artists.

CLIFF MATTHEWS MANAGEMENT & ENTERTAINMENT AGENCY

PO Box 95, Rotherham, South Yorkshire
S60 5YH
Tel/Fax: 01709 363 908
Tel: 01709 36747
Email: cliffmm@btinternet.com
Senior Personnel: Cliff Matthews

ARTISTES REPRESENTED:

Boom
Jack E Day
Johnny Foreigner
Kyla
Jack Page
Two Hot
Mark Ward

MAVERICK MANAGEMENTS LTD

Maverick House 15 Grand Manor Drive,
Lytham St. Annes, Lancashire FY8 4FY
Tel: 01253 795657 Fax: 01253 735899
Email: info@maverickmanagement.co.uk
Web Site: www.maverickmanagement.co.uk / www.showbizworks.com
Contact: Martin Blore
London Office: (Sales and Enquiries)
Maverick Management, Communications House, 26 York Street
London, W1U 6PZ
Tel: +44 (0)845 638 1808

CASSIE MAYER LTD

Number 5, Old Garden House,
The Lanterns, Bridge Lane, London
SW11 3AD
Tel: 020 7350 0880 Fax: 020 7350 0890
Email: info@cassiemayerltd.co.uk
Agent: Cassie Mayer

ARTISTES REPRESENTED:

Actresses:
Kacey Ainsworth
Sheila Allen
Gina Bellman
Nicky Croydon
Francesca Folan
Brenda Fricker
Katy Gleadhill
Beth Goddard
Louise Gold
Serena Gordon
Andrea Hart
Beverley Hills
Ginny Holder
Katherine Igoe
Rachel Joyce
Gillian Kirkpatrick
Janette Legge
Susan Lynch
Sara Mair-Thomas
Dearbhla Molloy
Natasha Nicholl
Heather Peace
Mary Jo Randle
Alyson Spiro
Frances Tomelty
Lou Wakefield
Jody Watson
Actors:
Paul Chahidi
Dermot Crowley
James Dreyfus
Kevin Elyot
Stuart Fox
Iain Fraser
Jimmy Garnon
Aden Gillett
Nicholas Gleaves
Sam Graham
Alexander Hanson
Lloyd Hutchinson
Dermot Kerrigan
Mark Lacey

Dominic Mafham
Owen McDonnell
Ian McElhinney
Nick Moorcroft
Jimmy Mulville
Will Norris
Hugh Quarshie
Alexei Sayle
Paul Shelley
Suzanne Richardson
Martha Ross
Naomi Slater
Helen Snow
Maureen Taylor
Sherill Turner
Sheila Tyson
Kate Van-Dike
Deborah Watling

MBA

(Formerly John Mahoney Management)
Concorde House, 18 Margaret Street, Brighton, East Sussex BN2 1TS
Tel: 01273 685 970 / 672 262
Email: mba.concorde@virgin.net
Web Site: www.mbagency.co.uk
Senior Personnel: Derek Keller, Peter Stanford, Andrea Todd

ARTISTES REPRESENTED:

Male:
Collin Baxter
Jeremy Blake
Paul Blake
Colin Campbell
Chris Coughlin
Mike Dalton
Jason Davis
Michael D'Cruze
James Duggan
Rufus Forde
Brendan Foster MBE
Ross Holland
Derek Hollis
Chris Hornby
Simon Johns
Alexander Khan
Simon Mathis
David Mayberry
Adam McConville
Ricardo Montez
Matthew Moxon
Grant Neal
Bryan Pilkington
Miguel Angel Plaza
Aaron Romano
Bill Rourke
Peter Snipp
Peter Stephens
Ronald Wood
Female:
Lyn Ashley
Debbi Blythe
Anita Chellamah-Nurse
Fiona Cuskelly
Helen Day
Aurelie Bargeme
Sally Goodman
Jenny Hanley
Kate Hayworth
Andrea Hoban
Diane Holland
Michelle Jackson-Read
Amani Johara
Sophie Leigh
Wendy Lovelock
June Marlow
Dani McCallum
Victoria McFarlane
Maria Morgan
Moya O'Shea

MCC SPORTS PROMOTIONS

96 Elborough Street, London SW18 5DL
Mobile: 07977 831519 (Mark Caswell)
Email: mccsports@mcaswell3.fsnet.co.uk
Web Site: www.southlondonfives.co.uk
Contact: Mark Caswell
For a complete range of sport and p.r. services.
Hire of models and promotional staff, film extras etc...
We represent and can supply the following:
Personalities from the world of sport; Entertainment; Models
Promotional Staff; Event Organisation; Authors

RICKY MCCABE ENTERTAINMENTS LTD

Po box 89 Upton, Wirral CH49 6WR
Tel: 0151 606 8118 Fax: 0151 606 8181
Email: r.mccabe@tiscali.co.uk
Senior Personnel: Peter Eyres

JAMES MCDERMOTT AGENCY

Suite 3, Acorn House, Longshot Lane, Bracknell, Berkshire RG12 1RL
Tel: 01344 305 588 Fax: 01344 30 55 80
Email: jfmcdermott@btconnect.com

DEBORAH MCKENNA LIMITED

Claridge House, 29 Barnes High Street, London SW13 9LW
Tel: 020 8876 7566 Fax: 020 8392 2462
Email: adam.kingl@deborahmckenna.com
Web Site: www.deborahmckenna.com
Managing Director: Borra Garson
Senior Personnel: Adam Kingl, Lauren Davis
Managers/Agents for the UK's top celebrity chefs and lifestyle presenters. Television and publishing deals plus endorsements and advertising. We are also agents for television scriptwriters.

ARTISTES REPRESENTED:

Stefan Gates
Sophie Grigson
Oliver Heath
Allegra McEvedy
Tony Tobin
John Torode

BILL MCLEAN PERSONAL MANAGEMENT

23B Deodar Road, Putney, London SW15 2NP
Tel: 020 8789 8191 Fax: 020 8789 8192
Email: bill.mclean@fsmail.net
Agent: Bill Mclean

MCLEAN-WILLIAMS MANAGEMENT

Thames Wharf Studios, Rainville Road, London W6 9HA
Tel: 020 7610 2929 Fax: 020 3080 0111
Email: alex@mclean-williams.com
Web Site: www.mclean-williams.com
Agent: Alex Mclean-Williams
Agency for actors and actresses working in all genres of the entertainment industry.

ARTISTES REPRESENTED:

Gareth Hunt
Susie Johns
Jon Lee
Anne Nolan
Maureen Nolan
Stefanie Powers
Adele Silva

MCLEOD AGENCY LTD

Established 1970
First Floor 6 The Square Hessle
East Yorkshire HU13 0AA
Tel: 01482 565 444 Fax: 01482 353 635
Email: info@themcleodagency.co.uk
Web Site: www.mcleodagency.co.uk
Senior Personnel: Liz Hugill
Entertainment Agency & Artiste Management.

ARTISTES REPRESENTED:

4 Sensations
The Backbeat Beatles
Billy Bean
Big Wolfe Oompah Band
Jim Bowen
Stephen Brailsford
Eric Bristow MBE
Brotherhood of Man
Bucks Fizz
Candlewick Green
Clown Steven
Co & Co
Norman Collier
Paul Derek
Tommy Docherty
Brian Duval
Edison Lighthouse
Berni Flint
Gidea Park (Beach Boys tribute)
Eve Graham
Gerry Grant (Roy Orbison)
David Gunson
Herman's Hermits
Emlyn Hughes OBE
Jokers Wild
Ned Kelly
David Kendall ACIB
Craig Kidd
Ivory Al Kilvington
Cliff Lazarenko
Craig Leach
Leodian String Quartet
Duncan MacKenzie
Bobby Martell
Steve Massam
Merseybeats
Geoff Miller

Mississippi Dixielanders
Morris and the Minors
Motown Magic
Brian Newbold
Outrageous Blues Brothers
Paper Lace
Brian Poole & Electrix
Dennis Priestley
Steven J Riley
Barry Roberts
Rollers Tribute Show
Shang-A-Lang
Paul Squire
Dennis Taylor
Tricks of the Trade
Vanity Fare (ex-chart band)
Venus
Andy Wilkins
Andy Wood (Ricky Martin, Tom Jones, Michael Bolton)
Dusty Young
Steve Love Band
Surrender
J.D. Adams
Stevie J
Mike Caine
Sarah Winters
Stephanie St James

KEN MCREDDIE LTD

36-40 Glasshouse Street, London
W1B 5DL
Tel: 020 7439 1456 Fax: 020 734 6530
Email: email@kenmcreddie.com
Web Site: www.kenmcreddie.com
Senior Personnel: Ken McReddie

MCS AGENCY

47 Dean Street, London W1D 5BE
Tel: 020 7734 9995 Fax: 020 7734 9996
Email: lara@mcsagency.co.uk
Web Site: www.mcsagency.co.uk
Senior Personnel: Keith Bishop

ARTISTES REPRESENTED:

Personalities:
Emma Bache
Paul Bloxham
Garry Bushell
Ian Carmichael
Michael Cole
Bobby Davro
Dr Lucy Glancey
Liz Halliday
Scott Henshall
Dr Tariq Idris
Josh Lewsey MBE BSc
Derek Laud
Nick Leeson
Neil & Christine Hamilton
Alan Pardew
Stuart Phillips
Simon Shaw
Eugene Sully
Jeff Turner
Zoe Tyler
Acting:
John Asquith
Francesca Baldwin
Robert Banks
Hayley Bennett-Jones
Princess Tamara Borbon
Malandra Burrows
Bobby Davro
Cassandra French
Sam Kane
Linda Lusardi
Jack Marsden
Cindy Marshall-Day
Clare McGhinn
Jodie McMullen
Susie Michelle
Jonathon Morris
Briony Price
Dave Prowse
Simon Ram
Jacqui Roberts
Matt Robinson
Jeff Rudom
Tony Scannell
Jodie Shaw
Diane Youdale

M.C.S. ENTERTAINMENTS

Beckford Business Centre Unit 10,
Beckford Street, Hamilton, Lanarkshire
ML3 0BT
Tel: 01698 401310
Email: john@mcsentertainments.co.uk
Contact: John Cummiskey

MERLIN CHILDREN'S ENTERTAINMENTS

29 Norwood Drive, Harrow, Middlesex
HA2 7PF
Tel/Fax: 020 8866 6327
Email: info@merlinents.co.uk
Web Site: www.merlinents.co.uk
Senior Personnel: Geoffrey & Clive Donald

ARTISTES REPRESENTED:

Merlins Children`s Entertainments

MERLIN ELITE

37 Lower Belgrave Street London
SW1W 0LS
Tel: 020 7823 5990 Fax: 020 7823 5298
Email: info@merlinelite.co.uk
Web Site: www.merlinelite.co.uk
Agent: Richard Thompson

ARTISTES REPRESENTED:

Males:
James Beattie
Ben Cohen
Kenny Dalglish
Les Ferdinand
Duncan James
Jay Kay
Graeme Le Saux
Matt Dawson MBE
Jamie Redknapp
Alec Stewart
Matthew Le Tissier
Russell Watson
Females:
Kelly Dalglish
Jodie Kidd
Amy Nuttall
Louise Redknapp
Diana Stewart

M.G. ENTERTAINMENTS

11 Kirkless Villas, Cale Lane,
New Springs, Wigan, Lancashire
WN2 1HQ
Tel: 01942 494 757 Fax: 01942 231 055
Mobile: 07880 590 662
Email: wendymgents@btinternet.com
Senior Personnel: Wendy Sweeney

ARTISTES REPRESENTED:

Josh Adams
Paul Adams (Ind Art)
Mike Alone
Amerez
Billy Flywheel
Terry Cotta
Dudley Doolittle
Keily Hampson
Harper
The Houghton Weavers
Billy Hunter
Jamie
Jeff Lee
Brad Leigh-Scott
Nostalgia
Dean Richards
Matt Rose
Carlo Paul Santanna
Janice Yorke

M.G. PROMOTIONS

19 Cobden Street Kidderminster,
Worcestershire DY11 6RR
Tel: 01562 745 415 Fax: 01562 825 968
Email: mgproms@aol.com
Web Site: www.m-gpromotions.com
Contact: Rose Hutton

ARTISTES REPRESENTED:

Norman Collier
Paul James (Elvis tribute)
J.T.B. Experience
Don MacLean MBE
Dave Silk (Magician)
Videoraces

MGA ENTERPRISES

118 Holme Lane, Sheffield S6 4JW
Tel: 01142 330 414 Fax: 01142 493 658
Email: ple@online.co.uk
Web Site: www.mgaenterprises.co.uk
Contact: Shaun Garratty, Maria Malia
Top northern agency representing actors, bands, models, music and extras who work in many industry productions.

ARTISTES REPRESENTED:

Performing Artistes:
David Bamford
Chrys Davies
Eulogy
Extreme Rhythm
Heart Of Glass (Blondie tribute)
Shyanglo
The Three Bees (official Bee Gees tribute band)
The Zephyrs
Actors:
David Bamford
Dean Burgin
Jimmy Carol
Steve Granger
Anthony Kirkham

Graham Rollason
Salvatori Vita
Actresses:
Ada Burch
Rachel Harper
Holly Jordan
Lois Lindsey
Nichol Malia
Crystal Powers
Saminda Rehman
Tania Michelle Smith
Stephanie Watson
Writers:
Mason Tyree
Set/Lighting Designers:
Ben Rogers
Presenters, DJs:
Jimmy Carol
DJ Salva
Lois Lindsey
Models:
Jessica Ashton-Davies
Stuntman:
Dave Coates
Costume Designer:
Victoria Ballandini

MICHAEL JOYCE MANAGEMENT
3rd Floor 33 Glasshouse Street London W1B 5DG
Tel: 020 3178 7190
Email: michael@michaeljoyce.tv
Web: www.michaeljoycemanagement.com
Contact: Michael Joyce

MIDLAND ENTERTAINMENT & MANAGEMENT AGENCY LTD
PO Box 259, Coventry, Warwickshire CV5 8YU
Tel/Fax: 024 7671 5544
Mob: 07778 792 521
Email: chrissy@midland-entertainment.com
Web: www.midland-entertainment.com
Senior Personnel: Chrissy Price
Specialising in: All Types of Artistes.
ARTISTES REPRESENTED:
Breeze - Function Band
Ian Irving (Comedian)
Los Charros-Salsa Band (Latin Dance)
Subterraneans - Party Band
Tropical Islanders Steel Band

MIKE HUGHES ENTERTAINMENTS
114 Woodsford Square London W14 8DT
Tel: 020 7602 2223
Email: mikehughesent@hotmail.co.uk
Contact: Michael Hughes

JOHN MILES ORGANISATION
Cadbury Camp Lane,
Clapton in Gordano, Bristol, BS20 7SB
Tel: 01275 856 770 / 854 675 Fax: 01275 810186
Email: john@johnmiles.org.uk
Web: www.johnmilesorganisation.org.uk
Contacts: John Miles
ARTISTES REPRESENTED:
Martin Bashir
Jamie Breese
Martin Brundle
Sue Cook
Tommy Cooper Estate
Noel Edmonds
George Ferguson
Nick Knowles
Alex Lovell
Timmy Mallett
Nigel Marven
Terry Nutkins
Des O'Connor
Mike Read
Carol Vorderman

GLENN MILLER ORCHESTRA
Directed by Ray Murray
6a Furzehill Parade, Shenley Road, Borehamwood, Hertfordshire WD6 1DX
Tel: 020 8905 1065 Fax: 020 8905 1074
Mobile: 07710 202711
Email: suemcvay@tinyworld.co.uk
Web: www.glennmillerorchestra.co.uk
Senior Personnel: Ray McVay, Sue McVay
ARTISTES REPRESENTED:
Glenn Miller Orchestra (UK) directed by Ray McVay
Ray McVay Orchestra

MILTON KEYNES THEATRE OF COMEDY LTD
The Workshop, Clickers Yard, Yardley Road, Olney, Buckinghamshire MK46 5DX
Tel: 01234 241 357 Fax: 01234 240 793
Mob: 078 7941 4110
Email: david.pibworth@btconnect.com
Web Site: www.mktoc.co.uk
Contact: David Pibworth
ARTISTES REPRESENTED:
Nostalgia:
A Night Of Musical Comedy
The Flanders and Swann Show
The Tom Lehrer Show
Touring Production:
Various

MIRACLE ARTISTS LTD
26 Dorset Street, London W1U 8AP
Tel: 020 7935 9222 Fax: 020 7935 6222
Email: info@miracle-artists.com
Web Site: www.miracle-artists.com
Senior Personnel: Steve Parker, Nick Peel
ARTISTES REPRESENTED:
10cc's Graham Gouldman & Friends
ABC
Acoustic Alchemy
Belinda Carlisle
Epica
The Gathering
Go West including Peter Cox
Graham Gouldman & Friends
Grip Inc
Tony Hadley
Jools Holland and his Rhythm & Blues Orchestra
Human League
Howard Jones
Kings X
Roger McGuinn
Moonspell
Morbid Angel
My Dying Bride
Nile
Peter Cox (from Go West)
The Quireboys
Uli Jon Roth
Sentenced
Stiff Little Fingers
Symphony X
Tapping The Vein
Terrorizer
Tiamat
Ruby Turner
UFO
Unleashed

MISSION CONTROL ARTIST AGENCY
Unit 3 City Business Centre
St. Olav's Court Lower Road, London SE16 2XB
Tel: 020 7252 3001 Fax: 020 7252 2225
Email: craig@missioncontrol.net
Web Site: www.missioncontrol.net
Contact: Craig D'Souza, Claire Wallace, Josh Byron, Tracey Roper, Charlotte Hunt, Billy Wood
ARTISTES REPRESENTED:
Mission Control Main Roster:
2 Play
3 Of A Kind
4 Poofs & A Piano
ABC
Alien Sex Fiend
Peter Andre & Katie Price
Apache Indian
Artful Dodger
Awesome 3
Axwell
Beatfreakz
Ben Macklin ft. Tiger Lily
Ben (Phats and Small)
Benny Benassi
Bez
Big Bass vs Michelle Narin
Big Brovaz
Black Legend
Blazin Squad
Boogie Pimps
B*Witched
Ali Campbell
DJ Casper
Chris Willis (David Guetta)
Coco (Fragma)
Coolio
Darude
DJ Luck + MC Neat
Estelle
Fatman Scoop
Natasha Hamilton
Intenso Project
Romina Johnson
Kelly Llorenna
Martin Kemp
Myleene Klass
Kele Le Roc

Lifford
Alison Limerick
LMC vs U2
Lonyo
Shane Lynch
Rachel Macfarlane
Madison Avenue
Lisa Maffia
Matt Goss
Christina Milian
Ministry of Sound Clubbers Guide Tour
Dannii Minogue
M&S Presents The Girl Next Door
Oxide and Neutrino
Pied Piper
Robbie Craig
Romeo
Sash
Scott and Leon
Shola Ama
So Solid Crew
Sonique
The Wideboys
Uniting Nations
Vula (Basement Jaxx)
Wayne Wonder

Mission Control Old School Roster:

2 Unlimited (Anita Doth)
911
Aswad
baby d
Pato Banton
Easther Bennett (Eternal)
Blackbox
Angie Brown
Belinda Carlisle
Chesney Hawkes
Culture Club
Alice Deejay
Jason Donovan
Double Trouble
D:ream
East 17
Frankie Goes to Hollywood
Go West including Peter Cox
Tony Hadley
Honeyz
The Human League
JT Taylor (Kool and the Gang)
JX
Katrina & The Waves
Liquid
Kym Mazelle
Musical Youth
Alexander O'Neal
Pasadenas
Real Thing
Rozalla
Shaun Ryder
SL-2
Snap feat. Turbo D
Sonia
Strike
Sybil
Technotronic
The Outhere Bros
Kenny Thomas
Urban Cookie Collective
Vengaboys
Caron Wheeler
Sharon Woolf

MISSION LOGISTICS

Riverbank House,
1 Putney Bridge Approach, London
SW6 3JD
Tel: 020 7371 0041
Athlete Representation

MISSION MUSIC

3 Plough Row, Deeping St. Nicholas,
Spalding, Lincolnshire PE11 3EW
Tel: 0034 9 6631 8562
Fax: 0034 6 7349 9857
Email: pat@missionmusic.co.uk
Web Site: www.missionmusic.co.uk
Contact: Patrick Johnston

MJE MANAGEMENT

Chaplin Suite, Appledorne,
Allimore Green, Haughton, Stafford,
ST18 9JQ
Tel: 01785 824 824 Tel: 0121 288 2402
Fax: 01785 824000 Mob: 07860 961600
Mob: 07590 500665
Email: mjemanagement@aol.com
Web Site: www.mjemanagement.com
Proprietor: Mike Davenport
Formed 31 years ago by Mike Davenport. Books comedians, vocalists, theatre and pantomime.

ARTISTES REPRESENTED:

Jon Bell
BPM Roadshow
Michael Brooks
Steve Case
Mitchell Craig
Scott David
Dave Diamond
Disco Nights
Steffi Gold
Scott Hindley
Emma Jenson
Tommy Keith
Natalie Knight
Peter Lee
Trevor Leeson
Shelley Marie
Steve McAvoy
Motown Magic
Jonathan Paul
Ashley Reeves (cocktail pianist)
Shirley Ann Turnbull
Lee Warwick

MN2S

4-7 Vineyard London SE1 1QL
Tel: 020 7378 7321
Email: info@mn2s.com
Web Site: http://mn2s.com/
Sharron Elkabas

MOCKINGBIRD MANAGEMENT

PO Box 52, Marlow, Buckinghamshire
SL7 2YB
Tel/Fax: 01491 579 214
Email: mockingbird@aol.com
Contact: Leon Fisk

MODEL PLAN CELEBRITIES & PRESENTERS

4th Floor, 4 Golden Square, London
W1F 9HT
Tel: 020 7287 8444 Fax: 020 7287 2555
Email: michelle@modelplanlondon.co.uk
Web Site: www.modelplan.co.uk
Agent: Sue Sammon, Michelle Davenport

ARTISTES REPRESENTED:

Celebrities:

Helen Adams
Dan Corsi
Jilly Johnson
Stuart Hosking

Presenters:

Emma Ford
Ruth Frances
Amanda Grant
Kevin Harris
Nell McAndrew
Franchesca Robinson
Kate Ryan
Sarah Whitefoot

MODEST! MANAGEMENT

The Matrix Complex,
91 Peterborough Road, London
SW6 3BU
Tel: 0207 384 6410 Fax: 0207 384 6411
Email: harry@modestmanagement.com
Web Site: www.modestmanagement.com
Agents: Harry Magee and Richard Griffiths

ARTISTES REPRESENTED:

Performers:

Alexandra Burke
JLS
Lemar
Leona Lewis
Ruth Lorenzo
Alison Moyet
Paul Potts
Ray Quinn
Rhydian Roberts
Diana Vickers

MONEY MANAGEMENT UK

22 Noel Street London W1F 8GS
Tel: 020 7287 7490 Fax: 020 7287 7499
Email: info@moneymanagementuk.com
Web: www.moneymanagementuk.com
Agent: Amanda Hart

ARTISTES REPRESENTED:

Donna Air
Dougie Anderson
Sophie Blake
Edith Bowman
Matt Brown
Lucie Cave
Joe Challands
Al Convy
Anthony Crank
Emily Newton Dunn
Abbie Eastwood
Rick Edwards
Sadie Frost
Zane Lowe
Sophie McDonnell
Miquita Oliver
Jayne Sharp

Lisa Snowdon
Melanie Sykes
Davinia Taylor
Joanna Taylor
Abi Titmuss

MONEYPENNY AGENCY & MANAGEMENT

The Stables, Westwood House,
Main Street, North Dalton, Driffield,
North Humberside YO25 9XA
Tel: 01377 217815 / 217662 Fax: 01377 217754
Email: nigel.morton@moneypennymusic.co.uk
Web Site: www.moneypennymusic.co.uk
Contact: Nigel Morton

MONKEYBIZ ENTERTAINMENT AGENCY

13 Homan House, Kings Avenue, London SW4 8DB
Tel: 020 8683 9373 Fax: 020 8683 9373
Mobile: 07930 128190
Email: info@monkeybizmanagement.com
Web: www.monkeybizmanagement.com/
Proprietor: Donald Deans
A new company with experienced personnel at dealing with top US and UK acts. We represent reggae, soca, african, soul, pep, R&B, acts, etc. Most of the acts have records out.

ARTISTES REPRESENTED:

SKA:
Laurel Aitken
The Claredonians
Winston Francis (Ind Art)
The Gaylads
Derrick Morgan
Rico
Max Romeo
African Hits:
Bunny Mack
Aura Msmang
Pan African Roadshow
Abdul Tee-Jay`s Rokoto (Sierra Leone)
Soukus Gang
Taxi Pata Pata
Taya Man
Artists With Past International Hits:
Ken Boothe
Judy Boucher
Dave & Ansel Collins
The Greyhound
Audrey Hall
John Holt
Tippa Irie
Janet Kay
Max Romeo
Trevor Walters
Soca Acts:
Arrow
Front Page
Byron Lee & The Dragoners
Shango
Storm
Gospel:
Denzil Dennis
The Golden Chords
Donna Marie
Jennifer Phillips
The Wades
Legendary Reggae Acts:
Abacush
Dennis Alcapone
Dave Barker
Dennis Bovell Dub Band
Al Campbell
Chosen Few
Alton Ellis
Peter Hunningale
Fred Locks
Ruddy Thomas
Soul Acts:
Black Velvet
Milly Jackson
The Manhattans
Wayne Marshall
Gwen McCrae
Noel McKoy
The Pasadenas
Precious WIlson & Eruptions
Radio DJs:
Daddy Ernie (Choice FM)
Chris Goldfinger (Radio One FM)
Rankin Ms P (GLR)
David Rodigan (Kiss FM)
Tribute Acts:
Pamela Maynard (Gladys Knight tribute)
Sol Ray (Nat King Cole tribute)
Popsi Williams (Barry White)

MOONLIGHT AGENCY

PO Box 54, Plymouth PL3 4XU
Tel: 01752 262 200 Fax: 01752 267 532
Email: andre@moonlightagency.co.uk
Web Site: www.moonlightagency.co.uk
Contact: Andre Baker

ARTISTES REPRESENTED:

Abba Sisters
E Dub-O
Georgia
Billy Hunter
Clive John
Steve Laister
Jeanette McFarlane
Stephan Miles
Quango
Retro
Tank Sherman
Sister Sister
Stee-V
Strung Out
Tempting Fate
Twice Shy
Ruby Washington

MORGAN & GOODMAN

Mezzanine, Quadrant House,
80-82 Regent Street, London W1B 5RP
Tel: 020 7437 1383
Email: mg1@btinternet.com
Proprietor: Tanya Greep

JANE MORGAN MANAGEMENT

Elsinore House 77 Fulham Palace Road, London W6 8JA
Tel: 020 7478 7479
Email: enquiries@janemorganmgt.com
Web Site: www.janemorganmgt.com
Senior Personnel: Jane Morgan
Specialises in the representation of sports broadcasters and sportsmen and women who now have a career in the media.

ARTISTES REPRESENTED:

Jonathan Agnew
Peter Alliss
Bill Beaumont OBE
Peter Brackley
Sir Trevor Brooking CBE
James Burridge
Mike Cattermole
Gabriel Clarke
Kevin Connelly
Robin Cousins MBE
Ian Darke
Susie Dent
Brendan Foster MBE
Louise Goodman
Hazel Irvine
Angus Loughran
Desmond Lynam OBE
Victoria Mather
Ally McCoist MBE
Jim McGrath
John Motson OBE
Rishi Persad
Steve Wilson

MORNINGSIDE MANAGEMENT

3 Old Rectory Drive, Thornhaugh,
Peterborough PE8 6HW
Tel: 05600 712 234
Email: steve@morningsidemanagement.com
Managing Director: Steve Barker
Promotes and manages artists (mostly within the theatre circuit) and also specialises in high quality tribute shows.

JAE MOSS ENTERPRISES

Riverside House, Feltham Avenue,
Hampton Court Surrey KT8 9BJ
Tel: 020 8979 3459 Fax: 020 8979 9631
Mobile: 07799 145999
Email: jmossent@aol.com
Web: www.jaemossenterprises.dsl.pipex.com/
Existing clients only.

ARTISTES REPRESENTED:

Krystal Archer
Lucille Barclay
Ruth Baxter
Kate Buxton
Hannah Chick
Emma Choy
Philip ClaytonSmith
Michelle Connolly
Don Crann
David Ephgrave
Gillian Hardie
Jemma Harris
David Kent
Gus Macgregor
Kevin Matthews
Drew McKay
Colin Pinrey
Mark Porter
Nova Reid
Karen Rush

Nicola Rutherford
Peter Saul
Isabella Seibert
Richard Siddway
Anna Stolli
Colin Twist
Anthony Whiteman
Paul Wright

MOUTHPIECE PRODUCTIONS LTD

PO Box 145 Inkberrow, Worcester
WR7 4EL
Tel: 01386 792 546
Email: info@mouthpieceuk.co.uk
Web:
www.mouthpiece-entertainments.co.uk
Contact: Keith Potts

MPC ENTERTAINMENT

MPC House, 15-16 Maple Mews,
Maida Vale, London NW6 5UZ
Tel: 020 7624 1184 Fax: 020 7624 4220
Email: mpc@mpce.com
Web Site: www.mpce.com
Senior Personnel: Michael P Cohen, Jonathan Cohen, Nick Canham, Sarah Rix, Matthew Mansfield.

ARTISTES REPRESENTED:

Josette Aitman
Bam Bam
Robin Banks
Jeremy Beadle
Tony Blackburn
David Boom
Allan Border
OJ Borg
Ian Botham MBE
Jono Buchanard
Wes Butters
Terry Christian
Gary Crowley
DJ Spoony
Andy Friendlander & Suzanne Duckett
Jon Gaunt
Jane Gazzo
Ian Healy
Alison Hulme
James Hyman
Jono Inverdale
Ben Jones
Charlie Jordan
Jacques Kallis
John Kearns
Lance Klusener
Justin Langer
Alex Lester
Jonah Lomu
Max
Alan Mullally
Mark Nicholas
Femi Oke
Richard Park
Steve Penk
Paul Phear
Natilie Pirks
Gary Player
Shaun Pollock
Mark Ramprakash
Mike Read
Jonty Rhodes
CeCe Sammy
Pat Sharp
Streetboy
Mark Taylor
Tayo
Natalie Du Toit
Trevor, Cueball & Ros
Shane Warne
Nicki Waterman
Steve Waugh
Russ Williams
Bob Woolmer

Excl with Austin Robinson (Aus):
David Boon
Allan Border
Wayne Grady

Excl with Paul Smith Promos (Aus):
John Buchanan
Ian Healy

Excl with Maestro Sports Mngt (SA):
Jacques Kallis

Excl with Fordham Company (Aus):
Mark Taylor (Aus)

Excl with Fiona Lomu (Manager):
Jonah Lomu

Excl with Mission Sports Management (UK):
Ian Botham MBE

Excl with Harley Medcalf:
Simon Katich
Justin Langer
Steve Waugh

Excl with Francois Brink:
Natalie Du Toit

MPL COMMUNICATIONS LTD

1 Soho Square, London W1D 3BQ
Tel: 020 7534 4100 / 0780 1189 745
Web Site: www.mplcommunications.com
Phone number is ex-directory.
Contact: Lillian Marshall

ARTISTES REPRESENTED:

Sir Paul McCartney

MR "E" ENTERPRISES

Little Greenfields Farm, Jack Haye Lane, Light Oaks, Stoke-on-Trent, Staffordshire
ST2 7NG
Tel: 01782 304 909
Mobile: 07831 311318
Email: info@mreenterprises.co.uk
Senior Personnel: Eddie Burke

ARTISTES REPRESENTED:

Eddie Burke
The Complete Childrens Party Co.
Hypno Comedy Show
Miracle of the Mindreading show
Mix and Mingle Magic & Balloonologist Group
Mr "E" The Magician
The Traditional Punch & Judy Show

MR MAGIC ENTERTAINMENTS

18 Church Street, Sutton-on-Hull,
East Yorkshire HU7 4TS
Tel: 01482 709 939 (Children's Parties)
Mob: 07787 557 412
Fax: 01482 787 362
Email: alan@mrmagicentertainments.co.uk
Web: www.mrmagicentertainments.co.uk
Contact: Alan Hudson
Provision of magicians, clowns, fire-eaters etc.

ARTISTES REPRESENTED:

Alan Hudson
Martyn James
Robert Jamieson
Juggling Jamie
James Long
Magic Hayley's Facepainting
Magic Philip
Jon Marshall
Mr Magic Entertainments
Nutty Norman
Punch & Judy
Tim Tagora
Billy Tempest

Side Shows:
Cleo (girl in the goldfish bowel)
Yvette
The Headless Lady
Gloria (the half-living lady)
Madame Penny Arcadia
The Amazing Martin (Escapology & Thrills)

MR SKETCHUM'S CARICATURES

69 Egerton Road, London N16 6UE
Mobile: 07719 262 736
Email: alfie@sketchum.co.uk
Web Site: www.sketchum.co.uk
Contact: Alfie Deliss
Alfie Deliss, also known as Mr Sketchum, a product of Chelsea College of Art available to sketch at all kinds of corporate and private events. See the website for lots of examples of 'live' sketches and more ...

ARTISTES REPRESENTED:

Mr Sketchum's Caricatures

MTC (UK) LTD

20 York Street, London W1U 6PU
Tel: 020 7935 8000 Fax: 020 7935 8066
Email: natasha@mtc-uk.com
Web Site: www.mtc-uk.com
For Presenters/TV Enquiries, contact: Natasha Clarke

ARTISTES REPRESENTED:

TV Presenters/Broadcasters:
Steve Backley MBE OBE
Alexandra Boyd
Dr Tim Brabants MBE
Pete Cohen
James Cracknell OBE
Annabel Croft
Robbie Earle MBE
Jonathan Edwards CBE
Professor Paul Gately
Paul Goodison MBE
Sally Gunnell OBE
James Hooper
Colin Jackson CBE
Dean Macey
Alistair Mann
Steve Parry
Natasha Rocca Devine
Babita Sharma
Lee Sharpe

Danny Steele
Di Stewart
Leon Taylor

MTM PRESENTATIONS
Avron House, 37 Highmeadow,
Ringley Wood, Radcliffe, Manchester
M26 1YN
Tel: 0161 725 9991 Fax: 0161 725 9199
Mob: 07970 205 060
Email: info@mtmpresentations.co.uk
Web Site: www.mtmpresentations.co.uk
Senior Personnel: Gaynor Green
ARTISTES REPRESENTED:
The Casablanca Steps
Street Theatre:
Artizani
Melvyn Artwarg
The Big Gals
Bread & Butter Theatre Company
Circus Fudge
Creature Features
The Curious Eyebrows
The Desperate Men
The Grand Theatre of Lemmings
Heir of Insanity - aerial, hand balance, artistic stilts
Bob & Bob Jobbins
Lady Christobel & Her Butler
The Smallest Theatre in the World
The Splott Brothers
The Amusing Sister Ruth!
What a Palaver
Zoot
Clowns:
The Ambassadors of Borrowash
Artizani
Bozo & Zizi with Fifi
The Brass Hoppers
Brodini's Magic
Calvero & Jan
Geoff Capes
Chester's Show Time
Chuckles
Circus Fudge
City of Coventry Corps of Drums
Stuart Clarke
Clown Matto
Crazy Chris
Crazy Tramps
Richard Cumming
The Custard Clowns
Dancing Diggers
Derby Midshipmen Carnival Band
Gus Dermody's Sheepdog Displays
Dingle Fingle
Dingle Fingle's Clowntown Crimewatch
Eagle & Vulture Show
Essex Dog Display Team
Flying Gunners Royal Artillery
Freddie The Fire Engine
The Game Goers Falconry
Gentle Jazz
Chris Goring
Yuri Grignoff
Harmony Hounds
The Hawk Experience
Heart of England Falconry
Bill Heslop
Elaine Hill
H&M Dog Display Team
The Imps Motorcycle Display Team
Ian Jay's Sponge Plunge
Jukalo
K9 Commandoes Dog Display
Kangaroos Gymnastic Display
Knights of Arkley
Lakeland Birds of Prey
Last Action Heroes
Brian Lecomber's Firebird Team
Gary Lees Great Escapes
Johnny & Barbara Ley
Mattie The Clown
Matto & Polo
Melton Mowbray Tally-Ho
Melton Mowbray Toy Soldiers
Motorcycle Mad Men!
Mr Topper
Mr Woo
Gerard Naprous
The Pathfinders
Phoenix New Orleons
Portsmouth Area VC Field Gun Display
The Red Arrows
Rockwood Dog Display
Royal Signals White Helmets
Saker Falconry
Scottish Academy
Sebastian's Incredibly Cool Band
South Cheshire Dog Team
Spangles
Spotty Dotty
Squires All American Marching Band
Suitcase Circus
Vander Brothers - Triple Wheel Spectacular
Richard Vobes
Warwick Girls Marching Band
Wax & Wain
Welsh Hawking Centre
John Whiteley
Yuri & Tanya

MUCH LOVED PRODUCTIONS LTD
The British Philharmonic Concert Orchestra
8 Oaks Farm Drive, Darton, Barnsley,
South Yorkshire S75 5BZ
Tel: 01226 380 175 Fax: 01226 380 566
Mob: 07802 959 594
Email: jeremy@mlpltd.com
Web Site: www.mlpltd.com
Senior Personnel: Mr JM Peaker, Mr M Peaker, Mrs JA Peaker
Specialising in all types of entertainment and corporate hospitality concerts. Shows and productions incorporating the British Philharmonic Concert Orchestra.

ARTISTES REPRESENTED:
The British Philharmonic Concert Orchestra

MULTI-MEDIA ENTERTAINMENTS
Treetops, Radford Lane, Lower Penn,
Wolverhampton, West Midlands WV3 8JT
Tel: 01902 761 126 Mobile: 07831 405 882
Email: mark@multi-mediaentertainments.co.uk
Web Site: www.multi-mediaentertainments.co.uk / www.mmel.co.uk
Senior Personnel: Mark Stokes
ARTISTES REPRESENTED:
Dean Bingham
Keith Cash
DJ Motor
Kris Krendo
KT Roadshow
Lady and the Tramp
Dave Peters
Tamzin
Centre Stage Disco Roadshow
Platinum Tracks Disco Roadshow

MUSIC BUSINESS MANAGEMENT
Labrican Healey Dell Nature Reserve
ROCHDALE OL12 6BG
Tel: 01706 524425
Email: info@mbmcorporate.co.uk
Web Site: www.mbmcorporate.co.uk
Anne Barrett

MUSIC FOR SCOTLAND
9-10 St. Andrew Square, Edinburgh
EH2 2AF
Tel: 0131 718 6069
Email: info@musicforscotland.co.uk
Web Site: www.musicforscotland.co.uk
Contact: Richard Lyon

MUSIC INTERNATIONAL
13 Ardilaun Road, London N5 2QR
Tel: 020 7359 5183 Fax: 020 7226 9792
Email: music@musicint.co.uk
Web Site: www.musicint.co.uk
Managing Director: Neil Dalrymple
Artist Manager: Rob Berry
ARTISTES REPRESENTED:
Sopranos:
Daniela Bechly
Rebecca Blankenship
Samantha Cole
Claire Debono
Sandra Ford
Alla Kravchuk
Fiona McAndrew
Constance Novis
Charlotte Page
Linda Tuvas
Counter-Tenors:
Iestyn Morris
Christopher Robson
Andrew Watts
Mezzo-Sopranos:
Alison Browner
Yvonne Burnett
Linda Finnie
Deborah Hawksley
Eirian James (Welsh & English Language)
Della Jones
Linda Ormiston
Pamela Helen Stephen
Tenors:
Ales Briscein
Simon Butteriss (buffo)
Hal Cazalet
Amos Christie

Daniel Hoadley
Neil Jenkins
Tyrone Landau
Robert Millner
Dominic Natoli
Tom Raskin
Baritones & Basses:
Ian Caddy
Alan Cemore
Julian Close
Julian Hubbard
Ivan Kusnjer
James Levesque
Donald Maxwell
Peter Mikulas
Geoffrey Moses
Sir John Tomlinson
John Wegner
Conductors:
Roderick Brydon
Michael Rosewell
Oliver Von Dohnanyi

MUSIC MAN ENTERTAINMENTS

52 Chapel Street, Billericay, Essex
CM12 9LS
Tel: 01277 630 367 / 01277 655 558
Fax: 01277 655 558
Contact: Mr Gary Edwards

THE MUSIC PARTNERSHIP LTD

41 Aldebert Terrace, London SW8 1BH
Tel: 020 7840 9590 Fax: 020 7735 7595
Email: office@musicpartnership.co.uk
Web Site: www.musicpartnership.co.uk
Directors: Louise Badger and Lawrence Kershaw
Musician's Agency.

ARTISTES REPRESENTED:

Anton Du Beke and Erin Boag
Louise Cannon
Geoffrey Dalton
Alan Fairs
Patrick Fourniller
Lesley Garrett
Gianluigi Gelmetti
Jacek Kaspszyk
Libra (Group)
Andras Ligeti
Enrique Diemecke
Marijn Simons
Kathleen Wilkinson
Roland Wood

MUSIC SCOTLAND INTERNATIONAL

24 Ochil Road, Alva, Clackmannanshire
FK12 5JT Scotland
Tel/Fax: 01259 760 126
Email: johndouglas@musicscotlandint.com
Web Site: www.musicscotlandint.com
Senior Personnel: John Douglas

MUSICAL AGENCY AND MANAGEMENT LTD

The Seedbed Centre, Langston Road,
Loughton, Essex IG10 3TQ
Tel: 020 8501 2469 Fax: 020 8502 6863
Email: info@manhattan-nights.co.uk / david@showtime.uk.com
Senior Personnel: David Fellerman
Producers and promoters of musical theatre.

ARTISTES REPRESENTED:

The Musical Celebration "Manhattan Nights"

MUSICAL ASSOCIATES (UK) LTD

64-66 Akeman Street, Tring, Hertfordshire
HP23 6AF
Tel: 01442 828 400 Fax: 01442 828 401
Email: info@musicalassociates.co.uk
Web Site: www.musicalassociates.co.uk
Senior Personnel: Rob McIntosh
Specialising in: session musicians for recordings, concerts, shows, musical entertainment, outdoor concerts & foreign tours.

MUSICIAN MANAGEMENT

132 Main Road, Quadring, Spalding,
Lincolnshire PE11 4PW
Tel: 01775 821 215
Email: music@tonyparkingson.co.uk
Web Site: www.tonyparkinson.co.uk
Senior Personnel: Tony Parkinson
Specialising in: Childrens Entertainment. for primary school concerts, music workshop tours.

ARTISTES REPRESENTED:

Artiste:
Tony Parkinson

MWM PERSONAL MANAGEMENT

"Colnbrook", 133 Tennyson Road,
Stockwood Park, Bedfordshire LU1 3RP
Tel/Fax: 01582 450 111
Email: michelle.worthington1e@virgin.net
Director: Mrs M Worthington

ARTISTES REPRESENTED:

Darren Day
Richard McCourt
Dominic Wood

MYTHOLOGY AGENCY

4th Floor 10 Greenland Street London
NW1 0ND
Tel: 020 3286 6604
Email: mark@mythology-live.com
Web Site: www.mythology-live.com
Mark Lewis

NAMES & FACES

Represented by Entertainment @ Drewry's
639 Norfolk House
London Gatwick Airport Gatwick
RH6 0NN
Tel: 08707 554 555 Fax: 01293 567100
Email: bernie@names-and-faces.co.uk
Contact: Bernie Wilson

ARTISTES REPRESENTED:

Beverley Sisters
Jess Conrad
Don Durbridge
Michael Fish MBE DSc
Christine Hamilton
David Hamilton
Cynthia Payne

NANCY HUDSON ASSOCIATES

3rd Floor, 50 South Molton Street,
London W1K 5SB
Tel: 020 7499 5548 Fax: 020 7499 0884
Email: agents@nancyhudsonassociates.com
Web: www.nancyhudsonassociates.com
Senior Personnel: Nancy Hudson, Charlotte Warner

ARTISTES REPRESENTED:

Male:
Tony Arunah Abbey
Robert Ashby
Robert Atiko
Jason Bailey
Nigel Barrett
Andy Beckwith
Marc Bolton
Arthur Bostrom
Christian Bradley
Paul Cameron
Pushpinder Chani
John Cormack
Tristram Davies
John Downham
Tanveer Ghani
Gerard Gilroy
Brian Gwaspari
Tim Hudson
Brian Jordan
Adrian Jubb
David Kershaw
Hugh Lloyd
Fabiano Martell
Roger Martin
Daniel Osgerby
Craster Pringle
Robert Purdy
Richard Roach
Robert McIntosh
Hassani Shapi
Matthew Sim
James Staddon
Richard Sutton
James Walmsley
Ian Warwick
Paul Williamson
Female:
Melissa Collier
Meneka Das
Sevilla Delofski
Beverley Denim
Susie Fairfax
Miranda Floy
Natasha Godfrey
Christine Handy
Nicola Harrison
Madeleine Howard
Liz Izen
Charlotte Jones
Emma Katz
Taryn Kay
Krishna Kumari
Sarah Lowries
Petra Markham
Zibba Mays

Polly Moore
Abbé Muschallik
Siobhan Nicholas
Lisa Peace
Sarah Quist
Nichola Rees
Annabel Reid
Erica Rossi
Nikki Leigh Scott
Maureen Sweeney
Phoebe Sweeney
Siren Turkesh
Karen Wallace-Jones
Amy Williams
Amber Worrall

THE NARROW ROAD COMPANY

3rd Floor, 76 Neal Street, London
WC2H 9PL
Tel: 020 7379 9598 Fax: 020 7379 9777
Email: amy@narrowroad.co.uk
Web Site: www.narrowroad.co.uk
Senior Personnel: Richard Ireson, Amy Ireson, James Ireson,
Lisa Dennis

ARTISTES REPRESENTED:

James Crossley
Anne Marie Davies
Stefan Dennis
Paul Hegarty
Jake McCarthy
Eddie Nestor
Kate O'Mara
Flik Swan
Rebecca Wheatley

THE NARROW ROAD COMPANY

2nd Floor, Grampian House
144 Deansgate, Manchester M3 3EE
Tel/Fax: 0161 833 1605
Email: manchester@narrowroad.co.uk
Web Site: www.narrowroad.co.uk
Director: Elizabeth Stocking

ARTISTES REPRESENTED:

Justine Adams
Karen Asemper
Christina Baily
Tim Beasley
Denton Brown
Jenna-Louise Coleman
Nigel Collins
Susan Cormack
Pauline Daniels
Marc Finn
Ralph Gassmann
Toby Hadoke
Marcus Hercules
Samuel James Hudson
Archie Kelly
Olwen May
Susan McArdle
Georgina Mellor
Helen Moon
Seamus O`Neill
Liam O'Brien
Colin Parry
Sara Roache
Debbie Shore
Richard Sinnott
Cyriack Stevenson
Amy Stratton
Val Tagger
Hayley Tamaddon
Kevin Tucker

NATION RECORDS LTD/QFM PUBLISHING

19 All Saints Road, Notting Hill, London
W11 1HE
Tel: 020 7792 8167 Fax: 020 7792 2854
Email: akination@btopenworld.com
Web Site: www.nationrecords.co.uk
Senior Personnel: Aki Nawaz
A&R: Rich McLean

ARTISTES REPRESENTED:

Asian Dub Foundation
Natasha Atlas
Charged
Fun-Da-Mental
Hard Kaur
Loop Guru
Lunar Drive
Recycler
TJ Rehmi
DJ Chebi I Sabbah
Swami
Transglobal Underground
Yam Yam

N.B. MANAGEMENT

PO Box 100, East Horsley, Surrey
KT24 6WN
Tel: 01483 282 666 Fax: 01483 284 777
Email: nick@bomford.com
Web Site: www.bomford.com
Senior Personnel: Nick Bomford
Orchestral Contractor, Concert Management

ARTISTES REPRESENTED:

Guildford Philharmonic
London Soloists Chamber Orchestra

NEM PRODUCTIONS (UK)

Priory House, 55 Lawe Road,
South Shields, Tyne and Wear NE33 2AL
Tel: 0191 427 6207 Fax: 0191 427 6323
Email: dave@nemproductions.com
Web Site: www.nemproductions.com
Contact: Dave Smith

ARTISTES REPRESENTED:

Pierre Bensusan
Thom Bresh
Bob Brozman
Clive Carroll
Johnny Dickinson
Tommy Emmanuel
Aziz Ibrahim
Joscho Stephan Trio
Woody Mann
Tony McManus
Dareth Pearson
John Renbourn

NEMESIS AGENCY LTD

1 Oxford Court, Manchester M2 3WQ
Tel: 0161 228 6646 Fax: 0161 228 6727
Email: enquiries@nmsmanagement.co.uk
Web Site: www.nemesisagency.co.uk
Agency Manager: Sam Coulson

NEMESIS CASTING LTD

Nemesis House, 1 Oxford Court,
Manchester M2 3WQ
Tel: 0161 228 6404 Fax: 0161 228 6727
Email: sheila@nmsmanagement.co.uk
Web Site: www.nemesiscasting.co.uk
Senior Personnel: Sheila Tollitt

NEON MANAGEMENT

34 Clare Lane, London N1 3DB
Tel: 020 7359 4884
Fax: 020 7359 5280
Email: info@neonmanagement.com
Web Site: www.neonmanagement.com
Agent: Dave Reid

ARTISTES REPRESENTED:

Calum Best
Bianca Gascoigne
Michael Greco
Gary Lucy
Michelle Marsh
Lee Otway
Luci Victoria

NETTWERK MANAGEMENT

Clearwater Yard, 35 Inverness Street,
Camden London NW1 7HB
Tel: 020 7424 7500
Fax: 020 7424 7501
Email: jason@nettwerk.com
Web Site: www.nettwerk.com
Agent: Jason Marcus

ARTISTES REPRESENTED:

The Pipettes

NEVS AGENCY

2nd Floor, Regal House, 198 Kings Road,
London SW3 5XP
Tel: 020 7352 4886 (Men) Tel: 020 7352 9496 (Girls) Fax: 020 7352 6068
Email: getamodel@nevs.co.uk
Web Site: www.nevs.co.uk
Senior Personnel: Paul Cavalier

NEW FACES

2nd Floor, The Linen Hall,
162-168 Regent Street, London
W1B 5TB
Tel: 020 7439 6900 Fax: 020 7287 5481
Email: val@newfacestalent.co.uk
Web Site: www.newfacestalent.co.uk
Agents: Val Horton, Tania Patti

New Faces is a dynamic presenters, actors and extras agency situated in the west end of London. The agency is aimed at giving highly talented people of today a platform from which to launch their career and established artists a professional, friendly, approachable and highly efficient service.

If you wish to be considered for representation, please send us a copy of your showreel (if appropriate), up-to-date CV or details of experience, photograph and SAE. All tapes are viewed and if we are interested we will contact you and arrange an interview.

For more information call Val or Cathy on 020 7439 6900.

NEW VISION ARTS MANAGEMENT

1 Canada Square, Canary Wharf Tower
London E14 5DY
Tel: 0870 444 2506 Fax: 0870 22 00 238
Email: paul@newvisionarts.com
Web Site: www.nvaentgroup.com
Agent: Paul Boadi
We are a young management company that represents top Premiership Footballers, Music Acts, Models, Actors/Actresses and TV Presenters.

ARTISTES REPRESENTED:

Addictive
Ebony Alleyne
Bashy

NEWLAND ARTISTES MANAGEMENT SERVICES

Newland House, 177 Boothferry Road, Hessle, North Humberside HU13 9BB
Tel: 01482 641 172 Fax: 01482 640 088
Email: newlandartistes@hotmail.co.uk
Senior Personnel: Stuart Adamson

NEWSUBSTANCE ARTISTS

Medius House, 2 Sheraton Street, London W1F 8BH
Tel: 0845 257 9611 Fax: 0870 622 1681
Email: info@newsubstance-artists.co.uk
Web: www.newsubstance-artists.co.uk
Contact: Matthew Stowe

NIC PICOT ENTERTAINMENT

25 Highfield, Watford Hertsfordshire WD19 5DY
Tel: 020 8421 2500
Email: lesleyp@nicpicot.co.uk
Web Site: www.nicpicot.co.uk
Partners - Nic Picot, Lesley Picot & Linda Laban
Specialising in magic, mix & mingle entertainment, celebrities & speakers, and all types of music & dance for corporate & private entertainment

NICE PEOPLE PRODUCTIONS LTD

12 Magnay Road, Drayton, Norwich NR8 6BT
Tel: 01603 426009 Fax: 01603 487580
Email: nicepeopleproductions@hotmail.com
Web: www.nicepeopleproductions.com
Contact: Paul Wortley

NICK ROSS

c/o Rachel Goodwin, PO Box 999, London W2 4XT
Tel: 020 7243 1325 Fax: 020 7792 9200
Mobile: 07966 491 256
Email: nickross@lineone.net
Web Site: www.nickross.com
Contact: Rachel Goodwin
Presenter Crimewatch (since 1984). Credits include Call Nick Ross, Westminster With Nick Ross, The Commission, A Week In Politics, Watchdog, Newsnight, breakfast TV, Man Alive, World at One, The World Tonight, documentaries, debates, chat shows and quizzes. Conference chairman and facilitator. President, trustee, ambassador of over a dozen charities inc UK Stem Cell Foundation.

ARTISTES REPRESENTED:

Nick Ross

NMP LIVE LTD

8 Blenheim Court Brook Way
Leatherhead, Surrey KT22 7NA
Tel: 01372 361004 Fax: 01372 374417
Email: live@nmp.co.uk
Web Site: www.nmplive.co.uk
Managing Directors: Neil Martin, Chris Banks.
Leading UK entertainment agency specialising in celebrity personal appearances, high profile entertainment, negotiating endorsements and advertising campaigns and presenting after-dinner, motivational & conference speakers.

ARTISTES REPRESENTED:

Kate Adie OBE
Samira Ahmed
Lucy Alexander
Kirstie Allsopp
Dave Alred MBE
Stephen K Amos
Ronni Ancona
Clive Anderson
Lord Archer
Michael Aspel OBE
Bill Bailey
Johnny Ball
Duncan Bannatyne OBE
Dave Bassett
Dr John Bird OBE
Roger Black MBE
Tony Blackburn
Nils Blyth
Erin Boag
Stefan Booth
Ian Botham MBE
Jeremy Bowen
Frankie Boyle
Kyran Bracken MBE LLB
Julia Bradbury
Lord Melvyn Bragg
Jo Brand
Gyles Brandreth
Sir Richard Branson
Rory Bremner
Erin Brockovich
Derren Brown
Jocelyn Brown
Fiona Bruce
Frank Bruno MBE
Rob Brydon
Professor Tanya Byron
James Caan
Alastair Campbell
Will Carling OBE
Alan Carr
Jimmy Carr
Todd Carty
Adrian Chiles
Oz Clarke
Jeremy Clarkson
Brendan Cole
Clive Coleman
Barry Cryer
Jamie Cullum
Jon Culshaw
Rob Curling
Edwina Currie
Paul Daniels
Jim Davidson OBE
Bobby Davro
Alan Dedicoat
Jack Dee
Katie Derham
Diversity
Alesha Dixon
Omid Djalili
Wayne Dobson
Craig Doyle
Geoffrey Durham
Greg Dyke
Huw Edwards
Escala
Richard Farleigh
Nick Ferrari
Sir Ranulph Fiennes Bt OBE
Flawless
Ben Fogle
Bruce Forsyth CBE
Stephen Fry
Chris Gardner
Frank Gardner OBE
Lesley Garrett
Uri Geller
Jacqueline Gold
Graham Gooch OBE
Bear Grylls
Tony Gubba
Sally Gunnell OBE
David Gunson
Krishnan Guru-Murthy
Christine Hamilton
Sir Stuart Hampson
Ainsley Harriott
Sahar Hashemi
Lenny Henry CBE
Harry Hill
Eamonn Holmes
Dame Kelly Holmes
Lord Michael Howard
John Humphrys
Konnie Huq
Sir Geoff Hurst MBE
Eddie Irvine
General Sir Michael Jackson
Judi James
Katherine Jenkins
Boris Johnson
Michael Johnson
Luke Johnston
Peter Jones
Jordan (AKA Katie Price)
Diane Louise Jordan
Journey South
Phil Jupitus
Vernon Kay
Patrick Kielty
Mark Lamarr
Allan Lamb MBE
Amanda Lamb
Nick Leeson
Allan Leighton
Dr David Lewis
Denise Lewis

Maureen Lipman CBE
Dominic Littlewood
Kenny Logan
Matt Lucas
Lulu
Lee Mack
Vanessa Mae
Lord Peter Mandelson
Andrew Marr
James Martin
Max Clifford
James May
Simon May
Davina McCall
Perry McCarthy
Gary McCausland
Martine McCutcheon
John McEnroe
Barry McGuigan MBE
Michael McIntyre
Michelle Mone
Chris Moon
Steve Nallon
Martina Navratilova
Jack Nicklaus
Archie Norman MP
Barry Norman
Dara O'Briain
Kev Orkian
Theo Paphitis
Richard Park
Joe Pasquale
Jeremy Paxman
Suzi Perry
Fiona Phillips
Fay Presto
Harry Redknapp
Doug Richard
Jonathan Ross
Nick Ross
Pete Sampras
George Sampson
June Sarpong
Nadia Sawalha
Leo Sayer
Phillip Schofield
David Seaman
Monica Seles
John Sergeant
Lee Sharpe
Peter Shilton MBE OBE
David Shukman
Junior Simpson
Heather Small
Tim Smit CBE
Peter Snow
Phil Spencer
Alastair Stewart OBE
Jackie Stewart
John Suchet
John Suchet
Claire Sweeney
Chris Tarrant
Jim Tavare
Dennis Taylor
Dennis Taylor
Hamish Taylor
Phil Tufnell
Bonnie Tyler
Tim Vine
Murray Walker OBE
David Walliams
Capt. Brian Walpole
Hayley Westenra
Simon Weston OBE
Jo Whiley
Toyah Wilcox
Rav Wilding
Serena Williams
Shaun Williamson (Barry, Eastenders)
Holly Willoughby
Quentin Willson
Richard Wilson
Henry Winkler
Professor Lord Robert Winston
Simon Woodroffe
Ian Wright
Paul Zerdin

NMP MANAGEMENT

8 Blenheim Court Brook Way
Leatherhead Surrey KT22 7NA
Tel: 01372 361 004 Fax: 01372 374 417
Email: management@nmp.co.uk
Web Site: www.nmpmanagement.co.uk
Managing Directors: Neil Martin, Chris Banks.
Client list encompasses both established and up-and-coming talent with emphasis towards television presenters, entrepreneurs, academics and topic experts.

ARTISTES REPRESENTED:

Mark Borkowski
Paul Daniels
Richard Farleigh
Sir Stuart Hampson
Dr Ian Johnston
Ross Kemp
Nick Leeson
Simon May
Gary McCausland
Debbie McGee
Kev Orkian
Quentin Willson
Prof Heinz Wolff

NOEL GAY ORGANISATION

19 Denmark Street, London WC2H 8NA
Tel: 020 7836 3941 Fax: 020 7287 1816
Email: info@noelgay.com
Web Site: www.noelgay.com
Chief Executive Officer: Alex Armitage
Managing Director: Nick Ranceford-Hadley

ARTISTES REPRESENTED:

Writers:
Paul Alexander
James Bachman
Danny Baker
Adrian Bean
Marc Blake
Margaret Cabourn-Smith
Johnny Candon
Sean Carson
Len Collin
Toby Davies
Tudor Davies
Margaret Doyle
Mark Evans
Simon Fanshawe
Fat Pie
Sir David Frost OBE
Kim Fuller
Micheal & Shaun Gallagher & Alan Kelly
Zoe Gardner
Matt Green
Jeremy Hardy
Sven Hughes
Robin Ince
Milton Jones
Paul Karensa
Danny Kelly
Beth Kilcoyne
Emma Kilcoyne
Rod Liddle
Christopher Lillicrap
Paul Litchfield
Geoff Lloyd
Hannah Mackay
Kelvin MacKenzie
Martel Maxwell
Dan Mersh
Rageh Omaar
Steve Parry
Chris Pell
Amanda Platell
Eve Pollard
Adrian Poynton
Steve Punt
Howard Read
Laurence Rickard
George Sawyer
Peter Skellern
Dr Pam Spurr
Richard Stilgoe
Lowri Turner
Dave Vitty
Ed Weeks
Phil Whelans
Arnold Widdowson
Liam Woodman
Male Voices:
Scott Ainslie
James Bachman
Danny Baker
Todd Carty
Tony Clarkin
Martin Collins
Mark Evans
Stephen Fry
Matt Green
Nick Hancock
Jeremy Hardy
Peter Harkness
Robin Ince
Jeremy Limb
Paul Litchfield
Geoff Lloyd
Toby Longworth
David Menkin
Dan Mersh
Pete Mitchell
Dave Mounfield
Nathan Osgood
Ian Payne
Steve Punt
Mark Roper
Dave Vitty
Johnnie Walker
Phil Whelans
Female Voices:
Nana Akua
Sam Battersea
Margaret Cabourn-Smith

Zoe Gardner
Lucy Montgomery
Barunka O'Shaughnessy
Su Pollard
Stephanie Street
Fleur Taylor
Miranda Wilson
Barbara Young
Male Performers:
4 Poofs & A Piano
James Bachman
Johnny Candon
Tudor Davies
Mark Evans
Fat Pie
Matt Green
Jeremy Hardy
Robin Ince
Milton Jones
Paul Karensa
Jeremy Limb
Paul Litchfield
Toby Longworth
Cal McCrystal
Dan Mersh
Chris Neill
Steve Parry
Adrian Poynton
Steve Punt
John Ratzenberger
Howard Read
Laurence Rickard
George Sawyer
Peter Skellern
Richard Stilgoe
Ed Weeks
Phil Whelans
Arnold Widdowson
Liam Woodman
Female Performers:
Sam Battersea
Margaret Cabourn-Smith
Zoe Gardner
Emma Kilcoyne
Su Pollard
Miranda Wilson
Presenters:
Anita Anand
Dalaz Azar
Felicity Barr
Rob Butler
Martin Collins
Leyla Daybelge
Margaret Doyle
Juliet Errington
Simon Fanshawe
Sir David Frost OBE
Jane Gazzo
Krishnan Guru-Murthy
Jeremy Hardy
Steve Harley
Robin Ince
Danny Kelly
Riz Lateef
Rod Liddle
Ben De Lisi
Geoff Lloyd
Kelvin MacKenzie
Martel Maxwell
Adela Meer
Louise Minchin
Pete Mitchell
Jon Monie
Sarah Montague
Gigi Morley
Chris Neill
Mary Nightingale
Mary-Ann Ochota
Rageh Omaar
Ian Payne
Amanda Platell
Eve Pollard
Su Pollard
Louisa Preston
Steve Punt
Steve Punt
Raj & Pablo
Angus Scott
Steph Seager
Lucy Siegle
Dr Pam Spurr
Lowri Turner
Geraint Vincent
Jeremy Vine
Dave Vitty
Johnnie Walker
Ross Westgate
Tim Wilcox
Sian Williams
Miranda Wilson
Julian Worricker

NOEL GEE ASSOCIATES LTD

7 Belvoir Close, Waddington, Lincoln
LN5 9DG
Tel: 01522 722771 Fax: 01522 874246
Mob: 07775 726524
Email: info@noelgee.co.uk
Web Site: www.noelgee.co.uk
Contact: Noel Utting

JOHN NOEL MANAGEMENT

Block B, Imperial Works Perren Street
London NW5 3ED
Tel: 020 7428 8400 Fax: 020 7428 8401
Email: john@johnnoel.com
Web Site: www.johnnoel.com
Agent: John Noel

ARTISTES REPRESENTED:

Ade Adepitan
Christine Bleakley
Russell Brand
Josie D'Arby
Tess Daly
Caroline Flack
Mariella Frostrup
Kirsty Gallacher
Diarmuid Gavin
Dermot O'Leary
Matthew Wright

NOMANIS

Unit 3, Delta Park Smugglers Way
London SW18 1EG
Tel: 020 8875 8844
Email: isla@nomanis.com
Web Site: www.nomanis.com
Isla Angus

NON STOP ENTERTAINMENTS

PO Box 10, Garston, Liverpool,
Merseyside L19 2RD
Tel: 0151 427 1910 (5 lines) Fax: 0151 494 9707 Mob: 07768 747 686
Email: info@nonstopentertainments.co.uk
Web: www.nonstopentertainments.co.uk
Senior Personnel: L Bather

ARTISTES REPRESENTED:

Available via office::
Tony Barton
Black Onyx
Stan Boardman
Frank Carson KSG
Norman Collier
Jimmy Cricket
Pauline Daniels
Ken Dodd OBE
The Grumbleweeds
Jimmy James & The Vagabonds
Joe Longthorne
Mike Miller
Hal Nolan
Duncan Norvelle
Pete Price
Julie Reed-Asquith
Stevie Riks
Danny Roman
Michael Starke
Sean Styles
Ricky Tomlinson
Roy Walker
Denny Waters

THE NORTH AMERICAN ACTORS ASSOCIATION (NAAA)

Tel/Fax: 020 7938 4722
Mob: 07710 133 065
Email: americanactors@aol.com
Web Site: www.naaa.org.uk
Chief Executive: Laurence Bouvard
THE source for genuine North American actors, all NAAA members are professional actors able to work without restriction both in the UK and North America. Log onto our website to access members' photos and agent details for all your casting needs. There ain't nothing like the Real Thing!

NORTH OF WATFORD ACTORS AGENCY

Bridge Mill, Hebden Bridge,
West Yorkshire HX7 8EX
Tel: 01422 845 361 Fax: 01422 846 503
Email: info@northofwatford.com
Web Site: www.northofwatford.com
Contact: John Greenwood

ARTISTES REPRESENTED:

Lisa Allen
Kate Bancroft
John Banfield
Karen Blick
Lara Bradban
Juliet Budd
Cerrie Burnell
Damian Christian
Dermot Daly
Carol Ann Dunne
Robert Garrett
Jo Gerard
Georgia Hartley

Jane Jefferson
Gillian Kerrod
Simon Lacy
Joe Logan
Dean Love
Anthony Marwood
Ruth McCaul
Mathew McGuirk
Marianne McNamara
Jeff Merchant
Nicola Moodie
Grant Moorhouse
Chris Orton
Timothy Richards
Cynthia H Rover
Peter Toon
Sherill Turner
Nicki Vincent

NORTH ONE MANAGEMENT

HGO8 Aberdeen Studios,
Highbury Grove, Islington, London
N5 2EA
Tel: 020 7359 9666 Fax: 020 7359 9449
Email: actors@northone.co.uk
Web Site: www.northone.co.uk
Contact: Martin Coles

ARTISTES REPRESENTED:

Male:
Randall Alleyne
Gergo Danka
Koray D'Jaffer
TJ Holmes
Robin Middleton
Mark Rawson
Michael Redston
Patrick Ross
Jason Simmons
Graham Townsend
Eoin Whelan
Female:
Clyta Rainford
Minnie Crowe
Gemma Harvey
Barbara Joslyn
Gemma Layton
Caroline Madden
Liz Mance
Jeanette Rourke
Aurelie Sauli-Koren
Victoria Stadler
Louise Taney
Claire Turvey

NORTHERN LIGHTS MANAGEMENT

Dean Clough Mills, Halifax,
West Yorkshire HX3 5AX
Tel: 01422 382 203 Fax: 01422 330 101
Email: northern.lights@virgin.net
Senior Personnel: Angie Forrest, Maureen Magee
No calls from actors seeking representation. By post only please with a sae.

ARTISTES REPRESENTED:

Jon Adamson
Keri Arnold
Lucy Atkinson
John Barber
Nicola Berry
Adrian Bouchet
Nick Chadwin
Emma Christie
Ian Connaughton
Jamie Cymbal
Philip Dinsdale
Thomas Frere
Kate Hampson
Elliot Head
Nikki Hellens
Edmund Herd
Lisa Howard
Lucy-Jo Hudson
Paul Hurstfield
Phil Jervis
Julian Kay
Joyce Kennedy
Clare Kerrigan
Andrew Kwame
Belinda Lazenby
Jonathan Le Billon
Maureen Lunt
Anthony McGuinness
Tony Monroe
George Neville
Mikey North
Adam Pepper
Stephanie Preacher
Jowanna Rose
Adrian Russell
Paul Sadot
Angela Saville
Helen Turaya
Declan Wilson

NORTHERN MUSIC COMPANY

Cheapside Chambers, 43 Cheapside,
Bradford, West Yorkshire BD1 4HP
Tel: 01274 306 361 Fax: 01274 730 097
Email: info@northernmusic.co.uk
Web Site: www.northernmusic.co.uk
Senior Personnel: A Farrow, Vicky Langham

ARTISTES REPRESENTED:

Jan Cyrka
Oceansize
One Minute Silence
Opeth
Paradise Lost
Skindred

NORTHGATE MUSIC PROMOTIONS

1 City Walls, Chester, Cheshire CH1 2JG
Tel: 01244 313 400 Fax: 01244 400 414
Email: pt@alexandersjazz.com
Web Site: www.alexandersjazz.com
Jazz & Blues Promoter and Agency

NORWICH ARTISTES

'Bryden' 115 Holt Road, Hellesdon
Norwich Norfolk NR6 6UA
Tel: 01603 407101 Fax: 01603 405314
Email: brian@norwichartistes.co.uk / norwichartistes@agents-uk.com
Web Site: www.norwichartistes.co.uk
Senior Personnel: Brian Russell

ARTISTES REPRESENTED:

Function Bands:
Alpha Connection
Lee Vasey Band
Liza Wolfe Band
Mike West Band
Scratch The Cat
Beat Connection
Julie Cooper Band
Dynamite
Zebra Express
Glamtastics
Kaleidoscope
Madison Square
Melodybeats
High Mileage
MInd The Gap
Mixed Feelings
Nightride
Agent Orange
Platinum Gold
Red Hot & Blue Orchestra
Sahara
Captain Scarlet
Danny & The Seniors
Party X
Lookalikes & Tributes:
Abba (Lookalike)
Beach Boys (Lookalike)
Beatles (Lookalike)
Bee Gees (Lookalike)
Blues Brothers (Lookalike)
Buddy Holly (Lookalike)
Celine Dion (Lookalike)
Cher (Lookalike)
Christine Aquilera (Lookalike)
Cliff Richard (Lookalike)
David Beckham (Lookalike)
Del Boy (Lookalike)
Diana Ross (Lookalike)
Elton John (Lookalike)
Elvis Presley (Lookalike)
Freddie Mercury (Lookalike)
George Michael (Lookalike)
James Bond (Lookalike)
John Cleese (Lookalike)
Lionel Ritchie (Lookalike)
Madonna (Lookalike)
Marilyn Monroe (Lookalike)
Patsy (Ad Fab) Lookalike
Queen (Lookalike)
Ricky Gervais (Lookalike)
Robbie Williams (Lookalike)
Rod Stewart (Lookalike)
Roy Orbison (Lookalike)
Shirley Bassey (Lookalike)
Take That (Lookalike)
Tina Turner (lookalike)
Tom Jones (Lookalike)
Whitney Houston (Lookalike)
Comedy:
Ajay (Comedienne / Singer)
Chris Bylett & Co
Sid Dennis
Terry Gauci
Gerry Graham
Ian Irving (Comedian)
Ivy League
Tim Lane
Andy Leach
Phil Lowen (Tom Jones)
Maxi Mann
Micky Zany
Simon Sands

Jimmy Tamley
Triple Cream
Alan Wallace
Kevin Woolley
Classical & Jazz:
MPR Jazz Ensemble
Francis Fox
Gary Grace
Paul Hill
Xenia Horne the Harpist
Classic Dixieland Jazz
Excelsior Jazz
Andy Kirkham
Louise
Dave Parker
Cindy Pennick
Savoir Faire
Samantha De Stefano
Cavatina Strings
Gallery Strings
Sole Bay Strings
Caricaturists:
BlazerMan
Phil Cole
Andy Davey
Steven Garner
David Lucas
Jed Pascoe
George Williams
Disco & Karaoke:
ArcAngel
Chevron
Compact
Connections
On Cue
Falcon
DJ Hunter
Mobile Nightclub
Pulse
North Sea Radio
Five Star
Time Street
Solo & Duo:
Daniel Arpels
Tim Ballard
Liza Wolfe Band
Eve Bridger
Johnny Cleveland
Bob Cushing
Evergreen
Intrigue
Rachel King
Andy Laine
Ian Larkin
Kate McCabe
Knight Moves
Tim Nesbitt
Sirens
Starrz
Richard Taylor
Tommy Thomas
Touche
Venue
Glam X
Close-Up & Mind Magic:
Sean Alexander
Olly Day
Mark Daynes
Carl Gamble
Sean Goodman
Bob Hannam
Graham P Jolley
Mist
Chris North
Dave Royal
Tony Sands
Kevin Woolley

NOTABLE MUSIC

1 Hinderton Drive, Heswall, Wirral
CH60 8QA
Tel/Fax: 0151 342 3955
Contact: Glenys Clark
Specialist in live music, classical and popular.

NSE CONSULTANCY

Minster Cottage, Broomers Corner,
Shipley, Horsham, West Sussex
RH13 8PS
Tel: 01403 741 321
Senior Personnel: Ian Long
Entertainment and Event Management.

ARTISTES REPRESENTED:

Richard Courtice
Jack Hawkins Showband

NVB ENTERTAINMENTS

80 Holywell Road, Studham, Dunstable,
Bedfordshire LU6 2PD
Tel: 01582 873 623 Fax: 01582 873 618
Email: nvbents@aol.com
Senior Personnel: Henri Harrison, Frances Harrison, John Lamb

ARTISTES REPRESENTED:

All Hands Around
Alvin Allstars
Amazing Bavarian Stompers
Mick Antony
Applejack the Clown
Lynsette Ashley & The LA Dancers
B Natural
Bambos
The Barron Knights
Richard Beare
Bellacappella
Cliff Bennett and the Rebel Rousers
Mike Berry & The Outlaws
Big Al's Jazzers
Jim Bowen
Brahms "N" Lizst
Ann & Ray Brett
John Brown
Buckmaster Puppets
Dame Lucy Bun & Reg
Caribbean Express
Casino
Mike Cassidy
Chairman Mal
Champagne Trio
Keith "The Thief" Charnley
The Classics
Colinski
Cougar
Robert Cox
Paul Cullen
Tony Dancer
Johnny Davey
Booby Dean
Déjà Vu
David Dell
Delphine Y Domingo
Desperate Dan
The Divas
DJ DI
Doctor Feelgood
Lonnie Donegan
Rufus Doors
The Dreamers
Terry Ducane
Emily
Espree
Essex Man
Man Ezeke
Fat Old Dad
Tony Fields
Steve Finn
Fluke
Flyin Hi
Jean & Mervin Fortune
Jed Fortune
Graham Fowell
Mandy Freeman
Frigidaires
The Fugitives
Full Circle
Kenny G as Elvis
Gidea Park (Beach Boys tribute)
Glamarama
Gold Dust
Mike Gold
Peter Hales
Andy Holloway Roadshow
Hollywood
Hollywood Hookers
Tracey Hughes & Sarinda
Infantasia
Nigel James
Karina Jordan
Junction 24
Just Jay
Gary Kemsley
Kevin King
Chris Knight
Knights of Soul
Lew Lewis
Lisa
Live 2 Jive
The Luvvers
Kenny Mac
Madison Square
Mick Maguire
Andy Mann
Marrakesh Express
Willie McCarthy
Me 'n Him
Johnny Morgan
Munich Bier Keller Men
Mustang
The Nadgers
Nash
Nashville Teens
Jo Norfolk
Tim Norty
Jed Pascoe
Troy Passion
Phyzical
Stephen Pierre
Maxwell Plum
Poison the Poteen
Brian Poole & Electrix
Powerhouse International
Alvin Printwhistle

Tony Rae
The Rapiers
Ian Richards
Ruth
George Saunders
Sandy Scott
Terry Seabrooke
September
Skyline
Solid Steel
Patricia Spero (Harpist)
Spirellas
Alan St John
Stars & Stripes Show (Elvis & Tina Turner)
Sterling String Quartet
Kevin Stewart & First Chapter
Ronnie Stewart
Jimmy Tamley
Tammy
Tease
Think Twice
Willie Thompson
George Thorby Orchestra
Tina
Trendsetter Disco
Triple Cream
Vauxhall Male Voice Choir
Vox Nouveau
Walls of Limerick
Wellington Bootles
Westenders Show
White Mountain Skunk Family
Wild at Heart
The Woodman
Woodstock
Word Girls
Antonio Zambardini

NYLAND MANAGEMENT

20 School Lane, Heaton Chapel,
Stockport, Cheshire SK4 5DG
Tel: 0161 442 2224
Email: nylandmgmt@freenet.co.uk
Senior Personnel: Patrick Nyland, Tony Nyland

ARTISTES REPRESENTED:

Actors:
Ross Adams
Tony Barton
Robert Booth
Liam Brown
Paul Chips
James Coleman
Danny Davies
John de Main
Seva Dhalivaal
Gareth Dickinson
Stan Finni
Charlie Flint
James Foy
Tom Garland Collins
Howard Harling
Jack Hudson
Eric Hulme
Ken Kitson
Jack Marsden
Robert Maxfield
Alex Mellor-Brooks
Amer Nazir
Tony Nyland
Seamus O'Neill
Mark Pepper
Malcolm Pitt
Philip Reis
Anthony Schaeffer
Harmage Singh-Kalirai
Bruce Jones (Les, Coronation Street)
Phil Taylor
Ricky Tomlinson
Keith Walton
John A Wilson
Stuart Wolfenden
Actresses:
Edwina Barratt
Stephanie Bishop
Julie Brown
Veronica Doran
Grace Ellis
Madelaine Evans
Mori Finni
Paula Frances
Sylvie Gatrill
Sandra Gough
Suzy Hallam
Elizabeth Holt
Adele Leonard
Cheryl Murray
Anne O'Brien
Helen Peddie
Jo Rafferty
Ros Simmons
Janet Spooner
Margo Stanley
Elizabeth Steele
Georgina Tattersall
Roberta Thayne
Joanne Venet

O2 PRODUCTIONS LTD

Chestnut Barn, North Stoke, Bath
BA1 9AT
Tel: 0117 932 9530 Fax: 0117 932 9531
Mob: 07836 784 999
Email: bill@o2productionsltd.co.uk
Musician Contractors: Bill Occleshaw, Leah Occleshaw
Musicians contracted for theatrical productions, recording sessions, TV & radio work. West End theatre and tours covered.

OBJECTIVE TALENT MANAGEMENT LTD

3rd Floor Riverside Building County Hall
Westminster Bridge Road, London
SE1 7PB
Tel: 020 7202 2300
Email: corrie@objectivetalentmanagement.com
Web Site: www.objectivetalentmanagement.com
Contact: Corrie McGuire

OCEAN LEISURE ENTERTAINMENT AGENCY

Digital Media Centre County Way
Barnsley, South Yorkshire S70 2JW
Tel: 01226 720732
Email: daveoceanleisure@aol.com
Web Site: www.oceanleisureagency.co.uk
Contact: David Hirst

OFF THE KERB PRODUCTIONS

Hammer House 113-117 Wardour Street
London W1F 0UN
Tel: 020 7437 0607 Fax: 020 7437 0647
Email: info@offthekerb.co.uk or west-end@offthekerb.co.uk
Web Site: www.offthekerb.co.uk
Senior Personnel: Addison Cresswell, Joe Norris
Please note all corporate, personal appearance and casting enquiries for all artistes to Fay Clayton in the West End office.
fay@offthekerb.co.uk

ARTISTES REPRESENTED:

Jo Brand
Kevin Bridges
Marcus Brigstocke
Brendon Burns
Alan Carr
Barry Castagnola
Tim Clark
Otis Lee Crenshaw
Cyderdelic
Jack Dee
Lee Evans
Simon Evans
Dave Fulton
John Gordillo
Jeff Green
Steve Gribbin
Rich Hall aka Otis Lee Crenshaw
Jeremy Hardy
Adam Hills
Phill Jupitus
Shappi Khorsandi
Mark Lamarr
Sean Lock
Michael McIntyre
Ian Moore
Richard Morton
Dara O'Briain
Andy Parsons
Jon Richardson
Rowland Rivron
Andy Robinson
Jonathan Ross
Simon Donald & Alex Collier aka Viz Boys
Mark Steel
Angelo Tsarouchas
Gavin Webster
Steve Weiner
Mike Wilmot

OI OI! AGENCY

Pinewood Film Studios, Pinewood Road,
Iver, Buckinghamshire SL0 0NH
Tel: 01753 655 514 Fax: 01753 785 163
Email: info@oioi.org.uk
Web Site: www.oioi.org.uk
Agent: Julie Fox

ARTISTES REPRESENTED:

Frances Da Costas

OLGA LTD

189 Bermondsey Street, London
SE1 3UW
Tel: 020 7407 5301 Fax: 020 7234 0336
Email: olgaltd@dircon.co.uk

ARTISTES REPRESENTED:
Paul O'Grady
Lily Savage

OMEGA PROMOTIONS
P O Box 244 Southport,
Merseyside PR9 7GJ
Tel: 01704 505222 Fax: 01704 232655
Email: info@omega-promotions.com
Web Site: www.omega-promotions.com
Contact: Gary Marriott

ONE FIFTEEN
1 Globe House Middle Lane Mews,
London N8 8PN
Tel: 020 8442 7560 Fax: 020 8442 7561
Email: paul@onefifteen.com,
enquiry@onefifteen.com
Web Site: www.onefifteen.com
Agent: Paul Loasby

ARTISTES REPRESENTED:
Addictive TV
Syd Barrett
Enjoy Destroy
David Gilmour
Jools Holland
Ian Hunter
Janice Long
Francesca Longrigg
Los
Orange Goblin
Mike Ralphs
Scoundrels
Swound!

OPERA & CONCERT ARTISTS
75 Aberdare Gardens, London NW6 3AN
Tel: 020 7328 3097 Fax: 020 7372 3537
Email:
enquiries@opera-and-concert-artists.co.uk
Agents: Judith Newton, Andrew Dugdale
Management of Opera singers only.

ARTISTES REPRESENTED:
Sopranos:
Jacqueline Bremar
Laure Meloy
Sofia Mihailidou
Kimberley Myers
Rachael Tovey
Elizabeth Woollett
Mezzos:
Linda Hibberd
Nadiya Petrenko
Valerie Reid
Mary Ann Stewart
Miranda Westcott
CounterTenor:
Jordi Domenech
Tenors:
Barry Coleman
Jonathan Finney
Unusan Kuloglu
Baritones:
Gareth Jones
Jacek Strauch
Bass:
Pawel Izdebski

ORBIT ENTERTAINMENTS AGENCY AND MANAGEMENT
77 Leyland Road, Penwortham, Preston,
Lancashire PR1 9QH
Tel/Fax: 01772 744 584
Mobile: 07702 939297
Senior Personnel: Kevin Hudson-Dean
Specialising in all types of entertainment and corporate hospitality.

ORDINARY PEOPLE LTD
8 Camden Road, London NW1 9DP
Enquiries/Membership Tel: 020 7267 7007 Models Tel: 020 7267 4141
Fax: 020 7267 5677
Email: sarah@ordinarypeople.co.uk
Web Site: www.ordinarypeople.co.uk
Senior Personnel: Sarah Robbie, Simon Lloyd
Specialises in: Photographic Work and Commercials.

DEE O'REILLY MANAGEMENT LTD
13 Alliance Court, Alliance Road,
London W3 0RB
Tel: 020 8993 7441 Fax: 020 8992 9993
Email: info@dorm.co.uk
Web Site: www.thedormgroup.com
Managing Director: Dee O'Reilly

ORGANISATION UNLIMITED
6 Santa Maria Way, Stourport-on-Severn,
Worcestershire DY13 9RX
Tel: 01299 827 197 Fax: 01299 827 191
Email: sales@organisationunlimited.co.uk
Web: www.organisationunlimited.co.uk
Senior Personnel: Susie Hunt

ORIENTAL ARTS (BRADFORD) LIMITED
Design Exchange, 24 Peckover Street,
Bradford, West Yorkshire BD1 5BD
Tel: 01274 370190 Fax: 01274 729 680
Email: info@orientalarts.org.uk
Senior Personnel: Champak Kumar Limbachia
Specialises in Promoting Asian Arts.

ORVAD ENTERPRISES LTD
Clifton House, 62 Cranley Road,
Burwood Park, Walton-On-Thames
Surrey KT12 5BS
Tel: 01932 232 649
Email: orvad@aol.com
Senior Personnel: Siovanya Bond

ARTISTES REPRESENTED:
Bobby Davro
FABBA
Masashi Fujimoto
Anne Michelle
Maurice Thorogood

SHARON OSBOURNE MANAGEMENT
Regent House, 1 Pratt Mews, London
NW1 0AD
Tel: 020 7383 5735 Fax: 020 7267 6746
Email: lynn@divinerecordings.fsnet.co.uk
Contact Agent: Lynn Seager

OSKA'S LTD
PO Box 362, Cardiff, South Glamorgan
CF10 1YQ Wales
Tel: 0870 443 0100 / 0700 535 6060
Email: artistesandagents@oskas.com
Web Site: www.oskas.com
Senior Personnel: Lorna Gilmore,
Jonathan Gilmore
Television, film and modelling agency. We represent actors, models and walk-ons, and have access to supporting artists for crowd scenes.

OTB PRODUCTIONS
5 Oldridge View, Tedburn St. Mary,
Exeter, Devon EX6 6AB
Tel: 01647 61237
Email: Dave@otbproductions.co.uk
Web Site: www.otbproductions.co.uk
Senior Personnel: Dave McCrory

ARTISTES REPRESENTED:
Jerry Cahil
Fos Brothers
The Green Road Show
Huckleberries
Nigel Mazlyn Jones
McCrory Brothers

OTTO PERSONAL MANAGEMENT LTD
Office 2,
Sheffield Independent Film Building
5 Brown Street, Sheffield S1 2BS
Tel: 0114 275 2592 Fax: 0114 279 5225
Email: admin@ottopm.co.uk
Web Site: www.ottopm.co.uk
Contact: John Langford
New Applicants Co-ordinator: Fran Larkin
Accounts: Christopher Wilkinson
Actors' co-operative Agency.

ARTISTES REPRESENTED:
Simon Ashland
Lisa Brookes
Noel Byrne
Penny Capper
Liz Carter
Helena Coates
Stephen Crane
Karl Dobby
Jeanne Golding
Corinne Handforth
Julie Higginson
John Langford
Francesca Larkin
Kate Layden
David Leverton
Laura McDonald
Alan Meadows
Blue Merrick
Susan Mitchell
Adele Eve Nelson
Robin Polley
Matthew Risdon
Stuart Rooker
Andrew Rosser

Julia Rounthwaite
Rob Snell
Christopher Wilkinson
Carys Williams
Mark Stuart Wood

OUTER SANCTUM
2nd Floor, Godfree Court, 29 Long Lane, London SE1 4PL
Tel: 020 7407 1407 Fax: 020 7407 7676
Email: katy@outersanctum.net
Web Site: www.outersanctum.net
Agent: Emily Harper
ARTISTES REPRESENTED:
Jo Wood
Ronnie Wood

OXYGEN MANAGEMENT LTD
Floors 1-3, 40a Old Compton Street, Soho, London W1D 4TU
Tel: 020 7529 9753 Fax: 020 7439 0794
Web Site: www.oxygenmanagement.com
Directors: Giles Cooper, Mark Reid
Oxygen Management - artist management of the future.

PAGE THREE MANAGEMENT
Suite D, 4-6 Canfield Place, London NW6 3BT
Contact by post only.
Postal enquiries only.
Senior Personnel: Hadleigh Scott
Specialising in Glamour Models

PALESTAR ENTERTAINMENT
1 Ivebury Court, 325 Latimer Road, London W10 6RA
Tel: 0208 9628 759
Email: trenton@palestar-entertainment.com
Web: www.palestar-entertainment.com
Agent: Trenton Harrison-Lewis
ARTISTES REPRESENTED:
Adam F
Grooverider
Malpractice
Poisonflow
Sonna Rele
Shakti

PALM COURT THEATRE PRODUCTIONS
Winkton Lodge Cottage, Salisbury Road, Winkton, Christchurch, Dorset BH23 7AR
Tel: 01202 484 185 Mob: 07836 717 567
Fax: 01202 471 920
Email: godwin@palm-court.demon.co.uk
Senior Personnel: Patricia Godwin
ARTISTES REPRESENTED:
The Palm Court Theatre Orchestra:
Concert Party
Patricia Godwin - Talks for afterdinner & other such occasions
Palm Court Theatre 'Hot Swing Seven'
Palm Court Theatre Ensemble
Palm Court Theatre Orchestra "Putting on the Ritz"
Palm Court Theatre Swing Orchestra
Palm Court Theatre Swingtet
Sophisticated Swing

JACKIE PALMER (JPA MANAGEMENT)
30 Daws Hill Lane, High Wycombe, Buckinghamshire HP11 1PW
Tel: 01494 520 978 / 525 938 Fax: 01494 510 479
Email: jackie.palmer@btinternet.com
Web Site: www.jackiepalmer.co.uk
Senior Personnel: Marylyn E A Phillips
ARTISTES REPRESENTED:
Television actor:
Loui Batley
Film & Television actor:
Aaron Johnson

PAN ARTISTS AGENCY
34 Wood House Lane, Sale, Cheshire M33 4JX
Tel: 0161 969 7419 Fax: 0161 962 6571
Email: panartists@btconnect.com
Web Site: www.panartists.co.uk
Senior Personnel: Wendy Simpson
Specialising in Television.

PANIC MANAGEMENT
Tel: 07778 788 735
Email: ghislain@panic-uk.com
Web Site: www.panic-uk.com
Managing Director: Ghislain Pascal
Celebrity PR and Management company.
ARTISTES REPRESENTED:
Anouska Beckwith
Tamara Beckwith
Martyn Lawrence Bullard
Emma B
Jacqueline Gold
Polly Graham
Nell McAndrew
Gabrielle Richens
Shebah Ronay
Ed Sanders
Nancy Sorrell
Amanda Stretton
Jesse Tobin
Stacey Young

PANMEDIA UK LIMITED
18 Montrose Crescent, Finchley London N12 0ED
Tel: 020 8446 9662
Email: enquiries@panmediauk.co.uk
Web Site: www.panmediauk.co.uk
Contact: Lili Panagi

PARADISE INTERNATIONAL AGENCY
1 Derwent Road, London SE20 8SW
Tel: 020 8659 3133 Fax: 020 8653 8096
Email: theirishdance@aol.com / ray742@btinternet.com
Web Site: www.pia.london.com
Contact: Mr Roger Hills

PARAGON SPORTS MANAGEMENT LTD
Falstaff House, Suite 18, Bardolph Road, Richmond, Surrey TW9 2LH
Tel: 020 8332 8640 Fax: 020 8332 8649
Mobile: 07718 535 335 (Mike Martin)
Email: mike.martin@paragonsportsmanagement.com
Web Site: www.paragonsportsmanagement.com
Director: Mike Martin
ARTISTES REPRESENTED:
Henry Blofeld OBE
Ravi Bopara
Annalise Braakensiek
Mark Butcher
Mike Catt
Alistair Cook
Angus Fraser
Jonathan Green
Pen Haddow
Ronnie Irani
Richard Johnson
Ed Joyce
Conor O'Shea
Monty Panesar
Gavin Peacock
Dermot Reeve OBE
Chris Sheasby
Andy Strauss
Jim Troughton
Phil Tufnell

PARAMOUNT INTERNATIONAL MANAGEMENT
204-226 Imperial Drive, Harrow, Middlesex HA2 7HH
Tel: 020 8429 3179 Fax: 020 8868 6475
Email: mail@ukcomedy.com
Web Site: www.ukcomedy.com
Senior Personnel: Jon Keyes, Helen Chown, Marsha Samuels
ARTISTES REPRESENTED:
Babben
Arj Barker
Ross Bennett
Sol Bernstein
Colin Cole
Sean Collins
Simon B Cotter
Trevor Crook
Sean Cullen
Phil Davey
Mike Dugan
Derek Edwards
Maria Esposito
Kitty Flanagan
Glen Foster
Emme Gay
Geechy Guy
Ewen Gilmor
Bruce Griffiths
Raoul Heertje
Rene Hicks
Adam Hills
Barry Hilton
Steve Hughes
Eddie Ifft
Dom Irrera
Steve Jameson

Pommy Johnson
Tony Krolo
Lehmo
Brendhan Lovegrove
Bruno Lucia
Sabrina Mathews
Mickey D
Greg Morton
Mr Zed
Patrice O'Neal
Russell Peters
Marcus Powell
Paul Provenza
Eleanor Quine
Carla Rhodes
Rick Right
Paul Rogan
Paul Sinha
Winston Spear
Tom Stade
Jovanka Steele
Eddy Strange
Marty Wilson
Tony Woods

PARAMOUNT STAGE PROMOTIONS

Casada 21 Queen Street, Grangemouth, Stirlingshire FK3 9AU
Tel: 01324 486833 Fax: 01324 871763
Email: para@blueyonder.co.uk
Contact: Christine Judge

PARK PROMOTIONS

PO Box 651, Oxford OX2 9RB
Tel: 01865 241 717 Fax: 01865 204 556
Email: info@parkrecords.com
Web Site: www.parkrecords.com
Managing Director: John Dagnell

ARTISTES REPRESENTED:

Davey Arthur
Wild Willy Barrett
The Guitar Orchestra
Rose Kemp
Abbie Lathe
Lindisfarne
Kirsty McSee
Gilbert O'Sullivan
Pentangle
Maddy Prior
Maddy Prior & The Carnival Band
Rock Salt and Nails
Steeleye Span
Kathryn Tickell

PARKER ENTERTAINMENTS LTD

PO Box 1288 Hemel Hempstead, Hertfordshire HP1 9HL
Tel: 01442 248987
Email: office@parker-entertainments.com
Web: www.parker-entertainments.com
Contact: Colin Parker

TERRY PARKER ENTERTAINMENTS

10 Swinnow Crescent, Stanningley, Pudsey, West Yorkshire LS28 6NZ
Tel: 0113 257 2637
Email: tpents@talktalk.net
Senior Personnel: Terry Parker, Matthew Parker

GARY PARKES MUSIC LTD

172 Haverstock Hill, Hampstead, London NW3 2AT
Tel: 020 7794 1581 Fax: 020 7431 5537
Email: gary@garyparkes.com
Web Site: www.garyparkes.com
Senior Personnel: Gary Parkes
Provide and represent pianists/vocalists/keyboardists and entertainers to top hotel venues and cruise companies in London and internationally.

PARLIAMENT COMMUNICATIONS

Verry House, Chine Crescent Road, Bournemouth, Dorset BH2 5LQ
Tel: 01202 242 424 Fax: 01202 242 428
Email: info@parliamentspeakers.com
Web Site: www.parliamentspeakers.com / www.noordinaryjoe.co.uk / www.derekredmond.com / www.andycave.net
Senior Personnel: Marek Kriwald
Specialising in: Business speakers and celebrity entertainment for the corporate sector. Captains of industry, politicians, business gurus, media personalities, sports stars, adventurers, entertainers and professional facilitators and presenters. Parliament is in direct contact with many of the speakers listed. We also work with managers of certain speakers.

ARTISTES REPRESENTED:

Kate Adie OBE
Kriss Akabusi MBE MA
Benedict Allen
Clive Anderson
Prof Ian Angell
Pamela Armstrong
Roger Black MBE
Sir Chris Bonington CBE
Karren Brady
Sir Richard Branson
Rory Bremner
Geoff Burch
Paul Burden
Kevin Cadle
Rene Carayol MBE
Will Carling OBE
Rhiannon Chapman
Rosemary Conley
Terence Conran
Steph Cook MBE BM Bch MA
Colin Coulson-Thomas
Garth Crooks
Barry Cryer
Graham Davies
Edward De Bono
FW de Klerk
Jonathan Dimbleby
Tommy Docherty
John Dolan
Tim Drake
Charles Dunstone
Tracy Edwards MBE
Sir Ranulph Fiennes Bt OBE
Martha Lane Fox
PY Gerbeau
Harvey Goldsmith CBE
Duncan Goodhew MBE
Mikhail Gorbachev
David Gower OBE
Stelios Haji-Ioannou
Adam Hart-Davis
Sir John Harvey-Jones
Bobby Hashemi
Sahar Hashemi
The Rt Hon Roy Hattersley
Ian Hislop
John Humphrys
Sir Douglas Hurd
Sir Bernard Ingham
Colin Jackson CBE
Charles Kennedy MP
Gene Kranz
Ken Lewis
Martyn Lewis CBE
Lawrence Leyton
James Lovell
Dame Ellen MacArthur
Shay McConnon
Sir Trevor McDonald
Tom McNab
David Mellor
Malcolm Milton
Diane Modahl
Michelle Mone
Bob Monkhouse OBE
Andrew Neil
Des O'Connor
Olé
Dr Marilyn Orcharton
The Rt Hon Christopher Patten
Jeremy Paxman
Allan Pease
Tom Peters
Faith Popcorn
Michael Portillo
Derek Redmond
Michael Rodd
Nick Ross
Ricardo Semler
Joe Simpson
Peter Sissons
Michael Tipper
Murray Walker OBE
Rex Warner
Ruby Wax
Nicholas Witchell
Simon Woodroffe

PARR'S THEATRICAL & TV AGENCY

The Tom Thumb Theatre, Eastern Esplanade, Cliftonville, Margate, Kent CT9 2LB
Tel/Fax: 01843 221 791
Email: parrandbond@onetel.com
Senior Personnel: Sarah Bond, Lesley Parr

PARTNERSHIP ENTERTAINMENTS LTD

Pinetum Broughton Hall Skipton BD23 3AE
Tel: 01756 796176

Email: alan@peelcruise.com
Web Site: www.peelcruise.com
Alan Cutler

PARTYWEB.CO.UK

127 Carterhatch Road, Enfield, Middlesex EN3 5LX
Tel: 020 8245 4348 Fax: 07092 033 538
Email: magicians@partyweb.co.uk
Web Site: www.partyweb.co.uk
Propietor: Charles Coleman
Total entertainment specialists. Close-up magicians, cabaret and stage magic, clowns, children's entertainers. Private or corporate events.

ARTISTES REPRESENTED:

Andy B
John Anscomb
Paul Anthony
Matt Barnard
Jason Bell
Berno The Clown
Alan Bertin
Jonathan Cann
Ali Cardabra
Sheba Cassini
Charlie The Clown (Ind Art)
John Clayton
Clown Violly
David Crofts
Andy Davey
Tony De La Fou
Dweebie The Robot
Charlie Farley
Geoff Felix
Anthony Freeman
Jason George
Gertie Glitter
Gingernutt the Clown
Leslie Guinness
Mel Harvey
Tania Holland
Julian The Juggler
Allin Kempthorne
Pamela Kempthorne
George Kovari Jnr/Snr
Leo the Clown
Paul Lytton
Magic Moments
Mattie The Clown
Jenny Mayers
Tony McNamara
Jeff Morgan
Mr Toots
Bruce Munton
Jim Naylor
Ricky Newby
Nicholi The Clown
Nutty Norman
Ian Parratt
Jed Pascoe
Colin Perrotton
Pinky the Clown
Pizzazz
Poz
Leslie Press
Steve Price
Noel Qualter
Rhubarb the Clown
John Roberts
John G Roberts
Salvo The Clown
Paul Slattery
Uncle Smartie
Snakey Sue
Saucy Sue
Tricky Ricky
Charlie Valentino
Walligog The Wizard
Wizard Stonering
Lynn Worthington
Zako the Clown

PASADENA ROOF ORCHESTRA

Priors, 178 Hall Lane, Upminster, Essex RM14 1AT
Email: info@pasadena-roof-orchestra.com
Web: www.pasadena-roof-orchestra.com
Contact: David Jones
Head Office Contact (Munich): Marcus Meyer
Professional Orchestra (11 piece). 1920's & 1930's Jazz and Dance Music.
UK Booking Management: Liz Biddle, Upbeat Management. Tel: 020 8668 3332 Fax: 020 8668 3922

ARTISTES REPRESENTED:

The Pasadena Roof Orchestra

PAUL STACEY MANAGEMENT

Tel: 020 7758 2785
Agent: Paul Stacey

ARTISTES REPRESENTED:

Reality Stars:
Du'aine Ladejo
Rebecca Loos
TV Presenters:
Julian Benn
Giles Vickers-Jones
Miscellaneous:
Scott Henshall
Lady Victoria Hervey
Princess Tamara
Performers:
All Angels
Brendan Cole

PAVEMENT ACTS

Flexbury, 35a Cargate Avenue, Aldershot, Hampshire GU11 3EW
Tel: 01252 323 432
Email: janet@activeart.org.uk
Senior Personnel: Janet Mary King
Historic street entertainment. Murder mystery weekends, etc. Musicians and actors.

PBJ MANAGEMENT LTD

7 Soho Street, London W1D 3DQ
Tel: 020 7287 1112 Fax: 020 7287 1191
Email: general@pbjmgt.co.uk
Web Site: www.pbjmgt.co.uk
Senior Personnel: Caroline Chignell, Peter Bennett-Jones

ARTISTES REPRESENTED:

Performers:
Ash Atalla
Rowan Atkinson
Bill Bailey
Julian Barrett
The Boosh (Julian Barratt & Noel Fielding)
Adam Buxton
Adam Buxton & Joe Cornish
Arnab Chanda
Antoine de Caunes
Mark Dolan
Harry Enfield
Tim FitzHigham
Lenny Henry CBE
Sean Hughes
Barry Humphries
Armando Iannucci
Eddie Izzard
Dom Joly
Kit & The Widow
The League of Gentleman
Tracey MacLeod
Tim Minchin
Lucy Montgomery
Dylan Moran
Chris Morris
Julia Morris
Vic Reeves & Bob Mortimer
Rob Rouse
Reece Shearsmith
Richard Sisson
Sarah Smith
Rhys Thomas
Glenn Wool
Marc Wootton
Gina Yashere
TV & Radio Presenters:
Mark Cousins
Edward Enfield
Mary Anne Hobbs
Simon Mayo
Anneka Rice
Suggs

P.C. THEATRICAL MODEL AGENCY

12 Carlisle Road, Colindale, London NW9 0HL
Tel: 020 8381 2229 / 020 8205 7666
Fax: 020 8933 3418
Email: twinagy@aol.com
Web Site: www.twinagency.com
Senior Personnel: Sandra Mooney
Specialising in identical twins/actors/models/children. Largest database of Identical Twins in the UK.

PELHAM ASSOCIATES

Brighton Media Centre, 9-12 Middle Street, Brighton, East Sussex BN1 1AL
Tel: 01273 323 010 Fax: 01273 202 492
Email: petercleall@pelhamassociates.co.uk
Web Site: www.pelhamassociates.co.uk
Contact: Peter Cleall
Representing actors of the highest quality for casting in all branches of the media - film, television, theatre, radio, commercials, corporate video, presentation and voice-overs.

PELLER ARTISTES LTD

14 West Street, Beighton, Sheffield,

South Yorkshire S20 1EP
Tel: 0114 247 2365 Fax: 0114 247 2156
London Office: 39 Princes Avenue, London N3 2DA Tel: 020 8343 4264
Fax: 070 9280 8252
Email: agent@pellerartistes.com
Web Site: www.pellerartistes.com
Senior Personnel: Johnnie Peller (London Office)
Specialising in Tribute Bands, Lookalikes, Television Celebrities & Soap Stars, Star Vocal & Comedy Artistes, Party & Function Bands, Magicians, Hypnotists and Speciality Entertainment, After Dinner Speakers and Sports Stars.

ARTISTES REPRESENTED:

Tribute Bands:
Abba Fever
Tina Ballentino (Tina Turner Tribute)
Bleach (Blondie Tribute)
Born 2 Run (Bruce Springstein Tribute)
But Seriously (Phil Collins tribute)
Nova Casper as Tina Turner
Claptonite (Eric Clapton Tribute)
Conmitments (Commitments Tribute)
Sophie D'Wilde as Kylie (Kylie Tribute)
Definitely Might Be (Oasis tribute)
Fab 4 (Beatles Tribute)
Fast Love (George Michael Tribute)
John Finch (Marti Pellow)
Frank & Dean (Frank Sinatra & Dean Martin Show)
Phil Fryer as Frank Sinatra
Lewis Gates as Elvis
Heroes (Jam & New Wave 78-83)
Jawonderquai (Jamiroquai Tribute)
Mikki Jay (Michael Jackson)
Jeni Jaye (Britney Spears)
Justine as Anastasia
The Karpenters (The Carpenters Tribute)
La Vida Loca (Ricky Martin & Enrique Eglasias)
Maxine Mazumder as Lulu
Money For Nothing (Dire Straits Tribute)
Navi As Michael Jackson
Oasisn`t (Oasis Tribute)
Police Force (Police tribute)
Queen Fever (Queen)
Red Mick (Simply Red Tribute)
Rolling Clones (Rolling Stones Tribute)
Sheer Shakira (Shakira Tribute)
Shomaddymaddy (Swowaddywaddy Tribute)
Status Clone (Status Quo Tribute)
Stayin' Alive (Bee Gees tribute)
Steve Steinman's Meatloaf 2
Robbie Supreme (Robbie Williams Tribute)
Time Warped (Rocky Horror Tribute)
Tom-Tastic (Tom Jones Tribute)
Gerry Trew (Rod Stewart)
Turn Back Time (Cher Tribute)
Celebrity Appearances:
Christine Hamilton
Keith Harris with Orville & Cuddles
Willie Thorne
John Virgo
Musical & Comedy:
Bad Manners
Jim Bowen
Chas 'n' Dave
Phil Cool
Paul Daniels
Go West including Peter Cox
Tony Hadley
Limahl
Function Bands:
Charm
Co-Stars
Fully Funktional
Lex Icon
Impromtu
Mike James
Liaison
Loose Wire
Platform Soul
Respect
Rivieras
Soul System
Sounds of Swing
Status Cymbal
Steelasophical Steel Band
Yes !!! Brazil Latin Band & Dancers
Hypnotists:
Ian Gray
Chris Lee
Adam Night
Magicians:
Corporate Illusion
Deans of Magic
Zane
Duos & Solos:
Laura Miles
Rio Madness
System X
XMY
Jazz/Brass/Easy Listening:
Jo Caleb Group
Barry Cole
Bob Drury
Jazz Pack
John Worthington
Soul Discretion

PEMBERTON ASSOCIATES (MANCHESTER)

193 Wardour Street, London W1F 8ZF
Tel: 020 7734 4144 Fax: 020 7734 2522
Email: barbara@pembertonassociates.com
Web: www.pembertonassociates.com
Senior Personnel: Barbara Pemberton, Mark Pemberton, Fay Hallam
Specialising in Actors/Actresses.

PENGUINS EVENTS LTD

Unit 12, Vansittart Estate, Windsor, Berkshire SL4 1SE
Tel: 01753 833 811 Fax: 01753 833 754
Email: richardb@penguins.co.uk
Web Site: www.penguins.co.uk
Senior Personnel: J Story, Gemma Pickering
Email: gemmap@penguinevents.co.uk
Themes, Discos, Entertainment, Bands, Corporate Entertainment, Conferences and team building.

PENNY ARCADE ENTERTAINMENTS

122 St Davids Crescent, Aspull, Wigan, Lancashire WN2 1ST
Tel/Fax: 01942 831 981
Email: neil@pennyarcadeagency.com
Contact: Caron Hilton
Manager: Neil Hilton

PENNY LANE PROMOTIONS

61a Hough Lane, Leyland PR25 2SA
Tel: 01772 422 388
Email: pennylane@themail.co.uk
Web: www.pennylanepromotions.co.uk
Contact: Tom Lane
Entertainment agency. Represent artists,singers, magicians, speakers and many others.

PERFORMANCE ACTORS AGENCY

137 Goswell Road, London EC1V 7ET
Tel: 020 7251 5716 Fax: 020 7251 3974
Email: info@performanceactors.co.uk
Web Site: www.performanceactors.co.uk
Contact: Lionel Guyett

ARTISTES REPRESENTED:

Shelley Atkinson
Cleo Barnham
Janet Behan
Gerard Bell
Kate Burdette
Alistair Cameron
Paul Christie
Lucy Cochrane
Olivette Cole-Wilson
Ellen Collier
Rosalind Cressy
Eva Crompton
Susie Emmett
Terence Frisch
Daniel Gentley
Karen Gledhill
Hilary Greatorex
Lionel Guyett
Hugh Hayes
Laura Hayes
Nicola Herring
Matt Jamie
Michael Larkin
Dorothy Lawrence
Moir Leslie
Olivia Maffett
Valerie Minifie
Nadia Morgan
Maz Nieviarovski
James Rayment
Richard Sandells
Lydia Tuckey
James Wrighton

PERFORMERS AGENCY

Southend Road, Corringham, Stanford-le-Hope, Essex SS17 8JT
Tel: 01375 672 053 Fax: 01375 672 353
Email: pdc@dircon.co.uk
Web Site: www.performerscollege.com
Senior Personnel: Mike Stephens, Jan Rogers
Specialising in Choreographers, Dancers, Singers.

ARTISTES REPRESENTED:

Brian Rogers

PERFORMING ACTS

c/o Choice Ltd Unit A, Derby Road Trade
Nottingham NG10 5HU
Tel: 0115 939 0251
Email: rs@performingacts.com
Web Site: www.performingacts.com
Robert Stevenson

PERFORMING ARTISTES (PART OF THE F4 GROUP)

F4 Group Ltd 24a High Street, Cobham
Surrey KT11 3EB
Tel: 01932 590 376 Fax: 01932 862 437
Email: ask@performingartistes.co.uk
Web Site: www.f4group.co.uk
Contacts: Stanley Jackson
Specialising in After Dinner entertainment, including: speakers, hosts, business and motivational/keynote speakers, celebrities for personal appearances, endorsements, advertising campaigns and corporate events.

ARTISTES REPRESENTED:

Rob Bonnet
Susan Bookbinder
John Cugley
Nik Gowing
Jimmy Greaves
Garry Herbert MBE
John Humphrys
Rob Nothman
Mike Osman
Eve Pollard
Garry Richardson
Stephen Sackur
Justin Webb
Peter White
Toby Young

PERFORMING ARTS

6 Windmill Street, London W1T 2JB
Tel: 020 7255 1362 Fax: 020 7631 4631
Email: info@performing-arts.co.uk
Web Site: www.performing-arts.co.uk
Senior Personnel: Richard Haigh

ARTISTES REPRESENTED:

Directors:
Annabel Arden
Bill Bankes-Jones
Lee Blakeley
James Conway
Jo Davies
Charles Edwards
Jonathan Moore
Jeremy Sutcliffe
Designers:
Charles Edwards
Roswitha Gerlitz
John Gunter
Sally Jacobs
Tanya McCallin
Alison Nalder
Joanna Parker
Brigitte Reiffenstuel
Rae Smith
Yannis Thavoris
Jenny Tiramani
Choreographers:
Kate Flatt
Leah Hausman
Michael Keegan-Dolan
Andrew George
Conductors:
Christopher Adey
Wyn Davies
Hilary Davan Wetton
Lighting Designers:
Andrew Bridge
Paule Constable
Simon Corder
Davy Cunningham
Wayne Dowdeswell
Nigel Edwards
Chris Ellis
Zerlina Hughes
Durham Marenghi
John B Read

PERROTTS FOLLY AGENCY

Treverryl, Trenance, Mawgan Porth, Newquay, Cornwall TR8 4DA
Tel/Fax: 01637 860 866
Email: jd@perrottsfolly.fsnet.co.uk
Web Site: www.perrottsfolly.com
Senior Personnel: Jackie Grinnell
Nationally Known folk and folk-comedy artistes plus the best jazz bands from the south-west including: Johnny Silvo & Jeremy Taylor.

ARTISTES REPRESENTED:

Johnny Silvo

PERSONAL APPEARANCES

20 North Mount, 1147-1161 High Road, Whetstone, London N20 0PH
Tel: 020 8343 7748 Fax: 020 8343 7748
Email: patsy@personalappearances.biz
Web Site: www.personalappearances.biz
Senior Personnel: Patsy Martin
Specialists in Public Relations and Personal Management

ARTISTES REPRESENTED:

Motivational Speakers:
Kriss Akabusi MBE MA
Steve Backley MBE OBE
Tony Ball MBE
Roger Black MBE
Geoff Capes
Will Carling OBE
Bob Champion MBE
Chris Cowdrey
Sharron Davies MBE
Derek Thompson & Bob Champion MBE
Richard Dunwoody MBE
Tracy Edwards MBE
Ieuan Evans MBE
Duncan Goodhew MBE
Barry McGuigan MBE
Chris Moon
Alan Mullery MBE
Ft Lt John Peters
Graham Taylor
Dame Tanni Grey Thompson OBE
Derek Thompson
After Dinner Speakers:
Kriss Akabusi MBE MA
Bob Anderson
Ron Atkinson
Steve Backley MBE OBE
Tony Ball MBE
Gordon Banks OBE
John Barnes MBE
Phil Bennett OBE
Bob “The Cat” Bevan MBE
Dickie Bird MBE
Roger Black MBE
Paul Boardman
Stan Boardman
Jim Bowen
Karren Brady
Sir Trevor Brooking CBE
Duggie Brown
Will Carling OBE
Frank Carson KSG
Mike Cassidy
Bob Champion MBE
Jack Charlton OBE
Gareth Chilcott
Ray Clemence MBE
Brian Close CBE
John Conteh
Chris Cowdrey
Graham Davies
Jonathan Davies
Clarrisa Dickson Wright
Tommy Docherty
David Duckham MBE
Richard Dunwoody MBE
Vince Earl
Frances Edmonds
Eddie “ The Eagle” Edwards
Ieuan Evans MBE
Fat Tony
Michael Fish MBE DSc
John Francome MBE
Raymond Froggatt
Dermot Gallagher
Duncan Goodhew MBE
Terry Griffiths OBE
Tony Gubba
David Gunson
Eric Hall
Christine Hamilton
Neil Hamilton
Ron “Chopper Harris”
Derek Hatton
Alex Hay
Rachael Heyhoe-Flint MBE
Matthew Hoggard
Tommy Horton
Dr Kevin Jones
Alan Kennedy
John Kettley
Roger Kitter
Dave Lee
Ian Lees (Sludge)
Rodney Marsh
Barry McGuigan MBE
Frank McLintock MBE
Geoff Miller
Chris Moon
Sir Stirling Moss OBE
Alan Mullery MBE
Keith O’Keefe
Lembit Opik
Martin Peters MBE
Jenny Pitman OBE
Richard Pitman
Jeff Probyn
Derek Quinnell
Ian Robertson
Steve Smith MBE (Lawyer & Author)

David Speedie
Ed Stewart
John Stirling
Stuart Storey
Dennis Taylor
John Taylor
Jerry Thomas
Mickey Thomas
Willie Thorne
David Trick
Roger Uttley OBE
John Virgo
Bob Webb
Jimmy White MBE
Lee Wilson
Rod Woodward
Frank Worthington

Toastmasters:
Alexander Michaels
Ken Tappenden MBE
Steven Warwick

Personal Appearances:
Kriss Akabusi MBE MA
Bob Anderson
Ron Atkinson
Cheryl Baker
Tony Ball MBE
Gordon Banks OBE
John Barnes MBE
Martin Bayfield
Phil Bennett OBE
Bob "The Cat" Bevan MBE
Dickie Bird MBE
Roger Black MBE
Jim Bowen
Karren Brady
Russ Bray
Sir Trevor Brooking CBE
Geoff Capes
Will Carling OBE
Frank Carson KSG
Bob Champion MBE
Jack Charlton OBE
Gareth Chilcott
Ray Clemence MBE
Kevin Connelly
John Conteh
Chris Cowdrey
Sharron Davies MBE
Roger De Courcey
Keith Deller
Clarrisa Dickson Wright
Kerry Dixon
Tommy Docherty
Vince Earl
Frances Edmonds
Eddie " The Eagle" Edwards
David Fairclough
Vanessa Feltz
Michael Fish MBE DSc
John Francome MBE
Dermot Gallagher
Bobby George
Duncan Goodhew MBE
Tony Green
Terry Griffiths OBE
Tony Gubba
Eric Hall
Christine Hamilton
Neil Hamilton
Derek Hatton
Alex Hay
Rachael Heyhoe-Flint MBE
Matthew Hoggard
Pat Jennings OBE KSG
Henry Kelly
Alan Kennedy
John Kettley
Ian Lavender
Adrian Lewis
Rodney Marsh
John McCririck
Barry McGuigan MBE
Frank McLintock MBE
Geoff Miller
Ken Morley
Sir Stirling Moss OBE
Alan Mullery MBE
Lembit Opik
Cynthia Payne
Martin Peters MBE
Jenny Pitman OBE
Richard Pitman
Duncan Preston
Jeff Probyn
Derek Quinnell
Ian Robertson
Tessa Sanderson CBE
Selina Scott
Peter Shilton MBE OBE
Oliver Skeete
Nicky Slater
Spanner in the Works
David Speedie
Ed Stewart
Stuart Storey
Dennis Taylor
John Taylor
Mickey Thomas
Derek Thompson
Willie Thorne
David Trick
Stuart Turner
John Virgo
Jimmy White MBE
William Roache MBE
Bob Wilson
Frank Worthington

Presenters:
Cheryl Baker
Roger Black MBE
Jim Bowen
Sir Trevor Brooking CBE
Geoff Capes
Bob Champion MBE
Jack Charlton OBE
Ray Clemence MBE
Sharron Davies MBE
Frances Edmonds
Eddie " The Eagle" Edwards
Tracy Edwards MBE
Vanessa Feltz
Michael Fish MBE DSc
John Francome MBE
Graham Goode
Tony Gubba
Christine Hamilton
David Hamilton
Neil Hamilton
Derek Hatton
Alex Hay
Jonty Hearnden
Henry Kelly
John Kettley
Ian Lavender
Rodney Marsh
John McCririck
Barry McGuigan MBE
Sir Stirling Moss OBE
Alan Mullery MBE
Richard Pitman
Duncan Preston
Ian Robertson
Jim Rosenthal
Tessa Sanderson CBE
Selina Scott
Ed Stewart
Stuart Storey
Dennis Taylor
John Taylor
Derek Thompson
John Virgo
Bob Wilson
Roger Black MBE
Sir Trevor Brooking CBE
Geoff Capes
Bob Champion MBE
Jack Charlton OBE
Ray Clemence MBE
Sir Henry Cooper OBE KSG
Sharron Davies MBE
Eddie " The Eagle" Edwards
John Francome MBE
Graham Goode
Tony Gubba
Alex Hay
Jimmy Hill OBE
Rodney Marsh
John McCririck
Barry McGuigan MBE
Sir Stirling Moss OBE
Alan Mullery MBE
Richard Pitman
Tessa Sanderson CBE
Dennis Taylor
Derek Thompson
Willie Thorne
Bob Wilson

Sports Personalities:
Kriss Akabusi MBE MA
Bob Anderson
Ron Atkinson
Gordon Banks OBE
John Barnes MBE
John Bentley
Dickie Bird MBE
Roger Black MBE
Karren Brady
Russ Bray
Sir Trevor Brooking CBE
Geoff Capes
Will Carling OBE
Bob Champion MBE
Jack Charlton OBE
Gareth Chilcott
Ray Clemence MBE
Brian Close CBE
John Conteh
Chris Cowdrey
Huw Davies
Sharron Davies MBE
Keith Deller
Kerry Dixon
Tommy Docherty
David Duckham MBE
Eddie " The Eagle" Edwards

Tracy Edwards MBE
Ieuan Evans MBE
David Fairclough
John Francome MBE
Dermot Gallagher
Bobby George
Duncan Goodhew MBE
Terry Griffiths OBE
Tony Gubba
Eric Hall
Ron "Chopper Harris"
Alex Hay
Rachael Heyhoe-Flint MBE
Matthew Hoggard
Pat Jennings OBE KSG
Alan Kennedy
Adrian Lewis
Duncan MacKenzie
Rodney Marsh
John McCririck
Frank McLintock MBE
Geoff Miller
Sir Stirling Moss OBE
Alan Mullery MBE
Jeff Probyn
Derek Quinnell
Ian Robertson
Jim Rosenthal
Tessa Sanderson CBE
Peter Shilton MBE OBE
Oliver Skeete
Nicky Slater
Steve Smith MBE (Lawyer & Author)
David Speedie
John Stirling
Stuart Storey
Dennis Taylor
John Taylor
Mickey Thomas
Derek Thompson
David Trick
Roger Uttley OBE
Jimmy White MBE
Bob Wilson
Frank Worthington

Golfing Personalities:

Jeremy Dale Golf Show
David Edwards
Alex Hay
Tommy Horton
Christy O'Connor Jnr
John Stirling

Comedians:

Paul Boardman
Stan Boardman
Jim Bowen
Adger Brown
Duggie Brown
Frank Carson KSG
Mike Cassidy
Kevin Connelly
Roger De Courcey
Derby Midshipmen Carnival Band
Vince Earl
Joe Goodman
Ian Irving (Comedian)
Aaron James
Roger Kitter
Dave Lee
Johnny More
Keith O'Keefe
Ted Robbins

John Stiles
Jerry Thomas
Adrian Walsh
Bob Webb
Lee Wilson
Rod Woodward

Entertainers:

Alan Bates (Hypnotist)
Bobby Davro
Aaron James
Graham P Jolley
Johnny More

Musicians/Singers:

Brahms "N" Lizst
Jess Conrad
Johnny More
Premier Cru Dance Band

PERSONAL MANAGEMENT (CHESTERFIELD)

57 Rutland Road, Chesterfield, Derbyshire S40 1ND
Tel: 01246 237 221 Fax: 01246 206 575
Email: pmanagement1234@aol.com
Senior Personnel: Peter Sadler and Margaret Sadler
Established for 20 years.

PERSONAL MANAGEMENT (HEBBURN)

6a St Johns Precinct, Hebburn, Tyne and Wear NE31 1LQ
Tel: 0191 483 5411 / 5040
Fax: 0191 483 5414
Email: perman@btconnect.com
Agent: Mr I Symonds

PERSONAL MANAGEMENT & CASTING

Creative House, 103 The Drive, Beckenham, Kent BR3 1EF
Tel: 020 8402 9553 Fax: 020 8289 2963
Email: jaine@casting.uk.net
Managing Director: Jaine Brent
Operations Manager: Dan Zegze

ARTISTES REPRESENTED:

We represent:

Lorraine Candy (Cosmopolitan Editor)
Martine McCutcheon
Dr Linda Papadopoulos (Celebrity Psychologist)
Tana Ramsey

Sole brand managers:

Atomic Kitten
Blue
Duel
Matt Dusk
Ruthie Henshall
Javine Hylton
Steve McFadden
Dannii Minogue
Nu
Gordon Ramsay
Sugababes
Claire Sweeney
Daniella Westbrook

Also represent for branding:

Big Brovaz
Andrea Bocelli
Busted
Holly Valance
Russell Watson
All DECCA classical artists

PERSONALITY ARTISTES LTD

Worldwide Headquarters PO Box 1
Poulten le Fylde Blackpool, Lancashire FY6 7WS
Tel: 01253 899 988 Fax: 01253 899 333
Mobile: 07860 479092
Email: info@personalityartistes.com
Web Site: www.personalityartistes.com
Contact: Mal Ford & Jean Parkes
Corporate Entertainment specialists and Artistes Management.

ARTISTES REPRESENTED:

Barricade (Comedy Duo)
Peter Grant
Harper (Comedy/Vocal Duo)
Siobhan Phillips

The Platters
Tony 'Bangor' Walsh (After Dinner)

PETE CROSS AGENCY LTD

4 Jason Place, Waterlooville, Hampshire
PO7 8BB
Tel/Fax: 023 9264 0170 / 023 9242 6579
Email: pete@pca.uk.com
Web Site: www.pca.uk.com
Senior Personnel: Pete Cross, Jane Cross

ARTISTES REPRESENTED:

Mr Sketchum's Caricatures

PETE MITCHELL ASSOCIATES

24 Briarwood Close, Fareham,
Hampshire PO16 0PS
Tel: 01329 511806 Fax: 08707 551 240
Email: pete@pmaweb.co.uk
Web Site: /www.pmaweb.co.uk
Senior Personnel: Mrs Del Mitchell,
Mr Peter Mitchell, Tayla Mitchell

ARTISTES REPRESENTED:

Miscellaneous:
Beverley Sisters
Boney M
Bootleg Beatles
John Boulter
Jim Bowen
Brotherhood of Man
Bucks Fizz
Clem Cantini`s Tornadoes
Frank Carson KSG
Norman Collier
Andy Collins
Con & Dec - The Batchelors
Jess Conrad
Counterfeit Kylie
Clem Curtis & the Foundations
Steve Daking
Martin Daniels
Craig Douglas
Dozy Beaky Mick & Tich
Easybeats
Edison Lighthouse
Nigel Ellery
The Four Pennies
The Fourmost
Gidea Park (Beach Boys tribute)
Herman's Hermits
Kenny
Carol Lee Scott (Grotbags)
Brother Lees
Don MacLean MBE
Pat Mooney
Johnny Moore
Paper Lace
Julie Rogers
The Rubettes featuring Bill Hurd
Tony Strudwick Band
Tight Fit
Unit 4 Plus 2
Vanity Fare (ex-chart band)
Wild at Heart
Tribute Bands:
Counterfeit Kylie
Four Tops Motown Show
Eric Haydock's Ex Hollies
John Hylton is Neil Diamond
The Real Abba Gold
Tribute Two (Sinatra, Dean Martin, Neil Diamond)
The Visitors (Abba tribute)
Comedy:
Mike Jerome
Hypnotists:
Nigel Ellery

JON PETERS ENTERTAINMENTS

14 Slaidburn Avenue, Rossendale,
Lancashire BB4 8JS
Tel: 01706 228 359 Fax: 01706 218 334
Email: jonpetersents@aol.com
Senior Personnel: Jon Peters, Lynne Miller

ARTISTES REPRESENTED:

Steve Chicane
Dave Just
David Lavelle

PETERS FRASER DUNLOP (PFD)

Drury House, 34-43 Russell Street,
London WC2B 5HA
Switchboard: 020 7344 1000
Fax: 020 7836 9543
Email: info@pfd.co.uk
Web Site: www.pfd.co.uk
Senior Personnel: Caroline Michel

ARTISTES REPRESENTED:

TV Presenters:
Richard Bacon
Jackie Brambles
Beechy Colclough
Twiggy Lawson
Dan Snow
Ruby Wax
Alex Zane
Authors/Writers:
Lord Paddy Ashdown
Louise Bagshawe
Alan Bennett
Richard Curtis
Michael Dibdin
David Dimbleby
Margaret Drabble
Simon Garfield
Nick Hornby
John Irving
Sir Jeremy Isaacs
Graham Linehan
Jonathan Lynn
Adrian Mitchell
Joanna Trollope
Danny Wallace
Ann Widdecombe
Derek Wilson
Actresses:
Hayley Atwell
Stephanie Beacham
Fiona Bell
Edith Bowman
Anna Brewster
Saffron Burrows
Natalie Cassidy
Toni Collette
Sophie Dahl
Jane Danson
Dawn French
Caroline Goodall
Kate Winslet
Gillian Kearney
Patsy Kensit
Keira Knightley
Miriam Margoyles OBE
Sienna Miller
Denise Van Outen
Elaine Paige
Sian Phillips
Stacey Roca
Jennifer Saunders
Lisa Stansfield
Nicola Stapleton
Meera Syal
Sandi Toksvig
Francis Wheen
Susannah York
Actors:
Matt Le Blanc
Marcus Brigstocke
Peter Capaldi
Michael Cashman
Henry Cavill
Peter Cellier
Craig Charles
Justin Lee Collins
Antony Cotton
Simon Day
Jason Donovan
Jamie Dornan
Kevin Doyle
Rupert Everett
James Frain
Ricky Gervais
David Haig
Tom Hardy
Nigel Harman
Lord Michael Hesseltine
James McAvoy
Ewan McGregor
Mike McShane
Stephen Merchant
Dominic Monaghan
Kieran O'Brien
Clive Rowe
Toby Sawyer
Andrew Scott
Mel Smith
Edward Speelers
Toby Stephens

JO PETERS MANAGEMENT LTD

56 Macready House, 75 Crawford Street,
London W1H 5LP
Tel: 020 7724 6555 / 6556
Fax: 020 7724 5296
Email: jo@jopeters.biz
Web Site: www.jopeters.biz
Agent: Jo Peters
Provide corporate entertainment and voice coaching.

PHA MODEL & CASTING MANAGEMENT

Tanzaro House, Ardwick Green North,
Manchester M12 6FZ
Tel: 0161 273 4444 Fax: 0161 273 4567
Email: info@pha-agency.co.uk
Web Site: www.pha-agency.co.uk
Senior Personnel: Lorna McDonough,
Robert F Lang

Represent models, extras and actors for commercials, corporate and TV work. Largest casting suites in Manchester also available for hire.

PHAB
High Notes, Sheerwater Avenue,
Woodham, Addlestone, Surrey KT15 3DS
Tel: 01932 348 174
Email: phabmusic@yahoo.co.uk
Senior Personnel: Philip HA Bailey

PHIL MCINTYRE ENTERTAINMENT LTD
3rd Floor 85 Newman Street
London W1T 3EU
Tel: 020 7291 9000 Fax: 020 7291 9001
Email: reception@mcintyre-ents.com
Web Site: www.mcintyre-ents.com
Chief Executive: Phil McIntyre
Promoter: Ed Smith
Agent: Lucy Ansbro
ARTISTES REPRESENTED:
Caroline Aherne
Jason Byrne
Craig Cash
Ben Elton
Peter Kay
Rob Newman
Mark Thomas
Victoria Wood OBE

PHILLIPS ENTERTAINMENT AGENCY
Also known as Tribute World.
4 Queen Victoria Road, Llanelli,
Carmarthenshire SA15 2TL Wales
Tel: 01554 750 525 Fax: 01554 758 336
Email: info@phillipsentertainments.com
Web: www.phillipsentertainments.com
Senior Personnel: Mr Alan Phillips
Representing the best in the UK tribute shows and acts.
ARTISTES REPRESENTED:
Groups:
Agenda
Deja Vue
Fat Barry's Soul Band
Monophonics
Sound Awake
Variations
Artistes:
Astra Review Show
Paul Daisley
Dave Devraux
Mike Doyle
Robbie Gould
Gemma Honey
Owen Money

NORMAN PHILLIPS ORGANISATION LIMITED
Osbourne House 34 Moat Drive,
Drayton Bassett, Tamworth, Staffordshire
B78 3UG
Tel: 01827 284466 Fax: 01827 285599
Email: info@normanphillips.co.uk
Web Site: www.normanphillips.co.uk
Senior Personnel: Norman Phillips, Lianne Phillips
ARTISTES REPRESENTED:
Intrigue
Spanner in the Works
Tropical Islanders Steel Band

HILDA PHYSICK AGENCY
78 Temple Sheen Road, London
SW14 7RR
Tel: 020 8876 0073 Fax: 020 8876 5561
Agent: Hilda Physick
ARTISTES REPRESENTED:
Milton Johns

PICCADILLY MANAGEMENT
Unit 131 23 New Mount Street,
Manchester M4 4DE
Tel: 0161 953 4057 Fax: 0161 953 4001
Email: piccadilly.management@virgin.net
ARTISTES REPRESENTED:
Female:
Carol Alexander
Charlotte Armer
June Broughton
Valerie Bundy
Sian Foulkes
Jude Fowler
Sharon Gatherer
Stacy Liu
Pauline Shanahan
Tania Staite
Elisa Williams
Male:
Kenan Ally
Michael Andrews
Tony Broughton
John Christian
Eric Coudrill
Martyn Cousins
Peter Foster
Zack Foster
Philip Fowler
Ross McCormack
Damon Young-Monaghan

PINEAPPLE AGENCY
Montgomery House,
159-161 Balls Pond Road, Islington,
London N1 4BG
Tel: 020 7241 6601 Fax: 020 7241 3006
Email: pineapple.agency@btconnect.com
Web Site: www.pineappleagency.com
Senior Personnel: David Paton
Specialising in Dancers & Choreographers.
ARTISTES REPRESENTED:
Sean Cheesman - Choreographer
Paul Harris Choreographer

P.J. ENTERTAINMENTS
Church View, Alveley, Bridge North,
Shropshire WV15 6NB
Tel/Fax: 01746 781 883
Web Site: www.flipanddippy.co.uk
Agent: Joanna Jones
Specialising in magic and allied arts, children's entertainment and corporate hospitality.
ARTISTES REPRESENTED:
Crackers
Crazy Clowns
Dippy the Clown
Flip the Clown
Magic Circus
Magic Faces
Glyn Peters
Dave Silk (Magician)
Smallworld Puppets
Russ Styler
Zeppo

PLANET EARTH ENTERPRISES
Cavendish House,
69/79 Fulham High Street,
London SW6 3JW
Tel: 020 7384 7666 Fax: 020 7384 7645
Email: tops.henderson@bmg.com
Management for Rick Astley.
Senior Personnel: Tony Henderson
ARTISTES REPRESENTED:
24/7
Rick Astley
Andrew Frampton

GRAHAM PLATTS MANAGEMENT
PO Box 3706 Sheffield S36 9WA
Tel: 01226 766709 Fax: 01226 766642
Email: grahamplatts@btconnect.com
Senior Personnel: Graham Platts
Specialise in the corporate market; tribute and cabaret artistes.

PLAYERS
PO Box 247, Waltham Cross,
Hertfordshire EN8 9ZX
Email: jay.stratford@btclick.com
Senior Personnel: Jay Stratford
Producing and distributing quality publicity material to active casting directors and producers. Commission free schemes and sponsorship to get actors seen.

PLI ENTERTAINMENTS
PO Box 441 Ashford, Kent TN23 9EL
Tel: 01233 623 003 Mob: 07931 467 388
Mob: 07748 642 923
Email: plientertainment@hotmail.co.uk
Web Site: www.plientertainment.co.uk
Contact: Phil Marks

PLUM PROMOTIONS (SOUTH WALES) LTD
35 Finsbury Terrace, Brynmill, Swansea
SA2 0AH
Tel: 01792 646278 Fax: 01792 475109
Contact: John Landon

PMA MANAGEMENT
(a division of PMA Productions Limited)
The Old Stables, 38 Church Street,
Barrowford, Nelson, Lancashire BB9 6EB
Tel / Fax: 01282 612 503 Production

Mobile: 07768 013 469
Email: info@pmaproductions.co.uk
Web Site: www.pmaproductions.co.uk
ADMINISTRATION:
Artistic Director / Producer: George Critchley
Specialising in: Pantomimes, Children's Theatre, Corporate Presentations and Theatre in education

ARTISTES REPRESENTED:

Lynette Creane
George Critchley

THE POLICE CHIEFS

20 Spencer Drive, Midsomer Norton, Radstock BA3 2DN
Tel: 07974 690 181
Email: bullit7@live.co.uk
Web: www.myspace.com/thepolicechiefs
Contact: Olly Wise

ARTISTES REPRESENTED:

The Police Chiefs

GORDON POOLE AGENCY LTD

The Limes, Brockley, Bristol, BS48 3BB
Tel: 01275 463 222
Email: gordon@gordonpoole.com, agents@gordonpoole.com
Web Site: www.gordonpoole.com
Senior Personnel: Gordon Poole, James Poole
Bands, Cabaret, Celebrities & After Dinner Speakers for Corporate & Private Parties. The Gordon Poole Agency is one of the premier suppliers of entertainment in the UK. The agency has been supplying quality entertainment for over 4 decades to Blue-Chip companies, Event Organisers, PR Companies, Private Parties and other agents.

ARTISTES REPRESENTED:

Kriss Akabusi MBE MA
Jamie Andrew
Dawn Annandale
Ron Atkinson
Nighat Awan
Stephen Backshall
Prof. Chris Baines
Luisa Baldini
Alan Ball MBE
Tony Ball MBE
Maurice Bamford
Gordon Banks OBE
Duncan Bannatyne OBE
Trevor Baylis OBE
Graham Bean
John Beattie
James Bellini
Phil Bennett OBE
Bob "The Cat" Bevan MBE
Karan Bilimoria
Roger Black MBE
Col John Blashford-Snell
Sir Chay Blyth CBE
Sir Chris Bonington CBE
Henry Bonsu
Roger Bootle
Jim Bowen
Kyran Bracken MBE LLB
Craig Brown
Bishop Pat Buckley
Bruce Bugess
Tony Bullimore
Will Carling OBE
Simon Carr
Frank Carson KSG
Barbara Cassani
Jack Charlton OBE
Gareth Chilcott
George Cohen MBE
Clive Coleman
Charles Collingwood
Ed Coode
Bill Copeland
John Craven OBE
Mike D'Abo & His Mighty Quintet
Howard Davies
Lynn Davies MBE
Syd Dennis
Tommy Docherty
Jill Douglas
David Duckham MBE
Richard Dunwoody MBE
Greg Dyke
Tracy Edwards MBE
Rachel Elnaugh
Nigel Farrell
Sir Ranulph Fiennes Bt OBE
John Francome MBE
Ros Gardner
Bill Giles
Robbie Glen
Graham Gooch OBE
Duncan Goodhew MBE
Martin Goodyer
Baroness Susan Greenfield
Jurgen Grobler
Bear Grylls
David Gunson
Terry Hanlon
Gavin Hastings OBE
James Hatfield MBE
Derek Hatton
Alex Hay
Austin Healey
Lord Healey MBE
David Hempleman-Adams
Garry Herbert MBE
Rachael Heyhoe-Flint MBE
Anthony Hilton
Dominic Holland
Damian Hopley
Peter Hudson
John Humphrys
Ben Hunt-Davis MBE
Douglas Hurd
Sir Bernard Ingham
Ian Irving (Comedian)
Dave Ismay
Tony Jardine
Dr Kevin Jones
Ian Keable
David Kendall ACIB
Miles Kington
Carol Klein
Allan Lamb MBE
Nick Leeson
Virginia Leng MBE
Dr David Lewis
Per Lindstrand
Tony Livesey
Lord Lichfield
Jonathan Margolis
Howard Marks
Andrew Marr
Trevor Marriott
John McCarthy
Perry McCarthy
Ian McCaskill
Wilf McGuiness
Paul McKenna
Dom Mee
David Mellor
Owen Money
Cliff Morgan OBE
Roy Noble
Lord Oaksey
Keith O'Keefe
Harvey Oliver
Lance Percival
Gervase Phinn (School Governor)
Gervase Phinn (School Governor)
Bertrand Piccard
Nicky Piper
Jenny Pitman OBE
Michael Portillo
Prof. Richard Holmes
Nigel Rees
Doug Richard
Emma Richards MBE
Dame Stella Rimington DCB MA
Ian Robertson
Peter Rowell
Roger Royle
Henry Sandon
John Sergeant
Sir Digby Jones
Sir Gerry Robinson
Paul Sloane
Tim Smit CBE
Ian St John
John Stalker
Oliver Steeds
Rebecca Stephens MBE
Jeff Stevenson
Col Bob Stewart DSO
John Stirling
Laurie Taylor
Ros Taylor
Polly Toynbee
Chris Vacher
Harvey Walden
Murray Walker OBE
Fred Wedlock
John Welch
Patience Wheatcroft
Barry Williams
Quentin Willson
Richard Wilson
Dave Wolfe
Prof Heinz Wolff
Sir Clive Woodward
Frank Worthington

PORTASS & CARTER ENTERTAINMENTS

The Music Shop, 26 Bridge Road, Sutton Bridge, Spalding, Lincolnshire PE12 9UA
Tel: 01406 350 407 / 350 266
Mobile: 07810 134 464
Senior Personnel: Nigel Portass

ARTISTES REPRESENTED:
Danny Ford & The Offbeats
Nigel Portass Band

POSITIVE MANAGEMENT
PO Box 161, Ormskirk, Lancashire
L39 3QG
Tel: 08702 407 508
Email: info@tomoconnor.co.uk
Web Site: www.tomoconnor.co.uk
Senior Personnel: Kevin O'Brien, Tom Murray
ARTISTES REPRESENTED:
Tom O'Connor

POSITIVE PLUS LTD
Berkeley House, Berkeley Street,
Ashton-under-Lyne, Lancashire OL6 7DT
Tel: 0161 339 9333 Fax: 0161 339 4242
Senior Personnel: Alistair Shackleton
ARTISTES REPRESENTED:
"The Bradshaws"
Billy Bradshaw
Chicagoland Blues Brothers
Mike Ford
Buzz Hawkins
Paul Keefe
Russell Shaun

BOB POTTER ENTERTAINMENT AGENCY
The Lakeside Complex, Wharf Road,
Frimley Green, Camberley, Surrey
GU16 6PT
Tel: 01252 836 464 Fax: 01252 836 777
Email: bobpotter@lakesidecomplex.com
Web Site: www.lakesidecomplex.com
Senior Personnel: Bob Potter OBE, Austin Brown

POWER PROMOTIONS
PO Box 61, Liverpool, Merseyside
L13 0EF
Tel: 0151 230 0070 - 5 Lines Fax: 0870 706 0202 Mob: 07850 779 466 (Lyn Staunton)
Email: tom@powerpromotions.co.uk
Web Site: www.powerpromotions.co.uk
Senior Personnel: Tom Staunton, Lyn Staunton
ARTISTES REPRESENTED:
Billy Butler - Radio
Paul Crone (tv presenter)
Tracy King
Wally Scott - Radio

PP PROMOTIONS
22 Torrington Court, Park North,
Swindon, Wiltshire SN3 2NF
Tel/Fax: 01793 643 280
Mobile: 07771 552974
Email: pppromotions@btconnect.com
Web Site: www.strip2tease.co.uk
Senior Personnel: Peter Prestridge
Specialising in male and female striptease, drag artists, comedians and stag & hen shows.

PRELUDE
Suite 3,Ground Floor Nimax House
20 Ullswater Crescent Coulsdon Surrey
CR5 2HR
Tel: 020 8660 6647 Fax: 010 8660 6657
Email: sales@preludeentertainment.co.uk
Web: www.preludeentertainment.co.uk
Managing Director: Rodney Prout
Administrator: Julianne Basten
Specialising in a variety of entertainment for corporate and private events.

PREMIER STAGE PRODUCTIONS LTD
Unit 16, Randalls Road
Mole Business Park Leatherhead
Surrey KT22 7BA
Tel: 01372 362722
Email: info@premier-productions.co.uk
Web: www.premier-productions.co.uk
Directors: Jason Francis and Nick George
Booking & Production Manager: Stephen Smart
Specialising in Children's Theatre Shows.

PRESENTER PROMOTIONS
123 Corporation Road, Gillingham,
Kent ME7 1RG
Tel/Fax: 01634 851 077
Email: info@presenterpromotions.com
Web Site: www.presenterpromotions.com
Senior Personnel: Colin Cobb
With over 20 years experience, we specialise in Presenters, Speakers, Voice Artistes. Offering a casting service free to production companies and specialist help to newcomers and artistes without an agent.

PRESTIGE ARTISTE MANAGEMENT
19 Coventry Road, Cubbinton,
Leamington Spa, Warwickshire CV32 7JN
Tel: 01926 313 355 Fax: 01926 313 355
Email: banger@primex.co.uk
Contact: Tony Walsh, Don Fardon

PREVIEW & REVIEW ENTERTAINMENT LTD
PO Box 99, Hockley, Essex SS5 4TN
Tel: 01702 202 036 Fax: 0871 871 2065
Email: info@eentertainments.com
Web Site: www.eentertainments.com
Senior Personnel: Mr D Stewart
The agents for many sporting legends including members of 1966 World Cup Team, Frank Bruno and many others.
ARTISTES REPRESENTED:
Sir Geoff Hurst MBE
Peter Shilton MBE OBE
George Cohen MBE
Ray Wilson MBE
Harry Redknapp
Alan Ball MBE
Dave Bassett
Ray Clemence MBE
Steven Clemence
Nobby Stiles MBE
Gordon Banks OBE
Graham Kelly
The Boys Of 66
Mad Mark Peters
Ian Irving (Comedian)
London Gospel Choir
Frank McLintock MBE
Sir Trevor Brooking CBE
Peter Bonetti

PRIMA ARTISTS
3 Sovereign House, West Hill Road,
St Leonards, Sussex TN38 0NH
Tel: 0845 5009393 Fax: 0845 5009394
Email: info@prima-artists.com
Web Site: www.prima-artists.com
Proprietor: Tony MacDonnell, Joan MacDonnell
Full member of NEAC. Specialists in music and entertainment for corporate events, exhibitions and private functions.
ARTISTES REPRESENTED:
4TE
Gimme Abba
Abba Inferno
Abbalicious
Paul Adams (Ind Art)
Darren Alboni as Simply Red
Alpha Connection
Amor
Andalus (Gypsy Kings)
Andy Nolan as Ronan Keating
Blue Attic
Stirling Austin
Bagatelle
Paul Eshelby Band
Ultimate Beatles
Camilla Shadbolt as Victoria Beckham
Rick Beech
The Bootleg BeeGees
Big Macs Wholly Soul Band
Perfect Blend
Blue Harlem
Sue Bradbury as Ab Fab's Patsy
Briefcase Blues Brothers
Chapman Brothers
Ultimate Blues Brothers
Caché
Cafe Society
Maurice Canham is Del Boy
Jazz Cannons
Sax in the City
The BB Collective
Crush
Dan Darling & His Lovely Chaps
Drop Dead Divas (Ind Art)
Price Wates Duo
E2
Simon Ellinas
Suspiciously Elvis
Tenors Encore
Essence
Kylie In Your Eyes
The Party Faithful
Fascinatin' Rhythm
John Parkin as Basil Fawlty
Feverish
Danny Foster
The Fugitives
Funky Divas
Funky Lipstik
Fuse

Gidea Park (Beach Boys tribute)
Blue Groove
Lesley Guinness (Edina from Ab Fab)
Lesley Guinness
Andy Harmon (David Beckham)
MIke Hatchard
Gordon Hendricks
Jeff Hooper
Hot Club Trio
Max Hutton (Robbie Williams)
Chip Jenkins
Ian Keable
Suzie Kennedy as Marilyn Monroe
Gipsy Kingdom
Robert Lamberti (George Michael)
Les Onions
Loaded
James Long
Lounge Sounds
Evelyne Brink as Madonna
Master Bavarian Brass
Mazaika Duo
Mimeworks
Miss Minogue
Kylie Monique
Mr Signature Man
Bruce Munton
Graeme Mykal
Al Nicholls Quintet
Jenis Adams as Michelle Obama
Ryan Seggs as Barak Obama
Izzy Ozzy
Palenké
Platinum Abba
Premier Cru Dance Band
Red Blooded Woman
Richard Reed
Regondi
The Roving Artist
Sav
Schwing
Oliver Sheen
Tim Shoesmith
Mike Newman SNR
Sol y Sombra
Solid Steel
Souled Out
David St John
Status Cymbal
Strawberry Strings
String mania
Stringfever
Red Hot Strings
Sway
The Citrus Brothers
Britney One More Time
Abba UK
Spencer Wood
Hui Ling Zhu

PRIMARY TALENT INTERNATIONAL

The Primary Building
10-11 Jockey's Fields, London
WC1R 4BN
Tel: 020 7400 4500 Fax: 020 7400 4501
Email: peterm@primary.uk.com
Web Site: www.primary.uk.com
Senior Personnel: Martin Hopewell,
Peter Maloney

ARTISTES REPRESENTED:

Lily Allen
Marc Almond
Vanessa Amorosi
Laurie Anderson
Tina Arena
Joseph Arthur
Asian Dub Foundation
The Ataris
Beans
Daniel Bedingfield
Natasha Bedingfield
Ben Folds
Bloodhound Gang
Blue States
John Cale
Cannibal Ox
Cassius
Chamonix
The Crystal Method
The Cure
Daft Punk
Def Jux
E1-P
Emery
Engerica
Everything But The Girl
Fall out boy
Fastball
Foolproof
Peter Gabriel
Mark Gardner
Laurent Garnier
Roland Gift
Bebel Gilberto
God Awfuls
Peter Hammill
Herbaliser
Indigo Girls
Joe Jackson
Basement Jaxx
Junkie XL
Ladytron
Lemon Jelly
Less Than Jake
Lucky jim
Mest
Kylie Minogue
Des Mitchell
Mojave 3
The Monkees
Morcheeba
Mouse on Mars
New Model Army
Nightmares On Wax
No Doubt
Oasis
Phoenix
Plaid
The Proclaimers
Lou Reed
Jonathan Richman
Ryuichi Sakamoto
Roger Sanchez
Ron Sexsmith
Shakatak
The Sisters of Mercy
Patti Smith
Speedy J
Ringo Starr
The Streets
Justin Sullivan
Matthew Sweet
The Androids
The Dropkick Murphys
The Eighties Matchbox B-Line Disaster
The Go
Tiger Lillies
Tower Of Power
Toy Dolls
Tricky
Tuck & Patti
Underworld
Unwritten Law
The Vandals
Rufus Wainwright
Zero 7
Gwen Stefani
The Pipettes
Lady Sovereign
Roger Sanchez
Rufus Wainwright
Acoustic Ladyland
Afrika Bambaataa
The Black Maria
The Pipettes
Adam F
David Byrne
Peter Doherty
Dizzee Rascal

PRIME PERFORMERS LTD

1-2 Faulkners Alley Cowcross Street
London EC1M 6DD
Tel: 020 7251 8222
Email: info@primeperformers.co.uk
Web Site: www.primeperformers.co.uk
Senior Personnel: Ian Walker,
Sally Dellow
Booking expert speakers for all your business events. Please Note that Prime Performers acts as consultants and not as artists agents for any of the personalities listed. Please call for further details, but here are just a few ...

ARTISTES REPRESENTED:

Abbamania
George Alagiah OBE
Ant & Dec
Zoe Ball
Amanda Barrie
Jasper Carrott OBE
Jeremy Clarkson
Billy Connolly
Sir Henry Cooper OBE KSG
Jack Dee
Frank Dick OBE
David Dimbleby
Gavin Esler
Vanessa Feltz
Kate Garraway
Uri Geller
Prof Germain Greer
John Grisham
Ainsley Harriott
Sir John Harvey-Jones MBE
Graham P Jolley
Martin Kemp
Joanna Lumley OBE
Denis Norden CBE
Michael Parkinson
Jeremy Paxman
Gail Porter

Anneka Rice
Andrew Sachs
Philip Schofield
Chris Tarrant
Jamie Theakston
Victoria Wood OBE

PRINCESS TALENT MANAGEMENT

Princess Studios Whiteleys Centre,
151 Queensway, London W2 4SB
Tel: 020 7985 1985 Fax: 020 7985 1989
Email: talent@princesstv.com
Web Site: www.princesstv.com
Agents: Jan Croxson, Kate Douglas, Angharad Allan
Princess Talent Management was launched in February 2000 and is the talent arm of Princess Productions.

ARTISTES REPRESENTED:

Emma Basden
Dave Berry
Charles Bickford
Jeff Brazier
Danann Breathnach
Kelly Brook
Vicki Butler-Henderson
Nigel Clarke
Ed Docx
Brian Dowling
Mark Eccleston
Jeremy Edwards
Sarra Elgan
Christian Furr
Andy Goldstein
Emma Griffiths
Sarah Hendy
Vernon Kay
Olivia Lee
Carole Machin
James McCourt
Steve McKenna
Ashley Mulheron
Nihal
Rachel Pierman
Johny Pitts
Mark Rumble
Janet Street-Porter
Mohini Sule
Jon Tickle
Giles Vickers-Jones

PRINCIPAL ARTISTES

4 Paddington Street, Off Baker Street,
London W1U 5QE
Tel: 020 7224 3414 Fax: 020 7486 4668
Email: principalartistes@aol.com
Senior Personnel: Pia Turner
Specialising in actors, singers & dancers, Musicians.

THE PRODUCTION ASSOCIATES (TPA)

23/24 Titan Court, Laporte Way, Luton
Bedfordshire LU4 8EF
Tel: 0845 226 8136 Fax: 0845 226 8137
Email: steve@theproductionassociates.com
Web: www.theproductionassociates.com
Contact: Steve Donnelly
TPA supplies the very best live entertainment for any event, venue or occasion.

PROFESSIONAL ARTISTES AGENCY

Autoquote House 755 - 757 City Road,
Mannor Top, Sheffield S12 2AA
Tel/ Fax: 0114 265 8182
Email: ebeighton@btconnect.com
Web Site: www.proartistesltd.co.uk
Contact: Tom West
Specialises in corprate events.

PROFESSIONAL SPORTS PARTNERSHIPS LTD

The Town House, 63 High Street,
Chobham Surrey GU24 8AF
Tel: 01276 858 930 Fax: 01276 856 974
Email: chris@profsports.com
Web Site: www.profsports.com
Contact: Chris Evans-Pollard

ARTISTES REPRESENTED:

Athletes & Olympians:
Jo Ankier
Sophie Broome
Simon Burnett
Chris Cook
Steve Cram MBE
Gail Emms
Fran Halsall
Katy Livingston
Caitlin McClatchey
Alex Partridge
Matthew Pinsent
Peter Reed
Nathan Robertson
Shirley Robertson OBE
Nick Thompson
Oliver Townend
Steve Williams MBE
Shelly Woods
Broadcasters:
Sue Barker OBE
Steve Cram MBE
Sean Fitzpatrick
PY Gerbeau
Matthew Pinsent
Ken Schofield
Jean Van de Velde
Golfers:
Jean Van de Velde
Yasin Ali
Barry Hume
Lynn Kenny
Bernard Gallacher OBE
Kyle Phillips
Joakim Backstrom
Celebrity Speakers:
Jo Ankier
Sue Barker OBE
Steve Cram MBE
Gail Emms
Sean Fitzpatrick
Bernard Gallacher OBE
PY Gerbeau
Alex Partridge
Matthew Pinsent
Peter Reed
Nathan Robertson
Shirley Robertson OBE
Ken Schofield
Steve Williams MBE

PROFESSOR MYSTRAL'S JUVENILE OMNIBUS

65 Penylan Road, Cardiff, CF23 5HZ
Wales
Tel: 029 2048 5544
Mobile: 07855 515350
Web Site: www.professormystral.co.uk
Proprietor: Frank Turvey
Children's/family entertainment under the names of Professor Mystral and Mister Magipatch.

ARTISTES REPRESENTED:

Mister Magipatch
Professor Mystral

PROFESSOR POTTY

45 David Newberry Drive,
Lee-on-the-Solent, Hampshire PO13 8FG
Tel: 0800 043 5945 Mob: 07920 779 410
Email: tensai@tensaimagic.com
Web Site: www.professorpotty.co.uk
Contact: Alan Vandome

ARTISTES REPRESENTED:

Professor Potty

PROMPT EVENTS

59 Crammond Glebe Road, Edinburgh
EH4 6NT
Tel: 0131 467 0066 Fax: 0870 130 1850
Email: prompt.events@ednet.co.uk
Contact: Richard Neville-Towle

THE PSYCHO MANAGEMENT CO LTD

Solly's Mill, Mill Lane, Godalming,
Surrey GU7 1EY
Tel: 01483 419 429 Fax: 01483 419 504
Email: agents@psycho.co.uk
Web Site: www.psycho.co.uk
Company Directors: Patrick Haveron, John Mabley
Psycho Management is the ultimate source for tribute bands and lookalikes in the UK and Europe.

ARTISTES REPRESENTED:

Nostalgia & Tribute Bands:
Abba Gold
Abba One
Atomic Blondie
Carte Blanche
Blues Brothers 2001
The Blues Brothers Experience
James Bond Orchestra
Carnival of the Bizarre
The Circus of Horrors
Completely Mad
The Counterfeit Concert
Disco Inferno
FABBA
Faith
The F.B.I. (Blues Brothers/Commitments tribute)
Greased Lightning
Green Dayz
Lady Madonna

Lady Marmalade
Mentallica
Platinum Abba
Probably Robbie
Pussycat Babes
Relax
Sounds of Abba
Super Troupers (Abba tribute)
Take This
Teen Spirit (Nirvana tribute)
The Fillers
The XFM Band
The Time Machine
Tom The Voice
Ultimate 80's
Utter Madness
Wham Duran
Zoo-2
Original Artists:
ABC
Toby Anstis
Bad Manners
The Beat
Sam Beeton
Bjorn Again
Bluetones
Boney M
Bootleg Beatles
Steve Brookstein
Bucks Fizz
Chas 'n' Dave
Cheeky Girls
The Commitments
Cut Up Boys
Doctor & the Medics
Drifters
The Foundations
Sir Bob Geldof
Go West including Peter Cox
Mark Goodier
Tony Hadley
Steve Harley & Cockney Rebel
Rolf Harris AM CBE
Heaven 17
Ronnie Herel (Radio 1)
Mary Anne Hobbs
Jools Holland
Hot Chocolate
Human League
Imagination
Incognito
Howard Jones
Kid Creole & the Coconuts
Limahl
Scott Mills
Modern Romance
Nemone
Nine Below Zero
Hazel O'Connor
Dave Pearce
Suzi Quatro
Sonna Rele
Rose Royce
Leo Sayer
The Selecter
Pat Sharp
Sister Sledge
Supergrass
The Supremes
JTQ James Taylor Quartet
Ten Years After
The Levellers
The Real Thing
The Specials
Toyah
Geno Washington
Wishbone Ash
Roy Wood
The Wurzels
Paul Young

PSYCHO MANAGEMENT COMPANY LTD

111 Clarence Road, Wimbledon,
London SW19 8QB
Tel: 020 8540 8122 Fax: 020 8715 2827
Surrey Office: Sollys Mill, Mill Lane,
Godalming, Surrey GU7 1EY
Tel: 01483 419429 Fax: 01483 419504
Email: john@psycho.co.uk
Web Site: www.circusofhorrors.co.uk / www.psycho.co.uk
Company Director: John Mabley
We specialise in providing speciality and weird acts for publicity stunts and TV management for Circus of Horrors and Carnival of the Bizarre. We also act as Media Company & Theatre bookers for: The Chinese State Circus, The Moscow State Circus, Cottle & Austen Circus, Circus Berlin.

ARTISTES REPRESENTED:
Solely Represented:
Abba Gold
Carnival of the Bizarre
The Circus of Horrors
The Counterfeit Concert
Disco Inferno
Dr Haze
Relax
Reload
Satanica
Gary Stretch
Teen Spirit (Nirvana tribute)
Wasp Boy
Also Represented:
Mangolian Laughing Boy

PULSE ENTERTAINMENTS & TODDLERS 2 TEENS LTD

136 Elliott Street, Tyldesley,
Manchester M29 8FJ
Tel: 01942 893092 Fax: 01942 892892
Email: sales@pulse-entertainers.co.uk
Web: www.pulse-entertainments.co.uk
Contact: Adrian Waring

TONY PUXLEY

Bay Tree Cottage, 1 Fairfield Road,
Burnham, Slough SL1 8AH
Tel: 01628 667 511
Email: vinegate@clara.net
Web Site: www.salenajones.co.uk
Senior Personnel: Tony Puxley

ARTISTES REPRESENTED:
Salena Jones

PVA ENTERTAINMENT CONSULTANTS

2 High Street, Westbury-on-Trym, Bristol,
Avon BS9 3DU
Tel: 0117 950 4504 Fax: 0117 959 1786
Email: tim@pvagroup.com, enquiries@pva.ltd.uk
Web Site: www.pva.ltd.uk
Senior Personnel: Pat Vincent, Tim Cowlin

ARTISTES REPRESENTED:
4-Real
Abbalike
The Amazing Mandrake
The Animals
Babewatch
Tony Ball MBE
Bar Fly
Stuart Barnes
Bath City Jazzmen
Beachcomber Stompers
Lennie Bennett
Bernardo
Dave Berry & The Cruisers
Best of British
Carte Blanche
Blue Note Jazzband
Bootleg Beach Boys
Bootleg Beatles
Bouncy Boxing
Jim Bowen
Brandysnaps Orchestra
Bromley Trio
Brotherhood of Man
Joe Brown
Bucking Bronco
Micky John Bull
Bungle Rye
Mr B Bunny
Eddie Burke
Caberfedh Scottish Dancers
Caberfedh Scottish Pipers
Canadian Log Rolling
Caribbean Harmonics
Casino Entertainment Services
The Charleston Chasers
The Charleys
Chico's Chilean Allstars
Gareth Chilcott
Chimes
Chinese Dragon Dancers
Chinese Lion Dancers
Circus Dropalot
Clown Bobby
John Conteh
Steve Conway
Sir Henry Cooper OBE KSG
Cossack Dancers
Barry Cryer
The Cufflinks
Mike D'Abo & His Mighty Quintet
The Dakotas
The Dance Band
Dancin' Easy
Graham Davies
Adam Daye
Daniel Dean
Denver Spur
Deuce
Diddly Eye Dudes
Dino
Jon Dolly
Dozy Beaky Mick & Tich
The Dreamers
Easybeats
Jack Edgar

Edison Lighthouse
English Mustard
Hugh Ferguson Band
Finesse
Flamingo Steel Band
Fon Moor Kuim
Wayne Fontana and the Mindbenders
Ricky Ford (Roy Orbison)
The Fortunes
The Four Pennies
The Fourmost
Ron Fowler Big Band
Ani Frank
Fred The Ted
Freddie & the Dreamers
Gaffer & Willis
Gee Baby I Love You
Gentlemen Of Jazz
Gidea Park (Beach Boys tribute)
Gipsy Kings
Gladiator Jousting
The Glitter Band
Great Western Marching Band
David Gunson
Gypsy
Gypsy's Kiss
Harvesters
Hawaiian Tropicana
Chip Hawkes
George Henry
Henry's Bootblacks
Herman's Hermits
Richard Hill
Joji Hirota
Hookey Band
Hop Till You Drop
Hopping Mad
Hot Strings
Tracie Hughes
The Hula Bluebirds
Human Gyroscope
It`s A Knockout
Ivy League
Mike James Band/Sound
Chris James
Mungo Jerry
The Joji Hirota Taiko Drummers
K J Music Sound
Kaz
King Swingers
Roger Kitter
Denny Laine
Laser Combat
The Syd Lawrence Orchestra
Steve Leaney
Don & Cindy Leather
Los Salerosos
Love Affair
Don MacLean MBE
Mainstreet Roadshow
The Manfreds
Marmalade
Steve Martin Roadshow
Masquerade
McCool
Piper Jimmy McQueen
Merengue-Mania
David Merlin (Magician)
Merseybeats
Michelle
Micky the Magical Clown
Middle Of The Road
The Glenn Miller Band
John Milner & Kim
Mimix
Mister Blue
Monte Carlo Casino
Gil Morris
Nina Myskow
Nashville Teens
New Sound Hurricane Force Steel Band
Old Fox Band
John Oliver Band and Singers
On The Edge
Paper Lace
Paradise Force Steel Band
Mike Pender's Searchers
Lance Percival
Phil & Die Heidelburger Band
Pinkertons
Brian Poole & Electrix
Charlotte Poulter
Prohibition Jazz Band
PVA Fun Casinos
PVA Outdoor Entertainment
Racey
Sir Steven Redgrave CBE
Regency Brass Ensemble
Marie-France Riboulet
Rob-E-Ryan
Robocop
The Rockin' Berries
Rodeo Bull
Root Doctors
Bungee Run
Salsa Y Ache
The Searchers
Nigel Shillitoe
Showaddywaddy
The Silver Beatles (Beatles tribute)
Simulators Unlimited
Soca Fire
Soirees Musicales
Solid Steel Ambassadors
Sounds of The Blues Brothers
St Lucia Steel Band
John Stalker
Piper Julian Steed
Steel Panacea
Jack Stephens
Steve & Megumi
Jeff Stevenson
Ronnie Stewart
John Stirling
Tony Strudwick Band
Sumo Wrestling
Piper Brian Supple
Sweet
Swing 39
The Swinging Blue Jeans
Jimmy Tamley
Patrick Tedbury
Tensai
The Three British Tenors
Tiare Tahiti
Titanic Tea Room Quartet
Top Catz
The Tornados
The Tremeloes
The Troggs
Twinkle
Ulysses The Statue
Vanity Fare (ex-chart band)
Viva Flamenco
Lenny Windsor
Steve Womack
Marty Wylde
Yes !!! Brazil Latin Band & Dancers
The Yetties
Paul Young
Rob Zikking

After Dinner Speakers:

Kriss Akabusi MBE MA
Clive Anderson
Ron Atkinson
Pam Ayres
Tony Ball MBE
Sir John Banham
Stuart Barnes
Chris Barrie
Bob "The Cat" Bevan MBE
Dickie Bird MBE
Roger Black MBE
Rabbi Lionel Blue
Jennie Bond
Ian Botham MBE
Jim Bowen
Geoff Boycott
Rory Bremner
Janet Brown
Joe Brown
Frank Carson KSG
Jack Charlton OBE
Gareth Chilcott
Jeremy Clarkson
Lord Coe OBE
John Conteh
Sir Henry Cooper OBE KSG
Mike Cowan
Barry Cryer
Edwina Currie
Graham Davies
Roger De Courcey
Angus Deayton
Frank Dick OBE
Tommy Docherty
Frances Edmonds
Gareth Edwards MBE
Brendan Foster MBE
John Francome MBE
Sir David Frost OBE
Bill Giles
Tony Gubba
David Gunson
Damon Hill OBE
Richard Hill
Ian Hislop
Roy Hudd OBE
Emlyn Hughes OBE
Sir Geoff Hurst MBE
Lee Hurst
Dave Ismay
Clive James
Diana Lamplugh OBE
Eddie Large
Denis Law
Martyn Lewis CBE
Jimmy Logan
Don MacLean MBE
Willie John McBride
Ian McCaskill
Rory McGrath
Lawrie McMenemy
John Motson OBE
Tiff Needell
Martin Nicholls

Tom O'Connor
Lord Oaksey
Alan Parry
Jeremy Paxman
Lance Percival
Sir Steven Redgrave CBE
Griff Rhys Jones
Sir Tim Rice
Steve Rider
Simon Rose
John Simonett
Tony Slattery
John Stalker
John Stirling
Rosie Swale
Dennis Taylor
Freddie Trueman OBE
Stuart Turner
Helen Vandervelde
Terry Venables
Ruby Wax
Dave Wolfe
Steve Womack
Sir Clive Woodward

THE Q BAND
20 Coombes Way, North Common Bristol BS30 8YP
Tel: 0117 940 0929 Tel: 0117 932 6244
Mob: 07801 627 859
Mob: 07853 944 227
Email: mail@theqband.co.uk
Web Site: www.theqband.co.uk
Contact: Brian Allen

ARTISTES REPRESENTED:
The Q Band

QUALITY ENTERTAINMENTS
PO Box 30, Gretton Gloucestershire GL54 5ZL
Tel: 01242 621 188 Fax: 01242 621 502
Email: mail@qualityents.co.uk
Web Site: www.qualityents.co.uk
Senior Personnel: Perry Bradley, Reg Bradley

ARTISTES REPRESENTED:
Discos:
A1
Apollo Disco
Casino Disco
Horizon Disco
Dave Jay
Magnum Disco
Sam's Wax
Spectrum Disco
Function Bands:
Gary Allcock Big Band
The Choice
First Impression
Tony Richards Sound Station
Jazz Bands:
Arthur Brown Jazzband
Doctors of Jazz
Eagle Jazz Band
Georgia Jazzmen
Jazz Ramblers
Martinique Jazzband
Tad Newton Jazzband
The Tailgate Jazz Band
Trent Valley Stompers
Zenith Hot Stompers
Strings Etc.:
The Burlington Quartet
Delamere String Quartet
Finesse
Palm Court Trio
The Pump Room Trio
The Quartz Quartet
St Nicholas String Quartet
The Strauss Quartet
Tea For Three
Harpists:
Emily Barter
Mary Benton
Audrey Douglas
Menir Heulyn
Christina Rhys
Patricia Spero (Harpist)
Catherine Thomas
Catrin Williams
Mexican Mariachi Bands:
Alkasalsa
Cuarteto Azteca
Orquesta Muracan
Steel Bands:
Caribbean Harmonics
Caribbean Melody
Caribbean Sounds
International Steelband
Pantonic Steelband
Phase One Steelband
Rhapsody Steel Band
Sun Jets

QUEEN B
3 Dorian Road Hornchurch Essex RM12 4AW
Tel: 01708 452 120
Email: pj@pjbands.com / pj@queenb.co.uk
Web Site: www.queenb.co.uk
Paul Jackson performing as Queen B - a tribute to Queen.

QUIDETAM LTD
PO Box 3698, London NW2 6ZA
Tel: 020 7748 3003 Fax: 020 7691 7632
Email: info@quidetam.com
Web Site: www.quidetam.com
Contact: Diane Hinds

ARTISTES REPRESENTED:
Nick Bateman
Dave Courtney
Amy Lame
Adrian Layment
Neil Rayment
Oliver Skeete
Vanessa Upton

R B ENTERTAINMENTS
Hazelmere Preston Road, Ribchester, Preston PR3 3XL
Tel: 01254 878096
Email: davehazelmere@aol.com
Web Site: www.rbentertainments.co.uk
Contact: David Reeve

RAGE
Tigris House, 256 Edgware Road, London W2 1DS
Tel: 020 7262 0515 Fax: 020 7402 0507
Email: coxy@ugly.org
Web Site: www.ugly.org
Senior Personnel: Mark French, Coxy
Modelling Agency

RAINBOW PRODUCTIONS
Rainbow House, 56 Windsor Avenue, London SW19 2RR
Tel: 020 8545 0700 Fax: 020 8545 0777
Email: info@rainbowproductions.co.uk
Web Site: www.rainbowproductions.co.uk
Managing Director: David Scott,
Sales & Marketing Director: Simon Foulkes
Rainbow Productions has over 70 celebrity cartoon characters to book for guest appearances. We also create bespoke brand mascots and props for events.

RAINBOW STRIPTEASE AGENCY
87 Herbert Gardens, London NW10 3BH
Tel: 020 8965 2826 Fax: 020 8965 2991
Mobile: 07802 885557
Email: mervyn87@aol.com
Senior Personnel: Mervyn Thomas
Female and Male Striptease/Stripograms agents for bars, pubs, clubs, stag and hen nights. Also Door Security.

ARTISTES REPRESENTED:
Ann Marie (striptease)
Dark Angel
Miss Jones
Raw Sex
Scarlet
Tony Silk

RAVENSCOURT MANAGEMENT
8-30 Galena Road, London W6 0LT
Tel: 020 8741 0707 Fax: 020 8741 1786
Email: info@ravenscourt.net
Web Site: www.ravenscourt.net
Contact: Christopher Price

RAY'S NORTHERN CASTING AGENCY
7 Wince Close, Middleton, Manchester M24 1UJ
Tel/Fax: 0161 643 6745
Email: rayscasting@yahoo.co.uk
Senior Personnel: Bobbie and Harold Ray
Specialising in Adults & Children - Multi Racial

RAZZAMATAZZ MANAGEMENT
Mulberry Cottage Park Farm
Haxted Road Lingfield, Surrey RH7 6DE
Tel: 01342 835 359 Fax: 01342 835 359
Email: razzamatazzmanagement@btconnect.com
Senior Personnel: Jill Shirley, Tony McGrogan

ARTISTES REPRESENTED:
Cheryl Baker

RBA MANAGEMENT LTD
The Annexe, 13-15 Hope Street,
Liverpool L1 9BH
Tel: 0151 708 7273 Fax: 0151 709 0773
Email: info@rbamanagement.co.uk
Web Site: www.rbamanagement.co.uk
Agency Manager: Freddy Carpen Juckes
Senior Personnel: Denise Kennedy

ARTISTES REPRESENTED:
Sufiah Ashraf
Tony Blaney
Roy Carruthers
Lisa Chae
Paul Codman
Elisa Cowley
Andrew James Davies
Emma Dears
Paul Green
Sarah Hogarth
Carolyn Hood
Stephen Ingham
Denise Kennedy
Aisling Leyne
Nicholas Mai
Angela Mounsey
Rebecca Ridgeway
Nevean Riley Mohamed
Ben Shevski
Bekah Sloan
Liam Tobin
Julie Walker
Kathryn Worthington

R.B.M. (RICHARD BUCKNALL MANAGEMENT)
See Richard Bucknall Management Listing

RDF MANAGEMENT
The Gloucester Building,
Kensington Village, Avonmore Road,
London W14 8RF
Tel: 020 7013 4100 Fax: 020 7013 4101
Email: vic.murray@rdfmanagement.com
Web Site: www.rdfmanagement.com
Agents: Michael Joyce, Debbi Allen, Vic Murray, Craig Latto

ARTISTES REPRESENTED:
Presenters (Males):
Ben Baldwin
Mike Brewer
Des Clarke
John Daly
Ortis Deley
Tim Dixon
Robert Elliot
Tim Fornara
Chris Hawkins
Mark Heyes
Jason Gardiner (Queer Eye for a Straight Guy)
Gethin Jones
Les Keen
Tim Lovejoy
Eddie Matthews
Angus Purden
Alex Riley
Adrian Simpson
Trev and Simon
Bradley Walsh
Presenters (Females):
Kaye Adams
LInzi Boyd
Sarah Champion
Dr Wendy Denning
Jemma Forte
Seetha Hallet
Nicky Hambleton-Jones
Sarah Heaney
Victoria Hollingsworth
Charlotte Hudson
Lisa I'Anson
Emma Lee
Debbie Lindley
Shauna Lowry
Clare Nasir
Melissa Peachy
Sue Perkins
Gail Porter
Lucy Porter
Lizzie Roper
Lucy Rusedski
Harriet Scott
Kat Shoob
Edwina Silver
Liza Tarbuck
Anthea Turner
Michelle Watt
Rebecca Wheatley
Thaila Zucchi
Stand Up Comedians:
LInzi Boyd
Des Clarke
Dr Wendy Denning
Kevin Eldon
James Holmes
Les Keen
Carey Marx
Gary McCausland
Owen O'Neill
Dan Tetsell
Jayne Tunnicliffe
Bradley Walsh
Actors:
Perry Benson
Jack Brough
Des Clarke
Dominic Coleman
Tony Craig
Mackay Crawford
Jamie Deeks
Ortis Deley
Andrew Dickens
Kevin Eldon
Graeme Garden
Simon Hickson
James Holmes
Paul Courtney Hyu
Les Keen
Andy Newton Lee
Daniel Macpherson
Daniel Maier
Trevor Neal
Phil Nice
Owen O'Neill
Robin Pirongs
Eric Potts
Danny Robins
Mark Roper
Richard Shelton
Dan Tetsell
Bradley Walsh
Jonathan Wrather
Actresses:
Peggy Batchelor
Cordelia Bugeja
Kelly Condron
Kate Copstick
Samantha Coughlin
Susan Earl
Kristina Erderly
Jemma Forte
Melissa George
Cicely Giddings
Lucy Jules
Janet Kidder
Oriane Messina
Charlotte Palmer
Sue Perkins
Wendi Peters
Lucy Porter
Lizzie Roper
Chandra Ruegg
Fay Rusling
Catherine Skinner
Jennie Mcalpine (Fizz, Coronation Street)
Liza Tarbuck
Jayne Tunnicliffe
Thaila Zucchi
Experts:
Mauricio Aguiar
Annie Ashdown
Anita Bean
LInzi Boyd
Dr Wendy Denning
Michelle Dewberry
Samantha Hamilton
Mark Heyes
Gary McCausland
Chris Mundle
Shay Shay
Derek Taylor
Ginette Vedrickas
Writers:
Rhodri Crooks
Kevin Eldon
James Hendrie
Simon Hickson
James Holmes
Trevor Neal
Geoff Thompson
Malcolm Williamson

RDL
132 Chase Way, London N14 5DH
Tel: 07050 055 167 Fax: 020 8361 3757
Email: rdldisco@aol.com
Web: www.mkentertainments.8k.com
Senior Personnel: C Jaques
Suppliers of DJ's, Karaoke and PA systems.

ARTISTES REPRESENTED:
Richard Black
Dizzy Wizzy Karaoke
David Martin
Natallia
Sanderina
Soundmoves Mobile Discos

REAL TALENT
24 Goodge Street, London W1T 2QF
Tel: 020 7436 5556 Fax: 020 7436 5557
Email: colindench@realtalent.co.uk
Web Site: www.realtalent.co.uk
Senior Personnel: Colin Dench
Management & Productions Co. Check website for current information.

ARTISTES REPRESENTED:
Ross Noble

REALITY CHECK MANAGEMENT
97 Charlotte Street, London W1T 4QA
Tel: 0207 907 1415 Fax: 0207 907 1423
Email: francesca@reality-m.com
Web Site: www.realitycheckmanagement.com
Contact: Francesca

ARTISTES REPRESENTED:
Actors:
Deborah Cox
Jo Emma
Chloe Fontaine
Jonny Grant
James Rees
Brian Wheeler
Performers:
Esme Bianca
Alex Cartana
Jaws
Anne Sharman
Presenters:
Jack Downes
Honey Hazel
Du'aine Ladejo
Paul Tennant
Jenny Topp
Jules Wheeler

RED ADMIRAL RECORDS
The Cedars, Elvington Lane, Hawkinge, Folkestone, Kent CT18 7AD
Tel: 01303 893 472 Mob: 07950 848 148 (Chris Ashman)
Email: info@redadmiralrecords.com
Web Site: www.redadmiralrecords.com
CEO: Chris Ashman

ARTISTES REPRESENTED:
Hardly Mozart
Rhythm of Blues
The Sharpee's
The Silent Kingdom
Rik Waller

RED ONION AGENCY & MANAGEMENT
Harmony Hall, Truro Road, London E17 7BY
Tel: 020 8520 3975 Fax: 020 8520 3975
Email: info@redonion.uk.com
Web Site: www.redonion.uk.com
Contact: Dee Curtis

ARTISTES REPRESENTED:
Citizen K Gospel Choir

RED ORANGE
20 Henderson Close St Albans AL3 6DY
Tel: 01727 568716
Email: miguel.santos@redorange.org.uk
Web Site: www.redorange.org.uk
Contact: Miguel Santos

JOAN REDDIN
Hazel Cottage, Wheeler End Common, Wheeler End, High Wycombe, Buckinghamshire HP14 3NL
Tel: 01494 882 729 Fax: 01494 521 727
Agent: Joan Reddin

ARTISTES REPRESENTED:
Jean Alexander
Gwyneth Owen
Anne Pichon
Katie Reddin-Clancy
Mollie Sugden

REDGATE PROPERTIES LTD
4 Little Borough Brockham RH3 7ND
Tel: 01737 843011
Email: sallymanningcomedy@sky.com
Web Site: www.sallymanningcomedy.com
Lord John Clack of Gerard's Bromley

REDROOFS AGENCY
Littlewick Green Maidenhead, Berkshire SL6 3QY
Tel: 01628 822982 Fax: 01753 785443
Email: junemrose@me.com
Web Site: www.redroofs.co.uk
Contact: June Rose

REDROOFS ASSOCIATES
Rooms 160-161 Main Admin Building, Pinewood Studios, Iver Heath, Buckinghamshire SL0 0NH
Tel: 01753 785 444 Fax: 01753 785 443
Email: agency2@redroofs.co.uk
Specialising in Children & Young Performers.
Agent: Sam Keston

MIKE REED PROMOTIONS
PO Box 122, Rochester, Kent ME2 1PQ
Tel: 01634 723 181 / 721414 Fax: 01634 721 414 Mobile: 07958 657 366
Email: info@mrp.eclipse.co.uk
Web Site: www.mikereedpromotions.com
Contact: Mike Reed.
See website for Artist Roster

DES REES SUNRISE GROUP
Elm Croft, Thornwood Common, High Road, Thornwood, Epping, Essex CM16 6LX
Tel: 07000 303130 Fax: 01992 575 705
Mobile: 07850 023522
Email: des.rees@btconnect.com
Web Site: www.sunrisegroup.co.uk
Contact: Des Rees
Britian's premier agency for all tribute acts. The one-stop-shop for tribute acts.

REGENCY AGENCY
25 Carr Road, Calverley, Pudsey, West Yorkshire LS28 5NE
Tel: 0113 255 8980 Fax: 0113 255 4833
Email: regencyagency@hotmail.co.uk

REID ENTERTAINMENTS
PO Box 85, Warrington, Cheshire WA2 0NZ
Tel: 01925 811 237 Fax: 01925 827 925
Email: reidentertainments@btconnect.com
Senior Personnel: Brian Wilson, Stephen Wilson

RENT-A-BAND
Burnside House, 10 Burns Court, Birstall, Batley, West Yorkshire WF17 9JZ
Tel/Fax: 01924 441 441
Email: bands@rent-a-band.org
Web Site: www.rent-a-band.org
Senior Personnel: Ken Baxter

ARTISTES REPRESENTED:
Jazz:
Dixielanders
The Good Time Jazz Band
Jazz All-Stars
Jazz Sounds
Society Swing
Ceilidh, Barn Dance, Hoe Down:
Mrs Delaney's Band
Finnegan`s Wake
Harvesters Ceilidh Band
Jackdaw Ceilidh Band
The Mother`s Delight Ceilidh Band
Russian, Ukranian, Hungarian:
Balalaika Orchestra
Krylati
Odessa
Troika
Tziganka - Russian Cossack Music & Dance Spectacular
Ragtime/Banjo:
Alexander's Rag Time Banjo Band
Banjo Boys
Chicago Swing Band
Downtown Sound
Roaring 20's Ragtime Band
Spanish:
Roberto Antonio
Duende
Fiesta Flamenca
Gonzales Ensemble
Pedro Romero
Bierkeller:
Bierfest
Bierstube Bavarian Musik
The Famous Steinhaus Bierkeller
Karneval Bavarian Band
Munchen Steht Bierkeller Band
French:
Sian De Lier
French Connection
French Impressions
L'Ensemble Paris
Pierre Et Les Garcons
Latin American:
Del-Rio Latin American Band
Made in Brazil
Sambaleros
South of the Border Sound
Viramundo

Greek:
Acropolis
The Bouzouki Brothers
Odyssey
Orpheus
P.C.G.
Medieval Elizabethan:
Brandy Wine Bridge
Courtlye Musicke
Grinnigogs
The Harvesters (Medieval Folk Music)
Pastyme Players
Italian:
Complesso Ravello
Europa Music
Ray Gallo Italian Band
Romantica Music
Toni's Accordian Sound
West Indian Steel Bands:
Caribbean Ambassadors
Caribbean Harmonics
North Stars Steel Band
Rainbow Steel Orchestra
Rhapsody Steel Band
Miscellaneous:
Adzido African Drummers and Dancers
Caliche
The Continentals
Cosmopolitan Music Sound
Guizer Scottish Music
Justin Israeli Music
Mabsant Welsh Band
Ping Xu
Punita Gupta/Jazz Indo
Salsa Pa'Gozar
Shananakins Irish Folk Band
Sharazad Arabian Sound
The Shillelagh Irish Band
Tiare Tahiti
Viramundo

REPRESENTATION UPSON EDWARDS

51 Bounds Green Road, London
N22 8HB
Te: 020 8888 2525 Fax: 056 007 565 16
Email: sarahupson2006@btconnect.com
Agent: Sarah Upson
Agency specialising in voice coaching.

RETURN ENTERTAINMENTS LTD

66/68 St Loyes Street, Bedford
MK40 1EZ
Tel: 01234 327 123 Fax: 01234 353 658
Email: phil.roberts@ceroccentral.com
Web Site: www.ceroccentral.com
Contact: Phil Roberts (Director)
Provision of Corporate Ceroc (learn-to-jive) Evenings & also Dancers for Promotional Events. We can supply: demonstrations of Ceroc, accompanying disco, teach large groups (in a fun fashion) how to jive.

SANDRA REYNOLDS AGENCY

Amadeus House, 27b Floral Street,
London WC2E 9DP
Tel: 020 7387 5858 Norwich Office:
Bacon House, 35 St Georges Street,
Norwich, NR3 1DA Tel: 01603 623 842
Email: tessa@sandrareynolds.co.uk
Web Site: www.sandrareynolds.co.uk
Managing Director: Tessa Reynolds,
Head Booker: Jessica Tracey
Representing commercial models, actors, actresses, supporting artists and children nationwide.

RHUBARB VOICE OVERS

1st Floor 1a Devonshire Road Chiswick
London W4 2EU
Tel: 020 8742 8683 Fax: 020 8742 8693
Email: enquiries@rhubarb.co.uk
Web Site: www.rhubarb.co.uk
Senior Personnel: Johnny Garcia
Rhubarb produces audio in-house from own talent base.

PENNY RICH

27 Hoxton Street, London N1 6NH
Tel: 020 7613 3886 Fax: 020 7729 8500
Email: penny@pennyrich.co.uk
Web Site: www.pennyrich.co.uk
Contact: Penny Rich
Specialising in Photographers, hair and make-up artists.
Studio hire and classic american airstream location service.

ARTISTES REPRESENTED:

Photographers:
Carl Fox
Esther Haase
Jean Paul Lefret
Dennis Pederson

THE CLIFF RICHARD ORGANISATION

PO Box 46c, Esher, Surrey KT10 0RB
Tel: 01372 467 752 Fax: 01372 462 352
Email: general@cliffrichard.org
Web Site: www.cliffrichard.org
Contact: Bill Latham

ARTISTES REPRESENTED:

Cliff Richard

RICHARD PRICE PR

Tel: 07733 248 025
Email: richard_price2@hotmail.com
Web Site: www.richardpricepr.com
Representing Australian Performers for Publicity, Appearances and Castings in the UK.

ARTISTES REPRESENTED:

Sam Atwell
Tim Campbell
Daniel Collopy
Dichen
Alan Fletcher (UK only)
Laurie Foell
Kip Gamblin
Kate Garven
Patrick Harvey
Christie Hayes
Brett Hicks-Maitland
Blair Mcdonough
Ben Nicholas
Mark Rafferty
Ben Unwin
Vida Las Vegas
Sharni Vinson

THE LISA RICHARDS AGENCY

108 Upper Leeson Street Dublin 4 Ireland
Tel: 00 3531 637 5000
Fax: 00 3531 667 1256
Email: info@lisarichards.ie
Web Site: www.lisarichards.ie
Managing Director: Lisa Cook
Agent: Jonathan Shankey
Specialising in Irish artistes.

ARTISTES REPRESENTED:

Ronan Keating

STELLA RICHARDS MANAGEMENT

42 Hazlebury Road, London SW6 2ND
Tel: 020 7736 7786 Fax: 020 7731 5082
Senior Personnel: Stella Richards
Specialises in Directors & Productions Designers. Existing Clients Only.

RICKY GRAHAM LEISURE

Kellingley Social Club Marine Villa Road,
Knottingley, West Yorkshire WF11 8ER
Tel: 01977 673500 Fax: 01977 671555
Email: info@rickygrahamleisure.co.uk, harryturnstyle@aol.com
Web Site: www.rickygrahamleisure.co.uk
Contact: Harry Haywood

THE RIGHT ADDRESS LTD

Second Floor, Salamander Quay West,
Park Lane, Harefield, Middlesex,
UB9 6NZ
Tel: 01895 827 800 Fax: 01895 827 801
Email: info@therightaddress.co.uk
Web Site: www.therightaddress.co.uk
Senior Personnel: Jane French, Jo'anna Tremaine, Rachael Robertson
Specialise in after dinner speakers, cabaret, bands and entertainment.

RIPPLE MANAGEMENT

344 Kings Road, London SW3 5UR
Tel: 020 7352 5628 Fax: 020 7351 7700
Email: ripple@ripplerecords.co.uk
Web Site: www.billwyman.com
Senior Personnel: Caroline Mccrink

ARTISTES REPRESENTED:

Bill Wyman
Bill Wyman & The Rhythm Kings

RJH MANAGEMENT

Gordon House, 6 Lissenden Gardens,
London NW5 1LX
Tel: 020 7482 8896 Fax: 020 7482 8897
Email: richard.hillgrove@rjhmanagement.com
Web Site: www.rjhmanagement.com
Agent: Richard Hillgrove

R.L.M. (RICHARD LAW MANAGEMENT)

58 Marylands Road, London W9 2DR
Tel: 020 7286 1706
Email: richard@rlmanagement.co.uk
Senior Personnel: Richard Law

ARTISTES REPRESENTED:

Laura Holiday

ROAR GROUP

Roar House 46 Charlotte Street London W1T 2GS
Tel: 020 7462 9060 Fax: 020 7462 9061
Email: jonathan@roarglobal.com
Web Site: www.roarglobal.com
Senior Personnel:Professor Jonathan Shalit

ARTISTES REPRESENTED:

Jonathan Ansell
Christopher Biggins
Tony Blackburn
Sonia Deol
Jennifer Ellison
Gizzi Erskine
Vernon Francois
Kate Halfpenny
Dani Harmer
Myleene Klass
Nina Myskow
Harriet Scott
Kate Silverton
Nicki Waterman

ROBERT CROSSLAND ENTERTAINMENTS LTD

Woodcroft, 16 Ashton Lane, Sale, Cheshire M33 6NS
Tel: 01619 627 820
Email: crosslandents@hotmail.com
Senior Personnel: Robert Crossland, Justine Crossland
Agency that covers a wide variety, from named acts to tributes and general cabaret.

ARTISTES REPRESENTED:

Boy-2-One
Franklyn
Janice Lacey
N.R.G.
Colin Paul and the Persuaders
Will Power
Carlo Sax
Sneezewort

GORDON ROBINSON ASSOCIATES

8 Lilac Avenue, Knutsford, Cheshire WA16 0AZ
Tel/Fax: 01565 652 188
Mobile: 07703 185642
Leisure Consultant dealing primarily with After Dinner Speakers.

ARTISTES REPRESENTED:

Speakers:
Al Conway
Barry Cryer
Tommy Docherty
Fred Eyre
Ray French
David Gunson
Alan Kennedy
Steve Kindon
Austin Knight
Duncan MacKenzie
Wilf McGuiness
Peter Moloney
Johnny More
Peter Parfitt
Cynthia Payne
Derek Redmond
Dean Richards
Tony Sherwood
John H Stracey
Rod Taylor
Captain Brian Walpole OBE
Ray Wilde
Dave Wolfe
Frank Worthington
Dusty Young

HARRY ROBSON ENTERTAINMENT

Office 2, Toll Bar Business Park, Newchurch Road, Stacksteads, Bacup, Lancashire OL13 0NA
Tel: 01706 220 338 Fax: 01706 879 224
Email: jason@hrentertainment.co.uk
Web Site: www.hrentertainment.co.uk
Senior Personnel: Harry Robson, Jason Duckworth
Providers of Fun Casinos, Murder & Mystery Magic, Race Nights, Theme Nights, etc. for conferences, parties, product launches, trade shows, etc.

ROCK ARTIST MANAGEMENT

Rothery House, 89 Henthorn Road, Clitheroe, Lancashire BB7 2LD
Tel: 01200 444 544 Fax: 01200 444 545
Mob: 07712 628 366
Email: rockartistmgmt@aol.com
Web: www.rockartistmanagement.com
Senior Personnel: Peter Barton

ARTISTES REPRESENTED:

9 Below Zero
999
Angelic Upstarts
Animals
The Animals
Don Ayrey Band
Aziz
Blackmores Night
Blodwyn Pig
The Blues Band
Colin Blunstone and Rod Argent
Boney M
Bucks Fizz
Trevor Burton
China Crisis
City Rockers
John Coghlans Quo
Company of Snakes
Hugh Cornwell
Creedence Clearwater Revived
The Damned
Simon Guitar Dean
Desmond Dekker
Doctor Feelgood
Mickey Dolenz
Eddie and the Hotrods
The Equals
Mike Estes Lynard Skynard
Fairport Convention
Fat Mattress
The Fortunes
The Foundations
Steve Gibbons
Gordon Giltrap
The Hamsters (Jimi Hendrix Tribute)
Jet Harris Shadows
Hawkwind
Uriah Heep
Herman's Hermits
Hot Chocolate
Mungo Jerry
Wilko Johnson Band
Alvin Lee
Limahl
Lindisfarne
Los Paraliticos
Eddie Lundon
The Manfreds
Glen Matlock ex Sex Pistols
Les McKeowns Bay City Rollers
Merseybeats
Middle Of The Road
Pentangle
Suzi Quatro
Quill
Racey
Noel Redding Experience
Oliver Dawson Saxon
The Searchers
Alan Silson Ex Smokie
Slack Alice
Slade II
Sounds of Smoke
Sweet
The Swinging Blue Jeans
T Rex
Tenpole Tudor
Thin Lizzy
The Tremeloes
The Troggs
TV Smith
UK Subs
Vibrators
Stan Webbs Chicken Shack
Johnny Guitar Williamson
Wishbone Ash
The Woolpackers
The Yardbirds

ROCK & ROWLES MANAGEMENT

24 Whitfield Avenue, Paddington, Warrington, Cheshire WA1 3NF
Tel: 01925 821 255
Email: johnrowles@bigpond.com
Web Site: www.johnrowles.com
Contact: Marilyn Roberts

ARTISTES REPRESENTED:

John Rowles

ROEDEAN MUSIC

16-17 Grafton House,
2-3 Golden Square, London W1F 9HR
Tel: 020 7434 7286 Fax: 020 7437 3852

Email: tonyhall@btconnect.com
Senior Personnel: Tony Hall, Simon Nixon, Leigh Pearson

ARTISTES REPRESENTED:

Paul Buckmaster (Europe)
Lynden David Hall
Real Thing

ROGER ALLEN MANAGEMENT

Howard Road, Hillsea Portsmouth
PO2 9PS
Tel: 02392 654820
Email: roger@rogerallenmanagement.com
Contact: Roger Allen

ROGUES & VAGABONDS MANAGEMENT

The Printhouse, 18 Ashwin Street, London E8 3DL
Tel: 020 7254 8130 Fax: 020 7249 8564
Email: rogues@vagabondsmanagement.com
Web: www.vagabondsmanagement.com
Agent: Ann Robson
Rogues is the oldest established actors' co-operative in London, with an excellent track record of finding work for actors and actresses, comedians and comediennes.

ARTISTES REPRESENTED:

Shane Armstrong
Jumanne Bailey
Eddie Beardsmore
Amanda Beckman
Chania Belle
Martin Belville
Nicola Borthwick
Theresa Brunskill
Simon de Cintra
Lizzie Conrad
Lisa Duffy
Michael Duncan
Sarah Durham
William Findley
George James
Nim Johnson
Charlotte McKinney
Sarah Niven
Wanda Opalinska
John Patrick Berry
Rebecca Peyton
Oliver Rice
Ian Rixon
Dan Schumann
Kirsten Shaw
Giles Stoakley

ROLE MODELS

12 Cressy Road, London NW3 2LY
Tel: 020 7284 4337 Fax: 020 7267 1030
Email: hiredhandsagency@aol.com
Web Site: www.hiredhandsmodels.com
Senior Personnel: Steve Barker

THE ROLLIN STONED

438 Archway Road, Highgate
London N6 4JH
Tel: 0870 766 9054 Fax: 020 8374 2127
Mob: 07720 046 886
Email: enquiries@rollinstoned.com
Web Site: www.rollinstoned.com
A typical two hour show includes not only all the classic crowd pleasing hits, but is spiced with enough eclectic selections from the deeper recesses of Stones Album archives to satisfy the most demanding of 'Buffs', all performed with the same vibrantly authentic attack and raw energy that characterised the original Stones shows in their prime.
With a Rollin Stoned show, the costumes are shamelessly camp gaudy and fab, the instruments genuinely vintage and the wit irreverent.

ARTISTES REPRESENTED:

The Rollin Stoned

RO-LO PRODUCTIONS

35 Dillotford Avenue, Coventry, West Midlands CV3 5DR
Tel: 024 7641 0388 Fax: 024 7641 6615
Email: rog@rogerlomas.com
Web Site: www.rogerlomas.com
Proprietor: Roger Lomas

ARTISTES REPRESENTED:

Bad Manners
The Fortunes
The Selecter
Roy Wood

ROOTS AROUND THE WORLD

The Barn, Fordwater Lane, Chichester, West Sussex PO19 6PT
Tel: 01243 789 786 Fax: 01243 789 787
Mobile: 07802 500050
Email: markringwood@btinternet.com
Web Site: www.rootsaroundtheworld.info
Senior Personnel: Mark Ringwood

ARTISTES REPRESENTED:

Asere
Atcha!
Alberto Balia
Tom Ball & Kenny Sultan
Dino Baptiste
Vera Bila & Kale
The Bissero Sisters
Clarence Bucard
Caribbean Carnival Extravaganza
Cimarron
JP Cormier
Dan Crary
Guy Davis
Gesuino Deiana
Romano Drom
Cordas et Cannas
Faire Winds
Beppe Gambetta
Eliza Gilkyson
Gwerinos
Boka Halat
Joji Hirota
Holmes Brothers
Chris Jagger
La Volee D'Castors
Carol Laula
Michael Messer
Aaron Monteverde
Big Bill Morganfield
Eduardo Niebla
Nuzha
Odetta
Ivo Papasov & His Bulgarian Wedding Band
Popa Chubby
Rag Foundation
Adel Salameh
Shichiseikai
Big Jim Sullivan
Hubert Sumlin
Taiko to Tabla
Toto la Momposina
The Transsylvanians
Trinidad Steel Band
Hank Wangford & The Lost Cowboys
Richard Wood
Steve Young (singer/songwriter)

ROSEBERY MANAGEMENT

Hoxton Hall, 130 Hoxton Street, London N1 6SH
Tel: 020 7684 0187 Mob: 07805 162731
Email: admin@roseberymanagement.com
Web: www.roseberymanagement.com
Manager: Ben West

ARTISTES REPRESENTED:

Male:
David Garrud
Andrew Heath
Paul Hessey
Phil Oakland
Neil Paskin
Ted Pleasance
Peter Tilly
Female:
Nona Alexander
Ruth Baldwin
Sophie Bevan
Sharron Byrne
Tor Clark
Caroline Norton
Julia Webber

ROSEMARY SQUIRES ENTERPRISES

2 The Meadows, Milford, Salisbury, Wiltshire SP1 2SS
Tel: 01722 322 479 All Electric Productions (Booking Agent): Tel: 01264 361 924
Email: fralock@tiscali.co.uk
Web Site: www.rosemarysquires.co.uk
Personal Manager: Frank Lockyer
Booking Agent:
All Electric Productions
Po Box 1805
Andover
SP10 3ZN

ARTISTES REPRESENTED:

Rosemary Squires

ROSSMORE PERSONAL MANAGEMENT

10 Wyndham Place, London W1H 2PU
Tel: 020 7258 1953 Fax: 020 7258 0124
Email: info@rossmoremanagement.com
Web: www.rossmoremanagement.com
Agents: Alison Lee, Fatima Malagueira, Sarah Mitchell

ARTISTES REPRESENTED:
Hugh Cornwell
Paul Danan
Matt DiAngelo
Dean Gaffney
Mohammed George
Rory Jennings
Joseph Kpobie
Louisa Lytton
Lorna Pegler
John Pickard
Nick Pickard
Scott Robinson
Frances Ruffelle
Ebony Thomas
Ricky Whittle (PC Calvin Valentine, Hollyoaks)

ROSTRUM

The Tree House, 4 Ferniebank Brae,
Bridge of Allan, Stirlingshire FK9 4PJ
Scotland
Tel: 01786 832 508
Mobile: 07778 295 641
Email: info@rostrum.co.uk
Web Site: www.rostrum.co.uk
Senior Personnel: Fiona Paterson
Sourcing music for private and corporate events.

ARTISTES REPRESENTED:
Andrea Jacobs-Gajic
Mark O'Keeffe

NIGEL ROUND MANAGEMENT AND ENTERTAINMENT AGENCY

119 Railway Road, Adlington, Chorley,
Lancashire PR6 9QX
Tel: 01257 480 103
Mobile: 07808 360 036
Email: nigel@nigelround.co.uk
Web Site: www.nigelround.co.uk
Senior Personnel: Nigel Round

ARTISTES REPRESENTED:
Comedians:
Bobby Bender
Stan Boardman
Jim Bowen
Cannon & Ball
Jimmy Carol
Frank Carson KSG
Johnny Casson
Chubby Live
Charlie Chuck
John Cooper Clarke
Norman Collier
Phil Cool
Jimmy Cricket
Terry Devon
Ken Dodd OBE
Vince Earl
Stu Francis
Keith Harris with Orville & Cuddles
Tony Jo
Mike Kelly
Lee Lard
Syd Little
Patrick McGuinness (Max & Paddy)
Mick Miller
Justin Moorhouse
Joe Pasquale
Billy Pearce
Ted Robbins
Chrissy Rock
Steve Royle
Scully
Brian Sharp
Tank Sherman
Frank Sidebottom
Dave Spikey
Jamie Sutherland
Venn Tracey
Roy Walker
Scarlett Ray Watt
Vocals:
Alix
Lyndsay B
Nathan Moore (Brother Beyond)
Chris Blackburn
Steve Brookstein
Charley
Tony dee
Diane Shaw (Diana Ross Tribute)
John Gillan
Cherie Jade
Sally Jaxx
Jennifer Jones
Keily
Hayley Kent
Michelle Lawson
Kerri Leigh
Mark McKenna
Victor Michael
Rosie Nicks
J D Powers
Johnny Prenton
Mike Quinn
Jamie Rae
Rebecca Ray
Rowetta (X-Factor)
Johnny Sax
Luke Stevenson
P J Stokes
James Stone
Jessica Stretton
Paul Sutton (Ronan Keating)
Jack T
Kev Simm (Liberty X)
Tribute Groups:
Marcus Andrew (Elton John)
Atomik-itton
Birmingham Blues Brothers
Bootleg Bowie
Boy George Experience
Dave Celec (Craig David)
Chubby Live
Dean Torkington (Meatloaf)
Fake That
Cecil Foster (Luther Vandross)
Gary Gibson (John Lennon)
Carmel Hunter (Tina Turner)
Jodie Jackson (Madonna)
Ky-Lee (Kylie Minogue)
Kylie Fever
Lady Gaa Gaa
Robert Lamberti (George Michael)
Dean Memphis (Shakin Stevens)
Nanarama
Terry Nash (Meatloaf)
Chris Nott (David Essex)
Lee Pashley (Robbie Williams tribute)
Almost Pink
Pure Bee Gees
Justine Riddock (Anastasia)
River Deep (Tina Turner)
Rumours Of Fleetwood Mac
Tony Scarth (Tom Jones)
Beautiful Sound (Beautiful South Tribute)
Sounds of Motown
Status Duo
Barry Steele - Roy Orbison Tribute
Robbie Supreme (Robbie Williams Tribute)
Viva La Coldplay
Wig Wam Glam
Emma Wilkinson (Dusty Springfield)
Xtreme Supreme
Z U2
TV Personality:
Sam Aston (Chesney, Coronation Street)
Rebecca Atkinson (Karen, Shamless)
Nicole Barber-Lane (Myra, Hollyoaks)
Ben Batt (Joe, Shamless)
Malandra Burrows
Sally Carmen (Kelly-Marie, Shamless)
Kelsey Beth Crossley (Scarlett, Emmerdale)
Lesley Dunlop (Brenda, Emmerdale)
Dom Brunt (Emmerdale)
Mark Charnock (Emmerdale)
Nicky Evans (Shane, Shamless)
Chris Fountain (Justin, Hollyoaks)
Craig Gazey (Graeme, Coronation Street)
Joe Gilgun (Eli, Emmerdale)
Ciaran Griffiths (Micky, Shamless)
Alan Halsall (Tyrone, Coronation Street)
Charlie Hardwick (Val, Emmerdale)
Joanna Higson (Shamless)
Suranne Jones (Karen, Coronation Street)
Gerard Kearns (Ian Shamless)
Michelle Keegan (Tina, Coronation Street)
Katherine Kelly (Beccy, Coronation Street)
Tom Lister (Carl, Emmerdale)
Tina Malone (Mimi, Shamless)
Luke Marsden (Big Brother)
Michelle Marsh
Gemma Merna (Carmel, Hollyoaks)
Jennifer Metcalfe (Mercedes, Hollyoaks)
Tina O'Brien (Sarah, Coronation Street)
Roxanne Pallett (Jo, Emmerdale)
Lucy Pargeter (Chasity, Emmerdale)
Deena Payne (Viv, Emmerdale)
Emma Rigby (Hannah, Hollyoaks)
Rebecca Ryan (Shamless)
Samantha Siddall (Mandy, Shamless)
Carley Stenson (Steph, Hollyoaks)
Bruce Jones (Les, Coronation Street)
Jennie Mcalpine (Fizz, Coronation Street)
Graeme Hawley (John, Coronation Street)
Jack P Shephard (David, Coronation Street)
Margi Clarke (Jackie, Coronation Street)
Michael Le Vell (Kevin,Coronation Street)
Hayley Tamaddon
Ryan Thomas (Jason, Coronation Street)
Elliott Tittensor (Carl, Shamless)
John Tomson
Dan Whiston (Dancing on Ice)
Ricky Whittle (PC Calvin Valentine, Hollyoaks)
Andrew Whyment (Kirk Coronation Street) (P.A.'s)
Shaun Williamson (Barry, Eastenders)
Speakers:
John Aldridge
Gordon Banks OBE

Craig Brown
Martin Byfield
Sir Bobby Charlton CBE
John Conti
Alan Curbishley
Keith Deller
Tommy Docherty
David Fairclough
Sir Alex Ferguson
Brian Flynn
Eric Gates
Jimmy Greaves
Ron "Chopper" Harris
Derek Hatton
Ricky Hatton
Steve Heighway
Eddie Hemmings
Norman Hunter
David Johnson
Dr Kevin Jones
Alan Kennedy
Steve Kindon
Denis Law
David Lloyd
Peter Lorimar
John Lowe
Duncan MacKenzie
Mike Maguire
Malcolm McDonald
Wilf McGuiness
Jan Molby
Alex Murphy
Peter Osgood
Steve Parkin
Graham Poll
Karl (The Hoaxer) Power
Norman Prince
James H Reeve
Andy Ritchie
Lawrie Sanchez
Tommy Smith MBE
Ian St John
Nobby Stiles MBE
Mike Summerbee
Phil Taylor
Stan Taylor
Micky Thomas
Carl Thompson
Phil Thompson
Sid Waddell
Mike Watkinson
Ronnie Whelan
Norman Whiteside
Frank Worthington
Ron Yates
DJs:
Adam Catterall (Rock FM)
Rob Charles (99mw)
Jonathon 18 (Clubland)
Ditch & Salty
David "Ditchy" Ditchfield
Jo Lloyd (Real Radio)
Pat Sharp
Mike Sweeney
Rick Vaughan (Rock FM)
Jude Vause
James Whale

THE ROVING ARTIST & CO
234 Peppard Road, Emmer Green,
Caversham, Berkshire RG4 8UA
Tel: 0118 947 6637 Fax: 0118 947 6813
Mobile: 0780 3085637
Email: charles@roving-artist.com
Web Site: www.roving-artist.com
Wandering silhouette cutters for your event, working under the artistic leadership of Charles Burns, Britain's foremost silhouette artist.

ARTISTES REPRESENTED:
Charles Burns - The Fine Artist
Michael Herbert - The Magician
Alison Turvey - The Paper Artist

ROYCE MANAGEMENT
29 Trenholme Road, London SE20 8PP
Tel/Fax: 020 8778 6861
Email: office@roycemanagement.co.uk
Senior Personnel: Amanda Fisher

ARTISTES REPRESENTED:
Actresses:
Marion Barron
Elaine Ives Cameron
Kate Dudley
Carol Duffy
Ally Holmes
Amanda Kernot
Jane Lambert
Ksenia Laurentieua
Rosemary MacVie
Catriona Martin
Jennifer Oscard
Amanda Richardson
Jane Tucker
Deborah Vale
Tessa Vale
Cookie Weymouth
Actors:
David Bannerman
Richard Bardsey
Gary Bates
Sean Buckley
Nigel Carrington
Ronald Chenery
Ben Craze
Paul Denzing
Gary Fairhall
Oliver Fishman
Alan Haines
Julian Harries
Paul Hutchinson
Eric Mason
Nayef Rashed
Geoffrey Serle
A.J. Simon
Noel Slattery
David Windle
Chris Yapp

RUMOUR ENTERTAINMENTS
2b Progressive Groby Road Audenshaw
M34 5HT
Tel: 0845 901 1520
Email: enquiries@rumour-entertainments.co.uk
Web: www.rumour-entertainments.co.uk
Contact: Wayne Williams

S M A TALENT LTD
The Cottage Church Street Fressingfield
Suffolk IP21 5PA
Tel: 01379 586 734 Fax: 01379 586 131
Email: olav@smatalent.com
Web Site: www.smatalent.com
Senior Personnel: Carolynne Wyper, Olav Wyper
Composers only and screen writers

ARTISTES REPRESENTED:
Composers:
John Altman
Tim Atack
George Callis
Willie Dowling
Matt Dunkley
Paul Heard
Roger Jackson
Paul Leonard-Morgan
Gregory Magee
Neil Martin
Mike Moran
Andrea Morricone
Alan Parker
Jean-Claude Petit
Craig Pruess
Ben Salisbury
Simon Slater
Martyn Swain
Graham Walker (Music Supervisor)

SABA COMMUNICATIONS LTD
Bethnel Green Training Centre,
Hanbury Street, London E1 5HZ
Tel: 020 7377 8545 / 020 776 6776
Fax: 020 337 1997
Email: tina.bennett@saba.org.uk
Web Site: www.saba.org.uk
PR contact: Tina Bennett
SABA Founder: John Downie

SAFE MANAGEMENT
St Ann's House Guildford Road
Lightwater Surrey GU18 5RA
Tel: 01276 476676 Fax: 01276 451109
Email: info@safemanagement.co.uk
Web Site: www.safemanagement.co.uk
Managing Director: Chris Herbert

ARTISTES REPRESENTED:
Kym Marsh

KEITH SALBERG AGENCY & PRODUCTIONS
34 Telford Avenue, Streatham Hill,
London SW2 4XF
Tel: 020 8671 1166 / 7
Senior Personnel: Keith Salberg
Specialising in: Concert Attractions, & Olde-Tyme Music Hall/Variety

ARTISTES REPRESENTED:
Bee and Bustle Olde Tyme Music Hall Company
Clinton Ford
Vince Hill One Man Show (S)
Hope & Keen
Lucken's Shetland Pantomime Ponies
Leslie Randall
The Temperance Seven
Ramon Villar Flamenco Playa Dance Company
The Yetties

SALVO THE CLOWN

(Founder of The Annual Clowns Directory)
13 Second Avenue, Kingsleigh Park, Thundersley, Essex SS7 3QD
Tel: 01268 745 791
Email: salvo@annualclownsdirectory.com
Web: www.annualclownsdirectory.com
Contact: Salvo

ARTISTES REPRESENTED:

Salvo The Clown

SANCTUARY ARTIST MANAGEMENT

Sanctuary House, 45-53 Sinclair Road, London W14 0NS
Tel: 020 7602 6351 Fax: 020 7603 5941
Email: deke.arlon@sanctuarygroup.com
Web Site: www.sanctuarygroup.com
Senior Personnel: Deke Arlon, Alison Thomas, Jamie Arlon
Chairman: Bob Ayling

LOESJE SANDERS

Pound Square, 1 North Hill, Woodbridge, Suffolk IP12 1HH
Tel: 01394 385 260 Fax: 01394 388 734
Email: loesje@loesjesanders.org.uk
Web Site: www.loesjesanders.com
Senior Personnel: Loesje Sanders

ARTISTES REPRESENTED:

Choreographers:
Kim Brandstrup
Marguerite Donlon
Javier de Frutos
Cathy Marston
Martino Müller
Christian Spuck
Lighting Designers:
Lucy Carter
Giuseppe Di Iorio
Simon Mills
Directors:
Brian Brady
Stephen Langridge
Antony McDonald
Designers Set & Costume:
Bob Bailey
Simon Banham
Ann Curtis
Gideon Davey
Peter J Davison
Johan Engels
Nicky Gillibrand
Craig Givens
Laura Hopkins
Ana Jebens
Patrick Kinmonth
Conor Murphy
John Otto
Jean-Marc Puissant
Robin Rawstorne
Emma Ryott
George Souglides
Peter Van Praet
Tatyana van Walsum
Jamie Vartan
Sue Willmington
Director/Designer:
Antony McDonald
Water Sculptor:
Mario Borza
Large Scale Projection Design:
Patrick Watkinson

SANGWIN ASSOCIATES

Queens Wharf, Queen Caroline Street, Hammersmith, London W6 9RJ
Tel: 020 8600 2670 Fax: 020 8600 2669
Email: info@sangwinassoc.com
Agents: Beth Sangwin

ARTISTES REPRESENTED:

Vicky Binns
Holly Davidson
David Easter
Connie Powney

SARABAND ASSOCIATES

265 Liverpool Road, Islington, London N1 1LX
Tel: 020 7609 5313 Fax: 020 7609 2370
Email: brynnewton@btconnect.com
Senior Personnel: Sara Randall, Bryn Newton

ARTISTES REPRESENTED:

Isabelle Amyes
Scott Anson
Matthew Cammelle
Peter Duncan
Jane Freeman
Polly Hemingway
Helen Lederer
Ruth Madoc
Brian Murphy
John Nettles
Lill Roughley
William Simons
Pam St Clement
Susan Tully

SARDI'S INTERNATIONAL ENTERTAINMENT CONSULTANTS

6 Redbridge Lane East, Redbridge, Ilford, Essex IG4 5ES
Tel: 020 8551 6720 Fax: 020 8551 1200
Email: Sardi's@axident.clara.net
Web Site: www.sardisonline.co.uk
Senior Personnel: Wendy Lewis, Maureen Shapiro

ARTISTES REPRESENTED:

Pianists:
Moira Hartley
Daniel Kieve
Dave Leonard
Nigel Stewart
Tony Williams
Pauline Willoughby
Duos:
Kwantum
The Human Jukebox
Two's Company
Receptions:
Charles Burns - The Fine Artist
Sophia Cantardi
Guy Carter (Caricaturist & Silhouettes)
Matthew Lawrence
Lord Geoffrey (The Balloon Man)
Luisa Calvo
Paper Magic
Jed Pascoe
Soul:
Darktown
Inside Out
Richie Milton & The Lowdown
Soul Sistas
Vocal Ensembles:
Bad Habits
Champagne Opera
Verona Madrigale
Themes:
El Advino Latin Duo/Band
Bollywood
Cockney Doodle-Do
Island Rhythm Hawaiian Band
Tony Liotti Italian Duo
Function Bands:
Baby Go Boom
L.A. Nights
Midnight Hour
Second Nature
Special Delivery
Streetwise
Three's Company
Tuxedo Junction
Cabaret:
Christopher Gee (1st class impressionist)
Ian Irving (Comedian)
Mervyn Jaye (Impressionist)
Marmon Magic
Phil Perry (Magician)
Soprano Bella (Musical)
Discos:
Ace of Clubs
Jingles
Sounds Magic
Warboy
Murder Mystery:
Golden Girl
Hooray Girl
Marching Bands:
Tonbridge Pipes & Drums

SARM MANAGEMENT

The Blue Building, 8-10 Basing Street, London W11 1ET
Tel: 020 7229 1229 Fax: 020 7221 9247
Email: roxanna@spz.com
Web Site: www.sarmstudios.com
Senior Personnel: Roxanna Ashton, Jill Sinclair

ARTISTES REPRESENTED:

Producers, Engineers & Programmers:
Pete Briquette
Phil Chill
Marcus Dravs
Brad Gilderman
Nigel Green
Trevor Horn
Garry Hughes
Rich Johnstone
Richard Lowe
Grant Mitchell
Ian Morrow
Mike Peden
Jeremy Stacey
Ali Thomson
Tim Weidner

SAS ENTERTAINMENT AGENCY

22 Homefield Close Copmanthorpe York

YO23 3RU
Tel/Fax: 01904 700707
Mob: 077 1440 9095
Senior Personnel: John Hatherley

SASHA LESLIE MANAGEMENT
In Association With Allsorts Drama For Children
34 Pember Road, London NW10 5LS
Tel/Fax: 020 8969 3249
Email: sasha@allsortsdrama.com
Web Site: www.allsortsdrama.com
Senior Personnel: Sasha Stevenson
Personal Managers of children and young adults for professional work in television and film.

ARTISTES REPRESENTED:
Leah Coombes
Georgina Moffat
Ben Newton
Anna Popplewell
Gregg Sulkin
Julia Winter

SATELLITE ARTISTS LTD
Studio House, 34 Salisbury Street, London NW8 8QE
Tel: 020 7402 9111 Fax: 020 7723 3064
Email: eliot@amimedia.co.uk
Web Site: www.amimedia.co.uk
Senior Personnel: Eliot Cohen, Peter Sullivan

ARTISTES REPRESENTED:
Fleetwood Max
The Headliners
Imagination
Mungo Jerry
Remi
Rockabeats
The Trybe
Anita Ward

SCA MANAGEMENT
77 Oxford Street, London W1D 2ES
Tel: 020 7659 2027 Fax: 020 7659 2116
Email: agency@sca-management.co.uk
Web Site: www.sca-management.co.uk
Senior Personnel: Gaynor Sheward, Carole Deamer

ARTISTES REPRESENTED:
Lise Cervi
Dean Crossley
Tom Eastwood
Dominik Golding
Rebecca Hackenberg
Michael Newman
Jon Samuel
Roy Skelton
Jamie Sweeney
Maggie Zolinsky

PETER SCHNABL
The Barn House, Cutwell, Tetbury, Gloucestershire GL8 8EB
Tel: 01666 502 133 Fax: 01666 502 998
Mobile: 07860 796283
Email: peter.schnabl@virgin.net
Senior Personnel: Peter Schnabl

ARTISTES REPRESENTED:
Loyd Grossman
Gerald Sinstadt

SCOTBASE ENTERTAINMENTS
103 Abercorn Street, Paisley, Renfrewshire PA3 4AT Scotland
Tel: 0141 849 0333 Fax: 0141 849 0111
Email: info@scotbase.com
Web Site: www.scotbase.com
Director: Robert Pope
Entertainment agency providing cabaret acts, bands, karaoke discos, children's entertainment, casino nights and children's entertainment.

SCOTT JORDAN ENTERTAINMENT LTD
25-29 Station Street, Sittingbourne, Kent ME10 3DU
Tel: 0845 094 1455
Email: enquiries@scottjordan.co.uk
Web Site: www.scottjordan.co.uk
Contact : Scott Jordan, Stephen Middleton
Entertainment booking agency providing quality tribute bands, function bands, comedians and magicians for weddings, private parties, and venues accross the U.K

SUSAN SCOTT LOOKALIKES
106 Tollington Park, Finsbury Park London N4 3RB
Tel: 020 7281 8029 Fax: 020 7281 1263
Mob: 07905 094 904 / 07847 633 348
Email: susan@lookalikes.info
Web Site: www.lookalikes.info
Senoir personnel: Helena Maroutzi, Susan Scott
Specialising in: All leading lookalikes and soundalikes.

SCOTTISH HIGHLAND ENTERTAINMENTS
27 Northpark Place, Eliburn, Livingston, West Lothian EH54 6TR Scotland
Tel: 01506 41 23 23 Mobile: 07968 150 566 Fax: 01506 41 45 83
Email: enquiries@entertaining-scotland.com
Web Site: www.entertaining-scotland.com
Senior Personnel: Malcolm J. Brown-Scott, Tracy C. Brown-Scott
Specialising in all forms of Scottish Traditional Entertainment (Pipers, Pipe Bands, Accordianists, Fiddlers, Ceilidh Bands, Dancers, Burns Speakers) and other contemporary entertainment (speakers, classical instrumentalists, jazz, disco, singers, magicians, caracaturists, function bands and many many more.

SCREENLITE AGENCY
Studio 61, Shepperton Studios, Studios Road, Shepperton, Middlesex TW17 0QD
Tel: 01932 566 977 / 592 271 / 592 272
Fax: 01932 572 507
Email: screenlite@dial.pipex.com
Web Site: www.screenliteagency.co.uk
Senior Personnel: Carlie Tovey, Kerry Tovey, Kate Reeves, Noel Tovey

DONALD SCRIMGEOUR ARTISTS AGENCY
49 Springcroft Avenue, London N2 9JH
Tel: 020 8444 6248 Fax: 020 8883 9751
Email: vwest@dircon.co.uk
Web Site: www.donaldscrimgeour.com
Senior Personnel: Donald Scrimgeour (Spain), Valerie West (London)
Representing Dancers, Choreographers, Teachers/Ballet Masters, Dance Producers, Conductors & Designers.

DAVE SEAMER ENTERTAINMENTS
46 Magdalen Road, Oxford OX4 1RB
Tel/Fax: 01865 240 054
Email: dave@daveseamer.co.uk
Web Site: www.daveseamer.co.uk
Senior Personnel: Dave Seamer

ARTISTES REPRESENTED:
Big Sand Steel Band
Celebration Showband
Dancin' Easy
The Jazz Menagerie
Dave Seamer Disco
Paul Seamer Disco
Uncle Dave's Disco
Uncle Dave's Magic Show

SEAMUS LYTE MANAGEMENT LTD
5 Oswald Building, Chelsea Bridge Wharf, 374 Queens Town Road, London SW8 4NU
Tel: 07930 391 401
Email: seamus@seamuslyte.com
Web Site: www.seamuslyte.com
Seamus Lyte Management was created to answer an increasing need from Presenters, Broadcasters and Producers to ensure expertise, quality and outstanding services.
Seamus Lyte Management represents several well known presenters on television today in the UK, Eire and the USA, as well as nurturing the 'stars' of tomorrow's top programmes.

ARTISTES REPRESENTED:
Jim Bellieni
James Braxton
Bill Burns
Claire Byrne
Jessica Callan
Brian Curran
Dane Bailey (Queer Eye for a Straight Guy)
Margaret Dane
Mai Davies
Nick Drake
Ryan Elliott
Lindsey Fallow
John Gonzalez
Bernard Hiller
Susan Hyatt

Jason Gardiner (Queer Eye for a Straight Guy)
Michael Levine
Lara Lewington
Sian Lloyd
Donal MacIntyre
Tonya Meli
Daniel Morris
Eileen Mulligan
Lembit Opik
Ali O'Sullivan
Peyton (Queer Eye for a Straight Guy)
Ashley Russell
Neil Sean
Abigail Thomas
Sarah van der Noot
Fran Warde
Halley Wolowiec

SEAVIEW MUSIC

28 Mawson Road, Cambridge CB1 2EA
Tel: 01223 508 431 Fax: 01223 508 449
Mob: 07801 234 343
Email: seaview@dial.pipex.com
Web Site: www.seaviewmusic.co.uk
Senior Personnel: Sarah Bruce
Seaview Music represents artists based in classical music who all do something a little different!

ARTISTES REPRESENTED:

The Carnival Band
The Chuckerbutty Ocarina Quartet
The Classic Buskers
Sambuca

DAWN SEDGWICK MANAGEMENT

3 Goodwins Court, Covent Garden, London WC2N 4LL
Tel: 020 7240 0404 Fax: 020 7240 0415
Email: laura@dawnsedgwickmanagement.com
Senior Personnel: Dawn Sedgwick
Also entertainment consultants.

ARTISTES REPRESENTED:

Mathew Horne
Dan Johnston
Colin Murphy
Ardal O'Hanlon
Simon Pegg
Catherine Tate

SELECT ENTERTAINMENTS

4 Pentland View, Kennoway, Leven, Fife KY8 5TY
Tel: 01333 353200 Fax: 01333 353203
Email: select-entertainments@fsmail.net
Contact: Grace Walsh

SELECTIVELY SPEAKING

17 St Johns Cresent, Harrogate, North Yorkshire HG1 3AB
Tel: 0870 330 0787 Fax: 0870 330 0788
Email: info@entertainment-zone.com
Web Site: www.entertainment-zone.com
Senior Personnel: Louise Parker
Specialises in supplying celebrity speakers and comedians to corporate events.

THE SESSION CONNECTION

110-112 Disraeli Road, London SW15 2DX
Tel: 020 8871 1212 Mob: 07801 070 362
Email: sessionconnection@mac.com
Web: www.thesessionconnection.com
Senior Personnel: Tina Hamilton
London's Longest Established Session Agency, providing Musicians and Singers for Tours, Sessions, TV, Videos, Commercials and Films

ARTISTES REPRESENTED:

Dawne Adams
Cristina Bonacci
Rachael Brown
Dave Clayton

SHAMROCK MUSIC LTD

9 Thornton Place, Marylebone London W1H 1FG
Tel: 020 7935 9719 Fax: 020 7935 0241
Email: lindy@abiryan.co.uk
Web Site: www.abiryan.co.uk
Manager: Lindy McManus

ARTISTES REPRESENTED:

John McManus - Composer (Film & TV)
Abi Ryan

SHANA GOLDMANS BRIGHTON

PO Box 23 Shipbourne Road, Tonbridge, Kent TN11 9NY
Tel: 01273 789252 Fax: 01323 472001
Email: casting@shana-goldmans.co.uk
Web Site: www.shana-goldmans.co.uk
Contact: Sarah Dormady

SHAPIRO INTERNATIONAL

6-26 Speirs Wharf, Glasgow G4 9TB
Tel: 0141 353 3996 Mob: 07973 106656
Email: info@shapirointernational.com
Web Site: www.shapirointernational.com
Contact: Frank Shapiro

SHARPER SOLUTIONS LTD

Elstree Film Studios, Shenley Road, Borehamwood, Hertfordshire WD6 1JG
Tel: 020 8207 2233 Fax: 020 8207 2255
Email: sandy@sharpersolutions.co.uk
Web Site: www.sharpersolutions.co.uk
Senior Personnel: Sandy Harper
Specialising in corporate and special event management.

VINCENT SHAW ASSOCIATES LTD

186 Shaftesbury Avenue, London WC2H 8JB
Tel: 020 7240 2927 Fax: 020 7249 2930
Email: info@vincentshaw.com
Web Site: www.vincentshaw.com
Director: Andrew Charles

ARTISTES REPRESENTED:

Actors:
Livy Armstrong
John Atterbury
Simon Aylin
Ilario Bisi-Pedro
David Brierley
Seb Craig
Manolis Emmanouel
Paul Fields
Ben Forgham
Roger Gartland
Alexander Giles
Andrew Jay
Michael Kilgarriff
David Kincaid
Robin Lloyd
Peter Rocca
Alex Scott-Fairley
Tim Swinton
Michael Witcomb
Actresses:
Mia Austen
Hayley Birbeck
Pamela Byrne
Paula Clarke
Alicia Devine
Amanda Fawsett
Sharon Gomez
Rebecca Kilgarriff
Jean Lloyd
Valerie Newbold
Clovissa Newcombe
Louisa Patikas
Mandy Rice-Davies
Catriana Sandison
Audrey Schoellhammer
Bita Taghavi
Sonya Vine

SHEPHERD MANAGEMENT LTD

4th Floor, 45 Maddox Street, London W1S 2PE
Tel: 020 7495 7813 Fax: 020 7499 7535
Email: info@shepherdmanagement.co.uk
Agent: Christina Shepherd

ARTISTES REPRESENTED:

Men:
Kieran Ahern
Dean Andrews
Michael Aspel OBE
Peter Baldwin
Peter Barrett
Terence Beesley
Geoffrey Beevers
Nicholas Blane
John Bowe
Tony Britton
Charlie Brown
James Bye
Thomas Craig
Bob Cryer
James Daffern
Richard Douglas
Greg Faulkner
Harry Gostelow
Glynn Grain
Andy Gray
Christopher Greet
Simon Harrison
Declan Harvey
Ben Hunter
George Innes
Bernard Kay
Nigel le Vaillant
Janek Lesniak
Crispin Letts

Des McAleer
Colin McCredie
Daniel Mendoza
Henry Miller
Basil Moss
Daragh O'Malley
Tomas O'Suilleabhain
Adrian Paul
Richard Pepper
Craig Pinder
James Quinn
Leslie Randall
Crispin Redman
Malcolm Rennie
Patrick Robinson
Kim Romer
Daniel Sharman
Rob Spendlove
Neil Stacy
Andy Taylor
Will Travis
Simon Ward
Oliver Williams
Jerome Willis
Matthew Wilson
Paul Young
Rik Young
Women:
Judy Buxton
Sue Cleaver
Susannah Corbett
Sarah Crowden
Seroca Davis
Fiona Dolman
Reanne Farley
Pauline Fleming
Helen Fraser
Hilary Gish
Megan Hall
Nelly Harker
Lisa Harrow
Julia Haworth
Karen Henthorn
Amy Huberman
Suranne Jones (Karen, Coronation Street)
Louise Kempton
Polly Maberly
Pat Mackie
Elizabeth Marmur
Siobhan McKay
Shelagh McLeod
Kerry Norton
Caroline O'Neill
Cecile Paoli
Rosie Rowell
Abbie Salt
Charlotte Salt
Jane Slavin
Ella Smith
Kerrie Taylor
Angela Thorne
Leslee Udwin
Manouk Van Der Meulen
Sophie Ward
Barbara Young

SHINING MANAGEMENT LTD

81 Oxford Street London W1D 2EU
Tel: 020 7734 1981 Fax: 020 7734 2528
Email: info@shiningvoices.com
Web Site: www.shiningvoices.com
Agents: Jennifer Taylor Cave, Clair Daintree
Voice artist agency for all types of projects.
Accounts/Admin address: PO BOx 1045, Chislehurst BR7 9AR. Please send all remittances/payments to this address.

ARTISTES REPRESENTED:

Karen Ascoe
Craig Barrett
Henry Blofeld OBE
Virgile Bramly
Paul Brennen
Janet Brown
John Brunning
Mike Burnside
Mark Cameron
Colin R Campbell
Katie Campbell
James Cannon
Katy Carmichael
Sarah Cartwright
Melissa Chapin
Kate Colgrave
Ellen Collier
Harvey Cook
Edmund Dehn
Donna Donovan
Felicity Duncan
Robert Elms
Craig Fairbrass
Howard Fiddy
Andy Grainger
Angie Greaves
Colin Griffiths-Brown
Brian Herring
Shash Hira
Tony Hirst
Ian Hughes
Amanda Hussain
Mickey Hutton
Taylor Jones
Dominic Keating
Alex Kerr
Stuart Laing
Tony Lockwood
Lucy Longhurst
Gary Martin
Lewis McKie
Chris McQuarry
Eric Meyers
Harry Miller
Tara Newley
Mary Ann O'Donoghue
Donna Pickup
Ben Price
David Pullan
Randall Lee Rose
Emma Rydal
Ben Small
Andy Styles
Mike Sweeney
Jennifer Thompson
Sandy Walsh
Howard Ward
Timothy Watson
Emma Weaver
Nigel Williams
Jonathan Wrather
Beverly Wright

SHOUT PROMOTIONS LTD.

PO Box 42 Atherton, Manchester
M46 0WX
Tel: 01942 888969
Email: info@shout123.co.uk
Web Site: www.shout123.co.uk
Contact: Steve Lowrey

SHOWSTOPPERS!

42 Foxglove Close, Witham,
Essex CM8 2XW
Tel: 01376 518486 Fax: 01376 510340
Email: mail@showstoppers-group.com
Web Site: www.showstoppers-group.com
Senior Personnel: Eve Regelous, Peter Regelous
Events Management, Promotions and Entertainments. Specialising in Celebrity Personal Appearances, Shopping Centre, Street, Specialty and Promotional Entertainment.

SHOWTIME CASTINGS LTD

112 Milligan Street, London E14 8AS
Tel: 020 7068 6816 Fax: 020 7987 3443
Email: gemma@showtimecastings.com
Web Site: www.showtimecastings.com
Contact: Gemma Faugh

SILENT WAY MANAGEMENT LTD

34 Percy Street London W1T 2DG
Tel: 020 7255 6910 Fax: 020 7255 6929
Manchester Office: The Old School House
George Leigh Street Manchester M4 6AF
Email: info@silentway.co.uk
Web Site: www.silentway.co.uk
Contact: Andrea Mills

ARTISTES REPRESENTED:

Brett Anderson
Simply Red

SILVEY ASSOCIATES

9-15 Neal Street, Covent Garden,
London WC2H 9PW
Tel: 020 7240 8410
Mobile: 07711 245 848
Email: denise@silveyassociates.co.uk
Web Site: www.silveyassociates.co.uk
Contact: Denise Silvey

ARTISTES REPRESENTED:

Actors:
James Clarkson
Jonny Hynes
Tim Morand
Actresses:
Amber Edlin
Kate Feldschreiber
Kerri Mclean
Rain Pryor

SIMON QUARMBY PRESENTS

Music Factory Hawthorne House
Ftitzwilliam Street Rotherdam S62 6EP
Tel: 01709 521830 Mob: 07753 792305
Email: simon@sqpresents.com
Web Site: www.sqpresents.com
Contact: Simon Quarmby

SIMPSON FOX ASSOCIATES LTD

52 Shaftesbury Avenue, London
W1D 6LP
Tel: 020 7434 9167 Fax: 020 7494 2887
Email: cary.parsons@simpson-fox.com
Contact: David Watson, Cary Parsons

ARTISTES REPRESENTED:

Designers:
Bob Crowley
Paul Farnsworth
Tim Goodchild
Sarah-Jane McClelland
Vicki Mortimer
Scott Pask
Di Seymour
Mark Thompson
Ultz
Joe Vanek
Philip Witcomb
Lighting Designers:
Oliver Fenwick
Howard Harrison
David Holmes
Hugh Vanstone
Directors:
Robert Allan Ackerman
Mark Clements
John Crowley
John Dove
Gary Griffin
Jane Howell
David Leveaux
Patrick Mason
Indhu Rubasingham
Ultz
Choreographers:
Peter Darling
Stuart Hopps
Stephen Mear
Meryl Tankard
Estates:
Sir Kenneth MacMillan (Estate)
Musical Directors:
Simon Lee

SINCERE MANAGEMENT

35 Bravington Road, London W9 3AB
Tel: 020 8960 4438 Fax: 020 8968 8458
Email: office@sinman.co.uk
Senior Personnel: Peter Jenner, Peter Kittle, Mushi Jenner,

ARTISTES REPRESENTED:

Billy Bragg
Dr Robert

SANDRA SINGER ASSOCIATES

21 Cotswold Road, Westcliff-on-Sea,
Essex SS0 8AA
Tel: 01702 331 616 Fax: 01702 339 393
Email: sandrasingeruk@aol.com
Web Site: www.sandrasinger.com
Senior Personnel: Sandra Singer
Film, TV, Musical Theatre Specialists, for adults and children. Specialist entertainment for Film & TV, Magic etc. Also represents composers and choreographers

ARTISTES REPRESENTED:

Miriam Ahmed
Akil
Maria Antonia
Teneisha Bonner
Aimee Bose
Colin Bower
Oliver Bower
Daryl Branch
Paul Cheneour (Flute)
Melissa Conner
Stuart Crawley
Daniel DeHaan
Kerry Duffield
Feeding the Fish
Gary Finan
Paul Fowler
Mark Franks
Matthew Garrett
Billy Herring
Rebecca Hood
Dani Jazzar
Lorenza Johnson
Junia
Larissa Kumana
Judy La Rose
Jodie Leigh
Jack Leonard
Victoria Leung
Bobby Lockwood
Eden Mackney
Maxine Mazumder as Lulu, Dusty
Claudia Morecroft
Cristian Morrell
Paul Moxon (composer)
Paper Magic
Sarah Parmenter
Scott Penrose
Rob Pheby
Sharon Prasad
Teresa Revill
Simon Roberts
Mabel Rogers
Jamie Savage
Aimee Singer
John Styles
Mark Sung
Lachlan Sutherland
Ayse Tezel
Nikki Trow
Muriel Vanel
Jane Victory
Amy Webb
Joanna Whitney
Sean Williams
James Wong
Anthony Wren
Tara Young

SJ MANAGEMENT

8 Bettridge Road, London SW6 3QD
Tel: 020 7371 0441 Fax: 020 7371 0409
Email: sj@susanjames.demon.co.uk
Senior Personnel: Susan James
Assistant to Susan James: John Carlin

ARTISTES REPRESENTED:

Lewis Collins
Ben Fielder
Anthony Inglis
Bogden Kominowski
Joanna Monro
Monroe Kent 111

SJM MANAGEMENT

St. Matthews Liverpool Road, Manchester
M3 4NQ
Tel: 0161 907 3443 Fax: 0161 907 3446
Mobile: 07715 108 768
Email: conrad@sjmconcerts.com
Office Manager: Simon Moran
Pa to Office Manager: Vicky Potts
Contact: Conrad Murray

ARTISTES REPRESENTED:

Beautiful South
The Coral
John Squire
Joe Strummer

SJS PROMOTIONS

159 Rotherham Road, Monk Bretton,
Barnsley, South Yorkshire S71 2LL
Tel/Fax: 01226 205 932
Tel: 01226 285 453
Email: sjspromotions@aol.com
Contact: Steve Jackson, Mark Jackson

ARTISTES REPRESENTED:

Clare Branigan
Cheeky Charlie
Dream Legion
Jimmy Echo
Endless Nights
Fatal Attraction
Chris Lee
New Dimension
Jonathan Redfearn
Ian Scott
Wired

SMA TALENT LTD

The Cottage, Church Street, Fressingfield,
Eye, Suffolk IP21 5PA
Tel: 01379 586734 Fax: 01379 586131
Email: carolynne@smatalent.com / olav@smatalent.com
Web Site: www.smatalent.com
Senior Personnel: Carolynne Wyper, Olav Wyper
Personnel: Jo Webster
Specialising in: Composers

ARTISTES REPRESENTED:

Composers:
John Altman
Tim Atack
Willie Dowling
Matt Dunkley
John Harle
Nick Harvey
Paul Heard
Roger Jackson
Srdjan Kurpjel & Marios Takoushis
Gregory Magee
Neil Martin
Mr Miller & Mr Porter
Mike Moran
Alan Parker
Jean-Claude Petit
Craig Pruess
Andrew Raiher
Ben Salisbury
Lawrence Shragge
Simon Slater
Martyn Swain
Music Supervisors:

Liz Shrek
Graham Walker (Music Supervisor)
Screen Writers:
J J Anderson
Gill Wiliams

SMAC ENTERTAINMENTS
Office No 1, Crofters House,
77 Green Burn Drive, Bucksburn,
Aberdeen AB21 9HB Scotland
Tel: 01224 710 280 Fax: 01224 710 286
Email: smacent@btconnect.com
Senior Personnel: Mr Andrew Gardiner
Kiss-o-gram Agency

SMART LIVE
30 Maiden Lane, London WC2E 7JS
Tel: 0207 836 0562 Fax: 0207 836 1044
Email: smartlive@smartgroupltd.co.uk
Web Site: www.smartlive.co.uk
Creating events with edge.
Special event production company comprising set designers, choreographers, and artistic directors. Technically, we boast sound engineers, lighting technicians and stage managers. We combine our creative and technical talents to stage the most amazing themed events ever.

SMARTYPANTS AGENCY LTD
San Marie Studios,
Guildprime Business Centre,
Southend Road, Billericay, Essex
CM11 2PZ
Tel: 01277 633772 / 633712
Fax: 01277 633998
Email: office@smartypantsagency.co.uk
Web Site: www.smartypantsagency.co.uk
Contac: Lisa-Marie Jobson, Catherine Spyrides & Keely Cook

SMC ENTERTAINMENTS
PO Box 101, Liverpool, Merseyside
L13 7JQ
Tel: 0845 465 0300 Fax: 0845 465 0301
Mob: 07717 090620
Email: info@smcentertainment.co.uk
Web Site: www.smcentertainment.co.uk
Senior Personnel: Paul Minney

SMILE TALENT
The Office, Hope Cottage, London Road, Newport, Saffron Walden, Essex
CB11 3PN
Tel: 020 8457 2702 Fax: 020 8457 2913
Email: info@smiletalent.com
Web Site: www.smiletalent.biz
Contact: Stephen Cornwall

CHRIS SMITH AND THE STRING OF PEARLS
13 Letchmore Road, Radlett,
Hertfordshire WD7 8HU
Tel: 01923 854 363
Email: info@stringofpearls.co.uk
Web Site: www.stringofpearls.co.uk
Contact: Chris Smith
Chris Smith and the String of Pearls, Britain's number one big party band. Playing today's mega pop hits of M People, Michael Jackson, Weather Girls, Tom Jones etc. Plus Frank Sinatra, Glenn Miller. Through the Swinging 60's with James Last.

ARTISTES REPRESENTED:
Chris Smith and the String of Pearls

DOUG SMITH ASSOCIATES
PO Box 1151, London W3 8ZJ
Tel: 020 8993 8436 Fax: 020 8896 1778
Email: mail@dougsmithassociates.com
Web: www.DougSmithAssociates.com
Senior Personnel: Doug Smith, Eve Carr

ARTISTES REPRESENTED:
Aluminum Babe
The King
Lonerparty
Patient Saints
Salt Tank

JIMMY SMITH
Hill Farm, Main Road, New Hackleton,
Northampton NN7 2DH
Tel: 01604 870 421 Fax: 01604 870 153
Email: jimmy@hackletonfams.co.uk

ARTISTES REPRESENTED:
The Hollies

SOLITAIRE MANAGEMENT & INTERNATIONAL BOOKING AGENCY
3 The Collops, Kingscourt, Co. Cavan, Ireland
Tel/Fax: 00 353 42 966 8792 Alan Mob: 00 353 086 2611 655 Barry Mob: 00 353 087 628 5636
Email: alan@solitaireagency.com
Web Site: www.solitaireagency.com
Solitaire Management and International Booking Agency is a company owned and run by Alan Whelan and Barry Heavey.
Initially, the company was set up to organise the world-wide booking of tours, corporate events and festivals for specific acts and productions.
In a short time, our artist roster has grown to include some of the best artists and shows from Ireland and around the world.

ARTISTES REPRESENTED:
Frances Black
Mary Black
Derby Browne
Jerry Fish & The Mudbug Club
Gaelforce Dance
Nina Hynes
On Eagles Wing
Sheoda
Juliet Turner

SOLO AGENCY LTD
53-55 Fulham High Street,
London SW6 3JJ
Tel: 020 7384 6644 Fax: 0870 749 3174
Email: soloreception@solo.uk.com
Web Site: www.solo.uk.com
Agent & Promoter: John Giddings
Promoter of the Isle of Wight Festival.
European promoter for U2, Madonna and The Rolling Stones.

ARTISTES REPRESENTED:
David Bowie
The Charlatans
Phil Collins
The Corrs
Iggy Pop
Il Divo
Ronan Keating
Meatloaf
Melanie C
N.E.R.D
Simple Minds
Starsailor
Rod Stewart
Suzanne Vega
Westlife
Wet Wet Wet

SOLOMON ARTISTES MANAGEMENT INTERNATIONAL
30 Clarence Street, Southend-on-Sea,
Essex SS1 1BD
General Tel: 01702 392 370 Clients Tel: 01702 437 118 Fax: 01702 392 385
Email: info@solomon-artistes.co.uk
Web Site: www.solomon-artistes.co.uk
Senior Personnel: Anita Houser
Office Manager: Helen Havis
Supporting artists agency.

SOME BIZARRE LTD
14 Tottenham Court Road, London
W1T 1JY
Tel: 020 7836 9995
Email: info@somebizarre.com
Web Site: www.somebizarre.com
Senior Personnel: Stevo Pearce

ARTISTES REPRESENTED:
Marc Almond
David Ball
Gary Lucas
Mainstream Distortion
Meka
MFF
Soft Cell
The Dark Poets
Zga vs. Figs

SOMETHIN' ELSE
20 - 26 Brunswick Place, London N1 6DZ
Tel: 020 7250 5500 Fax: 020 7250 0937
Email: info@somethinelse.com
Web Site: www.somethinelse.com
Head of Talent Management: Grant Michaels
Agent: Sarah Jane Cass
Assistant Agent: Richard Howells

ARTISTES REPRESENTED:
Liz Barker
Sonia Deol
Bobby Friction
Rachel Hopper
JK & Joel

Jeremy Kyle
Helen Mayhew
Emily Rose
Georgie Thompson
Kelli Young

SOUND ADVICE

30 Artesian Road, London W2 5DD
Tel: 020 7229 2219 Fax: 020 7229 9870
Email: mail@soundadvice.uk.com
Web Site: www.soundadvice.uk.com
Senior Personnel: Hugh Phillimore
Entertainment Consultants, Bookers and Event Organisers involved primarily with Music.

ARTISTES REPRESENTED:

Imelda May

SOUND ENTERTAINMENTS

16 Crofters Meadow, Lychpit,
Basingstoke, Hampshire RG24 8RX
Tel: 01256 354 573
Contact: Bernard Loake

SPEAK-EASY LTD

PO Box 648, Harrington, Northampton
NN6 9XT
Tel: 0870 0135 126
Email: enquiries@speak-easy.co.uk / first-name@speak-easy.co.uk
Web Site: www.speak-easy.co.uk
Presenters: Kate Moon
Voice Overs: Katie Matthews-Lee
Representing some of the finest established talent and rising stars including: Presenters/Journalists (TV & Radio); Conference Facilitators/Speakers; Voice Overs (Documentaries/Commercials/Corporate).

ARTISTES REPRESENTED:

Voice-Overs:
Sebastian Abineri
Stephen Armstrong
Nancy Baldwin
Eric Barton
Ian Bellion
Anna Bentinck
Melissa Berry
Tim Birkett
Nell Brady
Corie Brown
Robin Browne
Elisa Cannas
Tom Clarke-Hill
Eileen Colgan
Alison Colville
Andrew Conlan
Jane Copland
Sarah Coutts
Cita Crefeld
Rob Curling
Catrin Darnell
Mark Delacey
Rebecca Deren
Natasha Desborough
Hugh Dickson
Jacqueline Duff
Anthony Etherton
Adrian Finighan
Peter Forbes
Tilly Gerrard-Bannister
Piers Gibbon
Anna Godsiff
Michael Goldfarb
Tres Hanley
Peter Harlowe
Claire Harman
Kate Harper
Nick Harrison
Colm Hayes
Nuala Hayes
Mary Healy
Sophie Hein
Paul Herzberg
Tom Hodgkins
James Hornsby
Barbara Houseman
Robin Houston
Veronika Hyks
Ben Jackson
Peter Jefferson
Astley Jones
Ben Jones
Vanessa Keogh
Andy Kershaw
Gary King
Raewyn Lippert
Robin Lustig
Carolanne Lyme
Deborah Maclaren
Helen Madden
Helen Mark
Eddie Matthews
Ian Mayhew
Deborah McAndrew
Ian Michie
Adam D Millard
Marti Miller
Richard Mitchley
Elizabeth Moynihan
Jenni Murray
Eleanor Oldroyd
Katarina Olsson
Pat O'Regan
Rachel O'Shea
Melissa Pearce
Dave Benson Phillips
Michael Poole
Mark Rawson
Jack Roberts
Gavin Robertson
Zhivila Roche
Chris Saul
Paul Seed
Jan Shand
Peter Silverleaf
Tim Smith
David Symonds
Gary Terzza
Kiah Ross Tucker
Mike Turiansky
Jane Van Hool
Melinda Walker
Malcolm Ward
Liz Whiting
John Wilson
Alan Wogan
Ritchie Zealand
Presenters:
Sameena Alirkhan
Faye Barker
Chris Beardshaw
Karen Bowerman
Brigid Calderhead
Jamie Crawford
Rob Curling
Rob Dorsett
Piers Gibbon
Mark Gough
Melanie Hill
Robin Houston
Mishal Husain - Presenter
Veronika Hyks
Andy Kershaw
Sevi Lawson
Robin Lustig
Julie MacDonald
Helen Mark
Jenni Murray
Eleanor Oldroyd
Shane Osborn
Sam Pinkham
Lara Rostron
Valerie Sanderson
Philippa Tomson
Gordon Whistance
John Wilson
Alan Wogan
Amani Zain
Journalists/Corporate:
Rob Curling
Rob Dorsett
Melanie Hill
Mishal Husain - Presenter
Sevi Lawson
Robin Lustig
Julie MacDonald
Jenni Murray
Lara Rostron
Valerie Sanderson

SPEAKERS ASSOCIATES LTD

Thistles 15 Kinghom Park Maidenhead,
Berkshire SL6 7TX
Tel: 01628 636600
Email: info@speakersassociates.com
Web Site: www.speakersassociates.co.uk

ARTISTES REPRESENTED:

Deborah Meaden

SPEAKERS CORNER

207 High Road, London N2 8AN
Tel: 020 8365 3200 Fax: 020 8883 7213
Email: info@speakerscorner.co.uk
Web Site: www.speakerscorner.co.uk
Agent: Nick Gold
Specialising in After Dinner Speakers, Business and Motivational Speakers, Celebrities, Sports Personalities, Politicians, Awards Hosts and Cabaret for the Corporate Market.

SPEAKERS FOR BUSINESS

38 Bartholomew Close, London
EC1A 7HP
Tel: 020 7600 3993 Fax: 020 7600 3992
Email: info@sfb.com
Web Site: www.sfb.com
Senior Personnel: Tracey Ball

ARTISTES REPRESENTED:

Frank Dick OBE

Sir Ranulph Fiennes Bt OBE
Sahar Hashemi
Larry Hochman
John Humphrys
Steve McCauley
Steve McDermott
Chris Moon
Wally Olins
Miha Pogachnik
Sir Ken Robinson
Prof Richard Scase
Debra Searle
Dr David Starkey
Rebecca Stephens MBE
Col. Bob Stewart DSO
Tim Waterstone
Adrian Webster
Simon Woodroffe

SPEAKERS UK
27 Gloucester Street, London WC1N 3XX
Tel: 0845 458 3707
Email: info@speakers-uk.com
Web Site: www.speakers-uk.com
Contact: Dominic Morley
Specialises in motivational speakers.

SPEAKING VOLUMES
c/o The Swan Theatre, The Moors,
Worcester WR1 3EE
Tel: 01905 611 323 Fax: 01905 721 880
Email: chris@speakingvolumes.co.uk
Web Site: www.speakingvolumes.co.uk
Senior Personnel: Chris Jaeger
ARTISTES REPRESENTED:
Harvey Andrews
Phil Beer
Vin Garbutt
Gordon Giltrap
John Kirkpatrick
The Strawbs

SPEAKOUT CELEBRITIES & PRESENTERS LIMITED
Midlothian Innovation Centre, The Bush,
Roslin, Midlothian EH25 9RE
Tel: 0131 440 9226 Fax: 0131 440 3262
Email: info@speakoutuk.com / info@tmcentertainment.co.uk
Web Site: www.tmcentertainment.co.uk / www.speakoutuk.com
Director: Kenny Donaldson

ARTISTES REPRESENTED:
Some Artists are by arrangement with respective Agents
Speakers:
Kaye Adams
Kate Adie OBE
Kriss Akabusi MBE MA
Benedict Allen
Kirstie Allsopp
Matt Allwright
Clive Anderson
Jamie Andrew
Alexander Armstrong
Phil Ashby (Major)
Lord Paddy Ashdown
Steve Backley MBE OBE
Bill Bailey
Johnny Ball
Chris Barrie
Louise Batchelor
Mark Beaumont
Paul Bennett
Jackie Bird
Roger Black MBE
Sally Boazman
Jennie Bond
Sir Chris Bonington CBE
Frankie Boyle
Gyles Brandreth
Rory Bremner
Kevin Bridges
Arnold Brown
Craig Brown
Derren Brown
Guy Browning
Dee Cafari
Andy Cameron
Alastair Campbell
Will Carling OBE
Jimmy Carr
Jasper Carrott OBE
Andrew Castle
Craig Charles
Julian Clary
Lord Sebastian Coe
Roger Cook
Phil Cool
Quentin Cooper
Mark Cox
James Cracknell OBE
Alison Craig
Annabel Croft
John Culshaw
Edwina Currie
Declan Curry
Paul Daniels
Eric Davidson
Graham Davies
Jason Dawe
Angus Deayton
Alan Dedicoat
Hugh Dennis
Hilary Devey
Frank Dick OBE
Steven Dick
Charlie Dimmock
Tommy Docherty
Dougie Donnelly
Karen Dunbar
Penny Ferguson
Sir Ranulph Fiennes OBE
Donald Findlay QC
Stewart Francis
Jason Gardener MBE
Lord Edward "Eddie" George
Ricky Gervais
Dominic Gill
Robbie Glen
Duncan Goodhew MBE
Pete Goss MBE
Jeff Green
Bear Grylls
Sally Gunnell OBE
Dave Gunson
Pen Haddow
William Hague MP
Monty Halls
Caroline Hamilton
Richard Hammond
Alan Hansen
Neil Hanson
Sahar Hashemi
Gavin Hastings OBE
Scott Hastings
Tony Hawks
Alex Hay
Tim Healey
Sarah Heaney
Lenny Henry CBE
Craig Hill
Harry Hill
Dominic Holland
Dame Kelly Holmes
Armando Iannucci
Colin Jackson CBE
Clive James
Graham P Jolley
Miles Jupp
Natasha Kaplinsky
Lorraine Kelly
Baroness Helena Kennedy QC
Nick Knowles
Hardeep Singh-Kohli
Sanjeev Kohli
Alan Lamb MBE
Amanda Lamb
Paul Lambert
Nick Leeson
Jim Leishman
John Leslie
Maureen Lipman CBE
Gabby Logan BA
Gabby Logan BA
Michael Lynagh
Dame Ellen MacArthur
Fred MacAulay
Rob Maclean
Murdo Macleod
Sally Magnusson
Hayley Matthews
James May
Drew McAdam
Jane McCarry
Perry McCarthy
Alistair McGowan
Rory McGrath
Michael McIntyre
Steve McKenna
Mike Milligan
Dan Mills
Len Murray
Steve Nallon
Shereen Nanjiani
Terry Neason

Richard Noble OBE
Barry Norman
Tom O'Connor
Dara O'Briain
Bill Oddie
Neil Oliver
Dr Marilyn Orcharton
Denise Van Outen
Bruce Parry
Joe Pasquale
Dorothy Paul
Matthew Pinsent
Shaf Rasul
Sir Steven Redgrave CBE
Heather Reid OBE
Lesley Riddoch
Frank Robb
Ian Robertson
Tony Robinson
Nataylia Roni
Jez Rose
Jonathan Ross
Judith Ralston
Isobel Rutter
Ann Salter
Ben Saunders
Catriona Shearer
Roy Shephard
Robin Sieger
Robert Kilroy Silk
Kate Silverton
John Simonett
Joe Simpson
Tony Singh
Frank Skinner
Nicky Slater
Carol Smillie
Elaine C Smith
Phil Spencer
Ian St John
Sir John Stevens
Grant Stott
Arlene Stuart
Lord Alan Sugar
Jimmy Tarbuck OBE
Brian Taylor
Dennis Taylor
Daley Thopmson CBE
Willie Thorne
Sandi Toksvig
Isla Traquair
Lord David Trimble
Dr Chris & Dr Xand Van Tulleken
Debra Veal
Dougie Vipond
Alison Walker
Tommy Walsh
Ruby Wax
Sarah Webb MBE
Quentin Willson
Richard Wilson
Terry Wogan
Dave Wolfe
Prof Heinz Wolff
Chick Young
Kirsty Young

SPEAKS VOLUMES
The Mill House, Tyn-y-Caeau, Mold Road, Northop, Lower Soughton Clwyd
CH7 6BE
Tel: 01352 840911 Mob: 07739 800 101
Email: jomartinltd@gmail.com
Web Site: www.speaksvolumes.co.uk
Contact: Joanne Martin

SPECIAL EVENTS CONSULTANTS
26 Saddlers Rise, Norton, Runcorn, Cheshire, WA7 6PG
Tel/Fax: 01928 716 561 Tel: 01928 795 757
Email: info@special-events-consultants.co.uk
Web: www.special-events-consultants.co.uk
Contact: Laurence S Duckworth
Specialising in Race Nights, Disco Nights, Casino Nights and Murder Mystery.

KEN SPENCER PERSONAL MANAGEMENT
P.A.G. Promotions, 138 Sandy Hill Road, London SE18 7BA
Tel/Fax: 020 8854 2558
Email: pagandferret@hotmail.com
Senior Personnel: Ken Spencer
Classical artists and mainly classically-trained singers, sopranos and tenors. Occassionally represent pianists.

ARTISTES REPRESENTED:
Paul Arden-Griffith
Lord Arsenal`s All Stars
Geraldine Aylmer-Kelly
Evette Davis
Jay Flaxman
Paivi Payne
Pamela Smith

SPHINX MANAGEMENT & ENTERTAINMENT AGENCY
Unity House, 2 Unity Place, Westgate Rotherham, South Yorkshire S60 1AR
Tel: 01709 820 379 / 370 / 830 999 / 838 365 Fax: 01709 369 990
Senior Personnel: Mr Tony French, John O'Hara

ARTISTES REPRESENTED:
Abba Me - Abba You
Chameleon
Charm Skool
City Limits
Elesis
Good Rockin' Tonite
Koo-Ka-Choo
Respect
Sister System
Sam Sorono

SPLITTING IMAGES LOOKALIKE AGENCY
25 Clissold Court, Greenway Close, London N4 2EZ
Tel: 020 8809 2327 Fax: 020 8809 6103
Email: info@splitting-images.com
Web Site: www.splitting-images.com
Senior Personnel: Michael Fine
We have hundreds of lookalikes ranging from Tony Blair to Ruby Wax and Neil Diamond to Pierce Brosnan. Please call for further details.

THE SPORT ENTERTAINMENT AND MEDIA GROUP LTD
98 Cockfosters Road, Barnet, Hertfordshire EN4 0DP
Tel: 020 8447 4250 Fax: 020 8447 4251
Email: enquiries@semplc.com
Web Site: www.semplc.com
Agent: Jo Leigh
For a full listing of artists, please visit our website.

ARTISTES REPRESENTED:
Dennis Bergkamp
Anton Ferdinand
Rio Ferdinand
Fenton Gee
Thierry Henry
Sami Hyypia
Lennox Lewis
Jodie Marsh
Gavin McCann
Olof Mellberg
Charlie Nicholas
Marian Pahars
Emmanuel Petit
Micah Richards
Neil Ruddock
Kemal Shahin
Teemu Tainio
Jerome Thomas
David Thompson
Matthew Le Tissier
Stephen Warnock
Ian Wright

SPORTS WORKSHOP
56 Church Road, Crystal Palace, London SE19 2EZ
Tel: 020 8771 4700 Fax: 020 8771 4704
Mob: 07770 994 043 (Chris Snode)
Email: info@sportspromotions.co.uk
Web Site: www.sportspromotions.co.uk
Senior Personnel: Chris Snode
We supply sports models in all categories from Athletics to Wrestling.

SPOTLIGHT ENTERTAINMENTS
4a Bentinck Street, Hucknall, Nottingham, NG15 7EG
Tel: 0115 963 7642 Fax: 0115 953 8801
Mobile: 07711 257792
Email: neil.unwin@ntlworld.com
Senior Personnel: Neil A Unwin

ARTISTES REPRESENTED:
As Is (Band)
Roy Davendort
Finch & Young
Paul Francis
Louise Haywood (Annie Lennox)
Tony John
Graham P Jolley
K C Jay
Magenta
Savoir Faire

SPOTLIGHT ENTERTAINMENTS
Chantersell, Nether Lane, Nutley, East Sussex TN22 3LA
Tel: 01825 713 213 Fax: 0870 486 4484
Email: info@spotlight-ents.com
Web Site: www.spotlight-ents.com

Partner: Mr Siddons & Mrs Siddons

ARTISTES REPRESENTED:

Keith "The Thief" Charnley
Groovin' High
Graham P Jolley
Mandy Muden
Oliver Twist (Band)
Nick Reade
Spanner in the Works
The Amusing Sister Ruth!

SPOTLIGHT ENTERTAINMENTS (NORTHWEST)

PO Box 10 Tyldesley, Manchester, M29 8XW
Tel/Fax: 0161 790 6165
Email: spotlightents@ntlworld.com
Web Site: www.spotlightents.co.uk
Senior Personnel: Duane Letherbarrow
Cabaret agency.

SPROULE ENTERTAINMENTS

21 Brooklands Court, Hatfield Road
St Albans, Hertfordshire AL1 3NS
Tel: 01727 854 084 Fax: 01727 864460
Email: willsproule@yahoo.co.uk
Senior Personnel: Will Sproule
Represent freelance piano entertainments for hotel bookings.

PAUL SPYKER MANAGEMENTS

7 Garrick Street, London WC2E 9AR
Tel: 020 7462 0046 Fax: 020 7379 8282
Email: ps@pspy.com
Web Site: www.pspy.com
Senior Personnel: Paul Spyker

ARTISTES REPRESENTED:

Jaye Jacobs
Chris Quinten

S.T. ARTS MANAGEMENT

Suite 2 Cantilupe Road Ross-on-Wye HR9 7AN
Tel: 0845 408 2468
Email: agent@stagecoachagency.co.uk
Web Site: www.stagecoachagency.co.uk
Traquin Shaw-Young

ST JAMES'S MANAGEMENT

19 Lodge Close, Stoke D'Abernon, Cobham, Surrey KT11 2SG
Tel: 01932 860 666
Senior Personnel: Jacqueline Leggo

STABLES ENTERTAINMENTS

20 Grange Road, Long Eaton, Nottingham NG10 2EH
Tel: 0115 972 3399 Mob: 07970 117 172
Email: mail@stables-ents.co.uk
Web Site: www.stables-ents.co.uk
Proprietor: Reg Enderby, Darren Wright
Specialising in live bands and live tributes.

ARTISTES REPRESENTED:

AB/CD
Dizzy Lizzy (Thin Lizzy tribute)
Doctor & the Medics
The Earl Jackson Band
Once More Into the Bleach (Blondie)
Sounds of The Blues Brothers
The Full Shabang
The SJs (soul band)
Vogue (Madonna tribute)

BARRIE STACEY PROMOTIONS & PRODUCTIONS

Apartment 8, 132 Charing Cross Road, London WC2H 0LA
Tel: 020 7836 6220 / 4128
Fax: 020 7836 2949
Email: hopkinstacey@aol.com
Senior Personnel: Barrie Stacey, Jeff Howard
Specialising in Musicals and Stage Plays. First Class Children's Musicals - First Class Plays. Songbook Concerts, West End to Broadway, The Cole Porters Junglebook, Movie Memories.

ARTISTES REPRESENTED:

AM
Jamie Anderson
John Aston
Patrick Barr
Johnny Barrs
Sam Bern
Bonnie Bridgeman
Paul Carpenter
Lisa Cassidy
Stephen Cheriton
Guy Chinnery
Anna Church
Brendan Culshaw
Clare Cunliffe
Shelly Dartnell
David Whitfield
Marielle Dawson
Bob Flag
Pamela Flanagan
Julie Fox
Bob Grant
Tom Gribby
Keith Hopkins
Fiona Hunter
Isobel Hurle
Sam John
Debbie King
David Laughton
Audrey Maye
Kerry McDonald
Gary McErlane
Jenny McGrath
Mairi McHuffie
Colin McIntyre
Simon Money
John Pollendine
Geraldine Porterfield
Iain Potter
Stephen Russell-Bird
Nick Rutherford
Napoleon Ryan
Finn Silversten
Jason Summerfield
Gary Taylor
Edward Thorpe
Jeremy Todd
Jahangir uddin
Mark Underwood
Ben West
Derek Wright

HELEN STAFFORD MANAGEMENT

14 Park Avenue, Bush Hill Park, Enfield, Middlesex EN1 2HP
Tel: 020 8360 6329 Fax: 020 8482 0371
Email: helen.stafford@blueyonder.co.uk

STAFFORD LAW

Candle Way Broad Street Sutton Valence Kent ME17 3AT
Tel: 01622 840 038 Fax: 01622 840 039
Email: staffordlaw@btinternet.com
Web Site: www.stafford-law.com
Managing Director: Dominic Stafford Uglow
Consultants: David Law, Margherita Stafford

ARTISTES REPRESENTED:

Conductors:
Sergio Alapont
Angelo Cavallaro
Paul McGrath
Anu Tali
Sopranos:
Andrea Creighton
Delphine Gillot
Malin Hartelius
Eteri Lamoris
Tinuke Olafimihan
Patricia Rozario OBE
Yuri Maria Saenz
Eva Urbanova
Leontina Vaduva
Li Pink Zhang
Mariana Zvetkova
Mezzo Soprano:
U Hesse vd Steinen
Tenors:
Bonaventura Bottone
Donald George
Howard Haskin
Luis Lima
Reinaldo Macias
Gianni Mongiardino
Jorge Antonio Pita
Baritones & Basses:
Rodney Clarke
Graeme Danby
Peter Kajlinger
Ron Li-Paz
Gavin Taylor
Reuben Willcox
Samuel Youn
Giorgio Zancanaro

STAG ENTERTAINMENTS LTD

19 Elm Place, Aberdeen AB25 3SN Scotland
Tel/Fax: 01224 635 259
Email: info@stagentertainments.co.uk
Senior Personnel: Andy Irvine, Allan Doig

ARTISTES REPRESENTED:

Big Picture
Ceilidh UK
Crooked Jack
Gary Denis
George Duffus
Doug Duthie
Kyle Esplin
Graham Geddes

Headroom
Iron Broo (Ceilidh Band)
Billy Jeffrey
Craig McCallum
George McNeill
Peter Mitchell
Press-to-Play
Referendum
Shindig
Skirly Beat (Ceilidh Band)
Slinky
Rikki Stevens
The Stingrays
Storm
Alex Sutherland

STAGE CENTRE MANAGEMENT

41 North Road, London N7 9DP
Tel/Fax: 020 7607 0872 7700 3921
Email: stagecentre@aol.com
Co-Operative agency.

ARTISTES REPRESENTED:

David Ahmad
Elizabeth Cadwallader
Dominic Coddington
Philip Elvy
Graeme Eton
Duncan Foster
James Gitsham
Sarah Goddard
Leyla Holly
Claire Jeater
Terry Jermyn
Donna Lisa Kitching
Debbie Leigh-Simmons
Rachel Morris
Julia Munrow
Natalege Malene
Elliot Quinn
Victoria Ross
Joy Roston
Simon Spencer-Hyde

STAGE DOOR PRODUCTIONS & ENTERTAINMENT AGENCY

20 Dewar Drive, Millhouses, Sheffield
S7 2GQ
Tel/Fax: 0114 236 3083
Mobile: 07770 865953
Email: seanstagedoor@msn.com
Web: www.stagedoorproductions.co.uk
Sole Proprieter: Peter Wright
Secretary: Lucy Wright
Entertainment agency providing variety artists and
production/package shows.

STAGECOACH AGENCY UK

Suite 2 Cantilupe Road Ross-on-Wye
HR9 7AN
Tel: 0845 408 2468
Email: tarquin@stagecoachagency.co.uk
Web Site: www.stagecoachagency.co.uk
Tarquin Shaw-Young

STAGECOACH THEATRE ARTS PLC

The Courthouse, Elm Grove,
Walton-on-Thames, Surrey KT12 1LZ
Tel: 01932 254 333 Fax: 01932 222 894
Email: enquiries@stagecoach.co.uk
Web Site: www.stagecoach.co.uk
Co-Founding Directors: Stephanie Manuel, David Sprigg
The UK's original and largest part-time performing arts schools network for children aged 4-18years. Over 600 schools across the UK and Ireland teaching young people to sing, dance and act, at weekends, after-school and holiday workshops.

STAGESAFE

13 Portland Road, Street,
Somerset BA16 9PX
Tel: 01458 445 186 Mob: 07831 437 062
Email: info@stagesafe.co.uk
Web Site: www.stagesafe.co.uk
Senior Personnel: Chris Hannam
Stagesafe provide health and safety services to the live music, event and entertainment industries.

STAGESTRUCK MANAGEMENT

Stowe March, Barnet Lane, Elstree,
Borehamwood, Hertfordshire WD6 3RQ
Tel: 020 8953 8300 Fax: 020 8905 1511
Senior Personnel: Simon Caplan

STAGEWORKS MANAGEMENT AGENCY (BLACKPOOL)

Blackpool Pleasure Beach, Promenade,
Blackpool FY4 1EZ
Tel: 01253 342426/7 Fax: 01253 407715
Email: kelly.willars@stageworkswwp.com
Web Site: www.stageworkswwp.com
Contact: Amanda Thompson

STAGEWORKS WORLDWIDE PRODUCTIONS

525 Ocean Boulevard, Blackpool,
FY4 1EZ
Tel: 01253 342 426 / 7
Fax: 01253 407 715
Email: info@stageworkswwp.com
Web Site: www.stageworkswwp.com
Creative Director: Antony Johns
Skating - ice dancers, free skaters, pair skaters, adagio skaters, comedy skaters. Dancers. Actors. Singers. Models. Circus Artistes - Speciality acts, magicians, illusionists, costume characters, street performers. Promotional Personnel, Hosts and Hostesses, Guest Speakers. Choreographers, Directors, Producers.

STANLEY DALLAS

30 Hollies Way, Thurnby, Leicester
LE7 9RJ
Tel: 0116 241 6063 Fax: 0116 241 7753
Email: standal@sky.com
Contact: Stanley Dallas FEAA

STAR MANAGEMENT

Tel: 0870 242 2276
Email: carol@starmanagement.co.uk
Web Site: www.starmanagement.co.uk
Agent: Carol Meehan

ARTISTES REPRESENTED:

Jackie Bird
Ali Campbell
Alison Douglas
Nicola Jolly
Cathy Macdonald
Federico Martone
Shereen Nanjiani
Sarah O'Flaherty
Iain Duncan Smith
Louise White

STARDUST ENTERTAINMENTS AGENCY

1 West Well Close, Tingewick,
Buckingham Buckinghamshire
MK18 4QD
Tel/Fax: 01280 848 387
Mobile: 07721 613670 (Roger Tear)
Senior Personnel: Roger & Susan Tear

ARTISTES REPRESENTED:

Ajay (Comedienne / Singer)
Ballroom Glitz
Barnstorm Barn Dance Band
Black Velvet Band
Brass Monkeys Soul Band
Adger Brown
Buckin Bronco Rodeo Bull
Micky John Bull
Terry Burgess
Chris Bylett & Co
Casino Fun Time
Choice
Drew Christie
Chuckletruck
Clarendon String Quartet
Cockney Capers Show
Colinski
Counterfeit Beatles
Dad's Army Jazz Band
Daggers Drawn Murder Mystery
Disco Inferno
Dizzy Feet Disco
Fat Old Dad
Five Star Swing
Flash Show Cockney Duo
Focus
Rusty Ford & the Classics
Fortuna String Quartet
Mike Gancia
George - Caricaturist
Golden Age of Music Hall Show
Greased Lightning
Groove Company
Havana Boys Steel Band
Hookey Band
Horse Race Nights
Hot Trax Disco
Hurricane Force Steel Band
Junction Jugglers
Paul Levent
Malachi
Mick Martin`s Stag Show Exotica
Myles McKoy
Mini Grand Prix
Munich Bier Keller Men
New Dorne Valley
Adam Night

Nightbird
Richard C Parker
Poison Ivy 60's & 70's Show
Prestige
Queen B (Queen tribute)
Ian Richards
Royal Castle Jazz Band
Bierkeller Schunklers
Terry Seabrooke
Silver Stars Steel Band
Ron Smiley
Martin Smith
Society Jazz
Sounds Unlimited
Special F.X.
Stackyard Stompers Jazz Band
Stag Punch & Judy Show
Stag Show Exotica
Stardust Saucy Hen Show
Status Clone (Status Quo Tribute)
Greg Suggitt
Bruce Thompson
Walk Right Back (Everley Bros)
We'll Meet Again Show
Wild Honey

STARFINDERS INTERNATIONAL MANAGEMENT

113 Walton Road, East Molesey, Surrey KT8 0DR
Tel: 01483 203 438 Fax: 01483 229 018
Mobile: 07702 020652
Email: starfinders@btopenworld.com
Senior Personnel: Andina Treamer

ARTISTES REPRESENTED:

Andalus (Gypsy Kings)
Ronnie Beharry (Michael Jackson)
Bob "The Cat" Bevan MBE
Disco with Andina
DJ JD
DJ Jon
Eugene & The Hurricanes
Dave Ismay
Midas Sounds
Mr McDonut
Mark Peters
Carl Pettman
Starfinders Mobile Disco
Rod Stewart & Stone Cold Sober
Windsor Disco

STARLIGHT ENTERTAINMENTS

31 Brambling Drive, Westhoughton, Bolton, Lancashire, BL5 2SW
Tel/Fax: 01942 815 148
Email: starlightinfo@hotmail.co.uk
Contact: John Park

STARLINGS THEATRICAL AGENCY

45 Viola Close, South Ockendon, Essex RM15 6JF
Mobile: 07969 909 284
Email: julieecarter@aol.com
Web Site: www.tiptoestageschool.com
Senior Personnel: Spencer Carter, Juliee Carter
Specialising in Actors for all forms of media. (Also a theatre school).

Representing a wide variety of artists covering many genres of theatrical arts including: singers, dancers and actors - children through to adults.

STELLAMAX ENTERPRISES LTD

Nova House, 53 Nova Croft,
Off Broad Lane, Eastern Green, Coventry, Warwickshire CV5 7FJ
Tel: 024 7646 9585 Mob: 07899 045363
Email: max@stellamax.com
Web Site: www.stellamax.com
Senior Personnel: Max Roberts

ARTISTES REPRESENTED:

Clear Cut (4 piece)
The Mercury Tribute Show
Mr Sketchum's Caricatures
Pop Tease (5 piece)
The Sixth Revelation
The Masqueraders (5 piece)

STEPHANIE EVANS ASSOCIATES

Rivington House, 82 Great Eastern Street, London EC2A 3JF
Tel: 0870 609 2629 Fax: 0870 609 2629
Email: steph@stephanie-evans.com
Web Site: www.stephanie-evans.com
Contact: Stephanie Evans

STEPPIN' OUT ENTERTAINMENT & CORPORATE EVENTS

11 Beaumont Court, Oxford OX1 5AL
Tel/ Fax: 01865 327 772
Mobile: 07768 606 088
Email: enquiries@steppin-out.co.uk
Web Site: www.steppin-out.co.uk
Proprietor: Terry Penn
We provide a wide range of services within the event management and entertainment arena, including: Corporate Events, Wedding Services, Theme & Team Building Events, Sound & Lighting Equipment Hire DJ's/Discos, Karaoke, Bands, Musicians, Entertainers, Marquees, Fireworks and Outdoor/Giant Games.

STERNBERG-CLARKE

Ruffle House, Spencer court,
140 Wandsworth High street, London SW18 4JJ
Tel: 020 8877 1102 Fax: 020 8874 4402
Email: adam@sternbernclarke.co.uk
Web Site: www.sternbergclarke.co.uk
Senior Personnel: Adam Sternberg, Duncan Clarke

ARTISTES REPRESENTED:

Mr Sketchum's Caricatures

STEVE MARTIN ENTERTAINMENTS

45 Ramsgate LOUTH LN11 0NF
Tel: 01507 603145
Email: stevemartinentertainments@googlemail.com
Web: www.stevemartinentertainments.com
Steve Martin

STIRLING MANAGEMENT

490 Halliwell Road, Bolton BL1 8AN
Tel: 0845 017 6500
Email: admin@stirlingmanagement.co.uk
Web Site: www.stirlingmanagement.co.uk

STIVEN CHRISTIE MANAGEMENT

1 Glen Street, Tollcross, Edinburgh, Mid Lothian EH3 9JD Scotland
Tel: 0131 228 4040 / 07000 ACTORS
Fax: 0131 228 4645 Mobile: 07831 403030 (Douglas Stiven)
Email: info@stivenchristie.co.uk
Web Site: www.stivenchristie.co.uk
Senior Personnel: Douglas Stiven
Specialising in Actors/Actresses.
Please see our website for artistes rosta.

ANNETTE STONE ASSOCIATES

30-31 Peter Street, London W1F 0AR
Tel: 020 7734 0626
Email: annette@annettestone.com
Web Site: www.annettestone.com
Senior Personnel: Annette Stone

THE RICHARD STONE PARTNERSHIP

2 Henrietta Street, London WC2E 8PS
Tel: 020 7497 0849 Fax: 020 7497 0869
Email: chayes@richstonepart.co.uk
Web Site: www.vivienneclore.com
Agent: Cheryl Hayes
All artistes listed are exclusively represented.

ARTISTES REPRESENTED:

Male:
Roger Allam
Nick Atkinson
Bob Barrett
Duncan Bell
Peter Benson
John Bett
David Birrell
Raymond Bowers
Felix Bowness
Paul Bradley
Michael Fenton Stevens
John Carlisle
Nicholas Caunter
Ray Cooney
Tony Cownie
Greg Cruttwell
Ian Cullen
Peter Cutler
Charles Dale
Pip Donaghy
Robert Fitch
Philip Franks
Malcolm Freeman
William Gaminara
Ian Gelder
Grant Gillespie
David Hargreaves
Robert Harley

Nicky Henson
Lou Hirsch
Geoffrey Hughes
Kenny Ireland
David Jason
Simon Jones
Sam Kelly
David Killick
Jack Klaff
Will Knightley
Michael Knowles
Warren Llambias
Johnnie Lyne Pirkis
John McAndrew
Peter McEnery
Henry McGee
Tom McGovern
Stuart McGugan
Liam McMahon
Desmond McNamara
Colin Mace
Tony Mathews
Bill Maynard
Royce Mills
Sean Murray
Bill Pertwee
Philip Pope
Robert Putt
John Quentin
John Rogan
Simon Russell Beale
William Rycroft
Mark Saban
Andrew Sachs
Adrian Scarborough
Simon Scardifield
Luke Shaw
David Shaw-Parker
Charles Shirvell
Steve Steen
Richard Todd
Larrington Walker
David Warwick
Daniel Weyman
Andrew Williamson
Justin Edwards
Richard Orford
Fred Perry
Dave Allen
Jason Attar
Richard Bacon
Adam Bloom
Rory Bremner
Gideon Coe
Peter Curran
John Fortune
Mark Franks
Tony Gardner
Matt Green
Edward Hall
Ashley Hames
Dr Phil Hammond
Paul Hawkyard
Jon Holmes
Milton Jones
Paul Kaye
Dave Lamb
Derren Litten
Alex Lowe
Chris Moyles
Colin Murray
Chris Neill
Jeremy Nicholas
Ben Norris
Jim North
Patrick O'Connell
Mark Perry
Shaun Pye
Nick Revell
Jon Ronson
James Sherwood
John Sparkes
Richard Thomson
Paul Thorne
Richard Whiteley OBE
Anthony Wilson

Female:

Megan Arellanes
Zara Asante
Zoe Ball
Hetty Baynes
Elizabeth Bennett
Emma Bernbach
Cora Bissett
Liz Bonnin
Jane Booker
Jo Brand
Katy Brittain
Chloe Buswell
Kirsty Buswell
Jo Caulfield
Sarah Cawood
Gabrielle Cowburn
Catherine Cusack
Amanda Daniels
Kate Duchêne
Bella Enahoro
Susan Engel
Maria Esposito
Caroline Faber
Stephanie Fayerman
Briony Glassco
Anita Graham
Pippa Guard
Cate Hamer
Vivien Heilbron
Cathy Howse
Jay Hunt
Konnie Huq
Issy Van Randwyck
Trilby James
Emma Jones
Natasha Joseph
Liz Kettle
Nicola King
Amy Lame
Niamh Linehan
Louise Loughman
Carol Macready
Alexandra Mathie
Jules Melvin
Lucy Montgomery
Leah Muller
Barunka O'Shaughnessy
Charmaine Parsons
Katherine Porter
Marguerite Porter
Libby Potter
Saffron Oddy
Rebecca Saire
Judith Scott
Sophie Shaw
Gerda Stevenson
Jennie Stoller
Rebecca Thorn
Claire Yuille

STONEYPORT ASSOCIATES

65A Dundas Street, Edinburgh,
Mid Lothian EH3 6RS Scotland
Tel: 0131 539 8238 Fax: 0131 346 8237
Email: jb@stoneyport.demon.co.uk
Web Site: www.stoneyport.demon.co.uk
Senior Personnel: John Barrow, Bill Barclay, Martin Coull, Heather Macleod.
Specialising in Celtic/Folk, Blues & General Entertainment.

ARTISTES REPRESENTED:

Soloists:

Bill Barclay
Gill Bowman
Amos Garrett
Dick Gaughan
Mick Hanly (Irish)
Bert Jansch
Michael Marra
Tom Spiers
Andy M Stewart
Allan Taylor

Duos:

Eric Bogle and John Munro
Chris and Thomas (USA)
Alasdair Fraser & Natalie Haas
David Vernon (accordion) and Dick Lee (clarinet/reeds)
The Wrigley Sisters

Bands:

Burach
Colcannon (Australia)
Jim Condie
Deaf Shepherd
Fribo
Harem Scarem
International Guitar Night (USA)
La Boum!
Heather Macleod and The Healthy Measures (trio)
Malinky
The McCalmans
North Sea Gas
Parallelogram
The Poozies
Shepheard Spiers and Watson
Urban Trad (Belgium)
The Wild Cigarillos

Blues-Jazz:

Alex Yellowlees Hot Club Quartet
Scottish Guitar Quartet
Mike Whellans
Tam White

Rock:

Kenny Young and the Eggplants (USA trio)

Americana/Jazz Country:

Alison Brown Quartet (USA)

Folk Rock:

Mystery Juice

Irish Bands:

Dervish
Frankie Gavin and Tim Edey
Hibernian Rhapsody

MIKE STOREY ENTERTAINMENTS
Cliffe End Business Park, Dale Street, Longwood, Huddersfield, West Yorkshire
Tel: 0192 444 1245 Fax: 01484 657 055
Specialising in Irish and Country Music Acts
ARTISTES REPRESENTED:
Carolann 'B'
Club Class
Louisiana Blue
West Virginia
Jonny Williams

STUDIO ONE ASSOCIATES
Studio 1, 16 The Koko Building
Arches Industrial Estate, Spon End,
Coventry CV1 3JQ
Tel: +44 845 8733116
Mob: +44 247671720
Email: admin@studio1.co.uk
Web Site: www.studio1.co.uk
Managing Director: Mr Grant Wadey
ARTISTES REPRESENTED:
Bucks Fizz
DE Experience
Hazel Dean
Lee Pashley (Robbie Williams tribute)
Martha Reeves And The Vandellas
The Supremes
Three Degrees

STYLE ENTERTAINMENTS
PO Box 38, Robertsbridge,
East Sussex TN32 5XX
Tel: 01580 882 211 Mob: 07885 298 134
Email: info@styleentertainments.com
Web Site: www.styleentertainments.com
Senior Personnel: Terry Avann
Specialising in the booking of: Bands, Cabaret, Race Nights, TV & Sports Personalities and After-dinner speakers.

SUCCESS
Room 236, Linen Hall,
162-168 Regent street, London,
W1B 5TB
Tel: 020 7734 3356 Fax: 020 7494 3787
Email: ee@successagency.co.uk
Web Site: www.successagency.co.uk
Senior Personnel: Elena Gilbert, Elaine Payne
Specialising in Dancers & Choreographers

SUE RIDER MANAGEMENT LTD
Unit 41, Wimbledon 1 Deer Park Road
London SW19 3LT
Tel: 020 3432 7790
Email: susan@sueridermanagement.co.uk
Web: www.sueridermanagement.co.uk
Agent: Susan Rider
Talent representation for TV, radio, corporate & print.
ARTISTES REPRESENTED:
Mark Bailey
Clayton Byfield-Riches
Brian Cox
Miles Crawford
Beverley French
Amy Garcia
Mark Huggins
Susie Johns
Gia Milinovich
Hannah Sandling
Michael Schaeble
Nik & Eva Speakman

BOBBY SUMMERS
69A Bure Lane, Christchurch, Dorset
BH23 4DL
Tel: 01425 277 226 Mob: 07799 214 460
Fax: 01425 279 320
Contact: Bobby Summers
ARTISTES REPRESENTED:
Sing along Bobby
Bobby Summers

MICHAEL SUMMERTON MANAGEMENT LTD
Mimosa House, Mimosa Street,
London SW6 4DS
Tel: 020 7731 6969 Fax: 020 7731 0103
Email: msminfo@btconnect.com
Web Site: www.michaelsummerton.com
Director: Michael Summerton
Senior Personnel: Martin Taylor-Brown
Specialising in Choreographers & Dancers.
ARTISTES REPRESENTED:
Debbie Astell
Les Child
Arlene Phillips
Caroline Pope
Wanda Rokicki
Mitch Sebastian
Bruno Tonioli

SUNSHINE ENTERTAINMENTS (SIMON HARRIS LTD)
57 Rosebank Street, Leek, Staffordshire
ST13 6AG
Tel: 01538 398 121
Managing Director: Simon Harris
Provide singers, duos, groups, comedians and speciality.
ARTISTES REPRESENTED:
2 I D
3rd Element
Abba Dream
Maxine Adele
"Angels"
Backbeat
Becily B
Robbie Benson
Big Blue House
Big Business
Billy Flywheel
Marius Birks
Cargo
Carolina Blues Boys
Caroline
Chantilly Lace
Charmed
Darren Collings
Terry Conroy
Lonnie Cooke
Cool Memory
Cool Wave
DD King
Graham Dean
Denni Dee
Rob Derek
Disturbing The Peace
D.V.D
East & West
Eclipsed
Elmo
Embraced
Empathy
Flannelfoot 2
Footprints
Gemini
Brian St George
Paul Gibson
Neil Haywood
Hollywood Nites
Intermission
It Takes Two
Sarah Jane
Terry Jay
Dave Johns
Alec Johnson Band
Koko
Kool Breeze
Lenny Lee
Carol Lesley
Lovin' It
Diane Marsh
Dave Martin
Steve Michael
Midnight
Minus 2
Kelly Monroe
Tuesday Moore
Murphy's Marbles
Nothin Serious
Parka
Pink Cadillac
QV-J
R. John
Rhapsody In Blue
Davie Rhodes
Danny Roberts
Vicky Ross
Skinch
Sniezewort
Sound Advice
Alex Stepney
Scott Stevens
Stone Cold Sober
Straightjacket
Sugar Daddies
Take 2
Steven J Taylor
The Conspirators
The Tetleys
The Vicster
Timespan
Neil Timothy
Mark Trent
Twist & Shout
Rob Vincent
Whole Kaboodle

SUPERBAD TALENT LTD
2b Swanfield Street London E2 7DS
Tel: 020 7760 7553
Email: hello@superbadtalent.com

Web Site: www.superbadtalent.com
Kymberlee Jay

SUPERVISION MANAGEMENT

Zeppelin Building,
59-61 Farringdon Road, Farringdon,
London EC1M 3JB
Tel: 020 7916 2146 Fax: 020 7691 4666
Email: info@supervisionmgt.com
Contact: Paul Craig, James Sandom,
Cerne Canning
Worldwide Artiste Representation.

ARTISTES REPRESENTED:

Cajun Dance Party
Kaiser Chiefs
Cord
The Cribs
Cutcopy
Duels
Franz Ferdinand
Indigo Moss
Kubichek!
Late Off The Pier
Magnet
Mumm-ra
Neil's Children
Ripchord
Richard Swift
The Pistolas

JEFF SUTTON MANAGEMENT

Theatre Cottage, 113 Station Road,
Keadby, Scunthorpe, South Humberside
DN17 3BP
Tel: 01724 784 449 Fax: 01724 784 441
Mob: 07798 871 680
Email: jsm@agents-uk.com
Web Site: www.jeffsutton.co.uk
Agent: Jeff Sutton
Specialists in star names and production shows.

SWA ENTERTAINMENT

swaoffice@aol.com
1st Floor Suite, 1 Marguerite Close,
Bradwell, Gt Yarmouth, Norfolk
NR31 8RL
Tel: 01493 667 847
Email: info@swaentertainments.co.uk /
sawoffice@aol.com
Web Site: www.swaentertainments.co.uk
Director: Mrs Stuart
Specialising in live entertainments for hotels, clubs, TV and corporate. Dain Cordean - Britian's leading comedy magician. Biggest list of top tribute artistes available; named 60's band, top celebritys, Dream Boys, UK Famtasy Boys, Theatre shows.

ARTISTES REPRESENTED:

4 Sure
Audley Anderson
Nova Casper as Tina Turner
Chico
Complete Madness
Dain Cordean (Comedian)
Robin Cousins MBE
Sid Dennis
Dream Boys
Dreamers
Dave Evans
Paul Jackson
Jethro
Robert Lamberti (George Michael)
Tony Lewis (Robbie Williams)
Collen Nolan
Lee Pashley (Robbie Williams tribute)
Maxwell Plum
Rock Magic (Chris North and Belinda - Illusion)
Paul Sutton (Ronan Keating)
T Rextasy
Torvill and Dean
Gerry Trew (Rod Stewart)
UK Fantasy Boys

SWAMP MUSIC

PO Box 94, Derby DE22 1XA
Tel/Fax: 01332 332 336
Mobile: 07702 564804 (Chris Hall)
Email: chrishall@swampmusic.co.uk
Web Site: www.swampmusic.co.uk
Senior Personnel: Chris Hall
Many Cajun & Zydeco Bands available.

ARTISTES REPRESENTED:

The Bearcat Cajun Playboys
R Cajun & the Zydeco Brothers
Zydecomotion

SWAN ENTERTAINMENTS

52 Heathcote Drive Sileby Loughborough
Leicestershire LE12 7ND
Tel/Fax: 01509 814889
Senior Personnel: TC Woodward

ARTISTES REPRESENTED:

Jason Blake
John Daniels
Danni Jane
Dr Pesky
Expressive Harmony
Free & Eezy
Taylor Marcs
R.J. Nicholas
Platinum Jar
Bev Rae
Dillon Richards

SWEENEY ENTERTAINMENTS

Methven House 26 Stoke Road Methwold
Norfolk IP26 4PE
Tel: 01366 380333 Fax: 05601 158592
Email: info@sweeneyentertainments.co.uk
Web: www.sweeneyentertainments.co.uk
Contact: Julie Sweeney
Theatrical tour booking and production company.

SYLVANTONE PROMOTIONS

11 Saunton Avenue, Redcar, Cleveland
TS10 2RL
Tel: 01642 479 898 Fax: 0709 235 9333
Email: tonygoodacre /
sylviagoodacre@hotmail.com
Web Site: www.tonygoodacre.com
Senior Personnel: Tony Goodacre, Sylvia Goodacre
Specialists in traditional country music.

ARTISTES REPRESENTED:

Bluegrass Boogiemen (Holland) Int
Tony Goodacre Band
Tony Goodacre
Hill Billy Boogiemen (Holland) Int

TAKE THREE MANAGEMENT

110 Gloucester Avenue, Primrose Hill,
London NW1 8HX
Tel: 020 7209 3777 Fax: 020 7209 3770
Email: sara@take3management.com
Web Site: www.take3management.co.uk
Directors/Agents: Sara Cameron, Melanie Cantor, Vicki McIvor
Personal management agency specialising in television, radio and publishing.

ARTISTES REPRESENTED:

Females:
Louise Brady
Ginny Buckley
Caprice
Julia Carling
Kimberley Cohen
Vanessa Collingridge
Miriam Cooke
Tracey Cox
Bella Crane
Phillipa Davies
Tazeen Dhunna
Kirsty Duffy
Tessa Dunlop
Ruth England
Amanda Grant
Claire Halsey
Polly Hudson
Gemma Hunt
Ulrika Jonsson
Liv Kennard
Lara Logan
Tara Maguire
Saima Mohsin
Thalia Pellegrini
Claire Petulengro
Lisa Rogers
Anna Singleton
Nicole Smallwood
Gloria Thomas
Charlene White
Catherine York
Males:
Russell Amerasekera
Ricky Andalcio
Michael Anthony Bailey
Paul Coia
Chris Crudelli
Jamie Darling
Michael Douglas
Alvin Hall
Tim Hitchens
Eric Knowles
Gerard McCarthy
Stuart McQuitty
Andy Newton
Rhodri Owen
Fred Scott
Varun Sharma
Shovell (Live Percussion)
Dr Ian Stewart
Ivan Thomas
Mark Webster
Alan Williams

Expert:
Craig & Jane Hamilton-Parker

TALENT ARTISTS LTD

59 Sydner Road, London N16 7UF
Tel: 020 7923 1119 Fax: 020 7923 2009
Mob: 07967 029 551
Email: talent.artists@btconnect.com
Contact: Jane Wynn Owen

ARTISTES REPRESENTED:

Geoffrey Abbott
Stephen Ashfield
Kenneth Avery-Clark
Derek Barnes
Paul Bateman
Colin Bennett
Simon Buckley
Kaitlyn Carr
Sheila Carter
Vikki Coote
Marilyn Cutts
Mandy Demetriou
Richard Gauntlett
Susan Harriet
Graham Hoadly
Robert Howie
Josefine Isaksson
Nicola Keen
Malcolm McKee
Jonty Miller
Andy Morton
Richard O'Neal
Duncan Patrick
John Pattison
Jill Pert
John Rigby
Leanne Rogers
Fiz Shapur
Rosamund Shelley
David Shrubsole
Zoe Smith
Deborah Steel
Geraldine Stephenson
Judith Street
Sonia Swaby
Lisa Thorner
Victoria Ward
Nuala Willis
Michael Winsor

TALENT ENTERTAINMENTS AGENCY

Herronsgate, Saltmoor, Burrowbridge, Bridgwater, Somerset TA7 0RW
Tel: 01823 698 609 Mob: 07703 292 740
Fax: 01823 698 697
Email: mail@talent.uk.com
Web Site: www.talent.uk.com
Senior Personnel: Gillian White, Richard White, Nicolas White, Alexandra Rawle, Stefan Marusiak and Dave Richards.
Sole management and contact agent for several Celebrity Darts Players,The New Drifters, Horse Racing Celebrities and Broadcasters, plus many more artistes.

ARTISTES REPRESENTED:

Willie Carson OBE
Bob Champion MBE

TALENT INTERNATIONAL

61 Howland Way, London SE16 6HW
Tel/Fax: 020 7558 8190
Mobile: 07956 375 327
Email: info@talentinternational.com
Web Site: www.talentinternational.com
Senior Personnel: Michael Parlett
A full production service for music & Providers of Singers and musicians.

TALENT ONE

14 Fairfield Lane, Wolverley
Kidderminster, Worcestershire DY11 5QH
Tel: 01562 850 255 Mob: 07957 106 982
Email: admin@talentone.co.uk
Web Site: www.talentone.co.uk
Contact : Phil & Keith

ARTISTES REPRESENTED:

Natalie Brookes
Amanda Carr
Going Back
Chris King
Mamma-Mia
Session 60
Touch of Innocence

TALENT4 MEDIA LTD

Power Road Studios, 114 Power Road, Chiswick London W4 5PY
Tel: 020 8987 6416
Email: enquiries@talent4media.com
Web Site: www.talent4media.com
Contact: Joanna Carlton, Samantha Thomas

ARTISTES REPRESENTED:

Matt Baker
Alice Beer
Chris Brain
Pamela Brown
Sarah Cawood
John Craven OBE
Emily Hartridge
Paul Hendy
Chris Hollins
Chris Hopkins
Jenny Hull
Gloria Hunniford
Jonas Hurst
James Lamper
Jonathan Phang
Dean Piper
Rani Price
James Rylands
John Torode
Tim Vincent

TALKING CONCEPTS

PO Box 11914, Two Gates, Tamworth, B77 1WT
Tel: 01827 250 515 Fax: 0870 762 1535
Mob: 07870 154941
Email: ideas@talkingconcepts.co.uk
Web Site: www.talkingconcepts.co.uk
Senior Personnel: Jan Mattison
Specialising in after dinner/conference speakers, bands, cabaret artistes & themed entertainment.

TALKING HEADS - THE VOICE AGENCY

2-4 Noel Street, London W1F 8GB
Tel: 020 7292 7575 Fax: 020 7292 7576
Email: voices@talkingheadsvoices.com
Web Site: www.talkingheadsvoices.com
Senior Personnel: John Sachs
Specialising in Voice Overs, Atlantic, Character, Impressionists, Broadcasters, DJ's, Personalities, Actors, Foreign, Presenters and Documentaries.

ARTISTES REPRESENTED:

Females:
Nicky Adams
Clare Balding
Jenni Bale
Samantha Beckinsale
Sophie Benzing
Eva Birthistle
Claire Bloom
Laurence Bouvard
Jenny Burrell
Sarah Champion
Becky Chippendale
Nancy Crane
Suze Dawe
Alex Derbyshire
Elisabeth Dermot-Walsh
Hannah Emanuel
Fenella Fielding
Cassandra French
Beverley Fullen
Penny Gore
Sue Green
Mali Harries
Penny Haslam
Miranda Hewitt
Susannah Hitching
Carol Holt
Eiry Hughes
Gloria Hunniford
Janice Hunter
Jan Hyden Rowles
Lisa I'Anson
Elodie Kendall
Shirley King
Karen Krizanovich
Ruth Langsford
Jennifer Lawrence
Lela B
Tara Lester
Korenne Lofts
Skye Loneragan
Julia Marshall
Melanie Nicholson
Jo Parkerson
Amanda Phillips
Kate Sachs
Saffron
Dominica Warburton
Susie Webb
Anna Williamson
Serretta Wilson
Rebecca Wright
Males:
Edward Adoo
Stewart Alexander
John Anderson
Rod Arthur
John Beesley
Neil Bentley
Gary Bloom

Frank Bourke
Peter Bramhill
Andrew Brittain
Barry Clayton
Simon Clayton
Chris Cowdrey
Paul Coyte
John Craven OBE
Dermot Crowley
Rod Culbertson
Peter Curran
Mark Dexter
Reece Dinsdale
Kevin Duala
Greg Edwards
Robert Eims
Brian Ford
Graham Gold
David Graham
Richard Graham
Brian Greene
John Hammond
Jay Healy
Roger Hearing
Simon Hickson
Eamonn Holmes
Steven Hore
James Hyman
Michael Imerson
Chris Jarvis
David Jensen
Michael Kilgarriff
Bob Lampon
Martin Ledwith
Damien Lyne
Peter Mair
Noah Lee Margetts
Qarie Marshall
Dean Martin
David Mercer
Joe Mills
Trevor Neal
Tiff Needell
Nathan Nolan
Mike O'Malley
Nick Page
Craig Parker
Jonathan Pearce
John Pennington
Clarke Peters
John David Pohlhammer
David Prever
Steve Rider
Dave Roberts
David Rolston
Richard Ryder
John Sachs
John Sharian
Martin Sherman
Adam Sinclair
Allan Stewart
Darren Tighe
Harry Towb
Clive Tyldesley
Alec Westwood

TANWOOD THEATRICAL AGENCY

Tanwood School for Performing
Dowling Street, Swindon, Wiltshire
SN1 5QV
Tel: 01793 523 895
Email: Tanwood@tanwood.co.uk
Web Site: www.tanwood.co.uk
Founder/Principal: Mollie Tanner
Specialising in Young Adults and Children.

TAS MANAGEMENT

39 Coalbrook Grove, Woodhouse Mill, Sheffield S13 9XS
Tel: 0114 269 6457 Mobile: 07974 457458 Fax: 0114 269 2063
Email: terryashaw@btinternet.com
Senior Personnel: Terry & Ross Shaw
The Caring Agency. Your complete entertainment is our business.

TASTE OF CAIRO

22 Gilda Crescent Road Eccles
Manchester M30 9AG
Tel: 0161 7877 8578
Email: hello@tasteofcairo.com
Web Site: www.tasteofcairo.com
Tracey Gibbs

TAVISTOCK WOOD MANAGEMENT LTD

32 Tavistock Street, London WC2E 7PB
Tel: 020 7257 8725 Fax: 020 7240 9029
Email: wood@tavistockwood.com
Web Site: www.tavistockwood.com
Agent: Angharad Wood

ARTISTES REPRESENTED:

Actors:
Daniel Bruhl
Willem Defoe
Alex Kerr
Nikolai Kinski
Jack McElhorn
Linus Roache
Nicholas Roeg
Benjamin Ross
Dominic West
Benedict Wong
Will Young
Actresses:
Joanna David
Marie Gillian
Eva Green
Alexandra Maria Lara
Katy Saunders
Samantha Whittaker

BRIAN TAYLOR ASSOCIATES

50 Pembroke Road, Kensington, London W8 6NX
Tel: 020 7602 6141 Fax: 020 7602 6301
Email: briantaylor@nqassoc.freeserve.co.uk
Agent: Brian Taylor

ARTISTES REPRESENTED:

Female:
Sam Adams
Noriko Aida
Maev Alexander
Rita Anamagura
Lucy Austin
Denise Bryson
Alexandra Burn
Sandra Clark
Lynette Clarke
Nora Connolly
Melanie Downs
Grainne Gillis
Rebecca Hands-Wicks
Victoria Hayes
Sebrina Ishmael
Vicky Johnson
Pam Jolly
Koi Kimani
Sarah London
Joanna Loxton
Mary Ann O'Donoghue
Sally Plumb
Janene Possell
Jessica Punch
Ann Queensberry
Iris Russell
Elizabeth Sinclair
Amanda Symonds
Izabella Telezynska
Louise Vaughan
Margaret Wedlake
Male:
Tom Ambrose
Gary Calandro
Maitland Chandler
Alan Charlesworth
Richard Colvin
Robert Crofts
Jason Eblthite
Monty Fromant
Tim Hardy
Michael Hibberdine
Rupi Lal
Norman Mann
Roger Monk
Emmet Owens
Roger Parrott
Mike Rogers
Jimmy Roussounis
Paul Sirr
John Tallents
Christian Wilde
Russell Wootton
Menis Yousry

LAURIE TAYLOR ENTERTAINMENTS LTD

21 Crowborough Road,
Southend-on-Sea SS2 6LW
Tel: 01702 468 465
Mobile: 07717 223 710
Email: laurie@laurietaylor.co.uk
Senior Personnel: Laurie Taylor

ARTISTES REPRESENTED:

Angelique String Quartet
Craig Bowyer
Graham Davies
Graham P Jolley
Peter Moloney
Music Unlimited
Rupert Parker
Laurie Taylor Band
Valentine
Richard Vaughan
The Windwood Trio

TAYLOR MADE SPEAKERS
131 Battenhall Road, Battenhall,
Worcester WR5 2BU
Tel: 01905 767 465 Fax: 01905 767 489
Email: info@afterdinnerspeakers.org
Web Site: www.afterdinnerspeakers.org
Senior Personnel: David Taylor
After-dinner entertainment.

TCG ARTIST MANAGEMENT
Suite 43, 6 Langley Street, London
WC2H 9JA
Tel: 020 7240 3600 Fax: 020 7240 3606
Email: kristin@tcgam.co.uk
Web Site: www.tcgam.co.uk
Agent: Kristin Tarry

TEACHER STERN SELBY
37-41 Bedford Row, London WC1R 4JH
Tel: 020 7242 3191
Fax: 020 7242 1156 / 7405 2964
Email: g.shear@tsslaw.com
Web Site: www.tsslaw.com
Senior Personnel: Graham Shear
Specialising in Legal Representation

TEDGROUP
24 Titan Court, Laporte Way, Luton
LU4 8EF
General Tel: 01582 488 888
Fax: 01582 488877
Email: steve.donnelly@tedtalent.com
Web Site: www.teduk.com
Contact: Steve Donnelly

PAUL TELFORD MANAGEMENT
3 Greek Street, Soho London W1D 4DA
Tel: 020 7434 1100 Fax: 020 7434 1200
Email: paul@telford-mgt.com
Web Site: www.paultelford.net
Senior Personnel: Paul Telford, Kathryn Richards
Represents actors.

ARTISTES REPRESENTED:
4 Poofs & A Piano
Darren Day

TELSTAR ENTERTAINMENTS
5 The Lawley, Halesowen, West Midlands
B63 1JB
Tel: 01215 012 587
Email: telstarwmids@aol.com
Senior Personnel: Anne Palmer

TEMPLAR ENTERTAINMENT AGENCY
Rose Cottage, South End, Milton Bryan,
Bedfordshire, MK17 9HS
Tel: 01525 210 071 Fax: 01525 210 989
Email: plangbk@aol.com
Web Site: www.barronknights.com
Senior Personnel: Pete Langford

ARTISTES REPRESENTED:
The Barron Knights

TEMPLE'S ENTERTAINMENT AGENCY
2 Knowle Close, Abington Vale,
Northampton, NN3 3LW
Tel: 01604 639 198 Fax: 01604 628 204
Email: sue@temples-ents.co.uk
Web Site: www.temples-ents.co.uk
Managing Director: Sue Griffith-Temple
Est. 1987. Specialising in Acts for Outdoor Arenas and Attractions. A Family Business managed by the Third Generation of Temple's. Show & Gala specialists. "More Than A Century of Experience".

TERRY BLAMEY MANAGEMENT
PO Box 13196, London SW6 4WF
Tel: 020 7371 7627 Fax: 020 7731 7578
Email: alli@terryblamey.com
Agent: Terry Blamey

ARTISTES REPRESENTED:
Dani Minogue
Kylie Minogue

PAT TERRY ENTERTAINMENTS
24 Paddock Lane, Redditch,
Worcestershire B98 7XP
Tel: 01527 403 347 Fax: 01527 543 653
Senior Personnel: Pat Terry
Entertainment agency. Comedians, bands, discos, vocalists and many more...

TFA ARTISTE MANAGEMENT
40 Bowling Green Lane, Clerkenwell,
London EC1R 0NE
Tel: 020 7415 7070 Fax: 020 7415 7074
Email: tony@tfa-group.com
Web Site: www.tfa-group.com
Agent: Tony Fitzpatrick

ARTISTES REPRESENTED:
TV Presenters:
Tina Baker
Anne Diamond
Lotte Duncan
Rowena Johnson
Eric Lanlard
Diana Moran
Simon Rimmer
Julia Roberts
Sarah Walker

T.G.R. DIRECT ENTERTAINMENT AGENCY
88 Recreation Road Poole Dorset
BH12 2AL
Tel: 01202 721222 Fax: 01202 721802
Email: tatianaroc.tgrdirect@virgin.net
Managing Director: Tatiana Rocchiccioli
Representing dancers and vocalists.

THANK YOU FOR THE MUSIC LTD
200 London Road, Hadleigh, Benfleet,
Essex SS7 2PD
Tel: 01702 427 100 Fax: 01702 427 109
Email: michael@entertainers.co.uk
Web: www.thank-you-for-the-music.com
Agents: Michael Taylor, Leu Tucker
Entertainment agency/promoters.

THAT'S ENTERTAINMENT ASSOCIATES
Upham Hall, Green Lane, Kessingland,
Lowestoft, Suffolk NR33 7RP
Tel: 01502 742 011 Mob: 07970 421403
Email: kenny.cantor@virgin.net
Web: www.cantorstheatreschool.co.uk
Senior Personnel: Kenny Cantor
Supply, produce and direct various types of entertainment for holiday centres, cruise ships, etc.

ARTISTES REPRESENTED:
Kenny Cantor
Caron Heggie
Cedric Jemmett

THE ENTERTAINMENT CORPORATION
The Park, Oaksey, Malmesbury,
Wiltshire SN16 9SD
Tel: 01666 575 200 Fax: 01666 575 243
Email: admin@theentertainmentcorp.co.uk
Web Site: www.euroentcorp.co.uk
Presenting: The Moscow State Circus, The Chinese State Circus and Continental Circus Berlin.

ARTISTES REPRESENTED:
Continental Circus Berlin
The Chinese State Circus
Moscow State Circus

THE ELFIN NETWORK LLP T/A FIRST CONTACT AGENCY
Top Floor 206 Chalk Farm Road
Camden Lock LONDON NW1 8AB
Adam Elfin

THE ENTERTAINMENT AGENCY
Shoregate, Quayside,
Berwick-upon-Tweed TD15 1HE
Tel: 01289 330148 Fax: 01289 308408
Email:
malcolm@theentertainmentagency.co.uk
Web: www.theentertainmentagency.co.uk
Senior Personnel: Malcolm Murray & Elaine Murray

ARTISTES REPRESENTED:
2wice Nightley
4 For 1
Brenda Collins
Cosmos Cousins
Robbie Dale
Gary Dunn
Fever
Greggie G & Grazy Gang
Biby James Band
MInd The Gap
Planet X
Poison Ivy
Sahara
Splash
The Casino Band
Tracer
V
Waterfront
X Factor Tour

THE ENTERTAINMENT DEPARTMENT (UK) LTD
24 Titan Court Laporte Way
Luton LU4 8EF
Tel: 01582 488888
Email: steve.leatham@teduk.com
Web Site: www.teduk.com
Steve Leatham

THE FRASER LAWSON AGENCY
27 Heol y Delyn, Lisvane,
Cardiff CF14 0SR
Tel/ Fax: 02920 755020
Email: info@fraserlawson.co.uk
Web Site: www.fraserlawson.co.uk
Contact: Greg Lawson

THE ID AGENCY LTD
6 Paramount Court 41 University Street
LONDON WC1E 6JP
Tel: 0780 3581537
Email: info@theidagency.co.uk
Web Site: www.theidagency.co.uk
Barbara Adie

THE CHRIS LYNN AGENCY
17 Kimber Close Lancing, West Sussex
BN15 8QD
Tel/Fax: 01903 755 511
Tel: 07903 765 377
Email: chrislynn@btconnect.com
Contact: Jean Vallins

THE PRODUCTION SUITE LTD
11 Rydons Lane OLD COULSDON
CR5 1SU
Tel: 020 8407 2911
Email: agency@productionsuite.co.uk
Web Site: www.productionsuite.co.uk
Beverley Williams

THE SHOW TEAM PRODUCTIONS
36 Vine Street BRIGHTON BN1 4AG
Tel: 0845 467 1010
Email: andy@theshowteam.co.uk
Web Site: www.theshowteam.co.uk
Hannah Lee Weller

THE SPEAKERS AGENCY
3a High Street, Ibstock, Leicestershire
LE67 6LG
Tel: 01530 263221/267220
Fax: 01530 264018
Email: enquire@thespeakersagency.com
Web Site: www.thespeakersagency.com
ARTISTES REPRESENTED:
Moira Stewart

THE VILLAGE AGENCY LIMITED
43 Brook Green, London W6 7EF
Tel: 020 7734 5566 Fax: 020 7734 5553
Email: info@mvillage.co.uk,
paul@mvillage.co.uk
Web Site: www.thevillageagency.net
Contact: Paul Franklyn, Francesca Davies

THE YOUNG ACTORS THEATRE MANAGEMENT
70-72 Barnsbury Road, Islington,
London N1 0ES
Tel: 020 7278 2101 Fax: 020 7833 9467
Email: agent@yati.org.uk, info@yati.org.uk
Web Site: www.yati.org.uk
Contact: Dyana Daulby

THEOBALD DICKSON PRODUCTIONS
The Coach House, Swinhope Hall,
Swinhope, Market Rasen,
Lincolnshire LN8 6HT
Tel: 01472 399 011 Fax: 01472 399 025
Email: tdproductions@lineone.net
Senior Personnel: Bernard Theobald
Personal Management company.
ARTISTES REPRESENTED:
Barbara Dickson

THOMAS AND BENDA ASSOCIATION LTD
Flat 1, 15-16 Ivor Place,
London NW1 6HS
Fax: 020 7723 5509
Senior Personnel: Ann Thomas

THE IAN THOMAS ORGANISATION
Trevino, Halstead Drive, Menston, Ilkley,
West Yorkshire LS29 6AT
Tel: 01943 873364 Fax: 01943 877579
Mobile: 07768 296559
Email: itspeedway@aol.com
Web Site: www.it-org.co.uk
Proprietor: Ian Thomas
A company that provides both private and corporate entertainment indoors and outdoors, and also speciality acts on ice.
ARTISTES REPRESENTED:
Ray Allen
Richard Bott
Zac Cardelli
Arron Smith
Ian Thomas

JIM THOMPSON
Herricks, School Lane, Arundel,
West Sussex BN18 9DR
Tel: 01903 885 757 Fax: 01903 885 887
Email: jim@jthompson42.freeserve.co.uk
Specialising in Actors, Actresses, Presenters and Writers.

SYLVIA THORLEY ENTERTAINMENTS
2 Coastguard Cottages, Culver Down,
Sandown, PO36 8QT Isle of Wight
Tel: 01983 403583 Fax: 01983 402724
Email: roganddawn@btinternet.com
Senior Personnel: Roger Crawford, Dawn Crawford

THORNTON AGENCY
(For Dwarves, Midgets and Little People 5' and Under)
72 Purley Downs Road, South Croydon,
Surrey CR2 0RB
Tel/Fax: 020 8660 5588
Email: thorntons.leslie@tinyworld.co.uk
Web Site: www.dwarfs4hire.com
Senior Personnel: Leslie Collins

MELODY THRESH MANAGEMENT ASSOC LTD (MTM)
27 Ardwick Green North, Manchester
M12 6FZ
Tel: 0161 273 5445 Fax: 0161 273 5455
Email: melodythreshmtm@aol.com
Senior Personnel: Melody Thresh, Peter West
ARTISTES REPRESENTED:
From "Coronation Street":
Alan Halsall (Tyrone, Coronation Street)
Sally Lindsay
Ryan Thomas (Jason, Coronation Street)
Andrew Whyment (Kirk Coronation Street)
(P.A.'s)
From "24 Seven":
Sadie Pickering
From "Emmerdale":
Kelvin Fletcher
Charley Webb
From "Buried":
Smug Roberts

TICKETY BOO
2 Triq il-Barriera, Balzan BZN 06 Malta
Tel: 00 356 21 556 166
Fax: 00 356 2155 7316
Email: tickety-boo@tickety-boo.com
Web Site: www.tickety-boo.com
Senior Personnel: Steve Brown
ARTISTES REPRESENTED:
Billy Connolly
Pamela Stephenson

TICKLISH ALLSORTS
57 Victoria Road, Wilton, Salisbury
SP2 0DZ
Tel/Fax: 01722 744 949
Mob: 07721 992994
Email: garynunn@ntlworld.com
Web Site: www.ticklishallsorts.co.uk
Senior Personnel: Gary A Nunn
Childrens Entertainments, shows, puppets, musical comedy, workshops. Established 1981. Performances and workshops. RSPB National Touring Roadshows.

TIM RAFFLES ENTERTAINMENTS
Victoria House, 29 Swaythling Road,
West End, Southampton SO30 3AG
Tel/ Fax: 02380 465843
Mob: 07818 007109
Email: info@timrafflesentertainments.co.uk
Web: www.timrafflesentertainments.co.uk
Contact: Timothy Raffles

TIM SCOTT PERSONAL MANAGEMENT
284 Grays Inn Road, London WC1X 8EB
Tel: 020 7833 5733 / 020 7978 1358
Fax: 020 7278 9175
Mob: 07887 535 709
Email: timscott@btinternet.com
Agent: Tim Scott

TIME CONCERTS
Higher Bottoms, 4 Norbury Lane, Oldham, Lancashire OL8 2EW
Tel/Fax: 0161 633 3285
Email: chris@timeconcerts.co.uk
Senior Personnel: C Graham
ARTISTES REPRESENTED:
Bernard Manning
John Virgo
Graham (Grumbleweed) Walker
Janice Yorke

VICTORIA TINKER MANAGEMENT
Birchen Bridge House, Brighton Road, Mannings Heath, Horsham, West Sussex RH13 6HY
Tel/Fax: 01403 210 653
Email: victoriat@clara.co.uk
Specialising in Artistic Directors.
ARTISTES REPRESENTED:
Ken Caswell
Tony Edge
Dion McHugh

TLC CASTING LTD
4 Margaret Street, London W1W 8RF
Tel: 020 7436 7217 Fax: 020 7637 0816
Email: enquiries@tlccasting.com
Web Site: www.tlccasting.com
Senior Personnel: Tamsin Greet, Lindsey Hawkins
We specialise in booking celebrities for Advertising, PR and Corporate Events.

TMK MANAGEMENT AND AGENCY LIMITED
Musty Haulgh Farm, Granville Street, Briercliffe, Burnley, Lancashire BB10 2RA
Tel/Fax: 01282 831 325
Tel: 01282 456 467
Email: howardtmk@hotmail.co.uk
Web Site: www.tmkmanagement.com
Senior Personnel: Howard Uttley
ARTISTES REPRESENTED:
Debra Allan
Bernie
Paul Conner
Billy Dean (Elvis)
Dynamix
Face For Radio
Lynne George
Helen Claire
In 2 Deep
Lee Jaxon
Phillippa Lyons
Richard Muller
Mystery Machine
Gary Owen
Ritcie Penrose
Jo Jo Savage
Monty Scott
Shaan
Tameka
Vortex

TO HELL & BACK
Mob: 07941 197913
Email: meatloaf@meatloaf.org, dean.torkington1@btinternet.com
Web Site: www.meatloaf.org
Contact: Dean Torkington
Meat Loaf Tribute Band.

WARREN TOLLEY PRODUCTIONS LTD
59 Heron Way, Herons Reach, Blackpool, Lancashire FY3 8FA
Tel/Fax: 01253 399 114
Mobile: 07850 502001
Email: warren.tolley@virgin.net
Web: www.warrentolleyproductions.co.uk
Senior Personnel: Warren Tolley

TOM & LYNNE IVERS ENTERTAINMENTS
East Lynne Harpers Green Road Doe Hey BOLTON BL4 7HT
Tel: 01204 796 003
Email: tomandlynneivers@btinternet.com
Tome Ivers FEAA

TOMMY DEE ENTERTAINMENTS LTD
19 Kingswear Drive, Broughton, Milton Keynes MK10 9NZ
Tel: 01908 239088 Fax: 01908 239590
Email: tommy@tommydeeentertainments.com
Web: www.tommydeeentertainments.com
Contact: Thomas Taylor-Dowson

TONY BARRIE ASSOCIATES LTD
149 Kingfisher Drive, Merrow Park, Guildford, Surrey GU4 7EY
Tel/Fax: 01483 502 687
Mob: 07771 767 537
Contact: Tony Barrie
General entertainment agency.

TONY SMITH PERSONAL MANAGEMENT
55 Fulham High Street, London SW6 3JJ
Tel: 020 7384 8990 Fax: 020 7384 8994
Email: carol@ts-pm.com
Artist Manager: Carol Willis
ARTISTES REPRESENTED:
Nick Mason (Pink Floyd)
Genesis
Phil Collins
Mike & The Mechanics
Tony Banks

TOP HAT ENTERTAINMENTS
PO Box 7289, West Bromwich B71 1RA
Tel/Fax: 0121 588 6801 Mobile: 07775 623738 / 07773 149467
Email: kj58@vodafone.net
Senior Personnel: Kevin Jones
Specialising in all types of corporate entertainment: Soap stars, After Dinner Speakers, DJ's, Themed Events, Ladies Nights. Promotion staff, Models, Lookalikes. Everything for your entertainment needs.

TOP TALENT AGENCY
"Jason" Yester Road, Chislehurst, Kent BR7 5HN
Tel/Fax: 020 8467 0808
Email: top.talent.agency@virgin.net
Senior Personnel: John Day, Rita Day
General entertainment agency specialising in package shows. Cabaret, dance, bands, etc...

TOTS - TWENTIES
62 Buntingbridge Road, Ilford, Essex IG2 7LR
Tel: 020 8518 0200 Fax: 020 8518 0212
Mobile: 07702 031519
Email: sara@tots-twenties.co.uk
Web Site: www.tots-twenties.co.uk
Contact: Zena Zelique

TRACEY CHAPMAN
PO Box 50445, London W8 9BE
Tel: 020 8870 6303 Mob: 07803 082 443
Email: tracechapman@btinternet.com
Contact: Tracey Chapman
ARTISTES REPRESENTED:
Piers Morgan
Anne Robinson

TRADING FACES LTD
47 Dean Street, London W1D 5BE
Tel: 020 7287 0866 Fax: 0870 512 912
Email: enquiries@tradingfaces.co.uk
Web Site: www.tradingfaces.co.uk
Senior Personnel: Michelle Fowler, Vicki Michelle, Ann Michelle, Suzie Michelle
ARTISTES REPRESENTED:
Lord Ashdown
Michael Ball
Sue Barker OBE
Lord Patten of Barnes
Baroness Tanni Grey-Thompson
Chris Beardshaw
Chris Biggins
Brian Blessed
Sir Chris Bonington CBE
Jeremy Bowen
Bradley Wiggins
Karren Brady
Jeff Brazier
Rory Bremner
Derren Brown
Rob Brydon
James Caan
Alistair Campbell
Alan Carr

Jimmy Carr
Todd Carty
Alan Chambers
Adrian Chiles
Lord Sebastian Coe
Jon Culshaw
Gino D'Acampo
Lawrence Dallaglio
Frankie Dettori
Diversity
Jenny Eclair
Jennifer Ellison
Sir Ranulph Fiennes Bt OBE
Freddie Flintoff
Ben Fogle
Kate Garraway
Diarmuid Gavin
Edward 'Bear' Grylls
Nicky Hambleton-Jones
Ken Hames
Alison Hammond
Alan Hansen
Damon Hill OBE
Jools Holland
Eamonn Holmes
Dame Kelly Holmes
Colin Jackson CBE
Katherine Jenkins
Michael Johnson
Lord Digby Jones
Lorraine Kelly
Ross Kemp
Myleene Klass
Hardeep Singh-Kohli
Sally Lindsay
Gary Lineker OBE
Ken Livingstone
Laurence Llewelyn-Bowen
Sean Lock
Dame Ellen MacArthur
Lee Mack
Sir John Major
Peter Mandelson
Andrew Marr
James Martin
Davina McCall
Sir Trevor McDonald
Barry McGuigan MBE
Michael McIntyre
David Miliband MP
Chris Moon
Dermot Murnaghan
James Nesbitt
Flt. Lt. John Nichol
Mary Nightingale
Coleen Nolan
Jean Christophe Novelli
Dermot O'Leary
Jamie Oliver
Only Men Aloud
Patsy Palmer
Bruce Parry
Jeremy Paxman
Rupert Penry-Jones
Fiona Phillips
Jonathon Porritt
Michael Portillo
Gordon Ramsay
Sir Steven Redgrave CBE
Philip Schofield
Joe Simpson
John Simpson CBE
Sir Chris Hoy
Sir Ian Botham
Sir Matthew Pinsent
Debra Stephenson
Alistair Stewart
Alan Titchmarsh
Sam Torrance
Victoria Pendleton
Gok Wan
Ruby Wax
Denise Welch
Jack Whitehall
Anthony Worrall Thompson

TRANSART (UK) LTD

Cedar House, 10 Rutland Street, Filey, North Yorkshire YO14 9JB
Tel: 01723 515 819 Fax: 01723 514 678
Email: transartuk@transartuk.com
Web Site: www.transartuk.com
TransArt (UK) is a concert agency which represents, manages and promotes international classical musicians, both in the UK and throughout the world.

ARTISTES REPRESENTED:

Piano:
Nicholas Angelich
Giovanni Bellucci
Lazar Berman
Pietro de Maria
Jerome Ducros
Abdel Rahman El Bacha
Brigitte Engerer
Vladimir Feltsman
Bruno Leonardo Gelbar
Pascal Godart
Peter Katin
Cyprien Katsaris
Adrienne Krausz
Konstantin Lifschitz
Emile Naoumoff
Georges Pludermacher
Bruno Rigutto
Vladimir Viardo
Lilya Ziberstein
Organ:
Marie-Claire Alain
Violin:
Olivier Charlier
David Grimal
Alexander Markov
Josef Suk
Viola:
Miguel Da Silva
Cello:
Alexander Baillie
Anner Byslma
Henri Demarquette
Matt Haimovitz
Jerome Pernoo
Mstislav Rostropovich
Guitar:
John McLaughlin (classical)
Filomena Moretti
Conductors:
Christine Badea
Gabriel Chmura
James DePreist
Hiroyuki Iwaki
Karl Anton Rickenbacher
Yutaka Sado
Claudio Scimone
Jerzy Semkow
Michael Stern
David Wroe
Trio:
L'Archibudelli
Quartet:
Arpeggione Quartet
Violin & Piano:
Charlier/Engerer
Cello & Piano:
Pernoo/Ducros
Double Bass:
Marc Marder
Harp:
Marielle Nordmann
Clarinet:
Florent Heau
Horn:
Eric Ruske
Soprano:
Wilhelmenia Fernandez
Katarina Jovanovic
Françoise Pollet
Chamber Orchestra:
European Camerata
Wind Quartet:
Le Concert Impromptu

TRENDS AGENCY & MANAGEMENT LTD

Sullom Lodge, Sullom Side Lane, Barnacre, Preston PR3 1GH
Tel: 0871 200 3343 Fax: 01253 407 715
Email: info@trendsgroup.co.uk
Web Site: www.trendsgroup.co.uk
Senior Personnel: Antony Johns, Representing: Dougie Squires, Antony Johns, Patti Boulaye, Actors, Dancers, Singers, Directors, Choreographers.

TRIBUTE ENTERTAINMENT LTD

Unity House, 2 Unity Place, Rotherham, South Yorkshire S60 1AR
Tel: 01709 820379 Fax: 01709 369990
Email: tributebands@btconnect.com
Web: www.tribute-entertainment.co.uk
Contact: Tony French

TRINIFOLD MANAGEMENT

3rd Floor, 12 Oval Road, London NW1 7DH
Tel: 020 7419 4300 Fax: 020 7419 4325
Email: jane@judaspriest.com
Agent: Jane Andrews

ARTISTES REPRESENTED:

Judas Priest
Robert Plant
The Who

TRIPLE A MEDIA

30 Great Portland Street, London W1W 8QU
Tel/ Fax: 020 7738 0257
Tel: 020 33704988
Email: andy@tripleamedia.com, info@tripleamedia.com
Web Site: www.tripleamedia.com
Contact: Andy Hipkiss

TRIPLE CREAM ENTERTAINMENTS

38 Coombewood Drive, Benfleet, Essex SS7 3EA
Tel: 01268 566 991 Fax: 01268 566 992
Mobile: 07768 665646
Email: davekbrock@hotmail.com, info@triplecream.com
Web Site: www.triplecream.com
Senior Personnel: Dave Brock, Ruth Brock
General entertainment agency.

ARTISTES REPRESENTED:

Baby Go Boom
Adger Brown
Johnny Cassidy
Keith "The Thief" Charnley
Johnny Clark
Crisco
Escada
Joe Goodman
Terry Herbert
Ian Irving (Comedian)
Jimmy Jones
Lew Lewis
Wally Mardell
Mad Mark Peters
Steve Rawlings
Ian Richards
Triple Cream
Barry Williams

TROIKA TALENT

3rd Floor 74 Clerkenwell Road London EC1M 5QA
Tel: 020 7336 7868 Fax: 020 7490 7642
Email: helen@troikatalent.com / carl@troikatalent.com
Web Site: www.troikatalent.com
Agents: Conor McCaughan, Michael Duff, Melanie Rockcliffe

ARTISTES REPRESENTED:

Represented by Michael Duff::
Holly Aird
Amelia Bullmore
Nichola Burley
Pip Carter
Dan Clark
Nathan Constance
Joe Dempsie
Shaun Dingwall
Nicholas Gleaves
Keeley Hawes
Lena Headey
Paul Higgins
Ronny Jhutti
Sandra Jordan
Paul Keating
Joan Kempson
Lyndsey Marshal
Colm Meaney
Carol Morley
James Murray
Daniela Nardini
Craig Parkinson
Maxine Peake
Olivia Poulet
Melvil Poupaud
Kelly Reilly
Finlay Robertson
Claire Rushbrook
Nick Sidi
Juno Temple
Andrew Tiernan
Jack Whitehall
Represented by Conor McCaughan::
Paul Bettany
Andrew Birkin
Tom Burke
Paddy Considine
Richard Coyle
Alan Cumming
Michael Fassbender
Lucy Holt
Rachel Hurd-Wood
Daniel Kaluuya
James Lance
Susan Lynch
Simon McBurney
Celia Meiras
David Morrissey
Peter Serafinowicz
Rafe Spall
Ulrich Thomsen
David Walliams
Represented by Melanie Rockcliffe::
Jo Caulfield
Mark Chapman
Nina Conti
Sara Cox
Kevin Day
Emma B
Max Flint
Philipa Fordham
John Hegley
Simon Lipson
Matt Lucas
Fred MacAulay
Kate Marlow
Richard McCourt
Graham Norton
Christopher Parker
Caroline Reid
Griff Rhys Jones
Gaby Roslin
Arthur Smith
Jim Sweeney
Kate Thornton
Dom Wood

TROPICAL ENTERTAINMENTS MANAGEMENT AGENCY

34 Crest Road, London NW2 7LX
Tel: 020 8450 2084 Fax: 0870 706 4524
Email: enquiries@tropical-ents.co.uk
Web Site: www.tropical-ents.co.uk
Senior Personnel: Paul Cherrie
Specialising in world music, particularly Caribbean, Latin and African Music.

ARTISTES REPRESENTED:

Caché
Kaiso
Palenké
Rio Latino Dancers
Solid Steel
Trenchtown Experience (Bob Marley & The Wailers tribute)
Tropical Storm
Uthingo
Viramundo

TOMMY TUCKER AGENCY

Suite 66, 235 Earls Court Road, London SW5 9FE
Tel: 020 7370 3911
Email: TTTommytucker@aol.com
Senior Personnel: Tommy Tucker
Dance agency.

ARTISTES REPRESENTED:

Choreographers:
Sandy Borne
Kirsty Davide
Nicky Hinkley
Simon Shelton
+ 300 Dancers:

BILL TURNER MANAGEMENT

140 Beckett Road, Doncaster, South Yorkshire DN2 4BA
Tel: 01302 367 495 Fax: 01302 321 978
Email: bill@btmanagementuk.com

TWENTY-FIRST ARTISTS LTD

1 Blythe Road, London W14 0HG
Tel: 0207 348 4800
Email: info@wabbie.com
Contact: Anna Collins

ARTISTES REPRESENTED:

James Blunt
Sir Elton John

UBEEM (UNCLE BRIAN'S ENTERTAINMENT & EVENTS MANAGEMENT)

Burwell House, Folkton, Scarborough, North Yorkshire YO11 3UH
Tel: 01723 891 441
Mobile: 07801 969464
Email: s.reidfrow@btinternet.com
Web Site: www.ubeem.com
Senior Personnel: David Reid-Frow
Bands, catering, clown, car, disco, stilt-walkers, face painters, magicians, marquees and Punch & Judy.

UGLY MODELS

Tigris House, 256 Edgware Road, London W2 1DS
Tel: 020 7402 5564 Fax: 020 7402 0507
Email: info@ugly.org, coxy@ugly.org
Web Site: www.ugly.org
Senior Personnel: Marc French
Specialising in Character Models/Actors

UK BOOKING AGENCY

170 Domonic Drive, London SE9 3LE
Tel/Fax: 020 8857 8775
Email: stevegoddard@aol.com
Senior Personnel: Steve Goddard
We are a 'one-stop' organisation, piecing together a personal or total event package of ARTISTES and PROVISIONS. Working together with its sister company, 'Label Spinners', who organise the bookings of Artistes for personal or total event packages, from nightclubs to festivals. Specialising in booking events for universities, and artistes primarily DJs, Live

Bands and PAs.

ARTISTES REPRESENTED:

House & Trance:
Bah Samba (UK Live P.A.)
Disco Darlings (Duo or Single)
DJ Gregory (France)
DJ Yellow (France)
Terry Farley
Flaunt-It Party Nights
Steve "Good" Goddard (Soul & Funk)
Alex Gold
Hed Kandi Party Nights
Hoxton Whores (duo or single)
Jakatta
Kinky Malinky Party Nights
K-Klass
Laura V. (Live P.A. 'Changes' by Chris Lake)
Masters At Work (Kenny Dope Gonzales or Little Louie Vega - rarely together)
Joey Negro
Plush Da Funk Party Nights
Red Velvet Party Nights
Tony Richardson (Tony 'R' - Red Velvet resident)
Jim "Shaft" Ryan
Soul Avengerz
Soul Seekers (Duo)
Darren Tate
Steve Thomas
Jurgen Vries

Hard House & Hard Trance:
Billy (Daniel) Bunter
Marc French
Marshall Jefferson
Terry Marks
Slipmatt
Rob Tissera (Quake)

Hardbag (Hard House):
Billy (Daniel) Bunter
Marc French
Super Fast Oz
Steve Thomas

Techno & Tech-House:
Dave Angel
Tom Baker
Nathan Coles (wiggle)
Terry Francis (wiggle - Resident, Fabric, London)
Marshall Jefferson
Lulu
Jim Masters (Bass resident)
Derrick May (USA)
Darren Pearce (Peach - London)
Trevor Rockliffe
Brenda Russell (Bass resident)
Daz Saund
Craig Walsh

Old Skool Hardcore:
Altern 8 (Duo) - DJ & P.A
Aphrodite
DJ Vibes & Mc Lively
Mickey Finn
Jason Kaye (Top Buzz)
Ratpack (Duo)
DJ SY & MC Storm
Trubalsom
SL2 (Slipmatt, John Lime & MC Jay Jay)
Barney B (Pure X)

Old Skool UK Garage:
Booker T
Brasstooth
Karl "Tuff Enuff" Brown
DJ Face
DJ Ride
Scott Garcia
Hermit
Jason Kaye (Top Buzz)
Martin Larner
Mike "Ruffcut" Lloyd
Timmy Magic (Dream Team)
Master Stepz
Grant Nelson
Pied Piper
Ramsey & Fen
Mickey Simms
Daniel Ward
Norris "Da Boss" Windross

UK Garage:
Zed Bias
Karl "Tuff Enuff" Brown
DJ Luck
Ez
Scott Garcia
Jamieson
Jason Kaye (Top Buzz)
Mike "Ruffcut" Lloyd
Timmy Magic (Dream Team)
Master Stepz
Mikee B (Dream Team)
Pied Piper
Daniel Ward
Norris "Da Boss" Windross

Party & Personality:
Big Al
Larry Foster
Darren James
Alan Jones
Tony Pedra
Mike Steel
Terry Jones (Southport Weekender)

RNB/Hip-Hop/Soul:
Aitch B (Soul II Soul)
Bigger (Solar Radio)
Car Wash Party Nights (The Original)
Gary Dennis (Southport Weekender)
Gary Dennis (Southport Weekender)
DJ Swerve
Greg Edwards (Jazz FM)
Greg Edwards (Jazz FM)
Firin' Squad (Kiss FM)
Steve "Good" Goddard (Soul & Funk)
Ronnie Herel (Radio 1)
Chris Hill (Caister Soul Weekender/Lacy Lady)
Chris Hill (Caister Soul Weekender/Lacy Lady)
Scott James
Norman Jay (The Legend)
Jazzie B (Soul II Soul)
Terry Jones (Southport Weekender)
Tony Monson (Solar Radio)
Trevor Nelson
Rampage (BBC Radio London)
Shortee Blitz
Starlight Crew (Southport Weekender - RNB)
Stretch Taylor (Blues & Soul)

UK LIVE ENTERTAINMENT

18 Stane Grove, London SW9 9AL
Tel: 0845 873 3116 Fax: 02476 714095
Email: admin@studio1.co.uk
Web Site: www.studio1.co.uk
Contact: Grant Wadey
Coventry Office: 16 Koco Building, Arches Ind' Est', Spon End
Coventry, CV1 3JQ

ULTIMATE INTERNATIONAL

Atlas House, London Road, Hindhead, Surrey GU26 6AB
Tel: 01428 606 566 Fax: 01428 606 141
Email: info@partyplannersuk.com
Web Site: www.partyplannersuk.com
Senior Personnel: David L Starr

ARTISTES REPRESENTED:

Illusionists:
Phoenix
Pure Magic (Antonio Zambaldi)

Bands:
Academy
Basin Street
Bronx
Charade
Co-Stars
FBI
Louisiana Jazzmen
Louiza Friday Quartet
Mask
Mirror Image
Mission Blue
Musik Express
Odyssey 2000
Panama Cafe Orchestra
Piazza
Plutonics
Prestige
Sister Act
Sounds Easy
Spice
Spooky Big Sound
Superphonic

Instrumentals:
Blue Room Jazz
Jones & Co
Claire Madin (pianist)
Natalia Rogers (harpist)
Salieri Strings

Vocalists:
David Allacey (Sinatra)
Dawn Allacey
Charlene
Graham Hunter
Alan Mann
Will Rawlings (The Swing Years)

Comedians:
Kev Duncan (Comedy)
Tony Gerrard
Stuart Masters
Miles McKoy

Speciality Acts:
007 Casinos & Race Nights
Guy Carter (Caricaturist & Silhouettes)
Ray Cooper (Close Up Magic)
Mr Signature Man
Mark Tabbener
Tony Zambardi (Close Up Magic)

Presenters:
Ian Royce

Tributes:
David Allacey (Sinatra)
Elvis Himselvis
Gobbie Williams

The Rat Pack is Back
Impressionists:
Ken Duncan
Ventriloquists:
Paul Dumas
Hypnotists:
Chris Hare
Mickey Take

UNDERBELLY MANAGEMENT

83 Charlotte Street, London W1T 4PR
Tel: 0207 580 0154 Fax: 0207 580 0155
Mobile: 07787 517 060
Email: martyne@underbelly.co.uk
Web Site: www.underbelly.co.uk
Director: Ben Vincent
For Booking queries, contact: Martyne Green

ARTISTES REPRESENTED:

Musicians:
Carol (The Lady In The Moon)
Comedy Acts:
Fullmooners
Various:
Aaron Berg
Terry Clement
Jim Jeffries
Brian Lazanik
Papa CJ
Al Pitcher
Silky

UNIQUE ENTERTAINMENT UK

500 Chiswick High Road, Chiswick, London W4 5RG
Tel: 020 8987 8887 Fax: 020 8987 8886
Email: trevor@unique-entertainment.co.uk
Web: www.unique-entertainment.co.uk
Senior Personnel: Trevor Hamilton

UNIT ONE ENTERTAINMENT

Kings House, South King Street, Eccles, Manchester M30 8PH
Tel: 0161 7888444 Fax: 0161 7888555
Email: steve@unitoneentertainment.co.uk
Web: www.unitoneentertainment.co.uk
Bookings Officer: Steven Sayle
General entertainment and corporate agency.

UNITED AGENTS

12-26 Lexington Street, London W1F 0LE
Tel: 020 3214 0800 Fax: 020 3214 0801
Email: info@unitedagents.co.uk
Web Site: www.unitedagents.co.uk
Agents: Duncan Hayes, Ruth Young, Anthony Jones, Rosemary Scoular, Sean Gascoine, Maureen Vincent, Dallas Smith, Duncan Millership, Charles Walker, Lindy King, Rosemary Canter

ARTISTES REPRESENTED:

Jane Asher
Stephanie Beacham
Alan Bennett
Sanjeev Bhaskar
Raymond Blanc
Charley Boorman
Rob Brydon
Leslie Caron
Natalie Cassidy
Nick Cave
Craig Charles
James Corden
Richard Curtis
David Dimbleby
Jason Donovan
Tara Fitzgerald
Dawn French
Ricky Gervais
Clare Grogan
Susan Hampshire
Nigel Harman
Jane Horrocks
Kate Humble
Ruth Jones
Kate Winslet
Patsy Kensit
Keira Knightley
Kwame Kwei-Armah
Leigh Lawson
Louise Lombard
Zoe Lucker
Art Malik
Miriam Margoyles OBE
Sharon Maughan
Ewan McGregor
Gina McKee
Lee Mead
Stephen Merchant
Sienna Miller
Denise Van Outen
Roger Lloyd Pack
Elaine Paige
Nigel Planer
Lynn Redgrave
Eric Richard
Jennifer Saunders
Nadia Sawalha
Simon Schama
Victoria Smurfit
Dan Snow
Alison Steadman
Meera Syal
Sandi Toksvig
Ruby Wax
Colin Welland
June Whitfield
Sophie Winkleman
Susannah York
Benjamin Zephaniah

MEL UNSWORTH AGENCY

Eden House, 52 Bede Burn Road, Jarrow, Tyne and Wear NE32 5AS
Tel: 0191 489 3114 Fax: 0191 428 6547
Email: joanneunsworth@hotmail.com
Agent: Joanne Unsworth
Representing theatrical performers.

UPBEAT CLASSICAL MANAGEMENT

PO Box 479, Uxbridge, Middlesex UB8 2ZH
Tel: 01895 259 441 Fax: 01895 259 341
Email: info@upbeatclassical.co.uk
Web Site: www.upbeatclassical.co.uk
Management of concerts, special projects and artists including: Musical Classical, Early Music, World Music and Crossover.

ARTISTES REPRESENTED:

Piano:
Jeremy Menuhin
Violin:
Leland Chen
Viola:
Yuko Inoue
Guitar:
Carlos Bonell
Recorder:
Piers Adams
Conductor:
Stephen Bell
Ariel Zuckerman
Ensembles:
The Barkham Harp Quartet (4 Girls/4 harps)
David Rees-Williams Trio
St Petersburg String Quartet
Wihan String Quartet
Early Music:
The Clerks' Group
Red Priest
The Dufay Collective
Klezmer/Worldmusic:
The World Quintet (FKA Kol Simcha) (Klezmer band)

UPBEAT MANAGEMENT

Larg House Woodcote Grove, Coulsdon, Surrey CR5 2QQ
Tel: 020 8668 3332 Fax: 020 8668 3922
Email: info@upbeat.co.uk
Web Site: www.upbeat.co.uk
Senior Personnel (Entertainment): Liz Biddle, Beryl Korman
Specialising in Theatre Touring and large events for Festivals and corporate entertainment.

ARTISTES REPRESENTED:

Touring Shows:
Blake
Celtic Tenors
Ellington sings Ellington - featuring Lance Ellington
Forces Sweethearts (40's Nostalgia)
Forces Sweethearts at Christmas
In the Mood - With Five Star Swing
The Last Night at the Proms (Orchestral)
Libera
The London Community Gospel Choir
Olde Tyme Music Hall
Elio Pace
Pack Up Your Troubles (Singalong programme)
The Pasadena Roof Orchestra
Swing 'n' Sinatra
The Organist Entertains
Those Were the Days - With Rosemary Squires
Tribute Bands On Tour:
The Cavern Beatles
The Commitments
The Sensations (Tamla Motown/The Supremes tribute)
Stoned Again
Jazz Bands On Tour:
Kenny Ball & His Jazzmen
Five Star Swing
John Petters and his Rhythm
Bob Kerr's Whoopee Band (Jazz &

Comedy)
The New Squadronaires Orchestra
The Temperance Seven
The Glenn Miller Orchestra UK
The Glenn Miller Tribute Orchestra
The Ken Colyer Legacy New Orleans Jazz Band
The Pete Allen Jazz Band

UPFRONT ENTERTAINMENT AGENCY LIMITED

Unit 8-9, MCF Complex, New Road, Kidderminster, Worcestershire DY10 1AQ
Tel: 01562 69433 / 66350 Fax: 01562 69136
Email: brianupfront@aol.com
Web: www.upfrontentertainments.com
Contact: Brian Davies

ARTISTES REPRESENTED:

Tribute Artistes/Bands:
Abba Now
Darren Alboni as Simply Red
Marcus Andrew (Elton John)
Ballroom Glitz
Samantha Hill (Blondie)
Bootleg Bee Gees
Niqi Brown (Tina Turner)
Brian Collins (Van Morrison)
The Commitments
Sonia Dawn as Karen Carpenter
Dave Dean (Andy Williams)
Diamond Blues Brothers
John Ellis (Elton John)
Fake Bee Gees
Grease Is The Word
Ollie Hughes (Robbie Williams)
Kings Of Queen (Queen tribute)
Mike Lewis (Rolf Harris)
Bobby Memphis (Elvis)
Mersey Beatles
Mission Blue (Tamla Motown tribute)
Tracy Quinn (Madonna)
Tony Scarth (Tom Jones)
Sensations (Tamla Motown)
Sounds Of The Beachboys
The Royal Blues Brothers
Want You Back (Take That)
Peter White (Kenny Rogers)
Lookalikes:
Pauline Bailey (Marilyn Monroe)
Mark Billingham (Dame Edna Everidge)
Sue Bradbury as Ab Fab's Patsy
Maurice Canham is Del Boy
Stefan Feix (Del Boy)
Ron Fythe (Pierce Brosnan)
Andy Harmon (David Beckham)
Ray James (Alf Garnett)
Barbara Kealy (Joan Collins)
Mike Lewis (Rolf Harris)
The Rolf & Edna Show
Steve Rooney (Del Boy)
Meyrick Sheen (Jack Nicholson)
Tom Skehan (Tony Blair)

URBAN ASSOCIATES PERSONAL MANAGEMENT & PUBLIC RELATIONS

44 Montpelier Grove London NW5 2XG
Tel/Fax: 020 7482 1039
Email: urbanpr@aol.com
Web Site: www.theurbanassociates.com
Agents: Neil Howarth and Amanda Beckman

ARTISTES REPRESENTED:

Stephanie Beacham
Gaynor Faye
Claire King
Michelle King
Coleen Nolan
The Nolans
Claire Richards
Lisa Scott-Lee
Adele Silva
Gillian Taylforth
Denise Welch
Danniella Westbrook

URBAN TALENT

Nemesis House, 1 Oxford Court, Manchester M2 3WQ
Tel: 0161 228 6866 Fax: 0161 228 6727
Email: liz@nmsmanagement.co.uk
Web Site: www.urbantalent.tv
Senior Personnel: Liz Beeley
Represent actors and actresses.

ARTISTES REPRESENTED:

Barney Marwood

USP ARTISTES

24 Newman Street, London W1T 1AW
Tel: 0207 927 6600 Fax: 0207 927 6601
Email: dan@usp-group.com
Web Site: www.usp-group.com
Artistes Manager: Dan Green

ARTISTES REPRESENTED:

Radio Presenters:
Chris Brooks
Lisa Burke
David Croft
Guy Harris
Steve Harris
Christian O'Connell
Toni Phillips
Holly Samos
Tony Wrightson
Voiceover Artistes:
Ian Camfield
Daryl Denham
Justin Wilkes
Steve Wylie

ROXANE VACCA MANAGEMENT

73 Beak Street, London W1F 9SR
Tel: 020 7734 8085 Fax: 020 7734 8086
Email: roxane@roxanevacca.com
Web: www.Roxanevaccamanagement.com
Senior Personnel: Roxane Vacca

VALUE ADDED TALENT AGENCY (VAT)

1 Purley Place, London N1 1QA
Tel: 020 7704 9720 Fax: 020 7226 6135
Email: dan@vathq.co.uk
Web Site: www.vathq.co.uk
Senior Personnel: Dan Silver

ARTISTES REPRESENTED:

Alabama 3
DJ Paul Hartnoll
DJ Phil Hartnoll
Orbital
Silent Disco
Sparks
Warren Suicide
System 7 featuring Steve Hillage
The Larry Loveband

DENIS VAUGHAN MANAGEMENT

PO Box 2826, London N21 3WT
Tel: 020 7486 5353 Fax: 020 8224 0466
Email: dvaughanmusic@dial.pipex.com
Senior Personnel: Denis Vaughan

ARTISTES REPRESENTED:

A.B.C
Ace
Cheryl Baker
Bananarama
Chuck Berry
Frances Black
Boogie Brothers
Jose Carreras
Celtic Tenors
Chaka Khan
Chic
Petula Clark
Richard Clayderman
Bo Derek
Donovan
Ronnie Drew
Fairport Convention
Kelly Family
The Fureys
Gipsy Kings
Kid Creole & the Coconuts
Little Richard
Manhattan Transfer
Sergio Mendes & Brasil 2000
Nana Mouskouri
Chris Norman
Jessye Norman
Alexander O'Neal
Osibisa
Pointer Sisters
Demis Roussos
Jimmy Ruffin
Peter Sarstedt
Leo Sayer
Brendan Shine
Sister Sledge
Alan Stivell
Take Six
The Troggs
Village People
Dionne Warwick

VELRAG ARTS

Velrag House, 8 The Grange, Packington, Leicestershire LE65 1WW
Tel: 01530 415 152 Fax: 01530 412 931
Email: dave@velrag.co.uk
Web Site: www.velrag.co.uk
Contact: David Ismay
Corporate events - Golf days a speciality.

ARTISTES REPRESENTED:

Steve Cunningham
Dave Ismay
Don MacLean MBE

CLARE VIDAL-HALL

57 Carthew Road, London W6 0DU
Tel: 020 8741 7647 Fax: 020 8741 9459
Email: cvh@clarevidalhall.com
Web Site: www.clarevidalhall.com
Managing Director: Clare Vidal-Hall

ARTISTES REPRESENTED:

Theatre Directors:
Tim Baker
Karen Bruce
Jennie Darnell
John Doyle
Patricia Doyle
Jonathan Munby
Erica Whyman
Philip Wilson
Lighting Designers:
Jeanine Davies
Philip Gladwell
Mark Jonathan
Paul Keogan
Tina MacHugh
Tim Mitchell
Ben Ormerod
Bruno Poet
Malcolm Rippeth
Johanna Town
Choreographers:
Karen Bruce
Scarlett Mackmin
Designers (Film & TV):
John Ellis
Ian Fisher
Theatre Designers:
Mark Bailey
Patrick Connellan
David Farley
Kate Hawley (Costumes)
Anthony Lamble
Stephen Brimson Lewis
Niki Turner
Paul Wills
Matthew Wright
Composers/Musical Directors:
Steven Edis
Costume Designers (Film & TV):
Eric Doughney
Kate Hawley (Costumes)
Chris Marlowe

MICHAEL VINE ASSOCIATES

1 Stormont Road, London N6 4NS
Tel: 020 8347 2580
Email: info@michaelvineassociates.com
Web: www.michaelvineassociates.com
Senior Personnel: Michael Vine, Stephen Vine

ARTISTES REPRESENTED:

Christopher Caress
The Casablanca Steps
Bernie Clifton
Sally Franklyn
Luke Jermay
Lawrence Leyton
Andrew O'Connor
Sooty with Richard Cadell, Sweep and Soo
Adrian Walsh
Alan Wightman
Worbey and Farrell
In assocaiation with:
Objective Talent Management:
Barry & Stuart
Derren Brown
Pete Firman

VISCOUNT ENTERTAINMENTS

Brookdale House, 46 Kingfisher Avenue, Audenshaw, Manchester
Greater Manchester M34 5QH
Tel: 08450 170 819 Mob: 07794 051732
Email: viscountagency@btconnect.com
Web: www.viscountentertainment.co.uk
Contact: David Sands
Specialising in Children and Street Entertainers.

ARTISTES REPRESENTED:

Artemis UK
Marc Bant
Calvero
Carnival Carl
Caught In The Act Circus Workshop
Creature Features
Dance Fusion
Grand Theatre of Lemmings
Laurel and Hardy
Louby Lou
Pik and Mix Circus
Barrington Powell
Prixton Puppets
Professor Nik Nak
Brett Sirrell
Slim and Slam
Trumble
Ken Walmsley Punch and Judy

VITAL EDGE ARTIST AGENCY

PO Box 25965, London N18 1YT
Tel/Fax: 0870 350 1045
Email: info@vitaledgeagency.com
Web Site: www.vitaledgeagency.com
Contact: Mickey Jackson
Vital Edge are booking agents specialising in UK Garage, R&B DJs, MCs and live PAs, featuring a wide range of the top and most popular names throughout this music genre. Club tours featuring some of the best established UK promotions are also available, as are a selection of UK R&B artists.

THE VOICE BOX AGENCY LTD

1st Floor 100 Talbot Road, Old Trafford, Manchester M16 0PG
Tel: 0161 874 5741 Fax: 0161 888 2242
Email: elinors@thevoicebox.co.uk
Web Site: www.thevoicebox.co.uk
Contact: Elinor Stanton
Agency which represent voice-over artistes only.

ARTISTES REPRESENTED:

Ladies:
Sophie Allisstone
Robin Brunskill
Katrina Buchanan
Leah Charles
Leslie Churchill Ward
Jayne Dowell
Brigit Forsyth
Elaine Hill
Jenny Hull
Gloria Hunniford
Georgina Hunter
Janet James
Lorelei King
Anji Kreft
Marjorie Lofthouse
Maggie Mash
Diana Mather
Adrienne Posta
Sue Robbie
Joanna Ruiz
Gentlemen:
Allan Bardsley
Andrew Brittain
Paul Brown
Tom Clarke-Hill
John Craven OBE
Kieran Cunningham
Robin Galloway
Taff Girdlestone
Paul Guthrie
John Harrison
Martin Henfield
Chris Hopkins
Joe Mills
Martin Oldfield
Rob Rackstraw
Mark Radcliffe
Pete Reeves
Marc Silk
Phil Walker

VOICE SHOP

1st Floor, 1a Devonshire Road, London W4 2EU
Tel: 020 8742 7077 Fax: 020 8742 7011
Email: info@voice-shop.co.uk
Web Site: www.voice-shop.co.uk
Senior Personnel: Maxine Wiltshire
Voice-over and casting agency.

ARTISTES REPRESENTED:

Jimmy Akingbola
Ronni Ancona
Deborah Berlin
Martin Bishop
Kellie Bright
Glynis Brooks
Ray Brooks
Dylan Charles
Bernard Cribbins
Jon Culshaw
Joel Cutrara
Peter Dickson
James Faulkner
Jeremy Finch
Sally Grace
Jeffrey Holland
David Holt
Mitch Johnson
Eamonn Kelly
Stephen Kemble
Christopher Kent
Dean Kilbey
Baylen Leonard
Andy Mace
Georgia Mackenzie
Eve Matheson
Michael McClain
Kate McGoldrick
Aundrea Minto

Anna Naples
Mark Oxtoby
Davina Palmer
Tom Rivers
Liza Ross
Chris Sandford
Jamie Sandford
Jill Shilling
Melissa Sinden
Marc Smith
Luis Soto
Ken Stott
Sonya Vine
Keith Washington
Tracy Wiles

VRM ARTISTS
Laser House Waterfront Quay
Salford Quays Manchester M50 3XW
Tel: 0161 874 5741 Fax: 0161 888 2242
Email: elinors@thevoicebox.co.uk
Web Site: www.thevoicebox.co.uk
Contact: Elinor Stanton
Agency which represents presenters for corporate video, conferences and broadcast TV.
ARTISTES REPRESENTED:
Andrew Brittain
Tom Clarke-Hill
Brigit Forsyth
Robin Galloway
Philip Hayton
Martin Henfield
Georgina Hunter
Jeanette Lanz Bergin
Peter McCann
Nick Owen
Dianne Oxberry
Sue Robbie
Mark Simpkin

W M PRO ENTERTAINMENT AGENCY LIMITED
20 Bilsdale Way, Baildon, West Yorkshire BD17 5DG
Tel: 01274 589 854 / 580537
Fax: 01274 588 764
Email: wass@wm-pro.com
Web Site: www.wm-pro.com
Contact: Wassef Massaad
Specialises in music management

GINGER WALKER AGENCY
14 Gooding Rise, Tiverton, Devon EX16 5BX
Tel: 01884 256 389 / 0870 383 1988
Email: gingerwalker@eclipse.co.uk
Web Site: www.GingerWalker.co.uk
Senior Personnel: Ginger Walker, Sue Walker, Karen Cottrelt
ARTISTES REPRESENTED:
Elizabeth Jane Baldry
David Copperfield
Fifth Avenue
Geneva
Karisma
Les Martin Band
David Merlin (Magician)
Night Magic
On the Beach
Phoenix
Shannon & Co
Up 4 Grabs

WALKER PROMOTIONS
53 Ravensworth Road, Dunston, Gateshead, Tyne and Wear NE11 9AB
Tel: 0191 460 3030 Fax: 0191 4600 721
Mobile: 07836 531 929
Senior Personnel: D Weelock
ARTISTES REPRESENTED:
'Lucky' Jim Fallon

ALAN WALTERS MANAGEMENT
16 Davidia Court, Jasmin Grove, Waterlooville, Hampshire PO7 8BL
Tel: 023 9261 0405 Fax: 023 9243 0403
Email: awmanagement@aol.com
Senior Personnel: Alan Walters
General entertainment agency.
ARTISTES REPRESENTED:
John Burns
Checkers
Disco Services
Easy Living
Alan Mann
Moonlight
Paul Smith (disco entertainer)
Keith Venn

WAR ZONES
33 Kersley Road, London N16 0NT
Tel: 020 7249 2894 Fax: 020 7254 3729
Email: wz33@aol.com
Senior Personnel: Richard Hermitage
ARTISTES REPRESENTED:
Art Brut
Frank Black
Steel Pulse
The Wannadies

WARING & MCKENNA
11-12 Dover Street, Mayfair, London W1S 4LJ
Tel: 020 7629 6444 Fax: 020 7629 6466
Email: dj@waringandmckenna.com
Web Site: www.waringandmckenna.com
Senior Personnel: Daphne Waring, John Summerfield
ARTISTES REPRESENTED:
Laurie Brett
Wendy Craig
Ricky Groves
Zoie Kennedy
Robyn Page
David Spinx
Colin Tarrant

WARNER MUSIC & ENTERTAINMENTS (UK)
58 Withcote Avenue, Leicester LE5 6ST
Tel/ Fax: 0116 241 4067
Email: wmeukents@aol.com, info@warnermusic-ents.co.uk
Web Site: www.warnermusic-ents.com
Contact: Alan Warner
Specialising in theatres, clubs and cruising. Also Personal Management.

WAS/IS MANAGEMENT LTD
40 Ball Road, Malin Bridge, Sheffield, South Yorkshire S6 4LZ
Tel: 0114 281 9475 Fax: 0114 220 5445
Mob: 07725 571 570
Email: info@wasismanagement.com
Web Site: www.wasismanagement.com
Contact: Neil Tomlinson
General music entertainment agency, specialising on quirky and more unusual bands.

WAYNE DENTON ASSOCIATES LTD
4 Matthews Close, Rowley Regis, West Midlands B65 0AW
Tel/ Fax: 01216012808
Email: wayne@waynedenton.com, info@waynedenton.com
Web Site: www.waynedenton.com
Contact: Wayne Denton, Claire-Marie Swain, Jenny Lenton

JANET WELCH PERSONAL MANAGEMENT
Old Orchard, The Street, Ubley, Bristol BS40 6PJ
Tel/Fax: 0870 850 8874
Email: info@janetwelchpm.co.uk
Senior Personnel: Janet Welch
Specialising in Actors/Actresses

WELLIE BOOT PRODUCTIONS
P.O. Box 332, Rochdale, Lancashire OL12 7WD
Tel: 01706 353545 Fax: 01706 353545
Email: dale.mulgrew@zen.co.uk, jimmy@jimmycricket.co.uk
Web Site: www.jimmycricket.co.uk
Manager: Jimmy Cricket
Contact: Dale Mulgrew
Wellie Boot Productions is the ever popular Irish comedian Jimmy Cricket's entertainment Company. And There's More: We have many exciting shows and products featuring Jimmy on offer across all event platforms and we can provide creative solutions for your entertainment requirements.

WESSEX ENTERTAINMENTS
Ash Ponds, Lower Chillington, Ilminster, Somerset TA19 0PU
Tel/Fax: 01460 52109
Email: wessex.wessex@virgin.net
Web: www.wessexentertainments.co.uk
Senior Personnel: Paul Roberts, Alastair Cobb
General entertainment agency.
ARTISTES REPRESENTED:
Steve Finn
Barry Paull (as Elvis)
Pondlife - Function Band
Paul Roberts (pianist/organist)

WEST CENTRAL MANAGEMENT

4 East Block, Panther House,
38 Mount Pleasant, London WC1X 0AN
Tel/Fax: 020 7833 8134
Email: mail@westcentralmanagement.co.uk
Web: www.westcentralmanagement.co.uk
Contact: Leigh Kelly, Josh Darcy
Actors Co-operative agency.

ARTISTES REPRESENTED:

Cristina Contes
Rob Crompton
Josh Darcy
Adrian Deasley
Lizzy Dive
Matthew Eggleton
Uriel Emil
Miles Gallant
Malcolm Gerard
Leigh Kelly
Sue Maund
Caroline Olsson
David Richter
Lisa Rose
Charlotte Thompson
Jennifer Thorne
Jeremy Tiang
Katie Ventress
Melissa Woodbridge

WEST END THEATRICAL AGENCY

PO Box 634 Newcastle Tyne and Wear
NE5 9AU
Tel: 0191 268 4617
Email: info@westendagency.biz
Senior Personnel: John Thompson

JASON WEST AGENCY

Gables House, Saddlebow, King's Lynn,
Norfolk PE34 3AR
Tel: 01553 617 586 (3 Lines)
Fax: 01553 617 734
Email: info@jasonwest.com
Senior Personnel: Jason West

ARTISTES REPRESENTED:

Hit Recording Artistes:
Bad Manners featuring Buster Bloodvessel
The Barron Knights
BC Sweet
The Beat
Eric Bell Band
Cliff Bennett and the Rebel Rousers
Dave Berry & The Cruisers
Blackfoot Sue
The Blockheads
Liz Mitchell's Boney M
Brotherhood of Man
Miquel Brown
Christie
John Coghlans Quo
Jess Conrad
Clem Curtis & the Foundations
Billy Davis
Hazell Dean
Kiki Dee and Carmelo Luggeri
Desmond Dekker & The Aces
Gwen Dickeys Rose Royce
Doctor & the Medics
Dozy Beaky Mick & Tich
Eddie and the Hotrods
Edison Lighthouse
Eruption feat Precious Wilson
Fairport Convention
Fine Young Cannibals
Wayne Fontana and the Mindbenders
The Foundations
The Four Pennies
Dean Friedman
Steve Gibbons Band
Gidea Park (Beach Boys tribute)
The Glitter Band
Gonzalez
Jaki Graham
The Groundhogs
Herman's Hermits
Eddie Holman
Imagination
The Ivy League
Jimmy James & The Vagabonds
Mungo Jerry
The Jets
Wilko Johnson Band
Katrina Leskanich
Kursaal Flyers
Limahl
Limmie & Family Cookin
Love Affair
Kelly Marie
The Marvelette Revue
Middle Of The Road featuring Sally Carr
Mixtures
Modern Romance
Musical Youth
The New Seekers
New Tight Fit
Odyssey
Osibisa
Paper Lace
Billy Paul
Pickettywitch
The Pirates
Brian Poole & Electrix
Prince Buster
The Quarrymen
Racey
The Rah Band
The Rockin' Berries
The Rubettes
Jimmy Ruffin
Peter Sarstedt
The Selecter featuring Pauline Black
Sham 69
Showaddywaddy
Snowy White
The Strawbs
Hamish Stuart Band
Tavares
Thunderclap Newman
The Undertakers
Vanity Fare (ex-chart band)
Roy Wood's Army
By Arrangement With Respective Agents:
Apache Indian
Pato Banton
Elkie Brooks
Arthur Brown
The Commitments
Haddaway
Nazareth
Alexander O'Neal
Mica Paris
Heather Small
The Christians
T'Pau
ABC
The American Drifters
The Animals
Baccara
Bay City Rollers
The Bhundu Boys
Black Lace
Joycelyn Brown
Bucks Fizz
Eric Burden
Change
China Crisis
Con & Dec - The Batchelors
Doctor Feelgood
Dr Hook featuring Ray (Eye Patch) Sawyer
The Drifters
Chris Farlowe and The Norman Beaker Band
Gibson Brothers
Go West including Peter Cox
Peter Green Splinter Group
Tony Hadley
Heatwave
Heaven 17
Hot Chocolate
Human League
Howard Jones
Nik Kershaw
Kid Creole & the Coconuts
Kool & The Gang
Los Pacaminos feat Paul Young
The Manfreds
Marmalade
George McCrae
Merseybeats
Nolans
Hazel O'Connor
Ottowan
John Otway
The Pasadenas
Mike Pender's Searchers
Dawn Penn
Alan Price
Procol Harum
Suzi Quatro
Eddi Reader
Real Thing
Martha Reeves And The Vandellas
Santa Esmeralda & Leroy Gomez
Shakatak
Shalamar
The Sounds Of The Supremes featuring Kaaren Ragland
Space
The Supremes
Sweet
James Taylor Quartet
Temptations Review With Dennis Edwards
Kenny Thomas
Three Degrees
The Tremeloes
Ruby Turner
Bonnie Tyler
Midge Ure
Wishbone Ash
The Yardbirds
Paul Young

Zion Train
Zoot Money
Tributes:
12 Quo Bars (Status Quo)
3D
8 Tiz
80's Phantazie
Abacus
Abba Angels
Abba Babes
Abba Dream
The Abba Experience
Abba Forever
Abba Girls
Abba Rival
Abbamania
Abbamax
Abbasolutely Live
AC/DO (AC/DC tribute)
Atomic Blondie
Kate Axten (Shania Twain)
The Backbeat Beatles
Ballroom Glitz
The Bandit Beatles
Beachboys Inc
The Beached Boys
The 'B'Eagles (The Eagles tribute)
Beatels (Beatles)
The Beatless
The Beautiful Southmartins
Bee Gees - The Tribute
Bee Gees Fever
The Beetles - UK
Belooshi Blues Brothers
Be*Witched
The Bleach (Blondie tribute)
Blonde and Beyond (Blondie tribute)
Blondied (Blondie tribute)
Blues Brothers Connection
The Bogus Blues Brothers
The Bohemians (Queen tribute)
The Boogie Blues Brothers
Boogie Nights
Boogie Wonderland
Bootleg Beach Boys
Bootleg Beatles
Bootleg Bee Gees
Bootleg Slade
The Booze Brothers
The Briefcase Blues Brothers
The British Blues Brothers
Brothers Grimm
The Carpenters Experience
Carpenters Gold
Carwash
The Cavern Beatles
The Cheatles (The Beatles)
Cheeky Monkees
The Clashed (The Clash)
Closet Queen
Cocker Power (Joe Cocker tribute)
Complete Madness
Complete Stone Roses
Corrz
The Counterfeit Beatles
Dancing Queen (Abba)
Deliciously Dusty (Dusty Springfield tribute)
The Doors Are Open (Doors tribute)
The Double Diamond Blues Brothers
Ego A Go Go (Robbie Williams tribute)
Peter Elliot as George Michael, Stevie Wonder
Experienced (Jimi Hendrix tribute)
The Fab Four (The Beatles)
Feverish
Flairz
Fleetwood Bac
The Flirtations
Food Fighters (The Foo Fighters tribute)
Forge Michael (George Michael tribute)
Fragile (Yes Tribute)
Free Again (Free tribute)
Free At Last (Free)
Fresh Creem
The Funking Barstewards
Get Down On It
Godfatha (James Brown tribute)
Greased Lightning
Great Britney
Jimi Hendrix Tribute "Purple Haze"
John Henry (Frank Sinatra)
Buddy Holly & the Crickhits
In4XS
The Jamm
Mikki Jay (Michael Jackson)
Jean Genie (David Bowie tribute)
The J.Lo Show (Jennifer Lopez tribute)
KC and the Soul Revue
A Kick Up The 80's
Kinky (Kinks tribute)
Ky-Lee (Kylie Minogue)
The League (Human League tribute)
Robert Leslie (Neil Diamond)
Liberty Mountain (Elvis tribute)
Limehouse Lizzy (Thin Lizzy tribute)
Limpish Bizkit (Limp Bizkit)
Live Rust (Neil Young tribute)
Los Palmas Six (Madness tribute)
The Ludwig Beatles
M People Experience
The Machine (Pink Floyd)
Meatloaf 2
The Mersey Beatles
The Mimic Street Preachers
Mission Blue (Tamla Motown tribute)
Money 4 Nothing (Dire Straits)
Milli Munro (Shirley Bassey, Tina Turner, Whitney Houston)
Natural Wonder (Stevie Wonder tribute)
Mike Nelson as Bryan Ferry
The New Age Jam (The Jam tribute)
Night Fever
Numanesque (Gary Numan tribute)
Oasisn't (Oasis Tribute)
Okasis (Oasis tribute)
Once More Into the Bleach (Blondie)
One Night In Heaven
One Step Behind (Madness tribute)
Orange Alert (Stranglers Tribute)
The Other Commitments
Peatloaf
Phoney Beatles
The Photofit Police
Pink Fraud
Planet Pop
The Platforms
The Police Fraud Squad
Pretend Pretenders
Prince Buster Tribute Band
Pulse
QEII (Queen tribute)
Queen B (Queen tribute)
Queen on Fire (Queen tribute)
Quicksilver
Rats In The Kitchen (UB40 Tribute)
The Real Abba Gold
Reckless (Bryan Adams tribute)
Robbie's Angels (Robbie Williams tribute)
The Rolling Clones
The Rolling Tones
Carolyn Rowe (Dame Shirley Bassey)
S Club Heaven
Sabbath Bloody Sabbath
Salute The Supremes
Shadivarius - The Cliff and The Shadows Tribute Show
Shania (Shania Twain tribute)
Sharp Dressed Man (ZZ Top tribute)
Tracey Shields (Celine Dion)
Ann Shirley as Diana Ross
Kennie Simon (Errol Brown)
The Skatones (Madness tribute)
So Young (The Corrs tribute)
S.O.S. (Abba tribute)
Sound of the Suburbs
Sounds of The Blues Brothers
Southside
Spicey Girls
Stairway to Zeppelin
Status Clone (Status Quo Tribute)
Status Duo
Status Quid
Phil Steed (Tom Jones)
Stink 182
Stoned Again
The Strolling Bones
Super Troupers (Abba tribute)
Supernatural (Santana)
The Sus Sex Pistols
Swede Dreams (Abba)
T-Rextasy
Tamla Motion
Taste of Honey (Bee Gees Tribute)
Texus (Texas)
The Red Hot Silli Feckers
Think Floyd
Three B's (Tribute to the Bee Gees)
Tim Torode (Marc Bolan)
Toxic Twins (Aerosmith)
Trenchtown Experience (Bob Marley & The Wailers tribute)
UB4T
Uncovered (The Blues Brothers, The Commitments)
Upbeat Beatles
UU2
Vann The Mann
Vengaboyz
Village Boyz (Village People tribute)
Voulez Vous (Abba Tribute Show)
The Wanna Bee Gees
Westlives
Whole Lotta Led (Led Zeppelin)
Wizzards Of Ozz (Ozzy Osbourne tribute)
Cover Bands:
Atlantic Soul Machine
Below Average White Band
Big Macs Wholly Soul Band
The Boogie Brothers (Blues Brothers)
Eazy Street
Evening Mist
The Flying Emperors
Funk Soul Brothers
Funky Divas
Groovejuice

Hardcopy
Live
Mix'T Nutz
Monkhouse
MoonDance
Musik Express
Red Hot & Blue Orchestra
Red Roc & The Doctors Of Swing
The Sharp Cuts
Skyline
Space Boogie
Spice (MOR/Function Band)
Stax of Soul
Thumpasaurus
Uncovered (The Blues Brothers, The Commitments)
Upside Down
Venus
Vinyl Kutz
Zambu
Dance Bands & Orchestras:
The Casablanca Steps
The Grahamophones
The Pasadena Roof Orchestra
The Piccadilly Dance Orchestra
Shindig

TONY WEST ENTERTAINMENTS

PO Box 25, Formby, Liverpool,
Merseyside L38 0DA
Tel: 0151 929 2727 Fax: 0151 929 3030
Email: barbara@tonywestents.co.uk
Web Site: www.tonywestents.co.uk
Senior Personnel: Anthony West FEAA, Sheilagh O'Rourke, Barbara Brown
Suppliers of: Comedians, Vocalists, Speciality Acts, Tribute Acts, Showgroups, Musical and Multi Instrumental Artistes and Musicians.

ARTISTES REPRESENTED:

Colin Areety
Ban Buren and Co
Alan Black
Al Brown
Tony Brutus & Amanda
Bob Carolgees
Chimes Two
Christian
Donimo
Andy Eastwood
Paul Emmanuel
Kyle Esplin
John Evans
Four Past Midnight
Gordon Hopwood
Inspiration
Bobby Kaye
Latin Magic
Andy Leach
Lynx
Asa Murphy
Tom Pepper
Peter Price
Tracey Quinn
Tim Raffles & Co
Regency Duo
Don Reid
Jimmy Tamley
Tensai
Van Buren & Company
Duggie Webb
Sandi West
Kevin Whay

WESTEND EVENTS LTD

61-63 Great Queen Street, London
WC2B 5DA
Tel: 020 7404 4232 Fax: 020 7405 8405
Email: info@westendevents.co.uk
Web Site: www.westendevents.co.uk
Managing Director: Russell Davey
Specialises in organising parties , Murder Mystery Weekends and tribute nights.

WHAT MANAGEMENT

3 Belfry Villas, Belfry Avenue, Harefield,
Middlesex UB9 6HY
Tel: 01895 824 674 Fax: 01895 822 994
Mobile: 07860 590 190
Email: whatmanagement@blueyonder.co.uk
Senior Personnel: Mick Cater

ARTISTES REPRESENTED:

Carl Carlton & The Song Dogs
Los Pacaminos
Temposharks
Paul Young

WHATEVER ARTISTS MANAGEMENT LTD

F24 Argo House, Kilburn Park Road,
London NW6 5LF
Tel: 020 7372 4777 Fax: 020 7372 5111
Email: info@wamshow.biz
Web Site: www.wamshow.biz
Senior Personnel: Jenny Dunster
All types of entertainers booked for corporate and private events with full technical on-site management services.

ARTISTES REPRESENTED:

Magic:
Tariq Knight
Laura London
Richard McDougall
Nigel Mead
Nigel Mead
Peter Mehtab
Fay Presto
Romany
The Magic Waiters
Troy Von Majik
Ben Woodward
Dance:
Anton Du Beke and Erin Boag
Cuban Groove
Cuban Groove Latin Dance Company
Dance Rocks
Las Vegas Showgirls
Chris Marques & Jaclyn Spencer
Simply Ballroom
Solaris Snake Dancer
Tziganka - Russian Cossack Music & Dance Spectacular
Music:
China Grove
Covent Garden String Quartet
Kiki Dee
Iestyn Edwards
Festive Mibely
Jazz Functionaires
Jane McDonald
Mugenkyo Japanese Drummers
Ooh Baby Ooh
Oyster Opera
Penthouse
The Penthouse Experience
Perfectly Frank
Quiet Nights
Rat Pack Live from Las Vegas
Royal Philharmonic Concert Orchestra
Solid Steel
Star
Status Cymbal
String Diva Electric Violin Show
The Maida Vale Singers
The Three Waiters
Tziganka - Russian Cossack Music & Dance Spectacular
Andy Wood (Ricky Martin, Tom Jones, Michael Bolton)
Cabaret from the theatre:
Cuban Groove Latin Dance Company
Simply Ballroom
Toss
Comedy and Speciality:
Duo Du Sol - Acrobatic Duo
Entwine (Aerial Act as Seen on BBC1)
Gandini Juggling Project
Hui Ling's Chinese Circus
Judge The Poet
Men in Coats
Mimeworks
Mat Ricardo
Paul Zenon
Paul Zerdin
Modern Circus and Walkabout:
Anonymous
Chinese Circus
Duo Du Sol - Acrobatic Duo
Entwine (Aerial Act as Seen on BBC1)
Gandini Juggling Project
Hui Ling's Chinese Circus
Ian Marchant
Jason Maverick
Stewart Pemberton - Stage Juggler
Scarabeus
Scorch Ra - Fire and Juggling
Andy Sinclair - mime
The Wrong Size Stiltwalkers
Titan
Toss
Tuyo - Hand Balancers
Viva - Aerial Act

LAWRENCE WHEELER AGENCY LIMITED

59 Vicarage Farm Road, Wellingborough,
Northamptonshire NN8 5EU
Tel: 0870 4215366 / 67 Fax: 01933 385 351 Tel: 0870 4215366 / 67
Email: lwagency@ntlworld.com
Contact: James Honour

MICHAEL WHITEHALL

10 Lower Common South, London
SW15 1BP
Tel: 020 8785 3737 Fax: 020 8788 2340
Email: mwhitehall@email.emerson.com

ARTISTES REPRESENTED:

Jack Davenport

Leslie Grantham
Richard Griffiths

ALAN WHITEHEAD MANAGEMENT LTD

51 Chambers Grove Welwyn Garden City Hertfordshire AL7 4FG
Mob: 07957 358997 Fax: 01707 267 247
Email: alan_whitehead_uk@yahoo.com
Senior Personnel: Alan Whitehead
Specialising in management for the music industry, singers (male/female), groups etc.

ARTISTES REPRESENTED:
Kelly's Heroes
The Kit-Kat Dolls (Transexual Group)

WIENERWALD ENTERTAINMENTS

52 Helen Avenue, Feltham, Middlesex TW14 9LB
Tel/Fax: 020 8751 0417
Email: nrgft@hotmail.com
Senior Personnel: Keith Harmon
Specialising in Ethnic Acts, Classical Music and Motivational Speakers.

ARTISTES REPRESENTED:
Coco Express
Flamenco Fiesta
Japanesque
Kabbala
Katari Group
Merengada
The Mugenkyo Taiko Drummers

WIGAN PIER PROMOTIONS

PO Box 428, Wigan, Lancashire WN1 2ZP
Tel/Fax: 01257 251 908
Mob: 07989 614999
Email: anne.carlin1@btinternet.com
Web: www.wiganpierpromotions.co.uk
Senior Personnel: Anne Hurcombe
Entertainment supplier and events organiser. Solo, duos, trios, tributes, speciality acts, children's entertainment, DJs and comedians.

ARTISTES REPRESENTED:

MARTY WILDE PRODUCTIONS LTD

Thatched Rest, Queen Hoo Lane, Tewin, Hertfordshire AL6 0LT
Tel/Fax: 01438 798 395
Email: joyce@bigmgroup.freeserve.co.uk
Web Site: www.martywilde.com
Contact: Joyce Wilde

ARTISTES REPRESENTED:
Marty Wilde

WILIAMSON & HOLMES

9 Hop Gardens, St Martin's Lane, London WC2N 4EH
Tel: 020 7240 0407 Fax: 020 7240 0408
Email: jackie@williamsonandholmes.co.uk
Web: www.williamsonandholmes.co.uk
For actors and general enquiries, contact: Jackie Williamson
For all voice enquiries, contact: Sophie Reisch - sophie@williamsonandholmes.co.uk
For all children enquiries, contact: Danica Pickett
Williamson & Holmes represent actors in film, television, theatre, musical theatre, commercial and corporate work

DAVID WILKINSON ASSOCIATES

Wants to be contacted by existing clients only.
115 Hazlebury Road, London SW6 2LX
Tel: 020 7371 5188 Fax: 020 7371 5161
Email: info@dwassociates.net

ARTISTES REPRESENTED:
John Cameron
John Cleese
Chris Langham
John Morton
Arthur Robins
Susan Stranks

JOHN WILLCOCKS MEDIA AGENCY LTD

34 Carisbrooke Close, Enfield, Middlesex EN1 3NB
Tel: 020 8364 4556 Fax: 020 8292 5060
Mobile: 07710 295 586
Email: john.willcocks@blueyonder.co.uk
Senior Personnel: John Willcocks

WILLIAM MORRIS ENDEAVOR ENTERTAINMENT (UK) LTD

Centre Point, 103 New Oxford Street, London WC1A 1DD
Tel: 020 7534 6800 Fax: 020 7534 6900
Email: ccovington@wma.com
Web Site: www.wma.com
Contact: Cathie Covington

WILLOW PERSONAL MANAGEMENT

151 Main Street, Yaxley, Peterborough, Cambridgeshire PE7 3LD
Tel/Fax: 01733 240 392
Tel: 0700 900 945569
Email: pb@willowmanagement.co.uk
Web Site: www.willowmanagement.co.uk
Managing Director: Peter Burroughs
Specialist agency representing short actors from 3ft to 5ft tall.

NEWTON WILLS MANAGEMENT

The Studios, 29 Springvale Avenue, Brentford, Middlesex TW8 9QH
Mob: 07989 398 381
Email: newtoncttg@aol.com
Senior Personnel: Newton Wills, Christopher Socci

ARTISTES REPRESENTED:
Emile Andre Armstrong
Craig Ashley
Simon Brignull
James Cohan
Lauren Collins
Kelly Edwards
Ivan De Freitas
Paul Huntley-Thomas
Stuart Innes
Allan Jay
Therese Kesington
Myron Mckay
Rebecca Ostman
Christopher Palmer
Claire Phillips
Hannah Prince
Steven Ritchie
Morgan Roberts
Pearl Scott
Stuart Sumner
Stephanie Tavernier
Gemma West
Chris Wood

ALAN WILSON MANAGEMENT

29 Brunswick, Bracknell, Berkshire RG12 7YY
Tel/Fax: 01344 459 187
Mobile: 07774 810357
Email: alan@planet-marmalade.co.uk
Web Site: www.planet-marmalade.co.uk
Senior Personnel: Alan Wilson

ARTISTES REPRESENTED:
The 60's Storybook Show (with Dave Dee, Chip Hawkes, Mike D'Abo)
Marmalade

ALLAN WILSON ENTERPRISES

Queens House, Chapel Green Road, Hindley, Wigan, Lancashire WN2 3LL
Tel: 01942 258 565
Tel/Fax: 01942 255 158
Email: allan@allanwilson.co.uk
Senior Personnel: Allan Wilson

ARTISTES REPRESENTED:
David Franks
Mike Lester
Ray Marvin
Tony Stuart
Mike Watkins

WIM WIGT PRODUCTIONS LTD

98 Arundel Avenue, South Croydon, Surrey CR2 8BE
Tel: 0208 662 1235 Fax: 0208 654 2120
Email: info@wigt.nl
Web Site: www.wimwigt.com
Director, Sales, Bookings: Wim Wigt
Advertising, Promotion, Financial Administration : Herma Lueks

ARTISTES REPRESENTED:
Exclusive Worldwide:
The Big Chris Barber Band
Dutch Swing College Band (NL)
Traditional Jazz / Dixieland:
John Crocker Quartet (UK)
Down Town Jazzbnad (NL)
Fessor Big City Band (DK)
Doc Houlind & His Copenhagen Ragtime Orchestra (DK)
Huub Janssen's Amazing Jazzband (NL)
Jumpin' Jive (NL)
Oscar Klein, Romano Mussolini, Charlie

Antolini (A/CH/IT/G)
Rod Mason Hot Five (UK/G)
Midlife Revival Band (NL)
Papa Bue's Viking Jazzband (DK)
Prowizorka Jazzband (PL)
Stable Roof Jazzband (NL)
Storyville Jazzband (NL)
The Timeless Orchestra
Uralsky All Stars (Russ)
Swing, Jazz, Show & Dance:
Alice in Dixieland (NL)
The Budapest Ragtime Orchestra (H)
Handsome Harry Company (NL)
Jumpin' Jive (NL)
Sascha Klaar
Les Haricots Rouges (F)
Hazy Osterwald & Engelbert Wrobel's Swing Society (CH/G)
Titanic Ensemble (B)
Engelbert Wrobel's Swing Society (G)
Blues:
Sydney Ellis & her Yes Mama Band (USA)
Mojo Blues Band (A)
The John Slaughter Rhythm & Blues Band (UK)
Vocalists:
Angela Brown (USA)
Deborah Brown (USA)
Deborah J Carter (USA)
Eriko Ishihara (vocalist / pianist)
Diana Perez (USA)
Vandoorn Duo & Trio (NL)
Fay Victor (USA)
Zydeco:
Captain Gumbo (NL)
Argentinian:
Daniel Diaz
Gypsy Jazz & Swing:
Fapy Lapertin Trio (NL)
Capellino (NL)
Royal Gipsy Orchestra Roma Mirando Jnr
The Rosenberg Trio
Gospel:
The Jackson Singers (USA)
The Johnny Thompson Singers (USA)
Sydney Ellis & her Yes Mama Band (USA)
Lillian Boutte & her Music Friends
Mainstream Jazz:
John Crocker Quartet (UK)
Barbara Dennerlein
Lou Donaldson Quartet
Johnny Griffin
Archie Shepp Quartet
Archie Shepp & Jasper van't Hoff Duo
Shows:
Fire of Dance
Flames of the Dance
Highlights of Musicals
The Johann Strauss Gala

WINCHESTER ENTERTAINMENT

20 Greensmeade, Woodfalls, Salisbury, Wiltshire SP5 2NL
Tel/Fax: 01725 513487
Email: mail@winchester-entertainment.co.uk
Web: www.winchester-entertainment.co.uk
Senior Personnel: Keith Howard

ARTISTES REPRESENTED:

Mr Sketchum's Caricatures

DAVE WINSLETT ASSOCIATES

4 Zig Zag Road, Kenley, Surrey CR8 5EL
Tel: 020 8668 0531 Fax: 020 8668 9216
Email: info@davewinslett.com
Web Site: www.davewinslett.com
Senior Personnel: Dave Winslett FEAA

ARTISTES REPRESENTED:

Kate Bellingham
The Tony Charles Steel Band
Judith Hann
Monaco String Quartet
Maggie Philbin
Select Syncopators
Howard Stableford
Russ Stevens

WISE BUDDAH TALENT & VOICES

74 Great Titchfield Street, London W1W 7QP
Tel: 020 7307 1600 Fax: 020 7307 1601
Email: chris.north@wisebuddah.com / john.lawley@wisebuddah.com
Web Site: www.wisebuddah.com
Agent: Chris North

ARTISTES REPRESENTED:

Wise Buddah Talent:
Vicki Blight
Robin Burke
Mark Goodier
Simon Grant
Kevin Greening
Kevin Greening
Jon Hillcock
Greg James
Andy Jaye
Kam Kelly
Allan Lake
Steve Lamacq
Yannick Lawry
Nick Luscombe
Scott Mills
Nigell Mitchell
Michelle Mullane
Dave Pearce
Philippa T-J
Selena
Steve Smart
Christian Stevenson
Nick Wallis
Luke Wilkins
1:
Jim Davis
Mark Goodier
Kevin Greening
Gavin Inskip
Andy Jaye
Rebecca Jensen
Katherine Kingsley
Dave Pearce
Natasha Powell
Oli Smith
Christian Stevenson
Glyn Williams

WIZARDRY ENTERTAINMENTS LTD

Suite 3, 375 Chorley Road, Swinton, Manchester M27 6AY
Tel: 0161 728 5507 Fax: 0161 728 5509
Web Site: www.wizardry.co.uk
Contact: Carl Royle
Specialists in Corporate and Wedding Entertainment.

WOMENSPEAKERS.CO.UK

3a High Street, Ibstock, Leicestershire LE67 6LG
Tel: 01530 263221 Fax: 01530 264018
Email: info@womenspeakers.co.uk
Web Site: www.womenspeakers.co.uk
Managing Director: Sylvia Tidy-Harris
Agency which represents all women speakers from all walks of life

ARTISTES REPRESENTED:

Jane McDonald
Valerie Singleton

ALAN WOOD AGENCY

346 Gleadless Road, Sheffield, S2 3AJ
Tel: 0114 258 0338 Fax: 0114 258 0638
Email: alanwoodagency@aol.com
Web Site: www.alanwoodagency.co.uk
Contact: Alan Wood

ARTISTES REPRESENTED:

Paul Carrack

DAVE WOODBURY ENTERTAINMENTS

51 New Road, Bournemouth, Dorset BH10 7DP
Tel: 01202 576 633
Web Site: www.kissogram.it
Senior Personnel: Dave Woodbury
Specialising in stag & hen package shows, strippers, kissograms.

ARTISTES REPRESENTED:

Ladies:
Cherry B
Billie
Claire
Courtenay
Danielle
Sammy Dee
Elizabeth
Emmie
Frenchie
Gilly
Jenny
Kooki
Leanne
Lisa
Lucy
Martini
Dutch Michelle
Minx
Morgan
Mouse
Natasha
Sammy
Shona
Tammy Jo
Tina
Trinity
Trixie
Gentlemen:
Black Magic
Blade
Blaze

Buddy Brown
Chico
Dark Angel
Devon
Diablo
French Kiss
Heart Throb
Jay
Kane
King Shaft
Leo
Little Devil
Mac
Mr Tease
Paul Grant
Phoenix
Private 69
Rawhide
Rough Stuff
Smooth Rider
Jason Storm
Taurus
Wanderer

WORKSHOP NETWORK

Mercury House,
Shipstones Business Centre, Northgate,
Nottingham NG7 7FN
Tel: 08700 600 264 (Mon-Fri 9am - 5pm)
Tel: 07845 270 735 (after hours)
Email: info@workshopnetwork.co.uk
Web Site: www.workshopnetwork.co.uk
Business Development Manager: Gary Cicinskas
Finance Manager: Bronis Cicinskas
Administration: Amber Townshend
Workshop Network is an excellent, easy to use on-line service for those looking to book freelance creative workshop facilitators. Our workshop artists have had a minimum of three years workshop experience. Please visit our website for more information on all our artists.

WORLD OF FANTASY

(Swansflight Prods Ltd)
48 Uxbridge Road, Hampton, Middlesex TW12 3AD
Tel: 020 8941 1595 Fax: 020 8783 1366
Email: swansflight@aol.com
Web Site: www.swansflight.com
Managing Director: Sheila Denton de Gray
Company Secretary: Alan Flyng
Specialising in jousting, indoor themed events, outdoor entertainment and costume hire.

THE EDWARD WYMAN AGENCY

67 Llanon Road, Llanishen, Cardiff,
South Glamorgan CF14 5AH Wales
Tel: 029 2075 2351 Fax: 029 2075 2444
Email: edward.wyman@btconnect.com
Web Site: www.wymancasting.co.uk
Senior Personnel: Edward Wyman, Judith Gay
Parts Casting & TV Casting Agents for Actors, Walk-Ons and Extras. (English & Welsh Language)

THE WYSE AGENCY

1 Hill Farm Road, Whittlesford,
Cambridgeshire CB2 4NB
Tel: 01223 832288
Email: frances@dramawise.co.uk
Web Site: www.dramawise.co.uk
Managing Director: Frances Brownlie
Agency for young people from the ages of 8 years, as well as adults.

X-RAY TOURING LLP

2 Holford Yard London WC1X 9HD
Tel: 020 7749 3500 Fax: 020 7749 3501
Email: info@xraytouring.com
Web Site: www.xraytouring.com
Contact: Lucy Henrit

XS PROMOTIONS

57 Fonthill Road, Aberdeen AB11 6UQ
Scotland
Tel: 01224 595 969
Email: info@xsp.co.uk
Web Site: www.xsp.co.uk
Proprietor: Ean Jones
We cater for functions, corporate and social venues, specialising in weddings and traditional music. We represent the best entertainers in Scotland, and can provide bands, duo/trios and solo artistes (including pipers, harpists, vocalists, guitarists & violinists). We also can offer cabaret, comedy and circus acts and discos, as well as after dinner speakers and theme nights (murder mystery, casino, quiz & race).

ARTISTES REPRESENTED:

Function Bands (Ceilidh & Covers):
Country Edition
Illusion
Mak Folk
Bands:
Eclipse
Moonshine
Slipshod
Son Of A Gunn
Stewart Band
Duos & Trios:
Bedhead
Blue Casino
Horizon
Identity Crisis
Index
Made 2 Order
Mandate
Pepperpot
Reno
Savanah
Sullivan
Wonderland (Duo)
Solo Artists:
Mike Devine
Andy Fyfe
Roy Rhodes
Ronnie Sinclair
Caberet Acts:
Claude Bols
Andy Cameron
Crooked Jack
George Duffus
Jesse Garron
Inside Out
Jimmy Stirling
Comedy Acts:
Fake That
Mimics
Additional Entertainments:
Buchaneers (jazz)
Carl Howse (magician)
Linklater String Quartet
Pedro (caricaturist)
Garry Seagraves (magician)

YAKETY YAK

7a Bloomsbury Square, London
WC1A 2LP
Tel: 020 7430 2600 Fax: 020 7404 6109
Email: info@yaketyyak.co.uk
Web Site: www.yaketyyak.co.uk
Senior Personnel: Jolie Williams

ARTISTES REPRESENTED:

Guys:
Terry Alderton
Richard Allinson
John Altman
Robert Ashby
Dicken Ashworth
David Bamber
Marcus Bentley
Big Al
Jesse Birdsall
William Boyde
Ray Burdis
Tom Chadbon
John Challis
Brian Conley
Christian Coulson
Brian Deacon
Rupert Degas
Amerjit Deu
Pete Drummond
Richard Elis
Chris Ellison
Chris Evans
Craig Fairbrass
Max Flint
Jerome Flynn
Laurence Fox
Nickolas Grace
Stephen Greif
Derek Griffiths
Steven Hartley
Jeff Hordley
Gareth Hunt
Ralph Ineson
Fraser James
Robin Kermode
Dermot Kerrigan
Adrian Lester
Finbar Lynch
Steven Mackintosh
Mark Maier
Art Malik
Steve McFadden
Ewan McGregor
John McGuinn
Christian McKay
Simon Meacock
James Nesbitt
Daragh O'Malley
Con O'Neill
Stefano Paolini

Bill Petrie
Hugh Quarshie
Dr David Riley
Colin Salmon
Andrew Scarborough
Tony Selby
Jay Simpson
Hugo Speer
William Vanderpuye
Gary Waldhorn
Lee Williams
Nick Wilton
Peter Wingfield
Girls:
Kelly Adams
Jeni Barnett
Helen Baxendale
Lynda Bellingham
Isla Blair
Laurence Bouvard
Kate Buffery
Rebecca Callard
Sarah Cawood
Julie Dawn Cole
Nula Conwell
Sara Crowe
Niamh Cusack
Amanda Donohoe
Barbara Flynn
Rebecca Front
Alexandra Gilbreath
Valerie Gogan
Jan Goodman
Naomie Harris
Kelly Harrison
Amanda Holden
Lisa Jacobs
Gillian Kearney
Patsy Kensit
Sara Kestelman
Rebecca Lacey
Rosemary Leach
Cherie Lunghi
Carole Machin
Martine McCutcheon
Janet McTeer
Rhonda Millar
Cecilia Noble
Sally Oliver
Billie Piper
Gail Porter
Pauline Quirke
Jan Ravens
Jemma Richards
Marcella Riordan
Julia Sawalha
Nina Sosanya
Carmen Squire
Zara Turner
Anna Wing
Katherine Wogan

BRIAN YEATES ASSOCIATES

Home Farm House, London Road, Canwell, Sutton Coldfield, West Midlands B75 5SH
Tel: 0121 323 2200
Email: ashley@brianyeates.co.uk
Web Site: www.brianyeates.co.uk
Senior Personnel: Brian Yeates, Ashley Yeates

ARTISTES REPRESENTED:
1215
A 60's Night Out
Back to Broadway
Dave Berry
Bev Bevans
A Black Country Night Out
Frank Carson KSG
A Comedy Night Out
Dandy
Ezio
The Fortunes
The Ivy League
Just Aynuk
Ian 'Sludge' Lees
Gina Louise
Red Kiss
Sheratons
Alvin Stardust
Ten Days Late
The Father Teds
The Move
The Wise Guys
Lizzie Wiggins

YELLOW BALLOON PRODUCTIONS LTD

Freshwater House, Outdowns, Effingham, Surrey KT24 5QR
Tel: 01483 281 500 / 501 Fax: 01483 281 502 Mob: 07808 921 286
Email: yellowbal@aol.com
Senior Personnel: Mike Smith, Daryl Smith
Artiste Management and Consultancy.

ARTISTES REPRESENTED:
Argy Bargy
Baby Elvis
Caroline Cook
The Crack
Ruth Gordon
Chaz Hart
Bob James
Kim James
Sally James
Dave Lee
Kathy Lloyd
Roy Marlowe
Mistakes
Nick
Karen Noble
Mike Osman
Oxshott Royals
Adam Smith
Daryl Smith
Andy Street
Jay Taylor
Wild Women
Woppah

YORKSHIRE ENTERTAINMENT LTD

25 Chanterlands Avenue, Hull, East Yorkshire HU5 3SS
Tel: 01482 441 190 / 0845 345 1945
Fax: 01482 493 797
Email: duncan@yorkshireentertainment.co.uk
Web: www.yorkshireentertainment.co.uk
Contact: Duncan Wood

ARTISTES REPRESENTED:
Bacchus String Quartet
Baron Mad Dog's Oompah Band
Bejazzled
Bogus Brothers
Mike Brown Band
Casablanca Boys
Celebration
Chrissie Cullen Ceilidh Band
John Diver
Doghouse Skiffle Band
E2
Fret Monkey
Gaslight Jazz Band
Goosehorns
Philip Henderson (Piper)
Gary Jamieson
Leodian String Quartet
The Little Band - Ceilidh Band
Mad Dog's Little Big Band
Mister Sister
Morris and the Minors
Musica Viva String Quartet
Nite Train
Pure Silk
Reaction
Soul Train (Soul Band)
Sun, Sea & Sand (Steel Band)
The Lex Icon Corporation
Upside Down
V.I.P.

PHILIP YOUD ENTERTAINMENTS & MANAGEMENT

40 Armstrong Close, Locking Stumps, Birchwood, Warrington, Cheshire WA3 6DH
Tel: 01925 828 278 Fax: 01925 824 757
Email: lucyyoud@hotmail.com

ARTISTES REPRESENTED:
John Antony
David Dalton
Mitchell Grant
Natalie Kane
Pete Lyons
Dave Preston
Ricky Silvers
Lee Stevens

YOUNG ACTORS THEATRE & AGENCY

70-72 Barnsbury Road, London N1 0ES
Tel: 020 7278 2101 Fax: 020 7833 9467
Email: info@yati.org.uk
Web Site: www.yati.org.uk
Director: Andrew Harries
Agents: Dyana Daulby and Lucy O'Meara
Community Theatre and Management Agency.
The Community Theatre runs evening drama classes for all ages, from 6 upwards.
The Management Agency specialises in representation of children from the age of 6-17, as well as representing adults of all ages.

SCOTT-PAUL YOUNG ENTERTAINMENTS LTD

(Spy Productions)
Northern Lights House,
110 Blandford Road North, Langley,
Near Windsor, Berkshire SL3 7TA
Tel/Fax: 01753 693 250
Email: castingdirect@spy-ents.com
Web Site: www.spy-lightentsworld.com
Managing Director: Scott-Paul Young
Artists management and exclusive representation for films, television, commercials, theatre, sports and modelling events and all areas of the light entertainment industry.

ARTISTES REPRESENTED:

Melanie Beadle
Grahame Budd
Dov Citron
Julie Cornish
Jonathan Cullinane
Alan Dester
Marielle Dreier
Alan Evens
Michael Gabe
Tessa Gallagher
Darrie Gardener
Corcoran Hayes
Peter Irvine
Clare Jarvis
Mitch Jenkins
Omar Khan
Deboragh Klayman
Chrissy Lee
Helen Jessica Liggal
Jessica Marienson
Zara Martin
Peter Martindale
Rebecca McHugh
Lutz Michael
Jon Mohnani
Sonja Morenstern
Emma Netileton
Bernard Pellegrinetti
Rebecca Perry
Lynn Sarah Preston
Paul Richards
Paul Senn
James Watt
Gilda Waugh

ANN ZAHL PERSONAL MANAGEMENT

57 Great Cumberland Place, London
W1H 7LJ
Tel: 020 7724 3684 Fax: 020 7262 4143
Email: annz@freenetname.co.uk
Senior Personnel: Ann Zahl FEAA

ARTISTES REPRESENTED:

ZAP! ENTERTAINMENT LTD

14 Bryson Place, Larbert, Stirlingshire
FK5 4FZ
Tel: 0845 519 1220 Fax: 0845 519 1221
Email: info@zapentertainment.co.uk
Web Site: www.zapentertainment.co.uk
Contact: Dougie Jackson

ZEN DIRECTORIES

Central House, 1 Ballards Lane, London
N3 1LQ
Tel: 0203 115 0010 Fax: 0203 115 0035
Email: zendirectories@btconnect.com / info@zdcl.co.uk
Web Site: www.zdcl.co.uk
Managing Director: Zen Martinoli

ZIPPOS CIRCUS PRODUCTIONS LTD

Circus HQ, Enborne, Nr Newbury,
Berkshire RG20 0LD
Tel: 07836 641 277 Fax: 07050 244 867
BO: 0774 811811 / 07900 141516
Email: zipposcircus@yahoo.com
Web Site: www.zipposcircus.co.uk
Director: Martin Burton
Zippos Circus is a traditional style circus, featuring jugglers, acrobats, aerialists, clowns and horses. The show itself, and big top, are available for private and corporate functions.

ZISYS EVENTS

1 Alexander Place IRVINE KA12 0UR
Tel: 01294 238 918
Email: danny@zisysavmn.co.uk
Web Site: www.zisysavmn.co.uk
Danny Anderson

Major American Agencies

AGENCY FOR THE PERFORMING ARTS (APA)
405 S. Beverly Drive, Beverly Hills, California 90212
Tel: 00 1 310 888 4200 Fax: 00 1 310 888 4242
Web Site: www.apa-agency.com
Agent: Jeff Wilkins
ARTISTES REPRESENTED:
Abba Mania
Flex Alexander
Billy Talent
DJ Cobra
Janita
Judas Priest
Billy Ocean
Robert Plant
Adam Sandler
Greg Warren

AIM (ARTISTS INTERNATIONAL MANAGEMENT) INC
PMB 458, 9850 Sandalfoot Boulevard, Boca Raton, Florida 33428 USA
Tel: 00 1 561 498 1300 Fax: 00 1 561 498 2004
Email: aiminc1@aol.com
Web: www.artistsinternationalonline.net
Senior Personnel: Steve Green, Mark Lyman, Cheryl Sabol

ALLIANCE WORLDWIDE COMMUNICATIONS
Tel: 00 1 818 990 3378 Fax: 00 1 818 990 3377
Email: htaylor@alliancewc.com
Web Site: www.alliancewc.com
Agent: Heather Taylor
ARTISTES REPRESENTED:
Flavor Flav
Tara McNamara

AMERICAN PROGRAM BUREAU
313 Washington State. Ste. 225+ Newton, Massachusetts 02458
Tel: 00 1 617 965 6600 Fax: 00 1 617 965 6610
Email: apb@apbspeakers.com
Web Site: www.apbspeakers.com
The leading international agency for speakers and creative programming.
ARTISTES REPRESENTED:
Naomi Campbell
Michael Douglas
Richard Dreyfuss
Goldie Hawn
Larry King
Pres. Mary Robinson
Jane Seymour
Archbishop Desmond Tutu

ARTIST GROUP INTERNATIONAL
150 East 58th Street, 19th Floor, New York, New York 10155
Tel: 00 1 212 813 9292 Fax: 00 1 212 813 1972
Agent: Dennis Afra
ARTISTES REPRESENTED:
Def Leppard
Everclear
Billy Joel
Meat Loaf
Metallica
Motley Crue
Placebo
Poison
Rod Stewart

ASSOCIATED BOOKING CORPORATION (ABC)
501 Madison Ave. #501 New York, New York 10022 USA
Tel: 00 1 212 874 2400 Fax: 00 1 212 769 3649
Email: music@mindspring.com
Web Site: www.abcbooking.com

BARRA CUDA ENTERPRISES
PO Box 121, Anaheim, California 92815 USA
Tel: 00 1 714 991 5065 Fax: 00 1 714 991 9781
Email: cuda@barracuda-ent.com
Web Site: www.barracuda-ent.com
Agents: John Cuda, Sean Israel, Sharon Jacob

CAA (CREATIVE ARTISTS AGENCY)
9830 Wilshire Boulevard, Beverly Hills, Los Angeles, 91202-1825 USA
Tel: 00 1 310 288 4545 Fax: 00 1 310 288 4795 Nashville Office: 3310 West End, 5th Floor, Nashville TN37203 USA
Tel: 00 1 615 383 8787 Fax: 00 1 615 383 4937
Email: bwalker@caa.com

CAM (COLUMBIA ARTISTS MANAGEMENT) INC
165 West 57th Street, New York, New York 10019-2276 USA
Tel: 00 1 212 841 9500 Fax: 00 1 212 841 9744
Email: cami@cami.com
Web Site: www.cami.com

CHAOTICA
32 East 31st Street, 9th Floor, New York, New York 10016 USA
Tel: 00 1 212 725 5588 Fax: 00 1 212 725 6868
Email: inquire@chaotica.com

CREATIVE ARTISTS AGENCY
2000 Avenue of the Stars Los Angeles California 90067
Tel: 00 1 424 288 2000 Fax: 00 1 424 288 2900
Web Site: www.caatouring.com
Agent: Rob Light
Marketing Agent: Allison McGregor
ARTISTES REPRESENTED:
AC/DC
All American Rejects
Anastacia
Apocalyptica
Beastie Boys
Beck
Andrea Bocelli
Bon Jovi
Sarah Brightman
Mariah Carey
Tracy Chapman
Eric Clapton
John Cleese
Counting Crows
Jamie Cullum
Dixie Chicks
Bob Dylan
Eurythmics
Evanescence
Jamie Foxx
Nelly Furtado
Garbage
Green Day
PJ Harvey
Norah Jones
Annie Lennox
Lostprophets
Bette Midler
Alanis Morrissette
Morrissey
Phoenix
Corinne Bailey Rae
Razorlight
Lionel Richie
Seal
Simply Red
Usher

AL EMBRY INTERNATIONAL
PO Box 23162, Nashville, Tennessee 37202 USA
Tel: 00 1 615 327 4074 Fax: 00 1 615 329 4777
Email: alembry@alembryinternational.com
Web Site: www.alembryinternational.com
ARTISTES REPRESENTED:
The Dempseys
Fats Domino
Mickey Gilley
Jerry Lee Lewis
Jason D Williams

ENDEAVOR AGENCY
9601 Wilshire Boulevard, 3rd Floor, Beverley Hills, Los Angeles California 90210 USA
Tel: 00 1 310 248 2000 Fax: 00 1 310 248 2020
Agent: Chris Donnelly
ARTISTES REPRESENTED:
Jamie Bell
America Ferrara
Eva Green
Dustin Hoffman

Ashton Kutcher
Michael Moore
Jack Osbourne
Adam Sandler
Stuart Townsend

ENTERTAINMENT ARTISTS NASHVILLE

2409 21st Ave. S. Ste. 100 Nashville, Tennessee 37212 USA
Tel: 00 1 615 320 7041
Fax: 00 1 615 320 0856
Email: entartnash@aol.com
Web Site: www.entertainmentartists.com
Agent: Micky Bessone

ENTOURAGE TALENT ASSOCIATES

236 West 27th Street, 8th Floor, New York, New York 10001 USA
Tel: 00 1 212 633 2600 Fax: 00 1 212 633 1818
Email: booking@entouragetalent.com
Web Site: www.entouragetalent.com

GOODMAN PRODUCTIONS INC

340 West 57th Street Suite 5A New York, New York 10019 USA
Tel/Fax: 00 1 212 262 5437
Email: goodmanproductions@yahoo.com

ICM (INTERNATIONAL CREATIVE MANAGEMENT)

10250 Constellation Blvd, Los Angeles, California 90067 USA
Tel: 00 1 310 550 4000 Fax: 00 1 310 550 4100 New York Office: 852 8th Avenue, New York, New York 10019 Tel: 00 1 212 556 5600 Fax: 00 1 212 556 6847
Email: bsmith@icmtalent.com
Web Site: www.icmtalent.com
Contact Agent: Ben Smith

ARTISTES REPRESENTED:

Artists Roster:
Bryan Adams
Paul Anka
The Beach Boys
Jim Belushi & Sacred Hearts
Beyonce
Brandy
Foxy Brown
En Vogue
Fabolous
Aretha Franklin
Kathy Griffin
Iggy Pop
Joe
Jojo
Kelly Rowland
Kris Kristofferson
Jay Leno
Loverboy
Patti Lupone
Shirley MacLaine
Anne Murray
Anne Murray
Muse
Tony Orlando
Kelly Osbourne
Ray J
Joe Sample
David Sanborn
David Spade
The Strokes
Keith Sweat
The Temptations
Tommy Tune

Comedy Roster:
The Amazing Johnathan
Louie Anderson
Lester Barrie
Bill Bellamy
J. Anthony Brown
Brett Butler
George Carlin
Rodney Carrington
Carrot Top
Kate Clinton
Bobby Collins
Dave Coulier
Ellen De Generes
Andy Dick
Mike Epps
Firesign Theatre
Jeff Garlin
Adele Givens
Kathy Griffin
D.L. Hughley
A.J. Johnson
Jedda Jones aka “Ms. Dupre”
Jay Leno
Pam Matteson
Tracy Morgan
Myra J.
John Pinette
Jeff Richards
Chris Rock
Paul Rodriguez
Roseanne
Rita Rudner
Rudy Rush
Bob Saget
Russell Simmon’s Def Comedy Jam
Rickey Smiley
Sommore
David Spade
Aries Spears
Damon Wayans
John Witherspoon

JERRY KRAVAT ENTERTAINMENT

10th Floor, 404 Park Avenue South, New York, New York 10016 USA
Tel: 00 1 212 213 5270 Fax: 00 1 212 689 9140
Email: jkravat@parny.com
Web Site: www.parny.com

BUDDY LEE ATTRACTIONS INC

38 Music Square East, Suite 300, Nashville, Tennessee 37203 USA
Tel: 00 1 615 244 4336 Fax: 00 1 615 726 0429
Email: info@blanash.com
Web Site: www.buddyleeattractions.com
Contact: Tony Conway

Buddy Lee Attractions Inc is the oldest and largest privately-owned talent agency in the music industry. Staff of 21, representing 48 artistes.

Kansas City Office:
3821 NE West Park Drive, Kansas City, MO 64116 USA
Tel: 00 1 816 454 0839 Fax: 00 1 816 454 6629
Contact: Joan Saltel

Corpus Christi Office:
5105 Pryor Lane, Austin, TX 78734 USA
Tel: 00 1 512 328 8669 Fax: 00 1 512 328 8821
Contact: Jon Folk

New Waverly Office:
PO Box 1209, New Waverly, TX 77358 USA
Tel: 00 1 409 344 9114 Fax: 00 1 409 344 9110
Contact: Tony Lee

ARTISTES REPRESENTED:

Exclusive Representation:
Rhett Akins
Billy Block’s Western Beat Roots Revival
Chad Brock
Jeff Carson
Mark Chesnutt
Tammy Cochran
John Conlee
Earl Thomas Conley
Elizabeth Cook
Clint Daniels
Danny Davis & Nashville Brass
Kevin Denney
Joe Diffie
Dixie Chicks
Bobbie Eakes
Tyler England
Great Divide
Honky Tonk Tailgate Party
Hot Club Of Cowtown
Sonya Isaacs
Jamgrass Festival
Jenai
Michael Johnson
Doug Kershaw
Sammy Kershaw
Chris Knight
Tracy Lawrence
Danni Leigh
Bill Miller
Ronnie Milsap
Lorrie Morgan
Kevin Morris
Pinmonkey
Riders In The Sky
Rockin Roadhouse Tour
Tim Rushlow
Daryle Singletary
Connie Smith
Marty Stuart
Chalee Tennison
Aaron Tippin
Ricky Van Shelton
Clay Walker
Elbert West
Wild Horses
Hank Williams III

Lee Ann Womack
Billy Yates

LITTLE BIG MAN BOOKING

Little Big Man Building, 7th Floor, 155 Avenue of the Americas, New York, New York 10013 USA
Tel: 00 1 646 336 8520 Fax: 00 1 646 336 8522
Email: pr@littlebigman.com
Contacts: Martin Diamond, Larry Webman, Tammy Shin

LORDLY & DAME

51 Church Street, Boston, Massachussets 02116-5493 USA
Tel: 00 1 617 482 3593 Fax: 00 1 617 426 8019
Email: lordly@lordly.com
Web Site: www.lordly.com

MARS TALENT AGENCY

27 L'Ambiance Court, Bardonia, New York, New York 10954 USA
Tel: 00 1 845 627 1587 Fax: 00 1 845 627 1591
Email: marstalent@aol.com
Web Site: www.marstalent.com

MONTEREY PENINSULA ARTISTS

509 Hartnell Street, Monterey, California 93940 USA
Tel: 00 1 831 375 4889 Fax: 00 1 831 375 2623 Monterey Nashville: 124 12th Ave S, Ste 410, Nashville, Tennessee Tel: 00 1 615 251 4400 Fax: 00 1 615 251 4401 Monterey Chicago: 200 W Superior, Suite 202,Chicago,Illanois 60610 Tel: 00 1 312 640 7500 Fax: 00 1 312 640 7515
Email: info@mpartists.com

WILLIAM MORRIS AGENCY INC

1 William Morris Place Beverly Hills Los Angeles California 90212 USA
Tel: 00 1 310 859 4000 Fax: 00 1 310 859 4440 New York Office: 1325 Avenue of the Americas, New York, New York 10019 USA Tel: 00 1 212 586 5100 Fax: 00 1 212 246 3583
Email: bslater@wma.com
Web Site: www.wma.com
Contact Agent: Brad Slater

ARTISTES REPRESENTED:

Paula Abdul
Anastacia
Julie Andrews
Average White Band
Burt Bacharach
Shirley Bassey
Bee Gees
Harry Belafonte
Tony Bennett
Chuck Berry
Michael Bolton
Pat Boone
Sir Richard Branson
Glen Campbell
Mariah Carey
Jose Carreras
Diahann Carroll
Carol Channing
Gary Chapman
Ray Charles
Margaret Cho
Charlotte Church
Roy Clark
Natalie Cole
Joaquin Cortes
Bill Cosby
Andrae Crouch
Sheryl Crow
Billy Crystal
Culture Club
Craig David
Tommy Davidson
Phyllis Diller
Donovan
The Eagles
Missy Elliott
Eminem
The Flying Karamazov Brothers
Aretha Franklin
Peter Gabriel
Art Garfunkel
Kathie Lee Gifford
Whoopi Goldberg
Al Green
Herbie Hancock and the Headhunters
Don Henley
Gregory Hines
Maurice Hines - `Guys & Dolls`
Whitney Houston
Billy Idol
Enrique Iglesias
It Takes Two - M. McCoo & B. Davis Jr.
Jamiroquai
Wyclef Jean
Quincy Jones
Tom Jones
KC & The Sunshine Band
Alan King
The Kingston Trio
Robert Klein
Mark Knopfler
Diana Krall
Ladysmith Black Mambazo
Kenny Lattimore
Legends of Motown
Jerry Lewis
Little Richard
Kenny Loggins
Melissa Manchester
Barry Manilow
Mannheim Steamroller
Ziggy Marley & The Melody Makers
Jackie Mason
Johnny Mathis
Marilyn McCoo
Michael McDonald
Bill Medley (The Righteous Brothers)
Sergio Mendes
Jim Nabors
Willie Nelson
Aaron Neville
The Neville Brothers
Bob Newhart
Wayne Newton
Donny Osmond
Marie Osmond
Robert Palmer
Dolly Parton
Sandi Patty
Penn and Teller
Bernadette Peters
Regis Philbin
Carlos Ponce
Paula Poundstone
The Pretenders
Maxi Priest
Red Buttons
Della Reese
Debbie Reynolds
Keith Richards
Don Rickles
Righteous Brothers
Riverdance - The Show
Joan Rivers
Anne Robinson
Smokey Robinson
Jose Luis Rodriguez
Kenny Rogers
Ray Romano
Jon Secada
Neil Sedaka
Brian Setzer Orchestra
Shakira
The Smothers Brothers
Snoop Dogg
Sting
Donna Summer
Lily Tomlin
Joe Torry
Tower Of Power
Jethro Tull
Village People
The Who
Andy Williams
The Wilsons
CeCe Winans
Robert Wuhl

MVO LTD

307 Seventh Avenue, New York, New York 10001
Tel: 00 1 212 414 9380
Fax: 00 1 212 414 9886
Email: mvoltd@earthlink.net
Director: Marsha Vlasic

ARTISTES REPRESENTED:

Ben Folds
Elvis Costello
Iggy Pop
Le Tigre
Courtney Love
Moby
Van Morrison
Muse
Kelly Osbourne
Ozzy Osbourne
Lou Reed
Regina Spektor
The Strokes
The Bronx
The Mooney Suzuki
Neil Young

PARADISE ARTISTS

PO Box 1821, Ojai, California 93024-1821 USA

Tel: 00 1 805 646 8433
Fax: 00 1 805 646 3367
Email: bril@paradiseartists.com
Web Site: www.paradiseartists.com

ARTISTES REPRESENTED:

Billy Ocean

PINNACLE ENTERTAINMENT

30 Glenn Street, White Plains, New York 10603 USA
Tel: 00 1 914 686 7100 Fax: 00 1 914 686 4085
Email: pinnent@aol.com

PODELL TALENT AGENCY

9th Floor, 22 W. 21Street, New York, New York 10010
Tel: 00 1 212 941 9390
Fax: 00 1 212 941 9391
Email: noah@podeltalent.com
Web Site: www.podeltalent.com
Agent: CJ Strock
Assistant: Noah Perabo

ARTISTES REPRESENTED:

Alice Cooper
Erasure
Peter Gabriel
Cyndi Lauper

PREMIER TALENT AGENCY

17 East 67th Street, New York, New York 10021 USA
Tel: 00 1 212 758 4900
Fax: 00 1 212 755 3251
Email: premiertal@aol.com

PRODUCERS INC

11806 North 56th Street, Tampa, Florida 33617-1652 USA
Tel: 00 1 813 988 8333
Fax: 00 1 813 985 3293
Email: info@producersinc.com
Web Site: www.producersinc.com
Agents: Craig Hankenson, Meridith Hankenson, Steve Rudolf, Kathy Thompson

ROCK STEADY MANAGEMENT AGENCY

2022 84th St. Circle North West, Bradenton, Florida 34209
Tel: 00 1 941 792 7880
Fax: 00 1 941 794 8970
Email: rustyrsma@aol.com
Web Site: www.rocksteadyagency.com
President: Rusty Hooker

ARTISTES REPRESENTED:

Sade
Tina Turner

THE HOWARD ROSE AGENCY

9460 Wilshire Boulevard, Suite 310, Beverly Hills, California 90212 USA
Tel: 00 1 310 858 3838 Fax: 00 1 310 858 1995
Email: HRA@HowardRoseAgency.com

SPECIAL ARTISTS AGENCY

9465 Wilshire Blvd,Suite 470 Beverly Hills CA 90212 USA
Tel: 001 310 859 9688
Web Site: www.specialartists.com

ARTISTES REPRESENTED:

William Baldwin
Kim Basinger
Thora Birch
Kenneth Branagh
Jeff Bridges
Pierce Brosnan
Chevy Chase
Timothy Dalton
Tim Daly
Ted Danson
Joey Dedio
Cameron Diaz
Tate Donovan
Minnie Driver
David Duchovny
Hilary Duff
Anna Faris
Sarah Ferguson
America Ferrara
Jeff Goldblum
Gene Hackman
Dennis Hopper
Helen Hunt
Holly Hunter
Jon Lovitz
Kyle MacLachlan
Cheech Marin
Tim Matheson
Ewan McGregor
Julian McMahon
Jay Mohr
Mandy Moore
Brittany Murphy
Gary Oldman
Mandy Patinkin
Jean Reno
Eric Roberts
Tim Roth
David Schwimmer
Charlie Sheen
Martin Sheen
Tom Skerritt
Mary Steenburgen
Donald Sutherland
Mena Suvari
Holland Taylor
Benicio Del Toro
Tracey Ullman
Gene Wilder

TCI-TALENT CONSULTANTS INTERNATIONAL LTD

105 Shaw Road, 2nd Floor Piermont New York 10968 USA
Tel: 00 1 212 730 2701 Fax: 00 1 845 359 4609
Email: email@tciartists.com
Web Site: www.tciartists.com

THE GERSH AGENCY

232 North Canon Drive, Beverley Hills, Los Angeles California 90210
Tel: 00 1 310 274 6611 Fax: 00 1 310 274 1753
Web Site: www.gershcomedy.com
Agent: Matthew Blake, Miguel DeJesus

ARTISTES REPRESENTED:

Drew Carey
Dave Chappelle
Jamie Foxx
George Lopez
David Schwimmer
Pauly Shore

THE M.O.B. AGENCY

6404 Wilshire Boulevard, Ste. 505, Los Angeles California 90048
Tel: 00 1 323 653 0427
Fax: 00 1 323 653 0428
Email: mobster411@aol.com
Web Site: www.mobagency.com
Agent: Joy Collingbourne

ARTISTES REPRESENTED:

Minnie Driver
Fountains of Wayne
No Doubt
Oslo
Siouxie and the Banshees
Gwen Stefani

UNITED TALENT AGENCY

9560 Wilshire Boulevard, Beverley Hills, Los Angeles, California 90212
Tel: 00 1 310 273 6700
Fax: 00 1 310 786 4808
Email: lazarusb@unitedtalent.com
Web Site: www.unitedtalent.com
Agents: Rob Prinz, Nikki Wheeler, Steve Seidel, Billy Lazarus

UNIVERSAL ATTRACTIONS AGENCY INC

12th Floor 135 W. 26th Street. New York New York 10001 USA
Tel: 00 1 212 582 7575
Fax: 00 1 212 333 4508
Email: infopoll@universalattractions.com
Web Site: www.universalattractions.com
Agent: Jeff Epstein

RICHARD WALTERS ENTERTAINMENT

6464 Sunset Blvd, #740 Hollywood, CA 90028 USA
Tel: 00 1 323 463 8400
Fax: 00 1 323 463 4696
Email: rwetalent@aol.com

ARTISTES REPRESENTED:

Agent Roster:
Richard Walters
Artist Roster:
Gloria Gaynor

Concert Promoters

3A ENTERTAINMENT LTD

4 Princeton Court, 53-55 Felsham Road,

Putney, London SW15 1AZ
Tel: 020 8789 6111 Fax: 020 8789 6222
Email: aaaents@aol.com
Senior Personnel: Pete Wilson

ACADEMY MUSIC GROUP (AMG)
211 Stockwell Road, London SW9 9SL
Tel: 020 7787 3131 Fax: 020 7787 3136
Email:
enquiries@academy-music-group.co.uk
Web: www.academy-music-group.co.uk
Press and Communications: Louise Kovacs
Email:
louise@academy-music-group.co.uk
Operations: Richard Maides

ACORN ENTERTAINMENTS
PO Box 64, Cirencester, Gloucestershire GL7 5YD
Tel: 01285 644 622 Fax: 01285 642 291
Email: drussell@acornents.co.uk
Web Site: www.acornents.co.uk
Senior Personnel: Dudley Russell

ADASTRA
The Stables,Westwood House Main Street North Dalton, Driffield, East Yorkshire YO25 9XA
Tel: 01377 217 662 Fax: 01377 217 754
Email: adastra@adastra-music.co.uk
Web Site: www.adastra-music.co.uk
Senior Personnel: Chris Wade

A.I.R. LIMITED
AIR House, Spennymoor, County Durham DL16 7SE
Tel: 01388 814 632 Fax: 01388 812 445
Email: info@airagency.com
Web Site: www.airagency.com
Directors: Colin Pearson, John Wray

ASGARD
125 Parkway, London NW1 7PS
Tel: 020 7387 5090 Fax: 020 7387 8740
Email: info@asgard-uk.com
Web Site: www.asgard-uk.com
Senior Personnel: Paul Fenn, Paul Charles, Mick Griffiths

ASKONAS HOLT LTD
Lincoln House 300 High Holborn London WC1V 7JH
Tel: 020 7400 1700 Fax: 020 7400 1799
Email: info@askonasholt.co.uk
Web Site: www.askonasholt.co.uk
Chief Executives: Martin Campbell-White, Robert Rattray
Specialising in: Classical Music.

AVALON PROMOTIONS LTD
4a Exmoor Street, London W10 6BD
Tel: 020 7598 7333 Fax: 020 7598 7223
Email: info@avalonuk.com
Web Site: www.avalonuk.com
Head of Marketing: Mark Jackson
Avalon Promotions specialises in live artist bookings. Please see listing for 'Avalon Management' to refer to artists available for bookings.

BARRUCCI LEISURE ENTERPRISES LTD
45-47 Cheval Place, London SW7 1EW
Tel: 020 7225 2255 Fax: 020 7581 2509
Email: barrucci@barrucci.com
Senior Personnel: Bryan Miller, Carolynne Chandler
Promote concerts mostly in the Middle East and South Africa.

BIG BEAR MUSIC
PO BOX 944, Edgbaston, Birmingham B16 8UT
Tel: 0121 454 7020
Email: admin@bigbearmusic.com/
tim@bigbearmusic.com
Web Site: www.bigbearmusic.com
Senior Personnel: Tim Jennings, Jim Simpson
Big Bear Music promote jazz, blues and swing through concert and club tours, UK and European festivals, the Starbucks Birmingham International Jazz Festival and Marbella Jazz Festival (Spain).

DEREK BLOCK CONCERTS LTD
Suite D, 4-6 Canfield Place, L
ondon NW6 3BT
Tel: 020 7724 2101
Email: dbc@derekblock.co.uk
Web Site: www.derekblock.co.uk
Senior Personnel: Derek Block, Scott Miller, Paul Scarbrow

BOS PERFORMANCE MARKETING
Vine Cottage, Isington Lane, Isington, Alton, Hampshire GU34 4PW
Tel: 07967 724453
Email: chris@bospm.com
Web Site: www.wsom.co.uk
The Company offers; Marketing & Promotion for Venues, Festivals, Tours and Events; Poster & Leaflet Distribution; Direct Mail; Telemarketing; Media Competitions; Press Launches.
Contacts: Chris or Julie Maddocks

RICHARD BUCKNALL MANAGEMENT (RBM)
3rd Floor, 168 Victoria Street, London SW1E 5LB
Tel: 0207 630 7733 Fax: 0207 630 6549
Email: info@rbmcomedy.com
Web Site: www.rbmcomedy.com
Senior Personnel: Richard Bucknall, Rob Sandy

MEL BUSH ORGANISATION
26 Albany Business Park, Cabot Lane, Poole, Dorset BH17 7BX
Tel: 01202 691 891 Fax: 01202 691 896
Email: info@melbush.com
Senior Personnel: Mel Bush

CALIBRE PRODUCTIONS LTD
Chasewood Lodge Walford Road, Ross-on-Wye, Herefordshire HR9 5PQ
Tel: 01989 566 644 Fax: 01989 566 627
Email: admin@calibreproductions.co.uk
Web Site: www.calibreproductions.co.uk
Contact: Ed or Lynn O'Driscoll
Producers of "Beyond Broadway", "Kings Of Swing", " Masters of the Musical", "Absolute Swing", "A Night at the Opera", "Sounds of the 60s" and "Classic Response"

CARMEL ARTS
Heathcote Totteridge Green
London N20 8PA
Tel: 020 8445 1912
Email: carmelarts2001@aol.com
Contact: Ms Carmel Hart
Sector: Entertainment
Since 1993 Carmel Arts has produced concerts and gigs strongly represented by the presence of musicians and composers from Israel who have become internationally known soloists and ensembles through performing in such venues as the Albert Hall, Queen Elizabeth Hall, Purcell Room and Conway Hall. Many young musicians from this country too, have benefited from opportunities given to them to perform 'live'.

MRS CASEY MUSIC
PO Box 296, Matlock, Derbyshire DE4 3XU
Tel: 01629 827 012 Fax: 01629 821 874
Email: info@mrscasey.co.uk
Web Site: www.mrscasey.co.uk
Senior Personnel: Steve Heap
Publicity & Marketing Manager: Jess Adams
Festival and Event Organisers and consultants.

DUGGIE CHAPMAN ASSOCIATES
Clifton House 106 Clifton Drive Blackpool, Lancashire FY4 1RR
Tel: 01253 403177
Mobile: 07976 925 504
Email:
info@duggiechapmanassociates.co.uk
Web:
www.duggiechapmanassociates.co.uk
Director: Duggie Chapman
Artiste Booking: Beryl Johnson
Duggie Chapman Associates is Britain's longest running promoter of touring music hall presenting Star Variety Summer Shows and Pantomimes. Specialists in late bookings for managements. Name Package shows always available at short notice.

ALAN CLAYTON CONCERTS LTD
Alcaston Barn, Manor Farm, Alcaston, Church Stretton, Shropshire SY6 6RP
Tel: 01694 781689 Fax: 01694 781692
Email: alan_clayton@btconnect.com
Senior Personnel: Alan Clayton

CLIVE CONWAY PRODUCTIONS LTD
32 Grove Street, Oxford OX2 7JT
Tel: 01865 514 830 Fax: 01865 514 409
Email: info@celebrityproductions.org
Web www.cliveconwayproductions.com
Managing Director: Clive Conway
Producing celebrity entertainments featuring Britain's leading actors, writers, musicians and politicians.

TONY DENTON PROMOTIONS LTD
Charter House, 157 - 159 High Street, London N14 6BP
Tel: 020 8447 9411 Fax: 020 3232 0085
Email: info@tdpromo.com
Web Site: www.tdpromo.com
Director: Tony Denton, Peter Apps, Bennie Edwards

DEREK BLOCK PROMOTIONS LTD
Suite D, 4-6 Canfield Place, London NW6 3BT
Tel: 020 7724 2101
Email: dbp@derekblock.co.uk
Web Site: ww.derekblock.co.uk

DERI PROMOTIONS
9 Templars Close, Bognor Regis, West Sussex PO22 6RU
Tel/Fax: 01243 585 545
Email: deripromotions@btopenworld.com
Web Site: www.deripromotions.org.uk
Senior Personnel: Roy Cooper
Specialising in Country & Western.

DF CONCERTS
272 St Vincent Street, Glasgow, Strathclyde G2 5RL Scotland
Tel: 0141 566 4999 Fax: 0141 566 4998
Email: admin@dfconcerts.co.uk
Web Site: www.dfconcerts.co.uk
Managing Director: Geoff Ellis
www.gigsinscotland.com / www.tinthepark.com / www.kingtuts.co.uk
DF Concerts is one of Europe's leading concert promotion companies, bringing the best live music and events to audiences in Scotland, the company is also the promoter behind Scotland's most successful music festival, T in the Park.

ENTERTAINERS LTD
200 London Road, Hadleigh, Benfleet, Essex SS7 2PD
Tel: 01702 427100 Fax: 01702 427109
Email: enquiries@entertainers.co.uk
Web Site: www.entertainers.co.uk
Contact: Michael Taylor

ESIP LTD
PO Box 4702, Henley-on-Thames, Oxfordshire RG9 9AA
Tel: 0118 940 6812 Fax: 0870 122 4634
Email: ruben@esip.co.uk, info@esip.co.uk
Web Site: www.esip.co.uk
Director: John Ellson
Press and Marketing: Emma Perry
Promoter, Production and Tour Manager: Ruben Cordero
Events Producer: Dominic Nieper

FAMILY ENTERTAINMENTS
30 Stirling Place, Hove, East Sussex BN3 3YU
Tel: 01273 263637 Mobile: 07762 106959
Email: jdean@familyentertainments.com
Contact: Josh Dean

MALCOLM FELD AGENCY
Malina House, Sandforth Road, Sandfield Park, Liverpool, Merseyside L12 1JY
Tel: 0151 259 6565
Email: malcolm@malcolmfeld.co.uk
Web Site: www.malcolmfeld.co.uk
Senior Personnel: Malcolm Feld

THE FLYING MUSIC COMPANY LTD
PO Box 1959, London W11 2LY
Tel: 020 7221 7799 Fax: 020 7221 5016
Email: info@flyingmusic.co.uk
Web Site: www.flyingmusic.com
Directors: Derek Nicol and Paul Walden
General Manager: Mark Strange
Production Manager: Andy Sharrocks
Head of Marketing: Ginette Sinnott

GLASTONBURY FESTIVALS
Glastonbury Festival Office, 28 Northload Street, Glastonbury, Somerset BA6 9JJ
Tel: 01458 834 596
Email: office@glastonburyfestivals.co.uk
Web Site: www.glastonburyfestivals.co.uk
Manager: Dick Vernon

GLOBAL RADIO
30 Leicester Square, London WC2H 7LA
Tel: 020 7766 6000 Fax: 020 7766 6100
Email: info@thisisglobal.com
Web Site: www.thisisglobal.com
Chief Executive: Ashley Tabor
Group Programming Director: Richard Park
Sales Director: Mike Gordon

HARVEY GOLDSMITH PRODUCTIONS LTD
5th Floor,Langham House 308 Regent Street London W1B3AT
Tel: 020 7224 1992 Fax: 020 7224 0111
Email: mail@harveygoldsmith.com
Web Site: www.harveygoldsmith.com
Managing Director: Harvey Goldsmith

RAYMOND GUBBAY LTD
Dickens House 15 Took's Court, London EC4A 1LB
Tel: 020 7025 3750 Fax: 020 7025 3751
Email: info@raymondgubbay.co.uk
Web Site: www.raymondgubbay.co.uk
Chairman: Raymond Gubbay
Managing Director: Anthony Findlay
Deputy Managing Director: Cathy Lewis

JEF HANLON PROMOTIONS
Orchard House, 23 Lewes Road, Haywards Heath, West Sussex RH17 7SP
Tel: 01444 456717
Email: jef.hanlon@agents-uk.com
Contact: Jef Hanlon FEAA

HERITAGE MUSIC
50 Main Street, Peckleton, Leicester LE9 7RE
Tel: 01455 822 604 Fax: 01455 828 911
Mobile: 07970 440903
Email: orchestra@graff.plus.com
Web Site: www.grafforchestra.co.uk
Artistic Director: Celia Davies
Music Consultants & Production Company

JOHN HESSENTHALER ENTERTAINMENTS
6 Constable Court, Barn Street, Lavenham, Sudbury, Suffolk CO10 9RB
Tel: 01787 247 838 Fax: 01787 247 898
Email: john.hessenthaler@btinternet.com
Senior Personnel: John Hessenthaler
Stage PA & Lighting Systems, Stages, Disco Show. Act representation and Concert tours.

ADRIAN HOPKINS PROMOTIONS
P.O. Box 536, Headington, Oxford OX3 7LR
Tel: 01865 766 766 Fax: 01865 389521
Email: office@chesterhopkins.co.uk
Web Site: www.chesterhopkins.co.uk
Contact: Adrian Hopkins

CHESTER HOPKINS INTERNATIONAL
P.O. Box 536 Headington, Oxford OX3 7LR
Tel: 01865 766 766
Email: adrian@chesterhopkins.co.uk
Web Site: www.chesterhopkins.co.uk
Managing Director: Adrian Hopkins

DAVID HULL PROMOTIONS LTD
46 University Street, Belfast, BT7 1HB Northern Ireland
Tel: 028 9024 0360 Fax: 028 9024 7919

Email: info@dhpromotions.com/david@davidhullpromotions.com
Web: www.davidhullpromotions.com
Managing Director: David Hull
General Manager: Tony Brown
UK and Irish Celebrity and Personality Agency. UK and Ireland Tour Bookers. Representing the best in Irish Entertainment.

INTERNATIONAL ARTISTES LTD
4th Floor, Holborn Hall, 193-197 High Holborn, London WC1V 7BD
Tel: 020 7025 0600 Fax: 020 7404 9865
Email: reception@internationalartistes.com
Web Site: www.internationalartistes.com
Senior Personnel: Robert Voice, Michele Milburn, Phil Dale, Mandy Ward
Financial Directors: Paul Parnaby

INTERNATIONAL CLASSICAL ARTISTS
The Tower Building, 11 York Road, London SE1 7NX
Tel: 020 7902 0520 Fax: 020 7902 0530
Email: info@icartists.co.uk
Web Site: www.icartists.co.uk
Chairman/ Head of Artist Management: Stephen Wright
Senior Artist Manager: Cathy Carson

ITB (INTERNATIONAL TALENT BOOKING)
1st Floor, Ariel House, 74a Charlotte Street, London W1T 4QJ
Tel: 020 7637 6979 Fax: 020 7637 6978
Email: mail@itb.co.uk
Web Site: www.itb.co.uk
Agents: Rod MacSween, Barry Dickins, David Levy, Martin Horne, Mike Dewdney, Scott Thomas, Maria Hutt.

JAZZCO
Formerly Dankworth Management
Ten Acre Farm, Stonehill Road, Ottershaw, Chertsey, Surrey KT16 0AQ
Tel: 08450 008 007 / 01932455904
Email: les@jazzco.co.uk
Web Site: www..jazzco.co.uk

KENNEDY STREET ENTERPRISES LTD
Kennedy House, 31 Stamford Street, Altrincham, Cheshire WA14 1ES
Tel: 0161 941 5151 Fax: 0161 928 9491
Email: kse@kennedystreet.com
Managing Director: Danny Betesh

LEIGHTON-POPE ORGANISATION
8 Glenthorne Mews 115a Glenthorne Road, London W6 0LJ
Tel: 020 8741 4453 Fax: 020 8741 4289
Email: andrew@l-po.com
Web Site: www.l-po.com
Contact: Carl Leighton-Pope, Andrew Leighton-Pope

LINE-UP PMC
10 Matthew Close, Newcastle upon Tyne NE6 1XD
Tel / Fax: 0191 275 9745
Mob: 07808 300 906
Email: chrismurtagh@line-up.co.uk
Web Site: www.line-up.co.uk
Senior Personnel: Chris Murtagh

MARK LUNDQUIST MANAGEMENT & CONCERT PROMOTIONS
5 Tuckey Grove, Send Marsh, Ripley, Surrey GU23 6JG
Tel: 01483 224 118 Mobile: 07971 401510 Fax: 01483 479 417
Email: mark@marklundquist.com
Web Site: www.marklundquist.com
Contact: Mark Lundquist
Press And Marketing Officer: Canada Hepp
Established in 1990. Mark Lundquist specialises in personal representation of major recording artistes and bookings for Theatres, Art Centres, Festivals, Clubs, Corporate & Private Functions WORLD-WIDE.

JOHNNY MANS PRODUCTIONS LIMITED
Incorporating 'Real Publicity' & 'Encore Magazine'
PO Box 196, Hoddesdon, Hertfordshire EN10 7WG
Tel: 0845 467 0792
Email: johnnymansagent@aol.com, encoremags@aol.com
Web: www.johnnymansproductions.co.uk www.encoremagazine.org.uk
ADMINISTRATION:
Managing Director: Johnny Mans
Administration: Philip Crowe, Elliot Mans, David Perry.

MARSHALL ARTS LTD
Uint 6, Utopia Village, 7 Chalcot Road, London NW1 8LH
Tel: 020 7586 3831 Fax: 020 7586 1422
Email: info@marshall-arts.co.uk / barrie@marshall-arts.co.uk
Web Site: www.marshall-arts.co.uk
Managing Director: Barrie Marshall
Director: Doris Dixon
Agent: Ben Martin
Production Manager: Mike Stewart
International concert presentations.

MATPRO LTD
Cary Point, Babbacombe Downs Road, Torquay, Devon TQ1 3LU
Tel: 01803 322 233 Fax: 01803 322 244
Email: info@babbacombe-theatre.com
Web Site: www.babbacombe-theatre.com
Contact: Sharon Waring
Email: sharon@matpro-show.biz

PHIL MCINTYRE PROMOTIONS
3rd Floor 85 Newman Street London W1T 3EU
Tel: 020 7291 9000 Fax: 020 7291 9001
Email: info@mcintyre-ents.com
Web Site: www.mcintyre-ents.com
Director: Philip McIntyre
Managing Director: Paul Roberts

METROPOLIS MUSIC
69 Caversham Road, London NW5 2DR
Tel: 020 7424 6800 Fax: 020 7424 6849
Email: info@metropolismusic.com
Web Site: www.metropolismusic.com
Managing Director: Bob Angus
Director: Paul Hutton
Finance Director: Glyn Smith

JOHN MILES ORGANISATION
Cadbury Camp Lane, Clapton in Gordano, Bristol, BS20 7SB
Tel: 01275 856 770 / 854 675 Fax: 01275 810186
Email: john@johnmiles.org.uk
Web: www.johnmilesorganisation.org.uk
Contacts: John Miles

MUCH LOVED PRODUCTIONS LTD
The British Philharmonic Concert Orchestra
8 Oaks Farm Drive, Darton, Barnsley, South Yorkshire S75 5BZ
Tel: 01226 380 175 Fax: 01226 380 566
Mob: 07802 959 594
Email: jeremy@mlpltd.com
Web Site: www.mlpltd.com
Senior Personnel: Mr JM Peaker, Mr M Peaker, Mrs JA Peaker
Specialising in all types of entertainment and corporate hospitality concerts. Shows and productions incorporating the British Philharmonic Concert Orchestra.

NETT UK
45 Elizabeth Avenue, Hove, East Sussex BN3 6WA
Tel: 01273 565 627
Email: info@nettuk.com
Web Site: www.nettuk.com
Contact: Nick Taggart
Highly professional theatre production and management company for UK and overseas theatre, touring shows, events and concerts.
Full sales, marketing, public relations and I.T. departments.
Enquiries by email welcome.

PAUL BARKER LTD
Crosslands Barn, Main Street, Stanbury, Haworth, West Yorkshire BD22 0HB
Tel: 01535 643 686 Fax: 01535 648 586
Mobile: 07830 207123

Email: paul@paulbarker.com
Web Site: www.paulbarker.com
Concert promoter: Paul Barker
Promotes live bands and theatre concerts.

PLANIT PRODUCTIONS
Associated company of Planit Events Ltd
Planit Events Ltd Trinity House 15 Nottingham Road London SW17 7EA
Planit Events Tel: 020 8682 4900 Fax: 020 8682 0602
Email: enquiries@planitevents.co.uk
Web Site: www.planitevents.co.uk
Contact: David Ambrose

REGULAR MUSIC
42 York Place, Edinburgh, Mid Lothian EH1 3HU Scotland
Tel: 0131 525 6700 Fax: 0131 525 6701
Web Site: www.regularmusic.com
General Manager: Moira Mackenzie

RIVIERA ENTERTAINMENTS LTD
Suite D 4-6 Canfield Place, London NW6 3BT
Tel: 020 7724 2101
Email: riviera@derekblock.co.uk
Web Site: www.derekblock.co.uk

SHETLAND ARTS DEVELOPMENT AGENCY
Mareel Lerwick, Shetland ZE1 0WQ Scotland
Tel: +44 (0)1595 743843
Email: info@shetlandarts.org
Web Site: www.shetlandarts.org
Director: Gwilym Gibbons
Head of Development: Kathy Hubbard
Marketing Officer: Lisa Ward
Office Administrator: Lynda Anderson
Administrative Assistant: Helen Smith
Shetland Arts seeks to promote all art forms in Shetland, running an Arts Office and the Garrison Theatre in Lerwick, and Bonhoga Gallery in Weisdale Mill, and promotes a year round programme of music, craft, theatre, literature, visual arts, dance and film events.

SHOWPRO
Garden Studio, 30 Oakington Road, London W9 2DH
Mobile: 07932 602 323
Tel: 020 7286 7535
Email: showprolondon@talktalk.net
Contact: Rayner Bourton

SOLID ENTERTAINMENTS
46 Wellowgate, Grimsby, North East Lincolnshire DN32 0RA
Tel: 01472 349 222 Mobile: 07885 192345 Fax: 01472 362 275
Email: solidentertainments@live.co.uk
Web Site: www.solidentertainments.com
Contact Bookings Manager: Stephen Stanley
Concert promoter and ticket agency, plus supplier of coaches to concerts and crowd control barrier hire.

SOLO AGENCY LTD
53-55 Fulham High Street, London SW6 3JJ
Tel: 020 7384 6644 Fax: 0870 749 3174
Email: soloreception@solo.uk.com
Web Site: www.solo.uk.com
Agent & Promoter: John Giddings
Promoter of the Isle of Wight Festival.
European promoter for U2, Madonna and The Rolling Stones.

TKO PROMOTIONS LTD
PO Box 130, Hove, East Sussex BN3 6QU
Tel: 01273 550 088 Fax: 01273 540 969
Email: management@tkogroup.com
Web Site: www.tkogroup.com
Chairman: Jeffrey Kruge
Chief Executive & Head of Licensing: Howard Kruger, h.kruger@tkogroup.com

THE ORANGE
Charter Court 3 Linden Grove, New Malden, Surrey KT3 3BL
Tel: 020 8942 7722
Mob: 07958 96 76 66
Email: livegigs@mail.com
Web: myspace.com/orangepromotions
ADMINISTRATION:
Live Music Management.
Props: Orange Promotions
Contact: Phil Brydon

THEOBALD DICKSON PRODUCTIONS
The Coach House, Swinhope Hall, Swinhope, Market Rasen, Lincolnshire LN8 6HT
Tel: 01472 399 011 Fax: 01472 399 025
Email: tdproductions@lineone.net
Senior Personnel: Bernard Theobald
Personal Management company.

UK PRODUCTIONS LTD
Churchmill House, Ockford Road, Godalming, Surrey GU7 1QY
Tel: 01483 423 600 Fax: 01483 418 486
Email: mail@ukproductions.co.uk
Web Site: www.ukproductions.co.uk
Director: Martin Dodd
Production Manager: Andy Batty
Administrator: Jo Day

UPSET THE RHYTHM
Also a record label under the same name
363 North End Road, London SW6 1NW
Email: upset_the_rhythm@yahoo.com
Web Site: www.upsettherhythm.co.uk
Co-Concert Promotors: Andrew Doig & Andrew Hickson

VAMPIRES ROCK LTD
PO Box 8729, Newark, NG24 9BD
Tel: 01949 851 530 Fax: 01949 850 605
Email: nicky@vampiresrock.com
Web Site: www.vampiresrock.com
Director: Steven Murray
PR & Publicity: Jane Hirst
Merchandise & Website Information: Becky Cooney

WIM WIGT PRODUCTIONS LTD
98 Arundel Avenue, South Croydon, Surrey CR2 8BE
Tel: 0208 662 1235 Fax: 0208 654 2120
Email: info@wigt.nl
Web Site: www.wimwigt.com
Director, Sales, Bookings: Wim Wigt
Advertising, Promotion, Financial Administration : Herma Lueks

WOMAD LTD
Mill Lane, Box, Corsham, Wiltshire SN13 8PL
Tel: 01225 743 188 Fax: 01225 743 481
Email: info@womad.org
Web Site: www.womad.org
Artistic Director: Chris Smith

WONDERLAND PROMOTIONS LTD
15 Wellington Park, Belfast, County Antrim BT9 6DJ Northern Ireland
Tel: 02890 222 777 Fax: 02890 222 770
Email: enquiries@wonderlandpromotions.co.uk
Web www.wonderlandpromotions.co.uk
Contact: Eamonn McCann

Literary Agents

THE AGENCY (LONDON) LTD
24 Pottery Lane, Holland Park, London W11 4LZ
Tel: 020 7727 1346 Fax: 020 7727 9037
Email: info@theagency.co.uk
Web Site: www.theagency.co.uk
ADMINISTRATION:
Founded in 1995, The Agency represents screenwriters, directors, playwrights, composers, and children's authors & illustrators.
Company Secretary: Monique Campbell

AITKEN ALEXANDER ASSOCIATES
18-21 Cavaye Place, London SW10 9PT
Tel: 020 7373 8672 Fax: 020 7373 6002
Email: reception@aitkenalexander.co.uk
Web Site: www.aitkenalexander.co.uk
Chairman: Gillon Aitken
Joint Managing Directors: Clare Alexander and Sally Riley

AITKEN ALEXANDER ASSOCIATES LTD
18-21 Cavaye Place, London SW10 9PT
Tel: 020 7373 8672 Fax: 020 7373 6002
Email: reception@aitkenalexander.co.uk
Web Site: www.aitkenalexander.co.uk
ADMINISTRATION:
Contacts: Gillon Aitken, Clare Alexander, Lesley Thorne, Ayesha Karim, Matthew Hamilton, Andrew Kidd, Anna Stein.

ANDREW LOWNIE LITERARY AGENCY
36 Great Smith Street, London SW1P 3BU
Tel: 020 7222 7574 Fax: 020 7222 7576
Email: lownie@globalnet.co.uk
Web Site: www.andrewlownie.co.uk
Agent: Andrew Lownie
The Andrew Lownie Literary Agency (founded 1988) is one of Britain's leading non-fiction literary agencies and specialises in history and biography. All authors are personally represented by Andrew Lownie, himself a published author and former journalist.
Authors represented include Juliet Barker, Joyce Cary Estate, Tom Devine, Duncan Falconer, Laurence Gardner, Timothy Good, Lawrence James, Damien Lewis, Martin Pugh, David Roberts, MIchael Schuster, Desmond Seward and Mei Trow.

PAULINE ASPER MANAGEMENT LTD
Jacobs Cottage, Reservior Lane, Sedlescombe, Battle East Sussex TN33 0PJ
Tel: 01424 870 412
Email: paulineasper1@hotmail.com
Senior Personnel: Pauline Asper

ALAN BRODIE REPRESENTATION LTD
Paddock Suite, The Courtyard, 55 Charterhouse Street, London EC1M 6HA
Tel: 020 7253 6226 Fax: 020 7183 7999
Email: info@alanbrodie.com
Web Site: www.alanbrodie.com
Representing scripts for stage, screen and radio. We do not represent fiction, non-fiction or poetry.

CAMPBELL THOMSON & MCLAUGHLIN LTD
50 Albemarle Street, London W1S 4BD
Tel: 020 7297 4311 Fax: 020 7495 8961
Web Site: www.ctmcl.co.uk
Directors: John McLaughlin and Charlotte Bruton

ALEXANDRA CANN REPRESENTATION
52 Beauchamp Place, London SW3 1NY
Tel: 020 7584 9047
Email: mail@alexandracann.co.uk
Senior Personnel: Alexandra Cann

CASAROTTO RAMSAY & ASSOCIATES LTD
Waverley House, 7-12 Noel Street, London W1F 8GQ
Tel: 020 7287 4450 Fax: 020 7287 9128
Email: agents@casarotto.co.uk, info@casarotto.co.uk
Web Site: www.casarotto.co.uk
ADMINISTRATION:
Film and television department: Jeenne Casarotto
Theatrical Department: Tom Erhardt and Mel Kenyon
One of the UK's leading creative agencies, representing writers, directors, directors of photography, production designers, costume designers and editors.

JONATHAN CLOWES LTD
10 Iron Bridge House, Bridge Approach, London NW1 8BD
Tel: 020 7722 7674 Fax: 020 7722 7677
Email: admin@jonathanclowes.co.uk
Web Site: www.jonathanclowes.co.uk
Directors: Jonathan Clowes & Ann Evans

ROSICA COLIN LTD
1 Clareville Grove Mews, London SW7 5AH
Tel: 020 7370 1080 Fax: 020 7244 6441

COLMAN GETTY PR
28 Windmill Street, London W1T 2JJ
Tel: 020 7631 2666 Fax: 020 7631 2699
Email: info@colmangetty.co.uk, Lisa@colmangetty.co.uk
Web Site: www.colmangetty.co.uk
ADMINISTRATION:
Chief Executive: Dotti Irving
Events Manager: Lisa Perkins

CURTIS BROWN GROUP
5th Floor, Haymarket House, 28-29 Haymarket, London SW1Y 4SP
Tel: 020 7393 4400 Fax: 020 7393 4401
Email: jonathan@curtisbrown.co.uk
Web Site: www.curtisbrown.co.uk
Senior Personnel: Nick Marston
Agent: Jonathan Lloyd
Today, with over one hundred years of experience and more than twenty agents within our Book, Media, Actors and Presenters Divisions we represent many of the world's most popular and successful writers, directors, actors, playwrights and celebrities.

JUDY DAISH ASSOCIATES
2 St Charles Place, London W10 6EG
Tel: 020 8964 8811 Fax: 020 8964 8966
Email: judy@judydaish.com
Web Site: www.judydaish.com
ADMINISTRATION:
Senior Personnel: Judy Daish, Tracey Elliston, Howard Gooding
Representing writers, directors, designers and choreographers for theatre, film, television, radio and opera.

DENCH ARNOLD ASSOCIATES
10 Newburgh Street, London W1F 7RN
Tel: 020 7437 4551 Fax: 020 7439 1355
Email: contact@dencharnold.com
Web Site: www.dencharnold.com
Managaing Director: Elizabeth Dench

ED VICTOR AGENCY
6 Bayley Street, London WC1B 3HE
Tel: 020 7304 4100 Fax: 020 7304 4111
Email: charlie@edvictor.com
Contact: Ed Victor, Margaret Phillips, Sophie Hicks.

ELSPETH COCHRANE PERSONAL MANAGEMENT
16 Old Town, Clapham, London SW4 0JY
Tel: 020 7819 6256 Fax: 020 7819 4297
Email: elspeth@elspethcochrane.co.uk
Senior Personnel: Elspeth Cochrane

NORMA FARNES MANAGEMENT
9 Orme Court, London W2 4RL
Tel: 020 7727 1544 Fax: 020 7792 2110
Contact: Norma Farnes

LAURENCE FITCH LTD
258 Belsize Road, London NW6 4BT
Tel: 020 7316 1837 Fax: 020 7624 3629
Email: information@laurencefitch.com
Web Site: www.laurencefitch.com
Contact: Brendon Davis

JILL FOSTER LTD
1 Lyric Square, London W6 0NB
Tel: 020 3178 4409
Email: agents@jflagency.com
Web Site: www.jflagency.com
ADMINISTRATION:
Senior Personnel: Jill Foster, Alison Finch, Simon Williamson, Dominic Lord, Gary Wild
Founded in 1976, Jill Foster Ltd represents writers working in film, television, radio and theatre

SAMUEL FRENCH LTD
52 Fitzroy Street, Fitzrovia, London W1T 5JR
Tel: 020 7387 9373 Fax: 020 7387 2161
Email: theatre@samuelfrench-london.co.uk
Web: www.samuelfrench-london.co.uk

BLAKE FRIEDMANN LITERARY, TV AND FILM AGENCY
122 Arlington Road, London NW1 7HP
Tel: 020 7284 0408 Fax: 020 7284 0442
Email: info@blakefriedmann.co.uk

Web Site: www.blakefriedmann.co.uk
ADMINISTRATION:
Office Manager: Peter Calame
Fiction and Non-Fiction manuscripts: Carole Blake
Film and TV scripts: Julian Friedmann & Conrad Williams

ERIC GLASS LTD
25 Ladbroke Crescent, London W11 1PS
Tel: 020 7229 9500 Fax: 020 7229 6220
Email: eglassltd@aol.com
Senior Personnel: Janet Glass

THE ROD HALL AGENCY LTD
Suite 5.4b, The Old Fire Station, 140 Tabernacle Street, London EC2A 4SD
Tel: 020 7300 7266 Fax: 0871 918 6068
Email: office@rodhallagency.com
Web Site: www.rodhallagency.com
ADMINISTRATION:
Directors: Charlotte Knight, Tanya Tillett, Emily Hayward, Katie Langridge
Formed in May 1997 to represent playwrights and screenwriters, writers who also direct, directors and stage and screen rights in selected novels.

ROGER HANCOCK LTD
7 Broadbent Close, London N6 5JW
Tel: 020 8341 7243
Email: info@rogerhancock.com
ADMINISTRATION:
Contacts: Tim Hancock
Specializing in mainly comedy writers for film and television.

A.M. HEATH & COMPANY LTD
6 Warwick Court Holborn London WC1R 5DJ
Tel: 020 7242 2811 Fax: 020 7242 2711
Email: Victoria.Hobbs@amheath.com
Web Site: www.amheath.com
ADMINISTRATION:
Agent Contacts: Jennifer Custer, Bill Hamilton, Victoria Hobbs, Sarah Molloy, Euan Thorneycroft.

DAVID HIGHAM ASSOCIATES
5-8 Lower John Street, Golden Square, London W1F 9HA
Tel: 020 7434 5900 Fax: 020 7437 1072
Email: dha@davidhigham.co.uk
Web Site: www.davidhigham.co.uk
Contact: Nicky Lund, Georgina Ruffhead, David Perry.

AMANDA HOWARD ASSOCIATES LTD
21 Berwick Street, London W1F 0PZ
Tel: 020 7287 9277 Fax: 020 7287 7785
Email: mail@amandahowardassociates.co.uk
Web: www.amandahowardassociates.co.uk
ADMINISTRATION:
Senior Personnel: Amanda Fitzalan Howard, Mark Price, Kirsten Wright, Darren Rugg, Kevin Brady, Chloe Brayfield.
Amanda Howard Associates are leading talent and literary agents representing actors, presenters, producers, directors, designers, composers, voice-overs and writers of comedy, entertainment and drama. Our clients work across all forms of media, including television, radio, theatre and film productions.

TESSA LE BARS MANAGEMENT
54 Birchwood Road, Petts Wood, Orpington, Kent BR5 1NZ
Tel/Fax: 01689 837 084 Mob Tel: 07860 287 255
Email: tessa.lebars@ntlworld.com
Web Site: www.galtonandsimpson.com
Specialising in Mainly Comedy Writers. Member of Personal Managers Association. Existing Clients Only.

LEMON UNNA AND DURBRIDGE LTD
See The Agency (London) Ltd Listing

CHRISTOPHER LITTLE LITERARY AGENCY
10 Eel Brook Studios, 125 Moore Park Road, London SW6 4PS
Tel: 020 7736 4455 Fax: 020 7736 4490
Email: info@christopherlittle.net
Web Site: www.christopherlittle.net
ADMINISTRATION:
Contacts: Christopher Little, Emma Schlesinger
Commercial and literary full-length fiction and non-fiction (home 15%; US, Canada, translation, audio, motion picture 20%). No reading fee. No unsolicited submissions. No poetry, plays, science fiction, fantasy, textbooks, illustrated children's or short stories. Film scripts for established clients only. Founded 1979.

LUIGI BONAMI ASSOCIATES (LBA)
91 Great Russell Street, London WC1B 3PS
Tel: 020 7637 1234 Fax: 020 637 2111
Email: info@bonomiassociates.co.uk
Web Site: www.bonomiassociates.co.uk
Contacts: Luigi Bonomi, Amanda Preston, Ajda Vucicevic.

JOHNNY MANS PRODUCTIONS LIMITED
Incorporating 'Real Publicity' & 'Encore Magazine'
PO Box 196, Hoddesdon, Hertfordshire EN10 7WG
Tel: 0845 467 0792
Email: johnnymansagent@aol.com, encoremags@aol.com
Web Site: www.johnnymansproductions.co.uk, www.encoremagazine.org.uk
ADMINISTRATION:
Managing Director: Johnny Mans
Administration: Philip Crowe, Elliot Mans,

BLANCHE MARVIN (PMA)
21a St John's Wood High Street, London NW8 7NG
Tel/Fax: 020 7722 2313
Email: blanchemarvin17@hotmail.com
Web Site: www.blanchemarvin.com
ADMINISTRATION:
Managing Director: Blanche Marvin
Plays for theatre, film and TV. Critic and publisher of London theatre reviews.

M.B.A. LITERARY AGENTS LTD
62 Grafton Way, London W1T 5DW
Tel: 020 7387 2076 Fax: 020 7387 2042
Email: agent@mbalit.co.uk
Web Site: www.mbalit.co.uk
Contact: Diana Tyler and Meg Davis

BILL MCLEAN PERSONAL MANAGEMENT
23B Deodar Road, Putney, London SW15 2NP
Tel: 020 8789 8191 Fax: 020 8789 8192
Email: bill.mclean@fsmail.net
Agent: Bill Mclean

MUSICSCOPE
75 Furnival Street, Crewe CW2 7LH
Tel: 01270 617 653 Fax: 01270 583238
Email: info@musicscopeuk.com
Web Site: www.musicscopeuk.com
Partners: John Sinfield & David Jensen
Contact: John Sinfield
Copyright Holders.

PETERS FRASER DUNLOP (PFD)
Drury House, 34-43 Russell Street, London WC2B 5HA
Switchboard: 020 7344 1000 Fax: 020 7836 9543
Email: info@pfd.co.uk
Web Site: www.pfd.co.uk
Senior Personnel: Caroline Michel

POLLINGER LTD
9 Staple Inn, Holborn, London WC1V 7QH
Tel: 020 7404 0342 Fax: 020 7242 5737
Email: info@pollingerltd.com, timbates@pollingerltd.com
Web Site: www.pollingerltd.com
Agency Personnel: Tim Bates, Hayley Yeeles

ROBERT SMITH LITERARY AGENCY
12 Bridge Wharf, 156 Caledonian Road, London N1 9UU
Tel: 020 7278 2444 Fax: 020 7833 5680
Email: robertsmith.literaryagency@virgin.net
Agent: Robert Smith

THE SHARLAND ORGANISATION LTD
The Manor House, Manor Street, Raunds, Wellingborough, Northamptonshire NN9 6JW
Tel: 01933 626 600 Fax: 01933 624 860
Email: tso@btconnect.com
Web: www.sharlandorganisation.co.uk
Directors: Mike Sharland and Alice Sharland

SHEIL LAND ASSOCIATES LTD
52 Doughty Street, London WC1N 2LS
Tel: 020 7405 9351 Fax: 020 7831 2127
Email: info@sheilland.co.uk
Web Site: www.sheilland.co.uk
Agency Personnel: Lucy Fawcett and Holly Hawkins.

THE WYLIE AGENCY
17 Bedford Square, London WC1B 3JA
Tel: 020 7908 5900 Fax: 020 7908 5901
Email: mail@wylieagency.co.uk
Web Site: www.wylieagency.co.uk
Agent: Alba Ziegler Bailey

A.P. WATT LTD
20 John Street, London WC1N 2DR
Tel: 020 7405 6774 Fax: 020 7831 2154
Email: apw@apwatt.co.uk
Web Site: www.apwatt.co.uk
ADMINISTRATION:
Books Agent: Caradoc King, Derek Johns, Georgia Garrett

WILLIAM MORRIS ENDEAVOR ENTERTAINMENT (UK) LTD
Centre Point, 103 New Oxford Street, London WC1A 1DD
Tel: 020 7534 6800 Fax: 020 7534 6900
Email: ccovington@wma.com
Web Site: www.wma.com
Contact: Cathie Covington
Member of Agents' Association (GB)

Voice Over Agencies

ABCADS
49 Ashgrove, Steeple Claydon, Buckingham MK18 2LW
Tel: 01296 738 020
Email: info@abcdirectentertainments.co.uk
Web: www.abcdirectentertainments.co.uk
Senior Personnel: Len Illing, Catherine Brandon, Elise Illing, Charlotte Illing, William Illing

CALYPSO VOICES
25-26 Poland Street, London W1F 8QN
Tel: 020 7734 6415 Fax: 020 7437 0410
Email: calypso@calypsovoices.com
Web Site: www.calypsovoices.com
Senior Personnel: Jane Savage
Voice Over Agency - call for details.

CASTAWAY
Suite 3 15 Broad Court London WC2B 5QN
Tel: 020 7240 2345 Fax: 020 7240 2772
Email: sheila@castaway.org.uk
Web Site: www.castaway.org.uk
Senior Personnel: Sheila Britten
We have the widest range of carefully selected professional voice talent.

BRYAN DREW LTD
Quadrant House, 80/82 Regent Street, London W1B 5AU
Tel: 020 7437 2293 Fax: 020 7437 0561
Email: bryan@bryandrewltd.com
Web Site: www.bryandrewltd.com
Senior Personnel: Bryan Drew, Mina Parmar
Specialising in Actors, Actresses, Writers, Directors, Voice Overs

EARACHE VOICES
177 Wardour Street, London W1F 8WX
Tel: 020 7287 2291 Fax: 020 7287 2288
Email: alex@earachevoices.com
Web Site: www.earachevoices.com
Agent: Alex Lynch-White

EDDIE LOCK
2, The Old Parish Hall The Square Lenham Kent ME17 2PQ
Tel: 01622 858300 Mob: 07710 772207
Email: info@eddielock.com
Web Site: www.eddielock.co.uk / www.goldie.co.uk
Contact: Eddie Lock
Exclusive Worldwide Management & Agent of Goldie

EVANS O'BRIEN
2 Lampmead Road, London SE12 8QL
Tel: 020 8318 9058
Email: info@evansobrien.co.uk
Web Site: www.evansobrien.co.uk
Agent: Kate Evans

EXCELLENT VOICE COMPANY
19-21 Tavistock Street, London WC2E 7PA
Tel: 020 7520 5656
Email: info@excellentvoice.co.uk
Web Site: www.excellentvoice.co.uk
Voice Over agency representing over 100 of the UK's top voice artistes and 15 TV presenters. Website has a full casting engine and reels that can stream direct from the server or MP3 downloads for you to send direct to your clients. All artists have 25 second soundbite reels that allow you toi hear their complete range in a suitably short time frame for casting purposes. Please visit website for full Artiste Roster.

FOREIGN VERSIONS LTD
60 Blandford Street, London W1U 7JD
Tel: 020 7935 0993 Fax: 020 7935 0507
Email: info@foreignversions.co.uk
Web Site: www.foreignversions.co.uk
Senior Personnel: Margaret Davies
Provider of professional foreign language services to the media and communication industries.

GOLDMAN KING
16 St. Albans Road, Kingston upon Thames, Surrey KT2 5HQ
Tel: 020 8287 1199
Email: artistes@goldmanking.com
Web Site: www.goldmanking.com
Goldman King represent Comedians, Writers, Studio Warm-ups, Actors and Voice-Over Artistes. Our experienced comedy performers are available for castings and also corporate entertainment.

HARVEY VOICES LTD
4th Floor, 54-55 Margaret Street, London W1W 8SH
Tel: 020 7952 4361
Email: info@harveyvoices.co.uk
Web Site: www.harveyvoices.co.uk
Contact: Emma Harvey
Also represent children of all ages and Foreign Artistes

ROBERTA KANAL AGENCY
82 Constance Road, Twickenham, Middlesex TW2 7JA
Tel: 020 8894 2277 Fax: 020 8894 7952
Senior Personnel: Roberta Kanal

LATIN ARTS SERVICES (LAS) MUSIC
PO Box 57817, London SE23 3PT
Tel/Fax: 020 8291 9236 Mobile: 07956 446342
Email: info@latinartsgroup.com
Web Site: www.latinartsgroup.com
Senior Personnel: Hector Rosquete
Latin entertainment promoters. Our new show is The Mambo Boyz Salsa Show.

LIP SERVICE CASTING LIMITED
60-66 Wardour Street, London W1F 0TA
Tel: 020 7734 3393 Fax: 020 7734 3373
Email: bookings@lipservice.co.uk
Web Site: www.lipservice.co.uk
Also a roster of Foreign Artistes. Call for further details.

JOHN NOEL MANAGEMENT
Block B, Imperial Works Perren Street London NW5 3ED
Tel: 020 7428 8400 Fax: 020 7428 8401
Email: john@johnnoel.com
Web Site: www.johnnoel.com
Agent: John Noel

PRESENTER PROMOTIONS
123 Corporation Road, Gillingham, Kent ME7 1RG
Tel/Fax: 01634 851 077
Email: info@presenterpromotions.com
Web Site: www.presenterpromotions.com
Senior Personnel: Colin Cobb
With over 20 years experience, we specialise in Presenters, Speakers, Voice Artistes. Offering a casting service free to production companies and specialist help to newcomers and artistes without an agent.

QVOICE
4th Floor, Holborn Hall, 193-197 High Holborn, London WC1V 7BD
Tel: 020 7025 0660 Fax: 020 7025 0659
Email: sarah@qvoice.co.uk
Web Site: www.qvoice.co.uk
Agent: Nicola Richardson
Agent's Assistant: Sarah King

RABBIT VOCAL MANAGEMENT
Second Floor 18 Broadwick St London W1F 8HS
Tel: 020 7287 6466 Fax: 020 7281 6566
Email: info@rabbit.uk.net
Senior Personnel: Melanie Bourne

RHUBARB VOICE OVERS
1st Floor 1a Devonshire Road Chiswick London W4 2EU
Tel: 020 8742 8683 Fax: 020 8742 8693
Email: enquiries@rhubarb.co.uk
Web Site: www.rhubarb.co.uk
Senior Personnel: Johnny Garcia
Rhubarb produces audio in-house from own talent base.

SHINING MANAGEMENT LTD
81 Oxford Street London W1D 2EU
Tel: 020 7734 1981 Fax: 020 7734 2528
Email: info@shiningvoices.com
Web Site: www.shiningvoices.com
Agents: Jennifer Taylor Cave, Clair Daintree
Voice artist agency for all types of projects. Accounts/Admin address: PO Box 1045, Chislehurst BR7 9AR. Please send all remittances/payments to this address.

SPEAK-EASY LTD
PO Box 648, Harrington, Northampton NN6 9XT
Tel: 0870 0135 126
Email: enquiries@speak-easy.co.uk / firstname@speak-easy.co.uk
Web Site: www.speak-easy.co.uk
Presenters: Kate Moon
Voice Overs: Katie Matthews-Lee
Representing some of the finest established talent and rising stars including: Presenters/Journalists (TV & Radio); Conference Facilitators/Speakers; Voice Overs (Documentaries/Commercials/Corporate).

SUE TERRY VOICES
18 Broadwick Street, London W1F 8HS
Tel: 020 7434 2040 Fax: 020 7434 2042
Email: sue@sueterryvoices.co.uk
Web Site: www.sueterryvoices.co.uk
Contact: Sue Terry
Complete artist roster available on our website.

TALKING HEADS - THE VOICE AGENCY
2-4 Noel Street, London W1F 8GB
Tel: 020 7292 7575 Fax: 020 7292 7576
Email: voices@talkingheadsvoices.com
Web Site: www.talkingheadsvoices.com
Senior Personnel: John Sachs
Specialising in Voice Overs, Atlantic, Character, Impressionists, Broadcasters, DJ's, Personalities, Actors, Foreign, Presenters and Documentaries.

THE VOICEOVER GALLERY LTD
34 Stockton Road, Chorlton, Manchester M21 9ED
Tel: 0161 881 8844 Fax: 0161 718 1009
Email: info@thevoiceovergallery.co.uk
Web Site: www.thevoiceovergallery.co.uk
Agent: Marylou Thistleton-Smith
Marketing Assistant: Suzy Fitzpatrick
A voice over agency representing a number of celebrity & experianced voice over artists. To make things easier for our clients, we also have 2 voice over studios & an ISDN line.

VOICE & SCRIPT INTERNATIONAL
128 - 134 Cleveland Street, London W1T 6AB
Tel: 020 7692 7700 Fax: 020 7692 7711
ISDN: 020 7692 7722
Email: info@vsi.tv
Web Site: www.vsi.tv
Managing Director: Norman Dawood
Office Manager: Krista Raag
Services include; Script translation, Foreign-language voices, Subtitling, Dubbing, Deaf & hard of hearing services, Audio suites, DVD & video services, Avid offline & online.

THE VOICE BOX AGENCY LTD
1st Floor 100 Talbot Road, Old Trafford, Manchester M16 0PG
Tel: 0161 874 5741 Fax: 0161 888 2242
Email: elinors@thevoicebox.co.uk
Web Site: www.thevoicebox.co.uk
Contact: Elinor Stanton
Agency which represent voice-over artistes only.

VOICE SHOP
1st Floor, 1a Devonshire Road, London W4 2EU
Tel: 020 8742 7077 Fax: 020 8742 7011
Email: info@voice-shop.co.uk
Web Site: www.voice-shop.co.uk
Senior Personnel: Maxine Wiltshire
Voice-over and casting agency.

JENNI WATERS T/A VOICES
2 Kirkgate Lane, Wighton, Wells-next-the-Sea, Norfolk NR23 1PL
Tel: 01328 820 950 Fax: 01328 820 951
Contact: Jenni Waters

WIELAND AND BROOKS ASSOCIATES
PO Box 70, Feltham, Middlesex TW13 6FH
Tel: 020 8345 5905
Managing Director: Dave Wieland
Voice-over artistes representation, providing new international talent for TV, radio and film.

WILIAMSON & HOLMES
9 Hop Gardens, St Martin's Lane, London WC2N 4EH
Tel: 020 7240 0407 Fax: 020 7240 0408
Email: jackie@williamsonandholmes.co.uk
Web www.williamsonandholmes.co.uk
For actors and general enquiries, contact: Jackie Williamson
For all voice enquiries, contact: Sophie Reisch - sophie@williamsonandholmes.co.uk
For all children enquiries, contact: Danica Pickett
Williamson & Holmes represent actors in film, television, theatre, musical theatre, commercial and corporate work

WISE BUDDAH TALENT & VOICES
74 Great Titchfield Street, London W1W 7QP
Tel: 020 7307 1600 Fax: 020 7307 1601
Email: chris.north@wisebuddah.com / john.lawley@wisebuddah.com
Web Site: www.wisebuddah.com
Agent: Chris North

YAKETY YAK
7a Bloomsbury Square, London WC1A 2LP
Tel: 020 7430 2600 Fax: 020 7404 6109
Email: info@yaketyyak.co.uk
Web Site: www.yaketyyak.co.uk
Senior Personnel: Jolie Williams

Specialist Agents:

Animal Hire

NITA ANDERSON ENTERTAINMENT
165 Wolverhampton Road, Sedgley, Dudley, West Midlands DY3 1QR
Tel: 01902 882 211 / 681 224 Fax:

01902 883 356
Email: nitaandersonagency@hotmail.com
Web Site: www.nitaanderson.co.uk
Senior Personnel: Nita Anderson
Suppliers of Corporate Entertainment and After Dinner Speakers.

ANIMAL WORLD
28 Greaves Road, High Wycombe, Buckinghamshire HP13 7JU
Mobile: 07956 564715
Email: animalswork1@yahoo.co.uk
Web Site: www.animalswork.co.uk
Senior Personnel: Trevor Smith (07956 564715)
Established in1973. Specialising in providing animals to the entertainment industry, while ensuring their safety and protection from harm. Famous Animals who star on TV and in Films.

CIRCUS PROMOTIONS
36 St Luke's Road, Tunbridge Wells, Kent TN4 9JH
Tel: 01892 537 964 Fax: 01892 683 401
Mobile: 07973 512845
Email: info@heyprestoentertainments.co.uk
Web www.heyprestonentertainments.co.uk
Senior Personnel: Michael Alan Bonfield

Asian Artistes

THE A6 AGENCY
Willow Moorings Kegworth DE74 2EY
Mobile: 07889 745594
Email: michaelhobson2012@yahoo.co.uk
Web: www.snapshotproductions.co.uk
Senior Personnel: Michael Hobson
Specialising in outdoor and promotional attractions, jazz bands and silouette and origami artistes

BOMBAY BAJA BRASS BAND
53 Newquay Road, Walsall, WS5 3EL
Tel: 07710 040 183
Email: info@bombaybaja.com
Web Site: www.bombaybaja.com

DIVA ENTERTAINMENTS AGENCY
50-54 Farnham Road, Seven Kings, Ilford, Essex IG3 8QD
Tel: 020 8590 8050 Fax: 020 8590 8099
Email:
honeykalaria@divaentertainments.com
Web Site: www.divaentertainments.com
Contact: Honey Kalaria
Specialising in Bollywood/Asian acts

ICON ACTORS MANAGEMENT
Tanzaro House, Ardwick Green North, Manchester M12 6FZ
Tel: 0161 273 3344 Fax: 0161 273 4567
Email: nancy@iconactors.net
Web Site: www.iconactors.net
Contact: Rhian Salmon
Agent Director: Nancy Morris-Long
Represent actors for work in all areas of the industry. Casting suite available to hire.

JAZZ BARTON AGENCY
8 Rossby, Shinfield, Reading RG2 9FS
Mobile Tel: 07989 333745
Email: jazzkbarton@yahoo.co.uk
Bollywood Specialists representing Actors.
Bollywood Agent: Jazz Barton

MATTERS MUSICAL
The Loft, Rear of 8 West Street, Dorking, Surrey RH4 1BL
Tel: 01306 741 007 Fax: 01306 741 008
Email: info@mattersmusical.com
Web Site: www.mattersmusical.com
Senior Personnel: Frank Warren
Plus Dance Instruction/Demonstration for all the styles listed below.

NEW FACES
2nd Floor, The Linen Hall, 162-168 Regent Street, London W1B 5TB
Tel: 020 7439 6900 Fax: 020 7287 5481
Email: val@newfacestalent.co.uk
Web Site: www.newfacestalent.co.uk
Agents: Val Horton, Tania Patti
New Faces is a dynamic presenters, actors and extras agency situated in the west end of London. The agency is aimed at giving highly talented people of today a platform from which to launch their career and established artists a professional, friendly, approachable and highly efficient service.
If you wish to be considered for representation, please send us a copy of your showreel (if appropriate), up-to-date CV or details of experience, photograph and SAE. All tapes are viewed and if we are interested we will contact you and arrange an interview.
For more information call Val or Cathy on 020 7439 6900.

ORIENTAL ARTS (BRADFORD) LIMITED
Design Exchange, 24 Peckover Street, Bradford, West Yorkshire BD1 5BD
Tel: 01274 370190 Fax: 01274 729 680
Email: info@orientalarts.org.uk
Senior Personnel: Champak Kumar Limbachia
Specialises in Promoting Asian Arts.

PHA MODEL & CASTING MANAGEMENT
Tanzaro House, Ardwick Green North, Manchester M12 6FZ
Tel: 0161 273 4444 Fax: 0161 273 4567
Email: info@pha-agency.co.uk
Web Site: www.pha-agency.co.uk
Senior Personnel: Lorna McDonough, Robert F Lang
Represent models, extras and actors for commercials, corporate and TV work.
Largest casting suites in Manchester also available for hire.

ROGUES & VAGABONDS MANAGEMENT
The Printhouse, 18 Ashwin Street, London E8 3DL
Tel: 020 7254 8130 Fax: 020 7249 8564
Email:
rogues@vagabondsmanagement.com
Web www.vagabondsmanagement.com
Agent: Ann Robson
Rogues is the oldest established actors' co-operative in London, with an excellent track record of finding work for actors and actresses, comedians and comediennes.

BRIAN TAYLOR ASSOCIATES
50 Pembroke Road, Kensington, London W8 6NX
Tel: 020 7602 6141 Fax: 020 7602 6301
Email: briantaylor@nqassoc.freeserve.co.uk
Agent: Brian Taylor

Ballet

A.I.R. LIMITED
AIR House, Spennymoor, County Durham DL16 7SE
Tel: 01388 814 632 Fax: 01388 812 445
Email: info@airagency.com
Web Site: www.airagency.com
Directors: Colin Pearson, John Wray

ALEX JAY PERSONAL MANAGEMENT
8 Higher Newmarket Road, Newmarket, Nailsworth, Gloucestershire GL6 0RP
Tel/Fax: 01453 834 783
Email: alexjay@alex-jay-pm.freeserve.co.uk
Senior Personnel: Alex Jay
Specialising in artistes for film, television, theatre, commercials and TV & radio presenters.

DONALD SCRIMGEOUR ARTISTS AGENCY
49 Springcroft Avenue, London N2 9JH
Tel: 020 8444 6248 Fax: 020 8883 9751
Email: vwest@dircon.co.uk
Web Site: www.donaldscrimgeour.com
Senior Personnel: Donald Scrimgeour (Spain), Valerie West (London)
Representing Dancers, Choreographers, Teachers/Ballet Masters, Dance Producers, Conductors & Designers.

Balloon Sculpture

THE A6 AGENCY
Willow Moorings Kegworth DE74 2EY
Mobile: 07889 745594
Email: michaelhobson2012@yahoo.co.uk
Web: www.snapshotproductions.co.uk
Senior Personnel: Michael Hobson
Specialising in outdoor and promotional attractions, jazz bands and silouette and origami artistes

CHARLIE THE CLOWN
Flat 4 Carleton House 122A Hillfield Avenue London N8 7DQ
Tel: 07808 732 390
Email: info@charlietheclown.co.uk
Web Site: www.charlietheclown.co.uk
Senior Personnel: Lawrence Anthony
Specialising in children's entertainment for all ages. Choice of characters includes a clown, pirate, wizzard and story-teller. Entertainment includes clown and magic shows, singing and dancing, balloon, modelling & story-telling.

CIRCUS ALCHEMY
5 Beech Avenue, Rawmarsh, Rotherham, South Yorkshire S62 5HH
Tel: 01709 710 780 Fax: 01709 710 780
Email: albert@albertalchemy.com
Web Site: www.albertalchemy.com
Contact: Albert Alchemy
Fire-eating, escapology, stiltwalking, medieval jester. Magic for corporate, public and private functions.

CONTINENTAL DRIFTS
8 Hilton Grove, Hatherley Mews, Walthamstow, London E17 4QP
Tel: 020 8509 3353 Fax: 020 8509 9531
Email: info@continentaldrifts.co.uk
Web Site: www.continentaldrifts.co.uk
Senior Personnel: Mel Wilds, Chris Meikan
Event Production and Performance Specialists.
The finest in event entertainment and production, whether a single stilt walker or a fully choreographed show. Continental Drifts artists range from the bizarre to the beautiful and we have an in-house creative team to formulate ideas and realise your vision. Full technical production is available, along with fully trained event crews. Continental Drifts take a client-centred approach are are more than happy to meet with you to discuss your event requirements in full detail.

CROWD PULLERS (STREET PERFORMERS AND BANDS)
14 Somerset Gardens, London SE13 7SY
Tel: 020 8469 3900 Fax: 020 8469 2147
Mobile: 07831 150170
Email: jhole@crowdpullers.co.uk
Web Site: www.crowdpullers.co.uk
Senior Personnel: John Hole

D&S ARTISTES
19 Reffley Lane, King's Lynn, Norfolk PE30 3EF
Tel/Fax: 01553 671 693 Mobile: 07904 524 051
Email: info@dandsartistes.co.uk
Web Site: www.dandsartistes.co.uk
Senior Personnel: Alan Johnston, Mark Pearman
Specialising in groups, cabaret, children's entertainers, discos and celebrity appearances.

HEY PRESTO ENTERTAINMENTS AGENCY
36 St Luke's Road, Tunbridge Wells, Kent TN4 9JH
Tel: 01892 537 964 Fax: 01892 683 401
Mobile: 07973 512845
Email: info@heyprestoentertainments.co.uk
Web Site: www.heyprestoentertainments.co.uk
Senior Personnel: Michael Alan Bonfield

DAWN JUDD ENTERTAINMENTS
19 Ashness Gardens, Greenford, Middlesex UB6 0RL
Tel: 020 8902 3373 / 8903 5533 Fax: 020 8902 9538
Web: www.dawnjuddentertainments.co.uk
Senior Personnel: Dawn Judd

MR "E" ENTERPRISES
Little Greenfields Farm, Jack Haye Lane, Light Oaks, Stoke-on-Trent, Staffordshire ST2 7NG
Tel: 01782 304 909 Mobile: 07831 311318
Email: info@mreenterprises.co.uk
Senior Personnel: Eddie Burke

SALVO THE CLOWN
13 Second Avenue, Kingsleigh Park, Thundersley, Essex SS7 3QD
Tel: 01268 745 791
Email: salvo@annualclownsdirectory.com
Web Site: www.annualclownsdirectory.com
Contact: Salvo

Barber Shop Singers

THE A6 AGENCY
Willow Moorings Kegworth DE74 2EY
Mobile: 07889 745594
Email: michaelhobson2012@yahoo.co.uk
Web: www.snapshotproductions.co.uk
Senior Personnel: Michael Hobson
Specialising in outdoor and promotional attractions, jazz bands and silouette and origami artistes

LONDON MUSIC AGENCY
7 Rosewood Drive, Orchard Heights Ashford, Kent TN25 4QF
Tel: 01233 623 623 Mob: 07885 032 132
Email: enquiries@londonmusicagency.co.uk
Web: www.londonmusicagency.co.uk
Proprietor: Jenny Braby
Everything in entertainment for Private and Corporate functions, e.g. Jazz, String Quartets and all types of band, music and the unusual.

MATTERS MUSICAL
The Loft, Rear of 8 West Street, Dorking, Surrey RH4 1BL
Tel: 01306 741 007 Fax: 01306 741 008
Email: info@mattersmusical.com
Web Site: www.mattersmusical.com
Senior Personnel: Frank Warren
Plus Dance Instruction/Demonstration for all the styles listed below.

NEW FACES
2nd Floor, The Linen Hall, 162-168 Regent Street, London W1B 5TB
Tel: 020 7439 6900 Fax: 020 7287 5481
Email: val@newfacestalent.co.uk
Web Site: www.newfacestalent.co.uk
Agents: Val Horton, Tania Patti
New Faces is a dynamic presenters, actors and extras agency situated in the west end of London. The agency is aimed at giving highly talented people of today a platform from which to launch their career and established artists a professional, friendly, approachable and highly efficient service.
If you wish to be considered for representation, please send us a copy of your showreel (if appropriate), up-to-date CV or details of experience, photograph and SAE. All tapes are viewed and if we are interested we will contact you and arrange an interview.
For more information call Val or Cathy on 020 7439 6900.

STELLAMAX ENTERPRISES LTD
Nova House, 53 Nova Croft, Off Broad Lane, Eastern Green, Coventry, Warwickshire CV5 7FJ
Tel: 024 7646 9585 Mob: 07899 045363
Email: max@stellamax.com
Web Site: www.stellamax.com
Senior Personnel: Max Roberts

Barn Dance Band/Ceilidh/Folk Dance Band

THE A6 AGENCY
Willow Moorings Kegworth DE74 2EY
Mobile: 07889 745594

Email: michaelhobson2012@yahoo.co.uk
Web: www.snapshotproductions.co.uk
Senior Personnel: Michael Hobson
Specialising in outdoor and promotional attractions, jazz bands and silouette and origami artistes

ABDC ENTERTAINMENTS
La Loma, 18 Halls Farm Close,
Winchester, Hampshire SO22 6RE
Tel: 01962 885 628 Fax: 0845 3344981
YAK: 07092 035070
Email: anyact@abdc.co.uk
Web Site: www.abdc.co.uk
Senior Personnel: Henry Garfath, Barbara Hall
Entertainment agents offering a comprehensive one-stop service from single acts to complete events - everything from Acrobats to Zydeco - Specialists in Barn/Square Dances, Ceilidhs, Hoedowns & Line Dancing.

BAND OF TWO
26 Cumberland Court, 21 Cross Road,
Croydon, Surrey CR0 6TE
Tel: 020 8680 4302
Email: petefyfe@aol.com
Web Site: www.bandoftwo.com
Contact: Peter Fyfe
"Specialising in Goodtime Celtic/Irish Songs, Tunes and Folk Dances."

BARN DANCE LINE DANCE AGENCY
20 Shirley Avenue, Old Coulsdon, Surrey CR5 1QU
Tel: 020 8668 5714 Fax: 020 8645 6923
Email: info@barn-dance.co.uk
Web Site: www.barn-dance.co.uk
Senior Personnel: Derek Jones, Pamela Jones

DAVID CHARLES AGENCY
2 Betjeman Way, Hemel Hempstead,
Hertfordshire HP1 3HH
Tel: 01442 264 402 Mobile: 07767 813 231
Email: david@davidcharlesent.co.uk
Web Site: www.davidcharlesent.co.uk
Senior Personnel: David Charles, Penny Charles
Specialising in adult entertainment, bands and groups.

COMPACT MANAGEMENT & ENTERTAINMENT AGENCY
98 Shellards Road, Longwell Green,
Bristol, South Gloucestershire BS30 9DT
Tel: 0117 932 4344 Fax: 0117 932 6006
Mobile: 07831 446958
Email: paul@compactents.co.uk
Web Site: www.compactents.co.uk
Senior Personnel: Paul Wolf

CROWD PULLERS (STREET PERFORMERS AND BANDS)
14 Somerset Gardens, London SE13 7SY
Tel: 020 8469 3900 Fax: 020 8469 2147
Mobile: 07831 150170
Email: jhole@crowdpullers.co.uk
Web Site: www.crowdpullers.co.uk
Senior Personnel: John Hole

FLAT CAT BARN DANCE BAND
Oakleigh, Chitcombe Road, Broad Oak,
Rye, East Sussex TN31 6EU
Tel/Fax: 01424 882 046
Email: flatcatlangley@supanet.com
Web Site: www.flatcatband.com
Contact: Denis Langley
The Flat Cat Barn Dance Band, based in Hastings, are a well-established and accommodating band with a line-up comprising fiddle, concertina and guitars. An accordionist is also available if required. Their repertoire includes jigs, polkas, hornpipes and waltzes. A fun evening for all ages is guaranteed.

LONDON MUSIC AGENCY
7 Rosewood Drive, Orchard Heights
Ashford, Kent TN25 4QF
Tel: 01233 623 623 Mob: 07885 032 132
Email:
enquiries@londonmusicagency.co.uk
Web: www.londonmusicagency.co.uk
Proprietor: Jenny Braby
Everything in entertainment for Private and Corporate functions, e.g. Jazz, String Quartets and all types of band, music and the unusual.

MATTERS MUSICAL
The Loft, Rear of 8 West Street, Dorking,
Surrey RH4 1BL
Tel: 01306 741 007 Fax: 01306 741 008
Email: info@mattersmusical.com
Web Site: www.mattersmusical.com
Senior Personnel: Frank Warren
Plus Dance Instruction/Demonstration for all the styles listed below.

RENT-A-BAND
Burnside House, 10 Burns Court, Birstall,
Batley, West Yorkshire WF17 9JZ
Tel/Fax: 01924 441 441
Email: bands@rent-a-band.org
Web Site: www.rent-a-band.org
Senior Personnel: Ken Baxter

STELLAMAX ENTERPRISES LTD
Nova House, 53 Nova Croft, Off Broad Lane, Eastern Green, Coventry,
Warwickshire CV5 7FJ
Tel: 024 7646 9585 Mob: 07899 045363
Email: max@stellamax.com
Web Site: www.stellamax.com
Senior Personnel: Max Roberts

UPBEAT ENTERTAINMENT
236 Hythe Road Willesborough Kent
TN24 0QS
Tel: 01233 650 218 Fax: 01233 641 446
Mobile: 07974 260 479
Email: station2@tiscali.co.uk
Web: www.upbeat-entertainment.com
Senior Personnel: Kim Carney-Boeje

WINSTON THE SINGING FARMER
Nethergate Farm Guestwick, Dereham,
Norfolk NR20 5QR
Tel: 07748 186 489
Email: winston@singingfarmer.co.uk
Web Site: www.singingfarmer.co.uk
Contact: Winson

Caricaturists & Cartoonists

THE A6 AGENCY
Willow Moorings Kegworth DE74 2EY
Mobile: 07889 745594
Email: michaelhobson2012@yahoo.co.uk
Web: www.snapshotproductions.co.uk
Senior Personnel: Michael Hobson
Specialising in outdoor and promotional attractions, jazz bands and silouette and origami artistes

BELLTOWER ENTERPRISES
9 Hillside Road, Ashtead,
Surrey KT21 1RZ
Tel: 01372 277 703 Fax: 01372 278 406
Mobile: 07850 486 466
Email: music@dragonsfire.uk.com
Web Site: www.dragonsfire.uk.com
Senior Personnel: Nigel & Hilary Perona-Wright

CARICATURES & MAGIC
14 Mayfield Place, Brunswick Green,
Wideopen, Newcastle-upon-Tyne, Tyne and Wear NE13 7HY
Tel: 0191 236 3152
Mobile: 07802 748 579
Email: info@paullytton.com
Caricaturist, Paul Slattery & Magician, Paul Lytton
An unbeatable reputation with a complimentary blend of caricatures and magic for all your corporate entertainment needs.
Paul Slattery ~ A slick talent with any medium, be it pens, pencils or brushes. You will be both amazed and delighted at the lightening speed of Paul's caricaturing.
Paul Lytton ~ Specialising in close-up magic, you will be impressed, astonished and entertained !

DAVID CHARLES AGENCY

2 Betjeman Way, Hemel Hempstead, Hertfordshire HP1 3HH
Tel: 01442 264 402
Mobile: 07767 813 231
Email: david@davidcharlesent.co.uk
Web Site: www.davidcharlesent.co.uk
Senior Personnel: David Charles, Penny Charles
Specialising in adult entertainment, bands and groups.

COLEYS CARICATURES

61 Neville Road, Heacham, Norfolk PE31 7HD
Tel: 07879 243 117
Email: supacoley@hotmail.com
Web Site: www.coleyscaricatures.com
Contact: Phil Cole
Caricatures the perfect party or event entertainment, for staff christmas parties, birthdays, weddings, dinner parties or college balls. Ten minute on the spot sketches are drawn of guests on A3 size paper, this is a fun way of entertaining at corporate functions! Line or colour commissions also
available from photographs by post.
Also available for parties, Henna tattoos which last several weeks (by professional henna artist). As well as 1-3 day instant drying full colour realistic temporary tattoos: as used in the film "cape fear".
For either service, please view the information on the website. colour brochure also available on request. Feel free to ring me to discuss availability or any other questions that you or your clients may require.

COMPACT MANAGEMENT & ENTERTAINMENT AGENCY

98 Shellards Road, Longwell Green, Bristol, South Gloucestershire BS30 9DT
Tel: 0117 932 4344 Fax: 0117 932 6006
Mobile: 07831 446958
Email: paul@compactents.co.uk
Web Site: www.compactents.co.uk
Senior Personnel: Paul Wolf

CONTINENTAL DRIFTS

8 Hilton Grove, Hatherley Mews, Walthamstow, London E17 4QP
Tel: 020 8509 3353 Fax: 020 8509 9531
Email: info@continentaldrifts.co.uk
Web Site: www.continentaldrifts.co.uk
Senior Personnel: Mel Wilds, Chris Meikan
Event Production and Performance Specialists.
The finest in event entertainment and production, whether a single stilt walker or a fully choreographed show. Continental Drifts artists range from the bizarre to the beautiful and we have an in-house creative team to formulate ideas and realise your vision. Full technical production is available, along with fully trained event crews. Continental Drifts take a client-centred approach are are more than happy to meet with you to discuss your event requirements in full detail.

CROWD PULLERS (STREET PERFORMERS AND BANDS)

14 Somerset Gardens, London SE13 7SY
Tel: 020 8469 3900 Fax: 020 8469 2147
Mobile: 07831 150170
Email: jhole@crowdpullers.co.uk
Web Site: www.crowdpullers.co.uk
Senior Personnel: John Hole

DEVIL MANAGEMENT

PO Box 23, Spennymoor, County Durham DL16 7YZ
Tel: 01388 818 888 Fax: 01388 811 222
Email: steve@devilmanagement.com
Web Site: www.devilmanagement.com
Contact: Steve Dodds, Paul Carr

HEY PRESTO ENTERTAINMENTS AGENCY

36 St Luke's Road, Tunbridge Wells, Kent TN4 9JH
Tel: 01892 537 964 Fax: 01892 683 401
Mobile: 07973 512845
Email: info@heyprestoentertainments.co.uk
Web: www.heyprestoentertainments.co.uk
Senior Personnel: Michael Alan Bonfield

DAWN JUDD ENTERTAINMENTS

19 Ashness Gardens, Greenford, Middlesex UB6 0RL
Tel: 020 8902 3373 / 8903 5533
Fax: 020 8902 9538
Web: www.dawnjuddentertainments.co.uk
Senior Personnel: Dawn Judd

LONDON MUSIC AGENCY

7 Rosewood Drive, Orchard Heights Ashford, Kent TN25 4QF
Tel: 01233 623 623 Mob: 07885 032 132
Email: enquiries@londonmusicagency.co.uk
Web: www.londonmusicagency.co.uk
Proprietor: Jenny Braby
Everything in entertainment for Private and Corporate functions, e.g. Jazz, String Quartets and all types of band, music and the unusual.

MR SKETCHUM'S CARICATURES

69 Egerton Road, London N16 6UE
Mobile: 07719 262 736
Email: alfie@sketchum.co.uk
Web Site: www.sketchum.co.uk
Contact: Alfie Deliss
Alfie Deliss, also known as Mr Sketchum, a product of Chelsea College of Art available to sketch at all kinds of corporate and private events. See the website for lots of examples of 'live' sketches and more ...

JIM NAYLOR

The Cossack, Houghton Road, Stockbridge, Hampshire SO20 6LE
Tel: 01264 810 956
Email: jimnaylorcartoons@zoom.co.uk
Web: www.cartoonists.co.uk/naylor or www.ccgb.org.uk
Caricaturist and Cartoonist.
Available for Corporate Functions, Parties, Balls and Commissioned Portraits.
Caricatures for The Boardroom, Individual or Group as a gift or presentation, in black & white or colour.
Ring Jim Naylor on 01264 810 956 for a free client list, samples, letters of recommendation or just to pick his brains as to how you can make best use of his talents.

SPOT ON! CARICATURES

PO Box 6235, Leicester LE1 1AA
Tel: 0845 120 320
Mobile: 07793 677 794
Email: george@caricatures-uk.com
Web Site: www.caricatures-uk.com
Contact: George Williams
'TV Times' artiste George - The most off the cuff, dynamic, published Walkabout Caricaturist in the UK, ideal entertainment for Corporate functions, Weddings and Balls. Drawing one every 5 minutes, George turns caricaturing into a spectacle while drawing a crowd, creating a unique buzz and breaking the ice! Guaranteed quality with an individual edge!!

STELLAMAX ENTERPRISES LTD

Nova House, 53 Nova Croft, Off Broad Lane, Eastern Green, Coventry, Warwickshire CV5 7FJ
Tel: 024 7646 9585 Mob: 07899 045363
Email: max@stellamax.com
Web Site: www.stellamax.com
Senior Personnel: Max Roberts

UPBEAT ENTERTAINMENT

236 Hythe Road Willesborough Kent TN24 0QS
Tel: 01233 650 218 Fax: 01233 641 446
Mobile: 07974 260 479
Email: station2@tiscali.co.uk
Web: www.upbeat-entertainment.com
Senior Personnel: Kim Carney-Boeje

Chefs

CELEBRITY CHEFS UK

Tel: 01270 884 544 Mob: 0789 968 3180
Email: roemelbourne@aol.com
Web Site: www.celebritychefsuk.com
Contact: Rosemary Melbourne

CHEFS DU MONDE

13 Montagu Mews South, London W1H 7ER
Tel: 0871 250 1234

Email: anton@celebrity.co.uk
Web Site: www.chefdumonde.com
Agent: Anton Blanc
Celebrity Chefs for advertising, endorsements and corporate events.

STAN GREEN MANAGEMENT
PO Box 4, Dartmouth, Devon TQ6 0YD
Tel: 01803 770 046 Fax: 01803 770 075
Email: tv@stangreen.co.uk
Web Site: www.stangreen.co.uk
Senior Personnel: Stan Green
Production Manager: Adrian Worsley

DEBORAH MCKENNA LIMITED
Claridge House, 29 Barnes High Street, London SW13 9LW
Tel: 020 8876 7566 Fax: 020 8392 2462
Email: adam.kingl@deborahmckenna.com
Web Site: www.deborahmckenna.com
Managing Director: Borra Garson
Senior Personnel: Adam Kingl, Lauren Davis
Managers/Agents for the UK's top celebrity chefs and lifestyle presenters. Television and publishing deals plus endorsements and advertising. We are also agents for television scriptwriters.

PHA MODEL & CASTING MANAGEMENT
Tanzaro House, Ardwick Green North, Manchester M12 6FZ
Tel: 0161 273 4444 Fax: 0161 273 4567
Email: info@pha-agency.co.uk
Web Site: www.pha-agency.co.uk
Senior Personnel: Lorna McDonough, Robert F Lang
Represent models, extras and actors for commercials, corporate and TV work. Largest casting suites in Manchester also available for hire.

Child Representation

A & J MANAGEMENT
242a The Ridgeway, Botany Bay, Enfield, Middlesex EN2 8AP
Tel: 020 8342 0542
Email: info@ajmanagement.co.uk
Web Site: www.ajmanagement.co.uk
Senior Personnel: Joanne Mclintock Jamie Nichols
Specialising in Actors/Actresses/Children.

AGENCY K-BIS
Clermont Hall, Cumberland Road, Brighton, East Sussex BN1 6SL
Tel/Fax: 01273 566739
Email: k-bis@live.co.uk
Web Site: www.kbistheatreschool.co.uk
Senior Personnel: Marcia King, Robert Andrews
We are a theatrical agency mainly dealing with young people from 18 months to 22 years. We also represent adults in theatre, TV, film, voice overs, videos, radio, modelling and presenting.

ARTS MANAGEMENT (REDROOFS ASSOCIATES)
Agency Office, Littlewick Green Maidenhead, Berkshire SL6 3QY
Tel: 01628 822982 Fax: 01628 882461
Email: junemrose@me.com
Web Site: www.redroofs.co.uk
Contact: June Rose
Specialising in: Children and younger actors

BUBBLEGUM MODEL AGENCY
Pinewood Studios, Pinewood Road Iver Heath, Buckinghamshire SL0 0NH
Tel: 01753 632 867 Fax: 01753 652 521
Email: kids@bubblegummodels.com
Web Site: www.bubblegumodels.com
Senior Personnel: Penny Hobson, Nicola Barwell
Children and teenagers from newborn to 18 years.

CAPITAL ARTS THEATRICAL AGENCY
Wyllyotts Centre, Wyllyotts Place, Darkes Lane, Potters Bar, Hertfordshire EN6 2HN
Tel/Fax: 020 8449 2342
Mobile: 07885 232414
Email: capitalarts@btconnect.com
Senior Personnel: Kathleen Shanks
Specialising in Award Winning Children's Choir, Show Choir.

NORRIE CARR AGENCY
Holborn Studios, 49 Eagle Wharf Road, London, N1 7ED
Tel: 020 7253 1771 Fax: 020 7253 1772
Email: info@norriecarr.com
Web Site: www.norriecarr.com
Contact: Sally Peters. Kate Blakey
Specialising in: Kids, babies & Adults up to 80 years old.

CHILDSPLAY MODELS LLP
114 Avenue Road, Beckenham, Kent BR3 4SA
Tel: 020 8659 9860 Fax: 020 8778 2672
Email: info@childsplaymodels.co.uk
Web Site: www.childsplaymodels.co.uk
Partner: Wendy Lee
We cater from babies right up to adults.

SUSI EARNSHAW MANAGEMENT
Susi Earnshaw Theatre School, 68 High Street, Barnet, Hertfordshire EN5 5SJ
Tel: 020 8441 5010 Fax: 020 8364 9618
Email: casting@susiearnshaw.co.uk
Web Site: www.susiearnshaw.co.uk
Senior Personnel: Susi Earnshaw, Fran Proctor-Gibbs

DOREEN ENGLISH 95
4 Selsey Avenue, Bognor Regis, West Sussex PO21 2QZ
Tel/Fax: 01243 825 968
Senior Personnel: Gerry Kinner
Specialising in Children.

JABBERWOCKY AGENCY
Glassenbury Hill Farm, Glassenbury Road, Cranbrook, Kent TN17 2QF
Tel: 01580 714306 Fax: 01580 714346
Email: info@jabberwockyagency.com
Web Site: www.jabberwockyagency.com
Senior Personnel: Christina Yates
Casting Agents: Jessica Francis, Nicky Milford
Children's theatrical agency for artists from birth to 18 years.

PAT KEELING MODEL AGENCY
38 Northgate Street, Leicester LE3 5BY
Tel: 0116 262 2540 Fax: 0116 253 7712
Email: pat@patkeelingagency.freeserve.co.uk
Web: www.patkeelingagency.freeserve.co.uk
Senior Personnel: Pat Keeling
Specialising in Modeling for Male, Female & Children. Fashion Shows, Photographic Promotions. TV & Video Work.

KIDZ LTD
10 Ellendale Grange, Worsley, Manchester M28 7UX
Tel: 0870 241 4418
Email: info@kidzltd.com
Web Site: ww.kidzltd.co.uk
Professional Childrens Model & Casting Agency.

NEW FACES
2nd Floor, The Linen Hall, 162-168 Regent Street, London W1B 5TB
Tel: 020 7439 6900 Fax: 020 7287 5481
Email: val@newfacestalent.co.uk
Web Site: www.newfacestalent.co.uk
Agents: Val Horton, Tania Patti
New Faces is a dynamic presenters, actors and extras agency situated in the west end of London. The agency is aimed at giving highly talented people of today a platform from which to launch their career and established artists a professional, friendly, approachable and highly efficient service.
If you wish to be considered for representation, please send us a copy of your showreel (if appropriate), up-to-date CV or details of experience, photograph and SAE. All tapes are viewed and if we are interested we will contact you and arrange an interview.
For more information call Val or Cathy on 020 7439 6900.

P.C. THEATRICAL MODEL AGENCY
12 Carlisle Road, Colindale, London NW9 0HL

Tel: 020 8381 2229 / 020 8205 7666
Fax: 020 8933 3418
Email: twinagy@aol.com
Web Site: www.twinagency.com
Senior Personnel: Sandra Mooney
Specialising in identical twins/actors/models/children. Largest database of Identical Twins in the UK.

PHA MODEL & CASTING MANAGEMENT
Tanzaro House, Ardwick Green North, Manchester M12 6FZ
Tel: 0161 273 4444 Fax: 0161 273 4567
Email: info@pha-agency.co.uk
Web Site: www.pha-agency.co.uk
Senior Personnel: Lorna McDonough, Robert F Lang
Represent models, extras and actors for commercials, corporate and TV work. Largest casting suites in Manchester also available for hire.

REDROOFS ASSOCIATES
Rooms 160-161 Main Admin Building, Pinewood Studios, Iver Heath, Buckinghamshire SL0 0NH
Tel: 01753 785 444 Fax: 01753 785 443
Email: agency2@redroofs.co.uk
Specialising in Children & Young Performers.
Agent: Sam Keston

RHODES
5 Dymoke Road, Hornchurch, RM11 1AA
Tel: 01708 747 013 Fax: 01708 730 431
Email: rhodesarts@hotmail.com

SASHA LESLIE MANAGEMENT
34 Pember Road, London NW10 5LS
Tel/Fax: 020 8969 3249
Email: sasha@allsortsdrama.com
Web Site: www.allsortsdrama.com
Senior Personnel: Sasha Stevenson
Personal Managers of children and young adults for professional work in television and film.

SPORTS WORKSHOP
56 Church Road, Crystal Palace, London SE19 2EZ
Tel: 020 8771 4700 Fax: 020 8771 4704
Mob: 07770 994 043 (Chris Snode)
Email: info@sportspromotions.co.uk
Web Site: www.sportspromotions.co.uk
Senior Personnel: Chris Snode
We supply sports models in all categories from Athletics to Wrestling.

STAGECOACH THEATRE ARTS PLC
The Courthouse, Elm Grove, Walton-on-Thames, Surrey KT12 1LZ
Tel: 01932 254 333 Fax: 01932 222 894
Email: enquiries@stagecoach.co.uk
Web Site: www.stagecoach.co.uk
Co-Founding Directors: Stephanie Manuel, David Sprigg
The UK's original and largest part-time performing arts schools network for children aged 4-18years. Over 600 schools across the UK and Ireland teaching young people to sing, dance and act, at weekends, after-school and holiday workshops.

STARLINGS THEATRICAL AGENCY
45 Viola Close, South Ockendon, Essex RM15 6JF
Mobile: 07969 909 284
Email: julieecarter@aol.com
Web Site: www.tiptoestageschool.com
Senior Personnel: Spencer Carter, Juliee Carter
Specialising in Actors for all forms of media. (Also a theatre school). Representing a wide variety of artists covering many genres of theatrical arts including: singers, dancers and actors - children through to adults.

TANWOOD THEATRICAL AGENCY
Tanwood School for Performing Dowling Street, Swindon, Wiltshire SN1 5QV
Tel: 01793 523 895
Email: Tanwood@tanwood.co.uk
Web Site: www.tanwood.co.uk
Founder/Principal: Mollie Tanner
Specialising in Young Adults and Children.

TOTS - TWENTIES
62 Buntingbridge Road, Ilford, Essex IG2 7LR
Tel: 020 8518 0200 Fax: 020 8518 0212
Mobile: 07702 031519
Email: sara@tots-twenties.co.uk
Web Site: www.tots-twenties.co.uk
Contact: Zena Zelique

VISCOUNT ENTERTAINMENTS
Brookdale House, 46 Kingfisher Avenue, Audenshaw, Manchester Greater Manchester M34 5QH
Tel: 08450 170 819 Mob: 07794 051732
Email: viscountagency@btconnect.com
Web: www.viscountentertainment.co.uk
Contact: David Sands
Specialising in Children and Street Entertainers.

YOUNG ACTORS THEATRE & AGENCY
70-72 Barnsbury Road, London N1 0ES
Tel: 020 7278 2101 Fax: 020 7833 9467
Email: info@yati.org.uk
Web Site: www.yati.org.uk
Director: Andrew Harries
Agents: Dyana Daulby and Lucy O'Meara
Community Theatre and Management Agency.
The Community Theatre runs evening drama classes for all ages, from 6 upwards.
The Management Agency specialises in representation of children from the age of 6-17, as well as representing adults of all ages.

Children Entertainment

THE A6 AGENCY
Willow Moorings Kegworth DE74 2EY
Mobile: 07889 745594
Email: michaelhobson2012@yahoo.co.uk
Web: www.snapshotproductions.co.uk
Senior Personnel: Michael Hobson
Specialising in outdoor and promotional attractions, jazz bands and silouette and origami artistes

ALRIGHT CHARLIE
Flat 4 Carleton House 122a Hillfield Avenue London N8 7DQ
Tel: 07808 732 390
Email: info@alrightcharlie.co.uk
Web Site: www.alrightcharlie.co.uk
Senior Personnel: Lawrence Anthony
Charlie Chaplin Look Alike, Comedy waiter & Close-up Magician for all indoor and outdoor events.

ARTS MANAGEMENT (REDROOFS ASSOCIATES)
Agency Office, Littlewick Green Maidenhead, Berkshire SL6 3QY
Tel: 01628 822982 Fax: 01628 882461
Email: junemrose@me.com
Web Site: www.redroofs.co.uk
Contact: June Rose
Specialising in: Children and younger actors

BLACKPOOL'S MIDAS ENTERTAINMENTS
23 Ledbury Road, Blackpool, Lancashire FY3 7SR
Tel: 01253 395 062 No fax number
Web Site: www.blackpoolmidas.com
Represent Artistes, Groups, Duo's, Magicians. Also Disco/Karaoke P.A. Equipment Hire.

CHARLIE THE CLOWN
Flat 4 Carleton House 122A Hillfield Avenue London N8 7DQ
Tel: 07808 732 390
Email: info@charlietheclown.co.uk
Web Site: www.charlietheclown.co.uk
Senior Personnel: Lawrence Anthony
Specialising in children's entertainment for all ages. Choice of characters includes a clown, pirate, wizzard and story-teller. Entertainment includes clown and magic shows, singing and dancing, balloon, modelling & story-telling.

DAVE BENSON PHILLIPS

TV & RADIO PRESENTER – ENTERTAINER – BROADCASTER - ACTOR and WRITER of STUFF!

(Playdays. Fun Song Factory. Playhouse Disney. Get Your Own Back! Planet Cook!)

Loves to work * Loves to entertain
OPEN TO OFFERS

For enquiries, bookings and brochures, call +44(0)1903-248-258
Email: dave@davebensonphillips.co.uk

Or visit www.davebensonphillips.co.uk

Chester Benson Productions Ltd. P.O. Box 4227, Worthing, BN11 5ST

= = = = =

Dave Benson Phillips' entertainment company

Chester Benson Productions

We do *Children's and Family Events, Theatre Shows & Festivals*
Musical Concerts for Children, Sing & Sign Workshops
Circus Skills Workshops, GUNGE TANKS & Gameshows
INFLATABLES, GAMES & ATTRACTIONS, Celebrity DJ sessions
Corporate Events & Fun Training Workshops for Companies
and of course Television, Film, & Radio.
To view what we do, visit www.youtube.com/DaveBensonPhillipsTV

For enquiries, bookings and brochures, call +44(0)1903-248-258 or 07840-504-474
Email: dave@davebensonphillips.co.uk **or visit www.davebensonphillips.co.uk**
Chester Benson Productions Ltd. P.O. Box 4227, Worthing, BN11 5ST

CHESTER BENSON PRODUCTIONS
PO Box 4227, Worthing,
West Sussex BN11 5ST
Tel: 01903 248 258 Fax: 01903 700 389
Email: dave@davebensonphillips.co.uk
Web Site: www.davebensonphillips.co.uk
Proprietor: Dave Benson Phillips
A small company that's big on creating live shows and interactive experiences for children and adults. Over 20 years in the business, video & television! Producing "The all new Dave Benson Phillips Show", "Benson's Jumparound Activity Centres" and "Get Your Own Back". All shows are perfect for indoor/outdoor events.

CIRCUS ALCHEMY
5 Beech Avenue, Rawmarsh, Rotherham,
South Yorkshire S62 5HH
Tel: 01709 710 780 Fax: 01709 710 780
Email: albert@albertalchemy.com
Web Site: www.albertalchemy.com
Contact: Albert Alchemy
Fire-eating, escapology, stiltwalking, medieval jester. Magic for corporate, public and private functions.

COMPACT MANAGEMENT & ENTERTAINMENT AGENCY
98 Shellards Road, Longwell Green,
Bristol, South Gloucestershire BS30 9DT
Tel: 0117 932 4344 Fax: 0117 932 6006
Mobile: 07831 446958
Email: paul@compactents.co.uk
Web Site: www.compactents.co.uk
Senior Personnel: Paul Wolf

CONTINENTAL DRIFTS
8 Hilton Grove, Hatherley Mews,
Walthamstow, London E17 4QP
Tel: 020 8509 3353 Fax: 020 8509 9531
Email: info@continentaldrifts.co.uk
Web Site: www.continentaldrifts.co.uk
Senior Personnel: Mel Wilds,
Chris Meikan
Event Production and Performance Specialists.
The finest in event entertainment and production, whether a single stilt walker or a fully choreographed show. Continental Drifts artists range from the bizarre to the beautiful and we have an in-house creative team to formulate ideas and realise your vision. Full technical production is available, along with fully trained event crews. Continental Drifts take a client-centred approach are are more than happy to meet with you to discuss your event requirements in full detail.

DEVIL MANAGEMENT
PO Box 23, Spennymoor, County
Durham DL16 7YZ
Tel: 01388 818 888 Fax: 01388 811 222
Email: steve@devilmanagement.com
Web Site: www.devilmanagement.com
Contact: Steve Dodds, Paul Carr

D&S ARTISTES
19 Reffley Lane, King's Lynn,
Norfolk PE30 3EF
Tel/Fax: 01553 671 693
Mobile: 07904 524 051
Email: info@dandsartistes.co.uk
Web Site: www.dandsartistes.co.uk
Senior Personnel: Alan Johnston,
Mark Pearman
Specialising in groups, cabaret, children's entertainers, discos and celebrity appearances.

SUSI EARNSHAW MANAGEMENT
Susi Earnshaw Theatre School, 68 High
Street, Barnet, Hertfordshire EN5 5SJ
Tel: 020 8441 5010 Fax: 020 8364 9618
Email: casting@susiearnshaw.co.uk
Web Site: www.susiearnshaw.co.uk
Senior Personnel: Susi Earnshaw,
Fran Proctor-Gibbs

GALAXY EVENTS
Galaxy House, Mian Yard, 86 Wallis
Road, London E9 5LN
Tel: 0208 1330 558
Email: info@galaxy-events.co.uk
Web Site: www.galaxy-events.co.uk
Senior Personnel: Mel Harvey
Artist Management and Event Coordination.

GREAT WESTERN ENTERTAINMENT AGENCY
46 Critchill Road, Frome,
Somerset BA11 4HF
Tel: 01373 461 666
Mobile: 07774 694316
Senior Personnel: Graham Wilkin
Specialising in all types of entertainment.

HEART OF ENGLAND PROMOTIONS LTD
Old Hall, Wall Hill Road, Fillongley,
Coventry, Warwickshire CV7 8DX
Tel: 01676 540 333 Fax: 01676 540 365
Email: sales@heartofengland.co.uk
Web Site: www.heartofengland.co.uk
Senior Personnel: Stephen Hammon
Specialising in DJs, Comperes and Children's Entertainment

HEY PRESTO ENTERTAINMENTS AGENCY
36 St Luke's Road, Tunbridge Wells,
Kent TN4 9JH
Tel: 01892 537 964 Fax: 01892 683 401
Mobile: 07973 512845
Email: info@heyprestoentertainments.co.uk
Web www.heyprestoentertainments.co.uk
Senior Personnel: Michael Alan Bonfield

DAWN JUDD ENTERTAINMENTS
19 Ashness Gardens, Greenford,
Middlesex UB6 0RL
Tel: 020 8902 3373 / 8903 5533
Fax: 020 8902 9538
Web : www.dawnjuddentertainments.co.uk
Senior Personnel: Dawn Judd

JUNGLE JIM
The Lower House West Street, Denbury,
Newton Abbot, Devon TQ12 6DP
Tel: 01803 812 478 Mob: 07736 970 293
Email: jimmytamley@tiscali.co.uk
Web Site: www.junglejim.co.uk
Contact: Emma & Jimmy Tamley

MAGIC CATHERINE
4 Tamarind Court 75 Deepcut Bridge
Road Camberley, Surrey GU16 6QP
Tel: 01252 837 885 Mob: 07770 227 812
Email: catherine@magicentertainment.co.uk
Web Site: www.magicentertainment.co.uk
Contact: Catherine

MATTERS MUSICAL
The Loft, Rear of 8 West Street, Dorking,
Surrey RH4 1BL
Tel: 01306 741 007 Fax: 01306 741 008
Email: info@mattersmusical.com
Web Site: www.mattersmusical.com
Senior Personnel: Frank Warren
Plus Dance Instruction/Demonstration for all the styles listed below.

MR "E" ENTERPRISES
Little Greenfields Farm, Jack Haye Lane,
Light Oaks, Stoke-on-Trent, Staffordshire
ST2 7NG
Tel: 01782 304 909
Mobile: 07831 311318
Email: info@mreenterprises.co.uk
Senior Personnel: Eddie Burke

PROFESSOR POTTY
45 David Newberry Drive, Lee-on-the-
Solent, Hampshire PO13 8FG
Tel: 0800 043 5945 Mob: 07920 779 410
Email: tensai@tensaimagic.com
Web Site: www.professorpotty.co.uk
Contact: Alan Vandome

RAINBOW PRODUCTIONS
Rainbow House, 56 Windsor Avenue,
London SW19 2RR
Tel: 020 8545 0700 Fax: 020 8545 0777
Email: info@rainbowproductions.co.uk
Web Site: www.rainbowproductions.co.uk
Managing Director: David Scott,
Sales & Marketing Director: Simon
Foulkes
Rainbow Productions has over 70 celebrity cartoon characters to book for guest appearances. We also create bespoke brand mascots and props for events.

SALVO THE CLOWN
13 Second Avenue, Kingsleigh Park,
Thundersley, Essex SS7 3QD

Tel: 01268 745 791
Email: salvo@annualclownsdirectory.com
Web: www.annualclownsdirectory.com
Contact: Salvo

Choreographers

2MA
Springvale, Tutland Road, North Baddesley, Hants Southampton SO52 9FL
Tel: 023 8074 1354 Fax: 023 8074 1355
Mobile: 07730 662236
Email: mo.matthews@2ma.co.uk
Web Site: www.2ma.co.uk
Senior Personnel: Magee Matthews, Mo Matthews
Suppliers of gymnasts, acrobats and sports artistes. Martial arts, stunt men.

ARTS MANAGEMENT (REDROOFS ASSOCIATES)
Agency Office, Littlewick Green Maidenhead, Berkshire SL6 3QY
Tel: 01628 822982 Fax: 01628 882461
Email: junemrose@me.com
Web Site: www.redroofs.co.uk
Contact: June Rose
Specialising in: Children and younger actors

FUNKI FEATHERS DANCE PRODUCTIONS LTD
Sycamore House, 8 Sycamore Road, Bearwood Smethwick, West Midlands B66 4NL
Tel/Fax: 0121 420 4396
Mobile: 07958 945701 / 2
Email: funkifeathers@telco4u.net
Web Site: www.funkifeathers.co.uk
Contact: Julie-Ann Phillips
Dance/Promotional Group.
Providing dancers, costumes and production shows.

ALEX JAY PERSONAL MANAGEMENT
8 Higher Newmarket Road, Newmarket, Nailsworth, Gloucestershire GL6 0RP
Tel/Fax: 01453 834 783
Email: alexjay@alex-jay-pm.freeserve.co.uk
Senior Personnel: Alex Jay
Specialising in artistes for film, television, theatre, commercials and TV & radio presenters.

PAT KEELING MODEL AGENCY
38 Northgate Street, Leicester LE3 5BY
Tel: 0116 262 2540 Fax: 0116 253 7712
Email: pat@patkeelingagency.freeserve.co.uk
Web: www.patkeelingagency.freeserve.co.uk
Senior Personnel: Pat Keeling
Specialising in Modeling for Male, Female & Children. Fashion Shows, Photographic Promotions. TV & Video Work.

ROSEBERY MANAGEMENT
Hoxton Hall, 130 Hoxton Street, London N1 6SH
Tel: 020 7684 0187 Mob: 07805 162731
Email: admin@roseberymanagement.com
Web: www.roseberymanagement.com
Manager: Ben West

DONALD SCRIMGEOUR ARTISTS AGENCY
49 Springcroft Avenue, London N2 9JH
Tel: 020 8444 6248 Fax: 020 8883 9751
Email: vwest@dircon.co.uk
Web Site: www.donaldscrimgeour.com
Senior Personnel: Donald Scrimgeour (Spain), Valerie West (London)
Representing Dancers, Choreographers, Teachers/Ballet Masters, Dance Producers, Conductors & Designers.

TALENT ARTISTS LTD
59 Sydner Road, London N16 7UF
Tel: 020 7923 1119 Fax: 020 7923 2009
Mob: 07967 029 551
Email: talent.artists@btconnect.com
Contact: Jane Wynn Owen

Circuses & Circus Acts

NITA ANDERSON ENTERTAINMENT
165 Wolverhampton Road, Sedgley, Dudley, West Midlands DY3 1QR
Tel: 01902 882 211 / 681 224
Fax: 01902 883 356
Email: nitaandersonagency@hotmail.com
Web Site: www.nitaanderson.co.uk
Senior Personnel: Nita Anderson
Suppliers of Corporate Entertainment and After Dinner Speakers.

BILLY F ARATA
1 Vernon Avenue, Birmingham B20 1DB
Tel: 0121 554 4078 Fax: 0121 523 4603
Email: info@billy-smarts-circus.co.uk
Senior Personnel: Billy Arata
Specialises in Circuses & Variety Acts

CIRCUS ALCHEMY
5 Beech Avenue, Rawmarsh, Rotherham, South Yorkshire S62 5HH
Tel: 01709 710 780 Fax: 01709 710 780
Email: albert@albertalchemy.com
Web Site: www.albertalchemy.com
Contact: Albert Alchemy
Fire-eating, escapology, stiltwalking, medieval jester. Magic for corporate, public and private functions.

CIRCUS PROMOTIONS
36 St Luke's Road, Tunbridge Wells, Kent TN4 9JH
Tel: 01892 537 964 Fax: 01892 683 401
Mobile: 07973 512845
Email: info@heyprestoentertainments.co.uk
Web: www.heyprestonentertainments.co.uk
Senior Personnel: Michael Alan Bonfield

CONTINENTAL DRIFTS
8 Hilton Grove, Hatherley Mews, Walthamstow, London E17 4QP
Tel: 020 8509 3353 Fax: 020 8509 9531
Email: info@continentaldrifts.co.uk
Web Site: www.continentaldrifts.co.uk
Senior Personnel: Mel Wilds, Chris Meikan
Event Production and Performance Specialists.
The finest in event entertainment and production, whether a single stilt walker or a fully choreographed show. Continental Drifts artists range from the bizarre to the beautiful and we have an in-house creative team to formulate ideas and realise your vision. Full technical production is available, along with fully trained event crews. Continental Drifts take a client-centred approach are are more than happy to meet with you to discuss your event requirements in full detail.

CROWD PULLERS (STREET PERFORMERS AND BANDS)
14 Somerset Gardens, London SE13 7SY
Tel: 020 8469 3900 Fax: 020 8469 2147
Mobile: 07831 150170
Email: jhole@crowdpullers.co.uk
Web Site: www.crowdpullers.co.uk
Senior Personnel: John Hole

ES PROMOTIONS
Unit 24, Larkwood, Larkwood Close, Kettering, Northamptonshire NN16 9NQ
Tel: 01536 310 520 Fax 01536 358 113
Email: sales@es-promotions.com
Web Site: www.es-promotions.com
Financial Director: Dave Turner
The Agency supplies circus performers, children's entertainment, street entertainers, arena and aerial acts.
Outdoor event specialists, entertainment agency, team events, themed events, fun casino. Inflatables and unusual games for hire. Balloons, balloon gas, balloon releases and balloon decorating.

FOOL'S PARADISE
9 Colleton Crescent, Exeter, Devon EX2 4DG
Tel: 01392 454 160 Fax: 01392 848 384
Email: fools@foolsparadise.co.uk
Web Site: www.foolsparadise.co.uk
Senior Personnel: Jo Burgess, Nicki Street
Specialising in Acrobats, Circus, Comedians, Magicians, Mime, Outdoor, Puppets, Speciality Acts, Street Theatre.

GO ENTERTAINMENTS
The Arts Exchange, Dane Mill Congleton, Cheshire CW12 1LA

Tel: 01260 276 627 Fax: 01260 270 777
Email: info@arts-exchange.com
Web Site: www.arts-exchange.com
Contact: Phillip or Carol Gandey
Big tops up to 5000 people worldwide supply.

HATSTAND CIRCUS
Westferry Studios, 2nd Floor, Unit 98, 98 Milligan Street, London E14 8AS
Tel: 020 7538 3368 Mob: 07748 005 839
Email: helenahatstand@btconnect.com
Web Site: www.hatstandcircus.co.uk
Contact: Helena Hatstand
Bright and colourful and themed stilt characters, unique and unusual shows, juggling, UV show/blackout glo show, fire shows with fire eating and manipulation of fire props including fire whips. Meet and greet and mix and mingle.

DAWN JUDD ENTERTAINMENTS
19 Ashness Gardens, Greenford, Middlesex UB6 0RL
Tel: 020 8902 3373 / 8903 5533 Fax: 020 8902 9538
Web: www.dawnjuddentertainments.co.uk
Senior Personnel: Dawn Judd

LONDON CHINESE ACROBATICS
118 Albany Road, Leighton Buzzard, Bedfordshire LU7 1NS
Tel: 01525 633 944 Fax: 01525 370 642
Email: chineseacrobatic@hotmail.com
Web: www.chinesedance-acrobatic.co.uk
Contact: Jiang

MTM PRESENTATIONS
Avron House, 37 Highmeadow, Ringley Wood, Radcliffe, Manchester M26 1YN
Tel: 0161 725 9991 Fax: 0161 725 9199
Mob: 07970 205 060
Email: info@mtmpresentations.co.uk
Web Site: www.mtmpresentations.co.uk
Senior Personnel: Gaynor Green

NATIONAL FESTIVAL CIRCUS
Tober House, PO Box 2, Brierley Hill, West Midlands DY5 3LR
Tel: 01384 423 496
Email: clownsgalore123@AOL.com
Web: www.nationalfestivalcircus.co.uk

NEWSUBSTANCE ARTISTS
Medius House, 2 Sheraton Street, London W1F 8BH
Tel: 0845 257 9611 Fax: 0870 622 1681
Email: info@newsubstance-artists.co.uk
Web: www.newsubstance-artists.co.uk
Contact: Matthew Stowe

PSYCHO MANAGEMENT COMPANY LTD
111 Clarence Road, Wimbledon, London SW19 8QB
Tel: 020 8540 8122 Fax: 020 8715 2827
Surrey Office: Sollys Mill, Mill Lane, Godalming, Surrey GU7 1EY Tel: 01483 419429 Fax: 01483 419504
Email: john@psycho.co.uk
Web Site: www.circusofhorrors.co.uk / www.psycho.co.uk
Company Director: John Mabley
We specialise in providing speciality and weird acts for publicity stunts and TV management for Circus of Horrors and Carnival of the Bizarre. We also act as Media Company & Theatre bookers for: The Chinese State Circus, The Moscow State Circus, Cottle & Austen Circus, Circus Berlin.

SALVO THE CLOWN
13 Second Avenue, Kingsleigh Park, Thundersley, Essex SS7 3QD
Tel: 01268 745 791
Email: salvo@annualclownsdirectory.com
Web: www.annualclownsdirectory.com
Contact: Salvo

JEFF SUTTON MANAGEMENT
Theatre Cottage, 113 Station Road, Keadby, Scunthorpe, South Humberside DN17 3BP
Tel: 01724 784 449 Fax: 01724 784 441
Mob: 07798 871 680
Email: jsm@agents-uk.com
Web Site: www.jeffsutton.co.uk
Agent: Jeff Sutton
Specialists in star names and production shows.

WHATEVER ARTISTS MANAGEMENT LTD
F24 Argo House, Kilburn Park Road, London NW6 5LF
Tel: 020 7372 4777 Fax: 020 7372 5111
Email: info@wamshow.biz
Web Site: www.wamshow.biz
Senior Personnel: Jenny Dunster
All types of entertainers booked for corporate and private events with full technical on-site management services.

Classical Musicians

CAROLINE BAIRD ARTISTS
Pinkhill House, Oxford Road, Eynsham, Witney, Oxfordshire OX29 4DA
Tel: 01865 882 771
Email: caroline@cbartists.sol.co.uk
Web Site: www.carolinebairdartists.co.uk
Agent: Caroline Baird

PASADENA ROOF ORCHESTRA
Priors, 178 Hall Lane, Upminster, Essex RM14 1AT
Email: info@pasadena-roof-orchestra.com
Web: www.pasadena-roof-orchestra.com
Contact: David Jones
Head Office Contact (Munich): Marcus Meyer
Professional Orchestra (11 piece). 1920's & 1930's Jazz and Dance Music.
UK Booking Management: Liz Biddle, Upbeat Management. Tel: 020 8668 3332 Fax: 020 8668 3922

PRO ARTIST MANAGEMENT
54 Beaconsfield Road, London SE3 7LG
Tel: 020 8858 0785 Fax: 020 8269 1722
Mobile: 0794 108 3038
Email: info@proartist.co.uk
Web Site: www.proartist.co.uk
Agent: Aminah Domloge
Classical music artists, especially chamber music.

PATRICIA SPERO
Oaks Farm Vicarage Lane Chigwell Essex IG7 6LT
Email: patricia.spero@btinternet.com
Web: www.impulse-music.co.uk/spero.htm
Contacts: Patricia Spero

UPBEAT MANAGEMENT
Larg House Woodcote Grove, Coulsdon, Surrey CR5 2QQ
Tel: 020 8668 3332 Fax: 020 8668 3922
Email: info@upbeat.co.uk
Web Site: www.upbeat.co.uk
Senior Personnel (Entertainment): Liz Biddle, Beryl Korman
Specialising in Theatre Touring and large events for Festivals and corporate entertainment.

Classical Singers

BELLTOWER ENTERPRISES
9 Hillside Road, Ashtead, Surrey KT21 1RZ
Tel: 01372 277 703 Fax: 01372 278 406
Mobile: 07850 486 466
Email: music@dragonsfire.uk.com
Web Site: www.dragonsfire.uk.com
Senior Personnel: Nigel & Hilary Perona-Wright

DEVIL MANAGEMENT
PO Box 23, Spennymoor, County Durham DL16 7YZ
Tel: 01388 818 888 Fax: 01388 811 222
Email: steve@devilmanagement.com
Web Site: www.devilmanagement.com
Contact: Steve Dodds, Paul Carr

INGPEN & WILLIAMS LTD
7 St George's Court, 131 Putney Bridge Road, London SW15 2PA
Tel: 020 8874 3222 Fax: 020 8877 3113
Email: ds@ingpen.co.uk / hh@ingpen.co.uk
Web Site: www.ingpen.co.uk

Director: David Sigall
Artist Managers: Helen Hogh, Lulu Chivers
Senior Personnel: Thomas Hull, Jonathan Groves
Specialising in Opera and Classical Music

LONDON MUSIC AGENCY
7 Rosewood Drive, Orchard Heights Ashford, Kent TN25 4QF
Tel: 01233 623 623 Mob: 07885 032 132
Email: enquiries@londonmusicagency.co.uk
Web: www.londonmusicagency.co.uk
Proprietor: Jenny Braby
Everything in entertainment for Private and Corporate functions, e.g. Jazz, String Quartets and all types of band, music and the unusual.

MATTERS MUSICAL
The Loft, Rear of 8 West Street, Dorking, Surrey RH4 1BL
Tel: 01306 741 007 Fax: 01306 741 008
Email: info@mattersmusical.com
Web Site: www.mattersmusical.com
Senior Personnel: Frank Warren
Plus Dance Instruction/Demonstration for all the styles listed below.

QUIDETAM LTD
PO Box 3698, London NW2 6ZA
Tel: 020 7748 3003 Fax: 020 7691 7632
Email: info@quidetam.com
Web Site: www.quidetam.com
Contact: Diane Hinds

KEN SPENCER PERSONAL MANAGEMENT
P.A.G. Promotions, 138 Sandy Hill Road, London SE18 7BA
Tel/Fax: 020 8854 2558
Email: pagandferret@hotmail.com
Senior Personnel: Ken Spencer
Classical artists and mainly classically-trained singers, sopranos and tenors. Occassionally represent pianists.

PATRICIA SPERO
Oaks Farm Vicarage Lane Chigwell Essex IG7 6LT
Email: patricia.spero@btinternet.com
Web: www.impulse-music.co.uk/spero.htm
Contacts: Patricia Spero

UPBEAT MANAGEMENT
Larg House Woodcote Grove, Coulsdon, Surrey CR5 2QQ
Tel: 020 8668 3332 Fax: 020 8668 3922
Email: info@upbeat.co.uk
Web Site: www.upbeat.co.uk
Senior Personnel (Entertainment): Liz Biddle, Beryl Korman
Specialising in Theatre Touring and large events for Festivals and corporate entertainment.

SCOTT-PAUL YOUNG ENTERTAINMENTS LTD
Northern Lights House, 110 Blandford Road North, Langley, Near Windsor, Berkshire SL3 7TA
Tel/Fax: 01753 693 250
Email: castingdirect@spy-ents.com
Web Site: www.spy-lightentsworld.com
Managing Director: Scott-Paul Young
Artists management and exclusive representation for films, television, commercials, theatre, sports and modelling events and all areas of the light entertainment industry.

Clowns

THE A6 AGENCY
Willow Moorings Kegworth DE74 2EY
Mobile: 07889 745594
Email: michaelhobson2012@yahoo.co.uk
Web: www.snapshotproductions.co.uk
Senior Personnel: Michael Hobson
Specialising in outdoor and promotional attractions, jazz bands and silouette and origami artistes

CIRCUS ALCHEMY
5 Beech Avenue, Rawmarsh, Rotherham, South Yorkshire S62 5HH
Tel: 01709 710 780 Fax: 01709 710 780
Email: albert@albertalchemy.com
Web Site: www.albertalchemy.com
Contact: Albert Alchemy
Fire-eating, escapology, stiltwalking, medieval jester. Magic for corporate, public and private functions.

CIRCUS PROMOTIONS
36 St Luke's Road, Tunbridge Wells, Kent TN4 9JH
Tel: 01892 537 964 Fax: 01892 683 401
Mobile: 07973 512845
Email: info@heyprestoentertainments.co.uk
Web: www.heyprestonentertainments.co.uk
Senior Personnel: Michael Alan Bonfield

COMPACT MANAGEMENT & ENTERTAINMENT AGENCY
98 Shellards Road, Longwell Green, Bristol, South Gloucestershire BS30 9DT
Tel: 0117 932 4344 Fax: 0117 932 6006
Mobile: 07831 446958
Email: paul@compactents.co.uk
Web Site: www.compactents.co.uk
Senior Personnel: Paul Wolf

CONTINENTAL DRIFTS
8 Hilton Grove, Hatherley Mews, Walthamstow, London E17 4QP
Tel: 020 8509 3353 Fax: 020 8509 9531
Email: info@continentaldrifts.co.uk
Web Site: www.continentaldrifts.co.uk
Senior Personnel: Mel Wilds, Chris Meikan
Event Production and Performance Specialists.
The finest in event entertainment and production, whether a single stilt walker or a fully choreographed show. Continental Drifts artists range from the bizarre to the beautiful and we have an in-house creative team to formulate ideas and realise your vision. Full technical production is available, along with fully trained event crews. Continental Drifts take a client-centred approach are are more than happy to meet with you to discuss your event requirements in full detail.

CROWD PULLERS (STREET PERFORMERS AND BANDS)
14 Somerset Gardens, London SE13 7SY
Tel: 020 8469 3900 Fax: 020 8469 2147
Mobile: 07831 150170
Email: jhole@crowdpullers.co.uk
Web Site: www.crowdpullers.co.uk
Senior Personnel: John Hole

D&S ARTISTES
19 Reffley Lane, King's Lynn, Norfolk PE30 3EF
Tel/Fax: 01553 671 693
Mobile: 07904 524 051
Email: info@dandsartistes.co.uk
Web Site: www.dandsartistes.co.uk
Senior Personnel: Alan Johnston, Mark Pearman
Specialising in groups, cabaret, children's entertainers, discos and celebrity appearances.

HEART OF ENGLAND PROMOTIONS LTD
Old Hall, Wall Hill Road, Fillongley, Coventry, Warwickshire CV7 8DX
Tel: 01676 540 333 Fax: 01676 540 365
Email: sales@heartofengland.co.uk
Web Site: www.heartofengland.co.uk
Senior Personnel: Stephen Hammon
Specialising in DJs, Comperes and Children's Entertainment

HEY PRESTO ENTERTAINMENTS AGENCY
36 St Luke's Road, Tunbridge Wells, Kent TN4 9JH
Tel: 01892 537 964 Fax: 01892 683 401
Mobile: 07973 512845
Email: info@heyprestoentertainments.co.uk
Web: www.heyprestoentertainments.co.uk
Senior Personnel: Michael Alan Bonfield

DAWN JUDD ENTERTAINMENTS
19 Ashness Gardens, Greenford, Middlesex UB6 0RL
Tel: 020 8902 3373 / 8903 5533 Fax: 020 8902 9538
Web: www.dawnjuddentertainments.co.uk
Senior Personnel: Dawn Judd

LONDON MUSIC AGENCY
7 Rosewood Drive, Orchard Heights
Ashford, Kent TN25 4QF
Tel: 01233 623 623 Mob: 07885 032 132
Email:
enquiries@londonmusicagency.co.uk
Web: www.londonmusicagency.co.uk
Proprietor: Jenny Braby
Everything in entertainment for Private and Corporate functions, e.g. Jazz, String Quartets and all types of band, music and the unusual.

SALVO THE CLOWN
13 Second Avenue, Kingsleigh Park,
Thundersley, Essex SS7 3QD
Tel: 01268 745 791
Email: salvo@annualclownsdirectory.com
Web: www.annualclownsdirectory.com
Contact: Salvo

Cockney

PETER MORRIS
Primrose Cottage 11 Church Road,
Barling Magna, Southend-on-Sea Essex
SS3 0LS
Tel: 0800 970 8527 Tel: 01702 219 680
Mob: 07850 400 489
Email: peter.clan.morris@gmail.com
Contact: Peter Morris

Comedians & Comediennes

1ST CHOICE SPEAKERS UK LTD
52 Bois Moor Road Chesham,
Buckinghamshire HP5 1SN
Tel/Fax: 01494 773 020
Mobile: 07821 131 510
Email: enquiries@1stchoicespeakers.co.uk
Web Site: www.1stchoicespeakers.com
Managing Director: Pushpa Kasinather
Specialising in Celebrity Speakers for Cruise Ships, Conferences and Personal Appearances.
Speakers for After Dinner, Sports/Golf, Business, Keynote, Comedians and Product Launches.

AFTER DINNER SPEAKERS & COMEDIANS LIMITED
Chippings 2 The Old Saw Mills
Ripponden Halifax,
West Yorkshire HX6 4EN
Tel: 0845 4758866 Fax: 01422 884 494
Email: office@comedians.co.uk
Web Site: www.comedians.co.uk
Senior Personnel: Roger Davis, J. Mark Davis

VERN ALLEN ENTERTAINMENTS LIMITED
Suite 19, Basepoint Business Centre,
Yeoford Way, Marsh Barton Trading
Estate, Exeter EX2 8LB
Tel: 0870 383 1988 (2 lines)
Fax: 01392 426 421
Email: paul@vernallen.co.uk
Web Site: www.vernallen.co.uk
Senior Personnel: Paul Winteridge

GORDON BENNETT
16 Saxons Drive, Maidstone,
Kent ME14 5HS
Tel: 01622 672 128 Mob: 07930 758 083
Email: gordonbennett69@hotmail.com
Web Site: www.gordonbennett.biz
Contact: Gordon Bennett

CHAMBERS MANAGEMENT LTD
39-41 Parker Street London WC2B 5PQ
Tel: 020 7796 3588 Fax: 020 7796 3676
Email: hannah@chambersmgt.co.uk /
sophie@chabersmgt.co.uk
Web Site: www.chambersmgt.co.uk
Contact: Hannah Chambers
A management agency specialising in stand up comedians, comedian actors and presenters. Artists currently include 2 Perrier award winners and 2 Perrier nominees. We are also booking agents for a number of International Comedy Festivals.

DAVID CHARLES AGENCY
2 Betjeman Way, Hemel Hempstead,
Hertfordshire HP1 3HH
Tel: 01442 264 402
Mobile: 07767 813 231
Email: david@davidcharlesent.co.uk
Web Site: www.davidcharlesent.co.uk
Senior Personnel: David Charles, Penny Charles
Specialising in adult entertainment, bands and groups.

COMIC VOICE MANAGEMENT
2nd Floor, 28-31 Moulsham Street,
Chelmsford, Essex CM2 0HX
Tel: 0870 042 5656
Email: info@comicvoice.com
Web Site: www.comicvoice.com

COMPACT MANAGEMENT & ENTERTAINMENT AGENCY
98 Shellards Road, Longwell Green,
Bristol, South Gloucestershire BS30 9DT
Tel: 0117 932 4344 Fax: 0117 932 6006
Mobile: 07831 446958
Email: paul@compactents.co.uk
Web Site: www.compactents.co.uk
Senior Personnel: Paul Wolf

COSMIC COMEDY MANAGEMENT & CONSULTANCY
34 Cannon Court Road, Maidenhead,
Berkshire SL6 7QN
Tel/Fax: 01628 415 683
Email: joss@cosmiccomedy.co.uk
Web Site: www.cosmiccomedy.co.uk
Senior Personnel: Joss Jones
Comedy artiste representation and consultancy with over 15 years experience, promoting comedy venues and management.

CT ENTERTAINMENTS
PO Box 52, Newtownards, County Down
BT23 3FX Northern Ireland
Tel: 028 9042 8800 Fax: 028 9042 3999
Email: ctentertainment@ukgateway.net
Web Site: www.theuntouchables.info
Senior Personnel: Cecil Thompson
Comedians & DJ's also available

DEVIL MANAGEMENT
PO Box 23, Spennymoor, County
Durham DL16 7YZ
Tel: 01388 818 888 Fax: 01388 811 222
Email: steve@devilmanagement.com
Web Site: www.devilmanagement.com
Contact: Steve Dodds, Paul Carr

D&S ARTISTES
19 Reffley Lane, King's Lynn, Norfolk
PE30 3EF
Tel/Fax: 01553 671 693
Mobile: 07904 524 051
Email: info@dandsartistes.co.uk
Web Site: www.dandsartistes.co.uk
Senior Personnel: Alan Johnston, Mark Pearman
Specialising in groups, cabaret, children's entertainers, discos and celebrity appearances.

CHRISTOPHER GEE
32 Clydesdale Gardens, North Berstead
Bognor Regis, West Sussex PO22 9BE
Tel: 01243 861 171 Mob: 07794 218295
Email: christopher_gee@btinternet.com
Web Site: www.christopher-gee.com
Contact: Christopher Gee

TREVOR GEORGE ENTERTAINMENTS LTD
PO Box 135, Torquay, Devon TQ1 3ZW
Tel: 01803 615 600 / 700 Fax: 01803
615 888 Mobile: 07502 042 995
Email: anne@trevorgeorge.co.uk
Web Site: www.trevorgeorge.co.uk
Senior Personnel: Anne George, Beverley Korman

GOLDMAN KING
16 St. Albans Road, Kingston upon
Thames, Surrey KT2 5HQ
Tel: 020 8287 1199
Email: artistes@goldmanking.com
Web Site: www.goldmanking.com
Goldman King represent Comedians, Writers, Studio Warm-ups, Actors and Voice-Over Artistes. Our experienced

comedy performers are available for castings and also corporate entertainment.

GOOD SENSE OF HUMOUR
2 Porcupine Terrace, Penpillick, Par, Cornwall PL24 2RP
Mobile: 07940 418138 No fax
Email: jon@gsohcomedy.co.uk
Web Site: www.gsohcomedy.co.uk
Agent: Jon Briley
Representing the very best in stand-up comedians. To take a look out our artiste roster, please visit our website: http://www.gsohcomedy.co.uk/representation.html

GREAT WESTERN ENTERTAINMENT AGENCY
46 Critchill Road, Frome, Somerset BA11 4HF
Tel: 01373 461 666
Mobile: 07774 694316
Senior Personnel: Graham Wilkin
Specialising in all types of entertainment.

GT ARTISTES
4 Maple Avenue Allington Maidestone ME16 0DD
Tel: 01622 675 893 Mob: 07778 288 634
Email: tony.littley@btinternet.com
Web Site: www.gtartistes.com
Contact: Tony Littley

HEY PRESTO ENTERTAINMENTS AGENCY
36 St Luke's Road, Tunbridge Wells, Kent TN4 9JH
Tel: 01892 537 964 Fax: 01892 683 401
Mobile: 07973 512845
Email: info@heyprestoentertainments.co.uk
Web: www.heyprestoentertainments.co.uk
Senior Personnel: Michael Alan Bonfield

ROBERT C KELLY LTD
PO Box 5597 Glasgow, Strathclyde G77 9DH Scotland
Tel: 0141 533 5856
Email: robert@robertckelly.co.uk
Web Site: www.robertckelly.co.uk
Senior Personnel: Robert C Kelly

LIVE BUSINESS GROSVENOR PRODUCTIONS
136-144 New Kings Road Fulham London SW6 4LZ
Tel: 020 7384 2050
Email: jobs@livebusiness.co.uk
Web Site: www.livebusiness.co.uk
Contact: Peter Chittenden, Blain Fairman, Mark Dixon
Supplying entertainment of all kinds to the leisure industry and corporate clients as well as to individual private events.

MIRTH CONTROL MANAGEMENT
81 London Road West, Bath BA1 7JE
Mobile: 07976 283 456
Mobile 2: 07976 560 580
Email: leanna@mirthcontrol.org.uk
Web Site: www.mirthcontrol.org.uk
Contact: Leanna Race, Charlotte Hamilton
MCM, the artist management arm of Mirth Control, represents a diverse range of high-caliber stand-up comedians, comedy actors, impressionists, improvisers and writers, across live work, film, TV and radio. Mirth Control is also an authority on corporate bookings, and facilitates castings for both radio and television.

NMP LIVE LTD
8 Blenheim Court Brook Way Leatherhead, Surrey KT22 7NA
Tel: 01372 361004 Fax: 01372 374417
Email: live@nmp.co.uk
Web Site: www.nmplive.co.uk
Managing Directors: Neil Martin, Chris Banks.
Leading UK entertainment agency specialising in celebrity personal appearances, high profile entertainment, negotiating endorsements and advertising campaigns and presenting after-dinner, motivational & conference speakers.

OFF THE KERB PRODUCTIONS
Hammer House 113-117 Wardour Street London W1F 0UN
Tel: 020 7437 0607 Fax: 020 7437 0647
Email: info@offthekerb.co.uk or westend@offthekerb.co.uk
Web Site: www.offthekerb.co.uk
Senior Personnel: Addison Cresswell, Joe Norris
Please note all corporate, personal appearance and casting enquiries for all artistes to Fay Clayton in the West End office. fay@offthekerb.co.uk

PERSONALLY SPEAKING
Three Spires House, 16a Bird Street, Lichfield, Staffordshire WS13 6PR
Tel: 01543 263 136 Fax: 01543 262 402
Email: info@normanphillips.co.uk
Web: www.personally-speaking.co.uk
Senior Personnel: Lianne Phillips
Established 40 years as the UK's premier consultancy, supplying speakers and celebrities for every occasion including: Personal Appearances, After Dinner, Key Note and Business Speeches, Sporting Dinners, Conference and Award Ceremonies, Product Launches, Product Endorsements, Corporate Videos, Cabaret. Over 5000 speaker profiles available.

ROGUES & VAGABONDS MANAGEMENT
The Printhouse, 18 Ashwin Street, London E8 3DL
Tel: 020 7254 8130 Fax: 020 7249 8564
Email: rogues@vagabondsmanagement.com
Web: www.vagabondsmanagement.com
Agent: Ann Robson
Rogues is the oldest established actors' co-operative in London, with an excellent track record of finding work for actors and actresses, comedians and comediennes.

SCOTT JORDAN ENTERTAINMENT LTD
25-29 Station Street, Sittingbourne, Kent ME10 3DU
Tel: 0845 094 1455
Email: enquiries@scottjordan.co.uk
Web Site: www.scottjordan.co.uk
Contact : Scott Jordan, Stephen Middleton
Entertainment booking agency providing quality tribute bands, function bands, comedians and magicians for weddings, private parties, and venues accross the U.K

STELLAMAX ENTERPRISES
Nova House, 53 Nova Croft, Off Broad Lane, Eastern Green, Coventry, Warwickshire CV5 7FJ
Tel: 024 7646 9585 Mob: 07899 045363
Email: max@stellamax.com
Web Site: www.stellamax.com
Senior Personnel: Max Roberts

JEFF SUTTON MANAGEMENT
Theatre Cottage, 113 Station Road, Keadby, Scunthorpe, South Humberside DN17 3BP
Tel: 01724 784 449 Fax: 01724 784 441
Mob: 07798 871 680
Email: jsm@agents-uk.com
Web Site: www.jeffsutton.co.uk
Agent: Jeff Sutton
Specialists in star names and production shows.

TALENT ONE
14 Fairfield Lane, Wolverley Kidderminster, Worcestershire DY11 5QH
Tel: 01562 850 255 Mob: 07957 106 982
Email: admin@talentone.co.uk
Web Site: www.talentone.co.uk
Contact : Phil & Keith

PAUL ZENON
Tel: 07721 610 364
Email: gigs@paulzenon.com
Web Site: www.paulzenon.com
Personal Assistant: Sue Reed (Stranger Media Limited)
Comedian, Magician and Presenter.

Commentators

JANE MORGAN MANAGEMENT LTD
Elsinore House 77 Fulham Palace Road, London W6 8JA
Tel: 020 7478 7479
Email: enquiries@janemorganmgt.com
Web Site: www.janemorganmgt.com
Senior Personnel: Jane Morgan
Specialises in the representation of sports broadcasters and sportsmen and women who now have a career in the media.

Costume & Cartoon Caracters

THE A6 AGENCY
Willow Moorings Kegworth DE74 2EY
Mobile: 07889 745594
Email: michaelhobson2012@yahoo.co.uk
Web: www.snapshotproductions.co.uk
Senior Personnel: Michael Hobson
Specialising in outdoor and promotional attractions, jazz bands and silouette and origami artistes

CIRCUS ALCHEMY
5 Beech Avenue, Rawmarsh, Rotherham, South Yorkshire S62 5HH
Tel: 01709 710 780 Fax: 01709 710 780
Email: albert@albertalchemy.com
Web Site: www.albertalchemy.com
Contact: Albert Alchemy
Fire-eating, escapology, stiltwalking, medieval jester. Magic for corporate, public and private functions.

CONTINENTAL DRIFTS
8 Hilton Grove, Hatherley Mews, Walthamstow, London E17 4QP
Tel: 020 8509 3353 Fax: 020 8509 9531
Email: info@continentaldrifts.co.uk
Web Site: www.continentaldrifts.co.uk
Senior Personnel: Mel Wilds, Chris Meikan
Event Production and Performance Specialists.
The finest in event entertainment and production, whether a single stilt walker or a fully choreographed show. Continental Drifts artists range from the bizarre to the beautiful and we have an in-house creative team to formulate ideas and realise your vision. Full technical production is available, along with fully trained event crews. Continental Drifts take a client-centred approach are are more than happy to meet with you to discuss your event requirements in full detail.

PLANET 80S
PO Box 441 Ashford, Kent TN23 9EL
Tel: 07799 262 068
Email: planet80s@hotmail.co.uk
Web Site: www.planet80s.webs.com
Contacts : Phil Marks

RAINBOW PRODUCTIONS
Rainbow House, 56 Windsor Avenue, London SW19 2RR
Tel: 020 8545 0700 Fax: 020 8545 0777
Email: info@rainbowproductions.co.uk
Web Site: www.rainbowproductions.co.uk
Managing Director: David Scott,
Sales & Marketing Director: Simon Foulkes
Rainbow Productions has over 70 celebrity cartoon characters to book for guest appearances. We also create bespoke brand mascots and props for events.

Country/Folk Music

THE A6 AGENCY
Willow Moorings Kegworth DE74 2EY
Mobile: 07889 745594
Email: michaelhobson2012@yahoo.co.uk
Web: www.snapshotproductions.co.uk
Senior Personnel: Michael Hobson
Specialising in outdoor and promotional attractions, jazz bands and silouette and origami artistes

BAND OF TWO
26 Cumberland Court, 21 Cross Road, Croydon, Surrey CR0 6TE
Tel: 020 8680 4302
Email: petefyfe@aol.com
Web Site: www.bandoftwo.com
Contact: Peter Fyfe
"Specialising in Goodtime Celtic/Irish Songs, Tunes and Folk Dances."

BELLTOWER ENTERPRISES
9 Hillside Road, Ashtead, Surrey KT21 1RZ
Tel: 01372 277 703 Fax: 01372 278 406
Mobile: 07850 486 466
Email: music@dragonsfire.uk.com
Web Site: www.dragonsfire.uk.com
Senior Personnel: Nigel & Hilary Perona-Wright

DAVID CHARLES AGENCY
2 Betjeman Way, Hemel Hempstead, Hertfordshire HP1 3HH
Tel: 01442 264 402
Mobile: 07767 813 231
Email: david@davidcharlesent.co.uk
Web Site: www.davidcharlesent.co.uk
Senior Personnel: David Charles, Penny Charles
Specialising in adult entertainment, bands and groups.

DERI PROMOTIONS
9 Templars Close, Bognor Regis, West Sussex PO22 6RU
Tel/Fax: 01243 585 545
Email: deripromotions@btopenworld.com
Web Site: www.deripromotions.org.uk
Senior Personnel: Roy Cooper
Specialising in Country & Western.

LUCKY JIM FALLON
34 Borrowdale, Newcastle-upon-Tyne NE7 1QG
Tel: 0191 417 9859
Mobile: 07788 907384
Country Music, Line Dancing & Listening. Singer/Songwriter

FIRST TIME MANAGEMENT
Sovereign House, 12 Trewartha Road, Praa Sands, Penzance, Cornwall TR20 9ST
Tel: 01736 762 826 Fax: 01736 763 328
Email: panamus@aol.com
Web Site: www.songwriters-guild.co.uk / www.panamamusic.co.uk
Senior Personnel: Roderick G Jones

FOLK ENTERTAINMENTS LTD
20 Shirley Avenue, Old Coulsdon, Surrey CR5 1QU
Tel: 020 8668 5714 Fax: 020 8645 6923
Mobile: 07802 688 072
Email: americanthemeevents@btinternet.com
Web Site: www.american-theme.com

GT MANAGEMENT PROMOTIONS
99 Gnoll Park Road, Neath, West Glamorgan SA11 3BU
Tel: 01639 643555 Fax: 01639 641643
Email: gareth@gtmp.co.uk / gtdeliver12@tiscali.co.uk
Contact: Gareth Thomas

HEAD ON MANAGEMENT
88 Lewisham Way, New Cross, London SE14 6NY
Tel/Fax: 020 8469 2576
Mobile: 07796 447 302
Email: headonman@yahoo.co.uk
Web Site: www.headonmanagement.com
Senior Personnel: Nick Wren, Chloe Wren
Personal Band Management.
Live Event promotions, Euphoria-Live, DJ Events, Live 3D Graphics.

DENNIS HEANEY PROMOTIONS
Whitehall, 8 Ashgrove Road, Newry, County Down BT34 1QN Northern Ireland
Tel: 028 3026 8658 Fax: 028 3026 6673
Mobile: 07860 377 414
Email: dennis_heaney@hotmail.com
Web Site: www.susanmccann.com
Senior Personnel: Dennis Heaney

MATTERS MUSICAL
The Loft, Rear of 8 West Street, Dorking, Surrey RH4 1BL
Tel: 01306 741 007 Fax: 01306 741 008
Email: info@mattersmusical.com
Web Site: www.mattersmusical.com
Senior Personnel: Frank Warren
Plus Dance Instruction/Demonstration for all the styles listed below.

OTB PRODUCTIONS
5 Oldridge View, Tedburn St. Mary, Exeter, Devon EX6 6AB
Tel: 01647 61237
Email: Dave@otbproductions.co.uk
Web Site: www.otbproductions.co.uk
Senior Personnel: Dave McCrory

PERROTTS FOLLY AGENCY
Treverryl, Trenance, Mawgan Porth, Newquay, Cornwall TR8 4DA
Tel/Fax: 01637 860 866
Email: jd@perrottsfolly.fsnet.co.uk
Web Site: www.perrottsfolly.com
Senior Personnel: Jackie Grinnell
Nationally Known folk and folk-comedy artistes plus the best jazz bands from the south-west including: Johnny Silvo & Jeremy Taylor.

PVA ENTERTAINMENT CONSULTANTS
2 High Street, Westbury-on-Trym, Bristol, Avon BS9 3DU
Tel: 0117 950 4504 Fax: 0117 959 1786
Email: tim@pvagroup.com, enquiries@pva.ltd.uk
Web Site: www.pva.ltd.uk
Senior Personnel: Pat Vincent, Tim Cowlin

THE Q BAND
20 Coombes Way, North Common Bristol BS30 8YP
Tel: 0117 940 0929 Tel: 0117 932 6244
Mob: 07801 627 859
Mob: 07853 944 227
Email: mail@theqband.co.uk
Web Site: www.theqband.co.uk
Contact: Brian Allen

RED SKY PRODUCTIONS
PO Box 27, Stroud, Gloucestershire GL6 0YQ
Tel/ Fax: 01453 885088
Email: johnny@redskyrecords.co.uk
Contact: Johnny Coppin
We specialise in British musical productions. Shows available are an annual Christmas show - "All on a Winter's Night" - a feast of Christmas songs and stories touring December 2010", plus "Edge of Day" - A tribute to Laurie Lee, and "Songs on Lonely Roads" - The story of composer/poet Ivor Gurney.

RENT-A-BAND
Burnside House, 10 Burns Court, Birstall, Batley, West Yorkshire WF17 9JZ
Tel/Fax: 01924 441 441
Email: bands@rent-a-band.org
Web Site: www.rent-a-band.org
Senior Personnel: Ken Baxter

MIKE STOREY ENTERTAINMENTS
Cliffe End Business Park, Dale Street, Longwood, Huddersfield, West Yorkshire
Tel: 0192 444 1245 Fax: 01484 657 055
Specialising in Irish and Country Music Acts

SYLVANTONE PROMOTIONS
11 Saunton Avenue, Redcar, Cleveland TS10 2RL
Tel: 01642 479 898 Fax: 0709 235 9333
Email: tonygoodacre / sylviagoodacre@hotmail.com
Web Site: www.tonygoodacre.com
Senior Personnel: Tony Goodacre, Sylvia Goodacre
Specialists in traditional country music.

Creatives

THE LUXFACTOR GROUP (UK)
Fleet Place, Nelson Drive, Petersfield, Hampshire GU31 4SJ
Tel: 0845 370 0589 Fax: 0845 370 0588
Email: info@luxfactor.co.uk
Web Site: www.luxfactor.co.uk
Managing Director & Agent: Michael D. Finch
Primarily representing Lighting, Sound, Video, Set, Costume and Scenic Designers, LUXFactor picks up where others are left bewildered. With clients on four continents we truly are an international agency. LUXFactor Client Management operates on a flexible international timeline status and during "theatre' hours too!

CLARE VIDAL-HALL
57 Carthew Road, London W6 0DU
Tel: 020 8741 7647 Fax: 020 8741 9459
Email: cvh@clarevidalhall.com
Web Site: www.clarevidalhall.com
Managing Director: Clare Vidal-Hall

DJ's

A.I.B. ENTERTAINMENTS
Newhouse Business Park, Newhouse Road, Grangemouth, Stirlingshire FK3 8LL Scotland
Tel: 01324 664 111
Email: enquiries@aib-discos.co.uk
Web Site: www.aib-discos.co.uk
Senior Personnel: Alan Burt
Professional mobile discos for corporate events.

ALCHEMY PR
212a The Bridge, 12-16 Clerkenwell Road, London EC1M 5PQ
Tel: 020 7324 6260 Fax: 020 7324 6001
Email: matt@alchemypr.com
Web Site: www.alchemypr.com
Directort: Matt Learmouth

VERN ALLEN ENTERTAINMENTS LIMITED
Suite 19, Basepoint Business Centre, Yeoford Way, Marsh Barton Trading Estate, Exeter EX2 8LB
Tel: 0870 383 1988 (2 lines)
Fax: 01392 426 421
Email: paul@vernallen.co.uk
Web Site: www.vernallen.co.uk
Senior Personnel: Paul Winteridge

AVENUE ARTISTES LTD
PO Box 1573 Southampton, Hampshire SO16 3XS
Tel: 02380 760930 Fax: 02380 760930
Email: info@avenueartistes.com
Web Site: www.avenueartistes.com
Senior Personnel: Terry Rolph

PAUL BARRETT ROCK 'N' ROLL ENTERPRISES
21 Grove Terrace, Penarth, Vale Glamorgan CF64 2NG Wales
Tel: 01222 704279 Fax: 01222 709989
Email: barrettrocknroll@ntlworld.com
Web Site: www.rockabillyhall.com
Senior Personnel: Paul Barrett
Specialist booking agent for rock'n'roll style acts. Able to book any international act in this category from local heroes to living legends. Any and all 50s and early 60s acts available.

ANDREW BEAUCHAMP MANAGEMENT
Oaklands Business Centre, 64-68 Elm Grove, Worthing, West Sussex BN11 5LH
Tel: 07737 415 534
Email: abeauchampmgt@aol.com
Proprietor: Andrew Beauchamp

BLACKPOOL'S MIDAS ENTERTAINMENTS
23 Ledbury Road, Blackpool, Lancashire FY3 7SR
Tel: 01253 395 062 No fax number
Web Site: www.blackpoolmidas.com
Represent Artistes, Groups, Duo's, Magicians. Also Disco/Karaoke P.A. Equipment Hire.

COFFEE ARTISTS
5 Weyhill Close, Maidstone, Kent ME14 5SQ
Tel: 01622 222 222 Fax: 01622 222 223
Email: gelli@coffeeartists.com
Web Site: www.coffeeartists.com
Head of Artists: Gelli Graham

Artist Management: Steve Piper
Coffee Artists UK DJ and musicians booking agency representing a select rosta of dj's and musicians and arranging tours for the clubbing industry promoters, club owners and party goers across the world.

COMPACT MANAGEMENT & ENTERTAINMENT AGENCY

98 Shellards Road, Longwell Green, Bristol, South Gloucestershire BS30 9DT
Tel: 0117 932 4344 Fax: 0117 932 6006
Mobile: 07831 446958
Email: paul@compactents.co.uk
Web Site: www.compactents.co.uk
Senior Personnel: Paul Wolf

CT ENTERTAINMENTS

PO Box 52, Newtownards, County Down BT23 3FX Northern Ireland
Tel: 028 9042 8800 Fax: 028 9042 3999
Email: ctentertainment@ukgateway.net
Web Site: www.theuntouchables.info
Senior Personnel: Cecil Thompson
Comedians & DJ's also available

D&S ARTISTES

19 Reffley Lane, King's Lynn, Norfolk PE30 3EF
Tel/Fax: 01553 671 693
Mobile: 07904 524 051
Email: info@dandsartistes.co.uk
Web Site: www.dandsartistes.co.uk
Senior Personnel: Alan Johnston, Mark Pearman
Specialising in groups, cabaret, children's entertainers, discos and celebrity appearances.

ELASTIC ARTISTS AGENCY

101 Micawber Wharf 17 Micawber Street, London N1 7TB
Tel: 020 7336 8340 Fax: 020 7608 1471
Email: info@elasticartists.net
Web Site: www.elasticartists.net
Agents: Mark Lewis, Naomi Palmer, Rebecca Prochnik, Jon Slade, Sinan Or, Greg Lowe
Email: firstname@elasticartists.net

FIRST TIME MANAGEMENT

Sovereign House, 12 Trewartha Road, Praa Sands, Penzance, Cornwall TR20 9ST
Tel: 01736 762 826 Fax: 01736 763 328
Email: panamus@aol.com
Web Site: www.songwriters-guild.co.uk / www.panamamusic.co.uk
Senior Personnel: Roderick G Jones

FRESH ARTISTE MANAGEMENT

Fresh Events Ltd, PO Box 1700, Sheffield S7 1JZ
Tel: 0870 990 9216 Fax: 0870 990 9217
Email: paul@freshdjs.co.uk
Web Site: www.freshdjs.co.uk
Agent: Paul Lyman
Including: Trance & Hard Dance DJs, House DJs, Musicians and Vocalists.

GREAT WESTERN ENTERTAINMENT AGENCY

46 Critchill Road, Frome, Somerset BA11 4HF
Tel: 01373 461 666
Mobile: 07774 694316
Senior Personnel: Graham Wilkin
Specialising in all types of entertainment.

LES HART (SOUTHAMPTON) ENTERTAINMENTS

6 Crookhorn Lane, Purbrook, Waterlooville, Hampshire PO7 5QE
Tel: 023 9225 8373 Fax: 023 9225 8369
Email: rod@leshart.co.uk
Web Site: www.leshart.co.uk
Contact: Rod Watts

HEAD ON MANAGEMENT

88 Lewisham Way, New Cross, London SE14 6NY
Tel/Fax: 020 8469 2576
Mobile: 07796 447 302
Email: headonman@yahoo.co.uk
Web: www.headonmanagement.com
Senior Personnel: Nick Wren, Chloe Wren
Personal Band Management.
Live Event promotions, Euphoria-Live, DJ Events, Live 3D Graphics.

HEART OF ENGLAND PROMOTIONS LTD

Old Hall, Wall Hill Road, Fillongley, Coventry, Warwickshire CV7 8DX
Tel: 01676 540 333 Fax: 01676 540 365
Email: sales@heartofengland.co.uk
Web Site: www.heartofengland.co.uk
Senior Personnel: Stephen Hammon
Specialising in DJs, Comperes and Children's Entertainment

DAWN JUDD ENTERTAINMENTS

19 Ashness Gardens, Greenford, Middlesex UB6 0RL
Tel: 020 8902 3373 / 8903 5533 Fax: 020 8902 9538
Web: www.dawnjuddentertainments.co.uk
Senior Personnel: Dawn Judd

LONDON MUSIC AGENCY

7 Rosewood Drive, Orchard Heights Ashford, Kent TN25 4QF
Tel: 01233 623 623 Mob: 07885 032 132
Email: enquiries@londonmusicagency.co.uk
Web: www.londonmusicagency.co.uk
Proprietor: Jenny Braby
Everything in entertainment for Private and Corporate functions, e.g. Jazz, String Quartets and all types of band, music and the unusual.

MATTERS MUSICAL

The Loft, Rear of 8 West Street, Dorking, Surrey RH4 1BL
Tel: 01306 741 007 Fax: 01306 741 008
Email: info@mattersmusical.com
Web Site: www.mattersmusical.com
Senior Personnel: Frank Warren
Plus Dance Instruction/Demonstration for all the styles listed below.

NEW FACES

2nd Floor, The Linen Hall, 162-168 Regent Street, London W1B 5TB
Tel: 020 7439 6900 Fax: 020 7287 5481
Email: val@newfacestalent.co.uk
Web Site: www.newfacestalent.co.uk
Agents: Val Horton, Tania Patti
New Faces is a dynamic presenters, actors and extras agency situated in the west end of London. The agency is aimed at giving highly talented people of today a platform from which to launch their career and established artists a professional, friendly, approachable and highly efficient service.
If you wish to be considered for representation, please send us a copy of your showreel (if appropriate), up-to-date CV or details of experience, photograph and SAE. All tapes are viewed and if we are interested we will contact you and arrange an interview.
For more information call Val or Cathy on 020 7439 6900.

JOHN NOEL MANAGEMENT

Block B, Imperial Works Perren Street London NW5 3ED
Tel: 020 7428 8400 Fax: 020 7428 8401
Email: john@johnnoel.com
Web Site: www.johnnoel.com
Agent: John Noel

PHA MODEL & CASTING MANAGEMENT

Tanzaro House, Ardwick Green North, Manchester M12 6FZ
Tel: 0161 273 4444 Fax: 0161 273 4567
Email: info@pha-agency.co.uk
Web Site: www.pha-agency.co.uk
Senior Personnel: Lorna McDonough, Robert F Lang
Represent models, extras and actors for commercials, corporate and TV work. Largest casting suites in Manchester also available for hire.

RENT-A-BAND

Burnside House, 10 Burns Court, Birstall, Batley, West Yorkshire WF17 9JZ
Tel/Fax: 01924 441 441
Email: bands@rent-a-band.org
Web Site: www.rent-a-band.org
Senior Personnel: Ken Baxter

STELLAMAX ENTERPRISES LTD

Nova House, 53 Nova Croft, Off Broad Lane, Eastern Green, Coventry,

Warwickshire CV5 7FJ
Tel: 024 7646 9585 Mob: 07899 045363
Email: max@stellamax.com
Web Site: www.stellamax.com
Senior Personnel: Max Roberts

TALENT ONE
14 Fairfield Lane, Wolverley
Kidderminster, Worcestershire DY11 5QH
Tel: 01562 850 255 Mob: 07957 106 982
Email: admin@talentone.co.uk
Web Site: www.talentone.co.uk
Contact : Phil & Keith

UPFRONT ENTERTAINMENT AGENCY LIMITED
Unit 8-9, MCF Complex, New Road,
Kidderminster, Worcestershire DY10 1AQ
Tel: 01562 69433 / 66350
Fax: 01562 69136
Email: brianupfront@aol.com
Web: www.upfrontentertainments.com
Contact: Brian Davies

VALUE ADDED TALENT AGENCY (VAT)
1 Purley Place, London N1 1QA
Tel: 020 7704 9720 Fax: 020 7226 6135
Email: dan@vathq.co.uk
Web Site: www.vathq.co.uk
Senior Personnel: Dan Silver

Escapology

THE A6 AGENCY
Willow Moorings Kegworth DE74 2EY
Mobile: 07889 745594
Email: michaelhobson2012@yahoo.co.uk
Web: www.snapshotproductions.co.uk
Senior Personnel: Michael Hobson
Specialising in outdoor and promotional attractions, jazz bands and silouette and origami artistes

CIRCUS ALCHEMY
5 Beech Avenue, Rawmarsh, Rotherham,
South Yorkshire S62 5HH
Tel: 01709 710 780 Fax: 01709 710 780
Email: albert@albertalchemy.com
Web Site: www.albertalchemy.com
Contact: Albert Alchemy
Fire-eating, escapology, stiltwalking, medieval jester. Magic for corporate, public and private functions.

CONTINENTAL DRIFTS
8 Hilton Grove, Hatherley Mews,
Walthamstow, London E17 4QP
Tel: 020 8509 3353 Fax: 020 8509 9531
Email: info@continentaldrifts.co.uk
Web Site: www.continentaldrifts.co.uk
Senior Personnel: Mel Wilds,
Chris Meikan
Event Production and Performance Specialists.
The finest in event entertainment and production, whether a single stilt walker or a fully choreographed show. Continental Drifts artists range from the bizarre to the beautiful and we have an in-house creative team to formulate ideas and realise your vision. Full technical production is available, along with fully trained event crews. Continental Drifts take a client-centred approach are are more than happy to meet with you to discuss your event requirements in full detail.

GALAXY EVENTS
Galaxy House, Mian Yard, 86 Wallis Road, London E9 5LN
Tel: 0208 1330 558
Email: info@galaxy-events.co.uk
Web Site: www.galaxy-events.co.uk
Senior Personnel: Mel Harvey
Artist Management and Event Coordination.

THE MAGIC OF SHAHID MALIK
3 Selborne Villas, North Park Road,
Heaton, Bradford, West Yorkshire
BD9 4NN
Tel: 01274 499 065 Fax: 01274 490 179
Email: shahid@shahidmalik.co.uk
Web Site: www.shahidmalik.co.uk
Contact: Shahid Malik
International Magician and Illusionist.

STELLAMAX ENTERPRISES LTD
Nova House, 53 Nova Croft, Off Broad Lane, Eastern Green, Coventry,
Warwickshire CV5 7FJ
Tel: 024 7646 9585 Mob: 07899 045363
Email: max@stellamax.com
Web Site: www.stellamax.com
Senior Personnel: Max Roberts

Function Bands

1ST CALL ENTERTAINMENT
Redland Office Centre, 157 Redland Road, Bristol BS6 6YE
Tel: 01179 239 299
Mobile: 07980 863 468
Email: julian@firstcallentertainment.com
Web: www.1stcallentertainment.co.uk
Contact: Julian Franks

THE PETER DONEGAN BAND
21 Belsay Grove, Bedlington,
Northumberland NE22 5YU
Mob: 07563 379 245
Email: peter-donegan@hotmail.com
Web Site: www.peterdonegan.com
Contact: Peter Donegan

TIM GENTLE MUSIC
PO Box 154 Stockton-on-Tees, Cleveland
TS20 1XJ
Tel: 01642 557 979 Fax: 01642 557 677
Mob: 07850 515 058
Email: timgentle@hotmail.com
Web Site: www.thehitmen.eu
Contact: Tim Gentle

THE GRAFFITI CLASSICS
37 Twickenham Road, Leytonstone,
London E11 4BN
Tel/Fax: 020 8556 5949
Mob: 07956 909981
Email: info@graffiticlassics.com
Web Site: www.graffiticlassics.com
The Group's unique character and style has developed a refreshing insight into the world of classical music, the principal aim being to entertain, educate and bring an interactive involvement to all audiences of all ages and abilities.

INSTANT SUNSHINE
9 Ashdown Road, Epsom,
Surrey KT17 3PL
Tel: 01372 720 727
Email: instantsunshine@christiehouse.demon.co.uk
Web Site: www.instantsunshine.co.uk
Contact: Peter Christie

THE Q BAND
20 Coombes Way, North Common Bristol
BS30 8YP
Tel: 0117 940 0929 Tel: 0117 932 6244
Mob: 07801 627 859
Mob: 07853 944 227
Email: mail@theqband.co.uk
Web Site: www.theqband.co.uk
Contact: Brian Allen

TALENT ONE
14 Fairfield Lane, Wolverley
Kidderminster, Worcestershire DY11 5QH
Tel: 01562 850 255 Mob: 07957 106 982
Email: admin@talentone.co.uk
Web Site: www.talentone.co.uk
Contact : Phil & Keith

UPBEAT ENTERTAINMENT
236 Hythe Road Willesborough Kent
TN24 0QS
Tel: 01233 650 218 Fax: 01233 641 446
Mobile: 07974 260 479
Email: station2@tiscali.co.uk
Web: www.upbeat-entertainment.com
Senior Personnel: Kim Carney-Boeje

UPBEAT MANAGEMENT
Larg House Woodcote Grove, Coulsdon,
Surrey CR5 2QQ
Tel: 020 8668 3332 Fax: 020 8668 3922
Email: info@upbeat.co.uk
Web Site: www.upbeat.co.uk
Senior Personnel (Entertainment): Liz Biddle, Beryl Korman
Specialising in Theatre Touring and large events for Festivals and corporate entertainment.

Hypnotists

AFTER DINNER SPEAKERS & COMEDIANS LIMITED
Chippings 2 The Old Saw Mills Ripponden Halifax, West Yorkshire HX6 4EN
Tel: 0845 4758866 Fax: 01422 884 494
Email: office@comedians.co.uk
Web Site: www.comedians.co.uk
Senior Personnel: Roger Davis, J. Mark Davis

DAVID CHARLES AGENCY
2 Betjeman Way, Hemel Hempstead, Hertfordshire HP1 3HH
Tel: 01442 264 402
Mobile: 07767 813 231
Email: david@davidcharlesent.co.uk
Web Site: www.davidcharlesent.co.uk
Senior Personnel: David Charles, Penny Charles
Specialising in adult entertainment, bands and groups.

COMPACT MANAGEMENT & ENTERTAINMENT AGENCY
98 Shellards Road, Longwell Green, Bristol, South Gloucestershire BS30 9DT
Tel: 0117 932 4344 Fax: 0117 932 6006
Mobile: 07831 446958
Email: paul@compactents.co.uk
Web Site: www.compactents.co.uk
Senior Personnel: Paul Wolf

DCM (DAVE CARR MANAGEMENT)
PO Box 102 Spennymoor, County Durham DL16 9BF
Tel: 01388 817755
Email: seancarragent@yahoo.co.uk
Contacts: Sean Carr, David Johnston

DEVIL MANAGEMENT
PO Box 23, Spennymoor, County Durham DL16 7YZ
Tel: 01388 818 888 Fax: 01388 811 222
Email: steve@devilmanagement.com
Web Site: www.devilmanagement.com
Contact: Steve Dodds, Paul Carr

D&S ARTISTES
19 Reffley Lane, King's Lynn, Norfolk PE30 3EF
Tel/Fax: 01553 671 693
Mobile: 07904 524 051
Email: info@dandsartistes.co.uk
Web Site: www.dandsartistes.co.uk
Senior Personnel: Alan Johnston, Mark Pearman
Specialising in groups, cabaret, children's entertainers, discos and celebrity appearances.

DAWN JUDD ENTERTAINMENTS
19 Ashness Gardens, Greenford, Middlesex UB6 0RL
Tel: 020 8902 3373 / 8903 5533 Fax: 020 8902 9538
Web: www.dawnjuddentertainments.co.uk
Senior Personnel: Dawn Judd

MR "E" ENTERPRISES
Little Greenfields Farm, Jack Haye Lane, Light Oaks, Stoke-on-Trent, Staffordshire ST2 7NG
Tel: 01782 304 909
Mobile: 07831 311318
Email: info@mreenterprises.co.uk
Senior Personnel: Eddie Burke

STELLAMAX ENTERPRISES LTD
Nova House, 53 Nova Croft, Off Broad Lane, Eastern Green, Coventry, Warwickshire CV5 7FJ
Tel: 024 7646 9585 Mob: 07899 045363
Email: max@stellamax.com
Web Site: www.stellamax.com
Senior Personnel: Max Roberts

Ice Skaters

GO ENTERTAINMENTS
The Arts Exchange, Dane Mill Congleton, Cheshire CW12 1LA
Tel: 01260 276 627 Fax: 01260 270 777
Email: info@arts-exchange.com
Web Site: www.arts-exchange.com
Contact: Phillip or Carol Gandey
Big tops up to 5000 people worldwide supply.

Impressionists

VERN ALLEN ENTERTAINMENTS LIMITED
Suite 19, Basepoint Business Centre, Yeoford Way, Marsh Barton Trading Estate, Exeter EX2 8LB
Tel: 0870 383 1988 (2 lines)
Fax: 01392 426 421
Email: paul@vernallen.co.uk
Web Site: www.vernallen.co.uk
Senior Personnel: Paul Winteridge

DAVID CHARLES AGENCY
2 Betjeman Way, Hemel Hempstead, Hertfordshire HP1 3HH
Tel: 01442 264 402
Mobile: 07767 813 231
Email: david@davidcharlesent.co.uk
Web Site: www.davidcharlesent.co.uk
Senior Personnel: David Charles, Penny Charles
Specialising in adult entertainment, bands and groups.

COMPACT MANAGEMENT & ENTERTAINMENT AGENCY
98 Shellards Road, Longwell Green, Bristol, South Gloucestershire BS30 9DT
Tel: 0117 932 4344 Fax: 0117 932 6006
Mobile: 07831 446958
Email: paul@compactents.co.uk
Web Site: www.compactents.co.uk
Senior Personnel: Paul Wolf

D&S ARTISTES
19 Reffley Lane, King's Lynn, Norfolk PE30 3EF
Tel/Fax: 01553 671 693
Mobile: 07904 524 051
Email: info@dandsartistes.co.uk
Web Site: www.dandsartistes.co.uk
Senior Personnel: Alan Johnston, Mark Pearman
Specialising in groups, cabaret, children's entertainers, discos and celebrity appearances.

CHRISTOPHER GEE
32 Clydesdale Gardens, North Berstead Bognor Regis, West Sussex PO22 9BE
Tel: 01243 861 171 Mob: 07794 218295
Email: christopher_gee@btinternet.com
Web Site: www.christopher-gee.com
Contact: Christopher Gee

TREVOR GEORGE ENTERTAINMENTS LTD
PO Box 135, Torquay, Devon TQ1 3ZW
Tel: 01803 615 600 / 700 Fax: 01803 615 888 Mobile: 07502 042 995
Email: anne@trevorgeorge.co.uk
Web Site: www.trevorgeorge.co.uk
Senior Personnel: Anne George, Beverley Korman

GREAT WESTERN ENTERTAINMENT AGENCY
46 Critchill Road, Frome, Somerset BA11 4HF
Tel: 01373 461 666 Mobile: 07774 694316
Senior Personnel: Graham Wilkin
Specialising in all types of entertainment.

JANE MORGAN MANAGEMENT
Elsinore House 77 Fulham Palace Road, London W6 8JA
Tel: 020 7478 7479
Email: enquiries@janemorganmgt.com
Web Site: www.janemorganmgt.com
Senior Personnel: Jane Morgan
Specialises in the representation of sports broadcasters and sportsmen and women who now have a career in the media.

STELLAMAX ENTERPRISES LTD
Nova House, 53 Nova Croft, Off Broad Lane, Eastern Green, Coventry, Warwickshire CV5 7FJ
Tel: 024 7646 9585 Mob: 07899 045363

Email: max@stellamax.com
Web Site: www.stellamax.com
Senior Personnel: Max Roberts

Jazz & Blues

THE A6 AGENCY
Willow Moorings Kegworth DE74 2EY
Mobile: 07889 745594
Email: michaelhobson2012@yahoo.co.uk
Web: www.snapshotproductions.co.uk
Senior Personnel: Michael Hobson
Specialising in outdoor and promotional attractions, jazz bands and silouette and origami artistes

ACKER'S INTERNATIONAL JAZZ AGENCY
53 Cambridge Mansions, Cambridge Road, London SW11 4RX
Tel: 020 7978 5885
Mobile: 07985 713403
Email: pamela@ackersmusicagency.co.uk
Web Site: www.ackersmusicagency.co.uk
Proprietor: Pamela Frances Sutton
Personal Management and Exclusive Agency for Acker Bilk and his Paramount Jazz Band.
Non-Exclusive Agency for:

NICK ALLEN MANAGEMENT
7 Forewoods Common, Holt, Trowbridge, Wiltshire BA14 6PJ
Tel/Fax: 01225 782 281
Email: namanage@aol.com
Web Site: www.namrecording.com
Senior Personnel: Nick Allen

ANDREW BEAUCHAMP MANAGEMENT
Oaklands Business Centre, 64-68 Elm Grove, Worthing, West Sussex BN11 5LH
Tel: 07737 415 534
Email: abeauchampmgt@aol.com
Proprietor: Andrew Beauchamp

BIG BEAR MUSIC
PO BOX 944, Edgbaston, Birmingham B16 8UT
Tel: 0121 454 7020
Email: admin@bigbearmusic.com/ tim@bigbearmusic.com
Web Site: www.bigbearmusic.com
Senior Personnel: Tim Jennings, Jim Simpson
Big Bear Music promote jazz, blues and swing through concert and club tours, UK and European festivals, the Starbucks Birmingham International Jazz Festival and Marbella Jazz Festival (Spain).

THE JOHN BODDY AGENCY
10 Southfield Gardens, Twickenham, Middlesex TW1 4SZ
Tel: 020 8892 0133 / 8891 3809
Fax: 020 8287 0798
Email: jba@johnboddyagency.co.uk
Web Site: www.johnboddyagency.co.uk
Senior Personnel: John Boddy and Jonathan Boddy
Member of Agents Association (GB)

DAVID CHARLES AGENCY
2 Betjeman Way, Hemel Hempstead, Hertfordshire HP1 3HH
Tel: 01442 264 402
Mobile: 07767 813 231
Email: david@davidcharlesent.co.uk
Web Site: www.davidcharlesent.co.uk
Senior Personnel: David Charles, Penny Charles
Specialising in adult entertainment, bands and groups.

BARRY COLLINGS ENTERTAINMENTS
PO Box 1151 St Albans AL1 9WB
Tel: 01702 201880 Fax: 01702 201880
Email: barry-Collings@btconnect.com
Web Site: www.barrycollings.co.uk
Senior Personnel: Barry Collings, Lorraine Collings
All artistes available by arrangement with their respective managements.

COMPACT MANAGEMENT & ENTERTAINMENT AGENCY
98 Shellards Road, Longwell Green, Bristol, South Gloucestershire BS30 9DT
Tel: 0117 932 4344 Fax: 0117 932 6006
Mobile: 07831 446958
Email: paul@compactents.co.uk
Web Site: www.compactents.co.uk
Senior Personnel: Paul Wolf

CROMWELL MANAGEMENT
20 Drayhorse Road, Ramsey, Huntingdon, Cambridgeshire PE26 1SD
Tel: 01487 815 063 Fax: 01487 711 896
Email: tricvic@lineone.net
Web Site: www.jazzmanagement.ic24.net
Senior Personnel: V Gibbons, P A Gibbons

THE PETER DONEGAN BAND
21 Belsay Grove, Bedlington, Northumberland NE22 5YU
Mob: 07563 379 245
Email: peter-donegan@hotmail.com
Web Site: www.peterdonegan.com
Contact: Peter Donegan

D&S ARTISTES
19 Reffley Lane, King's Lynn, Norfolk PE30 3EF
Tel/Fax: 01553 671 693 Mobile: 07904 524 051
Email: info@dandsartistes.co.uk
Web Site: www.dandsartistes.co.uk
Senior Personnel: Alan Johnston, Mark Pearman
Specialising in groups, cabaret, children's entertainers, discos and celebrity appearances.

FIRST TIME MANAGEMENT
Sovereign House, 12 Trewartha Road, Praa Sands, Penzance, Cornwall TR20 9ST
Tel: 01736 762 826 Fax: 01736 763 328
Email: panamus@aol.com
Web Site: www.songwriters-guild.co.uk / www.panamamusic.co.uk
Senior Personnel: Roderick G Jones

GTA MUSIC CONSULTANTS AND AGENCY
14 Glamorgan Road Hampton Wick, Kingston-upon-Thames, Surrey KT1 4HP
Tel: 020 8943 9113 / 020 8412 0096
Fax: 020 8943 9112
Email: info@gtamusic.co.uk
Web Site: www.gtamusic.co.uk
Senior Personnel: Gilly Tarrant, David Kelly

LES HART (SOUTHAMPTON) ENTERTAINMENTS
6 Crookhorn Lane, Purbrook, Waterlooville, Hampshire PO7 5QE
Tel: 023 9225 8373 Fax: 023 9225 8369
Email: rod@leshart.co.uk
Web Site: www.leshart.co.uk
Contact: Rod Watts

JAZZCO
Ten Acre Farm, Stonehill Road, Ottershaw, Chertsey, Surrey KT16 0AQ
Tel: 08450 008 007 / 01932455904
Email: les@jazzco.co.uk
Web Site: www..jazzco.co.uk

THE JIVE ACES
Saint Hill Manor East Grinstead West Sussex RH19 4JY
Tel/Fax: 01342 300 075 Mobile: 07793 122 646
Email: bookings@jiveaces.com
Web Site: www.jiveaces.com
Manager: Peter Howell
Publicist: Grazia Clarkson
Promotions Manager: Alex Douglas
The UK's No1 Jive & Swing Band
A group of lads from London were drawn together by their love for a style and music that outclassed anything around. The music was hot jive that had the beat, energy and enthusiasm of Rock'n'Roll and the fun and rhythm of big band swing all rolled into one. The Jive Aces' unique sound comes from a combination of their own original tunes in true swing style as well as fresh arrangements of songs from the swing era.

LONDON MUSIC AGENCY
7 Rosewood Drive, Orchard Heights Ashford, Kent TN25 4QF
Tel: 01233 623 623 Mob: 07885 032 132

Email: enquiries@londonmusicagency.co.uk
Web: www.londonmusicagency.co.uk
Proprietor: Jenny Braby
Everything in entertainment for Private and Corporate functions, e.g. Jazz, String Quartets and all types of band, music and the unusual.

MATTERS MUSICAL
The Loft, Rear of 8 West Street, Dorking, Surrey RH4 1BL
Tel: 01306 741 007 Fax: 01306 741 008
Email: info@mattersmusical.com
Web Site: www.mattersmusical.com
Senior Personnel: Frank Warren
Plus Dance Instruction/Demonstration for all the styles listed below.

NATIONAL YOUTH JAZZ ORCHESTRA
2nd Floor, 5 Vigo Street,
London W1S 3HD
Tel: 020 7494 1733
Email: info@nyjo.org.uk
Web Site: www.NYJO.org.uk
Executive Chairman: Nigel Tully
Executive Director: Dr. Fiona Ord-Shrimpton

PERROTTS FOLLY AGENCY
Treverryl, Trenance, Mawgan Porth, Newquay, Cornwall TR8 4DA
Tel/Fax: 01637 860 866
Email: jd@perrottsfolly.fsnet.co.uk
Web Site: www.perrottsfolly.com
Senior Personnel: Jackie Grinnell
Nationally Known folk and folk-comedy artistes plus the best jazz bands from the south-west including: Johnny Silvo & Jeremy Taylor.

RENT-A-BAND
Burnside House, 10 Burns Court, Birstall, Batley, West Yorkshire WF17 9JZ
Tel/Fax: 01924 441 441
Email: bands@rent-a-band.org
Web Site: www.rent-a-band.org
Senior Personnel: Ken Baxter

ROSEBERY MANAGEMENT
Hoxton Hall, 130 Hoxton Street,
London N1 6SH
Tel: 020 7684 0187 Mob: 07805 162731
Email: admin@roseberymanagement.com
Web: www.roseberymanagement.com
Manager: Ben West

ROSEMARY SQUIRES ENTERPRISES
2 The Meadows, Milford, Salisbury, Wiltshire SP1 2SS
Tel: 01722 322 479 All Electric Productions (Booking Agent):
Tel: 01264 361 924
Email: fralock@tiscali.co.uk
Web Site: www.rosemarysquires.co.uk
Personal Manager: Frank Lockyer
Booking Agent:
All Electric Productions
Po Box 1805
Andover
SP10 3ZN

KEN SPENCER PERSONAL MANAGEMENT
P.A.G. Promotions, 138 Sandy Hill Road, London SE18 7BA
Tel/Fax: 020 8854 2558
Email: pagandferret@hotmail.com
Senior Personnel: Ken Spencer
Classical artists and mainly classically-trained singers, sopranos and tenors. Occassionally represent pianists.

STELLAMAX ENTERPRISES LTD
Nova House, 53 Nova Croft, Off Broad Lane, Eastern Green, Coventry, Warwickshire CV5 7FJ
Tel: 024 7646 9585 Mob: 07899 045363
Email: max@stellamax.com
Web Site: www.stellamax.com
Senior Personnel: Max Roberts

UPBEAT ENTERTAINMENT
236 Hythe Road Willesborough
Kent TN24 0QS
Tel: 01233 650 218 Fax: 01233 641 446
Mobile: 07974 260 479
Email: station2@tiscali.co.uk
Web: www.upbeat-entertainment.com
Senior Personnel: Kim Carney-Boeje

UPBEAT MANAGEMENT
Larg House Woodcote Grove, Coulsdon, Surrey CR5 2QQ
Tel: 020 8668 3332 Fax: 020 8668 3922
Email: info@upbeat.co.uk
Web Site: www.upbeat.co.uk
Senior Personnel (Entertainment): Liz Biddle, Beryl Korman
Specialising in Theatre Touring and large events for Festivals and corporate entertainment.

DAVE WINSLETT ASSOCIATES
4 Zig Zag Road, Kenley, Surrey CR8 5EL
Tel: 020 8668 0531 Fax: 020 8668 9216
Email: info@davewinslett.com
Web Site: www.davewinslett.com
Senior Personnel: Dave Winslett FEAA

Latin Dance

MAX COLLIE RHYTHM ACES
26 Wendover Road, Bromley,
Kent BR2 9JX
Tel: 020 8460 1139 Fax: 020 8466 7005
Email: max@maxcollie.fsnet.co.uk
Web Site: www.maxcollie.co.uk
Senior Personnel: Max Collie
Specialising in Traditional and New Orleans Jazz

FUNKI FEATHERS DANCE PRODUCTIONS LTD
Sycamore House, 8 Sycamore Road, Bearwood Smethwick, West Midlands B66 4NL
Tel/Fax: 0121 420 4396
Mobile: 07958 945701 / 2
Email: funkifeathers@telco4u.net
Web Site: www.funkifeathers.co.uk
Contact: Julie-Ann Phillips
Dance/Promotional Group.
Providing dancers, costumes and production shows.

LATIN ARTS SERVICES (LAS) MUSIC
PO Box 57817, London SE23 3PT
Tel/Fax: 020 8291 9236
Mobile: 07956 446342
Email: info@latinartsgroup.com
Web Site: www.latinartsgroup.com
Senior Personnel: Hector Rosquete
Latin entertainment promoters. Our new show is The Mambo Boyz Salsa Show.

LATIN MOTION
PO Box 8311, Birmingham B16 0LQ
Tel: 0121 454 5009 Fax: 0121 246 3555
Mob: 07973 402 911
Email: info@latinmotion.co.uk, mauricio@latinmotion.co.uk
Web Site: www.latinmotion.co.uk
Contact: Mauricio Reyes

LONDON MUSIC AGENCY
7 Rosewood Drive, Orchard Heights
Ashford, Kent TN25 4QF
Tel: 01233 623 623 Mob: 07885 032 132
Email: enquiries@londonmusicagency.co.uk
Web: www.londonmusicagency.co.uk
Proprietor: Jenny Braby
Everything in entertainment for Private and Corporate functions, e.g. Jazz, String Quartets and all types of band, music and the unusual.

MATTERS MUSICAL
The Loft, Rear of 8 West Street, Dorking, Surrey RH4 1BL
Tel: 01306 741 007 Fax: 01306 741 008
Email: info@mattersmusical.com
Web Site: www.mattersmusical.com
Senior Personnel: Frank Warren
Plus Dance Instruction/Demonstration for all the styles listed below.

RENT-A-BAND
Burnside House, 10 Burns Court, Birstall, Batley, West Yorkshire WF17 9JZ
Tel/Fax: 01924 441 441
Email: bands@rent-a-band.org
Web Site: www.rent-a-band.org
Senior Personnel: Ken Baxter

STELLAMAX ENTERPRISES LTD
Nova House, 53 Nova Croft, Off Broad Lane, Eastern Green, Coventry,

Warwickshire CV5 7FJ
Tel: 024 7646 9585 Mob: 07899 045363
Email: max@stellamax.com
Web Site: www.stellamax.com
Senior Personnel: Max Roberts

UPBEAT ENTERTAINMENT
236 Hythe Road Willesborough Kent TN24 0QS
Tel: 01233 650 218 Fax: 01233 641 446
Mobile: 07974 260 479
Email: station2@tiscali.co.uk
Web: www.upbeat-entertainment.com
Senior Personnel: Kim Carney-Boeje

Lookalikes & Soundalikes

A.I.R. LIMITED
AIR House, Spennymoor, County Durham DL16 7SE
Tel: 01388 814 632 Fax: 01388 812 445
Email: info@airagency.com
Web Site: www.airagency.com
Directors: Colin Pearson, John Wray

VERN ALLEN ENTERTAINMENTS LIMITED
Suite 19, Basepoint Business Centre, Yeoford Way, Marsh Barton Trading Estate, Exeter EX2 8LB
Tel: 0870 383 1988 (2 lines)
Fax: 01392 426 421
Email: paul@vernallen.co.uk
Web Site: www.vernallen.co.uk
Senior Personnel: Paul Winteridge

ALRIGHT CHARLIE
Flat 4 Carleton House 122a Hillfield Avenue London N8 7DQ
Tel: 07808 732 390
Email: info@alrightcharlie.co.uk
Web Site: www.alrightcharlie.co.uk
Senior Personnel: Lawrence Anthony
Charlie Chaplin Look Alike, Comedy waiter & Close-up Magician for all indoor and outdoor events.

ANDREW BEAUCHAMP MANAGEMENT
Oaklands Business Centre, 64-68 Elm Grove, Worthing, West Sussex BN11 5LH
Tel: 07737 415 534
Email: abeauchampmgt@aol.com
Proprietor: Andrew Beauchamp

CHANCE PROMOTIONS
The Nook, Bee Lane, Penwortham, Preston PR1 9TU
Tel: 01772 321 160
Email: info@legendschance.com
Web Site: www.legendschance.com
Managing Directors: Trevor Chance, Brenda Chance
Creative Musical director: Richard Chance
Choreographer: Wendy Holland
Company Production Manager: Tony Harvey
Specialising in Look/Sound Alike Shows & Tributes.

DAVID CHARLES AGENCY
2 Betjeman Way, Hemel Hempstead, Hertfordshire HP1 3HH
Tel: 01442 264 402
Mobile: 07767 813 231
Email: david@davidcharlesent.co.uk
Web Site: www.davidcharlesent.co.uk
Senior Personnel: David Charles, Penny Charles
Specialising in adult entertainment, bands and groups.

BARRY COLLINGS ENTERTAINMENTS
PO Box 1151 St Albans AL1 9WB
Tel: 01702 201880 Fax: 01702 201880
Email: barry-Collings@btconnect.com
Web Site: www.barrycollings.co.uk
Senior Personnel: Barry Collings, Lorraine Collings
All artistes available by arrangement with their respective managements.

COMPACT MANAGEMENT & ENTERTAINMENT AGENCY
98 Shellards Road, Longwell Green, Bristol, South Gloucestershire BS30 9DT
Tel: 0117 932 4344 Fax: 0117 932 6006
Mobile: 07831 446958
Email: paul@compactents.co.uk
Web Site: www.compactents.co.uk
Senior Personnel: Paul Wolf

DCM (DAVE CARR MANAGEMENT)
PO Box 102 Spennymoor, County Durham DL16 9BF
Tel: 01388 817755
Email: seancarragent@yahoo.co.uk
Contacts: Sean Carr, David Johnston

D&S ARTISTES
19 Reffley Lane, King's Lynn, Norfolk PE30 3EF
Tel/Fax: 01553 671 693 Mobile: 07904 524 051
Email: info@dandsartistes.co.uk
Web Site: www.dandsartistes.co.uk
Senior Personnel: Alan Johnston, Mark Pearman
Specialising in groups, cabaret, children's entertainers, discos and celebrity appearances.

STEVE ELSON
11 Ernest Gardens, London W4 3QU
Tel: 020 8995 5520 Fax: 020 8995 3835
Mobile: 07976 276 375
Email: steve@counterfeitstone.demon.co.uk
Web Site: www.thecounterfeitstones.net
Senior Personnel: Steve Elson
Production and management of The Counterfeit Stones - "A Rolling Stones Tribute Show".

ENTERTAINERS COMPANY LTD.
200 London Road, Hadleigh, Benfleet, Essex SS7 2PD
Tel: 01702 427 100 / 0870 233 0836
Fax: 01702 427 109 Mob: 07850 111616
Email: enquiries@entertainers.co.uk
Web Site: www.entertainers.co.uk / www.easytheatres.co.uk
Director: Michael Taylor (michael@entertainers.co.uk)
Senior Personnel: Ben Hatton
The one stop shop for entertainment.

ENTERTAINERS MANAGEMENT LTD
200 London Road, Hadleigh, Benfleet, Essex SS7 2PD
Tel: 01702 427 100 Fax: 01702 427 109
Mob: 07850 111616
Email: enquiries@entertainers.co.uk
Web Site: www.easytheatres.com
Senior Personnel: Ben Hatton
Director: Michael Taylor
Contact: michael@entertainers.co.uk
The UK's no 1 entertainment agency.

LIONEL FANTHORPE
48 Claude Road, Roath Cardiff CF24 3QA
Tel: 029 2049 8368 Mob: 07767 207 289
Fax: 029 2049 6832
Email: fanthorpe@aol.com
Web Site: www.lionel-fanthorpe.com
Contact: Lionel Fanthorpe

FAWLTY TOWERS - EDMOND WELLS AS JOHN CLEESE
2 The Maltings, Fenlane Beccles, Suffolk NR34 9BT
Tel: 01485 570 945 Mob: 07767 863 415
Email: info@johncleese.co.uk
Web Site: www.johncleese.co.uk
Contact: Edmond Wells

JEM FRAZER LIMITED
6 Shancara Court, Tingley, Wakefield, West Yorkshire WF3 1JP
Tel: 01132 529 062 Mob: 07870 666 840
Email: jem@jemfrazer.co.uk
Web Site: www.jemfrazer.co.uk
Contact : Jem Frazer
Please see ads : Haurel and Lardy, Ziddler, Funderbirds, Jem Frazer Characters, Hogwarts characters

CHRISTOPHER GEE
32 Clydesdale Gardens, North Berstead Bognor Regis, West Sussex PO22 9BE
Tel: 01243 861 171 Mob: 07794 218295
Email: christopher_gee@btinternet.com
Web Site: www.christopher-gee.com
Contact: Christopher Gee

TREVOR GEORGE ENTERTAINMENTS LTD
PO Box 135, Torquay, Devon TQ1 3ZW
Tel: 01803 615 600 / 700 Fax: 01803 615 888 Mobile: 07502 042 995
Email: anne@trevorgeorge.co.uk
Web Site: www.trevorgeorge.co.uk
Senior Personnel: Anne George, Beverley Korman

GOLDSTAR ENTERTAINMENT UK
Homefield, Rotherham Road, Middlecliffe, Barnsley, South Yorkshire S72 0HA
Tel: 01226 340 011 Fax: 01226 751 011
Email: lynn@goldstarents.freeserve.co.uk
Web: www.goldstarentertainment-uk.com
Senior Personnel: Lynn Winks

HEAD ON MANAGEMENT
88 Lewisham Way, New Cross, London SE14 6NY
Tel/Fax: 020 8469 2576
Mobile: 07796 447 302
Email: headonman@yahoo.co.uk
Web Site: www.headonmanagement.com
Senior Personnel: Nick Wren, Chloe Wren
Personal Band Management.
Live Event promotions, Euphoria-Live, DJ Events, Live 3D Graphics.

MATTERS MUSICAL
The Loft, Rear of 8 West Street, Dorking, Surrey RH4 1BL
Tel: 01306 741 007 Fax: 01306 741 008
Email: info@mattersmusical.com
Web Site: www.mattersmusical.com
Senior Personnel: Frank Warren
Plus Dance Instruction/Demonstration for all the styles listed below.

RENT-A-BAND
Burnside House, 10 Burns Court, Birstall, Batley, West Yorkshire WF17 9JZ
Tel/Fax: 01924 441 441
Email: bands@rent-a-band.org
Web Site: www.rent-a-band.org
Senior Personnel: Ken Baxter

SUSAN SCOTT LOOKALIKES LTD
106 Tollington Park, Finsbury Park London N4 3RB
Tel: 020 7281 8029 Fax: 020 7281 1263
Mob: 07905 094 904 / 07847 633 348
Email: susan@lookalikes.info
Web Site: www.lookalikes.info
Senoir personnel: Helena Maroutzi, Susan Scott
Specialising in: All leading lookalikes and soundalikes.

SPLITTING IMAGES LOOKALIKE AGENCY
25 Clissold Court, Greenway Close, London N4 2EZ
Tel: 020 8809 2327 Fax: 020 8809 6103
Email: info@splitting-images.com
Web Site: www.splitting-images.com
Senior Personnel: Michael Fine
We have hundreds of lookalikes ranging from Tony Blair to Ruby Wax and Neil Diamond to Pierce Brosnan. Please call for further details.

MANY FACES OF DEAN TAYLOR
116 Fullarton Crescent, South Ockendon, Essex RM15 5HZ
Tel: 01708 856 022 Mob: 07956 217 954
Email: Themanyfacesofdt@aol.com
Contact: Dean Taylor

UPBEAT ENTERTAINMENT
236 Hythe Road Willesborough Kent TN24 0QS
Tel: 01233 650 218 Fax: 01233 641 446
Mobile: 07974 260 479
Email: station2@tiscali.co.uk
Web: www.upbeat-entertainment.com
Senior Personnel: Kim Carney-Boeje

UPFRONT ENTERTAINMENT AGENCY LIMITED
Unit 8-9, MCF Complex, New Road, Kidderminster, Worcestershire DY10 1AQ
Tel: 01562 69433 / 66350
Fax: 01562 69136
Email: brianupfront@aol.com
Web: www.upfrontentertainments.com
Contact: Brian Davies

Models

B.M.A. MODELS LIMITED
The Stables, 346 High Street, Berkhamsted, Hertfordshire HP4 1HT
Tel: 01442 878 878 Fax: 01442 879 879
Email: info@bmamodels.com
Web Site: bmamodels.com
Senior Personnel: Lynn Campbell-Walter

BUBBLEGUM MODEL AGENCY
Pinewood Studios, Pinewood Road Iver Heath, Buckinghamshire SL0 0NH
Tel: 01753 632 867 Fax: 01753 652 521
Email: kids@bubblegummodels.com
Web Site: www.bubblegumodels.com
Senior Personnel: Penny Hobson, Nicola Barwell
Children and teenagers from newborn to 18 years.

ALISON CAMPBELL MODEL AGENCY
381 Beersbridge Road, Belfast, County Antrim BT5 5DT Northern Ireland
Tel: 028 9080 9809 Fax: 028 9080 9808
Email: info@alisoncampbellmodels.com
Web: www.alisoncampbellmodels.com
Senior Personnel: Alison Campbell
Various artistes for corporate & promotional events., inc Miss Northern Ireland

CELEBRATION MODEL MANAGEMENT
PO Box 91, Neston, Cheshire CH64 6LX
Mobile: 07776 236 367
Email: agents@celebration-manag.co.uk
Web Site: www.celebration-manag.co.uk
Senior Personnel: Dave Bradshaw, Tom Bradshaw
Model Agency representing glamour and fashion models to the model industry, corporate functions, page 3, nightclubs, promotions, company promotions.

DAVID CHARLES AGENCY
2 Betjeman Way, Hemel Hempstead, Hertfordshire HP1 3HH
Tel: 01442 264 402
Mobile: 07767 813 231
Email: david@davidcharlesent.co.uk
Web Site: www.davidcharlesent.co.uk
Senior Personnel: David Charles, Penny Charles
Specialising in adult entertainment, bands and groups.

CRAWFORDS
po box 44 394 London SW20 0YP
Tel: 020 8947 9999 Fax: 020 8879 1437
Email: nick@crawfords.tv
Web Site: www.crawfords.tv
Senior Personnel: Nicholas Young
Specialises in TV Commercials and Modelling

THE DAVID AGENCY
26-28 Hammersmith Grove, London W6 7BA
Tel: 020 7967 7001
Email: casting@davidagency.net
Web Site: www.davidagency.net
Contact: Leila Debs
Specialist in crowd and supporting artists.

DEREK'S HANDS & BODY PARTS
26-28 Hammersmith Grove, London W6 7BA
Tel: 020 8834 1609 Fax: 020 8834 1144
Email: casting@derekshands.com
Web Site: www.derekshands.com
Director: Laila Debs
Specialist Hands & Body parts Agency.

DREAMS INTERNATIONAL MODEL & CASTING AGENCY
Empire House, 175 Piccadilly, Mayfair, London W1J 9TB
Tel: 020 7359 4786 Fax: 020 7688 0771
Mobile: 07949 548904
Senior Personnel: Deborah Hillaire

E.K.A MODEL & ACTOR MANAGEMENT

The Warehouse Studios, Glaziers Lane, Culcheth, Warrington WA3 4AQ
Tel: 0871 222 7470 Fax: 0871 222 7471
Email: info@eka-agency.com
Web Site: www.eka-agency.com
Company Director: Debbie Ikin
Senior TV & Film Casting Agent: Rebecca Keeley
Actor Management: Kate Sinclair
Agents to talented and experienced models and actors 18 to 80 yrs of all nationalities. Photographic, Television Commercials and Programmes, Films. Main & Supporting Artistes. We are a large agency covering the North West, Midlands and all UK. 20 Staff. Casting and Photographic Studios available. Friendly and efficient service.
E.K.A Management and Eurokids & Adults Agency is part of Eurokids Ltd.

EVENTS CONNECT

15 Faversham House, 15 Jewbury, York YO31 7PL
Mobile Tel: 07904 376629.
Email: viviennelee01@aol.com
Web Site: www.eventsconnect.co.uk
Contact: Vivienne Lee
A Model Management company: representing fashion and photographic models in the York area.
Event Management: Events big and small, fashion show production a speciality, organisers of Miss York, an area final for Miss England
Public Relations: personal press and media promotion offered to models, actors, sports people.

GIRL MANAGEMENT

52 Broadwick Street, London W1F 7AH
Tel: 020 7434 7382 fax: 020 7434 7383
Email: dana@girlmanagement.com
Web Site: www.girlmanagement.com
Contact: Dana Malmstrom

HIDDEN TALENT MODEL & CASTING AGENCY

555 East Side Complex, Pinewood Studios, Pinewood Road, Iver Heath, Buckinghamshire SL0 0NH
Tel: 0870 240 6515 Fax: 01753 656092
Email: becks@hiddentalentmodel.co.uk
Web Site: www.hiddentalentmodel.co.uk

HIRED HANDS

12 Cressy Road, London NW3 2LY
Tel: 020 7267 9212 Fax: 020 7267 1030
Email: hirehandsagency@aol.com
Web Site: www.hiredhandsmodels.com
Senior Personnel: Steve Barker

JACLYN AGENCY

52 Bessemer Road, Norwich, Norfolk NR4 6DQ
Tel: 01603 622 027 Fax: 01603 612 532
Email: info@jaclyn2000.co.uk
Web Site: www.jaclyn2000.co.uk
Senior Personnel: Julian Sandiford, Henrietta Cassidy
Specialising in: Supporting Artistes for TV & Film Companies. Covers East Anglia, E. Midlands, N. London. Over one thousand professional artistes available.

PAT KEELING MODEL AGENCY

38 Northgate Street, Leicester LE3 5BY
Tel: 0116 262 2540 Fax: 0116 253 7712
Email:
pat@patkeelingagency.freeserve.co.uk
Web:
www.patkeelingagency.freeserve.co.uk
Senior Personnel: Pat Keeling
Specialising in Modeling for Male, Female & Children. Fashion Shows, Photographic Promotions. TV & Video Work.

LEE'S PEOPLE

16 Manette Street, London W1D 4AR
Tel: 020 7734 5775 Fax: 020 7734 3033
Mobile: 07970 527252 / 527152
Email: lee@lees-people.co.uk
Web Site: www.lees-people.co.uk
Senior Personnel: Lee Towsey

MAGIK MODELS

Unit B17 Bow House 153-159 Bow Road, London E3 2SE
Tel: 020 8980 3232
Email: michelle@magikmodels.co.uk
Web Site: www.magikmodels.co.uk
Senior Personnel: Michelle Morris
Magik manages and represents models for the photographic, television and film sector.

MODEL PLAN

4th Floor, 4 Golden Square, London W1F 9HT
Tel: 020 7287 8444 Fax: 020 7287 2555Fax: 020 7287 2555
Email: michelle@modelplanlondon.co.uk
Web Site: www.modelplan.co.uk
Agent: Michelle Davenport

NEVS AGENCY

2nd Floor, Regal House, 198 Kings Road, London SW3 5XP
Tel: 020 7352 4886 (Men) Tel: 020 7352 9496 (Girls) Fax: 020 7352 6068
Email: getamodel@nevs.co.uk
Web Site: www.nevs.co.uk
Senior Personnel: Paul Cavalier

ORDINARY PEOPLE LTD

8 Camden Road, London NW1 9DP
Enquiries/Membership Tel: 020 7267 7007 Models Tel: 020 7267 4141
Fax: 020 7267 5677
Email: sarah@ordinarypeople.co.uk
Web Site: www.ordinarypeople.co.uk
Senior Personnel: Sarah Robbie, Simon Lloyd
Specialises in: Photographic Work and Commercials.

PHA MODEL & CASTING MANAGEMENT

Tanzaro House, Ardwick Green North, Manchester M12 6FZ
Tel: 0161 273 4444 Fax: 0161 273 4567
Email: info@pha-agency.co.uk
Web Site: www.pha-agency.co.uk
Senior Personnel: Lorna McDonough, Robert F Lang
Represent models, extras and actors for commercials, corporate and TV work. Largest casting suites in Manchester also available for hire.

PREMIER SPECIAL

40-42 Parker Street, London WC2B 5PQ
Tel: 020 7333 0888 Fax: 020 7323 1221
Email: jess@premierspecial.com
Web Site: www.premierspecial.com
Agent: Jess Robertson

RAGE

Tigris House, 256 Edgware Road, London W2 1DS
Tel: 020 7262 0515 Fax: 020 7402 0507
Email: coxy@ugly.org
Web Site: www.ugly.org
Senior Personnel: Mark French, Coxy Modelling Agency

SANDRA REYNOLDS AGENCY

Amadeus House, 27b Floral Street, London WC2E 9DP
Tel: 020 7387 5858 Norwich Office: Bacon House, 35 St Georges Street, Norwich, NR3 1DA Tel: 01603 623 842
Email: tessa@sandrareynolds.co.uk
Web Site: www.sandrareynolds.co.uk
Managing Director: Tessa Reynolds, Head Booker: Jessica Tracey
Representing commercial models, actors, actresses, supporting artists and children nationwide.

ROLE MODELS

12 Cressy Road, London NW3 2LY
Tel: 020 7284 4337 Fax: 020 7267 1030
Email: hiredhandsagency@aol.com
Web Site: www.hiredhandsmodels.com
Senior Personnel: Steve Barker

SAMANTHA BOND MANAGEMENT

Unit 15, Elysium Gate, 126 - 128 New Kings Road, London SW6 4LZ
Tel: 020 7013 0918 Fax: 020 7736 2221
Email: enquiries@samanthabond.net
Web Site: www.samanthabond.net
Agent: Samantha Bond

SPORTS WORKSHOP
56 Church Road, Crystal Palace,
London SE19 2EZ
Tel: 020 8771 4700 Fax: 020 8771 4704
Mob: 07770 994 043 (Chris Snode)
Email: info@sportspromotions.co.uk
Web Site: www.sportspromotions.co.uk
Senior Personnel: Chris Snode
We supply sports models in all categories from Athletics to Wrestling.

UGLY MODELS
Tigris House, 256 Edgware Road,
London W2 1DS
Tel: 020 7402 5564 Fax: 020 7402 0507
Email: info@ugly.org, coxy@ugly.org
Web Site: www.ugly.org
Senior Personnel: Marc French
Specialising in Character Models/Actors

SCOTT-PAUL YOUNG ENTERTAINMENTS LTD
Northern Lights House, 110 Blandford Road North, Langley, Near Windsor,
Berkshire SL3 7TA
Tel/Fax: 01753 693 250
Email: castingdirect@spy-ents.com
Web Site: www.spy-lightentsworld.com
Managing Director: Scott-Paul Young
Artists management and exclusive representation for films, television, commercials, theatre, sports and modelling events and all areas of the light entertainment industry.

Motivational Speakers

1ST CHOICE SPEAKERS UK LTD
52 Bois Moor Road Chesham,
Buckinghamshire HP5 1SN
Tel/Fax: 01494 773 020
Mobile: 07821 131 510
Email: enquiries@1stchoicespeakers.co.uk
Web Site: www.1stchoicespeakers.com
Managing Director: Pushpa Kasinather
Specialising in Celebrity Speakers for Cruise Ships, Conferences and Personal Appearances.
Speakers for After Dinner, Sports/Golf, Business, Keynote, Comedians and Product Launches.

AFTER DINNER SPEAKERS & COMEDIANS LIMITED
Chippings 2 The Old Saw Mills
Ripponden Halifax,
West Yorkshire HX6 4EN
Tel: 0845 4758866 Fax: 01422 884 494
Email: office@comedians.co.uk
Web Site: www.comedians.co.uk
Senior Personnel: Roger Davis, J. Mark Davis

THE AKABUSI COMPANY
14 Doolittle Mill Froghall Road Ampthill
Bedfordshire MK45 2ND
Tel: 0870 444 1975 Fax: 0870 444 1976
Email: info@akabusi.com
Web Site: www.akabusi.com
Proprietor: Kriss Akabusi
Contact: Jane
Media Consultancy. Conference & Motivational Peak Performance Speaker.

STEVE CRAM
S & K Consulting, Tranwell House,
Tranwell Woods, Morpeth,
Northumberland NE61 6AQ
Tel/Fax: 01670 503 266
After Dinner Speaking, Motivational Speaking, Openings, Corporate Videos & Promotions, Radio & TV Presenting and TV Commentary.

DEREK REDMOND
Verry House, Chine Crescent Road,
Bournemouth BH2 5LQ
Tel 01202 242 434 Fax 01202 242 428
Email: info@derekredmond.com
Web Site: www.derekredmond.com
Contact: Derek Redmond
Former 400m athlete: Won Gold in the 4X400m with Black, Akabusi & Regis and his semi-final race in the Barcelona Olympics, has since become one of the most famous sporting images of modern times. Inspirational Speaker. Sports Commentator.

JON HOLMES MEDIA LTD
5th Floor, Holborn Gate, 26 Southampton Buildings, London WC2A 1PQ
Tel: 020 7861 2550 Fax: 020 7861 3067
Email: dominic@jonholmesmedia.com
Web Site: www.jonholmesmedia.com
Senior Personnel: Jon Holmes, Diana Van Bunnens
Client Manager: Dominic Van Bunnens
Email Address for specific contact person: firstname@jonholmesmedia.com

THE LONDON SPEAKER BUREAU
Elsinore House, 77 Fulham Palace Road,
London W6 8JA
Tel: 020 8748 9595 Fax: 020 8741 8723
Email: tom@londonspeakerbureau.co.uk
Web: www.londonspeakerbureau.co.uk
Senior Personnel: Tom Kenyon-Slaney, Brendan O'Connor, Lucinda Swan
Specialising in Business and Political Speakers.

PALM COURT THEATRE PRODUCTIONS
Winkton Lodge Cottage, Salisbury Road,
Winkton, Christchurch, Dorset BH23 7AR
Tel: 01202 484 185 Mob: 07836 717 567
Fax: 01202 471 920
Email: godwin@palm-court.demon.co.uk
Senior Personnel: Patricia Godwin

PERFORMING ARTISTES (PART OF THE F4 GROUP)
F4 Group Ltd 24a High Street, Cobham
Surrey KT11 3EB
Tel: 01932 590 376 Fax: 01932 862 437
Email: ask@performingartistes.co.uk
Web Site: www.f4group.co.uk
Contacts: Stanley Jackson
Specialising in After Dinner entertainment, including: speakers, hosts, business and motivational/keynote speakers, celebrities for personal appearances, endorsements, advertising campaigns and corporate events.

PERSONAL APPEARANCES
20 North Mount, 1147-1161 High Road,
Whetstone, London N20 0PH
Tel: 020 8343 7748 Fax: 020 8343 7748
Email: patsy@personalappearances.biz
Web Site: www.personalappearances.biz
Senior Personnel: Patsy Martin
Specialists in Public Relations and Personal Management

PERSONALLY SPEAKING
Three Spires House, 16a Bird Street,
Lichfield, Staffordshire WS13 6PR
Tel: 01543 263 136 Fax: 01543 262 402
Email: info@normanphillips.co.uk
Web: www.personally-speaking.co.uk
Senior Personnel: Lianne Phillips
Established 40 years as the UK's premier consultancy, supplying speakers and celebrities for every occasion including: Personal Appearances, After Dinner, Key Note and Business Speeches, Sporting Dinners, Conference and Award Ceremonies, Product Launches, Product Endorsements, Corporate Videos, Cabaret. Over 5000 speaker profiles available.

SPEAKERS UK
27 Gloucester Street, London WC1N 3XX
Tel: 0845 458 3707
Email: info@speakers-uk.com
Web Site: www.speakers-uk.com
Contact: Dominic Morley
Specialises in motivational speakers.

DAVE WINSLETT ASSOCIATES
4 Zig Zag Road, Kenley, Surrey CR8 5EL
Tel: 020 8668 0531 Fax: 020 8668 9216
Email: info@davewinslett.com
Web Site: www.davewinslett.com
Senior Personnel: Dave Winslett FEAA

Nostalgia/Tribute

ABBA GIRLS
11a Percy Road Leigh-on-Sea
Essex SS9 2LA
Tel: 01702 517419 Mob: 07702 543 117
Email: info@abbagirls.com
Web Site: www.abbagirls.com

Contacts: Colin Cross
Also availble as a duo

ABBA GOLD
1 Kingfisher Street, London E6 5JZ
Mob: 07771 801243 02036 590746
Email: info@abbagold.uk.com
Web Site: www.abbagold.uk.com / www.myspace.com/originalabbagold
Contact: Karen Graham

ABBA UK - TOP INTERNATIONAL ABBA TRIBUTE BAND
139 Merlin Avenue, Nuneaton, Warwickshire CV10 9QJ
Tel/Fax: 024 763 97991
Email: info@abbauk.co.uk
Web Site: www.abbauk.co.uk
Contact: Jackie
ABBA - one of the worlds greatest pop groups now stunningly recreated by Britain's Top International ABBA Tribute - ABBA UK. ABBA UK are available for performances world-wide bringing you the global phenomenon that was ABBA "BACK TO THE STAGE".

ACADEMY ARTISTES LTD
57 Rosebank Street, Leek, Staffordshire Staffordshire ST13 6AG
Tel: 01782 519 268 Fax: 01538 388 223
Managing Agency, Contacts Simon Harris & Mr Durber

A.I.R. LIMITED
AIR House, Spennymoor, County Durham DL16 7SE
Tel: 01388 814 632 Fax: 01388 812 445
Email: info@airagency.com
Web Site: www.airagency.com
Directors: Colin Pearson, John Wray

ALMOST ELTON
258 St. Johns Road, Yeovil, Somerset BA21 5QP
Tel: 07970 216 459
Email: matthewrock@almostelton.co.uk
Web Site: www.almosteltonjohn.com
Contact: Matthew Rock
A brilliant Elton John Tribute.

ANDERSSENS
4 Rothmans Avenue, Chelmsford, Essex CM2 9UE
Tel/Fax: 01245 476 187
Mob: 07850 589029
Email: john@cockneypride.co.uk
Web: www.pearlykingandqueen.co.uk
Senior Personnel: John Anderssen

B.D.A. (BRIAN DURKIN ASSOCIATES)
Bryson House, Chiltern Road, Culcheth, Warrington, Cheshire WA3 4LL
Tel: 01925 766 655 Fax: 01925 765 577
Email: briandurkin@btconnect.com
Web Site: www.bdaltd.co.uk
Senior Personnel: Brian Durkin

ANDREW BEAUCHAMP MANAGEMENT
Oaklands Business Centre, 64-68 Elm Grove, Worthing, West Sussex BN11 5LH
Tel: 07737 415 534
Email: abeauchampmgt@aol.com
Proprietor: Andrew Beauchamp

GORDON BENNETT
16 Saxons Drive, Maidstone, Kent ME14 5HS
Tel: 01622 672 128 Mob: 07930 758 083
Email: gordonbennett69@hotmail.com
Web Site: www.gordonbennett.biz
Contact: Gordon Bennett

THE JOHN BODDY AGENCY
10 Southfield Gardens, Twickenham, Middlesex TW1 4SZ
Tel: 020 8892 0133 / 8891 3809 Fax: 020 8287 0798
Email: jba@johnboddyagency.co.uk
Web Site: www.johnboddyagency.co.uk
Senior Personnel: John Boddy and Jonathan Boddy
Member of Agents Association (GB)

BOLDEAN PRODUCTIONS
42 Church Lane, Heacham, King's Lynn, Norfolk PE31 7HN
Tel: 01485 572 347
Email: roger.dean15@btinternet.com
Web Site: www.roger-dean.com
Contact: Roger Dean

JAMES BRANDON COMPANY
Cherry Tree House, 1 Cherry Tree Street,, Elsecar, South Yorkshire S74 8DG
Tel: 01226 742 886
Email: info@jamesbrandon.co.uk
Web Site: www.jamesbrandon.co.uk
Managing Director: James Brandon
Production and agency specialising in pantomime, tribute and variety shows, illusion, design and special effects. Radio, Media and road shows. Specialist in corporate events and one-off bespoke entertainments.

PAUL BRIDSON PRODUCTIONS
Motte House, Marford Hill, Marford, Wrexham, LL12 8SW Wales
Tel: 01244 571 708 / 709 Fax: 01244 571 722
Email: paul@paulbridson.co.uk
Web Site: www.paulbridson.co.uk
Contact: Paul Bridson
Artistes available via my office by arrangement with their respective management; Ken Dodd, Frank Carson, Jim Bowen, Stan Boardman, Jimmy Cricket. Other than those identified here, other circus, magical and speciality acts are available.

CASHBACK
35 Belfast Quay, Irvine, Ayrshire KA12 8PR
01294 276203 Mob: 07518 374 201
Email: ric@richerrington.co.uk
Web: www.richerrington.co.uk/cashback or www.myspace.com/cashbacktribute
Contact: Richard Herrington

CHANCE PROMOTIONS
The Nook, Bee Lane, Penwortham, Preston PR1 9TU
Tel: 01772 321 160
Email: info@legendschance.com
Web Site: www.legendschance.com
Managing Directors: Trevor Chance, Brenda Chance
Creative Musical director: Richard Chance
Choreographer: Wendy Holland
Company Production Manager: Tony Harvey
Specialising in Look/Sound Alike Shows & Tributes.

DAVID CHARLES AGENCY
2 Betjeman Way, Hemel Hempstead, Hertfordshire HP1 3HH
Tel: 01442 264 402 Mobile: 07767 813 231
Email: david@davidcharlesent.co.uk
Web Site: www.davidcharlesent.co.uk
Senior Personnel: David Charles, Penny Charles
Specialising in adult entertainment, bands and groups.

GRAHAM COLE MANAGEMENT
51 Grove Avenue, Weymouth, Dorset DT4 7RJ
Tel: 01305 777 253 Fax: 01305 788 853
Mob: 07767 872 157
Email: grahamcole@hotmail.co.uk
Senior Personnel: Derick Graham Cole

BARRY COLLINGS ENTERTAINMENTS
PO Box 1151 St Albans AL1 9WB
Tel: 01702 201880 Fax: 01702 201880
Email: barry-Collings@btconnect.com
Web Site: www.barrycollings.co.uk
Senior Personnel: Barry Collings, Lorraine Collings
All artistes available by arrangement with their respective managements.

COMPACT MANAGEMENT & ENTERTAINMENT AGENCY
98 Shellards Road, Longwell Green, Bristol, South Gloucestershire BS30 9DT
Tel: 0117 932 4344 Fax: 0117 932 6006
Mobile: 07831 446958
Email: paul@compactents.co.uk
Web Site: www.compactents.co.uk
Senior Personnel: Paul Wolf

DANSATAK
Worth House, 15 Worth Street, Carlton,

Nottingham NG4 1RX
Tel: 0844 888 7722 Fax: 08707 444 556
Email: info@dansatak.com
Web Site: www.dansatak.com
Senior Personnel: Scott Peters, Tony Sherwood

DEVIL MANAGEMENT
PO Box 23, Spennymoor, County Durham DL16 7YZ
Tel: 01388 818 888 Fax: 01388 811 222
Email: steve@devilmanagement.com
Web Site: www.devilmanagement.com
Contact: Steve Dodds, Paul Carr

DINGS ENTERTAINMENT
Suite 1 106A Bedford Road Wootton Bedford MK43 9JB
Tel: 01234 851 166 Fax: 01234 840 383
Email: ding@dings.com
Web Site: www.dings.com
Senior Personnel: Ian Davis FEAA

THE PETER DONEGAN BAND
21 Belsay Grove, Bedlington, Northumberland NE22 5YU
Mob: 07563 379 245
Email: peter-donegan@hotmail.com
Web Site: www.peterdonegan.com
Contact: Peter Donegan

ELITE PROMOTIONS
1A Thistle Place, Aberdeen AB10 1UZ Scotland
Tel: 01224 636 363 Fax: 01224 652 980
Email: info@elitepromotions.net
Web Site: www.elitepromotions.net
Senior Personnel: John Anderson, Kathleen Anderson
Wedding Co-ordinator: Susan Moultrie
Entertainment Consultants and Booking Agents - Supplying all entertainment sectors and corporate hospitality packages.

STEVE ELSON
11 Ernest Gardens, London W4 3QU
Tel: 020 8995 5520 Fax: 020 8995 3835
Mobile: 07976 276 375
Email: steve@counterfeitstone.demon.co.uk
Web Site: www.thecounterfeitstones.net
Senior Personnel: Steve Elson
Production and management of The Counterfeit Stones - "A Rolling Stones Tribute Show".

ELVIS SHMELVIS
Tel: 01727 858 606
Email: elvis@shmelvis.com
Web Site: www.shmelvis.com
Contact: Sue & Martin
Please see full page advert in the Corporate Entertainment & Hospitality section for more details.

ENTERTAINERS COMPANY LTD
200 London Road, Hadleigh, Benfleet, Essex SS7 2PD
Tel: 01702 427 100 / 0870 233 0836
Fax: 01702 427 109 Mob: 07850 111616
Email: enquiries@entertainers.co.uk
Web Site: www.entertainers.co.uk / www.easytheatres.co.uk
Director: Michael Taylor (michael@entertainers.co.uk)
Senior Personnel: Ben Hatton
The one stop shop for entertainment.

ENTERTAINERS MANAGEMENT LTD
200 London Road, Hadleigh, Benfleet, Essex SS7 2PD
Tel: 01702 427 100 Fax: 01702 427 109
Mob: 07850 111616
Email: enquiries@entertainers.co.uk
Web Site: www.easytheatres.com
Senior Personnel: Ben Hatton
Director: Michael Taylor
Contact: michael@entertainers.co.uk
The UK's no 1 entertainment agency.

ESPREE MUSIC MANAGEMENT
54 Craigerne Road, London SE3 8SN
Tel: 020 8293 1132 Fax: 020 8293 4055
Email: info@espreemusicmanagement.co.uk
Web: www.espreemusicmanagement.co.uk
Senior Personnel: Suzanne Miller, Libby Kemkaran

FAB PRODUCTIONS
Yew Tree Farm, Oglet Lane, Hale Village, Liverpool, Merseyside L24 5RJ
Tel: 0151 425 5070
Email: info@fabproductions.co.uk
Web Site: www.fabproductions.co.uk
Proprietor: Richard Blasbery

BRIAN GANNON MANAGEMENT
St James House, Kiln Lane, Milnrow, Rochdale, Lancashire OL16 3JF
Tel: 01706 374 411 Fax:01706 377 303
Email: nospambrian@briangannon.co.uk
Web Site: www.briangannon.co.uk
Senior Personnel: Brian Gannon

GLOBAL ENTERTAINMENT AGENCY
6 Digby Street, Ilkstone, Derbyshire DE7 5TG
Tel: 0115 917 2767 Fax: 0115 917 4458
Mob: 07836 614 203
Email: tony@global-ents.co.uk
Web Site: www.globalents.com
Contact: Tony Barry
Booking, Tribute Acts, Bands, Chart Acts, Wedding Entertainment, Magicians, Look-a-Likes, everything in entertainment.

GREAT WESTERN ENTERTAINMENT AGENCY
46 Critchill Road, Frome, Somerset BA11 4HF
Tel: 01373 461 666 Mobile: 07774 694316
Senior Personnel: Graham Wilkin
Specialising in all types of entertainment.

HEAD ON MANAGEMENT
88 Lewisham Way, New Cross, London SE14 6NY
Tel/Fax: 020 8469 2576
Mobile: 07796 447 302
Email: headonman@yahoo.co.uk
Web Site: www.headonmanagement.com
Senior Personnel: Nick Wren, Chloe Wren
Personal Band Management.
Live Event promotions, Euphoria-Live, DJ Events, Live 3D Graphics.

INTERNATIONAL MANAGEMENT & AGENCY LTD
2 Bond Terrace, Rishworth Street, Wakefield, West Yorkshire WF1 2HW
Tel: 01924 299 993 Fax: 01924 200 750
Email: lizmarston@im-agency.com
Web Site: www.im-agency.com
Senior Personnel: Norman Thewlis FEAA, Barry Marshall

JAKE, ELWOOD & THE BLACK RHINO BAND
c/o 35 Navigation Lane, West Bromwich, West Midlands B71 3NP
Tel: 0121 588 7692 Fax: 0121 588 7459
Email: annerley73@aol.com
Marketing Officer: Annerley Johnson

ANDREW JAMES
Tel: 07880 557 428
Email: andrew.rafferty@ntlworld.com
Web Site: www.easy-lover.co.uk / www.illinoisbluesbrothers.com
Contact: Andew James

LEE JAMES ASSOCIATES LTD
PO Box 61, York YO61 1WD
Tel: 01347 821121 Fax: 01347 824 499
Mobile: 07739 227 687
Email: leejamesltd@btconnect.com
Web Site: www.leejamesltd.com
Senior Personnel: Lee James, Gail James, Scott James

MICHAEL LA ROCHE MANAGEMENT
PO Box 35, Bexhill, East Sussex TN40 2WA
Tel: 01424 216 400 Fax: 01424 223644
Email: mlr@michaellaroche.com
Web Site: www.michaellaroche.com
Providing tribute and revival shows, call for further details.

LADIES OF ROCK
C/O 15 Yew Tree Court Alsager Cheshire ST7 2YQ
Tel: 01270 883 080 Mob: 07710 784 913
Email: tinacher@paularandell.com

Web Site: www.paularandell.com
Contact: Paula Randell

LEISURE MANAGEMENT
PO Box 48, Spennymoor, County Durham DL16 7YL
Tel: 01388 420 050 Fax: 01388 420 037
Email: info@lmpresents.com
Web Site: www.lmpresents.com
Senior Personnel: Alan Leightell

LONDON MUSIC AGENCY
7 Rosewood Drive, Orchard Heights Ashford, Kent TN25 4QF
Tel: 01233 623 623 Mob: 07885 032 132
Email: enquiries@londonmusicagency.co.uk
Web: www.londonmusicagency.co.uk
Proprietor: Jenny Braby
Everything in entertainment for Private and Corporate functions, e.g. Jazz, String Quartets and all types of band, music and the unusual.

MAD ENTERTAINMENTS AGENCY
56 New Croft, Weedon, Northampton NN7 4RJ
Tel: 01327 349 938
Mobile: 07788 570 747
Email: dd.colonel@btopenworld.com
Senior Personnel: David Dickens
Corporate Events & Product Launches catered for. Any type of Entertaiment catered for. Any Budget. Management for the Billy Fury Band & Darren H. (Elvis Presley Tribute). Agents for 60s, 70s & 80s Tribute Bands and Morris Dancers.

MARK WINDOWS
32 Lower Flat Brookfield Avenue Walthamstow E17 9EP
Tel/Fax: 020 8520 2627
Email: markwindowsfilms@yahoo.co.uk
Web Site: www.markwindows.com
GLAMTASTIC ROCKSHOW
An over the top funfest of 70s and 80s sounds with stunning impersonations and comic delivery that gets any audience jumping. Sixties show also available. Two slots or one hour cabaret. Mark Windows has worked for Hilton hotels, Armed forces, Holsen, Bass, Met Police, Channel 4, Carlton, and Revolution films to name a few.

MATTERS MUSICAL
The Loft, Rear of 8 West Street, Dorking, Surrey RH4 1BL
Tel: 01306 741 007 Fax: 01306 741 008
Email: info@mattersmusical.com
Web Site: www.mattersmusical.com
Senior Personnel: Frank Warren
Plus Dance Instruction/Demonstration for all the styles listed below.

GLENN MILLER ORCHESTRA
6a Furzehill Parade, Shenley Road, Borehamwood, Hertfordshire WD6 1DX
Tel: 020 8905 1065 Fax: 020 8905 1074
Mobile: 07710 202711
Email: suemcvay@tinyworld.co.uk
Web: www.glennmillerorchestra.co.uk
Senior Personnel: Ray McVay, Sue McVay

MUSICAL AGENCY AND MANAGEMENT LTD
The Seedbed Centre, Langston Road, Loughton, Essex IG10 3TQ
Tel: 020 8501 2469 Fax: 020 8502 6863
Email: info@manhattan-nights.co.uk / david@showtime.uk.com
Senior Personnel: David Fellerman
Producers and promoters of musical theatre.

NEVER 4 GET
14 Pavilion Court Northlands Road Southampton SO15 2NN
Tel: 02380 829 385 Mob: 07814 454 796
Email: lee@never4getmusic.com
Web Site: www.never4getmusic.com
Contact: Lee Cornick

PELLER ARTISTES LTD
14 West Street, Beighton, Sheffield, South Yorkshire S20 1EP
Tel: 0114 247 2365 Fax: 0114 247 2156
London Office: 39 Princes Avenue, London N3 2DA Tel: 020 8343 4264
Fax: 070 9280 8252
Email: agent@pellerartistes.com
Web Site: www.pellerartistes.com
Senior Personnel: Johnnie Peller (London Office)
Specialising in Tribute Bands, Lookalikes, Television Celebrities & Soap Stars, Star Vocal & Comedy Artistes, Party & Function Bands, Magicians, Hypnotists and Speciality Entertainment, After Dinner Speakers and Sports Stars.

PERSONALITY ARTISTES LTD
Worldwide Headquarters PO Box 1 Poulten le Fylde Blackpool, Lancashire FY6 7WS
Tel: 01253 899 988 Fax: 01253 899 333
Mobile: 07860 479092
Email: info@personalityartistes.com
Web Site: www.personalityartistes.com
Contact: Mal Ford & Jean Parkes
Corporate Entertainment specialists and Artistes Management.

PLANET 80S
PO Box 441 Ashford, Kent TN23 9EL
Tel: 07799 262 068
Email: planet80s@hotmail.co.uk
Web Site: www.planet80s.webs.com
Contacts : Phil Marks

THE POLICE CHIEFS
20 Spencer Drive, Midsomer Norton, Radstock BA3 2DN
Tel: 07974 690 181
Email: bullit7@live.co.uk
Web Site: www.myspace.com/thepolicechiefs
Contact: Olly Wise

THE PSYCHO MANAGEMENT CO LTD
Solly's Mill, Mill Lane, Godalming, Surrey GU7 1EY
Tel: 01483 419 429 Fax: 01483 419 504
Email: agents@psycho.co.uk
Web Site: www.psycho.co.uk
Company Directors: Patrick Haveron, John Mabley
Psycho Management is the ultimate source for tribute bands and lookalikes in the UK and Europe.

QUEEN B
3 Dorian Road Hornchurch Essex RM12 4AW
Tel: 01708 452 120
Email: pj@pjbands.com / pj@queenb.co.uk
Web Site: www.queenb.co.uk
Paul Jackson performing as Queen B - a tribute to Queen.

DES REES SUNRISE GROUP
Elm Croft, Thornwood Common, High Road, Thornwood, Epping, Essex CM16 6LX
Tel: 07000 303130 Fax: 01992 575 705
Mobile: 07850 023522
Email: des.rees@btconnect.com
Web Site: www.sunrisegroup.co.uk
Contact: Des Rees
Britian's premier agency for all tribute acts. The one-stop-shop for tribute acts.

RENT-A-BAND
Burnside House, 10 Burns Court, Birstall, Batley, West Yorkshire WF17 9JZ
Tel/Fax: 01924 441 441
Email: bands@rent-a-band.org
Web Site: www.rent-a-band.org
Senior Personnel: Ken Baxter

RICKY LOPEZ RATPACK AND SWING SHOW
Tel: 01727 858 606
Email: ricky@rickylopezratpack.com
Web Site: www.rickylopezratpack.com
Contact: Sue & Martin
Please see full page advert in the Corporate Entertainment & Hospitality section for more details.

THE ROLLIN STONED
438 Archway Road, Highgate London N6 4JH
Tel: 0870 766 9054 Fax: 020 8374 2127
Mob: 07720 046 886
Email: enquiries@rollinstoned.com
Web Site: www.rollinstoned.com
A typical two hour show includes not only

all the classic crowd pleasing hits, but is spiced with enough eclectic selections from the deeper recesses of Stones Album archives to satisfy the most demanding of 'Buffs', all performed with the same vibrantly authentic attack and raw energy that characterised the original Stones shows in their prime.
With a Rollin Stoned show, the costumes are shamelessly camp gaudy and fab, the instruments genuinely vintage and the wit irreverent.

ROSEMARY SQUIRES ENTERPRISES
2 The Meadows, Milford, Salisbury, Wiltshire SP1 2SS
Tel: 01722 322 479 All Electric Productions (Booking Agent): Tel: 01264 361 924
Email: fralock@tiscali.co.uk
Web Site: www.rosemarysquires.co.uk
Personal Manager: Frank Lockyer
Booking Agent:
All Electric Productions
Po Box 1805
Andover
SP10 3ZN

GARY RYAN - NEIL DIAMOND TRIBUTE
135 Hughes Street, Bolton BL1 3EZ
Tel: 07919 485 495
Email: g.ryan2@btinternet.com
Web Site: www.neildiamond-tribute.com
Contact: Gary Ryan

SCOTT JORDAN ENTERTAINMENT LTD
25-29 Station Street, Sittingbourne, Kent ME10 3DU
Tel: 0845 094 1455
Email: enquiries@scottjordan.co.uk
Web Site: www.scottjordan.co.uk
Contact : Scott Jordan, Stephen Middleton
Entertainment booking agency providing quality tribute bands, function bands, comedians and magicians for weddings, private parties, and venues accross the U.K

SAMANTHA STARR
80 Coronation Road, Wolverhampton Heath Town WV10 0QH
Tel: 01902 659 769 Mob: 07812 998 754
Email: sammystarr@blueyonder.co.uk
Web Site: www.samanthastarr.co.uk
Contact : Samantha Starr

STARS IN YOUR EYES LIMITED ENTERTAINMENT AGENCY
61a Hough Lane, Leyland PRESTON PR25 2SA
Tel: 01772 422 388 Fax: 01772 457 600
Mob: 07768 103 645
Email: info@staracts.com / startributes@yahoo.co.uk
Web Site: www.staracts.com
Senior Personnel: Rhoda Myers, Tom Lane
Corporate, Lookalikes / Tributes, Variety.

STELLAMAX ENTERPRISES LTD
Nova House, 53 Nova Croft, Off Broad Lane, Eastern Green, Coventry, Warwickshire CV5 7FJ
Tel: 024 7646 9585 Mob: 07899 045363
Email: max@stellamax.com
Web Site: www.stellamax.com
Senior Personnel: Max Roberts

STUDIO ONE ASSOCIATES
Studio 1, 16 The Koko Building Arches Industrial Estate, Spon End, Coventry CV1 3JQ
Tel: +44 845 8733116
Mob: +44 247671720
Email: admin@studio1.co.uk
Web Site: www.studio1.co.uk
Managing Director: Mr Grant Wadey

THE ILLINOIS BLUES BROTHERS
Tel: 07880 557 428
Email: andrew.rafferty@ntlworld.com
Web: www.theIllinoisbluesbrothers.com
Contact: Andrew Rafferty

TO HELL & BACK
Mob: 07941 197913
Email: meatloaf@meatloaf.org, dean.torkington1@btinternet.com
Web Site: www.meatloaf.org
Contact: Dean Torkington
Meat Loaf Tribute Band.

TRIBUTE TO BUDDY HOLLY
High House Farm Asheldham, Southminster, Essex CM0 7NX
Tel: 01621 778 886 Mob: 07889 426 343
Email: marcusejrobinson@hotmail.com
Contact: Marc Robinson

UKOM
3 Chapel Close, Humbleton, Hull East Yorkshire HU11 4NP
Tel: 01964 670 162 Mob: 07912 421 876
Email: steve@elvislovingyou.com
Web Site: www.elvislovingyou.com
Contact: Steve Caprice

ULTIMATE INTERNATIONAL
Atlas House, London Road, Hindhead, Surrey GU26 6AB
Tel: 01428 606 566 Fax: 01428 606 141
Email: info@partyplannersuk.com
Web Site: www.partyplannersuk.com
Senior Personnel: David L Starr

UNIQUE ENTERTAINMENT UK
500 Chiswick High Road, Chiswick, London W4 5RG
Tel: 020 8987 8887 Fax: 020 8987 8886
Email: trevor@unique-entertainment.co.uk
Web: www.unique-entertainment.co.uk
Senior Personnel: Trevor Hamilton

UPBEAT ENTERTAINMENT
236 Hythe Road Willesborough Kent TN24 0QS
Tel: 01233 650 218 Fax: 01233 641 446
Mobile: 07974 260 479
Email: station2@tiscali.co.uk
Web: www.upbeat-entertainment.com
Senior Personnel: Kim Carney-Boeje

UPBEAT MANAGEMENT
Larg House Woodcote Grove, Coulsdon, Surrey CR5 2QQ
Tel: 020 8668 3332 Fax: 020 8668 3922
Email: info@upbeat.co.uk
Web Site: www.upbeat.co.uk
Senior Personnel (Entertainment): Liz Biddle, Beryl Korman
Specialising in Theatre Touring and large events for Festivals and corporate entertainment.

JASON WEST AGENCY
Gables House, Saddlebow, King's Lynn, Norfolk PE34 3AR
Tel: 01553 617 586 (3 Lines)
Fax: 01553 617 734
Email: info@jasonwest.com
Senior Personnel: Jason West

Outdoor Arena Attractions

1ST CLASS ENTERTAINMENT AGENCY
2 Scotts Way, Riverhead, Sevenoaks, Kent TN13 2DG
Tel: 0870 755 6446 Fax: 08707 55 6471
Mobile: 07850 603 500
Email: email@1stclassentertainment.co.uk
Web: www.1stclassentertainment.co.uk
Senior Personnel: Brenda Pope, Alan Pope
Outdoor Event Specialists, Bands, Groups, Cabaret, Children's Entertainment, Disco, Toastmasters, Pipers, Complete Shows, Corporate Entertainment, Event Management + loads more.
Speciality acts include aerial displays, car stunts, dog displays, donkey derbies, It's A Knockout and many more.

THE A6 AGENCY
Willow Moorings Kegworth DE74 2EY
Mobile: 07889 745594
Email: michaelhobson2012@yahoo.co.uk
Web: www.snapshotproductions.co.uk
Senior Personnel: Michael Hobson
Specialising in outdoor and promotional

attractions, jazz bands and silouette and origami artistes

THE DAUBNEY VARIETY & GALA AGENCY LTD

1 Bent Lane, Staveley, Chesterfield, Derbyshire S43 3UG
Tel: 01246 477677
Email: info@daubneyagency.co.uk
Web Site: www.daubneyagency.co.uk
Contact: Margot Wilding
Fixers and finders for all outdoor requirements

STEVE ELSON

11 Ernest Gardens, London W4 3QU
Tel: 020 8995 5520 Fax: 020 8995 3835
Mobile: 07976 276 375
Email: steve@counterfeitstone.demon.co.uk
Web Site: www.thecounterfeitstones.net
Senior Personnel: Steve Elson
Production and management of The Counterfeit Stones - "A Rolling Stones Tribute Show".

ES PROMOTIONS

Unit 24, Larkwood, Larkwood Close, Kettering, Northamptonshire NN16 9NQ
Tel: 01536 310 520 Fax 01536 358 113
Email: sales@es-promotions.com
Web Site: www.es-promotions.com
Financial Director: Dave Turner
The Agency supplies circus performers, children's entertainment, street entertainers, arena and aerial acts.
Outdoor event specialists, entertainment agency, team events, themed events, fun casino. Inflatables and unusual games for hire. Balloons, balloon gas, balloon releases and balloon decorating.

GT ARTISTES

4 Maple Avenue Allington Maidestone ME16 0DD
Tel: 01622 675 893 Mob: 07778 288 634
Email: tony.littley@btinternet.com
Web Site: www.gtartistes.com
Contact: Tony Littley

HEAD ON MANAGEMENT

88 Lewisham Way, New Cross, London SE14 6NY
Tel/Fax: 020 8469 2576
Mobile: 07796 447 302
Email: headonman@yahoo.co.uk
Web Site: www.headonmanagement.com
Senior Personnel: Nick Wren, Chloe Wren
Personal Band Management.
Live Event promotions, Euphoria-Live, DJ Events, Live 3D Graphics.

HEY PRESTO ENTERTAINMENTS AGENCY

36 St Luke's Road, Tunbridge Wells, Kent TN4 9JH
Tel: 01892 537 964 Fax: 01892 683 401
Mobile: 07973 512845
Email: info@heyprestoentertainments.co.uk
Web: www.heyprestoentertainments.co.uk
Senior Personnel: Michael Alan Bonfield

PETER JOHNSON ENTERTAINMENTS LTD

Hastings Road, Hawkhurst, Kent TN18 4RT
Tel: 01580 754 822 Fax: 01580 754 808
Email: enquiries@peterjohnson.co.uk
Web Site: www.peterjohnson.co.uk
Senior Personnel: Peter Johnson, Mandy O'Nion
Specialising in all forms of Outdoor Entertainments. Arena Entertainments, Mix 'n' Mingle,Corporate Participation Attractions and Music and Dance Groups.

LIVE PROMOTIONS LTD

Riverside Quay, Double Street, Spalding, Lincolnshire PE11 2AB
Tel: 01775 768 661 Fax: 01775 768 665
Email: enquiries@livepromotions.co.uk
Web Site: www.truckfest.co.uk
Managing Director: Colin Ward
Specialising in: Outdoor Entertainment & Celebrities. The UK's leading automotive event specialists.

SALVO THE CLOWN

13 Second Avenue, Kingsleigh Park, Thundersley, Essex SS7 3QD
Tel: 01268 745 791
Email: salvo@annualclownsdirectory.com
Web: www.annualclownsdirectory.com
Contact: Salvo

STEPPIN' OUT ENTERTAINMENT & CORPORATE EVENTS

11 Beaumont Court, Oxford OX1 5AL
Tel/ Fax: 01865 327 772
Mobile: 07768 606 088
Email: enquiries@steppin-out.co.uk
Web Site: www.steppin-out.co.uk
Proprietor: Terry Penn
We provide a wide range of services within the event management and entertainment arena, including: Corporate Events, Wedding Services, Theme & Team Building Events, Sound & Lighting Equipment Hire DJ's/Discos, Karaoke, Bands, Musicians, Entertainers, Marquees, Fireworks and Outdoor/Giant Games.

TEMPLE'S ENTERTAINMENT AGENCY

2 Knowle Close, Abington Vale, Northampton, NN3 3LW
Tel: 01604 639 198 Fax: 01604 628 204
Email: sue@temples-ents.co.uk
Web Site: www.temples-ents.co.uk
Managing Director: Sue Griffith-Temple
Est. 1987. Specialising in Acts for Outdoor Arenas and Attractions. A Family Business managed by the Third Generation of Temple's. Show & Gala specialists. "More Than A Century of Experience".

Personal Appearances

1ST CHOICE SPEAKERS UK LTD

52 Bois Moor Road Chesham, Buckinghamshire HP5 1SN
Tel/Fax: 01494 773 020
Mobile: 07821 131 510
Email: enquiries@1stchoicespeakers.co.uk
Web Site: www.1stchoicespeakers.com
Managing Director: Pushpa Kasinather
Specialising in Celebrity Speakers for Cruise Ships, Conferences and Personal Appearances.
Speakers for After Dinner, Sports/Golf, Business, Keynote, Comedians and Product Launches.

CELEBRITY APPEARANCES

Three Spires House, 16a Bird Street, Lichfield, Staffordshire WS13 6PR
Tel: 01543 263 136 Fax: 01543 262 402
Email: info@normanphillips.co.uk
Web: www.celebrity-appearances.co.uk
Contact: Lianne Phillips
Established 40 years as the UK's premier consultancy supplying speakers and celebrities for every occasion including: Personal Appearances, After Dinner, Key Note and Business Speeches, Sporting Dinners, Conference and Award Ceremonies, Product Launches, Product Endorsements, Corporate Videos, Cabaret. Over 5000 speaker profiles available.

CROMWELL MANAGEMENT

20 Drayhorse Road, Ramsey, Huntingdon, Cambridgeshire PE26 1SD
Tel: 01487 815 063 Fax: 01487 711 896
Email: tricvic@lineone.net
Web Site: www.jazzmanagement.ic24.net
Senior Personnel: V Gibbons, P A Gibbons

ALEX JAY PERSONAL MANAGEMENT

8 Higher Newmarket Road, Newmarket, Nailsworth, Gloucestershire GL6 0RP
Tel/Fax: 01453 834 783
Email: alexjay@alex-jay-pm.freeserve.co.uk
Senior Personnel: Alex Jay
Specialising in artistes for film, television, theatre, commercials and TV & radio presenters.

JOHN KETTLEY

Weatherview House, 50 Beaumont Way, Hazlemere, High Wycombe, Buckinghamshire HP15 7BE
Tel: 01494 715 115 Fax: 01494 715 115

Email: kettley@britishweatherservices.co.uk
Web: www.britishweatherservices.co.uk
Contact: Jim Dale

NMP LIVE LTD
8 Blenheim Court Brook Way
Leatherhead, Surrey KT22 7NA
Tel: 01372 361004 Fax: 01372 374417
Email: live@nmp.co.uk
Web Site: www.nmplive.co.uk
Managing Directors: Neil Martin, Chris Banks.
Leading UK entertainment agency specialising in celebrity personal appearances, high profile entertainment, negotiating endorsements and advertising campaigns and presenting after-dinner, motivational & conference speakers.

OFF THE KERB PRODUCTIONS
Hammer House 113-117 Wardour Street
London W1F 0UN
Tel: 020 7437 0607 Fax: 020 7437 0647
Email: info@offthekerb.co.uk or westend@offthekerb.co.uk
Web Site: www.offthekerb.co.uk
Senior Personnel: Addison Cresswell, Joe Norris
Please note all corporate, personal appearance and casting enquiries for all artistes to Fay Clayton in the West End office. fay@offthekerb.co.uk

Presenters

ALL ELECTRIC PRODUCTIONS & DAVID FOSTER MANAGEMENT
40 Lidgate Street Poundbury Dorchester
Dorset DT1 3SJ
Tel: 01305 259605
Email: info@allelectricproductions.co.uk
Web: www.allelectricproductions.co.uk
Contact: David Foster
Agent / Personal Manager / Producer specialising in Theatre shows, Musical shows, Concert & Jazz, Speakers & Presenters.

DAVID ANTHONY PROMOTIONS
PO Box 286, Warrington,
Cheshire WA2 8GA
Tel: 01925 632 496 Fax: 01925 416 589
Mob: 07836 752 195
Email: dave@davewarwick.co.uk
Web Site: www.davewarwick.co.uk
Senior Personnel: Dave Warwick
Specialising in Presenters.

ARENA ENTERTAINMENT CONSULTANTS
Regents Court, 39 Harrogate Road,
Leeds, West Yorkshire LS7 3PD
Tel: 0113 239 2222 Fax: 0113 239 2016
Email: stars@arenaentertainments.co.uk
Web: www.arenaentertainments.co.uk
Senior Personnel: Barry McManus, Martin Nazaruk,
Hayley Germain.
MAIL FORWARDED BY ARRANGEMENT ONLY.

ASQUITH & HORNER PERSONAL MANAGEMENT
The Studio, 14 College Road, Bromley,
Kent BR1 3NS
Tel: 020 8466 5580 Fax: 020 8313 0443
Web Site: www.spotlightagent.info/ (Agents PIN 9858-0919-0728)
Senior Personnel: Anthony van der Elst, Helen Melville
Specialising in all types of performers and entertainment.
E-mail on application. Distinguished list of European and Eastern European artists available. For complete client list, please see website: www.spotlightagent.info (Agents PIN 9858-0919-0728).

ALISON CAMPBELL MODEL AGENCY
381 Beersbridge Road, Belfast, County Antrim BT5 5DT Northern Ireland
Tel: 028 9080 9809 Fax: 028 9080 9808
Email: info@alisoncampbellmodels.com
Web: www.alisoncampbellmodels.com
Senior Personnel: Alison Campbell
Various artistes for corporate & promotional events., inc Miss Northern Ireland

CUNNINGHAM MANAGEMENT LTD
Suite 50, London House, 271 King Street,
London W6 9LZ
Tel: 020 8233 2824 / 2820
Email:
info@cunningham-management.co.uk
Web:
www.cunningham-management.co.uk
Senior Personnel: Chloe Cunningham
Contact: Simon Fairclough
Manages TV presenters and speakers.
Specialises in inspirational people of achievement.

CURTIS BROWN GROUP
5th Floor, Haymarket House, 28-29
Haymarket, London SW1Y 4SP
Tel: 020 7393 4400 Fax: 020 7393 4401
Email: jonathan@curtisbrown.co.uk
Web Site: www.curtisbrown.co.uk
Senior Personnel: Nick Marston
Agent: Jonathan Lloyd
Today, with over one hundred years of experience and more than twenty agents within our Book, Media, Actors and Presenters Divisions we represent many of the world's most popular and successful writers, directors, actors, playwrights and celebrities.

PAUL DUDDRIDGE MANAGEMENT
32 Rathbone Place, London W1T 1JD
Tel: 020 7580 3580 Fax: 020 7580 3480
Email: paul@paulduddridge.com
Web Site: www.paulduddridge.com
Agents: Paul Duddridge, Mike Leigh

JACQUE EVANS MANAGEMENT LTD
Suite 1 14 Holmesley Road,
London SE23 1PJ
Tel: 020 8699 1202 Fax: 020 8699 5192
Email: jacque@jemltd.demon.co.uk
Web Site: www.jacqueevansltd.com
Senior Personnel: Jacque Evans
Specialising in Journalists, Broadcasters & Presenters.

JAMES GRANT MANAGEMENT LTD
94 Strand On The Green Chiswick
London W4 3NN
Tel: 020 8742 4950 Fax: 020 8742 4951
Email: enquiries@jamesgrant.co.uk
Web Site: www.jamesgrant.co.uk
Contacts: Paul Worsley, George Ashton, Alison Astall, John Knight, Anne-Marie Corbett

HARVEY VOICES LTD
4th Floor, 54-55 Margaret Street,
London W1W 8SH
Tel: 020 7952 4361
Email: info@harveyvoices.co.uk
Web Site: www.harveyvoices.co.uk
Contact: Emma Harvey
Also represent children of all ages and Foreign Artistes

JANE HUGHES MANAGEMENT
4 Dundrennan Close, Poynton, Stockport,
Cheshire SK12 1SQ
Tel: 01625 858 556 Mob: 07766 130 604
Email: gill@jhm.co.uk
We are a Management Company providing Presenters for TV/Radio and corporate work. We also producers/directors for all media.

INDEPENDENT TALENT GROUP LTD
Oxford House, 76 Oxford Street, London
W1D 1BS
Tel: 020 7636 6565 Fax: 020 7323 0101
Web Site:
www.independenttalent.com/presenters
Contact: Laura Hill, Jessica Stone

ALEX JAY PERSONAL MANAGEMENT
8 Higher Newmarket Road, Newmarket,
Nailsworth, Gloucestershire GL6 0RP
Tel/Fax: 01453 834 783
Email:
alexjay@alex-jay-pm.freeserve.co.uk

Senior Personnel: Alex Jay
Specialising in artistes for film, television, theatre, commercials and TV & radio presenters.

KBJ MANAGEMENT
5 Soho Square London W1D 3QA
Tel: 020 7434 6767
Fax: 020 7287 1191
Email: general@kbjmgt.co.uk
Web Site: www.kbjmgt.co.uk
Agent: Joanna Kaye
Corporate Booking Agent: Candida Alderson

JOHN KETTLEY
Weatherview House, 50 Beaumont Way, Hazlemere, High Wycombe, Buckinghamshire HP15 7BE
Tel: 01494 715 115 Fax: 01494 715 115
Email: kettley@britishweatherservices.co.uk
Web: www.britishweatherservices.co.uk
Contact: Jim Dale

COLIN LEWIN MANAGEMENT
PO Box 891, Gerrards Cross, Buckinghamshire SL9 0BS
Tel/Fax: 01494 874 326
Email: clm@enterprise.net
Web Site: www.andycollins.biz
Senior Personnel: Colin Lewin

JANE MORGAN MANAGEMENT LTD
Elsinore House 77 Fulham Palace Road, London W6 8JA
Tel: 020 7478 7479
Email: enquiries@janemorganmgt.com
Web Site: www.janemorganmgt.com
Senior Personnel: Jane Morgan
Specialises in the representation of sports broadcasters and sportsmen and women who now have a career in the media.

NEW FACES
2nd Floor, The Linen Hall, 162-168 Regent Street, London W1B 5TB
Tel: 020 7439 6900 Fax: 020 7287 5481
Email: val@newfacestalent.co.uk
Web Site: www.newfacestalent.co.uk
Agents: Val Horton, Tania Patti
New Faces is a dynamic presenters, actors and extras agency situated in the west end of London. The agency is aimed at giving highly talented people of today a platform from which to launch their career and established artists a professional, friendly, approachable and highly efficient service.
If you wish to be considered for representation, please send us a copy of your showreel (if appropriate), up-to-date CV or details of experience, photograph and SAE. All tapes are viewed and if we are interested we will contact you and arrange an interview.
For more information call Val or Cathy on 020 7439 6900.

NMP LIVE LTD
8 Blenheim Court Brook Way Leatherhead, Surrey KT22 7NA
Tel: 01372 361004 Fax: 01372 374417
Email: live@nmp.co.uk
Web Site: www.nmplive.co.uk
Managing Directors: Neil Martin, Chris Banks.
Leading UK entertainment agency specialising in celebrity personal appearances, high profile entertainment, negotiating endorsements and advertising campaigns and presenting after-dinner, motivational & conference speakers.

JOHN NOEL MANAGEMENT
Block B, Imperial Works Perren Street London NW5 3ED
Tel: 020 7428 8400 Fax: 020 7428 8401
Email: john@johnnoel.com
Web Site: www.johnnoel.com
Agent: John Noel

OFF THE KERB PRODUCTIONS
Hammer House 113-117 Wardour Street London W1F 0UN
Tel: 020 7437 0607 Fax: 020 7437 0647
Email: info@offthekerb.co.uk or westend@offthekerb.co.uk
Web Site: www.offthekerb.co.uk
Senior Personnel: Addison Cresswell, Joe Norris
Please note all corporate, personal appearance and casting enquiries for all artistes to Fay Clayton in the West End office. fay@offthekerb.co.uk

PRESENTER PROMOTIONS
123 Corporation Road, Gillingham, Kent ME7 1RG
Tel/Fax: 01634 851 077
Email: info@presenterpromotions.com
Web Site: www.presenterpromotions.com
Senior Personnel: Colin Cobb
With over 20 years experience, we specialise in Presenters, Speakers, Voice Artistes. Offering a casting service free to production companies and specialist help to newcomers and artistes without an agent.

PROFESSIONAL SPORTS PARTNERSHIPS LTD
The Town House, 63 High Street, Chobham Surrey GU24 8AF
Tel: 01276 858 930 Fax: 01276 856 974
Email: chris@profsports.com
Web Site: www.profsports.com
Contact: Chris Evans-Pollard

ROSEBERY MANAGEMENT
Hoxton Hall, 130 Hoxton Street, London N1 6SH
Tel: 020 7684 0187 Mob: 07805 162731
Email: admin@roseberymanagement.com
Web: www.roseberymanagement.com
Manager: Ben West

SOMETHIN' ELSE
20 - 26 Brunswick Place, London N1 6DZ
Tel: 020 7250 5500 Fax: 020 7250 0937
Email: info@somethinelse.com
Web Site: www.somethinelse.com
Head of Talent Management: Grant Michaels
Agent: Sarah Jane Cass
Assistant Agent: Richard Howells

TALENT4 MEDIA LTD
Power Road Studios, 114 Power Road, Chiswick London W4 5PY
Tel: 020 8987 6416
Email: enquiries@talent4media.com
Web Site: www.talent4media.com
Contact: Joanna Carlton, Samantha Thomas

SCOTT-PAUL YOUNG ENTERTAINMENTS LTD
Northern Lights House, 110 Blandford Road North, Langley, Near Windsor, Berkshire SL3 7TA
Tel/Fax: 01753 693 250
Email: castingdirect@spy-ents.com
Web Site: www.spy-lightentsworld.com
Managing Director: Scott-Paul Young
Artists management and exclusive representation for films, television, commercials, theatre, sports and modelling events and all areas of the light entertainment industry.

Public/Guest/After Dinner Speakers

1ST CHOICE SPEAKERS UK LTD
52 Bois Moor Road Chesham, Buckinghamshire HP5 1SN
Tel/Fax: 01494 773 020 Mobile: 07821 131 510
Email: enquiries@1stchoicespeakers.co.uk
Web Site: www.1stchoicespeakers.com
Managing Director: Pushpa Kasinather
Specialising in Celebrity Speakers for Cruise Ships, Conferences and Personal Appearances.
Speakers for After Dinner, Sports/Golf, Business, Keynote, Comedians and Product Launches.

ABCADS
49 Ashgrove, Steeple Claydon, Buckingham MK18 2LW
Tel: 01296 738 020
Email: info@abcdirectentertainments.co.uk
Web: www.abcdirectentertainments.co.uk
Senior Personnel: Len Illing, Catherine Brandon, Elise Illing, Charlotte Illing, William Illing

AFTER DINNER SPEAKERS & COMEDIANS LIMITED
Chippings 2 The Old Saw Mills
Ripponden Halifax, West Yorkshire
HX6 4EN
Tel: 0845 4758866 Fax: 01422 884 494
Email: office@comedians.co.uk
Web Site: www.comedians.co.uk
Senior Personnel: Roger Davis, J. Mark Davis

AFTER DINNER WORLD LIMITED
Chippings 2 The Old Saw Mills
Ripponden Halifax, West Yorkshire
HX6 4EN
Tel: 0845 388 1966
Email: mark@afterdinnerworld.co.uk
Web Site: www.afterdinnerworld.co.uk
Senior Personnel: Jared Davis

ALL ELECTRIC PRODUCTIONS & DAVID FOSTER MANAGEMENT
40 Lidgate Street Poundbury Dorchester
Dorset DT1 3SJ
Tel: 01305 259605
Email: info@allelectricproductions.co.uk
Web: www.allelectricproductions.co.uk
Contact: David Foster
Agent / Personal Manager / Producer specialising in Theatre shows, Musical shows, Concert & Jazz, Speakers & Presenters.

ALL STAR SPEAKERS
23 Tynemouth Street, London SW6 2PS
Tel: 020 7371 7512 Fax: 01892 750 089
Email: laura@allstarspeakers.co.uk
Senior Personnel: Laura Collins
Specialising in After Dinner Speakers, Comedians, Presenters, Sports Personalities and Celebrity Voice Overs.

AMAZING EVENTS
Sunshine Cottage Burton Row Brent Knoll
Somerset TA9 4BY
Tel: 0844 332 0129 Mob: 07791 157719
Email: robbie@amazingevents.co.uk
Web Site: www.amazingevents.co.uk
Managing Director: Robbie Burns
Corporate Hospitality and Event Management specialists working nationwide, providing; themed parties, murder mysteries, team building, conference support and entertainers including celebrities and after-dinner speakers.

NITA ANDERSON ENTERTAINMENT
165 Wolverhampton Road, Sedgley,
Dudley, West Midlands DY3 1QR
Tel: 01902 882 211 / 681 224 Fax: 01902 883 356
Email: nitaandersonagency@hotmail.com
Web Site: www.nitaanderson.co.uk
Senior Personnel: Nita Anderson
Suppliers of Corporate Entertainment and After Dinner Speakers.

ANFIELD AGENCY
PO Box 48 Carnforth Lancashire LA6 2UZ
Tel: 07803 576871
Email: info@anfieldagency.co.uk
Web Site: www.anfieldagency.co.uk
Contact: Kevin O'Brien
Specialises in After Dinner Speakers, Cabaret, Corporate and Summer Seasons

ARENA ENTERTAINMENT CONSULTANTS
Regents Court, 39 Harrogate Road,
Leeds, West Yorkshire LS7 3PD
Tel: 0113 239 2222 Fax: 0113 239 2016
Email: stars@arenaentertainments.co.uk
Web: www.arenaentertainments.co.uk
Senior Personnel: Barry McManus, Martin Nazaruk,
Hayley Germain.
MAIL FORWARDED BY ARRANGEMENT ONLY.

ASSOCIATED SPEAKERS
24a Park Road, Hayes, Middlesex
UB4 8JN
Tel: 020 8848 9048
Senior Personnel: E.A. Davis, P.A. Davis, D.M. Wood, K.A. Davis
Specialising in After Dinner & Multi National Corporation Speakers from Show-Business, Sport & the Media, plus Top TV & Theatre Celebrities for all Personal Appearances.

MICHAEL BLACK PERSONAL MANAGEMENT LTD
5 The Ridgeway, Radlett,
Hertfordshire WD7 8PZ
Tel: 01923 856 555 Fax: 01923 859 871
Mobile: 07798 525253
Email: michael@themichaelblack.co.uk
Web Site: www.michaelblack.co.uk
Senior Personnel: Michael Black
Specialising in All Corporate Work, Bands, Discos, After Dinner Speakers.

BRITISH & EUROPEAN SPORTS TALENT
13 Montagu Mews South,
London W1H 7ER
Tel: 0871 250 1234
Email: richard@celebrity.co.uk
Web Site: www.celebrity.co.uk/best
Agent: Richard Johnson
Sports personalities for advertising, endorsements and corporate events.

BRITISH SPEAKER BUREAU
BSB House, 12 Nottingham Place,
London W1U 5NB
Freephone: 0808 0001 001 Tel: 08712 501 234 Fax: 020 7224 6060
Email: info@bsb.co.uk
Web Site: www.bsb.co.uk
Contact: Simona Gambini, Ron Mowlam

BURNETT GRANGER ASSOCIATES
3 Clifford Street London W1S 2LF
Tel: 0207 437 8008 Fax; 0207 287 3239
Email: associates@burnettgranger.co.uk
Web Site: www.burnettgranger.co.uk
Senior Personnel: Barry Burnett, Lindsay Granger. Theatrical agents.

JILLIE BUSHELL ASSOCIATES
15 Claylands Place, The Oval, London
SW8 1NL
Tel: 020 7582 3048 Fax: 020 7793 8658
Mob: 07831 330 340
Email: info@jilliebushell.com
Web Site: www.jilliebushell.com
Senior Personnel: Jillie Bushell
Book entertainment, speakers/motivational speakers, presenters and Jazz & Blues for corporate functions.

BUSINESS SPEAKERS BUREAU
13 Montagu Mews South,
London W1H 7ER
Tel: 0871 250 1234
Email: elizabeth@bsb.co.uk
Web Site: www.bsb.co.uk
Agent: Elizabeth Van Cleef
Guest Speakers, Celebrities & Entertainers for Corporate events.

LEE CARROLL
Sandpiper House 9 Yateman Close
Bishop Sutton Bristol, BS39 5PU
Mobile: 07974 620 507
Email: gagman@blueyonder.co.uk
Web Site: www.leecarroll.com
Britain's brightest comedy star, available for after-dinner, cruising, cabaret and TV warm-ups. Unique, a clean comedy that's very funny!

CELEBRITY APPEARANCES
Three Spires House, 16a Bird Street,
Lichfield, Staffordshire WS13 6PR
Tel: 01543 263 136 Fax: 01543 262 402
Email: info@normanphillips.co.uk
Web: www.celebrity-appearances.co.uk
Contact: Lianne Phillips
Established 40 years as the UK's premier consultancy supplying speakers and celebrities for every occasion including: Personal Appearances, After Dinner, Key Note and Business Speeches, Sporting Dinners, Conference and Award Ceremonies, Product Launches, Product Endorsements, Corporate Videos, Cabaret. Over 5000 speaker profiles available.

THE CELEBRITY GROUP
13 Montagu Mews South,
London W1H 7ER

Tel: 0871 250 1234
Email: brad@celebrity.co.uk
Web Site: www.celebrity.co.uk
Agent: Brad Cohen
Celebrities for Advertising, Endorsements and Corporate Events.

CSA - CELEBRITY SPEAKERS LTD

90 High Street, Burnham,
Berkshire SL1 7JT
Tel: 01628 601 400 Fax: 01628 601 4101
Email: csa@speakers.co.uk
Web Site: www.speakers.co.uk
Senior Personnel: Alex Krywald

COMMERCIAL CASTING

12 Colas Mews, London NW6 4LH
Tel: 0207 372 0009 Fax: 0207 372 3141
Email: info@commercialcasting.com
Web Site: www.commercialcasting.com
Senior Personnel: Charles Benenson
Specialists in providing Celebrities for corporate events.

STEVE CRAM

S & K Consulting, Tranwell House,
Tranwell Woods, Morpeth,
Northumberland NE61 6AQ
Tel/Fax: 01670 503 266
After Dinner Speaking, Motivational Speaking, Openings, Corporate Videos & Promotions, Radio & TV Presenting and TV Commentary.

CUNNINGHAM MANAGEMENT LTD

Suite 50, London House, 271 King Street,
London W6 9LZ
Tel: 020 8233 2824 / 2820
Email: info@cunningham-management.co.uk
Web: www.cunningham-management.co.uk
Senior Personnel: Chloe Cunningham
Contact: Simon Fairclough
Manages TV presenters and speakers. Specialises in inspirational people of achievement.

DAVID DICKINSON PRODUCTIONS LTD

High Barn, Cocksheadhey Road,
Bollington, Macclesfield, Cheshire
SK10 5QZ
Tel/Fax: 01625 560 821 Mobile: 07836 601 278

DBA SPEAKERS

58 Station Avenue, Walton-on-Thames,
Surrey KT12 1NQ
Tel: 01932 228 544 Fax: 01932 224 961
Email: diana@dbaspeakers.com
Web Site: www.dbaspeakers.com
Senior Personnel: Diana Boulter, Sarah Hobbs

We provide leading business speakers & entertainers, including e-business, economy, finance, sport, motivation, future business, vision strategy and political commentators.

MALCOLM DERRICK THEATRICAL ENTERPRISES

Poolbank House, 266 Longbridge Lane,
Northfield, Birmingham B31 4RJ
Tel: 0121 475 8759 Mob: 0788 618 179
Senior Personnel: Malcolm Derrick
Specialists in After Dinner Speakers

MARK JAMES DORMER F.G. INT. P.T.

Park Parade, Hazlemere, High Wycombe,
Buckinghamshire HP15 7AA
Tel: 01296 655 468 Fax: 01296 655 468
Email: enquiries@toast-masters.co.uk
Web Site: www.toast-masters.co.uk
Toastmaster, Master of Ceremonies and Speech Writer.

NEIL DROVER - THE AGENCY

Event House, 437 Crow Road, Glasgow,
Strathclyde G11 7DZ Scotland
Tel: 0845 062 3377 Fax: 0141 334 4796
Email: neil@neildrover.com
Web Site: www.neildrover.com
Senior Personnel: Neil Drover, Angela Prentice, Julie Hume
Specialising in a variety of entertainment and corporate hospitality.

ELITE PROMOTIONS

1A Thistle Place, Aberdeen AB10 1UZ
Scotland
Tel: 01224 636 363 Fax: 01224 652 980
Email: info@elitepromotions.net
Web Site: www.elitepromotions.net
Senior Personnel: John Anderson, Kathleen Anderson
Wedding Co-ordinator: Susan Moultrie
Entertainment Consultants and Booking Agents - Supplying all entertainment sectors and corporate hospitality packages.

FAMOUS FACES

PO Box 69, Kingsbridge,
Devon TQ7 4WZ
Tel: 01548 559 165 Fax: 01548 559 165
Louise EspigTel: 08452
Email: ideas@famousfaces.co.uk
Web Site: www.famousfaces.co.uk
Contact: Jeremy Harmer
Famous Faces provide speakers, celebrities and cabaret artistes for promotional activities, conference and corporate entertainment, catering for all occasions and audiences.

GUILD OF INTERNATIONAL PROFESSIONAL TOASTMASTERS

12 Little Bornes, Dulwich,
London SE21 8SE
Tel: 020 8670 5585 Fax: 020 8670 0055
Web Site: www.ivorspencer.com
Life President: Ivor Spencer
The Guild Members officiate at functions all over the United Kingdom and undertake engagements abroad. They are expert organisers who arrange authentic British Banquets with the traditional ceremonies (Loving Cup, Baron of Beef, etc.) anywhere in the world. The Guild Toastmasters are experts at officiating on Royal occasions.
Conferences and Banquets from 12 to 10,000 guests organised.

HEART OF ENGLAND PROMOTIONS LTD

Old Hall, Wall Hill Road, Fillongley,
Coventry, Warwickshire CV7 8DX
Tel: 01676 540 333 Fax: 01676 540 365
Email: sales@heartofengland.co.uk
Web Site: www.heartofengland.co.uk
Senior Personnel: Stephen Hammon
Specialising in DJs, Comperes and Children's Entertainment

JLA (JEREMY LEE ASSOCIATES LTD)

80 Great Portland Street
London W1W 7NW
Tel: 020 7907 2800 Fax: 020 7907 2801
Email: talk@jla.co.uk
Web Site: www.jla.co.uk
Senior Personnel: Jeremy Lee

JON HOLMES MEDIA LTD

5th Floor, Holborn Gate, 26 Southampton Buildings, London WC2A 1PQ
Tel: 020 7861 2550 Fax: 020 7861 3067
Email: dominic@jonholmesmedia.com
Web Site: www.jonholmesmedia.com
Senior Personnel: Jon Holmes, Diana Van Bunnens
Client Manager: Dominic Van Bunnens
Email Address for specific contact person: firstname@jonholmesmedia.com

JOHN KETTLEY

Weatherview House, 50 Beaumont Way,
Hazlemere, High Wycombe,
Buckinghamshire HP15 7BE
Tel: 01494 715 115 Fax: 01494 715 115
Email: kettley@britishweatherservices.co.uk
Web: www.britishweatherservices.co.uk
Contact: Jim Dale

KRUGER COWNE LIMITED

Unit 18G Chelsea Wharf, 15 Lots Road,
London SW10 0QJ
Tel: 020 7352 2277 Fax: 020 7900 6545
Email: info@krugercowne.com
Web Site: www.krugercowne.com
Director: Gina Nelthorpe-Cowne
Chief Executive Officer: Mark Cowne
Kruger Cowne represent the 'creme de la creme' of after dinner and public speakers, presenters, hosts or entertainers including Bob Geldof KBE, John Simpson

CBE, Jamie Oliver, Sarah Duchess of York, Princess Michael of Kent, Uri Geller, Ruby Wax, Jerry Hall, Ranulph Fiennes KBE, OBE, Dr Jane Goodall DBE, John Sergeant, Martin Bell OBE and other top personalities.
Many of the people that we represent are also available for voice-over work for radio and television commercials, audio visual presentations and general narration.

THE LONDON SPEAKER BUREAU
Elsinore House, 77 Fulham Palace Road, London W6 8JA
Tel: 020 8748 9595 Fax: 020 8741 8723
Email: tom@londonspeakerbureau.co.uk
Web: www.londonspeakerbureau.co.uk
Senior Personnel: Tom Kenyon-Slaney, Brendan O'Connor, Lucinda Swan
Specialising in Business and Political Speakers.

NMP LIVE LTD
8 Blenheim Court Brook Way Leatherhead, Surrey KT22 7NA
Tel: 01372 361004 Fax: 01372 374417
Email: live@nmp.co.uk
Web Site: www.nmplive.co.uk
Managing Directors: Neil Martin, Chris Banks.
Leading UK entertainment agency specialising in celebrity personal appearances, high profile entertainment, negotiating endorsements and advertising campaigns and presenting after-dinner, motivational & conference speakers.

NON STOP ENTERTAINMENTS
PO Box 10, Garston, Liverpool, Merseyside L19 2RD
Tel: 0151 427 1910 (5 lines) Fax: 0151 494 9707 Mob: 07768 747 686
Email: info@nonstopentertainments.co.uk
Web: www.nonstopentertainments.co.uk
Senior Personnel: L Bather

OFF THE KERB PRODUCTIONS
Hammer House 113-117 Wardour Street London W1F 0UN
Tel: 020 7437 0607 Fax: 020 7437 0647
Email: info@offthekerb.co.uk or westend@offthekerb.co.uk
Web Site: www.offthekerb.co.uk
Senior Personnel: Addison Cresswell, Joe Norris
Please note all corporate, personal appearance and casting enquiries for all artistes to Fay Clayton in the West End office. fay@offthekerb.co.uk

PALM COURT THEATRE PRODUCTIONS
Winkton Lodge Cottage, Salisbury Road, Winkton, Christchurch, Dorset BH23 7AR
Tel: 01202 484 185 Mob: 07836 717 567
Fax: 01202 471 920
Email: godwin@palm-court.demon.co.uk
Senior Personnel: Patricia Godwin

PARLIAMENT COMMUNICATIONS
Verry House, Chine Crescent Road, Bournemouth, Dorset BH2 5LQ
Tel: 01202 242 424 Fax: 01202 242 428
Email: info@parliamentspeakers.com
Web Site: www.parliamentspeakers.com / www.noordinaryjoe.co.uk / www.derekredmond.com / www.andycave.net
Senior Personnel: Marek Kriwald
Specialising in: Business speakers and celebrity entertainment for the corporate sector. Captains of industry, politicians, business gurus, media personalities, sports stars, adventurers, entertainers and professional facilitators and presenters. Parliament is in direct contact with many of the speakers listed. We also work with managers of certain speakers.

PERFORMING ARTISTES (PART OF THE F4 GROUP)
F4 Group Ltd 24a High Street, Cobham Surrey KT11 3EB
Tel: 01932 590 376 Fax: 01932 862 437
Email: ask@performingartistes.co.uk
Web Site: www.f4group.co.uk
Contacts: Stanley Jackson
Specialising in After Dinner entertainment, including: speakers, hosts, business and motivational/keynote speakers, celebrities for personal appearances, endorsements, advertising campaigns and corporate events.

PERSONAL APPEARANCES
20 North Mount, 1147-1161 High Road, Whetstone, London N20 0PH
Tel: 020 8343 7748 Fax: 020 8343 7748
Email: patsy@personalappearances.biz
Web Site: www.personalappearances.biz
Senior Personnel: Patsy Martin
Specialists in Public Relations and Personal Management

PERSONALLY SPEAKING
Three Spires House, 16a Bird Street, Lichfield, Staffordshire WS13 6PR
Tel: 01543 263 136 Fax: 01543 262 402
Email: info@normanphillips.co.uk
Web: www.personally-speaking.co.uk
Senior Personnel: Lianne Phillips
Established 40 years as the UK's premier consultancy, supplying speakers and celebrities for every occasion including: Personal Appearances, After Dinner, Key Note and Business Speeches, Sporting Dinners, Conference and Award Ceremonies, Product Launches, Product Endorsements, Corporate Videos, Cabaret. Over 5000 speaker profiles available.

POSITIVE PLUS LTD
Berkeley House, Berkeley Street, Ashton-under-Lyne, Lancashire OL6 7DT
Tel: 0161 339 9333 Fax: 0161 339 4242
Senior Personnel: Alistair Shackleton

PROFESSIONAL SPORTS PARTNERSHIPS LTD
The Town House, 63 High Street, Chobham Surrey GU24 8AF
Tel: 01276 858 930 Fax: 01276 856 974
Email: chris@profsports.com
Web Site: www.profsports.com
Contact: Chris Evans-Pollard

PVA ENTERTAINMENT CONSULTANTS
2 High Street, Westbury-on-Trym, Bristol, Avon BS9 3DU
Tel: 0117 950 4504 Fax: 0117 959 1786
Email: tim@pvagroup.com, enquiries@pva.ltd.uk
Web Site: www.pva.ltd.uk
Senior Personnel: Pat Vincent, Tim Cowlin

THE RIGHT ADDRESS LTD
Second Floor, Salamander Quay West, Park Lane, Harefield, Middlesex, UB9 6NZ
Tel: 01895 827 800 Fax: 01895 827 801
Email: info@therightaddress.co.uk
Web Site: www.therightaddress.co.uk
Senior Personnel: Jane French, Jo'anna Tremaine, Rachael Robertson
Specialise in after dinner speakers, cabaret, bands and entertainment.

GORDON ROBINSON ASSOCIATES
8 Lilac Avenue, Knutsford, Cheshire WA16 0AZ
Tel/Fax: 01565 652 188
Mobile: 07703 185642
Leisure Consultant dealing primarily with After Dinner Speakers.

SELECTIVELY SPEAKING
17 St Johns Cresent, Harrogate, North Yorkshire HG1 3AB
Tel: 0870 330 0787 Fax: 0870 330 0788
Email: info@entertainment-zone.com
Web Site: www.entertainment-zone.com
Senior Personnel: Louise Parker
Specialises in supplying celebrity speakers and comedians to corporate events.

SPEAKERS ASSOCIATES LTD
Thistles 15 Kinghom Park Maidenhead, Berkshire SL6 7TX
Tel: 01628 636600
Email: info@speakersassociates.com
Web Site: www.speakersassociates.co.uk

SPEAKERS CORNER
207 High Road, London N2 8AN
Tel: 020 8365 3200 Fax: 020 8883 7213
Email: info@speakerscorner.co.uk
Web Site: www.speakerscorner.co.uk
Agent: Nick Gold
Specialising in After Dinner Speakers, Business and Motivational Speakers, Celebrities, Sports Personalities, Politicians, Awards Hosts and Cabaret for the Corporate Market.

SPEAKERS FOR BUSINESS
38 Bartholomew Close, London
EC1A 7HP
Tel: 020 7600 3993 Fax: 020 7600 3992
Email: info@sfb.com
Web Site: www.sfb.com
Senior Personnel: Tracey Ball

TALENT ONE
14 Fairfield Lane, Wolverley
Kidderminster, Worcestershire DY11 5QH
Tel: 01562 850 255 Mob: 07957 106 982
Email: admin@talentone.co.uk
Web Site: www.talentone.co.uk
Contact : Phil & Keith

TALKING CONCEPTS
PO Box 11914, Two Gates, Tamworth,
B77 1WT
Tel: 01827 250 515 Fax: 0870 762 1535
Mob: 07870 154941
Email: ideas@talkingconcepts.co.uk
Web Site: www.talkingconcepts.co.uk
Senior Personnel: Jan Mattison
Specialising in after dinner/conference speakers, bands, cabaret artistes & themed entertainment.

TAYLOR MADE SPEAKERS
131 Battenhall Road, Battenhall,
Worcester WR5 2BU
Tel: 01905 767 465 Fax: 01905 767 489
Email: info@afterdinnerspeakers.org
Web Site: www.afterdinnerspeakers.org
Senior Personnel: David Taylor
After-dinner entertainment.

TRADING FACES LTD
47 Dean Street, London W1D 5BE
Tel: 020 7287 0866 Fax: 0870 512 912
Email: enquiries@tradingfaces.co.uk
Web Site: www.tradingfaces.co.uk
Senior Personnel: Michelle Fowler, Vicki Michelle, Ann Michelle, Suzie Michelle

WELLIE BOOT PRODUCTIONS
P.O. Box 332, Rochdale, Lancashire
OL12 7WD
Tel: 01706 353545 Fax: 01706 353545
Email: dale.mulgrew@zen.co.uk,
jimmy@jimmycricket.co.uk
Web Site: www.jimmycricket.co.uk
Manager: Jimmy Cricket
Contact: Dale Mulgrew
Wellie Boot Productions is the ever popular Irish comedian Jimmy Cricket's entertainment Company. And There's More: We have many exciting shows and products featuring Jimmy on offer across all event platforms and we can provide creative solutions for your entertainment requirements.

Shows

ANDY EASTWOOD
PO Box 5004 Christchurch,
Dorset BH23 5WD
Tel: 01425 275 830 Mob: 07950 454 365
Email: andy@andyeastwood.com
Web Site: www.andyeastwood.com
Contacts: Andy Eastwood

LARRY JONES
Castle House 86 Teehey Lane, Wirral,
Merseyside CH63 8QU
Tel: 0151 608 8503 Mob: 07851 023695
Email: handl.jones@btconnect.com
Contact: Larry Jones

THE MAGIC OF MUSICALS
PO Box 31187 London E16 3FT
Tel : 020 7476 8440
Mob: 07702 543 117
Email: colin@abbagirls.com
Web Site: www.themagicofmusicals.co.uk
Contact: Colin

Soap Personalities

ANDREW BEAUCHAMP MANAGEMENT
Oaklands Business Centre, 64-68 Elm Grove, Worthing, West Sussex BN11 5LH
Tel: 07737 415 534
Email: abeauchampmgt@aol.com
Proprietor: Andrew Beauchamp

BURNETT GRANGER ASSOCIATES
3 Clifford Street London W1S 2LF
Tel: 0207 437 8008 Fax; 0207 287 3239
Email: associates@burnettgranger.co.uk
Web Site: www.burnettgranger.co.uk
Senior Personnel: Barry Burnett, Lindsay Granger. Theatrical agents.

Sports Personalities

AFTER DINNER WORLD LIMITED
Chippings 2 The Old Saw Mills
Ripponden Halifax, West Yorkshire
HX6 4EN
Tel: 0845 388 1966
Email: mark@afterdinnerworld.co.uk
Web Site: www.afterdinnerworld.co.uk
Senior Personnel: Jared Davis

ALL STAR SPEAKERS
23 Tynemouth Street, London SW6 2PS
Tel: 020 7371 7512 Fax: 01892 750 089
Email: laura@allstarspeakers.co.uk
Senior Personnel: Laura Collins
Specialising in After Dinner Speakers, Comedians, Presenters, Sports Personalities and Celebrity Voice Overs.

ARENA ENTERTAINMENT CONSULTANTS
Regents Court, 39 Harrogate Road,
Leeds, West Yorkshire LS7 3PD
Tel: 0113 239 2222 Fax: 0113 239 2016
Email: stars@arenaentertainments.co.uk
Web: www.arenaentertainments.co.uk
Senior Personnel: Barry McManus, Martin Nazaruk,
Hayley Germain.
MAIL FORWARDED BY ARRANGEMENT ONLY.

CELEBRITY APPEARANCES
Three Spires House, 16a Bird Street,
Lichfield, Staffordshire WS13 6PR
Tel: 01543 263 136 Fax: 01543 262 402
Email: info@normanphillips.co.uk
Web: www.celebrity-appearances.co.uk
Contact: Lianne Phillips
Established 40 years as the UK's premier consultancy supplying speakers and celebrities for every occasion including: Personal Appearances, After Dinner, Key Note and Business Speeches, Sporting Dinners, Conference and Award Ceremonies, Product Launches, Product Endorsements, Corporate Videos, Cabaret. Over 5000 speaker profiles available.

DEREK REDMOND
Verry House, Chine Crescent Road,
Bournemouth BH2 5LQ
Tel 01202 242 434 Fax 01202 242 428
Email: info@derekredmond.com
Web Site: www.derekredmond.com
Contact: Derek Redmond
Former 400m athlete: Won Gold in the 4X400m with Black, Akabusi & Regis and his semi-final race in the Barcelona Olympics, has since become one of the most famous sporting images of modern times. Inspirational Speaker. Sports Commentator.

FIGHTING TALK PROMOTIONS
30 Peterborough Way, Fellgate, Jarrow,
Tyne and Wear NE32 4XD
Tel: 0191 422 3816 Fax: 0191 422 3816
Mobile: 0775 251 5280
Email: md@boxingcelebrities.co.uk
Web Site: www.boxingcelebrities.co.uk
Contact: Martyn Devlin
Featuring and providing boxing celebrities for after dinner speaking, talk-ins and appearances at events. Specialising in artist booking, both direct and in collaboration with their agents.

FIRST ARTIST CORPORATION PLC
First Artist House, 87 Wembley Hill Road, Wembley, Middlesex HA9 8BU
Tel: 020 8900 1818 Fax: 020 8903 2964
Email: reception@firstartist.com
Web Site: www.firstartist.com
Chief Executive: Jon Smith
Contact: Corrinne Goodall
First Artist are one of the leading international sporting agencies looking after a myriad of football players and media personalities.

IMG WORLD
Pier House Strand On The Green
London W4 3NN
Tel: 020 8233 5000 Fax: 020 8233 5001
Web Site: www.imgworld.com

JON HOLMES MEDIA LTD
5th Floor, Holborn Gate, 26 Southampton Buildings, London WC2A 1PQ
Tel: 020 7861 2550 Fax: 020 7861 3067
Email: dominic@jonholmesmedia.com
Web Site: www.jonholmesmedia.com
Senior Personnel: Jon Holmes, Diana Van Bunnens
Client Manager: Dominic Van Bunnens
Email Address for specific contact person: firstname@jonholmesmedia.com

LITTLE TONE PROMOTIONS
Unit 1, Perfecta Works, Bordesley Street, Birmingham B5 5PG
Tel/Fax: 0845 124 9758
Mobile: 07976 916 208
Email: info@littletone.co.uk
Web Site: www.littletone.co.uk
Contact: Tony Diponio
Sports and entertainment promotions company.

NUFF RESPECT
The Coach House, 107 Sherland Road, Twickenham TW1 4HB
Tel: 020 8891 4145 Fax: 020 8891 4140
Email: nuff_respect@msn.com
Web Site: www.nuff-respect.co.uk
Agent: Sue Barrett

PARAGON SPORTS MANAGEMENT LTD
Falstaff House, Suite 18, Bardolph Road, Richmond, Surrey TW9 2LH
Tel: 020 8332 8640 Fax: 020 8332 8649
Mobile: 07718 535 335 (Mike Martin)
Email: mike.martin@paragonsportsmanagement.com
Web: www.paragonsportsmanagement.com
Director: Mike Martin

PERSONAL APPEARANCES
20 North Mount, 1147-1161 High Road, Whetstone, London N20 0PH
Tel: 020 8343 7748 Fax: 020 8343 7748
Email: patsy@personalappearances.biz
Web Site: www.personalappearances.biz
Senior Personnel: Patsy Martin
Specialists in Public Relations and Personal Management

PROFESSIONAL SPORTS PARTNERSHIPS LTD
The Town House, 63 High Street, Chobham Surrey GU24 8AF
Tel: 01276 858 930 Fax: 01276 856 974
Email: chris@profsports.com
Web Site: www.profsports.com
Contact: Chris Evans-Pollard

TALENT ONE
14 Fairfield Lane, Wolverley
Kidderminster, Worcestershire DY11 5QH
Tel: 01562 850 255 Mob: 07957 106 982
Email: admin@talentone.co.uk
Web Site: www.talentone.co.uk
Contact : Phil & Keith

SCOTT-PAUL YOUNG ENTERTAINMENTS LTD
Northern Lights House, 110 Blandford Road North, Langley, Near Windsor, Berkshire SL3 7TA
Tel/Fax: 01753 693 250
Email: castingdirect@spy-ents.com
Web Site: www.spy-lightentsworld.com
Managing Director: Scott-Paul Young
Artists management and exclusive representation for films, television, commercials, theatre, sports and modelling events and all areas of the light entertainment industry.

Stunt Specialists

2MA
Springvale, Tutland Road, North Baddesley, Hants Southampton SO52 9FL
Tel: 023 8074 1354 Fax: 023 8074 1355
Mobile: 07730 662236
Email: mo.matthews@2ma.co.uk
Web Site: www.2ma.co.uk
Senior Personnel: Magee Matthews, Mo Matthews
Suppliers of gymnasts, acrobats and sports artistes. Martial arts, stunt men.

CIRCUS ALCHEMY
5 Beech Avenue, Rawmarsh, Rotherham, South Yorkshire S62 5HH
Tel: 01709 710 780 Fax: 01709 710 780
Email: albert@albertalchemy.com
Web Site: www.albertalchemy.com
Contact: Albert Alchemy
Fire-eating, escapology, stiltwalking, medieval jester. Magic for corporate, public and private functions.

NEW FACES
2nd Floor, The Linen Hall, 162-168 Regent Street, London W1B 5TB
Tel: 020 7439 6900 Fax: 020 7287 5481
Email: val@newfacestalent.co.uk
Web Site: www.newfacestalent.co.uk
Agents: Val Horton, Tania Patti
New Faces is a dynamic presenters, actors and extras agency situated in the west end of London. The agency is aimed at giving highly talented people of today a platform from which to launch their career and established artists a professional, friendly, approachable and highly efficient service.
If you wish to be considered for representation, please send us a copy of your showreel (if appropriate), up-to-date CV or details of experience, photograph and SAE. All tapes are viewed and if we are interested we will contact you and arrange an interview.
For more information call Val or Cathy on 020 7439 6900.

Toastmasters & Masters Of Ceremonies

AFTER DINNER SPEAKERS & COMEDIANS LIMITED
Chippings 2 The Old Saw Mills
Ripponden Halifax, West Yorkshire HX6 4EN
Tel: 0845 4758866 Fax: 01422 884 494
Email: office@comedians.co.uk
Web Site: www.comedians.co.uk
Senior Personnel: Roger Davis, J. Mark Davis

MARK JAMES DORMER F.G. INT. P.T.
Park Parade, Hazlemere, High Wycombe, Buckinghamshire HP15 7AA
Tel: 01296 655 468 Fax: 01296 655 468
Email: enquiries@toast-masters.co.uk
Web Site: www.toast-masters.co.uk
Toastmaster, Master of Ceremonies and Speech Writer.

GALAXY EVENTS
Galaxy House, Mian Yard, 86 Wallis Road, London E9 5LN
Tel: 0208 1330 558
Email: info@galaxy-events.co.uk
Web Site: www.galaxy-events.co.uk
Senior Personnel: Mel Harvey
Artist Management and Event Coordination.

GUILD OF INTERNATIONAL PROFESSIONAL TOASTMASTERS
12 Little Bornes, Dulwich, London SE21 8SE

Tel: 020 8670 5585 Fax: 020 8670 0055
The Guild Members officiate at functions all over the United Kingdom and undertake engagements abroad. They are expert organisers who arrange authentic British Banquets with the traditional ceremonies (Loving Cup, Baron of Beef, etc.) anywhere in the world. The Guild Toastmasters are experts at officiating on Royal occasions.
Conferences and Banquets from 12 to 10,000 guests organised.

JAM HOT PRODUCTIONS
38 Surbiton Hill Park, Surbiton,
Surrey KT5 8ES
Tel: 020 8390 2275 Fax: 020 8390 2275
Mob: 07889 431 004
Email: bazmoran@btinternet.com
Contact: Barry Moran

LONDON MUSIC AGENCY
7 Rosewood Drive, Orchard Heights
Ashford, Kent TN25 4QF
Tel: 01233 623 623 Mob: 07885 032 132
Email: enquiries@londonmusicagency.co.uk
Web: www.londonmusicagency.co.uk
Proprietor: Jenny Braby
Everything in entertainment for Private and Corporate functions, e.g. Jazz, String Quartets and all types of band, music and the unusual.

TOASTMASTER PAUL DEACON
Chantry, Broomfield Hill, Great
Missenden, Buckinghamshire HP16 9HT
Tel: 01494 862 868
Email: toastmaster@pauldeacon.com
Web Site: www.pauldeacon.com
Toastmaster: Paul Deacon
International Toastmaster and Master of Ceremonies.

Ventriloquest

LARRY JONES
Castle House 86 Teehey Lane, Wirral,
Merseyside CH63 8QU
Tel: 0151 608 8503 Mob: 07851 023695
Email: handl.jones@btconnect.com
Contact: Larry Jones

JUNGLE JIM
The Lower House West Street, Denbury,
Newton Abbot, Devon TQ12 6DP
Tel: 01803 812 478 Mob: 07736 970 293
Email: jimmytamley@tiscali.co.uk
Web Site: www.junglejim.co.uk
Contact: Emma & Jimmy Tamley

JIMMY TAMLEY
The Lower House West Street, Denbury,
Newton Abbot, Devon TQ12 6DP
Tel: 01803 812 478 Mob: 07736 970 293
Email: jimmytamley@tiscali.co.uk
Web Site: www.jimmytamley.com
or www.junglejim.co.uk
Contact: Emma & Jimmy Tamley

Independent Artistes

ACOUSTIC MEDIA TONES
5 Ridgeway Drive, Dunstable,
Bedfordshire LU5 4QT
Tel/Fax: 01582 603 935
Email: mreid491@aol.com
Director: Mark Reid
Freelance songwriter.

THE AKABUSI COMPANY
14 Doolittle Mill Froghall Road Ampthill
Bedfordshire MK45 2ND
Tel: 0870 444 1975 Fax: 0870 444 1976
Email: info@akabusi.com
Web Site: www.akabusi.com
Proprietor: Kriss Akabusi
Contact: Jane
Media Consultancy. Conference & Motivational Peak Performance Speaker.

SEAN ALEXANDER
32 Dunnock Drive Costessey
Norwich NR8 5FF
Tel: 01603 746706 Mob: 07765 881894
Email: sean@seanalexandermagic.com
Web Site: www.seanalexandermagic.com
Contact: Sean Alexander
Please see full page ad within the Magicians & Illusionists section

ALMOST ELTON
258 St. Johns Road, Yeovil,
Somerset BA21 5QP
Tel: 07970 216 459
Email: matthewrock@almostelton.co.uk
Web Site: www.almosteltonjohn.com
Contact: Matthew Rock
A brilliant Elton John Tribute.

ALRIGHT CHARLIE
Flat 4 Carleton House 122a Hillfield
Avenue London N8 7DQ
Tel: 07808 732 390
Email: info@alrightcharlie.co.uk
Web Site: www.alrightcharlie.co.uk
Senior Personnel: Lawrence Anthony
Charlie Chaplin Look Alike, Comedy waiter & Close-up Magician for all indoor and outdoor events.

ANDSOME CABIN BUOYS
26 Cumberland Court, Cross Road,
Croydon, Surrey CR0 6TE
Tel: 020 8680 4302
Email: petefyfe@aol.com
Web Site: www.bandoftwo.com
Contact: Peter Fyfe
Specialising in Goodtime Sea Songs & Tunes.

BAND OF TWO
26 Cumberland Court, 21 Cross Road,
Croydon, Surrey CR0 6TE
Tel: 020 8680 4302
Email: petefyfe@aol.com
Web Site: www.bandoftwo.com
Contact: Peter Fyfe
"Specialising in Goodtime Celtic/Irish Songs, Tunes and Folk Dances."

THE BANDIT BEATLES
c/o Firbank, Vinegar Hill, Undy, Undy
Monmouthshire NP26 3EJ South Wales
Tel: 01633 882 211 Fax: 01633 882 211
Email: info@banditbeatles.com
Web Site: www.banditbeatles.com
Contact: Colin Smith

BANJAX
62 Collier Road, Hastings, East Sussex
TN34 3JB
Tel: 01424 716 576
Email: greenman@britishlibrary.net
Contact: Keith Leech
Specialising in Barn Dances, Ceilidhs and Folk Music.

ALAN BATES STAGE HYPNOTIST
Tudor Cottage, 11 Greeendale Road, Port
Sunlight Wirral Merseyside CH62 5DF
England
Tel/Fax: 0151 644 9693
Email: info@hypnotistalanbates.com
Web Site: www.hypnotistalanbates.com
Contact: Alan Bates
International Comedy Stage Hypnotist.

BE BOP DADDIES
Mobile Tel: 07973 919587 (John Davies)
Email: john@bebopdaddies.com
Web Site: www.bebopdaddies.com
Contact: John Davies
We are a visual and entertaining, authentic 1950's style Rock'n'Roll band, comprising of a Frontman Vocalist with pure attitude and a natural rapport with an audience, Lead Guitar/vocals, Double 'slap' Bass/vocals and Drums/vocals. The act comprises of all members of the band leaving the stage and performing...a sight to see! .

GORDON BENNETT
16 Saxons Drive, Maidstone,
Kent ME14 5HS
Tel: 01622 672 128 Mob: 07930 758 083
Email: gordonbennett69@hotmail.com
Web Site: www.gordonbennett.biz
Contact: Gordon Bennett

BOB "THE CAT" BEVAN M.B.E
Barelands Oast, Bells Yew Green,

Tunbridge Wells, Kent TN3 9BD
Tel: 01892 750 131 Fax: 01892 750 089
Mobile: 07336 250 335
Email: bob@bobthecatbevan.co.uk
Web Site: www.bobthecatbevan.co.uk
After Dinner Speaker, Comedian, Sports Personality and TV & Radio Presenter, Master of Ceremonies, Conference Host, script + speech writer.

BIG TELLY THEATRE COMPANY
Portstewart Town Hall, The Crescent, Portstewart, County Londonderry
BT55 7AB Northern Ireland
Tel/Fax: 028 7083 2588 / 6473
Email: info@big-telly.com
Web Site: www.big-telly.com
Contacts: Louise Rossington, Zoe Seaton Hannah McKensie

BIGTOPMANIA
Big top hire and performance for all events Featuring Pete Za and Friends
Swallows Croft, Chapmans Well, Launceston, Cornwall, PL15 9SG
Tel/Fax: 01409 211178
Mob: 07768 498 090
Email: info@junctionjugglers.com & peteza@madasafish.com
Web Site: www.junctionjugglers.com & www.bigtopmania.co.uk
Senior Personnel: Pete Wintercrane
Est.1987. Hundreds of shows annually. Family entertainment, cabaret or street style. Various acts from solo to major productions. Typically - fire eating, stilts, unicycling, circus, etc.

BLOWOUT SAX
South Lodge, North Parade, Bath, B.A.N.E.S. BA2 4EU
Tel: 01225 339 007
Mobile: 07773 737 880
Email: markarcher@blowoutsax.com
Web Site: www.blowoutsax.com
School Director: Mark Archer
School, shop and musicians.

BOMBAY BAJA BRASS BAND
53 Newquay Road, Walsall, WS5 3EL
Tel: 07710 040 183
Email: info@bombaybaja.com
Web Site: www.bombaybaja.com

BOO-BOO THE CLOWN
20 Abbey Drive, Ashby-de-la-Zouch, Leicestershire LE65 2LX
Tel: 01530 413 998 Fax: 01530 564 601
Email: davidcooper@ashby7777.fsbusiness.co.uk
Contact: David Cooper
Clown mix and mingle, face painting, balloon modelling, comedy magic, temporary tatoos, fun discos, Santa Claus.
One Day training courses in face painting, balloon modelling and childrens magic.
Jester/builder/wizard/angel/snowman/pan to dame/teddy bears/white rabbit - characters available.

SANDY BRECHIN
16/2 Panmure Place, Toll Cross, Edinburgh, EH3 9JJ Scotland
Tel/Fax: 0131 466 6559
Email: sandy@squeeze.demon.co.uk
Web Site: www.brechin-all-records.com

SHANE BROGAN MUSIC PRODUCTIONS
PO BOX 26253 Ayr South Ayrshire KA7 1YF Scotland, UK
Mob: 07762 472 187
Email: shane@shanebrogan.com
Web Site: www.shanebrogan.com
Musician: Shane D Brogan
Accordionist specialising in Jazz, Classical, Popular, Ethnic, Music, etc.; Pianist/Keyboardist; Composer/Arranger; Private Music Teacher.

CHARLES BURNS - SILHOUETTE ARTIST
234 Peppard Road, Emmer Green, Caversham, Berkshire RG4 8UA
Tel: 0118 947 6637 Fax: 0118 947 6813
Mobile: 0780 3085637
Email: charles@roving-artist.com
Web Site: www.roving-artist.com
Charles cuts astoundingly accurate portraits of your guests. Cut from black paper with scissors in just 90 seconds!

JAIK CAMPBELL
Mobile: 07949 949480
Email: jaik.campbell@tinyonline.co.uk
Web Site: www.jaikcampbell.com
Comedian/Presenter: Jaik Campbell

CARICATURES & MAGIC
14 Mayfield Place, Brunswick Green, Wideopen, Newcastle-upon-Tyne, Tyne and Wear NE13 7HY
Tel: 0191 236 3152
Mobile: 07802 748 579
Email: info@paullytton.com
Caricaturist, Paul Slattery & Magician, Paul Lytton
An unbeatable reputation with a complimentary blend of caricatures and magic for all your corporate entertainment needs.
Paul Slattery ~ A slick talent with any medium, be it pens, pencils or brushes. You will be both amazed and delighted at the lightening speed of Paul's caricaturing.
Paul Lytton ~ Specialising in close-up magic, you will be impressed, astonished and entertained !

CARRIESMATIC THEME PARTIES
21 Clermiston Crescent, Edinburgh, Mid Lothian EH4 7DY Scotland
Tel: 0131 336 3673
Mobile: 07952 945 749
Email: carriesmatic@yahoo.co.uk
Senior Personnel: Carrie Todd
Party entertainment for all ages.
Children's entertainer, fortune teller, storyteller and flamenco dance act. Outdoor events educational, interactive workshops with drama, dance, storymaking.

LEE CARROLL
Sandpiper House 9 Yateman Close Bishop Sutton Bristol, BS39 5PU
Mobile: 07974 620 507
Email: gagman@blueyonder.co.uk
Web Site: www.leecarroll.com
Britain's brightest comedy star, available for after-dinner, cruising, cabaret and TV warm-ups. Unique, a clean comedy that's very funny!

CASHBACK
35 Belfast Quay, Irvine, Ayrshire KA12 8PR
01294 276203 Mob: 07518 374 201
Email: ric@richerrington.co.uk
Web: www.richerrington.co.uk/ cashback or www.myspace.com/cashbacktribute
Contact: Richard Herrington

CHARLIE THE CLOWN
Flat 4 Carleton House 122A Hillfield Avenue London N8 7DQ
Tel: 07808 732 390
Email: info@charlietheclown.co.uk
Web Site: www.charlietheclown.co.uk
Senior Personnel: Lawrence Anthony
Specialising in children's entertainment for all ages. Choice of characters includes a clown, pirate, wizzard and story-teller. Entertainment includes clown and magic shows, singing and dancing, balloon, modelling & story-telling.

CHILDREN LOVE STORIES
14 Leaside Mansions, Fortis Green, London N10 3EB
Tel: 020 8883 0034
Email: info@childrenlovestories.com
Web Site: www.childrenlovestories.com
Contact: Siaran Brooks
Story Telling for Children, touring the UK at festivals, art centres etc.

CHRISTALA ROSINA POETRY CONCERTS
38 Merrymeet, Woodmansterne, Near Banstead, Surrey SM7 3HT
Tel: 01737 371 761 No fax number
Email: christalarosina@hotmail.com
Web Site: www.christalarosina.co.uk
Poetry Concerts: Modern Romantic poet, Christala Rosina, performs her beautiful, passionate and inspiring poetry to classical and celtic accompaniment by harpist, Luisa-Maria Cordell. Christala also works with other instrumentalists.

CHUCKLE THE CLOWN AND HAZEL
8 St Nicholas Close, Richmond, North Yorkshire DL10 7SP
Tel: 01748 821 621
Email: chuckle@clownhotline.com
Web Site: www.jollygoodfun.co.uk / www.clownhotline.com
Contact: Hazel Wood
Clown Show, Punch & Judy, Balloon Decorating, Balloon Twisting, Circus Workshops, Craft Workshop, Puppets, Face Painting, Temporary Tatoos, Disco & Games, Parachute Display, Hand Bells, Giant Bubbles, Stiltwalking, Clown Training & Workshops.
Prepared to work anywhere in the UK or abroad. Very versatile, excellent references, totally reliable and loads of fun.

CIRCUS ALCHEMY
5 Beech Avenue, Rawmarsh, Rotherham, South Yorkshire S62 5HH
Tel: 01709 710 780 Fax: 01709 710 780
Email: albert@albertalchemy.com
Web Site: www.albertalchemy.com
Contact: Albert Alchemy
Fire-eating, escapology, stiltwalking, medieval jester. Magic for corporate, public and private functions.

CIRCUS BERZERCUS
41 Danes Road, Exeter, Devon EX4 4LS
Tel: 01392 669 873
Email: admin@circusberzercus.co.uk
Web Site: www.circusberzercus.co.uk
Contact: Judith Sturman (Adminstrator)
Fun-filled family entertainment for theatres, fundraising and events as well as corporate work. Top notch comedy show. Workshops available covering many circus skills including juggling, plate spinning, tightrope, unicycling, diabolo, stilt walking, clowning and presentation, Send for free brochure.

COCKNEY DOODLE DO
Primrose Cotage Church Road, Barling Magna, Southend-on-Sea Essex SS3 0LS
Tel: 0800 970 8527 Tel: 01702 219 680
Mob: 07850 400 489
Email: clan.morris@boltblue.com
Contact: Peter Morris

STEVE CRAM
S & K Consulting, Tranwell House, Tranwell Woods, Morpeth, Northumberland NE61 6AQ
Tel/Fax: 01670 503 266
After Dinner Speaking, Motivational Speaking, Openings, Corporate Videos & Promotions, Radio & TV Presenting and TV Commentary.

DANCE FACTORY LTD
5 Wey Close, Ash, Aldershot, Hampshire GU12 6LY
Tel: 01252 338 019
Contact: J Roe
Dance School/Mobile Disco - all types of music and dance instruction included.

ALAN DARK
15 Hurrell Court, Hurrell Road, Kingsbridge, Devon TQ7 1HT
Tel: 0870 442 3284 Fax: 01548 857 748
Mobile: 07970 605 336
Email: alan.magic@virgin.net
Web Site: www.alandark.com
Magician/Entertainer: Alan Dark

IVOR DEMBINA
Email: dembonet@aol.com
Web Site: www.thinkbeforeyoulaugh.com
London based Jewish writer, stand-up comedian and resident host of the Hampstead Comedy Club.

THE PETER DONEGAN BAND
21 Belsay Grove, Bedlington, Northumberland NE22 5YU
Mob: 07563 379 245
Email: peter-donegan@hotmail.com
Web Site: www.peterdonegan.com
Contact: Peter Donegan

STACEY-JANE DOUGLAS
Buttercup Music Projects, PO Box 20482 London SE11 5WQ
Tel: 020 7735 4085
Email: info@staceyjanedouglas.co.uk
Web Site: www.staceyjanedouglas.co.uk
Visionary award-winning singer and guitarist, Stacey-Jane Douglas, has established her name within the contemporary field of music. Versatile within the genre of jazz, soul, folk and pop, her range and lively improvision make Stacey-Jane's voice into a lead instrument. Stacey-Jane has performed with artistes such as Jacqueline Dankworth, Tony Perry, and Valerie Ehenre.

DRAGONSFIRE
9 Hillside Road, Ashtead, Surrey KT21 1RZ
Tel: 01372 277 703 Fax: 01372 278 406
Email: music@dragonsfire.uk.com
Web Site: www.dragonsfire.uk.com
Contact: Nigel Perona-Wright

DROP DEAD DIVAS
34 Skylark Walk, Chelmsford CM2 8BA
Tel: 01245 347 977
Email: jo.ramjane@btopenworld.com
Web Site: www.dropdeaddivas.com
Contacts: Jo Ramjane

PAUL DUMAS ENTERPRISES
12 Malvern Close, Banbury, Oxfordshire OX16 9EL
Tel: 01295 258 120
Email: pauldumas@supernet.com
Entertainer: Paul Hilton

ANDY EASTWOOD
PO Box 5004 Christchurch, Dorset BH23 5WD
Tel: 01425 275 830 Mob: 07950 454 365
Email: andy@andyeastwood.com
Web Site: www.andyeastwood.com
Contacts: Andy Eastwood

EL ADIVINO
46 Merceron Houses, Globe Road, London E2 0PA
Tel/Fax: 020 8980 3243
Mobile: 07748 276539
Email: jocelyn@eladivino.net
Web Site: www.eladivino.net
Contact: L J Bouic
Spanish Gypsy Band

RON ELLIS
37 Regent Court, Lord Street, Southport, Merseyside PR9 0QQ
Tel/Fax: 01704 535 556
Mobile: 07931 745613
Email: ronellis50@hotmail.com
Web Site: www.ronellis.co.uk
After Dinner Speaker, D.J., Crime Novelist, Property Tycoon, Singer-Songwriter.

ELVIS SHMELVIS
Tel: 01727 858 606
Email: elvis@shmelvis.com
Web Site: www.shmelvis.com
Contact: Sue & Martin
Please see full page advert in the Corporate Entertainment & Hospitality section for more details.

ETERNAL FLAME
38 Houlton Road, Poole, Dorset BH15 2LN
Tel: 01202 686 500
Email: eternal-flame@ntlworld.com
Web Site: www.eternal-flame.com
Contact: R.G. Mitchener
Cabaret style Pop band plus new one hour fully costumed and choreographed Abba tribute show.

JOHN EVANS STRONGMAN LTD
142 Ilkeston Road, Heanor, Derbyshire DE75 7BP
Mobile: 07831 210393
Email: john@headbalancer.com
Web Site: www.headbalancer.com
International Strongman and Head Balancer; can balance a car on his head. Ideal stunts for TV Commercials, Promotional Events or Main Arena. Holder of 29 World Records. Also in the "Who's Who".

FABBA
Comforts Farm, Pallance Road, Cowes, Isle of Wight PO31 8LS
Tel/Fax: 01983 299 919
Email: fabba@fabba.com

Web Site: www.fabba.com
Senior Personnel: A. Skelton, G.Annett
Production: Pete Lindup
Live Abba tribute band as seen on Night Fever and Style Challenge. New variety show with stars in their eyes guests.

LUCKY JIM FALLON
34 Borrowdale, Newcastle-upon-Tyne
NE7 1QG
Tel: 0191 417 9859
Mobile: 07788 907384
Country Music, Line Dancing & Listening. Singer/Songwriter

LIONEL FANTHORPE
48 Claude Road, Roath Cardiff CF24 3QA
Tel: 029 2049 8368 Mob: 07767 207 289
Fax: 029 2049 6832
Email: fanthorpe@aol.com
Web Site: www.lionel-fanthorpe.com
Contact: Lionel Fanthorpe

FAT OLD DAD
19 Mandeville Road, Marks Tey,
Colchester, Essex CO6 1XT
Tel: 01206 210 716 Fax: 01206 212 620
Email: fodband@aol.com
Web Site: www.fatolddat.com
Contact: Vicki Gibbs
60's Music Fun Band.

FAWLTY TOWERS - EDMOND WELLS AS JOHN CLEESE
2 The Maltings, Fenlane Beccles, Suffolk
NR34 9BT
Tel: 01485 570 945 Mob: 07767 863 415
Email: info@johncleese.co.uk
Web Site: www.johncleese.co.uk
Contact: Edmond Wells

STUART & ALAN FELL
88 Attimore Road, Welwyn Garden City,
Hertfordshire AL8 6LP
Tel: 01707 335 435
Email: tarothejester@yahoo.com
Web Site: www.tarothejester.co.uk
Jesters, jugglers, fire eaters, stiltwalkers. Taro the Jester is "Jester of the Year".

FLAT CAT BARN DANCE BAND
Oakleigh, Chitcombe Road, Broad Oak,
Rye, East Sussex TN31 6EU
Tel/Fax: 01424 882 046
Email: flatcatlangley@supanet.com
Web Site: www.flatcatband.com
Contact: Denis Langley
The Flat Cat Barn Dance Band, based in Hastings, are a well-established and accommodating band with a line-up comprising fiddle, concertina and guitars. An accordionist is also available if required. Their repertoire includes jigs, polkas, hornpipes and waltzes. A fun evening for all ages is guaranteed.

ANTHONY FREEMAN
99 Wellfield Road, Hatfield,
Hertfordshire AL10 0BY
Tel/Fax: 01707 266 769
Email: jollyjester@onetel.com
Web Site: www.thejollyjester.com
Jester/Stiltwalker, Circus Skills, Workshops, Magic. Works Worldwide. A traditional jester with 31 years experience. Performing magic, juggling, stilts and fire eating, worldwide.

FUNKI FEATHERS DANCE PRODUCTIONS LTD
Sycamore House, 8 Sycamore Road,
Bearwood Smethwick, West Midlands
B66 4NL
Tel/Fax: 0121 420 4396
Mobile: 07958 945701 / 2
Email: funkifeathers@telco4u.net
Web Site: www.funkifeathers.co.uk
Contact: Julie-Ann Phillips
Dance/Promotional Group.
Providing dancers, costumes and production shows.

FUNKY FACES
1 Station Road, Pershore, Worcestershire
WR10 1NQ
Tel: 01905 763362 Mob: 07967 483 878
Email: joanne.kite@tesco.net
Proprietor: Mrs Joanne Kite
Face Painting.

FUZZY THE CHILDRENS ENTERTAINER
25 Norburn, Bretton, Peterborough
Cambridgeshire PE3 8NR
Tel/Fax: 01733 334 495
Email: info@mrfuzzy.co.uk
Web Site: www.mrfuzzy.co.uk

TIM GENTLE MUSIC
PO Box 154 Stockton-on-Tees,
Cleveland TS20 1XJ
Tel: 01642 557 979 Fax: 01642 557 677
Mob: 07850 515 058
Email: timgentle@hotmail.com
Web Site: www.thehitmen.eu
Contact: Tim Gentle

GERRY THE FLUTE
23 Hughes Crescent, Garden City,
Chepstow, Monmouthshire NP16 5DY
Tel: 07703 491 420
Email: gerryflute@o2.co.uk
Gerry Game is "Gerry The Flute", Busking Novelty Music Act. Sax Cymbal, Mince Strell, Trainee Leprechaun. Help me out if you're "Game for a laugh!"

GORDON GLENN
5 The Oaks, Walton-le-Dale, Preston,
Lancashire PR5 4LT
Tel: 01772 62 6736
Accordionist with very wide TV, Radio and Light Entertainment, plus more serious music featured on Festival Concerts.

JON GORDON
4 Mount Rise, Leeds, West Yorkshire
LS17 7QR
Tel: 0113 237 0056
Email: jon@occasionalmagic.co.uk
Web Site: www.occasionalmagic.co.uk / www.magic4business.co.uk
Contact: Jon Gordon

THE GRAFFITI CLASSICS
37 Twickenham Road, Leytonstone,
London E11 4BN
Tel/Fax: 020 8556 5949
Mob: 07956 909981
Email: info@graffiticlassics.com
Web Site: www.graffiticlassics.com
The Group's unique character and style has developed a refreshing insight into the world of classical music, the principal aim being to entertain, educate and bring an interactive involvement to all audiences of all ages and abilities.

GRAND THEATRE OF LEMMINGS
38 High Street, Manningtree,
Essex CO11 1AJ
Tel: 01206 391 632 Fax: 01206 392 402
Email: lemmings@dircon.co.uk
Web Site: www.lemmings.dircon.co.uk
Contact: David Danzig
The Lemmings specialise in visual comedy producing a range of street theatre acts and a touring theatre show.

AMY GREAVES
516 Redditch Road, Kings Norton,
Birmingham B38 8LU
Tel: 0121 459 3426
Email: amy.greaves@wlv.ac.uk
I am an experienced dancer who can adapt to many roles and parts. I am also experienced in choreography and teaching dance.

STEVE (STREET) GRIFFIN
Lynwood Farm Lyne Lane, Lyne,
Chertsey, Surrey KT16 0AL
Tel: 01932 565 686 Fax: 01932 568 934
Mobile: 07860 711009
Email: monsteraction@compuserve.com
Web Site: www.stevegriffin.co.uk
Equity Stunt Co-ordinator and Performer.

EMLYN 'GRIFF' GRIFFITHS
Garfield Lodge 30 Garfield Road,
Paignton, Devon TQ4 6AX
Tel: 01803 557 764 Mob: 07831 198 875
Email: garfieldlodge1@aol.com

THE GRINNIGOGS/CELTARABIA
Arnold Carr Farm Wood House Lane
Arnold Hull East Yorkshire HU11 5HX
Tel: 01964 562 073

Email: grinnigogs@pop3.poptel.org.uk
Web: www.historicalentertainers.co.uk
Contacts: Quentin Budworth, Amanda Lowe
Medieval Music and Street Theatre. Historical and themed entertainers. Archaic instruments - Modern technology.

R HARVEY CLASSICAL GUITAR
12 Dene Close, London SE4 2HB
Tel: 020 7639 6824
Email: Richard1960harve@aol.com

HATRICK AND FRIENDS
Laurieston Hall, Castle Douglas, Kirkcudbrightshire DG7 2NB Scotland
Tel: 01644 450 683
Email: johnw@lauriestonhall.demon.co.uk
Web Site: www.hatrickandfriends.co.uk
Contact: John Wheeler
Street Theatre, Circus & Silent Comedy Workshops and Storytelling.

HELENA HATSTAND
Special Skills Performer for Events Stilt Dancing/Fire/Whips/Juggling/Sparks
39 Old Church Road, Stepney, London E1 0QB
Tel/Fax: 020 7791 2541
Mobile: 07748 005839
Email: helenahatstand@btopenworld.com
Web Site: www.hatstandcircus.co.uk

HERE BE DRAGONS
14 Leaside Mansions Fortis Green, London N10 3EB
Tel: 020 8883 0034 Mobile: 07803 773160
Email: mike@herebedragons.info
Web Site: www.herebedragons.info
Contact: Mike Brook
Storyteller: Siaran Brooks
Website: www.childrenlovestories.com
Email: siaran@childrenlovestories.com
Band playing ' wild celtic music from Wales'. Mainly Festival Band.

HILARY THACKER
8 Bellevue Terrace, Edinburgh, Mid Lothian, EH7 4DT Scotland
Tel: 0131 556 7976
Email: hilary@hilarysbazaar.com
Web Site: www.hilarysbazaar.com
Belly Dancer

HOUGHTON WEAVERS (MANAGEMENT) LTD
22 Wingates Lane, Westhoughton, Bolton BL5 3LP
Tel: 01942 813 033
Email: hweavers@aol.com
Web Site: www.houghtonweavers.com
Senior Personnel: Phil McGuiver

IAN AND FRIENDS
35 Hibernia Point, Wolvercote Road, London SE2 9TL
Tel/Fax: 020 8310 4376 Mobile: 07860 183471
Email: info@ianandfriends.co.uk
Web Site: www.gingernutt.com
Contact: Ian Thom
Speciality Act. Puppets and characters including Gingernutt the Clown, Tofi-Stilt Clown and Bigwig the Ten Foot Magician.

GUY INGLE
Inglenock 15 Hawthorn Close, Ampthill, Bedford MK45 2TN
Tel: 01525 402 475-01525 753670
Mobile: 07811 364328
Email: info@princecharles.co.uk
Web Site: wwww.princecharles.co.uk / www.look-a-like.co.uk
Prince Charles Lookalike. Speaker
Guy Ingle "The Knoll" 12, Flithick Rd Ampt Hill.

INSTANT SUNSHINE
9 Ashdown Road, Epsom, Surrey KT17 3PL
Tel: 01372 720 727
Email: instantsunshine@christiehouse.demon.co.uk
Web Site: www.instantsunshine.co.uk
Contact: Peter Christie

ISRAEL FOLK DANCE INSTITUTE (ORANIM)
Balfour House, 741 High Road, London N12 0BQ
Tel/Fax: 020 8446 6427
Email: info@ifdiuk.org
Web Site: www.ifdiuk.org
Project Manager: Charlotte Casselson

ALAN JAMES
227 Corporation Road, Grimsby, North East Lincolnshire DN31 2PZ
Tel: 01472 360 619
Mobile: 07803 595941
Email: alanjames76@hotmail.com
Alan James tribute to John Lennon and Chris de Burgh. Alan finally got the seal of approval when he was personally invited onto the stage by Chris de Burgh to sing with him during his concert at Harewood House, Yorkshire, August 1998 and at Bridgewater Hall, Manchester in July 1999. Alan has also appeared on ITV's, Television series, "The Lookalikes".

ANDREW JAMES
Tel: 07880 557 428
Email: andrew.rafferty@ntlworld.com
Web Site: www.easy-lover.co.uk / www.illinoisbluesbrothers.com
Contact: Andew James

LEEANN JAMES
3 Gilbert House Old Coach Road, Runcorn, Cheshire WA7 1NJ
Tel: 07885 084 223
Email: leejay1@tiscali.co.uk
Web Site: www.leeannjames.com
Contact: Leeann James

THE MIKE JAMES SOUND & SINGERS
26 Hillcrest Road, Offerton, Stockport, Cheshire SK2 5QL
Tel: 0161 456 0067
Mobile: 07889 728180
Email: alanarnison@supanet.com
Web Site: www.mikejamessound.co.uk
International film/TV and recording artistes.

THE JIVE ACES
Saint Hill Manor East Grinstead West Sussex RH19 4JY
Tel/Fax: 01342 300 075
Mobile: 07793 122 646
Email: bookings@jiveaces.com
Web Site: www.jiveaces.com
Manager: Peter Howell
Publicist: Grazia Clarkson
Promotions Manager: Alex Douglas
The UK's No1 Jive & Swing Band
A group of lads from London were drawn together by their love for a style and music that outclassed anything around. The music was hot jive that had the beat, energy and enthusiasm of Rock'n'Roll and the fun and rhythm of big band swing all rolled into one. The Jive Aces' unique sound comes from a combination of their own original tunes in true swing style as well as fresh arrangements of songs from the swing era.

JIVING LINDY HOPPERS
c/o JLA (Jeremy Lee Associates)
80 Great Portland Street, London W1W 7NW
Tel: 020 7907 2800
Email: talk@jla.co.uk, suzypayne@jla.co.uk
Web Site: www.jla.co.uk
ADMINISTRATION:
Authentic Jazz Dance group managed by Jeremy Lee Associates.
Admin: Suzy Payne

JOLLY JESTERS
99 Wellfield Road, Hatfield, Hertfordshire AL10 0BY
Tel/Fax: 01707 266 769
Email: jollyjester@onetel.com
Web Site: www.thejollyjester.com
Contact: Robert Freeman
In a colourful costume, the Jolly Jester presents Magic, Juggling, Period Paperfolding, Traditional Wooden Stilts and Fire Eating. All in his own unique humourous style (As seen on TV !!) This can be in the form of a set act or meet & greet.

JON PICKARD
Inschfield, Clawdd Lane, New Radnor,

Presteigne, Powys LD8 2TU
Tel: 01544 350 275
Mobile: 07919 030 579
Email: root@jonpickard.co.uk
Web Site: www.jonpickard.co.uk
Contact: Jon Pickard
Provides a mix of Spanish / Classical / Flamenco / South American Solo Guitar Music. More than 20 years professional experience. Available for all live events including Corporate functions, Weddings, Formal Recitals etc., also Studio recording sessions. Usually based around Bristol/Bath but will travel anywhere, please ask re travel costs etc.
See website for full details.

LARRY JONES
Castle House 86 Teehey Lane, Wirral, Merseyside CH63 8QU
Tel: 0151 608 8503 Mob: 07851 023695
Email: handl.jones@btconnect.com
Contact: Larry Jones

JUMA STEEL BAND
14 Gordon Road, London E15 2DD
Tel: 020 8556 0926 Fax: 020 8539 3813
Mobile: 07710 420682
Email: majuentertain@aol.com
Web Site: www.jumaentertain.co.uk
Contact: Junior or Marcella Bailey
Steel Band.

KERNEL MARVO
1 Marsh-Farm Cottages, Wolferton, King's Lynn, Norfolk PE31 6HB
Tel: 01485 543 038
Web Site: www.kernelmarvo.co.uk
Contact: Keith Hodson
Clowning, Punch & Judy, Stilt walking, Face Painting and Magic.

JOHN KETTLEY
Television/Radio Weather Presenter
Weatherview House, 50 Beaumont Way, Hazlemere, High Wycombe, Buckinghamshire HP15 7BE
Tel: 01494 715 115 Fax: 01494 715 115
Email: kettley@britishweatherservices.co.uk
Web: www.britishweatherservices.co.uk
Contact: Jim Dale

BARRY KNIGHT
Amberley Cottage, 25 Station Road, North Mymms, Hatfield, Hertfordshire AL9 7PQ
Tel: 01707 260 408
Email: bkflyhigh@yahoo.com / bskuk@yahoo.com
Conductor and Producer.

LADIES OF ROCK
C/O 15 Yew Tree Court Alsager Cheshire ST7 2YQ
Tel: 01270 883 080 Mob: 07710 784 913
Email: tinacher@paularandell.com
Web Site: www.paularandell.com
Contact: Paula Randell

LAWRENSON AND BARNARD
6 Holne Chase, Morden Surrey SM4 5QB
Tel/Fax: 07958 356 754
Email: mattbarnard@hotmail.com
Web Site: www.barnard2.freeserve.co.uk
Senior Personnel: Matt Barnard
Comedy variety act - plate manipulation, sand dance, flaming feet, tap dancing.

CHRIS LEE
79 School Lane, Illingworth, Halifax, West Yorkshire HX2 9QJ
Tel/Fax: 01422 240 059 Mobile: 07767 302605
Email: chrisleetrance@hotmail.com
Web Site: www.chrisleetrance.com
International Stage Hypnotist.

RICARDO LEON
2 Orchard Road, South Croydon, Surrey CR2 9LU
Tel: 020 8651 3462
Email: ricardo@auragraph.fsnet.co.uk
Web Site: www.auragraph.co.uk
Contact: Ricardo Leon
Psychic demonstrator.

BRIAN LLEWELLYN
Llewellyn for Fun
287 North Road, Darlington, County Durham DL1 2JS
Tel/Fax: 01325 288 338
Email: llewellyn@ntlworld.com
Web Site: www.llewellyn4fun.com
Punch & Judy Show.

LONDON CHINESE ACROBATICS
118 Albany Road, Leighton Buzzard, Bedfordshire LU7 1NS
Tel: 01525 633 944 Fax: 01525 370 642
Email: chineseacrobatic@hotmail.com
Web Site: www.chinesedance-acrobatic.co.uk
Contact: Jiang

SHELLEY LOZANO
9 Barnes Road, Bitterne, Southampton, Hampshire SO19 5FG
Tel/Fax: 023 8044 2783 Mobile: 07747 804 447
Email: shellylozano@talktalk.net
Web Site: www.bcc.talktalk.net
After dinner speaker on big cat conservation or belly dance. Fire-eater, Limbo dancer, Belly Dancer, DJ and tv presenter.

MAGIC CATHERINE
4 Tamarind Court 75 Deepcut Bridge Road Camberley, Surrey GU16 6QP
Tel: 01252 837 885 Mob: 07770 227 812
Email: catherine@magicentertainment.co.uk
Web Site: www.magicentertainment.co.uk
Contact: Catherine

MAGIC MOMENTS
127 Carterhatch Road, Enfield, Middlesex EN3 5LX
Tel: 020 8245 4348 Fax: 07092 033 538
Email: magicmoments@partyweb.co.uk
Web Site: www.partyweb.co.uk/act/magicmoments
Contacts: Charlie Valentino
Colourful comedy magic/juggling with live bunny rabbit suitable for private shows as well as public mix & mingle.

THE MAGIC OF SHAHID MALIK
3 Selborne Villas, North Park Road, Heaton, Bradford, West Yorkshire BD9 4NN
Tel: 01274 499 065 Fax: 01274 490 179
Email: shahid@shahidmalik.co.uk
Web Site: www.shahidmalik.co.uk
Contact: Shahid Malik
International Magician and Illusionist.

CRAIG MCMURDO
The Foundry 100/2 Constitution Street, Edinburgh, Mid Lothian EH6 6AW Scotland
Tel: 08700 433 791 Fax: 0131 476 2259
Email: mail@craigmcmurdo.com
Web Site: www.craigmcmurdo.com
Singer/Voice Over Artiste/Actor.

MR METHANE!
c/o BO Productions, PO Box 201, Macclesfield, Cheshire SK11 7BS
Tel/Fax: 01625 424 137
Email: bookings@mrmethane.com
Web Site: www.mrmethane.com
Contacts: Barrie Barlow, Paul Oldfield
Anal Madness from the Man with the Rumbling Ring - Professional Flatulist capable of Controlled Anal Voicing.

MICK'S ENTERTAINMENTS
Oldwell House, Broad End Road, Walsoken, Wisbech, Cambridgeshire PE14 7BQ
Tel/Fax: 01945 461 383
Email: mick@unclemicks.co.uk
Web Site: www.unclemicks.co.uk
Uncle Mick Children's Entertainer, Punch and Judy, Magic Ventriloquism, Funfair, Rides and Stalls.

PETER MOORE
18 College Gardens, London SW17 7UG
Tel: 020 8767 2103 Mobile: 0585 113825
Email: peter@londontowncrier.com
Web Site: www.londonstowncrier.co.uk
Town Crier to the Mayor of London and Toastmaster and master of Ceremonies.

PETER MORRIS
Primrose Cottage 11 Church Road,

Barling Magna, Southend-on-Sea Essex SS3 0LS
Tel: 0800 970 8527 Tel: 01702 219 680
Mob: 07850 400 489
Email: peter.clan.morris@gmail.com
Contact: Peter Morris

MR SKETCHUM'S CARICATURES
69 Egerton Road, London N16 6UE
Mobile: 07719 262 736
Email: alfie@sketchum.co.uk
Web Site: www.sketchum.co.uk
Contact: Alfie Deliss
Alfie Deliss, also known as Mr Sketchum, a product of Chelsea College of Art available to sketch at all kinds of corporate and private events. See the website for lots of examples of 'live' sketches and more ...

MR ZEN
1 Ferniehill Street, Edinburgh, Mid Lothian EH17 7BE Scotland
Tel/Fax: 0131 664 4732
Hypnotist.

MY LITTLE MAKEOVER PARTY
Lyndhurst, 1 Station Road, Pershore, Worcestershire WR10 1NQ
Mob: 07967 483 878
Email: joanne.kite@tesco.net

ALAN MYATT
75 Victoria Street, Gloucester GL1 4EP
Tel/Fax: 01452 307 958 Mobile: 07973 472896
Email: alanmyatt@blueyonder.co.uk
Web Site: www.thememan.co.uk
Toast Master/Town Crier and Henry VIII Lookalike.

NATIONAL FESTIVAL CIRCUS
Tober House, PO Box 2, Brierley Hill, West Midlands DY5 3LR
Tel: 01384 423 496
Email: clownsgalore123@AOL.com
Web: www.nationalfestivalcircus.co.uk

NATIONAL YOUTH JAZZ ORCHESTRA
2nd Floor, 5 Vigo Street, London W1S 3HD
Tel: 020 7494 1733
Email: info@nyjo.org.uk
Web Site: www.NYJO.org.uk
Executive Chairman: Nigel Tully
Executive Director: Dr. Fiona Ord-Shrimpton

JIM NAYLOR
The Cossack, Houghton Road, Stockbridge, Hampshire SO20 6LE
Tel: 01264 810 956
Email: jimnaylorcartoons@zoom.co.uk
Web Site: www.cartoonists.co.uk/naylor or www.ccgb.org.uk
Caricaturist and Cartoonist.
Available for Corporate Functions, Parties, Balls and Commissioned Portraits.
Caricatures for The Boardroom, Individual or Group as a gift or presentation, in black & white or colour.
Ring Jim Naylor on 01264 810 956 for a free client list, samples, letters of recommendation or just to pick his brains as to how you can make best use of his talents.

NEVER 4 GET
14 Pavilion Court Northlands Road Southampton SO15 2NN
Tel: 02380 829 385 Mob: 07814 454 796
Email: lee@never4getmusic.com
Web Site: www.never4getmusic.com
Contact: Lee Cornick

NICK ROSS
c/o Rachel Goodwin, PO Box 999, London W2 4XT
Tel: 020 7243 1325 Fax: 020 7792 9200
Mobile: 07966 491 256
Email: nickross@lineone.net
Web Site: www.nickross.com
Contact: Rachel Goodwin
Presenter Crimewatch (since 1984). Credits include Call Nick Ross, Westminster With Nick Ross, The Commission, A Week In Politics, Watchdog, Newsnight, breakfast TV, Man Alive, World at One, The World Tonight, documentaries, debates, chat shows and quizzes. Conference chairman and facilitator. President, trustee, ambassador of over a dozen charities inc UK Stem Cell Foundation.

PADDY THE CLOWN
39 Elm Street, Roath, Cardiff, South Glamorgan CF24 3QS Wales
Tel: 029 2048 6550
Email: paddy@paddytheclown.com
Web Site: www.paddytheclown.com
Contact: Paddy Faulkner
Touring theatres nationwide. Also available for private functions, outdoor events and promotions. International Award Winning Show.

THE PALAZZO STRING QUARTET
33 Dryden Court, Renfrew Road, Kennington, London SE11 4NH
Tel: 020 7735 2160 Mobile: 07941 909314
Email: mphall@bigfoot.com
Contact: Michael Hall
This highly experienced and recorded string quartet offers the discerning client an unusually wide variety of background music for special occasions.

R. PARKER ENTERPRISES
5 Pennyford Close, Brockhill, Redditch, Worcestershire B97 6TW
Tel/Fax: 01527 62463 Mobile: 07802 605095
Email: rikip@rpe1.co.uk
Web Site: www.rpe1.co.uk
Compere, DJ and freelance Event Manager

PASADENA ROOF ORCHESTRA LTD
Priors, 178 Hall Lane, Upminster, Essex RM14 1AT
Email: info@pasadena-roof-orchestra.com
Web: www.pasadena-roof-orchestra.com
Contact: David Jones
Head Office Contact (Munich): Marcus Meyer
Professional Orchestra (11 piece). 1920's & 1930's Jazz and Dance Music.
UK Booking Management: Liz Biddle, Upbeat Management. Tel: 020 8668 3332 Fax: 020 8668 3922

GRAEME E PEARSON AND THE MUTINEERS
6 Lawson Crescent, South Queensferry, West Lothian EH30 9JE Scotland
Tel: 0131 331 1617
Mobile: 07817 362 171
Email: mutiny@onetel.com
Web Site: www.mutineers.com
Contact: Graeme E Pearson
Graeme E Pearson is a solo performer (guitar/banjo/vocals) and The Mutineers play as a duo, trio, four-piece or in any other permutation to suit the occasion. Traditional and contempory songs and entertainment - guitar, bajo, moothy.

PICTURE BOX
44 Neville Drive, Thornton-Cleveleys, Lancashire FY5 5EZ
Tel/Fax: 01253 828 391
Email: picture.box@virgin.net
Contact: David Whittle: Manager
Painter of Murals.

PLANET 80S
PO Box 441 Ashford, Kent TN23 9EL
Tel: 07799 262 068
Email: planet80s@hotmail.co.uk
Web Site: www.planet80s.webs.com
Contacts : Phil Marks

THE POLICE CHIEFS
20 Spencer Drive, Midsomer Norton, Radstock BA3 2DN
Tel: 07974 690 181
Email: bullit7@live.co.uk
Web Site: www.myspace.com/thepolicechiefs
Contact: Olly Wise

PREMIER CRU
The 'Leys', Chorleywood Road, Chorleywood, Hertfordshire WD3 4ER
Tel: 01923 771 791 Fax: 01923 771 091

Mobile: 07973 818622
Email: premiercru.theband@virgin.net
Web Site: www.premiercru-theband.com
Contact: Del Bingley, Linda Bingley
Function Band available for weddings, corporate events, private parties, awards evenings, etc. 6-15 piece.

PROFESSOR CRUMP
8 St Marks Road, London W7 2PW
Tel/Fax: 020 8566 1575
Mob: 07966 233 220
Email: paul@professorcrump.co.uk
Web Site: www.professorcrump.co.uk
Contact: Paul Goddard
Clown, Stilt, Character Entertainer plus Children's Entertainment.

PROFESSOR MYSTRAL'S JUVENILE OMNIBUS
65 Penylan Road, Cardiff, CF23 5HZ Wales
Tel: 029 2048 5544
Mobile: 07855 515350
Web Site: www.professormystral.co.uk
Proprietor: Frank Turvey
Children's/family entertainment under the names of Professor Mystral and Mister Magipatch.

BARBARA RAY
44 Alderson Drive, Bennetthorpe, Doncaster, South Yorkshire DN2 6BY
Tel: 01302 320 717 / 01262 468 551
Mob: 07766 196 621
Email: babs@barbara-ray.co.uk
Web Site: www.barbararay.co.uk
Comedy Ventriloquist/Puppets for all ages.

RHUBARB THE CLOWN
72 Hillside Road, London N15 6NB
Tel: 020 8800 5009 Mob: 07968 969 846
Email: rhubarbtheclown@onetel.com
Web Site: www.rhubarbtheclown.co.uk
With over 5000 perfomances in over a dozen countries, Rhubarb the Clown has a spectacular 45 minute show using uni-cycling (ordinary, 5' & 6'), juggling (including with fire), mime, magic, nose-flute and lots of silly business suitable for all ages and cultures in any venue. Accessible to special needs and the deaf, Also performs "clowning around" and as Rhubarb the Jester.

NICK RICHMOND
16 Skeldale Grove, Darlington, County Durham DL3 0GW
Tel: 01325 352 341
Mobile: 07708 177 007
Email: 007@seanconnerylookalike.com
Web: www.seanconnerylookalike.com
Sean Connery Lookalike

RICKY LOPEZ RATPACK AND SWING SHOW
Tel: 01727 858 606
Email: ricky@rickylopezratpack.com
Web Site: www.rickylopezratpack.com
Contact: Sue & Martin
Please see full page advert in the Corporate Entertainment & Hospitality section for more details.

THE ROLLIN STONED
438 Archway Road, Highgate
London N6 4JH
Tel: 0870 766 9054 Fax: 020 8374 2127
Mob: 07720 046 886
Email: enquiries@rollinstoned.com
Web Site: www.rollinstoned.com
A typical two hour show includes not only all the classic crowd pleasing hits, but is spiced with enough eclectic selections from the deeper recesses of Stones Album archives to satisfy the most demanding of 'Buffs', all performed with the same vibrantly authentic attack and raw energy that characterised the original Stones shows in their prime.
With a Rollin Stoned show, the costumes are shamelessly camp gaudy and fab, the instruments genuinely vintage and the wit irreverent.

ROUND MIDNIGHT LTD
Unit 8, 14-20 George Street, Moseley, Birmingham B12 9RG
Tel/Fax: 0121 440 8188
Email: rmtheatre@yahoo.com
Web Site: www.roundmidnight.org.uk
Director: C. Downes

GARY RYAN - NEIL DIAMOND TRIBUTE
135 Hughes Street, Bolton BL1 3EZ
Tel: 07919 485 495
Email: g.ryan2@btinternet.com
Web Site: www.neildiamond-tribute.com
Contact: Gary Ryan

SALVO THE CLOWN
(Founder of The Annual Clowns Directory)
13 Second Avenue, Kingsleigh Park, Thundersley, Essex SS7 3QD
Tel: 01268 745 791
Email: salvo@annualclownsdirectory.com
Web: www.annualclownsdirectory.com
Contact: Salvo

SANDOW CLOWNS
59 Thoresby Close, Bridlington, East Yorkshire YO16 7EN
Tel: 01262 671 492 Fax: 01262 675 543
Mob 1: 07969 933 236
Mob 2 :07964 274 186
Email: fossett@supanet.com
Web Site: www.sandowclowns.co.uk
Contact: Tom Bratby or Sheila Bratby
Clown show "circus party" on stage, in the round, schools, civic venues, galas.

SARA'S FACE PAINTING AND BALLOON MODELLING
53 Coombelands, Royston, Hertfordshire SG8 7DW
Tel: 01763 244 255 Mobile: 07767 814479
Email: saras.facepainting@ntlworld.com
Contact: Sara Willis-Wright
No job too big or too small!

CHRIS SMITH AND THE STRING OF PEARLS
13 Letchmore Road, Radlett, Hertfordshire WD7 8HU
Tel: 01923 854 363
Email: info@stringofpearls.co.uk
Web Site: www.stringofpearls.co.uk
Contact: Chris Smith
Chris Smith and the String of Pearls, Britain's number one big party band. Playing today's mega pop hits of M People, Michael Jackson, Weather Girls, Tom Jones etc. Plus Frank Sinatra, Glenn Miller. Through the Swinging 60's with James Last.

SNAKEY SUE
Tel: 020 8989 2560 Fax: 020 8989 2838
Email: sue@snakeysue.com
Web Site: www.snakeysue.com
Snakes, Belly Dancer, Tarot Reader.

SPECTRAL PRODUCTIONS
PO Box 3356, Brighton, East Sussex DN2 0DP
Tel: 0870 750 0679 Mobile: 07989 568321 / 07977 270724
Email: info@spectralproductions.com
Web Site: www.spectralproductions.com
Contact: Mark Bolwell
Ultraviolet Stage Shows, interactive performance, stilts, creative commissions, art and craft workshops.

SPENCER'S NIGHTHAWKS ORCHESTRA
21 Fulwoods Drive Leadenhall Milton Keynes MK6 5LA
Tel: 01797 223 691
Mobile: 07836 258 974
Email: spencers.nighthawks@virgin.net
Contact: Carl Spencer
Authentic ragtime to swing 8-piece band, also straight dance, Dixieland, New Orleans etc. TV, Radio, Records. Smaller outfits also available.

PATRICIA SPERO
Oaks Farm Vicarage Lane Chigwell Essex IG7 6LT
Email: patricia.spero@btinternet.com
Web: www.impulse-music.co.uk/spero.htm
Contacts: Patricia Spero

SPOT ON! CARICATURES
PO Box 6235, Leicester LE1 1AA

Tel: 0845 120 320
Mobile: 07793 677 794
Email: george@caricatures-uk.com
Web Site: www.caricatures-uk.com
Contact: George Williams
'TV Times' artiste George - The most off the cuff, dynamic, published Walkabout Caricaturist in the UK, ideal entertainment for Corporate functions, Weddings and Balls. Drawing one every 5 minutes, George turns caricaturing into a spectacle while drawing a crowd, creating a unique buzz and breaking the ice! Guaranteed quality with an individual edge!!

SAMANTHA STARR
80 Coronation Road, Wolverhampton
Heath Town WV10 0QH
Tel: 01902 659 769 Mob: 07812 998 754
Email: sammystarr@blueyonder.co.uk
Web Site: www.samanthastarr.co.uk
Contact : Samantha Starr

STATUS CYMBAL
The Different String Quartet
27 Kendal Steps, St George's Fields, London N2 9EA
Tel: 020 7402 7860 Fax: 020 7402 7172
Mobile: 07836 294833
Email: quartet@status-cymbal.co.uk
Web Site: www.status-cymbal.co.uk
Contact: Paul Appleyard
String quartet with a unique library of own arrangements - Vivaldi to The Verve.

BOBBY SUMMERS
69A Bure Lane, Christchurch, Dorset BH23 4DL
Tel: 01425 277 226 Mob: 07799 214 460
Fax: 01425 279 320
Contact: Bobby Summers

SUNBURST STORY THEATRE
23 Kings Road, Laindon,
Essex SS15 4AB
Tel/Fax: 01268 416 195
Email: charlie@crickcrack.com
Web Site: www.crickcrack.com
Crickcracking storytelling with music from Charlie Wilson. Lively, colourful and interactive. For children and family audiences. Voice overs also undertaken.

THE ILLINOIS BLUES BROTHERS
Tel: 07880 557 428
Email: andrew.rafferty@ntlworld.com
Web: www.theIllinoisbluesbrothers.com
Contact: Andrew Rafferty

THEM PEOPLE
35 Pomfret Ave Luton LU2 0JJ
Proprietor: Wanda Terrelonge
The UK's No.1 tribute to Heather Small and M-People. Truly a "sight for sore eyes".

TIGGER BLAKE
Tel: 01909 478 993 Mob: 07816 614 805
Email: Mssunnydale@aol.com
Contact: Sunny Dale

TOASTMASTER PAUL DEACON
Fellow of the National Association of Toastmasters
Chantry, Broomfield Hill, Great Missenden, Buckinghamshire HP16 9HT
Tel: 01494 862 868
Email: toastmaster@pauldeacon.com
Web Site: www.pauldeacon.com
Toastmaster: Paul Deacon
International Toastmaster and Master of Ceremonies.

TRIANGLE
c/o The Herbert, Jordan Well, Coventry, West Midlands CV1 5QP
Mgt: 02476 785 170 Mktg: 07899 872 215
Email: info@triangletheatre.co.uk
Web Site: www.triangletheatre.co.uk
Performance art, music, film and cabaret.
Artistic Directors: Richard Talbot and Carran Waterfield.
Two full-time staff, average 80 performances per year.
Current repertoire: The Whissell and Williams Training Camp
Chico Talks and The Singing Nun.
Policy: Live performances, music, film and video. Full workshop programme.
Museum Theatre.
Touring: 2-week residencies, 4-week tribute tours, available all year. Most venues considered. Average audience: 100.

TRIBUTE TO BUDDY HOLLY
High House Farm Asheldham, Southminster, Essex CM0 7NX
Tel: 01621 778 886 Mob: 07889 426 343
Email: marcusejrobinson@hotmail.com
Contact: Marc Robinson

ALEX TSANDER
Tel: 0117 907 7064 Mobile: 0771 9949554
Email: alex@summitother.co.uk
Hypnotist: "I Can't Believe It's Not Hypnosis". Only Hypnotist to always declare that there is no such thing as hypnosis. About 1000 shows since 1993.

THE CHRIS TURNER BAND
29 Hackton Lane, Hornchurch, Essex RM12 6PH
Tel: 01708 508 149
Email: amelia.reynolds@gmail.com
Contact: Amelia Reynolds
4 piece - 8 piece function band playing all styles of music to suit your event.

UKOM
3 Chapel Close, Humbleton, Hull East Yorkshire HU11 4NP
Tel: 01964 670 162 Mob: 07912 421 876
Email: steve@elvislovingyou.com
Web Site: www.elvislovingyou.com
Contact: Steve Caprice

VAN BUREN
41 High Street, Silverdale, Newcastle-under-Lyme, Staffordshire ST5 6NG
Tel: 01782 611 954
Email: avanburen@aol.com
Web Site: www.vanburen.org.uk
Contact: Andrew Van Buren
Specialising in Cabaret, TV, Outdoor shows, Theatre, Magic, Juggling, Unicycling, Plate Spinning and Illusion.

JOHN WHEELER
Laurieston Hall, Castle Douglas, Kirkcudbrightshire DG7 2NB Scotland
Tel: 01644 450 683
Email: johnw@lauriestonhall.demon.co.uk
Web: www.johnwheelerstoryteller.co.uk
Storyteller

WINSTON THE SINGING FARMER
Nethergate Farm Guestwick, Dereham, Norfolk NR20 5QR
Tel: 07748 186 489
Email: winston@singingfarmer.co.uk
Web Site: www.singingfarmer.co.uk
Contact: Winson

PAUL ZENON
Tel: 07721 610 364
Email: gigs@paulzenon.com
Web Site: www.paulzenon.com
Personal Assistant: Sue Reed (Stranger Media Limited)
Comedian, Magician and Presenter.

ZOOT
Shows,Walkabout, Meet and Greet, Circus Workshops Juggling, Unicycling, Stilts, Fire, Baloons
7 Gatefield Road, Sheffield S7 1RD
Tel: 0114 255 6289
Mobile: 07785 306812
Email: tim@zootstuff.f9.co.uk
Contact: Tim Byrom
Circus Performance and Street Theatre.

Magicians & Illusionists

AKA ZANE
29 Pegwell Avenue, Ramsgate, Kent CT11 0NL
Tel/Fax: 01843 850 036 Email: magic_zane@btinternet.com
Web Site: www.zanesmagicshop.com
Contact: Shane Robinson
Magic, Illusion, Cabaret and Close-up Magic.

SEAN ALEXANDER
32 Dunnock Drive Costessey Norwich NR8 5FF
Tel: 01603 746706 Mob: 07765 881894
Email: sean@seanalexandermagic.com
Web Site: www.seanalexandermagic.com
Contact: Sean Alexander
Please see full page ad within the Magicians & Illusionists section

MARK ANDREWS ENTERTAINMENTS
57 William Bristow Road, Coventry, Warwickshire CV3 5LP
Tel: 024 7650 2011 Email: mark@markandrews.co.uk
Web Site: www.markandrews.co.uk
Proprietor: Mark Andrews
Professional entertainment for children comedy magic shows. Traditional Punch & Judy shows.

AURORA'S CARNIVAL
23 Sunningdale Avenue Marlpool Heanor Derbyshire DE75 7BS
Tel: 01773 530093 Mob: 07710 788 671
Email: enquiries@aurorascarnival.co.uk
Web Site: www.aurorascarnival.co.uk
Contact: Chris Ehrenzeller
General entertainment agency.

MIKE AUSTIN
See Artiste Index & Essex Entertainments Listings

RICHARD BALLINGER - COMEDY MAGICIAN
Applemead 109 Severn Road, Weston-super-Mare, Avon BS23 1DS
Tel: 01934 418 184 Mobile: 07979 600797 Email: magic@richard-ballinger.co.uk
Web Site: www.richard-ballinger.co.uk
Comedy & Magic - Richard 1st designed to meet all needs. Any age - Any venue. Comedy, close-up magic. Corporate Events. Phone Richard for free information pack.

BAN BUREN & CO
See Artistes Index & Tony West Agency listing.

BERNIE
35 Premier Avenue, Ashbourne, Derbyshire DE6 1LH
Tel: 01335 344 523 Mob: 07931 346296
Email: magic@yourfingertips.co.uk
Web: www.magicatyourfingertips.co.uk
Contact: Bernie Pedley
Magical Entertainer - Award winning close-up magician, children's entertainer, inc.close-up magic featured on BBC "Live & Kicking".

BIG HAND PEOPLE LTD
PO Box 409, Betchworth
Surrey RH3 7YA
Tel: 01737 844 044 Fax: 01737 843 717
Email: alex@bighandpeople.co.uk
Web Site: www.bighandpeople.co.uk
Director: Alex Hogg
General entertainment agency.

CLIFFORD BRADLEY
See Artiste Index & Personal Appearances Listing

JAMES BRANDON
Cherry Tree House, 1 Cherry Tree Lane, Elsecar, South Yorkshire S74 8DG
Tel: 01226 742 886
Email: info@illusionist.uk.com
Web Site: www.illusionist.uk.com
James Brandon is one of the UK's most versatile performers, having worked in almost every area of the entertainment business. From cruise ships to theatres, cabaret to pantomime and countless appearances in the corporate field, James Brandon has created his own special brand of magic and illusion both at home and abroad.

THE JAMES BRANDON COMPANY
Cherry Tree House, 1 Cherry Tree Street,, Elsecar, South Yorkshire S74 8DG
Tel: 01226 742 886
Email: info@jamesbrandon.co.uk
Web Site: www.jamesbrandon.co.uk
Managing Director: James Brandon
Production and agency specialising in pantomime, tribute and variety shows, illusion, design and special effects. Radio, Media and road shows. Specialist in corporate events and one-off bespoke entertainments.

JACK BRYCE
26 Lake View Close, Holly Park Plymouth Devon PL5 4LX
Tel: 01752 219 928 Mob: 07775 978 783
Email: jbmagic@tiscali.co.uk or magic@jackbryce.co.uk
Contact: Jack Bryce

TERRY BURGESS
See Artiste Index, 1st Choice Speakers Ltd & Stardust Entertainments Agency Listings.

CARICATURES & MAGIC
14 Mayfield Place, Brunswick Green, Wideopen, Newcastle-upon-Tyne, Tyne and Wear NE13 7HY
Tel: 0191 236 3152 Mobile: 07802 748 579 Email: info@paullytton.com
Caricaturist, Paul Slattery & Magician, Paul Lytton
An unbeatable reputation with a complimentary blend of caricatures and magic for all your corporate entertainment needs.
Paul Slattery ~ A slick talent with any medium, be it pens, pencils or brushes. You will be both amazed and delighted at the lightening speed of Paul's caricaturing.
Paul Lytton ~ Specialising in close-up magic, you will be impressed, astonished and entertained !

MIKE CASSIDY
See Artiste Index, NVB entertainments & Personal Appearances Listings

KEITH "THE THIEF" CHARNLEY
See Artistes Index, Essex Entertainment Agency, Highfield Management & Promotions, London Music Agency, NMP Live Ltd, NVB Entertainments, Spotlight Entertainments, Stardust Entertainments Agency & Triple Cream Entertainments Listings.

STEVE CHARRETT
See Artiste Index & Prima Artists Listings.

COLINI THE MAGICIAN
See Artiste Index & Hire-a-Band Entertainment Agency Listing

COLINSKI
See Artiste Index, NVB Entertainments, Stardust Entertainments Agency & Tony Bennell Entertainments Listings.

CONFETTI MAGIC
Rocket Park, Half Moon Lane, Pepperstock, Luton, Bedfordshire, LU1 4LL
Tel: 01582 723502 Fax: 01582 485545
Email: ian@confettimagic.com
Web Site: www.confettimagic.com

ALISTAIR COOK
See Artiste Index, Arena Entertainment Consultants, J Gurnett Personal Management Ltd & NMP Live Ltd.

RAY COOPER
See Artiste Index, London Music Agency & Ultimate Representation listing.

ROBERT COX
Close-up magic & Cabaret.
See Artiste Index, CS Entertainments, Tony Bennell Entertainments & NVB Entertainments listing.

MIKE DANATA
See Artiste Index, Apollo Promotions & Upfront Entertainment Agency Listings.

MARTIN DANIELS
See Artiste Index and Chris Davis Management listing.

PAUL DANIELS
c/o International Artistes Lapley Hall, Lapley, Staffordshire ST19 9JR
Tel: 01785 841 991 Fax: 01785 841 992
Email: cdavis@intart.co.uk
Web Site: www.pauldaniels.co.uk
Contact: Chris Davis

ALAN DARK
15 Hurrell Court, Hurrell Road, Kingsbridge, Devon TQ7 1HT
Tel: 0870 442 3284 Fax: 01548 857 748
Mobile: 07970 605 336 Email: alan.magic@virgin.net
Web Site: www.alandark.com
Magician/Entertainer: Alan Dark

DAVID HAWKINS - CLOSE UP MAGICIAN
107 Butts Hill Road, Woodley, Reading, Berkshire RG5 4NT
Tel: 07850 740557 Fax: 0845 458 5301
Email: info@david-hawkins.co.uk
Web Site: www.david-hawkins.co.uk
Close-up magic for the corporate & private events. Member of The Magic Circle.

DAVID OAKLEY
See Artistes Index, The Horne Concert Agency, Anita Alraun Representation & Anglia Artistes (UK) Ltd listings.

CARL DEAN
Suite 33, 10 Barley Mow Passage, London W4 4PH
Tel: 07733 106540
Email: info@thedeansofmagic.biz
Web Site: www.thedeansofmagic.com
Also see Artiste Index & The Deans Of Magic Listing.

DANIEL DEAN
See Artiste Index & PVA Ltd Listing.

THE DEANS OF MAGIC
Suite 33, 10 Barley Mow Passage, London W4 4PH
Tel: 07733 106540
Email: info@thedeansofmagic.biz
Web Site: www.thedeansofmagic.com
Contact: Carl Dean & Claudine (The Deans Of Magic)
Illusionists of international acclaim. Carl Dean has over 25 years experience in the world of Magic working worldwide. They now specialise in spectacular shows for the corporate market for both grand and intimate events.

CHRIS DUGDALE
See Artiste Index & CKK Entertainment Listing

GEOFFREY DURHAM
See Artiste Index, NMP Live Ltd & International Artistes Listings.

DYNAMIC FX LTD
Regent House, 291 Kirkdale, London SE26 4QD
Tel: 0845 00 62442 Fax: 0845 00 62443
Email: mail@dynamicfx.co.uk
Web Site: www.dynamicfx.co.uk
Dynamic FX is the UK's leading magical entertainment company providing magicians, illusionists, pickpockets, mind readers and other unusual entertainers. All of our performers are unique and many are members of the world famous Magic Circle.

EXTRAVAGANZA ENTERTAINERS
34 Oak Tree Close, Hertford, Hertfordshire SG13 7RG
Tel: 01992 552 441 Mobile: 07973 310661 Email: chandmagic@aol.com
Web: www.extravaganzaentertainers.com
Contact: Michael Chandler
Children and adult parties, table hopping and close-up magic for adult functions & corporate magic.

FAY PRESTO
See Artiste Index Whatever Artiste Management Ltd Listings.

FLUKE
See Artiste Index, CKK Entertainment, Crowd Pullers (Street Performers and Bands), NVB Entertainments & Whatever Artists Management Ltd Listings.

FOOLS PARADISE
9 Colleton Crescent, Exeter EX2 4DG
Tel: 01392 454 160 Fax: 01392 848 384
Email: fools@foolsparadise.co.uk
Web Site: www.foolsparadise.co.uk
Director: Nicki Street

COLIN FRANCOME
See Artiste Index & Nic Picot Entertainment Listing

KEVIN GALLAGHER
134 Ashby Road, Burton-on-Trent, Staffordshire DE15 0LQ
Tel: 01283 500 130 (Day) Tel: 01283 563 448 (Eve) Email: magician@mystifier.co.uk
Web Site: www.mystifier.co.uk
Multi award winning close-up magician offering skilful mystification of the highest quality. Impossibilities under scrutinising conditions no problem.

DANIEL GOODWIN
See Artiste Index & Derek Bruce Entertainments Listing

JON GORDON
4 Mount Rise, Leeds, West Yorkshire LS17 7QR
Tel: 0113 237 0056 Email: jon@occasionalmagic.co.uk
Web Site: www.occasionalmagic.co.uk / www.magic4business.co.uk
Contact: Jon Gordon

PETER HALES
See Artiste Index & NVB Entertainments Listing

TERRY HERBERT
See Artiste Index & Triple Cream Entertainments listing.

GUY HOLLINGWORTH
See Artiste Index & CKK Entertainment Listing
Conjurer and sleight of hand artiste.
Web Site: www.guy-hollingworth.com

ALAN HUDSON
See Artiste Index & Mr Magic Entertainments Listing

TRACEY HUGHES & SARINDA
See Artiste Index & NVB Entertainments Listing

INTERNATIONAL MAGIC
89 Clerkenwell Road, London EC1R 5BX
Tel: 020 7405 7324 Email: admin@internationalmagic.com
Web Site: www.internationalmagic.com
Contact: Martin MacMillan

ROBERT JAMIESON
See Artiste Index & Mr Magic Entertainments Listing

PHIL JAY
See Artiste Index & CKK Entertainment Listing

ANTHONY JOHN
4 Mayfield Court, Eversley, Hook, Hampshire RG27 0RS
Tel/Fax: 0118 973 2778 Mobile: 07785 753414 Email: info@anthonyjohn.co.uk
Web Site: www.anthonyjohn.co.uk
Close up magic for every occasion. Member of the Magic Circle. Total satisfaction guaranteed!

JOHN LOVE
See Artistes Index, Anglia Artistes (UK) Ltd & The Horne Concert Agency listings.

GRAHAM P JOLLEY
See Artiste Index, Laurie Taylor Entertainments Ltd, Arena Entertainment

Consultants, Personal Appearances, Prime Performers Ltd, Personally Speaking Listings.

RICHARD JONES
See Artiste Index, Mainstream Events, Newton Wills Management & Productions & Judy Daish Assoc Listings.

IAN KEABLE
7 Harberton Road, London N19 3JS
Tel: 020 7263 0261 Mob: 07710 420 912
Email: ian@iankeable.co.uk
Web Site: www.iankeable.co.uk
Mind reader and magician for corporate functions. Brochure available on request.

PAUL KIEVE
See Artiste Index & CKK Entertainment Listing

LATIN MAGIC
See Artistes Index & Tony West Agency listing.

ROY LEE
See Artiste Index & Apollo Promotions Listing.

JOHN LENAHAN
See Artiste Index & JLA Listing

LESTER, MAN OF MAGIC
See Artiste Index & Apollo Promotions Listing

JULIE ILUSION
See Artiste Index & Derek Bruce Entertainments Listing

JAMES LUKINS
See Artiste Index & Apollo Promotions Listing

LYNX
See Artiste Index, Celebration Management Entertainment Group & Tony West Entertainments listings.

TERRY MACHIN
See Artiste Index & London Music Agency Listing

MAGIC BOB
See Artiste Index & MTM Presentations Listing

MAGIC CATHERINE
4 Tamarind Court 75 Deepcut Bridge Road Camberley, Surrey GU16 6QP
Tel: 01252 837 885 Mob: 07770 227 812
Email: catherine@magicentertainment.co.uk
Web Site: www.magicentertainment.co.uk
Contact: Catherine

MAGIC JUNIOR LIMITED
187 Goulden House, Bullen Street, London SW11 3HG
Tel: 0845 166 2169 Tel: 020 7801 0201
Fax: 020 7801 0272
Email: mj@magicjunior.com
Web Site: www.magicjunior.com
Contact: Magic Junior

MAGIC MOMENTS
127 Carterhatch Road, Enfield, Middlesex EN3 5LX
Tel: 020 8245 4348 Fax: 07092 033 538
Email: magicmoments@partyweb.co.uk
Web Site: www.partyweb.co.uk/act/magicmoments
Contacts: Charlie Valentino
Colourful comedy magic/juggling with live bunny rabbit suitable for private shows as well as public mix & mingle.

THE MAGIC OF SHAHID MALIK
3 Selborne Villas, North Park Road, Heaton, Bradford, West Yorkshire BD9 4NN
Tel: 01274 499 065 Fax: 01274 490 179
Email: shahid@shahidmalik.co.uk
Web Site: www.shahidmalik.co.uk
Contact: Shahid Malik
International Magician and Illusionist.

JON MARSHALL
See Artiste Index & Mr Magic Entertainments Listing

ROBIN MARTIN
See Artiste Index & The A6 Agency Listing.

SHAUN MCCREE
See Artiste Index, The A6 Agency & Arena Entertainment Consultants Listings.

RICHARD MCDOUGALL
See Artistes Index, CKK Entertainment, NMP Live Ltd & Whatever Artists Management Ltd Listings.

PETER MEHTAB
See Artiste Index, CKK Entertainment, Whatever Artists management Ltd & 1st Choice Speakers Ltd Listings.

MERLIN CHILDREN'S ENTERTAINMENTS
29 Norwood Drive, Harrow, Middlesex HA2 7PF
Tel/Fax: 020 8866 6327
Email: info@merlinents.co.uk
Web Site: www.merlinents.co.uk
Senior Personnel: Geoffrey & Clive Donald

DAVID MERLIN
Illusionist.
See Artiste Index, Hartbeat Entertainments Ltd, PVA Ltd, Ginger Walker Agency Listings.

MICHELLE
See Artiste Index & PVA Ltd Listing.

JOHN MILNER & KIM
See Artiste Index & PVA Ltd Listing

MALCOLM MILTON
See Artiste Index & Parliament Communications Listing.

MIRAGE
See Artiste Index and Arena Entertainments Consultants Listings.

MIST - THE ILLUSIONS OF SEAN ALEXANDER
1 Queens Court, The Street, Long Stratton, Norwich NR15 2XD
Tel: 07765 881 894 Email: sean@seanalexandermagic.com
Web Site: www.seanalexandermagic.com
Contact: Sean Alexander
Please see full page ad within the Magicians & Illusionists section

MR "E" THE MAGICIAN
See Artiste Index & Mr "E" Enterprises Listing.

MR MAGIC ENTERTAINMENTS
18 Church Street, Sutton-on-Hull, East Yorkshire HU7 4TS
Tel: 01482 709 939 (Children's Parties)
Mob: 07787 557 412 Fax: 01482 787 362 Email: alan@mrmagicentertainments.co.uk
Web: www.mrmagicentertainments.co.uk
Contact: Alan Hudson
Provision of magicians, clowns, fire-eaters etc.

MR TED'S MAGIC SHOW
Footlight Productions, 48 Hathaway Gardens, Chadwell Heath, Romford, Essex RM6 5TL
Tel: 020 8599 6253 Mob: 07737 046 066
Email: tedheath@talktalk.net
Contact: Ted Heath
Corporate, major private big parties.

BRUCE MUNTON
16 High Street, Gainsborough, Lincolnshire DN21 1BH
Tel/Fax: 01427 811150 Mobile: 07961 913609 Email:

spellboundpromotions@supanet.com
Web Site: www.brucemunton.com
Bruce has been entertaining as a close-up magician for more than a decade now and is an Associate Member of the prestigious Magic Circle.
Whether it be Mix & Mingle, Strolling or Table Magic, Bruce's award winning skills will amaze and entertain - bringing wonder to your audience.
Call today for availabiliy or for Bruce's free colour brochure.

HUGH NIGHTINGALE
See Artiste Index & CKK Entertainment listing.

NIGHTMARE
See Artiste Index & Celebration Management Entertainment Group Listing.

CHRIS NORTH & BELINDA
See Artiste Index, Barry Dye Entertainments, Highfield Management & Promotions & Anglia Artistes Listings.

MARC OBERON
See Artiste Index, Celebration Management Entertainment Group, Arena Entertainment Consultants & The Wizard - Marc Oberon Listings.

ANTHONY OWEN
Close-up magic and caberet. Member of the Magic Circle.

PARTYWEB.CO.UK
127 Carterhatch Road, Enfield, Middlesex EN3 5LX
Tel: 020 8245 4348 Fax: 07092 033 538
Email: magicians@partyweb.co.uk
Web Site: www.partyweb.co.uk
Propietor: Charles Coleman
Total entertainment specialists. Close-up magicians, cabaret and stage magic, clowns, children's entertainers. Private or corporate events.

MARC PAUL
Tel: 020 7025 0611 Fax: 020 7404 9865
Email: nhobbs@intart.co.uk
Officially, "The World's Greatest Mind Reader" and Memory expert. Corporate and motivational speaker and television presenter.
Web Site: www.marcpaul.co.uk
See Artiste Index & Magic International Artistes Ltd Listing.

PAUL RAY
58 Ennerdale Road, Shrewsbury SY1 3LD
Tel: 01743 445 328 Fax: 01743 445 327
Comedy Entertainer. Close up magic & stage.

DAVID PENN
See Artiste Index, Coach House Entertainment & CKK Entertainment Listings.

PHIL PERRY
Table topping and illusion
See Artiste Index, Steve Allen Entertainments, Dave Andrews Entertainments, Sardi's Enterprises & Style Promotions Listings.

PHILIP PARTRIDGE ENTERTAINMENT LTD
34 Winwood Road, East Didsbury, Manchester M20 5PE
Tel: 0161 448 2672 Mobile: 07970 871544 Email: magic@philippartridge.co.uk
Web Site: www.philippartridge.co.uk / www.magicphilip.co.uk (for family entertainment)
Contact: Philip Partridge
Philip makes your event memorable with his unique blend of Close-up Magic, the most personalised form of entertainment. Comedy Cabaret Magic will further enhance your event. His celebrity clients include the Beckhams & he has amazed HRH The Prince of Wales. Manchester United, Shell U.K. & PC World Business are among his corporate clients. He is a Close-up & Cabaret Magic award winner & has appeared on TV with Prince Charles, Ann Robinson & Ian Wright. He is a Magic Circle & Equity member & carries full Public Liability Insurance. MAGIC PHILIP guarantees to put a smile on children's faces of all ages with his action packed show full of colourful comedy magic,
balloon modelling & audience participation. Philip will also host the whole party adding special non-elimination games & can even offer take home balloon presents!

PJ THE MAGICIAN
See Artiste Index & PJ Entertainments Listing

RON POPPLE
See Artiste Index & The Home Concert Agency listing.

THE PRESTO PACK
See Artiste Index & Whatever Artiste Management Ltd Listing

CHRIS PRIEST
See Artiste Index & CKK Entertainment Listing

PROFESSOR MYSTRAL'S JUVENILE OMNIBUS
65 Penylan Road, Cardiff, CF23 5HZ Wales
Tel: 029 2048 5544 Mobile: 07855 515350
Web Site: www.professormystral.co.uk
Proprietor: Frank Turvey
Children's/family entertainment under the names of Professor Mystral and Mister Magipatch.

NICK READE
Close-up magic and caberet. Exhibition presenter.
Member of the Magic Circle.
See Artiste Index & Spotlight Entertainments listing.

JOHN RICHARD
See Artiste Index & London Music Agency Listing

RICHARD WYMARK
See Artistes Index, Barry Dye Entertainments & London Music Agency.

JOE RIDING
See Artiste Index & 1st Choice Speakers Ltd listing.

ALFONSO RIOS
See Artiste Index & Whatever Artiste Management Ltd Listing

SAFIRE
See Artiste Index, Ernest Colclough Enterprises & CKK Entertainment Listings.

TIM SAIET
See Artiste Index.

MARTIN SANDERSON
See Artiste Index & CKK Entertainment Listing

SAXON TYLNEY
See Artistes Index, Anglia Artistes (UK) Ltd & The Horne Concert Agency listings.

SCOTT JORDAN ENTERTAINMENT LTD
25-29 Station Street, Sittingbourne, Kent ME10 3DU
Tel: 0845 094 1455 Email: enquiries@scottjordan.co.uk
Web Site: www.scottjordan.co.uk
Contact : Scott Jordan, Stephen Middleton
Entertainment booking agency providing quality tribute bands, function bands, comedians and magicians for weddings, private parties, and venues accross the U.K

TERRY SEABROOKE
See Artiste Index, NVB Entertainments, 1st Choice Speakers Ltd, Johnny Mans Productions Limited, The Home Concert Agency & Stardust Entertainments Agency Listings.

GARRY SEAGRAVES
See Artiste Index & XS Promotions Listing

SEAN CARPENTER
See Artistes Index, Anglia Artistes (UK) Ltd listing & The Home Concert Agency listings.

ALAN SHAXON
See Artistes Index & 1st Choice Speakers Ltd listing.

JOHN SHEARER
See Artiste Index & Peter De Rance listing.

MICHAEL SHUTE
See Artiste Index & Apollo Promotions Listing

JOHN SIMONETT
See Artiste Index, Arena Entertainment Consultants, Personally Speaking, Gordon Poole Agency Ltd, 1st Choice Speakers Ltd, TMC Corporate Events and Entertainment Ltd, Personal Appearances & PVA Ltd Listings

RAY SPARKS
See Artiste Index & Complete Entertainment Services Listing

MARC SPELMANN - MAGIC-ILLUSION+PARANORMAL ENTERTAINMENT
Tel: 020 8341 7988 Mob: 07939 223 246
Email: info@marcspelmann.co.uk
Web Site: www.marcspelmann.co.uk
Marc Spelmann is a Paranormal Entertainer with a totally unique approach to the art of astonishment. Marc cultivates an air of mystery about himself, and has created some of the most abstract illusions ever to be screen on national television. Marc can tailor his act to your requirements, whether they be for celebrity galas to more intimate functions where he will mix & mingle amongst you. You are assured an evening of illusion and psychic phenomena you will never forget !

RICHARD ST JOHN
See Artiste Index & Joker Entertainments Listing

JACK STEPHENS
Cotswold House, 42 Netherstreet, Bromham, Chippenham, SN15 2DW
Tel/Fax: 01380 850 453 Email: jack-stephens@abra-cadabra.co.uk
Web Site: www.jackstephens.co.uk
See Artiste Index & PVA Ltd.

RUSS STEVENS
See Artiste Index & Dave Winslett Associates listing.

BILLY TEMPEST
See Artiste Index & Mr Magic Entertainments Listing

TENSAI MAGIC
45 David Newberry Drive, Lee-on-the-Solent, Hampshire PO13 8FG
Tel: 02392 550 807 Mob: 07920 779 410
Email: tensai@tensaimagic.com
Web Site: www.tensaimagic.com
Contact: Alan Vandome

THE MINISTRY OF FUN
127-129 Great Suffolk Street, London SE1 1PP
Tel: 020 7407 6077 Email: james@ministryoffun.net
Web Site: www.ministryoffun.net
Managing Director: James Lovell
General entertainment agency for magicians, peformers, human statues, etc.

UNCLE PETER'S MAGIC SHOW
Unit 4a, Keighley Business Centre, South Street, Keighley, West Yorkshire BD21 1SY
Tel: 01535 662 036 Fax: 01535 611 921
Mobile: 07885 802966 Email: itsmagic@supanet.com
Web Site: www.itsmagicuk.org.uk
Proprietor: Peter Greenwood
"Uncle Peter's Magic Show", a self contained mobile outfit for pre-school to teenage children. Also performs as an illusionist and stand-up patter act.

CHARLIE VALENTINO
127 Carterhatch Road, Enfield, Middlesex EN3 5LX
Tel: 020 8245 4348 Fax: 07092 033 538
Email: valentino@partyweb.co.uk
Web Site:
www.partyweb.co.uk/act/valentino
Contact: Charlie Valentino
Close-up miracles performed with deadpan comic humour.

VAN BUREN
41 High Street, Silverdale, Newcastle-under-Lyme, Staffordshire ST5 6NG
Tel: 01782 611 954 Email: avanburen@aol.com
Web Site: www.vanburen.org.uk
Contact: Andrew Van Buren
Specialising in Cabaret, TV, Outdoor shows, Theatre, Magic, Juggling, Unicycling, Plate Spinning and Illusion.

MICHAEL VINCENT
See Artiste Index and CKK Entertainment listing.

PETER WESTLAKE
See Artiste Index, CS Entertainments & 1st Choice Speakers Ltd Listing.

WHATEVER ARTISTS MANAGEMENT LTD
F24 Argo House, Kilburn Park Road, London NW6 5LF
Tel: 020 7372 4777 Fax: 020 7372 5111
Email: info@wamshow.biz
Web Site: www.wamshow.biz
Senior Personnel: Jenny Dunster
All types of entertainers booked for corporate and private events with full technical on-site management services.

THE WIZARD - MARC OBERON
5 Church Avenue, Daybrook, Nottingham NG5 6LB
Tel: 0115 920 6390 Email: marcoberon-wizard@aol.com
Web Site: www.marcoberon.com
Contact: Marc Oberon
Spectacular floating shapes fragment and reform. A thousand points of laser lights spin intricate patterns through the darkness. Original and memorable.

ANTONIO ZAMBARDINI
See Artiste Index & NVB Entertainments Listing

PAUL ZENON
Tel: 07721 610 364 Email: gigs@paulzenon.com
Web Site: www.paulzenon.com
Personal Assistant: Sue Reed (Stranger Media Limited)
Comedian, Magician and Presenter.

Industry Organisations

THE GUILD OF INTERNATIONAL SONGWRITERS & COMPOSERS
Sovereign House, 12 Trewartha Road, Praa Sands, Penzance, Cornwall TR20 9ST
Tel: 01736 762 826 Fax: 01736 763 328
songmag@aol.com
www.songwriters-guild.co.uk
Chairman: Roderick Jones

Casting Agencies/ Directors

BBC TV
BBC Television Centre, Wood Lane, London W12 7RJ
Tel: 020 8743 8000
Email: julian.bellamy@bbc.co.uk
Web Site: www.bbc.co.uk
BB1 Programme Controller: Peter Fincham
BB3 Casting Director: Julian Bellamy

SIOBHAN BRACKE
22A the Barons, St Margarets, Twickenham Middlesex TW1 2AP
Tel: 020 8891 5686 Fax: 020 8607 9452
Freelance Casting Director: Siobhan Bracke

LINDA BUTCHER
39 Arlington Road, Surbiton, Surrey KT6 6BW
Tel: 020 8399 7373

BWH AGENCY
Barley Mow Business Centre, 10 Barley Mow Passage, London W4 4PH
Tel: 020 8996 1661 Fax: 020 8996 1662
Email: andrew@thebwhagency.co.uk
Agent: Andrew Braidford

CAIRD LITTLEWOOD CASTING
PO Box MT 86, Leeds, West Yorkshire LS17 8YQ
Tel: 0113 288 8014 Fax: 0113 266 6068
Email: cairdlitt@aol.com
Casting Director: Angela Caird

CASTCALL CASTING SERVICES
106 Wilsden Avenue, Luton, Bedfordshire LU1 5HR
Tel: 01582 456 213 Fax: 01582 480 736
Email: info@castcall.co.uk
Web Site: www.castcall.co.uk
Senior Personnel: Ron O'Brien

THE CASTING COUCH
213 Trowbridge Road, Bradford-on-Avon, Wiltshire BA15 1EU
Tel: 07932 785 807 Fax: 01225 869 029
Email: moiratownsend@yahoo.co.uk
Contact: Moira Townsend

CASTNET
20 Sparrows Herne, Bushey WD23 1FU
Tel: 020 8420 4209 Fax: 020 8421 9666
Email: admin@castingnetwork.co.uk
Web Site: www.castingnetwork.co.uk
Contact: Alyson Sharon
CastNet is a unique FREE casting service to those seeking the best of British acting talent. We have thousands of vetted, trained UK actors on our database.

CHARKHAM CASTING
79 Mortimer Street, London W1W 7ST
Tel: 020 7436 4842 Fax: 020 7927 8336
Email: charkhamcasting@btconnect.com
Senior Personnel: Beth Charkham, Gary Ford

LEE DENNISON ASSOCIATES
Fushion, 27 Old Gloucester Street, London WC1N 3XX
Tel: 08700 111 100 (6 lines) Fax: 08700 111 020 (2 lines) New York Office: Fushion, #28, 1328 Broadway, Suite 524, New York 10001
Email: leedennison@fushion-uk.com
Web: www.ukscreen.com/crew/ldennison
Manager: Lee Dennison CDA
Established Casting Team for Film, Television, Music Videos and Promotional work for Worldwide markets.
Lee Dennison Associates are based in London & New York. Lee Dennison CDA is also Agency Consultant at Fushion Pukka Bosh.

DI CARLING CASTING
1st Floor, 49 Frith Street, London W1D 4SG
Tel: 020 7287 6446 Fax: 020 7287 6844
Mobile: 0774 8655 00

DREAMS INTERNATIONAL MODEL & CASTING AGENCY
Empire House, 175 Piccadilly, Mayfair, London W1J 9TB
Tel: 020 7359 4786 Fax: 020 7688 0771
Mobile: 07949 548904
Senior Personnel: Deborah Hillaire

E.K.A MODEL & ACTOR MANAGEMENT
The Warehouse Studios, Glaziers Lane, Culcheth, Warrington WA3 4AQ
Tel: 0871 222 7470 Fax: 0871 222 7471
Email: info@eka-agency.com
Web Site: www.eka-agency.com
Company Director: Debbie Ikin
Senior TV & Film Casting Agent: Rebecca Keeley
Actor Management: Kate Sinclair
Agents to talented and experienced models and actors 18 to 80 yrs of all nationalities. Photographic, Television Commercials and Programmes, Films. Main & Supporting Artistes. We are a large agency covering the North West, Midlands and all UK. 20 Staff. Casting and Photographic Studios available. Friendly and efficient service.
E.K.A Management and Eurokids & Adults Agency is part of Eurokids Ltd.

EUROKIDS & ADULTS INTERNATIONAL CASTING & MODEL AGENCY
The Warehouse Studios, Glaziers Lane, Culcheth, Warrington, Cheshire WA3 4AQ
Tel: 0871 222 7470 Fax: 0871 222 7471
Email: info@eka-agency.com
Web Site: www.eka-agency.com
Contact: Debbie Ikin
Agents to talented models and actors. Birth to 80 years of all nationalities. Photographic, television commercials & programmes, films. Main & supporting artistes. Extras for background work. We are a large agency covering the North West and Midlands. 20 staff. Casting & photographic studios available. Friendly & efficient service. Eurokids &adults agency is part of EuroKids Ltd

RICHARD EVANS CDG
10 Shirley Road, London W4 1DD
Tel: 020 8994 6304 Fax: 020 8742 1010
Email: contact@evanscasting.co.uk
Web Site: www.evanscasting.co.uk
Freelance Casting Director with extensive knowledge and 13 years' experience in straight and musical theatre, television, commercials and films.

GBM CASTING
Unit 2, 11 Dalsholm Place, Glasgow G20 0UH
Tel: 0141 948 0334
Mobile: 07967 187980
Email: gbmcasting@yahoo.co.uk
Web Site: www.gbmcasting.co.uk
Agent: Graham Miller
GBM Casting is one of Scotland's newest Casting Agencies, specialising in providing Supporting Artists to the TV, Film and Advertising Industries.

NINA GOLD
10 Kempe Road, London NW6 6SJ
Tel: 020 8960 6099 Fax: 020 8968 6777
Email: nina@ninagold.co.uk

HUBBARD CASTING
14 Rathbone Place, London W1T 1HT
Tel: 0207 631 4944 Fax: 0207 636 7117
Email: info@hubbardcasting.com
Web Site: www.hubbardcasting.com
London Contact: Ros & John Hubbard

SYLVIA HUGHES
Casting Suite, The Deanwater, Wilmslow Road, Woodford, Stockport, Cheshire SK7 1RJ
Tel: 0777 0520 007 Fax: 01565 723 707

ITV GRANADA
Quay Street, Manchester M60 9EA
Tel: 0161 832 7211 Fax: 0161 827 2180
Email: natalie.armisted@itv.com
Web Site: www.itv.com/granada
Senior Personnel: Judi Hayfield/Sue Slee
Advertising Officer: Natalie Armisted

JACLYN AGENCY
52 Bessemer Road, Norwich,
Norfolk NR4 6DQ
Tel: 01603 622 027 Fax: 01603 612 532
Email: info@jaclyn2000.co.uk
Web Site: www.jaclyn2000.co.uk
Senior Personnel: Julian Sandiford, Henrietta Cassidy
Specialising in: Supporting Artistes for TV & Film Companies. Covers East Anglia, E. Midlands, N. London. Over one thousand professional artistes available.

JUST CASTING
20th Century Theatre, 291 Westbourne Grove, London W11 2QA
Tel: 020 7229 3471 Fax: 020 7792 2143
Email: justcasting@btopenworld.com
Contact: Miss Leo Davis

RAY KNIGHT CASTING
21a Lambolle Place, Belsize Park, London NW3 4PG
Tel: 020 7722 1551 Fax: 020 7722 2322
Email: tony@rayknight.co.uk
Web Site: www.rayknight.co.uk
Senior Personnel: Tony Gerrard, Rachel Adamson, John Whelan, Judy Szucs

SUZY KOREL
20 Blenheim Road, London NW8 0LX
Tel: 020 7624 6435 Fax: 020 7372 3964
Email: suzy@korel.org
Casting Directors.

MUGSHOTS
50 Frith Street, London W1D 4SQ
Tel: 020 7292 0555 Fax: 020 7437 0308
Email: contact@mugshots.co.uk
Web Site: www.mugshots.co.uk
Contact: Jacqui Morris

THE NORTH AMERICAN ACTORS ASSOCIATION (NAAA)
Tel/Fax: 020 7938 4722
Mob: 07710 133 065
Email: americanactors@aol.com
Web Site: www.naaa.org.uk
Chief Executive: Laurence Bouvard
THE source for genuine North American actors, all NAAA members are professional actors able to work without restriction both in the UK and North America. Log onto our website to access members' photos and agent details for all your casting needs. There ain't nothing like the Real Thing!

PERSONAL MANAGEMENT & CASTING
Creative House, 103 The Drive, Beckenham, Kent BR3 1EF
Tel: 020 8402 9553 Fax: 020 8289 2963
Email: jaine@casting.uk.net
Managing Director: Jaine Brent
Operations Manager: Dan Zegze

RAY'S NORTHERN CASTING AGENCY
7 Wince Close, Middleton, Manchester M24 1UJ
Tel/Fax: 0161 643 6745
Email: rayscasting@yahoo.co.uk
Senior Personnel: Bobbie and Harold Ray
Specialising in Adults & Children - Multi Racial

SIMONE REYNOLDS
60 Hebdon Road, London SW17 7NN
Fax: 020 8767 0280

RHODES
5 Dymoke Road, Hornchurch, RM11 1AA
Tel: 01708 747 013 Fax: 01708 730 431
Email: rhodesarts@hotmail.com

RSC CASTING
1 Earlham Street, London WC2H 9LL
Tel: 020 7845 0507 Fax: 020 7845 0505
Email: sam.jones@rsc.org.uk
Web Site: www.rsc.org.uk
Casting Director: Sam Jones

SUZANNE SMITH
33 Fitzroy Street, London W1T 6DU
Tel: 020 7436 9255 Fax: 020 7436 9690
Email: zan@dircon.co.uk

LIZ STOLL CASTING DIRECTOR
Room 223 BBC Elstree Neptune House
Clarendon Road ELstree WD6 1JF
Tel: 020 8228 8285
Mobile: 07947 068 500
Email: liz.stoll@bbc.co.uk
Casting for television, theatre, corporate videos, training films and commercials.

JEREMY ZIMMERMANN CASTING
26-27 Oxendon Street, London SW1Y 4EL

Internet

RENTACROWD.CO.UK
40 St. Enoch Square, Glasgow G1 4DH
Tel: 0141 221 5664
Email: alana@rentacrowd.co.uk
Web Site: www.rentacrowd.co.uk
Contact: Alana
Rentacrowd.co.uk is one of Scotland's leading Casting Agencies, providing Supporting Artists/ Extras' and Character Models for: Commercials, T.V, Film and Photographic work. Please visit our website for more information on our artist roster.

STARNOW.CO.UK
Email: jeremy@StarNow.co.uk
Web Site: www.StarNow.co.uk
Contact: Cameron Mehlhopt; Jeremy Leslie
StarNow.co.uk is the UK's biggest online casting service. Apply for casting calls online and get discovered in our talent directory.

TALENTSPOT UK
Freepost TalentSpot UK
Tel: 0845 045 4111
Email: info@talentspotuk.com
Web Site: wwww.talentspotuk.com
Contact: Dean Ezekiel

Advisory Services

ACTORS' BENEVOLENT FUND
6 Adam Street, London WC2N 6AD
Tel: 020 7836 6378 Fax: 020 7836 8978
Email: office@abf.org.uk
Web: www.actorsbenevolentfund.co.uk
Patron: H.R.H. The Prince of Wales
President: Penelope Keith, O.B.E.
Registered Charity No. 206524
Founded in 1882 by Sir Henry Irving and a group of his friends, the A.B.F. provides assistance to members of the theatrical profession who because of old age, ill health or accident are suffering hardship. Financial help is provided by grants and allowances. Assistance can also be given with nursing home fees.

ANIMAL FREE ADVISORY SERVICE
Member of Animal Welfare Filming Federation
28 Greeves Road, High Wycombe, Buckinghamshire HP13 7JU
Mob: 07956 564715
Email: animalswork1@yahoo.co.uk
Web Site: www.animalswork.co.uk
Manager: Trevor Smith
Senior Personnel: Graham Johnson
Provides advisory service to production companies on the usage of animals, covering safety and legal requirements, whilst ensuring their safety and protection from harm.

TUFF THE SESSION AGENCY
United House, North Road, London N7 9DP
Tel: 020 7700 6262 Fax: 020 7700 6172
Email: jo.castello@btinternet.com
Web Site: www.tuffsessions.com
Contact: Jo Castello
The premier agency specialising in providing music solutions, from vocal training, session work, worldwide tours, to corporate events and advertising. Our blend of experienced musicianship, marketing and strong entertainment skills makes us perfect for any music related project.

TV, Film & Radio Production Companies

20TH CENTURY FOX FILM CO
20th Century House, 31 Soho Square, London W1D 3AP
Tel: 020 7437 7766 Fax: 020 7434 2170
Email: clare.mackintosh@fox.co.uk
Web Site: www.fox.co.uk
Managing Director: Peter Dignan
Marketing Manager: Clare Macintosh

AARDMAN ANIMATIONS
Gas Ferry Road, Bristol, Avon BS1 6UN
Tel: 0117 984 8485
Fax: 0117 984 8486 / 907 6677
Email: mail@aardman.com
Web Site: www.aardman.com
Head Of Developments: Liz Keynes
Animated film producers.

ABACUS FILM PRODUCTIONS
Lomond, Horse Hill, Norwood Hill, Horley, Surrey R86 0HN
Tel: 01293 862 318 Fax: 01293 863 790
Email: lomondabs@aol.com
Directors: Rob Trainer, Abbie Gaiche

ABOVE THE TITLE PRODUCTIONS LTD
Level 2, 10-11 St Georges Mews, London NW1 8XE
Tel: 020 7916 1984 Fax: 020 7722 5706
Email: ruth@abovethetitle.com
Web Site: www.abovethetitle.com
CEO: Bruce Hyman
MD: Helen Chatwell

ADELPHI MEDI CINE
adelphi mill grimshore lane bollington maccleffield cheshire SK10 5JB
Tel:0162 577 233 Fax:0162 575 853
Email: lifecyclesolutions@adelphigroup.com
Web Site: www.adelphigroup.com
Managing Director: Steve Firmer

ANIMAGE FILMS
62 Westcroft Close, London NW2 2RR
Tel/Fax: 020 7435 3883
Email: ruth@animagefilms.com
Web Site: www.animagefilms.com
Managing Director: Ruth Beni
Animation production.

ANVIL POST PRODUCTION LTD
Anvil Post Production Denham Media Park North Orbital Road Denham, Uxbridge, Middlesex UB9 5HL
Tel: 01895 833 522 Fax: 01895 835 006
Email: pam.nash@thomson.net
Web Site: www.anvil-post.com
Studio manager: Mike Anscombe

APEX TELEVISION
Vision Centre, Eastern Way, Bury St Edmunds, Suffolk IP32 7AB
Tel: 01284 724 900 Fax: 01284 700 004
Email: sales@apextv.co.uk
Web Site: www.apextv.co.uk
Contact: Peter Creswell

AVALON TELEVISION
4a Exmoor Street, London W10 6BD
Tel: 020 7598 8000 Fax: 020 7598 7300
Email: jenniferm@avalonuk.co.uk
Company Directors: Richard Allen Turner, Jon Thoday
Contact: Lee Tucker

BBC
Henry Wood House, London W1A 1AA
Tel: 020 7580 4468
Email: ldn-planning@bbc.co.uk
Web Site: www.bbc.co.uk/london

BBC RADIO WILTSHIRE
Broadcasting House, Prospect Place, Swindon, Wiltshire SN1 3RW
Tel: 01793 513 626 Fax: 01793 513 650
Email: amelia.claydon-smith@bbc.co.uk
Web Site: www.bbc.co.uk/wiltshire
Managing Editor: Tony Worgan
Contact: Amelia Claydon-Smith

BBC WORLD
Woodlands, 80 Wood Lane, London W12 0TT
Tel: 020 8433 2000 Fax: 020 8749 0538
Email: jane.gorard@bbcworld.co.uk
Web Site: www.bbcworld.co.uk
Director of Marketing: Jane Gorard
Head of Marketing: Seema Kotecha

BLACKMAN PRODUCTIONS
Butlers Wharf Business Centre, Old Barn Lane, Old Barn Studio, Churt, Farnham, Surrey GU10 2NA
Tel: 01428 602979
Email: Johnb@blackman-productions.co.uk
Web: www.blackman-productions.co.uk
Director: John Blackman

BLINK PRODUCTIONS
181 Wardour Street, London W1F 8WZ
Tel: 020 7494 0747 Fax: 020 7494 3771
Email: info@blinkprods.com
Web Site: www.blinkprods.com
Contact: Rob Connolly

BUENA VISTA INTERNATIONAL UK
3 Queen Caroline Street, London W6 9PE
Tel: 020 8222 1968 Fax: 020 8222 2795
Email: adrian.last@disney.co.uk
Web Site: www.bvimovies.co.uk
Contact Marketing Manager: Adrian Last

CANDLE
44 Southern Row, London W10 5AN
Tel: 020 8960 0111 Mobile: 07860 912192
Email: tony@candle.org.uk
Web Site: www.candle.org.uk
Managing Director: Tony Satchell
Creative Director: Charlie Spencer
Original composition for TV, Radio and Film.

CAPRICORN PROGRAMMES
4/5 Hithercroft Court, Lupton Road, Wallingford, Oxfordshire OX10 9BT
Tel: 01491 838 888 Fax: 01491 833 333
Email: louise@capricornprogs.com
Web Site: www.capricornprogs.com
Contact: Catherine Cornick or Louise Gray

CARNIVAL
12 Raddington Road, Ladbroke Grove, London W10 5TG
Tel: 020 8968 0968 Fax: 020 8968 0177
Email: info@carnival-films.co.uk
Web Site: www.carnival-films.co.uk
Proprietor: Brian Eastman
Assistant: Jude Likenaitzllky

CHANNEL FOUR TV CO LTD
124 Horseferry Road, London SW1P 2TX
Tel: 020 7396 4444
Email: klygo@channel4.com
Web Site: www.channel4.co.uk
Director of Programmes: Kevin Lygo
Press Office contact: Loretta de Souza

CHANNEL X COMMUNICATIONS
2nd Floor, Highgate Business Centre, 33 Greenwood Place, Kentish Town, London NW5 1LB
Tel: 020 7428 3999 Fax: 020 7428 3998
Email: carla.mcgilchrist@chxp.co.uk
Web Site: www.chxp.co.uk

THE CHILDREN'S COMPANY
211 Piccadilly, London W1J 9HF
Tel: 020 7917 9542 Fax: 020 7917 9543
Email: office@childrenscompany.com
Senior Personnel: Robert Howes
Children's TV production company.

CNN INTERNATIONAL
19-22 Rathbone Place, London W1P 1DF
Web Site: www.cnn.com
Bureau Chief: Tom Mintier

COLUMBIA TRISTAR FILMS
25 Golden Square, London W1F 9LU
Tel: 020 7533 1000 Fax: 020 7533 1015
Web Site: www.spe.sony.com

COSGROVE HALL FILMS
8 Albany Road, Chorlton, Manchester M21 0AW
Tel: 0161 882 2500 Fax: 0161 882 2555
Email: animation@chf.co.uk
Web Site: www.chd.uk.com

CRE8 STUDIOS
Town Hall Studios, Regent Circus, Swindon, Wiltshire SN1 1QF
Tel: 01793 463 210 Fax: 01793 463 223
Email: info@cre8studios.org.uk
Web Site: cre8studios.org.uk
Administrator: Julie Thorn

CREATIVE FILM PRODUCTION
68 Conway Road, London N14 7BE
Tel: 020 8447 8187
Email: wssales@creativefilm.co.uk
Web Site: www.creativefilm.co.uk
Producer: Phil Davies

CUTTING EDGE PRODUCTIONS
27 Erpingham Road, London SW15 1BE
Tel: 020 8780 1476 Fax: 020 8780 0102
Email: juliannorridge@btconnect.com
Director: Julian Norridge

DENHAM PRODUCTIONS
Quay West Studios, Old Newnham, Plymouth, Devon PL7 5BH
Tel: 01752 345 444 Fax: 01752 345 448
Email: info@denhams.demon.co.uk
Contact: Peter Edwards

WALT DISNEY & COMPANY
3 Queen Caroline Street, London W6 9PE
Tel: 020 8222 1000 Fax: 020 8222 2795
Email: zoe.hawkins@disney.co.uk
Web Site: www.disney.co.uk

DIVERSE LTD
6-12 Gorleston Street, Kensington, London W14 8XS
Tel: 020 7603 4567 Fax: 020 7603 2148
Email: reception@diverse.tv
Web Site: www.diverse.tv
Head of Post Production: Paul Bates
Executive Producer: Jane Lomas

DOMINO FILMS
7 King Harry Lane, St Albans, Hertfordshire AL3 4AS
Tel: 01727 750 153
Email: jo@dominofilms.co.uk
Producer/Director: Joanna Mack

THE DRAMA HOUSE
The Clockhouse, St Mary Street, Nether Stowey Somerset TA5 1LJ
Email: jack@dramahouse.co.uk
Web Site: www.dramahouse.co.uk
Chairman/Chief Executive: Jack Emery

THE EDGE PICTURE COMPANY
7 Langley Street, London WC2H 9JA
Tel: 020 7836 6262 Fax: 020 7836 6949
Email: kayla.ellis@edgepicture.com
Web Site: www.edgepicture.com
Managing Director: Philip Blundell
Creative Director: Pete Stevenson
Creative Director's Personal Assistant: Kayla Ellis

ENDBOARD PRODUCTIONS
114a Poplar Road, Bearwood, Birmingham B66 4AP
Tel: 0121 429 9779 Fax: 0121 429 9008
Email: anna@endboard.com,
Web Site: www.endboard.com
Producer/Director: Sunandan Walia
TV production factual, factual entertainment and drama. Also: Three fiction scripts in development for theatrical release.

FLICKS FILM
101 Wardour Street, London W1F 0UG
Tel: 020 7734 4892 Fax: 020 7287 2307
Email: flicks@btconnect.com
Web Site: www.flicksfilms.com
Managing Director: Terry Ward

FULCRUM TV
3rd Floor Bramah House 65-71 Bermondsey Street London SE1 3XF
Tel: 020 7939 3160
Fax: 020 7403 2260
Email: info@fulcrumtv.com
Web Site: www.fulcrumtv.com
Head of Production: Martin Long
Administrator: Sandra Leeming

GALA PRODUCTIONS LTD
25 Stamford Brook Road, London W6 0XJ
Tel: 020 8741 4200 Fax: 020 8741 2323
Email: info@galaproductions.co.uk
Producer: David Lindsay

GRANADA INTERNATIONAL
48 Leicester Square, London WC2H 7FB
Tel: 020 7491 1441 Fax: 020 7493 7677
Email: int.info@granadamedia.com
Web: www.granadamedia.com/international
Managing Director: Nadine Nohr

HARCOURT FILMS
58 Camden Square, London NW1 9XE
Tel: 020 7267 0882 Fax: 020 7267 1064
Email: jmarre@harcourtfilms.com
Web Site: www.harcourtfilms.com
Managing Director: Jeremy Marre

HAT TRICK PRODUCTIONS
10 Livonia Street, London W1F 8AF
Tel: 020 7434 2451 Fax: 020 7287 9791
Email: info@hattrick.com
Web Site: www.hattrick.com
Managing Director: Denise O'Donoghue

HAWKSHEAD
Shepherd's Building Central, Charecroft Way, Shepherd's Bush, London W14 0EE
Tel: 08703 331 700 Fax: 020 8222 4401
Email: info@hawksheadtv.com
Web Site: www.hawksheadtv.com
Managing Director: Sarah Beadsmoore

HEAVY ENTERTAINMENT LTD
222 Kensal Road, London W10 5BN
Tel: 020 8960 9001 / 2 Fax: 020 8960 9003 Tel: 0207 494 1000
Email: info@heavy-entertainment.com
Web Site: www.heavy-entertainment.com
Contacts: David Roper, Davy Nougarede
Producers of broadcast programmes, promotional video and audio, EPKs, VNRs, radio and TV commercials, media training, audio books, ISDN interviews and live events. Audio studios for hire. Duplication services available.

HIT ENTERTAINMENT
5th Floor, Maple House, 149 Tottenham Court Road, London W1T 7NF
Tel: 020 7554 2500
Email: submissions@hitentertainment.com
Web Site: www.hitentertainment.com
Live Events Manager: Jonathan Blazer

HOURGLASS PICTURES
27 Prince's Road, Wimbledon, London SW19 8RA
Tel: 020 8540 8786 Fax: 020 8544 0787
Email: productions@hourglass.co.uk
Web Site: www.hourglass.co.uk
Director: Martin Chilcott

ILLUMINATIONS
19-20 Rheidol Mews, Rheidol Terrace, London N1 8NU
Tel: 020 7288 8400 Fax: 020 7359 1151
Email: illuminations@illumin.co.uk
Web Site: www.illuminations.co.uk
Contacts: Linda Zuck, John Wyver

INDEPENDENT FILMS LTD
3rd Floor 7a Langley Street, London WC2H 9JA
Tel: 020 7457 474 Fax: 020 7457 475
Email: mail@independ.net
Web Site: www.independ.net
Executive Producer: Jani Guest, Richard Packer

INDEPENDENT IMAGE
Overhills, Old Coach House, Woldingham, Caterham, Surrey CR3 7BB
Tel: 01883 654 867 Fax: 01883 653 290
Email: info@indimage.com
Web Site: www.indimage.com
Managing Director: David Wickham

INITIAL FILM & TV
Shepherd's Building Central, Charecroft Way, Shepherd's Bush, London W14 0EH

Tel: 0870 333 1700 Fax: 0870 333 1800
Email: jane.shaw@endomuluk.com
Web Site: www.endemoluk.com
Managing Director: Malcolm Gerrie

ITN FACTUAL
16 Mortimer Street, London W1T 3JL
Tel: 020 7430 4401 Fax: 020 7430 4576
Email: itn.factual@itn.co.uk
Web Site: www.itn.co.uk
Head of ITN Factual: Philip Dampier

JACARANDA PRODUCTIONS
6 Studland Street, Hammersmith, London W6 0JS
Tel: 020 8741 9088 Fax: 020 8748 5670
Email: creatives@jacaranda.co.uk
Web Site: www.jacaranda.co.uk
Managing Director: Katy Eyre

LITTLE KING COMMUNICATIONS
The Studio, 2 Newport Road, Barnes, London SW13 9PE
Tel: 020 8741 7658 Fax: 020 8563 2742
Email: littleking@squaremail.co.uk
Managing Director: Simon Nicholas

MAC FILMS
Waterworks House, Seven Acres Lane, Batheaston, Bath BA1 8EL
Tel: 01225 859 777
Managing Director: Ian MacArthur

MAGPIE PRODUCTIONS
PO Box 465, Broxbourne, Hertfordshire EN10 7RN
Tel/Fax: 01992 465 465
Email: mikwapparatus@aol.com
Senior Personnel: Mick Wilkojc, Phil Ward-Large

MAYDAY MANAGEMENT
34 Tavistock Street, London WC2E 7PB
Tel: 020 7497 1100 Fax: 020 7497 1133
Email: paulbird@maydaymgt.co.uk
Director: Anne James, Steve Abbott

MENTORN BARRACLOUGH & CAREY
43 Whitfield Street, London W1T 4HA
Tel: 020 7258 6800 Tel: 020 7258 6888
Email: mbc@mentorn.co.uk
Web Site: www.mentorn.co.uk
Chairman: Tom Gutteridege

MERCHANT IVORY
46 Lexington Street, London W1R 3LH
Tel: 020 7437 1200 Fax: 020 7734 1579
Email: paul@merchantivory.co.uk
Web Site: www.merchantivory.com
Managing Director: Ismail Merchant
Executive Producer: Paul Bradley

MIGHTY MEDIA
PO Box 73, Bourne End, Buckinghamshire SL8 5FJ
Tel: 01628 522 002 Fax: 01628 526 530
Email: info@mightymedia.co.uk
Managing Director: David Hughes

GRANT NAYLOR PRODUCTIONS
Shepperton Studios, Studios Road, Shepperton, TW17 0QD
Tel: 01932 592 175 Fax: 01932 592 484
Email: enquiries@grantnaylor.co.uk
Web Site: www.reddwarf.co.uk
General Manager: Helen Norman

NEBRASKA PRODUCTIONS
12 Grove Avenue, London N10 2AR
Tel: 020 8444 5317 Fax: 020 8444 2113
Email: nebraskaprods@aol.com
Producer: Brian Harding

NOEL GAY ORGANISATION
19 Denmark Street, London WC2H 8NA
Tel: 020 7836 3941 Fax: 020 7287 1816
Email: info@noelgay.com
Web Site: www.noelgay.com
Chief Executive Officer: Alex Armitage
Managing Director: Nick Ranceford-Hadley

OBJECTIVE PRODUCTIONS LIMITED
29 Mount View Road, London N4 4SS
Tel: 020 8348 5899 Fax: 020 8348 3277
Email: mpvine@aol.com
Web Site: www.objectiveproductions.net

OCTOBER FILMS
Spring House, 10 Spring Place, London NW5 3BH
Tel: 020 7284 6868 Fax: 020 7284 6869
Email: mark.brickman@octoberfilms.co.uk
Web Site: www.octoberfilms.co.uk
Drama Feature & Film Head of Development: Mark Brickman

OPTIMUM PRODUCTIONS
32 Thames Eyot, Cross Deep, Twickenham, Middlesex TW1 4QL
Tel: 020 8892 1403 Fax: 020 8892 6014
Email: yvonne@optiprod.co.uk
Web Site: www.optiprod.co.uk
Producer/Director: Yvonne Hewett

PARALLAX INDEPENDENT
7 Denmark Street, London WC2H 8LZ
Tel: 012 0657 4909 Fax: 020 7497 8062
Directors co-operative: Sally Hibbin

PARK ENTERTAINMENT
4th Floor, 50-51 Conduit Street, London W1S 2YT
Tel: 020 7434 4176 Fax: 020 7434 4179
Email: patricia@parkentertainment.com
Web Site: www.parkentertainment.com
Managing Director: Jim Howell
Sales Executive: Denise Vickers
TV Distribution.
Television Sales Director: Patricia Kershaw

PATHE
Kent House, 14-17 Market Place, Great Titchfield Street, London W1N 8AR
Tel: 020 7323 5151 Fax: 020 7631 3568
Email: lucy.savage@pathe-uk.com
Web Site: www.pathe.co.uk
Sales Co-ordinator: Lucy Savage

PBF MOTION PICTURES
Lilac Cottage, Portsmouth Road, Ripley, GU23 6ER
Tel: 01483 225 179
Email: image@pbf.co.uk
Web Site: www.pbf.co.uk
Director: Peter Fairbrass

PELICULA FILMS
59 Holland Street, Glasgow G2 4NJ
Tel: 0141 287 9522 Fax: 0141 287 9504
Email: peliculafilms@btinternet.com
Managing Director: Mike Alexander

PEPPER
Slinsby Place, Long Acre, London WC2E 9AB
Tel: 020 7632 4240 Fax: 020 7497 9305
Email: mailus@pepperpost.tv
Web Site: www.pepperpost.tv
Head Of Production: Andrew Swepson

PHOTOPLAY PRODUCTIONS
21 Princess Road, London NW1 8JR
Tel: 020 7722 2500 Fax: 020 7722 6662
Email: photoplay@compuserve.com
Contacts: Kevin Brownlow, Patrick Stanbury

PICTURE PALACE PRODUCTIONS
13 Egbert Street, London NW1 8LJ
Tel: 020 7586 8763 Fax: 020 7586 9048
Email: info@picturepalace.com
Web Site: www.picturepalace.com
Chief Executive: Malcolm Craddock

PREMIERE PRODUCTIONS LTD
3 Colville Place, London W1T 2BH
Tel: 020 7255 1650
Please contact before sending material.

PROSPECT PICTURES
13 Wandsworth Plain, London SW18 1ET
Tel: 020 7636 1234 Fax: 020 7636 1236
Email: rhys@prospect-uk.com
Web Site: www.prospect-uk.com
Managing Directors: Tony McAvoy, Barry Lynch, Rhys John.

QUADRANT TELEVISION
17 West Hill, Wandsworth,
London SW18 1RB
Tel: 020 8870 9933 Fax: 020 8870 7172
Email: quadranttv@aol.com
Managing Director: Nick Cookson
Production & Post-Production: Simon Jessey

RIDLEY SCOTT AND ASSOCIATES
42-44 Beak Street, London W1F 9RH
Tel: 020 7437 7426 Fax: 020 7734 4978
Email: kai@rsafilms.co.uk
Web Site: www.rsafilms.co.uk

ROYAL 1 RADIO
Glasgow Royal Infirmary, 84-106 Castle Street, Glasgow, Strathclyde G4 0SF
Tel: 0141 211 4835
Email: mayrutherford@yahoo.com
Company Secretary: May Rutherford

SCALA PRODUCTIONS
4th Floor Portland House 4 Great Portland Street London W1W 8QF
Tel: 020 7734 7060 Fax: 020 7612 003
Email: scalaprods@aol.com
Contact: Nik Powell

SEPTEMBER FILMS
Glen House, 22 Glenthorne Road, Hammersmith, London W6 0NG
Tel: 020 8563 9393 Fax: 020 8741 7214
Email: sulagraham@septemberfilms.com
Web Site: www.septemberfilms.com
Chief Executive: David Green
Head Of Production: Elaine Day
Managing Director: Sally Miles

SEVENTH HOUSE FILMS
1 Hall Farm Place, Burburgh, Norwich, Norfolk NR9 3LW
Tel: 01603 749 068 Mob: 07740 785 316
Fax: 01603 749 069
Producer: Clive Dunn
Production Manager: Angela Rule

SILVER PRODUCTIONS
The Granary Lower Road, Britford, Salisbury SP5 4DY
Tel: 01722 336 221 Fax: 01722 336227
Email: info@silver.co.uk
Web Site: www.silver.co.uk
Production Unit Manager: Mark Tucker
Director: Ethem Cetintas

SKYLINE PRODUCTIONS
10 Scotland Street, Edinburgh, Mid Lothian EH3 6PS Scotland
Tel: 0131 557 4580 Fax: 0131 556 4377
Email: admin@skyline.uk.com
Web Site: www.skyline.uk.com
Company Director: Leslie Hills

SPEAK EASY PRODUCTIONS
Wildwood House, Stanley, Perth, Perth & Kinross PH1 4PX Scotland
Tel: 01738 828 524 Fax: 01738 828 419
Email: info@speak.co.uk
Web Site: www.speak.co.uk
Director: Jim Adamson

SPIRIT FILMS
1 Wedgewood Mews, 12-13 Greek Street, London W1D 4BA
Tel: 020 7734 6642 Fax: 020 7734 9850
Director: Simon Cheek

JON STATON PRODUCTIONS
2 Percy Street, London W1T 1DD
Tel: 020 7637 5825 Fax: 020 7436 9740
Email: jstaton@dircon.co.uk
Web Site: www.re-active.net
Contact: Jon Staton

TABLE TOP PRODUCTIONS
1 The Orchard, Bedford Park,
London W4 1JZ
Tel: 020 8994 1269 Fax: 020 8742 0507
Email: alvin@tabletopproductions.com
Web Site: www.tabletopproductions.com
Director: Alvin Rakoff
Production Manager: Ben Berry

TALENT TV
72-75 Red Lion Street,
London WC1R 4NA
Tel: 020 7421 7800 Fax: 020 7421 7811
Email: entertainment@talenttv.com
Web Site: www.talenttv.com
Managing Directors: John K Cooper, Tony Humphreys

TALKBACK PRODUCTIONS
20-21 Newman Street, London W1T 1PG
Tel: 020 7861 8000 Fax: 020 7861 8001
Email: lorraine.heggessey@talkbackthames.tv
Web Site: www.talkbackthames.tv
Directors: Griff Rhys Jones, Peter Fincham

TALKING HEADS PRODUCTION
2-4 Noel Street, London W1F 8GB
Tel: 020 7292 7575 Fax: 020 7292 7576
Email: johnsachs@talkingheadproductions.com
Web: www.talkingheadsproductions.com
Senior Personnel: John Sachs
Specialising in film production, music supervision, casting and supervision of animation and production.

TALKING HEADS - THE VOICE AGENCY
2-4 Noel Street, London W1F 8GB
Tel: 020 7292 7575 Fax: 020 7292 7576
Email: voices@talkingheadsvoices.com
Web Site: www.talkingheadsvoices.com
Senior Personnel: John Sachs
Specialising in Voice Overs, Atlantic, Character, Impressionists, Broadcasters, DJ's, Personalities, Actors, Foreign, Presenters and Documentaries.

TEMPEST FILMS
33 Brookfield, Highgate West Hill,
London N6 6AT
Tel: 020 8340 6435 Fax: 020 8340 9309
Email: tempest_films@btinternet.com
Producer: Jacky Stoller

THE GOOD FILM COMPANY
5/6 Eton Garages, Lambolle Place,
London NW3 4PE
Tel: 020 7794 6222 Fax: 020 7794 4651
Email: yanina@goodfilms.co.uk
Web Site: www.goodfilms.co.uk
Managing Director: Yalina Barry
Good Films is a film, video and multi-media production Service Company. We provide you with your own London office, fully equipped with the latest technology, for instant communications and production support, as well as complete production services - research, budgeting, location scouting, casting, scheduling, crewing and post production. The Company has wide experience in all areas of visual communications - commercials, corporate films, music video, interactive CD Rom, photographic and television.

THIN MAN FILMS
9 Greek Street, London W1D 4DQ
Tel: 020 7734 7372 Fax: 020 7287 5228
Email: info@thinman.co.uk
Director: Simon Channing Williams

TIGER ASPECT PRODUCTIONS
7 Soho Street, London W1D 3DQ
Tel: 020 7434 6700 Fax: 020 7434 1798
Email: website@tigeraspect.co.uk
Web Site: www.tigeraspect.co.uk
Managing Director: Andrew Zein

TOM DICK & DEBBIE PRODUCTIONS
21 Kings Meadow, Ferry Hinksey Road, Oxford OX2 0DP
Tel: 01865 201 564
Email: info@tomdickanddebbie.com
Web Site: www.tomdickanddebbie.com

TRANS WORLD INTERNATIONAL
Unit 2 3 Burlington Lane, Chiswick,
London W4 2TH
Tel: 020 8233 5400 Fax: 020 8233 5401
Email: clacy@imgworld.com
Web Site: www.imgworld.com
Managing Director: Eric Drossard
VP of Business Affairs: Buzz Hornett
VP Production & Development: Bill Sinrich
VP UK & Europe: Michael Mellor
Contact Agents:
Caroline Lacy

Guy Kinnings
Jo Walkley

TWO FOUR PRODUCTIONS
Quay West Studios, Old Newnham, Plymouth, Devon PL7 5BH
Tel: 01752 727 400 Fax: 01752 344 224
Email: charles.wace@twofour.co.uk
Web Site: www.twofour.co.uk
Managing Director: Charles Wace

UNITED INTERNATIONAL PICTURES (UIP)
12 Golden Square London W1A 2JL
Tel: 020 8741 9041 Fax: 020 8748 8990
Marketing Tel: 0207 534 5200
Email: deborah.sheppard@uip.com
Web Site: www.uip.com
Contact Marketing Manager: Deborah Sheppard
Contact Non-Theatrical Manager: Terry Jones

UNITED TELEVISION ARTISTS
Baird House, 15-17 St Cross Street, London EC1N 8UW
Tel: 020 7831 4433 Fax: 020 7831 6633
Email: uta@unitedtv.co.uk
Web Site: www.unitedtv.co.uk/uta
Director: Bill Kerr-Elliott

VERA MEDIA
30-38 Dock Street, Leeds, West Yorkshire LS10 1JF
Tel: 0113 242 8646 Fax: 0113 242 8739
Email: vera@vera-media.co.uk
Web Site: www.vera-media.co.uk
Partners: Alison Garthwaite, Catherine Mitchell

VIDEO ARTS LTD
6/7 St Cross Street, London EC1N 8UA
Tel: 020 7400 4800 Fax: 020 7400 4900
Email: info@videoarts.co.uk
Web Site: www.videoarts.com
Marketing Manager: Kim Whigfield

BRIAN WADDELL PRODUCTIONS
Strand Studios, 5-7 Shore Road, Holywood, County Down BT18 9HX Northern Ireland
Tel: 028 9042 7646 Fax: 028 9042 7922
Email: strand@bwpltv.co.uk
Web Site: www.bwpltv.co.uk
Director: Brian Waddell

WISE BUDDAH CREATIVE LTD
74 Great Titchfield Street, London W1W 7QP
Tel: 020 7307 1600 Fax: 020 7307 1601
Email: sam.leese@wisebuddah.com
Web Site: www.wisebuddah.com
Senior Personnel: Paul Plant

WORKING TITLE
Oxford House, 76 Oxford Street, London W1D 1BS
Tel: 020 7307 3000 Fax: 020 7307 3001
Email: aliza@workingtitlefilms.com
Web Site: www.workingtitlefilms.com
Contacts: Tim Bevan, Eric Fellner
Contact Eric Fellner's Personal Assistant: Aliza James
Email: aliza@workingtitlefilms.com
To submit Action Programme applications:
action@workingtitlefilms.com

SCOTT-PAUL YOUNG ENTERTAINMENTS LTD
(Spy Productions)
Northern Lights House, 110 Blandford Road North, Langley, Near Windsor, Berkshire SL3 7TA
Tel/Fax: 01753 693 250
Email: castingdirect@spy-ents.com
Web Site: www.spy-lightentsworld.com
Managing Director: Scott-Paul Young
Artists management and exclusive representation for films, television, commercials, theatre, sports and modelling events and all areas of the light entertainment industry.

ZENITH PRODUCTIONS
43-45 Dorset Street, London W1U 7NA
Tel: 020 7224 2440 Fax: 020 7224 1027
Email: general@zenith-entertainment.co.uk
Web: www.zenith-entertainment.co.uk
Managing Director: Ivan Rendall

Record Companies

ARISTA LABELS
Bedford House 69-79 Fulham High Street London SW6 3JW
Tel: 020 7384 7700 Fax: 020 7973 0332
Email: abigail.williams@bmg.co.uk
Web Site: www.bmg.co.uk
Contact Agent: Abigail Williams

ATOMIC MUSIC LTD
Elm House, 133 Long Acre, Covent Garden, London WC2E 9DT
Tel: 020 7379 3010 Fax: 020 7420 7979
Email: ben@atomic-london.com
Web Site: www.atomic-london.com
Artist Management: Ben Newton

BARELY BREAKING EVEN
PO Box 25896, London N5 1WE
Tel: 020 7607 0597 Fax: 020 7607 4696
Email: lee@bbemusic.com
Web Site: www.bbemusic.com
Agent: Lee Bright

BERLIN PRODUCTIONS
Caxton House, Caxton Avenue, Blackpool, Lancashire FY2 9AP
Tel: 01253 591 169 Fax: 01253 508 670
Email: berlin.studios@virgin.net
Web Site: www.berlinstudios.co.uk
Contact: Mr R Sharples

BGS PRODUCTIONS
Newtown Street, Kilsyth, Glasgow, Strathclyde, G65 0JX Scotland
Tel: 01236 821 081 Fax: 01236 826 900
Email: info@scotdisc.co.uk
Web Site: www.scotdisc.co.uk
Senior Personnal: Dougie Stevenson, Bill Garden

BMG ENTERTAINMENTS INTERNATIONAL LTD
50 Great Marlborough Street, London W1F 7JS
Tel: 0207 4405 280
Email: info.uk@bmg.com
Web Site: www.bmg.com
Managing Director (UK & Ireland): Tony Moss
Music Rights Management.

CHAMPION RECORDS
181 High Street, London NW10 4TE
Tel: 020 8455 2469 Fax: 020 8965 3948
Email: raj@championrecords.co.uk
Web Site: www.championrecords.co.uk
Senior Personnel: Mel Medalie

THE CHRYSALIS GROUP
The Chrysalis Building, 13 Bramley Road, London W10 6SP
Tel: 020 7221 2213 Fax: 020 7221 6455
Email: katy.farnell@chrysalis.com
Web Site: www.chrysalis.com
Advertising Manager: Nick Morgan
PA to Managing Director: Stephanie Welsh

COLUMBIA RECORDS
10 Great Marlborough Street, London W1F 7LP
Tel: 020 7911 8200 Fax: 020 7911 8600
Email: jo_headland@uk.sonymusic.co.uk
Web Site: www.sonymusic.co.uk
Contact: Jo Headland

DEFECTED RECORDS
8 Charterhouse Buildings, Goswell Road, London EC1M 7AN
Tel: 0207 439 9995 Fax: 0207 432 6470
Email: tonit@defected.co.uk
Web Site: www.defected.co.uk
Press & PR Manager: Toni Tambourine
Label Manager: Kieran Mansfield

DIGIMIX RECORDS
Sovereign House, 12 Trewartha Road, Praa Sands, Penzance, Cornwall TR20 9ST

Tel: 01736 762 826 Fax: 01736 763 328
Email: info@digimixrecords.com
Web Site: www.digimixrecords.com
Contact: Roderick Jones
International record company working all styles of music and artists.

WALT DISNEY RECORDS
3 Queen Caroline Street, London W6 9PE
Tel: 020 8222 1416 Fax: 020 8222 1163
Email: zoe.hawkins@disney.com

ELEKTRA ENTERTAINMENT
American record label owned by Warner Music Group Today operates under label Atlantic Records
Electric Lighting Station 46 Kensington Court London W8 5DA
Tel: 020 7983 5500 Fax: 020 7761 6018
Email: emma.elwood@atlanticrecords.co.uk
Web Site: www.warnermusic.com

EMI RECORDS (UK) LTD
EMI House, 43 Brook Green, London W6 7EF
Tel: 020 7605 5000 Fax: 020 7605 5050
Email: emma.salmon@emimusic.com
Web Site: www.emirecords.co.uk

EPIC RECORDS
10 Great Marlborough Street, London W1F 7LP
Tel: 020 7911 8200 Fax: 020 7911 8600
Email: matt.reynolds@uk.sonymusic.com
Web Site: www.sonymusic.co.uk
Vice President of Human Resources: Colin Blears

FICTION RECORDS
364-366 Kensington High Street, London W14 8NS
Tel: 020 7471 5352 / 07779 294 412
Fax: 020 7471 5344
Email: fictionrecords@umusic.com
Web Site: www.fictionrecords.co.uk
Contact: Natalie Nissim

TONY GIBBER PRODUCTIONS
116-120 Seven Sisters Road, London N7 6AE
Mobile (main): 07956 225891 Fax: 020 8883 2732 Tel: 020 7607 9928
Email: tony@music4ads.co.uk
Senior Personnel: Tony Gibber

GLASSHOUSE PRODUCTIONS LIMITED
Democracy Records
Upper York Street, (Private Road East), Earlsdon, Coventry, Warwickshire CV1 3GQ
Tel: 024 7622 3892 Fax: 024 7622 9341
Email: admin@glasshouseproductions.co.uk
Web: www.glasshouseproductions.co.uk
Senior Personnel: Amos Anderson, Maria Faser

GO BEAT
22 ST.Peters Square London W6 9NW
Tel: 020 8910 3333

GOTHAM RECORDS
PO Box 6003, Birmingham B45 0AR
Tel: 0121 477 9553 Fax: 0121 693 2954
Email: barry@gotham-records.com
Web Site: www.gotham-records.com
Senior Personnel: Barry Tomes, Mac Goatcher, Tara Tomes

GUT RECORDS
Byron House, 112a Shirland Road, London W9 2EQ
Tel: 020 7266 0777 Fax: 020 7266 7734
Email: beth@gutrecords.com
Web Site: www.gutrecords.com
Agent: Beth Claridge

KICK ASS RECORDS
196 Chester Road, Warrington WA4 6AR
Tel: 01925 243 368 Fax: 01925 652 096
Mob: 07970 007 503
Email: mail@kickass.co.uk
Web Site: www.kickass.co.uk
Contact: David Kwitchley

THE KRUGER ORGANISATION - TKO
PO Box 130, Hove, East Sussex BN3 6QU
Tel: 01273 550 088 Fax: 01273 540 969
Email: h.kruger@tkogroup.com
Web Site: www.tkogroup.com
Senior Personnel: Drn Jeffrey Kruger MBE, Howard Kruger
Specialising in Concert & Event Promotions and Management.

M.I.C (MUSIC IN CREATION)
9 Eton Close Canvey Island Essex SS8 9RU
Tel: 07890 676338
Email: jono35@hotmail.com ; jono35@hotmail.com j; ono35@hotmail
Web Site: www.somebodysmusic.com
John Milton
Theraputic / Relaxation

MOTOWN RECORDS
364-366 Kensington High Street, London W14 8NS
tel: 020 7471 5019 fax: 020 7471 5294
Email: rebecca.jane.ram@umusic.com
Web Site: www.umusic.com
Contact Press & Promotions Office: Becky Ram

MUTE RECORDS LTD
429 Harrow Road, London W10 4RE
Tel: 020 8964 2001 Fax: 020 8968 4977
Email: info@mutehq.co.uk
Web Site: www.mute.com

ONE LITTLE INDIAN
34 Trinity Crescent, London SW17 7AE
Tel: 020 8772 7600 Fax: 020 8772 7601
Email: info@indian.co.uk
Web Site: www.indian.co.uk
Contact: Derek Birkett

PARK PROMOTIONS
PO Box 651, Oxford OX2 9RB
Tel: 01865 241 717 Fax: 01865 204 556
Email: info@parkrecords.com
Web Site: www.parkrecords.com
Managing Director: John Dagnell

PARLOPHONE
EMI House, 43 Brook Green, London W6 7EF
Tel: 020 7605 5000 Fax: 020 7605 5050
Email: murray.chalmers@emimusic.com
Web Site: www.parlophone.co.uk
Contact Agent: Murray Chalmers

POLYDOR LTD
364-366 Kensington High Street, London W14 8NS
Tel: 020 7471 5400 Fax: 020 7471 5319
Email: dan.drake@umusic.com
Contact agent: Dan Drake

QUIDETAM LTD
PO Box 3698, London NW2 6ZA
Tel: 020 7748 3003 Fax: 020 7691 7632
Email: info@quidetam.com
Web Site: www.quidetam.com
Contact: Diane Hinds

RCA RECORDS
Bedford House, 69-79 Fulham High Street, London SW6 3JW
Tel: 020 7384 7500 Fax: 020 7371 9298
Email: abigail.williams@bmg.co.uk
Web Site: www.bmg.com

RED ADMIRAL RECORDS
The Cedars, Elvington Lane, Hawkinge, Folkestone, Kent CT18 7AD
Tel: 01303 893 472 Mob: 07950 848 148 (Chris Ashman)
Email: info@redadmiralrecords.com
Web Site: www.redadmiralrecords.com
CEO: Chris Ashman

RED BUS RECORDINGS & TV STUDIOS
Studio House, 34 Salisbury Street, London NW8 8QE
Tel: 020 7402 9111 Fax: 020 7723 3064
Email: eliot@amimedia.co.uk
Web Site: www.amimedia.co.uk

ROJON RECORDS
Mob: 07890 676338
Email: jono35@hotmail.com
Web Site: www.rojonrecords.com
Contact: John Milton
Rock /Heavy Metal.

SOME BIZARRE LTD
14 Tottenham Court Road,
London W1T 1JY
Tel: 020 7836 9995
Email: info@somebizarre.com
Web Site: www.somebizarre.com
Senior Personnel: Stevo Pearce

SOMEBODYS MUSIC
Mob: 07890 676338
Email: jono35@hotmail.com
Web Site: www..somebodysmusic.com
Senior Personnel: John Milton
Accoustic singer songwriters / acoustic music

SONY BMG (UK)
Bedford House 69-79 Fulham High Street
London SW6 3JW
Tel: 020 7384 7500 Fax: 020 7371 9298
Email: phil.youngman@sonybmg.com
Web Site: www.sonybmg.co.uk
Contact Agent: Phil Youngman

SUBLIMINAL RECORDS
The Courtyard, Fulham Palace, Bishops Avenue, London SW6 6EA
Tel: 020 7751 0792 Fax: 020 7736 9470
Email: helen@subliminalrecords.com
Contact: Helen Coates

TRACK RECORD
PO Box 107, South Godstone, Redhill, Surrey RH9 8YS
Tel: 01342 892 074 Fax: 01342 893 411
Email: ian.grant@trackrecords.co.uk
Web Site: www.trackrecord.co.uk
Senior Personnel: Ian Grant

UNIVERSAL MUSIC INTERNATIONAL
22 st Peters Sqaure, London W6 9MW
Tel: 020 7 747 4000 Fax: 020 7747 4499
Email: shane.oneill@umusic.com
Web Site: www.umusic.com
Contact Agent: Shane O'neill

UNIVERSAL MUSIC UK LIMITED
364-366 Kensington High Street,
London W14 8NS
Tel: 020 8910 5000 Fax: 020 8741 4901
Web Site: www.umusic.com

UNIVERSAL/ISLAND RECORDS LTD
22 St Peters Square, London W6 9NW
Tel: 020 7471 5300 Fax: 020 8748 1998
Press Office: 020 7471 5300
Email: ted.cummings@umusic.com
Web Site: www.islandrecords.com / www.umusic.com
Contact Agent: Shane O'Neil

UPSET THE RHYTHM
Also a record label under the same name
363 North End Road, London SW6 1NW
Email: upset_the_rhythm@yahoo.com
Web Site: www.upsettherhythm.co.uk
Co-Concert Promotors: Andrew Doig & Andrew Hickson

UNIVERSAL CLASSICS & JAZZ
364-366 Kensington High Street
London W14 8NS
Tel: 020 7471 5067 Fax: 020 7471 5270
Email: martin.williams@umusic.com
Web Site: www.deccaclassics.com
Contact Marketing Manager: Martin Williams

VIRGIN RECORDS
Kensal House, 553-579 Harrow Road,
London W10 4RH
Tel: 020 8964 6000 Fax: 020 8968 6533
Email: scott.steele@virginmusic.com
Web Site: www.vmg.co.uk
Contact agent: Scott Steele

WARNER BROS RECORDS
The Warner Building 28 Kensington Church Street, London W8 4EP
Tel: 020 7368 2500 Fax: 020 7761 6062
Email: emma.jenkins@warnermusic.com
Web Site: www.wea.co.uk
Contact Agent: Pete Black

Corporate Event Organiser

Casino Nights

1ST CALL VIVA VEGAS
144A Old South Lambeth Road, London SW8 1XX
Tel: 020 7820 0999 Fax: 020 7820 0998
Email: enquiries@vivavegas.co.uk
Web Site: www.vivavegas.co.uk
Manager: David Gant

AKA RHYTHM
306 Michelgrove Worthing West Sussex BN13 3XQ
Tel: 01903 871221 Mob: 07909 894939
Web Site: www.akarhythm.co.uk

ROYAL CASINO ENTERTAINMENTS
24 West Parade, Sea Mills, Bristol, Avon BS9 2JX
Tel: 0117 923 6777
Email: enquiries@theroyalecasino.co.uk
Web Site: www.theroyalecasino.co.uk
We are a mobile fun casino. We cater for weddings, corporate events, birthdays, stag nights, sport events etc.
Contact: Julie

Caterers

AT HOME
40 High Street, Cobham, Surrey KT11 3EB
Tel: 020 7499 695 Fax: 01932 867 617
Email: parties@athomecatering.co.uk
Web Site: www.athomecatering.com

BENTLEY'S ENTERTAINMENTS
7 Square Rigger Row, London SW11 3TZ
Tel: 020 7223 7900 Fax: 020 7978 4062
Email: charlotte@bentleys.net
Web Site: www.bentleys.net
Contact: Charlotte Jenkinson
Specialising in Party Organisation.

BLUE STRAWBERRY
Unit 53/54, Southbank Commercial Centre, 140 Battersea Park Road, London SW11 4NB
Tel: 020 7498 0017 Fax: 020 7498 3103
Email: enquiries@bluestrawberry.co.uk
Web Site: www.bluestrawberry.co.uk

CHELSEA CATERING
6 Newington Court Business Centre, Newington Causeway, London SE1 6DF
Tel: 020 7403 0538 Fax: 020 7407 0537
Email: sales@chelseacatering.co.uk
Web Site: www.chelseacatering.co.uk

EAT YOUR HEARTS OUT
The Basement, 108a Elgin Avenue, London W9 2HD
Tel: 020 7289 9446 Fax: 020 7266 3160
Email: eyho@dial.pypex.com

EPICURE CATERING & PARTY DESIGN LTD
The Trident Bus Centre, Bickersteth Road, London SW17 9SH
Tel: 020 8288 8882 Fax: 020 8516 7741
Email: catering@epicure.uk.com
Web Site: www.epicure.uk.com
Epicure are experianced quality caterers providing wonderful modern stylish food for parties and corporate events at competitive prices. We work with many venues, event-organisers and marquee companies. Whether you want a canapes, a barbeque, themed stalls or a full sit down dinners, Epicure do it all.

Children's Entertainment

CHARLIE THE CLOWN
Flat 4 Carleton House 122A Hillfield Avenue London N8 7DQ
Tel: 07808 732 390
Email: info@charlietheclown.co.uk
Web Site: www.charlietheclown.co.uk
Senior Personnel: Lawrence Anthony
Specialising in children's entertainment for all ages. Choice of characters includes a clown, pirate, wizzard and story-teller. Entertainment includes clown and magic shows, singing and dancing, balloon, modelling & story-telling.

CHESTER BENSON PRODUCTIONS
PO Box 4227, Worthing, West Sussex BN11 5ST
Tel: 01903 248 258 Fax: 01903 700 389
Email: dave@davebensonphillips.co.uk
Web Site: www.davebensonphillips.co.uk
Proprietor: Dave Benson Phillips
A small company that's big on creating live shows and interactive experiences for children and adults. Over 20 years in the business, video & television! Producing "The all new Dave Benson Phillips Show", "Benson's Jumparound Activity Centres" and "Get Your Own Back". All shows are perfect for indoor/outdoor events.

CHILDREN LOVE STORIES
14 Leaside Mansions, Fortis Green, London N10 3EB
Tel: 020 8883 0034
Email: info@childrenlovestories.com
Web Site: www.childrenlovestories.com
Contact: Siaran Brooks
Story Telling for Children, touring the UK at festivals, art centres etc.

PAUL DUMAS ENTERPRISES
12 Malvern Close, Banbury, Oxfordshire OX16 9EL
Tel: 01295 258 120
Email: pauldumas@supernet.com
Entertainer: Paul Hilton

JUNGLE JIM
The Lower House West Street, Denbury, Newton Abbot, Devon TQ12 6DP
Tel: 01803 812 478 Mob: 07736 970 293
Email: jimmytamley@tiscali.co.uk
Web Site: www.junglejim.co.uk
Contact: Emma & Jimmy Tamley

KATZ ENTERTAINMENT
6A Stiles Syston, Leicester LE7 2BX
Tel: 0116 260 5381 Fax: 0116 260 5381
Mob: 07816 032 887
Katz entertainment has been Police checked and is an equity member. The most exhilarating party packages for children entertainment. Kitty Kat, Disco Duck and Dino The Dinosaur are Katz animated furry friends. Excellent compere, party dances, fun and games, singing, mini disco and balloon modelling. Over seas experience in top hotels.

MAGIC CATHERINE
4 Tamarind Court 75 Deepcut Bridge Road Camberley, Surrey GU16 6QP
Tel: 01252 837 885 Mob: 07770 227 812
Email: catherine@magicentertainment.co.uk
Web Site: www.magicentertainment.co.uk
Contact: Catherine

MEL'S MAGICAL PARTIES
10 Mount Road, Hertford SG14 2AH
Tel: 01992 552026
Email: mel@melsmagic.co.uk
Web Site: www.melsmagic.co.uk
Contact: Melanie Partner

PHILIP PARTRIDGE ENTERTAINMENT LTD
34 Winwood Road, East Didsbury, Manchester M20 5PE
Tel: 0161 448 2672 Mobile: 07970 871544
Email: magic@philippartridge.co.uk
Web Site: www.philippartridge.co.uk / www.magicphilip.co.uk (for family entertainment)
Contact: Philip Partridge
Philip makes your event memorable with his unique blend of Close-up Magic, the most personalised form of entertainment. Comedy Cabaret Magic will further enhance your event. His celebrity clients

include the Beckhams & he has amazed HRH The Prince of Wales. Manchester United, Shell U.K. & PC World Business are among his corporate clients. He is a Close-up & Cabaret Magic award winner & has appeared on TV with Prince Charles, Ann Robinson & Ian Wright. He is a Magic Circle & Equity member & carries full Public Liability Insurance. MAGIC PHILIP guarantees to put a smile on children's faces of all ages with his action packed show full of colourful comedy magic,
balloon modelling & audience participation. Philip will also host the whole party adding special non-elimination games & can even offer take home balloon presents!

PROFESSOR MYSTRAL'S JUVENILE OMNIBUS
65 Penylan Road, Cardiff, CF23 5HZ Wales
Tel: 029 2048 5544 Mobile: 07855 515350
Web Site: www.professormystral.co.uk
Proprietor: Frank Turvey
Children's/family entertainment under the names of Professor Mystral and Mister Magipatch.

PROFESSOR POTTY
45 David Newberry Drive, Lee-on-the-Solent, Hampshire PO13 8FG
Tel: 0800 043 5945 Mob: 07920 779 410
Email: tensai@tensaimagic.com
Web Site: www.professorpotty.co.uk
Contact: Alan Vandome

Q20 THEATRE
19 Wellington Crescent, Shipley, West Yorkshire BD18 3PH
Tel/Fax: 0845 126 0632 (10am - 5 pm Mon-Fri)
Email: info@q20theatre.co.uk
Web Site: www.q20theatre.co.uk
Artistic Director: John Lambert
Specialising in Full Event Creation and Ful-Scale Theatre Production for over three decades. Entertainment for Children, Family and Adult audiences, sourced from our comprehensive database of UK performers. All types of act and performers, inculding the best lookalikes from a range of UK agencies.

JIMMY TAMLEY
The Lower House West Street, Denbury, Newton Abbot, Devon TQ12 6DP
Tel: 01803 812 478 Mob: 07736 970 293
Email: jimmytamley@tiscali.co.uk
Web Site: www.jimmytamley.com or www.junglejim.co.uk
Contact: Emma & Jimmy Tamley

Cigar Suppliers

BURLINGTON BERTIE
57 Houndsditch, London EC3A 7BE
Tel: 020 7929 2242 Fax: 020 7929 2232
Email: havanas@bbertie-cigars.com
Web Site: www.bbertie-cigars.com
Specialist Cigar Merchant. Stockist of Cigar Accessories, humidors, cutter cases etc.

C.GARS LTD
Rowan House, 28 Queens Road, Hethersett, Norwich NR9 3DB
Tel: 07000 088 088 Fax: 020 7604 3983
Email: sales@cgarsltd.co.uk
Web Site: www.cgarsltd.com
We are the largest mail order cigar merchants in the uk. Rapid delivery, lowest prices guaranteed. Largest range of cigars in the country.

CIGARS UNLIMITED
129 Waltham Green Court, Moore Park Road, London SW6 2DG
Tel: 020 7386 9000
Email: sales@cigarsunlimited.co.uk
Web Site: www.cigarsunlimited.co.uk
CigarsUnlimited are South West London's leading Cigar Retailer specialising in fine cigars, humidors, gifts and accessories. We are recognised Habanos Gold Medal Specialists, Davidoff Depositaires and stockists of Dunhill and other non - Havana cigars. Mailorder and Trade enquiries welcome.

HAVANA MISS
P.O. Box 26415 London SE10 8WW
Tel: 020 8691 6001
Email: enquires@havanamiss.co.uk
Web Site: www.havanamiss.co.uk

SIMPLYCIGARS.CO.UK
25 Tabor Road, London W6 0BN
Tel/Fax: 020 8834 7123
Email: www.simplycigars.co.uk
Simply Cigars are one of the UK's market leaders offering authentic mail order Cuban Havana cigars, guaranteed by Habanos, with the trusted English Market Selection seal of authenticity as well as a range of humidors and cigar accessories.

THE CUBAN CONNECTION
194 High Street, Rochester, Kent ME1 1EY
Tel: 01634 829 966 Mob: 07811 431 516
Web Site: www.cubanconnection.co.uk
We are the first dedicated cigar shop in kent. Specializing in pure cuban and nicaraguan 'fat cigars'.

Climate Suppliers

AGGREKO UK
Aggreko House, Orbital 2, Voyager Drive, Orbital Retail Centre, Cannock, Staffordshire WS11 8XP
Tel: 01543 476000 Fax: 01543 476001
Email: info@aggreko.co.uk
Web Site: www.aggreko.co.uk
Manager: Stuart Parsons
Aggreko provides rental energy solutions including power, temperature control and 100% oil-free compressed air systems to companies worldwide. Service Centres operate on a 27/7/365 basis.

ANDREWS SYKES HIRE LTD
Unit 20, Manners Avenue, Manners Industrial Estate, Ilkeston, Derbyshire DE7 8EF
Tel: 0115 930 0179
Email: nottingham@andrews-sykes.com
Web Site: www.andrews-sykes.com
Hire & Sales of air conditioning heating and pumps.

ARCOTHERM(UK) LTD
Unit 11, Ecclesbourne Park, Clover Nook Road, Cotes Park Industrial Estate, Somercotes, Alfreton, Derbyshire DE55 4RF
Tel: 0845 600 44 99
Email: enquiry@arcotherm.co.uk
Web Site: www.arcotherm.co.uk

CELTIC COOLING & HEATING LTD
3 Hill Rise, Llanderyn, Cardiff CF23 6UH
Tel: 029 2054 1342
Web Site: www.celticcooling.co.uk
Air Conditioning, Refrigeration, Commercial & Residential, Design, Install & Maintain.

CLIMATE CONTROL SOLUTIONS
12 Coppingford Close, Peterborough, Cambridgeshire PE2 8PE
Tel: 01733 315 159 Fax: 01733 894 377
Email: wayne.12@tiscali.co.uk

Coach & Car Hire

AMERICAN STRETCH LIMOUSINES
Holmlea, Town Street, South Killingholme, Immingham North Lincolnshire DN40 3DA
Tel: 01472 345 233 Mob: 07932 633227
Email: enquiry@americanstretchlimo.co.uk
Web Site: www.americanstretchlimo.co.uk
American stretched limousine hire and chauffeur drive.
4 Limos.

Corporate & Promotional Gifts

BURST
Unit 6, The Angerstein Business Park,
Horn Lane, Greenwich,
London SE10 0RT
Tel: 020 8858 8851 Fax: 020 8858 9496
Email: info@burstuk.com
Web Site: www.burstuk.com

CREATIVE PROMOTIONS LTD
79 West Regent Street, Glasgow G2 2AW
Tel: 0141 332 7471 Fax: 0141 331 2801
Email: enquiries@creativepromotions.co.uk
Web Site: www.creativepromotions.co.uk
Corporate merchandise, sold all over europe and the Far East. Promote your company by putting your name onto Pens, Keyrings, Caps, Conference items, give aways etc. Helping people with there advertising budgets.

CUFFLINKS PLUS
Emblem House, Mount Pleasant, Barnet, Hertfordshire EN4 9HH
Tel: 020 8441 9911 Fax: 020 8440 7771
Web Site: www.cufflinksdirect.co.uk
We have been a manufacturer to the trade since 1973. We make cufflinks and promotional items. We are in the jewellery industry and specialize in gold and silver. We produce long service award pins and have also made trophies for various TV award shows ie. Daily Star Award.

ELEGANCE
92 High Street, Croydon CR0 1ND
Tel: 020 8401 2222 Fax: 020 8406 1877
Email: elegance@hostapartyanywhere.com
Web Site: www.hostapartyanywhere.com

MITREPRIZE LTD
Mitre House, 96-98 Braemar Avenue, South Croydon, Surrey, CR2
Tel: 020 8668 4999 Fax: 020 8668 1487
Email: rob@mitreprize.co.uk
Web Site: www.thepromotionalpeople.com
Specialising in producing personalised products and accessories for any event; from clothing to bags, pens, folders, and give-aways. With 1000's of products in our catalogues we also have global sourcing facilities allowing us to find the best product for your event.

QUARRY FOLD STUDIO
Billinge End Road, Pleasington, Blackburn BB2 6QY
Tel: 01254 207 620 Fax: 01254 209 945
Email: julia.schofield@quarryfoldstudio.com
Web Site: www.quarryfoldstudio.com
Contact: Julia Schofield

WORLD OF EXPRESSIONS
92 Fulham Palace Road, London W6 9PL
Tel: 020 8741 9988 Fax: 020 8741 3626
Email: info@worldofexpressions.com
Web Site: www.worldofexpressions.com
We are a retail party and balloon shop. We do a decoration service for weddings, corporate events and any occasion.

Corporate Entertainment & Hospitality

1ST LEISURE SUPPLIES
137 Hankinson Road, Charminster, Bournemouth BH9 1HR
Tel: 01202 525223 Fax: 01202 525224
Email: carl@1stleisuresupplies.com
Web Site: www.1stleisuresupplies.com
Managing Director: Andy George

ACF HOSPITALITY LTD
Aldwick Court Farm, Redhill, Bristol BS40 5RF
Tel: 01934 862 305 Fax: 01934 863 308
Email: info@acfteambuilding.co.uk
Web Site: www.acfhospitality.co.uk
Sales/Marketing Director: Mr Mark Fanning

AKA RHYTHM
306 Michelgrove Worthing West Sussex BN13 3XQ
Tel: 01903 871221 Mob: 07909 894939
Web Site: www.akarhythm.co.uk

SEAN ALEXANDER
32 Dunnock Drive Costessey Norwich NR8 5FF
Tel: 01603 746706 Mob: 07765 881894
Email: sean@seanalexandermagic.com
Web Site: www.seanalexandermagic.com
Contact: Sean Alexander
Please see full page ad within the Magicians & Illusionists section

ALIVE NETWORK
Ground Floor Suite, Silk Mill Studios, Princess Street, Newcastle, Staffordshire ST5 1DD
Tel: 0845 108 5500 Fax: 0845 226 3119
Email: dave@alivenetwork.com
Web Site: www.alivenetwork.com
Reception: Ingrid Avramovic
Senior Entertainment Co-ordinator: Gemma Jane
Entertainment Co-ordinators: Paul Ridley, Tony Woolliscroft, Pete Bacanin, Rececca Corneby, James Woodroffe, Seth Fullbrook, Nick Taylor
Artist Management: Richard Cowen, Kate Howard
Administration: Nicolle Van Veelen, Yvonne Van Veelen
Managing Director: David Bevan
Alive Network is the UK's largest supplier of live entertainment for weddings, corporate events and parties. We only work with the very best artists, all of whom are strictly vetted for quality and reliability. We are the only entertainment agency to offer online availability checking & fee quoting for our artists. Over 1000 of the very best live bands (inc. Hipster, e2, Pure, Fully Functional, Carte Blanche, Platinum Gold, VIP, Rat Pack is Back, King Pleasure, Ray Gelato), DJs, Entertainers and Event Suppliers

ALMOST ELTON
258 St. Johns Road, Yeovil, Somerset BA21 5QP
Tel: 07970 216 459
Email: matthewrock@almostelton.co.uk
Web Site: www.almosteltonjohn.com
Contact: Matthew Rock
A brilliant Elton John Tribute.

ALRIGHT CHARLIE
Flat 4 Carleton House 122a Hillfield Avenue London N8 7DQ
Tel: 07808 732 390
Email: info@alrightcharlie.co.uk
Web Site: www.alrightcharlie.co.uk
Senior Personnel: Lawrence Anthony
Charlie Chaplin Look Alike, Comedy waiter & Close-up Magician for all indoor and outdoor events.

AMAZING EVENTS
Sunshine Cottage Burton Row Brent Knoll Somerset TA9 4BY
Tel: 0844 332 0129 Mob: 07791 157719
Email: robbie@amazingevents.co.uk
Web Site: www.amazingevents.co.uk
Managing Director: Robbie Burns
Corporate Hospitality and Event Management specialists working nationwide, providing; themed parties, murder mysteries, team building, conference support and entertainers including celebrities and after-dinner speakers.

BAND OF TWO
26 Cumberland Court, 21 Cross Road, Croydon, Surrey CR0 6TE
Tel: 020 8680 4302
Email: petefyfe@aol.com
Web Site: www.bandoftwo.com
Contact: Peter Fyfe
"Specialising in Goodtime Celtic/Irish Songs, Tunes and Folk Dances."

B.F.P ENTERTAINMENTS
3 Queens Road, Corfe Mullen, Wimborne, Dorset BH21 3NE
Tel: 0845 6441951 Mob: 07778 809968

Email: bfpentertainment@yahoo.co.uk
Web Site: www.thebfpagency.co.uk
Contact: Mike Banting

BIGSTAR ENTERTAINMENTS
37 Dovedale Avenue, Long Eaton, Nottingham NG10 3HP
Tel: 0115 972 4849 Fax: 0115 973 3003
Email: dick@bigstarentertainments.co.uk
Web Site: www.bigstarentertainments.co.uk
Contact: Dick Hill
Specialises in club and corprate entertainment.

THE BOLLYWOOD BOOKING AGENCY
53 Newquay Road, Walsall WS5 3EL
Tel:07710 040 183
Email: info@bollywoodbookingagency.com
Web: www.bollywoodbookingagency.com
Contact: Shin Kang
Specialising in: Corporate Events, Dancers, Bands and Musicians.

BOO-BOO THE CLOWN'S ENTERTAINMENTS & PROMOTIONS
170 Watling Street, Grendon, Atherstone, Warwickshire CV9 2PH
Tel: 01827 715 011 Fax: 01827 715 665
Email: info@clownsareus.co.uk
Web Site: www.clownsareus.co.uk
Senior Personnel: David Cooper
Various forms of Corporate and Speciality entertainment. Nation-wide agency for every type of corporate, adult, family and childrens event.

BOOK A BAND
Ledston Engine Cottages, Ridge Road, Kippax, Leeds LS1 6DG
Tel: 08707 430 601 Fax: 08707 430 602
Email: bands@book-a-band.co.uk
Web Site: www.book-a-band.co.uk
Senior Personnel: Lenny Phillip
Party bands, wedding bands and function bands available.

JACK BRYCE
26 Lake View Close, Holly Park Plymouth Devon PL5 4LX
Tel: 01752 219 928 Mob: 07775 978 783
Email: jbmagic@tiscali.co.uk or magic@jackbryce.co.uk
Contact: Jack Bryce

BUSINESS EVENT MANAGEMENT
Moulton Park Business Centre, Redhouse Road, Moulton Park, Northampton NN3 6AQ
Tel: 01604 497 770 Fax: 01604 670 446
Email: enquiries@businessevent.co.uk
Web Site: www.businessevent.co.uk
Senior Personnel: Geoff Morgan
Specialising in all types of bespoke corporate entertainment/hospitality.

CASHBACK
35 Belfast Quay, Irvine, Ayrshire KA12 8PR
01294 276203 Mob: 07518 374 201
Email: ric@richerrington.co.uk
Web Site: www.richerrington.co.uk/ cashback or www.myspace.com/cashback-tribute
Contact: Richard Herrington

CIRCA GROUP
16 Church Road, Tunbridge Wells, Kent TN1 1JP
Tel: 01892 517 500 Fax: 01892 527 702
Email: info@circagroup.co.uk
Web Site: www.circagroup.co.uk
Film and video production, projection and technical consultancy and corporate event organisers.

COCKNEY DOODLE DO
Primrose Cotage Church Road, Barling Magna, Southend-on-Sea Essex SS3 0LS
Tel: 0800 970 8527 Tel: 01702 219 680
Mob: 07850 400 489
Email: clan.morris@boltblue.com
Contact: Peter Morris

COLCLOUGH ENTERTAINMENT & EVENTS
Newton House, 1 Newton Drive, Blackpool, Lancashire FY3 8BT
Tel: 01253 302262 Mobile: 07711 473 874 Fax: 01253 300 072
Email: laurayne@colclough-entertainment.co.uk
Web Site: www.colclough-entertainment.co.uk
Senior Personnel: Laurayne Colclough

COMEDY STORE MANAGEMENT
1a Oxendon Street, London SW1Y 4EE
Tel: 020 7839 1862 / 2949 Fax: 020 7930 2951
Email: charlotte@thecomedystore.co.uk
Web Site: www.comedystoremanagement.co.uk
Senior Personnel: Don Ward, Charlotte Smith

CORPORATE EVENTS SCOTLAND
44 Speirs Wharf, Glasgow, Strathclyde G4 9TH Scotland
Tel: 0141 332 6626 Fax: 0141 353 3671
Email: events@corporateeventscotland.com
Web Site: www.corporateeventscotland.com
Managing Director: Mr Don Spence
Events Manager: Sally Matheson
National and international excellence and creativity in gala events, entertainment & hospitality, conferences, team building and speakers.

CORPORATE HOSPITALITY SERVICES LTD
7b Town Street Farsley Pudsey LS28 5EN
Tel: 0113 236 2000 Fax: 0113 256 2100
Email: info@chsevents.co.uk
Web Site: www.chsevents.co.uk
Business Development Manager: Jo Raunsoey

DANCE CRAZY MANAGEMENT
294-296 Nether Street, Finchley Central, London N3 1RJ
Tel: 020 8343 0848 Fax: 020 8343 0747
Email: dancecm@aol.com
Web Site: www.dancecrazy.co.uk
Contacts: Kelly Isaacs
Specialises in reording arts, pa management & promotion, touring american artistes, clowns and corprate entertainment. Also includes artistes covering 70's up to present day music.

THE PETER DONEGAN BAND
21 Belsay Grove, Bedlington, Northumberland NE22 5YU
Mob: 07563 379 245
Email: peter-donegan@hotmail.com
Web Site: www.peterdonegan.com
Contact: Peter Donegan

DROP DEAD DIVAS
34 Skylark Walk, Chelmsford CM2 8BA
Tel: 01245 347 977
Email: jo.ramjane@btopenworld.com
Web Site: www.dropdeaddivas.com
Contacts: Jo Ramjane

ANDY EASTWOOD
PO Box 5004 Christchurch, Dorset BH23 5WD
Tel: 01425 275 830 Mob: 07950 454 365
Email: andy@andyeastwood.com
Web Site: www.andyeastwood.com
Contacts: Andy Eastwood

ELVIS SHMELVIS
Tel: 01727 858 606
Email: elvis@shmelvis.com
Web Site: www.shmelvis.com
Contact: Sue & Martin
Please see full page advert in the Corporate Entertainment & Hospitality section for more details.

FAMOUS FACES
PO Box 69, Kingsbridge, Devon TQ7 4WZ
Tel: 01548 559 165 Fax: 01548 559 165
Louise EspigTel: 08452
Email: ideas@famousfaces.co.uk
Web Site: www.famousfaces.co.uk

Contact: Jeremy Harmer
Famous Faces provide speakers, celebrities and cabaret artistes for promotional activities, conference and corporate entertainment, catering for all occasions and audiences.

LIONEL FANTHORPE
48 Claude Road, Roath Cardiff CF24 3QA
Tel: 029 2049 8368 Mob: 07767 207 289
Fax: 029 2049 6832
Email: fanthorpe@aol.com
Web Site: www.lionel-fanthorpe.com
Contact: Lionel Fanthorpe

FAWLTY TOWERS - EDMOND WELLS AS JOHN CLEESE
2 The Maltings, Fenlane Beccles, Suffolk NR34 9BT
Tel: 01485 570 945 Mob: 07767 863 415
Email: info@johncleese.co.uk
Web Site: www.johncleese.co.uk
Contact: Edmond Wells

JEM FRAZER LIMITED
6 Shancara Court, Tingley, Wakefield, West Yorkshire WF3 1JP
Tel: 01132 529 062 Mob: 07870 666 840
Email: jem@jemfrazer.co.uk
Web Site: www.jemfrazer.co.uk
Contact : Jem Frazer
Please see ads : Haurel and Lardy, Ziddler, Funderbirds, Jem Frazer Characters, Hogwarts characters

CHRISTOPHER GEE
32 Clydesdale Gardens, North Berstead Bognor Regis, West Sussex PO22 9BE
Tel: 01243 861 171 Mob: 07794 218295
Email: christopher_gee@btinternet.com
Web Site: www.christopher-gee.com
Contact: Christopher Gee

TIM GENTLE MUSIC
PO Box 154 Stockton-on-Tees, Cleveland TS20 1XJ
Tel: 01642 557 979 Fax: 01642 557 677
Mob: 07850 515 058
Email: timgentle@hotmail.com
Web Site: www.thehitmen.eu
Contact: Tim Gentle

THE GRAFFITI CLASSICS
37 Twickenham Road, Leytonstone, London E11 4BN
Tel/Fax: 020 8556 5949 Mob: 07956 909981
Email: info@graffiticlassics.com
Web Site: www.graffiticlassics.com
The Group's unique character and style has developed a refreshing insight into the world of classical music, the principal aim being to entertain, educate and bring an interactive involvement to all audiences of all ages and abilities.

ANDREW JAMES
Tel: 07880 557 428
Email: andrew.rafferty@ntlworld.com
Web Site: www.easy-lover.co.uk / www.illinoisbluesbrothers.com
Contact: Andew James

LEEANN JAMES
3 Gilbert House Old Coach Road, Runcorn, Cheshire WA7 1NJ
Tel: 07885 084 223
Email: leejay1@tiscali.co.uk
Web Site: www.leeannjames.com
Contact: Leeann James

LADIES OF ROCK
C/O 15 Yew Tree Court Alsager Cheshire ST7 2YQ
Tel: 01270 883 080 Mob: 07710 784 913
Email: tinacher@paularandell.com
Web Site: www.paularandell.com
Contact: Paula Randell

LONDON CHINESE ACROBATICS
118 Albany Road, Leighton Buzzard, Bedfordshire LU7 1NS
Tel: 01525 633 944 Fax: 01525 370 642
Email: chineseacrobatic@hotmail.com
Web Site: www.chinesedance-acrobatic.co.uk
Contact: Jiang

MAD ENTERTAINMENTS AGENCY
56 New Croft, Weedon, Northampton NN7 4RJ
Tel: 01327 349 938 Mobile: 07788 570 747
Email: dd.colonel@btopenworld.com
Senior Personnel: David Dickens
Corporate Events & Product Launches catered for. Any type of Entertaiment catered for. Any Budget. Management for the Billy Fury Band & Darren H. (Elvis Presley Tribute). Agents for 60s, 70s & 80s Tribute Bands and Morris Dancers.

MAGIC CATHERINE
4 Tamarind Court 75 Deepcut Bridge Road Camberley, Surrey GU16 6QP
Tel: 01252 837 885 Mob: 07770 227 812
Email: catherine@magicentertainment.co.uk
Web Site: www.magicentertainment.co.uk
Contact: Catherine

MEDIA CIRCUS
Room 6, Roslin House, Sun Street, Hitchin, Hertfordshire SG5 1AE
Tel: 01737 852 151 Fax: 01737 852 101
Email: mark@webprojects.co.uk
Contact: Mark Walmsley
Spoof Paparazzi.

PETER MORRIS
Primrose Cottage 11 Church Road, Barling Magna, Southend-on-Sea Essex SS3 0LS
Tel: 0800 970 8527 Tel: 01702 219 680
Mob: 07850 400 489
Email: peter.clan.morris@gmail.com
Contact: Peter Morris

NEVER 4 GET
14 Pavilion Court Northlands Road Southampton SO15 2NN
Tel: 02380 829 385 Mob: 07814 454 796
Email: lee@never4getmusic.com
Web Site: www.never4getmusic.com
Contact: Lee Cornick

OPAL MOON SERVICES LTD
Opal House, 155 Castle Road, Bedford MK40 3RT
Tel/Fax: 01234 403 593 Mobile: 07970 932944
Email: opalfc@aol.com
Senior Personnnel: Amanda Lovell, Fausto Cataldo
Professional discos

CLIVE PANTO PRODUCTIONS
Water's Edge, Frogmill, Hurley, Berkshire SL6 5NL
Tel: 01628 826 999 Fax: 01628 820 000
Email: murder@clivepanto.co.uk
Web Site: www.clivepanto.co.uk
Proprietor: Clive Panto
Contact: Clive Panto
The original murder mystery based on all the gossip and scandal in your company. Also pantomimes, gameshows, sci-fi, films.

PERSONALITY ARTISTES LTD
Worldwide Headquarters PO Box 1 Poulten le Fylde Blackpool, Lancashire FY6 7WS
Tel: 01253 899 988 Fax: 01253 899 333
Mobile: 07860 479092
Email: info@personalityartistes.com
Web Site: www.personalityartistes.com
Contact: Mal Ford & Jean Parkes
Corporate Entertainment specialists and Artistes Management.

PLANET 80S
PO Box 441 Ashford, Kent TN23 9EL
Tel: 07799 262 068
Email: planet80s@hotmail.co.uk
Web Site: www.planet80s.webs.com
Contacts : Phil Marks

THE POLICE CHIEFS
20 Spencer Drive, Midsomer Norton, Radstock BA3 2DN
Tel: 07974 690 181
Email: bullit7@live.co.uk
Web: www.myspace.com/thepolicechiefs
Contact: Olly Wise

PRELUDE
Suite 3,Ground Floor Nimax House 20 Ullswater Crescent Coulsdon
Surrey CR5 2HR
Tel: 020 8660 6647 Fax: 010 8660 6657
Email: sales@preludeentertainment.co.uk
Web Site:
www.preludeentertainment.co.uk
Managing Director: Rodney Prout
Administrator: Julianne Basten
Specialising in a variety of entertainment for corporate and private events.

THE PRODUCTION ASSOCIATES (TPA)
23/24 Titan Court, Laporte Way, Luton
Bedfordshire LU4 8EF
Tel: 0845 226 8136 Fax: 0845 226 8137
Email:
steve@theproductionassociates.com
Web Site: www.theproductionassociates.com
Contact: Steve Donnelly
TPA supplies the very best live entertainment for any event, venue or occasion.

THE Q BAND
20 Coombes Way, North Common Bristol
BS30 8YP
Tel: 0117 940 0929 Tel: 0117 932 6244
Mob: 07801 627 859
Mob: 07853 944 227
Email: mail@theqband.co.uk
Web Site: www.theqband.co.uk
Contact: Brian Allen

Q20 THEATRE
19 Wellington Crescent, Shipley, West Yorkshire BD18 3PH
Tel/Fax: 0845 126 0632 (10am - 5 pm Mon-Fri)
Email: info@q20theatre.co.uk
Web Site: www.q20theatre.co.uk
Artistic Director: John Lambert
Specialising in Full Event Creation and Ful-Scale Theatre Production for over three decades. Entertainment for Children, Family and Adult audiences, sourced from our comprehensive database of UK performers. All types of act and performers, inculding the best lookalikes from a range of UK agencies.

RADIO CITY PRODUCTIONS
13 Montagu Mews South, London W1H 7ER
Tel: 0871 250 1234
Email: jim@celebrity.co.uk
Web Site: www.radio-city.co.uk
Agent: Jim Dameco
Music and Comedy for corporate entertainment.

RICKY LOPEZ RATPACK AND SWING SHOW
Tel: 01727 858 606
Email: ricky@rickylopezratpack.com
Web Site: www.rickylopezratpack.com
Contact: Sue & Martin
Please see full page advert in the Corporate Entertainment & Hospitality section for more details.

RIVIERA ENTERTAINMENTS
8, Boulevard d'Aguillon 06600 Antibes
France
Tel: 0033 493 776658 Fax: 0033 493 776672
Email: peter@rivieraentertainments.com
Web Site: www.rivieraentertainments.com

GARY RYAN - NEIL DIAMOND TRIBUTE
135 Hughes Street, Bolton BL1 3EZ
Tel: 07919 485 495
Email: g.ryan2@btinternet.com
Web Site: www.neildiamond-tribute.com
Contact: Gary Ryan

SCOTT JORDAN ENTERTAINMENT LTD
25-29 Station Street, Sittingbourne, Kent
ME10 3DU
Tel: 0845 094 1455
Email: enquiries@scottjordan.co.uk
Web Site: www.scottjordan.co.uk
Contact : Scott Jordan, Stephen Middleton
Entertainment booking agency providing quality tribute bands, function bands, comedians and magicians for weddings, private parties, and venues accross the U.K

SPEAKOUT CELEBRITIES & PRESENTERS LIMITED
Midlothian Innovation Centre, The Bush, Roslin, Midlothian EH25 9RE
Tel: 0131 440 9226 Fax: 0131 440 3262
Email: info@speakoutuk.com / info@tmcentertainment.co.uk
Web Site: www.tmcentertainment.co.uk / www.speakoutuk.com
Events Manager: Noel Rocks, Kenny Donaldson

PATRICIA SPERO
Oaks Farm Vicarage Lane Chigwell Essex
IG7 6LT
Email: patricia.spero@btinternet.com
Web Site: www.impulse-music.co.uk/spero.htm
Contacts: Patricia Spero

SPIRIT INTERNATIONAL ARTISTS LTD
Ivy House 35 High Street Bushey Herts
WD23 1BD
Tel: 020 8421 7171 Mob: 07921 113119
Email: angela@spiritartists.com
Web Site: www.spiritartists.com
Managing Director: David King

STARDREAM LTD
'Party House', Mowbray Drive, Blackpool, Lancashire FY3 7JR
Tel: 01253 302 602 Fax: 01253 301 000
Email: johnbarnett@stardream.co.uk
Senior Personnel: John & Danielle Barnett
Dealing in the supply of all forms of Corporate Entertainment.

SAMANTHA STARR
80 Coronation Road, Wolverhampton
Heath Town WV10 0QH
Tel: 01902 659 769 Mob: 07812 998 754
Email: sammystarr@blueyonder.co.uk
Web Site: www.samanthastarr.co.uk
Contact : Samantha Starr

BOBBY SUMMERS
69A Bure Lane, Christchurch, Dorset
BH23 4DL
Tel: 01425 277 226 Mob: 07799 214 460
Fax: 01425 279 320
Contact: Bobby Summers

SUPERBFUNCTIONS.COM
161(D) Ashley Road, Hale, Cheshire,
Tel: 0800 298 6338
Email: steve@superbfunctions.com
Web Site: www.superbfunctions.com
Proprietor: Mr McCrory
From DJs to Major Names, Tribute Bands, Theme Nights to After-Dinner Speakers.

JIMMY TAMLEY
The Lower House West Street, Denbury, Newton Abbot, Devon TQ12 6DP
Tel: 01803 812 478 Mob: 07736 970 293
Email: jimmytamley@tiscali.co.uk
Web Site: www.jimmytamley.com or www.junglejim.co.uk
Contact: Emma & Jimmy Tamley

MANY FACES OF DEAN TAYLOR
116 Fullarton Crescent, South Ockendon, Essex RM15 5HZ
Tel: 01708 856 022 Mob: 07956 217 954
Email: Themanyfacesofdt@aol.com
Contact: Dean Taylor

THE BOLLYWOOD THEME COMPANY
53 Newquay Road, Walsall WS5 3EL
Tel: 07710 040 183
Email:
www.bollywoodthemecompany.com
Web Site: www.bollywoodthemecompany.com
Contact: Shin Kang
Specialising in: Corporate Events, Christmas Parties & Event Management.

THE ILLINOIS BLUES BROTHERS
Tel: 07880 557 428

Email: andrew.rafferty@ntlworld.com
Web: www.theIllinoisbluesbrothers.com
Contact: Andrew Rafferty

THE MAGIC OF MUSICALS
PO BOX 31187 London E16 3FT
Tel: 020 7476 8440 Mob: 07702 543117
Email: colin@abbagirls.com
Web Site: www.themagicofmusicals.co.uk
Contacts: Colin

THE MAGIC OF MUSICALS
PO Box 31187 London E16 3FT
Tel : 020 7476 8440
Mob: 07702 543 117
Email: colin@abbagirls.com
Web Site: www.themagicofmusicals.co.uk
Contact: Colin

TRIBUTE TO BUDDY HOLLY
High House Farm Asheldham, Southminster, Essex CM0 7NX
Tel: 01621 778 886 Mob: 07889 426 343
Email: marcusejrobinson@hotmail.com
Contact: Marc Robinson

UKOM
3 Chapel Close, Humbleton, Hull East Yorkshire HU11 4NP
Tel: 01964 670 162 Mob: 07912 421 876
Email: steve@elvislovingyou.com
Web Site: www.elvislovingyou.com
Contact: Steve Caprice

VISION PROMOTIONS
Unit 8, Robinson Close, Telford Way Industrial Estate, Kettering, Northamptonshire NN16 8PU
Tel: 01536 312 106 Fax: 01536 312 961
Email: sales@visionpromotions.co.uk
Web Site: www.visionpromotions.co.uk
Contact: David Perkins

WHATEVER ARTISTS MANAGEMENT LTD
F24 Argo House, Kilburn Park Road, London NW6 5LF
Tel: 020 7372 4777 Fax: 020 7372 5111
Email: info@wamshow.biz
Web Site: www.wamshow.biz
Senior Personnel: Jenny Dunster
All types of entertainers booked for corporate and private events with full technical on-site management services.

Corporate Event Suppliers

ENTERTAINING OPTIONS LTD
8 Belmont, Bath BA1 5DZ
Tel: 01225 422 002 Fax: 01225 422 003
Email: info@entertainingoptions.co.uk
Web Site: www.entertainingoptions.co.uk
Top quality entertainers, musicians and activities, supplied nationwide by established corporate entertainment agenies. For showbands, speakers, stilt walkers, speciality acts and everything in between. Plus friendly advice.

ES PROMOTIONS
Unit 24, Larkwood, Larkwood Close, Kettering, Northamptonshire NN16 9NQ
Tel: 01536 310 520 Fax 01536 358 113
Email: sales@es-promotions.com
Web Site: www.es-promotions.com
Financial Director: Dave Turner
The Agency supplies circus performers, children's entertainment, street entertainers, arena and aerial acts.
Outdoor event specialists, entertainment agency, team events, themed events, fun casino. Inflatables and unusual games for hire. Balloons, balloon gas, balloon releases and balloon decorating.

GREGORY'S AMUSEMENTS
54 Mead Lane, Chertsey, Surrey KT16 8NW
Tel/Fax: 01923 570 501 Mobile: 07976 297735
Contacts: Michael & Ann Gregory

ICE SCULPTURE BY GLOBAL ICE
Unit 41, Halifax Road, The Metropolitan Centre, Greenford, Middlesex UB6 8XU
Tel: 020 8575 7112 Fax: 020 88131315
Email: ice0181@aol.com
Web Site: www.icesculpture.net
Senior Personnel: Glenn Harding, Tracy Dixon
Ice sculptures for corporate events, promotions and private functions. Virtually anything can be created in ice. UK delivery direct to the venue.

JAM HOT PRODUCTIONS
38 Surbiton Hill Park, Surbiton, Surrey KT5 8ES
Tel: 020 8390 2275 Fax: 020 8390 2275
Mob: 07889 431 004
Email: bazmoran@btinternet.com
Contact: Barry Moran

PETER JOHNSON ENTERTAINMENTS LTD
Hastings Road, Hawkhurst, Kent TN18 4RT
Tel: 01580 754 822 Fax: 01580 754 808
Email: enquiries@peterjohnson.co.uk
Web Site: www.peterjohnson.co.uk
Senior Personnel: Peter Johnson, Mandy O'Nion
Specialising in all forms of Outdoor Entertainments. Arena Entertainments, Mix 'n' Mingle,Corporate Participation Attractions and Music and Dance Groups.

LIVE BUSINESS GROSVENOR PRODUCTIONS
136-144 New Kings Road Fulham London SW6 4LZ
Tel: 020 7384 2050
Email: jobs@livebusiness.co.uk
Web Site: www.livebusiness.co.uk
Contact: Peter Chittenden, Blain Fairman, Mark Dixon
Supplying entertainment of all kinds to the leisure industry and corporate clients as well as to individual private events.

NEW YORK PRODUCTIONS
Unit 1 Shaws Building Deptford Terrace, Sunderland SR4 6DD
Tel: 0191 565 1222 Fax: 0191 565 1333
Email: Dave@newyorkproductions.co.uk
Web Site: www.newyorkproductions.co.uk
Contact: David Arkley

THEME CREATION
3 Campion Way, Dickens Heath, Solihull, B90 1RX
Tel/Fax: 0121 744 2500
Email: info@themecreation.co.uk
Web Site: www.themecreation.co.uk
Theme Creation for conferences and events. Suppliers of room decor, lighting, sound, starcloths and electrical installation services.

THEME TRADERS
The Stadium, Oaklands Road, London NW2 6DL
Tel: 020 8452 8518 Fax: 020 8450 7322
Email: mailroom@themetraders.com
Web Site: www.themetraders.com
Co-Director: Kim Einhorn.
Contact the Projects Office.
See our website for further details.

Costumiers

FANTASY DRESS HIRE
20 Abbey Drive, Ashby-de-la-Zouch, Leicestershire LE65 2LX
Tel: 01530 413 998 Fax: 01530 564 601
Email: davidcooper@ashby7777.fsbusiness.co.uk
Contact: David Cooper
Supply over 4000 different costumes, accessories, hats, wigs, masks & novelty items.
Period, traditional, fairy tale & nursery rhymes & cartoon characters a speciality.
Costumes can be made to order - hire/sale.

GABBYS
Unit 4, 131 Vauxhall Road, Liverpool L3 6BN
Tel/Fax: 0151 707 6555
Tel: 0151 255 1230
Email: gab10@btconnect.com

Web Site: www.gabbys.co.uk
General Manager: Gabriella Marie

TRENDS ENTERTAINMENT
Unit 4, 9 Chorley Road, Blackpool, FY3 7XQ
Tel: 01253 396 534
Email: info@trendsentertainment.com
Web Site: www.trendsentertainment.com
Contact: Antony Johns

Dance Floors

A1 EVENT SOLUTIONS
Station Yard, Holnes Chapel, Cheshire CW4 8AA
Tel: 01477 544 222 Fax: 01477 544 808
Email: sales@eventsolutions.co.uk
Web Site: www.eventsolutions.co.uk

ABINGER MARQUEE HIRE
54 Haydon Place, Guildford,
Surrey GU1 4NE
Tel: 01483 536 270 Fax: 01483 306 551
Email: info@guilfest.co.uk
Web Site: www.guilfest.co.uk
Manager: Tony Scott

BRISTOL (UK) LTD
1 Sutherland Court, Moor Park Industrial Centre, Tolpits Lane, Watford WD18 9SP
Tel: 01923 779 333 Fax: 01923 779 666
Email: tech.sales@bristolpaint.com
Web Site: www.bristolpaint.com
Managing Director: Mark Chapman
Manufactures of water-based paints and coatings for the Film, Television and Theatre sectors, and Exhibition & Visual Merchandising Industries. Also available: Reversible, instant lay, flat PVC studio / dance flooring which can be decorated with exclusive water based PVC painting system; Special range of paints and matching fabric for visual effects backings; Anti-Graffiti coating; Range of Fire protection products. Newly available: Stardust range of Glitter paints.

HARLEQUIN (BRITISH HARLEQUIN PLC)
Festival House, Chapman Way, Tunbridge Wells, Kent TN2 3EF
Tel: 01892 514888 Fax: 01892 514222
Email: enquiries@harlequinfloors.com
Web Site: www.harlequinfloors.com
Sales Manager: Rebecca Conway
Established in 1979, Harlequin produces a world renowned range of portable and permanent floors, together with three sprung floor systems.

MARLDON MARQUEES
111 Winner Street, Paignton,
Devon TQ3 3BP
Tel: 01803 524 425 Fax: 01803 666 888
Web Site: www.marldonmarquees.co.uk

PRINCIPAL FURNITURE LTD
Arkwright Road, Bicester, Oxon OX26 4UU
Tel: 01869 324 488 Fax: 01869 324 012
Email: sales@principalfurniture.co.uk
Web Site: www.principalfurniture.co.uk

Decorating & Event Theming

88 EVENTS COMPANY
Larchfield Court, Ibrox Business Park, Woodville Street Glasgow G51 2RQ
Tel: 0141 445 2288 Fax: 0141 445 1188
Email: info@88eventscompany.com
Web Site: www.88eventscompany.com

AMAZING PARTY THEMES
The Forum 277 London Road Burgess Hill West Sussex RH15 9QU
Tel: 0870 759 1901 Fax: 0870 759 1902
Email: info@amazingpartythemes.com
Web Site: www.amazingpartythemes.com
Contact: Steve

AWESOME EVENTS
Suite F19 Argo House Argo Business Centre Kilburn Park Road London NW6 5LF
Tel: 0845 644 6510 Fax:: 0845 644 6520
Email: sales@awesome-events.co.uk
Web Site: www.awesome-events.co.uk

ENTERTAINING OPTIONS LTD
8 Belmont, Bath BA1 5DZ
Tel: 01225 422 002 Fax: 01225 422 003
Email: info@entertainingoptions.co.uk
Web Site: www.entertainingoptions.co.uk
Top quality entertainers, musicians and activities, supplied nationwide by established corporate entertainment agenies. For showbands, speakers, stilt walkers, speciality acts and everything in between. Plus friendly advice.

Disco Equiptment

ADAM HALL LTD
10 The Seedbed Business Centre, Vanguard Way, Shoeburyness, Essex SS3 9QY
Tel: 01702 613 922 Fax: 01702 617 168
Email: mail@adamhall.co.uk
Web Site: www.adamhall.com
Contact: Mark Stimpson
Distributor and supplier of fittings and hardware for flight cases and loudspeaker cabinets. Own brand stands for lighting, sound and musical instruments. Newly launched Adam Hall Cables. Sole distributor of Amphenol Audio Connectors, Palmer Professional Audio Tools and Power Amplifiers.

KNIGHT SOUND & LIGHT
98-100 Uxbridge Road, Hanwell, London W7 3SU
Tel: 020 8579 0144 Fax: 020 8579 8222
Email: andy@knightsoundandlight.com
Web Site: www.knightsoundandlight.com
Sales, repair hire, installation, part exchange, export of professional sound and lighting equiptment.

MIDDLESEX SOUND & LIGHTING LTD
4-6 Village Way East, Rayners Lane, Harrow, Middlesex HA2 7LU
Tel: 020 8866 5500 Fax: 020 8866 3757
Email: msl@middlesexsound.co.uk
Web Site: www.middlesexsound.co.uk
We are a audio visual installation company for the bar club restaurant and leisure industry.

NEW YORK PRODUCTIONS
Unit 1 Shaws Building Deptford Terrace, Sunderland SR4 6DD
Tel: 0191 565 1222 Fax: 0191 565 1333
Email: Dave@newyorkproductions.co.uk
Web: www.newyorkproductions.co.uk
Contact: David Arkley

STAGE TWO LIMITED
Unit J, Penfold Estate, Imperial Way, Watford, Hertfordshire WD24 4YY
Tel: 01923 230 789 Fax: 01923 255 048
Email: info@stage-two.co.uk
Web Site: www.stage-two.co.uk
Hire or Sale of sound, lighting and special effects for all applications. Special effects Flash Pots, Maroons, Bullet Hits. Supplier of special effects for stage, films and TV.

STEVE YOUNG MOBILE DISCOS & EQUIP HIRE
20 Malden Road, Kentish Town, London NW5 3HN
Tel: 020 7485 1115 Fax: 020 7267 6769
Web Site: www.londondiscohire.co.uk

SULLIVANS ENTERTAINMENTS
33 Hornfair Road, Charlton London SE7 7BE
Tel: 020 8319 4848 Fax: 020 8319 3820
Mob: 0777 421 3469
Email: mikeatsullivans@aol.com

Effects & Fireworks & Lasers

CINEBUILD LTD
Broadcast Engineering Centre, Eastbourne Road, Blindley Heath, R7 6JP
Tel: 020 7582 8750
Email: cinebuild@btclick.com
Web Site: www.cinebuild.co.uk

Directors: Tony Neale, Patrick Neale
We supply all types of breakaway glass for television and film, plus sales and hire of special effects and props - snow, mist, rain, cobwebs and dust.

FANTASTIC FIREWORKS
Rocket Park, Half Moon Lane, Pepperstock, Luton, Beds LU1 4LL
Tel: 01582 485 555 Fax: 01582 485 545
Email: info@fantastic-fireworks.co.uk
Web Site: www.5nov.com
Contact: Rob Farow

LASER HIRE LTD
Fole Spring Farm, Fole, Uttoxeter, Staffordshire ST14 5EF
Tel: 01889 507 067 Fax: 01889 507 068
Email: info@laserhire.co.uk
Web Site: www.laserhire.co.uk

QUICKSILVER UK LTD
17 Hyde Road, Denton, Manchester M34 3AF
Tel: 0161 320 7232 Fax: 0161 335 9871
Email: contact@quicksilverfireworks.co.uk
Web Site: www.quicksilverfireworks.co.uk

STAGE ELECTRICS
Third Way, Avonmouth, Bristol, Avon BS11 9YL
Hire & Sales: 0117 938 4000 Accounts: 0117 937 9550 Admin: 0117 982 7282 Admin Fax: 0117 916 2825 Fax: 0117 916 2828
Email: bristol@stage-electrics.co.uk
Web Site: www.stage-electrics.co.uk
One of the UK's largest suppliers of technical equipment to the entertainment, leisure, conference and presentation industries.
Offering sales and hire of lighting, sound, rigging, staging and all related equipment.
Head of Marketing: Adam Blaxill
Managing Director: Dan Aldridge
London Branch: 175 Long Lane, London SE1 4PN
Tel: 020 7939 3000 Fax: 020 7939 3001
E-Mail: london@stage-electrics.co.uk
Exeter Branch: 1 Swan Units, Heron Road, Sowton Industrial Estate, Exeter EX2 7LL
Tel: 01392 824 100 Fax: 01392 891 116
E-Mail: exeter@stage-electrics.co.uk

Event Management

A.B.C. DIRECT EVENTS RESOURCES
49 Ashgrove, Steeple Claydon, Buckingham MK18 2LW
Tel: 01296 738 020
Email: info@abcdirectentertainments.co.uk
Web: www.abcdirectentertainments.co.uk
Senior Personnel: Len Illing, Catherine Brandon, Elise Illing, Charlotte Illing, William Illing
Researching for, and creative and imaginative planning of, events from the sublime to the spectacular, from classical to pop to pageant.

ACTIVE INTERNATIONAL GROUP LTD
9 Windy Ridge, Park Farm Road, Bromley, Kent BT1 2RQ
Tel: 020 8325 2222 Fax: 020 8325 2226
Email: info@active-group.co.uk
Web Site: www.active-group.co.uk
Managing Director: Matthew Lewis

ALTERNATIVE ARTS
Top Studio, Bethnal Green Training Centre, Deal Street, London E1 5HZ
Tel: 020 7375 0441 Fax: 020 7375 0484
Email: info@alternativearts.co.uk
Web Site: www.alternativearts.co.uk
Senior Personnel: Maggie Pinhorn, Liz Weston
Specialising in Event Management.

ARIA EVENTS MANAGEMENT LTD
The Inovation Centre Vienna Court, Kirkleatham Business Park, Redcar, Cleveland TS10 5SH
Tel: 01642 777 778 Fax: 01642 777 774
Email: sales@ariadirect.co.uk
Web Site: www.ariadirect.co.uk
Director: Mr A Pitfield
Health & safety, procurement, funding corporate, public sector and community events

ASCENSION LTD
1 Union Terrace, Marine Promenade, New Brighton, Wirral CH45 2JT
Tel: 0151 637 0055 Fax: 0151 637 0011
Email: all@mmia.u-net.com

ATLANTIC ENTERTAINMENTS
PO Box 4465, Bournemouth Bournemouth BH7 7WD
Tel: 01202 417 285 Fax: 01202 417 346
Email: atlantic.entertainments@virgin.net
contacts: Bridie Reid. Also deals with corporate management or Don Jones

BIG CAT GROUP LTD
Vincent House, 92-93 Edward Street, Birmingham B1 2RA
Tel: 0121 248 4697 Fax: 0121 248 4699
Email: info@bcguk.com
Web Site: www.bigcatgroup.com
Director: Mr Morgan

BLAZERS ENTERTAINMENT GROUP
PO Box 52, Marlow, Buckinghamshire SL7 2YB
Tel/Fax: 01491 579 214
Email: blazersentertain@aol.com
Web Site: www.blazersentertainment.co.uk
Contact: Leon Fisk

BRILLIANT EVENTS LTD
19 Presley Way, Crown Hill, Milton Keynes, Buckinghamshire MK8 0ES
Tel: 01908 563 263 Fax: 01908 567 267
Email: andrewm@brilliantevents.co.uk
Web Site: www.brilliantevents.co.uk

CELEBRATE IN STYLE
2 Foxhall Close, Norwell, Newark, Nottinghamshire NG23 6OQ
Tel: 01636 636 111 Fax: 01636 636 600
Email: admin@celebrateinstyle.net
Contact: Charlotte R Hall

COMEDY STORE MANAGEMENT
1a Oxendon Street, London SW1Y 4EE
Tel: 020 7839 1862 / 2949 Fax: 020 7930 2951
Email: charlotte@thecomedystore.co.uk
Web: www.comedystoremanagement.co.uk
Senior Personnel: Don Ward, Charlotte Smith

CATHERINE COOPER EVENTS
Tel: 020 7483 1181
Email: info13@catherinecooperevents.co.uk
Web: www.catherinecooperevents.co.uk
Contact: Catherine Cooper
Extensive contact in theatre, the media and beyond. Complete event management and public relations or work to your specification, to create memorable and unique occasions.

DOUB7E SEVEN EVENTS LTD
Authorised House 4 Endowood Road Sheffield, S7 2LZ
Tel: 0114 2362 874 Mob: 07966 060777
Email: roop@77events.co.uk
Web Site: www.77events.co.uk
Contact: Roop Mullins
We supply entertainment for private and corporate events, ranging from celebrities, bands, speakers to magicians and walkabout entertainment.

EVENT EVENT
9 Church Street Leominster, Herefordshire HR6 8NE
Tel/Fax: 01568 615 723
Email: sales@eventevent.co.uk
Web Site: www.eventevent.co.uk
Contact: Lorna Philip

EVENTS CONNECT
15 Faversham House, 15 Jewbury, York YO31 7PL

Mobile Tel: 07904 376629.
Email: viviennelee01@aol.com
Web Site: www.eventsconnect.co.uk
Contact: Vivienne Lee
A Model Management company: representing fashion and photographic models in the York area.
Event Management: Events big and small, fashion show production a speciality, organisers of Miss York, an area final for Miss England
Public Relations: personal press and media promotion offered to models, actors, sports people.

EXCLUSIVE EVENTS UK LTD
4 Cayley Court George Cayley Drive
Clifton Moor York Y0304WH
Tel: 01904 692 662 Fax: 01904 692 676
Email: enquies@exevents.com
Web Site: www.exevents.com
Events Manager: Kenny Robertson

G.S.P
Canalot Studios, 222 Kensal Road, London W10 5BN
Tel: 020 8968 9331 Fax: 020 8968 9332
Email: info@gsp-uk.com
Web Site: www.gsp-uk.com
Contact: Emma Gold, Jules Stevenson
Clients include Warners, MTV, BBC, Empay and Lastminute.com. Services include: Set design, Lighting and sound, wide range of amazing entertainment & performance artistes, Overall management & co-ordination, Novel invitation ideas and more.

GROWTH INDUSTRY
20 Huddersfield Road, Holmfirth, West Yorkshire HD9 2JF
Tel: 01484 688 219
Email: info@celebrateprojects.co.uk
Producing, promoting and developing arts, cultural and heritage events and initiatives. Working with clients and/or in partnerships to develop projects and events, long and short-term - offering experience and expertise in production, administration, funding and marketing.

DAVID HULL PROMOTIONS LTD
46 University Street, Belfast, BT7 1HB
Northern Ireland
Tel: 028 9024 0360 Fax: 028 9024 7919
Email: info@dhpromotions.com/ david@davidhullpromotions.com
Web Site: www.davidhullpromotions.com
Managing Director: David Hull
General Manager: Tony Brown
UK and Irish Celebrity and Personality Agency. UK and Ireland Tour Bookers. Representing the best in Irish Entertainment.

I.C.E. PRODUCTIONS
Warwick Corner, 42 Warwick Road, Kenilworth, Warwickshire CV8 1HE
Tel: 01926 864 800
Email: web@ice-productions.com/ birmingham@ice-productions.com
Web Site: www.ice-productions.com
Entertainment and Video Production services. Festival and Event production. Short films and pop promos.

THE INCREDIBLE EVENT COMPANY LTD
Magnum House, 33 Lord Street, Leigh, Lancashire WN7 1BY
Tel: 01942 260 080 Fax: 01942 680 608
Email: enquiries@incredibleevent.com
Web Site: www.incredibleevent.com
Contact: Anita Watson

MUSICTALKS
33 Palmeira Road, Bexleyheath, Kent DA7 4UU
Tel/ Fax: 020 8301 6366 Mob: 07798641400
Email: info@musictalks.biz
Web Site: www.musictalks.biz
Contact: Pauline Slane
MusicTalks realises that no two functions are the same, so each of our bespoke events are tailored to your individual needs, ensuring guests speak of the occasion long after they have gone home. With our professional, yet fun approach, you can be sure of commitment, adaptability and professionalism at all times. There isn't a problem that cannot be solved - just a solution waiting to be found! We welcome all enquiries both corporate and private.

NSE CONSULTANCY
Minster Cottage, Broomers Corner, Shipley, Horsham, West Sussex RH13 8PS
Tel: 01403 741 321
Senior Personnel: Ian Long
Entertainment and Event Management.

OUTER SANCTUM
2nd Floor, Godfree Court, 29 Long Lane, London SE1 4PL
Tel: 020 7407 1407 Fax: 020 7407 7676
Email: katy@outersanctum.net
Web Site: www.outersanctum.net
Agent: Emily Harper

Q20 THEATRE
19 Wellington Crescent, Shipley, West Yorkshire BD18 3PH
Tel/Fax: 0845 126 0632 (10am - 5 pm Mon-Fri)
Email: info@q20theatre.co.uk
Web Site: www.q20theatre.co.uk
Artistic Director: John Lambert
Specialising in Full Event Creation and Ful-Scale Theatre Production for over three decades. Entertainment for Children, Family and Adult audiences, sourced from our comprehensive database of UK performers. All types of act and performers, inculding the best lookalikes from a range of UK agencies.

RAINBOW PRODUCTIONS
Rainbow House, 56 Windsor Avenue, London SW19 2RR
Tel: 020 8545 0700 Fax: 020 8545 0777
Email: info@rainbowproductions.co.uk
Web Site: www.rainbowproductions.co.uk
Managing Director: David Scott,
Sales & Marketing Director: Simon Foulkes
Rainbow Productions has over 70 celebrity cartoon characters to book for guest appearances. We also create bespoke brand mascots and props for events.

SABA COMMUNICATIONS LTD
Bethnel Green Training Centre, Hanbury Street, London E1 5HZ
Tel: 020 7377 8545 / 020 776 6776 Fax: 020 337 1997
Email: tina.bennett@saba.org.uk
Web Site: www.saba.org.uk
PR contact: Tina Bennett
SABA Founder: John Downie

SHARPER SOLUTIONS LTD
Elstree Film Studios, Shenley Road, Borehamwood, Hertfordshire WD6 1JG
Tel: 020 8207 2233 Fax: 020 8207 2255
Email: sandy@sharpersolutions.co.uk
Web Site: www.sharpersolutions.co.uk
Senior Personnel: Sandy Harper
Specialising in corporate and special event management.

STEPPIN' OUT ENTERTAINMENT & CORPORATE EVENTS
11 Beaumont Court, Oxford OX1 5AL
Tel/ Fax: 01865 327 772 Mobile: 07768 606 088
Email: enquiries@steppin-out.co.uk
Web Site: www.steppin-out.co.uk
Proprietor: Terry Penn
We provide a wide range of services within the event management and entertainment arena, including: Corporate Events, Wedding Services, Theme & Team Building Events, Sound & Lighting Equipment Hire DJ's/Discos, Karaoke, Bands, Musicians, Entertainers, Marquees, Fireworks and Outdoor/Giant Games.

TALENTSPOT UK
Freepost TalentSpot UK
Tel: 0845 045 4111
Email: info@talentspotuk.com
Web Site: www.talentspotuk.com
Contact: Dean Ezekiel

THAT'S ENTEETAINMENT
The Old Telephone Exchange, Long Lane, Hermitage, Thatcham, Berkshire RG18 9QS

Tel: 01635 202 618 Fax: 01635 202 628
Mob: 07836 335 605
Email: dick@dicktee.com
Web Site: www.dicktee.com
Contact: Dick Tee
Event production and management company. From festivals and concerts to conferences and fashion shows.

THE BOLLYWOOD THEME COMPANY

53 Newquay Road, Walsall WS5 3EL
Tel: 07710 040 183
Email:
www.bollywoodthemecompany.com
Web Site: www.bollywoodthemecompany.com
Contact: Shin Kang
Specialising in: Corporate Events, Christmas Parties & Event Management.

TIME EVENTS

The Meeting House, 31 Prospect Place, Epsom, Surrey KT17 1WW
Tel: 01372 747 757 Fax: 01372 747 340
Email: sales@timeevents.co.uk
Operations Director: Russell Gilbey

UK BOOKING AGENCY

170 Domonic Drive, London SE9 3LE
Tel/Fax: 020 8857 8775
Email: stevegoddard@aol.com
Senior Personnel: Steve Goddard
We are a 'one-stop' organisation, piecing together a personal or total event package of ARTISTES and PROVISIONS. Working together with its sister company, 'Label Spinners', who organise the bookings of Artistes for personal or total event packages, from nightclubs to festivals. Specialising in booking events for universities, and artistes primarily DJs, Live Bands and PAs.

WIZARDRY ENTERTAINMENTS LTD

Suite 3, 375 Chorley Road, Swinton, Manchester M27 6AY
Tel: 0161 728 5507 Fax: 0161 728 5509
Web Site: www.wizardry.co.uk
Contact: Carl Royle
Specialists in Corporate and Wedding Entertainment.

WORLD WIDE PICTURES LTD

21-25 St.Anne's Court, London W1F 0BJ
Tel: 020 7434 1121 Fax: 020 7734 0619
Email: pics@worldwidegroup.ltd.uk
Web Site: www.worldwidegroup.ltd.uk

Event Organisers

1ST TROPICAL EVENT ORGANISERS

Office 2, 10 Silverhill Close, Strelley, Nottingham NG8 6QL
Tel: 07944432649 Tel: 0115 951 9864
Email: acts@african-caribbean-ents.com
Contact Manager: Kawbena

ANGEL EVENT MANAGEMENT

9 Abbey Road, Virginia Water, Surrey GU25 4RS
Tel/Fax: 01344 845 966
Email: rayna@angelevents.co.uk
Web Site: www.angelevents.co.uk
Proprietor: Rayna Angel

BYDAND LEISURE

39 Dunkeld Road, Perth, Perth & Kinross PH1 5RN Scotland
Tel/Fax: 01738 636 321 Mob: 07977 928721
Email: bignalky@tiscali.co.uk
Web Site: www.bydandleisure.co.uk
Proprietor: Mr Malcolm Gordon

MRS CASEY MUSIC

PO Box 296, Matlock, Derbyshire DE4 3XU
Tel: 01629 827 012 Fax: 01629 821 874
Email: info@mrscasey.co.uk
Web Site: www.mrscasey.co.uk
Senior Personnel: Steve Heap
Publicity & Marketing Manager: Jess Adams
Festival and Event Organisers and consultants.

CIRCA GROUP

16 Church Road, Tunbridge Wells, Kent TN1 1JP
Tel: 01892 517 500 Fax: 01892 527 702
Email: info@circagroup.co.uk
Web Site: www.circagroup.co.uk
Film and video production, projection and technical consultancy and corporate event organisers.

CORPORATE EVENTS SCOTLAND

44 Speirs Wharf, Glasgow, Strathclyde G4 9TH Scotland
Tel: 0141 332 6626 Fax: 0141 353 3671
Email:
events@corporateeventscotland.com
Web Site:
www.corporateeventscotland.com
Managing Director: Mr Don Spence
Events Manager: Sally Matheson
National and international excellence and creativity in gala events, entertainment & hospitality, conferences, team building and speakers.

DDA

192-198 Vauxhall Bridge Road, London SW1V 1DX
Tel: 020 7932 9800 Fax: 020 7932 4950
Email: info@ddapr.com
Web Site: www.ddapr.com
Public relations: now the pre-eminent consultancy in the sector
Event management: which was formed in 2001, manages the presence of many major film companies and producers at film festivals and markets around the world, including Cannes, Venice, Toronto and Berlin.The division also organises conferences, seminars and events for a wider,
non-film client base.
Productions: was formed in 1997, to produce the European Film Awards under auspices of the European Film Academy at every stage from the event itself to broadcast. The company is involved at every stage from the event itself through to the TV broadcast. We are also involved in other internationally recognised festivals.
Consulting: The establishment of this new division is intended to formalize our wide experience of corporate and crisis public relations in the film industry.

FIFTH ELEMENT EVENT DESIGN LTD

12 Talina Centre, Bagleys Lane, Fulham, London SW6 2BW
Tel: 020 7610 8630 Fax: 020 7610 8631
Email: office@fifth-element.co.uk
Web Site: www.fifth-element.co.uk

HEAVY ENTERTAINMENT LTD

222 Kensal Road, London W10 5BN
Tel: 020 8960 9001 / 2 Fax: 020 8960 9003 Tel: 0207 494 1000
Email: info@heavy-entertainment.com
Web Site: www.heavy-entertainment.com
Contacts: David Roper, Davy Nougarede
Producers of broadcast programmes, promotional video and audio, EPKs, VNRs, radio and TV commercials, media training, audio books, ISDN interviews and live events. Audio studios for hire. Duplication services available.

INCREDIBULL

5th floor Cheapside House 138 Cheapside London EC2V 6BJ
Tel: 020 7940 3800 Fax: 020 7940 3801
Email: hello@incredibull.com
Web Site: www.incredibull.com

IOGIG LTD

39 Equinox House Wakering Road, Barking, Essex IG11 8RN
Tel: 020 7112 8907
Email: ian@iogig.com
Web Site: www.iogig.com
Contact: Ian Taylor
We provide theatre and event production services for business and the entertainment industry, including planning, costing, set design and construction, sound and lighting design, equipment hire, management and all the disciplines required to stage high quality concerts, productions or events.

J.H. PROMOTIONS LTD
61 Crystal Avenue, Hornchurch, Essex RM12 6SJ
Tel: 08707 557 667 Fax: 08707 557 677
Email: enquiries@jhpromotions.com
Web Site: www.jhprom.com
Events Director: Julie Howsego
Established in 1992, we offer a wide range of entertainment services for adults and children alike, on a nation-wide basis. From a Mix & Mingle magician to a full fun fair!

ON EVENT PRODUCTION COMPANY
Acton House, Acton Grove, Acton Road Industrial Estate, Long Eaton, Nottingham NG10 1FY
Tel: 01159 222 959 Fax: 01159 735 918
Email: sales@lovingitlive.co.uk
Web Site: www.lovingitlive.co.uk
MD: Guy Eaton
Operations Director: Paul White
Production Director: Chris Vernon-Smith
Hire Manger: James Pemblington
We hire PA / Staging / Lighting / Truss & Power distribution for either dry hire or as a complete package with engineers and/or event management.

OVATION
Upstairs at the Gatehouse, Highgate Village, London N6 4BD
Tel: 020 8340 4256 Fax: 020 8340 3466
Email: events@ovationproductions.com
Web Site: www.ovationproductions.com / www.ovationtheatres.com
Partners: Katie & John Plews

TANO REA EVENT & MUSIC MANAGEMENT
58 Alexandra Road, London NW4 2RY
Tel: 020 8203 1747 Fax: 020 8203 1064
Email: tano.rea@btopenworld.com
Web Site: www.tanorea-events.com
Senior Personnel: Tano Rea

SMART LIVE
30 Maiden Lane, London WC2E 7JS
Tel: 0207 836 0562 Fax: 0207 836 1044
Email: smartlive@smartgroupltd.co.uk
Web Site: www.smartlive.co.uk
Creating events with edge.
Special event production company comprising set designers, choreographers, and artistic directors. Technically, we boast sound engineers, lighting technicians and stage managers. We combine our creative and technical talents to stage the most amazing themed events ever.

SPT EVENTS LTD
1 Greek Street Soho Square London W1D 4NQ
Tel: 020 7434 2067 Fax: 020 7434 1746
Email: schattalou@spteventsltd.co.uk
Web Site: www.spteventsltd.co.uk
Managing Director: Suzan Chattalou

THEME TRADERS
The Stadium, Oaklands Road, London NW2 6DL
Tel: 020 8452 8518 Fax: 020 8450 7322
Email: mailroom@themetraders.com
Web Site: www.themetraders.com
Co-Director: Kim Einhorn.
Contact the Projects Office.
See our website for further details.

THEMES UNLIMITED
17 St. Johns Cresent Harrogate, North Yorkshire HG1 3AB
Tel: 0870 330 0787 Fax: 0870 330 0788
Email: info@entertainment-zone.com
Web Site: www.entertainment-zone.com
Senior Personnel: Hayley Agars, Louise Parker
Specialising in theming for corporate events. Creating events from Mardi Gras to Hollywood Oscars.

UK BOOKING AGENCY
170 Domonic Drive, London SE9 3LE
Tel/Fax: 020 8857 8775
Email: stevegoddard@aol.com
Senior Personnel: Steve Goddard
We are a 'one-stop' organisation, piecing together a personal or total event package of ARTISTES and PROVISIONS. Working together with its sister company, 'Label Spinners', who organise the bookings of Artistes for personal or total event packages, from nightclubs to festivals. Specialising in booking events for universities, and artistes primarily DJs, Live Bands and PAs.

ULTIMATE INTERNATIONAL
Atlas House, London Road, Hindhead, Surrey GU26 6AB
Tel: 01428 606 566 Fax: 01428 606 141
Email: info@partyplannersuk.com
Web Site: www.partyplannersuk.com
Senior Personnel: David L Starr

UPFRONT TELEVISION LTD
39-41 New Oxford Street, London WC1A 1BN
Tel: 020 7836 7702 / 3 Fax: 020 7836 7701
Email: info@upfronttv.com
Web Site: www.celebritiesworldwide.com
Joint Managing Directors: Claire Nye, Richard Brecker
Established in 1991, Upfront Television has developed a reputation as England's leading independent production company, specialising in celebrity booking. Credits include the UK premieres of The Lord Of The Rings: The Two Towers & The Return Of The King, the Elle Style Awards 1998-2005, the Mobo Awards 2004, the Kerrang Awards, the Brit Awards, the Saatchi Gallery Launch and 1st Anniversary.

ZEST EVENTS
2 Swan Mews, Parsons Green Lane, London SW6 4QT
Tel: 020 7384 9336 Fax: 020 7384 9337
Email: parties@zestevents.com
Web Site: www.zestevents.com

Fairground Attractions

GREGORY'S AMUSEMENTS
54 Mead Lane, Chertsey, Surrey KT16 8NW
Tel/Fax: 01923 570 501 Mobile: 07976 297735
Contacts: Michael & Ann Gregory

SIRPS
c/o 66 Carolgate, Retford, Nottinghamshire DN22 6EF
Tel: 01493 842 097
Email: info@sirps.com
Web Site: www.sirp.co.uk
Chairman: Peter Williamson
The members of SIRPs own and operate a vast range of restored vintage fairground rides and attractions from the 1880s to 1950s. Available for corporate, media and private events throughout the UK.

Floral Hire

CHANTAL UK LTD
Unit 5 Stadium Business Court, Millenium Way, Pride Park, Derby DE24 8HP
Tel: 01332 204 555 Fax: 01332 204 666
Email: info@cukltd.com
Web Site: www.cukltd.com
Innovative florists, featuring luxury gift boutique in store located in Derby East Midlands. Exclusive stockists in the midlands of Amouage 'The most valuable perfume in the world'. Theme creation for private and corporate events.

FLOWERWORKS
15 Windsor Street, Uxbridge, Middlesex UB8 1AB
Tel: 01895 810 008
Email: sales@flowersuxbridge.co.uk
Web Site: www.flowersuxbridge.co.uk

MOYSES STEVENS LTD
157-158 Sloane Street
London SW1A 2AH
Tel: 020 7259 9303
Email: lucilla@moyses-stevens.co.uk
Web Site: www.moyses-stevens.co.uk
Events Director: Lucilla Bouchier

PEEBLES EXHIBITION FLORIST
Fillongley Mill Farm, Tamworth Road,

Fillongley, Coventry, Warwickshire CV7 8DZ
Tel: 01676 542 234 Fax: 01676 542 456
Email: martinpeebles@btinternet.com
Web Site: www.peeblesflorists.co.uk
Floral Displays for Banquets, Conferences, Corporate Events, County Shows, Hospitality, Launches, Open Days, Outdoor Events, Press Day, Weddings.

Funfair

GREGORY'S AMUSEMENTS
54 Mead Lane, Chertsey, Surrey KT16 8NW
Tel/Fax: 01923 570 501
Mobile: 07976 297735
Contacts: Michael & Ann Gregory

Ice Sculptures

DO ME A FAVOUR
12 Hunts Cross Shopping Centre, Speke Hall Road, Liverpool, Merseyside L24 9GB
Tel: 0151 486 5341
Email: info@domeafavour.ltd.uk
Web Site: www.domeafavour.ltd.uk
We design ice scultures, decorate balloons, champagne fountains and personlised printing. We also hire out bubble machines, smoke machines etc. For all you party requirements.

ICE CUBED
13 The Downs, Cheadle, Cheshire SK8 1JL
Tel: 0800 253671 Fax: 0161 491 6916
Email: icecubed@btinternet.com
Web Site: www.ice-cubed.co.uk
Ice delivered for all occasions. Hand carved ice sculptures. Vodka and spirit Luges.

ICE WORK LIMITED
Lamberhurst Road, Horsmonden, Tonbridge, Kent TN12 8DP
Tel: 01892 722 522 Fax: 01892 722 578
Email: info@icework.co.uk
Web Site: www.icework.co.uk
Ice sculptures make an elegant and attractive feature for any occasion. Using ice that is crystal clear, Ice Work introduces modern technology to sculpture production alongside traditional hand carving methods.

THE ICE BOX.COM
Unit A 35-36, New Covent Garden Market, London SW8 5EE
Tel: 020 7498 0800 Fax: 020 7498 0900
Email: info@theicebox.com
Web Site: www.theicebox.com

THE ICE MAN
Unit 27, Imex Business Park, Flaxley Road, Birmingham West Midlands B33 9AL
Tel: 0121 789 8384
Email: enquiries@the-ice-man.co.uk
Web Site: www.the-ice-man.co.uk
The Midland Premier Supplier of cubed ice, vodka luges and ice sculptures.

Karaoke

ASSOCIATED DISCOS & KARAOKES
28 East Street, Huntingdon, Cambridgeshire PE29 1WE
Tel: 01480 457 966
Email: andi.cooke@ntlworld.com
Web Site: www.associateddisco.co.uk
Disco techs and Karaoke equiptment hire.

BLADEN PROMOTIONS
Unit 3C, Stanlaw Abbey Business Centre, Dover Drive, Ellesmere Port CH65 9BF
Tel: 0151 355 4500 Fax: 0151 355 4700
Email: bladenpromotions@aol.com
Contact: Graham Reid

LEAPFROG INTERNATIONAL LTD
Riding Court Farm, Riding Court Road, Datchet, Berkshire SL3 9JU
Tel: 01753 580 880 Fax: 01753 580 881
Email: enq@leapfrog-int.co.uk
Web Site: www.leapfrog-int.co.uk
Leapfrog International is a dynamic Corporate Events Company, specialising in Team Building Programs, Interactive Games and Corporate Events. For events ideas, inspiration and consultation please contact our helpful and dedicated team.

O'SULLIVAN GROUP
18 Bankes Avenue, Orrell, Wigan, Lancashire WN5 8HU
Tel/Fax: 01942 515 000

SOUND & VISION EXPRESS LTD
Mead Road Cheltenham Gloucestershire GL53 7DU
Tel: 01242 222 721 Fax: 01242 255 065
Email: saveltd@btconnect.com
Web Site: www.cdkm.co.uk
Contact Manager: Pete French

SOUND FORCE
44 Church Road, Crystal Palace, London SE19 2ET
Tel: 020 8771 7221 Fax: 020 8771 1555
Email: soundforce.london@virgin.net

Lighting Equipment Sale & Hire

EVENTS SOUND & LIGHT LTD
Unit 34, Waterhouse Business Centre, Cromar Way, Chelmsford Essex CM1 2QE
Tel: 01245 392 260 Fax: 01245 392 261
Email: sales@eventsoundandlight.com
Web Site: www.eventsoundandlight.com
Contact: N. Hills

DRAX LIGHTING LTD
Unit 21B Icknield Way Farm, Tring Road, Dunstable, Bedfordshire LU6 2JX
Tel: 01582 475 614 Fax: 01582 475 669
Email: richard@draxlighting.com, info@draxlighting.com
Web Site: www.draxlighting.com
Contact: Richard Foster
Drax specialises in event lighting design and equipment supply for stage shows, outdoor productions and corporate events. Drax hire and sell quality lighting, sound and effects equipment for static, touring or short term use. Dry hire or hire with crew is available for both professional and amateur events, UK and worldwide. Hire equipment includes profiles, fresnels, PARs, floods, followspots, moving lights, rigging, special effects systems and dimmers. Control systems available include Avolites, Artistic Licence and Zero 88.

GLS LIGHT & SOUND PRODUCTION LTD
Alpha Building, Willments Industrial Estate, Hazel Road, Southampton SO19 7HS
Tel: 023 8043 6622 Fax: 023 8043 6633
Email: info@glslighting.com
Web Site: www.glslighting.com
Contact: Claire Lewis, Ms J Turner

HSL (HIRE) LTD
Unit E & F, Glenfield Park, Philips Road, Blackburn Lancashire BB1 5PF
Tel: 01254 698 808 Fax: 01254 698 835
Email: simon@hslgroup.com, contact@hslgroup.com
Web Site: www.hslgroup.com
Contact: Simon Stuart
Every client is special, each commission totally unique, our in house event management process ensuring that your project is carefully monitored, from the taking of your detailed instructions, through design and planning, and ultimately the installation and staging of the event itself.

NEW YORK PRODUCTIONS
Unit 1 Shaws Building Deptford Terrace, Sunderland SR4 6DD

Tel: 0191 565 1222 Fax: 0191 565 1333
Email: Dave@newyorkproductions.co.uk
Web: www.newyorkproductions.co.uk
Contact: David Arkley

SPARKS THEATRICAL HIRE
Unit 4, Cannon Wharf Business Centre, 35 Evelyn Street, Surrey Quays, London SE8 5RT
Tel: 020 7237 2872 Fax: 020 7237 8572
Email: enquiries@sparkshire.co.uk
Web Site: www.sparkshire.co.uk
Director: Paul Anderson

STAGE AUDIO SERVICES
Unit 2, Bridge Street Wordsley Stourbridge West Midlands DY8 5YU
Tel: 01384 263 629 Fax: 01384 263 6209
Email: kevinmobers@aol.com
Web Site: www.stageaudioservices.com
Contact: Kevin Mobers
Suppliers of Quality Sound, Lighting & Production Services.

STAGE ELECTRICS
Third Way, Avonmouth, Bristol, Avon BS11 9YL
Hire & Sales: 0117 938 4000 Accounts: 0117 937 9550 Admin: 0117 982 7282 Admin Fax: 0117 916 2825 Fax: 0117 916 2828
Email: bristol@stage-electrics.co.uk
Web Site: www.stage-electrics.co.uk
One of the UK's largest suppliers of technical equipment to the entertainment, leisure, conference and presentation industries.
Offering sales and hire of lighting, sound, rigging, staging and all related equipment.
Head of Marketing: Adam Blaxill
Managing Director: Dan Aldridge
London Branch: 175 Long Lane, London SE1 4PN
Tel: 020 7939 3000 Fax: 020 7939 3001
E-Mail: london@stage-electrics.co.uk
Exeter Branch: 1 Swan Units, Heron Road, Sowton Industrial Estate, Exeter EX2 7LL
Tel: 01392 824 100 Fax: 01392 891 116
E-Mail: exeter@stage-electrics.co.uk

THEME CREATION
3 Campion Way, Dickens Heath, Solihull, B90 1RX
Tel/Fax: 0121 744 2500
Email: info@themecreation.co.uk
Web Site: www.themecreation.co.uk
Theme Creation for conferences and events. Suppliers of room decor, lighting, sound, starcloths and electrical installation services.

VIKING SOUND & LIGHT LTD
Unit 9 Woodstock Close Standard Way Ind. Park, Northallerton North Yorkshire DL6 2NB
Tel: 01609 780190 Mob Tel: 07980 023154
Email: steve@vikingsound.co.uk
Web Site: www.vikingsound.co.uk
Contact: Steve Williams
Viking Sound are suppliers of PA systems, lighting systems, stage hire, installations, artist bookings and event managment.

Marquee & Furniture Hire

BANANA SPLIT PLC
6 Carlisle Road, London NW9 0HN
Tel: 020 8200 1234 Fax: 020 8200 1121
Email: mail@banana-split.com
Web Site: www.banana-split.com
Contact: Julie-Anne Posner
Established 25 years. Our specialist team organises all events, utilising their high quality marquees, lighting, balloons, discotheques and entertainment agency.

Memorabilia

DEAD FAMOUS
12 Nottingham Street, London W1U 5NE
Freephone: 080 800 808 808 Tel: 020 7224 5050
Email: info@dead-famous.co.uk
Web Site: www.dead-famous.com
Contact: Ron Mowlam

Murder Mystery

1ST CALL ENTERTAINMENT
Redland Office Centre, 157 Redland Road, Bristol BS6 6YE
Tel: 01179 239 299 Mobile: 07980 863 468
Email: julian@firstcallentertainment.com
Web: www.1stcallentertainment.co.uk
Contact: Julian Franks

ACCIDENTAL PRODUCTIONS LTD
36 Barratt Avenue, London N22 7EZ
Tel: 020 8881 8000 Fax: 020 8881 8008
Email: info@accidental.co.uk
Web Site: www.accidental.co.uk
Directors: Julie Foulds, Ian Williams
Providing Murder Mysteries, Games Shows, Themed Treasure Hunts, Film Days and Pantos of the highest calibre. We combine entertainment with competition and teambuilding. Attention to detail makes us stand out.

AS YOU LIKE IT PRODUCTIONS
18 Okeover Manor, 20-23 Clapham Common North Side, London SW4 0RH
Tel: 020 7627 8942
Email: info@asyoulikeitproductions.co.uk
Web: www.asyoulikeitproductions.co.uk
As You Like It Productions are dedicated in writing and producing original and effective corporate entertainment, team building and conferences. We also specialise in training and development using role play and forum theatre. Our aim is to help improve communication and promote team building skills within a corporation.

INITIATIVE UNLIMITED
13 Brook Business Park, Cowley Mill Road, Uxbridge, Middlesex UB8 2FX
Tel: 01895 234313 Fax: 01895 236651
Email: david@dmlmarketing.co.uk
Web Site: www.initiativeunlimited.co.uk
Senior Personnel: Adam Hayes
Specialises in actor management and representation. Our corporate events not only help improve employee motivation and productivity, they also help colleagues get to know each other better in a relaxed environment. Team building games can also help you achieve work-related objectives in an entertaining way. Who says its all work and no play?

MURDER BY DESIGN
Elmgrove Centre, Redland Road, Bristol BS6 6AH
Tel: 0117 942 0377
Mobile: 07980 863 468
Email: chris@murderbydesign.co.uk
Web Site: www.murderbydesign.co.uk
Proprietor: Chris Mills
Sales: Julian Franks
Over 25 years of experience in the "Murder" business.
South West HQ - work nationally. Large database of actors. Stock/Bespoke plots.

MYSTERY EVENTS
Unit 6, Herts Business Centre, London Colney, Hertfordshire AL2 1JG
Tel: 01727 827 888
Email: events@mysteryevents.co.uk
Web Site: www.mysteryevents.co.uk
We provide participation events including murder mystery, spy catcher, treasure hunts etc. for fun, parties and team building. You have a character, are a suspect and you could be the guilty person. Venues throughout the UK.

SCREAM BLUE MURDER
Moreland Avenue, Colnbrook, Slough SL3 0LR
Tel: 01629 733 058 Fax: 01629 735 425
Email: screambluemurder@aol.com
Web Site: www.screambluemurder.net
Contact: Tracey Sydee - Events Manager
Murder Mystery Evenings & Weekends. We do house murders, murder-grams & themed murders. Scripts personalised to your murder. Team events on site at our base - The Barn.

SPECIAL EVENTS CONSULTANTS
26 Saddlers Rise, Norton, Runcorn, Cheshire, WA7 6PG
Tel/Fax: 01928 716 561
Tel: 01928 795 757
Email: info@special-events-consultants.co.uk
Web: www.special-events-consultants.co.uk
Contact: Laurence S Duckworth
Specialising in Race Nights, Disco Nights, Casino Nights and Murder Mystery.

TEAM TASK EVENTS
4 Hopfield Close, Waterlooville, Hampshire PO7 7LJ
Tel/Fax: 02392 269 096
Email: teamtaskevent@aol.com
Web Site: www.teamtaskevents.co.uk

WESTEND EVENTS LTD
61-63 Great Queen Street, London WC2B 5DA
Tel: 020 7404 4232 Fax: 020 7405 8405
Email: info@westendevents.co.uk
Web Site: www.westendevents.co.uk
Managing Director: Russell Davey
Specialises in organising parties , Murder Mystery Weekends and tribute nights.

Party Planners

1ST TROPICAL EVENT ORGANISERS
Office 2, 10 Silverhill Close, Strelley, Nottingham NG8 6QL
Tel: 07944432649 Tel: 0115 951 9864
Email: acts@african-caribbean-ents.com
Contact Manager: Kawbena

ANGEL EVENT MANAGEMENT
9 Abbey Road, Virginia Water, Surrey GU25 4RS
Tel/Fax: 01344 845 966
Email: rayna@angelevents.co.uk
Web Site: www.angelevents.co.uk
Proprietor: Rayna Angel

BANANA SPLIT PLC
6 Carlisle Road, London NW9 0HN
Tel: 020 8200 1234 Fax: 020 8200 1121
Email: mail@banana-split.com
Web Site: www.banana-split.com
Contact: Julie-Anne Posner
Established 25 years. Our specialist team organises all events, utilising their high quality marquees, lighting, balloons, discotheques and entertainment agency.

LATIN ARTS SERVICES (LAS) MUSIC
PO Box 57817, London SE23 3PT
Tel/Fax: 020 8291 9236
Mobile: 07956 446342
Email: info@latinartsgroup.com
Web Site: www.latinartsgroup.com
Senior Personnel: Hector Rosquete
Latin entertainment promoters. Our new show is The Mambo Boyz Salsa Show.

THEME TRADERS
The Stadium, Oaklands Road, London NW2 6DL
Tel: 020 8452 8518 Fax: 020 8450 7322
Email: mailroom@themetraders.com
Web Site: www.themetraders.com
Co-Director: Kim Einhorn.
Contact the Projects Office.
See our website for further details.

TWIZZLE PARTIES & EVENTS
Studio 6, 26-28 Priests Bridge, London SW14 8TA
Tel: 020 8392 0860 Fax: 020 8487 8550
Email: party@twizzle.co.uk
Web Site: www.twizzle.co.uk
Proprietor: Peter Robertson

Photographic & Film Services

APOLLO PHOTOGRAPHERS LTD
PO Box 7002 Richmond TW10 6WP
Tel: 020 8241 8949 Fax: 020 8940 0144
Email: info@apollophotographers.co.uk
Web Site: www.apollophotographers.co.uk

DRAGON NEWS & PICTURE AGENCY
Communications House, 21 Walter Road, Swansea SA1 5NQ
Tel: 01792 464 800 Fax: 01792 475 264
Email: mail@dragon-pictures.com
Web Site: www.dragon-pictures.com
We take photographs for national newspapers, magazines, TV stills and PR in Wales. We have a very large picture library going back 25 years.

ELECTRIC FILM COMPANY
4-6 Eaton Grove, Hove, East Sussex BN3 3PH
Tel: 01273 208 208 Mob: 07831 279 362
Advertising commercial photography and video production.

JOE BANGAY PHOTOGRAPHY
River House, Riverwood Drive, Marlow, Buckinghamshire SL7 1QY
Tel: 01628 486 193 Fax: 01628 890 239
Email: william.b@btclick.com
Web Site: www.joebangay.com
Contacts: William and Joe Bangay
Casting, portrait and styling photography with established make up/hair team. Distribution of press material. Showbiz and Pop library from 1968 to the present. Theatre and Film Production Photography.
Stage, location, studio photography in the theatre, films and rock/pop music.

Puppetry & Puppeteers

MARK ANDREWS ENTERTAINMENTS
57 William Bristow Road, Coventry, Warwickshire CV3 5LP
Tel: 024 7650 2011
Email: mark@markandrews.co.uk
Web Site: www.markandrews.co.uk
Proprietor: Mark Andrews
Professional entertainment for children comedy magic shows. Traditional Punch & Judy shows.

JOHN FIELD - THEATRE AND PUPPETRY
1 Grange House, 229 Stoke Newington Church Street, London N16 9HL
Tel: 020 7690 7449
Email: johnfield.theatreandpuppetry@btinternet.com
The only agency in the UK dealing with puppetry and all its aspects. "If It Waggles - We Cover It". Ideal for indoor/outdoor corporate events.

Radio Hire

COMMUNICATION SPECIALISTS
Unit 6, Murrell Green Business Park, London Road, Hook, Hampshire RG27 9GR
Tel: 01256 766 600 Fax: 01256 766 500
Email: kervin@comm-spec.co.uk / info@comm-spec.co.uk
Web Site: www.comm-spec.com
Contact: Kervin Labrosse
Specialising in the supply, servicing and hire of all aspects of two-way radios. We also carry a large stock of accessories.

Security

BUSINESS AND ENTERTAINMENT SECURITY LTD
38 Ashtree Road, Norwich, Norfolk NR5 0LS
Tel: 01603 441 806 Fax: 01603 441 807
Mobile: 07976 240878
Email: besecurity@boltblue.com
Web Site: www.besecurity.co.uk
Director: Sean Stone
Provision of high and low profile security, personal security, corporate hospitality security, conference and private function security, event and venue security.

EXECUTIVE GROUP HOLDINGS
Executive House, Wilderspool Causeway, Warrington WA4 6PU
Tel: 01925 652 652 Fax: 01925 652 525
Email: info@bodyguard-protection.com
Web Site: www.executivegroupholdings.co.uk
Contact: Damien Scott

FREELANCE SECURITY SERVICES
16 Grosvenor Road, Aldershot, Hampshire GU11 1DP
Tel: 01252 319 582 Fax: 01252 342 648
Mobiles: 07802 669339 / 674283 / 07880 266891
Email: pat@freelancesecurity.co.uk
Web Site: www.freelancesecurity.co.uk
Contact: John Mitchell

SPECIALIZED SECURITY
Royal Highland Centre, Ingliston, Edinburgh EH28 8NF Scotland
Tel: 0131 333 4747 Fax: 0131 333 4848
Email: sales@specializedsecurity.co.uk
Web Site: www.specializedsecurity.co.uk
Senior Personnel: Tom Clements, Kara Campbell
Suppliers of personnel to concerts, events, festivals, sports stadia, film locations, personal security, retail, merchandising security. Security consultants to the entertainment world.

Sound Equipment Sale & Hire

EVENTS SOUND & LIGHT LTD
Unit 34, Waterhouse Business Centre, Cromar Way, Chelmsford Essex CM1 2QE
Tel: 01245 392 260 Fax: 01245 392 261
Email: sales@eventsoundandlight.com
Web Site: www.eventsoundandlight.com
Contact: N. Hills

E.S.S.
Unit 14, Bleakhill Way, Mansfield, Nottinghamshire NG18 5EZ
Tel: 01623 647 291 Fax: 01623 622 500
Email: richardjohn@orange.net
Partner: Phil McDaniel

KIRKPATRICK SOUND ENGINEERING
1 Clover Drive, The Paddocks, Pickmere, Knutsford, Cheshire WA16 0WF
Tel/Fax: 01565 733 200 Mobile: 07831 504 404
Email: roy@kirkpatrick4sound.co.uk
Web Site: www.kirkpatrick4sound.co.uk
Contact: Roy Kirkpatrick
Professional sound and communication systems and equipment. Sales, installation, hire and system design. Also Magnetic Induction Loop Systems.

MAC SOUND
1-2 Attenburys Park, Park Road, Altrincham, Cheshire WA14 5QE
Tel: 0161 969 8311 Fax: 0161 962 9423
Email: info@macsound.co.uk
Web Site: www.macsound.co.uk
Design: Clement Rawling
Sales: David Houghton
Hire: Andrew Simpson
Administration: Julie Murray
MAC Sound offers a complete sound design, equipment hire, engineering and personnel service for all types of theatre presentations and concerts. With over thirty years experience, we provide a free radio microphone planning and licensing service and offer quotations and site visits without obligation. Please visit our website or call for a current hire ratecard.

NEW YORK PRODUCTIONS
Unit 1 Shaws Building Deptford Terrace, Sunderland SR4 6DD
Tel: 0191 565 1222 Fax: 0191 565 1333
Email: Dave@newyorkproductions.co.uk
Web Site: www.newyorkproductions.co.uk
Contact: David Arkley

SDD SOUND & LIGHT LTD
Temple Gardens, Staines, Middlesex TW18 3NQ
Tel: 01784 455 666 Fax: 01784 455 642
Email: info@sddsoundandlight.com
Web Site: www.sddsoundandlight.com
Rental, sales, repair and installation of all types and brands of equipment from multi channel radio microphone systems to intelligent lighting. Visit our website for our catalogue.

STAGE AUDIO SERVICES
Unit 2, Bridge Street Wordsley Stourbridge West Midlands DY8 5YU
Tel: 01384 263 629 Fax: 01384 263 6209
Email: kevinmobers@aol.com
Web Site: www.stageaudioservices.com
Contact: Kevin Mobers
Suppliers of Quality Sound, Lighting & Production Services.

STAGE ELECTRICS
Third Way, Avonmouth, Bristol, Avon BS11 9YL
Hire & Sales: 0117 938 4000 Accounts: 0117 937 9550 Admin: 0117 982 7282
Admin Fax: 0117 916 2825 Fax: 0117 916 2828
Email: bristol@stage-electrics.co.uk
Web Site: www.stage-electrics.co.uk
One of the UK's largest suppliers of technical equipment to the entertainment, leisure, conference and presentation industries.
Offering sales and hire of lighting, sound, rigging, staging and all related equipment.
Head of Marketing: Adam Blaxill
Managing Director: Dan Aldridge
London Branch: 175 Long Lane, London SE1 4PN
Tel: 020 7939 3000 Fax: 020 7939 3001
E-Mail: london@stage-electrics.co.uk
Exeter Branch: 1 Swan Units, Heron Road, Sowton Industrial Estate, Exeter EX2 7LL
Tel: 01392 824 100 Fax: 01392 891 116
E-Mail: exeter@stage-electrics.co.uk

STUDIOHIRE (LONDON) LTD
8 Daleham Mews, London NW3 5DB
Tel: 020 7431 0212 Fax: 020 7431 1134
Email: mail@studiohire.net
Web Site: www.studiohire.net
Contact: Paul Tattersall, Sam Thomas
Hire of musical and theatrical equipment. See our new website for details and prices.
You name it, we've got it!

THAMES AUDIO LTD
Building 11, Shepperton Film Studios, Studios Road, Shepperton, Middlesex TW17 0QD
Tel: 01932 567 681 Fax: 01932 569 758
Email: info@thamesaudio.co.uk
Web Site: www.thamesaudio.co.uk
Directors: Pete Cox, Graham Simpson
Project Manager: James Tebb
Specialists in Sound Design and Equipment Hire for Theatre, Concerts and Live Events.

TMC
Hillam Road, Bradford, West Yorkshire BD2 1QN
Tel: 01274 370 966 Fax: 01274 308 706
Email: sales@tmc.ltd.uk
Web Site: www.tmc.ltd.uk
Contact: Chris Smith
Highly specialised from the outset. TMC (The Music Company) is regarded as one of Britain's foremost centres of expertise in sound and vision technology, a position acknowledged by many industry awards and citations.
Product lines include radio mics, loudspeakers, amplifiers, mixing consoles, DVD players, video projectors, Plasma Screens and tour guide systems.
TMC are agents for d&b audiotechnik, Funktion 1, Turbosound, Allen & Heath, Crest Audio, Sennheiser, Trantec, Sony, Pioneer and Sanyo. To name but a few ...
Emergency call out service also available.

VIKING SOUND & LIGHT LTD
Unit 9 Woodstock Close Standard Way Ind. Park, Northallerton North Yorkshire DL6 2NB
Tel: 01609 780190 Mob Tel: 07980 023154
Email: steve@vikingsound.co.uk
Web Site: www.vikingsound.co.uk
Contact: Steve Williams
Viking Sound are suppliers of PA systems, lighting systems, stage hire, installations, artist bookings and event managment.

Staging

ALISCAFF LTD
Kenrich House, Elizabeth Way, Harlow, Essex CM19 5TL
Tel: 01279 406 270 Fax: 01279 406 292
Email: colin_w@alistage.co.uk
Web Site: www.alistage.co.uk
Managing Director: Colin Wright
Technical: Graham Hards
Stage systems, domed canopies, roof systems, raked seating, catwalks.

ALISTAGE
Kenrich House, Elizabeth Way, Harlow, Essex CM19 5TL
Tel: 01279 406270 Fax: 01279 406292
Email: colin_w@alistage.co.uk
Web Site: www.alistage.co.uk
Managing Director: Colin Wright
Technical: Graham Hards
Modular stages for hire, sale and lease. Stage systems, domed canopies, roof systems, raked seating, catwalks.

BOWER WOOD PRODUCTION SERVICES
Unit 5, The Billings, 3 Walnut Tree Close, Guildford, Surrey GU1 4UL
Tel: 01483 300 926 Fax: 01483 450 926
Email: enquiries@bowerwood.com
Web Site: www.bowerwood.com
Contact: Graham Bower Wood, Nigel Mathias
Scenery Construction & Metal Fabrication for the Theatre, Opera, Cruise Ships, Exhibitions & Special Events.

MOVETECH UK
Emblem Works, Emblem Street, Bolton, Lancashire BL3 5BW
Tel: 01204 525 626 London Depot: Tel: 01992 574 602 Fax: 01992 560 385
Email: info@turntable.co.uk
Web Site: www.british.turntable.co.uk, www.movetechuk.com
British Turntable Company, leaders in creating dramatic movement, offer a range of low profile, self-assembly revolving stages, in diameters ranging from 2m to 10m. Highly portable, these revolves can be assembled by two men in as little as half an hour*, can be supplied for manual or powered operation and include options such as variable speed, indexing and/or static centre.
This range is in addition to the extremely comprehensive range of revolves available for sale or hire up to 25 tonne capacity and which include units suitable for outdoor location applications.
Competitively priced, all units are available from depots throughout the UK and Europe.
*Assembly time based on a 6m standard revolve on sound, level surface.

NEW YORK PRODUCTIONS
Unit 1 Shaws Building Deptford Terrace, Sunderland SR4 6DD
Tel: 0191 565 1222 Fax: 0191 565 1333
Email: Dave@newyorkproductions.co.uk
Web: www.newyorkproductions.co.uk
Contact: David Arkley

STAGE ELECTRICS
Third Way, Avonmouth, Bristol, Avon BS11 9YL
Hire & Sales: 0117 938 4000 Accounts: 0117 937 9550 Admin: 0117 982 7282 Admin Fax: 0117 916 2825 Fax: 0117 916 2828
Email: bristol@stage-electrics.co.uk
Web Site: www.stage-electrics.co.uk
One of the UK's largest suppliers of technical equipment to the entertainment, leisure, conference and presentation industries.
Offering sales and hire of lighting, sound, rigging, staging and all related equipment.

Head of Marketing: Adam Blaxill
Managing Director: Dan Aldridge

London Branch:
175 Long Lane, London SE1 4PN
Tel: 020 7939 3000 Fax: 020 7939 3001
E-Mail: london@stage-electrics.co.uk

Exeter Branch:
1 Swan Units, Heron Road, Sowton Industrial Estate, Exeter EX2 7LL
Tel: 01392 824 100 Fax: 01392 891 116
E-Mail: exeter@stage-electrics.co.uk

STAGE SYSTEM HIRE
5 Church Avenue, Daybrook, Nottingham NG5 6LB
Tel/Fax: 0115 920 6390
Mob: 07710 310 537
Email: marcoberonwizard@aol.com
Web Site: www.marcoberon.com
Contact: Marc Oberon
Hire of stages, catwalks and dance platforms.

Street Theatre

ALRIGHT CHARLIE
Flat 4 Carleton House 122a Hillfield Avenue London N8 7DQ
Tel: 07808 732 390
Email: info@alrightcharlie.co.uk
Web Site: www.alrightcharlie.co.uk
Senior Personnel: Lawrence Anthony
Charlie Chaplin Look Alike, Comedy waiter & Close-up Magician for all indoor and outdoor events.

DESPERATE MEN THEATRE COMPANY
Epstein Buildings, Mivart Street, Easton, Bristol, BS5 6JL
Tel: 0117 939 3902 Mob: 0777 5911 620
Email: office@desperatemen.com
Web Site: www.desperatemen.com
Creative Producer: Richard Headon

Corporate Days Out

Bunjee Jumping

SKY HIGH BUNGEE
PO Box 1882, Dronfield, Derbyshire S18 8BJ
Tel: 0114 289 0173 Fax: 0114 289 0830
Email: info@skyhighbunjee.com
Web Site: www.skyhighbungee.com
Corporate and mobile bunjee. We do bunjee jumping, reverse bunjee and zip wire.

THE UK BUNGEE CLUB
Rockwood Cottages, 43 Barnsley Road, Flockton, Wakefield, West Yorkshire WF4 4DW
Tel: 07000 286 433 Fax: 01924 849 452
Email: enquiries@ukbungee.co.uk
Web Site: www.ukbungee.co.uk
We are largest bungee club in the UK offering Nation-Wide locations. UK Bungee was established in 1992 and has successfully jumped over 100,000 people safely and helped to raise over £1,000,000 for good causes.

Clay Pigeon Shooting

CAMP HILL LTD
Kirklington, Bedale, North Yorkshire DL8 2LS
Tel: 01845 567 788 Fax: 01845 567 065
Email: gavin@camphill.co.uk
Web Site: www.camphill.co.uk
Yorkshire's leading provider of outdoor teambuilding programmes & corporate entertainment. We offer tailor made events as well as pre-packaged programmes allowing us to suit your budget, however big or small.
Contact Marketing Manager: Gavin Newman

COUNTRY PURSUITS UK
46 Clappers Meadow, Alfold, Cranleigh, Surrey GU6 8HJ
Tel: 01403 751 657 Fax: 01403 751 658
Email: office@countrypursuits.uk.com
Web Site: www.countrypursuits.uk.com
Country Pursuits UK is a family run business with 25 years experience in shooting and Corporate Hospitality. Specialising in

Country activities they are in great demand for Stag, Hen and Birthday parties, events are built around each customer's requirements.

GARLANDS LTD
Raddle Lane, Edingale, Tamworth, Staffordshire B79 9JR
Tel: 01827 383 300 Fax: 01827 383 360
Email: garland@dial.pipex.com
Clay Pigeon Shooting ground. We do practise and novice tuition. Also corporate days out by appointment.

HOLLAND & HOLLAND SHOOTING GROUNDS
Ducks Hill Road, Northwood, Middlesex HA6 2SS
Tel: 01923 825 349 Fax: 01923 836 266
Email: shooting.grounds@hollandandholland.com
Web Site: www.hollandandholland.com
'To host an event at Holland and Holland is to treat your guests to the very best in corporate multi activity hospitality. With 50 years experience of providing the ultimate day out where else would you go?'

Go-Kart

ANCASTER KART RACING CENTRE
Wood Lodge, Ancaster, Grantham, Lincolnshire NG32 3PY
Tel: 01400 230306 Fax: 01400 230153
Email: lesjohnson@lancasterkartracing.co.uk
Web Site: www.ancasterkarting.co.uk
Group bookings or arrive and drive sessions available. Phone for details.

BILLING KARTING
Billing Aquadrome,
Crow Lane, Little Billing, Northampton, Northamptonshire NN3 9DA
Tel: 07855 440059 No fax number
Email: kennykart@aol.com
Web Site: www.billingkarts.com

DAYTONA MILTON KEYNES
H4 Dansteed Way, Rooksley, Milton Keynes Buckinghamshire MK13 8NP
Tel: 0845 6445503 Fax: 01908 695 999
Email: mk@daytona.co.uk
Web Site: www.daytona.co.uk
Individuals and groups are welcome. Prices start from £20 per head.

SUPER KARTS
2 Pixmore Avenue, Letchworth Garden City, Hertfordshire SG6 1JS
Tel: 01462 485 959 Fax: 01462 625 600
Email: information@superkarts.co.uk
Web Site: www.superkarts.co.uk

SUTTON CIRCUIT
Sutton In The Elms, Leicester LE9 6QF
Tel: 01455 287078 Fax: 01455 287006
Email: kart@suttoncircuit.co.uk
Web Site: www.suttoncircuit.co.uk
The ultimate car circuit.

TRAQ MOTOR SPORT CIRCUITS
Jessops Way,
Croydon Surrey CR0 4TS
Tel: 020 8665 0222
Email: collivers@btinternet.com
Web Site: www.traq-motorracing.com
We have had over 35 years experience in motor-sport. We use Quads,Karts for Corporate Race Nights/Days. We have a floodlit track and a quality outdoor track. We are open 7 days a week and Kids are welcome. Minimoto race track available.

Hot Air Ballooning

BAILEY BALLOONS
44 Ham Green, Pill, Bristol BS20 0HA
Tel: 01275 375 300
Email: info@baileyballoons.co.uk
Web Site: www.baileyballoons.co.uk
Champagne balloon flights

BRITISH SCHOOL OF BALLOONING
Little London Ebernoe, Petworth, West Sussex GU28 9LF
Tel: 01428 707 307 Fax: 01428 707 815
Email: bsb@hotair.co.uk
Web Site: www.hotair.co.uk
Whether you are a single person joining one of our groups or a couple looking for that something special, each and every champagne balloon flight makes for an unforgettable and breathtaking aerial adventure. We Fly our balloons over the English countryside including Sussex, Surrey, Hampshire, Kent, Herts, Essex, Berkshire, Bath & the East Midlands.

HEAD IN THE CLOUDS
28 Connaught Road, Newbury, Berkshire RG14 5SP
Tel: 01635 437 19
Email: d.head@ndirect.co.uk
Web: www.headinthecloudsballoonflights.co.uk
We offer hot air balloon flights in and around Newbury, Oxford, Reading, Swindon and the area west of London each day throughout the year. Balloon flights and ballooning vouchers make excellent gifts for all occasions including weddings, birthdays, retirements, Christmas presents and corporate events.

HORIZON BALLOONING
Unit G5,
Blacknest Road, Blacknest, Alton, Hampshire GU34 4PX
Tel: 01420 520 505
Email: info@horizonballooning.co.uk
Web Site: www.horizonballooning.co.uk
As well as our champagne balloon rides we can supply a twelve month open dated gift voucher and offer exclusive balloon trips for two, great for romantic occasions, Valentines Day, wedding proposals and special anniversaries, birthdays or Christmas presents.

Multi-Day Activities

A DAY IN THE COUNTRY
Upper Aynho Grounds,
Aynho, Banbury, Oxon OX17 3AY
Tel: 01869 810 823 Fax: 01869 810 892
Email: jerry@adayinthecountry.co.uk
Web Site: www.adayinthecountry.co.uk

ACTIVATE OUTDOORS LTD
The Station,
Station Street, Lymington, Hampshire SO41 3BA
Tel/Fax: 01590 688 011
Email: enquiries@activateoutdoors.co.uk
Web Site: www.activateoutdoors.co.uk
Activate specialise in running outdoor team events for corporate groups. We design and deliver team building and training programmes at our exclusive 1000 acre site in the New Forest.

ANGLIA SPORTING ACTIVITIES
Hungarian Hall,
Pettistree, Woodbridge, Suffolk IP13 0JF
Tel/Fax: 01394 460 475
Email: enquiries@angliasport.co.uk
Web Site: www.angliasport.co.uk
A huge variety of activities to suit every group occasion and team building! Have fun and try new skills from Paintball and Off Road Rally Karts to Raft Building.

BROAD OAK EVENTS
Broad Oak Estate,
Broad Oak Lane, Green Head, Kingsley Moor, Stoke-on-Trent Staffs ST10 2EL
Tel: 01782 550 371 Fax: 01782 550 368
Email: sales@broadoakevents.co.uk
Web Site: www.broadoakevents.co.uk
Broad Oak Events are the market leaders in the corporate entertainment field. We can organise a variety of activities, events, entertainments, and team building throughout Europe. We exceed your expectations.

CAPITAL SPORT
The Red House,
College Road, Aston Clinton, Aylesbury, Buckinghamshire HP22 5EZ
Tel: 01296 631 671 Fax: 01296 631 703
Email: info@capital-sport.co.uk
Web Site: www.capital-sport.co.uk
A 20 year history of Creative multi-activity events.

HENLEY HILLBILLIES
Old Henley Farm, Buckland Newton, Dorchester, Dorset DT2 7BL
Tel/Fax: 01300 345 293
Email: mark@henley-hillbillies.freeserve.co.uk
Web Site: www.henleyhillbillies.co.uk
We are an Off Road driving and shooting centre in Dorset. Catering for small and large groups.

PLEASURE BEACH
Blackpool FY4 1EZ
Stageworks Worldwide Productions Tel: 01253 342 426 or 01253 336 341
Email: info@stageworkswwp.com
Web Site: www.stageworkswwp.com
Senior Personnel: Antony Johns
Conferences, meetings, gala dinners, presentation evenings, product launches, exhibitions, weddings, special events, team building. Park/rides available for private hire. Complete corporate event suppliers.

Paintball

ANCASTER KART RACING CENTRE
Wood Lodge, Ancaster, Grantham, Lincolnshire NG32 3PY
Tel: 01400 230306 Fax: 01400 230153
Email: lesjohnson@lancasterkartracing.co.uk
Web Site: www.ancasterkarting.co.uk
Group bookings or arrive and drive sessions available. Phone for details.

BAWTRY PAINTBALL FIELDS
Bawtry Forest,
Great North Road, Bawtry, Doncaster, South Yorkshire DN10 6NF
Tel: 0808 144 3777
Email: info@bawtrypaintballfields.co.uk
Web: www.bawtrypaintballfields.co.uk
BPF is the largest most well equipt venue in Europe, voted best paintball site in britain 2000/2002/2003/2004. This 385 acre site boasts a number of paintballing firsts including a wessex helicopter, Europes first tree fortress, the largest bridge on any site in britiain and the infamous 7ft 6inch predator.

CAMPAIGN PAINTBALL
54 Elane Road, London SW11 3AD
Tel: 01932 865 999 Fax: 01932 865 744
Email: info@campaignpaintball.co.uk
Web Site: www.campaignpaintball.co.uk

NATIONAL PAINTBALL PARK
Stocking Wood,
Penbridge Lane, Broxbourne, Hertfordshire EN10
Tel: 01707 660 088 Fax: 01707 660 087
Email: info@paintballparks.co.uk
Web Site: www.paintballparks.co.uk
Birmingham Office:
Shawbury Wood, Shawbury Lane, Coleshill, Birmingham B46
Hampshire Office:
Street End Cops, Hook Road, Rotherwick, Hampshire RG27
Themed adventure paintball parks. Ideal for stag and hens, corporate and junior events.

PAINTBALL WORLD
2 Woodgate Road, Wootton, Northampton Northamptonshire NN4 6ET
Tel: 01322 552818
Email: jwardb@globalnet.co.uk
Web Site: www.splatme.co.uk
We have been in paintball for 20 years and have numerous sites up and down the UK.

SKIRMISH PAINTBALL GAMES
Sandage Wood,
Fryers Farm Lane, Lane End, High Wycombe, Buckinghamshire HP14 3NP
Tel: 0800 316 1724 Fax: 01189 549935
Email: info@apl.tv
Web Site: www.apl.tv

TASKFORCE PAINTBALL GAMES
Paintball Site:
Just off Main A48, at Penllyn, Cowbridge CF71 3DS
Tel: 029 2059 3900 Fax: 029 2059 4053
Office Address: St Lythans Court, St Lythans, nr Wenvoe, Cardiff CF5 6BQ
Email: enquiries@taskforcepaintball.co.uk
Web Site: www.taskforcepaintball.co.uk
Dedicated 30 acre paintball site. Other activities include, archery, lazer clay shooting, team building, falconary and scuba diving.

Sailing

PLAIN SAILING
Brixham Marina, Brixham, Devon TQ5 9BP
Tel: 01803 853 843 Fax: 01803 854 242
Email: enquiries@plainsailing.co.uk
Web Site: www.plainsailing.co.uk
Yacht Charter and RYA Training Centre, for sail Power & Motor. Courses run all year round. Round Britain Experience, 12 weeks of circumnavigating the British Isles - 38 ft yacht.

PLYMOUTH SAILING SCHOOL
Queen Anne Battery, Coxside, Plymouth PL4 0LP
Tel: 01752 667 170 Fax: 01752 257 162
Email: school@plymsail.co.uk
Web Site: www.plymsail.co.uk
Plymouth Sailing School was established in 1957. An RYA Recognised Teaching Establishment offering Competent Crew/Helmsman to Yachtmaster Ocean, Powerboat Courses and the entire range of shorebased theory courses.

VANILLA
Hambleside,
Swanwick Shore Road, Swanwick, Southampton SO31 7EF
Tel: 01489 589 275 Fax: 01489 589 275
Email: info@vanillacatering.co.uk
Web Site: www.vanillacatering.co.uk

Wine Tasting

ENGLISH WINE CENTRE
Alfriston Roundabout,
Alfriston, East Sussex BN26 5QS
Tel: 01323 870 164 Fax: 01323 870 005
Email: bottles@englishwine.co.uk
Web Site: www.englishwine.co.uk
The English Wine Centre was established in 1972 to provide visitors with the opportunity to taste a range of English wine from different vineyards and winemakers.

LUNZER WINE EVENTS
Ground Floor,
28 Austin Friars, London EC2N 2QQ
Tel: 020 7720 4200
Email: peter@lunzer.co.uk
Web Site: www.lunzer.co.uk
Designing bespoke events for corporate clients since 1992, Peter Lunzer has utilised a talent for simplifying the subject of wine to enable hosts and their guests to pursue important matters of business in the relaxing surroundings of great venues whilst tasting delicious wines.

SNIFF & SPITT
74 St. Helens Road, Hastings, East Sussex TN34 2LN
Tel: 01424 427 702
Email: rebecca@sniffandspit.com
Web Site: www.sniffandspit.com
Corporate wine tasting in London and nationwide, a fun time with fine wine.

TASTE OF THE VINE LTD
Jeroboam House,
Sandy Lane, Grayswood, Haslemere, Surrey GU27 2DG
Tel: 01428 656 319 Fax: 01428 654 951
Email: events@tasteofthevine.co.uk
Web Site: www.tasteofthevine.co.uk
"Interactive entertainment shows based around wine, champagne, whisky, beer and cocktail challenges and events - a unique blend of comedy and theatre.

WINFIELD WINE EVENTS
38 The Avenue, London W13 8LP
Tel: 020 8997 4718 Fax: 020 8997 7619
Email: info@winfieldwines.co.uk
Web Site: www.winfieldwines.co.uk
Winfield Wine Events offer tailor-made wine tastings as corporate entertainment events. They specialise in team building blind tasting competitions, and also offer a free venue finding service.

Specialist Event Venues

Miscellaneous

BUSINESS DESIGN CENTRE
52 Upper Street, Islington Green, London N1 0QH
Tel: 020 7359 3535 Fax: 020 7 226 0590
Email: grahams@businessdesigncentre.co.uk
Web: www.businessdesigncentre.co.uk
Cap: 1,500 Banquet

CAESARS
156-160 Streatham Hill, London SW2 4RU
Tel: 020 8671 3000 Fax: 01306 711660
Mobile: 07860 414194
Email: info@caesars.co.uk
Web Site: www.caesars.uk.co.uk
Contact: Fred Batt
Maximum Capacity: 1,900
Ideal for banquets, concerts, product launches and fashion shows. Live & Recorded television programmes, video and photographic shoots.

CLIVEDEN
Taplow, Berkshire SL6 0JF
Tel: 01628 668 561 Fax: 01628 661 837
Email: reservations@clivedenhouse.co.uk
Web Site: www.clivedenhouse.co.uk
One of the World's leading hotels.

LEITH'S AT DARTMOUTH HOUSE
The English Speaking Union, 37 Charles Street, London W1J 5ED
Tel: 020 7499 4005 Fax: 020 7495 1886
Email: claire.patten@compass-group.co.uk
Web Site: www.unusualvenue.com
Sales Manager: Julia Dalgleish
Dartmouth House is an elegant mansion providing the perfect setting for a variety of events. The original building was constructed in the late 16th Century and converted in the late 19th Century, by Lord Revelstoke, into a beautiful town house with many interesting features. The rooms can be hired individually or the House in its entirety. Leith's are the caterers. The function rooms can cater from 20 to 150 people. Please call for further details.

EXCEL ARENA
1 Western Gateway, Royal Victoria Dock, London E16 1XL
General Sales: Tel: 020 7069 4602 Fax: 020 7069 4747
Email: info@excel-london.co.uk
Web Site: www.excel-london.co.uk
Cap: 100,000

MAINLINE PICTURES
37 Museum Street, London WC1A 1LQ
Tel: 020 7242 5523 Fax: 020 7430 0170
Email: tony.bloom@btinternet.com
Web Site: www.screencinemas.co.uk
Managing Director: Romaine Hart
London and out of London venues - cinemas, location shooting - interior & exterior, private cinema hire.

MINISTRY OF SOUND
103 Grant Street, London SE1 6DP
Tel: 020 7740 8728 Fax: 020 7403 5348
Email: met@ministryofsound.com
Web Site: www.ministryofsound.com/privatehire
Managing Director: Hector Dewar
Contact: Met Salih (private hire and special event co-ordinator).
5 rooms to hire, with 3 bars.Capacity 1200 people.
JBL Sound System throughout. 3 Phase Power. Modular Stage. Video Projection System.
We offer a full range of facilities in a central London location.

PLANET HOLLYWOOD
Restaurant and Bar Available for Private Hire
13 Coventry Street, London W1D 7DH
Tel: 020 7478 1558/ 07/ 43 Fax:020 7478 1503
Email: salesuk@planethollywood.com
Web: www.planethollywoodlondon.com
Capacity: Main Restaurant 300-500, used for a variety of purposes from film screenings to seminars and private parties. Rex Cinema bar capacity 190 cinema capacity 75 (seated)

THE RITZ
150 Piccadilly, London W1J 9BR
Tel: 020 7493 8181 Fax: 020 7493 2687
Email: enquire@theritzlondon.com
Web Site: www.theritzlondon.com
Contact: Andrew Hartley
Capacity: Reception 100 maximum, Dinner 50 max (private banqueting rooms).

THE SAVOY
The Strand, London WC2R 0EU
Tel: 020 7836 4343 Fax: 020 7872 8894
Email: info@the-savoy.co.uk
Web Site: www.savoygroup.com
Capacity: Cocktail reception: 800 max, Dinner: 500 max, Dinner Dance: 375 max, Conference 400 max (theatre style).

THE CIRCUS SPACE
Coronet Street, London N1 6HD
Tel: 020 7729 9522 Fax: 020 7729 9422
Email: jane@thecircusspace.co.uk
Web Site: www.thecircusspace.co.uk
ADMINISTRATION:
Joint Chief Executives: Jane Rice-Bowen and Kate White
Operations Director: Jonathan Dix
Higher Education Courses Director: Tim Roberts
Participation and Outreach Director: Eira Gibson
Director of Circus Development: Daisy Drury
Finance and Administration Director: Edward Halshaw
Head of Marketing and Communication: Philip Nichols
Venue Hire: Alex Horder (alex@thecircusspace.co.uk)

THE HOUSE OF ST. BARNABAS-IN-SOHO
1 Greek Street Soho Square London W1D 4NQ
Tel: 0207 437 1894 Fax: 0207 437 1746
Email: eluned.santos@houseofstbarnabas.org.uk
Web Site: www.houseofbarnabas.org.uk
Hiring Officer: Suzan Chattalou
Director: Eluned Santos

THE MAGIC CIRCLE HEADQUARTERS
12 Stephenson Way, London NW1 2HD
Admin: 020 7387 2222
Email: mail@magiccirclevenue.co.uk
Web: www.themagiccirclevenue.co.uk
ADMINISTRATION:
Props: The Magic Circle Headquarters
Sales Manager: Jackson Baugh
Capacity: Theatre; 162. Devant Room; 80 Theatre Style/ Dining, 100 Reception. Club Room; 50 Theatre Style/ Dining, 65 Reception.
Policy: In addition to seasonal shows the building is available for hire seven days a week. Ideal for a wide range of events and meetings - from conferences to product launches and promotions to corporate entertainment.
Located in Central London, next to Euston station, the venue has excellent national travel links and is easily accessible by public transport. Modern facilities include a fully equipped purpose built theatre, flexible meeting, dining and function rooms, a clubroom and bar; perfect for receptions and meetings and a magic museum showcasing one of the largest magic collections in Europe. There is a lift to all floors, induction loop in the theatre and disabled access throughout the building.

Museums & Galleries

THE BANQUETING HOUSE, WHITEHALL PALACE
Whitehall, London SW1A 2ER
Tel: 0870 751 5170 Events Tel: 0870 751 5185 / 5186
Marketing Tel: 0207 488 5775
Email: mike.nicholas@hrp.org.uk

Web Site: www.hrp.org.uk
Contact: Michael Nicholas
Capacity: Reception 500; Dinner 375.
Contact Visitors Services Manager: L Kennedy
Email: lin.kennedy@hrp.org.uk

BEAULIEU, NATIONAL MOTOR MUSEUM

John Montagu Building, Beaulieu, Brockenhurst, Hampshire SO42 7ZN
Tel: 01590 614 604 Fax: 01590 612 624
Email: conference@beaulieu.co.uk
Web Site: www.beaulieu.co.uk
Contact: Dinah Farrell
Capacity: Dining 300; Reception 600

THE BRITISH MUSEUM

Great Russell Street, London WC1B 3DG
Tel: 020 7323 8136 (Neil Ormondroyd)
Tel: 020 7323 8128 (Charlotte Stokes)
Fax: 020 7323 8137
Email: corporate@thebritishmuseum.ac.uk
Web Site: www.thebritishmuseum.ac.uk
Evening Events Contact: Heather Graham
Daytime Conferencing Contact: Neil Ormondroyd
Capacities: Dinner 500. Reception 1500.

CABINET WAR ROOMS

Clive Steps, King Charles Street, London SW1A 2AQ
Tel: 020 7930 6961 Fax: 020 7839 5897
Email: cwr@iwm.org.uk
Web Site: www.iwm.org.uk
Capacity: 200 Reception/Buffet occupying whole site. 50 seated dinner.
The historic site (21 rooms leading off two very long corridors) which sheltered Winston Churchill lies 3 metres below ground in the basement of the Government Offices Great George Street and can be hired for a variety of functions.

DULWICH PICTURE GALLERY

Gallery Road, London SE21 7AD
Tel: 020 8299 9284
Email: enterprise@dulwich.org.uk
Web: www.dulwichpicturegallery.org.uk
Contact: Liz Smith
The Dulwich Picture Gallery can cater for up to 350. The Linbury room and the Chapel are available throughout the day, whilst the Soane Galleries and the Cabinet Room are suitable for receptions and dinners.

IMPERIAL WAR MUSEUM

Lambeth Road, London SE1 6HZ
Tel: 020 7416 5394 Fax: 020 7416 5457
Email: cgresty@iwm.org.uk
Web Site: www.iwm.org.uk
Catherine Gresty
Capacity: Dinner 400, Reception 1,000.
The Imperial War Museum can be hired for a variety of events. Daytime meeting rooms are available to accommodate groups of 10-200 people. During the evening, maximum capacity for a dinner is 400, and 1,000 for a reception.

THE LONDON DUNGEON

28/34 Tooley Street, London SE1 2SZ
Tel: 020 7403 7221 Fax: 020 7378 1529
Bookings through: The Crown Group, 13 Bishopsgate, London EC2M 4QB Tel: 020 7236 2149
Email: marilyn.allen@crownsociety.co.uk
Web Site: www.thedungeons.com
Contact: Gill Butler
The venue has just completed an exciting refurbishment and relaunch. Up to 140 people for a silver service, sit-down meal and up to 400 people for a buffet meal.

LONDON'S TRANSPORT MUSEUM

The Piazza, Covent Garden, London WC2E 7BB
Tel: 020 7565 7292 Fax: 020 7565 7253
Email: corphire@ltmuseum.co.uk
Web Site: www.ltmuseum.co.uk
Events Co-ordinator: Victoria Goodfellow
Capacity: Reception: 400, Dinner: 100

THE NATIONAL FILM THEATRE

South Bank, London SE1 8XT
Tel: 020 7815 1304 Fax: 020 7815 1378
Email: lisa.moore@bfi.org.uk
Web Site: www.bfi.org.uk
Contact: Lisa Moore
Capacity: Stand up Buffet: 200, Meetings 460. NFT 1: 450; NFT2 160; NFT3 135 - All equiped with digital and video equipment.

NATIONAL MARITIME MUSEUM

Park Row, Greenwich, London SE10 9NF
Tel: 020 8312 6565 Admin: 020 8858 4422 Fax: 020 8312 6632
Email: egoody@nmm.ac.uk / jopole@nmm.ac.uk
Web Site: www.nmm.ac.uk
Events Office: Eleanor Goody, Jo Pole
The National Maritime Museum is a unique and beautiful complex in the heart of Greenwich offering a huge range of corporate entertaining opportunities, limited only by the imagination.

NATIONAL PORTRAIT GALLERY

2 St Martin's Place, Piccadilly, London WC2H 0HE
Tel: 020 7306 0055 Fax: 020 7306 0058
Email: adavies@npg.org.uk
Web Site: www.npg.org.uk
Contact: Event Manager
Dinner: 100, Reception 350

THE NATURAL HISTORY MUSEUM

Cromwell Road, South Kensington, London SW7 5BD
Tel: 020 7942 5434 Fax: 020 7942 5070
Email: functions@nhm.ac.uk
Web Site: www.nhm.ac.uk/functions
Contact: Ian Fraser
Capacity: Dinner 600, Dinner & Dance 450, Buffet 800, Cocktail Reception 1,250

ROYAL ACADEMY OF ARTS

Burlington House, Piccadilly, London W1J 0BD
Tel: 020 7300 5701 Fax: 020 7287 6312
Email: natalie.glaser@royalacademy.org.uk
Web Site: www.royalacademy.org.uk
Contact: Corporate Events Manager
Cap: Reception: 350 or 800 (depending on exhibition) Dinners: 100. No smoking, no dancing.

ROYAL AIR FORCE MUSEUM

Hendon, London NW9 5LL
Tel: 020 8358 4848 Fax: 020 8358 4981
Email: events@rafmuseum.com
Web Site: www.rafmuseum.com
Contact: Anne-Marie Henry
Capacity: Reception 1,000 max, Dinner 350 max

THE ROYAL OBSERVATORY GREENWICH

Romney Road, London SE10 9NF
Tel: 020 8312 6693 / 6644 / 8517 Fax: 020 8312 6572
Email: egoody@nmm.ac.uk / jrough@nmm.ac.uk
Web Site: www.nmm.ac.uk
Events Office: Eleanor Goody, Jo Rough

THE ROYAL PAVILION, BRIGHTON

4/5 Pavillion Buildings, Brighton, East Sussex BN1 1EE
Tel: 01273 292 815/3 Fax: 01273 292 871
Email: trish.baker@brighton-hove.gov.uk
Web Site: www.royalpavilion.org.uk
Capacity: Reception 200, Dinner 90

SCIENCE MUSEUM

Events Office Exhibition Road, London SW7 2DD
Tel: 020 7942 4340
Email: science.eventsoffice@nmsi.ac.uk
Web Site: www.sciencemuseum.org.uk
Capacity 2000

TOWER BRIDGE

Tower Bridge Exhibition London SE1 2UP
Tel: 020 7940 3972 Fax: 020 7403 4477
Email: enquiries@towerbridge.org.uk
Web Site: www.towerbridge.org.uk
Tower Bridge can host groups in the Victorian Engine Rooms, the Bridge Master's Dining Rooms, or over 40 metres above the Thames in the walkways.

THE TOWER OF LONDON

London EC3N 4AB
Tel: 020 7488 5762 Fax: 020 7480 5543
Email: events@hrp.org.uk
Web Site: www.hrp.org.uk
Functions Executive: Rosemary Ridyard
The Tower does offer a unique and fascinating venue for a special event.
Capacity: 15-300 guests in various suites.
The tower is now able to offer a superb reception facility in the White Tower, amongst the armour from King Henry VIII's court. From February 2001 the New Armouries banqueting and conference suites will be available.

THE VICTORIA & ALBERT MUSEUM

Cromwell Road, London SW7 2RL
Tel: 020 7942 2646 Fax: 020 7942 2645
Email: p.dacunha@vam.ac.uk
Web Site: www.vam.ac.uk
Contact: Pippa da Cunha
The V&A is one of the world's great museums and a vast treasure house of art and design. The magnificent victorian building offers remarkable rooms for entertaining.
Capacity: Reception 700, Seated Dinner 400, Dinner Dance 250.

Palaces & Stately Homes

HAMPTON COURT PALACE

Hampton Court Palace, East Molesey, Surrey KT8 9AU
Tel: 020 8781 9508 Fax: 020 8781 9509
Email: vikki.wood@hrp.org.uk
Web Site: www.hrp.org.uk
PR Officer: Vikki Wood
Capacity: The Great Hall: Reception 400, Dinner 280; Banqueting House: Receptions 100, Dinners 50.

KENSINGTON PALACE

The Orangery
State Apartments Kensington Gardens, London W8 4PX
Tel: 020 7376 2452 Fax: 020 7376 0198
Email: events@hrp.org.uk
Web Site: www.hrp.org.uk
Contact: Lorraine Rossdale
Capacity: Queen Anne's Orangery 300 for cocktail parties, 150 for dinners.

THE QUEEN'S HOUSE

Romney Road, London SE10 9NF
Tel: 020 8312 6693 / 6644 / 8517 Fax: 020 8312 6572
Email: egoody@nmm.ac.uk / jrough@nmm.ac.uk
Web Site: www.nmm.ac.uk
Events Office: Eleanor Goody, Jo Rough

SOMERSET HOUSE

Tel: 020 7845 4618
Email: corporate.events@somerset-house.org.uk
Web Site: www.somerset-house.org.uk
The courtyard at Somerset House hosts up to 2,700 for drinks and smaller groups can use the Hermitage Rooms and Navy Boardroom. A lecture theatre for 60 delegates is also available.

WARWICK CASTLE

Warwick, Warwickshire CV34 4QU
Tel: 01926 406 604 Fax: 01926 406 611
Corporate evenings: 0870 442 2374
Email: customer.information@warwick-castle.co.uk
Web Site: www.warwick-castle.co.uk
Contact: The Sales Office
Capacity: Marquee 2000 max; Receptions: 230; Dining: 50-130

WOBURN ABBEY

Woburn, Bedfordshire MK17 9WA
Tel: 01525 290 666 Fax: 01525 290 549
Email: catering@sculpturegallery.co.uk
Web Site: www.woburnabbey.co.uk

Sports Venues

ASCOT RACECOURSE

closed until end of 2005
The Grandstand, Ascot, Berkshire SL5 7JX
Tel: 01344 878 599 Fax: 01344 878 598
Email: businessandevents@ascot.co.uk
Web Site: www.ascot.co.uk
Contact: Gerry Skerritt

THE BELFRY

The De Vere Belfry, Wishaw, North Warwickshire B76 9PR
Tel: 01675 470 301 Fax: 01675 470 256/01675470178
Email: enquiries@thebelfry.com
Web Site: www.devereonline.co.uk
Contact: Sales Department
Guests at the Belfry enjoy the unique atmosphere of a major seniors golf tournament, which includes players - many of whom are former Ryder Cup stars - mixing openly with the guests.

BRANDS HATCH

Brands Hatch Circuits Ltd Fawkham, Longfield, Kent DA3 8NG
Tel: 01474 872 331 Ticketing: 0870 606 0611 Activities: 0870 512 5250 Fax: 01474 874 766
Email: rob.sorbel@motorsportvision.co.uk
Web Site: www.octagon.com
Corporate Sales: Rob Sorbel
Capacity: 300 per floor (2 floors) 450 acres of land for any event from a party of 10 to a conference of 1,000.

CHEPSTOW RACECOURSE

Chepstow Racecourse Chepstow Monmouthshire NP16 6BE Wales
Tel: 01291 622 260 Fax: 01291 627 061
Email: caroline.freiha@chepstow-racecourse.co.uk
Web: www.chepstow-racecourse.co.uk
Contact Commercial Manager: Caroline Freiha

DONINGTON PARK

Exhibitions Conference Centre, Donington Park, Castle Donington, Derby DE74 2RP
Tel: 01332 810 048 Fax: 01332 811 647
Email: martin.quilliam@livenation.co.uk
Web Site: www.donington-park.co.uk
Contact: Martin Quilliam

LIVERPOOL FOOTBALL CLUB

Anfield Road, Liverpool, Merseyside L4 0TH
Tel: 0151 263 9199 Fax:0151 260 0981
Email: events@liverpoolfc.tv
Web Site: www.liverpoolfc.tv
Contact: Sue Johnson
Merseyside Tourism Conference Venue of the Year 1998.
Here at Anfield we have a reputation for being one of the most successful football clubs on the pitch, however this success also applies off the pitch. The range and standard of facilities, food and service available are second to none, and with our own "onsite" team of professionals to co-ordinate and manage your individual event, Anfield is the perfect venue for any occasion.

SILVERSTONE SPORTS LTD

Silverstone Circuit
Silverstone, Northamptonshire NN12 8TN
Tel: 01327 320 330 Fax: 01327 320 333
Email: laurence.wiltshire@silverstone.co.uk
Contact: Hospitality Team
Conference and hospitality facilities for small to large groups.

TOTTENHAM HOTSPUR FOOTBALL CLUB

Bill Nicholson Way, 748 High Road, Tottenham, London N17 0AP
Tel: 020 8365 5010 Fax: 020 8365 5015
Web Site: www.tottenhamhotspur.com

WEMBLEY (LONDON) LTD

Elvin House, Stadium Way, Wembley, Middlesex HA9 0DW
Tel: 020 8902 8833
Email: benj@wembley.co.uk
Web Site: www.whatsonwembley.com / www.wembley.co.uk

WEST HAM FOOTBALL CLUB

Boelyn Ground, Green Street, Upton Park, London E13 9AZ
Tel: 020 8548 2748 Conference & Banqueting: 020 8548 2775

Fax: 020 8548 2758
Email: afordyce@westhamunited.co.uk
Web Site: www.whufc.com
Contact: Julie Brown
Various rooms, call for details
Contact Commercial Manager: Susan Page
spage@westhamunited.co.uk

WIMBLEDON GREYHOUND STADIUM

Plough Lane, Wimbledon, London SW17 0BL
Tel: 020 8946 8000 Fax: 0870 880 1111
Email: wmreserve@gralimited.co.uk
Web Site: www.wimbledonstadium.co.uk
Contact: Gaye Robinson, David West
Capacity: Dinner 420 max.
One of the finest Greyhound Stadiums in London.
Executive boxes available for up to 96 people. Two restaurants available with a joint capacity of 420 diners. Racing every Tuesday, Thursday, Friday & Saturday nights.

Themed Attractions & Leisure Parks

ALTON TOWERS

Alton Staffordshire ST10 4DB
Tel: 01538 704 692 Fax: 01538 704 099
Email: events@alton-towers.com
Web Site: www.alton-towers.co.uk
Special Event Manager: Liz Hulse
Alton Towers is the UK's Number One theme park with a host of exciting venues for the ultimate event, so if its a company fun day for 10,000 or a conference for 200 in our fabulous hotel, Alton Towers can deliver.

THE BEATLES STORY

Britannia Pavillion, Albert Dock, Liverpool, Merseyside L3 4AA
Tel: 0151 709 1963 Fax: 0151 708 0039
Email: info@beatlesstory.com
Web Site: www.beatlesstory.com
Manager: Louise Collier
The Beatles Story is a unique venue for corporate or private parties. In a replica of the original Cavern Club your party can really get into the mood of the swingin' 60's. With facilities for a buffet and dancing packages can be customised to suit your individual requirements. Go on-line at www.beatlesstory.com for further information.

BRIGHTON PIER

Brighton Pier, Madeira Drive, Brighton, East Sussex BN2 1TW
Tel: 01273 609 361 Fax: 01273 684 289
Email: info@brightonpier.co.uk
Web Site: www.brightonpier.co.uk
Contact: Suzannah Mascarenhas
At 1,722ft long and acknowledged as the finest pier ever built, Brighton Pier (Grade II listed building) now offers all the swagger and style of tradition balanced with the pace and excitement of today. Many pieces of history remain on the Pier. It is available for Corporate Events, Filming, Private Hire and almost anything else. Please call for further details.

CADBURY WORLD

Corporate Sales Office, 100 Icknield Port Road, Edgbaston, Birmingham B16 0AA
Tel: 0121 456 4545 Fax: 0121 454 9118
Email: cc.conferences@redcliffe.com
Web Site: www.redcliffe.com
Senior Sales Executive: Tracey Mason
Cadbury World offers clients a unique "Chocaholic Experience" combined with superb hospitality catering for many different styles of events. All Corporate Clients enjoy sole use of the facilities including a tour of the Attraction, a ride on the new £1m "Cadabra", the Cadbury Shop and the restaurant for dining.
Capacity: 50-300. Floor Space: 1,800sq ft plus a hexagonal well suitable for dancing.

CHESSINGTON WORLD OF ADVENTURES

Leatherhead Road, Chessington, Surrey KT9 2NE
Tel: 01372 731 546 Fax: 01372 731 519
Email: david.fisher@chessington.co.uk
Web Site: www.chessington.com
Special Event Co-ordinator: David Fisher
One of the UK's best theme parks. Call for details of corporate facilities.

CREALY ADVENTURE PARK

Sidmouth Road, Clyst St Mary, Exeter, Devon EX5 1DR
Tel: 01395 233 200 Fax: 01395 233 211
Email: fun@crealy.co.uk
Web Site: www.crealy.co.uk
General Manager: Angela Wright
Administrator/PA: Jenny Taffs
Capacity: Dining 150
Where Business is a Pleasure
Crealy Adventure Park guarantees maximum fun - whether for an annual meeting, fun day or evening party.

DRAYTON MANOR THEME PARK

Tamworth, Staffordshire B78 3TW
Tel: 01827 287 979 Fax: 01827 252 444
Email: info@draytonmanor.co.uk
Web Site: www.draytonmanor.co.uk
Whatever you're planning - conference, reception banquet, corporate entertainment - Drayton Manor is perfectly situated in the heart of England. Set in 280 acres of parkland and lakes, Drayton Manor not only offers you one of the country's leading theme parks, but is also an ideal venue for business & pleasure.

EXPLORERS CAFE & RESTAURANT

Drusillas Park, Alfriston, East Sussex BN26 5QS
Tel: 01323 874 100 Fax: 01323 874 101
Email: info@drusillas.co.uk
Web Site: www.drusillas.co.uk
Catering Manager: Malcolm Yarwood
Evening restaurant hire with seating for up to 150 people. Themed evenings and entertainment. Catering also available.

FLAMINGO LAND

Kirby Misperton, Malton, North Yorkshire Y017 6UX
Tel: 01653 668 287 Fax: 01653 668 280
Email: info@flamingoland.co.uk
Web Site: www.flamingoland.co.uk
Marketing Manager: Mark Crane
Capacity: Up to 500
Corporate days at Flamingo Land can consist of the hiring of a marquee accompanied by a barbecue lunch or, depending on the time of year, we can provide a buffet style lunch which would be available in one of our suites situated in the heart of the park. Group visits are also an option.

FOLLY FARM

Begelly, Kilgetty, Pembrokeshire SA68 0XA Wales
Tel: 01834 812 731 Fax: 01834 813 148
Email: admin@folly-farm.co.uk
Web Site: www.folly-farm.co.uk
General Manager: Chris Ebsworth
Fully equipped with conference facilities for all your corporate needs.

FUNLAND

The Trocadero, 1 Piccadilly Circus, London W1V 8DH
Tel: 020 7395 1704 Fax: 020 7395 1708
Email: info@funland.co.uk
Web Site: www.funland.co.uk
Operations Director: Max Claus
Sales & Marketing Executive: Judy Lowther
The World's leading indoor Entertainment Centre. Funland combines simulators, rides, the latest in hitech video games, ten-pin bowling, pool hall, dodgems and much, much more coming in the near future. For further information please call the Events Department.

HEIGHTS OF ABRAHAM

Matlock Bath, Derbyshire DE4 3PD
Tel: 01629 582 365 Ext: 256 Fax: 01629 581 128
Email: office@h-of-a.co.uk
Web Site: www.heights-of-abraham.co.uk
Ride high above the Derwant Valley in the cable cars. Go down two famous Show

Caverns. Picnic and play Areas. Woodland Walks. Hi Café. Gift Shops.

LEGOLAND, WINDSOR

Winkfield Road, Windsor, Berkshire SL4 4AY
Tel: 01753 626 102 Fax: 01753 626 200
Email: michelle.wynne@legoland.co.uk
Web Site: www.legoland.co.uk
Corporate Sales Executive: Michelle Wynne
Corporate Events Manager: Sheila Robbie
Set in 150 acres of mature parkland Legoland, Windsor is situated just two miles from Windsor. At the centre of the park is St.Leonards Mansion, an elegant Georgian house - providing two rooms for corporate use. From conferences to themed meal packages to exclusive use of the park in the evenings: We can cater for any event. Please call for more details.

THE LONDON AQUARIUM

County Hall, Westminster Bridge Road, London SE1 7PB
Tel: 020 7967 8026
Email: sales@londoncountyhall.com
Web Site: www.londoncountyhall.com

THE LONDON DUNGEON

28/34 Tooley Street, London SE1 2SZ
Tel: 020 7403 7221 Fax: 020 7378 1529
Bookings through: The Crown Group, 13 Bishopsgate, London EC2M 4QB Tel: 020 7236 2149
Email: marilyn.allen@crownsociety.co.uk
Web Site: www.thedungeons.com
Contact: Gill Butler
The venue has just completed an exciting refurbishment and relaunch. Up to 140 people for a silver service, sit-down meal and up to 400 people for a buffet meal.

THE BRITISH AIRWAYS LONDON EYE

Riverside Building, County Hall, Westminster Bridge Road, London SE1 7PB
Tel: 0870 220 2223 Fax: 0870 990 8882
Email: capsules@ba-londoneye.com
Web Site: www.ba-londoneye.com
A popular choice for drinks receptions; groups of up to 20 can occupy each pod. If no drinks or food, each pod can hold 25 people.

THE LONDON PLANETARIUM

See Madame Tussauds Listing
Email: michael.birch@madame-tussauds.com
Contact Events Marketing Manager: Michael Birch

LONDON ZOO HOSPITALITY

Zoological Gardens, Regents Park, London NW1 4RY
Tel: 020 7449 6374 Fax: 020 7722 0388
Email: joanna.green@zsl.org
Web Site: www.londonzoo.co.uk
For events enquiries, contact: Joanna Green
Maximum Capacity: Lunch/dinner 70-240; Reception 40-380; Dinner-Dance 100-220

MADAME TUSSAUDS & THE LONDON PLANETARIUM

Marylebone Road, London NW1 5LR
Main Tel: 020 7487 0200 Main Fax: 020 7465 0862 Specialist Event Contact Line: 020 7407 0224 Specialist Event Fax Line: 020 7465 0884
Email: events@madame-tussauds.com
Web Site: www.madametussauds.com
Head of Events: Michael Aldridge
Madame Tussauds: Capacity: Reception 600, Dinner 350. From cocktail parties to product launches and themed dinners, all the events take place within the exhibition, allowing your guests to mingle with the rich, famous and even dine with the Royal Family.
The Planetarium: Maximum Capacity: 300 Ideal for product launches and corporate presentations, offering the very latest multi-media facilities in a brand new theatre style auditorium. Also an interactive exhibition area for cocktails, buffets and themed dinners.

THE MILKYWAY ADVENTURE PARK

Clovelly, Bideford, North Devon EX39 5RY
Tel: 01237 431 255 Fax: 01237 431 735
Email: info@themilkyway.co.uk
Web Site: www.themilkyway.co.uk
Contact: Rob Weare
Indoor facilities cover 2.5 football pitches. We can offer hire of the entire site or merely parts of it for private groups. We have catering and fully licensed bar facilities. Hire of the Time Warp indoor play area. Archery, mini-golf and laser target shooting competitions. Hire of the Indoon Arena with PA system and informal bench seating for up to 700 people. Falconry tuition for individuals/small groups.

NEW PALACE

Marine Promenade, New Brighton, Wirral CH45 2JX
Tel: 0151 639 6041 Fax: 0151 639 6801
Email: david@wilkieleisuregroup.com
Managing Director: David Wilkie
New Palace indoor speed karting circuit for corporate events and party bookings. Also available is our luxury function suite available for corporate entertaining and private hire. Catering for up to 200 people with superb views across the River Mersey and ample free parking.

NEW PLEASUREWOOD HILLS

Leisure Way, Corton, Lowestoft, Suffolk NR32 5DZ
Tel: 01502 586 000 Fax: 01502 567 393
Email: info@pleasurewoodhills.com
Web Site: www.pleasurewoodhills.com
To hold a conference, there are various facilities ranging from a meeting room to an 800 seat theatre.
Please phone for more information.

OAKWOOD PARK

Canaston Bridge, Narberth, Pembrokeshire SA67 8DE Wales
Tel: 01834 891373 Fax: 01834 891 380
Email: marketing@oakwood-leisure.com
Web Site: www.oakwood-leisure.com
Marketing Manager: Zoe Snell
Marketing Officer: Shelley Upton
CC2000 (venue) available for 15-30 people with conference facilities and company packages. Please call for further details.

PAULTONS

Paultons Park Ltd, Ower, Romsey, Hampshire SO51 6AL
Tel: 023 8081 4442 Fax: 023 8081 3025
24 Hour Hotline: 023 8081 4455
Email: robgriffiths@paultons.co.uk
Web Site: www.paultonspark.co.uk
Marketing Manager: Rob Griffiths
Catering Manager: Gary Weldon-Jones
This park was once a country estate and has a magnificent setting with beautiful gardens landscaped with ponds, fountains and aviaries for exotic birds. The Cedar Room seats up to 180 people. Areas in the park can be provided where marquees can be erected. Ideal for company days out, meetings, seminars and private functions.

PLEASURE BEACH

Blackpool FY4 1EZ
Stageworks Worldwide Productions Tel: 01253 342 426 or 01253 336 341
Email: info@stageworkswwp.com
Web Site: www.stageworkswwp.com
Senior Personnel: Antony Johns
Conferences, meetings, gala dinners, presentation evenings, product launches, exhibitions, weddings, special events, team building. Park/rides available for private hire. Complete corporate event suppliers.

PLEASURELAND LTD

The Amusement Park on the Sands
Marine Drive, Southport, Merseyside PR8 1RX
General: 08702 200 204 Party Hotline: 08702 200 204 Fax: 01704 537 936
Email: mail@pleasurelandltd.freeserve.co.uk
Web Site: www.pleasureland.uk.com
Managing Director: Mrs A J Thompson
Marketing Manager: Joanne Cheetham
Amusement park with over 100 rides & attractions including the UK's tallest, fastest suspended looping rollercoaster,

Go karts & Family entertainment centre. Facilities available for hire.

ROLLERWORLD
Eastgates, Colchester, Essex CO1 2TJ
Tel: 01206 868 868 Fax: 01206 870 400
Web Site: www.rollerworld.co.uk
Contact: Andy Starr
Europe's largest Roller skating rink, and Quasar facilities available for group hire. Catering available. Please call for further details. Great for launch parties and video shoots, TV etc. Fully licenced bar + fast food cafe.

THORPE PARK
Staines Road, Chertsey, Surrey KT16 8PN
Tel: 01932 569 393 Fax: 01932 566 367
Email: nancy.edwards@thorpe-park.co.uk
Web Site: www.thorpe-park.com
General Manager: Peter Ronchetty
Corporate Services Executive: Lynne Paterson(01932 577129/109)
Sprawled over 500 acres, Thorpe Park offers private, unrestricted use of a number of top class venues plus unlimited access to our World Famous rides and attractions. Our corporate services team are here to provide advise and guidance for you to enjoy your day with your guests or colleagues. Company Days, Exhibitions, Meetings, Product Launches, Corporate Fundays, Team Building, Wedding Receptions - we have a variety of versatile venues from the Thorpe Belle Mississippi Paddle Steamer to The Palladium 600 seat conference theatre. Thorpe Park can be exclusively hired into the evening or you can hire specific rides to enjoy once the park is closed. Thorpe Park is the venue that has it all. Call us now for more details.

THE WICKSTEED PARK PAVILION
Wicksteed Park, Kettering, Northamptonshire NN15 6NJ
Tel: 01536 512 475 Fax: 01536 518 948
Email: john-wicksteed@tiscali.co.uk
Web Site: www.wicksteedpark.co.uk
Set within the grounds of Wicksteed Park, the pavilion offers a variety of rooms to cater for all occasions. From company meetings to exhibitions. It is also ideal for weddings, private parties and dinner dances whilst maintaining its romantic "air" for ballroom dancing. It can accommodate 750 seated guests.

WOBURN SAFARI PARK
Woburn, Bedfordshire MK17 9QN
Tel: 01525 290 406 (catering mngr direct line) Tel: 01525 290 407 (main office) Fax: 01525 290 715 (catering)
Email: catering@woburnsafari.co.uk
Web Site: www.woburnsafari.co.uk
Catering Manager: Alastair Crawford
Functions tailored to your needs. Conference area for up to 200. Top class in-house catering. Photocopying/faxing available. Excellent product launch setting. Amazing views over the lakes. Licensed bar upon request. Please call for further details.

Waterways

CUTTY SARK
The Cutty Sark Trust, 2 Greenwich Church Street, London SE10 9BG
Tel: 020 8858 2698 Fax: 020 8858 6976
Email: info@cuttysark.org.uk
Web Site: www.cuttysark.org.uk
Contact: Jonathon Bentall
Capacity: Reception 180, Dinner 80.
Sited in dry dock the upper deck is suitable for summer receptions and the between deck accommodates dinners.

THE "DIXIE QUEEN"
Thames Luxury Charters Ltd, 5 The Mews, 6 Putney Common, Putney SW15 1HL
Tel: 020 8780 1562 Fax: 020 8788 0072
Email: sales@thamesluxurycharters.co.uk
Web Site: www.thamesluxurycharters.co.uk
Contact: Sharon Ward
Capacity: 400 silver service; 520 buffet.
London's largest cruising function boat. A stunning $10 million conversion into a replica Mississippi Paddleboat that sets new standards for luxury on the Thames. Based near Tower Bridge. 10' high ceilings, 3 bars, spacious outside decks, extensive kitchens. Competitive charter rates based on numbers on board. Colour brochure available.

THE "ELIZABETHAN MISSISSIPPI PADDLE STEAMER"
5 The Mews, 6 Putney Common, London SW15 1HL
Tel: 020 8780 1562 Fax: 020 8788 0072
Email: info@mainstreamleisure.co.uk
Web Site: www.mainstreamleisure.co.uk
Contact: Nigel Scandrett
Capacity: 140 silver service one level or 200 using both decks. A replica 19th Century Paddle Boat with a 5 star restaurant and night club atmosphere. Guests can be picked up from any of 21 London Piers from Putney to the Thames Barrier.

HMS BELFAST
Morgans Lane, Tooley Street, London SE1 2JH
Tel: 020 7403 6246 Fax: 020 7407 0708
Email: jwilson@iwm.org.uk
Web Site: www.iwm.org.uk / www.conference-online.co.uk
Contact: Nicola Butler
Capacity: 20-400
Various quarters available for hire, including the Summer Quarter Deck, the Admiral's Quarters, the Ship's Company Dining Hall, the Ward and Ward Ante Room and the Gun Room. Luncheons, dinners, receptions, seminars and evening parties.

THE "LADY ROSE OF REGENTS" CANALBOAT
c/o Mainstream Leisure, 5 The Mews, 6 Putney Common, London SW15 1HL
Tel: 020 8788 2669 Fax: 020 8788 0073
Email: info@mainstreamleisure.co.uk
Web Site: www.mainstream.co.uk
Contact: Nigel Scandrett
Capacity: 40 silver service, 50 for Buffet.
The 70' wideboat of Edwardian Canalboat design is based in Little Venice and follows a colourful and historic cruising route through lock keeper's cottages. London Zoo and Snowdon's Aviary, into bustling Camden Lock and back.

MAINSTREAM EVENTS
5 The Mews, 6 Putney Common, Putney SW15 1HL
Tel: 020 8788 2669 Fax: 020 8788 0073
Email: info@mainstreamleisure.co.uk
Web Site: www.mainstreamleisure.co.uk
Senior Personnel: Nigel Scandrett
Own and operate eight riverboats in London and the Maidenhead area. Have Party Planning services in London and the Home Counties. Original venues a speciality. Represent a wide variety of artistes.

MILLENNIUM SAILS
Studio 4-5, Garnett Close, Watford, Hertfordshire WD24 7GN
Tel: 01923 211 703 / 020 8950 8998
Fax: 01923 211 704
Email: enquiries@millenniumsails.com
Web Site: www.millenniumsails.com
Senior Personnel: Tony Laurenson
Beautiful historic vessels, with corporate hospitality and cuisine. The 'SB May' offers the ultimate venue to see and enjoy the historic River Thames from a different perspective. The 'SB May' is licensed for 40 people when cruising and will accomodate 50 when in-situ at St Katherine's Dock.

ARTISTES

Please note that all Artistes can be cross-referenced with their agency entry in the 'Agents & Personal Managers' section, except where otherwise indicated. Entries marked 'Ind Art', 'Magic' or 'USA' can be found in their relevant sections. (Please refer to the Contents for page numbers)

Amsterdam ABS Agy/CRUISIN' MUSIC
Amy G Steve Draper Ents
Isabelle Amyes Saraband Assoc
An American Trilogy Entertainers Mgt Ltd
An Evening with Queen Victoria (with Prunella Scales) Clarion/Seven Muses
Ana Ann Stan Green Mngt
Rita Anamagura Brian Taylor Assoc
Anita Anand Noel Gay Artists Ltd
Anastacia Creative Artists Agency/William Morris Inc (USA)
Anatomik Continental Drifts/TEST AGENT C
Ancillary Barn Dance Line Dance Agy
Ronni Ancona NMP Live Ltd/Voice Shop
Ricky Andalcio Take Three Mngt
Andalus (Gypsy Kings) Andrew Beauchamp Mngt/Latin-Touch Ents/London Music Agy/Matters Musical/Prima Artists/Starfinders Int'l Mngt/Upbeat Entertainment
Terje Andersen Athole Still Int'l Ltd/TEST AGENT A
Adele Anderson Gavin Barker
Audley Anderson BCM Promos Ltd/SWA Ent
Ben Anderson Curtis Brown Grp
Bob Anderson ABDC Ents/CHAMPIONS (UK) PLC/Persnl Appearances
Brett Anderson 13 Artists/Silent way Management Ltd
Charley Anderson (Ex Selecter) Glasshouse Prods Ltd
Clive Anderson Curtis Brown Grp/NMP Live Ltd/PVA Ent Consultants/Parliament Comms/Speakout
Dan Anderson Border Leisure
Devon Anderson Big Bang Mngt Ltd
Dougie Anderson Money Management UK
Francesca Anderson Elinor Hilton Associates
Gerry Anderson David Hull Promos Ltd
Ian Anderson Derek Bruce Ents
J J Anderson SMA Talent Ltd
Jamie Anderson Barrie Stacey Promos & Prods
Jan Anderson CAM London
Stuart Anderson Jnr BGS PRODUCTIONS
John Anderson Talking Heads - The Voice Agy
June Anderson Askonas Holt Ltd
Larry Anderson Gordon Kellett Ents
Laurie Anderson Primary Talent Int'l
Louie Anderson ICM (USA)
Stuart Anderson Snr BGS PRODUCTIONS
Stephen Anderson Direct Persnl Mngt
Valdine Anderson Ingpen & Williams Ltd
Vass Anderson Anita Alraun Representation
Piotr Anderszewski Askonas Holt Ltd
Karen Andesson Dinosaur Promo/Dinosaur Mus
Martin André Ingpen & Williams Ltd
Peter Andre CHAMPIONS (UK) PLC/Can Associates Ltd
Peter Andre & Katie Price Mission Control Artist Agy
Alex Andrea Wendy Lee Mngt
Andrea Jacobs-Gajic Rostrum
Andre's Magical Madness Trevor George Ents Ltd
Jamie Andrew Gordon Poole Agy Ltd/Speakout
Andrew Kerry Association The Dixon Agy
Marcus Andrew (Elton John) Nigel Round Mgnt/Upfront Ent Agy Ltd
Andrew Oliver (Elton John) Advanced Ents
Rob Andrew MBE Celebrity Appearances/Persnly Spkng
Clive Andrews
Dave Andrews Dave Andrews Ents
David Lee Andrews Steve Draper Ents
Dean Andrews Angle Ents Ltd/Shepherd Mngt Ltd
Harvey Andrews Speaking Volumes
Julie Andrews William Morris Inc (USA)
Katie Andrews Agency K-Bis
Leela Andrews Agency K-Bis
Mark Andrews Dave Andrews Ents/Mark Andrews Ents (Magic)
Michael Andrews Piccadilly Mngt
Naveen Andrews Markham & Froggatt Ltd
Andrex Animal World
Leif Ove Andsnes IMG Artists
Andsome Cabin Buoys 'Andsome Cabin Buoys (Ind Art)
Andy B Partyweb.co.uk
Andy Irvine & Donal Lunny's Mozaik Adastra
Andy McGowan (Robbie Williams) Advanced Ents
Andy Nolan as Ronan Keating Funhouse Productions Ltd/Prima Artists
Carol Angel Angle Ents Ltd
Angel City Action Talent Int.
Dave Angel UK Booking Agy
Angel Eyes Devil Management
Angel Street Essex Ent Agy
Angelic Upstarts Rock Artist Mngt
Nicholas Angelich Transart (UK) Ltd
Angelique String Quartet Crown Ents/Fanfare 3000/Laurie Taylor Ents Ltd/The John Boddy Agency/Upbeat Entertainment
Ian Angell DBA Speakers
Prof Ian Angell Parliament Comms
Rob Angelo LRO Artist Mngt
"Angels" Head On Mngt/Les Hart (Southampton) Ents/Sunshine Ents
Angels of the North Barn Dance Line Dance Agy
Avril Angers Peter Charlesworth & Assoc
Ivan Anguelov Athole Still Int'l Ltd/TEST AGENT A
Angus & Julia Stone Sainted PR
David Angus Patrick Garvey Mngt
Christien Anholt Roger Carey Assoc
Animals Barry Collings Ents/Rock Artist Mngt
Animals and Friends BULLET MANAGEMENT LIMITED
The Animals Brian Gannon Mngt/Jason West Agy/John Hessenthaler Ents/PVA Ent Consultants/Rock Artist Mngt
Alexander Anissimov Askonas Holt Ltd
Anjali EC1 Music Agency
Paul Anka ICM (USA)
Jo Ankier Prof Sports Ptnr Ltd
kwaku Ankomah Burnett Granger Assoc
Jamie Anley Arlington Enterprises Ltd
Ann Marie (striptease) Rainbow Striptease Agy
Anna & José León London Music Agy
Anna Acton Louise Hillman/Katie Threlfall
Annabelle Derek Bruce Ents
Amanda Van Annan ANA
Dawn Annandale Gordon Poole Agy Ltd
Kerry Anne CeeBee Variety Agy
Anne-Marie (Tina Turner) G Entertaining
Luke Annersley Quartet Matters Musical
Annuals Free Trade Agy
Anonymous CKK Ent/Whatever Artists Mngt Ltd
Another Green World Magick Eye Records
John Anscomb Partyweb.co.uk
Paul Ansdell Jeffrey & White
Jonathan Ansell COLE KITCHENN PRSN MGT/ROAR Group
Scott Anson Saraband Assoc
Toby Anstis Hyper Agency/The Psycho Mngt Co Ltd
Ant & Dec CHAMPIONS (UK) PLC/Hackford Jones PR/James Grant Mngt Ltd/Prime Performers Ltd/The Commercial Agency
Adam Ant Tony Denton Promos Ltd
Ant Hill Mob The Dixon Agy
Antara Latin-Touch Ents
Ant-e-static Advanced Ents
Colin Anthony Matters Musical
Graham Anthony IMWP (UK) Ltd
Leigh Anthony Dinosaur Promo/Dinosaur Mus
Lysette Anthony Harvey Voices Ltd
Paul Anthony Partyweb.co.uk
Phil Anthony Derek Bruce Ents
George Anton Jonathan Altaras Assoc
Maria Antonia Sandra Singer Assoc
Esteban Antonio Johnny Mans Prods Ltd
Roberto Antonio Rent-A-Band
Antony & The Johnsons Dog Day Press
John Antony Philip Youd Ents & Mngt
Mick Antony NVB Ents
Dan Antopolski Avalon Mngt
Dave Antrobus David Forshaw Entp
David Antrobus M W Management
John Antrobus Tessa Le Bars Mngt
Mina Anwar Louise Hillman/Katie Threlfall
Apache M.S. Ent Grp
Apache Indian Jason West Agy/Mission Control Artist Agy/Tony Denton Promos Ltd
Apes & Japes Barn Dance Line Dance Agy
Aphrodite Fairplay Ents/Owen Hughes Ents/UK Booking Agy
Apocalyptica Creative Artists Agency/Helter Skelter Agy Ltd
Apollo Disco Quality Ents
Fiona Apple ITB
Applejack the Clown NVB Ents
Brian Appleton Richard Bucknall Mngt (RBM)
JJ Appleton COFFEE ARTISTS
Natalie & Nicole Appleton Freud Comms
Nicole Appleton CAM London
Apu Line-Up PMC/Matters Musical
Arbie the Robot Advanced Ents/CKK Ent
Arcadians Matters Musical
ArcAngel Norwich Artistes
David Arch ABC Direct Ents
Arch Enemy The Agency Group
Iain Archer Big Sister Promotions
Krystal Archer Jae Moss Entp
Lord Archer NMP Live Ltd
Mark Archer Blowout Sax
Martin Archer Hyper Agency
Tasmin Archer Republic Media
Robert Archibald Adrian King Assoc
Archie Bronson Outfit Big Sister Promotions/Free Trade Agy
Archive IE MUSIC
Arctic Monkeys 13 Artists/Bad Moon Publicity/Big Sister Promotions
John Arden CASAROTTO RAMSAY &

ASSOCIATES
Mark Arden Lip Service Casting Ltd
Paul Arden-Griffith Ken Spencer Persnl Mngt
Are You Experienced? (Jimi Hendrix) Andrew Beauchamp Mngt
Colin Areety Tony West Ents
Megan Arellanes The Richard Stone Prtnrshp
Gameo Arena Boo Boo's Entertainments
Tina Arena Primary Talent Int'l
Nancy Argenta Askonas Holt Ltd
Argentum Roadshow Highfield Mngt & Promos
Argy Bargy Yellow Balloon Prods Ltd
Charles Ariel Athole Still Music
Arion Duo Matters Musical
Ann Aris Amber Persnl Mngt Ltd
Julie Arkell Limelight Management
Lucy Arkhurst Emptage Hallett Ltd
Armada Jazzband Hartbeat Ents Ltd
Joan Armatrading Tribute Band Bulrush Mngt
Charlotte Armer Piccadilly Mngt
Lizzie Armistead CHAMPIONS (UK) PLC
Dan Armour Direct Persnl Mngt
The Armpit Jug Band The Horne Concert Agy
Alexander Armstrong M F Management Ltd/Speakout
Alun Armstrong Markham & Froggatt Ltd
Andre Armstrong Dance Funki Feathers Agy
Emile Andre Armstrong Newton Wills Mngt
Craig Armstrong IE MUSIC
Fiona Armstrong Knight Ayton Mngt
Julie Armstrong Adrian King Assoc
Lance Armstrong CHAMPIONS (UK) PLC
Linda Armstrong AIM
Livy Armstrong Vincent Shaw Assoc Ltd
Pamela Armstrong Parliament Comms
Richard Armstrong CBE Ingpen & Williams Ltd
Rosie Armstrong Grays Mngt & Asc
Sally Armstrong Grays Mngt & Asc
Shane Armstrong Rogues & Vagabonds Mngt
Stephen Armstrong Speak-Easy Ltd
William Armstrong Macfarlane Chard Talent Agency
David Arneil Hilary Gagan Assoc
Marie Arnet Hazard Chase Ltd
Alice Arnold Burnett Granger Assoc
Damian Arnold Burnett Granger Assoc
Keri Arnold Northern Lights Mngt
Pete Arnold First Time Mngt
Richard Arnold Capel & Land
Tanya Arnold Celebn Model Mngt
Tim Arnold Lena Davis/John Bishop Assoc
Tom Arnold Derek Bruce Ents
Arnold's Flea Circus Continental Drifts/TEST AGENT C
Kenny Aro Sandra Boyce Mngt
Arpeggione Quartet Transart (UK) Ltd
Daniel Arpels Norwich Artistes
Patricia Arquette Markham & Froggatt Ltd
Arrival (Abba) Camscott Leisure
Bennett Arron Jill Foster Ltd
Arrow Monkeybiz Ent Agy
Lucy Arrowsmith Form Talent
Lord Arsenal's All Stars Ken Spencer Persnl Mngt
Art Brut War Zones
Art Deco Murders Complete Ent Serv Ltd
Art Deco Swing Quartet Matters Musical
Artemis Manias (Gloria Estefan tribute) Andrew Beauchamp Mngt
Artemis UK Viscount Ents
Artful Dodger Mission Control Artist Agy
Davey Arthur Park Promotions
John Arthur Daly Pearson Associates
Joseph Arthur Primary Talent Int'l
Keith Arthur MATCHROOM SPORT LTD
Rod Arthur Talking Heads - The Voice Agy
Dave Arthur's Storybox John Field - Theatre and Puppe
The Artistes Bulrush Mngt
Artizani CKK Ent/MTM Presntns/The A6 Agy
Melvyn Artwarg MTM Presntns
As Is (Band) Spotlight Ents (Notts)
Amma Asante Judy Daish Assoc
Zara Asante The Richard Stone Prtnrshp
Brian Asawa Askonas Holt Ltd
Nicholas Asbury Louise Hillman/Katie Threlfall
Karen Ascoe Daly Pearson Associates/Shining Mngt Ltd
Karen Asemper The Narrow Road Company Ltd
Asere Roots Around The World
Ash Alan James PR Agency/Big Sister Promotions
Bob Ash London Music Agy
Melanie Ash Lime Actors Agy & Mngt Ltd
Kate Ashby Derek Bruce Ents
Phil Ashby (Major) Speakout
Robert Ashby Nancy Hudson Associates Ltd/Yakety Yak
Ceri Ashcroft Frontline Mngt Ltd
Annie Ashdown RDF Management
Ashdown Forest Ceildh Band Barn Dance Line Dance Agy
Lord Ashdown Trading Faces Ltd
Lord Paddy Ashdown CHAMPIONS (UK) PLC/Peters Fraser Dunlop (PFD)/Speakout
Russell Ashdown Agency K-Bis
Stephan Ashdown Agency K-Bis
Graham Ashe B.A.S.I.C.
Rosemary Ashe All Electric Productions & Dav/Hilary Gagan Assoc
Damian Asher Sandra Boyce Mngt
Jane Asher The Commercial Agency/United Agents
Stephen Ashfield Talent Artists Ltd
Andrew Ashford Actorum
Daisy Ashford ANA
David Ashford Downes Presenters Agy
Matthew Ashforde Qvoice
Carl Ashington Funhouse Productions Ltd/Gordon Kellett Ents
Simon Ashland Otto Persnl Mngt Ltd
Craig Ashley Newton Wills Mngt
David Ashley Hilary Gagan Assoc
Ashley Dean (hypnotist) Barrie Hawkins Leisure Service
Lyn Ashley MBA
Lynsette Ashley & The LA Dancers NVB Ents
Mike Ashman Athole Still Int'l Ltd/TEST AGENT A
Ashmore Kevin King Mngt
Sufiah Ashraf RBA Management Ltd
David Ashton Emptage Hallett Ltd
Holly Ashton M W Management
John Ashton Crescent Mngt
Marcia Ashton Burnett Granger Assoc
Jessica Ashton-Davies MGA Entp
Brittany Ashworth ICON Actors Mngt
Dicken Ashworth ICON Actors Mngt/Yakety Yak
Asian Dub Foundation Nation Recs Ltd/Primary Talent Int'l
Claire Askam Billboard Persnl Mngt
Andy Askins Comedy Store Mngt
Michael Aspel OBE NMP Live Ltd/Shepherd Mngt Ltd
Paul Aspinall Agency K-Bis
John Asquith MCS Agcy
Ross Assenhiem (DJ) Head On Mngt
Randeep Assi Lime Actors Agy & Mngt Ltd
Debbie Astell Michael Summerton Mngt
Asteria Matters Musical
Loulla Astin Jacque Evans Mngt Ltd
Rick Astley Planet Earth Entp Ltd/Tony Denton Promos Ltd
Charles Aston Grays Mngt & Asc
John Aston Barrie Stacey Promos & Prods
Sam Aston (Chesney, Coronation Street) Linton Mngt/Nigel Round Mgnt
Astra Review Show Phillips Ent Agy
Astralasia Magick Eye Records
Aswad Barry Collings Ents/Mission Control Artist Agy/Tony Denton Promos Ltd
At the Hop! Leisure Mngt
Tim Atack S M A Talent Ltd/SMA Talent Ltd
Ash Atalla PBJ Mngt Ltd
Naki Ataman Elaine Avon Artistes Mngt
The Ataris Primary Talent Int'l
Atcha! Roots Around The World
A-Team Book A Band
A-Tease Andrew Beauchamp Mngt
David Atherton Askonas Holt Ltd
Julie Atherton Louise Hillman/Katie Threlfall
Mike Atherton OBE MA Jon Holmes Media Ltd
Rachael Atherton Wendy Lee Mngt
Athlete 13 Artists
Robert Atiko Nancy Hudson Associates Ltd
Leo Atkin Circuit Persnl Mngt Ltd
Holly Atkins Emptage Hallett Ltd
Rachel Atkins Louise Hillman/Katie Threlfall
Barbara Atkinson Audrey Benjamin Agy
Dan Atkinson Avalon Mngt
Helen Atkinson Wood Limelight Management
James Atkinson Circuit Persnl Mngt Ltd
Rebecca Atkinson (Karen, Shamless) Nigel Round Mgnt
Kate Atkinson CASAROTTO RAMSAY & ASSOCIATES/Markham & Froggatt Ltd
Lucy Atkinson Northern Lights Mngt
Mark Atkinson Major Ent Agy
Michael Atkinson Amber Persnl Mngt Ltd
Nick Atkinson The Richard Stone Prtnrshp
Ron Atkinson Athole Still Int'l Ltd/Gordon Poole Agy Ltd/PVA Ent Consultants/Persnl Appearances/TEST AGENT A
Rowan Atkinson PBJ Mngt Ltd
Shelley Atkinson Performance Actors Agy
Atlanta Rhythm Section AIM Inc (USA)
Atlantic Soul Band BULLET MANAGEMENT LIMITED
Atlantic Soul Machine Henderson Mngt/Jason West Agy
Atlantico Athole Still Int'l Ltd/TEST AGENT A

Natasha Atlas Nation Recs Ltd
Atmosfear (illusion) Ron Martin Mngt
Atomic Blondie Jason West Agy/The Psycho Mngt Co Ltd
A-Tom-Ic Jones & The Explosive Reload Orchestra Direct Music Mngt Ltd
Atomic Kitten Personal Management & Casting
Atomik-itton Nigel Round Mgnt
Atoms For Peace 13 Artists
Atreyu The Agency Group
Jason Attar The Richard Stone Prtnrshp
Attention Seekers CKK Ent
John Atterbury Vincent Shaw Assoc Ltd
Blue Attic Prima Artists
Attic Jam Devil Management
Richard Attlee Dennis Lyne Agy/Harvey Voices Ltd
Michael Attwood Agency K-Bis
Shane Attwooll M W Management
Hayley Atwell Peters Fraser Dunlop (PFD)
Sam Atwell Richard Price PR
Moshe Atzmon Patrick Garvey Mngt
Li-Leng Au Anita Alraun Representation
Antony Audenshaw JLM Persnl Mngt
Tony Audenshaw Big Bang Mngt Ltd
Audioslave ITB
Auf Weiderseh'n Set Funhouse Productions Ltd
Ruth Augilera Burnett Granger Assoc
Aurora Harp-Flute Duo CS Ents
Louie Austen Lulu Le Vay
Mia Austen Vincent Shaw Assoc Ltd
Anthony Austin Grays Mngt & Asc
Christopher Austin Clarion/Seven Muses
Lucy Austin Brian Taylor Assoc
Mark Austin Capel & Land
Michelle Austin CAM London
Stirling Austin Prima Artists
Robert Austins Kerry Gardner Mngt
The Australian Pink Floyd Show The Agency Group
Automated Country Disco ABDC Ents
Autre Ne Veut 13 Artists
Peter Auty Ingpen & Williams Ltd
Avalon Highfield Mngt & Promos
Avenue D Ferrara PR
Average White Band Free Trade Agy/William Morris Inc (USA)
Charlotte Avery Emptage Hallett Ltd/Harvey Voices Ltd
Kenneth Avery-Clark Talent Artists Ltd
Liz Avis Linton Mngt
Aviv Quartets Pro Artist Management
Alan Avon Dinosaur Promo/Dinosaur Mus
Avon Jazz Band Derek Bruce Ents
Nighat Awan Gordon Poole Agy Ltd
Awesome 3 Mission Control Artist Agy
Awesome Duesome CeeBee Variety Agy
Emanuel Ax Askonas Holt Ltd
Kate Axten (Shania Twain) Jason West Agy
Axwell Mission Control Artist Agy
Sir Alan Ayckbourn CASAROTTO RAMSAY & ASSOCIATES
Simon Aylin Vincent Shaw Assoc Ltd
Geraldine Aylmer-Kelly Ken Spencer Persnl Mngt
Aynuk The Horne Concert Agy
Ayr Pipe Band Hireaband Ltd
Pam Ayres Acorn Ent/PVA Ent Consultants
Don Ayrey Band Rock Artist Mngt
Dalaz Azar Noel Gay Artists Ltd
Aziz Rock Artist Mngt
Khalid Aziz Jane Hughes Mngt
Lisa Aziz JLA
Shabana Azmi Brunskill Mngt Ltd
Aztec Angle Ents Ltd
Maricachi Aztlan Latin Arts Serv (LAS)
Azure Leo Mngt & Agy

B

Cherry B Dave Woodbury Ents
Lyndsay B Nigel Round Mgnt
B Natural NVB Ents
B52's Helter Skelter Agy Ltd
Keedie Babb Tony Clayman Promos
Babben Paramount Int'l Mngt
Babewatch PVA Ent Consultants
Babu Zukini Albert Alchemy Ent
Baby Boney M Entertainers Mgt Ltd
baby d Mission Control Artist Agy
Baby Elvis Yellow Balloon Prods Ltd
Baby Go Boom ABC Direct Ents/Sardi's Int'l Ent/Triple Cream Ents
Baby Grande Gordon Kellett Ents
Bacardi II Disco Clubline Promos
Baccara Jason West Agy/Tony Denton Promos Ltd
Bacchus String Quartet Yorkshire Ent
Burt Bacharach William Morris Inc (USA)
Emma Bache MCS Agcy
Bachelors John Hessenthaler Ents
James Bachman Noel Gay Artists Ltd
Back 2 The 80's Angle Ents Ltd
Back 2 the Future Angle Ents Ltd
Back To Back Entertainers Mgt Ltd
Back to Broadway Brian Yeates Assoc
Back to the Future Angle Ents Ltd
Backbeat Fairplay Ents/Henderson Mngt/Martin Ents/Sunshine Ents
The Backbeat Beatles Big Bang Mngt Ltd
Backbeat Beatles European Artistes Mngt
The Backbeat Beatles Henderson Mngt/Jason West Agy/McLeod Agy Ltd
Kristiane Backer Persnly Spkng
Charlotte Backhouse Agency K-Bis
Desmond Backhouse Fushion Pukka Bosh
Steve Backley MBE OBE Jon Holmes Media Ltd/MTC (UK) LTD/Persnl Appearances/Speakout
Backroom Boys Barn Dance Line Dance Agy
Stephen Backshall Gordon Poole Agy Ltd
Steve Backshall Jo Sarsby PR Ltd
Backstreet Soul Matters Musical/Upbeat Entertainment
Joakim Backstrom Prof Sports Ptnr Ltd
Richard Bacon Peters Fraser Dunlop (PFD)/The Richard Stone Prtnrshp
Bad Boys (Wham) Big Bang Mngt Ltd/David Charles Agy/Funhouse Productions Ltd
Bad Habits Sardi's Int'l Ent
Bad Manners Andrew Beauchamp Mngt/BULLET MANAGEMENT LIMITED/Barry Collings Ents/Henderson Mngt/Peller Artistes Ltd/Ro-Lo Prods/The Psycho Mngt Co Ltd
Bad Manners featuring Buster Bloodvessel Henderson Mngt/Jason West Agy
Bad Obsession (Guns + Roses) Head On Mngt
Bad Religion Gold Star PR
Zeinab Badawi Knight Ayton Mngt
Badboys (Male Revue Team) Steve Draper Ents
David Baddiel Avalon Mngt
Christine Badea Transart (UK) Ltd
Badly Drawn Boy Alan James PR Agency/Big Life Management
Badooba Matters Musical
Kate Badrick Barn Dance Line Dance Agy
Joan Baez Asgard
Bagatelle Prima Artists
Danny Bage Burnett Granger Assoc
The Baghdaddies Continental Drifts/Line-Up PMC/TEST AGENT C
Jessica Baglow Linton Mngt
Louise Bagshawe Peters Fraser Dunlop (PFD)
Bah Samba (UK Live P.A.) UK Booking Agy
Baha Beach Boys The Dixon Agy
Bahookie Ceilidh Band Hireaband Ltd
Adrian Bailey Alexandra Cann Reprsntn
Bill Bailey NMP Live Ltd/PBJ Mngt Ltd/Speakout
Bob Bailey Loesje Sanders
Donnaleigh Bailey JLM Persnl Mngt/Unleashed PR
Imogen Bailey Girl Management
Jason Bailey Nancy Hudson Associates Ltd
Jumanne Bailey Rogues & Vagabonds Mngt
Marion Bailey Kerry Gardner Mngt
Mark Bailey Clare Vidal-Hall/Sue Rider Mngt Ltd
Michael Anthony Bailey Take Three Mngt
Pauline Bailey (Marilyn Monroe) Upfront Ent Agy Ltd
Sarah Bailey CKK Ent/The Horne Concert Agy
Jessica Bailey-Woodward Tony Clayman Promos
Alexander Baillie Transart (UK) Ltd
Christina Baily The Narrow Road Company Ltd
Aly Bain & Phil Cunningham Adastra/Firefly Productions
Ed Baines CHAMPIONS (UK) PLC/Limelight Management
Prof. Chris Baines Gordon Poole Agy Ltd
Lisa Baird APM Ass
Bak 2 Bak Tony Bennell Ents
Bakehouse Matters Musical
Kees Bakels IMG Artists
Arthur Baker Stephen Budd Mngt
Carroll Baker Deri Promos
Cheryl Baker Denis Vaughan Mngt/Funky Beetroot Celebrity Manag/Liz Hobbs Grp Ltd/Persnl Appearances/Razzamatazz Mngt/Tony Clayman Promos
Danny Baker Noel Gay Artists Ltd
David Baker Adrian King Assoc
Edward Baker Duly Burnett Granger Assoc
George Baker All Electric Productions & Dav
Joe Don Baker Markham & Froggatt Ltd
Jules Baker CKK Ent
Keith Baker Associated Arts
Kenny Baker Johnny Mans Prods Ltd
Kevin Baker APM Ass
Lee Baker (Freddie Mercury) Funhouse Productions Ltd
Matt Baker Talent4 Media Ltd
Mike Baker CHAMPIONS (UK) PLC
Rae Baker Burnett Granger Assoc
Simon Baker Hazard Chase Ltd
Tim Baker Clare Vidal-Hall
Tina Baker TFA Artiste Management
Tom Baker UK Booking Agy

Tommy Baker CKK Ent
Bakerloo Line Hireaband Ltd
Gary Bakewell Daly Pearson Associates
Joan Bakewell Knight Ayton Mngt
Amie Bakker ANA
Balalaika London Music Agy
Balalaika Orchestra Matters Musical/Rent-A-Band
Balam Acab 13 Artists
Pepe Balderrama Brunskill Mngt Ltd
Clare Balding CHAMPIONS (UK) PLC/Talking Heads - The Voice Agy
Luisa Baldini Gordon Poole Agy Ltd
Elizabeth Jane Baldry Ginger Walker Agy
Ben Baldwin RDF Management
Clive Baldwin A.I.R. Ltd
Francesca Baldwin MCS Agcy
Nancy Baldwin Speak-Easy Ltd
Peter Baldwin Shepherd Mngt Ltd
Ruth Baldwin Rosebery Mngt
William Baldwin Special Artists Agency
Bernard Bale Johnny Mans Prods Ltd
Jenni Bale Talking Heads - The Voice Agy
Micah Balfour Susan Angel Kevin Francis Ltd
Alberto Balia Roots Around The World
Fairuza Balk Markham & Froggatt Ltd
David Ball Some Bizarre Ltd
Kenny Ball & His Jazzmen Barry Collings Ents/Jazzco/The John Boddy Agency/Upbeat Mngt
Johnny Ball Downes Presenters Agy/NMP Live Ltd/Speakout
Tom Ball & Kenny Sultan Roots Around The World
Martin Ball Brown & Simcocks
Tony Ball MBE Arena Ent Cons/DBA Speakers/Gordon Poole Agy Ltd/PVA Ent Consultants/Persnl Appearances
Michael Ball Trading Faces Ltd
Nicholas Ball The Commercial Agency
Nick Ball Lip Service Casting Ltd
Zoe Ball Prime Performers Ltd/The Richard Stone Prtnrshp
Victoria Ballandini MGA Entp
Jamie Ballard Brunskill Mngt Ltd
JG Ballard CASAROTTO RAMSAY & ASSOCIATES
Michael Ballard Billboard Persnl Mngt
Steve Ballard (Elvis Presley)
Tim Ballard Norwich Artistes
Tina Ballentino (Tina Turner Tribute) Peller Artistes Ltd
Edoardo Ballerini Markham & Froggatt Ltd
Balletto Di Milano A.I.R. Ltd
Richard Ballinger Richard Ballinger (Magic)
Balloonatic CKK Ent
Ballroom Glitz BCM Promos Ltd/Compact Mngt & Ent Agy/Derek Bruce Ents/G Entertaining/Henderson Mngt/Jason West Agy/Stardust Ents Agy/Upfront Ent Agy Ltd
Ballroom Glitz (70's show) Head On Mngt
James Balme David Anthony Promos
Andy Baloney Albert Alchemy Ent
Bam Bam MPC Ent
David Bamber Yakety Yak
Bamboleo Matters Musical
Bambos NVB Ents
Mattlas Bamert IMG Artists
David Bamford MGA Entp
Maurice Bamford Gordon Poole Agy Ltd
Ban Buren and Co Tony West Ents
Bananarama Denis Vaughan Mngt/Tony Denton Promos Ltd
Bananas In Pyjamas Paul Bridson Prods
Banchory Strathspey & Reel Soc. BGS PRODUCTIONS
Banco De Gaia CODA Ltd
Arthur Bancroft Derek Bruce Ents
Kate Bancroft North Of Watford Actors Agy
A Band Called Frank First Time Mngt
Harir Band Matters Musical
Have A Banana One-Man Band Matters Musical
JJ Vinten Band Matters Musical
John Leyton & Band BCM Promos Ltd
Lee Vasey Band Norwich Artistes
Liza Wolfe Band Norwich Artistes
Mardi Gras Jazz Band Matters Musical
Mike West Band Norwich Artistes
Band of Skulls 13 Artists
Band of Two Band of Two (Ind Art)/CKK Ent/Matters Musical
Band of West Mercia Constabulary Derek Bruce Ents
Paul Eshelby Band Prima Artists
The Anna Reay Band Barrie Hawkins Leisure Service
The PPS Band Barrie Hawkins Leisure Service
The Stirling Austin Swing Band Matters Musical
Woody's One-Man Band Matters Musical
Choro Bandido Matters Musical
The Bandit Beatles Arena Ent Cons
Bandit Beatles BULLET MANAGEMENT LIMITED
The Bandit Beatles Jason West Agy/Stars In Your Eyes Ltd Ent Agy/The Bandit Beatles (Ind Art)/The John Boddy Agency
Bandwise Barn Dance Line Dance Agy
John Banfield North Of Watford Actors Agy
Bang On a Can All-Stars Hazard Chase Ltd
Sir John Banham Arena Ent Cons/DBA Speakers/PVA Ent Consultants/Persnly Spkng
Simon Banham Loesje Sanders
Banish Misfortune Barn Dance Band ABDC Ents
Banjax Banjax (Ind Art)
Banjo Boys Rent-A-Band
Bill Bankes-Jones Performing Arts
Peter Bankole Susan Angel Kevin Francis Ltd
Gordon Banks OBE After Dinner World Ltd/Gordon Poole Agy Ltd/Nigel Round Mgnt/Persnl Appearances/Preview & Review Ents Ltd
Jeff Banks Celebrity Appearances
John Banks Sara Crouch Mngt
Liz Banks Peter Charlesworth & Assoc
Ray Banks Devil Management
Robert Banks MCS Agcy
Robin Banks MPC Ent
Sam Banks Audrey Benjamin Agy
Tony Banks Tony Smith Personal Management
Duncan Bannatyne OBE CHAMPIONS (UK) PLC/Curtis Brown Grp/Gordon Poole Agy Ltd/NMP Live Ltd
Wings Banned B.F.P Ents
Celia Bannerman Kerry Gardner Mngt
David Bannerman Royce Mngt
Matthew Bannister Knight Ayton Mngt
Trevor Bannister Daly Pearson Associates
Marc Bant Viscount Ents
Pato Banton Jason West Agy/Mission Control Artist Agy
John Banville Ed Victor Agency
Austin Baptiste Steel Band Austin Baptiste Ent Agy Ltd
The Austin Baptiste Coral Reef Steel Band Upbeat Entertainment
Dino Baptiste Roots Around The World
Bar Fly PVA Ent Consultants
The Bar Wizards Action Talent Int.
Baraka Continental Drifts/Matters Musical/TEST AGENT C
The Big Chris Barber Band Wim Wigt Prodns Ltd
John Barber Northern Lights Mngt
Nicole Barber-Lane (Myra, Hollyoaks) Lime Actors Agy & Mngt Ltd/Nigel Round Mgnt
Isabel Barbuk CCM
Alice Barclay Elinor Hilton Associates
Bill Barclay Stoneyport Associates
Barclay James Harvest Mad Mngt Ltd
Jim Barclay 1984 Persnl Mngt
Lucille Barclay Jae Moss Entp
Roger Barclay Macfarlane Chard Talent Agency
Matt Bardock Hatton Mcewan Ltd
John Bardon Brown & Simcocks
Richard Bardsey Royce Mngt
Allan Bardsley The Voice Box Agency Ltd
Barenaked Ladies The Agency Group
Daniel Barenboim Askonas Holt Ltd
Helen Barford The Actors File
Tracy Bargate Grays Mngt & Asc
Marilyn Bar-Ilan ICON Actors Mngt
Arj Barker Paramount Int'l Mngt
Dave Barker Monkeybiz Ent Agy
Faye Barker Speak-Easy Ltd
Hils Barker Int'l Artistes Ltd
Howard Barker Judy Daish Assoc
Liz Barker Somethin' Else
Ronnie Barker Chatto & Linnit Ltd
Stew Barker Derek Bruce Ents
Sue Barker OBE CHAMPIONS (UK) PLC/Persnly Spkng/Prof Sports Ptnr Ltd/Trading Faces Ltd
The Barkham Harp Quartet (4 Girls/4 harps) Upbeat Classical Mngt
Peter Barkworth Jonathan Altaras Assoc
Justin Barley Liz Hobbs Grp Ltd
Lou Barlow Big Sister Promotions
Patrick Barlow Jonathan Altaras Assoc
William Barlow Brunskill Mngt Ltd
Barn Dance Band Flat Cat Barn Dance Band
Barn Dance Experience Barn Dance Line Dance Agy
David Barnaby Actorum
Diane Barnard Jon Holmes Media Ltd
Matt Barnard Fool's Paradise/Partyweb.co.uk
Adrian Barnes Associated Arts
Carol Barnes Celebrity Appearances/Knight Ayton Mngt
Chris Barnes Dennis Lyne Agy
Derek Barnes Talent Artists Ltd
John Barnes MBE Athole Still Int'l Ltd/Jon Holmes Media Ltd/Persnl Appearances/TEST AGENT A
Lord Patten of Barnes Trading Faces Ltd
Michael Tudor Barnes Langford Assoc
Peter Barnes ANA/CASAROTTO RAMSAY & ASSOCIATES
Stuart Barnes PVA Ent Consultants
Angus Barnett Kerry Gardner Mngt
Greg Barnett Argyle Assoc
Jeni Barnett Yakety Yak

Barney B (Pure X) UK Booking Agy
Cleo Barnham Performance Actors Agy
Debbie Barnham (Estate) CASAROTTO RAMSAY & ASSOCIATES
Barnstorm ABDC Ents
Barnstorm Barn Dance Band Stardust Ents Agy
Dave Baron Creeme Ents
Baron Mad Dog`s Oompah Band Yorkshire Ent
Baroness Tanni Grey-Thompson Trading Faces Ltd
Barons of Bavaria CS Ents
Felicity Barr Noel Gay Artists Ltd
Liam Barr Jonathan Altaras Assoc
Patrick Barr Barrie Stacey Promos & Prods
Roy Barraclough Gavin Barker
Sarah Barrand CAM London
Paul Barrass Wendy Lee Mngt
Claire Barratt Arlington Enterprises Ltd
Edwina Barratt Nyland Mngt
Cristina Barreiro ANA
Barrel Organ London Music Agy
Bob Barrett The Richard Stone Prtnrshp
Camilla Barrett Agency K-Bis
Clare Barrett 1984 Persnl Mngt
Craig Barrett Shining Mngt Ltd
Gaynor Barrett Daly Pearson Associates
Joanna Barrett Agency K-Bis
Julian Barrett PBJ Mngt Ltd
Nigel Barrett Nancy Hudson Associates Ltd
Peter Barrett Shepherd Mngt Ltd
Sean Barrett Daly Pearson Associates
Syd Barrett One Fifteen
Wild Willy Barrett Park Promotions
Barricade (Comedy Duo) Personality Artistes Ltd
Rubens Barrichello 19 Entertainment
Amanda Barrie AIM/Burnett Granger Assoc/Prime Performers Ltd/Robert Smith Literary Agency
Chris Barrie JLA/PVA Ent Consultants/Speakout
Hannah Barrie Brunskill Management Ltd
June Barrie Louise Hillman/Katie Threlfall
Lester Barrie ICM (USA)
Maxine Barrie (Shirley Bassey) Chance Promos/Entertainers Mgt Ltd
Paul Barrie (Barry Manilow) Advanced Ents/Funhouse Productions Ltd
Andrew Barron Links Mngt
Carl Barron IMWP (UK) Ltd
The Barron Knights BCM Promos Ltd/Barron Knights/Entertainers Mgt Ltd/Jason West Agy/NVB Ents/Paul Bridson Prods/Templar Ent Agy
Marion Barron Royce Mngt
Jean Barrow Creeme Ents
John Barrowman Gavin Barker
Johnny Barrs Barrie Stacey Promos & Prods
Barry & Stuart Michael Vine Assoc
Aidan Barry Anita Alraun Representation
Becky Barry 1984 Persnl Mngt
Chantelle Barry Darren Gray Mngt
Daniel Barry Brunskill Management Ltd
Diane Barry Caledonian Music Agy
Jim Barry Mainstream Evts
Matthew Barry Susan Angel Kevin Francis Ltd
Rudolf Barshai Askonas Holt Ltd
Emily Barter Quality Ents
Barton & Paige European Artistes Mngt
The Chris Barton Band Matters Musical
Emma Barton AIM/Big Bang Mngt Ltd
Eric Barton Speak-Easy Ltd
John Barton CASAROTTO RAMSAY & ASSOCIATES
Tony Barton Non Stop Ents/Nyland Mngt
Alex Bartram Alpha Persnl Mngt
Emma Basden Princess Talent Mngt
Base Rate Kinsella Associates
The Basement Band Hire-A-Band Ent Agy
Bash Street Circus Kernow Ents
Bash Street Theatre Fool's Paradise
Martin Bashir John Miles Org
Yuri Bashmet International Classical Artist
Bashy New Vision Arts Management
Basin Street Ultimate Int'l
Kim Basinger Special Artists Agency
Gillian Baskeyfield Direct Persnl Mngt
Brodie Bass Brunskill Management Ltd
Campbell Bass CHAMPIONS (UK) PLC
Dave Bassett After Dinner World Ltd/NMP Live Ltd/Preview & Review Ents Ltd
Linda Bassett Jonathan Altaras Assoc
Franco Bassetti Crowd Pullers
Shirley Bassey William Morris Inc (USA)
Basshunter Insanity Artists
Alexandra Bastedo AIM
Bat For Lashes Dog Day Press
Tim Bat CKK Ent
Tim Bat Trick Show John Field - Theatre and Puppe
Louise Batchelor Speakout
Peggy Batchelor RDF Management
Nick Bateman Fox Artist Mngt Ltd/Peter Charlesworth & Assoc/RAGE
Paul Bateman Talent Artists Ltd
Alan Bates (Hypnotist) Alan Bates (Ind Art)/Persnl Appearances
Professor Brian Bates Knight Ayton Mngt
Gary Bates Royce Mngt
Richard Bates Sara Crouch Mngt
Anthony Batey Trevor George Ents Ltd
Bath City Jazzmen PVA Ent Consultants
Bathsheba's Wedding Tony Bennell Ents
Robert Bathurst ARG Management
Loui Batley Jackie Palmer (JPA Mngt)
Ben Batt (Joe, Shamless) Nigel Round Mgnt
Miriam Battan Athole Still Int'l Ltd/TEST AGENT A
Battant EC1 Music Agency
Julian Battersby Sara Crouch Mngt
Sam Battersea Noel Gay Artists Ltd
Battle Helter Skelter Agy Ltd
Eileen Battye Jeffrey & White
Zac Bauman Trevor George Ents Ltd
Bavarian Schunklers (Bavarian) Apple County
Bavarian Strollers Oompah Band Advanced Ents/Barrie Hawkins Leisure Service
The Bavarian Strollers CS Ents
Baverian Brassumpah Global Ent Agy
Juliet Bawden Jacque Evans Mngt Ltd
Helen Baxendale ARG Management/Yakety Yak
Sarah Baxendale JLM Persnl Mngt
Collin Baxter MBA
Keith Baxter Chatto & Linnit Ltd
Luke Baxter Liz Hobbs Grp Ltd
Ruth Baxter Jae Moss Entp
Sarah Baxter APM Ass
Bay City Rollers Brian Gannon Mngt/Jason West Agy/Tony Denton Promos Ltd
Martin Bayfield CHAMPIONS (UK) PLC/Louise Hillman/Katie Threlfall/Persnl Appearances
John Bayley & Five Go Jiving The John Boddy Agency
Marc Baylis COLE KITCHENN PRSN MGT
Scott Baylis Paul Bailey Agy
Scott Baylis Band Paul Bailey Agy
Trevor Baylis OBE Gordon Poole Agy Ltd/Persnly Spkng
Hetty Baynes The Richard Stone Prtnrshp
Duke Baysee Book A Band
Bayside The Agency Group
Carolyn Bazely Grays Mngt & Asc
BBC Big Band The John Boddy Agency
The BBC Big Band Matters Musical
BBMak Freud Comms
BC Sweet Global Ent Agy/Jason West Agy/John Hessenthaler Ents
The Beach Boys ICM (USA)
Stephanie Beacham Peters Fraser Dunlop (PFD)/United Agents/Urban Associates Personal Mana
Beachboys Inc Andrew Beauchamp Mngt/Compact Mngt & Ent Agy/Henderson Mngt/Jason West Agy
Beachbuggy CODA Ltd
Beachcomber Stompers PVA Ent Consultants
The Beached Boys Jason West Agy
Gary Beadle Lou Coulson Associates
Jeremy Beadle MPC Ent
Melanie Beadle Scott-Paul Young Ents Ltd
The 'B'Eagles (The Eagles tribute) Andrew Beauchamp Mngt/Head On Mngt/Jason West Agy
BEAK 13 Artists
Dave Beale Derek Bruce Ents
Simon Russell Beale The Richard Stone Prtnrshp
Adrian Bean Noel Gay Artists Ltd
Anita Bean RDF Management
Billy Bean After Dinner Spkers & Com/After Dinner World Ltd/McLeod Agy Ltd
Graham Bean Gordon Poole Agy Ltd
The Beanies Hire-A-Band Ent Agy
Beans Primary Talent Int'l
Jazz Beans David Charles Agy
The Bearcat Cajun Playboys Matters Musical/Swamp Music
Chris Beardshaw Speak-Easy Ltd/Trading Faces Ltd
Peter Beardsley Jon Holmes Media Ltd
Eddie Beardsmore Rogues & Vagabonds Mngt
Sue Beardsmore Celebrity Appearances
Beardyman CHAMPIONS (UK) PLC
Richard Beare NVB Ents
Armand Beasley Lime Actors Agy & Mngt Ltd
Tim Beasley The Narrow Road Company Ltd
Beastie Boys Creative Artists Agency/Free Trade Agy
The Beat Jason West Agy/The Psycho Mngt Co Ltd
Beat Street International Int'l Mngt & Agy Ltd
Beatels (Beatles) Jason West Agy
The Beatels Head On Mngt
Beatfreakz Mission Control Artist Agy
Beatlemania Doub7e Seven Events Ltd
Beatles Beat Cosmos Agy & Promos
Beatles Experience (Beatles Tribute) BCM Promos Ltd
Ultimate Beatles Prima Artists

Geoff Boyz Richard Bucknall Mngt (RBM)
Boyz Limited Int'l Mngt & Agy Ltd
Boyzaloud Angle Ents Ltd
Boyzonly BULLET MANAGEMENT LIMITED
Bozo & Zizi with Fifi MTM Presntns
BPM Roadshow MJE Mngt
BR549 Asgard
Annalise Braakensiek PARAGON SPORTS MANAGEMENT LTD
Dr Tim Brabants MBE MTC (UK) LTD
Sara Brace Kinsella Associates
Kyran Bracken MBE LLB Gordon Poole Agy Ltd/Jon Holmes Media Ltd/NMP Live Ltd
Peter Brackley Jane Morgan Mngt Ltd
Lara Bradban North Of Watford Actors Agy
Emmy Bradbury APM Ass
Jason Bradbury Arlington Enterprises Ltd
Julia Bradbury NMP Live Ltd
Sue Bradbury as Ab Fab's Patsy Prima Artists/Upfront Ent Agy Ltd
Christian Bradley Nancy Hudson Associates Ltd
Major David Bradley CHAMPIONS (UK) PLC
Paul Bradley The Richard Stone Prtnrshp
Steve Bradley Limelight Management
Bradley Wiggins CHAMPIONS (UK) PLC/Trading Faces Ltd
Alan Bradshaw AIM
Billy Bradshaw Positive Plus Ltd
Oliver Bradshaw Grays Mngt & Asc
Peter Bradshaw (Dramatic Rights) Judy Daish Assoc
"The Bradshaws" Positive Plus Ltd
Brian Brady Loesje Sanders
Karen Brady CHAMPIONS (UK) PLC
Karren Brady CHAMPIONS (UK) PLC/Parliament Comms/Persnl Appearances/Trading Faces Ltd
Louise Brady Take Three Mngt
Lucia Brady Dance Funki Feathers Agy
Nell Brady Speak-Easy Ltd
Paul Brady Asgard
Rachel Brady Form Talent
Billy Bragg CODA Ltd/Cooking Vinyl/Sincere Mngt
Lord Melvyn Bragg NMP Live Ltd
Brahms & Liszt Book A Band
Brahms "N" Lizst NVB Ents/Persnl Appearances
Stephen Brailsford McLeod Agy Ltd
Chris Brain Talent4 Media Ltd
Brakes Scream Promotions
Jackie Brambles Peters Fraser Dunlop (PFD)
Peter Bramhill Talking Heads - The Voice Agy
Tessa Bramley Limelight Management
Virgile Bramly Shining Mngt Ltd
Helen Brampton Jeffrey & White
Kenneth Branagh Premier PR/Special Artists Agency
Andrew Branch Adrian King Assoc
Daryl Branch Sandra Singer Assoc
Jo Brand CHAMPIONS (UK) PLC/NMP Live Ltd/Off The Kerb Prods/The Richard Stone Prtnrshp
Katy Brand Int'l Artistes Ltd
The Brand New Heavies Helter Skelter Agy Ltd
Russell Brand John Noel Mngt
James Brandon James Brandon
Gyles Brandreth CHAMPIONS (UK) PLC/Celebrity Appearances/Int'l Artistes Ltd/NMP Live Ltd/Persnly Spkng/Speakout
Kim Brandstrup Loesje Sanders
Brandy ICM (USA)
Brandy Wine Bridge Rent-A-Band/Tony Bennell Ents
Brandysnaps Orchestra PVA Ent Consultants
Clare Branigan SJS Promos
Kevin Brannagan ICON Actors Mngt
Mark Brannelly Derek Bruce Ents
Sir Richard Branson CHAMPIONS (UK) PLC/NMP Live Ltd/William Morris Inc (USA)/Parliament Comms
Betsy Brantley Markham & Froggatt Ltd
John Branwell Susan Angel Kevin Francis Ltd
The Brass Hoppers Crowd Pullers/MTM Presntns
Brass Monkeys Soul Band Stardust Ents Agy
Brass Routes Funhouse Productions Ltd
Brasshoppers The A6 Agy
Brasstooth UK Booking Agy
Ruth Bratt GOLDMAN KING/Paul Duddridge Mngt
Meredith Braun Susan Angel Kevin Francis Ltd
Kurt Braunohler Avalon Mngt
Danny Bravo London Music Agy
Fimber Bravo Matters Musical
James Braxton Seamus Lyte Management Ltd
Russ Bray Persnl Appearances
Vanessa Bray Hilary Gagan Assoc
Andrew Brazier Fushion Pukka Bosh
Jeff Brazier CHAMPIONS (UK) PLC/Hyper Agency/Princess Talent Mngt/Trading Faces Ltd
Alan Brazil CHAMPIONS (UK) PLC
Brazil Tropical Latin Arts Serv (LAS)
Bread & Butter Theatre Company Continental Drifts/MTM Presntns/TEST AGENT C
Breakin Convention Abstrakt PR
Spike Breakwell Kevin King Mngt
Julian Bream Hazard Chase Ltd
Bream Silver Band Derek Bruce Ents
Ann Brean Deri Promos
Mike Brearley OBE Jon Holmes Media Ltd/Persnly Spkng
Danann Breathnach Princess Talent Mngt
Sandy Brechin (Accordionist) Sandy Brechin (Ind Art)
Breeders 4.A.D.
Jamie Breese John Miles Org
Breeze Derek Bruce Ents
Breeze - Function Band Midland Ent & Mgnt Ltd
Cathy Breeze Hilary Gagan Assoc
Jacqueline Bremar Opera & Concert Artists
Richard Bremmer Emptage Hallett Ltd
Alan Bremner Hope Management
Rory Bremner NMP Live Ltd/PVA Ent Consultants/Parliament Comms/Speakout/The Richard Stone Prtnrshp/Trading Faces Ltd
Roy Bremner CHAMPIONS (UK) PLC
Brenda Tony Denton Promos Ltd
Adrian Brendel Ingpen & Williams Ltd
Alfred Brendel Ingpen & Williams Ltd
Barbara Brennan Daly Pearson Associates
Brid Brennan Jonathan Altaras Assoc
Christine Brennan Lime Actors Agy & Mngt Ltd
Herbie Brennan Ed Victor Agency
Liam Brennan Kerry Gardner Mngt
Pat Brennan Derek Bruce Ents
Patrick Brennan Dennis Lyne Agy
Paul Brennan/Carrig Matters Musical
Paul Brennan Band
Sarah Brennan Brunskill Mngt Ltd
Stephen Brennan Brunskill Mngt Ltd
Paul Brennen Shining Mngt Ltd
Carl Brent Fairplay Ents
Howard Brenton (German) CASAROTTO RAMSAY & ASSOCIATES
Thom Bresh NEM Prods (UK)
Bretforton Silver Band Derek Bruce Ents
Andrea Breth Ingpen & Williams Ltd
Ann & Ray Brett NVB Ents
Laurie Brett Big Bang Mngt Ltd/Waring & Mckenna
Martin Brett Louise Hillman/Katie Threlfall
Simon Brett CASAROTTO RAMSAY & ASSOCIATES
The Brew Band Graham Cole Mngt
Christine Brewer Askonas Holt Ltd
Mike Brewer RDF Management
Andrew D Brewis Matters Musical
Amanda Brewster Langford Assoc
Anna Brewster Peters Fraser Dunlop (PFD)
Yvonne Brewster Sandra Boyce Mngt
Brian Dee Group The John Boddy Agency
Brian Poole & the Tremoles Jean Levy PR Agency
Brian T Strollers Funhouse Productions Ltd
Sean Brickell Downes Presenters Agy
Alice Brickwood Actorum
Andrew Bridge Performing Arts
Bonnie Bridgeman Barrie Stacey Promos & Prods
Eve Bridger Norwich Artistes
Jeff Bridges Special Artists Agency
Kevin Bridges CHAMPIONS (UK) PLC/Off The Kerb Prods/Speakout
Leanna Bridges (Sooty) Brian Marshall Mngt
Bridie
Rebecca Bridle Circuit Persnl Mngt Ltd
Briefcase Blues Brothers Andrew Beauchamp Mngt/Prima Artists
The Briefcase Blues Brothers Head On Mngt/Jason West Agy
David Brierley Vincent Shaw Assoc Ltd
Emanuel Brierley ICON Actors Mngt
Effi Briest Asgard
Alexander Briger Askonas Holt Ltd
Barbara Griggs Limelight Management
Hope Briggs Ingpen & Williams Ltd
Johnny Briggs MBE AIM
Tracey Briggs ICON Actors Mngt
Chris Bright The A6 Agy
Bright Eyes Big Sister Promotions
Joe Bright Louise Hillman/Katie Threlfall
Kellie Bright Gordon & French/Voice Shop
Bright Lights Disco Tony Bennell Ents
Trisha Bright Gordon Kellett Ents
Sarah Brightman Creative Artists Agency
Brighton Jive Dancers Complete Ent Serv Ltd
Irena Brignull CASAROTTO RAMSAY & ASSOCIATES
Simon Brignull Newton Wills Mngt
Marcus Brigstocke Off The Kerb Prods/Peters Fraser Dunlop (PFD)
Brilliant Disguise Tony Bennell Ents
Richard Brimblecombe AIM
Dougie Brimson Jacque Evans Mngt Ltd

Eddy Brimson Jongleurs
Matthew Brind (Orchestrator/Arranger) Gavin Barker
Pete Briquette Sarm Mngt
Ales Briscein Music Int'l
Jen Brister Avalon Mngt
The Bristol Baroque Ensemble Graham Cole Mngt
Eric Bristow MBE McLeod Agy Ltd/Paul Bridson Prods
The British Blues Brothers Jason West Agy
The British Philharmonic Concert Orchestra Much Loved Prods Ltd
British Sea Power The Agency Group
British Whale Big Sister Promotions
Britney Baby BULLET MANAGEMENT LIMITED
Britney Back To School Andrew Beauchamp Mngt
Andrew Brittain Talking Heads - The Voice Agy/The Voice Box Agency Ltd/VRM Artists
Katy Brittain The Richard Stone Prtnrshp
Britten Oboe Quartet Pro Artist Management
Anji Britton CS Ents
Jasper Britton Kerry Gardner Mngt
Tony Britton Shepherd Mngt Ltd
Chris Broad Jon Holmes Media Ltd
Broad St G Entertaining
Graeme Broadbent Askonas Holt Ltd
Jim Broadbent Conway Van Gelder Grant Ltd
Paul Broadhurst CHAMPIONS (UK) PLC
David Broadley Angle Ents Ltd
Broadway Ensemble Derek Bruce Ents
Broadway UK Matters Musical
Sue Broberg Alpha Persnl Mngt
Chad Brock Buddy Lee Attrctns Inc (USA)
Erin Brockovich NMP Live Ltd
Mark Le Brocq Hazard Chase Ltd
Sam Brodie Unleashed PR
Brodini's Magic MTM Presntns
Simon Brodkin Avalon Mngt
Paul Brodrick Jill Foster Ltd
Steve Brody Lip Service Casting Ltd/Paul Duddridge Mngt
Shane Brogan Shane Brogan (Ind Art)
Neil Bromley 1984 Persnl Mngt
Bromley Trio PVA Ent Consultants
Bronx Crown Ents/Ultimate Int'l
Anna Brook Denmark Street Mngt
Apple Brook Grays Mngt & Asc
Jennifer Brook Anita Alraun Representation
Jonathan Brook Audrey Benjamin Agy
Kelly Brook COLE KITCHENN PRSN MGT/Jon Fowler Management Ltd/Premier PR/Princess Talent Mngt
Philip Brook Louise Hillman/Katie Threlfall
Orlando Brooke Actors Alliance
Ian Brooker M W Management
Bev Brookes CeeBee Variety Agy
Bruno Brookes Fox Artist Mngt Ltd
Emma Brookes Dance Funki Feathers Agy
Lisa Brookes Otto Persnl Mngt Ltd
Natalie Brookes Talent One
Ritchie Brookes Derek Bruce Ents
Tim Brooke-Taylor Jill Foster Ltd
Brookfield Band Barn Dance Line Dance Agy
Sir Trevor Brooking CBE CHAMPIONS (UK) PLC/Celebrity Appearances/Jane Morgan Mngt Ltd/Persnl Appearances/Persnly Spkng/Preview & Review Ents Ltd
Christopher Brooklyn City Actors Mngt
Bill Brookman - One Man Band Bill Brookman Prods Ltd
Chris Brooks USP Artistes
David Brooks Emptage Hallett Ltd
Elkie Brooks Jason West Agy/Tony Clayman Promos/Tony Denton Promos Ltd
Elliott Brooks Johnny Mans Prods Ltd
Glynis Brooks Voice Shop
Jeremy Brooks (Estate) CASAROTTO RAMSAY & ASSOCIATES
Michael Brooks MJE Mngt
Ray Brooks Voice Shop
Sara Brooks BAM Assoc Ltd
Sorcha Brooks Sara Crouch Mngt
Steve Brookstein Nigel Round Mgnt/The Psycho Mngt Co Ltd/Tony Denton Promos Ltd
Sarah Louise Broom Boogie Management
Sophie Broome Prof Sports Ptnr Ltd
Pierce Brosnan Jonathan Altaras Assoc/Premier PR/Special Artists Agency
The Brother Lees Entertainers Mgt Ltd
Brotherhood of Man BULLET MANAGEMENT LIMITED/Barry Collings Ents/Brian Gannon Mngt/Brotherhood Of Man Mngt/Compact Mngt & Ent Agy/Derek Bruce Ents/Entertainers Mgt Ltd/Henderson Mngt/Jason West Agy/McLeod Agy Ltd/PVA Ent Consultants/Paul Bridson Prods/Pete Mitchell Associates/Ron Martin Mngt
Chapman Brothers Prima Artists
Brothers Grimm Jason West Agy
Brothers in Soul DG Entp/Global Ent Agy
The Brothers Quay Judy Daish Assoc
Ultimate Blues Brothers Prima Artists
Lez Brotherston Judy Daish Assoc
Simon Brotherton Jon Holmes Media Ltd
Jack Brough RDF Management
June Broughton Piccadilly Mngt
Tony Broughton Piccadilly Mngt
Adger Brown CHAMPIONS (UK) PLC/Complete Ent Serv Ltd/G Entertaining/Persnl Appearances/Stardust Ents Agy/Tony Bennell Ents/Triple Cream Ents
Al Brown Tony West Ents
Alfie Brown KBJ Management
Angela Brown (USA) Wim Wigt Prodns Ltd
Angie Brown Fresh Artiste Management Ltd/Mission Control Artist Agy/Tony Denton Promos Ltd
Arnold Brown Jeremy Hicks Assoc/Speakout
Arthur Brown Jason West Agy
Arthur Brown Jazzband Quality Ents
Ben Brown Kruger Cowne Limited
Buddy Brown Dave Woodbury Ents
Charlie Brown Bees Knees Ents/Shepherd Mngt Ltd
Connor Brown Grays Mngt & Asc
Corie Brown Speak-Easy Ltd
Craig Brown Speakout
David Brown ICON Actors Mngt
Deborah Brown (USA) Wim Wigt Prodns Ltd
Denton Brown The Narrow Road Company Ltd
Derren Brown CHAMPIONS (UK) PLC/Michael Vine Assoc/NMP Live Ltd/Speakout/Trading Faces Ltd
Diego Brown & the Good Fairy Matters Musical
Duggie Brown After Dinner Spkers & Com/After Dinner World Ltd/Celebrity Appearances/Persnl Appearances/Persnly Spkng
Errol Brown BULLET MANAGEMENT LIMITED/Tony Denton Promos Ltd
Faith Brown Big Management (UK) Ltd (Ldn)/Celebrity Appearances/Persnly Spkng
Foxy Brown ICM (USA)
Gary Brown Martin Ents
Hamilton Brown (Lionel Richie) Chance Promos/Funhouse Productions Ltd
Ian Brown 13 Artists
Ian Brown (music) Fiction Records
Ian Brown Jill Foster Ltd
J. Anthony Brown ICM (USA)
Jackie Brown Celebn Model Mngt
James Brown Independent Talent Group Ltd
Janet Brown PVA Ent Consultants/Shining Mngt Ltd/Susan Angel Kevin Francis Ltd
Jocelyn Brown NMP Live Ltd
Joe Brown BULLET MANAGEMENT LIMITED/Entertainers Mgt Ltd/PVA Ent Consultants/Paul Bridson Prods
John Brown NVB Ents
Joycelyn Brown Jason West Agy
Julie Brown Nyland Mngt
June Brown AIM
Justin Brown IMG Artists
Karl "Tuff Enuff" Brown UK Booking Agy
Kayleigh Brown Lime Actors Agy & Mngt Ltd
Liam Brown Nyland Mngt
Lorna Brown Susan Angel Kevin Francis Ltd
Matt Brown Central Line Co-Op Persnl Mngt/Money Management UK
Matthew Brown London Music Agy
Melody Brown Grays Mngt & Asc
Mike Brown Band Yorkshire Ent
Miquel Brown Jason West Agy
Nikki Brown Inspiration Mngt
Niqi Brown (Tina Turner) Upfront Ent Agy Ltd
Pamela Brown Talent4 Media Ltd
Paul Brown Brunskill Mngt Ltd/The Voice Box Agency Ltd
Peter Brown Persnly Spkng
Pieta Brown Asgard
Rachael Brown The Session Connection
Rick Brown BTM Mngt & Agy
Roy "Chubby" Brown Handshake Ltd
Sam Brown The Agency Group
Steve Brown Chris Gordon Theatrical Agy
Tony Brown Martin Ents
W Brown Insanity Artists
Derby Browne SOLITAIRE MGT & INT AGCY
Jackson Browne Asgard
Orde Browne Central Line Co-Op Persnl Mngt
Robin Browne 1984 Persnl Mngt/Speak-Easy Ltd
Ronnie Browne BGS PRODUCTIONS
Alison Browner Music Int'l
Guy Browning JLA/Speakout
John Browning Patrick Garvey Mngt
Alistair and Jonathan Brownlee CHAMPIONS (UK) PLC
Polly Brown`s Picketty Witch Brian Gannon Mngt
Bob Brozman NEM Prods (UK)
Derek Bruce Derek Bruce Ents
Derek Bruce Big Band Derek Bruce Ents

Emily Bruce AXM
Fiona Bruce Avalon Mngt/Knight Ayton Mngt/NMP Live Ltd
Karen Bruce Clare Vidal-Hall
Ken Bruce Jo Gurnett Persnl Mngt
Mona Bruce Kerry Gardner Mngt
Tim Bruce ANA
Frans Brüggen Askonas Holt Ltd
Daniel Bruhl Tavistock Wood Management Ltd
Martin Brundle Celebrity Appearances/John Miles Org
Emily Bruni Markham & Froggatt Ltd
John Brunning Shining Mngt Ltd
Frank Bruno MBE CHAMPIONS (UK) PLC/Celebrity Appearances/NMP Live Ltd
Robin Brunskill The Voice Box Agency Ltd
Theresa Brunskill Rogues & Vagabonds Mngt
Michael Brunson Knight Ayton Mngt
Dominic Brunt Michelle Braidman Assoc
Polly Brunt Susan Angel Kevin Francis Ltd
Tony Brutus & Amanda Tony West Ents
Earl Brutus Universal/Island Records Ltd
Bryan Brown Chatto & Linnit Ltd
Debi Bryan Celebn Model Mngt
Dora Bryan OBE Burnett Granger Assoc
Kelle Bryan Big Management (UK) Ltd (Ldn)
Maureen Ann Bryan Audrey Benjamin Agy
Reeta Bryant Fushion Pukka Bosh
Jack Bryce (Magic) Jack Bryce
Rob Brydon NMP Live Ltd/Paul Duddridge Mngt/Trading Faces Ltd/United Agents
Roderick Brydon Music Int'l
Gareth Bryn Louise Hillman/Katie Threlfall
Phyllis Bryn Julson Ingpen & Williams Ltd
David Bryne as Del Boy Complete Ent Serv Ltd
David Bryon CHAMPIONS (UK) PLC
Ann Bryson Amanda Howard Assoc Ltd
Denise Bryson Brian Taylor Assoc
Vic Bryson Grays Mngt & Asc
BTO AIM Inc (USA)
Bubblegum Fairplay Ents
Buble Fever CHAMPIONS (UK) PLC
Clarence Bucard Roots Around The World
John Buchanan Dinosaur Promo/Dinosaur Mus/MPC Ent
Katrina Buchanan The Voice Box Agency Ltd
Keisha Buchanan Insanity Artists
Ken Buchanan Fighting Talk Promos
Grant Buchanan Marshall Jill Foster Ltd
Martin Buchanan KAL Mngt
Paul Buchanan Asgard
Jono Buchanard MPC Ent
Buchaneers (jazz) XS Promos
Pamela Buchner Adrian King Assoc
Buck 65 The Agency Group
Dave Buck Creeme Ents
Lloyd Buck Jo Sarsby PR Ltd
Buckcherry Scream Promotions
Clare Buckfield AIM/Amanda Howard Assoc Ltd
William Buckhurst Susan Angel Kevin Francis Ltd
Buckin Bronco Rodeo Bull Stardust Ents Agy
Bucking Bronco PVA Ent Consultants
Bishop Pat Buckley Gordon Poole Agy Ltd
Ginny Buckley Take Three Mngt
James Buckley CHAMPIONS (UK) PLC/Insanity Artists
Sarah Jane Buckley Lime Actors Agy & Mngt Ltd
Sean Buckley Royce Mngt
Simon Buckley Talent Artists Ltd
Paul Buckmaster (Europe) Roedean Music/Tony Hall Grp Of Cos
Buckmaster Puppets NVB Ents
The Original Bucks Fizz Action Talent Int.
Bucks Fizz BULLET MANAGEMENT LIMITED/Barry Collings Ents/Brian Gannon Mngt/Entertainers Mgt Ltd/Jason West Agy/McLeod Agy Ltd/Pete Mitchell Associates/Rock Artist Mngt/Studio One Assoc/The Psycho Mngt Co Ltd/Tony Denton Promos Ltd
The Budapest Ragtime Orchestra (H) Wim Wigt Prodns Ltd
Grahame Budd Scott-Paul Young Ents Ltd
Juliet Budd North Of Watford Actors Agy
Budgie Alan Cottam Agency
Michael Buerk CHAMPIONS (UK) PLC/Knight Ayton Mngt
Kate Buffery Yakety Yak
Tomasz Bugaj Patrick Garvey Mngt
Cordelia Bugeja RDF Management
Bruce Bugess Gordon Poole Agy Ltd
Angie Buggy Agency K-Bis
Bugz in the Attic Elastic Artists Agency Ltd/Toast Press
Marlan Bulger Audrey Benjamin Agy
Andy Bull Richard Bucknall Mngt (RBM)
Angela Bull Peter Charlesworth & Assoc
Clive Bull JLA
Dr David Bull Arlington Enterprises Ltd/June Ford-Crush
Micky John Bull Apple County/Compact Mngt & Ent Agy/Derek Bruce Ents/G Entertaining/PVA Ent Consultants/Stardust Ents Agy
Neil Bull Grays Mngt & Asc
Rhian Jayne Bull Indep Mngt Ltd
Martyn Lawrence Bullard Panic Management
Bulldog ABC Direct Ents
Bullet For My Valentine The Agency Group
Tony Bullimore Gordon Poole Agy Ltd/Ron Martin Mngt
Amelia Bullmore Troika Talent
Jeremy Bulloch Brown & Simcocks
Katy Bullock CHAMPIONS (UK) PLC
Dame Lucy Bun & Reg NVB Ents
Caroline Bunce Cardiff Casting
Deborah Bundy Anita Alraun Representation
Laura Bell Bundy United Talent Agency
Valerie Bundy Piccadilly Mngt
Bungle Rye PVA Ent Consultants
Mr B Bunny PVA Ent Consultants
Billy (Daniel) Bunter UK Booking Agy
Emma Bunton 19 Entertainment/Hall Or Nothing
Penny Bunton Kerry Gardner Mngt
Burach Sandy Brechin (Ind Art)/Stoneyport Associates
Ada Burch MGA Entp
Geoff Burch Cunningham Mngt Ltd/DBA Speakers/Parliament Comms/Persnly Spkng
Paul Burch Asgard
Paata Burchuladze Askonas Holt Ltd
Eric Burden Jason West Agy
Paul Burden Knight Ayton Mngt/Parliament Comms
Suzanne Burden Macfarlane Chard Talent Agency
William Burden Askonas Holt Ltd
Abigail Burdess GOLDMAN KING
Kate Burdette Performance Actors Agy
Ray Burdis Yakety Yak
Ian Burford Burnett Granger Assoc
Jennifer Burgess Elinor Hilton Associates
John Burgess Jessica & Carney Assoc
Kelly Burgess MAGIK MODELS
Lois Burgess M W Management
Michael Burgess Billboard Persnl Mngt
Paul Burgess Red Sky Prods
Sonny Burgess Paul Barrett Rock'N'Roll Entp
Terry Burgess Stardust Ents Agy
Tony Burgess Amber Persnl Mngt Ltd
Dean Burgin MGA Entp
Burgundy Wine CS Ents
Alan Buribayev IMG Artists
Alexandra Burke Modest! management
Andy Burke ICON Actors Mngt
Eddie Burke Derek Bruce Ents/Mr "E" Ents/PVA Ent Consultants
John Burke Amber Persnl Mngt Ltd
Kathy Burke Hatton Mcewan Ltd
Kevin Burke Adastra/Albert Alchemy Ent
Lisa Burke USP Artistes
Robin Burke Wise Buddah Talent & Voices
Stephen Burke CASAROTTO RAMSAY & ASSOCIATES
Tom Burke Troika Talent
George Burley Athole Still Int'l Ltd/TEST AGENT A
Nichola Burley Linton Mngt/Troika Talent
The Burlington Quartet Quality Ents
Burlington String Quartet Mainstream Evts
Kath Burlinson Billboard Persnl Mngt
Alexandra Burn Brian Taylor Assoc
Emma Burn Clic Agency
Cerrie Burnell North Of Watford Actors Agy
Guy Burnet Big Bang Mngt Ltd
Bryan Burnett David Anthony Promos
Julia Burnett Johnny Mans Prods Ltd
Kate Burnett Dennis Lyne Agy
Sally-Ann Burnett Audrey Benjamin Agy
Simon Burnett Prof Sports Ptnr Ltd
Yvonne Burnett Music Int'l
Paul Burnham Liz Hobbs Grp Ltd
Bill Burns Seamus Lyte Management Ltd
Brendon Burns Off The Kerb Prods
Charles Burns - The Fine Artist Charles Burns (Ind Art)/Sardi's Int'l Ent/The Roving Artist
Donnie Burns & Gaynor Fairweather Peter Charlesworth & Assoc
Gordon Burns David Anthony Promos/Paul Bridson Prods
John Burns Alan Walters Mngt
Mike Burns Events Connect/Lime Actors Agy & Mngt Ltd
Pete Burns Full Portion Media
Tanya Burns Dennis Lyne Agy
Terry Burns Wendy Lee Mngt
Mike Burnside Shining Mngt Ltd
Jenny Burrell Talking Heads - The Voice Agy
Paul Burrell CHAMPIONS (UK) PLC
Sheila Burrell Burnett Granger Assoc
James Burridge Jane Morgan Mngt Ltd
Zalie Burrow Peter Charlesworth & Assoc
Justin Burrows Lime Actors Agy & Mngt

Ltd
Lisa Burrows APM Ass
Malandra Burrows MCS Agcy/Nigel Round Mgnt
Saffron Burrows Peters Fraser Dunlop (PFD)
Maxine Burth ICON Actors Mngt
Adam Burton Louise Hillman/Katie Threlfall
John Burton Jeffrey & White
Trevor Burton Rock Artist Mngt
Carol Bush Billboard Persnl Mngt
Kate Bush Jukes Prods Ltd
Victoria Bush AIM/Burnett Granger Assoc
Garry Bushell MCS Agcy/Tony Clayman Promos
Gary Bushell Ron Martin Mngt
Kirsty Bushell Macfarlane Chard Talent Agency
Bushes & Briars Barn Dance Line Dance Agy
Busted Personal Management & Casting
Buster Martin Ents
Bustin' Loose Tony Bennell Ents
Bustles & Beaux Belltower Entp
Chloe Buswell The Richard Stone Prtnrshp
Kirsty Buswell The Richard Stone Prtnrshp
But Seriously (Phil Collins tribute) Peller Artistes Ltd
Lisa Butcher Independent Talent Group Ltd
Mark Butcher PARAGON SPORTS MANAGEMENT LTD
Billy Butler - Radio Power Promos
Brett Butler ICM (USA)
Rob Butler Noel Gay Artists Ltd
Stefan Butler Argyle Assoc
William Butler-Adams CHAMPIONS (UK) PLC
Vicki Butler-Henderson Arlington Enterprises Ltd/Princess Talent Mngt
Michelle Butt ICON Actors Mngt
Benjamin Butterfield Athole Still Int'l Ltd/TEST AGENT A
Simon Butteriss (buffo) Music Int'l
Wes Butters MPC Ent
Jez Butterworth Judy Daish Assoc
Tyler Butterworth Kerry Gardner Mngt
Angela Buttolph Curtis Brown Grp
Jenson Button 19 Entertainment
Adam Buxton PBJ Mngt Ltd
Adam Buxton & Joe Cornish PBJ Mngt Ltd
Judy Buxton Shepherd Mngt Ltd
Kate Buxton Jae Moss Entp
Buzzcocks Cooking Vinyl/Free Trade Agy
The Buzztones Goldstar Ent UK
B*Witched Mission Control Artist Agy
Liam Byatt Colette Fenlon Persnl Mngt
Paul Byatt Colette Fenlon Persnl Mngt
Semyon Bychkov International Classical Artist
James Bye Shepherd Mngt Ltd
Martin Byfield Nigel Round Mgnt
Clayton Byfield-Riches Sue Rider Mngt Ltd
Peter Bygott BAM Assoc Ltd
Anthony Bygraves Johnny Mans Prods Ltd
Max Bygraves OBE Johnny Mans Prods Ltd
Chris Bylett & Co Compact Mngt & Ent Agy/Complete Ent Serv Ltd/Norwich Artistes/Stardust Ents Agy
B-Yond Int'l Mngt & Agy Ltd
Amanda Byram Independent Talent Group Ltd
The Byrds Brian Gannon Mngt
Claire Byrne Seamus Lyte Management Ltd
David Byrne Primary Talent Int'l
Elianne Byrne Amber Persnl Mngt Ltd
Jason Byrne Karushi Mngt/Phil McIntyre Ent. Ltd
John Byrne CASAROTTO RAMSAY & ASSOCIATES
Matt Byrne (Robbie Williams) Chance Promos
Maurice Byrne Actorum
Noel Byrne Otto Persnl Mngt Ltd
Pamela Byrne Vincent Shaw Assoc Ltd
Sharron Byrne Rosebery Mngt
Brendon Byrnes Fushion Pukka Bosh
Tim Byrom The A6 Agy
Antoinette Byron Darren Gray Mngt
Kathleen Byron Jessica & Carney Assoc
Professor Tanya Byron NMP Live Ltd
Anner Byslma Transart (UK) Ltd
BZRK Hawthorn Ent

C

James Caan CHAMPIONS (UK) PLC/NMP Live Ltd/Trading Faces Ltd
Caberfedh Scottish Dancers PVA Ent Consultants
Caberfedh Scottish Pipers PVA Ent Consultants
Margaret Cabourn-Smith Noel Gay Artists Ltd
Caché Complete Ent Serv Ltd/Prima Artists/Tropical Ents Mngt Agy
Cactus Funhouse Productions Ltd
Peter Cadden Denmark Street Mngt
Ian Caddy Music Int'l
Richard Cadell Boogie Management
Cadenza Derek Bruce Ents
Giles Cadle Judy Daish Assoc
Kevin Cadle Parliament Comms
John Cadman Matters Musical
Elizabeth Cadwallader Stage Centre Mngt
Johnny Caesar Funhouse Productions Ltd
Caesars Free Trade Agy
Café du Monde Matters Musical
Dee Cafari Speakout
Café Goldstar Ent UK
Café Aman Matters Musical
Cafe Society Prima Artists
Cafe' Sol Band Barn Dance Line Dance Agy
Les Caffrey Lime Actors Agy & Mngt Ltd
Caged soul (Sting) Advanced Ents
Jerry Cahil OTB Prods
Matthew Cain Curtis Brown Grp
Shania Cain (Shania Twain Tribute) Bees Knees Ents
Mike Caine McLeod Agy Ltd
Rebecca Caine Athole Still Int'l Ltd/TEST AGENT A
Gemma Cairney Hyper Agency/Insanity Artists
Cajun Dance Party Supervision Management
R Cajun & the Zydeco Brothers Matters Musical/Swamp Music
Cake Free Trade Agy
Salvatore Calabrese Limelight Management
Gary Calandro Brian Taylor Assoc
Brigid Calderhead Speak-Easy Ltd
Adrian Cale All Electric Productions & Dav
John Cale Primary Talent Int'l
Jo Caleb Group Peller Artistes Ltd
Caledonia Dreamin' Andrew Beauchamp Mngt
Caledonian Heritage Pipes & Drums BGS PRODUCTIONS
Calexico CODA Ltd/Dog Day Press
Caliche Derek Bruce Ents/Rent-A-Band
Siempre Caliente CS Ents
Richard Calkin Burnett Granger Assoc
Ruth Calkin The Actors File
Ayden Callaghan Burnett Granger Assoc
Claire Callaghan Sandra Boyce Mngt
Laura Callaghan Agency K-Bis
Bill Callahan 13 Artists
Barry Callan APM Ass
Jessica Callan Seamus Lyte Management Ltd
Rebecca Callard Yakety Yak
George Callis S M A Talent Ltd
James Callis Emptage Hallett Ltd
Simon Callow CASAROTTO RAMSAY & ASSOCIATES/Sally Hope Assoc
Catherine Calloway Lime Actors Agy & Mngt Ltd
Gilian Cally Amber Persnl Mngt Ltd
Calvero Viscount Ents
Calvero & Jan MTM Presntns
Joe Calzaghe CHAMPIONS (UK) PLC
Cambiata CS Ents
Sylvain Cambreling International Classical Artist
Harry Cambridge as Luther Vandross Entertainers Mgt Ltd
Cambridge Jazz Company Highfield Mngt & Promos/Independent Talent Group Ltd
Camden Crawl Sainted PR
Cameo Colclough Entertainment/Elastic Artists Agency Ltd/Eleventh Hour Mngt Ltd
Cameo Dancers London Music Agy
Alistair Cameron Performance Actors Agy
Andy Cameron Peter De Rance/Speakout/XS Promos
Drew Cameron B.F.P Ents
Elaine Ives Cameron Royce Mngt
John Cameron David Wilkinson Assoc
Katherine Cameron Peter Charlesworth & Assoc
Mark Cameron Brunskill Management Ltd/Shining Mngt Ltd
Paul Cameron Nancy Hudson Associates Ltd
Rhona Cameron Richard Bucknall Mngt (RBM)
Ian Camfield USP Artistes
Crishna & Camilita Matters Musical
Camille Asgard
Nicholas Camm Amber Persnl Mngt Ltd
Matthew Cammelle Saraband Assoc
Campari Disco David Forshaw Entp
Al Campbell Monkeybiz Ent Agy
Alastair Campbell NMP Live Ltd/Speakout
Ali Campbell Mission Control Artist Agy/Star Management
Alistair Campbell CHAMPIONS (UK) PLC/Trading Faces Ltd
Colin Campbell MBA
Colin R Campbell Shining Mngt Ltd
Craig Campbell Avalon Mngt
Dallas Campbell KBJ Management
Gavin Campbell Celebrity Appearances
Glen Campbell The Kruger Organisation - TKO/William Morris Inc (USA)
H Ben Campbell M W Management
Jaik Campbell Jaik Campbell (Ind Art)

Katie Campbell Shining Mngt Ltd
Marvin Campbell Fushion Pukka Bosh
Naomi Campbell American Program Bureau/Premier Special/The Outside Organisation
Natalia Campbell Grays Mngt & Asc
Nicky Campbell Capel & Land/Inspirational Artiste Bkg
Richard Campbell APM Ass
Rita Campbell Action Talent Int.
Tim Campbell Frank PR/Richard Price PR
Tim Campbell MBE CHAMPIONS (UK) PLC
The Campbells BGS PRODUCTIONS
Danielle Campbell-Scott Liz Hobbs Grp Ltd
Ray Campi Paul Barrett Rock'N'Roll Entp
Jon Campling Frontline Mngt Ltd
Can You Feel The Force Tour John Hessenthaler Ents
Canadian Log Rolling PVA Ent Consultants
Dermot Canavan Elinor Hilton Associates
Candela The John Boddy Agency
Candide The John Boddy Agency
Candlewick Green McLeod Agy Ltd/Paul Bridson Prods
Johnny Candon Noel Gay Artists Ltd
Maurice Canham is Del Boy Prima Artists/Upfront Ent Agy Ltd
Jacquii Cann as Alison Moyet Entertainers Mgt Ltd
Jonathan Cann Partyweb.co.uk
Elisa Cannas Speak-Easy Ltd
Canned Heat ABS Agy
Cannibal Ox Primary Talent Int'l
Cannon & Ball Int'l Artistes Ltd/Nigel Round Mngt
Freddy Cannon Inspirational Artiste Bkg
James Cannon Shining Mngt Ltd
Louise Cannon The Music Ptnrshp Ltd
Jazz Cannons Prima Artists
Canny Band Apple County/Barn Dance Line Dance Agy
Brian Cant Amanda Howard Assoc Ltd
Cantabile All Electric Productions & Dav/CKK Ent
Sophia Cantardi Sardi's Int'l Ent
Clem Cantini's Tornadoes Pete Mitchell Associates
Kenny Cantor That's Ent Assoc
Matt Cantor CODA Ltd
Jerry Cantrell ITB
Laura Cantrell Asgard
Tom Cantrell Amber Persnl Mngt Ltd
Jake Canuzo Macfarlane Chard Talent Agency
Peter Capaldi Lip Service Casting Ltd/Peters Fraser Dunlop (PFD)
Harry Capehorn Harvey Voices Ltd
Capellino (NL) Wim Wigt Prodns Ltd
Geoff Capes Live Promos Ltd/MTM Presntns/Paul Bridson Prods/Persnl Appearances
Jamie Capewell Wendy Lee Mngt
Adam Caplin Limelight Management
Capoeira Twins (DJ) CODA Ltd
Penny Capper Otto Persnl Mngt Ltd
Capriccio String Quartet CS Ents
Caprice Crown Ents/Identity One Management/Les Hart (Southampton) Ents/Take Three Mngt/The CBS Grp
Capricorn 2 CMO Mngt Int'l Ltd
Brian Capron Markham & Froggatt Ltd
Captain Adequate Barn Dance Line Dance Agy
Captain Gumbo (NL) Wim Wigt Prodns Ltd
Captain Spanner Derek Bruce Ents
Captain Splash Albert Alchemy Ent
Gautier Capucon (Cello) Clarion/Seven Muses
Scott Capurro Int'l Artistes Ltd
Car Wash BULLET MANAGEMENT LIMITED
Car Wash Party Nights (The Original) UK Booking Agy
Elena Carapetis Darren Gray Mngt
Rene Carayol MBE CHAMPIONS (UK) PLC/Parliament Comms
Carazon
Carbon / Silicon Free Trade Agy
Ali Cardabra Partyweb.co.uk
Zac Cardelli Ian Thomas Org
Allan Cardew Agency K-Bis
Cardinal Jazz Apple County
Annette Carducci Judy Daish Assoc
The Care Bears Galaxy Evts
Care Bears Magic Show Paul Bridson Prods
Christopher Caress Michael Vine Assoc
Anita Carey Louise Hillman/Katie Threlfall
Drew Carey The Gersh Agency
Gerard Carey Gavin Barker
Mariah Carey Creative Artists Agency/William Morris Inc (USA)
Karen Cargill International Classical Artist
Cargo Sunshine Ents
Caribbean Ambassadors Rent-A-Band
Caribbean Carnival Extravaganza Roots Around The World
Caribbean Express NVB Ents
Caribbean Harmonics Derek Bruce Ents/PVA Ent Consultants/Quality Ents/Rent-A-Band/Steve Allen Ents
Caribbean Melody Quality Ents
Caribbean Sounds Quality Ents/Steve Allen Ents
Caribbean Steel Band Hire-A-Band Ent Agy
The Caribbeans Book A Band
Caricatures & Magic Caricatures & Magic (Magic)
Steve Caridge CHAMPIONS (UK) PLC
Carl Dominic Band Derek Bruce Ents
Carlin Discotheques London Music Agy
George Carlin ICM (USA)
Julia Carling Take Three Mngt
Will Carling OBE CHAMPIONS (UK) PLC/Celebrity Appearances/Gordon Poole Agy Ltd/NMP Live Ltd/Parliament Comms/Persnl Appearances/Persnly Spkng/Speakout
Belinda Carlisle Miracle Artists Ltd/Mission Control Artist Agy/Tony Denton Promos Ltd
John Carlisle The Richard Stone Prtnrshp
Mark Carlisle Denmark Street Mngt
Hayes Carll Asgard
Guillermo & Juan Carlos Matters Musical
Bob Carlton CASAROTTO RAMSAY & ASSOCIATES
Carl Carlton & The Song Dogs What Mngt
Timothy Carlton Susan Angel Kevin Francis Ltd
Carly Connor connor carly 13 Artists
Derek Carlyle Elinor Hilton Associates
Sally Carmen (Kelly-Marie, Shamless) Nigel Round Mngt
Colin Carmichael Liz Hobbs Grp Ltd
Hayley Carmichael Brunskill Mngt Ltd
Ian Carmichael MCS Agcy
Katy Carmichael Shining Mngt Ltd
Carmina Matters Musical
Tony Carnagie - Divas In Concert Scott Mackenzie Assoc
Tony Carnagie's Pop Goes The 80's Scott Mackenzie Assoc
Liz Carney Denmark Street Mngt
The Carnival Band Seaview Music
Carnival Carl Viscount Ents
Carnival Collective Continental Drifts/TEST AGENT C
Carnival of the Bizarre Psycho Mngt Co Ltd/The Psycho Mngt Co Ltd
Carnival On De Road Continental Drifts/TEST AGENT C
Jimmy Carol CeeBee Variety Agy/MGA Entp/Nigel Round Mgnt
Carol (The Lady In The Moon) Underbelly Management
Carolann 'B' Mike Storey Ents
Joseph Carole ANA
Bob Carolgees Tony West Ents
Carolina Blues Boys Sunshine Ents
Caroline Sunshine Ents
Caron Bosler Fushion Pukka Bosh
Leslie Caron United Agents
Jeremy Carpenter Hazard Chase Ltd
Paul Carpenter Barrie Stacey Promos & Prods
Sean Carpenter Anglia Artistes/The Horne Concert Agy
The Carpenters Experience Jason West Agy
Carpenters Gold Jason West Agy
The Carpenters Story Hal Carter Org
Alan Carr CHAMPIONS (UK) PLC/NMP Live Ltd/Off The Kerb Prods/Trading Faces Ltd
Amanda Carr Talent One
Colin Carr Caroline Baird Artists
Jimmy Carr CHAMPIONS (UK) PLC/Chambers Management Ltd/NMP Live Ltd/Speakout/Trading Faces Ltd
Kaitlyn Carr Talent Artists Ltd
Simon Carr Gordon Poole Agy Ltd
Vicki Carr Liz Hobbs Grp Ltd
Paul Carrack Alan Wood Agy/BULLET MANAGEMENT LIMITED
Cressida Carre APM Ass
Jose Carreras Denis Vaughan Mngt/William Morris Inc (USA)
Carribbean Sunrise CS Ents
Carrie Universal/Island Records Ltd
Carrig
Nigel Carrington Royce Mngt
Rebecca Carrington Richard Bucknall Mngt (RBM)
Rodney Carrington ICM (USA)
Claudia Carroll Macfarlane Chard Talent Agency
Clive Carroll NEM Prods (UK)
Diahann Carroll William Morris Inc (USA)
Dina Carroll Tony Denton Promos Ltd
Emma Carroll AXM
Johnny Carroll Malcolm Derrick Thtrcl Entp
Jonathan Carroll Gordon Kellett Ents
Lee Carroll Lee Carroll (Ind Art)/Tony Bennell Ents
Rob Carroll Billboard Persnl Mngt/Lip Service Casting Ltd
Tim Carroll Ingpen & Williams Ltd
Simon Carroll-Jones The Actors File
Carrot Top ICM (USA)
Jasper Carrott OBE HIGHFIELD ARTISTES HIGHFIELD P/Prime Performers Ltd/Speakout
Roy Carruthers RBA Management Ltd
Frank Carson KSG Arena Ent Cons/Brian Yeates Assoc/Celebrity

Appearances/Frank Carson/Gordon Poole Agy Ltd/Michael La Roche Mngt/Nigel Round Mgnt/Non Stop Ents/PVA Ent Consultants/Paul Bridson Prods/Persnl Appearances/Persnly Spkng/Pete Mitchell Associates
James Robert Carson Associated Arts
Jeff Carson Buddy Lee Attrctns Inc (USA)
Robert Carson Judy Daish Assoc
Sean Carson Noel Gay Artists Ltd
Silas Carson Kerry Gardner Mngt
Willie Carson OBE Athole Still Int'l Ltd/TEST AGENT A/Talent Ents Agy
Alex Cartana Reality Check Management
Alex Carter Laine Mngt Ltd
Deborah J Carter (USA) Wim Wigt Prodns Ltd
Guy Carter (Caricaturist & Silhouettes) Sardi's Int'l Ent/Ultimate Int'l
Jim Carter ARG Management/Conway Van Gelder Grant Ltd
Kate Carter Cardiff Casting
Kaz Carter Hyper Agency
Liz Carter Otto Persnl Mngt Ltd
Lucy Carter Loesje Sanders
Petronella Carter CKK Ent
Pip Carter Troika Talent
Richard Carter (George Michael) Entertainers Mgt Ltd
Ruth Carter Judy Daish Assoc
Sheila Carter Talent Artists Ltd
Jo Carthey Derek Bruce Ents
Sophie Cartman Amber Persnl Mngt Ltd
Sarah Cartwright Shining Mngt Ltd
Todd Carty AIM/NMP Live Ltd/Noel Gay Artists Ltd/Trading Faces Ltd
Tom Carty CASAROTTO RAMSAY & ASSOCIATES
Julian Caruso Derek Bruce Ents
Daragh Carville (French) CASAROTTO RAMSAY & ASSOCIATES
Carwash Global Ent Agy/Head On Mngt/Hireaband Ltd/Jason West Agy/Matters Musical
Casa Latina Arena Ent Cons/Latin Arts Serv (LAS)/Latin-Touch Ents
Casa Latina Allstars/Bugalu/Conjunto Salsanito Matters Musical
Casablanca 13 Artists
Casablanca Boys Yorkshire Ent
The Casablanca Steps Book A Band/CKK Ent/Jason West Agy/MTM Presntns/Matters Musical/Michael Vine Assoc
Jean-Claude Casadesus IMG Artists
Steve Case MJE Mngt
Cases Faces The A6 Agy
Daniel Casey Susan Angel Kevin Francis Ltd
Natalie Casey CAM London
Craig Cash Phil McIntyre Ent. Ltd
The Cash Cube Edge Ent Cons Ltd
Dave Cash Jacque Evans Mngt Ltd
Keith Cash Multi-Media Ents
Pat Cash CHAMPIONS (UK) PLC
Tommy Cash Deri Promos
Cashback - The Definitive Johnny Cash Tribute Cashback
Michael Cashman Peters Fraser Dunlop (PFD)
Casino NVB Ents
Casino Disco Quality Ents
Casino Entertainment Services PVA Ent Consultants
Casino Fun Time Stardust Ents Agy
Casino Royale (Casino) Essex Ent Agy
Casino Royale Steel Band Tony Bennell Ents
~Casinos~ The John Boddy Agency
DJ Casper Mission Control Artist Agy
Nova Casper as Tina Turner Andrew Beauchamp Mngt/Entertainers Mgt Ltd/Peller Artistes Ltd/SWA Ent/Stars In Your Eyes Ltd Ent Agy
Dave Cass Hire-A-Band Ent Agy
Barbara Cassani CHAMPIONS (UK) PLC/Gordon Poole Agy Ltd
David Cassidy Tony Denton Promos Ltd
John Cassidy Highfield Mngt & Promos
Johnny Cassidy Triple Cream Ents
Lisa Cassidy Barrie Stacey Promos & Prods/LJ Ents
Mike Cassidy NVB Ents/Persnl Appearances
Natalie Cassidy AIM/Peters Fraser Dunlop (PFD)/United Agents
Simon Cassidy Lime Actors Agy & Mngt Ltd
Sheba Cassini CKK Ent/Partyweb.co.uk
Simon Cassini CKK Ent
Cassius Primary Talent Int'l
Johnnie Casson After Dinner Spkers & Com
Johnny Casson Nigel Round Mgnt
Barry Castagnola Off The Kerb Prods
Crocodile Casting Int'l Artistes Ltd
Andrew Castle CHAMPIONS (UK) PLC/Speakout
Jennifer Castle Paul Duddridge Mngt
The Casuals Brian Gannon Mngt
Ken Caswell Victoria Tinker Mngt
The Cat Empire The Agency Group
Cat scratch fever Advanced Ents
Scratch The Cat Norwich Artistes
Christina Catalina City Actors Mngt
The Catch Steve Allen Ents
Catch 22 The Agency Group/Tony Bennell Ents
Emma Cater Sandra Boyce Mngt
Harriet Cater M W Management
Caterpillar Roadshow Hartbeat Ents Ltd
Catherine Michelle Carter (Cher) Advanced Ents
Grant Cathro Jill Foster Ltd
Juliette Caton AIM
Nathan Caton Int'l Artistes Ltd
Cats Claw Barn Dance Line Dance Agy
Cats Eyes Derek Bruce Ents
Cats Pyjamas Owen Hughes Ents
Cats Whiskers Barn Dance Band Barn Dance Line Dance Agy/Matters Musical
Mike Catt CHAMPIONS (UK) PLC/PARAGON SPORTS MANAGEMENT LTD
Hernan Cattaneo ITB
Adam Catterall (Rock FM) Nigel Round Mgnt
John Catterall Amber Persnl Mngt Ltd
Mike Cattermole Jane Morgan Mngt Ltd
Sarah Cattle Jonathan Altaras Assoc
Caught In The Act Circus Workshop Viscount Ents
Caught on the Hop The A6 Agy
Jo Caulfield The Richard Stone Prtnrshp/Troika Talent
William Caulfield David Hull Promos Ltd
Nicholas Caunter The Richard Stone Prtnrshp
Angelo Cavallaro Stafford Law
Katy Cavanagh Qvoice
Lucie Cave Money Management UK
Nick Cave United Agents
Mark Caven Harvey Voices Ltd
Brenda Cavendish Louise Hillman/Katie Threlfall
The Cavern Beatles Arena Ent Cons/Fab Prods
Cavern Beatles Henderson Mngt
The Cavern Beatles Jason West Agy/Mark Lundquist Management & Co/Stars In Your Eyes Ltd Ent Agy/Upbeat Mngt
Henry Cavill Peters Fraser Dunlop (PFD)
Vinette Cawan (Tina Turner & Diana Ross) Chance Promos
Garth Cawood Funhouse Productions Ltd
John-James Cawood Burnett Granger Assoc
Sarah Cawood Talent4 Media Ltd/The Richard Stone Prtnrshp/Yakety Yak
Robert Cawsey Daly Pearson Associates
Hal Cazalet Music Int'l
Dominic Cazenove Actorum/Alex Jay Persnl Mngt
Tony Jacklin CBE CHAMPIONS (UK) PLC
Bethan Cecil Louise Hillman/Katie Threlfall
Cee C Derek Bruce Ents
Ceilidh UK Stag Ents
Celebration B.D.A./Tony Bennell Ents/Yorkshire Ent
Celebration Reed & Brass Band Derek Bruce Ents
Celebration Showband Dave Seamer Ents
Dave Celec (Craig David) Nigel Round Mgnt
Celli Babies The John Boddy Agency
Peter Cellier Peters Fraser Dunlop (PFD)
Celtarabia Albert Alchemy Ent/Grinnigogs (Ind Art)
Celtic Feet Irish Dance Company Matters Musical
Celtic Fiddle Festival (Ireland, Scotland, Brittany) Adastra
Celtic Pride Andrew Beauchamp Mngt
Celtic Sounds Barn Dance Line Dance Agy
Celtic Tenors Denis Vaughan Mngt/Upbeat Mngt
Celtic Upstarts Andrew Beauchamp Mngt
Alan Cemore Music Int'l
Centenary Barbershop The Horne Concert Agy
Centre Of Attraction Dings Ent
Centre Stage Disco Roadshow Multi-Media Ents
Centurions Funhouse Productions Ltd
Century Steel Band Glasshouse Prods Ltd
Ceolsha Matters Musical
Lise Cervi SCA Mngt
Tom Chadbon Yakety Yak
James Chadwick (Frank Sinatra) Funhouse Productions Ltd
Nick Chadwin Northern Lights Mngt
Lisa Chae RBA Management Ltd
Paul Chahidi Cassie Mayer Ltd
Chain Gang Compact Mngt & Ent Agy
Chairman Mal M.S. Ent Grp/NVB Ents
Chaka Khan Denis Vaughan Mngt/Tony Denton Promos Ltd
George Chakiris Susan Angel Kevin Francis Ltd
Jay Chaldean Boo Boo's Entertainments
Chalford Brass Band Derek Bruce Ents
Joe Challands Money Management UK
John Challis Burnett Granger Assoc/Yakety Yak
Alan Chambers Trading Faces Ltd
Dwain Chambers CHAMPIONS (UK)

James Cowdery Wendy Lee Mngt
Chris Cowdrey After Dinner World Ltd/Jon Holmes Media Ltd/Persnl Appearances/Persnly Spkng/Talking Heads - The Voice Agy
Simon Cowell James Grant Mngt Ltd/The Commercial Agency
Elisa Cowley Lime Actors Agy & Mngt Ltd/RBA Management Ltd
Tony Cownie The Richard Stone Prtnrshp
Gerry Cowper Roger Carey Assoc
Nicola Cowper AIM
Brian Cox CHAMPIONS (UK) PLC/Conway Van Gelder Grant Ltd/Sue Rider Mngt Ltd
Deborah Cox Reality Check Management
Derek Cox Derek Boulton Productions
Donal Cox Audrey Benjamin Agy/Indep Mngt Ltd
Hugo Cox City Actors Mngt
Jane Cox Big Bang Mngt Ltd
John Cox Askonas Holt Ltd
Julie Cox Markham & Froggatt Ltd
Kelly Cox (Caricaturist) Doub7e Seven Events Ltd
Lara Cox Darren Gray Mngt
Prof Margaret Cox Knight Ayton Mngt
Mark Cox Speakout
Mike Cox LRO Artist Mngt
Rob Cox (close-up) Gown & Gauntlet Promos
Robert Cox CS Ents/NVB Ents/Tony Bennell Ents
Sara Cox Troika Talent
Sarah Cox Insanity Artists
Simon Cox Alexandra Cann Reprsntn
Tracey Cox Take Three Mngt
Graham Coxon CMO Mngt Int'l Ltd/United Talent Agency
John Coyle Fighting Talk Promos
Nadine Coyle Purple PR
Richard Coyle Troika Talent
Peter Coyote Markham & Froggatt Ltd
Paul Coyte Talking Heads - The Voice Agy
Anthony Cozens Jeffrey & White
Kerry Crabbe Judy Daish Assoc
The Crack Yellow Balloon Prods Ltd
Crackers P.J. Ents
James Cracknell OBE CHAMPIONS (UK) PLC/MTC (UK) LTD/Speakout
Cradle of Filth Helter Skelter Agy Ltd
Ali Craig Jeffrey & White
Alison Craig Speakout
Daniel Craig Harvey Voices Ltd/Premier PR
Fergus Craig Avalon Mngt
Jules Craig Grays Mngt & Asc
Mike Craig Arena Ent Cons/Colclough Entertainment/Persnly Spkng
Mitchell Craig MJE Mngt
Seb Craig Vincent Shaw Assoc Ltd
Thomas Craig Shepherd Mngt Ltd
Tony Craig RDF Management
Wendy Craig Waring & Mckenna
Steve Cram MBE CHAMPIONS (UK) PLC/Celebrity Appearances/Persnly Spkng/Prof Sports Ptnr Ltd/Steve Cram (Ind Art)
Bella Crane Take Three Mngt
Matthew Crane Tony Clayman Promos
Nancy Crane CASAROTTO RAMSAY & ASSOCIATES/Talking Heads - The Voice Agy
Sam Crane Emptage Hallett Ltd
Stephen Crane Otto Persnl Mngt Ltd
Tom Crane Insanity Artists
Heather Craney ARG Management
Kenneth Cranham Markham & Froggatt Ltd
Anthony Crank Money Management UK
Crank It Up Derek Bruce Ents
Don Crann Jae Moss Entp
Crannog Barn Dance Line Dance Agy
Geoff Crapes Global Ent Agy
Dan Crary Roots Around The World
Beverley Craven Blueprint Mngt
John Craven OBE Gordon Poole Agy Ltd/Talent4 Media Ltd/Talking Heads - The Voice Agy/The Voice Box Agency Ltd
Sarah Craven Celebn Model Mngt
The Crawfish Scrapers ABDC Ents
Crawford and Brown Owen Hughes Ents
Jamie Crawford Speak-Easy Ltd
Jo Crawford Sara Crouch Mngt
Mackay Crawford RDF Management
Michael Crawford Sally Hope Assoc
Miles Crawford Sue Rider Mngt Ltd
Peter Crawford Jane Hughes Mngt
Randy Crawford Tony Denton Promos Ltd
Crawford String Quartet CS Ents
Stuart Crawley Sandra Singer Assoc
Ben Craze Royce Mngt
Crazy Ape Book A Band/Steve Allen Ents
Crazy Cavan & The Rhythm Rockers Paul Barrett Rock'N'Roll Entp
Crazy Chris MTM Presntns
Crazy Clowns P.J. Ents
Crazy Diamond Gordon Kellett Ents
Crazy Frog Republic Media
Crazy 'K' Barn Dance David Charles Agy
Crazy Tramps MTM Presntns
Lynette Creane PMA Management
Creature Features CKK Ent/Continental Drifts/MTM Presntns/TEST AGENT C/Viscount Ents
Cred Zeppelin Andrew Beauchamp Mngt
Creedence Clearwater Revived Rock Artist Mngt
Vivien Creegor Cunningham Mngt Ltd
Cita Crefeld Speak-Easy Ltd
David Cregan CASAROTTO RAMSAY & ASSOCIATES
Andrea Creighton Stafford Law
David Crellin Amber Persnl Mngt Ltd
Otis Lee Crenshaw Off The Kerb Prods
Leila Crerar Burnett Granger Assoc
Pete Cresswell Derek Bruce Ents
Rosalind Cressy Performance Actors Agy
Crewneck Ceilidh Barn Dance Line Dance Agy
Bernard Cribbins Gavin Barker/Voice Shop
The Cribs Bad Moon Publicity/Big Sister Promotions/Supervision Management
Jimmy Cricket Book A Band/Compact Mngt & Ent Agy/Nigel Round Mgnt/Non Stop Ents/Paul Bridson Prods
Caroline Crier Harvey Voices Ltd
Crime and the City Solution 13 Artists
Martin Crimp Judy Daish Assoc
Scott Cripps Jeffrey & White
Crisco Triple Cream Ents
Ronald Crisp (Toastmaster) ABDC Ents
George Critchley PMA Management
John Crocker Quartet (UK) Wim Wigt Prodns Ltd
Annabel Croft CHAMPIONS (UK) PLC/Celebrity Appearances/MTC (UK) LTD/Speakout
David Croft USP Artistes
Jaq Croft Langford Assoc
David Crofts Partyweb.co.uk
Robert Crofts Brian Taylor Assoc
Brendan Croker Adastra
Eva Crompton Performance Actors Agy
Matthew Crompton Paul Duddridge Mngt
Rob Crompton West Central Mngt
James Cromwell Markham & Froggatt Ltd
Paul Crone (tv presenter) Power Promos
Emma Crook Fushion Pukka Bosh
Mackenzie Crook Karushi Mngt
Paul Crook (from 'Strictly Dance Fever) CKK Ent
Trevor Crook Paramount Int'l Mngt
Crooked Jack Stag Ents/XS Promos
Garth Crooks Parliament Comms
Rhodri Crooks RDF Management
Gary Croome Liz Hobbs Grp Ltd
Peter Cropper Ingpen & Williams Ltd
Craig Crosbie Brunskill Management Ltd
Lorraine Crosby Band The Dixon Agy
Chris Cross Trevor George Ents Ltd
Cyril Cross Anita Alraun Representation
Debbie Cross Celebn Model Mngt
James Cross B.A.S.I.C.
Keith Cross London Music Agy
Amanda Crossley Lime Actors Agy & Mngt Ltd
Dean Crossley SCA Mngt
Howard Crossley Jeffrey & White
James Crossley Narrow Road Company
Kelsey Beth Crossley (Scarlett, Emmerdale) Nigel Round Mgnt
Stuart Crossman Frontline Mngt Ltd
Andrae Crouch William Morris Inc (USA)
Norman Croucher OBE Persnly Spkng
Sheryl Crow William Morris Inc (USA)
Graham Crowden Jonathan Altaras Assoc
Sarah Crowden Shepherd Mngt Ltd
Crowdies House Andrew Beauchamp Mngt
Minnie Crowe North One Mngt
Sara Crowe Yakety Yak
Rodney Crowell Asgard
Crowjane Highfield Mngt & Promos
Bob Crowley Simpson Fox Assoc Ltd
Dermot Crowley Cassie Mayer Ltd/Talking Heads - The Voice Agy
Gary Crowley Curtis Brown Grp/MPC Ent
John Crowley Simpson Fox Assoc Ltd
Nick Crown London Music Agy
Nicky Croydon Cassie Mayer Ltd
Chris Crudelli Take Three Mngt
Marty Cruickshank Louise Hillman/Katie Threlfall
Ian Cruishank's Gypsy Jazz CS Ents
Sean Crummey David Hull Promos Ltd
Crush Prima Artists
Abigail Cruttenden Julian Belfrage Assoc
Hal Cruttenden IMWP (UK) Ltd
Greg Cruttwell The Richard Stone Prtnrshp
Barry Cryer All Electric Productions & Dav/Gordon Robinson Assoc/NMP Live Ltd/PVA Ent Consultants/Parliament Comms/Paul Bridson Prods
Bob Cryer Shepherd Mngt Ltd
Crystal Jongleurs
Billy Crystal William Morris Inc (USA)
The Crystal Method Primary Talent Int'l
Terry Crystal After Dinner World Ltd
Crystalle Kevin King Mngt
Cuarteto Azteca Latin-Touch Ents/Quality Ents

The Cuban Brothers Cosmos Agy & Promos/Get Involved Ltd
Cuban Groove Whatever Artists Mngt Ltd
Cuban Groove Latin Dance Company Whatever Artists Mngt Ltd
Cubanito Matters Musical
Ska Cubano Matters Musical
Lucy Cudden Paul Duddridge Mngt
Vesna Cudic CASAROTTO RAMSAY & ASSOCIATES
On Cue Norwich Artistes
Jose Cuenco Junior Wendy Lee Mngt
Cuff Billet Jazz Band The CBS Grp
The Cufflinks BCM Promos Ltd/PVA Ent Consultants
John Cugley Performing Artistes
Rod Culbertson Talking Heads - The Voice Agy
Michael Cule Kenneth Earle Persnl Mngt
Michael Culkin Julian Belfrage Assoc
Chrissie Cullen Ceilidh Band Yorkshire Ent
Ian Cullen The Richard Stone Prtnrshp
Paul Cullen NVB Ents
Richie Cullen Chris Gordon Theatrical Agy
Sean Cullen Paramount Int'l Mngt
Jonathan Cullinane Scott-Paul Young Ents Ltd
Jamie Cullum AIR/Creative Artists Agency/Kas Mercer/Mercenary PR/NMP Live Ltd
Matt Cullum Brunskill Mngt Ltd
Brendan Culshaw Barrie Stacey Promos & Prods
John Culshaw Speakout
Jon Culshaw Billy Marsh Assoc Ltd/NMP Live Ltd/Trading Faces Ltd/Voice Shop
Culture Ceilidh Band BGS PRODUCTIONS
Culture Club Mission Control Artist Agy/The Agency Group/Tony Denton Promos Ltd/William Morris Inc (USA)
Alan Cumming Troika Talent
Michael Cumming Alexandra Cann Reprsntn
Richard Cumming MTM Presntns
Des Cummings ICON Actors Mngt
Cumuli Wind Quintet Matters Musical
Francesca Cundy Susan Angel Kevin Francis Ltd
Clare Cunliffe Barrie Stacey Promos & Prods
Andrea Cunningham (Caricaturist) Upbeat Entertainment
Andy Cunningham London Music Agy
BJ Cunningham CHAMPIONS (UK) PLC
Davy Cunningham Performing Arts
Glen Cunningham Lime Actors Agy & Mngt Ltd
Kieran Cunningham The Voice Box Agency Ltd
Liam Cunningham ARG Management
Steve Cunningham Velrag Arts
Cupid's Stunts Glam Rock Band Hire-A-Band Ent Agy
Alan Curbishley Nigel Round Mgnt
The Cure Primary Talent Int'l
Curiosity Killed The Cat Tony Denton Promos Ltd
Curious Continental Drifts/TEST AGENT C
Curious Company CKK Ent
Curious Eyebrow Albert Alchemy Ent
The Curious Eyebrows MTM Presntns
Curious Potion Scott Mackenzie Assoc
Ben Curley ICON Actors Mngt
Rob Curling NMP Live Ltd/Speak-Easy Ltd
Laura Curnick Inspiration Mngt
Christian Curnyn Hazard Chase Ltd
Brian Curran Seamus Lyte Management Ltd
Paul Curran AIM
Peter Curran Talking Heads - The Voice Agy/The Richard Stone Prtnrshp
Edwina Currie NMP Live Ltd/PVA Ent Consultants/Persnly Spkng/Speakout
Simon Currie Jazz Quartet CS Ents
Tony Currie CHAMPIONS (UK) PLC
Declan Curry Speakout
Jayne Curry Devil Management
Simon Curry Jazz Band CS Ents/Central Events/Matters Musical
Mark Curry AIM
Tim Curry Jonathan Altaras Assoc
Lisa Marie Curtain Celebn Model Mngt
Ian Curteis Alexandra Cann Reprsntn
Kevin Curtin Hilary Gagan Assoc
Ann Curtis Loesje Sanders
Catie Curtis Asgard
Lucinda Curtis Daly Pearson Associates
Mac Curtis Paul Barrett Rock'N'Roll Entp
Richard Curtis Peters Fraser Dunlop (PFD)/United Agents
Ruth Curtis Direct Persnl Mngt
Clem Curtis & the Foundations BCM Promos Ltd/BULLET MANAGEMENT LIMITED/Big Bang Mngt Ltd/Brian Gannon Mngt/Entertainers Mgt Ltd/Funhouse Productions Ltd/Henderson Mngt/Jason West Agy/Mad Entertainments Agency/Pete Mitchell Associates
Tony Curtis Markham & Froggatt Ltd
Catherine Cusack The Richard Stone Prtnrshp
Niamh Cusack ARG Management/Yakety Yak
Sinead Cusack ARG Management
Bob Cushing Norwich Artistes
Fiona Cuskelly MBA
The Custard Clowns MTM Presntns
Custom Blue Athole Still Int'l Ltd/Athole Still Music/TEST AGENT A
Cut Up Boys Hyper Agency/The Psycho Mngt Co Ltd
Cutcopy Supervision Management
Trevor Cuthbertson Paul Duddridge Mngt
Peter Cutler The Richard Stone Prtnrshp
Joel Cutrara Voice Shop
Cutting Crew Tony Denton Promos Ltd
Marilyn Cutts Talent Artists Ltd
Cybernaut Magick Eye Records
Cyberstein Creations (Robotics) Continental Drifts/Kernow Ents/TEST AGENT C
Cyderdelic Off The Kerb Prods
Jamie Cymbal Northern Lights Mngt
Jan Cyrka Northern Music Co
Cyrus & Denver Glasshouse Prods Ltd

D

Josie D'Arby John Noel Mngt
Sophie D'Wilde as Kylie (Kylie Tribute) Peller Artistes Ltd
Francesco Da Mosto Independent Talent Group Ltd
Miguel Da Silva Transart (UK) Ltd
Da Vinci's Seasons (Jersey Boys - Four Seasons Tribute) Essential Ent
Mike D'Abo & His Mighty Quintet Gordon Poole Agy Ltd/PVA Ent Consultants
Gino D'Acampo CHAMPIONS (UK) PLC/Jeremy Hicks Assoc/Trading Faces Ltd
D'Accord ABDC Ents
Sue Dacre John Field - Theatre and Puppe
Daddy Ernie (Choice FM) Monkeybiz Ent Agy
Daddy G (Massive Attack) Elastic Artists Agency Ltd
Dad's Army Jazz Band Stardust Ents Agy
James Daffern Shepherd Mngt Ltd
Daft Punk Primary Talent Int'l/Sainted PR
Melanie Dagg ICON Actors Mngt
Daggers Drawn Murder Mystery Stardust Ents Agy
Roald Dahl (Estate) CASAROTTO RAMSAY & ASSOCIATES
Sophie Dahl Peters Fraser Dunlop (PFD)
Tove Dahlberg International Classical Artist
Daily Planet Matters Musical
Nicholas Daines CKK Ent
Lee Dainton Form Talent
Kareena Dainty M W Management
Charles Daish Gavin Barker
Paul Daisley Phillips Ent Agy
Daisy Dares You Insanity Artists
Steve Daking CHAMPIONS (UK) PLC/Pete Mitchell Associates
The Dakotas BCM Promos Ltd/BULLET MANAGEMENT LIMITED/Brian Gannon Mngt
Dakotas Henderson Mngt
The Dakotas PVA Ent Consultants
Marzia Dal Fabbro APM Ass
Michel Dalberto IMG Artists
Charles Dale The Richard Stone Prtnrshp
Jeremy Dale Golf Show Persnl Appearances
Jim Dale Eric Glass Ltd
John Dale Derek Bruce Ents
Robbie Dale The Ents Agency
Ron Dale Elaine Avon Artistes Mngt
Toby Dale Hilary Gagan Assoc
Antony Daley Agency K-Bis
Tom Daley CHAMPIONS (UK) PLC
Kelly Dalglish MERLIN ELITE
Kenny Dalglish MERLIN ELITE
Julia Dalkin Dennis Lyne Agy
Lawrence Dallaglio Jon Holmes Media Ltd/Trading Faces Ltd
Johnny Dallas B.A.S.I.C.
Lorna Dallas Garry Brown Assoc Ltd
Gabrielle Dall-Olio London Music Agy
Cathy Dalton Agency K-Bis
David Dalton Philip Youd Ents & Mngt
Geoffrey Dalton The Music Ptnrshp Ltd
Hattie Dalton CASAROTTO RAMSAY & ASSOCIATES
Mike Dalton MBA
Timothy Dalton Special Artists Agency
Dermot Daly North Of Watford Actors Agy
John Daly RDF Management
Tess Daly John Noel Mngt
Tim Daly Special Artists Agency
Damage Insanity Artists
Julia Damassa Central Line Co-Op Persnl Mngt
Damhsa Matters Musical
Damien O'hare Hamilton Hodell Ltd
Damion Angle Ents Ltd
The Damned Rock Artist Mngt
Vic Damone The Kruger Organisation -

TKO
Dampness Mike Malley Ents
Dan Darling & His Lovely Chaps Prima Artists
Dana David Hull Promos Ltd/Hazemead Ltd
Paul Danan Big Bang Mngt Ltd/Lip Service Casting Ltd/Rossmore Persnl Mngt
John Danbury Devil Management
Marc Danbury M W Management
Graeme Danby Stafford Law
The Dance Band PVA Ent Consultants
Carole Dance Elinor Hilton Associates
Dance Factory Dance Factory Ltd (Ind Art)
Dance Fusion Viscount Ents
Ngoma Drum & Dance Matters Musical
Dance On ABC Direct Ents
Dance reality Advanced Ents
Dance Rocks Whatever Artists Mngt Ltd
Tina Dancer Dance Funki Feathers Agy
Tony Dancer CS Ents/NVB Ents
Beckett Irish Dancers Matters Musical
Viramundo Dancers Matters Musical
Dancin' Easy Dave Seamer Ents/PVA Ent Consultants/Tony Bennell Ents
Dancing Bear Barn Dance Line Dance Agy
Dancing Diggers MTM Presntns
Dancing Fly Book A Band
Dancing in the Streets The Flying Music Co Ltd
Dancing Queen (Abba) Jason West Agy
Gavin Dando APM Ass
Suzanne Dando Jane Hughes Mngt
Leandro D'andrea Indep Mngt Ltd
Dandy Brian Yeates Assoc
Dane Bailey (Queer Eye for a Straight Guy) Seamus Lyte Management Ltd
Margaret Dane Seamus Lyte Management Ltd
Sophie Daneman Askonas Holt Ltd
D'Angelo ITB
Danger Glasshouse Prods Ltd
Dangerous age Advanced Ents
Dangerous Dave Fools Paradise
Nicholas Daniel Pro Artist Management
Paul Daniel CBE Ingpen & Williams Ltd
Daniel Smith Blues Band ABC Direct Ents
Danielle Bees Knees Ents/Dave Woodbury Ents
Danielle Body Art (Temporary Tatoos & Face Painting) Kaye Frankland Ent Agy
Amanda Daniels The Richard Stone Prtnrshp
Ann Daniels 1st Choice Speakers UK Ltd/Jon Holmes Media Ltd
Jack Daniels Band Derek Bruce Ents
Ben Daniels Markham & Froggatt Ltd
Charles Daniels Hazard Chase Ltd
Clint Daniels Buddy Lee Attrctns Inc (USA)
David Daniels Agency K-Bis/Askonas Holt Ltd
Gilly Daniels ICON Actors Mngt
John Daniels Swan Ents
Josh Daniels After Dinner Spkers & Com
Martin Daniels Chris Davis Management/Pete Mitchell Associates
Maxine Daniels B.A.S.I.C.
Paul Daniels CHAMPIONS (UK) PLC/Chris Davis Management/NMP Live Ltd/NMP MANAGEMENT/Paul Bridson Prods/Paul Daniels/Paul Madeley/Peller Artistes Ltd/Speakout
Pauline Daniels Non Stop Ents/The Narrow Road Company Ltd
Phil Daniels Emptage Hallett Ltd
Sarah Daniels CASAROTTO RAMSAY & ASSOCIATES
Tara Daniels Lime Actors Agy & Mngt Ltd
Gergo Danka North One Mngt
Danko Jones Scream Promotions
Jacqui Dankworth & Her Musicians Jazzco
Jacqui Dankworth The John Boddy Agency
The John Dankworth Quintet Jazzco
Colin Dann Alexandra Cann Reprsntn
Larry Dann KAL Mngt
Danni Derek Bruce Ents
Danni Jane Swan Ents
Danny Owen (Tom Jones) Advanced Ents
Jack Danson (Rod Stewart) Chance Promos
Jane Danson Peters Fraser Dunlop (PFD)
Ted Danson Special Artists Agency
Dante 13 Artists
Dante Ferrara CKK Ent/Leo Mngt & Agy/Matters Musical
Danú Adastra
Fuman Dar Jonathan Altaras Assoc
Paul Darby Lime Actors Agy & Mngt Ltd/Liz Hobbs Grp Ltd
Angela Darcy Daly Pearson Associates
James D'Arcy Markham & Froggatt Ltd
Josh Darcy West Central Mngt
Kay D'Arcy Sara Crouch Mngt
Matt Darey feat Marcella Woods Fresh Artiste Management Ltd
Darius Big Talent Group
Darius (close up magician) Barrie Hawkins Leisure Service
Alan Dark Alan Dark (Ind Art)
Dark Angel Complete Ent Serv Ltd/Dave Woodbury Ents/Rainbow Striptease Agy
The Dark Blues Discotheque Dark Blues Mngt
The Dark Blues Dark Blues Mngt
Shamus Dark Matters Musical
Dark side stilts Advanced Ents
Ian Darke Fighting Talk Promos/Jane Morgan Mngt Ltd
Darktown CS Ents/Sardi's Int'l Ent
Jamie Darling Take Three Mngt
Peter Darling Simpson Fox Assoc Ltd
Jonathan Darlington IMG Artists
Catrin Darnell Speak-Easy Ltd
Jennie Darnell Clare Vidal-Hall
Darren Campbell MBE Nuff Respect
Shelly Dartnell Barrie Stacey Promos & Prods
Darts Barry Collings Ents
Darude Mission Control Artist Agy
Ellie Darvill Elinor Hilton Associates
Emma Darwell-Smith Markham & Froggatt Ltd
Darwin's Wish Tony Bennell Ents
Meneka Das Nancy Hudson Associates Ltd
Nandita Das Brunskill Mngt Ltd
Das Orchester Bavarian Band ABDC Ents
Dash A.I.R. Ltd
Dashboard Confessional Kas Mercer/Mercenary PR
The Datsuns Helter Skelter Agy Ltd
Terence Dauncey BAM Assoc Ltd
Michael Daunt Independent Talent Group Ltd
Thomas Dausgaard IMG Artists
Dave & Amos Compact Mngt & Ent Agy/Derek Bruce Ents/G Entertaining
Dave & Danny Derek Bruce Ents
Chappers & Dave Hyper Agency
Dave Dee, Dozy, Beaky, Mich & Tich BULLET MANAGEMENT LIMITED/Hal Carter Org/Henderson Mngt
Roy Davendort Spotlight Ents (Notts)
Edward Davenport Susan Angel Kevin Francis Ltd
Jack Davenport Hamilton Hodell Ltd/Michael Whitehall
Dave's Get Up & Go Show Chester Benson Prods
Andy Davey Norwich Artistes/Partyweb.co.uk
Cathy Davey 13 Artists
Cyril Davey Fushion Pukka Bosh
Gavin Davey London Music Agy
Gideon Davey Loesje Sanders
Johnny Davey NVB Ents
Natalie Davey CKK Ent
Phil Davey Paramount Int'l Mngt
Craig David Helter Skelter Agy Ltd/The Outside Organisation/William Morris Inc (USA)
Eleanor David Markham & Froggatt Ltd
David Hedges Arena Personal Mngt
Jeremy David Elinor Hilton Associates
Joanna David Tavistock Wood Management Ltd
David Kidd (Tom Jones) Chord Theatrical & Corporate
Mansel David Audrey Benjamin Agy
Martin David John Bedford Ents Ltd
Scott David MJE Mngt
David Whitfield Barrie Stacey Promos & Prods
Kirsty Davide Tommy Tucker Agy
Eric Davidson Speakout
Holly Davidson Sangwin Associates
Jim Davidson OBE CHAMPIONS (UK) PLC/Int'l Artistes Ltd/NMP Live Ltd
Tommy Davidson William Morris Inc (USA)
Abigail Davies Brunskill Management Ltd
Alan Davies ARG Management/M F Management Ltd
Andrew James Davies RBA Management Ltd
Andy Davies Harvey Voices Ltd
Angela Davies Dennis Lyne Agy
Ann Davies Langford Assoc
Anne Marie Davies Narrow Road Company
Annette Davies Celebn Model Mngt
Ashley Davies Big Bang Mngt Ltd
Barry Davies Athole Still Int'l Ltd/TEST AGENT A
Ben Davies Harvey Voices Ltd
Chrys Davies MGA Entp
Danny Davies Nyland Mngt
David Davies Nuff Respect
David Broughton Davies Actorum
Emma Davies Burnett Granger Assoc
Geoffrey Davies Burnett Granger Assoc
Graham Davies Arena Ent Cons/CHAMPIONS (UK) PLC/Laurie Taylor Ents Ltd/PVA Ent Consultants/Parliament Comms/Persnl Appearances/Persnly Spkng/Speakout
Greg Davies Avalon Mngt/CHAMPIONS (UK) PLC/GOLDMAN KING
Howard Davies Gordon Poole Agy Ltd
Huw Davies Persnl Appearances
Ivor Davies Creeme Ents
Jeanine Davies Clare Vidal-Hall
Jo Davies Performing Arts
John Lloyd Davies Athole Still Int'l Ltd/TEST AGENT A
Jonathan Davies Persnl Appearances

Jonathan Davies MBE CHAMPIONS (UK) PLC
Karen Davies Adrian King Assoc
Leon Davies Louise Hillman/Katie Threlfall
Lestyn Davies International Classical Artist
Lynn Davies MBE Gordon Poole Agy Ltd/Jon Holmes Media Ltd
Mai Davies Seamus Lyte Management Ltd
Matthew Lloyd Davies Adrian King Assoc
Neal Davies Askonas Holt Ltd
Noel Davies Athole Still Int'l Ltd/TEST AGENT A
Phillipa Davies Take Three Mngt
Rachel Davies Jonathan Altaras Assoc
Ray Davies Asgard
Rhodri Davies (Harpist) The John Boddy Agency
Sharron Davies MBE Arena Ent Cons/Athole Still Int'l Ltd/Celebrity Appearances/Paul Bridson Prods/Persnl Appearances/Persnly Spkng/TEST AGENT A
Toby Davies Noel Gay Artists Ltd/Sara Crouch Mngt
Tristram Davies Nancy Hudson Associates Ltd
Tudor Davies Noel Gay Artists Ltd
Victoria Davies Audrey Benjamin Agy
Vincent Davies Amber Persnl Mngt Ltd
Windsor Davies Int'l Artistes Ltd
Wyn Davies Performing Arts
DaVinci Angle Ents Ltd
Billy Davis Derek Bruce Ents/Jason West Agy
Danny Davis & Nashville Brass Buddy Lee Attrctns Inc (USA)
David Davis CHAMPIONS (UK) PLC
Evette Davis Ken Spencer Persnl Mngt
Spencer Davis Group Alan Cottam Agency/Brian Gannon Mngt/Richard Martin Agy
Guy Davis Roots Around The World
Ian Davis Angle Ents Ltd
Jason Davis MBA
Jim Davis Wise Buddah Talent & Voices
Judy Davis Chatto & Linnit Ltd
Julienne Davis Lip Service Casting Ltd
Lena Davis Lena Davis/John Bishop Assoc
Phil Davis ARG Management
Seroca Davis Shepherd Mngt Ltd
The Sheena Davis Group Upbeat Entertainment
Skeeter Davis Deri Promos
Snake Davis (Saxophonist/Arranger) ABC Direct Ents
Steve Davis CHAMPIONS (UK) PLC/MATCHROOM SPORT LTD
Stuart Davis CHAMPIONS (UK) PLC
William Davis Persnly Spkng
Elise Davison Elinor Hilton Associates
Peter Davison Conway Van Gelder Grant Ltd
Peter J Davison Judy Daish Assoc/Loesje Sanders
Raine Davison ICON Actors Mngt
John Davitt Grays Mngt & Asc
Bobby Davro CHAMPIONS (UK) PLC/MCS Agcy/NMP Live Ltd/Orvad Enterprises/Persnl Appearances
Andy Davy London Music Agy
Jason Dawe Speakout
Suze Dawe Talking Heads - The Voice Agy
The Tim Dawes Jazz Band Upbeat Entertainment
Elizabeth Dawn MBE Arena Ent Cons
Sonia Dawn as Karen Carpenter Stars In Your Eyes Ltd Ent Agy/Upfront Ent Agy Ltd
Ashley Taylor Dawson Big Bang Mngt Ltd/Hyper Agency
Marielle Dawson Barrie Stacey Promos & Prods
Peter Dawson Direct Persnl Mngt
Tom Dawson Clic Agency
Josie Daxter Actors Alliance
Back In The Day Matters Musical
Clare Day Linkside Agy
Darren Day MWM Prsnl Mngt/Paul Telford Mngt
Helen Day MBA
Jack E Day Cliff Matthews Mngt & Ent Agy
Johnny Day David Hull Promos Ltd
Kevin Day Troika Talent
Olly Day Barry Dye Ents/Norwich Artistes
Robson Day Martin Ents
Simon Day Peters Fraser Dunlop (PFD)
Leyla Daybelge Noel Gay Artists Ltd
Mark Daydy Jill Foster Ltd
Adam Daye Derek Bruce Ents/PVA Ent Consultants/Trevor George Ents Ltd
Dave Dayes Jacque Evans Mngt Ltd
Kimberley Dayle (Britney Spears & Christina Aguilera Tribute) LRO Artist Mngt
Daniel Day-Lewis Julian Belfrage Assoc
Mark Daynes Norwich Artistes
Paul Dazeley Border Leisure
William Dazeley Askonas Holt Ltd
Michael D'Cruze MBA
DD King Sunshine Ents
Felipe De Algeciras Flamenco Dance Co CKK Ent
Marisa De Andrade Fushion Pukka Bosh
April De Angelis CASAROTTO RAMSAY & ASSOCIATES
Edward De Bono Parliament Comms
Antoine de Caunes PBJ Mngt Ltd
Roger De Courcey DHM Limited/PVA Ent Consultants/Persnl Appearances
DE Experience Studio One Assoc
Ellen De Generes ICM (USA)
Jules de Jongh Jane Hughes Mngt
FW de Klerk Parliament Comms
Tony De La Fou CKK Ent/Partyweb.co.uk
Sian De Lier Rent-A-Band
De Luca Equator Music
John de Main Nyland Mngt
Pietro de Maria Transart (UK) Ltd
Lynsey de Paul Cunningham Mngt Ltd/Langford Assoc
Richard De Sousa Sandra Boyce Mngt
Sebastian De Souza Insanity Artists
Rachel De Thame Arlington Enterprises Ltd
Magenta De Vine Harvey Voices Ltd
Sean De Vrind Louise Hillman/Katie Threlfall
Garold de Wyndham & Lady Pat ABDC Ents
Adam Deacon Insanity Artists
Brian Deacon Yakety Yak
Toastmaster Paul Deacon Toastmstr Paul Deacon(Ind Art)
Tom Deacon Avalon Mngt
Dead Kennedys ABS Agy
Dead Men Walking Tony Denton Promos Ltd
Dead or Alive Tony Denton Promos Ltd
Deadringer (Meatloaf tribute) Andrew Beauchamp Mngt/Devil Management
Deadringers Funhouse Productions Ltd
Deaf Heights Cajun Aces Cosmos Agy & Promos
Deaf Shepherd Stoneyport Associates
Kate Deakin Lime Actors Agy & Mngt Ltd
Billy Dean (Elvis) TMK Mngt & Agcy Ltd
Booby Dean NVB Ents
The Dean Brothers Deri Promos
Carl Dean & Claudine Carl Dean/Kevin King Mngt/The Deans of Magic (Magic)
Daniel Dean Johnny Mans Prods Ltd/PVA Ent Consultants
Dave Dean (Andy Williams) Upfront Ent Agy Ltd
Graham Dean Sunshine Ents
Hazel Dean Barry Collings Ents/Henderson Mngt/Studio One Assoc
Hazell Dean Jason West Agy
Letitia Dean CAM London/Inspirational Artiste Bkg
Peter Dean KAL Mngt
Roger Dean Sings Johnny Cash Boldean Productions
Rufus Dean Sandra Boyce Mngt
Simon Guitar Dean Rock Artist Mngt
Dean Taylor (Ali G, Austin Powers) Advanced Ents/Many Faces of Dean Taylor
Dean Torkington (Meatloaf) Advanced Ents/Nigel Round Mgnt
Bruce Deane Gordon Kellett Ents
The Deans of Magic Carl Dean
Deans of Magic Peller Artistes Ltd
The Deans of Magic The Deans of Magic (Magic)
Emma Dears RBA Management Ltd
Adrian Deasley West Central Mngt
Mark Folan Deasy ICON Actors Mngt
Death by Stereo Gold Star PR
Death Cab For Cutie The Agency Group
Death In Vegas EC1 Music Agency
Angus Deayton CHAMPIONS (UK) PLC/Independent Talent Group Ltd/PVA Ent Consultants/Speakout
Debate With Gravity Continental Drifts/TEST AGENT C
Debbie Boyd Band London Music Agy
Claire Debono Music Int'l
Johannes Debus Ingpen & Williams Ltd
Decade Dukeries Ents Ltd/JB Ents
Decadence Andrew Beauchamp Mngt
Decameron Red Sky Prods
Dave Decks and The Love Thing Owen Hughes Ents
Alan Dedicoat NMP Live Ltd/Speakout
Joey Dedio Special Artists Agency
Adam Rhys Dee Jonathan Altaras Assoc
Denni Dee Sunshine Ents
Diana Dee Derek Bruce Ents
Dolly Dee Steve Draper Ents
Dee Dowling Band The Dixon Agy
Jack Dee NMP Live Ltd/Off The Kerb Prods/Prime Performers Ltd
Janie Dee Jeffrey & White
Kiki Dee Whatever Artists Mngt Ltd
Kiki Dee and Carmelo Luggeri Jason West Agy/Tony Denton Promos Ltd
Nessi Dee Derek Bruce Ents
Nicki Dee Martin Ents
Rob Dee (Tribute to Billy Fury Solo or with Band) Advanced Ents
Sammy Dee Dave Woodbury Ents
Sara Dee Johnny Mans Prods Ltd
Simon Dee Derek Boulton Productions
Tony dee Nigel Round Mgnt
Tracy Dee
Craig Deegan Dukeries Ents Ltd

Alice Deejay Mission Control Artist Agy
Jamie Deeks RDF Management
Cat Deeley Inspirational Artiste Bkg
Timothy Deenihan Brunskill Mngt Ltd
Deep Purple The Agency Group
Deepest Purple Head On Mngt
Rob Deering Avalon Mngt
Deeva Dinosaur Promo/Dinosaur Mus
Darwin Deez Insanity Artists
Def Jux Primary Talent Int'l
Def Leppard Artist Group International/ITB
Def Shepherd Barn Dance Line Dance Agy
Jacqueline Defferary Markham & Froggatt Ltd
Definitely Might Be (Oasis tribute) Andrew Beauchamp Mngt/Peller Artistes Ltd
Willem Defoe Tavistock Wood Management Ltd
Phillip Defreitas CHAMPIONS (UK) PLC
Deftones ITB
Rupert Degas Yakety Yak
Jakki Degg Samantha Bond Management
Daniel DeHaan Sandra Singer Assoc
Edmund Dehn Shining Mngt Ltd
Gesuino Deiana Roots Around The World
Déjà Vu G Entertaining/NVB Ents
Deja Vue Phillips Ent Agy
DeKelten Derek Bruce Ents
Desmond Dekker Rock Artist Mngt
Desmond Dekker & The Aces Jason West Agy
Del Amitri G.A.A.
Mark Delacey Speak-Easy Ltd
Delamere String Quartet Quality Ents
Frank Delaney (Dramatic Rights) Judy Daish Assoc
Mark Delaney Anita Alraun Representation
Martin Delaney CAM London
Nicola Delaney Indep Mngt Ltd/M W Management
Paula Delaney Celebn Ents Mngt & Agy
Rob Delaney Avalon Mngt
Mrs Delaney's Band Rent-A-Band
Ortis Deley RDF Management
Junior Delgado Athole Still Int'l Ltd/TEST AGENT A
Deliciously Dusty (Dusty Springfield tribute) Jason West Agy
David Dell NVB Ents
Keith Deller Nigel Round Mgnt/Persnl Appearances
Elaine Delmar And Her Quartet Jazzco/The John Boddy Agency
Sevilla Delofski Nancy Hudson Associates Ltd
Delorian BCM Promos Ltd
Delphian Complex EC1 Music Agency
Delphic 13 Artists
Delphine Y Domingo Delphine Y Domingo (Ind Art)/NVB Ents
Julie Delpy Markham & Froggatt Ltd
Del-Rio Latin American Band Rent-A-Band
David Delve Kerry Gardner Mngt
Henri Demarquette Transart (UK) Ltd
Ivor Dembina Ivor Dembina (Ind Art)
Iris DeMent Asgard
Mandy Demetriou Talent Artists Ltd
Damien Dempsey Free Trade Agy
The Dempseys Al Embry Int'l (USA)
Joe Dempsie Troika Talent
George Demure Lulu Le Vay
Dame Judi Dench Julian Belfrage Assoc
Stéphane Denève IMG Artists
Daryl Denham USP Artistes
Beverley Denim Amber Persnl Mngt Ltd/CHAMPIONS (UK) PLC/Nancy Hudson Associates Ltd
Gary Denis Stag Ents
Barbara Dennerlein Wim Wigt Prodns Ltd
Kevin Denney Buddy Lee Attrctns Inc (USA)
Dr Wendy Denning RDF Management
Cathy Dennis 19 Entertainment
Denzil Dennis Monkeybiz Ent Agy
Gary Dennis (Southport Weekender) UK Booking Agy
Hugh Dennis CHAMPIONS (UK) PLC/Independent Talent Group Ltd/Lip Service Casting Ltd/Speakout
Les Dennis Curtis Brown Grp
Sid Dennis After Dinner World Ltd/Norwich Artistes/SWA Ent
Stefan Dennis Narrow Road Company
Syd Dennis Gordon Poole Agy Ltd
Denny & Dunipace Pipes & Drums BGS PRODUCTIONS
Richard Denny Persnly Spkng
Grace Dent Curtis Brown Grp
Susie Dent Jane Morgan Mngt Ltd
Denver Spur ABDC Ents/PVA Ent Consultants
Rachel Denyer Agency K-Bis
Paul Denzing Royce Mngt
Sonia Deol ROAR Group/Somethin' Else
James DePreist Transart (UK) Ltd
Dept Of Correction Continental Drifts/TEST AGENT C
Deptford Goth 13 Artists
Derby Midshipmen Carnival Band MTM Presntns/Persnl Appearances
Alex Derbyshire Talking Heads - The Voice Agy
Andrew Derbyshire Burnett Granger Assoc
Eileen Derbyshire Big Bang Mngt Ltd
Sam Derbyshire Big Bang Mngt Ltd
Victoria Derbyshire Avalon Mngt/Knight Ayton Mngt
Bo Derek Denis Vaughan Mngt
Paul Derek McLeod Agy Ltd
Rob Derek Sunshine Ents
Derek Thompson & Bob Champion MBE Persnl Appearances
Rebecca Deren Speak-Easy Ltd
Nadine Dereza CHAMPIONS (UK) PLC
Katie Derham NMP Live Ltd
Barbara Derkow Alexandra Cann Reprsntn
Gus Dermody's Sheepdog Displays MTM Presntns
Elisabeth Dermot-Walsh Talking Heads - The Voice Agy
Rick Derringer AIM Inc (USA)
Dervish Stoneyport Associates
Natasha Desborough Speak-Easy Ltd
Descarga Book A Band
Desire (Female Trio) Ron Martin Mngt
Desmond (Nat West Peacock) Animal World
Desperate Dan NVB Ents
The Desperate Men Fool's Paradise/MTM Presntns
Alan Dester Scott-Paul Young Ents Ltd
Destiny Owen Hughes Ents
Paul Detheridge Border Leisure
Detours B.D.A.
Detroit Soul Int'l Mngt & Agy Ltd
Frankie Dettori CHAMPIONS (UK) PLC/Celebrity Appearances/Persnly Spkng/Trading Faces Ltd
Amerjit Deu Yakety Yak
Deuce PVA Ent Consultants
Deuce Duo LJ Ents
dEUS Universal/Island Records Ltd
Bronya Deutsch 1984 Persnl Mngt
Matt Devereaux Anita Alraun Representation
Hilary Devey Speakout
Adam DeVine Avalon Mngt
Alicia Devine Vincent Shaw Assoc Ltd
Andy Devine Big Bang Mngt Ltd
Mike Devine XS Promos
Sydney Devine BGS PRODUCTIONS/Deri Promos
Matthew Devitt Emptage Hallett Ltd
Lisa Devlin Billboard Persnl Mngt
PJ Devlin (Elton John) Angle Ents Ltd
Devon Dave Woodbury Ents
Terry Devon Nigel Round Mgnt
Dave Devraux Phillips Ent Agy
Michelle Dewberry RDF Management
Emma Dewhurst Brunskill Management Ltd
Keith Dewhurst Alexandra Cann Reprsntn
Dexter & The Revelations The Dixon Agy
Mark Dexter Talking Heads - The Voice Agy
Dexy's Midnight Runners The Agency Group
Michelle DeYoung Askonas Holt Ltd
Dr Cecilia d'Felice Independent Talent Group Ltd
Seva Dhalivaal Nyland Mngt
Dhol Continental Drifts/TEST AGENT C
Ministry of Dhol Matters Musical
Tazeen Dhunna Take Three Mngt
Giuseppe Di Iorio Loesje Sanders
Diablo Dave Woodbury Ents
Mike Diabo & His Mighty Quintet John Hessenthaler Ents
Anne Diamond Inspirational Artiste Bkg/TFA Artiste Management
Diamond Blues Brothers Upfront Ent Agy Ltd
Dave Diamond MJE Mngt
Diamond Dogz Compact Mngt & Ent Agy
Dominik Diamond Paul Duddridge Mngt
Dustin Diamond Hyper Agency
Diamond Fun Casinos London Music Agy
Diamond Nights The Agency Group
Nikki Diamond Samantha Bond Management
Diamonds Funhouse Productions Ltd
Dawn Diamonds Derek Bruce Ents
Diane Shaw (Diana Ross Tribute) Advanced Ents/Nigel Round Mgnt
Matt DiAngelo Rossmore Persnl Mngt
Cameron Diaz Special Artists Agency
Daniel Diaz Wim Wigt Prodns Ltd
Joanne Diaz Johnny Mans Prods Ltd
Saul Dibb CASAROTTO RAMSAY & ASSOCIATES
John Dibble ANA
Michael Dibdin Peters Fraser Dunlop (PFD)
Elle Dible Paul Duddridge Mngt
Janet Dibley Lip Service Casting Ltd
Dichen Richard Price PR
Dick & Dom Action Talent Int./Insanity Artists
Andy Dick ICM (USA)
Bryan Dick Markham & Froggatt Ltd
Frank Dick OBE Celebrity Appearances/PVA Ent Consultants/Persnly Spkng/Prime Performers Ltd/Speakers For

Business/Speakout
Steven Dick Speakout
Andrew Dickens RDF Management
Gwen Dickey (solo) Andrew Beauchamp Mngt/Barry Collings Ents/Entertainers Mgt Ltd
Gwen Dickeys Rose Royce BULLET MANAGEMENT LIMITED/Jason West Agy
Bruce Dickinson The Agency Group
David Dickinson Billy Marsh Assoc Ltd/David Dickinson Prods. Ltd
Gareth Dickinson Nyland Mngt
Johnny Dickinson NEM Prods (UK)
Marvyn Dickinson ICON Actors Mngt
Matt Dickinson Jon Holmes Media Ltd
Sandra Dickinson AIM/Kerry Gardner Mngt
Harry Dickman Anita Alraun Representation
Barbara Dickson Adastra/Theobald Dickson Prods
Hugh Dickson Speak-Easy Ltd
Peter Dickson Hyper Agency/Voice Shop
Clarrisa Dickson Wright 1st Choice Speakers UK Ltd/Persnl Appearances
Dido Helter Skelter Agy Ltd
Die CODA Ltd
Die Apfelschnapps Steve Allen Ents
John Diedrich Burnett Granger Assoc
Different Levels Universal/Island Records Ltd
Different Strokes Get Involved Ltd
Joe Diffie Buddy Lee Attrctns Inc (USA)
Ani Difranco Helter Skelter Agy Ltd
Wendy Dignan David Anthony Promos
Phyllis Diller William Morris Inc (USA)
Jacqueline Dillon Lime Actors Agy & Mngt Ltd
Simone Dillon Brunskill Mngt Ltd
David Dimbleby Peters Fraser Dunlop (PFD)/Prime Performers Ltd/United Agents
Jonathan Dimbleby Parliament Comms
Dimitri Darren Gray Mngt
Michael Dimitri Kevin King Mngt
Charlie Dimmock Arlington Enterprises Ltd/Celebrity Appearances/Speakout
Dimmu Borgir The Agency Group
Peter Dineen M W Management
Fred Dinenage The CBS Grp
Dingle Fingle CKK Ent/MTM Presntns/The A6 Agy
Dingle Fingle's Clowntown Crimewatch MTM Presntns
Shaun Dingwall Troika Talent
Paul Dinnen Brunskill Mngt Ltd
Dino (Dean Martin) Funhouse Productions Ltd
Dino PVA Ent Consultants
Philip Dinsdale Northern Lights Mngt
Reece Dinsdale Jonathan Altaras Assoc/Talking Heads - The Voice Agy
Dion (Rap, Hip Hop) Glasshouse Prods Ltd
Celine Dion Joanna Burns PR/United Talent Agency
Dionne Andre's Absolute 80's The Dixon Agy
Dippy the Clown P.J. Ents
Dirrty (Christina Augilera) Henderson Mngt
Dirty Bug COFFEE ARTISTS
Dirty Hat Band Deri Promos
Dirty Projectors 13 Artists
Dirty Three Free Trade Agy
Disciples Derek Bruce Ents
Disco Darlings (Duo or Single) UK Booking Agy
Disco Disciples Advanced Ents
The Disco Disciples Direct Music Mngt Ltd
Headphone Disco Hyper Agency
Disco Inferno Andrew Beauchamp Mngt/Psycho Mngt Co Ltd/Stardust Ents Agy/The Psycho Mngt Co Ltd/Upbeat Entertainment
Disco Knights The Dixon Agy
Disco Madness Karaoke Disco David Forshaw Entp
Disco Nights MJE Mngt
Disco Services Alan Walters Mngt
Disco with Andina Starfinders Int'l Mngt
Disco's Here David Forshaw Entp
Disselbeck Alexandra Cann Reprsntn
Sacha Distel (Estate) Billy Marsh Assoc Ltd
Disturbing The Peace Sunshine Ents
Ditch & Salty Nigel Round Mgnt
David "Ditchy" Ditchfield Nigel Round Mgnt
Beth Ditto Purple PR/The Agency Group
Diva Int'l Mngt & Agy Ltd
Diva Diva Funhouse Productions Ltd
Diva Fever Insanity Artists
Joe DiVanna The London Spkr Bureau
The Divas NVB Ents
Divas Incongnito Matters Musical
Divas Live Advanced Ents
Lizzy Dive West Central Mngt
John Diver Yorkshire Ent
Diversions Classical Trio Hire-A-Band Ent Agy
Diversity CHAMPIONS (UK) PLC/Industry Music Group Ltd/NMP Live Ltd/Trading Faces Ltd
Divertimento Trio ABC Direct Ents/The John Boddy Agency
Divine Act CKK Ent
Sophie Dix Michelle Braidman Assoc
Dixie Chicks Buddy Lee Attrctns Inc (USA)/Creative Artists Agency/Helter Skelter Agy Ltd
Dixie De Luxe Doub7e Seven Events Ltd
Dixie Jazz Bandits Hire-A-Band Ent Agy
Dixieland All-Stars The John Boddy Agency
The Dixieland Swing Kings CS Ents
Dixielanders Rent-A-Band
Norma Dixit Sandra Boyce Mngt
Adrian Dixon Adrian King Assoc
Alesha Dixon Independent Talent Group Ltd/NMP Live Ltd
Hayley Dixon Identity One Management
Kerry Dixon Persnl Appearances
Kym Dixon Fushion Pukka Bosh
Lee Dixon CHAMPIONS (UK) PLC
Michael Dixon Markham & Froggatt Ltd
Nichola Dixon David Anthony Promos
Rico Dixon Linton Mngt
Robbie Dixon JB Ents
Shenton Dixon as Stevie Wonder Entertainers Mgt Ltd
Tim Dixon RDF Management
Jasmin Dizdar CASAROTTO RAMSAY & ASSOCIATES
Dizzee Rascal Primary Talent Int'l
The Dizzy Club Book A Band
Dizzy Feet Disco Stardust Ents Agy
Dizzy Lizzy (Thin Lizzy tribute) Stables Ents
Dizzy Wizzy Karaoke RDL
DJ Cobra Agency For the Performing Arts
DJ Cotton Dinosaur Promo/Dinosaur Mus
DJ DI NVB Ents
DJ Face UK Booking Agy
DJ Food CODA Ltd
DJ Format Big Sister Promotions
DJ Gregory (France) UK Booking Agy
DJ Jazzy Jeff Barely Breaking Even
DJ JD Starfinders Int'l Mngt
DJ Jon Starfinders Int'l Mngt
DJ Kentaro Elastic Artists Agency Ltd
DJ Krush CODA Ltd
DJ Luck UK Booking Agy
DJ Luck + MC Neat Mission Control Artist Agy
DJ Marky CODA Ltd
DJ Motor Multi-Media Ents
DJ Patife CODA Ltd
DJ Richie Martin Ents
DJ Ride UK Booking Agy
DJ Salva MGA Entp
DJ Sammy Action Talent Int.
DJ Spoony Elastic Artists Agency Ltd/MPC Ent
DJ Swerve Insanity Artists/UK Booking Agy
DJ SY & MC Storm UK Booking Agy
DJ Vibes & Mc Lively UK Booking Agy
DJ Vice (House, Garage, Dance) Glasshouse Prods Ltd
DJ Workshops Continental Drifts/TEST AGENT C
DJ Yellow (France) UK Booking Agy
DJ Zinc CODA Ltd
Koray D'Jaffer North One Mngt
Omid Djalili CHAMPIONS (UK) PLC/NMP Live Ltd
DJ's Disco Highfield Mngt & Promos
DK CODA Ltd
Oscar D'Leon Latin Arts Serv (LAS)
Karl Dobby Otto Persnl Mngt Ltd
Anita Dobson Burnett Granger Assoc
David Dobson Inspiration Mngt
Wayne Dobson NMP Live Ltd
Doc Cox Downes Presenters Agy
Tommy Docherty After Dinner World Ltd/Arena Ent Cons/Celebrity Appearances/Gordon Poole Agy Ltd/Gordon Robinson Assoc/McLeod Agy Ltd/Nigel Round Mgnt/PVA Ent Consultants/Parliament Comms/Paul Bridson Prods/Persnl Appearances/Persnly Spkng/Speakout
Doctor Feelgood Barry Collings Ents/Jason West Agy/John Hessenthaler Ents/NVB Ents/Rock Artist Mngt
Doctor & the Medics Andrew Beauchamp Mngt/Jason West Agy/Stables Ents/The Psycho Mngt Co Ltd
Doctors of Jazz Quality Ents/The Horne Concert Agy
Ed Docx Princess Talent Mngt
Bill Dod Arlington Enterprises Ltd
Ken Dodd OBE Int'l Artistes Ltd/Nigel Round Mgnt/Non Stop Ents/Paul Bridson Prods/Persnly Spkng
Paul Dodds Grays Mngt & Asc
Dogan Mehmet & the Deerhunters Adastra
Doghouse Skiffle Band Yorkshire Ent
Dogs Body Book A Band
The Dogs Andrew Beauchamp Mngt
Kate Doherty Sandra Boyce Mngt
Louise Doherty Gerald Goss Ltd
Paddy Doherty CHAMPIONS (UK) PLC/Insanity Artists
Peter Doherty Primary Talent Int'l
doktor cocacolamcdonalds Paul Duddridge Mngt
Joe Dolan Deri Promos
John Dolan Parliament Comms
Mark Dolan PBJ Mngt Ltd

Mick Dolan Red Sky Prods
Doldrums 13 Artists
Mickey Dolenz Rock Artist Mngt
Jon Dolly PVA Ent Consultants
Dolly Rockers Action Talent Int.
Fiona Dolman Shepherd Mngt Ltd
The Dolmen Graham Cole Mngt
Dolonos Funk Global Ent Agy
Buddy Dolphin Paul Duddridge Mngt
Dave & Dom Hyper Agency
Jordi Domenech Opera & Concert Artists
Placido Domingo AIR
Domino Bones Ferrara PR
David Domoney Jacque Evans Mngt Ltd
Don Leather Duo Tony Bennell Ents
Richie Don Action Talent Int.
Pip Donaghy The Richard Stone Prtnrshp
Siobhan Donaghy CMO Mngt Int'l Ltd
Alex Donald Harvey Voices Ltd
Howard Donald Fresh Artiste Management Ltd
Luke Donald MBE CHAMPIONS (UK) PLC
Lou Donaldson Quartet Wim Wigt Prodns Ltd
Lonnie Donegan Deri Promos/NVB Ents
Peter Donegan Peter Charlesworth & Assoc/The Peter Donegan Band
Tanya Donelly 4.A.D.
Donimo CKK Ent/Tony West Ents
Marguerite Donlon Loesje Sanders
The Donnas Big Sister Promotions
Ciaran Donnelly CASAROTTO RAMSAY & ASSOCIATES
Dougie Donnelly Speakout
Donnybrook Fair Barn Dance Line Dance Agy
Amanda Donohoe ARG Management/Yakety Yak
Peter Donohoe Askonas Holt Ltd
Donovan Brian Gannon Mngt/Denis Vaughan Mngt/The Agency Group/William Morris Inc (USA)
Donna Donovan Shining Mngt Ltd
Frances Donovan Jeremy Hicks Assoc
Jason Donovan Mission Control Artist Agy/Peters Fraser Dunlop (PFD)/United Agents
Rachel Donovan Actors Alliance
Tate Donovan Special Artists Agency
Trevor Donovan Insanity Artists
Don't You Want Me 80's Funhouse Productions Ltd
Doobie Brothers ITB
Dooby Doo Disco Derek Bruce Ents
Paul Doody As Marti Pellow Stars In Your Eyes Ltd Ent Agy
Doolally Crowd Pullers
Jack Doolan Emptage Hallett Ltd
Alice Dooley Louise Hillman/Katie Threlfall
Brian Dooley CASAROTTO RAMSAY & ASSOCIATES
Stacey Dooley Curtis Brown Grp
Dudley Doolittle M.G. Ents
Eliza Doolittle Insanity Artists
The Doors Are Open (Doors tribute) Jason West Agy
Rufus Doors NVB Ents
Veronica Doran Nyland Mngt
Charlie Dore Brunskill Management Ltd
Doreen Doreen Compact Mngt & Ent Agy
Simon Dorey Garston Ents Ltd
Tupele Dorgu JLM Persnl Mngt
Mark James Dormer Mark James Dormer (Ind Art)
Jamie Dornan Peters Fraser Dunlop (PFD)
John Dorney M W Management
Dorp Athole Still Int'l Ltd/TEST AGENT A
Nicholas Dorsett (X Factor) ENTERTAINMENT FX/Global Talent Management
Rob Dorsett Speak-Easy Ltd
Suzette Dorsey A.I.R. Ltd/Chimes Int'l Ents Ltd
Dotcomedy CKK Ent/Continental Drifts/TEST AGENT C
Roy Dotrice Eric Glass Ltd
Double Diamond blues brothers Advanced Ents
The Double Diamond Blues Brothers Jason West Agy
Double Jay Fairplay Ents
Double Trouble Mission Control Artist Agy
Eric Doughney Clare Vidal-Hall
Nick Doughty Jill Foster Ltd
Alison Douglas Star Management
Audrey Douglas Derek Bruce Ents/Quality Ents
Barry Douglas IMG Artists
Colin Douglas (Estate) Bernard Hunter Assoc
Craig Douglas Graham Cole Mngt/John Hessenthaler Ents/Pete Mitchell Associates
Jill Douglas Gordon Poole Agy Ltd
Michael Douglas American Program Bureau/Take Three Mngt
Richard Douglas Shepherd Mngt Ltd
Stacey-Jane Douglas Stacey-Jane Douglas (Ind Art)
Saba Douglas-Hamilton Jo Sarsby PR Ltd
Shaun Dovacton Fushion Pukka Bosh
John Dove Simpson Fox Assoc Ltd
Doves The Agency Group
Mira Dovreni Indep Mngt Ltd
Wayne Dowdeswell Performing Arts
Leilani Dowding Samantha Bond Management
Jayne Dowell The Voice Box Agency Ltd
Brian Dowling Princess Talent Mngt
Mike Dowling Highfield Mngt & Promos
Willie Dowling S M A Talent Ltd/SMA Talent Ltd
Down Town Jazzbnad (NL) Wim Wigt Prodns Ltd
Sir Edward Downes CBE Ingpen & Williams Ltd
Jack Downes Reality Check Management
Jackie Downey Susan Angel Kevin Francis Ltd
John Downham Nancy Hudson Associates Ltd
Rachael Downie Tony Clayman Promos
Paul Downing M W Management
Dr Kristina Downing-Orr Jacque Evans Mngt Ltd
Jay J Downs Elaine Avon Artistes Mngt
Kate Downs Samantha Bond Management
Melanie Downs Brian Taylor Assoc
Downtown Sound Rent-A-Band
Craig Doyle NMP Live Ltd
John Doyle Clare Vidal-Hall
Kevin Doyle Peters Fraser Dunlop (PFD)
Leon Doyle CHAMPIONS (UK) PLC
Lorna Doyle Crescent Mngt
Margaret Doyle Noel Gay Artists Ltd
Mike Doyle Int'l Artistes Ltd/Phillips Ent Agy
Patricia Doyle Clare Vidal-Hall
Susannah Doyle Lip Service Casting Ltd
Dozy Beaky Mick & Tich BCM Promos Ltd/Brian Gannon Mngt/Compact Mngt & Ent Agy/Jason West Agy/John Hessenthaler Ents/PVA Ent Consultants/Pete Mitchell Associates
DPA4 Book A Band
Dr & The Medics Global Ent Agy/Henderson Mngt/Tony Denton Promos Ltd
Dr Feelgood ABS Agy
Dr Haze Psycho Mngt Co Ltd
Dr Hook Alan Cottam Agency
Dr Hook featuring Ray (Eye Patch) Sawyer AIM Inc (USA)/Brian Gannon Mngt/Jason West Agy
Dr Ian Campbell MBE June Ford-Crush
Dr John Free Trade Agy
Dr Pesky Swan Ents
Dr Robert Sincere Mngt
Dr Southall CKK Ent
Dr Teeth Big Band Big Bear Music
Margaret Drabble Peters Fraser Dunlop (PFD)
DragonForce Helter Skelter Agy Ltd
Dragonsfire Arena Ent Cons/Belltower Entp/CS Ents/Dragonsfire (Ind Art)/London Music Agy/Matters Musical
Alan Drake Jonathan Altaras Assoc
Drake Fun casino Hartbeat Ents Ltd
Gabrielle Drake Kerry Gardner Mngt
Julius Drake IMG Artists
Nick Drake Seamus Lyte Management Ltd
Tim Drake Parliament Comms
D-Ran D-Ran Head On Mngt
Marcus Dravs Sarm Mngt
Julie Dray Brunskill Management Ltd
Zac Drayson Darren Gray Mngt
D:ream Mission Control Artist Agy
Dream Boys SWA Ent
The Dream Engine Fool's Paradise
Dream Legion SJS Promos
Dream Machine The Dixon Agy
The Dreamers BCM Promos Ltd/NVB Ents/PVA Ent Consultants
Dreamers SWA Ent
The Dreamweaver CKK Ent
Hayley Dredge London Music Agy
Marielle Dreier Scott-Paul Young Ents Ltd
Drenge 13 Artists
Dresden Dolls The Agency Group
Jackie Drew Frontline Mngt Ltd
Marc Drew (Lee) Broadwater Ents Assoc
Ronnie Drew Denis Vaughan Mngt
James Dreyfus Cassie Mayer Ltd/Lip Service Casting Ltd
Richard Dreyfuss American Program Bureau
The Drifters BULLET MANAGEMENT LIMITED/Brian Gannon Mngt/Jason West Agy/Mark Lundquist Management & Co
Drifters The Psycho Mngt Co Ltd
The Drifters Tony Denton Promos Ltd
Patricia Driscoll Downes Presenters Agy
Minnie Driver Special Artists Agency/The M.O.B. Agency
Romano Drom Roots Around The World
Drop Dead Divas (Ind Art) Drop Dead Divas/Prima Artists
Dropkick Murphys Scream Promotions
Dropping Clangers Barn Dance Line Dance Agy
Drops of Brandy Barn Dance Line Dance Agy
Michael Druiett Hazard Chase Ltd
Richard Drummie Blueprint Mngt
Kerr Drummond Curtis Brown Grp
Lauren Drummond AIM/Linton Mngt

Pete Drummond Yakety Yak
Drum'n'Didg/Mark Walker's Talking Drums Matters Musical
Bob Drury Peller Artistes Ltd
Peter Drury Jon Holmes Media Ltd
Greg Drysdale Clic Agency
Julius D'Silva Burnett Granger Assoc
Colonel Bob Stewart DSO June Ford-Crush
Yvette Du Sol CKK Ent
Dual Control Matters Musical
Dual Roles Barn Dance Line Dance Agy
Kevin Duala Talking Heads - The Voice Agy
Dub Pistols Get Involved Ltd
Terry Ducane NVB Ents
Kate Duchêne The Richard Stone Prtnrshp
David Duchovny Special Artists Agency
David Duckham MBE Gordon Poole Agy Ltd/Persnl Appearances
Ducktails 13 Artists
Jerome Ducros Transart (UK) Ltd
Neil Dudgeon Lip Service Casting Ltd
Kate Dudley Royce Mngt
William Dudley Judy Daish Assoc
Duel Personal Management & Casting
Duel Impact CKK Ent
Duels Big Sister Promotions/Helter Skelter Agy Ltd/Supervision Management
Duende Latin-Touch Ents/Rent-A-Band
Dale Duesing Askonas Holt Ltd
Anne-Marie Duff Gordon & French
Blythe Duff Brunskill Mngt Ltd
Hilary Duff Hackford Jones PR/Special Artists Agency
Jacqueline Duff Speak-Easy Ltd
Mary Duff Deri Promos
Stewart Duff Hireaband Ltd
Kerry Duffield Sandra Singer Assoc
Duffy 13 Artists
Carol Duffy Royce Mngt
Kirsty Duffy Take Three Mngt
Lisa Duffy Rogues & Vagabonds Mngt
Mike Dugan Paramount Int'l Mngt
Chris Dugdale CKK Ent
James Duggan MBA
Patrick Duggan APM Ass
John Duigan ARG Management
Duke Action Talent Int.
James Duke Band CKK Ent/Clubline Promos/The CBS Grp
The Duke Spirit The Agency Group
John Dulieu Brunskill Management Ltd
Paul Dumas Paul Dumas Entp (Ind Art)/Ultimate Int'l
Augustin Dumay Askonas Holt Ltd
Adrian Dunbar Markham & Froggatt Ltd
Karen Dunbar Speakout
Felicity Duncan Shining Mngt Ltd
Hugo Duncan David Hull Promos Ltd
Ken Duncan Ultimate Int'l
Kev Duncan (Comedy) Ultimate Int'l
Lindsay Duncan Conway Van Gelder Grant Ltd
Lotte Duncan TFA Artiste Management
Martin Duncan Askonas Holt Ltd
Michael Duncan Rogues & Vagabonds Mngt
Peter Duncan Chris Davis Management/Saraband Assoc
Mike Dundas Avenue Artistes Ltd
Lorna Dunkley Blackburn Sachs Assoc
Matt Dunkley S M A Talent Ltd/SMA Talent Ltd
Frank Dunlop CASAROTTO RAMSAY & ASSOCIATES
Lesley Dunlop (Brenda, Emmerdale) Jonathan Altaras Assoc/Nigel Round Mgnt
Marissa Dunlop Adrian King Assoc/Joe Bangay Entp
Tessa Dunlop Arlington Enterprises Ltd
Alan Dunn Matters Musical
Clive Dunn Peter Charlesworth & Assoc
Emily Newton Dunn Money Management UK
Enid Dunn Lime Actors Agy & Mngt Ltd
Gary Dunn The Ents Agency
Natasha Dunn Wendy Lee Mngt
Carol Ann Dunne North Of Watford Actors Agy
Neil E Dunne Fushion Pukka Bosh
Gary Dunnington Kerry Gardner Mngt
Dunno The Clown Hireaband Ltd
Adam Dunseath Denmark Street Mngt
Charles Dunstone Parliament Comms/Persnly Spkng
Richard Dunwoody MBE Athole Still Int'l Ltd/CHAMPIONS (UK) PLC/Full Portion Media/Gordon Poole Agy Ltd/Jon Holmes Media Ltd/Persnl Appearances/TEST AGENT A
Aurora Duo Matters Musical
Duo Du Sol - Acrobatic Duo Whatever Artists Mngt Ltd
Price Wates Duo Prima Artists
Sambossa Duo Matters Musical
Marcel Dupont & His French Band Upbeat Entertainment
Duppy Conquerors (Bob Marley tribute) Henderson Mngt
Duran Duran Frequency Media Group
Roberto Duran Fighting Talk Promos
Don Durbridge Names & Faces
Jon Durbridge Fushion Pukka Bosh
Richard Durden Julian Belfrage Assoc
Mark Durden-Smith KBJ Management
David Durham Burnett Granger Assoc
Geoffrey Durham NMP Live Ltd
Sarah Durham Rogues & Vagabonds Mngt
Charlotte Durjardin CHAMPIONS (UK) PLC
Chris Durlacher CASAROTTO RAMSAY & ASSOCIATES
Martin Durrant Crescent Mngt
Ray Durrant London Music Agy
Matt Dusk Personal Management & Casting
Dutch Swing College Band (NL) Wim Wigt Prodns Ltd
Dutch Uncles 13 Artists
Doug Duthie Stag Ents
Jacqueline Dutoit Jeffrey & White
Sanjay Dutt Jazz Barton Agency
Lara Dutta Jazz Barton Agency
Julian Dutton Richard Bucknall Mngt (RBM)
Nick Dutton ICON Actors Mngt
Brian Duval McLeod Agy Ltd
Janine Duvitski Susan Angel Kevin Francis Ltd
D.V.D Sunshine Ents
Dweebie The Robot Partyweb.co.uk
D.Y.C. CT Ents
Hayley Dye Barry Dye Ents
Danny Dyer Insanity Artists
Hal Dyer Anita Alraun Representation
Paul Van Dyk Alchemy PR
Greg Dyke Gordon Poole Agy Ltd/NMP Live Ltd
Bob Dylan Creative Artists Agency/ITB
Michael Dylan M W Management
Sara Dylan Billboard Persnl Mngt
Johnny Dymond Avenue Artistes Ltd
Dynamics Steel Band Funhouse Productions Ltd
Dynamite Norwich Artistes
Dynamix TMK Mngt & Agcy Ltd
Dynamix Sound Entertainments Liberty Entertainments
Dynamo CHAMPIONS (UK) PLC
Dynamo Productions CODA Ltd
The Dynamos Sixties Band CS Ents

E

E Dub-O Moonglight Agy
E1-P Primary Talent Int'l
E2 Paul Bailey Agy/Prima Artists/Yorkshire Ent
Colin Eade First Time Mngt
Eagle & Vulture Show MTM Presntns
Eagle Jazz Band Quality Ents
The Eagles William Morris Inc (USA)
Bobbie Eakes Buddy Lee Attrctns Inc (USA)
Elizabeth Earl A & J Mngt
Susan Earl RDF Management
Uncle Earl Adastra
Vince Earl Arena Ent Cons/B.D.A./Colclough Entertainment/Daly Pearson Associates/Nigel Round Mgnt/Persnl Appearances
Justin Townes Earle Asgard
Robbie Earle MBE MTC (UK) LTD
Steve Earle & The Dukes Asgard
Chas Early Paul Duddridge Mngt
Earth Wind For Hire Advanced Ents/Henderson Mngt
East & West Sunshine Ents
East 17 Mission Control Artist Agy
East Coast Blues Hire-A-Band Ent Agy
East Coast West C.D.E.C.
East of Ealing Adastra
David Easter Sangwin Associates
Richard Easter CASAROTTO RAMSAY & ASSOCIATES
Mike Easthope David Forshaw Entp
Abbie Eastwood Money Management UK
Andy Eastwood Andy Eastwood/Tony West Ents
Kyle Eastwood AIR
Paul Eastwood Trevor George Ents Ltd
Tom Eastwood SCA Mngt
Easy Living Alan Walters Mngt
Easy Rider ABDC Ents
Easy Street Barn Dance Line Dance Agy
Easy Weasel Barn Dance Line Dance Agy
Easybeats BCM Promos Ltd/Brian Gannon Mngt/PVA Ent Consultants/Pete Mitchell Associates
The Easybeats Garston Ents Ltd
Shirley Eaton Diamond Management
Eazy Street Complete Ent Serv Ltd/Crown Ents/Jason West Agy
Jason Eblthite Brian Taylor Assoc
Ebony Steel Band Matters Musical
Vincent Ebrahim BWH Agency
Christopher Eccleston Hamilton Hodell Ltd
John Eccleston Jonathan Altaras Assoc
Mark Eccleston Princess Talent Mngt
Jimmy Echo SJS Promos
Echoes of Ellington Jazz Orchestra The John Boddy Agency
Sharon Eckman Anita Alraun Representation
Jenny Eclair Avalon Mngt/Trading Faces Ltd
Eclectic Method Get Involved Ltd
Eclipse Continental Drifts/TEST AGENT C/XS Promos

Eclipse Strings Matters Musical
Eclipse The Band David Charles Agy
Eclipsed Sunshine Ents
Mister Ed COFFEE ARTISTS
Peter Edbrook M W Management
Tom Edden Frontline Mngt Ltd
Eddie and the Hotrods Jason West Agy/Rock Artist Mngt
Richard Ede Grays Mngt & Asc
The Terry Ede Quartet CS Ents
Sue Edelson Downes Presenters Agy
Helen Edgar Celebn Model Mngt
Jack Edgar PVA Ent Consultants
Lorna Edgar Celebn Model Mngt
Zoe Edgar Agency K-Bis
Tony Edge Victoria Tinker Mngt
Phillip Edgerley Burnett Granger Assoc
Joel Edgerton Markham & Froggatt Ltd
Steven Edis Clare Vidal-Hall
Edison Lighthouse Barry Collings Ents/Brian Gannon Mngt/Entertainers Mgt Ltd/Graham Cole Mngt/Jason West Agy/M.S. Ent Grp/McLeod Agy Ltd/PVA Ent Consultants/Pete Mitchell Associates
Edith Piaf - A celebration of a Legend The John Boddy Agency
Editors Hall Or Nothing
Amber Edlin Silvey Associates
Liz Edmiston Burnett Granger Assoc
Alison Edmonds Audrey Benjamin Agy
Frances Edmonds Arena Ent Cons/DBA Speakers/PVA Ent Consultants/Persnl Appearances
Francis Edmonds Persnly Spkng
Noel Edmonds John Miles Org
Ross Edmonds Downes Presenters Agy
Adrian Edmondson Jonathan Altaras Assoc
Kate Edmondson Independent Talent Group Ltd
Matt Edmondson Independent Talent Group Ltd
Dave Edmunds ABS Agy
John Edmunds Downes Presenters Agy
Antony Edridge Louise Hillman/Katie Threlfall
Educate Ltd SIMON WHITTAM PUBLIC-ITY
Edwardian Soirée Matters Musical
Charles Edwards Performing Arts
Christopher Edwards Jo Gurnett Persnl Mngt
Clive Edwards Kevin King Mngt
David Edwards Persnl Appearances
Derek Edwards Paramount Int'l Mngt
Eddie " The Eagle" Edwards Celebrity Appearances/Persnl Appearances
Gareth Edwards MBE Celebrity Appearances
Gareth Edwards DBA Speakers
Gareth Edwards MBE PVA Ent Consultants/Persnly Spkng
Gary Edwards London Music Agy
Glyn Edwards The A6 Agy
Glynn Edwards Derek Bruce Ents
Greg Edwards Talking Heads - The Voice Agy
Greg Edwards (Jazz FM) UK Booking Agy
Huw Edwards Independent Talent Group Ltd/Knight Ayton Mngt/NMP Live Ltd
Iestyn Edwards Whatever Artists Mngt Ltd
Jack Edwards Liz Hobbs Grp Ltd
Jeremy Edwards Hyper Agency/Princess Talent Mngt
Jonathan Edwards CBE CHAMPIONS (UK) PLC/MTC (UK) LTD
Justin Edwards The Richard Stone Prtnrshp
Katie Edwards Big Management (UK) Ltd (Ldn)
Kelly Edwards Newton Wills Mngt
Lynden Edwards Anita Alraun Representation
Mike Edwards Gailforce Mngt Ltd/Matters Musical
Nigel Edwards Performing Arts
Paul B Edwards Cosmic Comedy Mngt
Ray Edwards Audrey Benjamin Agy
Rick Edwards Action Talent Int./Insanity Artists/Money Management UK
Sian Edwards Ingpen & Williams Ltd
Steve Edwards Action Talent Int.
Terry Edwards CODA Ltd
Tracy Edwards MBE Gordon Poole Agy Ltd/Jon Holmes Media Ltd/Parliament Comms/Persnl Appearances/Persnly Spkng
Sarah Edwardson Daly Pearson Associates
Eels ITB
Mark Van Eeuwen Burnett Granger Assoc
E.F. Productions John Field - Theatre and Puppe
Big Joe Egan CHAMPIONS (UK) PLC
Francis Egerton Athole Still Int'l Ltd/TEST AGENT A
Norris Egg Albert Alchemy Ent
Matthew Eggleton West Central Mngt
Ego A Go Go (Robbie Williams tribute) Jason West Agy
Osaze Ehibor Grays Mngt & Asc
Eighteenth Day Of May Free Trade Agy
Eilidhs Ceilidh Barn Dance Line Dance Agy
Chiwetel Ejiofor Markham & Froggatt Ltd
Lisa Ekdahl Asgard
Bibs Ekkel's Tziganka Matters Musical
El Adivino El Adivino (Ind Art)
Abdel Rahman El Bacha Transart (UK) Ltd
El Equipo/Soneando Matters Musical
El Loco Compact Mngt & Ent Agy
El-Andalus Matters Musical
Elbow Alan James PR Agency
Elcka Universal/Island Records Ltd
Mark Elder CBE Ingpen & Williams Ltd
Kevin Eldon RDF Management
Lisa Eldridge Independent Talent Group Ltd
Electra CKK Ent/Crowd Pullers
Electrelane EC1 Music Agency
Electric Avenue Steve Allen Ents/Tony Bennell Ents
Electric Forecast Harvey Voices Ltd
Electric Fred Derek Bruce Ents
Former members of Electric Light Orchestra PTII Tony Denton Promos Ltd
Electric Six EC1 Music Agency
The Electrix BCM Promos Ltd
Electrix CKK Ent/Global Ent Agy/Major Ent Agy
Electrolux Deluxxe Management
Elesis Sphinx Mngt & Ent Agy
Elevation (tribute to U2) Fab Prods
Sarra Elgan Princess Talent Mngt
Sarah El-Hini Agency K-Bis
Elias String Quartet Ingpen & Williams Ltd
Anita Elilas APM Ass
Richard Elis Harvey Voices Ltd/Yakety Yak
Elite Jazz Band Derek Bruce Ents
Elizabeth Dave Woodbury Ents
Jane Elizabeth (actress, singer, presenter) Gown & Gauntlet Promos
Samantha Elka Creeme Ents
John Elkington Amber Persnl Mngt Ltd
Britt Elland Peter Charlesworth & Assoc
Jonathan Ellen Crescent Mngt
Justin Ellery Grays Mngt & Asc
Nigel Ellery Artsworld Int'l Mngt Ltd/Pete Mitchell Associates
Simon Ellinas London Music Agy/Prima Artists
Maria Ellingsen Markham & Froggatt Ltd
Ellington sings Ellington - featuring Lance Ellington Upbeat Mngt
"Ellingtonia" Jazzco
Lucy Ellinson 1984 Persnl Mngt
Bryany Joan Elliot KAL Mngt
Hayward Elliot Arena Personal Mngt
Peter Elliot as George Michael, Stevie Wonder Jason West Agy
Robert Elliot RDF Management
Viss Elliot Billboard Persnl Mngt
Missy Elliott William Morris Inc (USA)
Paul Mark Elliott Lip Service Casting Ltd
Peter J Elliott Kenneth Earle Persnl Mngt
Ryan Elliott Seamus Lyte Management Ltd
Alexander Ellis Langford Assoc
Alton Ellis Monkeybiz Ent Agy
Anna Ellis Mainstream Evts
Chris Ellis Performing Arts
Elaine Mackenzie Ellis Brunskill Mngt Ltd
Gabriella Ellis Insanity Artists
Grace Ellis Nyland Mngt
James Ellis Peter Charlesworth & Assoc
Janet Ellis First Artist Management
John Ellis Clare Vidal-Hall
John Ellis (Elton John) Funhouse Productions Ltd/Upfront Ent Agy Ltd
Steve Ellis' Love Affair BULLET MAN-AGEMENT LIMITED/Barry Collings Ents
Martyn Ellis Daly Pearson Associates
Ron Ellis Ron Ellis (Ind Art)
Sydney Ellis & her Yes Mama Band (USA) Wim Wigt Prodns Ltd
Vic Ellis (one man band) The A6 Agy
Sophie Ellis-Bextor Helter Skelter Agy Ltd/Insanity Artists/Premier Special
Chris Ellison CHAMPIONS (UK) PLC/Yakety Yak
Jennifer Ellison Can Associates Ltd/ROAR Group/Trading Faces Ltd
Nick Ellsworth Harvey Voices Ltd
Fionnuala Ellwood Daly Pearson Associates
Robin Ellwood Albert Alchemy Ent
Lawrence Elman Jonathan Altaras Assoc
Richard Elmes London Music Agy
Claudia Elmhirst Louise Hillman/Katie Threlfall
Poul Elming Ingpen & Williams Ltd
Elmo Dinosaur Promo/Dinosaur Mus/Sunshine Ents
Robert Elms Shining Mngt Ltd/Talking Heads - The Voice Agy
Rachel Elnaugh Gordon Poole Agy Ltd
Derek Elroy Sandra Boyce Mngt
Mac Elsey AXM
Rebecca Elsip Agency K-Bis
Jonathan Elsom Kerry Gardner Mngt
Donna Elson Creeme Ents
Ben Elton CASAROTTO RAMSAY & ASSOCIATES/Phil McIntyre Ent. Ltd
Elton Experience Hireaband Ltd
Terry Elvins Barn Dance Line Dance Agy
The Elvis Cleaning Company Hireaband Ltd
The Elvis Experience Steve Draper Ents
Elvis Himselvis Ultimate Int'l

Mark Goddard's Tribute to Elvis Barrie Hawkins Leisure Service
Elvis on Stilts Doub7e Seven Events Ltd
Elvis Presley Museum On Tour John Hessenthaler Ents
Elvis Shmelvis (Ind Art) David Charles Agy/Elvis Shmelvis
Suspiciously Elvis Prima Artists
Elvisly Yours Andrew Beauchamp Mngt
Philip Elvy Stage Centre Mngt
Geoff Elwell Barn Dance Line Dance Agy
Michael Elwyn Dennis Lyne Agy
ELXT90 Continental Drifts/TEST AGENT C
Richard Ely Central Line Co-Op Persnl Mngt
Kevin Elyot Cassie Mayer Ltd
Emaculate Int'l Mngt & Agy Ltd
E-Male CT Ents
Emalissa B.F.P Ents
David Emanuel Jacque Evans Mngt Ltd
Hannah Emanuel Talking Heads - The Voice Agy
Bella Emberg Gerald Goss Ltd/Paul Madeley
Mike Embley Knight Ayton Mngt
Embrace Big Sister Promotions/Sainted PR
Embraced Sunshine Ents
Louis Emerick COLE KITCHENN PRSN MGT/Funky Beetroot Celebrity Manag
Emerson String Quartet IMG Artists
Emery Primary Talent Int'l
Uriel Emil West Central Mngt
Emily NVB Ents
Emily Bowker Louise Hillman/Katie Threlfall
Eminem William Morris Inc (USA)
Emma B Panic Management/Troika Talent
Jo Emma Reality Check Management
Manolis Emmanouel Vincent Shaw Assoc Ltd
Colin Emmanuel Stephen Budd Mngt
Nathalie Emmanuel Big Bang Mngt Ltd
Paul Emmanuel Tony West Ents
Tommy Emmanuel NEM Prods (UK)
Wilfred Emmanuel-Jones CHAMPIONS (UK) PLC
Emmarald Les Hart (Southampton) Ents
Dom Brunt (Emmerdale) Nigel Round Mgnt
Mark Charnock (Emmerdale) Nigel Round Mgnt
Jonathan Emmett ANA
Susie Emmett Performance Actors Agy
Emmie Dave Woodbury Ents
Gail Emms CHAMPIONS (UK) PLC/Prof Sports Ptnr Ltd
Emotions Tony Denton Promos Ltd
Empathy Sunshine Ents
Emperors of Rhythm BULLET MANAGEMENT LIMITED
Empire State Band The John Boddy Agency
The Empire State Band The John Boddy Agency
Toby Hull & Emu Int'l Artistes Ltd
Dafydd Emyr Burnett Granger Assoc
En Vogue ICM (USA)
Bella Enahoro The Richard Stone Prtnrshp
Helene Enahoro Agency K-Bis
Toni Enahoro Agency K-Bis
Tenors Encore Prima Artists
End Of The Century Matters Musical
The End ITB
Endellion String Quaretet Hazard Chase Ltd
Endless Nights SJS Promos
Edward Enfield PBJ Mngt Ltd
Harry Enfield Conway Van Gelder Grant Ltd/PBJ Mngt Ltd
Susan Engel The Richard Stone Prtnrshp
Johan Engels Loesje Sanders
Brigitte Engerer Transart (UK) Ltd
Engerica Primary Talent Int'l
Sekar Enggal Matters Musical
Engineers Big Sister Promotions/Free Trade Agy
Alan England B.A.S.I.C.
Dinah England Associated Arts
England Football Squad 19 Entertainment
Ruth England Take Three Mngt
Tyler England Buddy Lee Attrctns Inc (USA)
English Baroque Ensemble Graham Cole Mngt
English Mustard PVA Ent Consultants
English Rose String Quartet Barrie Hawkins Leisure Service
English Serenata All Electric Productions & Dav
Enjoy Destroy One Fifteen
Jessica Ennis CHAMPIONS (UK) PLC
Jo Enright Int'l Artistes Ltd
Kerry Enright Wendy Lee Mngt
Enrique Experience Entertainers Mgt Ltd
Ensemble Bash Hazard Chase Ltd
Funky Butt Swing & Dance Ensemble Matters Musical
MPR Jazz Ensemble Norwich Artistes
Noise Ensemble Matters Musical
UK Chinese Ensemble Matters Musical
Firebird Entertainment Matters Musical
Starsound Entertainment Matters Musical
Surround Sounds Entertainment Matters Musical
John Enthoven Langford Assoc
Entwine (female duo) CKK Ent/Ron Martin Mngt
Entwine (Aerial Act as Seen on BBC1) Whatever Artists Mngt Ltd
Entwine Acrobatic Silk Show Continental Drifts/TEST AGENT C
Christine Entwisle Jonathan Altaras Assoc
Vicky Entwistle Big Bang Mngt Ltd
Envy The Dixon Agy
Envy & Other Sins Free Trade Agy
David Ephgrave Jae Moss Entp
Epica Miracle Artists Ltd
Hannah Epps APM Ass
Mike Epps ICM (USA)
Emile Epstein CKK Ent
Equals Brian Gannon Mngt
The Equals Rock Artist Mngt
Erasure Podell Talent Agency
Kristina Erderly RDF Management
Eriksonlaver Continental Drifts/TEST AGENT C
Sven Goran Eriksson Athole Still Int'l Ltd/TEST AGENT A
Eroica Trio IMG Artists
Hassan Erraji + Oriental Craze (Morocco) Adastra
Juliet Errington Noel Gay Artists Ltd
Errors 13 Artists
Gizzi Erskine ROAR Group
Eruption feat Precious Wilson Barry Collings Ents/Jason West Agy
Escada Crown Ents/Highfield Mngt & Promos/Triple Cream Ents
Escala CHAMPIONS (UK) PLC/NMP Live Ltd
Michelle Esclapez Louise Hillman/Katie Threlfall
Gavin Esler Prime Performers Ltd
Eso-Es Book A Band
Espiritu Negro Drummers & Dancer Folk Latin Arts Serv (LAS)
Kyle Esplin Stag Ents/Tony West Ents
Maria Esposito Paramount Int'l Mngt/The Richard Stone Prtnrshp
Espree NVB Ents/Tony Bennell Ents
Essence CS Ents/Highfield Mngt & Promos/Prima Artists
David Essex MP Promotions/Mel Bush Org/Tony Denton Promos Ltd
Essex Dog Display Team MTM Presntns
Essex Man NVB Ents
Esso Tiger Animal World
Michael Esswood CCM
Estate of Dame Iris Murdoch Ed Victor Agency
Estate of Douglas Adams Ed Victor Agency
Estate of Irving Wallace Ed Victor Agency
Estate of Sir Stephen Spender Ed Victor Agency
Gloria Estefan Joanna Burns PR
Estelle Mission Control Artist Agy
Elizabeth Estensen Burnett Granger Assoc/Louise Hillman/Katie Threlfall
Mike Estes Lynard Skynard Rock Artist Mngt
Cordas et Cannas Roots Around The World
Anne Etchells Crescent Mngt
Eternal Abba Eternal Flame (Ind Art)
Eternal Flame Eternal Flame (Ind Art)
Brian Keith Etheridge Avalon Mngt
Jan Etherington & Gavin Petrie Jill Foster Ltd
Anthony Etherton Speak-Easy Ltd
Graeme Eton Stage Centre Mngt
Chris Eubanh CHAMPIONS (UK) PLC
Eugene & The Hurricanes Starfinders Int'l Mngt
Eulogy MGA Entp
Euphoria Albums Tour Head On Mngt
Euphoria Live Head On Mngt
Eureeka Jazz Quartet Derek Bruce Ents
Europa Music Rent-A-Band
Europe Scream Promotions/The Agency Group
European Camerata Transart (UK) Ltd
Eurythmics Creative Artists Agency/G.A.A.
Malcolm Eva Barn Dance Line Dance Agy
Evanescence Creative Artists Agency/The Agency Group
Alan Evans London Music Agy
Alice Evans Premier PR
Dame Anne Evans Ingpen & Williams Ltd
Chris Evans ARG Management/Yakety Yak
Clare Evans CKK Ent
Dave Evans Barn Dance Line Dance Agy
Dave Evans & Barnstorm Folk Ents Ltd
Dave Evans SWA Ent
David Evans CASAROTTO RAMSAY & ASSOCIATES
Fiona Evans APM Ass
Ieuan Evans MBE Persnl Appearances
John Evans John Evans Strongman (Ind Art)/Tony West Ents
Jonathan Evans Alpha Persnl Mngt
Lee Evans Off The Kerb Prods
Liza Evans Jacque Evans Mngt Ltd
Lydia Evans Angle Ents Ltd

Madelaine Evans Nyland Mngt
Mark Evans David Anthony Promos/Noel Gay Artists Ltd
Michelle Evans Celebn Model Mngt
Nichola Evans Crescent Mngt
Nicky Evans (Shane, Shamless) AIM/Nigel Round Mgnt
Pippa Evans Chambers Management Ltd
Shaun Evans Hamilton Hodell Ltd
Simon Evans CHAMPIONS (UK) PLC/Off The Kerb Prods
Stewart Evans Robert Smith Literary Agency
Stuart Christian Evans Louise Hillman/Katie Threlfall
Tim Evans Jonathan Altaras Assoc
Victor Romero Evans Sandra Boyce Mngt
Warwick Evans Anita Alraun Representation
Eve 6 ITB
Alice Eve ARG Management
Rebecca Eve (Celine Dion/Shania Twain) Entertainers Mgt Ltd
Maya Even Knight Ayton Mngt
Evening Mist Jason West Agy
Evening Star Tony Bennell Ents
Alan Evens Scott-Paul Young Ents Ltd
Everclear Artist Group International
Henry Everett ANA
Jace Everett Asgard
Rupert Everett Peters Fraser Dunlop (PFD)
Evergreen Highfield Mngt & Promos/Norwich Artistes
The Everly Brothers The Agency Group
Clare Evers Action Talent Int.
Every Move A Picture The Agency Group
Every Time I Die The Agency Group
Everything But The Girl Primary Talent Int'l
Steve Evets Direct Persnl Mngt
Liz Ewing Kerry Gardner Mngt
Example Purple PR
The Eighties Experience Matters Musical
Experienced Fab Prods
Experienced (Jimi Hendrix tribute) Jason West Agy
Zebra Express Norwich Artistes
Expressive Harmony Swan Ents
Expresso KM Ents
Extravaganza Entertainments Extravaganza Ents (Magic)
Extreme Force David Charles Agy/M.S. Ent Grp
Extreme Rhythm MGA Entp
Kylie In Your Eyes Prima Artists
Alicya Eyo BWH Agency
Fred Eyre Gordon Robinson Assoc
Richard Eyre Judy Daish Assoc
Ez UK Booking Agy
Man Ezeke NVB Ents
Ezio Brian Yeates Assoc
George Ezra 13 Artists

F

The Fab Hartbeat Ents Ltd
Fab 4 (Beatles Tribute) Global Ent Agy/Peller Artistes Ltd
Fab Beatles All Electric Productions & Dav/ENTERTAINMENT FX/G Entertaining/Graham Cole Mngt/Vern Allen Ents Ltd
The Fab Four (The Beatles) Funhouse Productions Ltd/Head On Mngt/Jason West Agy
FABBA BULLET MANAGEMENT LIMITED/FABBA (Ind Art)/Orvad Enterprises/The Psycho Mngt Co Ltd
Katie Fabel Grays Mngt & Asc
Kyle Fabel Grays Mngt & Asc
Caroline Faber The Richard Stone Prtnrshp
Fabian Paul Barrett Rock'N'Roll Entp
Fabio Hyper Agency
Fabolous ICM (USA)
The Fabulous Doughboys Compact Mngt & Ent Agy
Fabulous Jazz Caverners Complete Ent Serv Ltd
Face 4 Radio Advanced Ents
Face For Radio TMK Mngt & Agcy Ltd
Face Value (Phil Collins) Head On Mngt
Jamie Facer Alexandra Cann Reprsntn
Facta 3 Derek Bruce Ents
Factor X (Boyband Tribute) Dansatak
Factory Floor 13 Artists
Candice Fagan Full Portion Media
Siobhan Fahey Ferrara PR
Joe Fahy Barn Dance Line Dance Agy
Kate Fahy Markham & Froggatt Ltd
Fair Play Continental Drifts/TEST AGENT C
Lynn Fairbairn Grays Mngt & Asc
Christopher Fairbank Markham & Froggatt Ltd
Craig Fairbrass Shining Mngt Ltd/Yakety Yak
Richard Fairbrass Jeremy Hicks Assoc
David Fairclough After Dinner World Ltd/Nigel Round Mgnt/Persnl Appearances
Faire Winds Roots Around The World
Susie Fairfax Nancy Hudson Associates Ltd
Gary Fairhall Royce Mngt
Fairhaven Holiday Cottages SIMON WHITTAM PUBLICITY
Josephine Fairley CHAMPIONS (UK) PLC
Fairly Famous Continental Drifts/TEST AGENT C
Fairport Convention Denis Vaughan Mngt/Jason West Agy/Rock Artist Mngt
Alan Fairs The Music Ptnrshp Ltd
Digby Fairweather's Half Dozen Jazzco
Fairy Tale Theatre B.A.S.I.C.
Faith The Psycho Mngt Co Ltd
Paloma Faith Insanity Artists
The Party Faithful Prima Artists
Faithless Helter Skelter Agy Ltd
Fake Bee Gees Big Bang Mngt Ltd/Upfront Ent Agy Ltd
Fake Rapper Action Talent Int.
Fake That Dansatak/Nigel Round Mgnt/XS Promos
Fakin' Stevens Henderson Mngt
Falcon Norwich Artistes
Jenni Falconer Hackford Jones PR/James Grant Mngt Ltd
Fall out boy Primary Talent Int'l
Andrew Fallaize Kerry Gardner Mngt
'Lucky' Jim Fallon 'Lucky' Jim Fallon (Ind Art)/Walker Promos
Lindsey Fallow Seamus Lyte Management Ltd
Andrew Falvey Susan Angel Kevin Francis Ltd
Georgie Fame The John Boddy Agency
Kelly Family Denis Vaughan Mngt
The Famous Steinhaus Bierkeller Rent-A-Band
John Famworth CHAMPIONS (UK) PLC
Brett Fancy Jonathan Altaras Assoc
Simon Fanshawe Noel Gay Artists Ltd
Fantasia Paul Bailey Agy
Fantazia CKK Ent/Matters Musical
Lionel Fanthorpe (Ind Art) Lionel Fanthorpe
Fapy Lapertin Trio (NL) Wim Wigt Prodns Ltd
Nicole Faraday Susan Angel Kevin Francis Ltd
Meg Faragher ANA
Mo Farah CHAMPIONS (UK) PLC
Don Fardon Howard Olson Promotions
Anna Faris Special Artists Agency
Richard Farleigh NMP Live Ltd/NMP MANAGEMENT
Charlie Farley Partyweb.co.uk
David Farley Clare Vidal-Hall
Reanne Farley Shepherd Mngt Ltd
Terry Farley UK Booking Agy
Chris Farlowe and The Norman Beaker Band Jason West Agy
Sarah Farmer Dance Funki Feathers Agy
Sir Tom Farmer CBE Persnly Spkng
Richard Farnes Ingpen & Williams Ltd
Brian Farnham CASAROTTO RAMSAY & ASSOCIATES
Jane Farnham Blackburn Sachs Assoc
Paul Farnsworth Simpson Fox Assoc Ltd
Anna Farnworth Hilary Gagan Assoc
Adam Farr Markham & Froggatt Ltd
Dean Farrar Chris Gordon Theatrical Agy
Debbie Farrell Trevor George Ents Ltd
Joanne Farrell AIM
Nicholas Farrell Markham & Froggatt Ltd
Nigel Farrell Gordon Poole Agy Ltd
Fascinatin' Rhythm Prima Artists
Michael Fassbender Troika Talent
Fast Love (George Michael Tribute) Peller Artistes Ltd
Fast Parts Barn Dance Line Dance Agy
Fastball Primary Talent Int'l
Fastlane Tony Bennell Ents
Fat Barry's Soul Band Phillips Ent Agy
Fat Chantz Steve Allen Ents
Fat Larry's Soul Band Book A Band
Fat Lizzy (Thin Lizzy tribute) Compact Mngt & Ent Agy/Graham Cole Mngt
Fat Mattress Rock Artist Mngt
Fat Old Dad Fat Old Dad (Ind Art)/NVB Ents/Stardust Ents Agy
Fat Pie Noel Gay Artists Ltd
Fat Tony Persnl Appearances
Fatal Attraction Devil Management/SJS Promos
Fatman Scoop Mission Control Artist Agy
Fats Domino Al Embry Int'l (USA)
Greg Faulkner Shepherd Mngt Ltd
James Faulkner Jonathan Altaras Assoc/Voice Shop
Lisa Faulkner ARG Management
Isabelle Faust Hazard Chase Ltd
Fausto Franco Kevin King Mngt
Adrian Fawcett CHAMPIONS (UK) PLC
Nick Fawcett Fushion Pukka Bosh
John Parkin as Basil Fawlty Prima Artists
Fawlty Towers - Edmond Wells as John Cleese (Ind Art) Fawlty Towers
Amanda Fawsett Vincent Shaw Assoc Ltd
Cecily Fay CKK Ent
Susan Fay Jeffrey & White
Gaynor Faye CAM London/Urban Associates Personal Mana
Stephanie Fayerman The Richard Stone Prtnrshp
FBI Ultimate Int'l
The F.B.I. (Blues Brothers/Commitments tribute) The Psycho Mngt Co Ltd

G

Entertainers Mgt Ltd
Lisa George Gerald Goss Ltd
Lynne George TMK Mngt & Agcy Ltd
Melissa George RDF Management
The George Michael Band Michael La Roche Mngt
Mohammed George Rossmore Persnl Mngt
Steven George Indep Mngt Ltd
Tom George Sandra Boyce Mngt
Richard Georgeson Dennis Lyne Agy
Georgia Moonglight Agy
Georgia & The McSmiths LJ Ents
Georgia Jazzmen Quality Ents
The Georgia Satellites AIM Inc (USA)
Michael Georgiades (Classical Guitarist) ABC Direct Ents
Georgie Star (Sinatra, Dean Martin + more) Advanced Ents
Jo Gerard North Of Watford Actors Agy
Malcolm Gerard West Central Mngt
PY Gerbeau CHAMPIONS (UK) PLC/Parliament Comms/Prof Sports Ptnr Ltd
Vassily Gerello Askonas Holt Ltd
Jose Maria Gererro Derek Boulton Productions
Larissa Gergieva Askonas Holt Ltd
Roswitha Gerlitz Performing Arts
Lisa Germano Gold Star PR
Dominique Gerrard Inspiration Mngt
Lisa Gerrard 4.A.D.
Tony Gerrard Compact Mngt & Ent Agy/Highfield Mngt & Promos/Tony Bennell Ents/Ultimate Int'l
Tilly Gerrard-Bannister Speak-Easy Ltd
Gerry George Johnny Mans Prods Ltd
Gerry The Flute Gerry The Flute (Ind Art)
Gerry & The Pacemakers BCM Promos Ltd/BULLET MANAGEMENT LIMITED/Barry Collings Ents/Chimes Int'l Ents Ltd/Entertainers Mgt Ltd/John Hessenthaler Ents/Paul Bridson Prods
Gershwin Gang Book A Band
Gertie Glitter Partyweb.co.uk
Ricky Gervais Peters Fraser Dunlop (PFD)/Speakout/United Agents
Get Cape Wear Cape Fly Free Trade Agy
Get Down On It Book A Band/Complete Ent Serv Ltd/Jason West Agy
Get Down On It (Kool & The Gang Tribute) Andrew Beauchamp Mngt
Tanveer Ghani Nancy Hudson Associates Ltd
Roann Ghosh Avalon Mngt
Lucia Giannecchini Brunskill Management Ltd
Giant Games Edge Ent Cons Ltd
The Giant Penguins CKK Ent/Continental Drifts/TEST AGENT C
Giant Sand ABS Agy/Hermana PR
Giant Steps Purple PR
The Giants Of Jazz Jazzco
Louise Gibb CKK Ent
Piers Gibbon Speak-Easy Ltd
Derek Gibbons Downes Presenters Agy
Geoff Gibbons BAM Assoc Ltd
Mandi Gibbons Celebn Ents Mngt & Agy
Steve Gibbons Rock Artist Mngt
Steve Gibbons Band Jason West Agy
Joyce Gibbs M W Management
Julie Gibbs Cardiff Casting
Alexandra Gibson Hazard Chase Ltd
Gibson Brothers Brian Gannon Mngt/Jason West Agy
Georgia Gibson Anita Alraun Representation
Gary Gibson (John Lennon) Nigel Round Mgnt
Michael Gibson Form Talent
Paul Gibson Sunshine Ents
Richie Gibson AIM
Cicely Giddings RDF Management
Gidea Park (Beach Boys tribute) Apple County/Barry Collings Ents/Brian Gannon Mngt/Entertainers Mgt Ltd/Henderson Mngt/Jason West Agy/McLeod Agy Ltd/NVB Ents/PVA Ent Consultants/Pete Mitchell Associates/Prima Artists/Stars In Your Eyes Ltd Ent Agy
Liewella Gideon Judy Daish Assoc
Mel Giedroyc Independent Talent Group Ltd
Michael Gielen Ingpen & Williams Ltd
Kathie Lee Gifford William Morris Inc (USA)
Roland Gift Primary Talent Int'l
Giggles The A6 Agy
Alan Gilbert IMG Artists
Faye Gilbert Judy Daish Assoc
Kenneth Gilbert Elinor Hilton Associates
Oliver Gilbert Actorum
Rhod Gilbert Comedy Store Mngt
Bebel Gilberto Primary Talent Int'l
Alexandra Gilbreath Yakety Yak
Alan Gilchrist Int'l Artistes Ltd
Eric Gilchrist Jazz and Blues Quintet CS Ents
James Gilchrist Hazard Chase Ltd
Brad Gilderman Sarm Mngt
Alexander Giles Vincent Shaw Assoc Ltd
Bill Giles All Electric Productions & Dav/Arena Ent Cons/Celebrity Appearances/Gordon Poole Agy Ltd/Limelight Management/PVA Ent Consultants/Persnly Spkng
Samatha Giles AIM
Rodney Gilfry Askonas Holt Ltd
Joe Gilgun (Eli, Emmerdale) Nigel Round Mgnt
Jo Gilgun Laine Mngt Ltd
Joseph Gilgun Big Bang Mngt Ltd/Insanity Artists
Brenda Gilhooly Avalon Mngt
Eliza Gilkyson Roots Around The World
Dominic Gill Speakout
Helen Gill AIM
John Gill - Retired Daly Pearson Associates
Lucinda Gill Liz Hobbs Grp Ltd
Merry-May Gill Line-Up PMC
Peter Gill CASAROTTO RAMSAY & ASSOCIATES
Peter Gill Jazz Band Tony Bennell Ents
Ian Gillan CODA Ltd
John Gillan Nigel Round Mgnt
Dana Gillespie GTA Music Cons & Agy
David Gillespie Jonathan Altaras Assoc
Grant Gillespie The Richard Stone Prtnrshp
Kate Gillespie Burnett Granger Assoc
Kim Gillespie Central Line Co-Op Persnl Mngt
Aden Gillett Cassie Mayer Ltd/Lip Service Casting Ltd
Geoff Gillett Hartbeat Ents Ltd
John Gillett Sara Crouch Mngt
Gillettes Global Ent Agy
Mickey Gilley Al Embry Int'l (USA)
Terry Gilliam CASAROTTO RAMSAY & ASSOCIATES
Marie Gillian Tavistock Wood Management Ltd
Mary Gilliatt Limelight Management
Nicky Gillibrand Loesje Sanders
Nick Gillingham MBE Celebrity Appearances/Jon Holmes Media Ltd/Persnly Spkng
Grainne Gillis Brian Taylor Assoc
Caroline Gillmer Darren Gray Mngt
Delphine Gillot Stafford Law
Gilly Dave Woodbury Ents/Martin Ents
Ewen Gilmor Paramount Int'l Mngt
Effie Gilmore APM Ass
Jimmie Dale Gilmore Asgard
Thea Gilmore Asgard
David Gilmour One Fifteen/The Agency Group
Emma Gilmour Peter Charlesworth & Assoc
Gerard Gilroy Nancy Hudson Associates Ltd
Gordon Giltrap Rock Artist Mngt/Speaking Volumes
Joe Giltrap Matters Musical
Ginger Beard Circus Albert Alchemy Ent
Gingerbeer Shindig Barn Dance Line Dance Agy
Gingernutt the Clown Ian & Friends/John Field - Theatre and Puppe/Partyweb.co.uk
Gipsy Kings Denis Vaughan Mngt/PVA Ent Consultants
Taff Girdlestone The Voice Box Agency Ltd
Girl Ambition JB Ents
The Girl from Nutbush Henderson Mngt
Girl from Nutbush (Tina Turner) Camscott Leisure
Laura Girling Kerry Gardner Mngt
Girls from Abbaland Andrew Beauchamp Mngt
Girls Roc Insanity Artists
Guy Gisbourne Derek Bruce Ents
Junior Giscombe Barry Collings Ents
Hilary Gish Shepherd Mngt Ltd
James Gitsham Stage Centre Mngt
Jeremy Gittins AIM/Susan Angel Kevin Francis Ltd
Rob Gittins Jill Foster Ltd
Characters from Give My Head Peace David Hull Promos Ltd
Give My Regards To Jolson A.I.R. Ltd
Adele Givens ICM (USA)/United Talent Agency
Craig Givens Loesje Sanders
Olayinka Giwa City Actors Mngt
Gladiator Jousting PVA Ent Consultants
Nathan Gladwell Amber Persnl Mngt Ltd
Philip Gladwell Clare Vidal-Hall
Gabrielle Glaister Emptage Hallett Ltd
Glam & Glitz Compact Mngt & Ent Agy/David Charles Agy
Glam R Us Continental Drifts/TEST AGENT C
Glam Stars Andrew Beauchamp Mngt
Glamarama NVB Ents
Glambusters Entertainers Mgt Ltd
Glamo Hireaband Ltd
Glamrus John Bedford Ents Ltd
Glamtastic Complete Ent Serv Ltd/Goldstar Ent UK
Glamtastics Norwich Artistes
Dr Lucy Glancey MCS Agcy
Jo Glanville Blackburn Limelight Management
Susannah Glanville Askonas Holt Ltd
Jim Glaser Deri Promos
Ty Glaser BWH Agency
Glasgow Phoenix Choir BGS PRODUC-TIONS
Briony Glassco The Richard Stone Prtnrshp
GLC Soundsystem Action Talent Int.
Katy Gleadhill Cassie Mayer Ltd
Jenny Gleave BWH Agency

Nicholas Gleaves Cassie Mayer Ltd/Lip Service Casting Ltd/Troika Talent
Karen Gledhill Performance Actors Agy
Glee Purple PR
Seán Gleeson Jonathan Altaras Assoc
Glen Fiddich Compact Mngt & Ent Agy
Robbie Glen Arena Ent Cons/Gordon Poole Agy Ltd/Peter De Rance/Speakout
Gordon Glenn Gordon Glenn (Ind Art)
Sammy Glenn Brunskill Management Ltd
Anthony Glennon Adrian King Assoc
Glitter Band BULLET MANAGEMENT LIMITED
The Glitter Band Brian Gannon Mngt/Graham Cole Mngt/Jason West Agy/John Hessenthaler Ents/PVA Ent Consultants
Glitterball
Glitz Blitz & 70's Hits The Flying Music Co Ltd
Gloria (the half-living lady) Mr Magic Ents (Magic)
Glory Days (Bruce Springstein) Head On Mngt
New Found Glory ITB
Gloucester Excelsior Band Derek Bruce Ents
Gloucester Police Band Derek Bruce Ents
Elaine Glover Susan Angel Kevin Francis Ltd
Jon Glover Daly Pearson Associates
Julian Glover Conway Van Gelder Grant Ltd
Julie Glover ICON Actors Mngt
Kate Glover Crescent Mngt
Richard Glover Karushi Mngt
The Go! Team Asgard
Go West including Peter Cox BULLET MANAGEMENT LIMITED/Barry Collings Ents/Blueprint Mngt/Jason West Agy/Miracle Artists Ltd/Mission Control Artist Agy/Peller Artistes Ltd/The Psycho Mngt Co Ltd
Gobbie Williams Ultimate Int'l
God Awfuls Primary Talent Int'l
Pascal Godart Transart (UK) Ltd
Beth Goddard Cassie Mayer Ltd
Sarah Goddard Stage Centre Mngt
Steve "Good" Goddard (Soul & Funk) UK Booking Agy
Godfatha (James Brown tribute) Jason West Agy
The Godfathers Autonomous Talent Bkg
Jeremy Godfrey Wise Buddah Music Radio Ltd
Natasha Godfrey BAM Assoc Ltd/Nancy Hudson Associates Ltd
Patrick Godfrey Markham & Froggatt Ltd
Janey Godley Int'l Artistes Ltd
Anna Godsiff Speak-Easy Ltd
Godsmack ITB
Christopher Godwin Daly Pearson Associates
Patricia Godwin - Talks for afterdinner & other such occasions Palm Court Thtre Prods
Tom Godwin Daly Pearson Associates
Glen Goei Markham & Froggatt Ltd
Chris Goffey Celebrity Appearances/Persnly Spkng
Valerie Gogan Yakety Yak
Simon Gogerly Stephen Budd Mngt
The Go-Go's Tony Denton Promos Ltd
Going Back Talent One
Alex Gold UK Booking Agy
Black & Gold Matters Musical
Gold Dust NVB Ents
Gold Fingers (Magician & Caricaturist) Doub7e Seven Events Ltd
Graham Gold Talking Heads - The Voice Agy
Jacqueline Gold CHAMPIONS (UK) PLC/NMP Live Ltd/Panic Management
Louise Gold Cassie Mayer Ltd/Gavin Barker/Lip Service Casting Ltd
Martin Gold After Dinner Spkers & Com
Mike Gold Derek Bruce Ents/Kevin King Mngt/NVB Ents
Steffi Gold MJE Mngt
Adrian Goldberg Knight Ayton Mngt
Whoopi Goldberg William Morris Inc (USA)
Craig Goldblatt CHAMPIONS (UK) PLC
Jeff Goldblum Special Artists Agency
Roger Goldby CASAROTTO RAMSAY & ASSOCIATES
Golden Age of Music Hall Show Stardust Ents Agy
The Golden Chords Monkeybiz Ent Agy
Golden Eagle Archery Display (minstrels troup) Gown & Gauntlet Promos
Golden Girl Sardi's Int'l Ent
Karl Golden CASAROTTO RAMSAY & ASSOCIATES
Sydney Golder Anita Alraun Representation
Michael Goldfarb Speak-Easy Ltd
Katie Goldfinch Agency K-Bis
Goldfinger The Agency Group
Chris Goldfinger (Radio One FM) Monkeybiz Ent Agy
Goldfrapp Purple PR
Goldie Eddie Lock
Dominik Golding SCA Mngt
Everick Golding Sandra Boyce Mngt
Jeanne Golding Otto Persnl Mngt Ltd
Goldner String Quartet Ingpen & Williams Ltd
Harvey Goldsmith CBE Kruger Cowne Limited/Parliament Comms
Andy Goldstein Princess Talent Mngt
Brett Goldstein Wendy Lee Mngt
John Golightly Audrey Benjamin Agy
Maria Golledge City Actors Mngt
Bella Gomez Fushion Pukka Bosh
Chad Gomez Grays Mngt & Asc
Sharon Gomez Vincent Shaw Assoc Ltd
Sisco Gomez Curtis Brown Grp
Jeanette Gondry (Harpist) The John Boddy Agency
Stella Gonet Markham & Froggatt Ltd
Gonzales Ensemble Rent-A-Band
Gonzalez Jason West Agy
John Gonzalez Seamus Lyte Management Ltd
Pablo González Patrick Garvey Mngt
Goo Goo Dolls Kas Mercer/Mercenary PR
Graham Gooch OBE After Dinner World Ltd/Arena Ent Cons/CHAMPIONS (UK) PLC/Gordon Poole Agy Ltd/NMP Live Ltd/Paul Bridson Prods/Persnly Spkng
Robin Good Angle Ents Ltd/Devil Management
Good Rockin' Tonight Funhouse Productions Ltd/Matters Musical/Paul Barrett Rock'N'Roll Entp
Good Shoes Free Trade Agy/Insanity Artists
The Good Time Jazz Band Rent-A-Band
Good Vibrations Henderson Mngt
Tony Goodacre Band Sylvantone Promos
Tony Goodacre Sylvantone Promos
Caroline Goodall Peters Fraser Dunlop (PFD)
Robin Goodchild Paul Duddridge Mngt
Tim Goodchild Simpson Fox Assoc Ltd
Graham Goode Persnl Appearances
Duncan Goodhew MBE Arena Ent Cons/Athole Still Int'l Ltd/Celebrity Appearances/Gordon Poole Agy Ltd/Parliament Comms/Persnl Appearances/Persnly Spkng/Speakout/TEST AGENT A
Mark Goodier Hyper Agency/The Psycho Mngt Co Ltd/Wise Buddah Talent & Voices
Goodison Avenue Goldstar Ent UK
Paul Goodison MBE MTC (UK) LTD
David Goodland Red Sky Prods
Henry Goodman ARG Management
Jan Goodman Yakety Yak
Joe Goodman London Music Agy/Persnl Appearances/Triple Cream Ents
Louise Goodman DBA Speakers/Jane Morgan Mngt Ltd
Sally Goodman MBA
Sean Goodman Norwich Artistes
Tim Goodman Alpha Persnl Mngt
Delta Goodrem Joanna Burns PR
Daisy Goodwin Taylor Herring Public Relation
Daniel Goodwin Derek Bruce Ents
Paul Goodwin Askonas Holt Ltd
Richard Goodwin Audrey Benjamin Agy
Peter Goodwright Johnny Mans Prods Ltd
Bob Goody Judy Daish Assoc
Martin Goodyer Gordon Poole Agy Ltd
Jilly Goolden Celebrity Appearances/Jeremy Hicks Assoc/Persnly Spkng
Claire Goose CAM London
Goosehorns Book A Band/Yorkshire Ent
Mikhail Gorbachev Parliament Comms
John Gordillo Off The Kerb Prods
Gordon & His Organ Hire-A-Band Ent Agy
Clive Gordon Alexandra Cann Reprsntn
Hannah Gordon Conway Van Gelder Grant Ltd
Jon Gordon Jon Gordon (Magic)
Ruth Gordon Yellow Balloon Prods Ltd
Serena Gordon Cassie Mayer Ltd
Penny Gore Talking Heads - The Voice Agy
Gorillaz CMO Mngt Int'l Ltd
Chris Goring MTM Presntns
Demetri Goritsas Lip Service Casting Ltd
Dave Gorman Avalon Mngt
Kate Gorman Darren Gray Mngt
Reg Gorman Darren Gray Mngt
Christina Gorna Jacque Evans Mngt Ltd
John Gorrie Kerry Gardner Mngt
Sandy Gort Jeremy Hicks Assoc
Pete Goss MBE Speakout
Howard Gossington Burnett Granger Assoc
Gossip Big Sister Promotions
Nicola Gossip Lime Actors Agy & Mngt Ltd
Harry Gostelow Shepherd Mngt Ltd
Cornelia Götz Athole Still Int'l Ltd/TEST AGENT A
Darren Gough CHAMPIONS (UK) PLC
Maria Gough Amber Persnl Mngt Ltd
Mark Gough Speak-Easy Ltd
Samuel Gough Hilary Gagan Assoc
Sandra Gough Nyland Mngt
Abdi Gouhad Adrian King Assoc
Gould Piano Trio Clarion/Seven Muses
Robbie Gould Phillips Ent Agy
Ellie Goulding Insanity Artists
Jon-Sel Gourkan Elinor Hilton

Associates
David Gower OBE Celebrity Appearances/Jon Holmes Media Ltd/Parliament Comms/Persnly Spkng
John Gower M W Management
Nik Gowing Performing Artistes
Edward Grace Frontline Mngt Ltd
Gary Grace Matters Musical/Norwich Artistes
Helen Grace Gavin Barker
Laura Grace A.I.R. Ltd
Nickolas Grace Yakety Yak
Sally Grace Voice Shop
Charlie Gracie Paul Barrett Rock'N'Roll Entp
Gracious K Insanity Artists
Grada Adastra
Michael Grade Inspirational Artiste Bkg
Timothy O'Grady & 'I Could Read The Sky' (Ireland) Adastra
Wayne Grady MPC Ent
Philippe Graffin Caroline Baird Artists
The Graffiti Classics CKK Ent/Graffiti Classics (Ind Art)
Graffiti Classics Matters Musical
Anita Graham The Richard Stone Prtnrshp
David Graham Talking Heads - The Voice Agy
Eve Graham McLeod Agy Ltd
Geoff Graham Peter De Rance
Gerry Graham Norwich Artistes
Graham Gouldman & Friends Miracle Artists Ltd
Herol Bomber Graham (Boxing) Doub7e Seven Events Ltd
Jaki Graham BCM Promos Ltd/Big Bang Mngt Ltd/Direct Music Mngt Ltd/Jason West Agy
Julie Graham Sally Hope Assoc
Kate Graham Gavin Barker
Katy Graham Agency K-Bis
Lesley Graham Jon Holmes Media Ltd/Liz Hobbs Grp Ltd
Mikey Graham Peter Charlesworth & Assoc
Polly Graham Panic Management
Richard Graham Talking Heads - The Voice Agy
Sam Graham Cassie Mayer Ltd
Tom Graham Louise Hillman/Katie Threlfall
The Grahamophones Jason West Agy
Chris Grahamson ICON Actors Mngt
Glynn Grain Shepherd Mngt Ltd
Andy Grainger Shining Mngt Ltd
Gawn Grainger Judy Daish Assoc
Gramma Funk Action Talent Int.
Grand Drive Free Trade Agy
The Grand Theatre of Lemmings CKK Ent/Fool's Paradise/Grand Thtre Lemmngs (Ind Art)/MTM Presntns
Grand Theatre of Lemmings Viscount Ents
Emma Granger London Music Agy
Steve Granger MGA Entp
Amanda Grant Model Plan Celebrities & Prese/Take Three Mngt
Barbara Grant Anita Alraun Representation
Bob Grant Barrie Stacey Promos & Prods
Brendan Grant Complete Ent Serv Ltd
Carrie Grant Taylor Herring Public Relation
Grant 'Daddy G' Marshall Ferrara PR
Gerry Grant (Roy Orbison) Compact Mngt & Ent Agy/McLeod Agy Ltd
Glen Grant London Music Agy
Jonny Grant Reality Check Management
Mark Grant CASAROTTO RAMSAY & ASSOCIATES
Mitchell Grant Philip Youd Ents & Mngt
Murray Grant Liz Hobbs Grp Ltd
Peter Grant Personality Artistes Ltd
Richard E Grant Independent Talent Group Ltd
Simon Grant Wise Buddah Talent & Voices
Tony Grant (Freddie Mercury tribute) Advanced Ents/European Artistes Mngt
Barry Grantham Audrey Benjamin Agy
Cathy Grantham Agency K-Bis
Leslie Grantham Michael Whitehall
Gillie Gratham Billboard Persnl Mngt
Harry Gration After Dinner World Ltd/Arena Ent Cons
Andy Gratton Celebrity Chefs UK
Trystan Gravelle Brunskill Mngt Ltd
The Gravelly Hillbillies The Agency Group
Tiffany Graves Burnett Granger Assoc
Andy Gray CHAMPIONS (UK) PLC/Shepherd Mngt Ltd
Arnold Gray Barn Dance Line Dance Agy
Cory Gray Central Ents
Elspet Gray Burnett Granger Assoc
Fenton Gray Burnett Granger Assoc
Ian Gray Peller Artistes Ltd
Linda Gray Roger Carey Assoc
Macy Gray Tribute Band Bulrush Mngt
Natasha Gray Burnett Granger Assoc
Simon Gray Judy Daish Assoc
Grease Is The Word Upfront Ent Agy Ltd
Greased (Greece show tribute) Andrew Beauchamp Mngt
Greased Lightning Henderson Mngt/Jason West Agy/Stardust Ents Agy/The Psycho Mngt Co Ltd/Upbeat Entertainment
The Great British Jazz Band Jazzco
The Great British Street Show Lawrenson & Barnard (Ind Art)
Great Britney Jason West Agy
Great Divide Buddy Lee Attrctns Inc (USA)
Emmy The Great Asgard
Great Glam Mothers The Dixon Agy
Great Legends of Rock Chance Promos
The Great Tymoni Boo Boo's Entertainments
Great Western Marching Band PVA Ent Consultants
Hilary Greatorex Performance Actors Agy
Amy Greaves Amy Greaves (Ind Art)
Angie Greaves Shining Mngt Ltd
Bob Greaves David Anthony Promos
Van Greaves Derek Bruce Ents
Buddy Greco Jean Levy PR Agency
Michael Greco Neon Management
Al Green William Morris Inc (USA)
Andy Green (world landspeed record) DBA Speakers
Chris Green CASAROTTO RAMSAY & ASSOCIATES
David Green Independent Talent Group Ltd
Green Day Creative Artists Agency
Green Dayz The Psycho Mngt Co Ltd
Eva Green Endeavor Agency/Premier PR/Tavistock Wood Management Ltd
Henrietta Green Celebrity Chefs UK/Jacque Evans Mngt Ltd
Jeff Green Off The Kerb Prods/Speakout
John Green Blujay Mngt Ltd
Jonathan Green PARAGON SPORTS MANAGEMENT LTD
The Leo Green Experience LM2 Entertainment
Lucinda Green MBE Celebrity Appearances/Persnly Spkng
Matt Green Noel Gay Artists Ltd/The Richard Stone Prtnrshp
Nigel Green Sarm Mngt
Paul Green RBA Management Ltd
Peter Green Splinter Group Jason West Agy
The Green Road Show OTB Prods
Simon Green Gavin Barker
Sue Green Talking Heads - The Voice Agy
Teddy Green Jeffrey & White
Tony Green Paul Madeley/Persnl Appearances
Tracy Green Actorum
Joyce Greenaway Actorum
Brian Greene Burnett Granger Assoc/Talking Heads - The Voice Agy
James Greene Susan Angel Kevin Francis Ltd
Leon Greene Jeffrey & White
Paddy Greene After Dinner Spkers & Com
Sarah Greene Conway Van Gelder Grant Ltd
Chris Greener Paul Madeley
Baroness Susan Greenfield Gordon Poole Agy Ltd
Prof Susan Greenfield Knight Ayton Mngt
Fay Greenhalgh Fushion Pukka Bosh
Kevin Greening Wise Buddah Talent & Voices
Culver Greenridge Cunningham Mngt Ltd
Heidi Greensmith CASAROTTO RAMSAY & ASSOCIATES
Greenwood Hire-A-Band Ent Agy
Amanda Greenwood BTM Mngt & Agy
Andrew Greenwood Athole Still Int'l Ltd/TEST AGENT A
Debbie Greenwood Jane Hughes Mngt
Karl Greenwood ICON Actors Mngt
Lisa Greenwood COLE KITCHENN PRSN MGT
Pippa Greenwood Arlington Enterprises Ltd
Will Greenwood MBE CHAMPIONS (UK) PLC
Darren Greer Dennis Lyne Agy
Prof Germain Greer Prime Performers Ltd
Christopher Greet Shepherd Mngt Ltd
Greggie G & Grazy Gang The Ents Agency
Constantine Gregory Emptage Hallett Ltd
John Gregory Athole Still Int'l Ltd/TEST AGENT A
Philippa Gregory Independent Talent Group Ltd
Roxy Gregory Celebn Model Mngt
Simon Gregson Langford Assoc
Victoria Gregson Dance Funki Feathers Agy
Stephen Greif Yakety Yak
David Greig CASAROTTO RAMSAY & ASSOCIATES
Tamsin Greig Sally Hope Assoc
Greta & The Stray Shots Folk Ents Ltd
Kumall Grewal Sandra Boyce Mngt
Sally Grey Kerry Gardner Mngt
The Greyhound Monkeybiz Ent Agy
Steve Gribbin Off The Kerb Prods
Tom Gribby Barrie Stacey Promos &

Prods
Rhian Grice M W Management
Guy Grieve Independent Talent Group Ltd
Richard Grieve Bronia Buchanan Ass
David Griffin Bernard Hunter Assoc
Gary Griffin Simpson Fox Assoc Ltd
Gordon Griffin Hilary Gagan Assoc
Johnny Griffin Wim Wigt Prodns Ltd
Kathy Griffin ICM (USA)
Patty Griffin Asgard
Steve (Street) Griffin Steve Griffin (Ind Art)
Bruce Griffiths Paramount Int'l Mngt
Derek Griffiths Yakety Yak
Emma Griffiths Princess Talent Mngt
Griff Griffiths ENTERTAINMENT FX/Emlyn 'Griff' Griffiths
Hilary Griffiths Athole Still Int'l Ltd/TEST AGENT A
Jaye Griffiths Harvey Voices Ltd
Lee Griffiths As Bobby Darin Entertainers Mgt Ltd
Ciaran Griffiths (Micky, Shamless) Nigel Round Mgnt
Terry Griffiths OBE Persnl Appearances
Picasso Griffiths CKK Ent
Rachel Griffiths Markham & Froggatt Ltd
Richard Griffiths Michael Whitehall
Roger Griffiths Emptage Hallett Ltd
Sara Griffiths Harvey Voices Ltd
Colin Griffiths-Brown Shining Mngt Ltd
Yuri Grignoff MTM Presntns
Sophie Grigson Deborah McKenna Ltd
David Grimal Transart (UK) Ltd
Ian Grimble Stephen Budd Mngt
Grimes 13 Artists
Frank Grimes Kerry Gardner Mngt
The Grimethorpe Colliery Band Arena Ent Cons
The Grimleys Entertainers Mgt Ltd
Leonid Grin IMG Artists
Ilya Gringolts IMG Artists
Grinnigogs Albert Alchemy Ent/Grinnigogs (Ind Art)/Matters Musical/Rent-A-Band
Michael Grinter Links Mngt
Grip Inc Miracle Artists Ltd
John Grisham Prime Performers Ltd
Tony Grisoni CASAROTTO RAMSAY & ASSOCIATES
Susan Gritton Askonas Holt Ltd
Vsevolod Grivnov Askonas Holt Ltd
Kemi-Anne Groarke Jonathan Altaras Assoc
Jurgen Grobler Gordon Poole Agy Ltd
Clare Grogan United Agents
Simon Groom Downes Presenters Agy
Blue Groove Prima Artists
Groove Central Grand CS Ents
The Groove Company CS Ents
Groove Company Stardust Ents Agy
Groove Nation CHAMPIONS (UK) PLC
Groovejuice Jason West Agy/John Hessenthaler Ents/Matters Musical
Grooverider Palestar Entertainment
Groovies Ghost Int'l Mngt & Agy Ltd
Groovin' High Spotlight Ents
Groovy Movie Continental Drifts/TEST AGENT C/The Dixon Agy
Andrew Grose Amber Persnl Mngt Ltd
Petite Et La Gross Matters Musical
Rebecca Gross Denmark Street Mngt
Loyd Grossman Celebrity Appearances/Persnly Spkng/Peter Schnabl
The Groundhogs Jason West Agy
Grouper Matters Musical
Hannah Grover Adrian King Assoc
David Groves Michelle Braidman Assoc
Kelly Groves Agency K-Bis
Ricky Groves Big Bang Mngt Ltd/Waring & Mckenna
Bryony Growden Fushion Pukka Bosh
Tom Grren Int'l Artistes Ltd
Andy Grubbs Audrey Benjamin Agy
Grumbleweeds Int'l Artistes Ltd
The Grumbleweeds Non Stop Ents
Grumbleweeds Paul Bridson Prods
Bear Grylls CHAMPIONS (UK) PLC/Cunningham Mngt Ltd/Gordon Poole Agy Ltd/NMP Live Ltd/Persnly Spkng/Speakout/The London Spkr Bureau
Edward 'Bear' Grylls Trading Faces Ltd
Pippa Guard The Richard Stone Prtnrshp
Guarneri Quartet Ingpen & Williams Ltd
Tony Gubba NMP Live Ltd/PVA Ent Consultants/Persnl Appearances
Eidur Gudjohnsen Athole Still Int'l Ltd/TEST AGENT A
Ann Guedes Judy Daish Assoc
Maggie Guess Grays Mngt & Asc
Jo Guest Samantha Bond Management
David Guetta ITB
Guildford Philharmonic N.B. Mngt
Guildhall Strings Hazard Chase Ltd
Lesley Guinness (Edina from Ab Fab) Mike Malley Ents
Lesley Guinness Prima Artists
Lesley Guinness (Edina from Ab Fab) Prima Artists
Leslie Guinness Partyweb.co.uk
The Guitar Orchestra Park Promotions
Guitarras Latinas Latin Arts Serv (LAS)
Guizer Scottish Music Int'l Artistes Ltd/Rent-A-Band
Roopa Gulati Jeremy Hicks Assoc
Shobna Gulati Burnett Granger Assoc
Maria Guleghina Askonas Holt Ltd
Jimmy Gulzar Upfront TV Ltd
Mickey Gunn Leo Mngt & Agy
Mike Gunn Comedy Store Mngt
Nathan Gunn Ingpen & Williams Ltd
Peter Gunn Brown & Simcocks
Sally Gunnell OBE CHAMPIONS (UK) PLC/DBA Speakers/MTC (UK) LTD/NMP Live Ltd/Speakout
Dave Gunson Speakout
David Gunson After Dinner World Ltd/Arena Ent Cons/Gordon Poole Agy Ltd/Gordon Robinson Assoc/McLeod Agy Ltd/NMP Live Ltd/PVA Ent Consultants/Persnl Appearances/Persnly Spkng
Ashley Gunstock Anita Alraun Representation
Ben Gunstone Nick Allen Mngt
John Gunter Performing Arts
Gupo Azteca Mexican Mariachi Latin Arts Serv (LAS)
Yana Gupta Jazz Barton Agency
Jane Gurnett Hamilton Hodell Ltd
Krishnan Guru-Murthy NMP Live Ltd/Noel Gay Artists Ltd
Jeremy Guscott CHAMPIONS (UK) PLC/Celebrity Appearances/Persnly Spkng
Paul Guthrie The Voice Box Agency Ltd
Steve Guttenberg Tony Clayman Promos
Reg Gutteridge OBE Fighting Talk Promos
Fran Guy Harvey Voices Ltd
François-Frédéric Guy International Classical Artist
Jennifer Guy Adrian King Assoc
Lionel Guyett Performance Actors Agy
Guys n' Dolls Brian Gannon Mngt/Kevin King Mngt
Gwalia Welsh Male Voice Choir London Music Agy
GWAR Scream Promotions
Brian Gwaspari Nancy Hudson Associates Ltd
Gwerinos Roots Around The World
Tammi Gwyn Louise Hillman/Katie Threlfall
Haydn Gwynne Markham & Froggatt Ltd
David Gyimah Jacque Evans Mngt Ltd
Gypsy PVA Ent Consultants
Gypsy & the Cat Purple PR
Gypsy Ensemble Latin Arts Serv (LAS)
Gypsy Jazz Matters Musical
Gypsy Kingdom Latin-Touch Ents
The Gypsy Kingdom Upbeat Entertainment
Gypsy's Kiss PVA Ent Consultants

H

Robbi 'H' CeeBee Variety Agy
Esther Haase Penny Rich
Rebecca Hackenberg SCA Mngt
Claire Hackett Jonathan Altaras Assoc
Leah Hackett Big Bang Mngt Ltd
Gene Hackman Special Artists Agency
The Hackney Ramblers Matters Musical
Kasia Haddad Sandra Boyce Mngt
Haddaway Jason West Agy
Pen Haddow CHAMPIONS (UK) PLC/DBA Speakers/Jeremy Hicks Assoc/PARAGON SPORTS MANAGEMENT LTD/Speakout
Krystof Hadek Markham & Froggatt Ltd
Cheryl Hadley Trevor George Ents Ltd
Tony Hadley BULLET MANAGEMENT LIMITED/Barry Collings Ents/Blueprint Mngt/Jason West Agy/Miracle Artists Ltd/Mission Control Artist Agy/Peller Artistes Ltd/The Psycho Mngt Co Ltd
Toby Hadoke The Narrow Road Company Ltd
Linal Haft Burnett Granger Assoc
Daisy Haggard Markham & Froggatt Ltd
Piers Haggard CASAROTTO RAMSAY & ASSOCIATES
Viviane Hagner International Classical Artist
William Hague MP JLA/Speakout
Hilary Hahn IMG Artists
David Haig Peters Fraser Dunlop (PFD)
Colin Haigh Anita Alraun Representation
Kenneth Haigh Peter Charlesworth & Assoc
Gary Hailes Adrian King Assoc/Cherry Parker Management
Phil and Simon Hailes Derek Bruce Ents
Emmanuelle Haim IMG Artists
Matt Haimovitz Transart (UK) Ltd
Alan Haines Royce Mngt
Ken Haines John Field - Theatre and Puppe
Ken Haines' Moving Tales John Field - Theatre and Puppe
Lindsay Haines Sandra Boyce Mngt
Luke Haines CEC Management/The Agency Group
Hair Of The Dog Complete Ent Serv Ltd
Bernard Haitink Askonas Holt Ltd
Stelios Haji-Ioannou Parliament Comms
Mika Hakkinen (Lookalike) Business Evt Mngt
Boka Halat Roots Around The World
Hale & Pace Int'l Artistes Ltd
Amanda Hale Markham & Froggatt Ltd

Charlie Hale After Dinner Spkers & Com
Rachel Hale Jeffrey & White
Sandra Hale Anita Alraun Representation
Halebopp Jazz Duo Hire-A-Band Ent Agy
Peter Hales NVB Ents
Halesowen Brass Band Derek Bruce Ents
Phil Haley & His Comments BCM Promos Ltd
The Half Human Video Show Fool's Paradise
Jill Halfpenny Scott Marshall Partners Ltd
Kate Halfpenny ROAR Group
Alex Hall Direct Persnl Mngt
Alvin Hall Take Three Mngt
Andrew Hall Kerry Gardner Mngt
Audrey Hall Monkeybiz Ent Agy
Deborah Hall Arlington Enterprises Ltd
Edward Hall The Richard Stone Prtnrshp
Eric Hall Persnl Appearances
Joe Hall BAM Assoc Ltd
Lynden David Hall Roedean Music/Tony Hall Grp Of Cos
Megan Hall Shepherd Mngt Ltd
Natasha Hall (from 'Strictly Dance Fever) CKK Ent
Peter Ruthven Hall Associated Arts
Rebecca Hall Julian Belfrage Assoc
Rich Hall aka Otis Lee Crenshaw Off The Kerb Prods
Roger Hall CASAROTTO RAMSAY & ASSOCIATES
Steve Hall Avalon Mngt
Stuart Hall Arena Ent Cons/Jane Hughes Mngt
Suzanne Hall Lime Actors Agy & Mngt Ltd
Terry Hall (The Specials) Ferrara PR
Vicky Hall Susan Angel Kevin Francis Ltd
William Hall Johnny Mans Prods Ltd
Suzy Hallam Nyland Mngt
Seetha Hallet RDF Management
Andrew Hallett Kerry Gardner Mngt
Andrew Halliday Burnett Granger Assoc
Jilly Halliday Jane Hughes Mngt
Liz Halliday MCS Agcy
Liam Halligan Knight Ayton Mngt
Kathryn Halliwell CKK Ent
Steve Halliwell Big Bang Mngt Ltd
Halloween Horror Frenzy Doub7e Seven Events Ltd
Matthew Halls Clarion/Seven Muses
Monty Halls Speakout
Ben De Halpert Crescent Mngt
Dominic Halpin & The Honey B's LM2 Entertainment
Alan Halsall (Tyrone, Coronation Street) Big Bang Mngt Ltd/Melody Thresh Mngt Assoc Ltd/Nigel Round Mgnt
Fran Halsall Prof Sports Ptnr Ltd
Jody Halse Billboard Persnl Mngt
Claire Halsey Take Three Mngt
Anthony Halstead Patrick Garvey Mngt
Nicky Hambleton-Jones RDF Management/Trading Faces Ltd
Cate Hamer The Richard Stone Prtnrshp
Ashley Hames The Richard Stone Prtnrshp
Ken Hames 1st Choice Speakers UK Ltd/Cunningham Mngt Ltd/The London Spkr Bureau/Trading Faces Ltd
Caroline Hamilton Julie Bushell Assoc/Speakout
Christine Hamilton After Dinner World Ltd/DBA Speakers/NMP Live Ltd/Names & Faces/Peller Artistes Ltd/Persnl Appearances/Persnly Spkng
David Hamilton Names & Faces/Persnl Appearances
George Hamilton IV Deri Promos
Dr Mark Hamilton Independent Talent Group Ltd
Natasha Hamilton Action Talent Int./Mission Control Artist Agy
Neil Hamilton After Dinner World Ltd/Persnl Appearances/Persnly Spkng
Samantha Hamilton RDF Management
Kathryn Hamilton-Hall Audrey Benjamin Agy
Craig & Jane Hamilton-Parker Take Three Mngt
The Hamish Birchall Trio Upbeat Entertainment
Tamantha Hammerschlag Judy Daish Assoc
Hammerstein CKK Ent
Peter Hammill Gailforce Mngt Ltd/Primary Talent Int'l
Steve Hammon Heart Of England Promos Ltd
Alison Hammond Trading Faces Ltd
John Hammond Talking Heads - The Voice Agy
Lilian Hammond Sandra Boyce Mngt
Lisa Hammond Susan Angel Kevin Francis Ltd
Dr Phil Hammond 1st Choice Speakers UK Ltd/The Richard Stone Prtnrshp
Richard Hammond Independent Talent Group Ltd/Speakout
Susan Hampshire Chatto & Linnit Ltd/United Agents
Christopher Hampson Grays Mngt & Asc
Kate Hampson Northern Lights Mngt
Keily Hampson M.G. Ents
Sir Stuart Hampson CHAMPIONS (UK) PLC/NMP Live Ltd/NMP MANAGEMENT
Hampsters Head On Mngt
Christopher Hampton (French/German) CASAROTTO RAMSAY & ASSOCIATES
Paul Hampton Dennis Lyne Agy
The Hamsters (Jimi Hendrix Tribute) John Hessenthaler Ents/Rock Artist Mngt
Derek Han IMG Artists
Herbie Hancock and the Headhunters William Morris Inc (USA)
Nick Hancock Independent Talent Group Ltd/Noel Gay Artists Ltd
Trevor Hancock Lime Actors Agy & Mngt Ltd
Corinne Handforth Otto Persnl Mngt Ltd
Vernon Handley CBE Clarion/Seven Muses
Marina Hands Markham & Froggatt Ltd
The Handsome Family CODA Ltd
Handsome Harry Company (NL) Wim Wigt Prodns Ltd
Rebecca Hands-Wicks Brian Taylor Assoc
Christine Handy Nancy Hudson Associates Ltd
Emma Handy Markham & Froggatt Ltd
Scott Handy Markham & Froggatt Ltd
Steve Hanks Band Deri Promos
Nesta Hanks Clic Agency
Jenny Hanley MBA
Tres Hanley Speak-Easy Ltd
Terry Hanlon Gordon Poole Agy Ltd
Mick Hanly (Irish) Stoneyport Associates
Judith Hann DBA Speakers/Dave Winslett Assoc/Persnly Spkng
John Hannah ARG Management/Lip Service Casting Ltd
Bob Hannam Norwich Artistes
Lisa Hannigan 13 Artists
Richard Hansell Burnett Granger Assoc
Andy Hanselman CHAMPIONS (UK) PLC
Alan Hansen CHAMPIONS (UK) PLC/Celebrity Appearances/Jon Holmes Media Ltd/Persnly Spkng/Speakout/Trading Faces Ltd
Ashia Hansen Nuff Respect
Hanson Cooking Vinyl
Alexander Hanson Cassie Mayer Ltd
Charlie Hanson Judy Daish Assoc
Christine Hanson - The Cremation of Sam McGee Firefly Productions
Julie Hanson David Anthony Promos
Neil Hanson Speakout
Susan Hanson BWH Agency/Peter Charlesworth & Assoc
Happy the Clown ABDC Ents
Harare Matters Musical
Harbour Lites Steel Band Avenue Artistes Ltd
Ed Harcourt 13 Artists
Hard Kaur Nation Recs Ltd
Diana Hardcastle Jonathan Altaras Assoc
Hardcopy Jason West Agy
Hardcore Derek Bruce Ents
Gillian Hardie Jae Moss Entp
Sean Hardie Alexandra Cann Reprsntn
Allison Harding M W Management
Bryone Harding Grays Mngt & Asc
Claire Harding KAL Mngt
Daniel Harding Askonas Holt Ltd
James Harding The Wylie Agency
Kate Harding Jane Hughes Mngt
Mike Harding CASAROTTO RAMSAY & ASSOCIATES
Niklas Harding Fresh Artiste Management Ltd
Hardly Mozart RED ADMIRAL RECORDS
Charlie Hardwick (Val, Emmerdale) Big Bang Mngt Ltd/Nigel Round Mgnt
Jeremy Hardy Noel Gay Artists Ltd/Off The Kerb Prods
Robert Hardy Chatto & Linnit Ltd
Sophie Hardy Broadwater Ents Assoc
Tim Hardy Brian Taylor Assoc
Tom Hardy Peters Fraser Dunlop (PFD)
Chris Hare Ultimate Int'l
David Hare CASAROTTO RAMSAY & ASSOCIATES
Sir David Hare CASAROTTO RAMSAY & ASSOCIATES
Harem Scarem Stoneyport Associates
Chris Hargreaves Lime Actors Agy & Mngt Ltd
David Hargreaves The Richard Stone Prtnrshp
Nelly Harker Shepherd Mngt Ltd
Jimmi Harkishin Gordon & French
Peter Harkness Noel Gay Artists Ltd
Timandra Harkness Jill Foster Ltd
John Harle SMA Talent Ltd
Harlem Gem Book A Band
Harlene Evans Band The Dixon Agy
Harlequin Disco Tony Bennell Ents
Harlequin Karaoke and Disco David Forshaw Entp
Robert Harley The Richard Stone Prtnrshp
Steve Harley Noel Gay Artists Ltd
Steve Harley & Cockney Rebel The Psycho Mngt Co Ltd
Harley Street Hire-A-Band Ent Agy
Howard Harling Nyland Mngt
Peter Harlowe Speak-Easy Ltd

Claire Harman Speak-Easy Ltd
Nigel Harman Peters Fraser Dunlop (PFD)/United Agents
Paris Harman MAGIK MODELS
Andy Harmer
Dani Harmer COLE KITCHENN PRSN MGT/ROAR Group
Jeffrey Harmer Adrian King Assoc/M W Management
Andy Harmon (David Beckham) Prima Artists/Upfront Ent Agy Ltd
Harmony Hounds Book A Band/MTM Presntns/The A6 Agy
Bethan (Harp) Matters Musical
Camilla (Harp) Matters Musical
Harper M.G. Ents
Chris Harper Louise Hillman/Katie Threlfall
Harper (Comedy/Vocal Duo) Personality Artistes Ltd
Helen Harper Gavin Barker
Kate Harper Speak-Easy Ltd
Rachel Harper MGA Entp
Sarah Harper Brunskill Management Ltd
Jerry Harpur Limelight Management
Manthe Harrap Fushion Pukka Bosh
Julian Harries Royce Mngt
Kathryn Harries Ingpen & Williams Ltd
Mali Harries Talking Heads - The Voice Agy
Susan Harriet Talent Artists Ltd
Amanda Harrington Girl Management
Ainsley Harriott CHAMPIONS (UK) PLC/Jeremy Hicks Assoc/NMP Live Ltd/Prime Performers Ltd
Harris & Day and the Rat Pack Orchestra Angle Ents Ltd
Anita Harris Chris Davis Management/Peter Charlesworth & Assoc
Bob Harris June Ford-Crush
Calvin Harris CHAMPIONS (UK) PLC
Emmylou Harris Asgard
Guy Harris USP Artistes
Jeannie Harris Peter Charlesworth & Assoc
Jemma Harris Jae Moss Entp
Jet Harris G Entertaining
Jet Harris Shadows Rock Artist Mngt
Keith Harris with Orville & Cuddles Camscott Leisure/Henderson Mngt/Nigel Round Mgnt/Peller Artistes Ltd
Kevin Harris Model Plan Celebrities & Prese
Kieron Harris APM Ass/Billboard Persnl Mngt
Martin Harris Circuit Persnl Mngt Ltd
Melanie Harris AIM
Mike Harris CHAMPIONS (UK) PLC
Naomie Harris ARG Management/Yakety Yak
Paul Harris Choreographer Pineapple Agy
Ron "Chopper" Harris Nigel Round Mgnt
Ron "Chopper Harris" Persnl Appearances
Steve Harris USP Artistes
Valentina Harris Celebrity Chefs UK/Fox Artist Mngt Ltd
Wee Willie Harris Paul Barrett Rock'N'Roll Entp
Zinnie Harris CASAROTTO RAMSAY & ASSOCIATES
Andrew Harrison Actorum/Adrian King Assoc
Andy Harrison Lip Service Casting Ltd
Claudia Harrison Markham & Froggatt Ltd
Edward Harrison ICON Actors Mngt
Ellie Harrison Arlington Enterprises Ltd/Jo Sarsby PR Ltd
Fiona Harrison Matters Musical
Howard Harrison Simpson Fox Assoc Ltd
John Harrison Derek Bruce Ents/The Voice Box Agency Ltd
Kelly Harrison Yakety Yak
Miles Harrison Jon Holmes Media Ltd
Nick Harrison Speak-Easy Ltd
Nicola Harrison Nancy Hudson Associates Ltd
Simon Harrison Shepherd Mngt Ltd
Tricia Harrison Sandra Boyce Mngt
Piers Harrisson Brunskill Mngt Ltd
Carly Harris-Sutcliffe Daly Pearson Associates
Lisa Harrow Shepherd Mngt Ltd
David Harrower CASAROTTO RAMSAY & ASSOCIATES
Keith Harrup Barn Dance Line Dance Agy
Harry Hazard Chase Ltd
Deborah Harry Tony Denton Promos Ltd
Flash Harry David Hull Promos Ltd
Jodie Harsh Curtis Brown Grp
Andrea Hart Cassie Mayer Ltd
Chaz Hart Yellow Balloon Prods Ltd
Colin Hart Fighting Talk Promos
Ian Hart ARG Management
James Hart Dukeries Ents Ltd
Josephine Hart Ed Victor Agency
Katherine Hart Arena Personal Mngt
Lindsay Hart Derek Bruce Ents
Miranda Hart CHAMPIONS (UK) PLC
Stacy Hart Louise Hillman/Katie Threlfall
Zoe Hart Louise Hillman/Katie Threlfall
Adam Hart-Davis Parliament Comms
Malin Hartelius Stafford Law
Cat Hartley Cunningham Mngt Ltd
Georgia Hartley North Of Watford Actors Agy
Jane Hartley Tony Clayman Promos
Moira Hartley Sardi's Int'l Ent
Steven Hartley Yakety Yak
Billy Hartman Brown & Simcocks
DJ Paul Hartnoll Value Added Talent Agy (VAT)
DJ Phil Hartnoll Value Added Talent Agy (VAT)
Emily Hartridge Talent4 Media Ltd
John Hartson CHAMPIONS (UK) PLC
John JK Harty Crescent Mngt
Harvesters PVA Ent Consultants
Harvesters Ceilidh Band Rent-A-Band
The Harvesters Duo The Horne Concert Agy
The Harvesters (Medieval Folk Music) Derek Bruce Ents/Rent-A-Band
Adam Paul Harvey AIM
Christopher Harvey Anita Alraun Representation
Declan Harvey Shepherd Mngt Ltd
Gemma Harvey Lime Actors Agy & Mngt Ltd/North One Mngt/The Actors File
Jan Harvey Brunskill Mngt Ltd
Jonathan Harvey Patrick Garvey Mngt
Lara Harvey Grays Mngt & Asc
Matt Harvey APM Ass
Mel Harvey Partyweb.co.uk
Naughty NIgel Harvey Devil Management
Nick Harvey SMA Talent Ltd
Patrick Harvey Richard Price PR
PJ Harvey Creative Artists Agency/Universal/Island Records Ltd
Richard Harvey R Harvey Classical (Ind Art)
Sarah Harvey APM Ass
Sir John Harvey-Jones Parliament Comms
Sir John Harvey-Jones MBE Prime Performers Ltd
Alexandra Harwood Judy Daish Assoc
John Harwood APM Ass
Richard Harwood Hazard Chase Ltd
Ronald Harwood Judy Daish Assoc
Stewart Harwood Susan Angel Kevin Francis Ltd
Bobby Hashemi Parliament Comms
Sahar Hashemi CHAMPIONS (UK) PLC/NMP Live Ltd/Parliament Comms/Speakers For Business/Speakout
Howard Haskin Stafford Law
Lynne-Marie Haslam Brian Marshall Mngt
Penny Haslam Talking Heads - The Voice Agy
Sadie Hasler Avalon Mngt
James Haspiel Robert Smith Literary Agency
Tamer Hassan Big Management (UK) Ltd (Ldn)
Erik Hassle Purple PR
Gavin Hastings OBE Arena Ent Cons/Celebrity Appearances/Gordon Poole Agy Ltd/Persnly Spkng/Speakout
Scott Hastings Speakout
MIke Hatchard Prima Artists
Molly Hatchet AIM Inc (USA)
Linzi Hateley Burnett Granger Assoc
James Hatfield MBE Gordon Poole Agy Ltd
Charlotte Hatherley Big Sister Promotions
Tim Hatley Judy Daish Assoc
Hatrick and Friends Hatrick & Friends (Ind Art)
Helena Hatstand CKK Ent/Complete Ent Serv Ltd
Helena Hatstand & Big Grey Continental Drifts/TEST AGENT C
Hatstand Opera Matters Musical
The Rt Hon Roy Hattersley Parliament Comms
Derek Hatton Gordon Poole Agy Ltd/Johnny Mans Prods Ltd/Nigel Round Mgnt/Persnl Appearances
Ricky Hatton Fighting Talk Promos/Nigel Round Mgnt
Leah Hausman Performing Arts
Havana Fanfare 3000
Havana Boys Steel Band Stardust Ents Agy
The Havana Boys Steve Allen Ents
Vaclav Havel CASAROTTO RAMSAY & ASSOCIATES
Greg Haver Stephen Budd Mngt
Giles Havergal Gavin Barker
Nigel Havers Inspirational Artiste Bkg
Hawaiian Tropicana PVA Ent Consultants
Keeley Hawes Troika Talent
The Hawk Experience MTM Presntns
Chip Hawkes PVA Ent Consultants
Dave Hawkes Hot Stuff Hartbeat Ents Ltd
John Hawkesworth CASAROTTO RAMSAY & ASSOCIATES
Buzz Hawkins Positive Plus Ltd
Charlie G Hawkins Big Bang Mngt Ltd
Charlotte Hawkins First Artist Management
Chris Hawkins RDF Management
David Hawkins CS Ents/David Hawkins - Close Up Magic
Jonnie Hawkins (X Factor) ENTERTAINMENT FX
Jack Hawkins Showband NSE Cons

Tony Hawks CHAMPIONS (UK) PLC/Independent Talent Group Ltd/Speakout
Deborah Hawksley Music Int'l
Jane Hawksley CASAROTTO RAMSAY & ASSOCIATES
Hawkwind Brian Gannon Mngt/Rock Artist Mngt
Paul Hawkyard The Richard Stone Prtnrshp
Kate Hawley (Costumes) Clare Vidal-Hall
Goldie Hawn American Program Bureau
Julia Haworth Shepherd Mngt Ltd
Hawthorne Heights The Agency Group
Alex Hay Celebrity Appearances/Gordon Poole Agy Ltd/Persnl Appearances/Persnly Spkng/Speakout
Lynn Robertson Hay Denmark Street Mngt
Paddy Haycocks Downes Presenters Agy
Mark Hayden Grays Mngt & Asc
Eric Haydock Band Brian Gannon Mngt
Eric Haydock's Ex Hollies Pete Mitchell Associates
Christopher Haydon Paul Duddridge Mngt
David Haye CHAMPIONS (UK) PLC
Chanelle Hayes Action Talent Int.
Christie Hayes Richard Price PR
Clarke Hayes M W Management
Colm Hayes Speak-Easy Ltd
Corcoran Hayes Scott-Paul Young Ents Ltd
Darren Hayes ITB
Hugh Hayes Performance Actors Agy
Laura Hayes Performance Actors Agy
Matt Hayes Curtis Brown Grp
Melvyn Hayes Peter Charlesworth & Assoc
Nuala Hayes Speak-Easy Ltd
Paul Hayes Hyper Agency/Limelight Management
Siobhan Hayes Amanda Howard Assoc Ltd
Stephen Hayes Stephen Budd Mngt
Victoria Hayes Brian Taylor Assoc
Haylayers Barn Dance Line Dance Agy
David Hayler Agency K-Bis/Brunskill Management Ltd
Sally Hayler Agency K-Bis
Mike Hayley Int'l Artistes Ltd
David Hayman Markham & Froggatt Ltd
Cynthia Haymon Athole Still Int'l Ltd/TEST AGENT A
Lindsey Haynes Sandra Boyce Mngt
Russ Haynes Sandra Boyce Mngt
Hayseed Dixie Free Trade Agy
Philip Hayton VRM Artists
Beth Hayward M W Management
Clive Hayward Dennis Lyne Agy
Robert Hayward Ingpen & Williams Ltd
Squire Ronnie Hayward Johnny Mans Prods Ltd
Louise Haywood (Annie Lennox) Spotlight Ents (Notts)
Neil Haywood Sunshine Ents
Kate Hayworth MBA
Ayesha Hazarika Harvey Voices Ltd
Honey Hazel Reality Check Management
Keeley Hazell Jon Fowler Management Ltd
Charles Hazlewood KBJ Management
He's the One - Robbie Williams Show The John Boddy Agency
Anthony Head Gordon & French
Elliot Head Northern Lights Mngt
Murray Head Daly Pearson Associates
Sarah Head Burnett Granger Assoc
Tyla Head Agency K-Bis
Lena Headey Troika Talent
Sheree Headington Liz Hobbs Grp Ltd
Nicola Headley Linton Mngt
The Headliners Satellite Artists Ltd
Headroom Stag Ents
Amanda Healer Amber Persnl Mngt Ltd
Austin Healey CHAMPIONS (UK) PLC/Gordon Poole Agy Ltd
Lord Healey MBE Gordon Poole Agy Ltd
Tim Healey Speakout
Health 13 Artists
Brendan Healy CHAMPIONS (UK) PLC
Ian Healy MPC Ent
Jay Healy Talking Heads - The Voice Agy
Mary Healy Speak-Easy Ltd
Matt Healy Big Bang Mngt Ltd
Camilla Heaney Kerry Gardner Mngt
Sarah Heaney RDF Management/Speakout
Paul Heard S M A Talent Ltd/SMA Talent Ltd
Roger Hearing Talking Heads - The Voice Agy
Barry Hearn MATCHROOM SPORT LTD
George Hearnden Barn Dance Line Dance Agy
Jonty Hearnden Independent Talent Group Ltd/Persnl Appearances
Heart and Soul Tony Bennell Ents
Heart of England Barn Dance Line Dance Agy
Heart of England Falconry MTM Presntns
Heart Of Glass (Blondie tribute) Advanced Ents/MGA Entp
Heart Throb Dave Woodbury Ents
Heartbeat Derek Bruce Ents
Heartbreakers Paul Barrett Rock'N'Roll Entp
Andrew Heath Rosebery Mngt
Katherine Heath Susan Angel Kevin Francis Ltd
Marcus Heath Anita Alraun Representation
Michael Heath Tony Clayman Promos
Oliver Heath Deborah McKenna Ltd
Roy Heath By Invitation Only
Duncan Heather Boogie Management
Elaine Heathfield Grays Mngt & Asc
Heatwave BULLET MANAGEMENT LIMITED/Entertainers Mgt Ltd/Jason West Agy/John Hessenthaler Ents/Owen Hughes Ents
Florent Heau Transart (UK) Ltd
Heaven 17 BULLET MANAGEMENT LIMITED/Jason West Agy/The Psycho Mngt Co Ltd/Tony Denton Promos Ltd
katie Hebb Anita Alraun Representation
Malcom Hebden Big Bang Mngt Ltd
Matt Hebden Daly Pearson Associates
Hed Kandi Party Nights UK Booking Agy
Hedgehog Pie Barn Dance Line Dance Agy
Hedgehoppers Anonymous Dinosaur Promo/Dinosaur Mus
James Hedley Amber Persnl Mngt Ltd
Lisa Heeley Agency K-Bis
Uriah Heep Duroc Media Ltd/Rock Artist Mngt
Raoul Heertje Paramount Int'l Mngt
Gareth Heesom Adrian King Assoc
Millgo Heff Derek Boulton Productions
Paul Hegarty Narrow Road Company
Caron Heggie That's Ent Assoc
John Hegley Troika Talent
Ralph Heid Blackburn International
Heights Purple PR
Steve Heighway Nigel Round Mgnt
Vivien Heilbron The Richard Stone Prtnrshp
Sophie Hein Speak-Easy Ltd
Paul Heiney Jo Gurnett Persnl Mngt/June Ford-Crush
Heir of Insanity - aerial, hand balance, artistic stilts CKK Ent/Continental Drifts/Crowd Pullers/Fool's Paradise/MTM Presntns/TEST AGENT C
Alan Held Askonas Holt Ltd
Helen Claire TMK Mngt & Agcy Ltd
Cornelia Helfricht Athole Still Int'l Ltd/TEST AGENT A
Hell is for Heroes Bad Moon Publicity/Helter Skelter Agy Ltd
Nikki Hellens Northern Lights Mngt
Robert Heller Arena Ent Cons
Hem CODA Ltd
Polly Hemingway Saraband Assoc
Wayne Hemingway MBE CHAMPIONS (UK) PLC
Manfred Hemm Athole Still Int'l Ltd/TEST AGENT A
Phil Hemming Circuit Persnl Mngt Ltd
Eddie Hemmings Nigel Round Mgnt
Joshua Hemmings Billboard Persnl Mngt
Roy G Hemmings Book A Band
Roy G. Hemmings Funhouse Productions Ltd
Roy G Hemmings & The Dictionary Of Soul Funhouse Productions Ltd
David Hempleman-Adams Gordon Poole Agy Ltd
Andy Henderson Jonathan Altaras Assoc
Craig Henderson AIM
Duncan Henderson Sandra Boyce Mngt
Karianne Henderson AIM
Philip Henderson (Piper) Yorkshire Ent
Barbara Hendricks Ingpen & Williams Ltd
Gordon Hendricks Prima Artists
James Hendrie RDF Management
Jimi Hendrix Tribute "Purple Haze" Jason West Agy
Nona Hendryx Asgard
Alastair Hendy Limelight Management
Paul Hendy Talent4 Media Ltd
Sarah Hendy Princess Talent Mngt
Martin Henfield The Voice Box Agency Ltd/VRM Artists
Don Henley William Morris Inc (USA)
Tim Henman CHAMPIONS (UK) PLC/IMG World
Geoff Hennesey APM Ass
Alana Hennings MAGIK MODELS
Danielle Henry Sandra Boyce Mngt
David Henry Susan Angel Kevin Francis Ltd
George Henry PVA Ent Consultants/Steve Allen Ents
Joe Henry Asgard
John Henry (Frank Sinatra) Jason West Agy
Junior Henry Fushion Pukka Bosh
Lenny Henry CBE NMP Live Ltd/PBJ Mngt Ltd/Speakout
Neil Henry Susan Angel Kevin Francis Ltd
Thierry Henry Sport Ent And Media Group
Zoe Henry Susan Angel Kevin Francis Ltd
Henry's Bootblacks PVA Ent Consultants
Henry's Cat Show Paul Bridson Prods

Jane Henschel Askonas Holt Ltd
Ruthie Henshall Conway Van Gelder Grant Ltd/First Artist Management/Personal Management & Casting
Scott Henshall MCS Agcy/Paul Stacey Management
Adam Henshaw Inspiration Mngt
Karen Henson Audrey Benjamin Agy
Nicky Henson The Richard Stone Prtnrshp
Karen Henthorn Shepherd Mngt Ltd
Judy Hepburn Sandra Boyce Mngt
Simon Hepworth Louise Hillman/Katie Threlfall
Her Majesty & The Wolves Insanity Artists
Herbaliser Primary Talent Int'l
Herbaliser DJs CODA Ltd
Aled Herbert Cardiff Casting
Johnny Herbert CHAMPIONS (UK) PLC
Garry Herbert MBE Athole Still Int'l Ltd/Gordon Poole Agy Ltd/Performing Artistes/TEST AGENT A
Michael Herbert - The Magician The Roving Artist
Terry Herbert Triple Cream Ents
Vince Herbert Associated Arts
Marcus Hercules The Narrow Road Company Ltd
Edmund Herd Northern Lights Mngt
Martin Herdman Brunskill Management Ltd
Here & Now Tour Tony Denton Promos Ltd
Here Be Dragons Here Be Dragons (Ind Art)
Ronnie Herel (Radio 1) Hyper Agency/The Psycho Mngt Co Ltd/UK Booking Agy
Randal Herley Jeffrey & White
Herman's Hermits BCM Promos Ltd/Brian Gannon Mngt/Compact Mngt & Ent Agy/Entertainers Mgt Ltd/Henderson Mngt/Jason West Agy/John Hessenthaler Ents/McLeod Agy Ltd/PVA Ent Consultants/Paul Bridson Prods/Pete Mitchell Associates/Rock Artist Mngt
Hermit UK Booking Agy
Hero (Enrique Tribute) Int'l Mngt & Agy Ltd
Heroes (Jam & New Wave 78-83) Peller Artistes Ltd
The Heros Deri Promos
Billy Herring Sandra Singer Assoc
Brian Herring Shining Mngt Ltd
Nicola Herring Performance Actors Agy
Richard Herring Avalon Mngt
Rainer Hersch CKK Ent
Kristin Hersh 4.A.D.
Barbara Hershey Markham & Froggatt Ltd
Lady Victoria Hervey Paul Stacey Management
Paul Herzberg Speak-Easy Ltd
Bill Heslop MTM Presntns
Julie Hesmondhalgh Lou Coulson Associates
Lord Michael Hesseltine Peters Fraser Dunlop (PFD)
Paul Hessey Rosebery Mngt
Menir Heulyn Quality Ents
Nick Hewer CHAMPIONS (UK) PLC
Nicholas Hewetson Julian Belfrage Assoc
James Hewitt Full Portion Media
Miranda Hewitt Talking Heads - The Voice Agy
Peter Hewitt CASAROTTO RAMSAY & ASSOCIATES
Julie Hewlett Daly Pearson Associates
Sherrie Hewson Bronia Buchanan Ass/CHAMPIONS (UK) PLC/COLE KITCHENN PRSN MGT
Hey Jude Int'l Mngt & Agy Ltd
Hey Negrita Fifth Element
Hey Sholay 13 Artists
Mark Heyes RDF Management
Rachael Heyhoe-Flint MBE Gordon Poole Agy Ltd/Persnl Appearances/Persnly Spkng
Nick Heyward Tony Denton Promos Ltd
Jean Heywood Burnett Granger Assoc
Hi-5 (Function Band) Camscott Leisure
Brian Hibbard Emptage Hallett Ltd
Linda Hibberd Opera & Concert Artists
Michael Hibberdine Brian Taylor Assoc
Emma Hibbert Peter Charlesworth & Assoc
Hibernian Rhapsody Stoneyport Associates
Stuart Hickey Brunskill Mngt Ltd
Simon Hickling (magician) Global Ent Agy
Simon Hickling Kaye Frankland Ent Agy
Dr Rob Hicks Limelight Management
Hinda Hicks Universal/Island Records Ltd
Jo Hicks Samantha Bond Management
Rene Hicks Paramount Int'l Mngt
Brett Hicks-Maitland Richard Price PR/Sandra Boyce Mngt
Louise Hickson Louise Hillman/Katie Threlfall
Simon Hickson RDF Management/Talking Heads - The Voice Agy
Brian Higgins Jongleurs
Prof Guy Higgins Derek Bruce Ents
Jack Higgins Colman Getty PR/Ed Victor Agency
Paul Higgins Troika Talent
Julie Higginson Otto Persnl Mngt Ltd
High Contrast CODA Ltd
High Highs 13 Artists
High Jinks Barn Dance Line Dance Agy
High Rise Rubber CKK Ent/Continental Drifts/TEST AGENT C
The High Society Show Max Collie Rhythm Aces
High time Advanced Ents
Darrel Higham Paul Barrett Rock'N'Roll Entp
Higher Motion Continental Drifts/TEST AGENT C
Highland Fiddle Orchestra BGS PRODUCTIONS
Highland Swing Matters Musical
Sara Highlands Anita Alraun Representation
Highley Band Derek Bruce Ents
Highlife London Music Agy
Highlights of Musicals Wim Wigt Prodns Ltd
Highly Strung Barn Dance Line Dance Agy
Charlie Higson Alexandra Cann Reprsntn
Joanna Higson (Shamless) Nigel Round Mgnt
Peter Higton Associated Arts/Dennis Lyne Agy
Hike Matters Musical
Bernard Hill ARG Management
Hill Billy Boogiemen (Holland) Int Sylvantone Promos
Chris Hill (Caister Soul Weekender/Lacy Lady) UK Booking Agy
Craig Hill Speakout
Damon Hill OBE CHAMPIONS (UK) PLC/Celebrity Appearances/PVA Ent Consultants/Trading Faces Ltd
Daniel Hill Judy Daish Assoc
Elaine Hill MTM Presntns/The Voice Box Agency Ltd
Elizabeth Hill Actors Alliance
Friday Hill Big Talent Group
Glen Hill Denmark Street Mngt
Harry Hill Avalon Mngt/NMP Live Ltd/Speakout
Jimmy Hill OBE Jon Holmes Media Ltd/Persnl Appearances
Melanie Hill Markham & Froggatt Ltd/Speak-Easy Ltd
Paul Hill Norwich Artistes
Richard Hill PVA Ent Consultants
Rupert Hill JLM Persnl Mngt
Stuart Hill Albert Alchemy Ent
Vince Hill Derek Franks Org/Johnny Mans Prods Ltd
Vince Hill One Man Show (S) Keith Salberg Agy & Prods
The Johnny Hillard Trio Matters Musical
Jon Hillcock Wise Buddah Talent & Voices
Bernard Hiller Seamus Lyte Management Ltd
The Hilliard Ensemble Hazard Chase Ltd
Carly Hillman AIM
Max Hillman Judy Daish Assoc
Adam Hills Jeffrey & White/Off The Kerb Prods/Paramount Int'l Mngt
Beverley Hills Cassie Mayer Ltd/Lip Service Casting Ltd
Anthony Hilton CHAMPIONS (UK) PLC/Gordon Poole Agy Ltd
Miles Hilton Barber 1st Choice Speakers UK Ltd
Barry Hilton Paramount Int'l Mngt
Lorraine Hilton ANA
Steve Hilton Stephen Budd Mngt
Rolf Hind Clarion/Seven Muses
Madge Hindle Sandra Griffin Mngt
Scott Hindley MJE Mngt
Paul Hine Lime Actors Agy & Mngt Ltd
Frazer Hines Billy Marsh Drama Ltd/Liz Hobbs Grp Ltd
Gregory Hines William Morris Inc (USA)
Maurice Hines - `Guys & Dolls` William Morris Inc (USA)
Nicky Hinkley Tommy Tucker Agy
Kathy Hipperson Louise Hillman/Katie Threlfall
Shash Hira Shining Mngt Ltd
Hired Hands Barn Dance Line Dance Agy
Junichi Hirokami Hazard Chase Ltd
Joji Hirota Matters Musical/PVA Ent Consultants/Roots Around The World
Lou Hirsch The Richard Stone Prtnrshp
Tony Hirst Brunskill Management Ltd/Shining Mngt Ltd
His Name is Alive 4.A.D.
Ian Hislop JLA/PVA Ent Consultants/Parliament Comms
The Hit Men Tim Gentle Music
Hit The Floor
Tim Hitchens Take Three Mngt
Susannah Hitching Talking Heads - The Voice Agy
Hitz Of The Blitz Entertainers Mgt Ltd
H&M Dog Display Team MTM Presntns
Daniel Hoadley Music Int'l
Graham Hoadly Talent Artists Ltd
Andrea Hoban MBA
Phil Hobbis (vocal) Apple County
Liz Hobbs MBE Liz Hobbs Grp Ltd

Mary Anne Hobbs PBJ Mngt Ltd/The Psycho Mngt Co Ltd
Kristy Hobden Agency K-Bis
Brent Hoberman CHAMPIONS (UK) PLC
Adrian Hobson Heart Of England Promos Ltd
Helen Hobson Gavin Barker
Nina Hobson Jeremy Hicks Assoc
Sophie Hobson Frontline Mngt Ltd
Larry Hochman Speakers For Business
Elise Hockley APM Ass
Chas Hodges Rock 'N' Roll Trio Paul Barrett Rock'N'Roll Entp
Hodges Dump Barn Dance Line Dance Agy/Derek Bruce Ents
Kathryn Hodges Denmark Street Mngt
Louise Hodges David Charles Agy
Tom Hodgkins Kerry Gardner Mngt/Speak-Easy Ltd
Amber Hodgkiss Linton Mngt
Leda Hodgson Hilary Gagan Assoc
Matt Hodgson Liz Hobbs Grp Ltd
Denise Hoey Grays Mngt & Asc
Dustin Hoffman Endeavor Agency
Holli Hoffman ANA
Dan Hogarth B.A.S.I.C.
Jane Hogarth Amber Persnl Mngt Ltd
Sarah Hogarth RBA Management Ltd
Alexandra Hogg M W Management
B J Hogg Brunskill Mngt Ltd
Matthew Hoggard CHAMPIONS (UK) PLC/Persnl Appearances
Simon Hoggart Arena Ent Cons
John Hogger Big Band Hire-A-Band Ent Agy
Hogs Head Barn Dance Line Dance Agy/Tony Bennell Ents
Hold Tight Derek Bruce Ents
Amanda Holden ARG Management/Yakety Yak
Bill Holden Johnny Mans Prods Ltd
Ellen Holden Linkside Agy
John Holden-White Paul Duddridge Mngt
Ginny Holder AIM/Cassie Mayer Ltd
Glenn Holderness Anita Alraun Representation
Sue Holderness Burnett Granger Assoc
Neil Holding After Dinner World Ltd
Hole In The Wall Gang David Hull Promos Ltd
Joanna Hole Actorum
Laura Holiday R.L.M.
Robert Holl Ingpen & Williams Ltd
Diane Holland MBA
Dominic Holland Gordon Poole Agy Ltd/Harvey Voices Ltd/Paul Duddridge Mngt/Persnly Spkng/Richard Bucknall Mngt (RBM)/Speakout
Elizabeth Holland Indep Mngt Ltd
Henry Holland Insanity Artists
Jeffrey Holland Voice Shop
Jolie Holland Asgard
Jools Holland One Fifteen/The Psycho Mngt Co Ltd/Trading Faces Ltd
Jools Holland and his Rhythm & Blues Orchestra Miracle Artists Ltd
Ross Holland MBA
Samantha Holland Kerry Gardner Mngt
Tania Holland Les Hart (Southampton) Ents/Partyweb.co.uk
David Hollett Markham & Froggatt Ltd
Jennifer Holliday Tony Denton Promos Ltd
The Hollies Entertainers Mgt Ltd/Jimmy Smith
Heinz Holliger Ingpen & Williams Ltd
Valerie Holliman Grays Mngt & Asc
Victoria Hollingsworth RDF Management
Guy Hollingworth CKK Ent
Chris Hollins Talent4 Media Ltd
Ellis Hollins Lime Actors Agy & Mngt Ltd
Chris Hollinshead ICON Actors Mngt
Derek Hollis MBA
Mark Hollis Darren Gray Mngt
Christer Holloman CHAMPIONS (UK) PLC
Andy Holloway Roadshow NVB Ents
Tribute to Buddy Holly (Ind Art) LRO Artist Mngt/Tribute to Buddy Holly
Buddy Holly & the Crickhits Jason West Agy
Leyla Holly Stage Centre Mngt
Hollywood NVB Ents
Hollywood & Broadway the Musicals The Flying Music Co Ltd
Hollywood Flairz Owen Hughes Ents
Gary Hollywood Susan Angel Kevin Francis Ltd
Hollywood Hookers NVB Ents
Hollywood Nites Dinosaur Promo/Dinosaur Mus/Fairplay Ents/Sunshine Ents
Paul Hollywood CHAMPIONS (UK) PLC
Sir Ian Holm Markham & Froggatt Ltd
Sarah Jane Holm Julian Belfrage Assoc
Catherine Holman Brunskill Mngt Ltd
Eddie Holman Jason West Agy
Ally Holmes Royce Mngt
Holmes Brothers Roots Around The World
Daren Elliot Holmes Jane Lehrer Assoc
David Holmes CODA Ltd/Simpson Fox Assoc Ltd
Eamonn Holmes Celebrity Appearances/David Hull Promos Ltd/First Artist Management/NMP Live Ltd/Talking Heads - The Voice Agy/Trading Faces Ltd
James Holmes RDF Management
Jon Holmes Jon Holmes Media Ltd/The Richard Stone Prtnrshp
Dame Kelly Holmes CHAMPIONS (UK) PLC/Colman Getty PR/NMP Live Ltd/Speakout/Trading Faces Ltd
Lucie Holmes Fushion Pukka Bosh
Lucy Ann Holmes Brunskill Management Ltd
Michael Holmes Form Talent
TJ Holmes North One Mngt
Paul Holowaty Linton Mngt
Carol Holt Talking Heads - The Voice Agy
David Holt Voice Shop
Elizabeth Holt Nyland Mngt
John Holt Monkeybiz Ent Agy
Lucy Holt Troika Talent
Michael Holt Associated Arts
Peter Holt Agency K-Bis
Matt Home Action Talent Int.
Sam Homer Creeme Ents
Ged Hone's Dixie Boys The A6 Agy
Manfred Honeck IMG Artists
Gemma Honey Phillips Ent Agy
The Honeycombs Graham Cole Mngt
Honeycombs2 C.D.E.C.
Lloyd Honeyghan Fighting Talk Promos
Honeyz Mission Control Artist Agy/Tony Denton Promos Ltd
Honky Tonk Tailgate Party Buddy Lee Attrctns Inc (USA)
Abigail Hood City Actors Mngt
Carolyn Hood RBA Management Ltd
Rebecca Hood Sandra Singer Assoc
Hookey Band Barn Dance Line Dance Agy/PVA Ent Consultants/Stardust Ents Agy
Joan Hooley Anita Alraun Representation
Hoolie Barn Dance Line Dance Agy
Hooper Henderson Mngt
James Hooper MTC (UK) LTD
Jeff Hooper Kevin King Mngt/Prima Artists
Robert A. Hooper CS Ents
Robin Hooper Kerry Gardner Mngt
Hooray Girl Sardi's Int'l Ent
Hootenanny 3 Matters Musical
Hootie & The Blowfish ITB
James Hooton Michelle Braidman Assoc
Rachel Hooton Chris Gordon Theatrical Agy
Hoover the Dog Matters Musical
Hop Till You Drop Barn Dance Line Dance Agy/PVA Ent Consultants
Hope & Keen Keith Salberg Agy & Prods
Jess Hope Derek Bruce Ents
Abigail Hopkins Fifth Element/Hilary Gagan Assoc
Chris Hopkins Talent4 Media Ltd/The Voice Box Agency Ltd
Duane Hopkins CASAROTTO RAMSAY & ASSOCIATES
Emma Hopkins AIM
John Hopkins Int'l Artistes Ltd
Keith Hopkins Barrie Stacey Promos & Prods
Laura Hopkins Loesje Sanders
Paul Hopkins (tribute to Roy Orbison) GM Ents
Rachel Hopkins Ron Martin Mngt
Damian Hopley Gordon Poole Agy Ltd
Dennis Hopper Special Artists Agency
Rachael Hopper Harvey Voices Ltd
Rachel Hopper Somethin' Else
Hopping Mad Barn Dance Line Dance Agy/PVA Ent Consultants
Stuart Hopps Simpson Fox Assoc Ltd
Dan Hopwood Independent Talent Group Ltd
Gordon Hopwood Tony West Ents
Horace X Matters Musical
Jeff Hordley Yakety Yak
Steven Hore Talking Heads - The Voice Agy
Myles Horgan Billboard Persnl Mngt
Horizon XS Promos
Horizon Disco Quality Ents
Kevin Horkin Jacque Evans Mngt Ltd
The Horn Belles Derek Bruce Ents
Louise Horn Celebn Model Mngt
Trevor Horn Sarm Mngt
Chris Hornby MBA
Clive Hornby Big Bang Mngt Ltd
Nick Hornby Peters Fraser Dunlop (PFD)
Alex Horne Avalon Mngt
Barbara Horne M W Management
David Horne Grays Mngt & Asc
Mathew Horne Dawn Sedgwick Mngt/Insanity Artists
Nicky Horne Harvey Voices Ltd
Xenia Horne the Harpist Hire-A-Band Ent Agy/Norwich Artistes
Bruce Hornsby The Agency Group
Graham Hornsby Crescent Mngt
James Hornsby Jeffrey & White/Speak-Easy Ltd
Laurie Hornsby The Horne Concert Agy
Inga Hornstra Darren Gray Mngt
Stuart Horobin Circuit Persnl Mngt Ltd
Jane Horrocks United Agents
Joanna Horton Susan Angel Kevin Francis Ltd
Sharon Horton Chris Gordon Theatrical Agy
Tommy Horton Persnl Appearances
Craig Revel Horwood (Director/Choreographer) Gavin Barker

Petrie Hosken Blackburn Sachs Assoc
Basil Hoskins M W Management
Nina Hossein Knight Ayton Mngt
Amir Hosseinpour Judy Daish Assoc
Tanya Hossick Elinor Hilton Associates
Hot & Horny David Charles Agy
Hot Chocolate BULLET MANAGEMENT LIMITED/Entertainers Mgt Ltd/Jason West Agy/Mark Lundquist Management & Co/Richard Martin Agy/Rock Artist Mngt/The Psycho Mngt Co Ltd/Tony Denton Promos Ltd
Hot Club (Jazz & Swing) Doub7e Seven Events Ltd
Hot Club Of Cowtown Buddy Lee Attrctns Inc (USA)
Hot Club Trio Prima Artists
The Hot Dogs Essential Ent
Hot Punch Barn Dance Line Dance Agy
Hot Strings PVA Ent Consultants
Hot Trax Disco Stardust Ents Agy
Hothouse Flowers Asgard
Hotline Tony Bennell Ents
John Hotowka Arena Ent Cons
Ian Houghton (Gene Pitney) Funhouse Productions Ltd
Simon Houghton
Houghton Weavers Houghton Weavers Ltd (Ind Art)
The Houghton Weavers M.G. Ents
Doc Houlind & His Copenhagen Ragtime Orchestra (DK) Wim Wigt Prodns Ltd
Gerard Houllier Athole Still Int'l Ltd/TEST AGENT A
Colin Hoult Avalon Mngt
Rufus Hound CHAMPIONS (UK) PLC
Sean Hourihan Mike Constantia Artiste Mngt L
Fred Housego Peter Charlesworth & Assoc
Barbara Houseman Speak-Easy Ltd
Housequake Int'l Mngt & Agy Ltd
Cherylee Houston Amber Persnl Mngt Ltd
Robin Houston Speak-Easy Ltd
Whitney Houston William Morris Inc (USA)
William Houston Markham & Froggatt Ltd
Queenie Hover Darren Gray Mngt
Roy Hover Darren Gray Mngt
Richard How Jonathan Altaras Assoc
How To Dress Well 13 Artists
Alan Howard Julian Belfrage Assoc
Barry Howard Peter Charlesworth & Assoc
Carmel Howard Louise Hillman/Katie Threlfall
Debbie Howard Lime Actors Agy & Mngt Ltd
Jan Howard Deri Promos
Jo Howard Elinor Hilton Associates
Jonathan Howard ICON Actors Mngt
Karl Howard JB Ents
Laura Howard Susan Angel Kevin Francis Ltd
Lisa Howard Northern Lights Mngt
Madeleine Howard Nancy Hudson Associates Ltd
Lord Michael Howard 1st Choice Speakers UK Ltd/Athole Still Int'l Ltd/NMP Live Ltd/TEST AGENT A
Russell Howard Avalon Mngt
Sammy Howard David Forshaw Entp
Raychel Howard-Jones (Vocalist/Presenter) Ron Martin Mngt
Laurence Howarth Richard Bucknall Mngt (RBM)
Peter Howarth Tony Clayman Promos
Brian Howe AIM Inc (USA)
Michael Howe AIM
Gwynne Howell CBE Ingpen & Williams Ltd
Jane Howell Simpson Fox Assoc Ltd
Rob Howell Judy Daish Assoc
Ursula Howells Chatto & Linnit Ltd
Emily Watson Howes Avalon Mngt
Howie B ITB
Howie D Insanity Artists
Josh Howie Chambers Management Ltd
Robert Howie Talent Artists Ltd
Mark Howland Associated Arts
Carl Howse (magician) XS Promos
Cathy Howse The Richard Stone Prtnrshp
Hoxton Whores (duo or single) UK Booking Agy
HOZZ Advanced Ents
HRH Princess Michael of Kent Kruger Cowne Limited
Anna Hruby Darren Gray Mngt
Jakub Hrusa IMG Artists
Julian Hubbard Music Int'l
Kevin Hubbard (Associate Producer) Hazemead Ltd
Amy Huberman Shepherd Mngt Ltd
Mark Huckett Grays Mngt & Asc
Huckleberries OTB Prods
Roy Hudd OBE AIM/PVA Ent Consultants
Alan Hudson Mr Magic Ents (Magic)
Alastair Hudson Alpha Persnl Mngt
Charlotte Hudson RDF Management
Jack Hudson Nyland Mngt
John Hudson Ingpen & Williams Ltd
Jules Hudson Arlington Enterprises Ltd
Kevin Hudson Funky Beetroot Celebrity Manag
Lucy-Jo Hudson Northern Lights Mngt
Oliver Hudson Linton Mngt
Peter Hudson Gordon Poole Agy Ltd
Polly Hudson Take Three Mngt
Richard Hudson Judy Daish Assoc
Samuel James Hudson The Narrow Road Company Ltd
Tim Hudson Nancy Hudson Associates Ltd
Joseph Hufton Agency K-Bis
Huge Book A Band
Monica Huggett (Violin) Clarion/Seven Muses
Mark Huggins Sue Rider Mngt Ltd
Will Huggins Kerry Gardner Mngt
Tracey Hughes & Sarinda NVB Ents
Chloe Hughes Wendy Lee Mngt
Dwain Arwel Hughes Hazard Chase Ltd
Eiry Hughes Talking Heads - The Voice Agy
Emlyn Hughes OBE McLeod Agy Ltd/PVA Ent Consultants
Enda Hughes CASAROTTO RAMSAY & ASSOCIATES
Garry Hughes Sarm Mngt
Geoffrey Hughes The Richard Stone Prtnrshp
Howard Hughes Harvey Voices Ltd
Ian Hughes Shining Mngt Ltd
Jenni Trent Hughes First Artist Management
Nerys Hughes Burnett Granger Assoc
Nicola Hughes Gavin Barker
Ollie Hughes (Robbie Williams) Upfront Ent Agy Ltd
Phil Hughes CASAROTTO RAMSAY & ASSOCIATES
Rebekah Hughes Direct Persnl Mngt
Rob Hughes (David Bowie) Funhouse Productions Ltd
Sally Hughes AIM
Samantha Hughes Peter Charlesworth & Assoc
Sarah Hughes Susan Angel Kevin Francis Ltd
Sean Hughes PBJ Mngt Ltd
Steve Hughes Comedy Store Mngt/Paramount Int'l Mngt
Sven Hughes Noel Gay Artists Ltd
Tracie Hughes Malcolm Derrick Thtrcl Entp/PVA Ent Consultants
Zerlina Hughes Performing Arts
D.L. Hughley ICM (USA)
Hugo and the Hugonotes Coach House Ent
Tara Hugo Brunskill Management Ltd
Victor Hugo Latin Quartet Latin Arts Serv (LAS)
Victor Hugo's Salsa Show with the Picante Dancers Latin Arts Serv (LAS)/Upbeat Entertainment
Chris Huhme CHAMPIONS (UK) PLC
Carla Huhtanen Hazard Chase Ltd
Hui Ling's Chinese Circus Whatever Artists Mngt Ltd
Hula Bluebirds London Music Agy
The Hula Bluebirds Matters Musical/PVA Ent Consultants
Hafdis Huld CEC Management
Cheska Hull (MIC) Insanity Artists
Jenny Hull Talent4 Media Ltd/The Voice Box Agency Ltd
Alison Hulme MPC Ent
Eric Hulme Nyland Mngt
Human Gyroscope PVA Ent Consultants
Human League BULLET MANAGEMENT LIMITED
The Human League Free Trade Agy
Human League Jason West Agy/Miracle Artists Ltd
The Human League Mission Control Artist Agy
Human League The Psycho Mngt Co Ltd/Tony Denton Promos Ltd
Human Statues Doub7e Seven Events Ltd
Ben Humble Fushion Pukka Bosh
Kate Humble United Agents
Barry Hume Prof Sports Ptnr Ltd
Alex Humes The Actors File
Amanda Humphrey Daly Pearson Associates
Jahe Humphrey CHAMPIONS (UK) PLC
Jake Humphrey Blackburn Sachs Assoc/CHAMPIONS (UK) PLC
The Humphrey Lyttelton Band The John Boddy Agency
Amy Humphreys The Actors File
Barry Humphries PBJ Mngt Ltd
Emma Humphries Alpha Persnl Mngt
Roger Humphries Deri Promos
Roger Humphries and Bite the Bullet Line Music Promotions
John Humphrys 1st Choice Speakers UK Ltd/Arena Ent Cons/Celebrity Appearances/Gordon Poole Agy Ltd/Kruger Cowne Limited/NMP Live Ltd/Parliament Comms/Performing Artistes/Persnly Spkng/Speakers For Business
Humpty Dumpty Show Paul Bridson Prods
Hundred Reasons Helter Skelter Agy Ltd
Gloria Hunniford Talent4 Media Ltd/Talking Heads - The Voice Agy/The Voice Box Agency Ltd
Peter Hunningale Monkeybiz Ent Agy
Tom Hunsinger CASAROTTO RAMSAY & ASSOCIATES

Anthony Hunt Adrian King Assoc
Dan Hunt CHAMPIONS (UK) PLC
Eliza Hunt Kerry Gardner Mngt
Gareth Hunt Mclean-Williams Management/Yakety Yak
Gemma Hunt Take Three Mngt
Helen Hunt Special Artists Agency
Jay Hunt The Richard Stone Prtnrshp
Sally Hunt Adrian King Assoc
Tommy Hunt (northern soul legend) Barry Collings Ents
Tristram Hunt Capel & Land
Ben Hunt-Davis MBE Gordon Poole Agy Ltd
Hunter Action Talent Int.
Alex Hunter CHAMPIONS (UK) PLC
The James Hunter Band Matters Musical
Ben Hunter Shepherd Mngt Ltd
Billy Hunter M.G. Ents/Moonglight Agy
Christopher Hunter Kerry Gardner Mngt
DJ Hunter Norwich Artistes
Fiona Hunter Barrie Stacey Promos & Prods
Georgina Hunter The Voice Box Agency Ltd/VRM Artists
Graham Hunter Ultimate Int'l
Holly Hunter Special Artists Agency
Ian Hunter One Fifteen
Janice Hunter Talking Heads - The Voice Agy
Kathryn Hunter Brunskill Mngt Ltd
Lucy Hunter Celebn Model Mngt
Neil Hunter CASAROTTO RAMSAY & ASSOCIATES
Norman Hunter After Dinner World Ltd/Nigel Round Mgnt
Rachel Hunter Can Associates Ltd/Premier Special
Reginald D. Hunter Int'l Artistes Ltd
Shaun Hunter (George Michael) Camscott Leisure
Carmel Hunter (Tina Turner) Advanced Ents/Nigel Round Mgnt
Paul Huntley-Thomas Newton Wills Mngt
Konnie Huq NMP Live Ltd/The Richard Stone Prtnrshp
Baron Douglas Hurd CH CBE PC CHAMPIONS (UK) PLC
Douglas Hurd Gordon Poole Agy Ltd
Sir Douglas Hurd Parliament Comms
Helen Hurd Elinor Hilton Associates
Rachel Hurd-Wood Troika Talent
Isobel Hurle Barrie Stacey Promos & Prods
Jonnie Hurn Kenneth Earle Persnl Mngt
Russell Hurn Downes Presenters Agy
Huron Kevin King Mngt
Elizabeth Hurran Jonathan Altaras Assoc
Hurricane Force Les Hart (Southampton) Ents
Hurricane Force Steel Band Stardust Ents Agy
Hurry The Jug Barn Dance Line Dance Agy
DJ Dave Hurst KM Ents
Sir Geoff Hurst MBE NMP Live Ltd/PVA Ent Consultants/Preview & Review Ents Ltd
Jonas Hurst Talent4 Media Ltd
Lee Hurst JLA/PVA Ent Consultants
Mark Hurst Paul Duddridge Mngt
Sally Hurst Louise Hillman/Katie Threlfall
Tony Hurst Big Bang Mngt Ltd
Paul Hurstfield Northern Lights Mngt
John Hurt Julian Belfrage Assoc
Hurts Purple PR
Mishal Husain - Presenter KBJ Management/Knight Ayton Mngt/Speak-Easy Ltd
Jenny Husey Argyle Assoc
Amanda Hussain Shining Mngt Ltd
Nasser Hussain OBE MA CHAMPIONS (UK) PLC/Jon Holmes Media Ltd
Shabana Hussain Audrey Benjamin Agy
Hussey AAA/Armstrong Academy Agy/Matters Musical
The Hustlers
Andrew Hutchings Adrian King Assoc
Reg Hutchings Barn Dance Line Dance Agy
Madeleine Hutchins Inspiration Mngt
Lloyd Hutchinson Cassie Mayer Ltd/Lip Service Casting Ltd
Paul Hutchinson Royce Mngt
Ron Hutchinson Judy Daish Assoc
Angela Huth CASAROTTO RAMSAY & ASSOCIATES
Max Hutton (Robbie Williams) Entertainers Mgt Ltd/Prima Artists
Mickey Hutton Shining Mngt Ltd
Timothy Hutton Markham & Froggatt Ltd
Huun - Huur - Tu (Tuva) Adastra
Richard Huw Lip Service Casting Ltd
Aldous Huxley (Estate) CASAROTTO RAMSAY & ASSOCIATES
Dmitri Hvorostovsky Askonas Holt Ltd
Susan Hyatt Seamus Lyte Management Ltd
Hybrid Continental Drifts/TEST AGENT C
Antony C. Hyde Frontline Mngt Ltd
Jonathan Hyde ARG Management
Patrick Hyde Inspiration Mngt
Jan Hyden Rowles Talking Heads - The Voice Agy
Veronika Hyks Speak-Easy Ltd
Javine Hylton COLE KITCHENN PRSN MGT/Personal Management & Casting
John Hylton is Neil Diamond Funhouse Productions Ltd/Pete Mitchell Associates
James Hyman MPC Ent/Talking Heads - The Voice Agy
Chrissie Hynde Gailforce Mngt Ltd
Jacquelyn Hynes Lime Actors Agy & Mngt Ltd
Jonny Hynes Silvey Associates
Nina Hynes SOLITAIRE MGT & INT AGCY
Hyper Hope Management
Hypno Comedy Show Mr "E" Ents
Nicholas Hytner Askonas Holt Ltd
Paul Courtney Hyu RDF Management
Sami Hyypia Sport Ent And Media Group

I

I Am Kloot Free Trade Agy
I Spatticus Head On Mngt
iamamiwhoami 13 Artists
Ian and Friends Ian & Friends/John Field - Theatre and Puppe
David Ian Taylor Herring Public Relation
Janis Ian Asgard/Cooking Vinyl
Armando Iannucci PBJ Mngt Ltd/Speakout
Lisa I'Anson RDF Management/Talking Heads - The Voice Agy
Grant Ibbs Susan Angel Kevin Francis Ltd
Aziz Ibrahim NEM Prods (UK)
Ice Graham Cole Mngt
Ice Fantasia Go Ents
Lex Icon Peller Artistes Ltd
Identity Crisis XS Promos
Jonathan Idiagbonya Derek Boulton Productions
Idlewild The Agency Group
Billy Idol ITB/William Morris Inc (USA)
Dr Tariq Idris MCS Agcy
Eddie Ifft Paramount Int'l Mngt
Alan Igbon Anita Alraun Representation
Iggy Pop ICM (USA)/MVO Ltd/Solo Agy Ltd
Enrique Iglesias William Morris Inc (USA)
Julio Iglesias ITB
Katherine Igoe Cassie Mayer Ltd
Leo 'The Lion' Ihenacho Hyper Agency
Il Divo Solo Agy Ltd/The Outside Organisation
William Ilkley Susan Angel Kevin Francis Ltd
The Illegal Eagles BULLET MANAGEMENT LIMITED/Derek Block Concerts/Hal Carter Org
Ray Illingworth Celebrity Appearances/Persnly Spkng
Illinois Blues Brothers Andrew James
Illusion XS Promos
Abba Illusion Barry Collings Ents
Ilogik Fresh Artiste Management Ltd
Imagination BULLET MANAGEMENT LIMITED/Jason West Agy/John Hessenthaler Ents/Satellite Artists Ltd/The Psycho Mngt Co Ltd/Tony Bennell Ents/Tony Denton Promos Ltd
Imagination feat Leee John Barry Collings Ents
Natalie Imbruglia Helter Skelter Agy Ltd
Michael Imerson Louise Hillman/Katie Threlfall/Talking Heads - The Voice Agy
Imogen Heap Purple PR
The Imposters - Ultimate 60's show Leisure Mngt
Impromtu DG Entp/Peller Artistes Ltd
The Imps Motorcycle Display Team MTM Presntns
Imran Mirza Elinor Hilton Associates
Celia Imrie M F Management Ltd
In 2 Deep TMK Mngt & Agcy Ltd
In The Cage (Genesis) Head On Mngt
In The Mood Matters Musical
In The Mood - Tribute to Glenn Miller with the Herb Miller Orchestra The Flying Music Co Ltd
In the Mood - With Five Star Swing Upbeat Mngt
In The Red (Boy Girl Duo) Bees Knees Ents
In4XS Andrew Beauchamp Mngt/Jason West Agy
Incandescence Continental Drifts/TEST AGENT C
Incarnation CKK Ent
Robin Ince Noel Gay Artists Ltd
Incognito The Psycho Mngt Co Ltd
The Incredibles Goldstar Ent UK
The Incredibly Strange Film Band Matters Musical
Index XS Promos
Indigo Broadwater Ents Assoc
Indigo Girls Primary Talent Int'l
Indigo Moon CKK Ent
Indigo Moss Supervision Management
Indulgence Chocolate Fountain Dave Andrews Ents
Ralph Ineson Gordon & French/Yakety Yak
Inez JB Ents
Infantasia Dings Ent/NVB Ents
Inflatables Tony Bennell Ents
In-Fusion Hawthorn Ent
Will Ing CASAROTTO RAMSAY & ASSOCIATES
Barrie Ingham AIM

Sir Bernard Ingham Gordon Poole Agy Ltd/Parliament Comms
Stephen Ingham RBA Management Ltd
Guy Ingle (Prince Charles) Guy Ingle (Ind Art)
Anthony Inglis SJ Mngt
Joe Inglis June Ford-Crush
Nick Ingram Adrian King Assoc
Pieta Inkinen IMG Artists
John Inman Int'l Artistes Ltd
Laurence Inman Elinor Hilton Associates
INME Helter Skelter Agy Ltd
Innersense Continental Drifts/TEST AGENT C
George Innes Shepherd Mngt Ltd
Neil Innes Jean Levy PR Agency
Stuart Innes Newton Wills Mngt
Inseparable Devil Management
Inside Out Derek Bruce Ents/Sardi's Int'l Ent/XS Promos
Clare Inskip Derek Bruce Ents
Gavin Inskip Wise Buddah Talent & Voices
Inspiration Tony West Ents
Instant Replay Cosmos Agy & Promos
Instant Sunshine (Ind Art) Instant Sunshine
Intenso Project Mission Control Artist Agy
Intermission Sunshine Ents
International Fun Casinos London Music Agy
International Guitar Night (USA) Stoneyport Associates
International Magic Int'l Magic (Magic)
International Steelband Quality Ents
International Wrestling Fairplay Ents
Interpol 13 Artists
Into the Bleach (Blondie tribute) Fab Prods/Head On Mngt/Henderson Mngt
Intrigue Fairplay Ents/G Entertaining/Norman Phillips Org Ltd/Norwich Artistes/The CBS Grp
John Inverdale Persnly Spkng
Jono Inverdale MPC Ent
The Invisible Men CKK Ent/Continental Drifts/Fool's Paradise/Fools Paradise/TEST AGENT C
Inxs The Agency Group
Tony Iommi Equator Music
Majid Iqbal Sandra Boyce Mngt
Ronnie Irani PARAGON SPORTS MANAGEMENT LTD
Jeni Ireland Sara Crouch Mngt
Kenny Ireland The Richard Stone Prtnrshp
Paul Ireland Louise Hillman/Katie Threlfall
Irelands Showbands Do You Come Here Often? David Hull Promos Ltd
Tippa Irie Monkeybiz Ent Agy
Irish Folk Rock Show Graham Cole Mngt
Irish Mist Matters Musical
Iron Broo (Ceilidh Band) Elite Promos/Stag Ents
Iron Maiden Scream Promotions
Ironically Maiden Head On Mngt
Dom Irrera Paramount Int'l Mngt
Eddie Irvine CHAMPIONS (UK) PLC/Celebrity Appearances/NMP Live Ltd
Hazel Irvine Jane Morgan Mngt Ltd
Peter Irvine Scott-Paul Young Ents Ltd
Ian Irving (Comedian) DBA Speakers/Gordon Poole Agy Ltd/Highfield Mngt & Promos/Midland Ent & Mgnt Ltd/Norwich Artistes/Persnl Appearances/Preview & Review Ents Ltd/Sardi's Int'l Ent/The CBS Grp/The Horne Concert Agy/Triple Cream Ents
John Irving Peters Fraser Dunlop (PFD)
Michael Irving Frontline Mngt Ltd
Sheen Irving Elinor Hilton Associates
Jane Irwin Ingpen & Williams Ltd
Sir Jeremy Isaacs Peters Fraser Dunlop (PFD)
Sonya Isaacs Buddy Lee Attrctns Inc (USA)
Chris Isaak ITB
Josefine Isaksson Talent Artists Ltd
Kazuo Ishiguro (Dramatic Rights) Judy Daish Assoc
Eriko Ishihara (vocalist / pianist) Wim Wigt Prodns Ltd
Sebrina Ishmael Brian Taylor Assoc
Isis String Quartet Tony Bennell Ents
Island Rhythm Hawaiian Band Sardi's Int'l Ent
Isle Of Oxney Band Barn Dance Line Dance Agy
Dave Ismay Gordon Poole Agy Ltd/PVA Ent Consultants/Starfinders Int'l Mngt/Velrag Arts
Nizar Al Issa Matters Musical
Issy Van Randwyck The Richard Stone Prtnrshp
It Takes Two Sunshine Ents
It Takes Two - M. McCoo & B. Davis Jr. William Morris Inc (USA)
It's A Knockout PVA Ent Consultants
The Ivy League BCM Promos Ltd/BULLET MANAGEMENT LIMITED/Brian Yeates Assoc
Ivy League Henderson Mngt
The Ivy League Jason West Agy
Ivy League Norwich Artistes/PVA Ent Consultants/Paul Bridson Prods
Hiroyuki Iwaki Transart (UK) Ltd
Pawel Izdebski Opera & Concert Artists
Liz Izen Nancy Hudson Associates Ltd
Eddie Izzard Conway Van Gelder Grant Ltd/PBJ Mngt Ltd

J

J Clown Esq Boo Boo's Entertainments
J & S Duo Derek Bruce Ents
Sammy J (Kylie) Entertainers Mgt Ltd
Simon J Garston Ents Ltd
Helen Jacey CASAROTTO RAMSAY & ASSOCIATES
Chris Jack ICON Actors Mngt
Jackdaw Ceilidh Band Rent-A-Band
Margaret Jackman Circuit Persnl Mngt Ltd
Wayne Jackman Jill Foster Ltd
Robbie Jacks Devil Management
Barbara Jackson B.A.S.I.C.
Barry Jackson Susan Angel Kevin Francis Ltd
Ben Jackson Speak-Easy Ltd
Colin Jackson CBE CHAMPIONS (UK) PLC/MTC (UK) LTD/Parliament Comms/Speakout/Trading Faces Ltd
David Jackson London Music Agy
The Earl Jackson Band Stables Ents
General Sir Michael Jackson NMP Live Ltd
Jeremy Jackson Action Talent Int.
Jilly Jackson Artsworld Int'l Mngt Ltd
Joe Jackson Primary Talent Int'l
La Toya Jackson Tony Denton Promos Ltd
Jodie Jackson (Madonna) Nigel Round Mgnt
Milly Jackson Monkeybiz Ent Agy
Paul Jackson SWA Ent
Philip Jackson Markham & Froggatt Ltd
Rachel Jackson Clic Agency
Roger Jackson S M A Talent Ltd/SMA Talent Ltd
Roy Jackson APM Ass
The Jackson Singers (USA) Wim Wigt Prodns Ltd
Tito Jackson Eleventh Hour Mngt Ltd
Tom Jackson Leo Mngt & Agy
Vicky Jackson Angle Ents Ltd
Michelle Jackson-Read MBA
Jacksonville Folk Ents Ltd
David Jacobs CBE DL All Electric Productions & Dav/Billy Marsh Assoc Ltd
Jaye Jacobs Paul Spyker Mngts
Lisa Jacobs Yakety Yak
Marc Jacobs Essex Ent Agy
Paul Jacobs Jacque Evans Mngt Ltd
Sally Jacobs Performing Arts
Tony Jacobs All Electric Productions & Dav/Matters Musical
Jacolly Puppets John Field - Theatre and Puppe
Jacqueline LRO Artist Mngt
Jacqueline Kington Burnett Granger Assoc
Jacques Cafe Band The John Boddy Agency
Jacques Lu Cont CODA Ltd
Melissa Jacques Adrian King Assoc
Jactito Theatre Co John Field - Theatre and Puppe
Jade The Dixon Agy
Cherie Jade Nigel Round Mgnt
Kieran Jae Adrian King Assoc
The Jagermeisters Umpah Band The Horne Concert Agy
Jagged Major Ent Agy
Chris Jagger Roots Around The World
Jade Jagger Insanity Artists
Jaguar Derek Bruce Ents
Jakatta UK Booking Agy
Jake & Elwood The Best Blues Brothers Show In The World ...... EVER!!! Handshake Ltd
Frankie Jakeman David Charles Agy
Vera Jakob Audrey Benjamin Agy
Jambalaya London Music Agy/Matters Musical/The CBS Grp
Jamelia Tony Denton Promos Ltd
Aaron James CHAMPIONS (UK) PLC/G Entertaining/Persnl Appearances/Steve Allen Ents
Adam James Angle Ents Ltd
Alan James as Chris de Burgh Entertainers Mgt Ltd
Alex James CMO Mngt Int'l Ltd
Mike James Band/Sound London Music Agy/Mike James Sound (Ind Art)/PVA Ent Consultants
Benedict James Adrian King Assoc
Biby James Band The Ents Agency
Bob James Yellow Balloon Prods Ltd
Brad James Fairplay Ents
Chris James Kevin King Mngt/PVA Ent Consultants
Chris james Hypnotic Entertainment Ltd Hartbeat Ents Ltd
Clive James PVA Ent Consultants/Speakout
Dee D James Derek Bruce Ents
Damien James Trevor George Ents Ltd
Danny James Cosmic Comedy Mngt
Darren James B.A.S.I.C.
Darren James (DJ) Head On Mngt
Darren James UK Booking Agy
Dolly James (Tina Turner Tribute) GM Ents
Duncan James Action Talent Int./Hackford Jones PR/Independent

Talent Group Ltd/MERLIN ELITE
Eirian James (Welsh & English Language) Music Int'l
Elliot James Alpha Persnl Mngt
Fraser James Yakety Yak
Gareth James (Comedy Vocalist) Ron Martin Mngt
George James Rogues & Vagabonds Mngt
Geraldine James Julian Belfrage Assoc
James Goff Orchestra ABC Direct Ents
Graham James Burnett Granger Assoc
James Graham Fushion Pukka Bosh
Greg James Big Talent Group/Hyper Agency/Wise Buddah Talent & Voices
Guy James B.A.S.I.C.
Ian James Les Hart (Southampton) Ents
Jack James Kerry Gardner Mngt
Janet James The Voice Box Agency Ltd
Jennifer James Derek Boulton Productions
Jimmy James & The Vagabonds BUL-LET MANAGEMENT LIMITED/Barry Collings Ents/Entertainers Mgt Ltd/Henderson Mngt/Int'l Mngt & Agy Ltd/Jason West Agy/Non Stop Ents/Paul Bridson Prods
J.P. James Compact Mngt & Ent Agy/Derek Bruce Ents
Judi James Knight Ayton Mngt/NMP Live Ltd
Kenny James Gordon Kellett Ents
Kim James Yellow Balloon Prods Ltd
Lee Roy James After Dinner Spkers & Com
Leeann James Leeann James
Lincoln James APM Ass
Louise James Derek Bruce Ents
Lyn James Darren Gray Mngt
Mark James CHAMPIONS (UK) PLC
Martyn James Mr Magic Ents (Magic)
Matt James Curtis Brown Grp
Mike James Peller Artistes Ltd
The Mike James Sound Tony Bennell Ents
Morgan Lee James Creeme Ents
Nicole James (X Factor Vocalist) Bees Knees Ents
Nigel James NVB Ents
Oscar James Susan Angel Kevin Francis Ltd
Paul James (Elvis tribute) M.G. Promos
Pedr James Judy Daish Assoc
Pete James GM Ents
Raji James Langford Assoc
Ray James (Alf Garnett) Upfront Ent Agy Ltd
Sally James Downes Presenters Agy/Yellow Balloon Prods Ltd
Scott James UK Booking Agy
Tony James The A6 Agy
Trevor James Matters Musical
Trilby James The Richard Stone Prtnrshp
Rob James-Collier Big Bang Mngt Ltd
Ben James-Ellis Gavin Barker
Louise Jameson COLE KITCHENN PRSN MGT/Conway Van Gelder Grant Ltd
Steve Jameson Paramount Int'l Mngt
Jamgrass Festival Buddy Lee Attrctns Inc (USA)
Jamie M.G. Ents
Jamie & The First Class CS Ents
Jamie Lidell Dog Day Press
Matt Jamie Performance Actors Agy
Jamie Reeves (Robbie Williams) Advanced Ents
Jamieson UK Booking Agy
Gary Jamieson Yorkshire Ent
Michelle Jamieson Inspiration Mngt
Peter Jamieson APM Ass
Robert Jamieson Mr Magic Ents (Magic)
Tom Jamieson Jill Foster Ltd
Jamiroquai Dave Woolf PR/ITB/William Morris Inc (USA)
The Jamm Head On Mngt/Henderson Mngt/Jason West Agy
We Be Jammin'! Matters Musical
Jan Steele Latin Jazz Band London Music Agy
Jan Wobble & The Invaders of the Heart EC1 Music Agency
Jane Bom-Bane Matters Musical
Sarah Jane Fairplay Ents/Sunshine Ents
Rebekah Janes M W Management
Janices Band Barn Dance Line Dance Agy
Janita Agency For the Performing Arts
Kaleem Janjua Amber Persnl Mngt Ltd
Bert Jansch Stoneyport Associates
Huub Janssen's Amazing Jazzband (NL) Wim Wigt Prodns Ltd
Samantha Janus CAM London
Japandroids 13 Artists
Japanesque Matters Musical/Wienerwald Ents
Kimberly Jaraj Brunskill Management Ltd
Antony Jardine Links Mngt
Tony Jardine Gordon Poole Agy Ltd
Sunna Jarman M W Management
Phillipe Jaroussky (Countertenor) Clarion/Seven Muses
Al Jarreau Marshall Arts Ltd
Russell Jarret Matters Musical
Nathan Stewart Jarrett Insanity Artists
Chris Jarvis Blackburn Sachs Assoc/Talking Heads - The Voice Agy
Clare Jarvis Scott-Paul Young Ents Ltd
Martin Jarvis As Tom Jones Barry Collings Ents/Stars In Your Eyes Ltd Ent Agy
David Jason The Richard Stone Prtnrshp
Jason Gardiner (Queer Eye for a Straight Guy) Curtis Brown Grp/RDF Management/Seamus Lyte Management Ltd
Jason Steele & Joanne Trevor George Ents Ltd
Java Function Band Hire-A-Band Ent Agy
Adil Mohammed Javed Lime Actors Agy & Mngt Ltd
Javine Tony Denton Promos Ltd
Jawonderquai (Jamiroquai Tribute) Peller Artistes Ltd
Jaws Reality Check Management
Lee Jaxon TMK Mngt & Agcy Ltd
Basement Jaxx Primary Talent Int'l
Sally Jaxx Nigel Round Mgnt
Jay Dave Woodbury Ents
Allan Jay Newton Wills Mngt
Andrew Jay Vincent Shaw Assoc Ltd
Becky Jay LJ Ents
Dave Jay Quality Ents
David Jay Disco The Horne Concert Agy
Gemma Jay CeeBee Variety Agy
Jenny Jay Sandra Boyce Mngt
Steve Jay (Jensen) B.A.S.I.C.
Jessica Jay CeeBee Variety Agy
Kenneth Jay Anita Alraun Representation
Mikki Jay (Michael Jackson) Barrie Hawkins Leisure Service/Compact Mngt & Ent Agy/Funhouse Productions Ltd/Jason West Agy/Peller Artistes Ltd
Norman Jay (The Legend) UK Booking Agy
Peter Jay Celebrity Appearances/Persnly Spkng
Phil Jay CKK Ent
Rikki Jay (International Comedy) Ron Martin Mngt
Sammie Jay Gordon Kellett Ents
Jay Tee (Justin Timberlake Tribute) Henderson Mngt
Terry Jay Sunshine Ents
Jayce ('Stars In Their Eyes' - Dolly Parton) Bees Knees Ents
Andy Jaye Wise Buddah Talent & Voices
Jani Jaye (B. Spears) Entertainers Mgt Ltd
Jeni Jaye (Britney Spears, Geri Haliwell) Apple County
Jeni Jaye (Britney Spears) Funhouse Productions Ltd
Jeni Jaye (Britney Spears, Geri Haliwell) G Entertaining
Jeni Jaye (Britney Spears) Henderson Mngt/Peller Artistes Ltd
Mervyn Jaye (Impressionist) Sardi's Int'l Ent
Sara Jaye Dance Funki Feathers Agy
Elisha Jayne Creeme Ents
Sara Jayne APM Ass
Sarah Jayne Dance Funki Feathers Agy
Ian Jay`s Sponge Plunge MTM Presntns
Dani Jazzar Sandra Singer Assoc
Jazmine Int'l Mngt & Agy Ltd
Jazz Afrique Int. Cabal Mngt
Jazz All-Stars Rent-A-Band
Jazz Chill London Music Agy
Jazz Collective Hireaband Ltd
Classic Dixieland Jazz Norwich Artistes
The Jazz Dynamos Matters Musical/Upbeat Entertainment
Excelsior Jazz Norwich Artistes
Jazz Express Derek Bruce Ents
Jazz Foundation Kernow Ents
Jazz Function Global Ent Agy
Jazz Functionaires Whatever Artists Mngt Ltd
Jazz Jamaica Allstars CODA Ltd
The Jazz Menagerie Dave Seamer Ents
Jazz Nights Dark Blues Mngt
Jazz Nutzz Tony Bennell Ents
Jazz Pack Peller Artistes Ltd
Jazz Ramblers Quality Ents
Jazz Sounds Rent-A-Band
Jazzie B (Soul II Soul) Elastic Artists Agency Ltd/UK Booking Agy
JBO Owen Hughes Ents
J.D. Adams McLeod Agy Ltd
Emma Jean Fushion Pukka Bosh
Jean Genie (David Bowie tribute) BUL-LET MANAGEMENT LIMITED/Compact Mngt & Ent Agy/Henderson Mngt/Jason West Agy
Wyclef Jean William Morris Inc (USA)
Claire Jeater Stage Centre Mngt
Ana Jebens Loesje Sanders
Kieron Jecchinis Actors Alliance
Jeepers Continental Drifts/TEST AGENT C
Jeepster Angle Ents Ltd
Jeeves & Wooster Animal World
Jack Jefferson Gavin Barker
Jane Jefferson North Of Watford Actors Agy
Marshall Jefferson UK Booking Agy
Peter Jefferson Speak-Easy Ltd
Darren Jeffery Ingpen & Williams Ltd
Billy Jeffrey Stag Ents
Susan Jeffrey Elinor Hilton Associates
Stephen Jeffreys CASAROTTO RAM-

SAY & ASSOCIATES
Jim Jeffries Athole Still Int'l Ltd/TEST AGENT A/Underbelly Management
Lionel Jeffries Liz Hobbs Grp Ltd
Ali Jehangit Fushion Pukka Bosh
Jekyll & Hyde Kevin King Mngt
Ann Jellicoe CASAROTTO RAMSAY & ASSOCIATES
The Jelly Rollers Crowd Pullers
Jem ITB
Jimmy Jemain as Cliff Richard Compact Mngt & Ent Agy/Entertainers Mgt Ltd/Funhouse Productions Ltd/GM Ents/Stars In Your Eyes Ltd Ent Agy
Cedric Jemmett That's Ent Assoc
Jenai Buddy Lee Attrctns Inc (USA)
Faye Jenelle Lime Actors Agy & Mngt Ltd
Amy Jenkins CASAROTTO RAMSAY & ASSOCIATES
Chip Jenkins Prima Artists
Graeme Jenkins Askonas Holt Ltd
Kate Jenkins Curtis Brown Grp
Katherine Jenkins CHAMPIONS (UK) PLC/NMP Live Ltd/The Agency Group/Trading Faces Ltd
Lois Jenkins Robert Smith Literary Agency
Mitch Jenkins Scott-Paul Young Ents Ltd
Neil Jenkins Music Int'l
Nia Jenkins (Harpist) The John Boddy Agency
Gerry Jenkinson Associated Arts
Karl Jenkinson Anita Alraun Representation
Stephen Jenn Brunskill Management Ltd
Martin Jenner David Charles Agy
Daniel Jennings The Actors File
Pat Jennings OBE KSG Persnl Appearances
Rory Jennings Rossmore Persnl Mngt
Jenny Dave Woodbury Ents
Jenny Fitzpatrick Burnett Granger Assoc
Ashley Jensen Hamilton Hodell Ltd
David Jensen Blackburn Sachs Assoc/Talking Heads - The Voice Agy
Rebecca Jensen Wise Buddah Talent & Voices
Emma Jenson Derek Bruce Ents/MJE Mngt
Ron Jeremy Hyper Agency
Luke Jermay Michael Vine Assoc
Terry Jermyn Stage Centre Mngt
Mike Jerome Dings Ent/Pete Mitchell Associates
Mungo Jerry Barry Collings Ents/Entertainers Mgt Ltd/Jason West Agy/PVA Ent Consultants/Paul Bridson Prods/Rock Artist Mngt/Satellite Artists Ltd
Jerusha LRO Artist Mngt
Phil Jervis Northern Lights Mngt
Jessie J CHAMPIONS (UK) PLC/Purple PR
Emma Jesson CHAMPIONS (UK) PLC/Persnly Spkng
Sammy Jessop David Charles Agy
Jethro SWA Ent
Jetplane Landing Bad Moon Publicity
Jets Henderson Mngt
The Jets Jason West Agy/Paul Barrett Rock'N'Roll Entp
Jewel The Agency Group
Emily Jewell Billboard Persnl Mngt
Lisa Jewell CASAROTTO RAMSAY & ASSOCIATES
Jewels Book A Band
Poppy Jhakra Amber Persnl Mngt Ltd
Ronny Jhutti Harvey Voices Ltd/Troika Talent
Jiggery Pokery Barn Dance Line Dance Agy
Jigsaw Graham Cole Mngt
Jimmy Mac Duo Derek Bruce Ents
Jingles Sardi's Int'l Ent
Jingo (Santana tribute) Andrew Beauchamp Mngt
Susan Louise Jinks Direct Persnl Mngt
Jive Aces The Jive Aces
Jive Romeros Paul Barrett Rock'N'Roll Entp
Jiving Lindy Hoppers JLA/Jiving Lindy Hoppers (Ind Art)
JK & Joel Hyper Agency/Somethin' Else
The J.Lo Show (Jennifer Lopez tribute) Jason West Agy
JLS Modest! management
Tony Jo Nigel Round Mgnt
Joa the Cockatoo (Sky TV) Animal World
Joanie Celebn Model Mngt
Joanna Eliot Elinor Hilton Associates
Bob & Bob Jobbins Fool's Paradise/MTM Presntns
Joe ICM (USA)
Joe Black Bees Knees Ents
Joe Public Funhouse Productions Ltd
Billy Joel Artist Group International
Dirk Joeres Patrick Garvey Mngt
Alfie Joey GOLDMAN KING
Jean Johansson AIM
Tore Johansson Stephen Budd Mngt
Amani Johara MBA
John & Paul (Beatles Tribute) Dansatak
Anthony John Anthony John (Magic)
Clive John Moonglight Agy
John Lewis (Elton John) Advanced Ents
Margaret John Sara Crouch Mngt
John Miller and his Orchestra Mark Lundquist Management & Co
Nicholas John Linkside Agy
John Petters and his Rhythm Upbeat Mngt
John Regis 1st Choice Speakers UK Ltd
Robbin John Audrey Benjamin Agy
Sam John Barrie Stacey Promos & Prods
Sir Elton John Marshall Arts Ltd/TWENTY-FIRST ARTISTS LTD
Tony John Spotlight Ents (Notts)
Victoria John City Actors Mngt
John Worthington Peller Artistes Ltd
Danny John-Jules Jonathan Altaras Assoc
Johnny and The Jailbirds Paul Barrett Rock'N'Roll Entp
Johnny and the Roccos Paul Barrett Rock'N'Roll Entp
Dave Johns Sunshine Ents
Milton Johns Hilda Physick Agency
Simon Johns MBA
Susie Johns Mclean-Williams Management/Sue Rider Mngt Ltd
Aaron Johnson Jackie Palmer (JPA Mngt)
A.J. Johnson ICM (USA)
Alec Johnson Band Sunshine Ents
Wilko Johnson Band Jason West Agy/Rock Artist Mngt
Boris Johnson NMP Live Ltd
Danyl Johnson CHAMPIONS (UK) PLC
Dave Johnson Duo/Trio Steve Allen Ents
David Johnson Nigel Round Mgnt
Denise Johnson Dukeries Ents Ltd
Diana Johnson Central Line Co-Op Persnl Mngt
Emma Johnson Hazard Chase Ltd
Emma Johnson & Friends Hazard Chase Ltd
Graham Johnson Askonas Holt Ltd
Jilly Johnson Big Management (UK) Ltd (Ldn)/Model Plan Celebrities & Prese
Kenny Johnson and Northwind Deri Promos
Lorenza Johnson Sandra Singer Assoc
Marilyn Johnson Susan Angel Kevin Francis Ltd
Martin Johnson CBE CHAMPIONS (UK) PLC/Jon Holmes Media Ltd
Matt Johnson Garston Ents Ltd
Meg Johnson Big Bang Mngt Ltd
Melissa Johnson Harvey Voices Ltd
Michael Johnson Buddy Lee Attrctns Inc (USA)/CHAMPIONS (UK) PLC/DBA Speakers/NMP Live Ltd/Trading Faces Ltd
Mitch Johnson Voice Shop
Nim Johnson Rogues & Vagabonds Mngt
Pete Johnson Jazz Global Ent Agy
Pommy Johnson Paramount Int'l Mngt
Richard Johnson Independent Talent Group Ltd/PARAGON SPORTS MANAGEMENT LTD
Romina Johnson Mission Control Artist Agy
Rowena Johnson TFA Artiste Management
Scarlett Johnson Lou Coulson Associates
Vernon Johnson Darren Gray Mngt
Vicky Johnson Brian Taylor Assoc
Wilko Johnson John Hessenthaler Ents
Camilla Johnson-Hill Independent Talent Group Ltd
Dan Johnston Dawn Sedgwick Mngt
Dr Ian Johnston NMP MANAGEMENT
Guy Johnston IMG Artists
Julia Johnston Sara Crouch Mngt
Luke Johnston NMP Live Ltd
Paul Johnston Adastra
Rich Johnstone Sarm Mngt
Rob Johnstone LJ Ents
Ben Joiner Burnett Granger Assoc
The Joji Hirota Taiko Drummers PVA Ent Consultants
Jojo ICM (USA)
JoKate Hope Management
Killing Joke Free Trade Agy
Joker Les Hart (Southampton) Ents
Jokers Wild Anglia Artistes/McLeod Agy Ltd
Graham P Jolley Arena Ent Cons/Barry Dye Ents/CHAMPIONS (UK) PLC/Laurie Taylor Ents Ltd/Norwich Artistes/Persnl Appearances/Persnly Spkng/Prime Performers Ltd/Speakout/Spotlight Ents/Spotlight Ents (Notts)
Casey Lee Jolleys Linton Mngt
Genevieve Jolliffe CASAROTTO RAMSAY & ASSOCIATES
Kira Jolliffe Independent Talent Group Ltd
Jolly Jesters Jolly Jesters (Ind Art)
Nicola Jolly Star Management
Pam Jolly Brian Taylor Assoc
Jolly Roger Derek Bruce Ents
Dom Joly PBJ Mngt Ltd
Gareth Jon-Clarke ANA
Willie Jonah Burnett Granger Assoc
Jonas3 KAL Mngt
Mark Jonathan Clare Vidal-Hall
Jones & Co Ultimate Int'l
Paul Jones & Dave Kelly GTA Music Cons & Agy/John Hessenthaler Ents
Alan Jones UK Booking Agy
Aled Jones Capel & Land/Tony Clayman

Promos
Aled Haydn Jones Hyper Agency
Arbel Jones Emptage Hallett Ltd
Astley Jones Speak-Easy Ltd
Barbara Jones Kaye Frankland Ent Agy
Ben Jones MPC Ent/Speak-Easy Ltd
Bimbo Jones Action Talent Int.
Charlotte Jones Nancy Hudson Associates Ltd
Danny Jones (McFly) Insanity Artists
David Jones Judy Daish Assoc
Della Jones Music Int'l
Derek Jones Garston Ents Ltd
Diana Jones Asgard
Dr Hilary Jones 1st Choice Speakers UK Ltd
Elton Jones Upbeat Entertainment
Emma Jones The Richard Stone Prtnrshp
Eric Jones After Dinner World Ltd
Gareth Jones Opera & Concert Artists
George Jones David Hull Promos Ltd
Gethin Jones RDF Management
Grace Jones Tony Denton Promos Ltd
Howard Jones Barry Collings Ents/Jason West Agy/Miracle Artists Ltd/The Psycho Mngt Co Ltd/Tony Denton Promos Ltd
Jack Jones Chimes Int'l Ents Ltd
Jade Jones CHAMPIONS (UK) PLC
Jedda Jones aka "Ms. Dupre" ICM (USA)
Jennifer Jones Nigel Round Mgnt
Jenny Jones Paul Bridson Prods
Jimmy Jones Michael La Roche Mngt/Triple Cream Ents
Julia Jones Jill Foster Ltd
Katie Rowley Jones Burnett Granger Assoc
Dr Kevin Jones After Dinner World Ltd/Arena Ent Cons/Gordon Poole Agy Ltd/Nigel Round Mgnt/Persnl Appearances
Kimberley Jones Agency K-Bis
Larry Jones Larry Jones
Laura Jones CASAROTTO RAMSAY & ASSOCIATES
Lord Digby Jones 1st Choice Speakers UK Ltd/CHAMPIONS (UK) PLC/Trading Faces Ltd
Maggie Jones Louise Hillman/Katie Threlfall
Mark Jones Boogie Management
Milton Jones CHAMPIONS (UK) PLC/Noel Gay Artists Ltd/The Richard Stone Prtnrshp
Nigel Mazlyn Jones OTB Prods
Norah Jones Creative Artists Agency
Paul Jones Chatto & Linnit Ltd
Peter Jones NMP Live Ltd
The Jones Project Matters Musical
Quincy Jones William Morris Inc (USA)
Rhydian Jones AIM
Richard Jones Judy Daish Assoc/Mainstream Evts
Robin Jones King Salsa Cindy Hacker Assoc
Robin Jones Latin Jazz Sextet Cindy Hacker Assoc
Ruth Jones United Agents
Sadie Jones CASAROTTO RAMSAY & ASSOCIATES
Salena Jones Tony Puxley
Simon Jones The Richard Stone Prtnrshp
Steve Jones Independent Talent Group Ltd
Suranne Jones (Karen, Coronation Street) Nigel Round Mgnt/Shepherd Mngt Ltd
Taylor Jones Shining Mngt Ltd
Terri Jones Celebn Model Mngt
Terry Jones (Southport Weekender) CASAROTTO RAMSAY & ASSOCIATES/UK Booking Agy
Thom Jones The Wylie Agency
Toby Jones Jonathan Altaras Assoc
Tom Jones William Morris Inc (USA)
Vinnie Jones COLE KITCHENN PRSN MGT
Wyn Jones Dennis Lyne Agy
Jonny Hates Jazz Tony Denton Promos Ltd
Jon's Elton (Elton John) Complete Ent Serv Ltd
Ulrika Jonsson Take Three Mngt
Miss Jools COFFEE ARTISTS
Jordan (AKA Katie Price) Can Associates Ltd/NMP Live Ltd
Brian Jordan Nancy Hudson Associates Ltd
Carolyn Jordan Hilary Gagan Assoc
Charlie Jordan MPC Ent
Clare Jordan Derek Bruce Ents
Diane Louise Jordan NMP Live Ltd
Elizabeth Jordan Audrey Benjamin Agy
Frankie Jordan Jeffrey & White
Gary Jordan Liz Hobbs Grp Ltd
Holly Jordan MGA Entp
James & Ola Jordan CHAMPIONS (UK) PLC
Karina Jordan NVB Ents
Kathleen Jordan Direct Persnl Mngt
Martin Lee Jordan JB Ents
Michael Jordan Jane Hughes Mngt
Neil Jordan CASAROTTO RAMSAY & ASSOCIATES
Nicholas Jordan Adrian King Assoc
Sandra Jordan Troika Talent
Tony Jordan Gordon Kellett Ents
Maria Jordon Steve Draper Ents
Sarah Jory Deri Promos
Stephanie Jory Paul Duddridge Mngt
Joscho Stephan Trio NEM Prods (UK)

Joseph Owen Hughes Ents
Chantelle Joseph Lime Actors Agy & Mngt Ltd
Jacqui Joseph Independent Talent Group Ltd
Lesley Joseph Inspirational Artiste Bkg
Natasha Joseph The Richard Stone Prtnrshp
Paterson Joseph Lip Service Casting Ltd
Josephine 13 Artists
Josh Fairplay Ents
Josh Lewsey MBE BSc MCS Agcy
Anthony Joshua CHAMPIONS (UK) PLC
Rosemary Joshua Askonas Holt Ltd
Barbara Joslyn North One Mngt
Natasha Jouhl Hazard Chase Ltd
Journey South Action Talent Int./Big Talent Group/NMP Live Ltd
Katarina Jovanovic Transart (UK) Ltd
Mark Jowett Audrey Benjamin Agy
David Joyce Limelight Management
Ed Joyce PARAGON SPORTS MANAGEMENT LTD
Jacqueline Joyce KAL Mngt
Leila Joyce Susan Angel Kevin Francis Ltd
Rachel Joyce Cassie Mayer Ltd
Jo Joyner Louise Hillman/Katie Threlfall
Jr Walker's All Stars Ron Martin Mngt
Kristjan Järvi International Classical Artist
JT Taylor (Kool and the Gang) Mission Control Artist Agy
J.T.B. Experience M.G. Promos
Adrian Jubb Nancy Hudson Associates Ltd
Jubilee G Entertaining
Judas Priest Agency For the Performing Arts/ITB/Trinifold Management
Sarah Judd Martin Ents
Tom Jude APM Ass
Judge The Poet Whatever Artists Mngt Ltd
Katherine Judkins ANA
Jug City Hire-A-Band Ent Agy
Juggling Jamie Mr Magic Ents (Magic)
Chantal Juillet (violin) Clarion/Seven Muses
Jukalo MTM Presntns
Juke Box Jive Book A Band/Funhouse Productions Ltd/Leisure Mngt/Paul Barrett Rock'N'Roll Entp
Peter Jukes Judy Daish Assoc
Jules (Ecclectic) Doub7e Seven Events Ltd
Gary Jules ITB
Lucy Jules RDF Management
Julian Lloyd Webber with Bossa Nova
Julian The Juggler Partyweb.co.uk
Julieanna Chris Gordon Theatrical Agy
Juliette and the Licks Kas Mercer/Mercenary PR/Scream Promotions/The Agency Group
Juma Steel Band Juma Steel Band (Ind Art)
Jump Jive London Music Agy
Jumpin' Henderson Mngt
Jumpin' Jive (NL) Wim Wigt Prodns Ltd
Junction 24 NVB Ents
Junction 6 Goldstar Ent UK
Junction Jugglers Bigtopmania/CKK Ent/Stardust Ents Agy
Ashwin Juneja Sandra Boyce Mngt
Barb Junga & Her Musicians Jazzco/Matters Musical
Junia Sandra Singer Assoc
Junior BCM Promos Ltd/Barry Collings Ents/CKK Ent
Tony Junior Devil Management
Junkie XL Primary Talent Int'l
John Junkin Persnly Spkng
Phil Jupitus NMP Live Ltd
Phill Jupitus Off The Kerb Prods
Laura Jupp Agency K-Bis
Miles Jupp Richard Bucknall Mngt (RBM)/Speakout
Vladimir Jurowski IMG Artists
Just Aynuk Brian Yeates Assoc
Just Bono (U2 & Bono Tribute) Bees Knees Ents
Just Crazy Derek Bruce Ents
Just Dave Derek Bruce Ents
Dave Just Jon Peters Ents
Just Fred GM Ents
Just George CKK Ent
Just Jack Free Trade Agy/Insanity Artists
Just Jay NVB Ents
Just Korrs Henderson Mngt
Just Magic ABDC Ents
Justin Israeli Music Rent-A-Band
Justine as Anastasia Peller Artistes Ltd
JX Mission Control Artist Agy

K

K C Jay Spotlight Ents (Notts)
K Groove Matters Musical
K J Music Sound PVA Ent Consultants
Kenny K LRO Artist Mngt
K9 Commandoes Dog Display MTM Presntns
Kaaren Ragland's The Supremes Ron Martin Mngt
Kabbala Cabal Mngt/Wienerwald Ents
Aron Kader Avalon Mngt
Eddie Kadi Insanity Artists
Dieter Kaegi Athole Still Int'l Ltd/TEST AGENT A
Bert Kaempfert Orchestra Derek Boulton Productions
Si Kahn Adastra
Kai Fish 13 Artists
Kaiso London Music Agy/Matters Musical/Tropical Ents Mngt Agy
Peter Kajlinger Stafford Law
Kajol Jazz Barton Agency
Kurley Kale Barn Dance Line Dance Agy
Stuart Kale Athole Still Int'l Ltd/TEST AGENT A
Kaleidoscope Norwich Artistes
Merve Kalgidim Agency K-Bis
Kalichstein/Laredo/Robinson Piano Trio Askonas Holt Ltd
Jacques Kallis MPC Ent
Jean Kalman Judy Daish Assoc
Daniel Kaluuya Troika Talent
Liam Kam & Grant Hodgson CASAROTTO RAMSAY & ASSOCIATES
Antonie Kamerling Emptage Hallett Ltd
Shawn Kan Billboard Persnl Mngt
Kanda Bongo Man (Congo) Adastra
Kane Dave Woodbury Ents
"Handy" Andy Kane Celebrity Appearances/David Anthony Promos
Eden Kane Hal Carter Org
Gordon Kane Amber Persnl Mngt Ltd
Hosh Kane Louise Hillman/Katie Threlfall
Jonathan Kane (Elton John) Chance Promos
Kadi Kane CeeBee Variety Agy
Michael Kane LJ Ents
Natalie Kane Philip Youd Ents & Mngt
Patricia Kane Anita Alraun Representation
Richard Kane Kerry Gardner Mngt
Russ Kane Blackburn Sachs Assoc
Russell Kane Avalon Mngt/CHAMPIONS (UK) PLC
Sam Kane MCS Agcy
Sarah Kane (Estate) CASAROTTO RAMSAY & ASSOCIATES
Tim Kane Elinor Hilton Associates
Wendy Kane Hawthorn Ent
Kangaroos Gymnastic Display MTM Presntns
Kangeroo Moon Matters Musical
Kaniki Matters Musical
Sarah Kants Markham & Froggatt Ltd
Dunajska Kapelye Matters Musical
Juliette Kaplan Langford Assoc
Natasha Kaplinsky KBJ Management/Speakout
Klowns Karaoke Hire-A-Band Ent Agy
Karen Western Dancers A.I.R. Ltd
Karena Marie Compact Mngt & Ent Agy
Paul Karensa Noel Gay Artists Ltd
Kariba Latin Arts Serv (LAS)
Karina Gem Prods
Karisma Derek Bruce Ents/Ginger Walker Agy
Karizma G Entertaining
Miriam Karlin OBE Burnett Granger Assoc
Katarina Karnéus Ingpen & Williams Ltd
Karneval Bavarian Band Rent-A-Band
The Karpenters (The Carpenters Tribute) Peller Artistes Ltd
Theresa Kartell M W Management
Kasabian Hall Or Nothing/ITB
Kasai Masai (Africa) Adastra
Mamta Kash Kerry Gardner Mngt
Tim Kash Form Talent
Jacek Kaspszyk The Music Ptnrshp Ltd
Ganiat Kasumu Jonathan Altaras Assoc
Katari Group Matters Musical/Wienerwald Ents
Katary Latin-Touch Ents
Katatonia The Agency Group
Kate (harpist) Matters Musical
Kate Winslet Peters Fraser Dunlop (PFD)/Premier PR/United Agents
Simon Katich MPC Ent
Katie Gibbons & Take 6 Cromwell Mngt
Peter Katin Transart (UK) Ltd
Kerry Katona The Commercial Agency
Katrice JB Ents
Katrina (from Katrina & the Waves) Barry Collings Ents
Katrina & The Waves Brian Gannon Mngt/Mission Control Artist Agy
Katrina Leskanich Jason West Agy
Cyprien Katsaris Transart (UK) Ltd
Emma Katz Nancy Hudson Associates Ltd
Amy Kaur Tony Clayman Promos
Kavana Action Talent Int./Tony Denton Promos Ltd/Unleashed PR
Anne Kavanagh M W Management
Anthony Kavanagh Lime Actors Agy & Mngt Ltd
Sarah Kavanagh-Jones Agency K-Bis
Tomono Kawamura Matters Musical
Bernard Kay Shepherd Mngt Ltd
Janet Kay Monkeybiz Ent Agy/Sandra Boyce Mngt
Jay Kay Dave Woolf PR/MERLIN ELITE
Julian Kay Northern Lights Mngt
Peter Kay Phil McIntyre Ent. Ltd
Serena Kay Ingpen & Williams Ltd
Taryn Kay Nancy Hudson Associates Ltd
Vernon Kay Hackford Jones PR/NMP Live Ltd/Princess Talent Mngt
Kay Ward's Baker Street Devil Management
Bobby Kaye Tony West Ents

Gorden Kaye Markham & Froggatt Ltd
Jason Kaye (Top Buzz) UK Booking Agy
Melody Kaye KAL Mngt
Paul Kaye The Richard Stone Prtnrshp
Kayley B.F.P Ents
Kaytu Nick Allen Mngt
Kaz PVA Ent Consultants
Lanie Kazan The Kruger Organisation - TKO
Rob Kazinsky Big Bang Mngt Ltd
Robert Kazinsky Burnett Granger Assoc
Michael Kazirakos Langford Assoc
KC & The Sunshine Band Tony Denton Promos Ltd/William Morris Inc (USA)
KC and the Soul Revue Jason West Agy
Ian Keable Arena Ent Cons/Gordon Poole Agy Ltd/Ian Keable (Magic)/Prima Artists
Kevin Keagan CHAMPIONS (UK) PLC
Barbara Kealy (Joan Collins) Upfront Ent Agy Ltd
Roy Kean Audrey Benjamin Agy
Sidney Kean M W Management
Keane The Agency Group
Dillie Keane Gavin Barker
Fergal Keane OBE Kruger Cowne Limited
Shirley Keane Grays Mngt & Asc
Gillian Kearney Jonathan Altaras Assoc/Peters Fraser Dunlop (PFD)/Yakety Yak
Martha Kearney KBJ Management
Sean Kearney Grays Mngt & Asc
Tracy Kearney Wendy Lee Mngt
Gerard Kearns (Ian Shamless) Nigel Round Mngt
John Kearns MPC Ent
Laura Kearsey Billboard Persnl Mngt
Dominic Keating Shining Mngt Ltd
Frank Keating Judy Daish Assoc
Paul Keating Troika Talent
Ronan Keating Solo Agy Ltd/The Lisa Richards Agy/The Outside Organisation
Ben Keaton Richard Bucknall Mngt (RBM)
Paul Keefe Positive Plus Ltd
Michelle Keegan (Tina, Coronation Street) Hyper Agency/Nigel Round Mngt
Michael Keegan-Dolan Performing Arts
Mark Keeley's Elvis Show Henderson Mngt
Gemma Keeling Audrey Benjamin Agy
Les Keen RDF Management
Nicola Keen Talent Artists Ltd
Simon Keenlyside Askonas Holt Ltd
Keily Nigel Round Mgnt
Claire Keirnan Celebn Model Mngt
Adam Keisner CKK Ent
Andy Keith Artiste & Musical
Penelope Keith OBE Burnett Granger Assoc
Tommy Keith MJE Mngt
Kele Okereke 13 Artists
Christopher Kelham Kerry Gardner Mngt
Kate Kelland APM Ass
J.D. Kelleher Dennis Lyne Agy
Natasha Kellett Sandra Boyce Mngt
Dave Kelly & The Blues Call GTA Music Cons & Agy
Alistair Kelly Linkside Agy
Archie Kelly The Narrow Road Company Ltd
Catherine Kelly Darren Gray Mngt
Danny Kelly Noel Gay Artists Ltd
Dave Kelly GTA Music Cons & Agy/Harvey Voices Ltd
Alannah Davis Kelly Linkside Agy
Dean Kelly Billboard Persnl Mngt/Harvey Voices Ltd
Eamonn Kelly Voice Shop
Gerard Kelly Markham & Froggatt Ltd
Gerry Kelly David Hull Promos Ltd
Graham Kelly Preview & Review Ents Ltd
Henry Kelly Persnl Appearances
Jane Kelly Derek Bruce Ents
Kelly Joe Phelps CODA Ltd
Jon Kelly Stephen Budd Mngt
Kam Kelly Wise Buddah Talent & Voices
Katherine Kelly (Beccy, Coronation Street) Nigel Round Mgnt
Kieran Kelly Jacque Evans Mngt Ltd
Kris Kelly Deri Promos
Leigh Kelly West Central Mngt
Kelly Llorenna Action Talent Int./Mission Control Artist Agy
Lorraine Kelly Speakout/Trading Faces Ltd
Mike Kelly After Dinner Spkers & Com/Nigel Round Mgnt
Ned Kelly Funhouse Productions Ltd/McLeod Agy Ltd
Polly Kelly Richard Bucknall Mngt (RBM)
Rae Kelly Amber Persnl Mngt Ltd
Kelly Rowland ICM (USA)/Purple PR
Sam Kelly The Richard Stone Prtnrshp
Spencer Kelly Curtis Brown Grp
Tony Kelly Barn Dance Line Dance Agy
Kellys Eye Barn Dance Line Dance Agy
Kelly's Heroes Alan Whitehead Mngt Ltd/Barn Dance Line Dance Agy/Matters Musical
Pat Kelman Inspiration Mngt
Anita Kelsey Matters Musical
Edward Kelsey Markham & Froggatt Ltd
Stephen Kemble Voice Shop
Kemistry Duo London Music Agy
Dee Kemp Barn Dance Line Dance Agy
Martin Kemp AIM/Mission Control Artist Agy/Prime Performers Ltd
Rose Kemp Park Promotions
Ross Kemp ARG Management/NMP MANAGEMENT/Trading Faces Ltd
Freddy Kempf IMG Artists
Teddy Kempner Kerry Gardner Mngt
William Kempsel AXM
Joan Kempson Troika Talent
Allin Kempthorne CKK Ent/Partyweb.co.uk
Pamela Kempthorne CKK Ent/Partyweb.co.uk
Louise Kempton Shepherd Mngt Ltd
Gary Kemsley NVB Ents
Harriet Kemsley Louise Hillman/Katie Threlfall
Ken Morgan Band with Carla Hendriks ABDC Ents
David Kendall ACIB After Dinner World Ltd/Arena Ent Cons/Gordon Poole Agy Ltd/McLeod Agy Ltd/Persnly Spkng
Elodie Kendall Talking Heads - The Voice Agy
Felicity Kendal Chatto & Linnit Ltd
Kenneth Kendall Jeremy Hicks Assoc
Kendall String Quartet Doub7e Seven Events Ltd
Kenisha Stephen Budd Mngt
Liv Kennard Take Three Mngt
Kennedy & Brent Fairplay Ents
Alan Kennedy After Dinner World Ltd/Gordon Robinson Assoc/Nigel Round Mgnt/Persnl Appearances
Angus Kennedy Alpha Persnl Mngt
Bryan Kennedy Jeffrey & White
Caroline Kennedy Lime Actors Agy & Mngt Ltd
Claire Kennedy Dinosaur Promo/Dinosaur Mus
Denise Kennedy RBA Management Ltd
Fiona Kennedy Limelight Management
Baroness Helena Kennedy QC Speakout
Johnny Kennedy The Horne Concert Agy
Joyce Kennedy Northern Lights Mngt
Kenneth Kennedy Audrey Benjamin Agy
Kevin Kennedy Burnett Granger Assoc
Phil Kennedy Blackburn Sachs Assoc
Rebecca Kennedy Indep Mngt Ltd
Sarah Kennedy CASAROTTO RAMSAY & ASSOCIATES/Richard Bucknall Mngt (RBM)
Suzie Kennedy as Marilyn Monroe Doub7e Seven Events Ltd/Prima Artists
Zoie Kennedy Waring & Mckenna
Kenneth Baker (Caricatures) Barrie Hawkins Leisure Service
Kenny Brian Gannon Mngt/Pete Mitchell Associates
Kenny G The Agency Group
Gerard Kenny Cromwell Mngt
Jason Kenny CHAMPIONS (UK) PLC
Louise Kenny (Shania Twain) Andrew Beauchamp Mngt
Lynn Kenny Prof Sports Ptnr Ltd
Yvonne Kenny Askonas Holt Ltd
Les Kenny-Green Alpha Persnl Mngt
Nathan Kenshaw Celebn Model Mngt
Patsy Kensit Peters Fraser Dunlop (PFD)/United Agents/Yakety Yak
Anne Kent Audrey Benjamin Agy
Christopher Kent Voice Shop
David Kent Jae Moss Entp
Hayley Kent Nigel Round Mgnt
Jonathan Kent Judy Daish Assoc
Lisa Kent (Director/Choreographer) Gavin Barker
Richard Kent Adrian King Assoc
Sayan Kent Elinor Hilton Associates
Stacey Kent The John Boddy Agency
Zachary Kenton Agency K-Bis
Rebecca Kenyon Frontline Mngt Ltd
Kenzie Big Talent Group/Identity One Management
Paul Keogan Clare Vidal-Hall
Vanessa Keogh Speak-Easy Ltd
Vanessa Jayne Kerfoot Amber Persnl Mngt Ltd
Tonya Kerins Susan Angel Kevin Francis Ltd
Robin Kermode Yakety Yak
Chris Kern & Siam Derek Bruce Ents
Suzanne Kern The Horne Concert Agy
David Kernan Brunskill Management Ltd
Amanda Kernot Royce Mngt
Kernow Pyrotechnics Kernow Ents
Alex Kerr Shining Mngt Ltd/Tavistock Wood Management Ltd
David Kerr CASAROTTO RAMSAY & ASSOCIATES
Paul Kerr Matters Musical
Yasmin Kerr Markham & Froggatt Ltd
Julian Kerridge Markham & Froggatt Ltd
Clare Kerrigan Northern Lights Mngt
Craig Kerrigan Sandra Boyce Mngt
Dermot Kerrigan Cassie Mayer Ltd/Yakety Yak
Jonathan Kerrigan CAM London
Patricia Kerrigan Markham & Froggatt Ltd
Gillian Kerrod North Of Watford Actors Agy
Bob Kerr's Whoopee Band (Jazz & Comedy) Acker's Int'l Agy/London Music Agy/Upbeat Mngt
Kerry's Gold LRO Artist Mngt
Andy Kershaw Speak-Easy Ltd

David Kershaw Nancy Hudson Associates Ltd
Doug Kershaw Buddy Lee Attrctns Inc (USA)
Nik Kershaw Jason West Agy/Tony Denton Promos Ltd
Sammy Kershaw Buddy Lee Attrctns Inc (USA)
Dervia Kerwan Conway Van Gelder Grant Ltd
Kesh Band Barn Dance Line Dance Agy
Therese Kesington Newton Wills Mngt
Sara Kestelman Jonathan Altaras Assoc/Yakety Yak
Keta Matters Musical
Jon Ketilsson Athole Still Int'l Ltd/TEST AGENT A
Billy Kettle Derek Bruce Ents
Liz Kettle The Richard Stone Prtnrshp
John Kettley Persnl Appearances
Sara Kewly Crescent Mngt
Christopher Key Anita Alraun Representation
Alicia Keys Helter Skelter Agy Ltd
Marjorie Keys Jeffrey & White
Richard Keys Athole Still Int'l Ltd/Jon Holmes Media Ltd/TEST AGENT A
Pia de Keyser Paul Duddridge Mngt
Kezia Tony Clayman Promos
KFS Elite Promos
Sergei Khachatrian Askonas Holt Ltd
Sergey Khachatryan Askonas Holt Ltd
Khaliq BTM Mngt & Agy
Khalisha Matters Musical
Alexander Khan MBA
Amir Khan CHAMPIONS (UK) PLC
Junaid Khan Linton Mngt
Muzz Khan Direct Persnl Mngt
Omar Khan Scott-Paul Young Ents Ltd
Shaheen Khan Judy Daish Assoc
Rahul Khanna Brunskill Mngt Ltd
Anjana Khatwa Arlington Enterprises Ltd
Nadia Khiavi Agency K-Bis
Rachel Khoo CHAMPIONS (UK) PLC
Shappi Khorsandi Off The Kerb Prods
Raymond Khoury CASAROTTO RAMSAY & ASSOCIATES
Kick Back Derek Bruce Ents
Kick Up The 80s Head On Mngt
A Kick Up The 80's Jason West Agy
Kickback Band LRO Artist Mngt
Kid Creole & the Coconuts BULLET MANAGEMENT LIMITED/Denis Vaughan Mngt/Jason West Agy/Malcolm Feld Agy/The Psycho Mngt Co Ltd/Tony Denton Promos Ltd
Kid Koala CODA Ltd
Kid;Coda Kitchenware Mngt
Craig Kidd McLeod Agy Ltd
David Kidd Chord Theatrical & Corporate
Jennifer Kidd Brunskill Mngt Ltd
Jodie Kidd MERLIN ELITE
Janet Kidder RDF Management
Angelique Kidjo Universal/Island Records Ltd
Kids (Kylie & Robbie) Advanced Ents
Patrick Kielty David Hull Promos Ltd/M F Management Ltd/NMP Live Ltd
Terry Kiely AIM
Daniel Kieve Sardi's Int'l Ent
Paul Kieve CKK Ent
Dean Kilbey Voice Shop
Emma Kilbey Sara Crouch Mngt
Melanie Kilburn Markham & Froggatt Ltd
Beth Kilcoyne Noel Gay Artists Ltd
Emma Kilcoyne Noel Gay Artists Ltd
Michael Kilgarriff Talking Heads - The Voice Agy/Vincent Shaw Assoc Ltd
Rebecca Kilgarriff Vincent Shaw Assoc Ltd
David Killick The Richard Stone Prtnrshp
Jeremy Killick 1984 Persnl Mngt
Preece Killick Kenneth Earle Persnl Mngt
Debbie Killingback Sandra Boyce Mngt
The Kills Big Sister Promotions/Sainted PR
Russell Kilmister M W Management
Ivory Al Kilvington McLeod Agy Ltd
Al Kilvinston & The Aces Funhouse Productions Ltd
Koi Kimani Brian Taylor Assoc
Christine Kimberley Anita Alraun Representation
Sue Kimberley ICON Actors Mngt
Francesca Kimpton Cunningham Mngt Ltd
Kin Derek Bruce Ents/Firefly Productions
David Kincaid Vincent Shaw Assoc Ltd
Glen Kinch Central Line Co-Op Persnl Mngt
Kind Of Jazz Steve Allen Ents
Kinda Magic (Illusionists) Ron Martin Mngt
Tania Kindersley (Dramatic Rights) Judy Daish Assoc
Clare Kindon Derek Bruce Ents
Steve Kindon After Dinner World Ltd/Gordon Robinson Assoc/Nigel Round Mgnt
The King Doug Smith Assoc
Alan King William Morris Inc (USA)
Allan King Compact Mngt & Ent Agy/Knight Ayton Mngt
Anthony King Jongleurs
Barbara King AIM
Basil King Grays Mngt & Asc
Ben E King Entertainers Mgt Ltd
Beryl King City Actors Mngt
Chris King Talent One
Claire King Daly Pearson Associates/Urban Associates Personal Mana
Danny King Complete Ent Serv Ltd
D.D. King Dinosaur Promo/Dinosaur Mus
Debbie King Barrie Stacey Promos & Prods/Tony Clayman Promos
Evelyn Champagne King Tony Denton Promos Ltd
Gary King Speak-Easy Ltd
Holly King Circuit Persnl Mngt Ltd
Jacqueline King Jeffrey & White
James King Hyper Agency/Knight Ayton Mngt
Jason King (international male vocalist) BCM Promos Ltd
Joanne King Sandra Boyce Mngt
Kevin King Kevin King Mngt/NVB Ents
Larry King American Program Bureau
Lorelei King The Voice Box Agency Ltd
Lucy King Agency K-Bis
Michelle King Urban Associates Personal Mana
Mike King Derek Bruce Ents
Nicola King The Richard Stone Prtnrshp
King Pleasure & the Biscuit Boys Big Bear Music
Rachel King Norwich Artistes
Richard Lloyd King Daly Pearson Associates
Ruby King Jeffrey & White
King Salsa Latin Arts Serv (LAS)
Selena King
King Shaft Dave Woodbury Ents/Derek Bruce Ents
Shirley King Talking Heads - The Voice Agy
Sid & Billy King Paul Barrett Rock'N'Roll Entp
Simon King (Freddie Starr tribute) BCM Promos Ltd
Stephanie King CeeBee Variety Agy
King Sunny Ade CODA Ltd
King Swingers PVA Ent Consultants
Teri King Jacque Evans Mngt Ltd
Tony King Kernow Ents
Tracy King Dinosaur Promo/Dinosaur Mus/Power Promos
Kingdom Choir Matters Musical
Gipsy Kingdom Prima Artists
Desiree Kingerod CKK Ent
Edward Kingham Kerry Gardner Mngt
Kings of Convenience CODA Ltd
Kings Of Queen (Queen tribute) Advanced Ents/Upfront Ent Agy Ltd
Kings X Miracle Artists Ltd
Kingsativa (Bob Marley) Advanced Ents
Noel Kingsbury Limelight Management
Katherine Kingsley Wise Buddah Talent & Voices
Steve Kingsley Les Hart (Southampton) Ents
Alex Kingston Lou Coulson Associates
The Kingston Trio William Morris Inc (USA)
Miles Kington Arena Ent Cons/Gordon Poole Agy Ltd
The Kinks Asgard
Kinky (Kinks tribute) Compact Mngt & Ent Agy/Henderson Mngt/Jason West Agy
Kinky Malinky Party Nights UK Booking Agy
Kinlochard Ceilidh Band BGS PRODUCTIONS
Patrick Kinmonth Loesje Sanders
Rory Kinnear Markham & Froggatt Ltd
Brooke Kinsella CAM London
Nikolai Kinski Tavistock Wood Management Ltd
Tim Kirby Anita Alraun Representation
Roy Kirby's Paragon Jazz Derek Bruce Ents
Amelia Kirk 1984 Persnl Mngt
Anne Kirkbride Big Bang Mngt Ltd
Emma Kirkby Hazard Chase Ltd
Anna Kirke Amber Persnl Mngt Ltd/City Actors Mngt
Andy Kirkham Norwich Artistes
Anthony Kirkham MGA Entp
Jen Kirkman Avalon Mngt
Andy Kirkpatrick CHAMPIONS (UK) PLC
Gillian Kirkpatrick Cassie Mayer Ltd/Lip Service Casting Ltd
John Kirkpatrick Speaking Volumes
Ralph Kirshbaum Ingpen & Williams Ltd
Dominic Kirwan Chimes Int'l Ents Ltd/Deri Promos
Colm Kirwen Jeffrey & White
Kisen Limelight Management
Kiskadee Advanced Ents
Kiss ITB
Evgeny Kissin Askonas Holt Ltd
Kit & The Widow PBJ Mngt Ltd
Michael Kitchen M F Management Ltd
Donna Lisa Kitching Stage Centre Mngt
Kit-E-Kat Animal World
Ken Kitson Nyland Mngt
Jayne Kitt Cherry Parker Management
Roger Kitter PVA Ent Consultants/Persnl Appearances/Tony Clayman Promos
KJ Band (functions) Apple County
K.J. Music Zone Derek Bruce Ents/G Entertaining
KK Stephen Budd Mngt
K-Klass UK Booking Agy

Sascha Klaar Wim Wigt Prodns Ltd
Jack Klaff The Richard Stone Prtnrshp
Franz Klammer Athole Still Int'l Ltd/TEST AGENT A
We Are Klang Avalon Mngt
Jessie Klass Blackburn Sachs Assoc
Myleene Klass Hackford Jones PR/Mission Control Artist Agy/ROAR Group/Trading Faces Ltd
Klaxons Alan James PR Agency/Big Life Management/Big Sister Promotions
Deboragh Klayman Scott-Paul Young Ents Ltd
Beverly Klein Jeffrey & White
Carol Klein Curtis Brown Grp/Gordon Poole Agy Ltd
Jeff Klein ITB
Lucy Klein Fushion Pukka Bosh
Oscar Klein, Romano Mussolini, Charlie Antolini (A/CH/IT/G) Wim Wigt Prodns Ltd
Robert Klein William Morris Inc (USA)
Klezmania Matters Musical
Klezmer Festival Band Adastra
Lance Klusener MPC Ent
Richard Klvac ANA
Katie Knapman Arlington Enterprises Ltd
Janet Knechtel John Field - Theatre and Puppe
Ashley Knight Matters Musical
Austin Knight Gordon Robinson Assoc
Barry Knight Barry Knight (Ind Art)
Beverley Knight Dave Woolf PR
Brian Knight BAM Assoc Ltd
Carmen Knight Audrey Benjamin Agy
Chris Knight Buddy Lee Attrctns Inc (USA)/NVB Ents
Kristian Knight Derek Bruce Ents
Michele Knight Jacque Evans Mngt Ltd
Natalie Knight MJE Mngt
Paul Knight Garston Ents Ltd
Richard Knight CKK Ent
Sharron Knight Celebn Ents Mngt & Agy
Tariq Knight Whatever Artists Mngt Ltd
Keira Knightley Peters Fraser Dunlop (PFD)/United Agents
Will Knightley The Richard Stone Prtnrshp
Gary Knights Steve Allen Ents
Knights of Arkley MTM Presntns
Knights of Soul NVB Ents
Mark Knopfler William Morris Inc (USA)
Chris Knott as David Essex GM Ents
Christian Knott Lime Actors Agy & Mngt Ltd
Christopher Knott Indep Mngt Ltd
Eric Knowles All Electric Productions & Dav/Paul Bridson Prods/Take Three Mngt
Michael Knowles The Richard Stone Prtnrshp
Nick Knowles John Miles Org/Speakout
Tony Knowles CHAMPIONS (UK) PLC
Alexis Knox Curtis Brown Grp
Patrick Knox Grays Mngt & Asc
Frankie Knuckles ITB
Bobby Knutt Funhouse Productions Ltd
Sally Knyvette Sandra Griffin Mngt
Zoltán Kocsis IMG Artists
Hardeep Singh-Kohli CASAROTTO RAMSAY & ASSOCIATES/Speakout/Trading Faces Ltd
Sanjeev Kohli Speakout
Roddy Kohn Jeremy Hicks Assoc
Koko Sunshine Ents
Kokomo (tribute to Beach Boys) BCM Promos Ltd
Bogden Kominowski SJ Mngt
Koo-Ka-Choo Fairplay Ents/Henderson Mngt/Sphinx Mngt & Ent Agy
Kooki Dave Woodbury Ents
Kooks 13 Artists
Kool & The Gang Brian Gannon Mngt/Jason West Agy/Tony Denton Promos Ltd
Kool Breeze Sunshine Ents
KooL Karaoke Disco David Forshaw Entp
Justine Koos ANA
Kopelman Pro Artist Management
Yiolanda Koppell Downes Presenters Agy
Kopy Katz Book A Band
Korgis Barry Collings Ents
Jyrki Korhonen Athole Still Int'l Ltd/TEST AGENT A
Korn ITB
Senya Koroma Grays Mngt & Asc
Kosheen CODA Ltd
Koshka (Russia/Scotland) Adastra
Aicha Kossoko Brunskill Management Ltd
Ravi Kothakota Argyle Assoc
Kadialy Kouyate Matters Musical
Stephen Kovacevich International Classical Artist
Kovari Crowd Pullers
George Kovari Jnr/Snr Partyweb.co.uk
Magdelena Kozená Askonas Holt Ltd
Joseph Kpobie Rossmore Persnl Mngt
Kracatoa Albert Alchemy Ent
Krackers Hire-A-Band Ent Agy
Henning Kraggerud IMG Artists
Diana Krall William Morris Inc (USA)
Larry Kramer CASAROTTO RAMSAY & ASSOCIATES
Krankies Henderson Mngt
Anna Krantz Blujay Mngt Ltd
Gene Kranz Parliament Comms
Adrienne Krausz Transart (UK) Ltd
Alla Kravchuk Music Int'l
Lenny Kravitz ITB
Roberta Kray Robert Smith Literary Agency
Krazy Kat Theatre John Field - Theatre and Puppe
Anji Kreft The Voice Box Agency Ltd
Kremlin Ballet Go Ents
The Kremlinaires Matters Musical
Kris Krendo Multi-Media Ents
Miranda Krestovnikoff Jo Sarsby PR Ltd
Charles Kriel Athole Still Int'l Ltd/TEST AGENT A
Thor Kristinsson Argyle Assoc
Kris Kristofferson ICM (USA)
Emmanuel Krivine Askonas Holt Ltd
Karen Krizanovich Blackburn Sachs Assoc/Talking Heads - The Voice Agy
Carsten Kroeyer Stephen Budd Mngt
Tony Krolo Paramount Int'l Mngt
Kruder & Dorfmeister CODA Ltd
Krust CODA Ltd
Krylati Rent-A-Band
Krys Dinosaur Promo/Dinosaur Mus/Fairplay Ents
Krystalettes Funhouse Productions Ltd
K's Choice ITB
Karolina Ksiazek Celebn Model Mngt
KT Roadshow Multi-Media Ents
KTP CEC Management
Kubichek! Free Trade Agy/Supervision Management
Kula Shaker 13 Artists
Unusan Kuloglu Opera & Concert Artists
Kultur Shock Gold Star PR
Larissa Kumana Sandra Singer Assoc
Akshay Kumar Jazz Barton Agency
Angela Kumari Elinor Hilton Associates
Krishna Kumari Nancy Hudson Associates Ltd
Simon Kunz Emptage Hallett Ltd
Kareena Kupoor Jazz Barton Agency
Darren Kuppan ICON Actors Mngt
Srdjan Kurpjel & Marios Takoushis SMA Talent Ltd
Kursaal Flyers Jason West Agy
Ivan Kusnjer Music Int'l
Ashton Kutcher Endeavor Agency
Kutski Fresh Artiste Management Ltd
Kwabana Continental Drifts/TEST AGENT C
Andrew Kwame Northern Lights Mngt
Kwantum Sardi's Int'l Ent
Kwame Kwei-Armah United Agents
Terry Kyan Jill Foster Ltd
Paul Kybert Derek Bruce Ents
Susan Kyd Kerry Gardner Mngt
Kyla Cliff Matthews Mngt & Ent Agy
Jeremy Kyle Somethin' Else
Ky-Lee (Kylie Minogue) David Charles Agy/Jason West Agy/Nigel Round Mgnt
Kylie Fever Dansatak/Nigel Round Mgnt
Kylie Tribute - Faye Arena Ent Cons

L

Thelma L'Estrange (soprano) Gown & Gauntlet Promos
La Bottine Souriante (Quebec) Adastra
La Boum! Stoneyport Associates
La Clave Latin Arts Serv (LAS)/Latin-Touch Ents
La Doors Andrew Beauchamp Mngt
La Musette ABDC Ents
L.A. Nights Sardi's Int'l Ent
Judy La Rose Sandra Singer Assoc
La Roux Insanity Artists
Peter La Scalla Devil Management
The LA Session Band Book A Band
La Tour The CBS Grp
La Vida Loca (Ricky Martin & Enrique Eglasias) Camscott Leisure/Peller Artistes Ltd
La Volee D'Castors Roots Around The World
John Labanowski Dennis Lyne Agy
L'Abba D'Abba Leisure Mngt
Adam Lacey Broadwater Ents Assoc
Janice Lacey Robert Crossland Ent Ltd
Mark Lacey Cassie Mayer Ltd
Rebecca Lacey ARG Management/Yakety Yak
William Lacey Ingpen & Williams Ltd
Lacuna Coil The Agency Group
Simon Lacy North Of Watford Actors Agy
Du'aine Ladejo Paul Stacey Management/Reality Check Management
Ladies and Gentlemen (George Michael tribute) Henderson Mngt
Ladies Of Rock (Ind Art) Ladies of Rock
Lady and the Tramp Multi-Media Ents
Lady Boys of Bangkok Go Ents
Lady Christobel & Her Butler CKK Ent/Fool's Paradise/MTM Presntns
Lady Gaa Gaa Nigel Round Mgnt
Lady Go Go B.F.P Ents
Lady Madonna The Psycho Mngt Co Ltd
Lady Marmalade The Psycho Mngt Co Ltd
Lady Sings The Blues Big Bear Music
Lady Sovereign Primary Talent Int'l
The Ladybirds Head On Mngt
The Ladykillers Head On Mngt
Ladysmith Black Mambazo William Morris Inc (USA)

Ladytron Primary Talent Int'l
Johnny Laff Compact Mngt & Ent Agy
Chris Lafferty Dukeries Ents Ltd
Christopher Lafferty KAL Mngt
Marcy Lafferty The Kruger Organisation - TKO
Kieran Lagan Jonathan Altaras Assoc
Lagbaja CODA Ltd
Emil Lager Actorum
Lorna Laidiaw Amber Persnl Mngt Ltd
Andy Laine Norwich Artistes
Cleo Laine The John Boddy Agency
Denny Laine PVA Ent Consultants
Denny Laine Band Brian Gannon Mngt
Cleo Laine & John Dankworth Jazzco
Jamie Laing CHAMPIONS (UK) PLC
Stewart Laing Judy Daish Assoc
Stuart Laing Shining Mngt Ltd
Martina Laird Gordon & French
Steve Laister Moonglight Agy
Adam Lake Burnett Granger Assoc
Allan Lake Wise Buddah Talent & Voices
Catherine Lake Linkside Agy
Lakeland Birds of Prey MTM Presntns
Seth Lakeman Big Sister Promotions/Dave Woolf PR
Leanne Lakey BWH Agency
Rupi Lal Brian Taylor Assoc
Steve Lamacq Wise Buddah Talent & Voices
Rob Lamar Ron Martin Mngt
Mark Lamarr NMP Live Ltd/Off The Kerb Prods
Alan Lamb MBE Speakout
Allan Lamb MBE Celebrity Appearances/Gordon Poole Agy Ltd/NMP Live Ltd/Persnly Spkng
Amanda Lamb NMP Live Ltd/Speakout
Dave Lamb The Richard Stone Prtnrshp
George Lamb Insanity Artists
Gina Lamb Lime Actors Agy & Mngt Ltd
Lambchop CODA Ltd/Dog Day Press
Jane Lambert Royce Mngt
Mark Lambert Jonathan Altaras Assoc
Paul Lambert Speakout
Robert Lamberti (George Michael) Advanced Ents/Andrew Beauchamp Mngt/Barry Collings Ents/Nigel Round Mgnt/Prima Artists/SWA Ent
Anthony Lamble Clare Vidal-Hall
Mark Lambourne Linkside Agy
Lady Lucinda Lambton 1st Choice Speakers UK Ltd
Amy Lame RAGE/The Richard Stone Prtnrshp
Gemma Lamonby Celebn Model Mngt
Glenn Lamont Amber Persnl Mngt Ltd
Katy Lamont AIM
Lord Norman Lamont CHAMPIONS (UK) PLC
Ray Lamontagne Big Sister Promotions
Eteri Lamoris Stafford Law
James Lamper Talent4 Media Ltd
Diana Lamplugh OBE PVA Ent Consultants
Bob Lampon Talking Heads - The Voice Agy
David Lan Judy Daish Assoc
Keith Lancaster Grays Mngt & Asc
James Lance Troika Talent
Tyrone Landau Music Int'l
Peter Landi Actorum/Sandra Boyce Mngt
Harry Landis Peter Charlesworth & Assoc
Kristine Landon-Smith Judy Daish Assoc
Lisa Landry Avalon Mngt
David Lane Jill Foster Ltd
Melody Lane Angle Ents Ltd
Natalie Lane (Shania Twain) Entertainers Mgt Ltd
Penny Lane KAL Mngt
Tim Lane Norwich Artistes
Steve Lane's Southern Stompers London Music Agy
Geoffrey Lang Billboard Persnl Mngt
K.D. Lang Asgard
John Langdon Jeremy Hicks Assoc
Bernard Langer OBE CHAMPIONS (UK) PLC
Bernhard Langer OBE CHAMPIONS (UK) PLC
Justin Langer MPC Ent
Bonnie Langford Billy Marsh Assoc Ltd
Darren Langford Circuit Persnl Mngt Ltd
John Langford Otto Persnl Mngt Ltd
Lloyd Langford GOLDMAN KING
Chris Langham David Wilkinson Assoc
Rebecca Langhurst Athole Still Int'l Ltd/TEST AGENT A
Mark Langley Devil Management
Stephen Langridge Loesje Sanders
Ruth Langsford David Hull Promos Ltd/First Artist Management/Talking Heads - The Voice Agy
Sara Langton Mike Constantia Artiste Mngt L
Junior Lanigan Kerry Gardner Mngt
Eric Lanlard TFA Artiste Management
Jeanette Lanz Bergin VRM Artists
Laptop Universal/Island Records Ltd
Alexandra Maria Lara Tavistock Wood Management Ltd
L'Archibudelli Transart (UK) Ltd
Lee Lard Nigel Round Mgnt
Jaime Laredo Askonas Holt Ltd
Eddie Large Int'l Artistes Ltd/PVA Ent Consultants
Larkin' About CKK Ent
Francesca Larkin Otto Persnl Mngt Ltd
Ian Larkin Norwich Artistes
Mary Larkin Daly Pearson Associates
Michael Larkin Performance Actors Agy
Martin Larner UK Booking Agy
L'Arpeggiata Clarion/Seven Muses
Marek Larwood Avalon Mngt
Las Vegas Showgirls Whatever Artists Mngt Ltd
Laser Combat PVA Ent Consultants
Marina Laslo Tony Clayman Promos
Ruth Lass Jonathan Altaras Assoc
Last Action Heroes MTM Presntns
Last Chance Owen Hughes Ents
Last Man Jack Barn Dance Line Dance Agy
The Last Night at the Proms (Orchestral) Upbeat Mngt
Last Tram Tae Auchenshuggle Hireaband Ltd
Jacek Laszczkowski Ingpen & Williams Ltd
Lee Latchford-Evans Identity One Management/Unleashed PR
Late Off The Pier Supervision Management
Riz Lateef Noel Gay Artists Ltd
Richard Latham Elinor Hilton Associates
Abbie Lathe Park Promotions
Sam Lathem Langford Assoc
Latin Fiesta CS Ents/Latin Arts Serv (LAS)/Matters Musical
Latin Jazz
Latin Magic Tony West Ents
Bhangra Latina Matters Musical
Factor Latino Matters Musical
Latino Heat (Ricky Martin tribute) Henderson Mngt
Heather Latona Celebn Model Mngt
Kenny Lattimore William Morris Inc (USA)
Derek Laud MCS Agcy
David Laughton Barrie Stacey Promos & Prods
Carol Laula Firefly Productions/Roots Around The World
Cyndi Lauper Podell Talent Agency
Laura Miles Peller Artistes Ltd
Laura V. (Live P.A. 'Changes' by Chris Lake) UK Booking Agy
Laurel & Hardy (Lookalikes) Kaye Frankland Ent Agy
Laurel and Hardy Viscount Ents
Lee Lauren Dance Funki Feathers Agy
Laurence Bolwell (David Bowie) Apple County
Pascal Laurent Brunskill Management Ltd
Ksenia Laurentieua Royce Mngt
Laurie Holloway Trio The John Boddy Agency
Hugh Laurie Lip Service Casting Ltd
Jon Laurimore Louise Hillman/Katie Threlfall
David Lavelle Jon Peters Ents
Ian Lavender Hilary Gagan Assoc/Persnl Appearances
Justin Lavender Athole Still Int'l Ltd/TEST AGENT A
Paul Lavent Compact Mngt & Ent Agy
Lauren Laverne Independent Talent Group Ltd
Paul Laverty Alexandra Cann Reprsntn
Avril Lavigne Helter Skelter Agy Ltd
Lucien Laviscount Linton Mngt
Denis Law Celebrity Appearances/Nigel Round Mgnt/PVA Ent Consultants/Persnly Spkng
Duncan Law Adrian King Assoc/M W Management
Edward Law Elinor Hilton Associates
Jude Law Julian Belfrage Assoc/Premier PR
Sallyanne Law Daly Pearson Associates
Steven Law Sara Crouch Mngt
Jim Lawless CHAMPIONS (UK) PLC
Stephen Lawless Askonas Holt Ltd
Sue Lawley OBE Kruger Cowne Limited
Sarah Lawn Elinor Hilton Associates
Lawnmower blues Advanced Ents
Andrew Lawrence Chambers Management Ltd
Annie Lawrence Creeme Ents
Cassie Lawrence (Female Vocalist) Ron Martin Mngt
Chris Lawrence Tony Clayman Promos
Debi Lawrence Devil Management
Denise Lawrence & Her Band CS Ents
Dorothy Lawrence Performance Actors Agy
Eleanor Lawrence Emptage Hallett Ltd
The Gloria Lawrence Band Bulrush Mngt
Greg Lawrence as Fats Domino Entertainers Mgt Ltd
Jennifer Lawrence Talking Heads - The Voice Agy
Matthew Lawrence Sardi's Int'l Ent
Phil Lawrence Gordon Kellett Ents
Sasha Lawrence Gordon Kellett Ents
Steve Lawrence LRO Artist Mngt
The Syd Lawrence Orchestra Acker's Int'l Agy/Derek Bruce Ents/PVA Ent Consultants/The John Boddy Agency
Tracy Lawrence Buddy Lee Attrctns Inc (USA)
Sarah Lawrie Grays Mngt & Asc
Lawros Disco David Forshaw Entp

Yannick Lawry Wise Buddah Talent & Voices
Brian Laws Barn Dance Line Dance Agy
Karen Laws CASAROTTO RAMSAY & ASSOCIATES
Aletta Lawson Sandra Boyce Mngt
Charles Lawson Brown & Simcocks
Denis Lawson Conway Van Gelder Grant Ltd
Leigh Lawson United Agents
Lord Lawson Inspirational Artiste Bkg
Maria Lawson Global Talent Management
Mark Lawson Wendy Lee Mngt
Michelle Lawson Nigel Round Mgnt
Nigella Lawson CHAMPIONS (UK) PLC/Colman Getty PR/Ed Victor Agency/Inspirational Artiste Bkg
Pete Lawson CASAROTTO RAMSAY & ASSOCIATES
Samantha Lawson Alpha Persnl Mngt
Sevi Lawson Speak-Easy Ltd
Twiggy Lawson Peters Fraser Dunlop (PFD)
Mikki Lawton Devil Management
Malcolm Laycock Derek Boulton Productions
Kate Layden Otto Persnl Mngt Ltd
Layla Continental Drifts/TEST AGENT C
Adrian Layment RAGE
Layo & Bushwacka ITB
Gemma Layton North One Mngt
Stephen Layton Hazard Chase Ltd
Brian Lazanik Underbelly Management
Cliff Lazarenko McLeod Agy Ltd
Stefanos Lazaridis Athole Still Int'l Ltd/TEST AGENT A
Belinda Lazenby Northern Lights Mngt
The Lazy Jumpers (Spain) Big Bear Music
Martino Lazzeri Jane Lehrer Assoc
Jonathan Le Billon Northern Lights Mngt
Le Concert Impromptu Transart (UK) Ltd
Antoni Le Faux Dance Funki Feathers Agy
Le Jazz Hot Hireaband Ltd
Le La Les Continental Drifts/TEST AGENT C
Kele Le Roc Mission Control Artist Agy
Graeme Le Saux MERLIN ELITE
Le Tigre MVO Ltd
Nigel le Vaillant Shepherd Mngt Ltd
Le Vent Du Nord Adastra
Stewart Lea Derek Bruce Ents
Andy Leach Norwich Artistes/Tony West Ents
Craig Leach McLeod Agy Ltd
Patricia Leach Audrey Benjamin Agy
Rosemary Leach Yakety Yak
Charles Leadbeater The London Spkr Bureau
Peter Leafe Indep Mngt Ltd
The League (Human League tribute) Jason West Agy
The League of Gentleman PBJ Mngt Ltd
Terry Leahy CHAMPIONS (UK) PLC
Steve Leaney PVA Ent Consultants
Leanne Dave Woodbury Ents
Adrian Leaper Hazard Chase Ltd
Amanda Lear Tony Denton Promos Ltd
Louise Lear Limelight Management
Don & Cindy Leather Derek Bruce Ents/PVA Ent Consultants/The Horne Concert Agy
David Leavitt The Wylie Agency
Nigel Leck Knight Ayton Mngt
Pip Leckenby Associated Arts
Jenny Lecoat Jill Foster Ltd
Brian Lecomber's Firebird Team MTM Presntns
Dennis Lecoriere - Voice of Dr Hook John Hessenthaler Ents
Led Zed Fab Prods
Helen Lederer Langford Assoc/Saraband Assoc
Martin Ledwith Talking Heads - The Voice Agy
A K Lee ABDC Ents
Alvin Lee Rock Artist Mngt
Andy Newton Lee RDF Management
Annabel Lee Dennis Lyne Agy
Billy Lee as Tom Jones Chance Promos/G Entertaining/Stars In Your Eyes Ltd Ent Agy
Byron Lee & The Dragoners Monkeybiz Ent Agy
Carol Lee Gordon Kellett Ents
Chris Lee Chris Lee (Ind Art)/Funhouse Productions Ltd/Peller Artistes Ltd/SJS Promos
Chrissy Lee Scott-Paul Young Ents Ltd
Colin Lee Athole Still Int'l Ltd/TEST AGENT A
Lee Combs CODA Ltd
Dave Lee Persnl Appearances/Yellow Balloon Prods Ltd
Emma Lee RDF Management
Gavin Lee Burnett Granger Assoc
Ha Young Lee International Classical Artist
Iain Lee Karushi Mngt
Jackie Lee Broadwater Ents Assoc
Jakson Lee Vern Allen Ents Ltd
Jason Lee Chris Gordon Theatrical Agy
Jeff Lee M.G. Ents
Jon Lee Mclean-Williams Management
Lenny Lee Fairplay Ents/Sunshine Ents
Olivia Lee Princess Talent Mngt
Peter Lee MJE Mngt
Ricky Lee Lucas Management
Rustie Lee Celebrity Appearances/Persnly Spkng
Sadie Lee Devil Management
Samantha Lee Linkside Agy
Scooter Lee Deri Promos
Carol Lee Scott (Grotbags) Johnny Mans Prods Ltd/Paul Bridson Prods/Pete Mitchell Associates
Simon Lee Simpson Fox Assoc Ltd
Steve Lee Highfield Mngt & Promos
Vicki Lee Taylor Jeffrey & White
Tony Lee Mike Malley Ents
Wendy Lee Jill Foster Ltd
Paul Leegan (Lonnie Donegan) Compact Mngt & Ent Agy/Cromwell Mngt
Jan Leeming SIMON WHITTAM PUBLICITY
Veronica Leer Brunskill Mngt Ltd
Brother Lees Paul Bridson Prods/Pete Mitchell Associates
Gary Lees Great Escapes MTM Presntns
Ian 'Sludge' Lees Brian Yeates Assoc
Ian Lees (Sludge) Persnl Appearances
Nick Leeson Gordon Poole Agy Ltd/MCS Agcy/NMP Live Ltd/NMP MANAGEMENT/Speakout
Trevor Leeson MJE Mngt
Kirsty Lee-Turner Daly Pearson Associates
Johnny Leeze B.D.A.
Jean Paul Lefret Penny Rich
Legacy Advanced Ents
Legend LRO Artist Mngt
David Legend - The Music of Legend David Rees Management
The "Legendary" Drifters Book A Band
Legendary Lynn CKK Ent
Legends Chance Promos
Legends of Motown William Morris Inc (USA)
George Leggat Anita Alraun Representation
Robin Leggate Askonas Holt Ltd
Janette Legge Cassie Mayer Ltd
Val Lehman Darren Gray Mngt
Paul Lehmann (actor, mimic) Gown & Gauntlet Promos
Lehmo Paramount Int'l Mngt
Lei Aloha Matters Musical
Sam Leifer CASAROTTO RAMSAY & ASSOCIATES
Sergei Leiferkus Askonas Holt Ltd
Cameron Leigh Argyle Assoc
Danni Leigh Buddy Lee Attrctns Inc (USA)
Ethan Leigh CeeBee Variety Agy
Jodie Leigh Sandra Singer Assoc
Kerri Leigh Nigel Round Mgnt
Debbie Leigh-Simmons Stage Centre Mngt
Sophie Leigh MBA
Victoria Leigh Wendy Lee Mngt
Brad Leigh-Scott M.G. Ents
Alexis Leighton AXM
Allan Leighton NMP Live Ltd
Kellie Leish JB Ents
Jim Leishman Elite Promos/Speakout
Lela B Talking Heads - The Voice Agy
David Leland CASAROTTO RAMSAY & ASSOCIATES
Lemar Joanna Burns PR/Modest! management/United Talent Agency
Eddy Lemar Anita Alraun Representation
Paul Lemming ICON Actors Mngt
Lemon Jelly Primary Talent Int'l
Ute Lemper Tony Clayman Promos
John Lenahan JLA
Virginia Leng MBE Gordon Poole Agy Ltd
The Lennerockers Paul Barrett Rock'N'Roll Entp
Anthony Lennon Sandra Boyce Mngt
Lyndsey Lennon Billboard Persnl Mngt
Steve Lennon Louise Hillman/Katie Threlfall
Annie Lennox 19 Entertainment/Creative Artists Agency
Kate Lennox Derek Bruce Ents
Jay Leno ICM (USA)
L'Ensemble Paris Rent-A-Band
Rula Lenska Daly Pearson Associates
Leo Dave Woodbury Ents
Leo the Clown Partyweb.co.uk
Leodian String Quartet McLeod Agy Ltd/Yorkshire Ent
Leon Markham & Froggatt Ltd
Glen Leon as Tom Jones Entertainers Mgt Ltd
Jose Leon Complete Ent Serv Ltd
José Leon/Sol Y Sombra Matters Musical
Ricardo Leon Ricardo Leon (Ind Art)
Tim Leon Audrey Benjamin Agy
Adele Leonard Nyland Mngt
Andy Leonard Derek Bruce Ents
Baylen Leonard Voice Shop
Dave Leonard Sardi's Int'l Ent
Jack Leonard Sandra Singer Assoc
Jonathan Leonard Cherry Parker Management
Lydia Leonard Markham & Froggatt Ltd
Maurice Leonard Hazemead Ltd
Sugar Ray Leonard CHAMPIONS (UK) PLC
Paul Leonard-Morgan S M A Talent Ltd
The Leonardo String Quartet CS Ents

Leonora Hartbeat Ents Ltd
Elizabeth Leonskaya IMG Artists
Leopold String Trio Ingpen & Williams Ltd
Dr. Armand Leroi Knight Ayton Mngt
Beresford LeRoy Sandra Boyce Mngt
Leroy Johnson & The Flicks The Dixon Agy
Les Compagnons Du Bal CS Ents
Les Encompetants Scream Promotions
Les Girls Can-Can Dancers Book A Band
Les Haricots Rouges (F) Wim Wigt Prodns Ltd
Les Onions Prima Artists
Carol Lesley Paul Bailey Agy/Sunshine Ents
John Leslie Speakout
Moir Leslie Performance Actors Agy
Ralph Leslie Crowd Pullers
Robert Leslie (Neil Diamond) Advanced Ents/Jason West Agy
David Muniz and David Lesniak Curtis Brown Grp
Janek Lesniak Shepherd Mngt Ltd
Less Than Jake Primary Talent Int'l
Adrian Lester ARG Management/Yakety Yak
Alex Lester MPC Ent
Mike Lester Allan Wilson Entp
Tara Lester Talking Heads - The Voice Agy
Virginia Lester Audrey Benjamin Agy
Let Loose Insanity Artists
Let Me Entertain You (Robbie Williams) Arena Ent Cons/Scott Mackenzie Assoc
Petra Letang CAM London
Lethal Bizzle (V2 Music) Ablaze Music Management
Let's Hang On Derek Block Concerts
Kathy Lette Ed Victor Agency
Alton Letto Susan Angel Kevin Francis Ltd
Crispin Letts Shepherd Mngt Ltd
Dominic Letts Sandra Boyce Mngt
Letz Zep Handshake Ltd
Victoria Leung Sandra Singer Assoc
David Leveaux Simpson Fox Assoc Ltd
Paul Levent Derek Bruce Ents/G Entertaining/Kaye Frankland Ent Agy/Stardust Ents Agy
Clare Lever Lime Actors Agy & Mngt Ltd
David Leverton Otto Persnl Mngt Ltd
James Levesque Music Int'l
Lawry Levin Avalon Mngt
Joshua Levine APM Ass
Michael Levine Judy Daish Assoc/Seamus Lyte Management Ltd
Ilya Levinsky Askonas Holt Ltd
Marianne Levy Paul Duddridge Mngt
Jona Lewie Gables & TTH Mngt
Lara Lewington Seamus Lyte Management Ltd
Adrian Lewis Persnl Appearances
AJ Lewis Brian Marshall Mngt
Carys Lewis Indep Mngt Ltd
Damian Lewis Markham & Froggatt Ltd
Dr David Lewis Cunningham Mngt Ltd/Gordon Poole Agy Ltd/NMP Live Ltd
Denise Lewis CHAMPIONS (UK) PLC/NMP Live Ltd
Lewis Dixon (Michael Buble tribute) Essential Ent
Dutch Lewis Derek Bruce Ents
Francine Lewis Tony Clayman Promos
Gareth Lewis Judy Daish Assoc
James Lewis Stephen Budd Mngt
Jerry Lewis William Morris Inc (USA)
Jerry Lee Lewis AIM Inc (USA)/Al Embry Int'l (USA)
June Lewis Anita Alraun Representation
Ken Lewis Parliament Comms
Laya Lewis Insanity Artists
Lennox Lewis CHAMPIONS (UK) PLC/Sport Ent And Media Group
Leona Lewis Modest! management
Lew Lewis NVB Ents/Triple Cream Ents
Linda Lewis The Agency Group/Tony Clayman Promos
Linda Gail Lewis Paul Barrett Rock'N'Roll Entp
Martin Lewis Knight Ayton Mngt
Martyn Lewis Celebrity Appearances/Persnly Spkng
Martyn Lewis CBE PVA Ent Consultants/Parliament Comms
Mike Lewis (Rolf Harris) Upfront Ent Agy Ltd
Natasha Lewis Wendy Lee Mngt
Norma Lewis BTM Mngt & Agy
Paul Lewis Ingpen & Williams Ltd
Ray Lewis Brian Gannon Mngt
Stephen Brimson Lewis Clare Vidal-Hall
Tony Lewis (Robbie Williams) Chance Promos/SWA Ent
Lexicon Corperation Global Ent Agy
Johnnie Ley The A6 Agy
Johnny & Barbara Ley MTM Presntns
Jon "Lofty" Ley Ley Ent Prods
Stephen Ley The Actors File
Aisling Leyne RBA Management Ltd
Barbara Ley's Circus Trampoline Time Ley Ent Prods
Matthew Leys CASAROTTO RAMSAY & ASSOCIATES
Keelan Leyser
Matilda Leyser Brunskill Mngt Ltd
Paul Leyshon Harvey Voices Ltd
Lawrence Leyton Michael Vine Assoc/Parliament Comms
Dan Li Amber Persnl Mngt Ltd
Liaison Ace Music Ents/Peller Artistes Ltd/The CBS Grp
Libby Purves OBE Jo Gurnett Persnl Mngt/June Ford-Crush
Libera Upbeat Mngt
Hans Liberg JLA
Liberty Mountain (Elvis tribute) Jason West Agy
Libra (Group) The Music Ptnrshp Ltd
Libby Liburd Denmark Street Mngt
Ralph Liddell Barn Dance Line Dance Agy
Rod Liddle Noel Gay Artists Ltd
Stuart Liddle BGS PRODUCTIONS
Lido 66 Matters Musical
Tom Erik Lie Athole Still Int'l Ltd/TEST AGENT A
Jack Liebeck Ingpen & Williams Ltd
Life And Soul Derek Bruce Ents
Life of Riley Hawthorn Ent
Lifford Mission Control Artist Agy
Konstantin Lifschitz Transart (UK) Ltd
Andras Ligeti The Music Ptnrshp Ltd
Helen Jessica Liggal Scott-Paul Young Ents Ltd
Jeannie Lightbrown Darren Gray Mngt
Terry Lightfoot & His Band Acker's Int'l Agy/Barrie Hawkins Leisure Service/Cromwell Mngt
Robert Lightfoot Frontline Mngt Ltd
Terry Lightfoot & His Jazzmen Jazzco
Lighthouse Family Kitchenware Mngt
Lights Out By Nine Alan Cottam Agency
Like A Rolling Stone Compact Mngt & Ent Agy
Like Father Like Son Andrew Beauchamp Mngt
Kylie Likely Funhouse Productions Ltd
Lil Chris Insanity Artists
Tracey-Anne Liles Frontline Mngt Ltd
John Lill Askonas Holt Ltd
Adam Lilley 1984 Persnl Mngt
Alexandra Lilley Kerry Gardner Mngt
Valerie Lilley Emptage Hallett Ltd
Christopher Lillicrap Noel Gay Artists Ltd
Amelia Lilly CHAMPIONS (UK) PLC
Lily & The Boys Elite Promos
Richard Lily ICON Actors Mngt
Luis Lima Stafford Law
Limahl Barry Collings Ents/Fox Artist Mngt Ltd/Jason West Agy/Peller Artistes Ltd/Rock Artist Mngt/The Psycho Mngt Co Ltd/Tony Denton Promos Ltd
Jeremy Limb Noel Gay Artists Ltd
Roger Limb London Music Agy
Tommy Limb David Forshaw Entp
Beverley Limbrick Billboard Persnl Mngt
Limehouse Lizzy (Thin Lizzy tribute) Andrew Beauchamp Mngt/Head On Mngt/Jason West Agy
Alison Limerick Blueprint Mngt/Mission Control Artist Agy/Tony Denton Promos Ltd
Limit Int'l Mngt & Agy Ltd
Limited Company GB Promos & Ent Agy
Limmie & Family Cookin Jason West Agy
Limousine Derek Bruce Ents/Tony Bennell Ents
Limp Bizkit ITB
Limpish Bizkit (Limp Bizkit) Jason West Agy
Linchpin Helter Skelter Agy Ltd/Scream Promotions
Andrew Lincoln Markham & Froggatt Ltd
Robert Linden Crescent Mngt
Peter Lindford Dennis Lyne Agy
Lindisfarne Park Promotions/Rock Artist Mngt
Debbie Lindley RDF Management
Gillian Lindsay Athole Still Int'l Ltd/TEST AGENT A
Robert Lindsay Hamilton Hodell Ltd
Sally Lindsay Melody Thresh Mngt Assoc Ltd/Trading Faces Ltd
Shona Lindsay Burnett Granger Assoc
Lois Lindsey MGA Entp
Per Lindstrand Gordon Poole Agy Ltd
Pete Lindup B.A.S.I.C.
Graham Linehan Peters Fraser Dunlop (PFD)
John Linehan David Hull Promos Ltd
Niamh Linehan The Richard Stone Prtnrshp
Rosaleen Linehan Brunskill Mngt Ltd
Gary Lineker OBE CHAMPIONS (UK) PLC/Celebrity Appearances/Jon Holmes Media Ltd/Persnly Spkng/Trading Faces Ltd
Sophie Linfield Jonathan Altaras Assoc
Linford Christie OBE Nuff Respect
Jahja Ling Hazard Chase Ltd
Mark Lingwood M W Management
Linklater String Quartet XS Promos
Gemma Linsey Dance Funki Feathers Agy
Illona Linthwaite Jeffrey & White
Richard Linton Discoteque Fanfare 3000
Louis Lintz Jelly Roll Jazz Band London Music Agy
Tony Liotti Italian Duo Sardi's Int'l Ent
Ron Li-Paz Stafford Law
Eugene Lipinski Emptage Hallett Ltd
Maureen Lipman CBE Conway Van Gelder Grant Ltd/NMP Live Ltd/Speakout
Raewyn Lippert Speak-Easy Ltd

Johann Lippowitz CHAMPIONS (UK) PLC
David Lipsky The Wylie Agency
Simon Lipson Troika Talent
Elaine Lipworth Jacque Evans Mngt Ltd
Liquid Mission Control Artist Agy
Liquid Engineering Barn Dance Line Dance Agy
Steve Lironi Stephen Budd Mngt
Lisa Dave Woodbury Ents/NVB Ents
Lisa B Jane Hughes Mngt
Lisa Williams Handshake Ltd
Ben De Lisi Noel Gay Artists Ltd
Listen To My Music Show With Chris Dean Big Band Derek Boulton Productions
Jane Lister CS Ents
Moira Lister Chatto & Linnit Ltd
Tom Lister (Carl, Emmerdale) Big Bang Mngt Ltd/Nigel Round Mgnt
Danny Litchfield Armstrong Academy Agy
Paul Litchfield Noel Gay Artists Ltd
Derren Litten The Richard Stone Prtnrshp
Little Annie Anxiety Autonomous Talent Bkg
The Little Band Barn Dance Line Dance Agy
Little Big Band Matters Musical
Little Boots 13 Artists
The Little Band - Ceilidh Band Yorkshire Ent
Little Devil Dave Woodbury Ents
Little Feat Free Trade Agy
Kirsty Little CKK Ent
Mark Little Chris Davis Management
Little Mothers Universal/Island Records Ltd
Ralf Little Action Talent Int.
Little Richard Denis Vaughan Mngt/William Morris Inc (USA)
Little River Band AIM Inc (USA)/Brian Gannon Mngt
Syd Little Nigel Round Mgnt
Tasmin Little Askonas Holt Ltd
Victoria Little M W Management
Little Wonder (David Bowie Tribute) Andrew Beauchamp Mngt
Trevor Littledale Argyle Assoc
Littler Britain Barrie Hawkins Leisure Service
Matt Littler Big Bang Mngt Ltd
Dominic Littlewood Arlington Enterprises Ltd/NMP Live Ltd
Robin Littlewood Darren Gray Mngt
Steve Littlewood (Freddie Mercury) Angle Ents Ltd
Julian Littman Brunskill Mngt Ltd
Stacy Liu Piccadilly Mngt
Live Jason West Agy
Live 2 Jive NVB Ents
Live At Handshake Ltd
Live Rust (Neil Young tribute) Jason West Agy
Brooks Livermore AIM
Rebecca Livermore Alpha Persnl Mngt
Tony Livesey David Anthony Promos/Gordon Poole Agy Ltd
Livewire (AC/DC tribute) Andrew Beauchamp Mngt
Ricky Livid Creeme Ents
Livin' Joy Action Talent Int.
The Living End ITB
Living In A Box Tony Denton Promos Ltd
Living Large Upbeat Entertainment
Katy Livingston Prof Sports Ptnr Ltd
Ken Livingstone CHAMPIONS (UK) PLC/Trading Faces Ltd
Li-Wei IMG Artists
LK Universal/Island Records Ltd
Warren Llambias The Richard Stone Prtnrshp
Brian Llewellyn Brian Llewellyn (Ind Art)
Carl Llewellyn CHAMPIONS (UK) PLC
Grant Llewellyn Hazard Chase Ltd
Gareth Llewelyn Actorum
Laurence Llewelyn-Bowen Fresh Partners/Inspirational Artiste Bkg/Trading Faces Ltd
Danielle Lloyd Action Talent Int.
David Lloyd Celebrity Appearances/Nigel Round Mgnt/Persnly Spkng
Freddie Lloyd David Forshaw Entp
Geoff Lloyd Noel Gay Artists Ltd
Gwilym Lloyd The Actors File
Hugh Lloyd Nancy Hudson Associates Ltd
Jean Lloyd Vincent Shaw Assoc Ltd
Jeremy Lloyd Alexandra Cann Reprsntn
Joe Lloyd Gordon Kellett Ents
Kathy Lloyd Yellow Balloon Prods Ltd
Marrie Lloyd (Cher Tribute) GM Ents
Mike "Ruffcut" Lloyd UK Booking Agy
Nathaniel A. Lloyd Audrey Benjamin Agy
Robert Lloyd Askonas Holt Ltd
Jeffrey Lloyd- Roberts Ingpen & Williams Ltd
Robin Lloyd Vincent Shaw Assoc Ltd
Sara Lloyd Louise Hillman/Katie Threlfall
Sharon Lloyd Anita Alraun Representation
Sian Lloyd Seamus Lyte Management Ltd
Julian Lloyd Webber IMG Artists
Adrian Lloyd-James Grays Mngt & Asc
Maggie Lloyd-Williams Susan Angel Kevin Francis Ltd
Julie Llusion Derek Bruce Ents
LMC vs U2 Mission Control Artist Agy
Ken Loach Judy Daish Assoc
Loaded Owen Hughes Ents/Prima Artists
Michelle Lobo Arena Personal Mngt
The Local Yokels CS Ents
Locarno Big Band London Music Agy
Lochs, Jocks & Two Guiness Barrells Andrew Beauchamp Mngt
Kate Lock Kerry Gardner Mngt
Sean Lock CHAMPIONS (UK) PLC/Off The Kerb Prods/Trading Faces Ltd
Lockdown Project Deluxxe Management
Ollie Locke Curtis Brown Grp/Insanity Artists
Fred Locks Monkeybiz Ent Agy
Bobby Lockwood Sandra Singer Assoc
Damaris Lockwood Sara Crouch Mngt
Tony Lockwood Shining Mngt Ltd
Thomas Lockyer Markham & Froggatt Ltd
Lococo Face Painters Crowd Pullers
Locodice Hope Management
Lodger Universal/Island Records Ltd
Meat Loef GM Ents
Marjorie Lofthouse The Voice Box Agency Ltd
Korenne Lofts Talking Heads - The Voice Agy
Logan Alan Cottam Agency
Gabby Logan BA CHAMPIONS (UK) PLC/Jon Holmes Media Ltd/Speakout
George Logan Int'l Artistes Ltd
Jimmy Logan PVA Ent Consultants
Joe Logan North Of Watford Actors Agy
Johnny Logan BULLET MANAGEMENT LIMITED
Kenny Logan Jon Holmes Media Ltd/NMP Live Ltd
Lara Logan Take Three Mngt
Stephan Loges International Classical Artist
Kenny Loggins William Morris Inc (USA)
Lolly Action Talent Int.
Jamie Lomas Big Bang Mngt Ltd
The Lomax Brothers Mike Constantia Artiste Mngt L
Louise Lombard United Agents
Jonah Lomu MPC Ent
Caroline Loncq Emptage Hallett Ltd
Richard Loncraine CASAROTTO RAMSAY & ASSOCIATES
London All Stars Steel Band Mainstream Evts
London Beat ft. Jimmy Helms Barry Collings Ents
London Chinese Acrobats ABDC Ents/CKK Ent/London Chinese Acrobatics
The London Community Gospel Choir Upbeat Mngt
London Concertante Matters Musical
London Elektricity CODA Ltd
London Gospel Choir Preview & Review Ents Ltd
Laura London CHAMPIONS (UK) PLC/Whatever Artists Mngt Ltd
The London Pops Orchestra Matters Musical
The London Ragtime Orchestra Cromwell Mngt/Matters Musical
Sarah London Brian Taylor Assoc
London School of Samba Matters Musical
London Soloists Chamber Orchestra N.B. Mngt
London Symphony Orchestra Dvora Lewis PR
Skye Loneragan Talking Heads - The Voice Agy
Lonerparty Doug Smith Assoc
Lonesome Bones Barn Dance Line Dance Agy
James Long Mr Magic Ents (Magic)/Prima Artists
Janice Long One Fifteen
Kerry Long Dance Funki Feathers Agy
Lisa Marie Long Blackburn Sachs Assoc
Hayley Longhurst Liz Hobbs Grp Ltd
Lucy Longhurst Shining Mngt Ltd
Brenda Longman Hilary Gagan Assoc
Francesca Longrigg One Fifteen
Joe Longthorne Non Stop Ents/Tony Clayman Promos
Adam Longworth Karushi Mngt
Toby Longworth Noel Gay Artists Ltd
Lonnie Donegan Band feat. Peter Donegan Adastra
Angela Lonsdale Funky Beetroot Celebrity Manag
Lonyo Mission Control Artist Agy
Abba (Lookalike) Norwich Artistes
Beach Boys (Lookalike) Norwich Artistes
Beatles (Lookalike) Norwich Artistes
Bee Gees (Lookalike) Norwich Artistes
Blues Brothers (Lookalike) Norwich Artistes
Buddy Holly (Lookalike) Norwich Artistes
Celine Dion (Lookalike) Norwich Artistes
Cher (Lookalike) Norwich Artistes
Christine Aquilera (Lookalike) Norwich Artistes
Cliff Richard (Lookalike) Norwich Artistes
David Beckham (Lookalike) Norwich Artistes
Del Boy (Lookalike) Norwich Artistes
Diana Ross (Lookalike) Norwich Artistes

Elton John (Lookalike) Norwich Artistes
Elvis Presley (Lookalike) Norwich Artistes
Freddie Mercury (Lookalike) Norwich Artistes
George Michael (Lookalike) Norwich Artistes
James Bond (Lookalike) Norwich Artistes
John Cleese (Lookalike) Norwich Artistes
Lionel Ritchie (Lookalike) Norwich Artistes
Madonna (Lookalike) Norwich Artistes
Marilyn Monroe (Lookalike) Norwich Artistes
Patsy (Ad Fab) Lookalike Norwich Artistes
Queen (Lookalike) Norwich Artistes
Ricky Gervais (Lookalike) Norwich Artistes
Robbie Williams (Lookalike) Norwich Artistes
Rod Stewart (Lookalike) Norwich Artistes
Roy Orbison (Lookalike) Norwich Artistes
Shirley Bassey (Lookalike) Norwich Artistes
Take That (Lookalike) Norwich Artistes
Tina Turner (lookalike) Norwich Artistes
Tom Jones (Lookalike) Norwich Artistes
Whitney Houston (Lookalike) Norwich Artistes
Looney Toons Compact Mngt & Ent Agy
Loop Guru Nation Recs Ltd
Rebecca Loos Paul Stacey Management
Loose Covers Book A Band
Loose Wire Peller Artistes Ltd
Rodrigo Lopes Hyper Agency
George Lopez The Gersh Agency
Jennifer Lopez Joanna Burns PR
Leon Lopez Big Bang Mngt Ltd/Funky Beetroot Celebrity Manag
Ricky Lopez Ratpack and Swing Show (Ind Art) Ricky Lopez Ratpack and Swing
Lord Geoffrey (The Balloon Man) Sardi's Int'l Ent
Malcolm Lord After Dinner World Ltd
LORDI Scream Promotions
Eric Loren Lip Service Casting Ltd
Peter Lorenzelli Amber Persnl Mngt Ltd
Ruth Lorenzo CHAMPIONS (UK) PLC/Industry Music Group Ltd/Modest! management
Lorika Barn Dance Line Dance Agy
Peter Lorimar Nigel Round Mgnt
Lorraine Candy (Cosmopolitan Editor) Personal Management & Casting
Mary Lorson Free Trade Agy
Los One Fifteen
Los Albertos Complete Ent Serv Ltd
Los Charros CS Ents/Latin Arts Serv (LAS)/Latin-Touch Ents/Matters Musical
Los Charros-Salsa Band (Latin Dance) Midland Ent & Mgnt Ltd
Los Chicos Latin-Touch Ents
Los de Abajo CODA Ltd
Los Kaos CKK Ent
Los Latinos Latin Arts Serv (LAS)
Los Madrigales Latin-Touch Ents
Los Pacaminos Mark Lundquist Management & Co/What Mngt
Los Pacaminos feat Paul Young Jason West Agy
Los Palmas Six (Madness tribute) Andrew Beauchamp Mngt/Apple County/Jason West Agy
Los Paraliticos Rock Artist Mngt
Los Pistoleros Matters Musical
Los Ricardos (Knife Thrower/Fire Eater) Joker Ents
Los Salerosos PVA Ent Consultants
Los Soneros Latin Arts Serv (LAS)/Matters Musical
The Joe Loss Ambassadors Joe Loss Ltd
The Lost And Lonely Rebels Richard Bucknall Mngt (RBM)
Lostprophets Big Sister Promotions/Creative Artists Agency/ITB/Insanity Artists
Dame Felicity Lott Askonas Holt Ltd
Louby Lou Viscount Ents
Nicola Loud Patrick Garvey Mngt
Louise Loughman The Richard Stone Prtnrshp
Angus Loughran Jane Morgan Mngt Ltd
Amy Loughton Actorum
Louie Rockerfella And The Dixie Mafia Band (Elvis) Head On Mngt
Laura Louis Clic Agency
Louise Norwich Artistes
Amber Louise Martin Ents
Gina Louise Brian Yeates Assoc
Louisiana Blue Mike Storey Ents
Louisiana Jazzmen Ultimate Int'l
Louiza Friday Quartet Ultimate Int'l
Lounge Sounds Prima Artists
Michael Lovatt City Actors Mngt
Love Affair BCM Promos Ltd/Brian Gannon Mngt/Compact Mngt & Ent Agy/Jason West Agy/John Hessenthaler Ents/PVA Ent Consultants
Courtney Love MVO Ltd
Dean Love North Of Watford Actors Agy
John Love Anglia Artistes/The Horne Concert Agy
Love Machine BULLET MANAGEMENT LIMITED
Sharon O Love Fresh Artiste Management Ltd
Steve Love Band McLeod Agy Ltd
The House of Love Asgard
Love Train Advanced Ents
Brendhan Lovegrove Paramount Int'l Mngt
Tim Lovejoy RDF Management
Alex Lovell John Miles Org
James Lovell Parliament Comms
Wendy Lovelock MBA
Loverboy ICM (USA)
Ophelia Lovibond BWH Agency
Lovin' It Sunshine Ents
Loving Jahband (Roots, Rock, Reggae) Glasshouse Prods Ltd
Gary Lovini Gerald Goss Ltd
Jon Lovitz Special Artists Agency
Low Free Trade Agy
Andy Fairweather Low Asgard
Belinda Low Audrey Benjamin Agy
Amelia Lowdell Emptage Hallett Ltd
Adam Lowe Lime Actors Agy & Mngt Ltd
Alex Lowe The Richard Stone Prtnrshp
Arthur Lowe (Estate) Bernard Hunter Assoc
Daisy Lowe Insanity Artists
Georgia Lowe Associated Arts
John Lowe CHAMPIONS (UK) PLC/Nigel Round Mgnt
Nick Lowe Asgard
Pearl Lowe Independent Talent Group Ltd
Rebecca Lowe Jon Holmes Media Ltd
Richard Lowe Sarm Mngt
Roy Lowe Trio The Horne Concert Agy
Ry Cooder & Nick Lowe Asgard
Stephen Lowe Judy Daish Assoc
Zane Lowe Money Management UK
Phil Lowen (Tom Jones) G Entertaining/Norwich Artistes
Jan Lower Grays Mngt & Asc
The Lowland Band of the Scottish Division BGS PRODUCTIONS
Sarah Lowries Nancy Hudson Associates Ltd
Shauna Lowry Harvey Voices Ltd/RDF Management
Joanna Loxton Brian Taylor Assoc
Shelley Lozano Shelley Lozano (Ind Art)
Chloe Lucas BAM Assoc Ltd
David Lucas Norwich Artistes
Gary Lucas Some Bizarre Ltd
Matt Lucas NMP Live Ltd/Troika Talent
Pete Lucas G Entertaining/Kaye Frankland Ent Agy
Lucci COFFEE ARTISTS
Bruno Lucia Paramount Int'l Mngt
Lucia Fiorini Trio
Lucifire Continental Drifts/TEST AGENT C
Lucken's Shetland Pantomime Ponies Keith Salberg Agy & Prods
Zoe Lucker United Agents
Lucky jim Primary Talent Int'l
Steve Lucock Devil Management
Lucy Continental Drifts/Dave Woodbury Ents/TEST AGENT C
Lucy and The Celebrities CS Ents
Gary Lucy Big Bang Mngt Ltd/CAM London/Neon Management
Ludwig Beatles BULLET MANAGEMENT LIMITED/Compact Mngt & Ent Agy
The Ludwig Beatles Head On Mngt/Jason West Agy
Christa Ludwig Ingpen & Williams Ltd
Stuart Luis CKK Ent/The A6 Agy
Luisa Calvo Sardi's Int'l Ent/Steve Allen Ents
Nicola Luisotti IMG Artists
Luke & Floyd Country Duo Folk Ents Ltd
Merveille Lukeba Insanity Artists
LULS 13 Artists
Lulu NMP Live Ltd/UK Booking Agy
Eliza Lumley Burnett Granger Assoc
Joanna Lumley OBE Conway Van Gelder Grant Ltd/Prime Performers Ltd
Lunar Drive Nation Recs Ltd
Lunasa Adastra
Urban Strawberry Lunch Matters Musical
Eddie Lundon Rock Artist Mngt
Cherie Lunghi CAM London/Yakety Yak
Francis Lunn Liz Hobbs Grp Ltd
Jonathan Lunn Judy Daish Assoc
Maureen Lunt Northern Lights Mngt
Patti Lupone ICM (USA)
Linda Lusardi MCS Agcy
Nick Luscombe Wise Buddah Talent & Voices
Alex Lush Jane Hughes Mngt
Lush Life Blues Duo Mainstream Evts
Don Lusher Big Band Jazzco
Tim Lusscombe (Writer/Director) Gavin Barker
Robin Lustig Speak-Easy Ltd
Michelle Luther Louise Hillman/Katie Threlfall
Tommy Luther Louise Hillman/Katie Threlfall
Luton Male Voice Choir London Music Agy
Nat Luurtsema Avalon Mngt
The Luvvers NVB Ents
Charlie Luxton KBJ Management
Sandy Lyle CHAMPIONS (UK) PLC
Carolanne Lyme Speak-Easy Ltd
David Lyms Jeffrey & White

Michael Lynagh Speakout
Desmond Lynam OBE Jane Morgan Mngt Ltd
Tom Lynam Alpha Persnl Mngt
Claire Lynch Band Adastra
Bet Lynch Experience Andrew Beauchamp Mngt
Finbar Lynch Yakety Yak
John Lynch Markham & Froggatt Ltd
Kenny Lynch Alan Field Assoc
Samantha Lynch BAM Assoc Ltd
Shane Lynch AIM/Mission Control Artist Agy
Susan Lynch Cassie Mayer Ltd/Troika Talent
Trish Lynch Downes Presenters Agy
Nicholas Lyndhurst Chatto & Linnit Ltd
Damien Lyne Talking Heads - The Voice Agy
Lynn Continental Drifts/TEST AGENT C
Jonathan Lynn Peters Fraser Dunlop (PFD)
Lynryd Skynyrd The Agency Group
Lynx Tony West Ents
Ed Lyon Ingpen & Williams Ltd
Lisa Lyon The A6 Agy
Steve Lyon Stephen Budd Mngt
Darryn Lyons Full Portion Media
Greta Lyons Audrey Benjamin Agy
Pete Lyons Philip Youd Ents & Mngt
Phillippa Lyons TMK Mngt & Agcy Ltd
The Humphrey Lyttelton Band Remembers Humph & celebrates his music Jazzco
Louisa Lytton Action Talent Int./Rossmore Persnl Mngt
Paul Lytton Partyweb.co.uk

M
M People Experience Jason West Agy/John Hessenthaler Ents
Yo-Yo Ma Askonas Holt Ltd
Baaba Maal Free Trade Agy
Brittan Maassen Frontline Mngt Ltd
Polly Maberly Shepherd Mngt Ltd
Mabsant Welsh Band Rent-A-Band
Mac Dave Woodbury Ents
Annie Mac Get Involved Ltd
Johnny Mac LJ Ents
Kenny Mac NVB Ents
Tony Mac Derek Bruce Ents
Cal MacAnineh Markham & Froggatt Ltd
Dame Ellen MacArthur Parliament Comms/Persnly Spkng/Speakout/Trading Faces Ltd
Ishbel MacAskill Firefly Productions
Fred MacAulay Speakout/Troika Talent
David Maccreedy Dennis Lyne Agy
Aimie Macdonald Langford Assoc
Cathy Macdonald Star Management
Fraser MacDonald CASAROTTO RAMSAY & ASSOCIATES
Julie MacDonald Speak-Easy Ltd
Rory MacDonald International Classical Artist
Sheena Macdonald Curtis Brown Grp
Toby Macdonald CASAROTTO RAMSAY & ASSOCIATES
Jennifer MacDonald-Anderson Sandra Boyce Mngt
Sarah MacDonnell
Andy Mace Voice Shop
Colin Mace The Richard Stone Prtnrshp
Dean Macey CHAMPIONS (UK) PLC/MTC (UK) LTD
Rachel Macfarlane Action Talent Int./Mission Control Artist Agy
Gus Macgregor Jae Moss Entp
Joanna MacGregor Ingpen & Williams Ltd
Niall Macgregor Markham & Froggatt Ltd
Sue MacGregor Knight Ayton Mngt
Carole Machin Princess Talent Mngt/Yakety Yak
Terry Machin London Music Agy
Machine Head Helter Skelter Agy Ltd
The Machine (Pink Floyd) Jason West Agy
Melanie MacHugh M W Management
Tina MacHugh Clare Vidal-Hall
Reinaldo Macias Stafford Law
Bradley Macintosh Action Talent Int./Insanity Artists
Ewen MacIntosh Form Talent/Hyper Agency
Donal MacIntyre Seamus Lyte Management Ltd
Bunny Mack Monkeybiz Ent Agy
Johnny Mack (Rod Stewart) Compact Mngt & Ent Agy
Lee Mack Avalon Mngt/NMP Live Ltd/Trading Faces Ltd
Sophie Mackaill Tony Clayman Promos
Fulton Mackay (Estate) Bernard Hunter Assoc
Hannah Mackay Noel Gay Artists Ltd
Stewart MacKay Curtis Brown Grp
Duncan MacKenzie 1st Choice Speakers UK Ltd/After Dinner World Ltd/Celebrity Appearances/Gordon Robinson Assoc/McLeod Agy Ltd/Nigel Round Mgnt/Persnl Appearances/Persnly Spkng
Georgia Mackenzie Voice Shop
Kelvin MacKenzie Noel Gay Artists Ltd
Sir Charles Mackerras Askonas Holt Ltd
Gina Mackey Matters Musical
Doon Mackichan Lip Service Casting Ltd
Christine Mackie Jane Lehrer Assoc
Joanna Mackie M W Management
Pat Mackie Shepherd Mngt Ltd
Philip Mackie (Estate) Judy Daish Assoc
Andrew Mackintosh Jessica & Carney Assoc
Ken Mackintosh & His Orchestra Austin Baptiste Ent Agy Ltd
Millie MacKintosh Insanity Artists
Steven Mackintosh Yakety Yak
Jjarone Macklin-Page Tony Clayman Promos
Scarlett Mackmin Clare Vidal-Hall
Eden Mackney Sandra Singer Assoc
Elliet Mackrell/Didgeridoo Matters Musical
Kyle MacLachlan Special Artists Agency
Shirley MacLaine ICM (USA)
Deborah Maclaren Speak-Easy Ltd
Steve Maclaren Athole Still Int'l Ltd/TEST AGENT A
Carla Maclean Audrey Benjamin Agy
Don MacLean MBE Celebrity Appearances/Derek Bruce Ents/M.G. Promos/PVA Ent Consultants/Persnly Spkng/Pete Mitchell Associates/The Horne Concert Agy/Velrag Arts
Hilary Maclean Jonathan Altaras Assoc
Rob Maclean Speakout
Paul Macleavy By Invitation Only
Heather Macleod and The Healthy Measures (trio) Stoneyport Associates
Joanna Macleod AIM
Murdo Macleod Speakout
Tracey MacLeod PBJ Mngt Ltd
Sir Kenneth MacMillan (Estate) Simpson Fox Assoc Ltd
Stephen Macmillan Dennis Lyne Agy
Susannah MacMillan Judy Daish Assoc
Joseph Macnab 1984 Persnl Mngt
Ian MacNeil Judy Daish Assoc
Stuart Maconie Amanda Howard Assoc Ltd
Daniel Macpherson RDF Management
Don Macpherson CASAROTTO RAMSAY & ASSOCIATES
Sean MacRae LJ Ents
Carol Macready The Richard Stone Prtnrshp
Macumba Line-Up PMC
Rosemary MacVie Royce Mngt
MAD Continental Drifts/TEST AGENT C
Mad Dog's Little Big Band Yorkshire Ent
The Mad Hatters Dings Ent
The Mad Hatter's Tea Party Galaxy Evts
Mad Manners Goldstar Ent UK
Mad Petes Karaoke Disco David Forshaw Entp
Madame Penny Arcadia Mr Magic Ents (Magic)
Madassa Compact Mngt & Ent Agy
Caroline Madden North One Mngt
Helen Madden Speak-Easy Ltd
John Madden CASAROTTO RAMSAY & ASSOCIATES
Joanna Maddison Gerald Goss Ltd
The Maddisons David Forshaw Entp
Made 2 Order XS Promos
Made in Brazil Latin Arts Serv (LAS)/Latin-Touch Ents/Rent-A-Band
Richard Madeley James Grant Mngt Ltd/Taylor Herring Public Relation
Diana Madill June Ford-Crush
Claire Madin (pianist) Ultimate Int'l
Madison Avenue Mission Control Artist Agy
Madison Heights ABC Direct Ents
Madison Square Highfield Mngt & Promos/NVB Ents/Norwich Artistes/Paul Bailey Agy/Steve Allen Ents/The CBS Grp
Madness ITB
Philip Madoc Emptage Hallett Ltd
Ruth Madoc Saraband Assoc
Madonna (By Debbie Nunn) Barrie Hawkins Leisure Service/Henderson Mngt
Evelyne Brink as Madonna Prima Artists
Vanessa Mae NMP Live Ltd
Olivia Maffett Performance Actors Agy
Lisa Maffia Mission Control Artist Agy
Dominic Mafham Cassie Mayer Ltd/Lip Service Casting Ltd
Gregory Magee S M A Talent Ltd/SMA Talent Ltd
Phillip Magee (X Factor) ENTERTAINMENT FX
Magenta Spotlight Ents (Notts)
Magenkyo (Taiko Drummers) Glasshouse Prods Ltd
Maggot Full Portion Media
Magic BULLET MANAGEMENT LIMITED
Magic - A Kind Of Queen Leisure Mngt
Magic Catherine (Magic) Magic Catherine
Magic Circus P.J. Ents
Magic Faces P.J. Ents
Magic Hayley's Facepainting Mr Magic Ents (Magic)
Magic Junior Magic Junior Limited
Magic Matt CKK Ent
Magic Mirror Theatre Co John Field - Theatre and Puppe
Magic Moments Magic Moments (Ind Art)/Partyweb.co.uk
Magic Mushroom Band Magick Eye Records
The Magic Of Abba The John Boddy

Agency
The Magic Of Motown Entertainers Mgt Ltd
The Magic of Sinatra The Flying Music Co Ltd
Magic Of The Dance The Leighton-Pope Org
The Magic of the Musicals The Flying Music Co Ltd
Magic Philip Mr Magic Ents (Magic)
Magic Singh Fools Paradise
Timmy Magic (Dream Team) UK Booking Agy
Magical Night With The Stars Entertainers Mgt Ltd
Magical World of the Musicals The Flying Music Co Ltd
Magicians Upbeat Entertainment
Magnet Supervision Management
Magnétophone 4.A.D.
Marcello Magni Brunskill Mngt Ltd
Magnum The Agency Group
Magnum Disco David Forshaw Entp/Quality Ents
Sally Magnusson Speakout
Maguin Matters Musical
Clare Maguire 13 Artists
Francis Maguire Julian Belfrage Assoc
Mick Maguire NVB Ents
Mike Maguire After Dinner Spkers & Com/Nigel Round Mgnt
Sarah Maguire Actorum
Sean Maguire Insanity Talent Management
Tara Maguire Take Three Mngt
Zak Maguire AIM
Janet Maher ICON Actors Mngt
Rebecca Mahon Central Line Co-Op Persnl Mngt
Mahoney Continental Drifts/TEST AGENT C
Sarah Mahony Grays Mngt & Asc
Llinos Mai Cardiff Casting
Nicholas Mai RBA Management Ltd
Sharon Maiden Louise Hillman/Katie Threlfall
Daniel Maier RDF Management
Mark Maier Yakety Yak
Sarah Maile Agency K-Bis
Mainstream Distortion Some Bizarre Ltd
Mainstreet Roadshow PVA Ent Consultants
Peter Mair Talking Heads - The Voice Agy
Sara Mair-Thomas Cassie Mayer Ltd
Emily Maitlis Independent Talent Group Ltd
Majical Cloudz 13 Artists
Sir John Major Trading Faces Ltd
Majorstuen Adastra
Mak Folk XS Promos
Makerfield Owen Hughes Ents
Makin Trax Owen Hughes Ents
Cynthia Makris Athole Still Int'l Ltd/TEST AGENT A
Malachi Stardust Ents Agy
Christian Malcolm AIM
Male / Female Strippers Steve Draper Ents
Male Order The Dixon Agy
Nichol Malia MGA Entp
Malibu Roadshow Clubline Promos
Art Malik United Agents/Yakety Yak
Roma Malik Wendy Lee Mngt
Shahid Malik Shahid Malik (Ind Art)
Jesse Malin ITB
Sidney Malin Grays Mngt & Asc
Malinky Stoneyport Associates
Julia Mallam Jonathan Altaras Assoc
Timmy Mallett Hyper Agency/John Miles Org
Allan Mallinson Ed Victor Agency
Paul Mallon Amber Persnl Mngt Ltd
Penny Mallory CHAMPIONS (UK) PLC/Cunningham Mngt Ltd
Dr Pippa Malmgren CHAMPIONS (UK) PLC
Raul Malo Asgard
Gareth Malone Curtis Brown Grp
JO Malone Curtis Brown Grp
Tina Malone (Mimi, Shamless) Nigel Round Mgnt
Rob Malone Lucas Management
Michael Maloney Markham & Froggatt Ltd
Malpractice Palestar Entertainment
Malthouse Barn Dance Line Dance Agy
Matthew Malthouse Gavin Barker
Christopher Maltman Askonas Holt Ltd
Malvern Hills District Brass Band Derek Bruce Ents
Mamadou Matters Musical
Mama's Gun Blujay Mngt Ltd
The Mambo Boys Latin Arts Serv (LAS)/Upbeat Entertainment
Mambo Jambo Adastra
Mamma-Mia Talent One
Man from Funkle (70s) Apple County
The Management Hire-A-Band Ent Agy
Manaia Matters Musical
Liz Mance North One Mngt
Melissa Manchester William Morris Inc (USA)
Manchester String Quartet Matters Musical
Sam Mancuso Audrey Benjamin Agy
Mandate XS Promos
Mandelino Matters Musical
Lord Peter Mandelson NMP Live Ltd
Peter Mandelson Trading Faces Ltd
Mandolin Express Matters Musical
Mandrake David Charles Agy
Serena Maneesh Helter Skelter Agy Ltd
Jason Manford Karushi Mngt
The Manfreds Acker's Int'l Agy/BULLET MANAGEMENT LIMITED/Compact Mngt & Ent Agy/Derek Franks Org/Entertainers Mgt Ltd/Jason West Agy/John Hessenthaler Ents/PVA Ent Consultants/Rock Artist Mngt
Mary Mangan Dance Funki Feathers Agy
Sue Manger Darren Gray Mngt
Mangles Wurzels Apple County
Mango Acoustic CHAMPIONS (UK) PLC
Mangolian Laughing Boy Psycho Mngt Co Ltd
Manhattan Transfer Denis Vaughan Mngt
Manhattans Int'l Mngt & Agy Ltd
The Manhattans Monkeybiz Ent Agy
Manhatten Nights LRO Artist Mngt
Mani Ferrara PR
Manic Street Preachers Hall Or Nothing
Barry Manilow William Morris Inc (USA)
Alan Mann Alan Walters Mngt/Ultimate Int'l
Alistair Mann MTC (UK) LTD
Andy Mann Artsworld Int'l Mngt Ltd/NVB Ents
Caroline Mann ANA
John Mann Cosmic Comedy Mngt
Maxi Mann Norwich Artistes
Norman Mann Brian Taylor Assoc
Woody Mann NEM Prods (UK)
Mannheim Steamroller William Morris Inc (USA)
Amanda-Jane Manning Adrian King Assoc
Bernard Manning Show Fairplay Ents
Bernard Manning Michael La Roche Mngt/Time Concerts
Katy Manning Peter Charlesworth & Assoc
Anelia Manova (Sheryl Crow) Andrew Beauchamp Mngt
Lucy Mans Johnny Mans Prods Ltd
Nigel Mansell OBE CHAMPIONS (UK) PLC/Celebrity Appearances
Nancy Mansfield Kerry Gardner Mngt
Richard Mansfield Actors Alliance
Sarah Manton Jeffrey & White
Marade Advanced Ents/Derek Bruce Ents
Anthony Marber Athole Still Int'l Ltd/TEST AGENT A
Patrick Marber Judy Daish Assoc
Marc D (Pop Idol) ENTERTAINMENT FX
Marc Dillon (Pop Idol 2004) ENTERTAINMENT FX
Sonia Marceau Alpha Persnl Mngt
Joseph Marcell Markham & Froggatt Ltd
Jane March AIM
Marianne March ANA
Ian Marchant Whatever Artists Mngt Ltd
Marconi Union ABS Agy
Taylor Marcs Swan Ents
Fiz Marcus ANA
Frank Marcus (Estate) CASAROTTO RAMSAY & ASSOCIATES
Stephen Marcus COLE KITCHENN PRSN MGT
Wayne Marcus CeeBee Variety Agy
Wally Mardell Triple Cream Ents
Marc Marder Transart (UK) Ltd
The Mardi Gras Joymakers Parade Band The John Boddy Agency
Durham Marenghi Performing Arts
Juanita Margerison Inspiration Mngt
Noah Lee Margetts Talking Heads - The Voice Agy
Harry Margolis & His Big Band 'Glenn Miller' Sound Ent Direct
Jonathan Margolis Gordon Poole Agy Ltd
Nicky Margolis Audrey Benjamin Agy
Miriam Margoyles OBE Peters Fraser Dunlop (PFD)/United Agents
Maria Derek Bruce Ents
Maria Louisa CKK Ent/Crowd Pullers
Maria Vincent and the Millionaires Advanced Ents
Mariachi Azteca Latin-Touch Ents/London Music Agy
Mariachi Lajara Matters Musical
Mariachi Tequila Matters Musical
Donna Marie Monkeybiz Ent Agy
Marie France Riboulet Derek Bruce Ents
Kelly Marie Henderson Mngt/Jason West Agy/M.S. Ent Grp
Natasha Marie The Horne Concert Agy
Nicole Marie Bees Knees Ents
Shelley Marie Fairplay Ents/MJE Mngt
Jessica Marienson Scott-Paul Young Ents Ltd
Julie Marie-Taylor Paul Duddridge Mngt
Marie-Therese (Marie McCormack) Universal/Island Records Ltd
Carlos Marin Athole Still Int'l Ltd/TEST AGENT A
Cheech Marin Special Artists Agency
Ion Marin Askonas Holt Ltd
Mario Basilisco (flamenco guitar) Barrie Hawkins Leisure Service
Marjin Entertainment CKK Ent
Clayton Mark (Elvis) Chance Promos
Helen Mark Speak-Easy Ltd
Mark Mark Productions CKK Ent

Mark Mason is Robbie Williams Graham Cole Mngt
Alex Marker Associated Arts
Petra Markham Nancy Hudson Associates Ltd
Alexander Markov Transart (UK) Ltd
Ben Marks Indep Mngt Ltd
Catherine Marks Magic Catherine
Gareth Marks Burnett Granger Assoc
Howard Marks Gordon Poole Agy Ltd
Roger Marks Society Band Hartbeat Ents Ltd
Terry Marks UK Booking Agy
Kate Marlais Grays Mngt & Asc
Ziggy Marley Cooking Vinyl
Ziggy Marley & The Melody Makers William Morris Inc (USA)
Marlo Henderson Mngt
June Marlow MBA
Kate Marlow Troika Talent
Tim Marlow Curtis Brown Grp
Chris Marlowe Clare Vidal-Hall
Claire Marlowe Burnett Granger Assoc
Clive Marlowe Anita Alraun Representation
Corinna Marlowe 1984 Persnl Mngt
Roy Marlowe Yellow Balloon Prods Ltd
Marmalade Alan Wilson Mngt/BCM Promos Ltd/BULLET MANAGEMENT LIMITED/Barry Collings Ents/Brian Gannon Mngt/Compact Mngt & Ent Agy/Derek Bruce Ents/Entertainers Mgt Ltd/Henderson Mngt/Jason West Agy/PVA Ent Consultants/Paul Bridson Prods
Marmon Magic Sardi's Int'l Ent
Elizabeth Marmur Shepherd Mngt Ltd
Maroon 5 ITB
The Marques Brothers Hire-A-Band Ent Agy
Chris Marques & Jaclyn Spencer Whatever Artists Mngt Ltd
Andrew Marr Ed Victor Agency/Gordon Poole Agy Ltd/NMP Live Ltd/Trading Faces Ltd
Michael Marra Stoneyport Associates
Marrakesh Express London Music Agy/NVB Ents
Andrew Marriner Ingpen & Williams Ltd
Lucy Marriot Brunskill Management Ltd
Trevor Marriott Gordon Poole Agy Ltd
Luke Marsden (Big Brother) Nigel Round Mgnt
Gerry Marsden Jean Levy PR Agency
Jack Marsden MCS Agcy/Nyland Mngt
Joseph Marsden Amber Persnl Mngt Ltd
Steve Marsden Derek Bruce Ents
Diane Marsh Sunshine Ents
Janet Marsh Lime Actors Agy & Mngt Ltd
Jodie Marsh Sport Ent And Media Group
Kym Marsh Safe Management
Madeleine Marsh Limelight Management
Michelle Marsh Neon Management/Nigel Round Mgnt
Rodney Marsh Persnl Appearances
Steve Marsh Independent Talent Group Ltd
Terry Marsh Fighting Talk Promos
Lyndsey Marshal Troika Talent
Chloe Marshall Jon Holmes Media Ltd
Gary Marshall After Dinner Spkers & Com/CHAMPIONS (UK) PLC
Gary Marshall Roadshow The CBS Grp
Harley Marshall BGS PRODUCTIONS
Jon Marshall Mr Magic Ents (Magic)
Julia Marshall Talking Heads - The Voice Agy
Melanie Marshall (Soul Train) Brian Marshall Mngt
Qarie Marshall Talking Heads - The Voice Agy
Richard Marshall The Actors File
Marshall Star (Tina Turner, Shirley Bassey) Advanced Ents
Tom Marshall City Actors Mngt
Tony Marshall Susan Angel Kevin Francis Ltd
Wayne Marshall Askonas Holt Ltd/Monkeybiz Ent Agy
Cindy Marshall-Day MCS Agcy
Cathy Marston Loesje Sanders
Bobby Martell McLeod Agy Ltd
Fabiano Martell Nancy Hudson Associates Ltd
Jo Martell Sara Crouch Mngt
Lena Martell BGS PRODUCTIONS
Naomi Martell Cardiff Casting
Terri Martell Compact Mngt & Ent Agy
Martin + Thornbury Matters Musical
Les Martin Band Ginger Walker Agy
Benedict Martin ANA
Martin Buttrich Hope Management
Caroline Martin Markham & Froggatt Ltd
Catriona Martin Royce Mngt
Corinne Martin Peter Charlesworth & Assoc
Dave Martin Matters Musical/Sunshine Ents
David Martin 1st Choice Speakers UK Ltd/Grays Mngt & Asc/RDL
Dean Martin Blackburn Sachs Assoc/Talking Heads - The Voice Agy
Demetri Martin Chambers Management Ltd
Derek Martin JLM Persnl Mngt
Martin Fry Of ABC BULLET MANAGEMENT LIMITED/Blueprint Mngt
Gary Martin Shining Mngt Ltd
Martin Glenn CHAMPIONS (UK) PLC/Jon Holmes Media Ltd
James Martin CHAMPIONS (UK) PLC/NMP Live Ltd/Trading Faces Ltd
Martin James (Comedy Illusion) Ron Martin Mngt
Janis Martin Paul Barrett Rock'N'Roll Entp
John Martin Colclough Entertainment
Juan Martin (solo & with dance group) Adastra
Kitty Martin Frontline Mngt Ltd
Neil Martin S M A Talent Ltd/SMA Talent Ltd
Peter Martin Big Bang Mngt Ltd
Ricky Martin Latin Arts Serv (LAS)
Steve Martin Roadshow PVA Ent Consultants
Robin Martin The A6 Agy
Roger Martin Nancy Hudson Associates Ltd
Sian Martin Athole Still Int'l Ltd/Athole Still Music/Jonathan Altaras Assoc/TEST AGENT A
Martin Solveig Defected Records
Stew Martin Derek Bruce Ents
Zara Martin Independent Talent Group Ltd/Scott-Paul Young Ents Ltd
Peter Martindale Scott-Paul Young Ents Ltd
Malcolm Martineau Askonas Holt Ltd
Martinez and Fabrigez Continental Drifts/TEST AGENT C
Antonio Gil Martinez Brunskill Mngt Ltd
Melanie Martinez CASAROTTO RAMSAY & ASSOCIATES
Martini Dave Woodbury Ents
Martinique Jazzband Quality Ents
Al Martino Derek Franks Org/Jean Levy PR Agency/The Kruger Organisation - TKO
Mick Martin`s Stag Show Exotica Stardust Ents Agy
Ayk Martirossian Askonas Holt Ltd
Steve Martland Band Hazard Chase Ltd
Federico Martone Star Management
Chris Martyn as Robbie Williams, Mick Hucknall Entertainers Mgt Ltd/Stars In Your Eyes Ltd Ent Agy
The Marvelette Revue Jason West Agy
Nigel Marven John Miles Org
Ray Marvin Allan Wilson Entp
Kernel Marvo Kernel Marvo (Ind Art)
Anthony Marwood North Of Watford Actors Agy
Barney Marwood Urban Talent
Jerry Marwood Inspiration Mngt
Carey Marx RDF Management
Maggie Mash The Voice Box Agency Ltd
Mask Ultimate Int'l
Rob Maskell B.A.S.I.C.
Scott Maslen Jonathan Altaras Assoc
Anthony Mason London Music Agy
Beni Mason Blackburn International
Catherine Mason The Horne Concert Agy
Eric Mason Royce Mngt
Jackie Mason William Morris Inc (USA)
Nick Mason (Pink Floyd) Tony Smith Personal Management
Patrick Mason Simpson Fox Assoc Ltd
Rod Mason Hot Five (UK/G) Wim Wigt Prodns Ltd
Rosanna Mason Grays Mngt & Asc
Rosemary Mason Judy Daish Assoc
Rupert Mason Audrey Benjamin Agy
Tony Mason 1st Choice Speakers UK Ltd
Masons Apron Barn Dance Line Dance Agy
Masquerade CS Ents/Hire-A-Band Ent Agy/PVA Ent Consultants
Steve Massam McLeod Agy Ltd
Anna Massey Markham & Froggatt Ltd
Massive Attack Sainted PR
Diego Masson Ingpen & Williams Ltd
Master Bavarian Brass Prima Artists
Master Stepz UK Booking Agy
Masters At Work (Kenny Dope Gonzales or Little Louie Vega - rarely together) Defected Records/UK Booking Agy
Jim Masters (Bass resident) UK Booking Agy
Stuart Masters Ultimate Int'l
Fay Masterson JLM Persnl Mngt
Simon Masterton-Smith Anita Alraun Representation
Francis Maston APM Ass
Matchbook Romance Gold Star PR
Matchbox Paul Barrett Rock'N'Roll Entp
Mates Owen Hughes Ents
Mates of State Free Trade Agy
Diana Mather The Voice Box Agency Ltd
Victoria Mather Jane Morgan Mngt Ltd
Eve Matheson Voice Shop
Tim Matheson Special Artists Agency
Arthur Mathews Marie-Louise Hogan
Sabrina Mathews Paramount Int'l Mngt
Tony Mathews The Richard Stone Prtnrshp
Sean Mathias Judy Daish Assoc
Alexandra Mathie The Richard Stone Prtnrshp
Jamie Mathieson Jongleurs
Johnny Mathis William Morris Inc (USA)
Simon Mathis MBA

Matisyahu The Agency Group
Glen Matlock ex Sex Pistols Rock Artist Mngt/Tony Denton Promos Ltd
Matt and Kim 13 Artists
Matt Dawson MBE CHAMPIONS (UK) PLC/MERLIN ELITE
Matt Goss Mission Control Artist Agy/The Agency Group
Mattafix Big Sister Promotions
Pam Matteson ICM (USA)
Yvonne Matthew Darren Gray Mngt
Dave Matthews Band ITB
David Matthews Grays Mngt & Asc
Eddie Matthews RDF Management/Speak-Easy Ltd
Hayley Matthews Speakout
Katie Matthews Lime Actors Agy & Mngt Ltd
Kevin Matthews Jae Moss Entp
Richard Matthews Frontline Mngt Ltd
Scott Matthews Asgard
Mattie The Clown MTM Presntns/Partyweb.co.uk
Matto & Polo MTM Presntns
Mustapha Matura Judy Daish Assoc
Sharon Maughan United Agents
Sue Maund West Central Mngt
Garth Maunders Lime Actors Agy & Mngt Ltd
Jason Maverick CKK Ent/Crowd Pullers/Fool's Paradise/Whatever Artists Mngt Ltd
Max Continental Drifts/MPC Ent/TEST AGENT C
Max and OB Action Talent Int.
Max Cherry and the Cherrypickers Steel Band Barrie Hawkins Leisure Service
Robert Maxfield Nyland Mngt
Anna Maxim Agency K-Bis
Jenny Maxim Agency K-Bis
Maximo Park Big Sister Promotions
Maximum Rhythm 'n' Blues The Flying Music Co Ltd
Maximum Who Compact Mngt & Ent Agy
Ernest Maxin Johnny Mans Prods Ltd
Donald Maxwell Music Int'l
Ian Maxwell Cunningham Mngt Ltd
Lisa Maxwell AIM/Diamond Management
Martel Maxwell Noel Gay Artists Ltd
Alan May Barn Dance Line Dance Agy
Derrick May (USA) UK Booking Agy
Diana May Burnett Granger Assoc
Imelda May Sound Advice
James May Arlington Enterprises Ltd/NMP Live Ltd/Speakout
Jesse May MATCHROOM SPORT LTD
Olwen May The Narrow Road Company Ltd
Simon May NMP Live Ltd/NMP MANAGEMENT
Sophia May Action Talent Int.
Tina May The John Boddy Agency
Tina May & Her Musicians Jazzco
Victoria May ICON Actors Mngt
Rik Mayall Brunskill Mngt Ltd
John Mayall & The Bluesbreakers ITB
David Mayberry MBA
Audrey Maye Barrie Stacey Promos & Prods
John Mayer ITB
Jonathan Mayer Matters Musical
Jenny Mayers Partyweb.co.uk
Tessa Mayes Knight Ayton Mngt
Mayfair Derek Bruce Ents
Mayhem Roadshow Highfield Mngt & Promos
Helen Mayhew Somethin' Else
Ian Mayhew Billboard Persnl Mngt/Speak-Easy Ltd
Paul Mayhew-Archer CASAROTTO RAMSAY & ASSOCIATES
Arne Maynard Limelight Management
Bill Maynard The Richard Stone Prtnrshp
Maynard Flip Flap Continental Drifts/TEST AGENT C
Pamela Maynard (Gladys Knight tribute) Monkeybiz Ent Agy
Simon Mayo PBJ Mngt Ltd
Royston Mayoh Kenneth Earle Persnl Mngt
Zibba Mays Nancy Hudson Associates Ltd
Mazaika London Music Agy
Mazaika Duo Prima Artists
Kym Mazelle Full Portion Media/Mission Control Artist Agy/Tony Denton Promos Ltd
Mazeppa Cossacks Arena Ent Cons
Maxine Mazumder as Lulu, Dusty Entertainers Mgt Ltd/Sandra Singer Assoc
Maxine Mazumder as Lulu Peller Artistes Ltd
Franz Mazura Ingpen & Williams Ltd
Gary Wolstenholme MBE CHAMPIONS (UK) PLC
MC Lars The Agency Group
Drew McAdam Speakout
Des McAleer Shepherd Mngt Ltd
Colin McAllister Knight Ayton Mngt
Gary McAllister CHAMPIONS (UK) PLC
Deborah McAndrew Speak-Easy Ltd
Fiona McAndrew Music Int'l
John McAndrew The Richard Stone Prtnrshp
Nell McAndrew Model Plan Celebrities & Prese/Panic Management
Lucia Mcanespie Actorum
Charlie McArdle (TV Presenter) Alex Jay Persnl Mngt
John McArdle Lou Coulson Associates
Susan McArdle The Narrow Road Company Ltd
Gerard McArthur Brunskill Mngt Ltd
James McAvoy Peters Fraser Dunlop (PFD)
Steve McAvoy MJE Mngt
Willie John McBride After Dinner World Ltd/Celebrity Appearances/PVA Ent Consultants/Persnly Spkng
Simon McBurney Troika Talent
Kate McCabe Anglia Artistes/Norwich Artistes
Mike McCabe Complete Ent Serv Ltd
Milo McCabe Paul Duddridge Mngt
David McCaffrey Sandra Boyce Mngt
Andrew McCaldon Jeremy Hicks Assoc
Davina McCall CHAMPIONS (UK) PLC/NMP Live Ltd/Trading Faces Ltd
Tanya McCallin Performing Arts
Craig McCallum Stag Ents
Dani McCallum MBA
The McCalmans Stoneyport Associates
Chris McCalphy BAM Assoc Ltd
Gavin McCann Sport Ent And Media Group
Kate McCann Lime Actors Agy & Mngt Ltd
Lee McCann Fushion Pukka Bosh
Peter McCann VRM Artists
Rory McCann Emptage Hallett Ltd
Susan McCann Dennis Heaney Promos
Cathleen McCarron Brunskill Management Ltd
Jane McCarry Speakout
Gerard McCarthy David Hull Promos Ltd/Take Three Mngt
Jake McCarthy Narrow Road Company
John McCarthy Gordon Poole Agy Ltd/Jeremy Hicks Assoc
Maggie McCarthy Kerry Gardner Mngt
Michael McCarthy Burnett Granger Assoc
Perry McCarthy CHAMPIONS (UK) PLC/Gordon Poole Agy Ltd/NMP Live Ltd/Speakout
Willie McCarthy NVB Ents
Jesse McCartney Hackford Jones PR
Sir Paul McCartney MPL Communications Ltd/Marshall Arts Ltd/The Outside Organisation
Ian McCaskill Arena Ent Cons/Celebrity Appearances/Gordon Poole Agy Ltd/PVA Ent Consultants/Paul Bridson Prods/Persnly Spkng
Ruth McCaul North Of Watford Actors Agy
Maria McCaul Tony Clayman Promos
Steve McCauley Speakers For Business
Gary McCausland NMP Live Ltd/NMP MANAGEMENT/RDF Management
Leon McCawley Clarion/Seven Muses
Michael McClain Voice Shop
Liz McClarnon Insanity Artists/The Outside Organisation
Caitlin McClatchey Prof Sports Ptnr Ltd
Stacey McClean Insanity Artists
Sarah-Jane McClelland Simpson Fox Assoc Ltd
Martina McClements Direct Persnl Mngt
Kevin McCloud KBJ Management
Ally McCoist MBE Jane Morgan Mngt Ltd
Liz McColgan Jon Holmes Media Ltd
Shay McConnon Parliament Comms
Adam McConville MBA
Ciaron McConville APM Ass
Marilyn McCoo William Morris Inc (USA)
McCool PVA Ent Consultants
Brendon McCormack Leo Mngt & Agy
Mark McCormack Avenue Artistes Ltd
Ross McCormack Piccadilly Mngt
Laura McCormick Gordon Kellett Ents
James McCourt Princess Talent Mngt
Martin McCourt CHAMPIONS (UK) PLC
Richard McCourt MWM Prsnl Mngt/Troika Talent
Eugene McCoy Daly Pearson Associates
Simon McCoy Adrian King Assoc
Sylvester McCoy Bronia Buchanan Ass
George McCrae BULLET MANAGEMENT LIMITED/Barry Collings Ents/Entertainers Mgt Ltd/Jason West Agy/Tony Denton Promos Ltd
Gwen McCrae Monkeybiz Ent Agy
Pete McCray (UB40 Tribute) GM Ents
Colin McCredie Shepherd Mngt Ltd
Laura McCree David Anthony Promos
Shaun McCree Arena Ent Cons/The A6 Agy
John McCririck Paul Madeley/Persnl Appearances
McCrory Brothers OTB Prods
Glenn McCrory Fighting Talk Promos
Helen McCrory Conway Van Gelder Grant Ltd
Cal McCrystal Noel Gay Artists Ltd
Catherine McCulloch KAL Mngt
Ian McCulloch After Dinner World Ltd
Nick McCullock (Neil Diamond) Chance Promos
Colleen McCullogh Capel & Land
Terry McCuster David Forshaw Entp
Martine McCutcheon Freud

Comms/Insanity Talent Management/NMP Live Ltd/Personal Management & Casting/Yakety Yak
Barrie McDermott After Dinner World Ltd
Helen McDermott Ron Martin Mngt
Steve McDermott Speakers For Business
Chas McDevitt Paul Barrett Rock'N'Roll Entp
Jon Mcdiarmid City Actors Mngt
Alastair McDonald BGS PRODUCTIONS
Antony McDonald Loesje Sanders
Ian McDonald David Forshaw Entp
Jane McDonald Whatever Artists Mngt Ltd/Womenspeakers.co.uk
Kerry McDonald Barrie Stacey Promos & Prods
Laura McDonald Otto Persnl Mngt Ltd
Lee McDonald Sandra Boyce Mngt
Lisa McDonald Wendy Lee Mngt
Malcolm McDonald Nigel Round Mgnt
Michael McDonald William Morris Inc (USA)
Penelope McDonald Elinor Hilton Associates
Tom McDonald Brunskill Mngt Ltd
Sir Trevor McDonald Capel & Land/Knight Ayton Mngt/Parliament Comms/Trading Faces Ltd
Chris McDonnell Liz Hobbs Grp Ltd
Owen McDonnell Cassie Mayer Ltd
Sophie McDonnell Money Management UK
Blair Mcdonough Richard Price PR
Catherine McDonough City Actors Mngt
Richard McDougall Anita Alraun Representation/CKK Ent/Whatever Artists Mngt Ltd
Matt McDowall Fushion Pukka Bosh
Malcolm McDowell Markham & Froggatt Ltd
Ian McElhinney Cassie Mayer Ltd
Jack McElhorn Tavistock Wood Management Ltd
Gwynne McElveen Elinor Hilton Associates
Peter McEnery The Richard Stone Prtnrshp
John McEnroe CHAMPIONS (UK) PLC/NMP Live Ltd
Gary McErlane Barrie Stacey Promos & Prods
Allegra McEvedy Deborah McKenna Ltd
Johnny McEvoy B.D.A.
Kerry McFadden Inspirational Artiste Bkg
Steve McFadden Personal Management & Casting/Yakety Yak
Colin McFarlane Emptage Hallett Ltd
Jeanette McFarlane Moonglight Agy
Victoria McFarlane MBA
Greg Mcfarnon Billboard Persnl Mngt
May McFettridge David Hull Promos Ltd
McFli Dansatak
Joe McGann Jonathan Altaras Assoc
Stephen McGann AIM
McGee & Mooney (Children's ITV) Brian Marshall Mngt
Debbie McGee Chris Davis Management/NMP MANAGEMENT/Paul Madeley
Henry McGee The Richard Stone Prtnrshp
Johnny McGee David Charles Agy
Mark McGhee Athole Still Int'l Ltd/TEST AGENT A
Jimmy McGhie Avalon Mngt/Paul Duddridge Mngt
Clare McGhinn MCS Agcy
Andrew McGillan BAM Assoc Ltd
Sean McGinley Daly Pearson Associates
Lawrence McGinty Knight Ayton Mngt
Chris McGlade After Dinner Spkers & Com/Kevin King Mngt
Clare McGlinn Tony Clayman Promos
Kate McGoldrick Voice Shop
Susan McGoun 1984 Persnl Mngt
Peter McGovern Persnly Spkng
Tom McGovern The Richard Stone Prtnrshp
Alistair McGowan CHAMPIONS (UK) PLC/Speakout
Kevin McGowan Lime Actors Agy & Mngt Ltd
Maddie McGowan Jacque Evans Mngt Ltd
Angela McGrath Darren Gray Mngt
Jenny McGrath Barrie Stacey Promos & Prods
Jim McGrath Jane Morgan Mngt Ltd
Joe McGrath Tessa Le Bars Mngt
John McGrath (Estate) CASAROTTO RAMSAY & ASSOCIATES
Maeve McGrath Brunskill Mngt Ltd
Paul McGrath Stafford Law
Rory McGrath Curtis Brown Grp/PVA Ent Consultants/Speakout
Sarah McGrath Dance Funki Feathers Agy
Geraldine McGreevy Askonas Holt Ltd
Paul McGreevy ICON Actors Mngt
Ewan McGregor CHAMPIONS (UK) PLC/Peters Fraser Dunlop (PFD)/Special Artists Agency/United Agents/Yakety Yak
Kat McGregor Big Bang Mngt Ltd
Kate McGregor Louise Hillman/Katie Threlfall
Carol McGriffin Debi Allen Associates
Stuart McGugan The Richard Stone Prtnrshp
Barry McGuigan MBE After Dinner World Ltd/CHAMPIONS (UK) PLC/Celebrity Appearances/Fighting Talk Promos/NMP Live Ltd/Persnl Appearances/Persnly Spkng/Trading Faces Ltd
Byron McGuiness Direct Persnl Mngt
Wilf McGuiness 1st Choice Speakers UK Ltd/After Dinner World Ltd/Gordon Poole Agy Ltd/Gordon Robinson Assoc/Nigel Round Mgnt
John McGuinn Yakety Yak
Roger McGuinn Miracle Artists Ltd
Anthony McGuinness Northern Lights Mngt
Frank McGuinness CASAROTTO RAMSAY & ASSOCIATES
Paddy McGuinness Phil McIntyre Ent. Ltd
Bill McGuire Curtis Brown Grp
Iago McGuire Clic Agency
Lesley McGuire Daly Pearson Associates
Mike McGuire After Dinner Spkers & Com
Suzie McGuire David Anthony Promos
Victor McGuire Lou Coulson Associates
Mathew McGuirk North Of Watford Actors Agy
Heather McHale AIM
Mairi McHuffie Barrie Stacey Promos & Prods
Dion McHugh Victoria Tinker Mngt
Erin McHugh Agency K-Bis
Greg McHugh Insanity Artists
John McHugh Fushion Pukka Bosh
Rebecca McHugh Scott-Paul Young Ents Ltd
Rory McIlroy CHAMPIONS (UK) PLC
Alan McInally CHAMPIONS (UK) PLC
Joanne McIntosh A & J Mngt
Colin McIntyre Barrie Stacey Promos & Prods
Kate McIntyre Fox Artist Mngt Ltd
Michael McIntyre CHAMPIONS (UK) PLC/NMP Live Ltd/Off The Kerb Prods/Speakout/Trading Faces Ltd
Charlotte McKay Wendy Lee Mngt
Christian McKay Kerry Gardner Mngt/Yakety Yak
Drew McKay Jae Moss Entp
John McKay CASAROTTO RAMSAY & ASSOCIATES
Myron Mckay Newton Wills Mngt
Siobhan McKay Shepherd Mngt Ltd
Gina McKee United Agents
Malcolm McKee Talent Artists Ltd
Roxanne McKee Big Bang Mngt Ltd
Shaun McKee Actors Alliance
Ed McKeever CHAMPIONS (UK) PLC
Nuala McKeever David Hull Promos Ltd
Gillian McKeith First Artist Management
Michael McKell CAM London
Kenneth McKeller Peter De Rance
Bernard McKenna Jill Foster Ltd
Breffni McKenna Louise Hillman/Katie Threlfall
James McKenna Jonathan Altaras Assoc
Jimmy McKenna Big Bang Mngt Ltd
Liam McKenna Harvey Voices Ltd/Kerry Gardner Mngt
Mark McKenna Nigel Round Mgnt
Paul McKenna Gordon Poole Agy Ltd
Steve McKenna Princess Talent Mngt/Speakout
Virginia Mckenna Brunskill Mngt Ltd
Loreena McKennitt Helter Skelter Agy Ltd
Brendan McKensey Darren Gray Mngt
Jack McKenzie Adrian King Assoc
Jade McKenzie CeeBee Variety Agy
Linsey Dawn McKenzie David Charles Agy
Liza McKenzie Devil Management
Erin McKeown Asgard
Les McKeowns Bay City Rollers BULLET MANAGEMENT LIMITED/Rock Artist Mngt
Mark McKerracher Burnett Granger Assoc
Alex McKie Arlington Enterprises Ltd
Lewis McKie Shining Mngt Ltd
Charlotte McKinney Rogues & Vagabonds Mngt
Miles McKoy Ultimate Int'l
Myles McKoy M.S. Ent Grp/Stardust Ents Agy
Noel McKoy Monkeybiz Ent Agy
Sarah McLachlan Helter Skelter Agy Ltd
Ian McLarnon Burnett Granger Assoc
Annette McLaughlin Kerry Gardner Mngt
Faye McLaughlin Lime Actors Agy & Mngt Ltd
John McLaughlin (classical) Transart (UK) Ltd
Andrea McLean First Artist Management
Don McLean Asgard
Katie McLean ANA
Kerri Mclean Silvey Associates
Alex McLeish Athole Still Int'l Ltd/TEST AGENT A
Shelagh McLeod Shepherd Mngt Ltd
Frank McLintock MBE Persnl Appearances/Preview & Review Ents Ltd
Rob McLoughlin David Anthony Promos
Graham McLusky Gerald Goss Ltd

Julian McMahon Special Artists Agency
Liam McMahon The Richard Stone Prtnrshp
Tony McMahon Anita Alraun Representation
Jim McMail Hireaband Ltd
John McManus - Composer (Film & TV) Shamrock Music Ltd
Michelle McManus Big Talent Group
Tony McManus NEM Prods (UK)
Lawrie McMenemy 1st Choice Speakers UK Ltd/Celebrity Appearances/Jon Holmes Media Ltd/PVA Ent Consultants/Persnly Spkng
Peter McMichael M W Management
Andrew McMillan CHAMPIONS (UK) PLC
Lynette McMorrough Burnett Granger Assoc
Jodie McMullen MCS Agcy
Craig McMurdo Craig McMurdo (Ind Art)
Craig McMurdo & That Swing Thang Hireaband Ltd
Tom McNab Parliament Comms
Kevin R McNally Hatton Mcewan Ltd
Desmond McNamara The Richard Stone Prtnrshp
Marianne McNamara North Of Watford Actors Agy
Tara McNamara Alliance Worldwide Communicati
Tony McNamara Partyweb.co.uk
Sarah McNeale Brunskill Mngt Ltd
Dave McNeill Avalon Mngt
George McNeill Stag Ents
Ian Mcniece Markham & Froggatt Ltd
Emer McParland ABC Direct Ents
Frankie McPolin Downes Presenters Agy
Chris McQuarry Shining Mngt Ltd
Barry McQueen Funhouse Productions Ltd
Molly McQueen Hackford Jones PR
Piper Jimmy McQueen PVA Ent Consultants
Stuart McQuitty Take Three Mngt
Hamish McRae Jon Holmes Media Ltd
Tom Mcrae ITB
Briony McRoberts Louise Hillman/Katie Threlfall
Kirsty McSee Park Promotions
Mike McShane Peters Fraser Dunlop (PFD)
Mike McStat Peter Charlesworth & Assoc
Janet McTeer ARG Management/M F Management Ltd/Yakety Yak
Ray McVay Orchestra Glenn Miller & Ray McVay Orch
Me 'n Him NVB Ents
Me One Universal/Island Records Ltd
Simon Meacock Yakety Yak
David Mead Asgard
Lee Mead United Agents/Wendy Lee Mngt
Nigel Mead Whatever Artists Mngt Ltd
Lesley Meade Daly Pearson Associates
Deborah Meaden CHAMPIONS (UK) PLC/Speakers Associates Ltd
Jonathan Meades Capel & Land
Rhiannon Meades Actors Alliance
Penny Meadmore Limelight Management
Robert Meadmore Kerry Gardner Mngt
Lisanne Meadowcroft Celebn Model Mngt
Alan Meadows Otto Persnl Mngt Ltd
Brian Meadows Fighting Talk Promos
Shane Meadows CASAROTTO RAMSAY & ASSOCIATES
Stephanie Meadows Limelight Management
Danille Meagher Curtis Brown Grp
Natasha Mealey MAGIK MODELS
Colm Meaney Troika Talent
Stephen Mear Simpson Fox Assoc Ltd
Graeme Mearns Daly Pearson Associates
Meat Katie CODA Ltd
Meat Loaf Artist Group International
Meat The Blues Devil Management
Meatloaf Solo Agy Ltd
Meatloaf 2 Jason West Agy
Meatloaf Experience Broadwater Ents Assoc
Meatloaf II Fairplay Ents
Tim Meats M W Management
Mechanical Fracture CKK Ent/Continental Drifts/TEST AGENT C
Stephen Medcalf Athole Still Int'l Ltd/TEST AGENT A
Paul J Medford Gavin Barker/Jonathan Altaras Assoc
Mediaeval Baebes All Electric Productions & Dav
Medicine8 ITB
Carl Medland Fushion Pukka Bosh
Bill Medley (The Righteous Brothers) William Morris Inc (USA)
Dom Mee Gordon Poole Agy Ltd
Andrew Meehan CASAROTTO RAMSAY & ASSOCIATES
Richard Meek Burnett Granger Assoc
Sally Meen First Artist Management
Adela Meer Noel Gay Artists Ltd
Zubin Mehta Askonas Holt Ltd
Peter Mehtab CKK Ent/Whatever Artists Mngt Ltd
Celia Meiras Troika Talent
Meka Some Bizarre Ltd
Mekon CODA Ltd
Mel And Sue Richard Bucknall Mngt (RBM)
Mel Day Broadwater Ents Assoc
Melanie C Solo Agy Ltd
Mikael Melbye Askonas Holt Ltd
Verity Anne Meldrum Liz Hobbs Grp Ltd
Melek CKK Ent
Charlotte Melen Paul Duddridge Mngt
Tonya Meli Seamus Lyte Management Ltd
Olof Mellberg Sport Ent And Media Group
Mel Mellers Vern Allen Ents Ltd
David Mellor Arena Ent Cons/Gordon Poole Agy Ltd/Parliament Comms
Georgina Mellor The Narrow Road Company Ltd
Will Mellor Big Bang Mngt Ltd/CAM London
Alex Mellor-Brooks Nyland Mngt
George Melly with Digby Fairweather's Half-Dozen Jazzco
Alexander Melnikov IMG Artists
The Melody Fakers Upbeat Entertainment
Melodybeats Norwich Artistes
Laure Meloy Opera & Concert Artists
Mel's Magic Galaxy Evts
Melton Mowbray Tally-Ho MTM Presntns
Melton Mowbray Toy Soldiers MTM Presntns
Katie Melua Marshall Arts Ltd/Republic Media
Gino Melvazzi Anita Alraun Representation
Josephine Melville Dennis Lyne Agy
Jules Melvin The Richard Stone Prtnrshp
Rickie & Melvin Hyper Agency
Members Of The Public CEC Management/The Agency Group
Memphis Belle Orchestra Advanced Ents
Bobby Memphis (Elvis) Upfront Ent Agy Ltd
Memphis King Angle Ents Ltd
Dean Memphis (Shakin Stevens) Nigel Round Mgnt
Men in Black David Charles Agy/The Dixon Agy
Men in Coats Jongleurs/Whatever Artists Mngt Ltd
Men, Women and Children The Agency Group
Sergio Mendes William Morris Inc (USA)
Sergio Mendes & Brasil 2000 Denis Vaughan Mngt
Carla Mendonca BWH Agency
Daniel Mendoza Shepherd Mngt Ltd
Chris Menges CASAROTTO RAMSAY & ASSOCIATES
David Menkin Noel Gay Artists Ltd
Mens Club Int'l Mngt & Agy Ltd
Freddie Mensah Mike Constantia Artiste Mngt L
Louise Mensch Curtis Brown Grp
Mentallica Andrew Beauchamp Mngt/The Psycho Mngt Co Ltd
Jeremy Menuhin Upbeat Classical Mngt
Anouschka Menzies Harvey Voices Ltd
Sean Meo IMWP (UK) Ltd
Steven Meo Emptage Hallett Ltd
David Mercer Blackburn Sachs Assoc/CASAROTTO RAMSAY & ASSOCIATES/Talking Heads - The Voice Agy
Nick Mercer John Field - Theatre and Puppe
Jeff Merchant North Of Watford Actors Agy
Stephen Merchant Peters Fraser Dunlop (PFD)/United Agents
Mercury - The Queen Tribute Mark Lundquist Management & Co
Mercury (Queen) Lee James Assoc Ltd
Mercury Rev Free Trade Agy
The Mercury Tribute Show Stellamax Entp Ltd
Guy Meredith Jill Foster Ltd
Merengada Matters Musical/Wienerwald Ents
Merengue-Mania PVA Ent Consultants
David Merlin (Magician) Ginger Walker Agy/Hartbeat Ents Ltd/PVA Ent Consultants
Merlins Children`s Entertainments Merlin Children's Ents
Merlyn Derek Bruce Ents
Anthony Merna Lime Actors Agy & Mngt Ltd
Gemma Merna (Carmel, Hollyoaks) Big Bang Mngt Ltd/Lime Actors Agy & Mngt Ltd/Nigel Round Mgnt
Melissa Merran CKK Ent
Jason Merrels ARG Management
Blue Merrick Otto Persnl Mngt Ltd
Joy Merriman Anita Alraun Representation
Chris Merritt Askonas Holt Ltd
Tift Merritt Asgard
Katharine Merry Nuff Respect
Merry Xmas Every Body Tale John Hessenthaler Ents
Mersey Beatles Henderson Mngt
The Mersey Beatles Jason West Agy
Mersey Beatles Upfront Ent Agy Ltd
Merseybeats Brian Gannon Mngt/Jason West Agy/John Hessenthaler

Ents/McLeod Agy Ltd/PVA Ent Consultants/Paul Bridson Prods/Rock Artist Mngt
The Merseybeats BULLET MANAGEMENT LIMITED/Dansatak
Dan Mersh Noel Gay Artists Ltd
Paul Merson After Dinner World Ltd/CHAMPIONS (UK) PLC
Paul Merton Int'l Artistes Ltd
Peter Merton Barn Dance Line Dance Agy
Zienia Merton Langford Assoc
Maria Mescki Linton Mngt
The Mesh Band Steve Allen Ents
Meskalin Head On Mngt
Camille Meskill Audrey Benjamin Agy
Michael Messer Roots Around The World
Oriane Messina RDF Management
Mest Primary Talent Int'l
Metallica Artist Group International/Kas Mercer/Mercenary PR
Metalworks (Gamelan Orchestra) Matters Musical
Samuel Metcalf Indep Mngt Ltd
Jennifer Metcalfe (Mercedes, Hollyoaks) Big Bang Mngt Ltd/Hyper Agency/Nigel Round Mgnt
Jesse Metcalfe Action Talent Int.
Paul Metcalfe (Rod Stewart) BULLET MANAGEMENT LIMITED/Ron Martin Mngt
Metric Scream Promotions
Metric Foot Barn Dance Line Dance Agy
Metro Riots The Agency Group
Metropolis Book A Band
Mew Free Trade Agy
David Meyer 1984 Persnl Mngt
Edgar Meyer IMG Artists
Jake Meyer Cunningham Mngt Ltd
Michael Meyer (Estate) CASAROTTO RAMSAY & ASSOCIATES
Paul Meyer Pro Artist Management
Eric Meyers Shining Mngt Ltd
Ben Meyjes Markham & Froggatt Ltd
Menno Meyjes CASAROTTO RAMSAY & ASSOCIATES
MFF Some Bizarre Ltd
Miami International Roadshow Clubline Promos
MIB Band CHAMPIONS (UK) PLC
Michael Bublé The Leighton-Pope Org
Enrique Diemecke The Music Ptnrshp Ltd
Michael Jackson (By Navi) Henderson Mngt
Lutz Michael Scott-Paul Young Ents Ltd
Steve Michael Sunshine Ents
Victor Michael Nigel Round Mgnt
Alexander Michaels Persnl Appearances
Barbara Michaels Gordon Kellett Ents
David Michaels Harvey Voices Ltd/Kerry Gardner Mngt
Kate Michaels Garston Ents Ltd
Lee Michaels (Robbie Williams) Camscott Leisure
Lenny Michaels CeeBee Variety Agy
Micheal King (Elvis) Advanced Ents
Faye Michel APM Ass
Michèle (Magician/Fire eater/Belly dancer) ABC Direct Ents
Michelle PVA Ent Consultants
Anne Michelle Orvad Enterprises
Dutch Michelle Dave Woodbury Ents
Kitty Michelle CeeBee Variety Agy
Louise Michelle Liz Hobbs Grp Ltd
Susie Michelle MCS Agcy
Vicki Michelle Liz Hobbs Grp Ltd
Ian Michie Speak-Easy Ltd
Mick the Knife (Sinatra) Advanced Ents
Mickey D Paramount Int'l Mngt
William Mickleborough Grays Mngt & Asc
Anne Micklethwaite Grays Mngt & Asc
Micky the Magical Clown PVA Ent Consultants
Micky Zany Barry Dye Ents/Highfield Mngt & Promos/Norwich Artistes
Paul Mico Avenue Artistes Ltd
Midas Sounds Starfinders Int'l Mngt
Midas Touch Cosmos Agy & Promos/Hireaband Ltd
Middle Of The Road BCM Promos Ltd/Barry Collings Ents/Brian Gannon Mngt/PVA Ent Consultants/Rock Artist Mngt
Middle Of The Road featuring Sally Carr Jason West Agy
Jayne Middlemiss Hackford Jones PR/James Grant Mngt Ltd/The Commercial Agency
Philip Middlemiss Brown & Simcocks
John Middleton Amber Persnl Mngt Ltd
Robin Middleton North One Mngt
Lucy Middleweek Indep Mngt Ltd
General Midi Hope Management
Midlake Free Trade Agy
The Midlands Artists Variety Music Hall Show Derek Bruce Ents
Bette Midler Creative Artists Agency
Midlife Revival Band (NL) Wim Wigt Prodns Ltd
Midnight Sunshine Ents
Midnight Affair Trevor George Ents Ltd
Midnight Beast Insanity Artists
Midnight Dynamos BCM Promos Ltd
Midnight Express Dave Andrews Ents/Les Hart (Southampton) Ents
Midnight Group Fairplay Ents
Midnight Hour Sardi's Int'l Ent
Midnight Oasis London Music Agy
Midnight Showband Hartbeat Ents Ltd
Midtown ITB
The Mighty Juke Box Band Book A Band
Miguel's All Star Steel Band The John Boddy Agency
Sofia Mihailidou Opera & Concert Artists
Mika Purple PR
Mika Bomb CODA Ltd
Mike & The Mechanics Tony Smith Personal Management
Magic Mike Devil Management
Mikee B (Dream Team) UK Booking Agy
Mike's Disco David Forshaw Entp
Mikey Dread - Channel One (Roots Reggae) Sound System Glasshouse Prods Ltd
Izabella Miko Emptage Hallett Ltd
Peter Mikulas Music Int'l
Milburn Freedom Management
Greg Milburn Lime Actors Agy & Mngt Ltd
Oliver Milburn ARG Management
High Mileage Norwich Artistes
Alastair Miles Ingpen & Williams Ltd
Annie Miles Kerry Gardner Mngt/Louise Hillman/Katie Threlfall
Debbie Miles Derek Bruce Ents/Tony Bennell Ents
Gaynor Miles Anita Alraun Representation
Leigh Miles Jo Gurnett Persnl Mngt
Nick Miles Big Bang Mngt Ltd
Sarah Miles Chatto & Linnit Ltd
Stephan Miles Moonglight Agy
Stuart Miles SIMON WHITTAM PUBLICITY
Christina Milian Mission Control Artist Agy
David Miliband MP Trading Faces Ltd
Gia Milinovich Sue Rider Mngt Ltd
~Military Bands~ The John Boddy Agency
Milk & Sugar (UK) Fresh Artiste Management Ltd
Milk Kan Free Trade Agy
Tony Millan & Mike Walling Jill Foster Ltd
Rhonda Millar Yakety Yak
Adam D Millard Speak-Easy Ltd
Rosie Millard Knight Ayton Mngt
Millenium 2000 (Robbie Williams tribute) Cosmos Agy & Promos
Millennium (Robbie Williams Tribute) Dansatak
Todd Miller And The Joe Loss Orchestra & Singers ABC Direct Ents/Derek Bruce Ents/Joe Loss Ltd
Bill Miller Buddy Lee Attrctns Inc (USA)
Buddy Miller Asgard
Dr. Scott Miller Knight Ayton Mngt
Geoff Miller After Dinner World Ltd/CHAMPIONS (UK) PLC/Jon Holmes Media Ltd/McLeod Agy Ltd/Persnl Appearances
The Glenn Miller Band PVA Ent Consultants
Glenn Miller Orchestra (UK) directed by Ray McVay Glenn Miller & Ray McVay Orch/The John Boddy Agency
Harry Miller Shining Mngt Ltd
Henry Miller Shepherd Mngt Ltd
John Miller & His Orchestra "The Glenn Miller Connection" The John Boddy Agency
Jonty Miller Talent Artists Ltd
Kerry Miller (Kylie Minogue) Chance Promos
Louise Miller Martin Ents
Lulu Miller Linkside Agy
Miller Magic John Hessenthaler Ents
Marti Miller Speak-Easy Ltd
Mick Miller ETM Ltd/Nigel Round Mgnt
Mike Miller Non Stop Ents
Pauline Miller Anita Alraun Representation
Mr Miller & Mr Porter SMA Talent Ltd
Sienna Miller Peters Fraser Dunlop (PFD)/United Agents
Teo Miller Stephen Budd Mngt
T'Nia Miller The Actors File
Vincent Miller 4.A.D.
Sophie Millett Daly Pearson Associates
Charles Millham Susan Angel Kevin Francis Ltd
David Milliband MP CHAMPIONS (UK) PLC
Sarah Millican CHAMPIONS (UK) PLC/Chambers Management Ltd
Mike Milligan Speakout
Millionaire Big Sister Promotions
Paddy Millner (Little Richard tribute) Graham Cole Mngt
Robert Millner Music Int'l
Adrian Mills Downes Presenters Agy/June Ford-Crush
Ben Mills Action Talent Int.
Bob Mills Paul Duddridge Mngt
Christopher Mills Kerry Gardner Mngt
Dan Mills Speakout
Dave Mills COFFEE ARTISTS
Hayley Mills Chatto & Linnit Ltd
Joe Mills Talking Heads - The Voice Agy/The Voice Box Agency Ltd
Royce Mills The Richard Stone Prtnrshp
Scott Mills Big Talent Group/Hyper Agency/The Psycho Mngt Co Ltd/Wise

Buddah Talent & Voices
Simon Mills Loesje Sanders
Alexandra Milman Susan Angel Kevin Francis Ltd
Lisa Milne Askonas Holt Ltd
Steven Milne Ron Martin Mngt
John Milner & Kim PVA Ent Consultants
Max Milner Burnett Granger Assoc
Jeremy Milnes KAL Mngt
Sherrill Milnes Ingpen & Williams Ltd
Ronnie Milsap Buddy Lee Attrctns Inc (USA)
Malcolm Milton Parliament Comms
Paul Milton Grays Mngt & Asc
Richie Milton & The Lowdown Sardi's Int'l Ent
Xanthe Milton Curtis Brown Grp
Miltra as Foxy Cleopatra Doub7e Seven Events Ltd
Mimbo The A6 Agy
Mimbre Continental Drifts/Fool's Paradise/TEST AGENT C
Mimeworks Continental Drifts/Prima Artists/TEST AGENT C/Whatever Artists Mngt Ltd
The Mimic Street Preachers Jason West Agy
Mimics XS Promos
Mimix PVA Ent Consultants
Tony Minchella Derek Bruce Ents
Louise Minchin Noel Gay Artists Ltd
Tim Minchin CHAMPIONS (UK) PLC/PBJ Mngt Ltd
MInd The Gap Highfield Mngt & Promos/Norwich Artistes/The Ents Agency
The Mindbenders Brian Gannon Mngt
Ann Ming Robert Smith Literary Agency
Anthony Minghella Judy Daish Assoc
Dominic Minghella CASAROTTO RAMSAY & ASSOCIATES
Mini Grand Prix Stardust Ents Agy
Valerie Minifie Performance Actors Agy
Miniscule Continental Drifts/TEST AGENT C
Miniscule Of Sound CKK Ent
Ministry of Sound Clubbers Guide Tour Mission Control Artist Agy
Karl Minns Avalon Mngt
Annie Minogue COFFEE ARTISTS
Ceilidh Minogue Hireaband Ltd
Dani Minogue Terry Blamey Management
Dannii Minogue Helter Skelter Agy Ltd/Mission Control Artist Agy/Personal Management & Casting/The Commercial Agency/Tony Denton Promos Ltd
Kylie Minogue Primary Talent Int'l/Terry Blamey Management
Minstrels Gallery London Music Agy
Medieval Minstrels Matters Musical
Alan Minter Fighting Talk Promos/Paul Bridson Prods
Aundrea Minto Voice Shop
John Minton The Horne Concert Agy
Minus ITB
Minus 2 Sunshine Ents
Minx Dave Woodbury Ents
Miracle of the Mindreading show Mr "E" Ents
Mirage Arena Ent Cons
Tim Mirfin Askonas Holt Ltd
Mirror & Dee C.D.E.C.
Mirror Image Ultimate Int'l
Antonietta Mirto Grays Mngt & Asc
Inam Mirza ANA
Katya Mirza Cherry Parker Management
Mischief La Bas Continental Drifts/TEST AGENT C
Mischief Labas Hireaband Ltd
Miscilly Music Coach House Ent
Annilese Miskimmon Judy Daish Assoc
Miss Behave CKK Ent/Continental Drifts/TEST AGENT C
Miss Jemella (Exotic Python Act) Joker Ents
Miss Jones Rainbow Striptease Agy
Miss Kylie & Dancers Camscott Leisure
Miss Minogue Big Bang Mngt Ltd/Prima Artists
Miss Moneypenny Andrew Beauchamp Mngt
Miss Northern Ireland Alison Campbell Model Agy
Miss T Bees Knees Ents
Miss Van Dyke Steve Draper Ents
Miss York Events Connect
Mission Blue (Tamla Motown tribute) Jason West Agy/Kaye Frankland Ent Agy/Les Hart (Southampton) Ents
Mission Blue Ultimate Int'l
Mission Blue (Tamla Motown tribute) Upfront Ent Agy Ltd
Mississippi Dixielanders McLeod Agy Ltd
Mist Norwich Artistes
Mistakes Yellow Balloon Prods Ltd
Mister Blue PVA Ent Consultants
Mister Magipatch Prof Mystral's Omnibus
Mister Sister Yorkshire Ent
Mister Ted's Magic Show Mr Ted's Magic Show (Magic)
Misterfield Magic Show Hire-A-Band Ent Agy
Jimi Mistry Jonathan Altaras Assoc
Misty in Roots ABS Agy
Adrian Mitchell Peters Fraser Dunlop (PFD)
Andrew Mitchell Alpha Persnl Mngt
Boney M-featuring Liz Mitchell Barrie Hawkins Leisure Service
Clare Mitchell Dennis Lyne Agy
David Mitchell Int'l Artistes Ltd
Des Mitchell Primary Talent Int'l
Grant Mitchell Sarm Mngt
Joni Mitchell ITB
Lisa Mitchell Purple PR
Nigell Mitchell Wise Buddah Talent & Voices
Pete Mitchell Noel Gay Artists Ltd
Peter Mitchell Stag Ents
Sasha Mitchell Louise Hillman/Katie Threlfall
Susan Mitchell Otto Persnl Mngt Ltd
Tim Mitchell Clare Vidal-Hall
Richard Mitchley Speak-Easy Ltd
Nina De Mitri Lime Actors Agy & Mngt Ltd
The Mix The CBS Grp
Mix and Mingle Magic & Balloonologist Group Mr "E" Ents
Mixed Feelings Book A Band/Crown Ents/Fanfare 3000/Highfield Mngt & Promos/Norwich Artistes/The CBS Grp
Mixolydian Steel Band Tony Bennell Ents
Mix'T Nutz Jason West Agy
Mixtures Jason West Agy
Miles Mlambo Agency K-Bis
Hanno Müller-Brachmann Askonas Holt Ltd
Moby MVO Ltd
Jeanne Mockford Langford Assoc
Diane Modahl Parliament Comms
Modern Romance BULLET MANAGEMENT LIMITED/Barry Collings Ents/CREATIVE PRODUCTIONS/Jason West Agy/Kevin King Mngt/The Psycho Mngt Co Ltd
Aidan Moffat 13 Artists
Georgina Moffat Sasha Leslie Mngt
Karl Moffatt Wendy Lee Mngt
Georgia Moffett Kerry Gardner Mngt
Mogul Athole Still Int'l Ltd/TEST AGENT A
Mogwai Asgard
Mohair Marshall Arts Ltd
Jon Mohnani Scott-Paul Young Ents Ltd
Jay Mohr Special Artists Agency
Saima Mohsin Take Three Mngt
Mojave 3 4.A.D./Primary Talent Int'l
Mojo Blues Band (A) Wim Wigt Prodns Ltd
Gretchen Mol Lou Coulson Associates
Jan Molby After Dinner World Ltd/Nigel Round Mgnt
Stephen Molden Colette Fenlon Persnl Mngt
Nicolae Moldoveanu Clarion/Seven Muses
Phillipa Mole Fox Artist Mngt Ltd
Alfred Molina Lou Coulson Associates
Stephen Mollett Jill Foster Ltd
Elsa Mollien Markham & Froggatt Ltd
Fiona Mollison Kerry Gardner Mngt
Dearbhla Molloy Cassie Mayer Ltd
Ryan Molloy Burnett Granger Assoc
Terry Molloy M W Management
Moloko ITB
John Moloney Int'l Artistes Ltd
Peter Moloney Gordon Robinson Assoc/Laurie Taylor Ents Ltd
Ryan Moloney Hyper Agency
Monaco Hireaband Ltd
The Monaco String Quartet Crown Ents
Monaco String Quartet Dave Winslett Assoc/Matters Musical
The Monaco String Quartet The John Boddy Agency
Dominic Monaghan Peters Fraser Dunlop (PFD)
Greg Monaghan Barry Dye Ents
Katharine Monaghan Burnett Granger Assoc
Patrick Monahan CHAMPIONS (UK) PLC
Monarchy (Queen Tribute) Henderson Mngt
Susan Moncrieff Nuff Respect
Michelle Mone 1st Choice Speakers UK Ltd/CHAMPIONS (UK) PLC/NMP Live Ltd/Parliament Comms
Mark Monero Hatton Mcewan Ltd
Money 4 Nothing (Dire Straits) Jason West Agy
Money For Nothing (Dire Straits Tribute) Advanced Ents/Peller Artistes Ltd
Kevin Money DBA Speakers
Owen Money Gordon Poole Agy Ltd/Phillips Ent Agy
Simon Money Barrie Stacey Promos & Prods
Drummond Money-Coutts Curtis Brown Grp
Gianni Mongiardino Stafford Law
David Monico M W Management
Jon Monie Noel Gay Artists Ltd
Kylie Monique Prima Artists
Anthony Monjaro Adrian King Assoc
Roger Monk Brian Taylor Assoc
The Monkees Primary Talent Int'l
Monkey Universal/Island Records Ltd
Funk Monkeys David Charles Agy
Monkhouse Jason West Agy
Bob Monkhouse OBE Parliament Comms

Roger Monkhouse Comedy Store Mngt
Edward Monks Agency K-Bis
Monophonics Phillips Ent Agy
Joanna Monro SJ Mngt
Mary Monro Audrey Benjamin Agy
Kelly Monroe Sunshine Ents
Monroe Kent 111 SJ Mngt
Mick Monroe After Dinner Spkers & Com
Sue Monroe All Electric Productions & Dav
Tony Monroe Northern Lights Mngt
Tony Monson (Solar Radio) UK Booking Agy
Monster (REM tribute) Andrew Beauchamp Mngt
Monster Truck Show Go Ents
Sarah Montague Noel Gay Artists Ltd
Monte Carlo Casino PVA Ent Consultants
Monteiro Piano Duo IMG Artists
Gabriela Montero Big Life Management
Aaron Monteverde Roots Around The World
Ricardo Montez MBA
Colin Montgomerie Brian Maclaurin Agency/CHAMPIONS (UK) PLC
Diane Montgomery Fushion Pukka Bosh
Lucy Montgomery Noel Gay Artists Ltd/PBJ Mngt Ltd/The Richard Stone Prtnrshp
Roger Montgomery London Music Agy
Samantha Montgomery Lime Actors Agy & Mngt Ltd
Michelle Montuori Bees Knees Ents
Edgaras Montvidas International Classical Artist
Monty Jo Sarsby PR Ltd
Nicola Moodie North Of Watford Actors Agy
Doug Moody Darren Gray Mngt
Ron Moody Eric Glass Ltd
Barry Moon G Entertaining
Chris Moon CHAMPIONS (UK) PLC/DBA Speakers/NMP Live Ltd/Persnl Appearances/Speakers For Business/Trading Faces Ltd
Georgina Moon Kenneth Earle Persnl Mngt
Helen Moon The Narrow Road Company Ltd
Johnny Moon Compact Mngt & Ent Agy/Derek Bruce Ents
MoonDance Jason West Agy
Moondog Beatles Compact Mngt & Ent Agy
Maggie Moone SIMON WHITTAM PUBLICITY
Pat Mooney Pete Mitchell Associates
Moonlight Alan Walters Mngt
Moonshine Barn Dance Line Dance Agy/XS Promos
Moonspell Miracle Artists Ltd
Ian Moor Angle Ents Ltd
Melanie Moorcraft Agency K-Bis
Nick Moorcroft Cassie Mayer Ltd
Sam Moore & Friends Brian Gannon Mngt
Alfie Moore CHAMPIONS (UK) PLC
Andy Moore ICON Actors Mngt
Brian Moore Jon Holmes Media Ltd
Christy Moore Asgard
Dominique Moore Sandra Boyce Mngt
Gary Moore ITB
Ian Moore Off The Kerb Prods
Jamie Moore Matters Musical
Johnny Moore Pete Mitchell Associates
Jonathan Moore Performing Arts
Juliet Moore Grays Mngt & Asc
Mandy Moore Helter Skelter Agy Ltd/Special Artists Agency
Margaret Moore Inspiration Mngt
Michael Moore Celebrity Chefs UK/Endeavor Agency
Sir Patrick Moore Paul Madeley
Peter Moore Peter Moore (Ind Art)
Polly Moore Nancy Hudson Associates Ltd
Richard Moore Emptage Hallett Ltd
Sally Moore (Madonna) Doub7e Seven Events Ltd/Funhouse Productions Ltd
Sally Moore as Celine Dion, Madonna Advanced Ents/Entertainers Mgt Ltd/Henderson Mngt
Sir Roger Moore Diamond Management
Stephen Moore Markham & Froggatt Ltd
Tuesday Moore Sunshine Ents
Vivienne Moore The Actors File
Allison Moorer Asgard
Adrian Moorhouse MBE Arena Ent Cons
Grant Moorhouse North Of Watford Actors Agy
Ian Moorhouse Funhouse Productions Ltd
Justin Moorhouse Nigel Round Mgnt
Moorish Delta 7 Ablaze Music Management
Julia Moorley Celebn Model Mngt
Moose (P.F. Project) (DJ) Head On Mngt
Mop Top Beatles Advanced Ents
Mark Moraghan COLE KITCHENN PRSN MGT
John Moraitis M W Management
David Morales ITB
Diana Moran TFA Artiste Management
Dylan Moran PBJ Mngt Ltd
Janet Moran Audrey Benjamin Agy
Josh Moran Amber Persnl Mngt Ltd
Mike Moran S M A Talent Ltd/SMA Talent Ltd
Nicky Moran The Horne Concert Agy
Tara Moran Susan Angel Kevin Francis Ltd
Tim Morand Silvey Associates
Morbid Angel Miracle Artists Ltd
Morcheeba CMO Mngt Int'l Ltd/Primary Talent Int'l
Johnny More Gordon Robinson Assoc/Persnl Appearances
More-Alanis-Set Andrew Beauchamp Mngt
Morecambe & Wise (Estate) Billy Marsh Assoc Ltd
Claudia Morecroft Sandra Singer Assoc
Sonja Morenstern Scott-Paul Young Ents Ltd
Filomena Moretti Transart (UK) Ltd
Morgan Dave Woodbury Ents
Adrian Lewis Morgan Elinor Hilton Associates
Ashley Morgan Colette Fenlon Persnl Mngt
Bethan Morgan Cardiff Casting
Caryl Morgan Louise Hillman/Katie Threlfall
Chris Morgan Cardiff Casting
Cliff Morgan OBE Celebrity Appearances/Gordon Poole Agy Ltd/Persnly Spkng
Dan Morgan Lip Service Casting Ltd
Derrick Morgan Monkeybiz Ent Agy
Emily Morgan Jonathan Altaras Assoc
Francine Morgan Susan Angel Kevin Francis Ltd
Garfield Morgan AIM
Jared Morgan Cardiff Casting
Jeff Morgan CKK Ent/Mainstream Evts/Partyweb.co.uk
Johnny Morgan NVB Ents
Karl F. Morgan Susan Angel Kevin Francis Ltd
Lorrie Morgan Buddy Lee Attrctns Inc (USA)
Maria Morgan MBA
Nadia Morgan Performance Actors Agy
Piers Morgan Tracey Chapman
Ric Morgan Grays Mngt & Asc
Sally Morgan Limelight Management
Sue Morgan Celebn Model Mngt
Tracy Morgan ICM (USA)
Big Bill Morganfield Roots Around The World
Naoko Mori Emptage Hallett Ltd
Eleanor Moriarty Susan Angel Kevin Francis Ltd
Erick Morillo Subliminal Records
Carol Morley Troika Talent
Gigi Morley Amanda Howard Assoc Ltd/Noel Gay Artists Ltd
James Morley ICON Actors Mngt
Ken Morley Arena Ent Cons/Chris Davis Management/Paul Madeley/Persnl Appearances
Vanessa Morley Actorum
Daniel Mornin Judy Daish Assoc
Paul Morocco CKK Ent
Cristian Morrell Sandra Singer Assoc
Penny Morrell Burnett Granger Assoc
Andrea Morricone S M A Talent Ltd
Ade Morris Associated Arts
Adrian Morris Grays Mngt & Asc
Morris and the Minors Book A Band/McLeod Agy Ltd/Yorkshire Ent
Aubrey Morris (Estate) Bernard Hunter Assoc
Chris Morris PBJ Mngt Ltd
Daniel Morris Seamus Lyte Management Ltd
Deirdra Morris Burnett Granger Assoc
Delmozene Morris Grays Mngt & Asc
Dewi Morris Jon Holmes Media Ltd/Sara Crouch Mngt
Gil Morris PVA Ent Consultants
Gill Morris Compact Mngt & Ent Agy
Graham Morris Derek Bruce Ents
Iestyn Morris Music Int'l
Jonathon Morris MCS Agcy
Julia Morris PBJ Mngt Ltd
Kevin Morris Buddy Lee Attrctns Inc (USA)
Libby Morris Kerry Gardner Mngt
Peter Morris (Ind Art) Peter Morris
Rachel Morris Stage Centre Mngt
Siwan Morris CAM London
Sonya Louis Morris Lime Actors Agy & Mngt Ltd
Jackie Morrison Susan Angel Kevin Francis Ltd
Nathaniel Morrison Burnett Granger Assoc
Stephen Morrison Avalon Mngt
Van Morrison Inspirational Artiste Bkg/MVO Ltd
Alanis Morrissette Creative Artists Agency
Morrissey Autonomous Talent Bkg/Best PR/Creative Artists Agency
David Morrissey Premier PR/Troika Talent
Ian Morrow Sarm Mngt
Laila Morse CAM London
Caroline Mortimer Burnett Granger Assoc
Vicki Mortimer Simpson Fox Assoc Ltd
Andy Morton Talent Artists Ltd
Greg Morton Paramount Int'l Mngt
John Morton David Wilkinson Assoc

Richard Morton Off The Kerb Prods
Samantha Morton Conway Van Gelder Grant Ltd
Mosaic (Band) Kaye Frankland Ent Agy
Moscow Ballet - La Classique A.I.R. Ltd
Moscow By Night A.I.R. Ltd
Johannes Moser IMG Artists
Albert Moses Cherry Parker Management
Geoffrey Moses Music Int'l
Andrew Moss Hyper Agency
Basil Moss Shepherd Mngt Ltd
Chloe Moss CASAROTTO RAMSAY & ASSOCIATES
David Moss The A6 Agy
Miles Moss ICON Actors Mngt
Natalie Moss Grays Mngt & Asc
Roger Moss Hilary Gagan Assoc
Sir Stirling Moss OBE Persnl Appearances
Trude Mostue Jacque Evans Mngt Ltd
The Mother`s Delight Ceilidh Band Rent-A-Band
Mothers Ruin Barn Dance Line Dance Agy
Rory Motion Adastra
The Motivators Steve Allen Ents
Motley Crue Artist Group International/Kas Mercer/Mercenary PR/Scream Promotions
Motorcycle Mad Men! MTM Presntns
Motorhead The Agency Group
Motown Magic MJE Mngt/McLeod Agy Ltd
Motown Show Mark Lundquist Management & Co
John Motson OBE Jane Morgan Mngt Ltd/Jon Holmes Media Ltd/PVA Ent Consultants
Bob Mould Free Trade Agy
Fran Moulds Avalon Mngt
Dave Mounfield Noel Gay Artists Ltd
Angela Mounsey RBA Management Ltd
Margaret Mountford Taylor Herring Public Relation
Robert Mountford Burnett Granger Assoc
Mouse Dave Woodbury Ents
Mouse on Mars Primary Talent Int'l
Nana Mouskouri Denis Vaughan Mngt
Mouth and Trousers Continental Drifts/TEST AGENT C
Move-it Derek Bruce Ents
Moves A Foot Barn Dance Line Dance Agy
Knight Moves Norwich Artistes
Guy Mowbray Jon Holmes Media Ltd
Patrick Mower Burnett Granger Assoc
Gina Moxley Alexandra Cann Reprsntn
Sue Moxley Tony Clayman Promos
Matthew Moxon MBA
Paul Moxon (composer) Sandra Singer Assoc
Patrick Moy Brunskill Mngt Ltd
Alison Moyet Helter Skelter Agy Ltd/Modest! management
Dave Moylan The A6 Agy
Chris Moyles The Richard Stone Prtnrshp
Elizabeth Moynihan Speak-Easy Ltd
Vince Cable MP Capel & Land
Mr C ITB
Mr Doo (clown & juggler) Austin Baptiste Ent Agy Ltd/Derek Bruce Ents
Mr "E" The Magician Mr "E" Ents
Mr Fizzbangs Continental Drifts/TEST AGENT C
Mr Green and Mr Orange Continental Drifts/TEST AGENT C
Mr Hudson Insanity Artists
Mr Jellyspoon The A6 Agy
Mr Lobster Albert Alchemy Ent
Mr Magic Entertainments Mr Magic Ents (Magic)
Mr McDonut Starfinders Int'l Mngt
Mr Methane BO Prods Ltd/Mr Methane! (Ind Art)
Mr Motivator Celebrity Appearances
Mr Scruff (DJ) CODA Ltd
Mr Signature Man Prima Artists/Ultimate Int'l
Mr Sketchum's Caricatures KM Ents/Kaleidoscope/Mr Sketchum's Caricatures/Pete Cross Agency Ltd/Stellamax Entp Ltd/Sternberg-Clarke/The CBS Grp/Winchester Ent
Mr Swing Dansatak
Mr Tease Dave Woodbury Ents
Mr Toots London Music Agy/Partyweb.co.uk
Mr Topper MTM Presntns
Mr Woo MTM Presntns
Mr Zed Paramount Int'l Mngt
Mr Zen Mr Zen (Ind Art)
Maksim Mrvica (pianist) Mel Bush Org
Ms Dynamite Helter Skelter Agy Ltd
M&S Presents The Girl Next Door Mission Control Artist Agy
Aura Msmang Monkeybiz Ent Agy
Sergio Muchado CASAROTTO RAMSAY & ASSOCIATES
The Muck Spreaders Barn Dance Band Hire-A-Band Ent Agy
The Muckers Barn Dance Line Dance Agy
Mud Brian Gannon Mngt
Mud II ft. members of Les Grays Mud Hal Carter Org
Mandy Muden Spotlight Ents
Michael Mueller Kerry Gardner Mngt
Mugenkyo Japanese Drummers Whatever Artists Mngt Ltd
The Mugenkyo Taiko Drummers Line-Up PMC/Matters Musical/Wienerwald Ents
Huntley Muir Judy Daish Assoc
Shalva Mukeria Athole Still Int'l Ltd/TEST AGENT A
Anj Mukerji Liz Hobbs Grp Ltd
Mukka Matters Musical
Stephen Mulhern James Grant Mngt Ltd
Ashley Mulheron Princess Talent Mngt
Tiffany Mulheron AIM
Alan Mullally MPC Ent
Peter Mullan Markham & Froggatt Ltd
Michelle Mullane Wise Buddah Talent & Voices
Gary Mullen (Freddie Mercury) Funhouse Productions Ltd/Hireaband Ltd
Muller Cleobury Mortimer Band Derek Bruce Ents
Leah Muller The Richard Stone Prtnrshp
Martino Müller Loesje Sanders
Richard Muller TMK Mngt & Agcy Ltd
Alan Mullery MBE CHAMPIONS (UK) PLC/Persnl Appearances/Persnly Spkng
Eileen Mulligan Seamus Lyte Management Ltd
Lawrence Mullin Louise Hillman/Katie Threlfall
The Mullova Ensemble Askonas Holt Ltd
Viktoria Mullova Askonas Holt Ltd
Jimmy Mulville Cassie Mayer Ltd
Heidi Mumford Tony Clayman Promos
Mumm-ra Supervision Management
Mums Porridge Barn Dance Line Dance Agy
Jonathan Munby Clare Vidal-Hall
Munchen Steht Bierkeller Band Rent-A-Band
Marc Munden CASAROTTO RAMSAY & ASSOCIATES
Chris Mundle RDF Management
Munich Bier Keller Men Derek Bruce Ents/NVB Ents/Stardust Ents Agy/Tony Bennell Ents
Simon Munnery Avalon Mngt
Matt Munro Jnr. Chimes Int'l Ents Ltd/Tony Clayman Promos
Milli Munro (Shirley Bassey, Tina Turner, Whitney Houston) Derek Bruce Ents/Henderson Mngt/Jason West Agy
Teddi Munro Apple County
Julia Munrow Stage Centre Mngt
Emma Munro-Wilson Matters Musical
Bruce Munton Bruce Munton (Magic)/CKK Ent/Partyweb.co.uk/Prima Artists/The A6 Agy
Murder, My Lord Clive Panto Prods
Murder Mystery Southern ABDC Ents
Kelly Murdoch Agency K-Bis
Laura Murdoch Agency K-Bis
Annika Murfitt Alpha Persnl Mngt
Dermot Murnaghan Celebrity Appearances/KBJ Management/Trading Faces Ltd
Alex Murphy After Dinner World Ltd/Nigel Round Mgnt
Asa Murphy Tony West Ents
Ben Murphy Compact Mngt & Ent Agy
Brian Murphy Saraband Assoc
Brittany Murphy Special Artists Agency
Cillian Murphy Lou Coulson Associates
Colin Murphy Dawn Sedgwick Mngt
Conor Murphy Loesje Sanders
Hannah Murphy Wendy Lee Mngt
Kevin Murphy Brunskill Management Ltd
Miriam Murphy Hazard Chase Ltd
Pat Murphy After Dinner World Ltd
Tom Murphy Alexandra Cann Reprsntn
Murphys Law Barn Dance Line Dance Agy
Murphy's Marbles Sunshine Ents
Al Murray - The Pub Landlord Avalon Mngt/CHAMPIONS (UK) PLC
Andy Murray CHAMPIONS (UK) PLC
Ann Murray Askonas Holt Ltd
Anne Murray ICM (USA)
Charlie Murray Identity One Management
Cheryl Murray Nyland Mngt
Colin Murray CHAMPIONS (UK) PLC/The Richard Stone Prtnrshp
Jaime Murray ARG Management
James Murray Troika Talent
Jenni Murray Speak-Easy Ltd
Jim Murray Limelight Management
Len Murray Speakout
Robert Murray Hazard Chase Ltd
Sean Murray The Richard Stone Prtnrshp
Olly Murs CHAMPIONS (UK) PLC
Makosi Musambasi Full Portion Media/Unleashed PR
Abbé Muschallik Nancy Hudson Associates Ltd
Muse Hall Or Nothing/ICM (USA)/MVO Ltd
Ben Musgrave CASAROTTO RAMSAY & ASSOCIATES
Toby Musgrave Jeremy Hicks Assoc
The Music Big Sister Promotions
Lost In Music Matters Musical
Music & Motion Disco David Forshaw Entp
Music Unlimited Laurie Taylor Ents Ltd
Musica Viva String Quartet Yorkshire Ent
The Musical Celebration "Manhattan

Nights" Musical Agny & Mngt Ltd
Showstopper! The Improvised Musical Matters Musical
Musical Youth Jason West Agy/Mission Control Artist Agy
Musik Express ABC Direct Ents/Jason West Agy/The CBS Grp/Ultimate Int'l
Mustang NVB Ents
Olli Mustonen International Classical Artist
Anjula Mutanda First Artist Management
Tam Mutu Jeffrey & White
Mutya, Keisha, Siobhan Insanity Artists
My Bloody Valentine Universal/Island Records Ltd
My Chemical Romance The Agency Group
My Dying Bride Miracle Artists Ltd
My Morning Jacket Bad Moon Publicity
Anjali Myachadna Burnett Granger Assoc
Philip Myall Alexandra Cann Reprsntn
Alan Myatt Alan Myatt (Ind Art)/Derek Bruce Ents
Josephine Myddleton Frontline Mngt Ltd
Jill Myers Direct Persnl Mngt
Johnny Myers Alpha Persnl Mngt
Kimberley Myers Opera & Concert Artists
Pat Myers (Freddie Mercury) BULLET MANAGEMENT LIMITED
Graeme Mykal Prima Artists
Patrick Myles AIM
Peter Mylet GM Ents
Mylo CODA Ltd
Mark Mylod CASAROTTO RAMSAY & ASSOCIATES
Marc Mynard (DJ) Head On Mngt
Myra J. ICM (USA)
Nina Myskow Hazemead Ltd/PVA Ent Consultants/ROAR Group
Mystery Jets 13 Artists/Alan James PR Agency
Mystery Juice Stoneyport Associates
Mystery Machine TMK Mngt & Agcy Ltd
Myths & Legwarmers John Field - Theatre and Puppe

N

Jim Nabors William Morris Inc (USA)
Rafael Nadal CHAMPIONS (UK) PLC
The Nadgers NVB Ents
Nadie (Kylie) Advanced Ents
William Nadylam Markham & Froggatt Ltd
Kent Nagano International Classical Artist
Parminder Nagra ARG Management/M F Management Ltd
Rupinder Nagra Brunskill Mngt Ltd
Phyllis Nagy (French) CASAROTTO RAMSAY & ASSOCIATES
Alison Nalder Performing Arts
Steve Nallon NMP Live Ltd/Speakout
Nanarama Nigel Round Mgnt
Shereen Nanjiani Speakout/Star Management
Fidel Nanton Anita Alraun Representation
Emile Naoumoff Transart (UK) Ltd
Harry Napier Actorum
Anna Naples Voice Shop
Gerard Naprous MTM Presntns
Narasirato Adastra
Daniela Nardini Harvey Voices Ltd/Troika Talent
Andi Jon Narsi M W Management
Nash NVB Ents
Nash Ensemble of London Ingpen & Williams Ltd
Jason Nash Avalon Mngt
Kate Nash 13 Artists/Fiction Records
Rebecca Nash Askonas Holt Ltd
Sarah Nash M W Management
Terry Nash (Meatloaf) Entertainers Mgt Ltd/Nigel Round Mgnt/Stars In Your Eyes Ltd Ent Agy
Willow Nash ANA
Nashville Teens Brian Gannon Mngt/NVB Ents/PVA Ent Consultants
Clare Nasir RDF Management
Nina Nastasia CODA Ltd
Natalege Malene Stage Centre Mngt
Natalia Action Talent Int.
Natallia RDL
Natasha Dave Woodbury Ents/LRO Artist Mngt
Ben Nathan Actorum
National Festival Circus National Fest Circus (Ind Art)/Paul Bridson Prods
The National Free Trade Agy
The National Youth Jazz Orchestra (NYJO) Jazzco/Nat Youth Jazz Orch (Ind Art)/The John Boddy Agency
Ali Natkiel Lime Actors Agy & Mngt Ltd
Dominic Natoli Music Int'l
Natural Wonder (Stevie Wonder tribute) Jason West Agy
James Naughtie JLA
Bill Naughton (Estate) CASAROTTO RAMSAY & ASSOCIATES
Naughty Rhythms John Hessenthaler Ents
Tino Navas (Juggler) Kaye Frankland Ent Agy
Navi As Michael Jackson Advanced Ents/Big Bang Mngt Ltd/Peller Artistes Ltd
Martina Navratilova NMP Live Ltd
Jim Naylor ABDC Ents/CKK Ent/Jim Naylor (Ind Art)/Partyweb.co.uk/The A6 Agy
Oliver Naylor City Actors Mngt
Harsh Nayyar Sandra Boyce Mngt
Nazareth AIM Inc (USA)/Alan Cottam Agency/Jason West Agy
Amer Nazir Nyland Mngt
Alan Neal Lime Actors Agy & Mngt Ltd
Grant Neal MBA
Luke Neal Markham & Froggatt Ltd
Trevor Neal RDF Management/Talking Heads - The Voice Agy
Ben Nealon Kerry Gardner Mngt
Steve Nealon ANA
Joanna Neary Avalon Mngt
Terry Neason Speakout
Tiff Needell 1st Choice Speakers UK Ltd/Blackburn Sachs Assoc/Celebrity Appearances/PVA Ent Consultants/Persnly Spkng/Talking Heads - The Voice Agy
Sir Richard Needham 1st Choice Speakers UK Ltd
Ian Needle APM Ass
Joey Negro UK Booking Agy
Neighbourhood Watch Continental Drifts/TEST AGENT C
Neil & Christine Hamilton MCS Agcy/Robert Smith Literary Agency
Andrew Neil 1st Choice Speakers UK Ltd/Arena Ent Cons/CHAMPIONS (UK) PLC/Celebrity Appearances/Parliament Comms/Persnly Spkng
Charlie Neil Celebrity Appearances
Hildegard Neil AIM
Ron Neild David Forshaw Entp
Sam Neill M F Management Ltd
Neil's Children Supervision Management
Michael Neilson Adrian King Assoc
Nellie Belle Barn Dance Line Dance Agy
Adele Eve Nelson Otto Persnl Mngt Ltd
Bill Nelson The Agency Group
Grant Nelson UK Booking Agy
John Nelson IMG Artists
Martin Nelson Anita Alraun Representation
Mary Elliott Nelson Grays Mngt & Asc
Mike Nelson as Bryan Ferry Jason West Agy
Trevor Nelson UK Booking Agy
Willie Nelson William Morris Inc (USA)
Thomas Nelstrop Paul Duddridge Mngt
Nemone The Psycho Mngt Co Ltd
N.E.R.D Solo Agy Ltd
Bibi Nerheim ICON Actors Mngt
Franco Nero Chatto & Linnit Ltd
Nerys Jones (Victoria Beckham) Advanced Ents
James Nesbitt ARG Management/Trading Faces Ltd/Yakety Yak
Sally Nesbitt Sara Crouch Mngt
Tim Nesbitt Norwich Artistes
Eddie Nestor Narrow Road Company
Emma Netileton Scott-Paul Young Ents Ltd
John Nettles Saraband Assoc
Julie Neubert Alpha Persnl Mngt
Günter Neuhold Athole Still Int'l Ltd/TEST AGENT A
Never 4 Get (Ind Art) Never 4 Get
Aaron Neville William Morris Inc (USA)
The Neville Brothers William Morris Inc (USA)
Charles Neville Crescent Mngt
Gary Neville CHAMPIONS (UK) PLC
George Neville Northern Lights Mngt
Richie Neville The Commercial Agency
The New Age Jam (The Jam tribute) Jason West Agy
New Amen Corner BCM Promos Ltd/Brian Gannon Mngt
The New Chevrons Dukeries Ents Ltd
New Digswell Banjo Band London Music Agy
New Dimension SJS Promos
New Dorne Valley Stardust Ents Agy/Tony Bennell Ents
New Drifters Big Bang Mngt Ltd
The New English Mandolin Orchestra/The Fretful Federation Matters Musical
New Hurricane Force (steel band) Apple County
The New Ivyleague Compact Mngt & Ent Agy
New Model Army Primary Talent Int'l
The New Originals Andrew Beauchamp Mngt/Book A Band
New Orleans Mardi Gras Max Collie Rhythm Aces
New Pornographers Free Trade Agy
New Recruits Entertainers Mgt Ltd
New Rope String Band Adastra
The New Royals (Covers - Rock, Soul, Pop) Glasshouse Prods Ltd
The New Seekers Hal Carter Org/Jason West Agy/Tony Denton Promos Ltd
New Simba Steelband Steve Allen Ents
New Sound Hurricane Force Steel Band PVA Ent Consultants
The New Squadronaires Orchestra David Coleman/Upbeat Mngt
New Tight Fit Jason West Agy
New York Cafe Band The John Boddy Agency
Louise Mai Newberry Billboard Persnl

Mngt
Flora Newbigin Jonathan Altaras Assoc
Brian Newbold McLeod Agy Ltd
Valerie Newbold Vincent Shaw Assoc Ltd
Gary Newbon Persnly Spkng
Ricky Newby Partyweb.co.uk
Newclear Waste Hartbeat Ents Ltd
Clovissa Newcombe Vincent Shaw Assoc Ltd
Newfolks Matters Musical
Bob Newhart William Morris Inc (USA)
Chris Newland Actors Alliance
Tara Newley Shining Mngt Ltd
Victoria Newlyn Louise Hillman/Katie Threlfall/Sara Crouch Mngt
Alec Newman Markham & Froggatt Ltd
Alison Newman CAM London
Jimmy C Newman & His Cajun Band Deri Promos
Leah Newman MAGIK MODELS
Michael Newman SCA Mngt
Nanette Newman Chatto & Linnit Ltd
Randy Newman ITB
Richard Newman Big Bang Mngt Ltd
Rob Newman Phil McIntyre Ent. Ltd
Joanna Newsom Asgard/Dog Day Press
Nicky Newsome Funhouse Productions Ltd
Andy Newton Take Three Mngt
Ben Newton Sasha Leslie Mngt
Tad Newton Jazzband Quality Ents
Victoria Newton/Katmandhu Matters Musical
Wayne Newton William Morris Inc (USA)
Tad Newton's Jazz Friends Tony Bennell Ents
Next Move (4 piece party band) BCM Promos Ltd
Nextmen Athole Still Int'l Ltd/Athole Still Music/TEST AGENT A
Ngati Ranana Matters Musical
Nice Mum Jeremy Hicks Assoc
Phil Nice RDF Management
Flight Lieutenant John Nichol Persnly Spkng
Flt. Lt. John Nichol 1st Choice Speakers UK Ltd/Trading Faces Ltd
Ben Nicholas Richard Price PR
Charlie Nicholas Sport Ent And Media Group
Sir David Nicholas CBE Knight Ayton Mngt
Jeremy Nicholas Brunskill Management Ltd/Harvey Voices Ltd/Louise Hillman/Katie Threlfall/The Richard Stone Prtnrshp
Mark Nicholas MPC Ent
Paul Nicholas Inspirational Artiste Bkg
R.J. Nicholas Swan Ents
Siobhan Nicholas Nancy Hudson Associates Ltd
Nicholi The Clown Partyweb.co.uk
Natasha Nicholl Cassie Mayer Ltd
Al Nicholls Quintet Prima Artists
Alec Nicholls Paul Duddridge Mngt
Davey Nicholls Angle Ents Ltd/Devil Management
Emma Nicholls Steve Draper Ents
Martin Nicholls PVA Ent Consultants
Sue Nicholls Brown & Simcocks
Jeb Loy Nichols Asgard
Audrey Nicholson Audrey Benjamin Agy
Melanie Nicholson Talking Heads - The Voice Agy
Sarah Nicholson Derek Bruce Ents
Nick Yellow Balloon Prods Ltd
Andy Nick Edge Ent Cons Ltd
Nickelback The Agency Group
Nicki Broadwater Ents Assoc
Jack Nicklaus NMP Live Ltd
Jonathan Nickoll Matters Musical
Rosie Nicks Nigel Round Mgnt
Susan Nickson CASAROTTO RAMSAY & ASSOCIATES
Nico & the band (Elvis) Advanced Ents
Ada Nicodemou Darren Gray Mngt
Lesley Nicol Daly Pearson Associates
Tanya Nicole Audrey Benjamin Agy/Tony Clayman Promos
Nicolinda Matters Musical
Lucas Nicoll Burnett Granger Assoc
Adam Nicolson Capel & Land
Eduardo Niebla Roots Around The World
Beth Nielsen Chapman Asgard
David Nielson Fushion Pukka Bosh
Maz Nieviarovski Performance Actors Agy
Nigel the Clown Albert Alchemy Ent
Night & Day Fairplay Ents
Adam Night Complete Ent Serv Ltd/Peller Artistes Ltd/Stardust Ents Agy
Night Fever Jason West Agy
Night Games Malcolm Feld Agy
Night Magic Ginger Walker Agy
Night Music Crown Ents/Highfield Mngt & Promos
A Night Of Musical Comedy Milton Keynes Theatre of Comed
A Night of Romantic Opera The John Boddy Agency
Nightbird Stardust Ents Agy
Mobile Nightclub Norwich Artistes
Annie Nightingale Curtis Brown Grp
Arthur Nightingale Anita Alraun Representation
Hugh Nightingale CKK Ent
Jake Nightingale Jessica & Carney Assoc
Mary Nightingale Noel Gay Artists Ltd/Trading Faces Ltd
Nightmare Of You Big Sister Promotions/Kas Mercer/Mercenary PR/The Agency Group
Nightmares On Wax Primary Talent Int'l
Nightride G Entertaining/Norwich Artistes
Bill Nighy Markham & Froggatt Ltd
Jo-Anne Nighy AIM
Mary Nighy Markham & Froggatt Ltd
Nihal Princess Talent Mngt
Nikita (X-factor contestant) Hireaband Ltd
Alex Nikitas Circuit Persnl Mngt Ltd
Nile Miracle Artists Ltd
Paul Nilon Ingpen & Williams Ltd
Caroline Nin Matters Musical
Professor Nincompoop Devil Management
Nine Below Zero The Psycho Mngt Co Ltd
Nine Inch Nails Universal/Island Records Ltd
Isobil Nisbet Chatto & Linnit Ltd
Neil Nisbet Chatto & Linnit Ltd
Nite Train Yorkshire Ent
Nite Vibes Disco David Charles Agy
Sarah Niven Rogues & Vagabonds Mngt
Sam Nixon 19 Entertainment
Nizlopi Free Trade Agy/Republic Media/Scream Promotions
N-Joy Gordon Kellett Ents
No Abode (Irish Duet, Folk) Glasshouse Prods Ltd
No Doubt Primary Talent Int'l/The M.O.B. Agency
No Exit Derek Bruce Ents
No Limits Derek Bruce Ents
No Strings Continental Drifts/TEST AGENT C
No Strings Attached Matters Musical
John Noakes Downes Presenters Agy
Cecilia Noble Jonathan Altaras Assoc/Yakety Yak
Emma Noble Daly Pearson Associates
Ian Noble Lena Davis/John Bishop Assoc
Karen Noble Yellow Balloon Prods Ltd
Louise Noble Celebn Model Mngt
Lucy Noble Tony Clayman Promos
Richard Noble OBE Arena Ent Cons/Celebrity Appearances/Persnly Spkng/Speakout
Ross Noble Real Talent
Roy Noble Gordon Poole Agy Ltd
Simon Nock Dennis Lyne Agy
Phil Nodding CASAROTTO RAMSAY & ASSOCIATES
Kieri Noddings Sandra Boyce Mngt
Noisettes Big Sister Promotions/Insanity Artists
Anne Nolan Mclean-Williams Management
Coleen Nolan Trading Faces Ltd/Urban Associates Personal Mana
Collen Nolan SWA Ent
Denise Nolan Ron Martin Mngt
Hal Nolan Hazemead Ltd/Non Stop Ents
Linda Nolan Yvette Hales Agy
Maureen Nolan Mclean-Williams Management
Nathan Nolan Talking Heads - The Voice Agy
Nolans Jason West Agy
The Nolans Urban Associates Personal Mana
Damon Noone Leo Mngt & Agy
Nora-Jane Noone Gavin Barker
Peter Noone BULLET MANAGEMENT LIMITED
Norali Jones Tribute - Come Away With Me Andrew Beauchamp Mngt
Arto Noras Patrick Garvey Mngt
Rob Norbury Lime Actors Agy & Mngt Ltd
Simon Norbury 1984 Persnl Mngt
Denis Norden CBE Prime Performers Ltd
Marielle Nordmann Transart (UK) Ltd
Jo Norfolk NVB Ents
Archie Norman MP NMP Live Ltd
Barry Norman NMP Live Ltd/Speakout
Chris Norman Denis Vaughan Mngt
Daniel Norman Askonas Holt Ltd
Jessye Norman Denis Vaughan Mngt
Judy Norman Actorum
Norman Roy Orchestra Advanced Ents
Russell Norman (Director) Hazemead Ltd
Amanda Normansell (Patsy Cline) Deri Promos
Normski Paul Duddridge Mngt
Ben Norris The Richard Stone Prtnrshp
Carli Norris Gavin Barker
Hermione Norris ARG Management/Conway Van Gelder Grant Ltd
Maggie Norris Kerry Gardner Mngt
Steve Norris 1st Choice Speakers UK Ltd
Will Norris Cassie Mayer Ltd
Chris North Norwich Artistes
Gemma North ICON Actors Mngt
Jim North The Richard Stone Prtnrshp
Mikey North Northern Lights Mngt
North Mississippi All Stars Cooking Vinyl

Philip North Cardiff Casting
Sam North CASAROTTO RAMSAY & ASSOCIATES
North Sea Gas BGS PRODUCTIONS/Stoneyport Associates
North Stars Steel Band Rent-A-Band
Jeremy Northam M F Management Ltd
Northern Lights Derek Bruce Ents
Northern Star Hireaband Ltd
Susanna Northern Denmark Street Mngt
Northern Xposure Int'l Mngt & Agy Ltd
Cassie Northwood Celebn Model Mngt
Caroline Norton Rosebery Mngt
Graham Norton Troika Talent
Jim Norton Lou Coulson Associates
John Norton Cardiff Casting
Kerry Norton Shepherd Mngt Ltd
Tim Norty NVB Ents
Duncan Norvelle Non Stop Ents
Nostalgia M.G. Ents
Not Chocolate Direct Music Mngt Ltd
Not Fade Away (Rolling Stones tribute) Andrew Beauchamp Mngt
Not The "Blues Brothers" David Charles Agy
The Long Notes Matters Musical
Nothin Serious Sunshine Ents
Rob Nothman Performing Artistes
Lloyd Notice Jeffrey & White
Chris Nott (David Essex) Nigel Round Mgnt
Heather Nova Free Trade Agy
Troia Nova Matters Musical
Jean Christophe Novelli CHAMPIONS (UK) PLC/Full Portion Media/Trading Faces Ltd
Constance Novis Music Int'l
Now 80's Henderson Mngt
Now And Then Highfield Mngt & Promos
Now Live Advanced Ents
Rick Nowels Stephen Budd Mngt
N.R.G. Robert Crossland Ent Ltd
N-Trance Action Talent Int./Insanity Artists
Nu Personal Management & Casting
Nuages CS Ents/Matters Musical
Luke Nugent B.A.S.I.C.
Null Nomine Daunce Matters Musical
Gary Numan Cooking Vinyl/The Agency Group
Numanesque (Gary Numan tribute) Jason West Agy
Debbie Nunn (Madonna) G Entertaining
Judy Nunn Darren Gray Mngt
Vernon Nurse Anita Alraun Representation
Kathryn Nutbeem Brunskill Mngt Ltd
Paolo Nutini 13 Artists
Nutkhut CKK Ent
Terry Nutkins John Miles Org
Phil Nutley Arlington Enterprises Ltd
Danny Nutt Dennis Lyne Agy
Amy Nuttall MERLIN ELITE
Andrew Nutter Celebrity Chefs UK
Richard Nutter ICON Actors Mngt
Nutty Norman Mr Magic Ents (Magic)/Partyweb.co.uk
Nuzha Roots Around The World
Anna Nygh Jonathan Altaras Assoc
Laura Nykänen Athole Still Int'l Ltd/TEST AGENT A
Tony Nyland Nyland Mngt
Michael Nyman Band Hazard Chase Ltd
Dave Nystrom Avalon Mngt
Nzinga Matters Musical

O

Dara O Briain NMP Live Ltd/Off The Kerb Prods/Speakout
Tom O'Connor PVA Ent Consultants/Positive Mngt/Speakout
Rynagh O'Grady Dennis Lyne Agy
Seamus O'Neill Nyland Mngt/The Narrow Road Company Ltd
John O'Callaghan Fresh Artiste Management Ltd
Steven O'Donnell Jonathan Altaras Assoc
Chris O'Dowd Gordon & French
Mark O'Shea All Electric Productions & Dav
Steve O'Toole KAL Mngt
Paul Oakenfold ITB/Pivotal PR
Meredith Oakes (German) CASAROTTO RAMSAY & ASSOCIATES
Phil Oakland Rosebery Mngt
David Oakley Anglia Artistes/Anita Alraun Representation/The Horne Concert Agy
Robin Oakley DBA Speakers
Lord Oaksey Celebrity Appearances/Gordon Poole Agy Ltd/PVA Ent Consultants/Persnly Spkng
Oasis Big Sister Promotions/Hall Or Nothing/Ignition Management/Primary Talent Int'l
Oasisn't (Oasis Tribute) Entertainers Mgt Ltd/Henderson Mngt/Jason West Agy/John Hessenthaler Ents/Peller Artistes Ltd
Samuel Oatley Susan Angel Kevin Francis Ltd
Ob Jay Da Upbeat Entertainment
Jenis Adams as Michelle Obama Prima Artists
Ryan Seggs as Barak Obama Prima Artists
Marc Koska OBE June Ford-Crush
Suzi Digby OBE June Ford-Crush
Claire Oberman Burnett Granger Assoc
Tina Oberman (Dusty Springfield) Funhouse Productions Ltd
Tracy-Ann Oberman CAM London/Qvoice
Marc Oberon The Wizard - M Oberon (Magic)
The Oberon String Quartet CKK Ent
Objayda Matters Musical
Oblivious Brothers Dave Andrews Ents
Kirsten O'Brian Big Talent Group
Anne O'Brien Nyland Mngt
Billy O'Brien CASAROTTO RAMSAY & ASSOCIATES
Brett O'Brien Langford Assoc
Helen O'Brien Avalon Mngt
Kieran O'Brien Peters Fraser Dunlop (PFD)
Kirsten O'Brien Paul Duddridge Mngt
Leyland O'Brien ICON Actors Mngt
Liam O'Brien The Narrow Road Company Ltd
Richard O'Brien Jonathan Altaras Assoc
Tina O'Brien (Sarah, Coronation Street) Nigel Round Mgnt
Jeanette Obstoj Jukes Prods Ltd
Joe O'Byrne ICON Actors Mngt
Tony O'Callaghan Macfarlane Chard Talent Agency
Brendan O'Casey Alexandra Cann Reprsntn
Billy Ocean Agency For the Performing Arts/Paradise Artists/Tony Denton Promos Ltd
Ocean Colour Scene Asgard/Frequency Media Group
Oceansize ITB/Northern Music Co
Arnold Oceng Susan Angel Kevin Francis Ltd
Mary-Ann Ochota Noel Gay Artists Ltd
Christian O'Connell USP Artistes
Eddie O'Connell Kerry Gardner Mngt
Jack O'Connell Insanity Artists
Patrick O'Connell The Richard Stone Prtnrshp
Andrew O'Connor Michael Vine Assoc
Derrick O'Connor Kerry Gardner Mngt
Des O'Connor John Miles Org/Parliament Comms
Frances O'Connor Markham & Froggatt Ltd
Francis O'Connor Dennis Lyne Agy
Hazel O'Connor Jason West Agy/Langford Assoc/The Psycho Mngt Co Ltd
Christy O'Connor Jnr Persnl Appearances
Sinead O'Connor Bad Moon Publicity
Terry O'Connor After Dinner World Ltd
Peter McNeil O'Conor Jonathan Altaras Assoc
Octavius Steel Band Essex Ent Agy
Michael Odam Associated Arts
Odd Sox Barn Dance Line Dance Agy
Oddballs Compact Mngt & Ent Agy
Bill Oddie All Electric Productions & Dav/Speakout
Matt Odell Elinor Hilton Associates
Odessa Rent-A-Band
Odetta Roots Around The World
O'Djangle Barn Dance Line Dance Agy
David O'Doherty Chambers Management Ltd
Damien O'Donnell CASAROTTO RAMSAY & ASSOCIATES
Daniel O'Donnell MP Promotions
Mary Ann O'Donoghue Brian Taylor Assoc/Shining Mngt Ltd
Rowan O'Duffy Johnny Mans Prods Ltd
Odysseus Matters Musical
Odyssey BULLET MANAGEMENT LIMITED/Jason West Agy/Rent-A-Band/Tony Denton Promos Ltd
Odyssey 2000 Ultimate Int'l
Michael Offei Peter Charlesworth & Assoc
Sarah O'Flaherty Star Management
Noriko Ogawa Hazard Chase Ltd
Ellen O'Grady Burnett Granger Assoc
Paul O'Grady Olga Ltd
Paula O'Grady Kerry Gardner Mngt
Oh Boy 'Show' Mike Constantia Artiste Mngt L
Oh Boy! It's Rock 'n' Roll feat. The Vernon Girls, John Leyton & Rockin' Horse Hal Carter Org
Oh Land 13 Artists
Oh Susanna CODA Ltd
Oh! What A Night Handshake Ltd
Oonagh O'Hagan Curtis Brown Grp
Steve O'Halloran Arena Personal Mngt
Ardal O'Hanlon Dawn Sedgwick Mngt
Lisa O'Hannon Circuit Persnl Mngt Ltd
Maggie O'Hara The Horne Concert Agy
Mary Margaret O'Hara Asgard
Gavan O'Herlihy Emptage Hallett Ltd
Adanna Oji Links Mngt
Ok Go Free Trade Agy
Sally Okafor Billboard Persnl Mngt
Okasis (Oasis tribute) Jason West Agy
Femi Oke MPC Ent
Keith O'Keefe Gordon Poole Agy Ltd/Persnl Appearances
Mark O'Keeffe Rostrum
Sophie Okonedo Markham & Froggatt Ltd/Premier PR
O.K.T.C. Book A Band
Tinuke Olafimihan Stafford Law

P

Eve Pollard Noel Gay Artists Ltd/Performing Artistes
Su Pollard Noel Gay Artists Ltd
John Pollendine Barrie Stacey Promos & Prods
Françoise Pollet Transart (UK) Ltd
Robin Polley Otto Persnl Mngt Ltd
Shaun Pollock MPC Ent
Christian Poltera Pro Artist Management
Polyphony Hazard Chase Ltd
Pomegranate Continental Drifts/TEST AGENT C
Carlos Ponce William Morris Inc (USA)
Pondlife - Function Band Wessex Ents
Jocelyn Pook Ensemble Hazard Chase Ltd
Pooka Universal/Island Records Ltd
Brian Poole John Hessenthaler Ents/M.S. Ent Grp
Brian Poole & Electrix BCM Promos Ltd/BULLET MANAGEMENT LIMITED/Brian Gannon Mngt/Entertainers Mgt Ltd/Funhouse Productions Ltd/Jason West Agy/McLeod Agy Ltd/NVB Ents/PVA Ent Consultants
Michael Poole Anita Alraun Representation/Speak-Easy Ltd
Shelly Poole Republic Media
The Poor Boys Rock Band The Horne Concert Agy
Imogen Poots BWH Agency
The Poozies Stoneyport Associates
Pop Fiction CT Ents
Pop of Ages Advanced Ents/ENTER-TAINMENT FX
The Pop Tarts Head On Mngt/Mike Constantia Artiste Mngt L
Pop Tease (5 piece) Stellamax Entp Ltd
Popa Chubby Roots Around The World
Faith Popcorn Parliament Comms
Angela Pope CASAROTTO RAMSAY & ASSOCIATES
Benjamin Pope Clarion/Seven Muses
Caroline Pope Michael Summerton Mngt
Frank Pope Jo Sarsby PR Ltd
Lauren Pope Girl Management/MAGIK MODELS
Philip Pope The Richard Stone Prtnrshp
Meghan Popiel Emptage Hallett Ltd
Popkorn Int'l Mngt & Agy Ltd
Popmania (vocal & dance) Apple County
Ron Popple The Horne Concert Agy
Anna Popplewell Sasha Leslie Mngt
Poptease Advanced Ents
David Porcelijn Patrick Garvey Mngt
Jonathon Porritt Trading Faces Ltd
Mary Portas CHAMPIONS (UK) PLC
Nigel Portass Band Portass & Carter Ents
Elisa Portelli Jane Hughes Mngt
Eugene Porter Paul Bailey Agy
Gail Porter Prime Performers Ltd/RDF Management/Yakety Yak
Katherine Porter The Richard Stone Prtnrshp
Lucy Porter RDF Management
Marguerite Porter The Richard Stone Prtnrshp
Mark Porter Jae Moss Entp
Melissa Porter Arlington Enterprises Ltd
Geraldine Porterfield Barrie Stacey Promos & Prods
Portia John Bedford Ents Ltd
Michael Portillo CHAMPIONS (UK) PLC/DBA Speakers/Parliament Comms/Trading Faces Ltd
Portishead 13 Artists/CODA Ltd
Portrayal Of A Legend Tony Bennell Ents
Portsmouth Area VC Field Gun Display MTM Presntns
Saskia Portway Audrey Benjamin Agy
The Posies Free Trade Agy
Kjartan Poskitt Tessa Le Bars Mngt
Janene Possell Brian Taylor Assoc
Robert Post Helter Skelter Agy Ltd
Adrienne Posta The Voice Box Agency Ltd
Elaine Postil CCM
Pete Postlethwaite Markham & Froggatt Ltd
Postman Pat The A6 Agy
Dennis Potter (Estate) Judy Daish Assoc
Gareth Potter Cardiff Casting
Iain Potter Barrie Stacey Promos & Prods
John Potter DBA Speakers
Libby Potter The Richard Stone Prtnrshp
Martin Potter Lime Actors Agy & Mngt Ltd
Potts CKK Ent
Eric Potts RDF Management
Paul Potts Modest! management
Olivia Poulet Troika Talent
Charlotte Poulter PVA Ent Consultants
Nicholas Pound Burnett Granger Assoc
Paula Poundstone William Morris Inc (USA)
Melvil Poupaud Troika Talent
Malcolm Povah London Music Agy
Richard Povall Direct Persnl Mngt
Duncan Pow Big Management (UK) Ltd (Ldn)/CAM London
Powder Blue Devil Management
Powderfinger Helter Skelter Agy Ltd
Barrington Powell Viscount Ents
Graham Powell Barry Dye Ents
Gwyneth Powell Dennis Lyne Agy
Helena Frith Powell Knight Ayton Mngt
James Powell B.A.S.I.C.
Jenny Powell Arlington Enterprises Ltd
Jo Powell Jeffrey & White
Marcus Powell Paramount Int'l Mngt
Natasha Powell Wise Buddah Talent & Voices
Paul Powell CASAROTTO RAMSAY & ASSOCIATES
Stuart Powell BAM Assoc Ltd
Tristram Powell CASAROTTO RAMSAY & ASSOCIATES
Jack Power Jeffrey & White
Karl (The Hoaxer) Power Nigel Round Mgnt
Lawrence Power Ingpen & Williams Ltd
Samantha Power Louise Hillman/Katie Threlfall
Power & Soul The Dixon Agy
Thomas Power Grays Mngt & Asc
Will Power Robert Crossland Ent Ltd
Powerhouse International NVB Ents
Crystal Powers MGA Entp
Gwen Powers Darren Gray Mngt
J D Powers Nigel Round Mgnt
Samantha Powers Dinosaur Promo/Dinosaur Mus
Stefanie Powers Mclean-Williams Management
Connie Powney Sangwin Associates
Powys & Jones Paul Bridson Prods
Adrian Poynton Noel Gay Artists Ltd
Poz Partyweb.co.uk
Jerome Pradon Hilary Gagan Assoc
Michael Praed CAM London
Mr. Praganza Head On Mngt
Juliet Prague Grays Mngt & Asc
Sharon Prasad Sandra Singer Assoc
Udayan Prasad CASAROTTO RAMSAY & ASSOCIATES
Guy Pratt Richard Bucknall Mngt (RBM)
Stephanie Preacher Northern Lights Mngt
Prefab Sprout Kitchenware Mngt
The Prefects Mainstream Evts
Gentlemen Prefer Matters Musical
Christoph Prégardien Askonas Holt Ltd
Sally Preisig John Field - Theatre and Puppe
Premier Brass Matters Musical
Premier Cru Dance Band Mainstream Evts/Persnl Appearances/Premier Cru (Ind Art)/Prima Artists
Jodie Prenger Gavin Barker
Johnny Prenton Nigel Round Mgnt
John E Prescott as Elvis Doub7e Seven Events Ltd
John E Prescott G Entertaining
Lord John Prescott CHAMPIONS (UK) PLC
Megan Prescott Insanity Artists
Reg Presley Stan Green Mngt
Leslie Press Partyweb.co.uk
Press-to-Play Stag Ents
Max Pressure Steve Draper Ents
Prestige Stardust Ents Agy/Tony Bennell Ents/Ultimate Int'l/Upbeat Entertainment
Prestige Fun Casino Dave Andrews Ents
Fay Presto CHAMPIONS (UK) PLC/NMP Live Ltd/Whatever Artists Mngt Ltd
Presto Puppets John Field - Theatre and Puppe
Presto the Magic Rabbit Galaxy Evts
Adam Preston CASAROTTO RAMSAY & ASSOCIATES
Dave Preston Philip Youd Ents & Mngt
Duncan Preston Burnett Granger Assoc/Persnl Appearances
Johnny Preston Paul Barrett Rock'N'Roll Entp
Lisa Preston Kaye Frankland Ent Agy
Louisa Preston Noel Gay Artists Ltd
Lynn Sarah Preston Scott-Paul Young Ents Ltd
Pretend Pretenders Andrew Beauchamp Mngt/Jason West Agy
The Pretenders Gailforce Mngt Ltd/William Morris Inc (USA)
The Pretentious Juggler Anglia Artistes
Stan Pretty Adrian King Assoc
Pretty Things ABS Agy
Tristan Prettyman Asgard
David Prever Talking Heads - The Voice Agy
Augustus Prew BWH Agency
Alan Price Cromwell Mngt/Jason West Agy
Ben Price Shining Mngt Ltd
Brendan Price Langford Assoc
Briony Price MCS Agcy
David Price Darren Gray Mngt/London Music Agy
David Price Hot Jazz Trio/Quartet London Music Agy
Kenneth Price Daly Pearson Associates
Nigel Price Matters Musical
Pete Price Non Stop Ents
Peter Price Tony West Ents
Rani Price Talent4 Media Ltd
Steve Price Partyweb.co.uk
Tom Price Karushi Mngt
Chris Priest CKK Ent
Maxi Priest William Morris Inc (USA)
Susan Priest Dance Funki Feathers Agy
Dennis Priestley McLeod Agy Ltd
Joe Priestley as Elvis Presley GM Ents
Luanna Priestman Crescent Mngt
Prime Cuts CODA Ltd
Primo CKK Ent/Continental Drifts/Global

Ent Agy/TEST AGENT C
Prince Buster Jason West Agy
Prince Buster Tribute Band Jason West Agy
Hannah Prince Newton Wills Mngt
James Prince Derek Bruce Ents/Les Hart (Southampton) Ents
Norman Prince After Dinner World Ltd/Nigel Round Mgnt
Peter Prince CASAROTTO RAMSAY & ASSOCIATES/Kevin King Mngt
Princess Tamara Paul Stacey Management
Craster Pringle Nancy Hudson Associates Ltd
Alvin Printwhistle NVB Ents
Andy Prior & His Orchestra Leo Mngt & Agy
Maddy Prior Park Promotions
Maddy Prior & The Carnival Band Park Promotions
Tim Prior BAM Assoc Ltd
Priscilla, Queen of the Desert Insanity Artists
Bryonie Pritchard Grays Mngt & Asc
Christopher Pritchard Fushion Pukka Bosh
Helen Pritchard Linkside Agy
Pritchard vs Dainton Insanity Artists
Private 69 Dave Woodbury Ents
Private Invitation Book A Band
Prixton Puppets Viscount Ents
Probably Robbie BULLET MANAGEMENT LIMITED/The Psycho Mngt Co Ltd
P.J. Proby BCM Promos Ltd
Jeff Probyn After Dinner World Ltd/Persnl Appearances
The Proclaimers Primary Talent Int'l
Procol Harum Jason West Agy
Mike Procter CHAMPIONS (UK) PLC
Prof "P" Punch & Judy The Horne Concert Agy
Prof. Richard Holmes Gordon Poole Agy Ltd
The Professionals Advanced Ents
Professor Crump Professor Crump (Ind Art)
Professor Mystral Prof Mystral's Omnibus
Professor Nik Nak Viscount Ents
Professor Popup John Field - Theatre and Puppe
Professor Potty Professor Potty
Proffessionals Funhouse Productions Ltd
Prohibition Hire-A-Band Ent Agy
Prohibition Jazz Band PVA Ent Consultants
The Teak Project Matters Musical
Elena Prokina Pro Artist Management
Pronghorn Continental Drifts/TEST AGENT C
Greg Proops Int'l Artistes Ltd
Ronnie Prophet Deri Promos
Amanda Protheroe-Thomas David Anthony Promos
Alex Proud KBJ Management
Danielle Proud KBJ Management
Paul Provenza Paramount Int'l Mngt
Prowizorka Jazzband (PL) Wim Wigt Prodns Ltd
Dave Prowse Johnny Mans Prods Ltd/MCS Agcy
Craig Pruess S M A Talent Ltd/SMA Talent Ltd
Jonathan Pryce Julian Belfrage Assoc
Paula Pryke Limelight Management
Andy Pryor Susan Angel Kevin Francis Ltd
Rain Pryor Silvey Associates
Psapp Big Sister Promotions
Public Enemy United Talent Agency
Katie Puckrik Inspirational Artiste Bkg
Puddle of Mudd ITB
Rob Pue Avalon Mngt
Robert Pugh Emptage Hallett Ltd
Pugwash Barn Dance Line Dance Agy
Pui Fan Lee Adrian King Assoc
Manuel Puig (Estate) CASAROTTO RAMSAY & ASSOCIATES
Monserrat Roig De Puig Actorum
Jean-Marc Puissant Loesje Sanders
Pull Tiger Tall Big Sister Promotions
David Pullan Louise Hillman/Katie Threlfall/Shining Mngt Ltd
Ben Pullen Markham & Froggatt Ltd
Jim Pullin Jill Foster Ltd
Pulp Universal/Island Records Ltd
Pulp Culture European Artistes Mngt
Pulse Devil Management/Jason West Agy/Norwich Artistes
Pump Action Barn Dance Line Dance Agy/Tony Bennell Ents
The Pump Room Trio Quality Ents
Punch & Judy Galaxy Evts/Mr Magic Ents (Magic)
Jessica Punch Brian Taylor Assoc
Punish The Atom Big Sister Promotions
Punita Gupta/Jazz Indo Rent-A-Band
Vasda Punjab Matters Musical
Punt and Dennis Richard Bucknall Mngt (RBM)
Steve Punt Noel Gay Artists Ltd
Puppets From Off The Planet Vern Allen Ents Ltd
The Puppini Sisters Republic Media
Alice Purcell Dennis Lyne Agy
Angus Purden RDF Management
Robert Purdy AIM/Nancy Hudson Associates Ltd
Pure Abba Dansatak
Pure Bee Gees Nigel Round Mgnt
Pure Liberty BCM Promos Ltd
Pure Magic (Antonio Zambaldi) Ultimate Int'l
Pure Silk Yorkshire Ent
Pure X 13 Artists
Puressence ITB/Universal/Island Records Ltd
Purple Haze Andrew Beauchamp Mngt
The Purple Puppets ABDC Ents/Liberty Entertainments
Christopher Purves Hazard Chase Ltd
Peter Purves Downes Presenters Agy
Neal Purvis & Robert Wade CASAROTTO RAMSAY & ASSOCIATES
Pussycat Babes The Psycho Mngt Co Ltd
Nikolai Putilin Askonas Holt Ltd
Stephanie Putson Kerry Gardner Mngt
Robert Putt The Richard Stone Prtnrshp
Puttin' on the Ritz Deri Promos
Nick Putz The A6 Agy
PVA Fun Casinos PVA Ent Consultants
PVA Outdoor Entertainment PVA Ent Consultants
David Pyatt (Horn) Clarion/Seven Muses
Jane Pye Dance Funki Feathers Agy
Shaun Pye The Richard Stone Prtnrshp
Jim Pyke Brunskill Management Ltd

Q

The Q Band The Q Band
Q (Kwabena Manso) Jonathan Altaras Assoc
Rizwaan Muazzam Qawwali Autonomous Talent Bkg
QEII (Queen tribute) Academy Artistes Ltd/Andrew Beauchamp Mngt/BULLET MANAGEMENT LIMITED/Dinosaur Promo/Dinosaur Mus/Head On Mngt/Henderson Mngt/Jason West Agy
Q-Tones Les Hart (Southampton) Ents
Geoff Quaife Barn Dance Line Dance Agy
Noel Qualter Partyweb.co.uk
Quango Moonglight Agy
David Quantick Amanda Howard Assoc Ltd
The Quarrymen Jason West Agy
Hugh Quarshie Cassie Mayer Ltd/Yakety Yak
The James Taylor Quartet Barrie Hawkins Leisure Service
The Val Kelly Jazz Quartet Matters Musical
The Quartz Quartet Quality Ents
Suzi Quatro BULLET MANAGEMENT LIMITED/Barry Collings Ents/Entertainers Mgt Ltd/Jason West Agy/Jive Ent/John Hessenthaler Ents/Paul Bridson Prods/Rock Artist Mngt/The Psycho Mngt Co Ltd/Tony Denton Promos Ltd
Finley Quaye Ferrara PR
Queen B (Queen tribute) Andrew Beauchamp Mngt/BULLET MANAGEMENT LIMITED/Barry Collings Ents/Compact Mngt & Ent Agy/Global Ent Agy/Henderson Mngt/Jason West Agy/Mike Malley Ents/Stardust Ents Agy/Stars In Your Eyes Ltd Ent Agy/The John Boddy Agency
Queen Fever (Queen) Peller Artistes Ltd
Jackson Queen Highfield Mngt & Promos
Queen on Fire (Queen tribute) BULLET MANAGEMENT LIMITED/Jason West Agy/Mike Malley Ents
Queen Victoria School Pipes & Drum BGS PRODUCTIONS
The Queen's Piper - Jim Motherwell BGS PRODUCTIONS
The Queens John Bedford Ents Ltd
Ann Queensberry Brian Taylor Assoc
Dee Quemby Lena Davis/John Bishop Assoc
Caroline Quentin Amanda Howard Assoc Ltd/Inspirational Artiste Bkg
John Quentin The Richard Stone Prtnrshp
The Quest Project Universal/Island Records Ltd
Lisa Quibell APM Ass
Quicksilver ABDC Ents/Jason West Agy/Matters Musical
Quiet Nights Whatever Artists Mngt Ltd
Pearce Quigley Julian Belfrage Assoc
Quill ABC Direct Ents/Direct Music Mngt Ltd/Rock Artist Mngt
Denis Quilley (Estate) Bernard Hunter Assoc
Denis Quilligan City Actors Mngt
Quilombo Continental Drifts/TEST AGENT C
Peter Quince ANA
Eleanor Quine Paramount Int'l Mngt
Kerry Quiney Derek Bruce Ents
Anthony Quinlan Big Bang Mngt Ltd
Andrea Quinn Clarion/Seven Muses
Elliot Quinn Stage Centre Mngt
James Quinn Shepherd Mngt Ltd
Jimmie Quinn Derek Bruce Ents
The Mighty Quinn Glasshouse Prods Ltd
Mike Quinn Nigel Round Mgnt
Patricia Quinn Jonathan Altaras Assoc
Ray Quinn Modest! management

Raymond Quinn Colette Fenlon Persnl Mngt
Tommy Quinn Derek Bruce Ents/The CBS Grp
Tracey Quinn Tony West Ents
Tracy Quinn (Madonna) Upfront Ent Agy Ltd
Derek Quinnell Persnl Appearances
Chris Quinten Darren Gray Mngt/Funhouse Productions Ltd/Paul Spyker Mngts
Quintessential Swing Band Doub7e Seven Events Ltd
Quintette Matters Musical
The Quireboys Miracle Artists Ltd
Pauline Quirke ARG Management/Yakety Yak
Sarah Quist Nancy Hudson Associates Ltd
QV-J Sunshine Ents

R

R. John Sunshine Ents
R We Them (REM tribute) Andrew Beauchamp Mngt
The Rabbit Redford Show Ian & Friends
Racey Barry Collings Ents/Brian Gannon Mngt/Jason West Agy/PVA Ent Consultants/Rock Artist Mngt
Rachel Parga (Sophie Ellis Bextor) Advanced Ents
Racine Free Trade Agy
Rob Rackstraw The Voice Box Agency Ltd
Daniel Radcliffe ARG Management
Mark Radcliffe The Voice Box Agency Ltd
Jo Lloyd (Real Radio) Nigel Round Mgnt
North Sea Radio Norwich Artistes
Radiohead 13 Artists
Amber Rae Complete Ent Serv Ltd
Bev Rae Swan Ents
Corinne Bailey Rae Creative Artists Agency
Jamie Rae Nigel Round Mgnt
Roisin Rae Jeffrey & White
Tony Rae Advanced Ents/NVB Ents
Gerry Rafferty Asgard
Jo Rafferty Nyland Mngt
Mark Rafferty Richard Price PR
Paul Raffield Susan Angel Kevin Francis Ltd
Tim Raffles & Co Tony West Ents
Jamie Rafn CASAROTTO RAMSAY & ASSOCIATES
Rag Foundation Roots Around The World
Nick Raggett Louise Hillman/Katie Threlfall
Raggle Taggle Cielidh David Charles Agy
Rags & Tatters Barn Dance Line Dance Agy
The Rah Band Jason West Agy
Aishwarya Rai Jazz Barton Agency
Andrew Raiher SMA Talent Ltd
Rainbow Steel Orchestra Rent-A-Band
Isobel Raine Louise Hillman/Katie Threlfall
Moses Raine CASAROTTO RAMSAY & ASSOCIATES
Alistair Raines Angle Ents Ltd
Joseph Raisbrook ANA
Raj & Pablo Noel Gay Artists Ltd
Anna Rajan Jacque Evans Mngt Ltd
The Rakes CEC Management/Free Trade Agy
Philip Ralph Jeffrey & White
Mike Ralphs One Fifteen
Judith Ralston Speakout
Ram Andrew Beauchamp Mngt
Simon Ram MCS Agcy
The Ramblers Barn Dance Line Dance Agy
D Ramirez Hope Management
John Ramm Jonathan Altaras Assoc
Rampage (BBC Radio London) UK Booking Agy
Charlotte Rampling Diamond Management
Mark Ramprakash MPC Ent
Andrew Ramsay Sara Crouch Mngt
Gordon Ramsay CHAMPIONS (UK) PLC/Personal Management & Casting/Trading Faces Ltd
Katrina Ramsay M W Management
Louie Ramsay Brunskill Mngt Ltd
Emma Ramsdale London Music Agy
Steve Ramsden Daly Pearson Associates
Chris Ramsey Avalon Mngt
Ramsey & Fen UK Booking Agy
Tana Ramsey Personal Management & Casting
Derek Randall After Dinner World Ltd
Leslie Randall Keith Salberg Agy & Prods/Shepherd Mngt Ltd
Richard Randall June Ford-Crush
Vicki Randall Argyle Assoc
Mary Jo Randle Cassie Mayer Ltd
Random Acts Of Jazz CKK Ent
Random Jig Barn Dance Line Dance Agy
Rang-a-Tang CHAMPIONS (UK) PLC
Rankin Ms P (GLR) Monkeybiz Ent Agy
Paul Rankin Limelight Management
Steve Ransome Band Elite Promos
Esther Rantzen CBE Billy Marsh Assoc Ltd/Celebrity Appearances
The Rapiers NVB Ents
Dale Rapley Louise Hillman/Katie Threlfall
Esther Rappaport Darren Gray Mngt
Nayef Rashed Royce Mngt
Tom Raskin Music Int'l
Shaf Rasul CHAMPIONS (UK) PLC/Speakout
The Rat Pack Mike Malley Ents
The Rat Pack is Back Ultimate Int'l
Rat Pack Live from Las Vegas Whatever Artists Mngt Ltd
The Rat Pack Live Entertainers Mgt Ltd
Steven Rathman Wendy Lee Mngt
Gerald Ratner CHAMPIONS (UK) PLC
Ratpack (Duo) UK Booking Agy
Rats In The Kitchen (UB40 Tribute) Compact Mngt & Ent Agy/G Entertaining/Henderson Mngt/Jason West Agy
Paul Rattee Grays Mngt & Asc
Sir Simon Rattle Askonas Holt Ltd
Rattle the Boards Barn Dance Line Dance Agy
Ratz alley Advanced Ents
John Ratzenberger Noel Gay Artists Ltd
Nina Rautio Athole Still Int'l Ltd/TEST AGENT A
Jennifer Raven Matters Musical
Mark Ravenhill CASAROTTO RAMSAY & ASSOCIATES
Jan Ravens Amanda Howard Assoc Ltd/Yakety Yak
The Raveonettes ITB
Ronnie Ravey Creeme Ents
Raw Deal Les Hart (Southampton) Ents
Raw Sex Rainbow Striptease Agy
Rawhide Dave Woodbury Ents
Jeff Rawle Jonathan Altaras Assoc
Rawless CHAMPIONS (UK) PLC
Ian Rawlings Darren Gray Mngt
Steve Rawlings Crowd Pullers/Triple Cream Ents
Will Rawlings (The Swing Years) Ultimate Int'l
Penelope Rawlins M W Management
Melvyn Rawlinson John Field - Theatre and Puppe
Sophie Raworth Arlington Enterprises Ltd
Kate Rawson Dennis Lyne Agy
Mark Rawson North One Mngt/Speak-Easy Ltd
Robin Rawstorne Loesje Sanders
Adil Ray Independent Talent Group Ltd
Barbara Ray Barbara Ray (Ind Art)
Ray J ICM (USA)
Lisa Ray Brunskill Mngt Ltd
Rebecca Ray Nigel Round Mgnt
Sol Ray (Nat King Cole tribute) Monkeybiz Ent Agy
James Rayment Performance Actors Agy
Neil Rayment RAGE
The Raymond and Mr Timpkins Revue Jongleurs
Emily Raymond Markham & Froggatt Ltd
Steve Raymond Band Derek Bruce Ents
Sonya Raymono Arena Personal Mngt
Adam Rayner Jonathan Altaras Assoc
Jay Rayner Curtis Brown Grp
Vince Rayner (Comedy) Essex Ent Agy
Elise Raynor Downes Presenters Agy
Rachel Raynor CeeBee Variety Agy
Lisa Raynsford Wendy Lee Mngt
Soni Razdan Brunskill Mngt Ltd
Razorlight Creative Artists Agency/The Agency Group
Razzle Dazzle Matters Musical/Paul Barrett Rock'N'Roll Entp
Chris Rea G.A.A.
Martin Rea Jonathan Altaras Assoc
Reaction Yorkshire Ent
Dean Read Peter Charlesworth & Assoc
Howard Read Noel Gay Artists Ltd
John B Read Performing Arts
Mike Read BULLET MANAGEMENT LIMITED/Fox Artist Mngt Ltd/John Miles Org/MPC Ent
Nick Reade Spotlight Ents
Eddi Reader Jason West Agy
The Real Abba Gold Arena Ent Cons/Jason West Agy/Mark Lundquist Management & Co/Pete Mitchell Associates
Real Easy Hireaband Ltd
The Real Macaws Book A Band
Tata Real Wendy Lee Mngt
Real Thing Barry Collings Ents/Jason West Agy/Mission Control Artist Agy/Paul Bridson Prods/Roedean Music/Tony Hall Grp Of Cos
Really Hot Chilli Peppers Head On Mngt
Ray Reardon Paul Bridson Prods
Jonathan Reason Inspiration Mngt
Rebound London Music Agy
Reckless (Bryan Adams tribute) Jason West Agy
Recloose Elastic Artists Agency Ltd
Recycler Nation Recs Ltd
Red Alert (Shakin' Stevens) Advanced Ents/Funhouse Productions Ltd
Red Army Chorus & Dance Ensemble Chimes Int'l Ents Ltd
The Red Arrows MTM Presntns
Red Blooded Woman Action Talent Int./Prima Artists

Red Buttons William Morris Inc (USA)
Red Dragon Continental Drifts/TEST AGENT C
Red Herrings Barn Dance Line Dance Agy
Red Hot & Blue Orchestra Jason West Agy/Mike Constantia Artiste Mngt L/Norwich Artistes
Red Hot and Blue Advanced Ents/Steve Allen Ents
Red Hot Chillies Steve Allen Ents
Red Hot Poker Band Hireaband Ltd
Red Hot Silli Feckers Mike Malley Ents
Red Hunter Derek Bruce Ents
Red Kiss Brian Yeates Assoc
Red Mick (Simply Red Tribute) Peller Artistes Ltd
Red Priest Upbeat Classical Mngt
Red River Band Barn Dance Line Dance Agy
Red Roc & The Doctors Of Swing Jason West Agy
Red Shed Upbeat Entertainment
The Red Stripe Band Matters Musical
Red Velvet Party Nights UK Booking Agy
Katie Reddin-Clancy Joan Reddin
Noel Redding Experience Rock Artist Mngt
David Redfearn CHAMPIONS (UK) PLC
Jonathan Redfearn SJS Promos
Ian Redford Markham & Froggatt Ltd
Luke Redford B.A.S.I.C.
Jacqueline Redgewell Circuit Persnl Mngt Ltd
David Redgrave Grays Mngt & Asc
Jemma Redgrave Conway Van Gelder Grant Ltd
Lynn Redgrave United Agents
Sir Steven Redgrave CBE Athole Still Int'l Ltd/CHAMPIONS (UK) PLC/PVA Ent Consultants/Speakout/TEST AGENT A/Trading Faces Ltd
Vanessa Redgrave Gavin Barker
Georgina Redhead Daly Pearson Associates
Redhouse Alan Cottam Agency
Nick Reding Markham & Froggatt Ltd
Amanda Redington Liz Hobbs Grp Ltd
Harry Redknapp Athole Still Int'l Ltd/NMP Live Ltd/Preview & Review Ents Ltd/TEST AGENT A
Jamie Redknapp MERLIN ELITE
Louise Redknapp MERLIN ELITE
Amanda Redman Lip Service Casting Ltd
Crispin Redman Shepherd Mngt Ltd
Derek Redmond CHAMPIONS (UK) PLC/Derek Redmond/Gordon Robinson Assoc/Parliament Comms
James Redmond CAM London
Natasha Redmond Grays Mngt & Asc
Siobhan Redmond Conway Van Gelder Grant Ltd
Michael Redston North One Mngt
Reduced Brass Band Company London Music Agy
Redwing Barn Dance Line Dance Agy
Elaine Redwood Anita Alraun Representation
John Redwood Persnly Spkng
Alex Reece Universal/Island Records Ltd
Gary Reece David Forshaw Entp
Georgia Reece CAM London
Raymond Reece Fushion Pukka Bosh
Amanda Reed Indep Mngt Ltd
Lou Reed MVO Ltd/Primary Talent Int'l/The Wylie Agency
Peter Reed Prof Sports Ptnr Ltd
Peter G Reed Billboard Persnl Mngt
Richard Reed CHAMPIONS (UK) PLC/Prima Artists
Julie Reed-Asquith Non Stop Ents
Reeds & Keys With Gina Hire-A-Band Ent Agy
Reef Helter Skelter Agy Ltd
Emily Reef Martin Ents
Christopher Reeks Anita Alraun Representation
Reel Big Fish The Agency Group
Reel McCoy Tony Bennell Ents
'ReelinandaRockin' Derek Franks Org
Reeltime ABDC Ents/Barn Dance Line Dance Agy
James Rees Reality Check Management
Nichola Rees Nancy Hudson Associates Ltd
Nigel Rees Arena Ent Cons/Gordon Poole Agy Ltd/Persnly Spkng
Sarah Rees Form Talent
Sean Rees Argyle Assoc
Della Reese William Morris Inc (USA)
Sian Reese-Williams Louise Hillman/Katie Threlfall
David Rees-Williams Trio Upbeat Classical Mngt
Dermot Reeve OBE Arena Ent Cons/Celebrity Appearances/PARAGON SPORTS MANAGEMENT LTD/Persnly Spkng
James H Reeve Nigel Round Mgnt
Alex Reeves Lip Service Casting Ltd
Martha Reeves And The Vandellas Jason West Agy/Studio One Assoc/Tony Denton Promos Ltd
Ashley Reeves (cocktail pianist) MJE Mngt
Pete Reeves The Voice Box Agency Ltd
Peter Reeves ETM Ltd
Saskia Reeves Markham & Froggatt Ltd
Vic Reeves & Bob Mortimer PBJ Mngt Ltd
Referendum Stag Ents
Fionn Regan The Agency Group
Joan Regan Johnny Mans Prods Ltd
Mark Regan MBE CHAMPIONS (UK) PLC
Regency Brass Ensemble PVA Ent Consultants
Regency Duo Tony West Ents
Regondi Prima Artists
Regurgitator Free Trade Agy
Saminda Rehman MGA Entp
TJ Rehmi Nation Recs Ltd
Alison Reid Louise Hillman/Katie Threlfall
Annabel Reid Nancy Hudson Associates Ltd
Anne Reid Conway Van Gelder Grant Ltd
Benji Reid Abstrakt PR
Caroline Reid Troika Talent
David Reid Blackburn International
Don Reid Creeme Ents/Tony West Ents
Jack Reid Grays Mngt & Asc
Nova Reid Jae Moss Entp
Heather Reid OBE Speakout
Peter Reid Athole Still Int'l Ltd/Jon Holmes Media Ltd/TEST AGENT A
Sheila Reid Susan Angel Kevin Francis Ltd
Valerie Reid Opera & Concert Artists
Brigitte Reiffenstuel Performing Arts
Kelly Reilly Troika Talent
Megan Reilly Gold Star PR
Philip Reis Nyland Mngt
Jennifer Reischel Peter Charlesworth & Assoc
Relative Strangers Les Hart (Southampton) Ents
Relax Psycho Mngt Co Ltd/The Psycho Mngt Co Ltd
Sonna Rele Palestar Entertainment/The Psycho Mngt Co Ltd
Reload Psycho Mngt Co Ltd
Re-Load (Tom & Robbie) Camscott Leisure
John Relyea Askonas Holt Ltd
R.E.M. G.A.A.
Remembering Humph The John Boddy Agency
Remi Satellite Artists Ltd
Lola Remi Frontline Mngt Ltd
John Renbourn NEM Prods (UK)
Gordon Rennie Sara Crouch Mngt
Malcolm Rennie Shepherd Mngt Ltd
Reno XS Promos
Jean Reno Special Artists Agency
Noelle Reno Curtis Brown Grp
Vadim Repin IMG Artists
Replica Creeme Ents
Reservoir Cats Paul Barrett Rock'N'Roll Entp
Respect Advanced Ents/Mike Constantia Artiste Mngt L/Peller Artistes Ltd/Sphinx Mngt & Ent Agy
Resurrection feat John Altman Andrew Beauchamp Mngt
Retro Moonglight Agy
Retronym COFFEE ARTISTS
The Retros Tony Bennell Ents
Reuben The Agency Group
Nick Revell The Richard Stone Prtnrshp
Revelution Disco David Forshaw Entp
Paul Revere Fushion Pukka Bosh
Elizabeth Revill BAM Assoc Ltd
Teresa Revill Sandra Singer Assoc
Revolution The Dixon Agy
Revolutionaires Devil Management
Richard Reynard Burnett Granger Assoc
Jaime Robbie Reyne Darren Gray Mngt
Debbie Reynolds William Morris Inc (USA)
Helen Reynolds Wendy Lee Mngt
Jay Reynolds Stephen Budd Mngt
Lee Reynolds Brunskill Mngt Ltd
Rob Reynolds (Elvis Reborn) Vern Allen Ents Ltd
Ruth Reynolds Girl Management
Yasmina Reza CASAROTTO RAMSAY & ASSOCIATES
Rhapsody In Blue Sunshine Ents
Rhapsody Steel Band Quality Ents/Rent-A-Band
Carla Rhodes Paramount Int'l Mngt
Davie Rhodes Sunshine Ents
Gary Rhodes The Outside Organisation
Jonty Rhodes MPC Ent
Mark Rhodes 19 Entertainment
Mary Rhodes Jo Sarsby PR Ltd
Nick Rhodes Frequency Media Group
Roy Rhodes XS Promos
Teddy Tahn Rhodes Askonas Holt Ltd
Rhubarb the Clown Partyweb.co.uk/Rhubarb The Clown (Ind Art)
Eunice Rhymes Derek Bruce Ents
Christina Rhys Quality Ents
Gruff Rhys CODA Ltd
Ieuan Rhys Emptage Hallett Ltd
Jean Rhys (Estate) CASAROTTO RAMSAY & ASSOCIATES
Griff Rhys Jones PVA Ent Consultants/Troika Talent
Paul Rhys Markham & Froggatt Ltd
Drew Rhys-Williams Alpha Persnl Mngt
Rhythm & Lites Disco David Forshaw Entp

Rhythm Chaps Book A Band
Rhythm Machine Hartbeat Ents Ltd
Rhythm Method ABDC Ents
Rhythm Nation Int'l Mngt & Agy Ltd
Rhythm of Blues RED ADMIRAL RECORDS
Rhythm of the Night Derek Bruce Ents
Rockin' In Rhythm Matters Musical
Rhythmworks Matters Musical
Brae Riach Ceilidh Band Barn Dance Line Dance Agy
Marie-France Riboulet PVA Ent Consultants
Ricardo Fox Artist Mngt Ltd
Mat Ricardo Crowd Pullers/Whatever Artists Mngt Ltd
Anneka Rice PBJ Mngt Ltd/Prime Performers Ltd
Carl Rice ICON Actors Mngt
Damien Rice 13 Artists
Dr Gillian Rice Jacque Evans Mngt Ltd
Oliver Rice Rogues & Vagabonds Mngt
Rachel Rice Markham & Froggatt Ltd
Sir Tim Rice PVA Ent Consultants
Mandy Rice-Davies Vincent Shaw Assoc Ltd
Mal Rich G Entertaining/Persnly Spkng
Rich Thair CODA Ltd
Richard & Judy The Commercial Agency
Cliff Richard The Cliff Richard Org
Doug Richard CHAMPIONS (UK) PLC/Gordon Poole Agy Ltd/NMP Live Ltd
Eric Richard United Agents
John Richard London Music Agy
Richard Street's The Temptations Ron Martin Mngt
Ben Richards CAM London
Claire Richards Urban Associates Personal Mana
Dean Richards CHAMPIONS (UK) PLC/Gordon Robinson Assoc/Jon Holmes Media Ltd/M.G. Ents
Dillon Richards Swan Ents
Doyle Richards Kenneth Earle Persnl Mngt
Emma Richards MBE Gordon Poole Agy Ltd
Gareth Richards Avalon Mngt
Ian Richards After Dinner World Ltd/Essex Ent Agy/G Entertaining/Highfield Mngt & Promos/NVB Ents/Stardust Ents Agy/Steve Allen Ents/Triple Cream Ents
Jeff Richards ICM (USA)
Jemma Richards Yakety Yak
Josha Richards Emptage Hallett Ltd
Julian Richards Knight Ayton Mngt
Kate Richards Derek Bruce Ents
Keith Richards William Morris Inc (USA)
Maurey Richards M W Management
Micah Richards Sport Ent And Media Group
Paul Richards Scott-Paul Young Ents Ltd
Tony Richards Sound Quality Ents
Timothy Richards North Of Watford Actors Agy
Tom Richards Darren Gray Mngt
Vicky Richards Dance Funki Feathers Agy
Amanda Richardson Royce Mngt
Anna Richardson M F Management Ltd
Anna Ryder Richardson Arlington Enterprises Ltd
Ben Richardson Arena Personal Mngt
Garry Richardson After Dinner World Ltd/Performing Artistes
Ian Richardson Diamond Management
James Richardson Curtis Brown Grp
Jon Richardson CHAMPIONS (UK) PLC/Off The Kerb Prods
Kieran Richardson Hyper Agency
Kieron Richardson (Hollyoaks actor) Lime Actors Agy & Mngt Ltd/Unleashed PR
Liz Richardson Grays Mngt & Asc
Miranda Richardson Conway Van Gelder Grant Ltd
Rebecca Richardson Kenneth Earle Persnl Mngt
Steve Richardson Dave Andrews Ents
Suzanne Richardson MBA
Tony Richardson (Tony 'R' - Red Velvet resident) UK Booking Agy
Gabrielle Richens Panic Management
Lionel Richie Creative Artists Agency/Marshall Arts Ltd
Richie Taylor Tribute Show Angle Ents Ltd
Jonathan Richman Primary Talent Int'l
Gillian Richmond CASAROTTO RAMSAY & ASSOCIATES
Julie Richmond Harvey Voices Ltd
Laura Richmond Amber Persnl Mngt Ltd
Nick Richmond Nick Richmond (Ind Art)
Phil Richmond Owen Hughes Ents
Sarah Richmond Fushion Pukka Bosh
Wayne Richmond Gem Prods
Bernard Richter Athole Still Int'l Ltd/TEST AGENT A
David Richter West Central Mngt
Rick Waller (Pop Idol 2003) ENTERTAINMENT FX
John Rickard (Neil Diamond) Entertainers Mgt Ltd
Laurence Rickard Noel Gay Artists Ltd
Karl Anton Rickenbacher Transart (UK) Ltd
Dominic Rickhards Gavin Barker
Adam Rickitt CAM London
Don Rickles William Morris Inc (USA)
Ian Rickson Judy Daish Assoc
Ricky Martin Show BULLET MANAGEMENT LIMITED
Rico Monkeybiz Ent Agy
Louisa Riddell Audrey Benjamin Agy
Ken Riddington Bernard Hunter Assoc
Lesley Riddoch Speakout
Justine Riddock (Anastasia) Nigel Round Mgnt
Steve Rider Blackburn Sachs Assoc/PVA Ent Consultants/Talking Heads - The Voice Agy
Riders In The Sky Buddy Lee Attrctns Inc (USA)
Angela Ridgeon Burnett Granger Assoc
Rebecca Ridgeway RBA Management Ltd
Jeremy Rifkin CHAMPIONS (UK) PLC
Emma Rigby (Hannah, Hollyoaks) Big Bang Mngt Ltd/Hyper Agency/Nigel Round Mgnt
John Rigby Talent Artists Ltd
Mark Rigby Lime Actors Agy & Mngt Ltd
Suzanne Rigden Audrey Benjamin Agy
Dame Diana Rigg ARG Management
Chestor Riggon Dinosaur Promo/Dinosaur Mus
DJ Ashley Riggs KM Ents
Rick Right Paramount Int'l Mngt
Right Stuff Funhouse Productions Ltd
The Right Thing Hireaband Ltd
Righteous Brothers William Morris Inc (USA)
Eric Rigler BGS PRODUCTIONS
Bruno Rigutto Transart (UK) Ltd
Stevie Riks Non Stop Ents
Alex Riley RDF Management
Billy Lee Riley Paul Barrett Rock'N'Roll Entp
Brendan Riley Cosmic Comedy Mngt
David Riley Arlington Enterprises Ltd
Dr David Riley Yakety Yak
Julie Riley Amber Persnl Mngt Ltd
Nevean Riley Mohamed RBA Management Ltd
Rachel Riley KBJ Management
Steven J Riley Devil Management/McLeod Agy Ltd
Talay Riley Purple PR
Yvonne Riley Grays Mngt & Asc
Stella Rimington Capel & Land
Dame Stella Rimington DCB MA DBA Speakers/Gordon Poole Agy Ltd
Shane Rimmer Emptage Hallett Ltd
Simon Rimmer CHAMPIONS (UK) PLC/TFA Artiste Management
Rin Tin Tin CKK Ent/Continental Drifts/TEST AGENT C
Ring O'Bells Barn Dance Line Dance Agy
Rio CS Ents/CT Ents
Rio Latino Dancers Tropical Ents Mngt Agy
Rio Madness Peller Artistes Ltd
Marcella Riordan Yakety Yak
Rip Off The Machine Head On Mngt
Rip Rock Brothers Garston Ents Ltd
Ripchord Barn Dance Line Dance Agy/Supervision Management/The Agency Group
Malcolm Rippeth Clare Vidal-Hall
Caroline Rippin Johnny Mans Prods Ltd
Angela Rippon Knight Ayton Mngt
Matthew Risdon Otto Persnl Mngt Ltd
Riski Bizniz Hire-A-Band Ent Agy
Risky Continental Drifts/TEST AGENT C
Aileen Ritchie CASAROTTO RAMSAY & ASSOCIATES
Andy Ritchie Nigel Round Mgnt
Chris Ritchie Devil Management
Guy Ritchie Creative Artistes Agency
Howard Ritchie Harvey Voices Ltd
Ian Ritchie Candle
Mark Ritchie Gordon Kellett Ents
Steven Ritchie Newton Wills Mngt
La Cuba Ritmo Matters Musical
River Deep (Tina Turner) Nigel Round Mgnt
Sandy Rivera Defected Records
Riverdance - The Show Gerry Lundberg Public Relation/William Morris Inc (USA)
Darren Rivers (Elvis) Funhouse Productions Ltd
Joan Rivers William Morris Inc (USA)
Malcolm Rivers Athole Still Int'l Ltd/TEST AGENT A
Tom Rivers Voice Shop
Wayne Rivers as Garth Brooks GM Ents
Riviera Breeze Crown Ents
The Rivieras ABC Direct Ents
Rivieras Peller Artistes Ltd
The Rivieras Tony Bennell Ents
Rowland Rivron Off The Kerb Prods
Jenna Rix Agency K-Bis
Ian Rixon Rogues & Vagabonds Mngt
Michael Roach GTA Music Cons & Agy
Pat Roach Peter Charlesworth & Assoc
Richard Roach Nancy Hudson Associates Ltd
Linus Roache Tavistock Wood Management Ltd
Sara Roache The Narrow Road Company Ltd
Roachford G.A.A.
Roadstar Helter Skelter Agy Ltd
Roaring 20's Ragtime Band Rent-A-

Band
The Roaring 20's Entertainers Mgt Ltd
Rob By Nature (Robbie Williams) Entertainers Mgt Ltd
Rob Idol Dansatak
Rob Lamberti (George Michael Tribute) Big Bang Mngt Ltd/Henderson Mngt
Andrew Robb Darren Gray Mngt
David Robb Emptage Hallett Ltd
Frank Robb Speakout
Jackie Robb Jill Foster Ltd
Robbie Craig Action Talent Int./Mission Control Artist Agy
Sue Robbie The Voice Box Agency Ltd/VRM Artists
Robbie Williams Experience The Dixon Agy
Robbie's Angels (Robbie Williams tribute) Jason West Agy
Robbing Williams Camscott Leisure/Fab Prods/Head On Mngt
Heather Robbins Daly Pearson Associates
Ted Robbins CHAMPIONS (UK) PLC/Nigel Round Mgnt/Persnl Appearances
Robert Hylton Urban Classicism Abstrakt PR
Robert L Hughes BCM Promos Ltd
Robert McIntosh Nancy Hudson Associates Ltd
Robert Randolph & The Family Band Asgard
Andrew Roberts Capel & Land
Barry Roberts Arena Ent Cons/McLeod Agy Ltd
Cerianne Roberts Grays Mngt & Asc
Daniel Roberts Louise Hillman/Katie Threlfall
Danny Roberts Sunshine Ents
Dave Roberts Talking Heads - The Voice Agy
Dave Roberts Karaoke Disco David Forshaw Entp
Dr Alice Roberts Arlington Enterprises Ltd
Eric Roberts Special Artists Agency
Jack Roberts Speak-Easy Ltd
Jacqui Roberts MCS Agcy
Jason Roberts Fox Artist Mngt Ltd
John Roberts CKK Ent/Partyweb.co.uk/The A6 Agy
John G Roberts Partyweb.co.uk
Joshua Roberts Hyper Agency
Judith Roberts Darren Gray Mngt
Julia Roberts TFA Artiste Management
Lea Roberts After Dinner Spkers & Com/After Dinner World Ltd
Lee Roberts LJ Ents
Lisa Roberts Celebn Model Mngt/Wendy Lee Mngt
Martin Roberts Independent Talent Group Ltd
Morgan Roberts Newton Wills Mngt
Nicola Roberts Insanity Artists
Paul Roberts (pianist/organist) Wessex Ents
Rachel Victoria Roberts Peter Charlesworth & Assoc
Rhydian Roberts Modest! management
Simon Roberts Kerry Gardner Mngt/Sandra Singer Assoc
Smug Roberts Melody Thresh Mngt Assoc Ltd
Tony Roberts Derek Bruce Ents
Veronica Roberts Susan Angel Kevin Francis Ltd
Viet Roberts Celebn Model Mngt
Clive Robertson Langford Assoc
David Robertson Direct Persnl Mngt
Finlay Robertson Troika Talent
Gavin Robertson Speak-Easy Ltd
Ian Robertson Gordon Poole Agy Ltd/Persnl Appearances/Speakout
Liz Robertson Burnett Granger Assoc/Jonathan Altaras Assoc
Nathan Robertson Prof Sports Ptnr Ltd
Samuel Robertson Insanity Artists
Shirley Robertson OBE Prof Sports Ptnr Ltd
Rob-E-Ryan PVA Ent Consultants
Roberyto Pla Latin Jazz Band Latin Arts Serv (LAS)
Arthur Robins David Wilkinson Assoc
Danny Robins RDF Management
Franchesca Robinson Chase Personal Management/Model Plan Celebrities & Prese
Andy Robinson Matters Musical/Off The Kerb Prods
Anne Robinson Tracey Chapman/William Morris Inc (USA)
Barry Robinson Tony Clayman Promos
Daniel Robinson APM Ass
James Robinson B.A.S.I.C.
Jason Robinson MBE CHAMPIONS (UK) PLC
Jeffrey Robinson Arena Ent Cons/Persnly Spkng
Sir Ken Robinson Speakers For Business
Mae Louis Robinson Grays Mngt & Asc
Marc Robinson (Buddy Holly) Compact Mngt & Ent Agy/Funhouse Productions Ltd
Marc Robinson as Buddy Holly & The Counterfeit Crickets Henderson Mngt
Pres. Mary Robinson American Program Bureau
Matt Robinson Argyle Assoc/MCS Agcy
Patrick Robinson Shepherd Mngt Ltd
Paul Robinson Martin Ents
Scott Robinson Action Talent Int./Rossmore Persnl Mngt
Smokey Robinson William Morris Inc (USA)
Timothy Robinson Askonas Holt Ltd
Tony Robinson Jeremy Hicks Assoc/Speakout
Jackie Robinson-Brown Sandra Boyce Mngt
Marisa Robles (harp) Clarion/Seven Muses
Robo Max 2000 CKK Ent
Robocop PVA Ent Consultants
Sir Bobby Robson CBE Athole Still Int'l Ltd/TEST AGENT A
Christopher Robson Music Int'l
Darren Robson (Magician) Doub7e Seven Events Ltd
Harry Robson Leo Mngt & Agy
Laura Robson CHAMPIONS (UK) PLC
Nigel Robson Ingpen & Williams Ltd
Philippa Robson ANA
Richard Robson Stephen Budd Mngt
Samantha Robson CAM London
Robyn Hitchcock and The Venus 3 Free Trade Agy
Stacey Roca Peters Fraser Dunlop (PFD)
Barry Rocard Linkside Agy
Natasha Rocca Devine MTC (UK) LTD
Peter Rocca Vincent Shaw Assoc Ltd
Zack De La Rocha ITB
Susan Roche Jacque Evans Mngt Ltd
Tony Roche CASAROTTO RAMSAY & ASSOCIATES
Zhivila Roche Speak-Easy Ltd
Helen Rochelle Anita Alraun Representation
James Rochfort Kerry Gardner Mngt
Rock Back the Clock Funhouse Productions Ltd/Paul Barrett Rock'N'Roll Entp
Chris Rock ICM (USA)
Chrissy Rock Kenneth Earle Persnl Mngt/Nigel Round Mgnt
Justin Rock Agency K-Bis
Rock Legacy Goldstar Ent UK
Rock Magic (Chris North and Belinda - Illusion) Anglia Artistes/Barry Dye Ents/Highfield Mngt & Promos/SWA Ent
Michael Rock Bees Knees Ents
Roxanna Rock Agency K-Bis
Rock Salt and Nails Park Promotions
Rockabeats Satellite Artists Ltd
The Rockin' Berries BTWS (Ents) Ltd/Barry Collings Ents/Compact Mngt & Ent Agy/Entertainers Mgt Ltd/Jason West Agy/PVA Ent Consultants/Paul Bridson Prods
Rockin' On Heaven's Door Mark Lundquist Management & Co
Rockin Roadhouse Tour Buddy Lee Attrctns Inc (USA)
Rockin Ron Kevin King Mngt
Rockin' The Joint Paul Barrett Rock'N'Roll Entp
Trevor Rockliffe UK Booking Agy
Rock'n'Roll Magic Entertainers Mgt Ltd
Amy Rockson Indep Mngt Ltd
Rocksy and Granit Fools Paradise
Rockwood Dog Display MTM Presntns
Rocky and Diesel ITB
Rocky Horrible Show Andrew Beauchamp Mngt
Rocky Meats The Blues Leisure Mngt
Cleo Rocos Eleventh Hour Mngt Ltd
Michael Rodd Arena Ent Cons/Parliament Comms
Saskia Roddick Agency K-Bis
Alison Roddy Ingpen & Williams Ltd
Ben Roddy Anita Alraun Representation
Roddy Frame The Agency Group
Katie Roddy APM Ass
Rodeo Bull PVA Ent Consultants
Joan Rodgers CBE Ingpen & Williams Ltd
David Rodigan (Kiss FM) Monkeybiz Ent Agy
Rodney P Athole Still Int'l Ltd/Athole Still Music/TEST AGENT A
Carmen Rodriguez Indep Mngt Ltd
Jose Luis Rodriguez William Morris Inc (USA)
Paul Rodriguez ICM (USA)
Rod's Highlights (Rod Stewart tribute) Andrew Beauchamp Mngt
Alex Roe AIM
Gillian Roe Audrey Benjamin Agy
Nicholas Roeg Tavistock Wood Management Ltd
Rog CKK Ent
John Rogan The Richard Stone Prtnrshp
Lizzie Rogan Cardiff Casting
Paul Rogan Paramount Int'l Mngt
Peter Rogan 1984 Persnl Mngt
Pascal Rogé Clarion/Seven Muses
Sir Roger Bannister CBE Persnly Spkng
Anne Rogers Burnett Granger Assoc
Ben Rogers MGA Entp
Brian Rogers Performers Agy
Chris Rogers Blackburn Sachs Assoc
Dudley Rogers Jeffrey & White
Erica Rogers ICON Actors Mngt
Glenn Rogers Experience Line Music Promotions

Graham Rogers Knight Ayton Mngt
Jean Rogers Downes Presenters Agy
Julie Rogers Pete Mitchell Associates/Peter Charlesworth & Assoc
Katherine Rogers Louise Hillman/Katie Threlfall
Kenny Rogers William Morris Inc (USA)
Leanne Rogers Talent Artists Ltd
Lisa Rogers Take Three Mngt
Mabel Rogers Sandra Singer Assoc
Malcolm Rogers Anita Alraun Representation
Mike Rogers Brian Taylor Assoc
Natalia Rogers (harpist) Ultimate Int'l
Nile Rogers & Chic Free Trade Agy
Rogues Andrew Beauchamp Mngt
Nicholas Rohl CASAROTTO RAMSAY & ASSOCIATES
Wanda Rokicki Michael Summerton Mngt
Abdul Tee-Jay`s Rokoto (Sierra Leone) Monkeybiz Ent Agy
Natalie Roles Emptage Hallett Ltd
The Rolf & Edna Show Upfront Ent Agy Ltd
David & Penny Rolfe Barn Dance Line Dance Agy
Roll Out The Barrel David Coleman
Rolla Coaster Fanfare 3000
Graham Rollason MGA Entp
Rollers Tribute Show McLeod Agy Ltd
The Rollin Stoned The Rollin Stoned
The Rolling Clones Compact Mngt & Ent Agy
Rolling Clones (Rolling Stones Tribute) G Entertaining
The Rolling Clones Jason West Agy/Johnny Mans Prods Ltd
Rolling Clones (Rolling Stones Tribute) Peller Artistes Ltd
The Rolling Tones Jason West Agy
Doug Rollins Langford Assoc
Henry Rollins Free Trade Agy
Arlene Rolph Ingpen & Williams Ltd
David Rolston Talking Heads - The Voice Agy
Roma Rad Continental Drifts/TEST AGENT C
Danny Roman Non Stop Ents
Aaron Romano MBA
Ray Romano William Morris Inc (USA)
Romantica Music Rent-A-Band
Romany Whatever Artists Mngt Ltd
Max Romeo ABS Agy/Monkeybiz Ent Agy
Kim Romer Shepherd Mngt Ltd
Marcus Romer Judy Daish Assoc
John Romero Complete Ent Serv Ltd
Pedro Romero Rent-A-Band
Ronaldo the Third The Horne Concert Agy
Shebah Ronay Panic Management
Tanya Ronder Kerry Gardner Mngt
Nataylia Roni Speakout
Ronnie & The Rex Matters Musical
Jon Ronson The Richard Stone Prtnrshp
Stuart Rooker Otto Persnl Mngt Ltd
Kathryn Rooney Liz Hobbs Grp Ltd
Kevin Rooney Emptage Hallett Ltd
Steve Rooney (Del Boy) Upfront Ent Agy Ltd
Rooster Kas Mercer/Mercenary PR
Root Doctors PVA Ent Consultants
The Roots Helter Skelter Agy Ltd
Levi Roots CHAMPIONS (UK) PLC
David Roper Susan Angel Kevin Francis Ltd
Lizzie Roper RDF Management
Mark Roper Noel Gay Artists Ltd/RDF Management
Susan Roquette Kenneth Earle Persnl Mngt
Sigur Ros Best PR/Joanna Burns PR
Rosanna Hart American Diva's Show Funhouse Productions Ltd
Karen Rosario Lime Actors Agy & Mngt Ltd
Dorothea Röschmann Askonas Holt Ltd
Roscoe
Martin Roscoe Hazard Chase Ltd
Martin Roscoe & Peter Donohoe Hazard Chase Ltd
Beatrice Rose Actorum
Bernard Rose CASAROTTO RAMSAY & ASSOCIATES
Chrystal Rose Peter Charlesworth & Assoc
Clifford Rose Markham & Froggatt Ltd
Coralie Rose AIM
Elizabeth Rose ICON Actors Mngt
Emily Rose Somethin' Else
Jez Rose ABC Direct Ents/Speakout
John Rose Langford Assoc
Jowanna Rose Northern Lights Mngt
Lisa Rose West Central Mngt
Lyn Rose David Forshaw Entp
Mary Rose Anita Alraun Representation
Matt Rose M.G. Ents
Natalie Rose Agency K-Bis
Nicholas J Rose City Actors Mngt
Pat Rose Derek Bruce Ents
Peter Rose Askonas Holt Ltd
Randall Lee Rose Shining Mngt Ltd
Rose Royce featuring Gwen Dickey Barry Collings Ents
Simon Rose PVA Ent Consultants
Timna Rose Sara Crouch Mngt
Rose-Marie David Hull Promos Ltd
Roseanne ICM (USA)
Sonya Roseman Celebn Model Mngt
The Rosenberg Trio Wim Wigt Prodns Ltd
Amy Rosenthal CASAROTTO RAMSAY & ASSOCIATES
Jack Rosenthal CASAROTTO RAMSAY & ASSOCIATES
Jim Rosenthal Jon Holmes Media Ltd/Persnl Appearances/Persnly Spkng
Michael Rosewell Music Int'l
Rosie Swale-Pope MBE 1st Choice Speakers UK Ltd
Hanna Rosin The Wylie Agency
Christala Rosina Christala Rosina Poetry Concer
Gaby Roslin Conway Van Gelder Grant Ltd/Troika Talent
Annette Ross Linkside Agy
Benjamin Ross Tavistock Wood Management Ltd
Charlie Ross CHAMPIONS (UK) PLC
David Ross Susan Angel Kevin Francis Ltd
Diana Ross ITB
Edward Ross Agency K-Bis
Elizabeth Ross Alpha Persnl Mngt
Hermione Ross Jeremy Hicks Assoc
John Ross B.A.S.I.C.
Jonathan Ross CHAMPIONS (UK) PLC/NMP Live Ltd/Off The Kerb Prods/Speakout
Katie Ross Lime Actors Agy & Mngt Ltd
Katy Ross Linton Mngt
Liza Ross Voice Shop
Louisa Ross Fushion Pukka Bosh
Martha Ross MBA
McIntosh Ross Asgard
Michael Ross Agency K-Bis
Michael T Ross Langford Assoc
Nick Ross Advanced Ents/NMP Live Ltd/Nick Ross (Ind Art)/Parliament Comms
Patrick Ross North One Mngt
Paul Ross Paul Duddridge Mngt
Vicky Ross Sunshine Ents
Victoria Ross Stage Centre Mngt
Andrew Rosser Otto Persnl Mngt Ltd
Erica Rossi Nancy Hudson Associates Ltd
Marco Rossi BAM Assoc Ltd
Jane Rossington Chris Davis Management
Adrian Ross-Jones Audrey Benjamin Agy
Joy Roston Stage Centre Mngt
Lara Rostron Speak-Easy Ltd
Mstislav Rostropovich Transart (UK) Ltd
Colin Rote Elinor Hilton Associates
David Roth Audrey Benjamin Agy
Joanna Roth Lip Service Casting Ltd
Tim Roth Markham & Froggatt Ltd/Special Artists Agency
Uli Jon Roth Miracle Artists Ltd
Laila Rouass CAM London
Mark Rough CHAMPIONS (UK) PLC
Rough Stuff Dave Woodbury Ents
Lill Roughley Saraband Assoc
Round Midnight Ltd Round Midnight Ltd (Ind Art)
Julia Rounthwaite Otto Persnl Mngt Ltd
Bill Rourke MBA
Jeanette Rourke North One Mngt
Josh Rouse Asgard
Rob Rouse PBJ Mngt Ltd
Demis Roussos Denis Vaughan Mngt
Jimmy Roussounis Brian Taylor Assoc
Route 66 Tony Bennell Ents
Michael Roux Jr CHAMPIONS (UK) PLC
Cynthia H Rover North Of Watford Actors Agy
The Roving Artist Prima Artists
The Roving Artist & Co CKK Ent
John Row Continental Drifts/TEST AGENT C
Peter Rowan Adastra
Bridget Rowe Jacque Evans Mngt Ltd
Carolyn Rowe (Dame Shirley Bassey) ABC Direct Ents/Jason West Agy
Christopher Rowe Kerry Gardner Mngt
Clive Rowe Peters Fraser Dunlop (PFD)
John Rowe Kerry Gardner Mngt
Matthew Rowe Clarion/Seven Muses
Peter Rowell Gordon Poole Agy Ltd
Rosie Rowell Shepherd Mngt Ltd
Rowetta (X-Factor) Nigel Round Mgnt
Guy Rowland The Horne Concert Agy
Kevin Rowland (Dexy's Midnight Runners) Ferrara PR
Tim Rowland Linkside Agy
John Rowles Rock & Rowles Mngt
Geoff Rowley Jill Foster Ltd
Samantha Rowley Unleashed PR
Sean Rowley Get Involved Ltd
J K Rowling Colman Getty PR
Phil Rowson Amber Persnl Mngt Ltd
Charlie Rox Goldstar Ent UK
Roxanne Creeme Ents/Derek Bruce Ents
Roxanne (Pop Idol 2004) ENTERTAINMENT FX
Roxy Magic Johnny Mans Prods Ltd
Roxy Music The Agency Group
Alvin Roy Jazzband Tony Bennell Ents
John Roy Avalon Mngt
Pipes & Drums Of Royal Artillery ABC Direct Ents
Royal Castle Jazz Band Stardust Ents Agy

Dave Royal Norwich Artistes
The Royal Family BULLET MANAGEMENT LIMITED
Royal Gipsy Orchestra Roma Mirando Jnr Wim Wigt Prodns Ltd
Dance Band Of H.M. Royal Marines ABC Direct Ents
Marching Band Of H.M. Royal Marines ABC Direct Ents
Royal Philharmonic Concert Orchestra The John Boddy Agency/Whatever Artists Mngt Ltd
The Royal Scots Dragoon Guards BGS PRODUCTIONS
Royal Signals White Helmets MTM Presntns
Ian Royce Colin Lewin Mngt/Int'l Artistes Ltd/Ultimate Int'l
Rose Royce The Psycho Mngt Co Ltd/Tony Denton Promos Ltd
Carl Royle The A6 Agy
Carol Royle Emptage Hallett Ltd
Eva Royle (Celine Dion, Lisa Stansfield) G Entertaining
Joe Royle Athole Still Int'l Ltd/TEST AGENT A
Roger Royle Gordon Poole Agy Ltd
Steve Royle Nigel Round Mgnt
Rozalla Action Talent Int./Tony Denton Promos Ltd
Patricia Rozario OBE Stafford Law
RTE Vanbrugh Quartet Hazard Chase Ltd
Indhu Rubasingham Simpson Fox Assoc Ltd
Rubber Ritchie CKK Ent
The Rubble Derek Bruce Ents
The Rubettes BULLET MANAGEMENT LIMITED/Brian Gannon Mngt/Compact Mngt & Ent Agy/Entertainers Mgt Ltd/Funhouse Productions Ltd/Hal Carter Org/Jason West Agy
The Rubettes featuring Bill Hurd Barry Collings Ents/Pete Mitchell Associates
Ruby Goe Purple PR
Jarka Rudavska Grays Mngt & Asc
Tony Rudd Trevor George Ents Ltd
Xavier Rudd Helter Skelter Agy Ltd
Anah Ruddin Alpha Persnl Mngt
Neil Ruddock CHAMPIONS (UK) PLC/Sport Ent And Media Group
Peter Rudeforth Ensemble London Music Agy
Andy Rudge Hawthorn Ent
David Rudkin CASAROTTO RAMSAY & ASSOCIATES
Shelley Rudman Brian Maclaurin Agency
Rita Rudner ICM (USA)
Rudolpho & His Amazing Bouncing Bed Ley Ent Prods
Jeff Rudom MCS Agcy
Rudy The Soul Man LRO Artist Mngt
Chandra Ruegg RDF Management
Frances Ruffelle COLE KITCHENN PRSN MGT/Rossmore Persnl Mngt
Jimmy Ruffin Denis Vaughan Mngt/Entertainers Mgt Ltd/Jason West Agy
Rufus Returns Barn Dance Line Dance Agy
Rugrats The A6 Agy
Joanna Ruiz The Voice Box Agency Ltd
Andy Rumble Hazemead Ltd
Rumble Band Advanced Ents
Mark Rumble Princess Talent Mngt
Rumours Of Fleetwood Mac BULLET MANAGEMENT LIMITED/Hal Carter Org/Nigel Round Mgnt/The Flying Music Co Ltd
Rumpelstiltskin Continental Drifts/TEST AGENT C
Bungee Run PVA Ent Consultants
Opera On The Run Matters Musical
Running on Empty Barn Dance Line Dance Agy
Runrig The Agency Group
Rupert Bear Show Paul Bridson Prods
Lucy Rusedski RDF Management
Rush The Agency Group
Debbie Rush Lime Actors Agy & Mngt Ltd
Rush Hour Hire-A-Band Ent Agy
Jason Rush Louise Hillman/Katie Threlfall
Jennifer Rush Tony Denton Promos Ltd
Karen Rush Jae Moss Entp
Poppy Rush Lime Actors Agy & Mngt Ltd
Rudy Rush ICM (USA)
Claire Rushbrook Troika Talent
Tim Rushlow Buddy Lee Attrctns Inc (USA)
Verity Rushworth Big Bang Mngt Ltd
Eric Ruske Transart (UK) Ltd
Fay Rusling RDF Management
Martin Russell Complete Ent Serv Ltd/John Bedford Ents Ltd
Adrian Russell Northern Lights Mngt
Ashley Russell Seamus Lyte Management Ltd
Brenda Russell (Bass resident) UK Booking Agy
Craig Russell Langford Assoc
Iris Russell Brian Taylor Assoc
Jasmine Russell Brunskill Mngt Ltd
Johnny Russell Deri Promos
Paul Russell Dennis Lyne Agy
Rob Russell Funhouse Productions Ltd
Steve Russell London Music Agy
Willy Russell CASAROTTO RAMSAY & ASSOCIATES
Stephen Russell-Bird Barrie Stacey Promos & Prods
Russian Classical Ballet Chimes Int'l Ents Ltd
Russian Tornado Matters Musical/The John Boddy Agency
Adam Rust Brunskill Mngt Ltd
Les Rustines Continental Drifts/TEST AGENT C
Ruth NVB Ents
Greg Rutherford CHAMPIONS (UK) PLC
Nicola Rutherford Jae Moss Entp
Nick Rutherford Barrie Stacey Promos & Prods
Tony Rutherford JB Ents
Isobel Rutter Speakout
Abi Ryan Shamrock Music Ltd
Amanda Ryan Markham & Froggatt Ltd
Amy Ryan Kerry Gardner Mngt
Analicia Ryan Angle Ents Ltd
Anita Ryan Devil Management
Brendan Ryan Derek Bruce Ents
Carl Ryan APM Ass
Christopher Ryan Kerry Gardner Mngt
Gary Ryan (Neil Diamond) Gary Ryan - Neil Diamond Trib
Jim "Shaft" Ryan UK Booking Agy
Justin Ryan Knight Ayton Mngt
Kate Ryan Model Plan Celebrities & Prese
Kathie Ryan Gordon Kellett Ents
Lee Ryan Action Talent Int./Big Talent Group
Michelle Ryan Premier PR
Naomi Ryan Burnett Granger Assoc
Napoleon Ryan Barrie Stacey Promos & Prods
Rebecca Ryan (Shamless) Laine Mngt Ltd/Nigel Round Mgnt
Anna Ryberg Athole Still Int'l Ltd/TEST AGENT A
William Rycroft The Richard Stone Prtnrshp
Emma Rydal Shining Mngt Ltd
Chris Ryder The A6 Agy
Jack Ryder CAM London
Keith Ryder Solo Act Hire-A-Band Ent Agy
Kym Ryder Big Bang Mngt Ltd
Richard Ryder Talking Heads - The Voice Agy
Katie Ryder Richardson Brunskill Mngt Ltd
Shaun Ryder Ferrara PR/Mission Control Artist Agy
Georgina Rylance Markham & Froggatt Ltd
Mark Rylance Markham & Froggatt Ltd
James Rylands Talent4 Media Ltd
Peter Rylands Amber Persnl Mngt Ltd
Emma Ryott Loesje Sanders

S

S Club 3 Insanity Artists
S CLUB Party Action Talent Int.
Malachi S Complete Ent Serv Ltd
S O H N 13 Artists
S Steps Club 7 Cosmos Agy & Promos
S W Storm & Island Fury ABDC Ents
Richard Saade Paul Duddridge Mngt
Abdelkader Saadoun Matters Musical
Mark Saban The Richard Stone Prtnrshp
DJ Chebi I Sabbah Nation Recs Ltd
Sabbamangalang Bodo Agy
Sabbath Bloody Sabbath Jason West Agy
Amelia Saberwal Billboard Persnl Mngt
Alex Sabga Sandra Boyce Mngt
Sabrina Action Talent Int.
Andrew Sachs Prime Performers Ltd/The Richard Stone Prtnrshp
John Sachs Talking Heads - The Voice Agy
Kate Sachs Talking Heads - The Voice Agy
Quinny Sacks Jonathan Altaras Assoc
Stephen Sackur Performing Artistes
Kevin Sacre Big Bang Mngt Ltd
Howard Saddler Michelle Braidman Assoc
Sade Rock Steady Management Agency
Paul Sadler Paul Duddridge Mngt
Yutaka Sado Transart (UK) Ltd
Paul Sadot Northern Lights Mngt
S.A.E Derek Bruce Ents
Yuri Maria Saenz Stafford Law
Saffron Talking Heads - The Voice Agy
Saffron Oddy The Richard Stone Prtnrshp
Safire CKK Ent/Colclough Entertainment
Safri Duo Helter Skelter Agy Ltd
Sanjay Sag Liz Hobbs Grp Ltd
Jonny Lee Sage Gem Prods
Bob Saget ICM (USA)/United Talent Agency
Sanju Sahai Matters Musical
Sahara Advanced Ents/London Music Agy/Norwich Artistes/Steve Allen Ents/The Ents Agency/Tony Bennell Ents
Sailor Barry Collings Ents
Amber Sainsbury Emptage Hallett Ltd
Steve Saint Hawthorn Ent
Rebecca Saire The Richard Stone Prtnrshp
Hari Sajjan Sandra Boyce Mngt

Ryuichi Sakamoto Primary Talent Int'l
Saker Falconry MTM Presntns
Toby Salaman Kerry Gardner Mngt
Salamander B.F.P Ents
Adel Salameh Roots Around The World
Salem 13 Artists
The Salford Jets BULLET MANAGEMENT LIMITED
Salieri Strings Ultimate Int'l
Arkin Salih Jo Gurnett Persnl Mngt
Ben Salisbury S M A Talent Ltd/SMA Talent Ltd
Peter Sallis Jonathan Altaras Assoc
Colin Salmon ARG Management/Yakety Yak
Zoe Salmon David Hull Promos Ltd
The Salon String Quartet The Horne Concert Agy
Esa-Pekka Salonen International Classical Artist
Salsa Pa'Gozar Rent-A-Band
Salsa Y Ache PVA Ent Consultants
Abbie Salt Shepherd Mngt Ltd
Charlotte Salt Shepherd Mngt Ltd
Salt Tank Doug Smith Assoc
Ann Salter Speakout
Godfrey Salter Audrey Benjamin Agy
Salute The Supremes Jason West Agy
Salute To The Rat Pack The John Boddy Agency
Salvo The Clown Partyweb.co.uk/Salvo The Clown
Sam I Am CKK Ent
Samantha Starr Derek Bruce Ents/Samantha Starr
Samara Book A Band
Liza Samari CKK Ent
Sambaleros Rent-A-Band
Sambuca Seaview Music
Baron Samedi (Lookalike) Joker Ents
Ronald Samm Ingpen & Williams Ltd
Sammy Dave Woodbury Ents
CeCe Sammy MPC Ent
Holly Samos USP Artistes
Joe Sample ICM (USA)
Pete Sampras NMP Live Ltd
George Sampson NMP Live Ltd
Val Sampson Limelight Management
Narinder Samra Sandra Boyce Mngt
Sam's Wax Quality Ents
Samsara CKK Ent
John Samson Audrey Benjamin Agy
Clifford Samuel Brunskill Management Ltd
Jon Samuel SCA Mngt
Howard Samuels Peter Charlesworth & Assoc
Mike Samuels Trevor George Ents Ltd
David Sanborn ICM (USA)/Marshall Arts Ltd
Lawrie Sanchez David Hull Promos Ltd/Nigel Round Mgnt
Roger Sanchez Primary Talent Int'l
Richard Sandells Performance Actors Agy
Sanderina RDL
Ed Sanders Panic Management
Rachel Sanders Fushion Pukka Bosh
Martin Sanderson CKK Ent
Nikki Sanderson Linton Mngt
Tessa Sanderson CBE CHAMPIONS (UK) PLC/Paul Bridson Prods/Persnl Appearances
Valerie Sanderson Speak-Easy Ltd
Chris Sandford Voice Shop
Jamie Sandford Voice Shop
Catriana Sandison Vincent Shaw Assoc Ltd
Adam Sandler Agency For the Performing Arts/Endeavor Agency
Hannah Sandling Sue Rider Mngt Ltd
Henry Sandon All Electric Productions & Dav/B.D.A./Gordon Poole Agy Ltd
Sandow Clowns Sandow Clowns (Ind Art)
Graham Sandry Linkside Agy
Julian Sands ARG Management
Myra Sands Langford Assoc
Simon Sands After Dinner Spkers & Com/Compact Mngt & Ent Agy/Norwich Artistes
Tony Sands Norwich Artistes
Paul Sandys Actorum
Justin Sane Devil Management
Sangeeta Matters Musical
Ian Sansom Capel & Land
David Sant CKK Ent
Santa Esmeralda & Leroy Gomez Jason West Agy
Carlo Paul Santanna M.G. Ents
Yo Santhaveesuk Burnett Granger Assoc
Laura Dos Santos Brunskill Mngt Ltd
Saosin Scream Promotions
Miguel Sapochnik CASAROTTO RAMSAY & ASSOCIATES
Sapphire Hire-A-Band Ent Agy
Sarabanda Latin-Touch Ents
Sarah Duchess of York Kruger Cowne Limited
Sarah Jane (Kylie) Advanced Ents
Shireen Sarkhoy Direct Persnl Mngt
June Sarpong NMP Live Ltd
Peter Sarstedt Barry Collings Ents/Denis Vaughan Mngt/Jason West Agy
Sash Mission Control Artist Agy
Gerard Sassu Agency K-Bis
Satanica Psycho Mngt Co Ltd
Brooke Satchwell Darren Gray Mngt
Kotono Sato Matters Musical
Satoshie Tomiie ITB
Zita Sattar Jonathan Altaras Assoc
Satu Salo CS Ents
Saturation Point Hope Management
Saturday Morning Pictures CRUISIN' MUSIC
Sauce City Jazz Derek Bruce Ents
Saudade (Salsa) Doub7e Seven Events Ltd
Chris Saul Speak-Easy Ltd
Darren Saul Kerry Gardner Mngt
Peter Saul Jae Moss Entp
Aurelie Sauli-Koren North One Mngt
Daz Saund UK Booking Agy
Ben Saunders Cunningham Mngt Ltd/Speakout/The London Spkr Bureau
Gemma Saunders Kerry Gardner Mngt
George Saunders CS Ents/NVB Ents
James Saunders CASAROTTO RAMSAY & ASSOCIATES
Jennifer Saunders Peters Fraser Dunlop (PFD)/United Agents
Junior Saunders Jo Sarsby PR Ltd
Katy Saunders Tavistock Wood Management Ltd
Rachel Saunders Angle Ents Ltd
Sautrie Matters Musical
Sav Prima Artists
Jamie Savage Sandra Singer Assoc
Jo Jo Savage TMK Mngt & Agcy Ltd
Lily Savage Olga Ltd
The Savages Book A Band
Savanah XS Promos
Angela Saville Northern Lights Mngt
Philip Saville CASAROTTO RAMSAY & ASSOCIATES
Sir Jimmy Saville Qvoice
Savoir Faire CS Ents/David Charles Agy/Hire-A-Band Ent Agy/Norwich Artistes/Spotlight Ents (Notts)/Steve Allen Ents
Julia Sawalha AIM/ARG Management/Yakety Yak
Nadia Sawalha AIM/NMP Live Ltd/United Agents
Nadim Sawalha AIM
Sawdid Continental Drifts/TEST AGENT C
Annie Sawle ICON Actors Mngt
George Sawyer Noel Gay Artists Ltd
Toby Sawyer Peters Fraser Dunlop (PFD)
Wolf Sawyerr Actorum
Carlo Sax Bees Knees Ents/Robert Crossland Ent Ltd
Johnny Sax Nigel Round Mgnt
Oliver Dawson Saxon Alan Cottam Agency/Assassination Music Promos/Rock Artist Mngt
Say Anything Helter Skelter Agy Ltd
Say Lou Lou 13 Artists
Leo Sayer Denis Vaughan Mngt/NMP Live Ltd/The Psycho Mngt Co Ltd/Tony Denton Promos Ltd
Phil Sayer Downes Presenters Agy
Ami Sayers Crescent Mngt
Goldie Sayers CHAMPIONS (UK) PLC
Alexei Sayle Cassie Mayer Ltd/G.A.A./Lip Service Casting Ltd
Ian Saynor Louise Hillman/Katie Threlfall
Sazzu JB Ents
Greta Scacchi Conway Van Gelder Grant Ltd
Boz Scaggs ITB
Amanda Scala Devil Management
Prunella Scales Conway Van Gelder Grant Ltd
Scalextrix Roadshow Advanced Ents
Lindsay Scandrett CKK Ent
Sean Scanlan Brunskill Management Ltd
Sean Scannell Vern Allen Ents Ltd
Tony Scannell MCS Agcy
Scarabeus CKK Ent/Whatever Artists Mngt Ltd
Scaramouch The CBS Grp
Adrian Scarborough The Richard Stone Prtnrshp
Andrew Scarborough Yakety Yak
Jacqui Scarborough Audrey Benjamin Agy
Simon Scardifield The Richard Stone Prtnrshp
Scarlet Rainbow Striptease Agy
Captain Scarlet Norwich Artistes
Scarlet Fusion Continental Drifts/TEST AGENT C
Scarlet Heights Funhouse Productions Ltd
Tony Scarth (Tom Jones) Nigel Round Mgnt/Upfront Ent Agy Ltd
Prof Richard Scase Speakers For Business
Caroline Scattergood Lena Davis/John Bishop Assoc
Kristen Schaal Avalon Mngt
Michael Schaeble Sue Rider Mngt Ltd
Anthony Schaeffer Nyland Mngt
Simon Schama United Agents
Simon Schatzberger Lip Service Casting Ltd
Claudia Schiffer 19 Entertainment/Premier Special
Jonathan Schippers COFFEE ARTISTS
James Schlesinger Brunskill Mngt Ltd
Peter Schmeichel MBE CHAMPIONS (UK) PLC
Barry Schmidt Bavarian Band Derek

Bruce Ents/The Horne Concert Agy
Jan Schmidt Oompah Band Les Hart (Southampton) Ents
David Schneider Conway Van Gelder Grant Ltd/Curtis Brown Grp
Rob Schneider Int'l Artistes Ltd
Yorg Schneider Athole Still Int'l Ltd/TEST AGENT A
Papa Schnitzel's Bavarian Dance Band Crown Ents/Matters Musical
Audrey Schoellhammer Vincent Shaw Assoc Ltd
Carl Schofield Artiste & Musical
Ken Schofield Prof Sports Ptnr Ltd
Philip Schofield Prime Performers Ltd/Trading Faces Ltd
Phillip Schofield James Grant Mngt Ltd/NMP Live Ltd
John Scholes Darren Gray Mngt
John Scholey Barn Dance Line Dance Agy
Liz Scholey Folk Ents Ltd
Wolfgang Schöne Ingpen & Williams Ltd
Stephanie Schonfield AIM
Michael Schonwandt Ingpen & Williams Ltd
The School Disco Band CS Ents
Schooner Leo Mngt & Agy/Paul Bridson Prods
Michael Schumacher (Lookalike) Business Evt Mngt
Howard Schuman CASAROTTO RAMSAY & ASSOCIATES
Dan Schumann Rogues & Vagabonds Mngt
Bierkeller Schunklers Derek Bruce Ents/Stardust Ents Agy
Daniel Schutzmann Langford Assoc
David Schwimmer Markham & Froggatt Ltd/Special Artists Agency/The Gersh Agency
Schwing CHAMPIONS (UK) PLC/Prima Artists
Claudio Scimone Transart (UK) Ltd
Scissor Sisters CODA Ltd
Terri Scoble KAL Mngt
Paul Scofield Chatto & Linnit Ltd
Scooby Don't Tony Bennell Ents
Scooch Insanity Artists
Scooter the Clown KM Ents
Scorch Ra - Fire and Juggling Whatever Artists Mngt Ltd
Scorpions ITB
Band Of the Scots Guards ABC Direct Ents
Dance Band Of Scots Guards ABC Direct Ents
Pipes & Drums Of 1st Battalion Scots Guards ABC Direct Ents
Scott and Leon Mission Control Artist Agy
Andrew Scott ARG Management/Peters Fraser Dunlop (PFD)
Angus Scott Noel Gay Artists Ltd
Barni Scott Derek Bruce Ents
Scott Brothers A Better Class Of Act
Brough Scott MA Jon Holmes Media Ltd
Caroline Scott Dennis Lyne Agy
Clare Scott 1984 Persnl Mngt
Darrell Scott Lime Actors Agy & Mngt Ltd
Dixon J Scott Devil Management/Martin Ents
Emily Scott Girl Management
Fred Scott Take Three Mngt
Gary Scott M.S. Ent Grp
Gemma Scott Tony Clayman Promos
Harriet Scott RDF Management/ROAR Group
Ian Scott SJS Promos
Ian Scott as Tom jones Advanced Ents/Complete Ent Serv Ltd
Jack Scott Paul Barrett Rock'N'Roll Entp
Jane Scott Crescent Mngt
John Scott Independent Talent Group Ltd
Hannah Scott Joynt Arlington Enterprises Ltd
Judith Scott The Richard Stone Prtnrshp
Katie Scott Jacque Evans Mngt Ltd
Martin Scott Martin Ents
Mick Scott Barn Dance Line Dance Agy
Monty Scott TMK Mngt & Agcy Ltd
Nikki Leigh Scott Nancy Hudson Associates Ltd
Pearl Scott Newton Wills Mngt
Roger Scott Derek Bruce Ents/The Horne Concert Agy
Sandy Scott NVB Ents
Sarah Lee Scott CeeBee Variety Agy
Sean Scott Hyper Agency
Selina Scott Knight Ayton Mngt/Persnl Appearances
Shirley Ann Scott Gordon Kellett Ents
Stevie Scott Caledonian Music Agy
Susan Scott Arena Personal Mngt
Tom Scott Mike Constantia Artiste Mngt L
Tommy Scott BGS PRODUCTIONS
Victoria Scott Darren Gray Mngt
Tim Scott Walker Brunskill Mngt Ltd
Sue Scott-Davison Lip Service Casting Ltd
Alex Scott-Fairley Vincent Shaw Assoc Ltd/Wendy Lee Mngt
Scottish Academy MTM Presntns
Scottish Blues Brothers Cosmos Agy & Promos
The Scottish Blues Brothers Hireaband Ltd
Scottish Ceilidh Bands Matters Musical
Scottish Guitar Quartet Stoneyport Associates
Lisa Scott-Lee Urban Associates Personal Mana
Isabel Scott-Plummer The Actors File
Scotts Castle Holidays SIMON WHITTAM PUBLICITY
Scoundrels One Fifteen
Scratch Perverts CODA Ltd
Scream Concerts Tour John Hessenthaler Ents
Screaming Ballerinas CEC Management
The Screaming Beavers Book A Band
Screaming Beavers Head On Mngt
The Screaming Beavers Henderson Mngt/Mike Constantia Artiste Mngt L
Scritti Politti Helter Skelter Agy Ltd
Scully Nigel Round Mgnt
Sea Of Bees 13 Artists
Terry Seabrooke Johnny Mans Prods Ltd/NVB Ents/Stardust Ents Agy/The Horne Concert Agy
Seafood Cooking Vinyl
Harvey Seager Funhouse Productions Ltd
Steph Seager Noel Gay Artists Ltd
Garry Seagraves (magician) XS Promos
Jenny Seagrove M F Management Ltd
Seal Creative Artists Agency/ITB
Seal Club Clubbing Club Bad Moon Publicity
Dave Sealey The Horne Concert Agy
David Seaman CHAMPIONS (UK) PLC/NMP Live Ltd
Dave Seamer Disco Dave Seamer Ents
Paul Seamer Disco Dave Seamer Ents
Sean Bolger June Ford-Crush
Sean Finch & The Street Band Book A Band
Jay Sean Dave Woolf PR
Neil Sean Seamus Lyte Management Ltd
The Searchers Alan Field Assoc/Entertainers Mgt Ltd/Jean Levy PR Agency/PVA Ent Consultants/Rock Artist Mngt/The John Boddy Agency
Debra Searle MBE Persnly Spkng
Debra Searle Speakers For Business
Simon Sebag-Montefiore Capel & Land
Mitch Sebastian Michael Summerton Mngt
Tim Sebastian Knight Ayton Mngt
Nina Sebastiane Jane Hughes Mngt
Sebastian's Incredibly Cool Band MTM Presntns
Marta Sebestyen Adastra
Jon Secada William Morris Inc (USA)
Second 2 Everleys Hawthorn Ent
Second 2 None Hawthorn Ent
Second Nature Martin Ents/Sardi's Int'l Ent
Second Time Around David Charles Agy
The Secret Garden Animal World
Secret Machines 13 Artists
Secret Police (Police tribute) Henderson Mngt
Neil Sedaka William Morris Inc (USA)
Becki Seddiki Unleashed PR
Paul Seed Speak-Easy Ltd
Seether ITB
Viviane Segade Dance Funki Feathers Agy
Leif Segerstam Patrick Garvey Mngt
Elizabeth Segojame Daly Pearson Associates
Isabella Seibert Jae Moss Entp
Seiji Elastic Artists Agency Ltd
Jerry Seinfield United Talent Agency
Tony Selby Jane Lehrer Assoc/Yakety Yak
Select Company Derek Bruce Ents
Select Syncopators Dave Winslett Assoc
The Selecter Ro-Lo Prods/The Psycho Mngt Co Ltd
The Selecter featuring Pauline Black Jason West Agy
Selena Wise Buddah Talent & Voices
Monica Seles NMP Live Ltd
Keiron Self Jill Foster Ltd
Susannah Self Athole Still Int'l Ltd/TEST AGENT A
Will Self The Wylie Agency
Catherine Selford CKK Ent
Jeannie Selly Deri Promos
Alice Selwyn Brunskill Management Ltd
Rebecca Semark Alpha Persnl Mngt
Jerzy Semkow Transart (UK) Ltd
Ricardo Semler Parliament Comms
David Semple Jill Foster Ltd
Martin Semple CHAMPIONS (UK) PLC
The Senators B.D.A./Colclough Entertainment/Henderson Mngt
Jerry Senfluk Kevin King Mngt
Mike Sengelow Actorum
Alison Senior Langford Assoc
Danny & The Seniors Norwich Artistes
Paul Senn Scott-Paul Young Ents Ltd
The Sensations (Tamla Motown/The Supremes tribute) Upbeat Mngt
Sensations (Tamla Motown) Upfront Ent Agy Ltd
Captain Sensible Brian Gannon Mngt
Sensky String Trio Highfield Mngt & Promos

Productions & Dav/Rosemary Squires Entp
St Andrews Pipe Band Derek Bruce Ents
Isla St Clair Johnny Mans Prods Ltd/SIMON WHITTAM PUBLICITY
Andrew St Clair James Grays Mngt & Asc
Pam St Clement Saraband Assoc
St Etienne EC1 Music Agency
St George & The Trombone Barn Dance Line Dance Agy
St Germain (UK/Asia/Aus) CODA Ltd
Alan St John NVB Ents
Barrie St John Book A Band
Christine St John Jeffrey & White
David St John Derek Bruce Ents/Prima Artists
Ian St John 1st Choice Speakers UK Ltd/After Dinner World Ltd/Arena Ent Cons/Gordon Poole Agy Ltd/Jon Holmes Media Ltd/Nigel Round Mgnt/Persnly Spkng/Speakout
Richard St John (Escapologist/Illusionist) Joker Ents
St Lucia Steel Band PVA Ent Consultants
St Nicholas String Quartet Quality Ents
St Petersburg String Quartet Upbeat Classical Mngt
Cris St Valery Jane Hughes Mngt
Stable Roof Jazzband (NL) Wim Wigt Prodns Ltd
Howard Stableford Dave Winslett Assoc
Staccato CS Ents
Melanie Stace BULLET MANAGEMENT LIMITED/Tony Clayman Promos
Ben Stacey Agency K-Bis
Jeremy Stacey Sarm Mngt
John Stacey Gavin Barker
Stackyard Stompers Jazz Band Stardust Ents Agy
Matt Stacy Indep Mngt Ltd
Neil Stacy Shepherd Mngt Ltd
James Staddon Nancy Hudson Associates Ltd
Tom Stade Comedy Store Mngt/Paramount Int'l Mngt
Victoria Stadler North One Mngt
Staff Trek Clive Panto Prods
Stag Punch & Judy Show Stardust Ents Agy
Stag Show Exotica Stardust Ents Agy
Stairway to Zeppelin Andrew Beauchamp Mngt/Jason West Agy
Tania Staite Piccadilly Mngt
Stak It Up Steve Allen Ents
John Stalker Arena Ent Cons/Gordon Poole Agy Ltd/PVA Ent Consultants/Paul Bridson Prods/Persnly Spkng
Stallions Big Bang Mngt Ltd
Terence Stamp Markham & Froggatt Ltd
Richard Stamper CS Ents
Stan Francisco Athole Still Int'l Ltd/TEST AGENT A
Joe Standerline Lime Actors Agy & Mngt Ltd
Jill Stanford The Actors File
Ruth Stanford Dukeries Ents Ltd
Benjamin Stanley APM Ass
Margo Stanley Nyland Mngt
Siobhan Stanley Kerry Gardner Mngt
Stan Stanley Avalon Mngt
Fiona Stansbury BAM Assoc Ltd
Lisa Stansfield Peters Fraser Dunlop (PFD)/The Agency Group
Ashley Stanton Adrian King Assoc
Barry Stanton Jonathan Altaras Assoc
Stanton Warriors CODA Ltd
Mark Stanway Audrey Benjamin Agy
Stuart Staples Asgard
Brendan Stapleton CKK Ent
Nicola Stapleton Peters Fraser Dunlop (PFD)
Brendan Stapleton's Amazing Animates John Field - Theatre and Puppe
Star Fanfare 3000/Highfield Mngt & Promos/The CBS Grp/Whatever Artists Mngt Ltd
Five Star Norwich Artistes
Star Spangled Express (tributes to Buddy Holly, Roy Orbison & The Everley Brothers) Advanced Ents
Alvin Stardust BULLET MANAGEMENT LIMITED/Barry Collings Ents/Brian Yeates Assoc
Stardust Experience The Dixon Agy
Stardust Saucy Hen Show Stardust Ents Agy
Starfinders Mobile Disco Starfinders Int'l Mngt
Michael Starke Dennis Lyne Agy/Non Stop Ents
Dr David Starkey Speakers For Business
Carol Starks Lou Coulson Associates
Starlight Crew (Southport Weekender - RNB) UK Booking Agy
Ringo Starr Primary Talent Int'l
Stevie Starr Mike Malley Ents
Pierce Starre Lime Actors Agy & Mngt Ltd
Starrz Norwich Artistes
Stars & Bars Line Dance Disco ABDC Ents
Stars from the Commitments Brian Gannon Mngt
Stars from the Gladiators Big Bang Mngt Ltd
Stars of the Future, Produced by Stephanie King CeeBee Variety Agy
Stars & Stripes Show (Elvis & Tina Turner) Funhouse Productions Ltd/NVB Ents
Starsailor Solo Agy Ltd
Starship featuring Mickey Thomas AIM Inc (USA)
Starskey & Hutch Andrew Beauchamp Mngt
State Of Quo Head On Mngt
A Static Lullaby The Agency Group
Station Book A Band/Quality Ents
Station to Station Upbeat Entertainment
Candi Staton Tony Denton Promos Ltd
Status Clone (Status Quo Tribute) BULLET MANAGEMENT LIMITED/Funhouse Productions Ltd/Jason West Agy/Peller Artistes Ltd/Stardust Ents Agy
Status Cymbal CKK Ent/Peller Artistes Ltd/Prima Artists/Status Cymbal (Ind Art)/Whatever Artists Mngt Ltd
Status Cymbal String Quartet CS Ents
Status Duo Jason West Agy/Nigel Round Mgnt
Status Go Compact Mngt & Ent Agy
Status Quid Jason West Agy
Status Quo Duroc Media Ltd/Fifth Element/The Agency Group
Imelda Staunton ARG Management/Conway Van Gelder Grant Ltd
Stax Atlantic Head On Mngt
Stax of Soul Arena Ent Cons/BULLET MANAGEMENT LIMITED/Big Wheel Ents Ltd/European Artistes Mngt/Head On Mngt/Jason West Agy
Stayin' Alive (Bee Gees tribute) Camscott Leisure/Compact Mngt & Ent Agy/Funhouse Productions Ltd/Peller Artistes Ltd
Alison Steadman United Agents
Lynda Steadman Harvey Voices Ltd/Peter Charlesworth & Assoc
Sheila Steafel Lip Service Casting Ltd
Geoffrey Steatfeild Markham & Froggatt Ltd
Andy Steed Langford Assoc
Maggie Steed Jonathan Altaras Assoc
Phil Steed (Tom Jones) David Charles Agy/Jason West Agy
Piper Julian Steed PVA Ent Consultants
Tim Steed Jonathan Altaras Assoc
Oliver Steeds Gordon Poole Agy Ltd
Ben Steel Funky Beetroot Celebrity Manag
Deborah Steel Talent Artists Ltd
Mark Steel Off The Kerb Prods
Mike Steel UK Booking Agy
Steel Panacea PVA Ent Consultants
Steel Pulse Free Trade Agy/War Zones
Steel Street Blues Hire-A-Band Ent Agy
Steelasophical Steel Band Peller Artistes Ltd
Barry Steele - Roy Orbison Tribute Nigel Round Mgnt
Carrie Steele Devil Management
Danny Steele MTC (UK) LTD
Elizabeth Steele Nyland Mngt
Fraser Steele Jill Foster Ltd
Glynne Steele Billboard Persnl Mngt
Jovanka Steele Cosmic Comedy Mngt/Paramount Int'l Mngt
Martin Steele (Male Vocalist) Ron Martin Mngt
Theo Fraser Steele Markham & Froggatt Ltd
Steeleye Span Park Promotions
Steel'n'Lace Hire-A-Band Ent Agy
Steely Dan ITB
Steve Steen The Richard Stone Prtnrshp
Mary Steenburgen Special Artists Agency
Stee-V Moonglight Agy
Gwen Stefani Primary Talent Int'l/The M.O.B. Agency
Samantha De Stefano Norwich Artistes
Roman Stefanski M W Management
Caroline Stein Athole Still Int'l Ltd/TEST AGENT A
Rick Stein OBE CHAMPIONS (UK) PLC
U Hesse vd Steinen Stafford Law
Steve Steinman's Meatloaf 2 Henderson Mngt/Peller Artistes Ltd
Shirley Stelfox AIM
Stellastar Big Sister Promotions
Jeff Stelling CHAMPIONS (UK) PLC/JLA
Randi Stene Askonas Holt Ltd
Stan Stennett B.A.S.I.C.
Carley Stenson (Steph, Hollyoaks) Big Bang Mngt Ltd/Hyper Agency/Nigel Round Mgnt
Malcolm Stent Celebrity Appearances/Persnly Spkng/The Horne Concert Agy
Markus Stenz Ingpen & Williams Ltd
Step It Up Martin Ents
Stephanie St James McLeod Agy Ltd
Anna Stephany Ingpen & Williams Ltd
Henry Stephen Argyle Assoc
Pamela Helen Stephen Music Int'l
Huw Stephens Hyper Agency
Jack Stephens By Invitation Only/Jack Stephens/PVA Ent Consultants
Peter Stephens MBA
Rebecca Stephens MBE DBA Speakers/Fox Artist Mngt Ltd/Gordon Poole Agy Ltd/Persnly Spkng/Speakers For Business
Simon Stephens CASAROTTO RAMSAY

& ASSOCIATES
Toby Stephens Peters Fraser Dunlop (PFD)
Debra Stephenson Tony Clayman Promos/Trading Faces Ltd
Denise Stephenson Emptage Hallett Ltd
Geraldine Stephenson Talent Artists Ltd
Julia Stephenson June Ford-Crush
Michelle Stephenson Sandra Boyce Mngt
Pamela Stephenson Tickety Boo
Paul Stephenson Elinor Hilton Associates
Alex Stepney After Dinner World Ltd/Sunshine Ents
Rev Obadiah Steppenwolfe III Jongleurs
Will Stepper (Reggae) Glasshouse Prods Ltd
Stereo MC's Universal/Island Records Ltd
Stereoironics Andrew Beauchamp Mngt
Stereophonics Kas Mercer/Mercenary PR
Stereotonics Head On Mngt
Andrew Sterling Hire-A-Band Ent Agy
Mike Sterling Arena Ent Cons
Sterling String Quartet CS Ents/NVB Ents
David Stern IMG Artists
Michael Stern Transart (UK) Ltd
Sam Stern Curtis Brown Grp
Rachel Sternberg Alpha Persnl Mngt
Steve & Aska Derek Bruce Ents
Steve & Megumi PVA Ent Consultants
Steve Preston (As Elvis Presley) Henderson Mngt
David Stevens Limelight Management
Gary Stevens The Horne Concert Agy
Jean Stevens Direct Persnl Mngt
Sir John Stevens Speakout
Jonathan Stevens London Music Agy
Kenny Stevens Dinosaur Promo/Dinosaur Mus
Lee Stevens Philip Youd Ents & Mngt
Michael Fenton Stevens The Richard Stone Prtnrshp
Nikki Stevens Ron Martin Mngt
Norman Stevens Derek Bruce Ents
Rachel Stevens 19 Entertainment
Rik Stevens (David Bowie tribute) Chord Theatrical & Corporate
Rikki Stevens Stag Ents
Rob Stevens Gordon Kellett Ents
Russ Stevens Dave Winslett Assoc
Scott Stevens Sunshine Ents
Steve Stevens Apple County
Sufjan Stevens ITB
Tony Stevens Colclough Entertainment
Zak Stevens After Dinner Spkers & Com
Christian Stevenson Wise Buddah Talent & Voices
Cyriack Stevenson The Narrow Road Company Ltd
Gerda Stevenson The Richard Stone Prtnrshp
Jeff Stevenson Artsworld Int'l Mngt Ltd/Gordon Poole Agy Ltd/PVA Ent Consultants
Jessica Stevenson CASAROTTO RAMSAY & ASSOCIATES/Jonathan Altaras Assoc
Juliet Stevenson Markham & Froggatt Ltd
Leo Stevenson Jacque Evans Mngt Ltd
Luke Stevenson Nigel Round Mgnt
Mark Stevenson Elinor Hilton Associates
Ray Stevenson Lip Service Casting Ltd
Sonia Stevenson Limelight Management
Steve's Disco David Forshaw Entp
Stevie J McLeod Agy Ltd
Alastair Stewart OBE Capel & Land/NMP Live Ltd
Alec Stewart CHAMPIONS (UK) PLC/MERLIN ELITE
Alistair Stewart Trading Faces Ltd
Allan Stewart Talking Heads - The Voice Agy
Andy M Stewart Stoneyport Associates
Stewart Band XS Promos
Col Bob Stewart DSO Gordon Poole Agy Ltd
Brent Stewart Audrey Benjamin Agy
Cathie Stewart Deri Promos
Christopher Stewart Jonathan Altaras Assoc
Dean Stewart Devil Management
Di Stewart MTC (UK) LTD
Diana Stewart Brunskill Mngt Ltd/MERLIN ELITE
Col. Bob Stewart DSO Speakers For Business
Ed Stewart Jo Gurnett Persnl Mngt/Persnl Appearances/Ron Martin Mngt
Kevin Stewart & First Chapter NVB Ents
Gavin Stewart Hilary Gagan Assoc
Dr Ian Stewart Take Three Mngt
Jackie Stewart NMP Live Ltd
Mary Ann Stewart Opera & Concert Artists
Moira Stewart The Speakers Agency
Nigel Stewart Sardi's Int'l Ent
Paul Stewart Gordon Kellett Ents
Rod Stewart Artist Group International/Solo Agy Ltd
Ronnie Stewart NVB Ents/PVA Ent Consultants
Russ Stewart & The Fake Faces Compact Mngt & Ent Agy
Rod Stewart & Stone Cold Sober Starfinders Int'l Mngt
Tina Stewart Harvey Voices Ltd
Adam Steyning-Williams Agency K-Bis
Stickleback Plasticus Fool's Paradise
Sticks and Stones CKK Ent
Sticks Band Barn Dance Line Dance Agy
Stiff Little Fingers Miracle Artists Ltd
Jake Stigers COFFEE ARTISTS
John Stiles Persnl Appearances
Nobby Stiles MBE After Dinner World Ltd/Nigel Round Mgnt/Preview & Review Ents Ltd
Richard Stilgoe Noel Gay Artists Ltd
Still Life Crowd Pullers
Still Living Statues CKK Ent/Continental Drifts/TEST AGENT C
Stiltskin Chimes Int'l Ents Ltd
Sting Markham & Froggatt Ltd/William Morris Inc (USA)
The Stingrays Stag Ents
Stink 182 Jason West Agy
Colin Stinton Kerry Gardner Mngt/Lip Service Casting Ltd
Stipe (REM Tribute) Andrew Beauchamp Mngt
Jimmy Stirling XS Promos
John Stirling Gordon Poole Agy Ltd/PVA Ent Consultants/Persnl Appearances/Persnly Spkng
Mathew Stirling APM Ass
Rachael Stirling Harvey Voices Ltd
Shaken Not Stirred Matters Musical
Alan Stivell Denis Vaughan Mngt
Giles Stoakley Rogues & Vagabonds Mngt
Paula Stockbridge Louise Hillman/Katie Threlfall
Mary Stockley Harvey Voices Ltd
Malcolm Stoddard Burnett Granger Assoc
Deborah Stoddart Pro Artist Management
Kevin Stokes Complete Ent Serv Ltd
P J Stokes Nigel Round Mgnt
Jennie Stoller The Richard Stone Prtnrshp
Anna Stolli Jae Moss Entp
The Marsh Town Stompers Matters Musical
The Sugarfoot Stompers Matters Musical
Stone Cold Sober Sunshine Ents
James Stone Nigel Round Mgnt
Joss Stone Dave Woolf PR
Lesley Stone Inspiration Mngt
Marty Stone Garston Ents Ltd
Stoned Again Compact Mngt & Ent Agy/Entertainers Mgt Ltd/Henderson Mngt/Jason West Agy/Upbeat Mngt
Stonefoxx Action Talent Int.
Kay Stonham CASAROTTO RAMSAY & ASSOCIATES
Alison Stonier Agency K-Bis
Stooshe Insanity Artists
Miriam Stoppard Harvey Voices Ltd
Jayne Storey CHAMPIONS (UK) PLC
Stuart Storey Persnl Appearances
Storm Advanced Ents/Monkeybiz Ent Agy/Stag Ents
Graeme Storm CHAMPIONS (UK) PLC
Jason Storm Dave Woodbury Ents
Maddie Storm Gordon Kellett Ents
Ricky Storm (Billy Fury/Elvis tributes) Graham Cole Mngt
Stormm Athole Still Music
Storm/Ritchie Athole Still Int'l Ltd/TEST AGENT A
Rob Storr Louise Hillman/Katie Threlfall
Story Of The Year The Agency Group
Storyville Jazzband (NL) Wim Wigt Prodns Ltd
Grant Stott Speakout
Kathryn Stott & Noriko Ogawa Hazard Chase Ltd
Ken Stott ARG Management/M F Management Ltd/Voice Shop
Stourport on Severn Brass Band Derek Bruce Ents
Edward Stourton Curtis Brown Grp
John H Stracey After Dinner World Ltd/Broadwater Ents Assoc/CHAMPIONS (UK) PLC/Fighting Talk Promos/Gordon Robinson Assoc
Antony Strachan Dennis Lyne Agy
Gordon Strachan Athole Still Int'l Ltd/TEST AGENT A
Michaela Strachan Jo Sarsby PR Ltd
Straight Eight CS Ents
Straight Jacket circus Advanced Ents
Straight Up Funhouse Productions Ltd
Straightjacket Sunshine Ents
Mark Straker Langford Assoc
Anna Stranack Adrian King Assoc
Eddy Strange Paramount Int'l Mngt
The Strangelings Continental Drifts/TEST AGENT C
Alan Strangeway Direct Persnl Mngt
Strangeways Hire-A-Band Ent Agy
The Stranglers ABS Agy/CRUISIN' MUSIC/Dorothy Howe Publicity & Press/Scream Promotions
Susan Stranks David Wilkinson Assoc
Michael Strassen Hilary Gagan Assoc
Strate Linze Hire-A-Band Ent Agy
Amy Stratton The Narrow Road Company Ltd

Jacek Strauch Opera & Concert Artists
Peter Straughan CASAROTTO RAMSAY & ASSOCIATES
Andrew Strauss CHAMPIONS (UK) PLC
Andy Strauss PARAGON SPORTS MANAGEMENT LTD
The Johann Strauss Gala Wim Wigt Prodns Ltd
Strauss Quartet Derek Bruce Ents
The Strauss Quartet Quality Ents
Strawberry Strings Complete Ent Serv Ltd/Crown Ents/Prima Artists
Strawberry the Clown CKK Ent
The Strawbs Jason West Agy/Speaking Volumes
The Strayhorns Upbeat Entertainment
Tania Strecker Independent Talent Group Ltd
Andy Street Yellow Balloon Prods Ltd
Bruce Jones (Les, Coronation Street) Nigel Round Mgnt/Nyland Mngt
Jennie Mcalpine (Fizz, Coronation Street) Nigel Round Mgnt/RDF Management
Graeme Hawley (John, Coronation Street) Amber Persnl Mngt Ltd/Nigel Round Mgnt
Ian Street Indep Mngt Ltd
Jack P Shephard (David, Coronation Street) Nigel Round Mgnt
Judith Street Talent Artists Ltd
Margi Clarke (Jackie, Coronation Street) Nigel Round Mgnt
Michael Le Vell (Kevin,Coronation Street) Nigel Round Mgnt
Patrick Street Adastra
Matthew Street Ragtime Jazz Band David Forshaw Entp
Stephanie Street Noel Gay Artists Ltd
Stephen Street Gailforce Mngt Ltd
Time Street Norwich Artistes
Streetboy MPC Ent
Streetlevel Leo Mngt & Agy
Janet Street-Porter Ed Victor Agency/Inspirational Artiste Bkg/Princess Talent Mngt
The Streets Primary Talent Int'l/Toast Press
Streetwise Sardi's Int'l Ent
Stretch Continental Drifts/TEST AGENT C
Gary Stretch Psycho Mngt Co Ltd
Stretch People Crowd Pullers
Amanda Stretton Panic Management
Jessica Stretton Nigel Round Mgnt
Stephen Strickland Jazz Trio Mainstream Evts
Strictly Come Dancing Band Insanity Artists
Virginia Stride Argyle Assoc
Striding Edge Barn Dance Line Dance Agy
Strike Mission Control Artist Agy
String Diva Electric Violin Show Whatever Artists Mngt Ltd
String mania John Oliver Org/Prima Artists
Berny Stringel Jill Foster Ltd
Nick Stringer Kerry Gardner Mngt
Ken Stringfellow Free Trade Agy
Stringfever Matters Musical/Prima Artists
Strings Attached London Music Agy/Tony Bennell Ents
Cavatina Strings CS Ents/Norwich Artistes
Gallery Strings Norwich Artistes
Peacock Strings Matters Musical
Red Hot Strings Prima Artists
S Strings Matters Musical
Sapphire Strings Matters Musical
Sole Bay Strings Norwich Artistes
Z Strings Matters Musical
Strippagrams Steve Draper Ents
Michael Strobel Grays Mngt & Asc
The Strokes ICM (USA)/MVO Ltd
The Strolling Bones Jason West Agy/The John Boddy Agency
Stromenti Matters Musical
Mark Strong Markham & Froggatt Ltd
Sir Roy Strong Knight Ayton Mngt
Dr Mike Stroud OBE Cunningham Mngt Ltd
Struck It Rich Country Band Folk Ents Ltd
Shelley Von Struckel Knight Ayton Mngt
Tony Strudwick Band PVA Ent Consultants/Pete Mitchell Associates
Alexis Strum Tony Clayman Promos
Joe Strummer SJM Management
Strung Out Moonglight Agy
Jane Struthers Jacque Evans Mngt Ltd
Harry Strutter's Hot Rhythm Orchestra London Music Agy/The John Boddy Agency
Sassy Stryker David Charles Agy
Arlene Stuart Speakout
Dean Stuart Les Hart (Southampton) Ents
Hamish Stuart Band Jason West Agy
Stuart Hosking Model Plan Celebrities & Prese
Kirsty Stuart Markham & Froggatt Ltd
Lise Stuart Sandra Boyce Mngt
Marty Stuart Buddy Lee Attrctns Inc (USA)
Moira Stuart Knight Ayton Mngt
Robert Stuart Actors Alliance
Tony Stuart Allan Wilson Entp
Stubborn Heart 13 Artists
Sophie Stuckey Susan Angel Kevin Francis Ltd
Ruben Studdard 19 Entertainment
Amy Studt 19 Entertainment
Neil Stuke ARG Management
Stush Action Talent Int.
Russ Styler P.J. Ents
Andy Styles Shining Mngt Ltd
John Styles Sandra Singer Assoc
Prof John Styles John Field - Theatre and Puppe
Sean Styles Non Stop Ents
The Stylistics Tony Denton Promos Ltd
Stylus Athole Still Int'l Ltd/TEST AGENT A
ash Stymest Curtis Brown Grp
Ensemble Suavis Matters Musical
Subterraneans - Party Band Midland Ent & Mgnt Ltd
John Suchet All Electric Productions & Dav/NMP Live Ltd
Sue Lloyd Burnett Granger Assoc
Saucy Sue Partyweb.co.uk
Suede 13 Artists
Suffolk Punch Country Duo Hire-A-Band Ent Agy
Sugababes Helter Skelter Agy Ltd/Personal Management & Casting/Purple PR
Sugar & Spice Tony Bennell Ents
Sugar Creek Trio Paul Barrett Rock'N'Roll Entp
Sugar Daddies Sunshine Ents
Lord Alan Sugar CHAMPIONS (UK) PLC/Frank PR/Speakout/Taylor Herring Public Relation
Sara Sugarman Judy Daish Assoc
Mollie Sugden Joan Reddin
Greg Suggitt Stardust Ents Agy
Suggs Amanda Howard Assoc Ltd/PBJ Mngt Ltd
Warren Suicide Value Added Talent Agy (VAT)
Suitcase Circus MTM Presntns
Josef Suk Transart (UK) Ltd
Mohini Sule Princess Talent Mngt
Gregg Sulkin Sasha Leslie Mngt
Sullivan XS Promos
Big Jim Sullivan Roots Around The World
Justin Sullivan Primary Talent Int'l
Kate Sullivan AAA/Armstrong Academy Agy
Ronnie O'Sullivan CHAMPIONS (UK) PLC/Frank PR
Eugene Sully MCS Agcy
Sultans Of Ping ABS Agy
Sum 41 The Agency Group
Daniel Sumegi Ingpen & Williams Ltd
Hubert Sumlin Roots Around The World
Donna Summer William Morris Inc (USA)
Mike Summerbee After Dinner World Ltd/Nigel Round Mgnt
Jason Summerfield Barrie Stacey Promos & Prods
Summerhill Folly Barn Dance Line Dance Agy
Bobby Summers Bobby Summers
Gene Summers Paul Barrett Rock'N'Roll Entp
Hilary Summers Ingpen & Williams Ltd
Kyle Summers Steve Allen Ents
Mike Summers Band Leo Mngt & Agy
Cassie Sumner Unleashed PR
Stuart Sumner Newton Wills Mngt
Sumo Wrestling PVA Ent Consultants
Sun Jets Quality Ents
Joe Sun Line Music Promotions
Sun, Sea & Sand (Steel Band) Yorkshire Ent
Sun Sea and Sand Band Book A Band
Sunblaze Steel Band Tony Bennell Ents
Sunburst Story Theatre Sunburst Story Thtre (Ind Art)
Adam Sunderland Amber Persnl Mngt Ltd
Sunfly Tony Bennell Ents
Mark Sung Sandra Singer Assoc
Chris Sunley Susan Angel Kevin Francis Ltd
Sunny Daye Creeme Ents/Tigger Blake
Sunshine CT Ents
Supafly Inc Action Talent Int.
Super 400 Universal/Island Records Ltd
Super Fast Oz UK Booking Agy
Super Furry Animals Best PR/The Agency Group
Super Jumper Daubney Variety & Gala Agcy Lt
Super Kings CeeBee Variety Agy
Super Troopers Essex Ent Agy
Super Troupers (Abba tribute) Jason West Agy/The Psycho Mngt Co Ltd
Superbad Head On Mngt
Superfly Continental Drifts/TEST AGENT C
Supergrass 13 Artists/The Psycho Mngt Co Ltd
Supernatural (Santana) Jason West Agy
Superphonic Ultimate Int'l
Superstition Andrew Beauchamp Mngt/Steve Allen Ents
Supertramp CODA Ltd
Piper Brian Supple PVA Ent Consultants
Supreme (Robbie Williams) Funhouse Productions Ltd/Hireaband Ltd
Robbie Supreme (Robbie Williams Tribute) Nigel Round Mgnt/Peller Artistes Ltd
The Supremes Brian Gannon

Mngt/Jason West Agy/Studio One Assoc/The Psycho Mngt Co Ltd/Tony Denton Promos Ltd
Alex Surguy Linkside Agy
Alan Suri Grays Mngt & Asc
Dave Surman LJ Ents
Nancy Surman Associated Arts
Surreal Madrid CODA Ltd
Surrender McLeod Agy Ltd
Survivor Brian Gannon Mngt
The Sus Sex Pistols Jason West Agy
Lolly Susi AIM
Sus-Sex Pistols Head On Mngt
Michelle Sutcliffe Fighting Talk Promos
Alex Sutherland Stag Ents
Ben Sutherland ICON Actors Mngt
Donald Sutherland Special Artists Agency
Jamie Sutherland CHAMPIONS (UK) PLC/Nigel Round Mgnt
Kiefer Sutherland Markham & Froggatt Ltd
Lachlan Sutherland Sandra Singer Assoc
Liz Sutherland Sandra Boyce Mngt
Michael Sutherland Derek Bruce Ents/Mike Malley Ents
Isobel Suttie APM Ass
Isy Suttie Avalon Mngt
Dudley Sutton BWH Agency
James Sutton Big Bang Mngt Ltd
Paul Sutton (Ronan Keating) Camscott Leisure/Funhouse Productions Ltd/Nigel Round Mgnt/SWA Ent/Stars In Your Eyes Ltd Ent Agy
Richard Sutton Nancy Hudson Associates Ltd
Mena Suvari Special Artists Agency
Sin Svegler Jeffrey & White
Sonia Swaby Talent Artists Ltd
Swags to Riches Bush Band ABDC Ents
Martyn Swain S M A Talent Ltd/SMA Talent Ltd
Rosie Swale PVA Ent Consultants/Persnly Spkng
Swami Nation Recs Ltd
Swamp Continental Drifts/TEST AGENT C
Swamp Circus Theatre CKK Ent
Billy Swan Paul Barrett Rock'N'Roll Entp
Flik Swan Narrow Road Company
Robert Swan OBE The London Spkr Bureau
Martha Swann Adrian King Assoc
Michelle De Swarte KBJ Management
Joe Swash Big Bang Mngt Ltd
Sway Prima Artists
Crispin Swayne Cunningham Mngt Ltd
The Sweat Band Book A Band
Keith Sweat ICM (USA)
Swede Dreams (Abba) Jason West Agy
Sweeney Compact Mngt & Ent Agy
Claire Sweeney Billy Marsh Assoc Ltd/NMP Live Ltd/Personal Management & Casting
Jamie Sweeney SCA Mngt
Jim Sweeney Troika Talent
Maureen Sweeney Nancy Hudson Associates Ltd
Mike Sweeney BULLET MANAGEMENT LIMITED/Nigel Round Mgnt/Shining Mngt Ltd
Phoebe Sweeney Nancy Hudson Associates Ltd
Sweet ABS Agy/BULLET MANAGEMENT LIMITED/Barry Collings Ents
The Sweet Brian Gannon Mngt
Sweet Jason West Agy/PVA Ent Consultants/Rock Artist Mngt
Sweet Dreams Owen Hughes Ents
Sweet Escape Garston Ents Ltd
Matthew Sweet Primary Talent Int'l
Shaun Sweet After Dinner Spkers & Com
Neal Swettenham Adrian King Assoc
Andrew Swift Peter Charlesworth & Assoc
Jeremy Swift ARG Management
Joe Swift Arlington Enterprises Ltd
Nick Swift Jeremy Hicks Assoc
Richard Swift Dog Day Press/Helter Skelter Agy Ltd/Supervision Management
Steve Swift Lime Actors Agy & Mngt Ltd
Swill & The Swaggerband Adastra
Walter Swinburn Jon Holmes Media Ltd
Clare Swinburne AIM
Swing 39 Les Hart (Southampton) Ents/PVA Ent Consultants
Swing Kings Int'l Mngt & Agy Ltd
Swing 'n' Sinatra Upbeat Mngt
Swinging at the Cotton Club The John Boddy Agency
The Swinging Blue Jeans BCM Promos Ltd
Swinging Blue Jeans BULLET MANAGEMENT LIMITED
The Swinging Blue Jeans Barry Collings Ents/Hal Carter Org
Swinging Blue Jeans Henderson Mngt
The Swinging Blue Jeans PVA Ent Consultants/Rock Artist Mngt/The John Boddy Agency
Tilda Swinton Hamilton Hodell Ltd
Tim Swinton Vincent Shaw Assoc Ltd
Anne Swithinbank Celebrity Appearances/Limelight Management
Alicia Swordes Links Mngt
Swound! One Fifteen
Meera Syal Peters Fraser Dunlop (PFD)/United Agents
Sybil Mission Control Artist Agy/Tony Denton Promos Ltd
Alice Sykes Independent Talent Group Ltd
Andrew Sykes Sandra Boyce Mngt
Melanie Sykes Hackford Jones PR/Inspirational Artiste Bkg/Money Management UK
Paul Sylvester (Mr Soulman) Trevor George Ents Ltd
Tamzin Sylvester Knight Ayton Mngt
Sylvester the Jester Derek Bruce Ents/The A6 Agy
Paul Symington Wendy Lee Mngt
Amanda Symonds Brian Taylor Assoc/Lip Service Casting Ltd
David Symonds Speak-Easy Ltd
Emily Symons AIM
Symphony X Miracle Artists Ltd
Sylvia Syms Brown & Simcocks
System 7 featuring Steve Hillage Value Added Talent Agy (VAT)
System X Peller Artistes Ltd
SYT Magick Eye Records
Magda Szabanski Markham & Froggatt Ltd
Szapora Matters Musical
Szymanowski Pro Artist Management

T

Jack T Nigel Round Mgnt
T Rex Brian Gannon Mngt/Rock Artist Mngt
T-Rextasy Andrew Beauchamp Mngt/Arena Ent Cons/Fab Prods/Henderson Mngt/Jason West Agy/John Hessenthaler Ents
T Rextasy Mark Lundquist Management & Co
T-Rextasy Michael La Roche Mngt
T Rextasy SWA Ent
T2 Action Talent Int.
Taala Matters Musical
Michel Tabachnik Patrick Garvey Mngt
Mark Tabbener Ultimate Int'l
Roger Tabor All Electric Productions & Dav
Adam Tabraham AXM
Tabu Int'l Mngt & Agy Ltd
Tacky Horror Show Andrew Beauchamp Mngt
Tafelmusik Clarion/Seven Muses
Patrick Taggart Indep Mngt Ltd
Val Tagger The Narrow Road Company Ltd
Bita Taghavi Vincent Shaw Assoc Ltd
Maggie Tagney Amber Persnl Mngt Ltd
Tim Tagora Mr Magic Ents (Magic)
Dalip Tahil CAM London
Taiko Drummers The John Boddy Agency
Taiko Meantime Matters Musical
Taiko to Tabla Matters Musical/Roots Around The World
The Tailgate Jazz Band Quality Ents
Teemu Tainio Sport Ent And Media Group
Johnny Tait Apple County
Julian Tait Anita Alraun Representation
Takaleed Matters Musical
Take 2 Sunshine Ents
Mickey Take Ultimate Int'l
Take Six Denis Vaughan Mngt
Take This Dansatak/The Psycho Mngt Co Ltd
George Takei COLE KITCHENN PRSN MGT
Kyoko Takezawa IMG Artists
Taking Back Sunday Helter Skelter Agy Ltd
Rachel Talalay CASAROTTO RAMSAY & ASSOCIATES
Fred Talbot David Anthony Promos
Ian Talbot Burnett Granger Assoc
Jasmine Talbot Agency K-Bis
Richard Talbot Arena Personal Mngt
Anu Tali Stafford Law
John Tallents Brian Taylor Assoc
The Tallis Scholars Hazard Chase Ltd
Talon (Eagles) Head On Mngt
Hayley Tamaddon Big Bang Mngt Ltd/Nigel Round Mgnt/The Narrow Road Company Ltd
Tamala Motown Gold Lee James Assoc Ltd
Tame Impala 13 Artists
Tame Valley (Brass) The A6 Agy
Tameka TMK Mngt & Agcy Ltd
Tamla Motion Global Ent Agy/Int'l Mngt & Agy Ltd/Jason West Agy
Tamla Motown Experience Graham Cole Mngt
Jimmy Tamley G Entertaining/Jimmy Tamley/Jungle Jim/NVB Ents/Norwich Artistes/PVA Ent Consultants/Tony Bennell Ents/Tony West Ents
Jimmy Tamlin Compact Mngt & Ent Agy
Mary Tamm Langford Assoc
Tammy NVB Ents
Tammy Jo Dave Woodbury Ents
Louis Tamone Langford Assoc
Tamzin Multi-Media Ents
Tandem Derek Bruce Ents
Steve Tandy After Dinner Spkers & Com/Derek Bruce Ents/Persnly Spkng
Louise Taney North One Mngt

Tang COFFEE ARTISTS
Muhai Tang IMG Artists
Tanglefoot Barn Dance Line Dance Agy
Tango Experience Latin Arts Serv (LAS)
Tango Passion The Flying Music Co Ltd
Tango Select Matters Musical
Tango Siempre/Subitango! Matters Musical
Manisha Tank Knight Ayton Mngt
Meryl Tankard Simpson Fox Assoc Ltd
Alex Tanner Alex Jay Persnl Mngt
James Tanner CHAMPIONS (UK) PLC
James & Chris Tanner Limelight Management
Roxanne Tanner Agency K-Bis
Pat Tansey Persnly Spkng
Patrick Tansey Derek Bruce Ents/The Horne Concert Agy
Tanya Gem Prods
Mariachi Tapatio Matters Musical
Los Tapatios Matters Musical
Tapestry Les Hart (Southampton) Ents
Tapestry of Music The A6 Agy
Ken Tappenden MBE Persnl Appearances
Tapping The Vein Miracle Artists Ltd
Tarantinos Head On Mngt
Jimmy Tarbuck OBE Int'l Artistes Ltd/Speakout
Liza Tarbuck RDF Management
Mauricio Taricco Athole Still Int'l Ltd/TEST AGENT A
William Tarmey Arena Ent Cons
Taro The Jester Stuart & Alan Fell (Ind Art)
Chris Tarrant Brian Maclaurin Agency/NMP Live Ltd/Prime Performers Ltd
Colin Tarrant Waring & Mckenna
Ingrid Tarrant First Artist Management
Tarrot Lee (Radio DJ) ENTERTAINMENT FX
Tartan Craic Andrew Beauchamp Mngt
A Taste of Honey BULLET MANAGEMENT LIMITED
Taste of Honey (Bee Gees Tribute) Apple County/G Entertaining/Henderson Mngt/Jason West Agy/Michael La Roche Mngt
A Taste Of Tina Trevor George Ents Ltd
Daniel Tatarsky Billboard Persnl Mngt
Catherine Tate Dawn Sedgwick Mngt/Taylor Herring Public Relation
Darren Tate UK Booking Agy
Mark Tate CKK Ent
Sid Tate The Horne Concert Agy
Georgina Tattersall Nyland Mngt
Tatty and Scruffy Continental Drifts/TEST AGENT C
Julia Taudevin Elinor Hilton Associates
Taurus Dave Woodbury Ents
Jim Tavare Avalon Mngt/NMP Live Ltd
Tavares BULLET MANAGEMENT LIMITED/Brian Gannon Mngt/Jason West Agy/Tony Denton Promos Ltd
Stephanie Tavernier Newton Wills Mngt
Taxi Pata Pata Monkeybiz Ent Agy
Taxi To The Ocean ABS Agy
Taya Man Monkeybiz Ent Agy
Kathy Tayler Jane Hughes Mngt
Gillian Taylforth Urban Associates Personal Mana
Allan Taylor Stoneyport Associates
Andy Taylor Frequency Media Group/Shepherd Mngt Ltd
Ann Taylor Ingpen & Williams Ltd
Laurie Taylor Band Laurie Taylor Ents Ltd
Ben Taylor Big Sister Promotions/Free Trade Agy
Blondell Taylor Sandra Boyce Mngt
Bob Taylor Compact Mngt & Ent Agy
Brian Taylor Barn Dance Line Dance Agy/Speakout
Cass Taylor Blackburn International
Davinia Taylor Money Management UK
Dean Taylor (Little Britain) Funhouse Productions Ltd/Many Faces of Dean Taylor
Dennis Taylor After Dinner World Ltd/CHAMPIONS (UK) PLC/Celebrity Appearances/McLeod Agy Ltd/NMP Live Ltd/PVA Ent Consultants/Persnl Appearances/Persnly Spkng/Speakout
Derek Taylor RDF Management
Fleur Taylor Noel Gay Artists Ltd
Gary Taylor Barrie Stacey Promos & Prods
Gavin Taylor Stafford Law
Giles Taylor Susan Angel Kevin Francis Ltd
Graham Taylor Persnl Appearances
Gwen Taylor Gavin Barker
Hamish Taylor NMP Live Ltd
Holland Taylor Special Artists Agency
Hugo Taylor Insanity Artists
JTQ James Taylor Quartet The Psycho Mngt Co Ltd
Jay Taylor Yellow Balloon Prods Ltd
Joanna Taylor Money Management UK
John Taylor Frequency Media Group/Persnl Appearances
Karen Taylor Avalon Mngt
Kerrie Taylor Shepherd Mngt Ltd
Laurie Taylor Gordon Poole Agy Ltd
Prof Laurie Taylor Arena Ent Cons/Persnly Spkng
Leon Taylor Doub7e Seven Events Ltd/MTC (UK) LTD
Lewis Taylor Universal/Island Records Ltd
Taylor Made Int'l Mngt & Agy Ltd
Maggie Taylor Audrey Benjamin Agy
Margherita Taylor Hackford Jones PR/James Grant Mngt Ltd/The Commercial Agency
Mark Taylor Liz Hobbs Grp Ltd/MPC Ent
Mark Taylor (Aus) MPC Ent
Martin Taylor Adastra
Maureen Taylor MBA
Michael Taylor Derek Bruce Ents
Mick Taylor Blues Band John Hessenthaler Ents
Mike Taylor (Solo Sax) CS Ents
Nathan Taylor Harvey Voices Ltd/Hilary Gagan Assoc
Pauline Taylor CMO Mngt Int'l Ltd
Phil Taylor CHAMPIONS (UK) PLC/MATCHROOM SPORT LTD/Nigel Round Mgnt/Nyland Mngt
James Taylor Quartet Jason West Agy/The John Boddy Agency
Richard Taylor Norwich Artistes
Rod Taylor After Dinner World Ltd/Gordon Robinson Assoc
Roger Taylor Frequency Media Group/G.A.A.
Ros Taylor Gordon Poole Agy Ltd
Russell Jarret & Simon Taylor Matters Musical
Sean Taylor Adastra
Shane Taylor Emptage Hallett Ltd
Stan Taylor Nigel Round Mgnt/Persnly Spkng/Tony Bennell Ents
Steven J Taylor Sunshine Ents
Stretch Taylor (Blues & Soul) UK Booking Agy
Cherie Taylor-Battiste Sandra Boyce Mngt
Ed Taylor-Gooby Inspiration Mngt
Tayo CODA Ltd/MPC Ent
Simon Tcherniak Dennis Lyne Agy
Te Vaka (Pacific Isles/New Zealand) Adastra
Tea For Three Quality Ents
The Tea Party ITB
Clare Teal The John Boddy Agency
Howard Teale Kerry Gardner Mngt
Owen Teale Markham & Froggatt Ltd
Sean Teale Insanity Artists
Lizzie Tear Harvey Voices Ltd
Robert Tear Askonas Holt Ltd
Tease NVB Ents
Teaser Goldstar Ent UK
Technotronic Mission Control Artist Agy
Patrick Tedbury PVA Ent Consultants
Teddybears Free Trade Agy
Teebee CODA Ltd
Teen Spirit (Nirvana tribute) Psycho Mngt Co Ltd/The Psycho Mngt Co Ltd
Teenage Fan Club Big Sister Promotions
Trond Teigen Anita Alraun Representation
Tejedor Firefly Productions
Izabella Telezynska Brian Taylor Assoc
Yuri Temirkanov IMG Artists
Temperance Be Damned Barn Dance Line Dance Agy
The Temperance Seven Jazzco/Keith Salberg Agy & Prods/The John Boddy Agency/Upbeat Mngt
Billy Tempest Mr Magic Ents (Magic)
Katherine Templar Paul Duddridge Mngt
Julien Temple CASAROTTO RAMSAY & ASSOCIATES
Juno Temple Troika Talent
Temple of Sound Autonomous Talent Bkg
Peter Temple Harvey Voices Ltd
Victoria Temple-Morris Paul Duddridge Mngt
Temples 13 Artists
James Templeton Adrian King Assoc
Temposharks What Mngt
The Temptations ICM (USA)/Ron Martin Mngt
Temptations Review With Dennis Edwards Brian Gannon Mngt/Jason West Agy
Tempting Fate Moonglight Agy
Ten Days Late Brian Yeates Assoc
Ten Years After Alan Cottam Agency/The Psycho Mngt Co Ltd
Paul Tennant Reality Check Management
Tennessee Tooters Steve Allen Ents
Chalee Tennison Buddy Lee Attrctns Inc (USA)
Helen Tennison APM Ass
Bradley (Tenor) Matters Musical
Caledon/Scottish Tenors All Electric Productions & Dav
Tenors Incognito CKK Ent/Matters Musical
Tenors Unlimited CKK Ent/Matters Musical
Tenpole Tudor Rock Artist Mngt
Tensai CKK Ent/Complete Ent Serv Ltd/PVA Ent Consultants/Tony West Ents
Tequila Slammers Doub7e Seven Events Ltd
Tequilaville David Charles Agy
David Terence Adrian King Assoc
Teresa McGinley (Louise Redknapp) Advanced Ents
Terrain G Entertaining
Hayley Terris Avalon Mngt

Terrorizer Miracle Artists Ltd
Terrorvision Free Trade Agy
Christopher Terry Actors Alliance
Terry Dactyl and the Dinosaurs Gables & TTH Mngt
Frank Terry (Charlie Chaplin) The A6 Agy
Mark Terry Fushion Pukka Bosh
Michelle Terry Brunskill Mngt Ltd
Terry Mills (Radio / Compare / DJ) ENTERTAINMENT FX
Ray Terry Band Paul Bailey Agy
Terry's Karaoke Disco David Forshaw Entp
Gary Terzza Speak-Easy Ltd
Test-Icicles Big Sister Promotions
Dan Tetsell RDF Management
Tewkesbury Town Band Derek Bruce Ents
Texus (Texas) Jason West Agy
Ayse Tezel Sandra Singer Assoc
TGK COFFEE ARTISTS
Th' Legendary Shack*Shackers Asgard
Hilary Thacker Hilary Thacker
Thank You For The Music Entertainers Mgt Ltd
That Swing Thang Cosmos Agy & Promos
Baroness Thatcher House Of Lords
That'll Be The Day - Touring Review Derek Block Concerts
Thats The Way it Was - Elvis Show - EXCLUSIVE
Yannis Thavoris Performing Arts
Roberta Thayne Nyland Mngt
The 007 Performers Doub7e Seven Events Ltd
The Ailerons CMO Mngt Int'l Ltd
The Alexander Brothers BGS PRODUCTIONS
The Alias Insanity Artists
The Amazing Magnus The A6 Agy
The Amazing Martin (Escapology & Thrills) Mr Magic Ents (Magic)
The Amusing Sister Ruth! Edge Ent Cons Ltd/MTM Presntns/Spotlight Ents
The Amusionist Uncle Peter Magic Show (Magic)
The Androids Primary Talent Int'l
The Answer Scream Promotions
The Automatic Big Sister Promotions
The Banderas Border Leisure
The Be Be See CEC Management
The Beach boys Inc Advanced Ents
The Beat Up Big Sister Promotions
The beehives Advanced Ents
The Best of Joyce Grenfell David Coleman
The Big Blowout Band Blowout Sax
The Big Deal Elite Promos
The Big Pink Insanity Artists
The Black Maria Primary Talent Int'l
The Bluetones CRUISIN' MUSIC/Cooking Vinyl/Doub7e Seven Events Ltd
The Bond Girls Doub7e Seven Events Ltd
The Bootleg Shadows Global Ent Agy
The Bootleggers (covers) Doub7e Seven Events Ltd
The Boy Least Likely To Free Trade Agy
The Boys Next Door CHAMPIONS (UK) PLC
The Bright Space Free Trade Agy
The Broken Family Band Free Trade Agy
The Bronx Big Sister Promotions/MVO Ltd
The Bruvvers The John Boddy Agency
The Cameleonz Insanity Artists
The Casino Band The Ents Agency
The Chancers Advanced Ents
The Chemical Brothers Pivotal PR
The Chicago Blues Brothers Derek Block Concerts/Lee James Assoc Ltd
The Chieftains Asgard
The Christians Jason West Agy
The Citrus Brothers Prima Artists
The Collective Mike Malley Ents
The Concretes EC1 Music Agency
The Conspirators Sunshine Ents
The Crystals Chimes Int'l Ents Ltd
The Curvettes Dansatak/Lee James Assoc Ltd
The Dark Poets Some Bizarre Ltd
The Decemberists Free Trade Agy
The Divine Comedy 13 Artists
The Dixie Four The John Boddy Agency
The Dolly Parton Story David Coleman
The Dropkick Murphys Primary Talent Int'l
The Dufay Collective Upbeat Classical Mngt
The Eighties Matchbox B-Line Disaster CEC Management/Primary Talent Int'l
The Exploders Gold Star PR
The Fabs Hireaband Ltd
The Fabulous Baker Brothers CHAMPIONS (UK) PLC
The Fall Dorothy Howe Publicity & Press
The Father Teds Brian Yeates Assoc
The Fillers The Psycho Mngt Co Ltd
The First Class Tony Bennell Ents
The Five Browns IMG Artists
The Flanders and Swann Show Milton Keynes Theatre of Comed
The Flirts Dansatak
The Frames Free Trade Agy
The Frank and Dean Show Doub7e Seven Events Ltd
The Fratelli's ITB
The Freelance Hellraiser CODA Ltd
The Full Shabang Stables Ents
The Funsters Advanced Ents
The Future Sound of London Freedom Management
The Futureheads Alan James PR Agency/Best PR/Big Life Management
The Gangsters Of Ska Devil Management
The Gap Band Eleventh Hour Mngt Ltd
The Glenn Miller Orchestra UK Upbeat Mngt
The Glenn Miller Tribute Orchestra David Coleman/Upbeat Mngt
The Go Primary Talent Int'l
The Grainger String Quartet ABDC Ents
The Guild Freedom Management
The Headless Lady Mr Magic Ents (Magic)
The Heartbreakers Purple PR
The Human Jukebox Sardi's Int'l Ent
The Inflations Angle Ents Ltd
The Ivories Big Sister Promotions
The Jazz Canons LM2 Entertainment
The Jones Gang Mark Lundquist Management & Co
The Ken Colyer Legacy New Orleans Jazz Band Upbeat Mngt
The Kit-Kat Dolls (Transexual Group) Alan Whitehead Mngt Ltd
The Krystalettes CHAMPIONS (UK) PLC
The Larry Loveband Value Added Talent Agy (VAT)
The Levellers The Psycho Mngt Co Ltd
The Lex Icon Corporation Yorkshire Ent
The Light Brigade Ceilidh Band ABDC Ents
The Likeness Head On Mngt
The Little Ones Free Trade Agy
The Maccabees 13 Artists/Insanity Artists/Toast Press
The Macdonald Brothers (X-factor contestants) Hireaband Ltd
The Magic Numbers 13 Artists
The Magic Waiters Whatever Artists Mngt Ltd
The Maida Vale Singers Whatever Artists Mngt Ltd
The Masqueraders (5 piece) Stellamax Entp Ltd
The Members Of The Spoof Paparazzi Doub7e Seven Events Ltd
The Men They Couldn't Hang Adastra
The Mend Insanity Artists
The Mescalites Scream Promotions
The Mob Advanced Ents
The Mooney Suzuki MVO Ltd
The Morning After Girls Scream Promotions
The Motorettes Kitchenware Mngt
The Move Brian Yeates Assoc
The New Amen Corner Direct Music Mngt Ltd
The Nextmen Elastic Artists Agency Ltd
The On Offs CEC Management
The Only Way Is Essex CHAMPIONS (UK) PLC/Insanity Artists
The Ordinary Boys Big Sister Promotions
The O'Reely's London Music Agy
The Organist Entertains Upbeat Mngt
The Oscar Performers Doub7e Seven Events Ltd
The Others CEC Management
The Outhere Bros Mission Control Artist Agy
The Paul Weller Experience Head On Mngt
The Perishers Big Sister Promotions/Helter Skelter Agy Ltd
The Pete Allen Jazz Band Upbeat Mngt
The Pioneers EC1 Music Agency
The Pipettes Alan James PR Agency/Nettwerk Management/Primary Talent Int'l
The Pistolas Supervision Management
The Platters Personality Artistes Ltd
The Presnyakov Brothers Judy Daish Assoc
The Pretend Pretenders Matters Musical
The Race Big Sister Promotions
The Real Thing BULLET MANAGEMENT LIMITED/The Psycho Mngt Co Ltd/Tony Denton Promos Ltd
(The Real) Tuesday Weld Big Sister Promotions
The receders Advanced Ents
The Red Hot Silli Feckers Jason West Agy
The Reservoir Cats Paul Barrett Rock'N'Roll Entp
The Rhythm Makers (Steel Band) ABC Direct Ents
The Rifles Big Sister Promotions
The Risk CHAMPIONS (UK) PLC
The Riverbrew Advanced Ents
The Royal Blues Brothers Upfront Ent Agy Ltd
The RPJ Band CHAMPIONS (UK) PLC
The Rumble Strips Insanity Artists
The Rushes CMO Mngt Int'l Ltd
The Saturdays CHAMPIONS (UK) PLC
The Secret's Out (party band) Apple County
The Select Syncopators Jazz Ensemble Austin Baptiste Ent Agy Ltd
The Silent Kingdom RED ADMIRAL RECORDS

The SJs (soul band) Stables Ents
The Snow Queen David Coleman
The Soho Dolls Helter Skelter Agy Ltd
The Soul Funksters BCM Promos Ltd
The Soul Kings Hireaband Ltd
The Sound Explosion Big Sister Promotions
The Specials The Psycho Mngt Co Ltd
The Spurting Man Fools Paradise
The Stargazers Paul Barrett Rock'N'Roll Entp
The Strollers Paul Barrett Rock'N'Roll Entp
The Stylites Advanced Ents
The Subways Alan James PR Agency/Gailforce Mngt Ltd
The Summer Of Love Direct Music Mngt Ltd
The Sunshine Underground Big Sister Promotions
The Swains Scott Mackenzie Assoc
the Sweet Soul Music Band Angle Ents Ltd
The Switches CEC Management
The Television Personalities Big Sister Promotions
The Temple Brothers Play Everly BCM Promos Ltd
The Tetleys Sunshine Ents
The The Free Trade Agy
The Three Bs - Ball, Barbra & Bilk The John Boddy Agency
The Three Waiters Fanfare 3000/Whatever Artists Mngt Ltd
The Timeless Orchestra Wim Wigt Prodns Ltd
The Ting Tings Purple PR
The Tom Lehrer Show Milton Keynes Theatre of Comed
The Tootsie Rollers CHAMPIONS (UK) PLC
The Two Beatles LRO Artist Mngt
The Undertones The Agency Group
The Untouchables CT Ents
The Unusual Suspects Adastra
The Upbeat Beatles CHAMPIONS (UK) PLC
The Upside Down Band (Ecclectic) Doub7e Seven Events Ltd
The Vicster Sunshine Ents
The View ITB
The Vox Lirika Opera Company David Coleman
The Wideboys Action Talent Int./Mission Control Artist Agy
The Wise Guys Brian Yeates Assoc
The Wombats Insanity Artists
The World of the Bee Gees The John Boddy Agency
The World Quintet (FKA Kol Simcha) (Klezmer band) Upbeat Classical Mngt
The Wrong Size Stiltwalkers Whatever Artists Mngt Ltd
The XFM Band The Psycho Mngt Co Ltd
The X-Men Big Bang Mngt Ltd
The Zico Chain CEC Management
Jamie Theakston ARG Management/Lip Service Casting Ltd/Prime Performers Ltd
Theatre Of Adventure Continental Drifts/TEST AGENT C
Them People Them People (Ind Art)
Theme Park 13 Artists
Themoula Fushion Pukka Bosh
Thepetebox Insanity Artists
Therapy? Helter Skelter Agy Ltd
There Only Make Believe David Coleman
Louis Theroux Capel & Land
Marcel Theroux KBJ Management
These New Puritans 13 Artists
They Might Be Giants Free Trade Agy
They Will Rock You Entertainers Mgt Ltd
Sophia Thierens Burnett Granger Assoc
Thin Lizzy John Hessenthaler Ents/Rock Artist Mngt/The Agency Group
Thingumajig Barn Dance Line Dance Agy/Matters Musical
Think Floyd Andrew Beauchamp Mngt/Head On Mngt/Jason West Agy
Think Twice NVB Ents
Thirsty Work Barn Dance Line Dance Agy
Thirteen Senses 13 Artists
This Way Up CT Ents
Thistle Dubh Ceilidh Band Hireaband Ltd
Ian Thom John Field - Theatre and Puppe
Sandi Thom Helter Skelter Agy Ltd
Abigail Thomas Seamus Lyte Management Ltd
Adam Thomas AIM
Anstey Thomas Grays Mngt & Asc
Bethan Thomas BAM Assoc Ltd
BJ Thomas Chimes Int'l Ents Ltd
Carryl Thomas Gavin Barker
Catherine Thomas Quality Ents
Dan Thomas CKK Ent
Delyth Thomas Judy Daish Assoc
Drew Thomas Judy Daish Assoc
Ebony Thomas Rossmore Persnl Mngt
Gareth Thomas Emptage Hallett Ltd
Gloria Thomas Take Three Mngt
Ian Thomas All Star Spkrs/Ian Thomas Org
Ione Thomas CHAMPIONS (UK) PLC
Ivan Thomas Take Three Mngt
Iwan Thomas CHAMPIONS (UK) PLC/Nuff Respect
Jacob Dylan Thomas Frontline Mngt Ltd
Jerome Thomas Sport Ent And Media Group
Jerry Thomas G Entertaining/Persnl Appearances
Joe Thomas Chris Gordon Theatrical Agy
John Thomas Candle
Katherine Thomas Derek Bruce Ents
Kenny Thomas Barry Collings Ents/Big Bang Mngt Ltd/Henderson Mngt/Jason West Agy/Mission Control Artist Agy/Tony Denton Promos Ltd
Keziah Thomas London Music Agy
Mark Thomas Phil McIntyre Ent. Ltd
Michael Tilson Thomas International Classical Artist
Mickey Thomas Persnl Appearances
Micky Thomas Nigel Round Mgnt
Rhys Thomas PBJ Mngt Ltd
Ruddy Thomas Monkeybiz Ent Agy
Ryan Thomas (Jason, Coronation Street) Melody Thresh Mngt Assoc Ltd/Nigel Round Mgnt
Sarah Thomas Langford Assoc
Simon Thomas CAM London
Steve Thomas UK Booking Agy
Tommy Thomas Norwich Artistes
Zoe Thomas Circuit Persnl Mngt Ltd
Marsha Thomason ARG Management
Ben Thompson Linton Mngt
Blair Thompson Albert Alchemy Ent
Bruce Thompson Derek Bruce Ents/Stardust Ents Agy/The A6 Agy
Carl Thompson Nigel Round Mgnt
Charlotte Thompson West Central Mngt
Dame Tanni Grey Thompson OBE Persnl Appearances/Persnly Spkng
David Thompson Sport Ent And Media Group
Derek Thompson CHAMPIONS (UK) PLC/Jonathan Altaras Assoc/Liz Hobbs Grp Ltd/Persnl Appearances
Emma Thompson Hamilton Hodell Ltd
Geoff Thompson RDF Management
Georgie Thompson Somethin' Else
Ian Thompson Athole Still Int'l Ltd/TEST AGENT A
Jemma Thompson ICON Actors Mngt
Jennifer Thompson Shining Mngt Ltd
Joanne Thompson Dinosaur Promo/Dinosaur Mus
The Johnny Thompson Singers (USA) Wim Wigt Prodns Ltd
Lawrie Thompson Kevin King Mngt
Lee Thompson CKK Ent
Mark Thompson Simpson Fox Assoc Ltd
Michael Thompson Patrick Garvey Mngt
Michael Thompson Wind Quartet Patrick Garvey Mngt
Nick Thompson Prof Sports Ptnr Ltd
Phil Thompson Nigel Round Mgnt
Richard Thompson Asgard/Cooking Vinyl
Shelley Thompson Sara Crouch Mngt
Vernon Thompson Peter Charlesworth & Assoc
Wendy Dawn Thompson Ingpen & Williams Ltd
Willie Thompson NVB Ents
Ulrich Thomsen Troika Talent
Alex Thomson Knight Ayton Mngt
Ali Thomson Sarm Mngt
Gabriel Thomson Hamilton Hodell Ltd
John Thomson ARG Management
Richard Thomson The Richard Stone Prtnrshp
Daley Thopmson CBE CHAMPIONS (UK) PLC/Speakout
George Thorby Orchestra NVB Ents
Rebecca Thorn The Richard Stone Prtnrshp
Angela Thorne Shepherd Mngt Ltd
Jane Thorne Actors Alliance
Jennifer Thorne West Central Mngt
Michelle Thorne Identity One Management
Paul Thorne The Richard Stone Prtnrshp
Willie Thorne CHAMPIONS (UK) PLC/Paul Bridson Prods/Peller Artistes Ltd/Persnl Appearances/Persnly Spkng/Speakout
Lisa Thorner Talent Artists Ltd
Emma Thornett Arena Personal Mngt
The Thorns ITB
Benjamin Thornton Agency K-Bis
Danny Thornton Lime Actors Agy & Mngt Ltd
Frank Thornton Daly Pearson Associates
Kate Thornton Troika Talent
Patrick Thornton Inspiration Mngt
Maurice Thorogood Orvad Enterprises
Richard Thorp Daly Pearson Associates
Simon Thorp ANA
Will Thorp Gavin Barker
Edward Thorpe Barrie Stacey Promos & Prods
Harriet Thorpe Gavin Barker
Marianne Thorsen Ingpen & Williams Ltd
Those Were the Days - With Rosemary Squires Upbeat Mngt
Thoughts of Chairman Alf (Warren Mitchell) Johnny Mans Prods Ltd
The Three Bees (official Bee Gees tribute band) MGA Entp
The Three British Tenors PVA Ent Consultants

Three B's (Tribute to the Bee Gees) Jason West Agy
Three Degrees Barry Collings Ents/Brian Gannon Mngt/Jason West Agy/Studio One Assoc/Tony Denton Promos Ltd
Three Men and a Bass (Rock & Pop) Book A Band/Doub7e Seven Events Ltd
Three Tenors In Concert - Tenorissimo David Coleman
Three, The Real McKoy Int'l Mngt & Agy Ltd
Threepenny Bit Entertainers Mgt Ltd
Three's Company Sardi's Int'l Ent
David Threlfall Chatto & Linnit Ltd
Annabel Thrower Grays Mngt & Asc
Thumpasaurus Jason West Agy
Thunderclap Newman Alan Cottam Agency/Jason West Agy
Claire Thurgood Daly Pearson Associates
Sophie Thursfield Brunskill Management Ltd
Philip Thurston Candle
Tiamat Miracle Artists Ltd
Jeremy Tiang West Central Mngt
Tiare Tahiti PVA Ent Consultants/Rent-A-Band
Kathryn Tickell Park Promotions
Jon Tickle Princess Talent Mngt
Ticklish Allsorts ABDC Ents
Andrew Tiernan Troika Talent
Malcolm Tierney Gavin Barker
Tiga Big Sister Promotions
Tiger Universal/Island Records Ltd
Tiger Lillies Primary Talent Int'l
Charlie Tighe Adrian King Assoc
Darren Tighe Talking Heads - The Voice Agy
Tight Fit Pete Mitchell Associates
Tight Squeeze Barn Dance Line Dance Agy
Glenn Tilbrook The Agency Group
Paula Tilbrook Big Bang Mngt Ltd
Peter Tilbury Jill Foster Ltd
Tilly and the Wall Best PR
Peter Tilly Rosebery Mngt
David Tilt Derek Bruce Ents
Tim Burgess Insanity Artists
Britney One More Time Prima Artists
The Time Machine The Psycho Mngt Co Ltd
Time of Your LIfe Barn Dance Line Dance Agy
Time Slip Devil Management
Time Warped (Rocky Horror Tribute) Peller Artistes Ltd
Timespan Sunshine Ents
Timotei Animal World
Neil Timothy Sunshine Ents
Tina Dave Woodbury Ents/Derek Bruce Ents/NVB Ents
Tina Turn Compact Mngt & Ent Agy
Tindersticks Asgard/Universal/Island Records Ltd
Norman Tinsel The A6 Agy
Tipitina Big Bear Music
Michael Tipper Parliament Comms
Aaron Tippin Buddy Lee Attrctns Inc (USA)
Brian Tipping Peter Charlesworth & Assoc
Jenny Tiramani Performing Arts
Tricky Ricky Partyweb.co.uk
Chris Tisdall Avalon Mngt
Rob Tissera (Quake) UK Booking Agy
Matt le Tissier CHAMPIONS (UK) PLC
Matthew Le Tissier MERLIN ELITE/Sport Ent And Media Group
Titan Whatever Artists Mngt Ltd
Titanic Ensemble (B) Wim Wigt Prodns Ltd
Titanic Tea Room Quartet PVA Ent Consultants
Alan Titchmarsh Arlington Enterprises Ltd/Trading Faces Ltd
Abi Titmuss Money Management UK/Taylor Herring Public Relation
Elliott Tittensor (Carl, Shamless) Nigel Round Mgnt
Elliot Tittensor Linton Mngt
Luke Tittensor Linton Mngt
The Tivoli String Trio / Quartet David Forshaw Entp
Ray Tizzard Int'l Artistes Ltd
Derek Tobias Audrey Benjamin Agy
Toby Tobias Lena Davis/John Bishop Assoc
Amon Tobin CODA Ltd
Jesse Tobin Panic Management
Liam Tobin RBA Management Ltd
Tony Tobin Deborah McKenna Ltd
Jeremy Todd Barrie Stacey Promos & Prods
Richard Todd The Richard Stone Prtnrshp
Sian Todd Argyle Assoc
Tofi The Clown Ian & Friends
Kara Tointon Big Bang Mngt Ltd
Natalie Du Toit MPC Ent
Sandi Toksvig Peters Fraser Dunlop (PFD)/Speakout/United Agents
Gill Tolliday Les Hart (Southampton) Ents
Alexandra Tolstoy Independent Talent Group Ltd
Tom The Voice BULLET MANAGEMENT LIMITED/The Psycho Mngt Co Ltd
Tómas Tómasson Athole Still Int'l Ltd/TEST AGENT A
Tombo the Clown Derek Bruce Ents
Frances Tomelty Cassie Mayer Ltd/Lip Service Casting Ltd
Carolyn Tomkinson Actorum
Lily Tomlin William Morris Inc (USA)
Sir John Tomlinson Music Int'l
Ricky Tomlinson Action Talent Int./Non Stop Ents/Nyland Mngt/Paul Bridson Prods
Scott Tomlinson The A6 Agy
Martin Tomms ICON Actors Mngt
Paul F Tompkins Avalon Mngt
Ronnie Toms APM Ass
Steve Toms Form Talent
Sally Tomsett Kenneth Earle Persnl Mngt
Bob Tomson Brunskill Mngt Ltd
John Tomson Nigel Round Mgnt
Philippa Tomson Speak-Easy Ltd
Tom-Tastic (Tom Jones Tribute) Peller Artistes Ltd
Tonbridge Pipes & Drums Sardi's Int'l Ent
Bruno Tonioli Michael Summerton Mngt
Toni's Accordian Sound Rent-A-Band
Paul Tonkinson Comedy Store Mngt/Karushi Mngt
Tony Christie Chris Davis Management/Republic Media
Tony Xu Direct Persnl Mngt
Too Darn Hot Matters Musical/Upbeat Entertainment
Too Hot to Handle CS Ents
Too Special Caledonian Music Agy
Stanley Toohey London Music Agy
Robert Took Direct Persnl Mngt
Tool ITB
David Toole Direct Persnl Mngt
Claire Toomey Free Trade Agy
Patrick Toomey Kerry Gardner Mngt
Peter Toon North Of Watford Actors Agy
Top Catz PVA Ent Consultants
Top Hat 'N Tales The CBS Grp
Top Secret Beatles Advanced Ents
Top Tunes Disco David Forshaw Entp
Jenny-Ann Topham M W Management
Paul Topham LJ Ents
Toploader Freud Comms
Jenny Topp Reality Check Management
Mister Topper Devil Management
TOPS 13 Artists
Bryan Torfeh Hilary Gagan Assoc
The Tornados BCM Promos Ltd/Graham Cole Mngt/John Hessenthaler Ents/PVA Ent Consultants
Benicio Del Toro Special Artists Agency
John Torode CHAMPIONS (UK) PLC/Deborah McKenna Ltd/Talent4 Media Ltd
Tim Torode (Marc Bolan) Jason West Agy
Sam Torrance CHAMPIONS (UK) PLC/Trading Faces Ltd
Joe Torry William Morris Inc (USA)
Yan Pascal Tortelier IMG Artists
Andrew Tortise International Classical Artist
Torvill and Dean SWA Ent
Toss Whatever Artists Mngt Ltd
Total Beach Boys Funhouse Productions Ltd
Toto la Momposina Roots Around The World
Sarah Totty Lime Actors Agy & Mngt Ltd
Touch & Go Int'l Mngt & Agy Ltd
Touch of Innocence Talent One
Touche Norwich Artistes
Touriste Deluxxe Management
Tournament CS Ents
Sylvestra Le Touzel Markham & Froggatt Ltd
Bramwell Tovey IMG Artists
Rachael Tovey Opera & Concert Artists
Harry Towb Talking Heads - The Voice Agy
Tower Of Power Primary Talent Int'l/William Morris Inc (USA)
Princes In The Tower Matters Musical
Alan Towers The Horne Concert Agy
Towers Of London Hall Or Nothing/ITB
Justyn Towler ICON Actors Mngt
Johanna Town Clare Vidal-Hall
Oliver Townend Prof Sports Ptnr Ltd
Sam Townend Lime Actors Agy & Mngt Ltd
Graham Townsend North One Mngt
Paul Townsend Grays Mngt & Asc
Stuart Townsend Endeavor Agency
Toxic Twins (Aerosmith) Jason West Agy
Toy Dolls Primary Talent Int'l
Toyah The Psycho Mngt Co Ltd/Tony Denton Promos Ltd
Polly Toynbee Gordon Poole Agy Ltd
T'Pau Brian Gannon Mngt/Jason West Agy/Tony Denton Promos Ltd
Tracer The Ents Agency
Stan Tracey Quartet Jazzco
Stan Tracey The John Boddy Agency
Stan Tracey Octet Jazzco
Ven Tracey Creeme Ents
Venn Tracey Nigel Round Mgnt
Trade 2 Universal/Island Records Ltd
The Traditional Punch & Judy Show Mr "E" Ents
The Tragically Hip Helter Skelter Agy Ltd
Train ITB
Michelle Trainer Celebn Model Mngt
Trammps Tony Denton Promos Ltd

Lisa Tramontin Grays Mngt & Asc
Trans Am CODA Ltd/Hermana PR
Transglobal Underground Nation Recs Ltd
The Transsylvanians Roots Around The World
Tranters Folly Barn Dance Line Dance Agy
Isla Traquair Speakout
Trash The Flying Music Co Ltd
Traveling Lite Disco David Forshaw Entp
Lily Travers Brunskill Mngt Ltd
Pat Travers Band AIM Inc (USA)
Travesty Head On Mngt
Travis Big Sister Promotions/Helter Skelter Agy Ltd/Sainted PR
Gus Travis David Forshaw Entp
Steve Travis John Hessenthaler Ents
Will Travis Shepherd Mngt Ltd
William Travis Jonathan Altaras Assoc
Travissing Andrew Beauchamp Mngt
Trebeka Matters Musical
Lucy Tregear Gavin Barker
Donald Trelford Celebrity Appearances
The Tremeloes BULLET MANAGEMENT LIMITED/Barry Collings Ents/Brian Gannon Mngt/Compact Mngt & Ent Agy/Entertainers Mgt Ltd/Hal Carter Org
Tremeloes Henderson Mngt
The Tremeloes Jason West Agy/PVA Ent Consultants/Paul Bridson Prods/Rock Artist Mngt/The John Boddy Agency
Martin Trenaman CASAROTTO RAMSAY & ASSOCIATES
Camilla Trench Agency K-Bis
Trenchtown Experience (Bob Marley & The Wailers tribute) Entertainers Mgt Ltd/Jason West Agy/Matters Musical/Tropical Ents Mngt Agy
Jean Trend ANA
Trendsetter Disco NVB Ents
Trendspotting Andrew Beauchamp Mngt
Mark Trent Sunshine Ents
Martin Trent Elinor Hilton Associates
Trent Valley Stompers Quality Ents
Trev and Simon RDF Management
Trevor, Cueball & Ros MPC Ent
Trevor Woodman MBE Nuff Respect
Gerry Trew (Rod Stewart) Entertainers Mgt Ltd/Funhouse Productions Ltd/Peller Artistes Ltd/SWA Ent/Stars In Your Eyes Ltd Ent Agy
T-Rex Major Ent Agy
T.Rextacy Head On Mngt/The John Boddy Agency
Triangle Derek Bruce Ents
The Goldrush (Crosby, Stills & Nash tribute) Matters Musical
Tribute To Joe Cocker Andrew Beauchamp Mngt
Tribute To Chris De Burgh Alan James
Tribute To John Lennon Alan James
Tribute To The Carpenters Brian Gannon Mngt/John Hessenthaler Ents
Tribute to the Supremes Graham Cole Mngt
Tribute To The Tops Entertainers Mgt Ltd
Tribute Two (Sinatra, Dean Martin, Neil Diamond) Pete Mitchell Associates
David Trick After Dinner World Ltd/Persnl Appearances
Tricks of the Trade McLeod Agy Ltd
Trickstars Anglia Artistes
Tricky Primary Talent Int'l/Universal/Island Records Ltd
Joachim Trier CASAROTTO RAMSAY & ASSOCIATES
Thomas Trilby CKK Ent
Trilogy Border Leisure
Lord David Trimble Speakout
Trinidad Steel Band Roots Around The World
Trinity Advanced Ents/Dave Woodbury Ents
London Trio Matters Musical
Trio Wanderer Pro Artist Management
Trion Con Brio (classical) Apple County
Triple Cream Dings Ent/NVB Ents/Norwich Artistes/Triple Cream Ents
Triple 'X' Showgirls David Charles Agy
Sally Ann Triplett Burnett Granger Assoc
Lauren Tritton Direct Persnl Mngt
Triumph Band Barn Dance Line Dance Agy
Triumph Motors RBL Pipe Band Derek Bruce Ents
Trixie Dave Woodbury Ents
The Troggs BULLET MANAGEMENT LIMITED/Brian Gannon Mngt/Denis Vaughan Mngt/Derek Franks Org/Entertainers Mgt Ltd/Hal Carter Org
Troggs Henderson Mngt
The Troggs PVA Ent Consultants/Paul Bridson Prods/Rock Artist Mngt/Stan Green Mngt
Troika Rent-A-Band
Joanna Trollope Peters Fraser Dunlop (PFD)
The Trolls Galaxy Evts
Tropical Heat CS Ents
Tropical Heatwave Complete Ent Serv Ltd/Tony Bennell Ents
Tropical Islanders Steel Band Derek Bruce Ents/Midland Ent & Mgnt Ltd/Norman Phillips Org Ltd
Tropical Sound CS Ents
Tropical Storm Matters Musical/Tropical Ents Mngt Agy
Tropicalia Band CS Ents
Tropicalisimo (Latin Show) Latin Arts Serv (LAS)
Mark Trotman M W Management
Laura Trott CHAMPIONS (UK) PLC
Del Boy Trotter Henderson Mngt
Thomas Trotter Patrick Garvey Mngt
David Troughton Markham & Froggatt Ltd
Jim Troughton PARAGON SPORTS MANAGEMENT LTD
Sam Troughton Markham & Froggatt Ltd
Nikki Trow Sandra Singer Assoc
Verne Troyer Hyper Agency
Simon Trpceski IMG Artists
Trubalsom UK Booking Agy
Simeon Truby Amber Persnl Mngt Ltd
Freddie Trueman OBE PVA Ent Consultants
Tommy Truesdale BGS PRODUCTIONS
Trumble Viscount Ents
Trumpeters of London Matters Musical
Trunkles Ceilidh Band Hire-A-Band Ent Agy
Matthew Trusler Hazard Chase Ltd
Truss & Bucket Band Matters Musical
The Truth CeeBee Variety Agy
The Trybe Satellite Artists Ltd
Alex Tsander Alex Tsander (Ind Art)
Angelo Tsarouchas Off The Kerb Prods
Sam Tsui Insanity Artists
Travelling By Tuba Matters Musical
Tuck & Patti Primary Talent Int'l
Tucker Brian Marshall Mngt/Tony Clayman Promos
Jane Tucker Royce Mngt
Kevin Tucker The Narrow Road Company Ltd
Kiah Ross Tucker Speak-Easy Ltd
Lennie Tucker Associated Arts
Lydia Tuckey Performance Actors Agy
Phil Tufnell CHAMPIONS (UK) PLC/NMP Live Ltd/PARAGON SPORTS MANAGEMENT LTD
Tulisa Contostavlos CHAMPIONS (UK) PLC/COLE KITCHENN PRSN MGT
Jethro Tull William Morris Inc (USA)
DJ Andy Tullett KM Ents
Nicola Tully Sandra Boyce Mngt
Susan Tully Saraband Assoc
Tumbledown Dick Tony Bennell Ents
Tunde Free Trade Agy
Tommy Tune ICM (USA)
Jayne Tunnicliffe RDF Management
KT Tunstall Big Sister Promotions/Dave Woolf PR/Pivotal PR
Helen Turaya Northern Lights Mngt
Turbozone Continental Drifts/TEST AGENT C
Mike Turiansky Speak-Easy Ltd
Turin Brakes CMO Mngt Int'l Ltd
Siren Turkesh Nancy Hudson Associates Ltd
Turktown Troupers Barn Dance Line Dance Agy
Turn Back Time (Cher Tribute) Peller Artistes Ltd
Turn It Loose European Artistes Mngt
Mark-Anthony Turnage International Classical Artist
Shirley Ann Turnbull MJE Mngt
Andrew Turner Celebrity Chefs UK
Anthea Turner RDF Management
Beverley Turner Arlington Enterprises Ltd
Brian Turner CHAMPIONS (UK) PLC/Persnly Spkng
Chris Turner Barn Dance Line Dance Agy
The Chris Turner Band The Chris Turner Band(Ind Art)
Dylan Turner AIM
Evelyn Turner Daly Pearson Associates
Jeff Turner MCS Agcy
Jessica Turner Jonathan Altaras Assoc
John Turner -Retired Daly Pearson Associates
Juliet Turner SOLITAIRE MGT & INT AGCY
Lacey Turner Big Bang Mngt Ltd
Leo Turner The Horne Concert Agy
Lowri Turner Noel Gay Artists Ltd
Martin Turner Kerry Gardner Mngt
Niki Turner Clare Vidal-Hall
Ruby Turner Jason West Agy/Miracle Artists Ltd
Ryan Turner LRO Artist Mngt
Sherill Turner MBA/North Of Watford Actors Agy
Simon Turner Sandra Boyce Mngt
Stephanie Turner Kerry Gardner Mngt
Stuart Turner PVA Ent Consultants/Persnl Appearances
Tina Turner Rock Steady Management Agency
Tina Turner Tribute Band Graham Cole Mngt
Trik Turner COFFEE ARTISTS
Zara Turner Yakety Yak
Jeremy Turner-Welch Louise Hillman/Katie Threlfall
Turning Point Mike Constantia Artiste Mngt L
Alicia Turrell Agency K-Bis
Alison Turvey - The Paper Artist The Roving Artist

Claire Turvey North One Mngt
Philippa Tuttiett Curtis Brown Grp
Tutto Matto Athole Still Int'l Ltd/TEST AGENT A
Archbishop Desmond Tutu American Program Bureau
Linda Tuvas Music Int'l
Tuxedo Class Disco Crown Ents/Matters Musical
Tuxedo Junction Sardi's Int'l Ent
Tuyo - Hand Balancers Whatever Artists Mngt Ltd
TV Smith Rock Artist Mngt
Tweedy & Alexis CKK Ent
Matchbox Twenty ITB
Twice Shy Moonglight Agy
Twilight Zone Disco The CBS Grp
Twinkle PVA Ent Consultants
Twist & Shout Sunshine Ents
Colin Twist Jae Moss Entp
Two Gallants Free Trade Agy
Two Hearts Derek Bruce Ents
Two Hot Cliff Matthews Mngt & Ent Agy
Two Left Feet Barn Dance Line Dance Agy
Two Out Of Three The Dixon Agy
Two Tone Collective (By Arrangement) Glasshouse Prods Ltd
Milo Twomey Kerry Gardner Mngt
Two's Company Sardi's Int'l Ent
Tygers of Pan Tang Alan Cottam Agency
Tykes Barn Dance Line Dance Agy
Clive Tyldesley Talking Heads - The Voice Agy
Blakeston Tyler Funhouse Productions Ltd
Bonnie Tyler Jason West Agy/NMP Live Ltd/The Leighton-Pope Org
Tom Tyler Susan Angel Kevin Francis Ltd
Zoe Tyler MCS Agcy
Saxon Tylney Anglia Artistes/The Horne Concert Agy
Ihor Tymchak The A6 Agy
Bernadette Tynan Arlington Enterprises Ltd
Tyneside Pipers The A6 Agy
Mason Tyree MGA Entp
Cathy Tyson CAM London
Mike Tyson CHAMPIONS (UK) PLC
Sheila Tyson MBA
Margaret Tyzack Markham & Froggatt Ltd
Tziganarama Matters Musical
Tziganka - Russian Cossack Music & Dance Spectacular ABDC Ents/London Music Agy/Rent-A-Band/The John Boddy Agency/Whatever Artists Mngt Ltd

U

U2 Universal/Island Records Ltd
U2 Magic Entertainers Mgt Ltd
U2 Pop (U2) Advanced Ents
The U.A. Roadshow Highfield Mngt & Promos
UB40 ITB
UB4T Jason West Agy
UB4T & The Allska's Head On Mngt
Uber and Alice Continental Drifts/TEST AGENT C
Victor Ubogo Bsc Jon Holmes Media Ltd
Jahangir uddin Barrie Stacey Promos & Prods
Leslee Udwin Shepherd Mngt Ltd
Ayako Uehara IMG Artists
UFO Miracle Artists Ltd
The Ugs CKK Ent
Charlotte Uhlenbroek Billy Marsh Assoc Ltd
Uillean Pipers Matters Musical
Abba UK Prima Artists
UK Beach Boys (Beach Boys Tribute) Advanced Ents
UK Chinese Acrobatic Company CKK Ent/Matters Musical
UK Fantasy Boys SWA Ent
Space UK Matters Musical
UK Storm Big Bang Mngt Ltd
UK Subs Rock Artist Mngt
Ukulele Orchestra of Great Britain Matters Musical
Tracey Ullman Special Artists Agency
Ultima Border Leisure
Ultimate 80's The Psycho Mngt Co Ltd
The Ultimate British Invasion Brian Gannon Mngt
Ultimate Madness (Madness Tribute) Entertainers Mgt Ltd/Henderson Mngt/Int'l Mngt & Agy Ltd
Ultimate Psychic Experience ft. Shaun Dennis and Alan Bates Chimes Int'l Ents Ltd
Ultra Nate Tony Denton Promos Ltd
Ultrabeat Action Talent Int.
Ultraista 13 Artists
Ultz Simpson Fox Assoc Ltd
Jonathan Ulysses Fresh Artiste Management Ltd
Ulysses The Statue PVA Ent Consultants
Unclassified Mime CKK Ent
Uncle Bernard`s Band Barn Dance Line Dance Agy
Uncle Dave`s Disco Dave Seamer Ents
Uncle Dave's Magic Show Dave Seamer Ents
Uncle Funk Advanced Ents
Uncle Mick's Entertainments Mick's Ents(Ind Art)
Uncle Peter's Magic Show Uncle Peter Magic Show (Magic)
Uncle Wiggy Tony Bennell Ents
Uncovered (The Blues Brothers, The Commitments) Jason West Agy
Undecided Hawthorn Ent
Under The Honeytunnel Magick Eye Records
Underoath Helter Skelter Agy Ltd
The Undertakers BULLET MANAGEMENT LIMITED/Jason West Agy
Underwolves Universal/Island Records Ltd
Carrie Underwood 19 Entertainment
Mark Underwood Barrie Stacey Promos & Prods
Nick Underwood Amber Persnl Mngt Ltd
Rory Underwood MBE After Dinner World Ltd/Jon Holmes Media Ltd
Tom Underwood Denmark Street Mngt
Tony Underwood BSc BA Jon Holmes Media Ltd
Underworld Jukes Prods Ltd/Primary Talent Int'l
Undisputed Owen Hughes Ents
Unforgetable - The Nat King Cole Story David Coleman
Unicorn Disco Derek Bruce Ents
Union Gap BCM Promos Ltd/BULLET MANAGEMENT LIMITED
Unit 4 Plus 2 Brian Gannon Mngt/Pete Mitchell Associates
Unit Six Tony Bennell Ents
Uniting Nations Mission Control Artist Agy
Unkle Bob Big Sister Promotions
Unknown Pleasures (Joy Division) Head On Mngt
Unleashed Miracle Artists Ltd
Uno Hoo Steve Allen Ents
Untitled Music Project CEC Management
Untouched Insanity Artists
Un-Used Toys ENTERTAINMENT FX
Ben Unwin Richard Price PR
Jo Unwin Lip Service Casting Ltd
Unwritten Law Primary Talent Int'l
Up 4 Grabs Ginger Walker Agy
Tim Hain & Jamside Up! Matters Musical
Upbeat Beatles Entertainers Mgt Ltd/Jason West Agy
Stephen Uppal Hyper Agency
Upside Down Book A Band/Jason West Agy/Yorkshire Ent
Vanessa Upton RAGE
Uralsky All Stars (Russ) Wim Wigt Prodns Ltd
Urban Cookie Collective Action Talent Int./Mission Control Artist Agy
Keith Urban The Leighton-Pope Org
Urban Trad (Belgium) Stoneyport Associates
Eva Urbanova Stafford Law
Midge Ure Jason West Agy/Tony Denton Promos Ltd
Urgent Live Turkeys Line-Up PMC
Justin Urquhart Stewart DBA Speakers
Amanda Ursell IMWP (UK) Ltd
US4 (U2 tribute) Advanced Ents/Henderson Mngt/Hireaband Ltd
Anastasia Ushakova-Carter Agency K-Bis
Usher Creative Artists Agency
Simon Usher Dennis Lyne Agy
The Usual Suspects Highfield Mngt & Promos
Uthingo Matters Musical/Tropical Ents Mngt Agy
Utter Madness Michael La Roche Mngt/Mike Malley Ents/The John Boddy Agency/The Psycho Mngt Co Ltd
Roger Uttley OBE Athole Still Int'l Ltd/Persnl Appearances/TEST AGENT A
UU2 Andrew Beauchamp Mngt/Head On Mngt/Jason West Agy
UVX Magick Eye Records

V

V The Ents Agency
Magic V B.F.P Ents
Chris Vacher Gordon Poole Agy Ltd
Leontina Vaduva Stafford Law
Holly Valance Curtis Brown Grp/Jon Fowler Management Ltd/Personal Management & Casting
Ricky Valance Brian Gannon Mngt
Deborah Vale Royce Mngt
Ella Vale Amber Persnl Mngt Ltd
Tessa Vale Royce Mngt
Valentine Laurie Taylor Ents Ltd
Anthony Valentine AIM
David Valentine Compact Mngt & Ent Agy
Kim Valentine Chris Gordon Theatrical Agy
Robert Valentine Lena Davis/John Bishop Assoc
Bobby Valentino Line-Up PMC/Matters Musical
Charlie Valentino Charlie Valentino (Magic)/Partyweb.co.uk
Richard Van Allen Askonas Holt Ltd
Van Buren & Company Colclough Entertainment/Tony West Ents

Advertisers' Index

Contents

continued on page 5

Contents

continued from page 3

Supplies & Services

Suppliers & Services

Advertisers' Index

VENUE FINDER INDEX

Listed below are all the London and Provincial venues in the British Theatre Directory with the town or city in which they can be found. The venues can be found alphabetised under the town or city name in the London or Provincial venues section.

The Comedy Store - London
The Comedy Store Manchester - Manchester
Comedy Theatre - London
Community Centre - Leominster
Compass Theatre and Arts Centre - Uxbridge
Concordia Leisure Centre - Cramlington
Congress Theatre - Cwmbran
The Congress Theatre - Eastbourne
Connaught Theatre - Worthing
Contact Theatre - Manchester
Coppenhall Leisure Centre - Crewe
Cork Opera House - Cork
The Corn Exchange - Brighton
The Corn Exchange - Bourne
The Corn Exchange - Newbury
The Corn Exchange - Wallingford
The Corn Exchange - King's Lynn
The Corn Hall - Cirencester
Cornbow Hall - Halesowen
Coronation Hall Theatre - Ulverston
The Coronet Theatre - London
Corran Hall - Oban
Corwen Leisure Centre - Corwen
Corwen Pavilion - Corwen
Cotswold Leisure Centre - Cirencester
The Courtyard - Hereford
The Courtyard Theatre At Ballyearl - Newtownabbey
Gordon Craig Theatre - Stevenage
Craigavon Civic Centre - Craigavon
Cramphorn Theatre - Chelmsford
Crawley Leisure Centre - Crawley
Crescent Theatre - Birmingham
Cresset Theatre - Peterborough
Criccieth Memorial Hall - Criccieth
Criterion Theatre - London
Crook Log Sports Centre - Bexleyheath
Crosby Civic Hall - Liverpool
Crowtree Leisure Centre - Sunderland
Crucible Theatre - Sheffield
Charles Cryer Studio Theatre And Scenery Workshop - Carshalton
Crystal Palace Outdoor Concert Bowl - London
Cullen Community Centre - Cullen
Cullen Town Hall - Cullen
Culm Valley Sports Centre - Callumpton
Cumbernauld Theatre - Glasgow
Cumnock Town Hall - Cumnock
Curve Theatre - Leicester
The Customs House - South Shields
DA Hall - Millport
Dalbeattie Town Hall - Dalbeattie
Dalry Public Hall - Dalry
Dancehouse Theatre - Manchester
Daneside Theatre - Congleton
Darlington Civic Theatre - Darlington
Dartington Arts - Totnes
Darvel Town Hall - Darvel
Darwen Library Theatre - Darwen
Daventry Leisure Centre - Daventry
Dawlish Leisure Centre - Dawlish
De La Warr Pavilion - Bexhill-on-Sea
De Montfort Hall - Leicester
De Valence Pavilion - Tenby
Deepings Leisure Centre - Peterborough
Deeside Leisure Centre - Queensferry
Denholme Mechanics Institute - Bradford
Denny Civic Theatre - Dumbarton
Derby Room - Leigh
Derby Theatre - Derby
Devonshire Park Theatre - Eastbourne
Dewsbury Town Hall - Dewsbury
Didcot Leisure Centre - Didcot
Digital - Brighton
Dollar Civic Centre - Dollar
The Dolphin Centre - Darlington
The Dome - Doncaster
Dominion Theatre - London
The Donald Roy Theatre - Hull
Doncaster Civic Theatre - Doncaster
Donmar Warehouse - London
Dorking Halls - Dorking
Dover Town Hall - Dover
Down Leisure Centre - Downpatrick
Dronfield Sports Centre - Dronfield
Dublin Gate Theatre - Dublin 1
Duchess Theatre - London
Dudley Concert Hall - Dudley
Dufftown Community Centre - Dufftown
Duke Of York's Theatre - London
Dukes Hall - Hornchurch
The Dukes Theatre & Cinema - Lancaster
Dundee Repertory Theatre - Dundee
Dundonald International Ice Bowl - Belfast
Dunes Family Entertainment Centre - Mablethorpe
Dunlop Village Hall - Dunlop
Dylan Thomas Theatre - Swansea
Ealing Town Hall - London
Earls Court Arena - London
Eastgate Theatre & Arts Centre - Peebles
Eaves Green Community Centre - Chorley
Eden Court Theatre - Inverness
Eden Theatre - Bishop Auckland
The Edinburgh Corn Exchange - Edinburgh
Edinburgh Festival Theatre - Edinburgh
Edinburgh International Conference Centre - EICC - Edinburgh
Edinburgh Playhouse - Edinburgh
Egremont Market Hall - Egremont
Electric Ballroom - London
Electric Theatre - Guildford
Elgin Community Centre - Elgin
Elgin Town Hall - Elgin
The Elgiva - Chesham
Elizabethan Suite - Bury
Ellesmere Port Civic Hall - Ellesmere Port
Ellesmere Town Hall - Ellesmere
Elmesthorpe Village Hall - Elmesthorpe
Embassy Centre - Skegness
Empire Theatre - Sunderland
Enderby Civic Centre - Leicester
Enderby Leisure Centre - Enderby
Epsom Playhouse - Epsom
The Epstein Theatre - Liverpool
Etcetera Theatre Club - London
Everyman Theatre - Cheltenham
Ewell Court House - Ewell
ExceL Arena - London
Exeter University Great Hall - Exeter
Fairfield Halls - Croydon
Falkirk Town Hall - Falkirk
Falmouth Arts Centre - Falmouth
Farnham Maltings - Farnham
Farrer Theatre - Windsor
Felixstowe Leisure Centre - Felixstowe
Ferneham Hall - Fareham
Festival Hall - Nottingham
Ffestiniog Village Hall - Ffestiniog
Ffwrnes - Llanelli
Findochty Town Hall - Findochty
Fishermen's Hall - Buckie
Fleming Hall - Aberlour
Fleming Park Leisure Centre - Eastleigh

12 Venue Finder Index

Vera Fletcher Hall - Thames Ditton
Floral Hall - Southport
Floral Pavilion Theatre and Conference Centre - Wirral
Formby Hall - Manchester
Forres House Community Centre - Forres
Fort Regent Leisure Centre - St Helier
Fortune Theatre - London
Forty Hall Banqueting Suite - Enfield
Forum 28 - Barrow-in-Furness
Forum Theatre - Billingham
Friargate Theatre - York
The Fridge Bar - London
Frome Memorial Theatre - Frome
Fulham Town Hall - London
Fulton Hall - Fenwick
The Furnace - Swindon
Futurist Theatre - Scarborough
G Live - Guildford
Gaiety Theatre - Dublin 2
Gaiety Theatre - Ayr
Gaiety Theatre - Douglas
Gala Theatre - Durham
Garrick Playhouse - Altrincham
Garrick Theatre - London
Garrison Theatre - Lerwick
Gatehead Hall - Gatehead
GBS Theatre (RADA) - London
Georgian Theatre - Stockton-on-Tees
Georgian Theatre Royal - Richmond
The John Gielgud Studio (RADA) - London
Gielgud Theatre - London
Glades Arena - Kidderminster
Glasgow Pavilion - Glasgow
Glasgow Royal Concert Hall - Glasgow
University of Glasgow Student's Union - Glasgow
Globe Theatre - Blackpool
Glyndebourne Festival Opera - Lewes
Goldsmith College - London
Gracie Fields Theatre - Rochdale
Grand Hall - Kilmarnock
Grand Opera House - York
Grand Opera House - Belfast
Grand Pavilion - Porthcawl
Grand Theatre - Blackpool
Grand Theatre - Wolverhampton
Grand Theatre - Lancaster
Grange Arts Centre - Oldham
The Grange Theatre - Ellesmere Port
Grantham Guildhall Arts Centre - Grantham
Grantham Meres Leisure Centre - Grantham
Granville Theatre - Ramsgate
Great Hall,Cardiff University Students' Union - Cardiff
Greenford Hall - Greenford
Greenwich Theatre - London
University Of Greenwich Union - London
Grimsby Auditorium - Grimsby
Grosvenor Ballroom - Wallasey
Grove Theatre - Dunstable
Guild Hall - Preston
Guildford Spectrum - Guildford
Guildhall - Portsmouth
Guildhall - Cambridge
Guildhall - Bath
Gloucester Guildhall - Gloucester
Guildhall Theatre - Derby
Guildhall Winchester - Winchester
Gulbenkian Theatre - Canterbury
Gwyn Hall - Neath
Hackney Empire - London
Hackney Town Hall Assembly Hall - London
Haigh Hall - Wigan
Hailsham Pavilion - Hailsham
Halesowen Leisure Centre - Halesowen
Halesworth Rifle Hall - Halesworth
Half Moon Young People's Theatre (YPT) - London
Hall For Cornwall - Truro
Haltemprice Leisure Centre - Hull
HambletonForum - Northallerton
Hammersmith Town Hall - London
Hampstead Theatre - London
Harden Memorial Hall - Bingley
The Harlequin Theatre and Cinema - Redhill
The Harlington - Fleet
Harpenden Public Halls - Harpenden
Harrogate International Centre - Harrogate
Harrogate Theatre - Harrogate
Hatfield Leisure Centre - Hatfield
Haverhill Arts Centre - Haverhill
Hawth Theatre - Crawley
Hawthorn Leisure and Recreational Centre - Pontypridd
Hayes Green Community Centre - Cannock
Haymarket Theatre - Basingstoke
Hayocks Hall - Stevenston
Helmsley Arts Centre - York
Henley Indoor Sports Centre - Henley-on-Thames
Her Majesty's Theatre - London
Heriot-Watt University Student's Union - Edinburgh
Hertford Theatre - Hertford
Heswall Hall - Heswall
The Hexagon Theatre - Reading
Heywood Civic Centre - Heywood
Highbury Theatre Centre - Sutton Coldfield
Hippodrome Circus - Great Yarmouth
His Majesty's Theatre - Aberdeen
Hitchin Town Hall - Hitchin
The HMV Forum - London
HMV Hammersmith Apollo - London
Holden Hall - Keighley
Holyhead Concert Hall - Holyhead
Holywell Leisure Centre - Holywell
Honley Community Centre - Honley
The Hope and Anchor - London
Hornsea Floral Hall - Hornsea
Horseshoe - Blackpool
Hove Town Hall - Hove
Hucknall Leisure Centre - Hucknall
Huddersfield Town Hall - Huddersfield
The Hull Arena - Hull
Hull City Hall - Hull
Hull New Theatre - Hull
Hull Truck Theatre - Hull
Huntingdon Hall - Worcester
Huthwaite Leisure Centre - Sutton-in-Ashfield
Huyton Suite - Huyton
Hyndburn Sports centre - Accrington
Hythe Social Centre - Egham
ICA Theatre - London
The i.e. Theatre - Axminster
IndigO2 Arena - London
INEC - Kerry
Inglis Memorial Hall - Edzell
Institute Hall - Stewarton
The International Centre Telford - Telford
Ipswich Regent and Corn Exchange - Ipswich
Island Arts Centre - Lisburn
Jacksons Lane - London
Jazz Cafe - London
Jermyn Street Theatre - London
Jersey Opera House - St Helier
Jerwood Theatre Downstairs -
Jerwood Theatre Upstairs -
The Jerwood Vanbrugh Theatre - London

John Phillips Hall - Bangor
Joymount Town Hall - Carrickfergus
Katherine Brennan Hall - Dublin 2
Keith Community Centre - Keith
Kelsey Kerridge Sports Centre - Cambridge
Kendal Town Hall - Kendal
Kenneth More Theatre - Ilford
Kensington Leisure Centre - London
Kenton Theatre - Henley-on-Thames
Kenwood Concerts -
Kessington Hall - Bearsdon
Key Theatre - Peterborough
King George's Hall - Blackburn
King's Hall Conference Centre - Belfast
King's Lynn Arts Centre - King's Lynn
King's Theatre - Edinburgh
King's Theatre - Glasgow
The King's Theatre - Southsea
Kings Hall - Herne Bay
Kings Hall/Winter Garden - Ilkley
King's Head Theatre (Islington) - London
Kings Theatre - Chatham
Kirkcudbright Town Hall - Kirkcudbright
Kirklands Community Centre - Ilkley
Knighton Community Centre - Knighton
Knowsley Village Hall - Knowsley Village
KOKO - London
Komedia Bath - Bath
Komedia Brighton - Brighton
Laban Theatre - London
Lady Cathcart Community Centre - Buckie
Lakes Leisure Kendal - Kendal
University of Essex Lakeside Theatre - Colchester
Lambeth Town Hall - London
Lamplight Arts Centre - Stanley
Lancastrian Suite - Chorley
The Landmark Theatre - Ilfracombe
Latchmere Leisure Centre - London
The Laverton Hall - Westbury
The Lawn in Lincoln - Lincoln
Layard Theatre - Wimborne
Leas Cliff Hall - Folkestone
Leatherhead Leisure Centre - Leatherhead
Leeds Grand Theatre and Opera House - Leeds
Leeds Playhouse -
Leeds University Union - Leeds
Leighton Buzzard Theatre - Leighton Buzzard
Leighton House Museum - London
Leisure World - Bridlington
Lenzie Public Hall - Lenzie
Leominster Leisure Centre - Leominster
LG Arena - Birmingham
Liberty Hall - Dublin 1
Library Theatre - Manchester
Library Theatre - Sheffield
The Library Theatre - Luton
Lichfield Garrick Theatre - Lichfield
Lighthouse, Poole's Centre For The Arts - Poole
Limelight Theatre - Aylesbury
Lincoln Drill Hall - Lincoln
Lincoln Theatre Royal - Lincoln
Literary Institute - Egham
Little Angel Theatre "Home of British Puppetry" - London
Little Theatre - Leicester
Little Theatre - Rhyl
Live Theatre - Newcastle upon Tyne
Liverpool Empire - Liverpool
Liverpool Everyman and Playhouse Theatre - Liverpool
Liverpool Olympia - Liverpool
University of Liverpool - Liverpool
Llanelli Entertainment Centre - Llanelli
Llantrisant Leisure Centre - Llantrisant
Lochgelly Centre Theatre - Lochgelly
Lochside Leisure Centre - Forfar
The Logan Hall - London
London Coliseum - London
London Palladium - London
University College London Union - London
University of London Union - London
Longfield Suite - Manchester
Longmore Hall - Keith
Lords Meadow Leisure Centre - Crediton
Lossiemouth Community Centre - Lossiemouth
Lossiemouth Town Hall - Lossiemouth
Loughborough Town Hall - Loughborough
Lowther Pavilion - Lytham St Anne's
Ludlow Assembly Rooms - Ludlow
Lurgan Town Hall - Craigavon
Lyceum Theatre - London
Lyceum Theatre - Crewe
Lyceum Theatre - Sheffield
Lymington Community Centre - Lymington
Lyric Hammersmith - London
Lyric Theatre - Belfast
Lyric Theatre - London
Macclesfield Leisure Centre - Macclesfield
MacOwan Theatre (LAMDA) - London
Maddermarket Theatre - Norwich
Magnet Leisure Centre - Maidenhead
Magnum Theatre - Irvine
Maidstone Leisure Centre-Mote Hall - Maidstone
Majestic Theatre - Retford
Maltings Arts Theatre - St Albans
The Maltings Public Hall Conference & Banqueting Centre - Ely
Malvern Theatres - Malvern
Manchester Arena - Manchester
Manchester Academy - Manchester
Manchester Central - Manchester
Manchester Metropolitan University Students' Union - Manchester
Manor Pavilion Theatre - Sidmouth
March Town Hall - March
Marina Theatre - Lowestoft
Marine Hall - Fleetwood
Marine Theatre - Lyme Regis
Market Place Theatre and Arts Centre - Armagh
The Marlowe Theatre - Canterbury
Martlets Hall - Burgess Hill
Mayflower Theatre - Southampton
The Medieval Hall - Salisbury
Medina Theatre - Newport
Meltham Civic Hall - Meltham
Melton Theatre - Melton Mowbray
Memorial Hall & Theatre - Barry
Mercury Theatre - Colchester
Merlin Theatre - Frome
Mermaid Conference & Events Centre - London
Metro Radio Arena - Newcastle-upon-Tyne
Michael Sobell Sports Centre - Aberdare
Middlesbrough Theatre - Middlesbrough
Middleton Arena - Manchester
The Middleton Hall - Hull
Midlands Arts Centre - Birmingham
The Mill at Sonning Theatre - Reading
The Mill Hall - Rayleigh
The Millennium Forum - Londonderry
Millfield Theatre - London
Millport Town Hall - Millport
Milton Keynes Theatre - Milton Keynes
The Milton Rooms - Malton
Minack Theatre - Penzance

Mitchell Theatre - Glasgow
The Mole Hall - West Molesey
Moles Club - Bath
Monaco Ballroom - Wigan
Morton Hall - Newmilns
Motherwell Concert Hall - Motherwell
Motherwell Theatre - Motherwell
Motorpoint Arena Cardiff - Cardiff
Motorpoint Arena,Sheffield - Sheffield
The Mowlem Theatre - Swanage
Mull Theatre - Isle of Mull
Music Hall - Aberdeen
The National Bowl - Milton Keynes
National Centre For Early Music - York
National Concert Hall - Dublin 2
National Gallery of Ireland - Dublin 2
National Stadium - Dublin 8
National Theatre - London
National Theatre (Abbey Theatre) - Dublin 1
National Theatre (Peacock Theatre) - Dublin 1
Netherton Arts Centre - Dudley
The Nettlefold - London
Neuadd Buddug Theatre - Bala
Neuadd Dwyfor - Pwllheli
The Nevis Centre - Fort William
New Alexandra Theatre - Birmingham
New Farm Loch Community Centre - Kilmarnock
New Greenham Arts - Newbury
New London Theatre - London
New Theatre - Cardiff
The New Theatre - Oxford
New Theatre Royal - Portsmouth
The New Vic - Newcastle-under-Lyme
New Victoria Theatre - Woking
New Walk Museum - Leicester
New Wimbledon Theatre - London
New Windmill Hall - Upminster
The New Wolsey Theatre - Ipswich
Newbiggin Sports & Community Centre - Newbiggin-by-the-Sea
Newcastle Centre - Newcastle
Newport Leisure Centre - Newport
Newry Town Hall - Newry
Newton Aycliffe Leisure Centre - Newton Aycliffe
NIA Academy - Birmingham
Noel Coward Theatre - London
North Devon Leisure Centre - Barnstaple
North Pier Theatre - Blackpool
Northcott Theatre - Exeter
Northcroft Leisure Centre - Newbury
Northern Stage - Newcastle-upon-Tyne
Northwich Memorial Hall - Northwich
Norwich Playhouse - Norwich
Norwich Puppet Theatre - Norwich
Nottingham Arts Theatre - Nottingham
Nottingham Playhouse - Nottingham
Nova Centre - Prestatyn
Novello Theatre - London
Novello Theatre - Ascot
Nuffield Theatre - Lancaster
Nuffield Theatre - Southampton
o2 Academy Brixton - London
O2 Arena - London
Oak Tree Leisure Centre - Mansfield
Oakengates Theatre - Telford
Oasis Leisure Centre - Swindon
Oceana Club - Brighton
Octagon Theatre - Yeovil
Octagon Theatre - Bolton
The Old Rep Theatre, Birmingham - Birmingham
The Old Vic Theatre - London
Oldham Theatre Workshop - Oldham
Olympia Theatre - Dublin 2
One Touch Theatre - Inverness
Open Air Theatre - London
Opera House - Buxton
Opera House Manchester - Manchester
Oran Mor - Glasgow
The Orchard Theatre - Dartford
Oswaldtwistle Civic Theatre - Accrington
Oxford Playhouse - Oxford
Oxford Town Hall - Oxford
Pacific Road Arts Centre - Birkenhead
The Paget Rooms - Penarth
Paisley Arts Centre - Paisley
Paisley Museum - Paisley
Palace Theatre - Westcliff-on-Sea
Palace Theatre - Kilmarnock
Palace Theatre - Manchester
Palace Theatre - Redditch
Palace Theatre - Newark
Palace Theatre - London
The Palace Theatre - Mansfield
The Palace Theatre - Paignton
Paradise Room - Blackpool
Park and Dare Theatre - Treorchy
Parterre Hall - Irvine
Pater Hall - Pembroke Dock
Patti Pavilion - Swansea
The Pavilion - Llandrindod Wells
The Pavilion - Exmouth
The Pavilion at Huncote - Huncote
Pavilion Ballroom - Ayr
Pavilion Garden on the Sands - Broadstairs
Pavilion Gardens - Buxton
Pavilion Theatre - Worthing
Pavilion Theatre - Brighton
Pavilion Theatre - Cromer
Pavilion Theatre - Rhyl
Pavilion Theatre - Weymouth
Pavilion Theatre & Ballroom - Bournemouth
The Pavilion Theatre Gorleston - Great Yarmouth
Peacock Theatre - London
Pegasus Theatre - Oxford
Penyrheol Theatre - Swansea
People's Theatre - Newcastle-upon-Tyne
Perth Concert Hall - Perth
Perth Theatre - Perth
Peterlee Leisure Centre - Peterlee
Philharmonic Hall - Liverpool
Phoenix Square: Film and Digital Media - Leicester
Phoenix Theatre - London
Phoenix Theatre - Blyth
Piccadilly Theatre - London
The Pickaquoy Centre - Kirkwall
Piece Hall - Halifax
Pier Theatre - Bournemouth
Pinner Youth & Community Centre - Pinner
Pitlochry Festival Theatre - Pitlochry
Pittville Pump Room - Cheltenham
Plas Madoc Leisure Centre - Wrexham
The Platform - Morecambe
Playbox Theatre Company - Warwick
Players' Theatre - London
The Playhouse - Harlow
The Playhouse Theatre - London
PLAYHOUSE Whitley Bay - Whitley Bay
Plaza Theatre - Stockport
Plaza Theatre - Romsey
Plowright Theatre - Scunthorpe
Plymouth Pavilions - Plymouth
The Point Dance & Arts Centre - Eastleigh

Pomegranate Theatre - Chesterfield
Pontardawe Arts Centre - Swansea
Pontefract Town Hall - Pontefract
Portadown Town Hall Theatre - Craigavon
Portgordon Community Centre - Portgordon
Portslade Town Hall - Portslade
Poulton Youth and Community Centre - Poulton le Fylde
Powys Dance - Powys
Prichard Jones Hall - Bangor
Prince Edward Theatre - London
Prince of Wales Centre - Cannock
Prince of Wales Theatre - London
Princes Hall - Aldershot
Princes Theatre - Clacton-on-Sea
The Princess Theatre and Arts Centre - Burnham-on-Sea
Princess Pavilion - Falmouth
The Princess Royal Theatre - Port Talbot
Princess Theatre - Hunstanton
Princess Theatre - Torquay
The Priory Centre - St Neots
Putney Leisure Centre - London
Pye Green Community Centre - Hednesford
Pyle Life Centre - Bridgend
Pyramid and Parr Hall - Warrington
Quarterhouse - Folkestone
The Quay Theatre - Sudbury
Quayside Leisure Centre - Kingsbridge
Queen Elizabeth Hall - London
Queen Mary College - London
The Queen's Hall - Edinburgh
Queen's Theatre - London
Queen's Theatre - Hornchurch
Queen's Theatre - Barnstaple
Queen's University Concert Halls - Belfast
Queen's Hall - Dunoon
Queens Hall - Ilkley
The Questors Theatre - London
Rada Studios - London
Radcliffe Civic Suite - Manchester
The Radlett Centre - Radlett
Rainton Meadows Arena - Houghton le Spring
Ramsbottom Civic Hall - Ramsbottom
The Ramshorn Theatre - Glasgow
Reading Town Hall - Reading
Redbridge Drama Centre - London
The Redgrave Theatre - Bristol
Regal Centre - Worksop
Regal Theatre - Ipswich
The Regent Centre - Christchurch
Regent Theatre - Stoke-on-Trent
The Regis Centre - Bognor Regis
Reid Concert Hall, University of Edinburgh - Edinburgh
Reid Hall - Forfar
Retford Leisure Centre - Retford
Retford Town Hall - Retford
Rhayader Leisure Centre - Rhayader
Rhoda McGaw Theatre - Woking
Rhyl Town Hall - Rhyl
Riccarton Community Centre - Kilmarnock
Richmond Theatre - Richmond
Rivermead Leisure Complex - Reading
Riverside Arts Centre - Sunbury
Riverside Leisure Centre - Morpeth
The Riverside Leisure Centre - Exeter
Riverside Studios - London
Riverside Theatre - Coleraine
Riverside Theatre - Woodbridge
Riviera International Conference Centre - Torquay
Paul Robeson Theatre - Hounslow
Robin Howard Dance Theatre - London
Rock City - Nottingham
Romiley Forum - Stockport
The Rondo Theatre - Bath
Rose Hall - Wigan
Rosehill Theatre - Whitehaven
Roses Theatre - Tewkesbury
Rothes Halls - Glenrothes
Rotunda Pillar Room - Dublin 1
The Roundhouse - London
Royal & Derngate - Northampton
Royal Albert Hall - London
Royal Centre -
Royal Concert Hall - Nottingham
Royal Court Theatre - Liverpool
Royal Court Theatre - London
Royal Dublin Society Concert Hall - Dublin 4
Royal Exchange Theatre - Manchester
Royal Festival Hall - London
Royal Hall - Harrogate
Royal Highland Centre - Edinburgh
Royal Hippodrome - Eastbourne
Royal International Pavilion - Llangollen
Royal Lyceum - Edinburgh
Royal Northern College of Music - Manchester
Royal Opera House - London
Royal Pump Rooms - Leamington Spa
Royal Shakespeare Theatre, Swan Theatre, Courtyard Theatre - Stratford-upon-Avon
Royal Spa Centre - Leamington Spa
Rugeley Road Pavilion - Hednesford
Rugeley Rose Theatre - Rugeley
Runnymede Hall - South Benfleet
The Ryan Centre - Stranraer
Sadler's Wells - London
The Sage Gateshead - Gateshead
Salisbury Guildhall - Salisbury
Salisbury Playhouse - Salisbury
Sallis Benney Theatre - Brighton
Saltire Leisure Centre - Arbroath
Sands Centre - Carlisle
Sanquhar Town Hall - Sanquhar
Sauchie Hall - Sauchie
Savoy Theatre - Monmouth
Savoy Theatre - London
Scottish Exhibition & Conference Centre - Glasgow
Ronnie Scott's - London
Seaburn Centre - Sunderland
Seagull Theatre - Lowestoft
Seaham Leisure Centre - Seaham
Sean Hollywood Arts Centre - Newry
Secombe Theatre - Sutton
Settle Victoria Theatre - Settle
Shaftesbury Theatre - London
Shakespeare's Globe - London
Shanklin Theatre - Shanklin
Sharley Park Leisure Centre - Clay Cross
Shavington Leisure Centre - Shavington
Shaw Theatre - London
Sheffield City Hall - Sheffield
Sheldonian Theatre - Oxford
Shelf Village Hall - Halifax
Shelley Theatre - Marlow
Shepherd's Bush Empire - London
Sheringham Little Theatre - Sheringham
Sherman Theatre - Cardiff
Shildon Sunnydale Leisure Centre - Shildon
Shinfield Players Theatre & Arts Centre - Reading
Shoestring Theatre - London
Silk Cabaret Venue - Wellingborough
Silsden Town Hall - Keighley
Simmonscourt Pavilion - Dublin 4

LONDON VENUES

100 CLUB
100 Oxford Street, London W1D 1LL
Tel: 020 7636 0933 Fax: 020 7436 1958
Email: info@the100club.co.uk
Web Site: www.the100club.co.uk
ADMNISTRATION:
Contact: Jeff Horton
Please contact Jenny at the 100Club via email if you wish to hire the venue: jenny@the100club.co.uk

ABBEY COMMUNITY CENTRE
34 Great Smith Street, London SW1P 3BU
Tel: 020 7222 0303 Fax: 020 7233 3308
Email: enquiries@theabbeycentre.org.uk
Web Site: www.theabbeycentre.org.uk
ADMINISTRATION:
Executive Director: Lainya Offside-Keivani
Contact:
lainya.keivani@theabbeycentre.org.uk
Conference Support and Reception: George Banya/ Georgine Deadman
Capacity (Parker Morris Hall); Theatre Style: 200, Cabaret: 80.
TECHNICAL:
Paker Morris Hall:
DIMENSIONS: 16.3 x10.91m, 53'6"x 35'10" (excluding stage).
AUDIO VISUAL: Free Wi-Fi, Hi-tech data projector, Flip chart. EXTRAS: for additional charges you can use roving microphones, LCD video projection unit, LCD data projector, display panels, flipcharts, pads and pens (1 set included per room).

THE ACADEMY
Cleveland Road, Uxbridge, Middlesex UB8 3PH
Tel: 01895 269 269 Fax: 01895 269 699
Email: adamphilpot@brunel.ac.uk
Web Site: www.brunelstudents.com
ADMINISTRATION:
Contact: Adam Philpot
Capacity: 600
Recent artists include; LTJ Bukem, Rat Pack, Chesney Hawkes, Judge Jules.
TECHNICAL:
8kw Sound system.
Comprehensive lighting rig.

ADELPHI THEATRE
409-412 Strand, London WC2R 0NS
SD/ Mgmt: 020 7836 1166 / 7379 5723
Admin: 020 7240 0880 BO: 0844 412 4651 Fax: 020 7379 5709
Email: info@reallyuseful.co.uk
Web Site: www.reallyuseful.co.uk
ADMINISTRATION:
Props: The Really Useful Group Ltd.
Licensing Authority: Westminster City Council
Chief Executive: André Ptaszynski
Policy: Large spectacular musicals, revues and plays. Venue hire ideal for; Conferences, AGM's, Product Launches, Seminars, Meetings, Training Courses.
Perfs: Variable according to production; Mats. Wed and Sat.
Seats: 1,500 + 2 Wheel chair. Royal Room; 10. Dress Circle Bar; 30 (60 standing). Four Bars.
TECHNICAL:
STAGE: Proscenium Stage, Flat; Pros. opening 10.82m; Depth of Stage 9.75m main + 6.8m rear; Height to bottom of iron 6.72m; Height of Grid 18.30m; Height of fly floors (to fly rail) 10.36m; Distance between fly floors 13.72m approx; Dock Door (Size and position) 2.74m x 2.74m; Height of Stage from street 4.28m below street; Wing space 2.10m approx each side. Orchestra Pit accomm. 20. Flying Facilities: 39 counterweight sets stage right; Length of flying bars 12.80m; Cradle capacities 685kg; Height under fly floors 8.68m.
LIGHTING: No house desk. Dimmers 378
BACKSTAGE FACILITIES: Stage Management: 6 head sets and 12 cue lights. Dressing Roms 15; Wardrobe and wig room 2 washing machines; Band Rooms 2.
FACILITIES FOR DISABLED PEOPLE: Ramp FoH 2 wheelchair positions Adapted toilet Infrared hearing aid system.

THE ALBANY
Theatre and community centre.
Douglas Way, Deptford, London SE8 4AG
Admin: 020 8692 0231 BO: 020 8692 4446 Fax: 020 8469 2253
Email: senay.gaul@thealbany.org.uk
Web Site: www.thealbany.org.uk
ADMINISTRATION:
The Albany is a lively, intimate and friendly venue with an exciting programme of the very best in theatre, live music, cabaret, family shows, club nights and multimedia events in informal cabaret-style seating.
CEO/Artistic Director: Gavin Barlow
Operations & Administration: Senay Gaul
Room Bookings & Venue Hires: Lily Hannell
Production & Events: Ben Stephens
Head of Communications: Amber Massie-Bloomfield
Box Office: Vicky Harrison
Front of House: Kate Miners (reception@thealbany.org.uk)
Policy: Variety of events, including music, theatre, dance, spoken word, clubs and family events.
Capacity: Main Auditorium: 300 seated/ 500 standing. Studio/ Conference Rooms: 12 - 100.

ALDWYCH THEATRE
49 Aldwych, London WC2B 4DF
SD: 020 7836 5537
Web Site: www.aldwychtheatre.com
ADMINISTRATION:
Props: Nederlander Theatres (Aldwych) Ltd
Management: Michael Codron Plays Ltd
Theatre Manager: Steve Hughes
Policy: Usual West End policy
Perfs: Variable according to production
Seats: 1,200, 4 Drinks Bars, Coffee facilities.
TECHNICAL:
STAGE: Proscenium Stage, Pros. opening 9.65m, height of Pros 6.44m, Rake 1:24. Depth of S.Line 12.09m. Height of Grid 15.39 D.S., 14.9m U.S. 40 Lines counterweight. Scenery Flying Ht 7.62m, Flying Bars 10.97m. W/Widths P.S. 2.99m, O.P. 2.13m D.S. 0.91m US. Prompt Corner P.S.
LIGHTING/SOUND/OTHER: Switchboard - Rank Strand Mini LIght Palette 90, 146 ways. Dips 10 each side. Spots bars available. Dressing rooms 15, accom 52, showers. Scene Dock P.S. Dock doors, 4.27m from stage level. 2990mm H x 2590mm W. Beam Obstruction 200m H x 150mm W Centre Top. Air conditioned.

THE EDWARD ALLEYN THEATRE
Dulwich College, Dulwich Common, London SE21 7LD
Admin: 020 8299 9232
Email: baskervilleh@dulwich.org.uk
Web Site: www.dulwich.org.uk/enterprises-ltd
ADMINISTRATION:
Director of Drama: Peter Jolly
Manager: Carol Morris
Technical Manager: Carol Morris
Theatre Co-ordinator: Heather Baskerville
The Edward Alleyn Theatre is a modern multi-purpose studio theatre producing Dulwich College productions. The theatre also has a programme of specialist Children's Theatre on Saturday mornings and in the holidays, together with Holiday Drama and Music courses. The theatre is also available for hire throughout the year. The flexible stage and seating areas provide a variety of layouts for drama, opera, dance and specialist events. Welcoming foyer facilities make it an ideal venue for conferences and lectures.
Rehearsal facilities: The theatre is available as a rehearsal space. There is also a separate, self -contained rehearsal room which is a footprint of the stage.
Capacity: 160-180
TECHNICAL:
Opening 8.75m, depth 6m, height 4.8m. Fully equipped with computerised lighting, sound and recording facilities. Baby grand piano. Workshop, laundry and 3 dressing rooms. Please apply to the theatre for full

specifications.

ALMEIDA THEATRE

Almeida Street, Islington, London N1 1TA
Admin: 020 7288 4900 BO: 020 7359 4404 Press: 020 7292 8330
Email: info@almeida.co.uk
Web Site: www.almeida.co.uk
ADMINISTRATION:
Artistic Director: Michael Attenborough
General Manager: Natasha Bucknor
Theatre Manager: Helen Noble
Policy: A full-time producing theatre presenting a varied programme of new work, rarely performed classics and international theatre and music.
Capacity: 321.
TECHNICAL:
LIGHTING: Strand 520i lighting control. Strand LD 90 Dimmers with 170 ways of dimming. A wide range of luminaires (250+) including: Source 4 profiles, Strand fresnels & PC's and Thomas Parcans.
SOUND: A comprehensive selection of equipment including: Yamaha 02R mixing desks, Akai S6000 samplers, Meyer speakers etc.
Apply to theatre for full information.

ANGEL COMMUNITY CENTRE

Raynham Road, Edmonton, London, N18 2JF
Tel: 020 8351 1610
Email: paul.adams@enfield.gov.uk
Web Site: www.enfield.gov.uk
ADMINISTRATION:
Props: London Borough of Enfield
For Bookings contact: Paul Adams

APOLLO THEATRE

31 Shaftesbury Avenue, London W1D 7EZ
Mgt: 020 7395 0780 BO: 0844 482 9671
SD: 020 7851 2711
Email: general@nimaxtheatres.com
Web Site: www.nimaxtheatres.com
ADMINISTRATION:
Props: Nimax Theatres Ltd, 11 Maiden Lane, London WC2E 7NA
Policy: Plays, Musicals, Comedy, Concerts.
Chief Executive: Nica Burns
General Manager: Laurence Miller
Operations Manager: Darren Atkins
For all bookings and production enquiries please contact Nica Burns (CEO).
Facilities may be made available for day time, late night and weekend use for private and press receptions, conferences and meetings - Contact Laurence Miller (Commercial Director): Tel: 020 7395 0794 and Email:
laurence.miller@nimaxtheatres.com
Seats: 775
3 Bars,Entertainment Suites.
TECHNICAL:
STAGE: Flat; Pros. Opening 9.14m; Ht of Pros. 6.71m; Depth of Stage 7.87m - 8.42m; Ht of Grid 14.63m; 2 Hemp. 36 C/W, Prompt Cnr. P.S.
LIGHTING: Board: Strand Gemini II, 120 circuits. Situated O.P. Circle Box.
SOUND: Please contact venue.
OTHER: Dressing Rooms: 11.
Membership: SOLT.

APOLLO VICTORIA

17 Wilton Road, London SW1V 1LG
Admin: 020 7834 6318 (Switchboard)
BO: 0844 8871 3001 (ATG Tickets) Tech Mgr. 020 7834 6318
Web Site: www.atgticket.com
ADMINISTRATION:
Props: Ambassadors Theatre Group
General Manager: Pippa Campbell
Technical Manager: Oliver Baldock
Policy: Major musicals.
Perfs: 7.30pm. Matinees 2.30pm
Seats: 2300. Bars.
TECHNICAL:
STAGE: Pros. opening 14.02m; Pros. Ht. 10.06m; Floats to Back Wall 7.32m; PS Wall to O.P. Wall 22.56m; Grid to Stage 21.64m. Flying System: 38 Counterweight Bars: 28 single, 18 double.
LIGHTING: Switchboard: Impact Lighting Board.
SOUND: Pleaee contact venue.
OTHER: Dressing Rooms: 10 and 2 suites.
Membership: SOLT.

ARTS DEPOT

5 Nether Street, Tally Ho Corner, North Finchley, London, N12 0GA
Admin: 020 8369 5455 BO Tel: 020 8369 5454 Fax: 020 8369 5476
Email: info@artsdepot.co.uk
Web Site: www.artsdepot.co.uk
ADMINISTRATION:
Director: Tracy Cooper
Artsdepot was conceived by the local community and built to provide new and improved services, in fact a larger version of The Bull Arts Centre in High Barnet.
Policy: Theatre, Music, Dance, Comedy, Spoekn Word, Children.
Pentland Theatre: Seats: 395, 500 standing.
Studio Theatre: Seats: 148
Gallery and Cafe / Bar
For more information on venue hire contact; Events Department on 020 8369 5471 or events@artsdepot.co.uk.

ARTS EDUCATIONAL SCHOOLS LONDON

Cone Ripman House 14 Bath Road Chiswick London W4 1LY
Tel: 020 8987 6666 Fax: 020 8987 6699
Email: julietaylor@artsed.co.uk
Web Site: www.artsed.co.uk
ADMINISTRATION:
Principal: Jane Harrison
Deputy Principal and the Director of the School of Music Theatre: Chris Hocking
Director of Marketing and Communication: Julie Taylor
Policy: Plays, Dance, Musical Theatre, Rehearsal space, Studio Space, Conference and Seminars, Two Theatres.
Perfs: normally 7.30pm.
Seats: Main Theatre; 140; Studio Theatre; 150. Refreshment facilities available.
For more information on venue hire contact Frank Daniel (Facilities Manager) on Tel: 0208 987 6691.
TECHNICAL:
STAGE: 7.6m wide, with a 4.9m depth and a 2m apron in front of the proscenium. Height 4.1m; Height to grid 8.15m; 28 line double purchase counterweighted flying system. Computerised lighting control and 16-4-2 sound capability.
Full technical staff and facilities. Rehearsal Facilities: available for hire. Dressing Rooms unlimited.

ARTS THEATRE

6-7 Great Newport Street, London WC2H 7JB
BO: 0207 836 8463
Email: info@artstheatrewestend.co.uk
Web Site: www.artstheatrewestend.com
ADMINISTRATION:
Managing Director: Lizzie Scott
Technical Manager: David Warwick
Box Office Manager: Jane Elizabeth
Seats: 350
For more information on venue hire contact: Louis Hartshorn on email: louis@artstheatrewestend.co.uk.
Upstairs at the Arts: Capacity - 50 seated
TECHNICAL:
STAGE: Pros. opening 6.17m; Ht. of Pros. 3.96m; Depth of S/Line 6.10m + 2.43 Apron. 6.10m; Ht. of Grid 12.50m; 31 lines, 15 Hemp, 16 C/W; Prompt Cnr. P.S.
OTHER: Dressing Rooms: 3.

ASHCROFT THEATRE

Park Lane, Croydon, Surrey CR9 1DG
Mgt: 020 8681 0821 BO: 020 8688 9291
Fax: 020 8603 3838 Fax (Mkt): 020 8603 3862
Email: info@fairfield.co.uk
Web Site: www.fairfield.co.uk
ADMINISTRATION:
Props: Fairfield (Croydon) Ltd.
A registered charity.
Chief Executive: Simon Thomsett
Technical Manager: Chris Whybrow
Head of Operations: John Bartliff
Policy: As well as receiving weekly touring productions of drama, musicals, ballet and opera, the theatre also stages children's shows, one-night events, concerts and films, conferences, product launches and award ceremonies for such companies as Nestlé UK Ltd, Kingston Polytechnic and The International Light Rail Conference.
Capacity: 749.
TECHNICAL:
STAGE: Concert Platform, mechanical variable sections.
LIGHTING: In addition to the 200 + lantern stock available for hire, the theatre offers a Strand 530I with Strand EC90 digital dimmers driving 156 circuits. With

the ability to control intelligent units, this board can easily control 500 circuits and run over 500 cues.
SOUND SYSTEM: The theatre can provide up to a 3.5Kw PA system, with up to 2Kw of foldback backstage, 2 stereo compressor limiters, 2 quad gates, 10 channels of graphic, 2 x 1 in 3 out delays, CD, minidisc, cassette, 4 Revox and a selection of mixers.
ADDITIONAL: Stage Management: Full communications and cueing systems (including CCTV). Dressing Rooms: 8, accom. 200; 3 showers; Orchestra Pit 28.90 orch. music stands, 2 Steinway concert D type Grand Pianos; seating 120 orch. max 250 choir seating. Staff: 5 Technicians - Casual Crew.
A registered charity.

BARBICAN - THE PIT

Barbican Centre, Silk Street, London EC2Y 8DS
Mgt: 020 7638 4141 SD: 020 7382 7676
BO: 020 7638 8891 Fax: 020 7382 7277
Email: theatre@barbican.org.uk
Web Site: www.barbican.org.uk
ADMINISTRATION:
Managing Director: Sir Nicholas Kenyon
Head of Theatre: Tony Racklin
BITE - Theatre Production Manager: Simon Bourne
Status: The venue is funded by Corporation of London.
Policy: International small-scale contemporary theatre & performance work.
Non-performance activities: Available for hire subject to programming. Willing to premiere shows.
Performance Schedule: No fixed schedule, call box office for details, 020 7638 8891.
Seats: 202
Catering: 1 bar and coffee points (see Barbican Centre catering facilities).
Access: (See Barbican Centre Access facilities).
Facilities for the disabled: 2 wheelchair spaces.
TECHNICAL:
STAGE: Open stage. Performing area 8m X 10m (7.5m with 4th side auditorium) - offstage areas limited. No rake - floor planks, crossover to SR at rear normally created by scenery or masking. Average fixed bar height 4.2m. Black masking. Get-in via lorry lift from street level, dock doors 3.1m X 3.1m. Tallescope. Scale stage plan available, 1:25.
LIGHTING: Strand Gemini II+ board, 144 circuits, operated on platform at back of auditorium - no supply for temporary board - 90 spots, 45 fresnels, 29 parcans, 14 pcs, 11 floods.
SOUND: Cadac A series 40:10:10 desk, operated in platform at back of auditorium - one flown 1 floor standing speaker in all four corners of auditorium, plus central cluster - 2 X Denon mini disc players - 1 X Akai s300i sampler - 1 X Amiga sequencer - CD player - 3 effects units - mics shared with Barbican Theatre.
Acoustics suitable for music and spoken word.
STAGE MANAGEMENT: Prompt position on lighting/sound platform at back of auditorium - cue lights, 12 outstations, and headsets, 8 outstations - show relay/Tannoy to dressing rooms.
Backstage: Dressing rooms shared with Barbican Theatre - green room - band room - 2 quick change rooms - wardrobe as for Barbican Theatre. Refreshments available in green room. Rehearsal facilities as for Barbican Theatre. Staff and security facility shared with theatre.
Backstage facilities accessible to disabled performers and staff.

Cinema 1
Tel: 0171 382 7000
ADMINISTRATION:
Props: Corporation of London,
Programme Planner: Robert Rider.
Policy: Independent film repertory and new releases.
Performances: Usually 2 evening perfs and week-end matinees, Saturday Childrens Cinema Club.
Seats: 280 plus 2 wheelchair spaces.
Full projections, lighting, sound, video, simultaneous interpretation.

Cinemas 2 and 3
Available for conferences, meetings and private screenings. Cinema 2 used for public cinema (see Cinema 1).
Seats: 253 and 153 respectively, plus one wheelchair space in each auditorium.

Other Facilities:
Barbican Art Gallery, Concourse & Foyer Gallery, 1400 sq.m.; open air Sculpture Court; City of London Lending Library; 3 public restaurants; private function rooms; 5 conference rooms; 2 trade exhibition halls, 8000 sq.m. gross; parking for 454 cars.

BARBICAN CENTRE

Silk Street, Barbican, London EC2Y 8DS
Mgt: 020 7638 4141 BO: 020 7638 8891
SD: 020 7382 7676 Fax: 020 7382 7270
Email: info@barbican.org.uk
Web Site: www.barbican.org.uk
ADMINISTRATION:
Managing Director: Sir Nicholas Kenyon
Head of Programming: Louise Jeffries
Head of Theatre: Tony Racklin
BITE - Theatre Production Manager: Simon Bourne
Head of Music: Huw Humphreys
Head of Cinema: Robert Rider
Facilities for the disabled: Barbican Hall, 16 wheelchair spaces plus escorts; Barbican Theatre, 11 wheelchair spaces plus escorts; The Pit, 2 wheelchair space plus escort. Lifts, chairlifts and assistance available, ring box office on 020 7638 8891. Level access and free parking on presentation of disabled car registration certificate.

For more information on hiring, contact the venue on: artistichire@barbican.org.uk
Theatre Capacity: 1,160

BARBICAN HALL

Barbican Centre, Silk Street, Barbican, London EC2Y 8DS
Mgt: 020 7638 4141 BO: 020 7638 8891
Fax: 020 7382 7377
Email: info@barbican.org.uk
Web Site: www.barbican.org.uk
Seats: Barbican Hall 1991, fixed rake, continental style;
TECHNICAL:
STAGE: Open Concert Platform.
Performing area 20.13m X 12.4m, 10.3m to 6.7m high. No rake - floor beech, unsprung, no crossover, stage heated. Timber surround at rear - drawn. Rear half of stage is a series of mechanical risers. Get-in via goods lift. Scale stage and lighting plans available.
LIGHTING: ETC Expression 2x board, 168 circuits, operated from control room at rear of stalls . 2 followspots if required.
SOUND: Midas XL200 48:8 desk, operated at rear of stalls - Renkus Heinz central cluster speaker system - stocks of AKG, Sennheiser, Shure and Sony Mics. Soundcraft 8000 24:8:8 control room rear of stalls.
STAGE MANAGEMENT: Prompt corner left, right or centre backstage - cue lights, talkback - show relay to dressing rooms.
BACKSTAGE: 21 dressing rooms, access by lifts and stairs - green room - band room. Backstage bar. Rehearsal rooms and pianos, excellent. Advice given on accommodation. Many staff - security, personnel.

BARBICAN THEATRE

Barbican Centre, Silk Street, London EC2Y 8DS
SD: 020 7628 3351 BO: 020 7628 8891
Fax: 020 7382 7277
Email: theatre@barbican.org.uk
Web Site: www.barbican.org.uk
Managed by the Barbican Centre.
ADMINISTRATION:
Head of Theatre: Tony Racklin
BITE Production Manager: Simon Bourne
Status: The venue is funded by Corporation of London.
Policy: international theatre, opera and contemporary dance. Willing to premiere shows.
Performance Schedule: Matinees usually Sat or Sun.
Non-performance activities: Available for hire subject to programming.
Seats: 1168
Catering: 2 private bars , Theatre bars, stalls floor and gallery bar, (also see Barbican Centre catering facilities).
Acess: (See Barbican Centre Access facilities).
Facilities for the disabled: 8 wheelchair spaces plus escorts; infra-red audio system; parking; lifts to all levels; special toi-

lets and assistance available.
TECHNICAL:
STAGE: Open Stage. Performing area 15m X 15m - pros opening up to 15m X 9m - wing widths 10m SR, 10m SL, 6m US - Raked stage 1 in 15 (removable), floor surface variable, dance floor available, backstage and understage crossovers, stage heated. Height of grid 30m - 67 powered hoists, 0.2m apart - 500kg permitted on bars - maximum flying height 10m - various masking. 30 X 15A/45A independent circuits. Various stage machinery. Get-in via truck lift, dock doors 4m X 6m. Tallescope. Safety curtain. Scale stage, fly and lighting plans available, 1:25 and 1:50.
LIGHTING: Obsession 2, 480 ways, 380 X 3kw, 100 X 5kw, operated from control room at rear of stalls - 300 spots, 100 fresnels, Strand - 4 X CSI followspots, operated from No 1 FOH bridge.
SOUND: Cadac E Series mixing desk - Beyer, Calrec, Sennheiser, AKG and Neumann mics - Akai sampler, Denon midi disk systems - purpose-built sound editing suite - PA system. Acoustics suitable for music and spoken word.
Stage Mgt: Prompt corner SL and rear of stalls - twin light cue system, 30 outstations - show relay/Tannoy to dressing rooms.
Backstage: 21 dressing rooms, accommodating 88 - green room - band room - quick change rooms - wardrobe on 7th floor, fully equipped. Rehearsal room and piano. Staff (for main Stage and Pit) - 16 stage, 10 lighting, 3 sound, 5 wardrobe - casuals available - security personnel. Backstage facilities accessible to disabled performers and staff.
Membership: SOLT; TMA.

BATTERSEA ARTS CENTRE

Venue undergoing restoration, capacity unknown until 2016
Lavender Hill, London SW11 5TN
Mgt: 020 7223 6557 BO: 020 7223 2223
Fax: 020 7978 5207 Admin: 020 7326 8239
Email: boxoffice@bac.org.uk, mailbox@bac.org.uk
Web Site: www.bac.org.uk
ADMINISTRATION:
Artistic Director: David Jubb
Executive Manager: Rebecca Holt
Technical Manager: Kevin Miles
Theatre: Multi-purpose performance space. Capacity: 200 +
Lower Hall Capacity: 100 - 200
Recreation Room Capacity: 50 - 100
Policy: To work with artists and audiences towards the development of innovative forms of theatre.
For venue hire contact the theatre on: venues@bac.org.uk.
TECHNICAL:
STAGE (Theatre): The playing area (on floor) is normally 27 feet x 21 feet.
LIGHTING: 6 X Harmony 1k Fresnels all with Barndoors, 10 X Cantata 1.2k Fresnels all with Barndoors, 10 X Cantata 1.2k Profiles 18/32 with Rotary Gobo Gate, 15 X 650w Prelude Fresnels all with Barndoors, 8 X Thomas Pars all CP 62.
LX Desk: ETC Express:- 120 Channels 2k per way Digital.
SOUND: Soundcraft K1 Sound Desk 16-4, 1 X Denon DCD -425 single C.D. Programmable, 1 X Denon DRM 550 single cassette unit, 2X EV P1250 PWR Amps, 1 X EV XP200 Cross Over, 4 X EV S x 200 Midd and Top Speakers, 2 X EV Sb 120 Bass Speakers, 1 X Alesis Quadravert, Relevant Cables, Patch Bay.
Please contact the Technical Manager for full technical specifications.

BATTERSEA TOWN HALL

Lavender Hill, Battersea, London SW11 5TN
Tel: 020 7326 8211 BO: 020 7223 2223
Email: venues@bac.org.uk
Web Site: www.bac.org.uk
ADMINISTRATION:
Props: London Borough of Wandsworth
Town Hall Manager: Rachel Twigg
Artistic Director: David Jubb
Technical Manager: Daniel Palmer. Tel: 020 7326 8251
Events Team: Tel: 020 7326 8211 Email: venues@bac.org.uk
Seated Capacity: Grand Hall 350 theatre style 500, standing 600.

LILIAN BAYLIS STUDIO THEATRE

Rosebery Avenue, London EC1R 4TN
Tel: 020 7863 8198 Fax: 020 7863 8199
Email: reception@sadlerswells.com
Web Site: www.sadlerswells.com
ADMINISTRATOR:
Props: Sadlers Wells
Chief Executive & Artistic Director: Alistair Spalding
Technical Manager: Roman Bezdyk (020 7863 8063 or roman.bezdyk@sadlerswells.com)
Cap: 180 + 2 wheelchair spaces.
TECHNICAL:
STAGE: Performance Area; 15m wide by 8m deep. Maple floor. Flat.
LIGHTING: Console and dimmers:
Control Room Console: Strand 530i, 1200 intensity channels, 600 scroller/moving light attributes, Tracker ball and rotary controls, 98 x 2.5k Strand LD90 dimmers, 10 x 5k Strand LD90 dimmers. Booms: There are 8 booms, 4 either side, each rigged with the following: Shin: 26 ETC Source 4 575w fixed beam profile, Mid: Selecon Rama HP 1200 1.2kW Fresnel Head: ETC Source 4 Par 575w with wide lens. Additional lighting stock: 6 x 19 ETC Source 4 575w fixed beam profile, 12 x 26 ETC Source 4 575w fixed beam profile, 12 x 36 ETC Source 4 575w fixed beam profile, 6 x 50 ETC Source 4 575w fixed beam profile, 24 x Selecon Rama HP1200 1.2kW Fresnel, 6 x Selecon Arena 2.5kW Fresnel, 20 x Thomas Par 64 1kW (CP60/CP61/CP62 - please ask for details), 16 x ETC Source 4 Par 575w (with lenses in narrow, medium, wide, extra wide), 7 x 4-cell Strand Coda 4 x 500w asymmetrical cells, 12 x Wybron 7.5" CXI colour changer (with backplates for Thomas Parcan or ETC Source 4 profile)
SOUND: FOH Speakers; 4 x Martin CT2 full range speakers split left and right and powered by Crown K1 amps with CT controller, 2 x Martin CTX sub bass speakers powered by Crown K1 amp, 4 x Tannoy T12 high and low in-fills powered by Crown K1 amps. Monitor Speakers: 4 x Tannoy T12, 2 x Yamaha P1600 AMPS. Control Room monitoring: 2 x Tannoy Reveals, 1 x Intem 500 amp. Mixer: Allen & Heath GL 2800 24 Channel 10 aux 12x 4 Matrix, Sonifex RB DA6 Distribution amp. Playback: 1 x CD Player Tascam RW 70, 1 x CD Player Denon DN - C635, 1 x Minidisc Player Sony MD MDS-E10, 1 x Cassette player Tascam 112R Single cassette. Outboard Processing: 1 x BSS FCS 966 2 x 30 way graphic EQ, 1 x DBX 1231 2 x 31 way graphic EQ, 1 x Yamaha SPX 990 effects, 1 x DBX 166XL limiter/gate/compressor, 1 X DBX Drive 260, 1 x Behringer Multigate XR 440
COMMUNICATIONS AND AUDIO VISUAL: Intercom; 3 x Tec-Pro wired beltpacks and headsets (Clearcom compatible), Cue lights, 4 Patchable, Backstage calls and Show Relay to dressing rooms.
AV Equipment: 1 x fixed colour camera with full stage view routed to: prompt desk, control room and dressing rooms, 1 x Panasonic MX70 Digital AV mixer, 1 x Marantz DVD Player DV 4610, 1 x Sony DV / Mini DV Recorder / Player DSR - 45AP, 1 x Mitsubishi XL5950LU projector (5000 lumens) with 2 interchangeable lens: 1.85-2.35:1 2.4-3.3:1
DRESSING ROOMS AND WARDROBE: Large room available for use as wardrobe or storage area. Equipped with : 1 washing machine, 1 tumble dryer. Dressing Rooms: 3 accomm 21. Shower and Basin facilities. All dressing rooms have mirrors, audio show relay, paging calls and a video feed of the main stage.
ADDITIONAL: 1 upright rehearsal piano for onstage use.

BECK THEATRE

Grange Road, Hayes, Middlesex UB3 2UE
Mgt/Admin: 020 8561 7506 BO: 020 8561 8371 Fax: 020 8569 1072
Email: enquiries@becktheatre.org.uk
Web Site: www.becktheatre.org.uk
ADMINISTRATION:
Props: HQ Theatres Ltd.
Theatre Director: Louise Clifford
Operations Manager: Jack Schofield
Contact: jack@becktheatre.org.uk
Theatre Administrator: Kay Grover
Perfs: Open 7 days per week. Variable, generally 8.00 p.m. for plays and single

performance concerts.
Policy: Major theatre tours and concerts, children's shows, pantomime, films, plus local amateur and daytime conference hirings. Cabaret performances, dance evenings, folk, jazz, dance workshop, fringe theatre, etc.
Capacity:
Theatre: Deluxe tiered, fixed auditorium seats: 600. With orchestra pit/thrust stage: 564.
Second Performance Area: Foyer area seating up to 120 around central performance floor of semi-sprung Canadian maple, dimensions up to 30' x 30'.
Extra: Licensed bar, kiosk, coffee shop.
Rooms available for private functions and meetings of up to 70; in-house catering.
Exhibition areas in foyer and function rooms.

BLACKHEATH HALLS

23 Lee Road, Blackheath, London SE3 9RQ
Tel: 020 8318 9758 BO: 020 8463 0100
Email: h.benton@trinitylaban.ac.uk
Web Site: www.blackheathhalls.com
ADMINISTRATION:
General Manager: Keith Murray
Operations Manager: Hannah Benton
Policy: Classical, Jazz, Folk, Contemporary, Opera, Musicals, Rock & Pop, Exhibitions, Recordings and Rehearsals. Available for hire, presents own events and co-presents.
Cafe Bar available for hire seating 50 - standing 150.
The Great Hall cap: 600 Seated, 1000 standing. Recital Room 160 seated, 250 standing.
For information on hiring the Great Hall or Recital Room please e-mail Caroline Foulkes: c.foulkes@trinitylaban.ac.uk
TECHNICAL:
Recital Room: 60' x 30', stage 18' x 9' max.
Great Hall: 90' x 60', stage 50' x 25'.

THE BLOOMSBURY THEATRE

15 Gordon Street, London WC1H 0AH
Mgt: 020 7679 2777 BO: 020 7388 8822
SD: 020 7679 2922 Tech: 020 7679 1361 Fax: 020 7383 4080
Email: admin@thebloomsbury.com
Web Site: www.thebloomsbury.com
ADMINISTRATION:
Director: Peter Cadley
Theatre Administrator: Shalini Simpson
Accountant: Gabriel Emordi
Theatre Coordinator: Frank Penter
Technical Manager: Nick Funnell (Syd)
Policy: All-year round programme of visiting Theatre
Dance, Concerts, Comedy and Opera, including
occasional in-house productions and 12 weeks of Student Productions (UCL) during October and Spring Terms.
Capacity: 547 seats. Standing room: 35.
Full Catering facilities and Licensed Bar.
TECHNICAL:
STAGE: Stage Width; Wall to Wall 79'3" 24.16m, Stage Left wing 21'7" 6.6m, Stage Right wing 26'72 8.1m. Pros. Width 29'11" 9.12m, Height 23' 7.03m. Stage Depth; Main Stage 30'8" 9.35m. Maximum flying width 39'4" 12m. 23 double purchase counterweight sets. Cinema Screen; On counter weights 6 and 7 (Set 5 does not fly); Size of screen 9m x 4.4m to 6m x 3m (top and side masking moves). Get-In; Access through Front Doors off Gordon Street; Door Height 2.12m; Door Width 1.23m (with doors), 1.31m (doors removed); Diagonal clearance 2.39m (with doors), 2.47m (doors removed).
LIGHTING: Lantern Stock; 11 x ETC Source 4 - 19 Degree 575W Profile, 10 x Freedom 18/32 - 600w Profile, 18 x Sil 30 - 1kw Profile, 8 x ETC Source 4 Zoom - 575w Profile, 10 x Starlette PC - 1kw, 14 x Alto - 2kw, 32 x Cantata F - 1kw, 2 x Starlette - 2kw Fresnel, 27 x Parcan - (CP61 or CP62 heads), 2 x Parcans - (short nose), 6 x Berkey Cyc Battens 650w - 4 compartment, 2 x Followspot - Pani 1202 , 1200w HMI, long throw. Rigging; Internally wired bars 3 x 18 Way I.W.Bs, Advance Bars - 2 x 12 Way I.W.B, 6 x Shin Stands, 4 x Stands (Max height 8'), 6 x Ballet booms (Max height 8') (20 x Boom arms approx.), 8 x Ladders 3 Rung. Control; ETC Ion control desk OR Strand 520i 250 channel Lighting board; 136 ways of dimming. 128 x 2.5kw , 8 x 5kw. (Hard wired. Strand LD90)
SOUND: Amps; 4 x Yamaha P2500, 1 x ARX SX1500, 1 x Yamaha P2350. Speakers; F.O.H; 2 x Martin Bass Bins, 4 x Martin W3s, 2 x Martin EM56. Onstage; 4 x RCF 312-a Active Monitor, 3 x JBL EON 15. Various microphones and stands available. Desk; Roland M-400 digital live mixing console OR 1 x Allen and Heath GL2800 (32:8:2) (permanent position at rear of Stalls). Playback; 1 x Dennon DN - D4000 Dual CD Player; 1 x Sony DVP NS300 DVD Player; 1 x Tascam CD-401 mk2 CD Player; 1 x Tascam MD301 mk2 Minidisc Player / Recorder. Processing; 2 x DBX 231 Graphic Equaliser, 1 x Yamaha Q2031 Graphic Equaliser, 2 x DBX 266XL dual channel Compressor/Gate, 1 x T.C.Electronic D.TWO Multitap Delay unit, 1 x Alesis Akira Digital multi effects unit, 1 x Yamaha SPX 990 Digital multi effects unit.
BACKSTAGE FACILITIES: Dressing Rooms; 4, accomm. 31. Green Room, Laundry Room (washing machine, tumble dryer).
ADDITIONAL: Communications; Tecpro Masterstation, 6 x Tecpro Beltpacks and Headsets, Prompt Desk with 6 cuelights, FOH paging, Backstage paging, and built in headset. Av Equipment; 1 x Panasonic PTD3500E data projector (3500 ANSI lumens) (extra cost); 1x Laser Pointer.

BORDERLINE

Orange Yard, Manette Street, London W1D 4JB
Tel: 020 7734 5547
Email: borderline@mamaco.com
Web Site: www.meanfiddler.com
ADMINISTRATION:
General Business Manager: Gemma Gilford. (gemma.gilford@mamaco.com)
Technical Manager: Matt Felton
Venue Manager: Gemma Gilford
Capacity: 300
TECHNICAL:
Contact the Technical Manager for full technical specifications; matt.felton@mamaco.com
SOUND: Mixing Desk; Yamaha LS9-32 (Monitor mixes from FOH. PA System; 4x Meyer MSL2, 2x Meyer 650 Subs, 2x Martin 215 mkIII Subs Powered by Crown. Monitors (4 mixes); 2x D&B Max 15, 2x Martin LE12, 1x JBL SR4733A Drum fill Powered by Crest. FOH Rack; 1x Klark Technic DN3600 Dual Graphic EQ, 1x Denon CD player, 1x Tascam Mini Disc player/recorder, 1x Panasonic DVD 554 DVD player.
LIGHTING: 1x Avolites Azure 2000, 6x LED parcans, 4x Anolis 144 LED Strip, 5x iPix Satellites, 6x Robe DJScan250 moving mirror club lights.
ADDITIONAL: AV [non-recordable video feed]: 1x Sanyo PLC-WXU30 Projector, 1x Kramer VP Series Video Scaler and Matrix 2x Widescreen TV 1x Widescreen Projector Screen [Drop down].

BRICK LANE MUSIC HALL

443 North Woolwich Road, Silvertown, London E16 2DA
Tel: 020 7511 6655
Email: admin@bricklanemusichall.co.uk
Web Site: www.bricklanemusichall.co.uk
ADMINISTRATION:
Props: London Borough of Newham
Capacity: 180 theatre style
Theatre Director: Vincent Hayes
Manager: Zara Kattan
Technical Manager: Oliver Savage
All correspondence through the Theatre Director.

BRITTEN THEATRE ROYAL COLLEGE OF MUSIC

Prince Consort Road, London SW7 2BS
Switchboard: 020 7591 4300 Fax: 020 7591 4737
Email: info@rcm.ac.uk
Web Site: www.rcm.ac.uk
ADMINISTRATION:
Props: Royal College of Music
Theatre Co-ordinator: Paul Tucker
Technical Manager: Keiran Taylor
Policy: One of London's best-kept secrets, this is an elegant theatre producing Royal College of Music Operas, Concerts, etc. Also available to hire for dance, conferences, product launches, concerts, filming etc. Opened in 1986.
Seats: 400 on 3 levels.

TECHNICAL:
STAGE: Pros width 9.06m, height 5.18m; Perf area (without masking) width 10.43m, depth 9.28m; wings widths SR 2.22m, SL 1.82m, US nil; rake flat level standard configuration; floor maple strip on ply; height of grid 12.70m; basic flying details counterweight, single purchase 35 set at 0.23cm spacing no tab track available; max weight on bars 400kg; max flying height 12.35m, basic masking available serge flats, legs, boards, tabs + wipe. Black;Stage power supply 19 X 13amp 240 outlets, stage machinary traps, Forestage dimensions: width 9.35m max, depth 3.58m entrances SL and SR; Orchestra pit dimensions: width 9.35m , depth 9.3m accommodates 80 max.
The stage is suitable for dance and barefoot dance and there is a cross over upstage.
LIGHTING: Board; Strand 530 consle c/w 400 channels of Genius Pro software, Tracker Moving Light software, Networker System software; dimmers 120 saturated configuration, 100 X 2.4kw, 20 X 5kw, 3 phase, (LD90); operation centre rear dress circle; temporary power supply 3 phase, 63 amp per phase, (USR), Luminaires: 12 X Cantata 11/26 1.2kw, 2 X Cantata 18/32 1.2kw, 22 X Harmony 15/28 1kw, 8 X Patt.264 1kw, 15 X Prelude 16/30 650w, 4 X Prelude 22/40 650kw, 1 X Solo follow spot 2kw, 1 X Cadenza F 2kw, 11 X Cadenza PC 2kw, 12 X Cadenza PC 1.2kw, 6 X Patt. 743 1kw, 1 Prelude F 650w, 24 X Prelude PC 650w, 24 X P.64 240v 1kw (CP61, CP62 only), 8 X Spill Ring for P.64, 2 X P.750, Beamlight 1kw, 12 X Coda 500/3 (3 X 500w), Misc: 2 X 4'6" stands, 4 X turtles, 1 X 16 way internally wired bar, 3 X 14 way internally wired bar, 2 X 6 way internally wired bar (1/2 width); Effect equipment 8 X Scroller Rainbow Pro 8, 33 colours, 2 X Moving Light, Strand Pirouette, 1 X Control for above units.
SOUND: 1 X Soundcraft 8-4-2, located SR corner, amplifiers 3 X AGM SC-500, microphones 1 X SM58, 1 X single cassette, house system show relay and tannoy to all dressing rooms, no foyer PA.
The theatre is designed with acoustics for music and the spoken word without amplification.

THE BROADWAY THEATRE BARKING

Broadway, Barking, Essex IG11 7LS
Mgt: 020 8507 5610 BO: 020 8507 5607
Email: admin@thebroadwaybarking.com
Web Site: www.thebroadwaybarking.com
ADMINISTRATION:
Props: London Borough of Barking & Dagenham
CEO / Artistic Director: Karena Johnson
Marketing Manager: Barry Burke
Technical & Buildings Manager: Cameron Murray
Policy: All forms of touring entertainment including plays, musicals, comedy acts, ballet, opera, concerts, jazz, rock, country, folk etc.
Seated: 341. Standing Capacity: 850
Licensed bar & coffee lounge.

TECHNICAL:
For full technical specifications contact the Technical Manager on cameron.murray@thebroadwaybarking.com.

BROADWAY THEATRE CATFORD

Catford Broadway, Catford, London SE6 4RU
Admin: 020 8314 9472 BO Tel: 020 8690 0002
Email: martin / kath / helen @broadwaytheatre.org.uk
Web Site: www.broadwaytheatre.org.uk
ADMINISTRATION:
Props: London Borough of Lewisham
Artistic Director: Martin Costello
Technical Manager: Kath O'Sullivan
Box Office and Marketing Manager: Helen Haylett
Policy: Touring, Pantomime, Concerts, Variety, Musical, Opera, Location Filming (1932 art deco theatre)
Perfs: variable.
Cap: 800. Three Bars.
TECHNICAL:
STAGE: Proscenium Stage, slight rake, pros. opening 9.14m. Ht. of Pros 6.10m, Depth of S/line 7.92, Ht. of Grid 5.49m, 9 lines 1 C/W 7 hemp; scenery flying Ht. 5.49m; Flying Bars 9.14m; W/Widths P.S. 1.52m, O.P. 1.52m; Prompt Cnr. P.S.
LIGHTING: Switchboard: M.24 Control with Back Up F/X Unit, 60 x 2K.W. (14 F.O.H.) Portable. 10 Harmony 16/30, 6 Prelude 15/28, 4 T.Spot, 8 264, 4 CCT Minuette Profile, 2 23, 12 Harmony P.C. 1 K.W. 12 743, 2 Minuette, 4 123, 4 243 (2K.W.) 22 PAR Cans (240v) Medium, 12 Coda 500W. Floods, 4 4 Circuit Code Groundrows. Follow Spots. Pani H.M.I. 1200.
SOUND: Equipment: 6.5k Rig - Yamaha PM 3000 40 Channel Mixer - Speakers left and right flown T/R4 clusters by Clair Brothers, Crest Audio amps 2 x 4801 High/Superhigh, 2 x 8001 Meds, 2 x 8001 Lows - crossover unit - programmable equalisers/spectrum analyzer - 5 D.I. Boxes - Effects include equalisers, Compressors and Noise gates - Foldback 4 Clair Brothers Audio 12 am monitors -1 High Speed Revox B77 - 1 Dennon Cassette Deck & CD with remote.
OTHER: Dressing Rooms 7, accom. 200; 2 Showers; Orchestra Pit 28.
Membership: TMA.
Studio Theatre: Cap 80

BROMPTON LIBRARY

210 Old Brompton Road, London SW5 0BS
Tel: 020 7373 3111 / 7361 3010 Fax: 020 7938 1445
Email: librariesandarts@rbkc.gov.uk
Web Site: www.rbkc.gov.uk/leisureandlibraries/libraries/yourlibraries.aspx
ADMINISTRATION:
Props: Royal Borough of Kensington and Chelsea
Room Bookings Manager: Craig Bateman or Elisabeth Brown.
Meeting Room seated capacity: 30
TECHNICAL:
Room 24' x 23' with rostra. Small kitchen and toilet facilities available. Suitable for meetings, quiet private functions. Not licensed.

BUSH HALL

310 Uxbridge Road, London W12 7LJ
Tel: 020 8222 6955
Email: notes@bushhallmusic.co.uk
Web Site: www.bushhallmusic.co.uk
ADMINISTRATION:
Managing Director: Charlie Raworth
Director: Emma Hutchinson
Senior Manager (Live Music & Events): Kath Borer
Web Producer: Tara Spinks
Capacity: Seated: 150. Standing: 400

TECHNICAL:
STAGING: Performance Hall dimensions;19.36 L x 9.958 W, Dance Floor dimensions; 4.88 L x 4.88 W. 6 x Aluminium deck sections, 8ft x 4ft, on 900mm legs. (Set up as 16ft x 12ft stage.), 1 x Set of Aluminium deck steps onto stage, stage left., 2 x Aluminium deck sections, 4ft x 4ft, supporting speaker stacks, on 600mm legs.
LIGHTING: 12 x Thomas Par cans - Par 64 long nose (4 par cans to right of stage, 4 par cans to left of stage and 4 par cans overhead), 2 x Source Four Juniors, 2 x Mirror ball spots, 12 x Thomas Par cans lighting the ceiling - Par 64 short nose, Various coloured gels, 088 12 channel XL master desk.
SOUND: 8 x Martin Audio W8LM Line Array Speaker, 4 x Martin Audio WMX Sub Bass Speaker, 1 x Amplifier Rack to drive the above, 2 x XTA DPA224 Digital Processors, 6 x Martin Audio LE1200 Monitor Speaker, 2 x QSC PLX2402 Monitor Amplifier, 1 x Midas Venice 320 - 24+4S Channel Control Desk, 1 x Klark Teknik DN360 Graphic Equaliser - Foh, 2 x BSS FDS960 Graphic Equaliser - Monitors, 1 x Yamaha SPX900 Multi Effects Unit, 1 x TC Electronics M1 Multi Effects Unit, 3 x DBX 166XL Twin Compressor / Gate, 1 x Drawmer DS201 Twin Gate. Various Microphones and stands available. 1 x Emo Passive DI Box, 5 x BSS AR133 Active DI Boxes, 1 x 24/8 Multicore (Note Without Monitor Splits).

CAMBRIDGE THEATRE

Earlham Street, London WC2H 9HU
Mgt: 020 7850 8711 BO: 020 7850 8715
SD: 020 7850 8710 Fax: 020 7836 9076
Email: info@rutheatres.co.uk

Web Site: www.reallyuseful.co.uk
ADMINISTRATION:
Props: Really Useful Theatres Ltd
Theatre Manager: Chris Green
General Manager, Production: Robert Jude
Chief Electrician: David Jarrett. (davidjarrett@reallyuseful.co.uk)
Policy: Musicals, Comedy, Concerts, Television, Plays.
Facilities may be made available for day time, late night and weekend use for private and press receptions, conferences and meetings.
For Venue Hire contact the theatre on: venuehire@reallyuseful.co.uk
Capacity: 1,283
3 Bars, Entertainment Suite.
TECHNICAL:
STAGE: Flat stage, Canadian Maple Tongue and Groove. Lift/Revolves etc; 1 stage lift, 17' 9" (5.41m) x 8' 10" (2.91m). Pros. Opening; 29' 6" (8.99m). Height of Pros. 25' 2" (7.76m). Depth of stage (from safety curtain) 30' 11" (9.43m). Height of Steel Grid 50' (15.24m). Height of fly floors (to fly rail); 25' (7.62m) stage right and 18' 10" (5.76m) to underside of CW Wall Frame. Distance between fly floors; 41' (12.5m) DS 40' (12.19m) US. Dock Door; 20' (6.90m) high x 8' (2.43m) wide. Height of Stage from street, 5'6" (1.67m) above pavement level. Hoist or Winches above get-in, 1 Tonne electric hoist. Wing space; Rear dock 24' (7.31m) x 15'(4.56m) deep x 16' 3" (4.95m) high. Orchestra Pit accommodates approx. 18.
LIGHTING: Board; Strand Galaxy II. Dimmers, 280. House Spots, 2 x Colorarc 2kw.
SOUND: Please contact venue.
BACKSTAGE FACILITIES: Stage Management; Headsets (Clear Com compatible) cue lights Tannoy System. Dressing Rooms, 18; 2 band rooms; wardrobe facilities. 3 x VIP Rooms. No Kitchen.
FACILITIES FOR DISABLED PEOPLE: 4 removable seats in stalls. Level access. Adapted toilet. Infrared hearing aid system.
Membership: SOLT

CECIL SHARP HOUSE

2 Regents Park Road, Camden, London NW1 7AY
Tel: 020 7485 2206 Fax: 020 7284 0534
Email: info@efdss.org
Web Site: www.cecilsharphouse.org
Home of English Folk Dance and Song Society.
ADMINISTRATION:
Props: EFDSS
Chief Executive: Katy Spicer
Marketing and Communications Director: Tessa Norton
Capacity: Contains 6 spaces. Kennedy Hall; 500 standing / 420 seated (300 chairs, 120 on tiered seating). Trefusis Hall: 150 standing / 120 seated. Storrow Hall; 60.
Available for hire; ideal for rehearsals. Conact Hiring Administrator, Jessica Grimshaw, on 020 7485 2206 ext. 24 (Hirings Manager) or hire@efdss.org. Facilities include sprung floors, grand piano, bar, cafeteria and garden.

CENTRAL HALL, WESTMINSTER

Storeys Gate, Westminster, London SW1H 9NH
Mgt: 020 7222 8010 Fax: 020 7222 6883
Email: info@c-h-w.com, events@c-h-w.com
Web Site: www.c-h-w.com
ADMINISTRATION:
Props: Methodist Church.
General Manager: Paul Southern
Head of Sales and Events: Stuart Ryding
Administrator: Karin Parkinson (kparkinson@c-h-w.com)
Policy: Concerts, Meetings, Conferences, Exhibitions, Trade Shows, Banqueting & Receptions.
Capacity: Great Hall - 2160; Lecture Hall - 500; Library - 500. Other rooms available ranging from 8 - 500.
TECHNICAL:
Open Stage with Choir risers. Thrust Stage Extension: 40' x 60'. 4-manual organ, grand piano on request.
Sound Equipment: 24-4-2 Yamaha PM1200 Console Apogee Speakers. Foldback. 4kW continuous sound power. New lifts - improved get-in facilities.

CHARING CROSS THEATRE

The Arches, Villiers Street, London WC2N 6NL
Tel: 0207 930 5868
Email: jon@charingcrosstheatre.co.uk
Web Site: www.charingcrosstheatre.co.uk
Senior Personnel: Jon Chai
Commercial theatre producers.
A 265 seat proscenium arch theatre in the heart of the West End. Promoting theatre, comedy and music. Also available to hire for rehearsal space, auditions, conferences and screenings. There is a separate restaurant and three bars. Intelligent Lighting are responsible for all technical aspects of the theatre, they can be contacted through the mainline number. Stage Right are responsible for all Technical aspects of the theatre.
Email: technical@charingcrosstheatre.co.uk
STAGE: Access SL and SR. Hemp flying with no tower. 12 bars 6.1m long, maximum dead height 5.4m. Fly floor is SR.
SOUND: In house Bose speaker system. Communications consist of backstage and FOH paging controlled SR and a tech pro technical intercom with 8 headsets and belt packs.
LIGHTING: ETC Smart Fade 2496 DMX Desk. 4 x ETC source 4 Junior zoom, 10 x CCT Starlette Fresnels, , 10 x Par Cans
POWER: 3 phase power situated SL; supply 1 sound - single phase 16amp ceeform, single phase 32amp ceeform, single phase 63amp ceeform, 3 # 63amp ceeofrm. All protected by 30m amp ELCB. Supply 2 lighting - 3 # 63amp ceeform. Protected by 100m amp ELCB.

CHATS PALACE

42-44 Brooksby's Walk, Homerton, Hackney, London E9 6DF
Tel: 020 8533 0227
Email: info@chatspalace.com
Web Site: www.chatspalace.com
ADMINISTRATION:
Capacity; Seated: 100. Standing: 200.
TECHNICAL:
STAGE: Floor area 5.5m x 6m deep, pros opening 5.5m x 3m. Rubberised dancefloor available. Black curtains / white cyclorama / black brick wall. Backstage crossover - just! Stage units form raked seating or can make 5m x 4m stage for music, etc. Traverse, round, other variations possible.
LIGHTS: Zero 88 Fat Frog programmable board. 18 circuit @2kw, operated from back balcony. 50 various fresnels, profiles, PCs and floods, and follow spot.
SOUND: 16.4.2 sound mixing desk operated from back of hall OR 20.2 mixing desk operated from back balcony. 2kW turbosound rig with 1kW monitoring.10 mics, 4 DI boxes, 2xCD, MD, DA, MC. Also available - projector (video/DVD/etc) and screen, 2 x slide projector, turntables and mixer, upright piano (good). Acoustic suitable for music and spoken word.
BACKSTAGE FACILITIES: One dressing room, stage right. Some wing space both sides.

CHINGFORD ASSEMBLY HALL

Station Road, Chingford, London E4 7EN
Booking: 020 8496 8018
Email: assemblyhall.bookings@walthamforest.gov.uk
Web Site: www.walthamforest.gov.uk
ADMINISTRATION:
Props: Waltham Forest Council
Capacity: Main hall / lounge concerts, 400. Dancing, open floor, 350. Dancing with tables, 200. Dinners, weddings with small dance floor, 250. Full seating, 435. Licensed Bar.
Policy: Touring, Pantomime, Concerts, Variety, Music Hall, Drama, Dances, Dinners, Conferences, Weddings, etc.
TECHNICAL:
STAGE: Main Hall Dimensions: 59' x 54'. Stage 30' x 24'
LIGHTING: Control; Strand MX console 48 way (30 Ways available). (Minimum) 4 x 1000 watt Powercans, 4 x 1000 watt T spots 4 x 1000 watt Area floods, 10 x 500 watt Fresnels 1 x 2000 watt CSI follow spots (operators not supplied) Studio Master 12 way, 7 line inputs (all XLR).
SOUND: Tape deck, 2 x Wedge monitors Talk back from stage to lighting, sound

controls and dressing rooms 3 Cabaret microphones SM48.
Backstage Facilities; Dressing Rooms x 2
ADDITIONAL: Grand / Upright Piano

CHURCHILL THEATRE

High Street, Bromley, Kent BR1 1HA
Admin/SD: 020 8464 7131 BO: 0844 871 7620 Fax: 020 8290 6968
Email: bromleystagedoor@theambassadors.com
Web Site: www.atgtickets.com
ADMINISTRATION:
Props: Ambassadors Theatre Group Ltd
Marketing Manager: Jamie Leadbeatter
Head of Creative Learning: Kiaran Hall
Technical Manager: Ed Brimley
Theatre Manager: Gavin Schuman
Policy: Co-Productions are combined with touring shows to provide a comprehensive mix of plays, musicals, opera, dance, pantomime, family shows and concerts.
Extensive Education Programme: contact the Education Officer, Liam Shea, for more details.
Perfs: Evenings Monday-Saturday 7.45. Thursday and Saturday matinees 2.30.
Seats: 785 (760 when orchestra pit used). Two Bars.
TECHNICAL:
STAGE: Apron; Flat; Pros. opening 9.15m-13.7m variable; ht. of Pros. 7.01m; Depth of S/Line 15.09m; Ht. of Grid 14.46m; 50 (47-50 storage only) lines c/w, Scenery Flying Ht. 5.49m; Flying Bars 16.4m; W/Widths P.S. 10.87m, O.P. 10.67m; Prompt Cnr. P.S. or O.P.
LIGHTING: Strand 520i with 350 channels 350 attributes. Radio remote. Fully networked. 4 streams of DMX512 available on stage, control box, dimmer room and auditorium. XTBA DMX available on stage. Dimmers; 144 x 2.5kw, 24 x 5kw patchable to 350 circuits. Temp supplies; 200A TPN+E USL, 100 TPN+E DSR, 3 63A single sound supply DSL. Lanterns; 97 profiles, 64 fresnel/PC, 100 parcans, 6 iris 4, 10 Coda 4, 2 Robert Julia + Korrigan follow-spots. Some of the equipment is on a chargable use basis.
SOUND: Soundcraft Venue 32:8:2 desk with 8-way matrix, operated from back of stalls, CD player, 3 minidisc. Acoustics suitable for music and spoken word.
ADDITIONAL: Dressing Rooms 12, accom. 135 inc. Band and Chorus; 6 Showers; Orchestra Pit :15 plus.

COCKPIT THEATRE

Gateforth Street Off Church Street
London NW8 8EH
Admin: 020 7258 2920 BO/Reservations: 020 7258 2925
Email: dave@thecockpit.org.uk, mail@thecockpit.org.uk
Web Site: www.thecockpit.org.uk
ADMINISTRATION:
Props: City of Westminster College.
Theatre Manager: Dave Wybrow
Technical Co-ordinator and Theatre Technician: Deb Jones
Policy: Incoming companies/shows & exhibitions.
Seats: In the Round 220; Thrust 180.
Upstairs Rehearsal Studios for Hire.
Bar, Large dressing rooms, workshop, foyer capacity 240. Large loading dock doors. Hire rates £300-£400 per show day.
Disabled Access at street level to auditorium and disabled toilets.
TECHNICAL:
STAGE: Adaptable stage, Round/Thrusts/End.
LIGHTING: Switchboard: Strand 60 way, 3 x 3 preset; F.O.H. Spots 19 Patt. 223, 27 Patt. 264, 4 Patt. 123, 12 Patt. 23.
SOUND: 2 Ferrograph, 1 Garrard in Lighting/ Control Box above stage; Speakers 4 floating 12 in Axion 7 positions.
OTHER: Dressing Rooms 2; accom. 20; 2 Showers.
For full technical specifications contact Theatre Technician, deb@thecockpit.org.uk

COLLAGE ARTS

The Chocolate Factory, Wood Green, London, N22 6XJ
Tel: 020 8365 7500 Fax: 020 8365 8686
Email: info@collage-arts.org
Web Site: www.collage-arts.org
ADMINISTRATION:
Executive Director: Manoj Ambasna
Administrator: Sam Clarke
Collage Arts runs events and projects. It organises exhibitions, literature events and community festivals. Currently the Arts Development Programme concentrates on building relationships with community, organisations and education to deliver a range of comprehensive arts projects with an educational element. Our work challenges issues around social exclusion, both within and outside the education sector. Collage Arts develops, and manages a wide range of projects, including artists' residencies, creative mentoring scheme, and work with HMP Holloway. Collage Arts offers advice and support through regular surgery sessions. Various studios available for hire. For more information contact Administrator, Sam Clarke, on 020 8365 7500 or via email sam@collage-arts.org.

THE COMEDY STORE

1A Oxendon Street, London SW1Y 4EE
Club: 020 7839 6642 Mgt: 020 7930 2949 BO: 0844 871 7699 Fax: 020 7024 2069 (Admin Office)
Email: london@thecomedystore.co.uk
Web Site: www.thecomedystore.co.uk
ADMINISTRATION:
General Manager: Loki McKay
For hiring enquiries, contact Loki Mckay: loki@thecomedystore.co.uk
Head of Technical: Simon Mason
Capacity: 400
TECHNICAL:
STAGE: Steel Deck 12 x 8 ft minus 4ft radial curves on front corners. Expandable to 16 x 10 ft. Black, pleated tabs on back wall (removable).
LIGHTING: Control: Avolites Pearl Expert. Fixtures (moving); Martin MAC250 Kryptons x 4, Martin MiniMAC x 2, Clay Paky HP Minicsans x 4. Fixtures (generic); Source 4 Parcans x 4, Source 4 Parnels x 6, Source 4 Zoom profiles x 4, Source 4 Junior profiles x 4, Strand 650w fresnels x 6, Strand 300w fresnels x 4, Strand 16/30 profiles x 4, Strand 28/40 profiles x 4, Crown shortcan/floorcans Parcans (Silver) x 6 Thomas shortcan Parcans (Silver) x 2, Altmann 20 cell MR16 battens x 2, Jem 24/7 Hazer x 2.
SOUND: 12 channel stage box, 8 channel extension snake. Control: Allen & Heath iLive-112. Main output: 18 x HK Audio CT108, 2 x HK Audio CDR210C Subs, 1 x HK Audio DFC, 7x HK Audio VX2400 Amplifiers. Fold Back; 4 x PS8 Nexo fold back wedges, 1 x LS400 Nexo sub. Proccessing; 3 x Xilica 4in 8out Speaker controllers, 2 x Nexo PS8 Controller (Analogue), 2 x Focusrite twintrack vocal Compressors, 1 x Yamaha SPX990 effects unit. Induction Loop for the hard of hearing covering one large area of seating. Various Microphones available. Playback; Denon DN1800F 2 deck CD player, Sony MDS JE440 minidisc player, G5 Macintosh with iTunes. Audio Recording Suite; Pro Tools HD1 on G5 Macintosh, Pro Tools 192 Digital I/O, Focusrite Octopre C/W Digital Card, Tascam CD-RW750, Genelic 8030A Monitors x 2, Beyer Dynamic DT100 and DT150 Headphones.
AV: Cameras; Fixed focus Sony Super Exware, Pan/tilt remote controlled Sony Super Exware, Fisheye lensed fixed focus Sony Exware. Data Projector; Sony VPL-CX86 3000 lumens. Control; Extron Matrix 8x8, Extron Switcher/scaler, VGA input points from control and stage positions to matrix, 2 x Sony 250Gb Hard Disc/DVD recorder, 4 x Sony LCD TV screens around the venue for show monitoring, 2 x Sony 42" Plasma Screens for overspill viewing.
DRESSING ROOMS; 1 w/ door leading directly to the stage. Accommodates 8. Shower and toilet facilities.

THE CORONET THEATRE

28 New Kent Road, London SE1 6TJ
Tel: 020 7701 1500
Email: info@coronetlondon.co.uk
Web Site: www.coronetlondon.co.uk
ADMINISTRATION:
Policy; Live music venue.
Capacity: Ground Floor: 1,990; Seated Circle: 572; First Floor Club Room: 410; Second Floor Club Room: 110; VIP Room: 90.
TECHNICAL:

STAGE: Dimensions; L = 6.865m, W = 11.303m, H = 10.541m
SOUND: FOH Control; 1 x Yamaha M7CL digital desk, 1 x Sony/denon CD player, 1 x Comms system FOH to Mons consisting 1 x base station, 2 x belt pack, 2 x headset. d&b Speaker System Infill; 4 x d&b C4 top cabinets, 4 x d&b C4 sub cabinets, 2 x d&b D12 amplifier. d&b Speaker System Flying; PA1and PA2: Approximately 2' advanced from the downstage edge and 17' centres, 12 x d&b J8 cabinets, 2 x d&b J12 cabinets, 6 x d&b J sub, 14 x d&b D12 amplifier, 2 x d&b flying frames and associated rigging. Monitor Control; 1 x Yamaha M7CL digital desk. Monitor System; 10 x d&b M4 monitors, 5 x d&b D12 amplifier. DJ Equipment; 2 x Technics 1210 turntables, 2 x Pioneer CDJ 1000, 1 x Pioneer DJM 800 mixer.
LIGHTING: Back Truss; 2 x 1t points fitted with 1t double braked motors, 32ft 20" box truss, Back truss normal trim 20-25ft, Back truss max trim 30ft, Back truss weight in standard configuration 900kg, Truss maximum load 1400kg UDL, Truss ladder and fall arrestor, 4 x bar6 Par64 Par cans CP61, 4 x bar4 Par36L/64 ACL, 4 x Mole Fay 4lite, 6 x Robe Colourspot 700E AT moving head profile (two on drop bars), 4 x Martin Atomic 3000 Strobe. Front Truss; 2 x 1T points fitted with 1T double braked motors, 40ft 20" box truss, Front truss normal trim c.27ft, Front truss max trim 40ft, Front truss weight in standard configuration 850kg, Truss maximum load 1150kg UDL, Truss ladder and fall arrestor, 4 x bar6 Par64 Par cans CP62, 3 x Source4 15-30 degree zoom profile spots, 4x GLP Impression RZ 122 Zoom LED Washes, 4x Robe Colourspot 250AT, 4 x Mole Fay 2lite. Additional Equipment; 1 x Jem 24/7 hazer, 1 x Fan for the above, 1 x Magnum Smoke machine, 4 x Robe Colourspot 700E AT, 6 x Pixeltrack LED batten, 6 x Tanktrap and pipe. Installed Control; 1 x Avolites Pearl Expert, 1 x Avolites Art2000 48 way 16A dimmer, 2 x DMX buffer splitter, 1 x KES 54 way hot power distribution system, 4 x DMX from control to stage (house rig uses 1), 5 pin. Additional; 1 x DHA double gobo rotator, 2 x Pixeltrak Battens (in Main room bar), 2 x iShow4 Multicolour effect lights (in Main room bar).
DRESSING ROOMS; 3.

CRITERION THEATRE

2 Jermyn Street, London SW1Y 4XA
Mgt/ SD: 020 7839 8811 BO: 0844 847 1778 Fax: 020 7925 0596
Email: admin@criterion-theatre.co.uk
Web Site: www.criterion-theatre.com
ADMINISTRATION:
Props: Criterion Theatre Trust
General Manager: Fiona Callaghan
Theatre Manager: Emma Bentley
Duty Manager: Joe Cartwright
Technicians: Tim Ingram and Chris Davies
Policy: Plays, revues, Comedy Venue
Perfs: Variable according to production
Seats: 580. Two licensed bars.
To hire the Criterion Theatre please contact Fiona Callaghan on admin@criterion-theatre.co.uk.
TECHNICAL:
STAGE: Proscenium Stage: Pros. opening 7.62m. Ht. of pros. 3.81m. Depth of S/line 6.63m. Ht. of grid 6.71m: 27 lines, Hemp; Scenery flying ht. 6.40m; Flying bars as required; W/Widths P.S.2. 74m; O.P. 3.05m; Prompt Cnr D.S.L.
Please contact theatre for details of lighting and sound facilities.

CHARLES CRYER STUDIO THEATRE AND SCENERY WORKSHOP

39 High Street, Carshalton, Surrey SM5 3BB
BO: 020 8770 6990 Tech: 020 8770 6989
Email: gina.gillam@sutton.gov.uk
Web Site: www.suttontheatres.co.uk
ADMINISTRATION:
Theatre Manager: Gina Gillam
Technical Manager: Stuart Caswell
Administrator: Diane Cash
Policy: Producing, small-scale touring, one nighters, collaborations. Theatre, music, dance, mime, comedy - professional and community. Hire, box office splits; fees sometimes paid. Arts project proposals and co-production proposals welcomed.
Seats: 68 - 125, (Average 95 for theatre/dance). Fixed seats, up to 100 additional loose seats depending on performance requirements. Standing; 180.
For more information on venue hire contact the Administrator, Diane Cash, on diane.cash@sutton.gov.uk or 020 8770 6988.
TECHNICAL:
Full sound/lighting. Rehearsal Room. Restaurant,Bar. 2 x Dressing Rooms. Fully equipped workshop - paint frame, building/welding.
For more information on Technical Specifications contact the venue.

CRYSTAL PALACE OUTDOOR CONCERT BOWL

Senior Park Ranger, Crystal Palace Park, Thicket Road, Penge, London SE20 8DT
Gen Enq: 020 8778 7148 (Adam Jenkins)
Email: jenkins.adam@bromley.gov.uk
Web Site: www.bromley.gov.uk
ADMINISTRATION:
Assistant Manager: Patrick Philips
Senior Park Ranger/Bookings contact: Adam Jenkins
Capacity: Standing (e.g. pop concert): 12,000- 16,000;
Seated: 8,000 (e.g. classical concert)

DOMINION THEATRE

268-269 Tottenham Court Road, London W1T 7AQ
Mgt: 020 7580 1889 BO: 0870 1690116
SD: 020 7927 0900 Fax: 020 7927 0970
Wheelchair & Disabled Access Enquiries: 020 7927 0929
Email: david.pearson@nederlander.co.uk
Web Site: www.dominiontheatre.co.uk
ADMINISTRATION:
Props: Nederlander Dominion Ltd
General Manager: David Pearson
Policy: Major West End House.
Seated capacity: 2,174, Stalls: 1,372; Circle: 802; Boxes: 2 (12 seats) (retained by house).
TECHNICAL:
STAGE: Size: Width 22m (72') wide x 12m (39') deep. Forestage 1.83m (6'). Pros Opening: 15.2m (49'10") width x 9m (29'6") ht. Flying system: 72 Bar, Counterweight 0.05m 0 (2") bars @ 0.2m (6") centres. Height to Grid: 20.42m (67') front, 20m (65'7") back. Stage to Audit. Ht. 1.12m (3'8"). Equipment Access: via dock door, off Great Russell Street (street level). Dock Door: 5.64m (18'6") ht. x 2.4m (8'). Hoist: 500kg capacity on 2.5m (8') arm on stage of dock doors. Power Supply: 4 x 400 amp, 3 phase , 1 x 100 amp, single phase, 240V (sound) with independent earths. F. S. Positions: throw upper circle to approx. 28m (92'). Mixer Desk Pos.: Rear stalls 1.78m (5'10") wide x 4.74m (15'6") long (can be extended). Mixer to stage - 35m (110').
LIGHTING: Board: House Light Controls: Front Truss Pos: Located above stage apron. Hanging Points: 13 permanent FOH. 7 above stage apron, 3 above orchestra pit, 3 above stalls row F. 0.5 metric ton SWL per point. 3 x follow spot positions- upper circle houselights located lighting gallery, prompt corner.
SOUND: Please contact venue.
OTHER: Orchestra Pit: 16.5m (55') long x 2.3m (7'6") wide at centre. Depth from stage 3m (9'8") capacity 30. max. Size with Rows ABCD removed: 16.5m (55') x 7.5m (24'6") wide at centre. Depth from stage : 2.28m (7'6").

DONMAR WAREHOUSE

41 Earlham Street, London WC2H 9LX
Mgmt: 020 7438 9200 BO: 020 7438 9205 SD: 020 7438 9200 Fax: 020 7438 9211 Donmar Warehouse Projects: 020 7240 4882
Email: davidgriffiths@theambassadors.co m
Web Site: www.donmarwarehouse.com
ADMINISTRATION:
Props: Ambassador Theatre Group Ltd/ Donmar Warehouse Projects Ltd
General Manager of the London division: Richard Wingate
Theatre Manager: David Griffiths
Deputy Theatre Manager: Emily Revell
Policy: Plays, Musicals etc
Seats: 251 & 20 standing. 2 licenced bars.
TECHNICAL: OPEN STAGE THEATRE
STAGE: 7130 mm x 8280 mm.

Technical Galleries Above Stage 6200mm.
Grid Height 8000mm. Two dressing rooms.
LIGHTING: 108 Arri Dimmers & Strand 520 desk. 150 lanterns. SOUND: 24-8-2 (8x8) Desk, 10 speakers, 2 CD players.

DUCHESS THEATRE

3 - 5 Catherine Street, London WC2B 5LA
Mgt: 020 7632 9601 SD: 020 7632 9600
BO: 0207 632 9602
Email: general@nimaxtheatres.com
Web Site: www.nimaxtheatres.com
ADMINISTRATION:
Props: Nimax Theatres Ltd, 1 Lumley Court, Off 402 Strand, London, WC2R ONB Tel: 020 7395 0780 Fax: 0207 240 4540
Policy: Plays, Musicals, Comedy, Concerts
Chief Executive: Nica Burns
General Manager: Samantha Clark
Facilities may be made available for day time, late night and weekend use for private and press receptions, conferences and meetings. Contact Laurence Miller ((Production Department) via 0845 434 9290 or laurence.miller@nimaxtheatres.com
Seats: 482
2 Bars,
TECHNICAL:
STAGE: 8.4m x 4.4m flat; Pros Opening 7.32m; Ht of Pros. 4.27m; Depth of Stage 7.40m; Ht of Grid 11.58m; 21 lines, plus tabs, under required; Prompt Cnr. P.S.
LIGHTING: Board: Strand Gemini II, 114 circuits.
Situated rear of Dress Circle.
OTHER: Dressing rooms: 8
Membership: SOLT.

DUKE OF YORK'S THEATRE

St Martin's Lane, London WC2N 4BG
Mgt: 020 7565 6486 BO: 020 7565 6485
SD: 020 7565 6500 Fax: 020 7565 6465
Email: gracechristie@theambassadors.com
Web Site: www.atgtickets.com/dukeofyorks
Props: Ambassador Theatre Group
Theatre Manager: Grace Christie
General Manager of London Theatres: Richard Wingate
Box Office Manager: Calvin Hunter
Policy: Plays & Musicals
Cap: 659. 2 bars, hospitality room.
Access car park - Upper St Martin's Lane. Station - Leicester Square tube, Charing Cross Branch. Coach terminal - Victoria.
TECHNICAL:
STAGE: prosc wide 26'3" (9m), height pelmet/safety curtain 19' (5.79m), house curtain out dead 18'2" (5.53m), house border width 31'4" (9.55m), height of underside of grid 55'8" (16.96m), fly rail height from stage 35'6" (10.82m), height to underneath fly floor 31'2" (9.50m), distance between fly rails 31'7" (9.63m), get-in below street level 12'4" (3.74m), depth of stage from back of iron 36'2" (11.02m), P.S. to wall to O.P. wall 43'0" (13.11m), wing space P.S. 6'0" (1.83m), wing space O.P. 5'6" (1.68m), depth under stage first level 7'3" (2.21m), depth under stage to basement 12'5" (3.78m). Flying Facilities - 42 rope sets, set centres 10'9" (3.8m), distance between sets 6' (1.83m), 7 counter weight systems, drops can be located anywhere, 2 winches located between front of iron and pros 10'2" (3.1m), house & safety curtains operated manually, electric chain hoist 1 tonne located by scene dock door. P.S. height to underside of old lighting gallery 21'6" (6.55m). Safety curtain height 31'2" (9.5m), width 28'8 (8.74m). Width of dock doors 3'9" (1.14m), width of alley 4'9" (1.45m), height of stage from floors of stalls 75cm. Masking - Various sizes, 3 tabs, 6 borders, 3 legs.
LIGHTING AND SOUND: 1 x Strand 520i desk. 140 ways 2.5k dimmers. Power in stage area. 1 x 63a 3-phase. 2 x 32a single phase. Extra power can be wired if needed. 4 x speakers FOH and 2 x foldback onstage. 3 x CD players. 1 x 10-way mixing desk. 1 x 5m 58 microphone.
BACKSTAGE FACILITIES: 7 dressing rooms plus 1 company office, access by stage door - wardrobe at top of building with 13amp power points. Staff - 3 stage, 3 LX, Stage Door keeper.
FACILITIES FOR THE DISABLED: 2 wheelchair spaces, level access. Sennheiser Dual-channel infrared system for audio enhancement (all performances) and visual interpretation (certain performances). Assistance available. Contact Theatre Management.

EALING TOWN HALL

Uxbridge Road, New Broadway, Ealing, London W5 2BY
Switchboard: 020 8825 5000 Tel/ Fax: 020 8825 6060
Email: halls@ealing.gov.uk
Web Site: www.ealing.gov.uk
ADMINISTRATION:
Props: London Borough of Ealing
Capacity: Theatre style - in Victoria Hall 470, Princes Hall 150, Queens Hall 150, Elizabeth Cantell Room 120, Nelson Room 80, Telfer Room 80.

ELECTRIC BALLROOM

184 Camden High Street, London NW1 8QP
Tel: 020 7485 9006
Email: admin@electricballroom.co.uk
Web Site: www.electricballroom.co.uk
ADMINISTRATION:
Venue Hire Managers: Trena Robinson; Kate Fuller; Margaret Gibson
Email: admin@electricballroom.co.uk
The main dance hall holds up to 800 people and upstairs holds a capacity of 300 plus V.I.P bar altogther 1100.
TECHNICAL:
STAGE: 4ft high x 30ft wide x 20ft deep. Stage to ceiling height 17feet
SOUND: Martin Wavefront 8 Speakers: 4 stacks per side (3xW8T, 1xW8S, 4xW8S). QSC PLX series and Lab Gruppen amplifiers used throughout. FOH: Soundcraft MH4 48 channel Mixing Desk. Klark Teknik DN360 graphic and BSS System controllers. 10 Drawmer Compressors & 10 Drawmer Gates. 2 Focusrite compressors. TC D-Two Delay. 3 Yamaha Multi Effects units including SPX2000.
Monitors: Soundcraft SM12 48 channel Monitor Desk. The stage monitor system offers 10 bi-amped mixes through Martin LE700A wedges and H3T fills. BSS graphics on all monitor mixes. TC Multi Effects unit. KT Square One 8 channel dynamics. QSC amplifiers used throughout. Full range of microphones and stands including Shure, Sennheiser and AKG.
LIGHTING: 12k par cans on back truss and 6 mac 500's. 12k par cans on mid truss and 4 mac 600's. 12k on front ladders. 16k ACL's on back ladders. 6 mac 500's and 4 source 4 profile spots on front truss. 6 x floor cans. 2 mac 500's on spkr stacks. Tour hazer. Avolites Pearl 2008 desk. 4 high end data flash strobes.
ADDITIONAL: 1 Production Office. 3 Dressing Rooms.

ETCETERA THEATRE CLUB

Oxford Arms, 265 Camden High Street, London NW1 7BU
Admin Tel: 020 7482 4857 BO: 020 7482 4857
Email: admin@etceteratheatre.com
Web Site: www.etceteratheatre.com
ADMINISTRATION:
Management: Maude Madlyn
Policy: To continue our current successful two shows a night policy, as well as a Monday night slot for 'one-off' performances, presenting a popular and varied programme with an emphasis on new work. To maintain and enhance the theatre's high media profile and to continue to provide the opportunity for small theatre companies, with limited finances, to stage productions in Central London. Studio theatre with seating capacity of 42.
TECHNICAL:
STAGE: Flat; 5.40m (w) x 4.00m (d) to back wall, 5.40m (w) x 3.70m (d) to chimney breast. Grid Height: 3.25m. Clearance Height: 2.75m. Get-In; ground floor side entrance, Door Dimensions approx 1.10m (w) x 1.80m (h). Staircase width approx 1.10m (w). Double Door Dimensions approx 2.20m (w) x 1.80m (h).
LIGHTING: Lighting console located in control room. Console: Zero 88 Level 12. 12 way analogue 2 preset lighting desk with timed fades. House lights controlled

via an independent dimmer in the control room. Dimming; 2 x Green Ginger, 6 channels, 24 x 15a outlets. Patchable via 38 overhead 15a outlets. Independent Power. 4 x 13a adaptable outlets on US wall. Lantern Stock: Fresnels; 3 x Minuette Fresnel 500w, 6 x Pattern 123 Fresnel 500w, 4 x Parcans PAR64, 2 x Parcans PAR64 SN, 4 x Pinspot PAR36 with int. Transformer, 2 x Sun Flood. Profiles; 1 x Strand SL 23/50 600w, 3 x Strand Quartet 22/40 500w, 2 x Patten 23 30o 500w, 1 x Minuette Profile 500w. Limited birdies, cables, grelcos, gobos and holders etc. (please ring for availability). Visiting companies must supply their own gel although a small stock of pre-cut colour is available FOC.
SOUND: Audio Tie Lines, 12 XLR tie lines USL terminating in the control room. Control: Yamaha MG12/4. 12 input channels, capable of taking XLR, TRS Phone Jack and RCA line input. Installed Loudspeaker System. 2 x JBL Control 1 mounted SL & SR powered by Samson Servo 260 amplifier Outboard Equipment. 1 x Tascam 122 Cassette Deck. 1 x Sony Mini-disc Player/Recorder. 1 x Sony CD Player. All of the above are housed in a rack located in the control room. Microphones; 3 x Shure Beta 58 (equivalent), 2 x Microphone stands, Cables, connectors etc. please contact us for more information.
BACKSTAGE FACILTIES: 1 Dressing Rooms, accomm. 5 people. Additional space in the technical room, opposite the dressing room, accomm. 2 people. Audio show relay system; Full show relay system to dressing rooms and control box.

EVENTIM APOLLO

Queen Caroline Street, Hammersmith, London W6 9QH
Mgt: 020 8563 3800
Email: info@eventimapollo.com
Web Site: www.eventimapollo.com
ADMINISTRATION:
Theatre Manager: Darren Murphy
Capacity (All Seated): 3632.
Capacity (Standing in Stalls): 5039.
TECHNICAL:
STAGE: 24.1m x 9.5m (79ft x 31ft). No rake. Up to 3.7m (12ft) extension pos. without loss of seats. Permanent crush barrier. Perm. speaker platforms, each 3.7m x 2.4m (12ft x 8ft). Pros. opening 19.2m wide x 10.7m high (63ft x 35ft). Safety curtain in use. Ht. to grid 16.8m (55ft). 22 line double purchase counterweight system. Stage power supply: 3 phase. 400 amps (lights), 1 phase 100 amps (sound), 3 phase 100 amps various with earth leakage trip. Stage water supply. Position for lighting truss in front of pros. arch. Cable run to auditorium sound control positions; rear stalls, 55m, front circle 73m. Two CS spots.
OTHER: Dressing Rooms 2 master + 7, accom. up to 42; Private stage bar. Showers. Catering Space. Get-in (3ft) ramp direct to stage from car park. Promoter's Office. Restricted parking.

EXCEL ARENA

1 Western Gateway, Royal Victoria Dock, London E16 1XL
General Sales: Tel: 020 7069 4602 Fax: 020 7069 4747
Email: info@excel-london.co.uk
Web Site: www.excel-london.co.uk
ADMINISTRATION:
Managing Director: David Pegler
Director of Conferences & Events: James Rees
Email: jamesrees@excel-london.co.uk
Marketing Manager, Conferences and Events: Gemma Parkhouse
Email: gemmaparkhouse@excel-london.co.uk
Cap: 100,000

FAIRFIELD HALLS

Park Lane, Croydon, Surrey CR9 1DG
Mgt/SD: 020 8681 0821 BO: 020 8688 9291 Marketing Fax: 020 8603 3862
Admin Fax: 020 8603 3838
Email: info@fairfield.co.uk
Web Site: www.fairfield.co.uk
ADMINISTRATION:
Props: Fairfield (Croydon) Ltd
Chief Executive: Simon Thomsett
Technical Manager: Chris Whybrow
Head of Operations: John Bartliff
Policy: Concert Hall, Music, Films, Pop, Jazz, Opera, Comedy, Conferences, Ballet.
Capacity: Seats: 1998 max.
Foyer, Coffee shop, Restaurant, Bars, Banqueting & Conference Rooms.
TECHNICAL:
STAGE: Concert Platform, mechanical variable sections.
LIGHTING: Switchboard: Strand Lightboard 'M' commanding 120 channels 200amp 3 phase and 60 amp single phase power supplies available for temporary supply; F.O.H. spots 42 CCT profiles. 2 spot bars available on electric hoist. Selection of lamps; P.A.R. cans and fresnels.
Get-in via platform lift, Direct Access & Parking. No flying facilities, but good grid provision and soft blacks for upstage masking.
SOUND EQUIPMENT: 7kw fully integrated Meyer sound system with permanent mixing position.
OTHER: Dressing Rooms: 7, accom. 200; 3 showers; Orchestra Pit 28.90 orch. music stands, 2 Steinway concert D type Grand Pianos; seats 120 orch. max 250 choir seats.
Staff: 5 Technicians - Casual Crew.
A registered charity.

FORTUNE THEATRE

Russell Street, London WC2B 5HH
Mgt: 020 7010 7910 BO: 0844 871 7627
SD: 020 7010 7900 Mgt Fax: 020 7010 7911
Web Site: www.atgtickets.com
ADMINISTRATION:
Props: Ambassador Theatre Group Ltd
General Manager of London Theatres: Richard Wingate
Theatre Manager: Alice Miller
Box Office Sales Manager: Stefan Couper
Policy: Plays
Seats: 432
TECHNICAL:
STAGE: Pros. opening 7.77m; Ht. of Pros. 5.49m; Depth of S/Line 8.53m; Ht. of Grid 12.80m; 26 lines, 16 Hemp, 10 C/W; Prompt Cnr. P.S.
LIGHTING: Switchboard: Ovation memory board (64 way).
Paging facilities to backstage and F.O.H.
SOUND: Please contact venue.
OTHER: Dressing Rooms 6 (dress 18).
Membership: SOLT

THE FORUM

9-17 Highgate Road, Kentish Town, London NW5 1JY
Tel: 020 7428 4080 Info Line: 020 7428 4099 BO:0844 847 2405(Ticketmaster)
Email: info@theforumlondon.com
Web Site: www.theforumlondon.com
Press and Marketing: Laura Bailey
Capacity: 2,300 max.

THE FRIDGE BAR

Town Hall Parade, Brixton Hill, London SW2 1RJ
Tel: 020 7326 5100
Email: info@fridgebar.com
Web Site: www.fridgebar.com
ADMINISTRATION:
Capacity: 300 Max Standing.

FULHAM TOWN HALL

Fulham Broadway, London SW6 1ET
General Tel: 020 8748 3020 Events Tel: 0845 337 0314
Email: events@lbhf.gov.uk
Web Site: www.lbhf.gov.uk
ADMINITRATION:
Props: London Borough of Hammersmith & Fulham
For bookings contact;
Manager: Helen Pinnington
Assistant/ Technicial Manager: Rob James
Tel: 020 8753 2135/2136 Fax: 020 8753 2353
TECHNICAL:
No amplified music is allowed in the concert hall.

The Grand Hall:
CAPACITY: 450 for lecture, concert or show, 250 for dinner, 230 for dinner dance
STAGE: Floor area 70' x 44' / 21.3m x 13.5m = 295m2, Stage area 28' x 15' / 8.5m x 4.5m.
BACKSTAGE FACILITIES: 2 x Cloakrooms, 2 x Dressing Rooms, Grand piano.

The Concert Hall:
CAPACITY: Dinner 100, Standing Reception 200, Theatre Style 200.

GARRICK THEATRE

2 Charing Cross Road, London WC2H 0HH
Mgt: 020 7520 5692 BO: 020 7520 5693
SD: 020 7520 5690
Email: adam.ellacott@nimaxtheatres.com
Web Site: www.nimaxtheatres.com
ADMINISTRATION:
Props: Nimax Theatres Ltd
Policy: Plays, Musicals, Comedy, Concerts.
Chief Executive: Nica Burns
Theatre Manager: Adam Ellacott
Operations Director: Darren Atkins
Theatre Operations Manager: Hayley Spong
PA to Nica Burns: Stephanie Creed
Facilities may be made available for day time, late night and weekend use for private and press receptions, conferences and meetings - Contact Laurence Miller: 0845 434 9290, Fax: 0207 240 4540 and Email: laurence.miller@nimaxtheatres.com
Seats: 734
3 Bars, Small Entertainment Suite.
TECHNICAL:
STAGE: raked 1:30; Pros. Opening 8.82m; Depth of Stage 9.60m. Ht of Pros. 6.10m; Ht of Grid 15.24m; 52 lines; 44 Hemp. 8 moveable counterweights; Prompt Cnr. as required.
LIGHTING: Board: Strand Gemini II, 120 circuits.
Situated O.P. Stage Box
OTHER: Dressing Rooms: 10
Membership: SOLT.

GBS THEATRE (RADA)

62-64 Gower Street, London WC1E 6ED
BO: 020 7908 4800 Mgt: 020 7636 7076
Hire: 020 7307 5061
Email: bookings@rada.ac.uk, enquiries@rada.ac.uk
Web Site: www.rada.ac.uk
ADMINISTRATION:
Props: Royal Academy of Dramatic Art
Venue Hire Co-Ordinator: Naomi Dixon
Stage Manager: Dave Agnew
RADA venues are available for hire, along with various rehearsal rooms and other specific spaces in the newly opened complex.
Cap: 70 max (multi-format)

THE JOHN GIELGUD THEATRE(RADA)

62-64 Gower Street, London WC1E 6ED
BO: 020 7908 4800 Tel: 020 7636 7076
Hire: 020 7307 5060
Email: bookings@rada.ac.uk, enquiries@rada.ac.uk
Web Site: www.rada.ac.uk
ADMINISTRATION:
Props: Royal Academy of Dramatic Art
Venue Hire and Events Co-ordinator: Stacie Novotny
bookings@radaenterprises.org
Stage Manager: Dave Agnew
RADA venues are available for hire, along with various rehearsal rooms and other specific spaces in the newly opened complex.
Cap: 50 max.

GIELGUD THEATRE

Shaftesbury Avenue, London W1D 6AR
Mgt: 020 7292 1321 (Manager) Tel: 020 7292 1322 (Assistant Manager) BO: 0844 482 5130 SD: 020 7292 1320
Email: delfont@delmack.co.uk
Web Site: www.delfontmackintosh.co.uk
ADMINISTRATION;
Props: Delfont Mackintosh Theatres Limited
Novello Theatre, Aldwych, London WC2B 4LD
Tel: 020 7379 4431 Fax: 020 7240 3831
Policy: Plays, Musicals, Comedy, Concerts.
Chief Executive: Richard Johnston
Theatre Manager: Louise Bolland
Chief Electrician: David Bodman
For all bookings and production enquiries contact Richard Johnston (Chief Executive). Facilities may be made available for day time, late night and weekend use for private and press receptions, conferences and meetings - Contact Louise Bolland 020 7292 1321
Seats: 981 + 10 standing
3 Bars, Entertainment Suite.
TECHNICAL:
STAGE: raked 1: 48; Pros. Opening 9.14m; Ht of Pros. 8.15m; Depth of Stage 10.82m; Ht of Grid 15.70m; 42 C/W sets; Prompt Cnr. P.S.
LIGHTING: Board: Strand 520, 137 circuits.
Situated Stalls Box P.S.
OTHER: Dressing rooms: 15, showers 2
Membership: SOLT

GOLDSMITH COLLEGE

Conference Office, Loring Management Centre, St James, New Cross London SE14 6AD
Tel: 020 7919 7133
Email: conference-services@gold.ac.uk
Web Site: www.gold.ac.uk
ADMINISTRATION:
Contact: Caroline Rondel. ext 7132
Room booking: Sarah Cloherty
Email: roombookings@gold.ac.uk or ext 7522
Policy: Lectures, conferences, concerts and rehearsals. Full hospitality service.
The Great Hall Cap (main building): 600, with balcony - 720

GREENWICH THEATRE

Crooms Hill, London SE10 8ES
Admin: 020 8858 4447 BO: 020 8858 7755 Fax: 020 8858 8042
Email: info@greenwichtheatre.org.uk
Web Site: www.greenwichtheatre.org.uk
ADMINISTRATION:
Props: Greenwich Theatre Ltd.
Artistic and Executive Director: James Haddrell
Marketing Manager: TBC
Technical Manager: Neil Fulcher
Policy: Varied length runs of drama, musical theatre and children's shows.
Perfs: Mon-Sat. 8.00; Mat. Sat. 2.30.
Seats: 421. Full Restaurant and Bar facilities.
For information on hiring the venue contact Greenwich Theatre on; operations@greenwichtheatre.org.uk
TECHNICAL:
For full Technical Specifications contact the Technical department on; technical@greenwichtheatre.org.uk.
STAGE: Wooden, No rake. Height; 17ft 10 inches (5.44m). Above the whole stage area is a grid, with clearance of 25ft 4 inches (7.72m) that reduces to 24ft 3 inches (7.39m) upstage of Lx Bar 5. Get In; doorway approx. 5ft (1.52m) wide by 10ft (3.04m). 16ft / 4.88m above street level. SWL of winch is 250 kg.
COMMUNICATIONS: Tecpro Communications Master Station feeds the stage, auditorium, stage basement and the Technical Management Office. There are also controls for 3 Bell and 2 telephone ringers, clock and timer.
LIGHTING: Permanent FOH rig, 6 Patt 264 Profiles 1kw, 12 Cantata 18/32 Profiles 1.2kw. Profiles; 12 Source 4 15-30 575w, 4 Cantata 26/44 1.2kw, 10 Patt 264 1kw, 10 Patt 23 Mk I 500w, 4 Patt 23 Mk II 500w. Fresnels; 5 Patt 123 500w, 30 Patt 743 1kw, 18 Patt 243 2kw. Floods; 12 AC1001 1kw. Pars; 6 Par 64 Short Nose 1kw, 24 Par 64 Standard Nose 1kw, Par Lamp stock - CP62. Followspot; 1 Patt 293 with colour magazines 2kw. Control; Strand 430 with Genius pro software V 2.8.5 and designers remote, A DMX outlet for scrollers etc. is on the SL gantry. Dimmers; 132 2kw, 4 5kw. Additional Equipment; 4 400W Ultra Violet Guns, 1 Le Maitre G300 Smoke Generator / Haze Machine with remote, 1 Le Maitre 6 way Pyro Controller with three pods and bomb tank, 4 Adjustable Height Lighting Stands 5ft - 10ft, 4 Heavy Boom Bases.
SOUND: Soundcraft Venue II 16:8:2, 2 Shure SM58 Microphones, 1 AKG D202 Microphone, 1 Tandy PZM microphone, 3 Boom Style Microphone Stands, 1 Table Microphone Stand, 3 M33 HX Cassette Deck, 1 Denon DCD 910 CD Player, 1 Teac 3340 1/4 4 Track with infra red stop facility, 1 Technics SL QX 300 record deck with EMO R1AA preamplifier, 1 Yamaha SPX900 Multi Effects Unit, 4 Channel Remote Start/Stop Unit for Revox and Denon Tape Machine Built into Sound Desk, 2 Bose 802 Hanging Brackets, 8 Bose 802 Speakers, 2 JBL Control 5 Speakers, 2 JBL Control 1 Speakers, 4Crest LA901 Stereo Amplifiers, 2 Quad 405 Stereo Amplifiers.
BACKSTAGE FACILITIES: Dressing

Rooms; 4, accommodates 20. Wardrobe equipped with sewing machines and irons. Full laundry facilities available.

UNIVERSITY OF GREENWICH UNION

Cooper Building, King William Walk, London SE10 9JH
Tel: 020 8331 7629 Fax: 020 8331 9255
Email: d.ford@gre.ac.uk
Web Site: www.suug.co.uk
ADMINISTRATION:
Commercial Services Manager: Lisa Connellan or Email: l.connellan@gre.ac.uk
Capacity: 200

HACKNEY EMPIRE

291 Mare Street, Hackney, London E8 1EJ
Mgt: 020 8510 4500 BO: 020 8985 2424
SD: 020 8510 4515
Email: info@hackneyempire.co.uk
Web Site: www.hackneyempire.co.uk
ADMINISTRATION:
Policy: Comedy, variety, music, dance to drama, opera and family shows.
Creative Director: Susie Mckenna (susie@hackneyempire.co.uk)
Box Office Manager: Jonathan Christian (jonathan.christian@hackneyempire.co.uk)
Marketing Manager: Dom Draper (dom@hackneyempire.co.uk)
Technical Manager: Othman Read
Capacity: 1,300 seated raked tiered, plus 250 standing.
For further information on hiring contact Jennie Jacques on 020 8510 4529 or email at jennie.jacques@hackneyempire.co.uk., or Sam Williams, email: sam.williams@hackneyempre.co.uk.
TECHNICAL:
STAGE: Proscenium arch, Performing area 11.59m x 9.75m - 12.2m, pros opening 10.26m x 6.7m, wing widths 3.05m, SR, 3.05m SL, 2.44m US. Stage raked, 1 in 31 floor hardboard on oak tongue and groove, suitable for all dance, backstage crossover, understage heated. Please contact the Technical Manager for further specifications; othman.read@hackneyempire.co.uk

HACKNEY TOWN HALL ASSEMBLY HALL

Mare Street, Hackney, London E8 1EA
Tel: 020 8356 5505 (Town Hall Reception) Mgt: 020 8356 5505 (Events)
Email: venuehire@hackney.gov.uk
Web Site: www.hackneyvenues.com
ADMINISTRATION:
Props: London Borough of Hackney
Capacity: 550 Standing, 420 (theatre-style no tables), 300 (banqueting-style with tables)

HALF MOON YOUNG PEOPLE'S THEATRE (YPT)

43 Whitehorse Road, London E1 0ND
Tel: 020 7265 8138 Box Office: 020 7709 8900 Fax: 020 7709 8914
Email: admin@halfmoon.org.uk
Web Site: www.halfmoon.org.uk
ADMINISTRATION
Director: Chris Elwell
Production and Technical Manager: Fred Beaufort
Leading provider of professional theatre training, youth theatre and arts projects for young people across London. Regular programme of shows for young people.
Capacity: 66- 90
TECHNICAL:
STAGE: Black box studio
LIGHTING: General cover will be pre-rigged.
SOUND: 1x minidisc player, 1 x CD player and 1 x cassette deck available. For microphones monitor speakers or any other sound requirements, please contact us in advance.
DRESSING ROOMS: 1, toilet facilities available.

HAMMERSMITH TOWN HALL

King Street, Hammersmith, London W6 9JU
Tel: 020 8753 1001 Events: 020 8753 2135
Email: events@lbhf.gov.uk
Web Site: www.lbhf.gov.uk
ADMINISTRATION:
Props: London Borough of Hammersmith and Fulham
Capacity: Assembly Hall; 1000 standing, 900 concert seated, 350 dinner/dance.
Small Hall: 120
TECHNICAL:
Assembly Hall Dimensions: Ceiling height 9.2m. Floor area 84'x65'/25.6m x 19.8m = 497m2. Stage area 46'x22'/14m x 6.7m.

HAMPSTEAD THEATRE

Eton Avenue, Swiss Cottage, London NW3 3EU
Admin: 020 7449 4200 BO: 020 7722 9301 Tech: 020 7449 4196 Fax: 020 7449 4201
Email: info@hampsteadtheatre.com
Web Site: www.hampsteadtheatre.com
ADMINISTRATION;
Props: Hampstead Theatre Ltd.
Artistic Director: Edward Hall
Executive Producer: Greg Ripley-Duggan
Head of Production: Tom Nickson
Email: tomn@hampsteadtheatre.com
Policy: Four-eight week runs of new plays - each individually cast.
Perfs: Mon-Sat at 7.30pm. Mats. Sat. 3.00pm.
Seats: 325. Bar (licensed) open 10.00-11.00.
TECHNICAL:
STAGE: Flexible end on / thrust. Pros opening adjustable: 13m-10.8m wide, 6.3m high. Full Stage Width: 15m. Full Stage Depth 9.2m. Main Stage Elevator: 10.8m x 7.2m. Fore Stage Elevator 10.8m x 3.5m (max). Main Elevator can form adjustable rake and contains modular removable sections. Fore Stage Elevator trapped and can raise / lower to form orchestra pit or apron (removes front 3 rows of seats). Front 6 rows of seats on air wagons to allow adjustment for end on / thrust / fore stage settings.
GRID HEIGHT: 10.6m, Max flying height 9.8m. 20 Counterweight sets plus facility for spot hemp sets. Clearance between fly floors 13m, Clearance under fly floors 6.3m
Get In: thru full height dock doors at truck level.
LIGHTING: Strand 520i desk, through Strand SLD96 dimmers (192x15A, 12x25A), Full kit list available.
SOUND: Yamaha O2R96 Digital desk, SFX / Showman Sound Control, Tascam Mini Disk, Denon CD player, 8 Meyer UPM 1P Speakers (4 as part of FOH system / 4 as required), 2 x Meyer UMS 1P Subs, 8 x Tannoy Pro V12 Speakers, 8 JBL Control 25 (Auditorium surround system), 5 x MC2 Audio T1500 Stero Amplifiers. Operated from Rear control box or rear of stalls (10 seats).
STAGE MANAGEMENT: Prompt desk in Rear Control Box or DSL. 10 cue lights. 2 sets radio cans. Wired cans through out stage. Video stage monitor and infra red monitor in control box and on stage as required. Show relay / paging to dressing rooms.
DRESSING ROOMS: 3, on first floor, accommodating 16 (4+4+8), all with toilets and showers. Accessible toilets on Dressing Room and Stage levels. Full wardrobe facilities.
Rehearsal Room: 11m x7m, Sprung wooded floor, natural light c/w kitchenette and SM facilities. Limited access for rehearsal sets.

HAROLD PINTER THEATRE

Panton Street, London SW1Y 4DN
Mgt: 020 7321 5310 BO: 020 7321 5306
SD: 020 7321 5300
Email: haroldpintermanagement@theambassadors.com
Web Site: www.atgtickets.com
ADMINISTRATION:
Props: The Ambassador Theatre Group
Theatre Manager: Rachael Lund Email: racharllund@theambassadors.com
Policy: Plays
Seats: 834
TECHNICAL:
STAGE: Proscenium Stage, Raked 4%; Pros. opening 7.55m; Ht. of Pros. 5.18m; Depth of S/Line 7.50m; Ht. of Grid 11.76m; 32 lines Hemp; Scenery Flying Ht. 5.49m; Flying Bars 8.53m; W/Widths p.s. 1.68m; O.P. 3.05m; Prompt Cnr. P.S.; Dock Door 3.10m x 1.07m.
LIGHTING: Strand S20i(V2.SE) 350 channels + 250 attributes

SOUND: Please contact venue.
ADDITIONAL: Dressing Rooms 8; 4 Showers; Orchestra Pit 12 approx.
No Scenery Dock; Storage limited.
Membership: SOLT.

HER MAJESTY'S THEATRE

Haymarket, London SW1Y 4QL
SD: 020 7850 8750 BO: 0844 412 4653
Email: venuehire@reallyuseful.co.uk
Web Site: www.reallyusefultheatres.co.uk
ADMINISTRATION;
Props: Really Useful Theatres Ltd, 65 Drury Lane, London WC2B 5SP; Tel: 020 7557 7300 and Fax: 020 7240 2511.
Policy: Plays, Musicals, Comedy, Concerts.
Theatre Manager: John Fitzsimmons
Facilities may be made available for day time, late night and weekend use for private and press receptions, conferences and meetings.
Seats: 1145.
3 Bars, Entertainment Suites.
TECHNICAL:
STAGE: Flat; Pros. Opening 10.52m; Ht of Pros. 8.84m; Depth of Stage 15.09m; Ht of Grid 17.37m; 50 C/W lines; Prompt Cnr. P.S.
LIGHTING: Lighting Board: Strand Galaxy II, 350 Circuits.
Situated rear of Dress Circle
OTHER: Dressing rooms: 18
Membership: SOLT

THE HOPE AND ANCHOR

207 Upper St, Islington, London N1 1RL
Tel: 020 7354 1312
ADMINISTRATION:
General Manager: James Smith
Capacity: 50
Policy: Up and Coming Bands

ICA THEATRE

Institute of Contemporary Arts The Mall, London SW1Y 5AH
Tel: 020 7930 0493 BO: 020 7930 0493
Email: events@ica.org.uk
Web Site: www.ica.org.uk
ADMINISTRATION:
Executive Director: Gregor Muir
Head of Events: Emilia Bromiley
Technical Manager: Sam Martin
Capacity: 350 standing, 180 theatre style.
TECHNICAL:
STAGE: Ply floor 74' x 33' Grid over whole area 14'6". Seating primarily on four movable bleachers enabling various endstage traverse thrust and round layouts up to a maximum capacity of 206 seats.
LIGHTING: 48 way Micron. Switch patching 3 ways on 12 channels. 174 Grid outlets. Lanterns: 12 x Patt. 23, 12 x Sil 30, 18 x Cantata Fres., 6 x harmony Fres., 14 x Parcans (1K), 2 x 15/28 Profiles, 2 x 22/40 Profiles.
SOUND: 2 x Revox B77; 1 x Revox A77; 1 x Tascam 8 x 4 x 1 Mixer. Bose Speaker System.

INDIGO2 ARENA

Millenium Way, Greenwich, London SE10 0AX
General Enq: 0208 463 2000 BO: 03333 219 999 (Ticketmaster)
Email: customerservices@theo2.co.uk
Web Site: www.theO2.co.uk
ADMINISTRATION:
Props: AEG Worldwide
General Manager: Jan Chadwick
For Corporate Sales and Special Events telephone 020 8463 2730 or Email: sales@theo2.co.uk
All enquiries to be made via Customer Services.
TECHNICAL:
STAGE: Depth - 8.4 M; Width - 16.5 M; Height - 1.22 M; Upstage edge to mixer - 19.4 M
Tour Power: 2 x 125A 3 phase/Ceeform; Iso Tour Power:
1 x 32A 3 phase/Ceeform; Outside Broadcast: 1 x 125A 3 phase/Ceeform; 1 x 63A 3 phase/Ceeform; 1 x 32A 3 phaseCeeform
LIGHTING: The lighting system at Indigo features state of the art Vari-Lite VL3000 series fixtures, Martin Atomic 3000 Strobes and Highend Systems Whole Hog IPC Consoles. The VL3000 moving light package consists of 15 VL3500 Wash fixtures and 20 VL3000 Spot fixtures. The brand new VL3500 Wash fixtures have an extra wide aperture for projecting dramatic beam effects. The VL3000 Spot fixtures feature 3 rotating gobo wheels, for projecting dynamic pattern effects; a remote control iris, for precise beam, control; and 10° to 60° motorized and focus optics for unbeatable versatility.
DRESSING ROOMS: The back of house area is located stage right. All rooms have been designed with multiple telephone/fax lines, internet connections, power outlets and wireless technology. 3 x Dressing rooms with en-suite facilities; 1 x Dressing room; 1 x Artists Lounge; 1 x Production office; 1 x Kitchen, 1 x wc/shower room

INSTITUTE OF INDIAN CULTURE

Bhavan Centre, 4a Castletown Road, West Kensington, London W14 9HQ
Tel: 020 7381 3086 / 4608 Fax: 020 7381 8758
Email: info@bhavan.net
Web Site: www.bhavan.net
Executive Director: Dr. M.N. Nandakumara
Theatre Capacity: 295 Seats
Rehearsal Rooms: Cap: Haithi Hall: 100. Dance Studio and Art Gallery also available.
Our auditorium is suitable for concerts, dances and dramas. It is fitted with light and sound. The other hall has a wooden floor and moveable chairs. Other rooms are suitable for meetings. All these spaces are for hire.

JACKSONS LANE

Opp Highgate Tube, 269a Archway Road, London N6 5AA
Admin: 020 8340 5226 BO: 020 8341 4421
Email: admin@jacksonslane.org.uk
Web Site: www.jacksonslane.org.uk
ADMINISTRATION:
Props: Haringey Borough Council
Artistic Director: Adrian Berry
General Manager: Ruth Turner
Theatre Technician: Nick Waddel
Email: technical@jacksonslane.org.uk
Policy: To provide a programme of music, drama, dance, mime and cabaret, representing multi-cultural interests. Training will play a large part in our programme, and many of our staff are trainees and volunteers.
Location: Alongside the Archway Road (A1), opposite Highgate tube. Served by buses 43, 134, X43, 263. Terms: Hire of theatre (negotiable); box office split.
Seats/Capacity: 166
Bars: one in foyer, one in auditorium.
TECHNICAL:
STAGE: End on, flat stage, semi-sprung wood floor, raked. 11m x 8m deep (without wing masking/ black tabs). 8m x 7m deep APPROX. (with wing masking/ black tabs). Grid Height: 6.2m. Get-In: Via 1.5m x 3.5m stage door from Archway Road (A1 facing north). Red route restrictions apply; parking for one hour between 10am and 4pm. Unrestricted parking after 7pm. Underground station car park charges £3 per day.
LIGHTING: Control: Strand 91703 300 Console 125ch 24sub. Lanterns: 10 x 1k Starlette fresnels, 6 x Par 64 (assorted lenses - please check with us), 2 x 650 w Minuette profiles, 6 x 1k Compact 6 fresnels, 12 x 1.2k ETC Source 4, 15/30 zoom profiles, 7 x 1.2k ETC Source 4, 25/50 zoom profiles, 4 x 500w Quartet fresnels, 2 x 3 cell 500w flood units. All lanterns are compete with barn doors, gel frames and shutters as appropriate.
SOUND: Allen and Heath GL 3300. Playback; Numark CDn22 Dual CD Player, 2x RCF Art 315a Powered speakers (Fixed Position). Various Microphones available.
ADDITIONAL: Infrared hearing systems fitted, 1x FXlab Small Hazer, 1x Martin magnum 650 Smoke Machine, 1x 30cm Mirror ball. Video Projector; NEC NP100 2000 lumen Projector. Projection Screen; Matt white front projection screen surface. 9m wide x 5.95m drop.
DRESSING ROOMS; 3, accomm. 20. Iron and ironing board available.
For more information contact Joe Boxshall on joe@jacksonslane.org.uk.

JAZZ CAFE

5 Parkway, Camden Town, London NW1 7PG
Admin: 0207 485 6834 Restaurants: 0207 688 8899 Tickets: 0844 847 2514
Email: boxoffice@thejazzcafelondon.co.uk

Web Site: www.jazzcafe.co.uk
ADMINISTRATION:
General Manager: Sarah Libretto
Capacity: 420

JERMYN STREET THEATRE

16B Jermyn Street, London SW1Y 6ST
Mgt Tel: 020 7434 1443 BO: 020 7287 2875
Email: info@jermynstreettheatre.co.uk
Web Site: www.jermynstreettheatre.co.uk
ADMINISTRATION:
Artistic Director: Anthony Biggs
General Manager: Penny Horner
Technical Manager: Thom Collins
Seats: 70 theatre style
TECHNICAL:
STAGE: 8 metres long x 4 metres deep x 3.5 metres high (to grid).
LIGHTING: Dimming; 36x 2.5kw channels. 6 x Zero88 Betapack 6x10amp Units. 2x 15amp sockets per channel, fuse blown indicator and local channel test control. Fed by a 3 phase 63 amp supply. Control Desk; Jands Event Plus, 48/96 (wide mode) 2 preset desk with 1000 memories operated via 50 pages of 20 scene masters per page or the cross fade memory(stack) section. In addition the desk can run up to 99 chases of up to 99 steps each. DMX; 4 DMX outlets along the FOH bar. The end of the DMX line is located beside the lighting booth. House Lighting; Overstage 6x M16 'Birdie' spotlights and sunken eyeball lamps over the seating provide primary House lighting which is controlled by a Mode Electronics 4 channel digital dimmer, which can also supply any rig socket for additional lighting purposes.
SOUND: Replay; 2x Denon 720R Cassette player/recorders, 1x Denon DN1000F Instant play CD player, 1x Sony MDS-JE510 MiniDisc player/recorder. Mixing Desk; Allen & Heath Mix Wizard 14/2/2. 10 x mono line or mic input channels. 2x stereo input channels. 6 x Auxiliary sends per channel (these can be set to pre or post-fade in groups of 1-4 and 5-6 depending on requirements.). 4 band EQ per channel (Hi and Low mid are swept). 4 x stereo FX returns. 2 x Pairs of sub groups. Comprehensive PFL functions. EQ; 2x Behringer DSP-8000 Ultra curve digital stereo graphics. 1 with delay functions to drive the main house speakers, and 1 to drive the monitor system. Speakers; Martin Em series passive two-way compact cabinets. Primary PA: 6 x EM15 75w permanent boxes flown slightly upstage of front of the auditorium. SB150 sub-bass cabinet, set inside the SL stage wall. 4 extra monitor speakers that can be placed anywhere around the stage. 2x WMM0.5 75w boxes and 2x trapezoidal EM26 125w boxes. All speaker connections are Neutrik NL4 Speakons, wired 1+ as in phase and 1- as out phase. Various Microphones available.
STAGE MANAGEMENT: 2 x ring system based on the Tecpro configuration. Outlets are for belt pack and head set are located in the two backstage sound boxes and the control room. 2 x Loud speaker stations located by the lower level dressing rooms and the administration office. The Theatre has a stock of 4 x 2 ring belt packs with single sided headsets. Circuit A runs to the stage outlets whilst B covers the
DRESSING ROOMS: 2, with fridges, sofas, microwaves, kettles, iron + ironing board. Third available.

JERWOOD THEATRE DOWNSTAIRS

Please see the Royal Court Theatre, London.
Email: info@royalcourttheatre.com
Web Site: www.royalcourttheatre.com
Capacity: 389
For Venue Hire contact Events Manager on hires@royalcourttheatre.com

JERWOOD THEATRE UPSTAIRS

Please see Royal Court Theatre, London.
Email: info@royalcourttheatre.com
Web Site: www.royalcourttheatre.com
Capacity: 72-100
For Venue Hire contact Events Manager on hires@royalcourttheatre.com

THE JERWOOD VANBRUGH THEATRE

62-64 Gower Street, London WC1E 6ED
BO: 020 7908 4800 Mgt: 020 7636 7076
Fax: 020 7323 3865
Email: bookings@rada.ac.uk, enquiries@rada.ac.uk
Web Site: www.rada.ac.uk
ADMINISTRATION:
Props: Royal Academy of Dramatic Art
Theatre Director: Edward Kemp
Venue Hire and Events Co-ordinator: Claire Rivers
Production Manager: Dave Agnew
RADA venues are available for hire, along with various rehearsal rooms and other specific spaces in the newly opened complex.
Cap: 183 - Stalls and Circle Seating

KENNETH MORE THEATRE

Oakfield Road, Ilford, Essex IG1 1BT
Mgt: 020 8553 4464 BO: 020 8553 4466
Fax: 020 8553 5476
Email: admin@kmtheatre.co.uk
Web Site: www.kmtheatre.co.uk
ADMINISTRATION:
Props: London Borough of Redbridge
Lessees: Redbridge Theatre Co Ltd
General Manager: Steven Day
Policy: Amateur and Professional Productions, Tours, Exhibitions, Recitals, Conferences, etc. Experimental productions in Studio, Costume Hire.
Seats: 358 with 3 wheelchair spaces in main auditorium. Licensed bar; hearing-aid loop.
TECHNICAL:
STAGE: Proscenium Stage with 1.83m removable apron over orchestra pit; Pros. arch 9.14m x 4.42m; S/Line to back wall 6.71m (with crossover behind wall); Ht. of Grid 12.04m; 28 X 12.08m lines C/W; Scenery Flying Ht. 10.97m; Flying Bars 9.14m; W/Widths 2.44m each side with direct access to large scene dock and workshop O.P.; Prompt Cnr. P.S. Counterweighted Trap-Door Centre Stage. 1:25 plans available.
LIGHTING: Eurolight Applause & back-up 106 way at rear of auditorium. 3 F.O.H. bars set in ceiling; 2 F.O.H. perches; 2 int. wired bars. 10 x strand SL, 4 x Patt. 264, 14 x Patt. 743, 6 x T84, 4 x Sil 15, 6 x Sil 30, 8 x Starlette Fresnel, 10 X Cantata Fresnel, 23 x Par Cans, 12 x AC1001, 3 x 3 CCT Battens, 2 x C.S.I. Follow Spots.
SOUND: Equipment: Soundcraft Delta 24/4/2 situated rear of auditorium, 8/4/2 Studiomaster mixer situated in control room, 2 X EAW speakers mounted centre F.O.H, 2 x Pairs Bose 802 mounted left and right F.O.H., 1 x Pair Rogers RM1Monitors, Denon DR-M33 and Technics M260 Cassette decks. Denon DCD910 CD player, 2 x Quad 405 and 1 x Turner B502 amps, 6 x AKG D2000, 3 x AKG CMS mics, 5 Sennheiser gun mics, 4 x Shure SM58, 1 X Yamaha SPX 90 effects unit.
DRESSING ROOMS: 6 (excl. large green room which can be used occasionally), accom. 45; 2 x Showers; Orchestra pit 3.40m x 12.08m.
Membership: TMA

KENSINGTON LEISURE CENTRE

Closed for redevelopment until early 2015
Walmer Road, London W11 4PQ
Tel: 020 7727 9747
Web Site: www.better.org.uk
ADMINISTRATION:
Large space available for functions, concerts, and sports events.
A number of break out rooms available.
Technical information available on request.

KING'S HEAD THEATRE (ISLINGTON)

115 Upper Street, Islington, London N1 1QN
BO: 020 7478 0160 Admin: 020 7226 8561
Email: info@kingsheadtheatre.com
Web Site: www.kingsheadtheatre.com
ADMINSTRATION:
Artistic Director: Adam Spreadbury-Maher
Capacity: 118

KOKO

1A Camden High Street, London NW1 7JE

Tel: 0870 432 5527 BO: 0844 847 2258
Email: info@koko.uk.com
Web Site: www.koko.uk.com
Formally known as Camden Palace
ADMINISTRATION:
General Manager: Mike Hamer
Production Manager: Kristina Riddington.
Email: kristina@koko.uk.com
Corporate/ Private Hire Contact: Annette Morris
Email: annette@koko.uk.com
Cap: Standing 1410, Theatre style 300, Banquet style 210, Reception 1000.
Custom built 50K JBL sound system.

LABAN THEATRE

Laban, Creekside London SE8 3DZ
Tel: 020 8691 8600 Events: 020 8469 9452 Fax: 020 8691 8400
Email: B.brady@trinitylaban.ac.uk, info@trinitylaban.ac.uk
Web Site: www.thetrinitylaban.ac.uk
ADMINISTRATION:
Senior Technician: Fay Patterson
Email: f.patterson@trinitylaban.ac.uk
Production Manager: Karsten Tinapp
Email: k.tinapp@trinitylaban.ac.uk
At the heart of an award winning building, the Bonnie Bird Theatre is London's most exciting venue for contempory dance, physical theatre and live art events.
Capacity: Bonnie Bird Theatre - 300 Theatre Style.
For Technical information, contact the production department on 020 8691 9502.

LAMBETH TOWN HALL

Brixton Hill, London SW2 1RW
Facilities Department: 020 7926 1010
Council Tel: 020 7926 1000
Email: fmhelpdesk@lambeth.gov.uk
Web Site: www.lambeth.gov.uk
ADMINISTRATION:
Props: London Borough of Lambeth
Facilities Manager: Louise Polton
For hiring enquiries, contact the Facilities Team: Marcia Griffiths and Sally Leedhan.
Assembly Hall Capacity: 350 (Standing), 300 (Theatre Style), 200 (Banquet)
General Purpose Hall used for dances, weddings etc.

LATCHMERE LEISURE CENTRE

Burns Road, Battersea, London SW11 5AD
Tel: 020 7207 8004 Fax: 020 7924 3783
Email: enquiries@latchmereleisurecentre.co.uk
Web Site: www.latchmereleisurecentre.co.uk
Administration:
Props: London Borough of Wandsworth
Manager: Ed Lane

LEICESTER SQUARE THEATRE

6 Leicester Place London WC2H 7BX
Tel: 020 7534 1740 BO: 08448 733433
Email: martin@leicestersquaretheatre.com
Web Site: www.leicestersquaretheatre.com
Props: London International Arts Theatre Ltd
Contact: Martin Witts
Capacity: 400
2 bars, second loung theatre, capacity 70

LEIGHTON HOUSE MUSEUM

12 Holland Park Road, London W14 8LZ
Tel: 020 7602 3316 Hires Tel : 020 7603 1123 (Sally Dobinson) Front Desk Tel: 020 7471 9160 (Gen Enquiries) Bkg Fax: 020 7371 2467
Email: sally.dobinson@rbkc.gov.uk
Web Site: www.rbkc.gov.uk/leighton-housemuseum
ADMINISTRATION:
Props: London Borough of Kensington & Chelsea
Bookings Contact: Sally Dobinson.
Capacity: Main Studio - 150 Standing, 100 Concert, 60 Dinner.
Opening times: Monday to Sunday 10.00am - 5.30pm. Closed Tuesdays.
Atmospheric period building licensed for use as a Concert Hall. Available from 6.30pm - 10.00pm. Limited dressing room facility. Theatrical entertainment not permitted.
Exhibition gallery available for the visual arts. (11am - 5.30pm Mon-Fri and to 5pm Sat and Sun.)
Admission fees: £5 entry. £1 for any concession. Free admittance for art fund members.

LITTLE ANGEL THEATRE "HOME OF BRITISH PUPPETRY"

14 Dagmar Passage, London N1 2DN
Admin: 020 7359 8581 BO: 020 7226 1787
Email: info@littleangeltheatre.com
Web Site: www.littleangeltheatre.com
ADMINISTRATION:
Technical Manager: David Duffy
Front of House Supervisor: Alex Carter
Policy: Resident & Touring Puppet Theatre.
Perfs: Wednesday to Sunday. Varied.
Disabled Access.
Seats: 100
TECHNICAL:
Proscenium Puppet Stage.

THE LOGAN HALL

Institute of Education, University of London, 20 Bedford Way, London WC1H 0AL
Admin: 020 7612 6143 Admin Fax: 020 7612 6126
Email: venuehire@ioe.ac.uk
Web Site: www.20bedfordway.com
ADMINISTRATION:
Props: Institute of Education
Conference Officer: Sharon Fisher
Policy: University multipurpose Hall used for national and international conferences, TV events, lectures, debates, graduation ceremonies, concerts, Arangetram, book launches and fashion events.
Seats: 933. A soft drinks bar can be provided in the adjoining Crush Hall.
TECHNICAL:
STAGE: Open flat stage; 12 movable rostra. Front projection screen. Ceiling mounted data projector. White, black, white silk swagged backcloths. Gold front curtain and two sets of grey stage traverse curtains in fixed positions.
LIGHTING: Strand Series 300 lighting control. 60 channel fixed lighting rig of Selecon HP's, Pat 743's, source 4 selecon performer follow spot.
SOUND: Allen & Heath GL 3300 mixing desk. Flexible mic/line patching system, allowing up to 24 channels. Shure dynamic mics, AKG condensers, 6 channel Sennheiser and UHF wireless system. Recording to cassette, CD or mini disc.
OTHER: Dressing room to accomm 60, 2 showers, 30 music stands. Induction loop for hearing aid users. One Steinway concert grand piano. One Yamaha 5ft 2in grand piano.
Seats: 30 max orchestra.

LONDON COLISEUM

St Martins Lane, London WC2N 4ES
Admin: 020 7845 9397 BO: 020 7845 9300 SD: 020 7845 9397 Tech: 020 7845 9459 Admin Fax: 020 7845 9296
Email: marketing@eno.org
Web Site: www.eno.org
ADMINISTRATION:
Owners: English National Opera.
Artistic Director: John Berry
Music Director: Edward Gardner OBE
Director of Marketing: Claire Round
Technical Director: Geoff Summerton (technical@eno.org)
Perfs: Normally 7.30.
Seats: 2,500 on four levels. Licensed Bars and Buffets serving full refreshment on all levels.
For more information on hiring the London Coliseum for performances, please call Lynne Adam, Director of Theatre Management, on 020 7845 9211 or Email: ladam@eno.org.
TECHNICAL:
STAGE: Proscenium stage flat surface; prosc. opening width 15.149m x height 8.525m; false prosc. width 12.16 - 13.999m x height 7.2 - 8.76m. Grid 21.6m high; 63 lines; counterweight. Flying Bars 16.76m long. Wing width P/S 3.05m, O/P 3.05m. Prompt corner O/P.
LIGHTING:
Control Board/Switchboard - Rank Strand 550i, 360 Channels; Front of House permanent positions available; Control Board - Rank Strand 550i, 360 Hardwired circuits to basic rig, 96 DMX Circuits for additional equipment; Follow spots - 2 x 2k Xenon KUPO.
Front of House Rig - Dome: 7 x 2k

Circuits, 7 x RJ710 SX Profiles 9/26 degrees; Upper Circle Front: 6 x 2k Circuit, 12 x Par64 (CP61), 12 x 1.2k Sil 30 degrees. Dress Circle Front: 5 x 2k Circuits, 4 x RJ714SX Profiles 15/38 degrees, 1 x RJ710SX Profiles 9/26 degrees. PS & OP Galleries: 15 x 2k Circuits per side, 15 x RJ710SK Profiles 9/26 degrees per side. PS & OP Box Rooms: 4 x 2k Circuits per side, 6 x RJ614SX Profiles 15/38 degrees per side. PS & OP Speaker Booms: 4 x 2k Circuits per side, 3 x RJ614SX Profiles 15/38 degrees, 4 x Par64 120v (No2/FFP) per side. PS & OP Pros Booms: 9 x 2k Circuits per side, 9 x 1.2k Cantata Fresnel, 1 x 1.2k Sil 30 degrees Profile per side.
Lighting Positions Behind Iron Curtain - PS & OP Perch: 10 x 2k Circuits per side; PS & OP Boom: 5 x 2k Circuits per side; PS & OP Ladders: 4 x 2k Circuits per ladder; PS & OP Bridge: 10 x 2k Circuits; Front Bridge: 12 x 2k Circuits; Under Bridge: 15 x 2k Circuits; Batten 2 (Bar 25): Provision for 23 x 2k Circuits, 6 x 5k Circuits; Batten 3 (Bar 34): Provision for 23 x 2k Circuits, 6 x 5k Circuits; Iris 4 Bar (Bar 37): Provision for 23 x 2k Circuits, 6 x 5k Circuits; 2k Bar (Bar 54): Provision for 23 x 2k Circuits, 6 x 5k Circuits; Iris 5 Bar No 2 (two tonner): Provision for 12 x 2 Circuits, 4 x 5k Circuits; Ground Rows: Provision for 8 x Orion Ground Row units; Dip: Provision for 10 x 2k Circuits, 2 x 5k Circuits per side.

LONDON PALLADIUM

Argyll Street, London W1F 7TF
Mgt: 020 7850 8771 BO: 0844 412 4655
SD: 020 7850 8770
Email: gareth.parnell@reallyuseful.co.uk
Web Site: www.reallyusefultheatres.co.uk
ADMINISTRATION:
Props: Really Useful Theatres Ltd, 65 Drury Lane, London WC2B 5SP; Tel: 020 7557 7300 and Fax 020 7240 2511.
Policy: Musicals, Comedy, Concerts, Television.
Theatre Manager: Gareth Parnell
For all bookings contact James Harrison (Concerts and Hirings Manager). Facilities may be made available for day time, late night and weekend use for private and press receptions, conferences and meetings. (venuehire@reallyuseful.co.uk)
Seats: 2,318
4 Bars, Café, Entertainment Suites.
TECHNICAL:
STAGE: Flat; Pros. Opening 14.48m; Ht of of Grid 16.76m; 60 lines, C/W; Depth of Stage 12.34m; Revolving Stage 9.75m & 5.45m; Circular Centre Lift 3.66m; Prompt Cnr. P.S.
LIGHTING: Board: Strand Galaxy II, 298 Circuits. Situated rear of Royal Circle.
OTHER: Dressing rooms: 24
Membership: SOLT.

UNIVERSITY COLLEGE LONDON UNION

25 Gordon Street, London WC1H 0AY
Tel: 020 7679 2500
Email: stuart.janes@ucl.ac.uk
Web Site: www.uclunion.org
ADMINISTRATION:
General Manager: David Squires. Tel: 020 7679 7216
or Email: d.squires@ucl.ac.uk
Commercial Services Manager: Tim Cary. Tel: 020 7679 2535, Email: t.cary@ucl.ac.uk
Events Manager: Stuart Janes
Marketing and Communications Manager: Tony Withstandley
Tel: 020 7679 7902, Email: t.withstandley@ucl.ac.uk
Seats/Capacity: 550

UNIVERSITY OF LONDON UNION

Malet Street, London WC1E 7HY
Admin Tel: 020 7664 2000 Hire Tel: 020 7664 2020 Hire Fax: 020 7436 4606
Mgmt: 020 7664 2084
Email: conference@ulu.lon.ac.uk, d.easton@ulu.lon.ac.uk
Web Site: www.ulu.co.uk
ADMINISTRATION:
Conference Manager: Donna Easton
Capacity: The Venue; 220 Theatre Style + 80 balcony seating. Seminar Rooms; 25 - 110 Theatre Style. Boardrooms; 15 - 40. The Upper Hall; 200 Theatre Style.

LYCEUM THEATRE

21 Wellington Street, London WC2E 7RQ
Mgt: 020 7420 8190 SD: 020 7420 8100
BO: 0844 844 0005 Admin: 020 7420 8193 Admin Fax: 020 7240 4155
Email: rainierkoeners@theambassadors.com
Web Site: www.lyceumtheatrelondon.org.uk
ADMINSTRATION:
Props: Ambassadors Theatre Group
Area General Manager: Ranier Koeners
Theatre Manager: Beth Morgan
Deputy Theatre Manager: Luke Hudson
Box Office Manager: Steve Anstee
Stage Manager: Mick Brown
Seats: 1,800-2,116

LYRIC HAMMERSMITH

Lyric Square King Street, London W6 0QL
BO & Gen Enquiries: 0208 741 6850
Admin: 020 8741 6824 Mgt Tel: 020 8741 6822
Email: enquiries@lyric.co.uk
Web Site: www.lyric.co.uk
ADMINISTRATION:
Props: Lyric Theatre Hammersmith Trust
Artistic Director: Sean Holmes
Executive Director: Jessica Hepburn
Senior Producer: Imogen Kinchin
Finance Manager: Anju Odedra
Head of Production: Seamus Benson

Policy: Producing and Receiving House. Limited runs of new plays and classics, and international work, live music, youth work.
Seats: 550 max.
Studio: Visiting small scale companies, predominantly new plays, classic revivals and international plays. Seats: 125
Rehearsal space capacity: 80.

TECHNICAL:
STAGE: Proscenium Stage, Flat, Pros. opening 8.2mts. Ht. of Pros. 6.95m; Depth of S/Line 9.1m; Elevator Forestage 2m; Ht. of Grid 15m; 38 lines, C/W; Flying Bars 10.5m; Gt-in Goods Lift 1.8m x 3m deep. Ht. 2.5m. Dressing Rooms 8; Orchestra Pit.
LIGHTING: Switchboard: Strand 550; 350 channels, 133 x 2kw, 15 x 5kw.
SOUND: Equipment: Yamaha M2500 32:8:2, 6 X Meyer UPA-1C, 2 x Meyer USW-1.
STUDIO THEATRE: Approx. 11m square; Ht. of Grid 4.8m. Switchboard: ETC Microvision, 120 channels, 104 x LD90 2.5kw. Sound Equipment: Midas Venice 240, 16:4:2. 4 x Meyer UMS-1P.
REHEARSAL SPACE: Expansive square space measuring 11.5 metres (38ft) by 10.5 metres (35ft) wide and has a 4.5metres (15ft) high ceiling providing a large airy space to work in. The adaptable space also incorporates facilities to rig theatre lighting, stage-sets and scenery, allowing performances to take place.

LYRIC THEATRE

Shaftesbury Avenue, London W1D 7ES
Mgt: 020 7494 5840 BO: 0844 412 4661
SD: 020 7494 5841
Email: david.holder@nimaxtheatres.com
Web Site: www.nimaxtheatres.com
ADMINISTRATION:
Props: Nimax Theatres Ltd, 11Maiden Lane, London, WC2E 7NA Telephone: 020 7395 0780 Fax: 0207 240 4540
Policy: Plays, Musicals, Comedy, Concerts.
Chief Executive: Nica Burns
Theatre Manager: David Holder
Chief Electrician: Tony Priestly
For all bookings and production enquiries please contact Nica Burns (CEO), Laurence Miller (Commercial Director). Facilities may be made available for day time, late night and weekend use for private and press receptions, conferences and meetings - Contact Laurence Miller: 0845 434 9290, Fax: 0207 240 4540 and Email: laurence.miller@nimaxtheatres.com
Seats: 932. VIP Room (7m x 3.2m) 20 Seated, 35 standing.
4 Bars.
TECHNICAL:
STAGE: flat; Pros. Opening 9.14m, Ht of Pros. 7.32m; Depth of Stage 12.65m; Ht of Grid 15.24m; 25 lines, 7 S.P/19 D.P C/W; Prompt Cnr. P.S.
LIGHTING: Lighting Board: Strand Galaxy II, 192 circuits. Situated rear of Upper

Circle.
OTHER: Dressing rooms: 14
Membership: SOLT.

MACOWAN THEATRE (LAMDA)

Logan Place, Kensington, London W8 6QN
Mgt: 020 7373 6932 BO: 0844 847 0550
Fax: 020 7370 1980
Email: enquiries@lamda.org.uk, boxoffice@lamda.org.uk
Web Site: www.lamda.org.uk
ADMINISTRATION:
Props: London Academy of Music and Dramatic Art
Head of Development & Communications: Georgina Grant Haworth
Operational Facilities Manager: James Medhurst
Technical Director: Robert Gale
Policy: Productions by LAMDA, student actors and technicians. Club licence.
Seats: 120
TECHNICAL:
STAGE: Flexible seating, mainly proscenium. Sprung wood floor. Pros 13.3m by 5.47m. Depth S/Line 9.2m. Grid 10.85m. 9 Counterweights, some hemps. Flying Bars 11.58m DS, 10.15m US. Wings 0.83m PS, 1.47m OP. PS prompt. Tallescope.
LIGHTING: Strand 520. 84 2kw dimmers. Position SL FOH. 50 Profiles, 30 Fresnels, 30 Parcans, 2 Follow Spots. Lantern stocks are varied for teaching requirements.
SOUND: Equipment: Yamaha PM1200. Position SRFOH. Again a wide stock of other equipment for teaching.
OTHER: Dressing Rooms 2, accom. 30; 5 Showers; Orchestra Pit 12. Wardrobe department.

MERMAID CONFERENCE & EVENTS CENTRE

Puddle Dock, Blackfriars, London EC4V 3DB
Tel: 020 7236 1919 Fax: 020 7236 1819
Email: info@the-mermaid.co.uk
Web Site: www.the-mermaid.co.uk
ADMINISTRATION:
General and Marketing Manager: Louise Stone
Technical Manager: Andy Munro
Auditorium: Seats - 600 on one raked level; Loop system for the hard of hearing. Disabled facilities. Servery and 2 large bars.
Reception Capacity: 400
TECHNICAL:
End stage, 14.8m wide; 23.8m deep; Dock Door direct off street, 4.6m high, 4.6m wide; 0.8m drop to stage level; Revolve manual, 6.1m diam. Trap DSC. Communications: 1 channel ring intercom; Cue lights patchable to 14 positions; dressing room paging and show relay

MILLFIELD THEATRE

Silver Street, Edmonton, London N18 1PJ
Mgt and BO: 020 8807 6680 Marketing Tel: 020 8887 7313
Email: boxoffice@enfield.gov.uk
Web Site: www.millfieldartscentre.co.uk
ADMINISTRATION:
Props: Enfield Borough Council
General Manager: Paul Everett
Operations Manager: Marc Day
Marketing Manager: Alice Plunkett
Email: alice.plunkett@enfield.gov.uk
Policy: Amateur and professional productions, tours, concerts and recitals, conferences, trade fairs, etc.
Perfs: Variable.
Seats: Variable 321 to 362.
Theatre bar, light refreshments.
For Millfield Theatre hire enquiries please contact Hannah Pender on Hannah.Pender@enfield.gov.uk.
TECHNICAL:
STAGE: Complete adjustable performance area. Depth 3.46m-7.63m. Width up to 14.15m Optional Pros. variable. Width up to 9.1m Depth up to 5.2m. Electrically operated lowering/mobile grid. 10 hemp sets. 3 tab tracks. 5 x wipe tracks. Flying bars 11m. Prompt corner PS, F.O.H. Direct get-in PS. Scene dock OP. Sprung floor over entire performance area. Control room at rear of auditorium.
LIGHTING: Control: Strand 520i with Lighting Board; 60 x 2.5kw dimmers and 6 x independants linked through patch bay to outlets throughout of performance area. 5 spot bars + 2 F.O.H. side booms + 2 stage side booms with 20 x 1kw Profiles, 24 x 1kw Fresnels, 30 x Parcans, 12 x 650w Profiles, 12 x 500w Fresnels, 4 x 500w Profiles, 8 x 500w Floods, 6 x Coda 4 Battens, 4 x 1kw Floods. 2 x 2kw followspot. 5 x 1kw PC Remote colour-change equipment available. 12 x Source 4 Profiles.
Sound: Equipment: Soundcraft 324 Live + Shure 10/2 desk. 30 mic lines, permanent auditorium PA + tie-lines to other areas. Denon 1050 Minidisc, Sony 530 Minidisc, 6 x Sennheiser UHF Radio, 4 x Shure UHF Radio Mics and two cassette decks. SPX90 effects unit and SPX 900, CD player, 2 Stereo delays, gate. Shure/AKG/Sennheiser Micro-phones.
OTHER: Dressing Rooms 8, accom. 65; 2 Showers; Shallow orchestra pit for up to 30. Full disabled access and facilities. Car park available.

NATIONAL THEATRE

South Bank, London SE1 9PX
Admin: 020 7452 3333 BO: 020 7452 3000 Fax: 020 7452 3344
Email: tours@nationaltheatre.org.uk
Web Site: www.nationaltheatre.org.uk
Director: Nicholas Hytner
Executive Director: Tessa Ross
Head of Production: Mark Dakin
Head of Technical Resources: Rob Barnard
Director of Marketing: Alex Bayley
Olivier Capacity: 110 - 1160
Lyttelton Capacity: 890
Dorfman Capacity: 250 - 400
Open in 1976, designed by Sir Denys Lasdun.
Policy: To present an ecletic mix of new plays and classics.
No performance on Sunday - evening shows starts at 7.30pm, matinees on Saturday and one other day at 2 - 2.30pm.
Other activities: Art and photography exhibitions, live foyer music daily, platform perfomances and other events throughout the year, conducted tours of the building, educational workshops, bookshop, outdoor performance events during summer.

TECHNICAL:
Olivier Theatre.
STAGE: Open stage. Thrust format, No rake - revolving stage with integral stage elevators, backstage and understage crossovers. Height of grid 26.4m. 127 computer controlled electric hoists at 0.5m centres, 200kg per hoist - maximum fly height 11m. Get-in via scenery lift 6.7m x 3.8m x 6m. Plans and elevations available.
LIGHTING: Strand 500 board with extensive repertoire lighting rig, some moving lights available.
SOUND: Cadac desk, computer assisted J console, operated from rear of auditorium in control box - 48 inputs, 12 subgroups, 12 main groups - Tannoy, D&B and meyer speakers and amps - Sennheiser radio mic system - Siap acoustic enhancement system.
STAGE MANAGEMENT: Extensive comms, Clearcom Matrix system and Clearcom radio communication system.
BACKSTAGE FACILITIES: Dressing rooms, accommodate approx 50 - laundry and wardrobe facilities. Canteen and staff bar.

Lyttelton Theatre
STAGE: Proscenium arch. performing area 18m x 15m - pros opening 13.6 - 10.4m x 5-9m. Stage can be raked - floor hardboard on gurjun, suitable for dance, backstage and understage crossovers. Height to grid 23.6m - 73 counterweight sets, single purchase, 0.2m apart - 500kg permitted on bars - maximum flying height 23m. Main elevator 13.6m x 12m - orchestra pit on 3 elevators, 4.5m x 1.6m. Main stage has integrated revolve, 11.5m diameter. Get-in via dick door at street level. Plans and elevation available.
LIGHTING: Strand 500 control system with extensive repertoire lighting rig and some moving lights
SOUND: Cadac Concert Series Desk, operated from rear of stalls (window opens) - EV speaker system - cueing at rear of stalls.
BACKSTAGE: - as Olivier Theatre

Cottesloe Theatre

STAGE: Flixible courtyard theatre.
Performing area up to 9.9m x 19m, wing widths 2.5m SR/SL. Floor can be raked - floor hardboard on gurjun strip, partially suitable for dance. 12 motorised flying bars - 125kg permitted on bars - maximum flying height 7.59m - black soft and hard masking - white filled cloth cyclorama. 5 trap apertures in stage end. Get-in via dock door 1.5m above stagewith door aperture 1.3m x 3m. Plans and elevation available
LIGHTING:- as Lyttelton Theatre
BACKSTAGE: - as Olivier Theatre - band room
COMMUNICATIONS: Clearcom - Both wired and wireless
For the disabled: 3 wheelchair spaces in the Olivier, 4 in the Lyttelton, 2 in the Cottesloe - lift to mezzanine restaurant - infra-red audio system - audio - described/captioned and signed performances - assistance available, contact Lyttelton Information Desk.

NEW LONDON THEATRE

Drury Lane and Parker Street, London WC2B 5PF
Mgt/SD: 020 7242 9802 Booking: 0844 412 4654 (SEE Tickets)
Email: james.harrison@reallyuseful.co.uk
Web Site: www.ruttheatres.com
ADMINISTRATION:
Props: Really Useful Stage Production Co Ltd
Theatre Manager: Cuqui Rivera
Maintenance Engineer: Dennis Barthram
Policy: As normal West End Theatre; Conferences.
Perfs: Variable.
Seats: 1024. Two Bars & One Coffee Bar.

TECHNICAL:
STAGE: Proscenium or Round Stage, Flat with 4.88m diam. revolve; Apron Stage; Front of Apron to Back Wall 11.81m; Pros. opening 17.68m variable; Depth of S/Line 8.53m; Ht. of Grid 16.76m; 39 lines, C/W; Scenery Flying Ht. 16.15m; Flying Bars 17.68m; W/Widths P.S. 5.33m; Prompt Cnr. either side or upstage. Theatre in The Round: 10 Electric Motor Flying Bars.
LIGHTING: Switchboard: Strand IDM Mk. 2a, rear gallery; 120 ways; F.O.H. Spots 2 Patt. 765, 35 Patt. 773, 65 Patt. 763; Dips 25 circuits.
SOUND: Equipment: Stagesound, 6 channel 2 group, 2 Stereo Grams, 2 Stereo Tape rear gallery; 100v line speakers, 2 Pros. SL/SR. 3 on stage.
OTHER: Dressing Rooms 9, accom. 40; 12 Showers. Orchestra Pit 18.
Membership: SOLT

NEW WIMBLEDON THEATRE

93 The Broadway, Wimbledon, London SW19 1QG
Mgt/SD: 020 8545 7900 BO: 0844 871 7646 Fax: 020 8543 6637
Email: wimbstagedoor@theambassadors.com
Web Site: www.atgtickets.com
ADMINISTRATION:
Props: Ambassadors Theatre Group (Venues) Ltd
Executive General Manager: Callum Kemp
Administration & Events Manager: Emma Brack
Theatre Manager: Lisa Mart
Technical Manager: Stuart Graham
Marketing Manager: Nicci Allt
Policy: Touring, pantomime, opera, ballet, concerts, amateur productions.
Also facilities for use of visiting film and television companies and conferences.
Willing to premier show. Also Studio - contact General Manager for details.
Perfs: Times vary. Mats usually Thursday and Saturday.
Seats: 1600, four fully licenced bars.
Studio seats: 80, one fully licenced bar.
TECHNICAL:
STAGE: Proscenium stage raked in 1 in 40, pros opening 10.40m, Height of pros 6.30m. Max Height House Header 6.00m. Depth of setting line 10.60m. Total depth of stage 12.87m. Height of grid 15.45m. 40 Counterweight and 18 Hemp. O/P Fly Floor. Scenery Flying Clearance height 7.33m. Prompt Corner P.S. 13 way cue board with answer headphone intercom system.
LIGHTING: Switchboard: Strand 520 -240 circuits - control rear stalls. Lighting Equipment: Strand 520 (software version 2.5e) with 2 monitors in rear stalls position. Designer position in stalls with control point. Riggers control in auditorium and stage. 240 circuits (inc. 36 5k's) controlled by EC90 dimmers (80 FOH, 12 Orchestra, 208 Backstage). Blues and Whites working light backstage. Lanterns: 20 x Source4 19 degree profiles. 6 x Harmony 15/28 profiles, 20 x1k Fresnels. 50 x Par 64's, 10 x Coda 4 500w flood units. Power: 400 amp 3 phase supply USR. 63 amp 3 phase clean sound supply with outlets SL and SR (adaptors also available).
BACKSTAGE COMMUNICATIONS:
Headsets to all positions, Cue lights to all backstage positions controlled from moveable prompt desk.
SOUND: Soundcraft mixing desk 20-4-2 in rear stalls position.
Auditorium cover - Stalls 2 x Martins, Backstage 2 Channel, 4 Position Foldback.

NOEL COWARD THEATRE

(Formerly the Albery Theatre)
St Martins Lane, London WC2N 4AH
Mgt: 020 7759 8010 BO: 0844 482 5140
SD: 020 7759 8010
Email: NoelCowardManagers@delmack.co.uk
Web Site: www.delfontmackintosh.co.uk
ADMINISTRATION:
Props: Delfont Mackintosh Theatres
Theatre Manager: Laura Day
Policy: Plays & Musicals.
Perfs: Variable according to Production.
Seats: 882, plus 21 Standing. Three Licensed Bars.
TECHNICAL:
Stage: Proscenium Stage, Temp c/w avail. Var. speed house tabs. Flat; Pros. opening 9.6m; Ht. of Pros. 6.55m; Depth of S/Line 11.58m; Ht. of Grid 15.85m; 55 lines Hemp, 6 Motor; Scenery Flying Ht. 15.24m; Flying Bars 11.89m; W/Widths P.Ss 1.90m; O.P. 1.90m; Prompt Cnr. as required (normally D.S.L.).
Lighting: Switchboard: 4 CTT Sil 30, 4ADB Fres. Strand MMS, 200 Channel Capacity with special facilities, rear of stalls; circuit distribution F.O.H. 60; Flys 82; Stage 54 F.O.H. Spots 22 Patt. 264, 8 Patt 23.
Sound: Equip: I/R Hearing. As required, F.O.H. Amplification System.
Other: Dressing Rooms 16; Bathrooms 5; 1 Shower; Orchestra Pit 8.
Joint Stage Door with Wyndham's Theatre.
Membership: SOLT.

NOVELLO THEATRE

5 Aldwych, London WC2B 4LD
Tel: 020 7759 9611 BO: 0844 4825170
Email: novellomanagers@delmack.co.uk
Web Site: www.delfontmackintosh.co.uk
ADMINISTRATION:
Props: Delfont Mackintosh Theatres
Theatre Manager: Gloria Louis
Technical Manager: Gavin Miller
Policy: Theatrical productions of all types.
Perfs: No set times.
Seats: 1,081. Bars on each floor.
TECHNICAL:
STAGE: Proscenium Stage, slight rake. Pros opening 9.60m(w) x 6.40m(h). Depth of slight line 9.75m. Ht. of Grid 17.37m. 31 lines ets. Scenery flying ht. 9.14m. Flying bars 12.19m D/S, 11.58m U/S. Working widths S/L 3.05m D/S 0.91m U/S; S/R 3.66m D/S with dock 5.49m x 4.27m. Prompt corner S/R. Orchestra Pit: 18-20.
LIGHTING: Electrics: Gemini lighting board, disk backup, Permus dimmers, 144 ways. Lantern Stock: 8 Sil 30 (1kw axial), 2 Prelude 16/30, 12 Patt. 23, 20 Patt. 743, 12 Patt. 53, 6 Patt. 49, 12 Furse 500w floods. Cue light system. Generator capable of running entire installation.
OTHER: Dressing Rooms: 16, accom. 44; 2 Showers.
Membership: SOLT

O2 ACADEMY BRIXTON

211 Stockwell Road, London SW9 9SL
Tel: 020 7771 3000 BO: 0844 477 2000
Email: mail@o2academybrixton.co.uk
Web Site: www.O2academybrixton.co.uk
ADMINISTRATION:
General Manager: Nigel Downs
Assistant General Manager: Octavia

Harwood
Stage Manager: Josh Rosen
Tel: 020 787 3116. Email: josh@o2academybrixton.co.uk
Capacity: 4,921 max. All Seated: 2,391.
Circle: 1,083 seated; 78 standing

O2 ARENA

Peninsula Square, Millenium Way, Greenwich, London SE10 0DX
BO Tel: 0844 8560202 General Enq: 0208 463 2000
Email: customerservices@theo2.co.uk
Web Site: www.theo2.co.uk
ADMINISTRATION:
Props: AEG Worldwide
For Corporate Sales and Special Events telelphone 020 8463 2149 or Email: sales@theo2.co.uk
All enquiries to be made via Customer Services.

THE OLD VIC THEATRE

The Cut, London SE1 8NB
Mgt/SD: 020 7928 2651 Mgt Fax: 020 7261 9161 Box Office: 0844 871 7628
Email: ovtcadmin@oldvictheatre.com
Web Site: www.oldvictheatre.com
ADMINISTRATION:
Chief Executive: Sally Greene
Artistic Director: Kevin Spacey
Theatre Manager: Liz Sillit
Development Director: Vivien Wallace
Business Director: Kate Varah
Facilities Manager: Deano McCullagh
Theatre Operations Manager: Dan Kujawski
Policy: Resident Theatre Company
Perfs: Eves Mon-Sat at 7.30pm; Mats Wed & Sat (times/days may vary depending on production). Panto: Thurs-Sun Sun Shows: one-off events (check first)
Seats: 1,077 (Three Bars)
The Old Vic has one rehearsal studio for hire on a daily or weekly basis. For more information, hire rates and availability, please contact the General Manager's office on 020 7981 0981 or email hires@oldvictheatre.com.
TECHNICAL:
STAGE: Proscenium Stage, Raked 1:22; Pros. opening 8.50m; Depth from iron 10.11m; Perm. Fore-stage 1.50m, Forestage extension 3m; Rear Stage 9.5m x 9.5m; Ht. of Pros. 6.10m; Ht. of Grid 15.60m; 53 double purchase C/W bars; Flying Bars 11.00m; W/Widths P.S. 7.00m, O.P. 7.00m; Prompt cnr. O. P. or P.S. Access equipment: 1 Tallescope, 2 x Focus Bridges and a selection of ladders, inc 12 rung Zarges.
LIGHTING: Control: 2 x ETC Expressions (identical to ARRI Imagine 3) with full tracking back up, capable of supporting 600 channels, 1024 dimmers, with 2 playbacks, 3.5" drive and dual display. Operated from control room at rear of the dress circle, with remote control facility onstage. Console or remote monitors can be moved to stalls during production periods. DMX and Ethernet patchable to various outlets around the stage.
Electrical: 144 Permus Dimmers installed - 22 x 5K 122 x 2.5K - but facility on SR for additional temporary installation. 12 switchable 15A independents distributed around the stage and auditorium. Auxiliary mains supply pannel on-stage comprising 2 x 100A three phase busbars, 3 x 63A C17 three phase sockets, 3 x 63A C17 single phase sockets. Additional three phase supply on SL fly floor for motors or stage machinery.
Lighting equipment: 28 x Sil 15 1K Axial 40 x Patt 264. These are usually FOH, and schematic layout is available on request, but it is not a fixed rig. No follow spots but position for up to four spots available at rear of upper circle slightly to SL of centre. NB. Due to construction of the circle fronts, no circle front or upper circle front lighting positions available.
SOUND: The theatre has no sound equipment, but it is equipped with approx 60 3pin XLR tie lines. A 6 inch duct connects the sound mixing position at the rear of the stalls to the orchestra pit, and a further duct links to the sub-stage room with position for amplifier racks, complete with 3 x 32A C17 single phase power supplies (all on the same phase). Proscenium boom positions available for speakers, as well as points for central overhead cluster and rear auditorium speaker mountings on all levels.
COMMUNICATIONS: RTS two channel headset system capable of supporting 17 belt packs. 20 outlets throughout building, 10 belt packs (325's), 16 Beyer Headsets with master station in prompt desk.
STAGE MANAGEMENT: Cue lights - 24 fixed positions, 12 remotable, fully patchable into 20 way control on prompt desk. Prompt desk also provides BT ringing supply, either manually controlled or on a standard pattern, as well as a digital clock/stopwatch.
CCTV: although the theatre does not supply a camera, BNC tie lines are provided to a variety of camera positions, and two 9" monitors are available.
BACKSTAGE FACILITIES: Dressing Rooms for 36 persons; 4 Bathrooms. Male & Female Band Rooms (pit capacity 24 musicians).
Maintenance, Wardrobe & Laundry Room.

OPEN AIR THEATRE

Regent's Park Theatre Ltd. Open Air Theatre, Inner Circle, Regent's Park, London NW1 4NR
BO: 0844 8264242 Mgt: 08443 753460
Email: admin@openairtheatre.com
Web Site: www.openairtheatre.com
ADMINISTRATION:
Props: Department of Culture, Media and Sport
Lessees: Regent's Park Theatre Ltd
Artistic Director: Timothy Sheader
Executive Director: William Village
Head of Visitor Services and Estates: Eleanor Williams
Commercial Director: Andy Locke
Theatre Administrator: Lydia Lewis
Policy: Regent's Park Theatre is a non-profit distributing Company founded in 1962 whose main function is to present Summer Seasons of plays and musicals at the Open Air Theatre.
Perfs: Mon/Sat 7.45 ; Mats. Wed/Thurs & Sat. 2.15; Mid May, June, July, August and first part of September.
Seats: 1200. Refreshment; Fully Licensed Bars. buffet (cold) and barbecue available before performance from 6.30. Bar open until midnight.
TECHNICAL:
Technical facilities vary according to production.
The Theatre is leased to the New Shakespeare Company by the Department of Culture, Media and Sport and is not generally available for hire.
Membership: SOLT

PALACE THEATRE

Shaftesbury Avenue, London W1D 5AY
Mgt/SD: 020 7434 0088 Fax: 020 7734 6157
Email: venuehire@reallyuseful.co.uk
Web Site: www.rutheatres.com
ADMINISTRATION:
Props: Really Useful Theatres Ltd. Head Office
Licensing Authority: City of Westminister.
Theatre Manager: Anna Charles
Chief Electrician: Kriss Buddle
Policy: Usual West End Policy of Commercial Theatre Seats: Capacity: 1,383. Bars in all parts.
TECHNICAL:
STAGE: 8'x4' hardboard sections, 32'x32' total area. Pros. Opening; 10.25m (33'7"), Stage Height; 10.2m (33'5"), Stage Depth; 12.95m (42'6"). Grid Height; 21.10m (69'3"). Get In; Mid stage left (Dock Door only) 1.83m (6') wide, 3.96 (13') high. Orchestra Pit; Accomm. 22
LIGHTING: Control; Strand 500 Series positioned in FoH Auditorium left box. 234 x dimmers. Follow Spot position; 2 x U/C FOH. 4 x on stage positions.
SOUND: Positioned at rear of stalls.
COMMUNICATIONS: 2 channel RTS headset system and radio cans for trucks.
BACKSTAGE FACILITIES; 15 x Dressing Rooms. Band room (under O/S seats). Wardrobe facilities.
FACILITIES FOR THE DISABLED: Infrared hearing aid system. Level access from Shaftesbury Avenue. Adapted toilet.
Membership: SOLT

PEACOCK THEATRE

Portugal Street, (off Kingsway) London WC2A 2HT
SD: 020 7863 8268 BO Tel: 0844 412 4322

Email: reception@sadlerswells.com
Web Site: www.sadlerswells.com
ADMINISTRATION:
Managed by Sadler's Wells Trust Ltd (Tel: 020 7863 8198)
Marketing Manager: Sammie Squire
Events Manager: Georgia Mackie
Director of Technical and Production: Emma Wilson
Tel: +44 (0)20 7863 8174
Email: emma.wilson@sadlerswells.com
Seats: 974 (675 Stalls, 283 + 14 open boxes + 2 wheelchair 1st Circle)
2 Bars, Entertainment Suite
TECHNICAL
STAGE: Pros. Opening 12.8m 42', Height 5.9m 19'7", Iron Opening (Between the guidelines) 14.8m 48'9". Depth of Stage: Iron to wall (upstage of iron) 9.7m 32', Front of stage to back wall 10.7m 35'3". Wings/Stage Left: Iron to wall (from iron guide to wall) 2.6m 8'4", Stage centre to side wall 10.1m 33', Height under fly floor 6.7m 22'. Wings/Stage right: Iron to wall (from iron guide to wall) 2.6m 8'4", Stage centre to side wall 9.4m 30'9", Height under fly floor 6.7m 22'. Upstage Dock (Positioned Centrally): Opening 6.9m 20', Depth 3.8m 12'8", Height 6.2m 19'9", Width 10m 32'10". Flying and Rigging: 52 single purchase counterweight line sets, Grid Height 15m 20cm 49', Length of bars 14m 46', All fly bars safe working load 204 kg 450 lbs. Load-in / dock doors: Height from Stage 5.1m 16'9", Width of door 3m 9'10", Height of door 5.3m 17'17", Distance from road to dock door 35.5m 116' 6", Hoist Safe working load 1000 kg 1 tonne. Orchestra Pit: accomm. 40 musicians, with one exit/entrance stage left. Half is open, half is understage. Full Depth 3.97m (sides); 4.07m (centre). Rear under-stage section 13.16m wide x 2.97m deep x 2.04m high. Front section with curved frontage is on an electric screw-jack lift and can form a forestage in its up position (this floor is not sprung). Pit Lift 11.28m wide x 1m either side; 2m centre. Height from Stage to Auditorium level 1.1m. Height from Stage to Pit floor Level 2.28m. Orchestral equipment: 1 x lit RAT conductors stand, 25 x lit RAT music stands, 35 x padded chairs.
STAGE EQUIPMENT: 6 pairs of black legs 8' x 24' drop 2.44m x 7.32m, 7 black borders 50' x 9' drop 15.24m x 2.74m, 1 full black tab (without fullness) 40' x 24' drop 12.19m x 7.32m, 1 full black tab (without fullness) 46' x 24' drop 14.02m x 7.32m, 1 pair of half blacks (without fullness) each 26' x 24' drop 7.92m x 7.32m, 1 black gauze (sharkstooth) 46' x 24' drop 14.02m x 7.32m, 1 plastic white Cyclorama 40' x 28' drop 12.19m x 8.53m. One black Harlequin dance floor is available to cover an area 14.63m wide x 9.75m deep (48' wide x 32' deep) with an additional roll to cover the forestage when the Orchestra Pit lift is in the raised position.
LIGHTING: Console and dimmers: Strand 520i (450 channels, 450 attributes), 145 x 2.4kW Dimmers (300A 3phase supply), 16 x 5kW Dimmers. Front of House Equipment: Front of House Bridge (permanently rigged) (19 dimmers), 18 x 26° ETC Source 4 750W fixed beam profile, 2 x 1kW Fresnel for tab warmers, 2 x Teclumen Arena 1200T Follow spots. Additional Lighting Stock: 14 x 19° ETC Source 4 575W fixed beam profile, 22 x 26° ETC Source 4 575W fixed beam profile, 30 x 36° ETC Source 4 575W fixed beam profile, 6 x 50° ETC Source 4 575W fixed beam profile, 18 x Strand Brio 25-50° 600W zoom profile, 28 x Strand Brio 18-30° 600W zoom profile, 12 x Selecon Arena 2kW 8" fresnel (with barndoors), 36 x Selecon Rama HP 1.2kW 7" fresnel (with barndoors), 10 x CCT Starlette PC 1kW PC (with barndoors), 70 x 240V PAR64 1kW (CP62, CP61, CP60 - please ask for details), 24 x Source 4 PAR 575W with VNSP, NSP, MFL & WFL lenses, 20 x ADB ACP1001 1250W asymmetric cyc flood, 6 x Thomas D10004p 1.25KW 4 Cell Asymmetric Flood, 110v Par 64 Available on request. Follow Spots: 2 x Arena Plus 1200w MSR: Beam angle 8° - 22° variable, colour changer, iris. Lighting Rigging Equipment: 10 x Boom Bases, 25 x D-rig boom arms (500mm), 80 x Standard Boom Arms.
SOUND: FOH Speakers: 4 x d&b Ci60 (2 mid fill & 2 circle), each driven by a D&B E-PAC amp, 2 x d&b Ci90 (stalls), each driven by a D&B E-PAC amp, 4 x d&b E3 (stalls delays), driven in L&R pairs by 2x D&B E-PAC amps, 4 x d&b E3 (circle delays), driven in L&R pairs by 2x D&B E-PAC amps, 4 x d&b E15X subs each driven by an D&B E-PAC amp (paired left and right), 2 x d&b C690 (stage side fill at 2 meters) driven by Crown micro tech 600. Monitor Speakers: 5 x d&b Max 12, 1 x Yamaha P7000S amps, 1 x Yamaha P2500 (Plus 2 x JBL eon10 Please ask for details). Mixers: 1 x Allen & Heath GL4000 32ch, 8 group, 10 aux, 4 matrix, 1 x Soundcraft Spirit E12 12ch (+ 2 stereo), 2 aux, 1 x Soundcraft Spirit Folio 8ch (+ 2 stereo), 3 aux, Mixing positions are either rear of stalls by removing 14 seats giving an area of 3.5m x 2.2m or in a booth at the rear of the circle, area 3.5m x 2.5m including fixed worktop. Playback: 1 x CD player Denon DN c615, 1 x CD player Denon DCD-625, 2 x Mini-Disc recorder Sony MDS-E12, extra mini disk recorder and tape players available on request. Outboard Processing: 1 x Lexicon MPX 550 Effects Unit, 1 x Yamaha SPX 90 Effects Unit, 1 x KT Square One Dynamics 8 channel compressor/limiter/gate, 1 x dbx 1066 2 channel compressor/limiter/gate, 2 x BSS FCS-960 2 channel 30 band graphic equalizer, 2 x dbx 1231 2 channel 31 band graphic equalizer. Audio Tie-Lines: Patchable audio infrastructure based around 32 Sends and 16 Returns at both control positions (3pin XLR). Infrastructure also includes the following (all patchable): Speaker (NL4 Speakon), Video (BNC), DMX (5pin XLR), Cat5 Ethernet (Ethercon). Various Microphones Available.
STAGE COMMUNICATIONS: Intercom; Two channel wired Stonewood Audio intercom system (Tecpro compatible), 6 x single channel beltpacks, 6 x dual channel beltpacks, 4 x HME DX200 wireless radio comms, interfacing with wired system. Operates on 2.4 Ghz. 8 x cue lights controlled from prompt corner DSR or control box, with patch Show relay to backstage areas. Paging from DSR prompt corner, control box and stage door, to backstage and FOH bars/foyer.
BACKSTAGE FACILITIES: Wardrobe equipment: Iron, Ironing Board, Front Loading Automatic Washing Machine, Tumble Dryer, Spin Dryer, 4 Wardrobe Rails, Steamer. Dressing Rooms: 10, accomm. 31, with WC and shower facilities. Green Room accomm. 8, with Kettle, Fridge, Microwave, Water cooler. Company Office, accomm. 2, with WC, safe, phone line, Wi-Fi broadband.
ADDITIONAL: Effects: 1 x JEM ZR22 - DMX smoke machine, 1 x Smoke Factory Captain K - DMX smoke machine, 1 x Cirro Lite Strata CS6 - Haze machine. AV Equipment; 1 x fixed colour camera with full stage view routed to: prompt desk and fly floor, 1 x fixed b&w infrared camera with full stage view routed to: prompt desk and fly floor, 1 x movable b&w camera with wide angle lens, suitable for conductor relay etc., 1 x 9" colour video monitor, 1 x 9" b&w video monitor, 2 x 12" b&w video monitors.

PHOENIX THEATRE

110 Charing Cross Road, London WC2H 0JP
SD: 020 7438 9600 Mgt: 020 7438 9610
BO: 0844 871 7627 SD Fax: 020 7438 9611
Email: phoenixtheatremanagement@theambassadors.com
Web Site: www.atgtickets.com/venues/phoenix
ADMINISTRATION:
Prop: Ambassadors Theatre Group Ltd
General Manager: Claire Dixon
Theatre Manager: Jamie Brent
Box Office Sales Manager: Stephen Reynolds
Chief Electrician: Gary Hamilton
Policy: Plays, Musicals
Seats: 1,045 and Five Bars
TECHNICAL:
STAGE: Proscenium Stage, Flat; Pros. opening 9.52m; Ht. of Pros. 7.57m; Depth of S/Line 8.54m; Ht. of Grid 15.39m; 44 lines inc. House Tabs, Scenery flying Ht. 14.63m; Double-Purchase C/W Lift 325lb normal. Flying Bars 11.28m; W/Widths P.S. 2.74m, P.O. 2.13m; Prompt Cnr. P.S. Stage Extension: 2.74 Depth, 11.90 Width, 6.20

Height, Flying Height 5.85, 3 pile Winches (adjustable positioning).
LIGHTING: Switchboard: located in O.P. Stage Box Dress Circle level but position is variable; 120 ways; 6 2kw Rank/Strand Cadenzas; Dip 6 each side plus Dips for Ground row and Float. Lighting Control: ARRI 250 120 way in house.
SOUND: Please contact venue.
BACKSTAGE FACILITIES: Dressing Rooms: 17; 2 Showers. Plus Dressing Rooms with Showers. Orchestra Pit 16.
Membership: SOLT

PICCADILLY THEATRE

16 Denman Street, London W1D 7DY
Mgt: 020 7478 8810 BO: 0844 871 7627
SD: 020 7478 8800
Email: piccadillytheatemanagement@theambassadors.com
Web Site: www.atgtickets.com/venues/piccadilly
ADMINISTRATION:
Props: Ambassador Theatre Group Ltd
Area General Manager: Clare Dixon
Theatre Manager: Jay Bourley
Box Office Sales Manager: Lyndsey Craft
Policy: Plays, Musicals, Ballet etc
Seats: Variable capacity auditorium - Small 792 seats; large 1,200.
Licensed Bars.

TECHNICAL:
STAGE: Proscenium Flat Unit Stage, removable completely or in part; Pros. Opening 9.70m; Ht. of Pros. 6.40m; Depth of S/Line 11.58m; Ht. of Grid 16.54m; 40 lines C/W. Hemp as required; Scenery Flying Ht. 15.09m; Flying Bars 11.73m; W/Widths P.S. 3.35m, O.P. 4.27m; Prompt Cnr. variable.
LIGHTING: Switchboard: MMS 200 channels, 320 memories. Many special facilities. F.O.H. Spots: 22 T Spots; 12 Patt. 264; 2 Patt. 765 Follow Spots; 4 Battens, 3 circuit; Floats 3 circuit, if required.
SOUND: Equipment: F.O.H. Stereo Amplification System and as required.
ADDITIONAL: Dressing Rooms 17, accom. 60; Orchestra Pit 28. Air Cooled Theatre.
Membership: SOLT

PLAYERS' THEATRE

12 Bentinck Street, London W1U 2ER
Tel: 020 7839 1134 Mob: 07770 281746
Email: enquiries@playerstheatre.co.uk
Web Site: www.playerstheatre.co.uk
ADMINISTRATION:
Props: Players Theatre Club
Chairman of Players' Restoration Committee: Bill Halson
Promotion: Laura Davies
Policy: Victorian Music Hall, Melodrama & Pantomime.
Outside hire available

THE PLAYHOUSE THEATRE

Northumberland Avenue, London WC2N 5DE
BO: 0844 871 7627 Mgt: 020 7925 7740
SD: 020 7925 7730 SD Fax: 020 7925 7743
Email: playhousetheatremanagement@theambassadors.com
Web Site: www.atgtickets.com/venues/playhouse
ADMINISTRATION:
Props: Ambassador Theatre Group
Theatre Manager: Aine O'Sullivan
Technical Manager: Ben Evans
Policy: Varied
Seats: 813. Four Licensed Bars plus 75 seat Restaurant.
TECHNICAL:
STAGE: 13.6m x 8.7m Prosc. width 7.88m. Height to Grid 13.2m. Flying: 34 Counter Weight sets at 200mm centres. Two advance F.O.H. bars on electric winches for lighting and loud speakers. Understage: 19th Century system with traps, bridges and sliders restored to full working order.
LIGHTING: In control room at rear of circle; 108 2.5kW and 12.5kW Permus Dimmers on 300A TPN supply. Dimmer circuits are paralleled to up to four locations.
Touring Power: 160A TPN on stage right fly gallery for lighting 60A SPN below stage for sound.
SOUND AND COMMUNICATION: A basic 'in house' system is available, comprising a Soundcraft 200SR 12/4/2 mixer. 6 x MartinCx2 loudspeakers with Yamaha amplifiers, 1 x CD Player, 1 x Tape Deck. The sound control room is located at the rear of the circle and connected by tie lines to a rack room via speaker, microphone and communication tie lines.
DRESSING ROOMS: Five with total spaces for 25 artists. Wardrobe/ Laundry and Company Office.
STAGE MANAGER: Portable Sm desk can be moved SR or SL with 12-way cue lights front of house and dressing room paging, bar bells and Tecpro compatible communication system with SM station, LX, Saver and 3 portable belt packs.

PRINCE EDWARD THEATRE

Old Compton Street, London W1D 4HS
SD: 020 7440 3020 BO: 0844 482 5151
Mgt: 0207 440 3021
Email: petmanagers@delmack.co.uk
Web Site: www.delfontmackintosh.co.uk
ADMINISTRATION:
Props: Delfont Mackintosh Theatres Ltd
Theatre Manager: Rodger Johnson
General Manager: Graham Bradbury
Chief Electrician: Gavin McGrath
Seats: 1,619. 4 Bars.
If you would like to discuss venue hire call 020 7440 3021 or email petmanagers@delmack.co.uk
TECHNICAL:
STAGE: Proscenium Stage Flat 0.25' hardboard surface on timber floor. Pros. Opening 13.38m; Ht. of Pros. 9.27m; Depth of S/Line 9.75m; Depth of Apron 2.70m; Ht. of Grid 19.84m; 47 lines C/W single purchase; Maximum height for Flown Scenery 10.57m; Flying Bars 14.90m average; Distance from Centre of Stage to O.P. wall 10.62m; Centre of Stage to P.S. wall 11.53m; Ht. of fly floors 10.87m; Width between Fly floors 19m; Prompt Cnr. P.S.
LIGHTING: Switchboard: Control and. Spots. As required.
SOUND: Please contact venue.
ADDITIONAL: Dressing Rooms 30, accom. 95; 4 Showers. Orchestra Pit 25.
Membership: SOLT

PRINCE OF WALES THEATRE

31 Coventry Street London W1D 6AS
Mgt: 020 7766 2102 BO: 0844 482 5115
SD: 020 7766 2100
Email: powmanagers@delmack.co.uk
Web Site: www.delfontmackintosh.co.uk
ADMINISTRATION:
Props: Delfont Mackintosh Theatres Ltd.
Lessees: Prince of Wales Theatre Ltd.
General Manager: Jaime Nabeta
Chief Electrician: George Green
Policy: Musical and Plays.
Perfs: Mon - Thurs & Sat 7.30pm, Fri 5pm & 8.30pm, Sat 3pm
Seats: 1,135
Bars: Delfont Room, American Bar
Wheelchair access and disabled toilet.
Infra red for hard of hearing
TECHNICAL:
STAGE: Performing area 12.8m x 8.23m (42'1" x 27'); Proscenium opening 12.8m x 6.55m (42'1" x 21'). Stage has no rake and is constructed of oil tempered hardboard over wood. Suitable for dance (not barefoot). No lino available. Grid height 14.78m (48') 33 counter weight sets, double purchase, 0.2m apart, 300kg permitted on bars. No tab track. Maximum flying height 14.4m (45'7"). Steel safety curtain with drencher. Descent time 24 secs. Orchestra pit 12.9m x 4.8m (42'4" x 15'9") seats 20. Stage get-in via dock door Whitcombe Court 2.59m x 2.74m (8'2" x 8'8") Tallescope available and access tower to 6m.
LIGHTING: 6 x 72 way ETC sensor racks to 16A outlets/socapex outlets, + ethernet infrastructure, + independant tech power (13A) at all lighting positions - operated from biograph room over rear circle. STM & PERMUS 400 amp 3 phase, FOH Lighting Bridge.
SOUND: Please contact venue.
STAGE MANAGEMENT: Prompt corner stage left. Show relay/calls to dressing rooms, calls to F.O.H. 4 followspot positions operated from biograph room.
BACKSTAGE FACILITIES: 17 dressing rooms on 5 floors, access via stage door in Whitcombe Street. Quick change either side of stage. Wardrobe on 4th floor with 10 power points. Washing and drying equipment not supplied. Rehearsal piano available in front stalls and in stalls bar. Stalls bar floor suitable for dance.

PUTNEY LEISURE CENTRE

Dryburgh Road, Putney, London SW15 1BL
Tel: 020 8785 0388 Fax: 020 8789 2387
Email: enquiries@putneyleisurecentre.co.uk
Web Site: www.pfpleisure.org
ADMINISTRATION:
Props: London Borough of Wandsworth
Manager: Tracy McNeela
Dryburgh Halls Capacity: Main Hall, 250. Small Hall, 60

QUEEN ELIZABETH HALL

The South Bank Centre Belvedere Road London SE1 8XX
Reception: 020 7921 0633 BO: 0844 847 9911
Email: events@southbankcentre.co.uk
Web Site: www.rfh.org.uk
ADMINISTRATION:
Props: South Bank Board
Operations Director: Catherine Mallyon
Bookings Manager: Pamela Showha
Head of Commercial Trading: Sue Mcainsh
Email: sue.mcainsh@southbank.co.uk
Seats:Up to 914 Theatre Style. Shares common Buffet/Bar in Foyer with Purcell Room.
TECHNICAL:
STAGE: Open Stage with Thrust Extension.
LIGHTING: Switchboard: Galaxy III, rear of auditorium; 240-ways;
F.O.H. Spots; 24 Harmony Profiles (IK); 36 harmony fresnels (IK); 2 HMV 2500 Zoom, 2 Nielhammer Follow Spots. Plus full stock of lighting equipment.
SOUND: Soundcraft Delta with Court Acoustic Amp and speakers permanently installed.
BACKSTAGE FACILITIES: 8, accom 98; 5 showers; Orchestra Pit by arrangement. Laundry facilities.
Part of the South Bank complex, incorporating the Royal Festival Hall, The Queen Elizabeth Hall, The Purcell Room and the Hayward Gallery.

QUEEN MARY COLLEGE

Students Union, 432 Bancroft Road, London E1 4DH
Tel: 020 7882 7068 Switchboard: 020 7882 5555 Tel: 020 7882 8458
Email: jamie.russell@qmsu.org, e.crooks@qmul.ac.uk
Web Site: www.qmsu.org
ADMINISTRATION:
Contact: Jamie Russell
Drapers Bar Capacity: 150 - 900

QUEEN'S THEATRE

51 Shaftesbury Avenue, London W1D 6BA
SD: 020 7292 1350 BO: 0844 482 5160
Fax: 020 7292 1362
Email: queensmanagers@delfontmackintosh.com
Web Site: www.delfontmackintosh.co.uk
ADMINISTRATION:
Props: Delfont Mackintosh Theatres.
Policy: Plays, Musicals, Comedy, Concerts.
Box Office Manager: David Oakley
For all bookings and production enquiries contact Delfont Mackintosh Theatres Ltd.
Facilities may be made available for day time, late night and weekend use for private and press receptions, conferences and meetings -
Seats: 1097
4 Bars, 2 Private Entertainment Rooms.
For theatre hire please contact Nick Shaw on 020 7292 1350
TECHNICAL:
STAGE: Raked 1:24; Pros. Opening 9.14m; Ht of Pros. 6.79m; Depth of Stage 11.72m; Ht of Grid 15.24m; 32 lines; C/W; Prompt Cnr. O.P..
LIGHTING: Lighting Board: Strand Gemini II, 144 circuits.
Situated O.P. Box Stalls.
SOUND: Please contact venue.
OTHER: Dressing rooms: 12
Membership: SOLT

THE QUESTORS THEATRE

Mattock Lane, Ealing, London W5 5BQ
Mgt: 020 8567 0011 BO: 020 8567 5184
Fax: 020 8567 2275
Email: enquiries@questors.org.uk
Web Site: www.questors.org.uk
ADMINISTRATION:
Props: The Questors Ltd
Executive Director: Andrea Bath. Email: andrea@questors.org.uk
Theatre Administrator: Jane Mason.
Email: jane@questors.org.uk
House and Technical Manager: Mike Hagan
Email: mike@questors.org.uk
Marketing Coordinator: Ian Briggs. Email: ian@questors.org.uk
Policy: Largest and best equipped Community Theatre in Europe. Regular visits from Professional Companies.
Venue comprises Playhouse, Studio, 3 large rehearsal rooms which are available for hire, Scenic Workshop, Large Wardrobe, various other meeting rooms and gallery space.
Perfs: Eves. 7.45 Mats. 2.30
Seats: Playhouse 320-400, Studio 80-100. Two bars, catering facilities available. Car Park. All FOH and Backstage facilities fully accessible.
TECHNICAL:
NB Playhouse only, Studio details available from the Theatre.
STAGE; performing area 7.3m x 8.2m. Prosc. opening variable from 7.3-10.97m x 5.5m. Wing width 6.10m SL. No rake. Limited flying facilities. Full set of scale plans available.
LIGHTING; ETC Insight 3 control console with Reflection backup, 144 channels (126 x 3kW dimmable, 8 x 5kW dimmable, 10 x 3kW switchable), 5 bridges and 2 side galleries provide positions for an adaptable rig, patch panels allow circuits to be allocated flexibly to dimmer channels, luminaire rig included in hire.
SOUND; Control Box: Soundcraft mixing desk 16-8-2. FOH speakers - main overstage cluster and 4 x proscenium speakers permanently wired. Additional speaker outlets at low and high level allow for multiple sound sources. Racked equipment. 4 x minidisc recorders. 2 x CD (one recordable). 1 x cassette. 1 x DAT machine. 4 x stereo amplifiers permanently assigned. 5 x stereo amplifiers that can be patched (input and output as required). Comprehensive patch panel to allow flexible interconnection. 5 x distribution panels at stage level allowing interconnection of audio lines. Various microphones.
STAGE MANAGEMENT; Prompt desk with communication to dressing rooms, control box, auditorium sound desk, FOH, and 8 outstations.
BACKSTAGE FACILTIES: 2 x dressing rooms with showers and toilets, wheelchair-accessible toilet backstage, backstage kitchen, video monitors of stage area.
OTHER FACILITIES; FOH public address system, infra-red hearing aid facility, piano available for hire.

RADA STUDIOS

16 Chenies Street, London WC1E 7EX
Admin/BO: 020 7307 5060 Fax: 020 7307 5062
Email: studiosboxoffice@rada.ac.uk
Web Site: www.radaenterprises.org
ADMINISTRATION:
General Manager: Stacie Novotny
Seats: 200 max.
Disabled access, licensed bar on ground floor.
The Drill Hall, just off Tottenham Court Road, in London's West End, has a 200 seat theatre,
Studio Theatre, a 50-seat cabaret-style. Club Theatre ,four rehearsal studios, four meeting rooms, a bar, an extensive programme of courses and classes (with changing rooms/ shower facilities) and is open seven days a week.
TECHNICAL:
Recently upgraded lighting system and in-house PA system.
Rehearsal rooms and fully accessible darkroom suite.

REDBRIDGE DRAMA CENTRE

Churchfields, South Woodford, London E18 2RB
BO: 020 8504 5451 BO Fax: 020 8505 6669
Email: admin@redbridgedramacentre.co.uk
Web Site: www.redbridgedramacentre.co.uk
ADMINISTRATION:
Head of Centre: Keith Homer
Admin and Box Office Manager: Sally

Polden
Technical Team: Chris Bocking, Ben Ward
Policy: Work suitable for all ages, schools and family audiences.
Capacity: 100 - flexible space.

RICHMOND THEATRE

The Green, Richmond, Surrey TW9 1QJ
Mgt: 020 8332 4500 BO: 0844 871 7651
SD: 020 8332 4500 SD Fax: 020 8332 4509 Tech: 020 8332 4500
Email: christiaandevilliers@theambassadors.com
Web Site: www.atgtickets.com/richmond
ADMINISTRATION:
Props: Ambassadors Theatre Group (Venues) Ltd
General Manager: Christiaan Devilliers
Marketing Manager: Samantha Preston
Technical Manager: Ken Savva
Policy: Touring Drama, Opera and Ballet, Concerts and Pantomime.
Perfs: Evenings at 7.45 pm, Matinees Wed and Sat.
Seats: 818 on three levels. Three licensed bars and entertaining suite.
TECHNICAL:
STAGE: Proscenium raked 1:24. Pros opening 8.16m. Ht. of Pros. 7.0m. Depth of Stage 9.1m. Ht. to Grid 14.0m. Wings 5.5m. P.S. 3.0m O.P. x over stage level. Flying system 35 sets single purchase counterweight 350kg S.W.C., bars 10m long. Get-in street level P.S. Removable rostra (row A) over orchestra pit 10m x 2m approx.
LIGHTING: Control: Strand 520i at rear of stalls. Dimmers 168 x 2.5kw and 12 x 5kw. Lanterns. Full permanent F.O.H. rig - details on application.
SOUND : Full wiring infrastructure for sound control on stage or by prior arrangement at rear of stalls. Details of equipment on application. Full cuelight system, ring intercom and paging to all the usual areas.
ADDITIONAL: Dressing Rooms 9, accom. 26 on 3 floors; 8 Showers; Green Room; Bandroom; Wardrobe and Laundry.

RIVERSIDE STUDIOS

Closed for redevelopment until 2018
Crisp Road, Hammersmith, London W6 9RL
Mgt: 020 8237 1000 BO: 020 8237 1111
Fax: 020 8237 1001
Email: online@riversidestudios.co.uk
Web Site: www.riversidestudios.co.uk
ADMINISTRATION:
Artistic Director: William Burdett-Coutts
Programme Manager: Michael Harris
Technical Director: Ruari Cormack
Technical Manager: James Donovan
Opening Times: 7 days a week.
Capacity: Studio 2 - 400 (seated); Studio 3 - 156. Cinema - 200 (seated).
TECHNICAL:
Studio 2:
STAGE: Dimensions: 18m x 21m. Normal Stage Area: Open: 6-9m x 15m (depending on seating layout), With wings: 6-9m x 12m (depending on seating layout), Height to Grid: 6.9m, Bars normally dead around 5.5m, Average lantern lens height: 5.2m, Main Access Door: 4m(w) x 2.5m(h). Stage Flooring: Concrete. Harlequin Liberty sprung wooden floor is available, maximum area 15m x 9m. No screw fixing or similar to either the concrete or Harlequin floor is possible. Black Harlequin Cascade Dance floor is available on request. Rigging: 48 point hoists SWL 150kg on tracking system position to suit. Usual configuration: 8 bars (15m width). Electric power: Production lighting is via 3 phases, 800 amps per phase. Production Sound is via 63A 1 phase. Other Available: 125A 3 phase Cee-form, 63A 1 phase Cee-form.
SOUND: ALLEN & HEATH GL3300 824C Mixing Console, 4 x LOGIC SYSTEM LS15 500W 8ohm Passive Loudspeaker, 2 x LOGIC SYSTEM Ethos B1 15 500W 4ohm Bass, 3 x LAB GRUPPEN IP 2100 2 x 700W Power Amplifier, BSS Minidrive FDS336 2 Input 6 Output Speaker Management Sys, 2 x Fender 115-ELC onstage monitors w/amp.
LIGHTING: Desk: Strand 530i, Dimmers: ADB EUROTRACK 96 x 3Kw, 48 x 5Kw. Lighting stock: Variable & shared between both Studio's 2 & 3: We maintain a stock of generic lanterns: ETC Source Four zoom & fixed degree profiles. ETC Source Four Parnel. Strand Patt 743 Fresnel. Cantata PC1.2kW. Coda 1kW Flood. Parcan CP62/61/60. Arri 2kW Fresnel (pole op). All lanterns on 16A Cee-form. Limited colour stock.
BACKSTAGE FACILITIES: Dressing Rooms: Up to 5 available. No Green Room. Wardrobe: Washing machine and dryer available.
Studio 3: 11m x 11m. (Normal Stage Area 11m x 5.5m)
Cinema: 16/35mm projection facilities.
A multi-resource arts centre also including bar, restaurant, gallery, rehearsal space and TV studio
Ex BBC film studios available for performance or commercial hire. Easy get-in access from street.

PAUL ROBESON THEATRE

Centrespace, Treaty Centre, High Street, Hounslow, MIddlesex TW3 1ES
Hire Enquiries: 0845 456 2796 (Option 7)
Email: hounslow-info@laing.com
Web Site: www.hounslow.info
ADMINISTRATION:
Props: London Borough of Hounslow
Press Officer: Michelle Morley
For Admin Enquiries please contact: Jason Sykes, 1st Floor, Centrespca, Treaty Centre, High Street, Hounslow, TW3 1ES
Policy: Mixed programme of evening performances including theatre, dance, multicultural events, music and children's shows. Daytime activities include youth workshops, children's events and senior citizen events. The theatre is also available for commercial and community hire. Closed Sundays.
Seats: 20-280
Community Room - adjacent to the theatre, can be used as Green Room or as a separate facility.
TECHNICAL:
STAGE: No actual stage. Performance space same level as row A; Performance Space: 39ft x 18ft (inc. cross over and tab bunching); Performance Area: 25ft x 14ft; Height to Grid: 30ft; Flying Lines: None, 3 x Wipe Tracks D.S./C.S./U.S.; Tabs: Black tabs at rear & mid stage, plus legs and borders; House Tabs: Blue/Green (Motorised); Cinema Screen: Picture Size 18ft x 9ft max (C.S.); Cinema Projector: Elmo Lx 2200 16mm; Slide Projector: Elmo Omnigraphic 552 Xenon; Power Supply: One 32A Cee Form (P.S.) 16 x 13A sockets (S.R.).
LIGHTING: Lighting Desk: Zero 88, Sirius 48; Dimmers: Electrosonic ES6000 series 2kw/chan also 4 x Non dim circuits (1kw each); Stage Bars: 3, 1 x 12 way, 1 x 10 way, 1 x 6 way (all internally wired); Stage Dips: 4 (U.S.L.), (All stage bars and dips are patchable across 22 circuits); F.O.H. Bridges: 2 each 6 way (both paired and internally wired); Follow Spot: 1 x Strand Solo 1kw CSI; Lanterns: Various types of luminaries are available.
SOUND: Sound Desk: Yamaha MC2404 II 24 Chn. Main Amps: Harrison Xi 600 (300w/chn) Mustang 200 (100w/chn); House Speakers: 4 x Tannoy Puma (Flown above pros), 2 x Yamaha S2 15ES (floor level); Foldback System: A basic 2 mix monitor system is available; Yamaha CDX480 CD player. Tape Decks: Revox B77 (1/2 Track 1/4 inch) JVC TD-X502, Denon M12 XR (Cassette Decks); Effect Units: Alesis Midiverb ll; EMP100; Yamaha Comp/LIM. Equalisation: Citronic SPX 7-21 Graphic (Pre Set).
Mics: Various types of vocal and instrument mics are available along with 5 passive D.I.s.
BACKSTAGE FACILITIES: Dressing Room, 2. Shower facilities available.

ROBIN HOWARD DANCE THEATRE

The Place, 17 Dukes Road London WC1H 9PY
Admin: 020 7121 1101 BO: 020 7121 1100
Email: info@theplace.org.uk, theatre@theplace.org.uk
Web Site: www.theplace.org.uk
ADMINISTRATION:
Props: Contemporary Dance Trust.
Theatre Director: Eddie Nixon
Director of Communications: Rosie Neave (Tel: 020 7121 1021)
Technical Manager: Graeme McGinty
Director of Administration & Finance: David Burnie
Policy: Independant Dance Companys.

Presented for 30 weeks. Theatre available for hire in remaining 22 weeks.
Perfs: 8.00pm (or by arrangement).
Seats: 300. Bar and Café.
TECHNICAL:
STAGE: Open Stage, flat; sprung wooden floor with grey/black lino covering. Total stage area 15.5m x 11m. Normal performance area 10.5m x 9m (black legs in position). Height to grid 6m. White Cyclorama Available.
LIGHTING: Equipment: Arri Imagine 250, 92 Strand LD90 Dimmers (60 Patchable via 263 outlets), 40 x Patt 743, 30 x Sil 30, 8 x ADB 1 KW PC, 16 x Prelude 16/30 650w, 3 x Patt 243, 16 Patt 23 650w, 8 x AC1001, 20 x Par 64 (CP62 only) 8 x 3m vertical booms, 6 x colour Chromatics for Sil 30. Tallescope.
SOUND: Equipment: Soundcraft Venue 16:8:2 Mixer, Tascam DA30 DAT Machine, 2 x Tascam 112 Cassette Decks, Denon CD Player, Revox B77, (available on request Denon DN 990 Mini Disc Recorder), Yamaha SPX 900, 4 Bose 802 Speakers, 2 Bose 302 Speakers, 2 Bose 1800 Amplifiers, 1 x Yamaha P2100 Amplifier, 2 x Crown D60 Amplifiers, 2 Bose Equalisers, 1 x Yamaha Graphic Equaliser, 4 x Stage Monitors (Purpose Built), 3 x Sure SM58, 2 x AKG 451, 1 x Crown PCC 160, 1 x AKG D112, 4 x Di boxes, 5 x boom mic stands, Tecpro intercom system.
OTHER: Dressing Rooms: 2, accom. 16, show relay & tannoy.

ROSE THEATRE

24-26 High Street Kingston KT1 1HL
Tel: 020 8546 6983 Fax: 020 8546 8783
BO: 020 8174 0090
Email: admin@rosetheatrekingston.org
Web Site: www.rosetheatrekingston.org
ADMINISTRATION:
Executive Producer: Jerry Gunn
Emeritus Director: Sir Peter Hall
Chief Executive: Robert O'Dowd
Assistant Producer: Naomi Webb
Director of Marketing and Communications: Sarah Lowry
Head of Production: Wayne Parry
Theatre Manager: Lesley Rowden
Policy: The Rose is a producing theatre that also presents a wide range of drama, music, comedy, dance, and events.
The Main Auditorium (capacity for 900, including cushion area)
The design of the auditorium took its inspiration from the Elizabethan Rose Theatre, situated on London's Bankside and has the same lozenge shaped stage, semi-circular seating configuration and pit area, where audiences can sit on cushions to watch performances.
The Gallery (capacity for 60 people, no fixed seating)
Cafe and Bar

THE ROUNDHOUSE

Chalk Farm Road, London NW1 8EH
Admin: 020 7424 9991 Events: 0300 6789 222 BO: 0300 6789 222
Email: hello@roundhouse.org.uk
Web Site: www.roundhouse.org.uk
ADMINISTRATION
Commercial & Operations: Heather Walker
Development & Communications: Ellie Sleeman
Finance & ICT: Michael Dixon
Capacity: 1,800
Main Space: Receptions and parties for up to 1,800; conferences for up to 1,500; dinners for up to 1,100. Circle Bar and Torquil's Bar & Terrace; informal meetings for 20+ people or receptions for up to 120. The Studio Theatre; suitable for screenings, product launches and meetings for up to 100 people.
For Hire, contact the venue on hire@roundhouse.org.uk or telephone 020 7424 6771.

ROYAL ALBERT HALL

Kensington Gore, London SW7 2AP
Mgt: 020 7589 3203 BO: 0845 401 5045
Fax: 020 7959 0546
Email: programming@royalalberthall.com
Web Site: www.royalalberthall.com
ADMINISTRATION:
Chief Executive: Chris Cotton
Corporate Sales Executive: Rob Morrison
Tel: 020 7959 0607, Email: robm@royalalberthall.com
Media Partnerships Executive: Sean Carrigan
Tel: 020 7959 0531, Email: seanc@royalalberthall.com.
Programming Department:
Tel: 020 7589 3203, Email: programming@royalalberthall.com
Policy: Concerts - Pop, Rock, Jazz, Classical, Meetings and Conferences, Sporting Events, Ballet.
Perfs: Varies according to type of show. Evening concerts normally 7.30pm.
Seats: 5,200. 13 Bars on each level and 3 Restaurants.
TECHNICAL:
Senior Technical Manager: Ollie Jeffery
Contact: oliverj@royalalberthall.com
Concert platform and arena. 9 rows raised choir stalls behind concert platform (1-4 removeable/adjustable).
Dressing Rooms: 6 principal, 5 choir for up to 200 each.

ROYAL COURT THEATRE

Sloane Square, London SW1W 8AS
Admin: 020 7565 5050 BO: 020 7565 5000 Fax: 020 7565 5001
Email: info@royalcourttheatre.com
Web Site: www.royalcourttheatre.com
ADMINISTRATION:
Artistic Director: Vicky Featherstone
Executive Director: Lucy Davies
Literary Manager: Christopher Campbell
Head of Production: Niall Black
Head of Communications: Becky Wootton
Theatre Manager: Rachel Dudley
Jerwood Theatre Downstairs: Cap 389
Jerwood Theatre Upstairs: Cap 72-100 (flexible seating)

ROYAL FESTIVAL HALL

The South Bank Centre, Belvedere Road, London SE1 8XX
Switchboard: 020 7960 4200 BO: 0844 847 9911
Email: events@southbankcentre.co.uk
Web Site: www.southbankcentre.co.uk
ADMINISTRATION:
Props: South Bank Board
Head of Corporate Development: Matthew Holt
Head of Planning: Pamela Showhan
Development Events Manager: Kelly Palmer
Seats:Up 2,788
Exhibition and meeting places include the Thames Pavillion, Waterloo Bar, Hungerford Bar, Sunley Pavilion, Chelsfield Room. Record shop and book shop. Foyers are open for free events, exhibitions, etc., from 10am every day. Self-Service Cafeteria, Bars and buffets and "People's Palace" Restaurant. Part of the South Bank Centre complex, incorporating the Royal Festival Hall, the Queen Elizabeth Hall, Purcell Room and Hayward Gallery.
TECHNICAL:
STAGE: Open Thrust Stage 17.25m x 6.76m. Height of main stage 0.79m. Height of stage with first riser 0.91m. No proscenium, no rake, no flying, wood floor, backstage crossover, stage heated. Minimum height to ceiling 9.3m/10.06m. Choir seating behind stage. For dance 'proscenium opening' and Orchestra Pit can be installed by arrangement.
GET IN: 50m. Flat run to goods lift direct to stage level or through front of house doors. Scenery lift (limited in size) available. Backstage facilities accessible to disabled performers and staff.
TECHNICAL STAFF: Two Production Technicians available 8am-10pm for set-up, rehearsal and performance. Normally a Production Manager is allocated to each project. Get-in/get-out time is by arrangement with SBC depending on requirements and on venue availability.
LIGHTING AND SOUND: The RFH has restricted in-house LX equipment and sound system. Southbank Centre has an extensive stock of sound, lighting, video and rigging equipment all available at competitive rates. P.A.system and Closed Circuit TV to foyer, talkback, Callboy, Show relay to dressing rooms. Detailed stage plans, technical equipment lists and extra technical information are available on request.
DRESSING ROOMS: 20, accom. 250; 19 Showers; Orchestra Pit 53. Prop. Store, Wardrobe.

ROYAL OPERA HOUSE
Floral Street, Covent Garden, London WC2E 9DD
Tel: 020 7240 1200 BO: 020 7304 4000
Email: mark.duffy@roh.org.uk
Web Site: www.roh.org.uk
ADMINISTRATION:
Chief Executive: Alex Beard
Creative Director, ROH 2: Deborah Bull
Head of Development: Amanda Saunders
Head of Development Events: Caroline Dalziel
Director of Finance: Sally O'Neill
Head of Marketing: Layla Amirshahi
Head of Production: David Pritchard
Director of Press and Communications: Christopher Millard
Capacity Main House: 2,256; Linbury Studio Theatre: approx 420; Clore Studio Upstairs: approx 170. The Royal Opera House can be hire for commercial events. For more information on Venue Hire contact Hire Manager, Mark Duffy: Tel: +44 (0)20 7212 9482 or Email: mark.duffy@roh.org.uk
TECHNICAL:
Head of Technical: Geoffrey Wheel. Tel: 020 7212 9233

SADLER'S WELLS
Rosebery Avenue, Islington, London, EC1R 4TN
BO: 0844 412 4300 SD: 020 7863 8198
Events: 020 7863 8065 Fax: 020 7863 8199
Email: reception@sadlerswells.com
Web Site: www.sadlerswells.com
ADMINISTRATION:
Executive Director: Laura Stevenson
Head of Events and Catering: Zuzana Galikova
4 Rehearsal studios, 3 of which have sprung floors.
Capacity: 1,500

SAVOY THEATRE
Savoy Court, The Strand, London WC2R 0ET
Admin: 020 7845 6050 BO: 0844 871 3046 SD: 020 7845 6050
Email: savoytheatremanagement@theambassadors.com
Web Site: www.atgtickets.com/venues/savoy-theatre
ADMINISTRATION:
Props: Savoy Theatre Ltd and Ambassador Theatre Group Ltd
Theatre Manager: Glen Cottenden
Box Office Manager: Mark Armstrong
Seated Capacity: 1,100 (Play), 1,130 (using small orchestra pit), 1,090 (using large orchestra pit)
Membership: SOLT, TMA
TECHNICAL:
STAGE: Area: Proscenium opening 9.0m wide x 7.5m high. Depth of stage from back of proscenium ot back wall 9.3m. Depth of rear stage from back wall of stage 5.0m (approx.,). Width of rear stage 7.3m. Depth of apron from back of proscenium to stage edge 1.2m. Width of apron 8.4m. Width of stage side wall to side wall 18.6m at centre stage. Centre line to stage left wall 9.3m. Centre line to stage right wall 9.3m. Wing space stage left 3.0m (approx) x 9.4m deep. Wing space stage right 2.5m (approx) x 9.4m deep. Height to underside of grid 15.8m. Clearance under fly floors 7.0m. Width of orchestra pit 10.0m. Depth of small orchestra pit 4.0m (25-30 musicians approx.). Depth of large orchestra pit 6.2m (50 musicians approx.). Access to pit from under stage area left and right. Stage floor - Hardboard on plywood on bearers on demountable steel framework. Equipment and scenery access via door in stage right wall at fly floor level. Electric hoist on jib lifts equipment from Carting Lane through trap in fly floor to stage level. Stage access - up left and up right. Pass door - downstage left.
Rigging: 42 No. 450kg single purchase counterweight sets. 40 cross stage sets, 2 up/downstage sets. Typical pipe length - 10.0m; 4 lines. 3 No. 250kg hand winches and pipes in rear dock. 2 No. FOH trusses suspended from electric chain hoists provide support for lighting and sound rigs. Truss capacity - 1000kg.
Drapes: House curtain and border. Black and coloured borders, legs and travellers. Side masking by legs on tracks under fly floors.
LIGHTING: Strand Galaxy 4 lighting control with tracking back up and printer located in control room at rear of Dress Circle. Designers location at stalls level has colour monitors and ability to connect designers remote. Riggers remote and data lines located throughout stage and auditorium. House lights are controlled from lighting control room or S.M. position stage left. Orchestra pit lights from S.M. position. Dimmers - 244 Strand EC90MD. 214 No. 2.4kW, 30 No. 5.0kW, Spot and Cyc bars - 4. Luminaires - 20 No. Cantata 11/26 1,200 watt, 16 No. Cantat 18/32 1,200 watt, 16 No. Cantata 26/44 1,200 watt, 10 No. Prelude 600 watt, 40 No. Cantata Fresnels 1,200 watt, 10 No. Cadenza Fresnels 2,000 watt, 36 No. Parcans, 4 No. Iris 4 cyc units 1,000 watt, 4 No. Iris 1 cyc units 1,000 watt, 12 No. Nocturne floods 500 watt, 2 No. Solo follow spots.
SOUND AND COMMUNICATIONS: Substantial wiring infrastructure and sound box distribution system.
Permanent system of installed BOSE 102 delay loudspeakers set into stalls ceiling. Electro-voice S40 loudspeakers set into auditorium walls at all levels for effects. Portable loudspeakers - 4 No. Electro-Voice 5200, 4 No. Galaxy-Hotspots. Systems complete with associated power amps, graphic equalisers, etc. Small 'in-house' 4-1 sound mixer provided for shows not requiring more sophistication. Larger shows requiring 'in-house' mixing position may use location centre of dress circle level. Outboard equipment includes - DAT, CD, cassette and tape machines. Building wide communications provide paging and show relay signals. Show relay camera on circle front relays video signal to monitors FOH and backstage. SM desk may be located stage left or right. Cue lights and technical intercom connection points location at all key areas. Hard of hearing facilities provided at all levels.
ADDITIONAL: Accommodation: Orchestra room and crew room under stage.
Dressing Rooms: 18. Total capacity 60.

RONNIE SCOTT'S
Jazz club
47 Frith Street, London W1D 4HT
Tel: 020 7439 0747 Fax: 020 7437 5081
Email: ronniescotts@ronniescotts.co.uk
Web Site: www.ronniescotts.co.uk
ADMINISTRATION:
Club Capacity: 220
Ronnie's Bar: 140-capacity lounge bar on first floor.
Theatre Owners: Sally Greene and Mike Watts
Managing Director: Simon Cooke
For more information on Venue Hire, please email events@ronniescotts.co.uk or phone.

SECOMBE THEATRE
42 Cheam Road, Sutton, Surrey SM1 2SS
Mgt: 020 8770 6988 BO: 020 8770 6990
Tech: 020 8770 6989
Email: gina.gillam@sutton.gov.uk, diane.cash@sutton.gov.uk
Web Site: www.suttontheatres.co.uk
ADMINISTRATION:
Props: London Borough of Sutton
Press & Publicity: Kate Puleston
Theatre and Arts Services Manager: Gina Gillam
Marketing Manager: Kate Puleston
Tel: 020 8770 6987, Email: kate.puleston@sutton.gov.uk
Venues Administration: Diane Cash
Policy: Mixed programme, professional one nighters, drama, tours, variety, dance, cinema, children's shows, pantomime, annual talent show, amateur theatre, lettings.
Seats: 341 (Max. 390). Foyer Bar, Foyer Buffet. Second performance space/letting room available.
TECHNICAL:
For more information, contact the Technical Team on:
theatretechnicians@sutton.gov.uk
STAGE: Prosc. Opening: Width: 8.23 metres (27'), Height: 4.52 metres (14' 10"), Depth: 8.54 metres (28'), Depth from tab line: 7.31 metres (24'). Height to grid: 9.15 metres (30'), Wing space S/R (O.P.): 5.35 metres (17' 7"), Wing space S/L (P.S.): 3.28 metres (10' 9"), Height of stage from floor: 1.17 metres (3' 10").
LIGHTING: ETC Express 96/144 Lighting Desk, 66 circuits (48 onstage, 18 FOH) +

6 independents, All circuits rated at 2.5kw.
FOH Lighting Rig is permanent consisting of: 12 ETC Source four zoom Juniors 25-50, 12 Source four Par EA, and 3 S4 zooms 25-50. On stage: 13 ETC Source four zoom Juniors 25-50, 30 ETC Parnell, 22 ETC source four Par MCM, 2 RJ cricket Follow spots and stands, 4 internally wired bars over stage (hand winched), 6-wheeled boom bases, 8 Chroma Q Scrollers inc power to fit ETC Pars.
SOUND: Allen & Heath GL2800 48-8-3 Mixing Desk, 2 x C Audio 1000w per channel amplifiers, Behringer Crossover, CS 400X Peavey Power Amp, Studiomaster 800c power amplifier, Drawmer LX20 expander/compressor, Art Alpha Multi Fx Processor, Yamaha, Rev 500 Digital Reverb unit, CD Player, Minidisc Player, Cassette Player, DAT Player, 2 x Logic Systems LS152A 800w fixed position FOH speakers, 2 x Logic Systems LS218A 1600w FOH Bass speakers, 2 x Bose 802 fixed position FOH speakers, 2 x Bose 802 mobile stage speakers, 2 x Peavey 112 Ti Stage Monitor wedges - SM58's, AKG CS1000's and 3 Float/floor microphones, Various microphones Stands, Various microphones XLR cables, 1 x 8 way XLR stage box with 15' TAIL.
ADDITIONAL (By prior arrangement): Le Maitre pyroflash system with 2 pods, 2 follow spots - Silhouette 15 - (2kw), 4 x Genius Micro Scanners, 1 x Strobe, 1 x Black Night U.V., 1 x Gem Mini Smoke Machine, Snow machine. 1x Glitter ball, 12 Silhouette 1000w Profiles, 12 Par Cans, 6 pairs - usually 3 colour wash, 4x Silhouette 30 (1kw), 10x Starlette Fresnel (1kw), 3x Starlette P.C. (1kw), 24x Parcans 240v (1kw), 15x Minuette Flood (500w). Other sound equipment available on request; Spirit Folio F1 Mixing Desk, Digital Sound control from PC.

SHAFTESBURY THEATRE

210 Shaftesbury Avenue, London WC2H 8DP
Mgt/SD: 020 7379 3345 BO: 020 7379 5399 Mgt Fax: 020 7836 8181
Email: davidscarr@shaftesburytheatre.com
Web Site: www.shaftesburytheatre.com
ADMINISTRATION:
Props: The Theatre of Comedy Company
Theatre Manager: David Scarr
House Manager: Rebecca Storey
Master Carpenter: Jimmy Quinn
Chief Electrician: Peter Goodman
Seats: 1,300

SHAKESPEARE'S GLOBE

21 New Globe Walk, Bankside, London SE1 9DT
Admin/SD: 020 7902 1400 BO: 020 7401 9919 Front of House: 020 7902 1480
Fax: 020 7902 1401
Email: info@shakespearesglobe.com
Web Site: www.shakespeares-globe.org
ADMINISTRATION:
Artistic Director: Dominic Dromgoole
Chief Executive: Neil Constable
Executive Producer: Sacha Millroy
Seats: 1000 (standing) including 700 standing (Groundlings) in uncovered yard.
For venue hire, contact the theatre on: +44 (0)20 7928 9444 (option 2)
TECHNICAL:
Height: 33 ft to the eaves, diameter: 100 ft, circumference: 300 ft.
Stage height: 5ft, length: 44ft, breadth: 25ft.
Theatre season: May-September, the remainder of the year used as an educational resource by Globe Education Department.

SHAW THEATRE

100 - 110 Euston Road, London NW1 2AJ
Tel: 020 7666 9037 Fax: 020 7666 9025
BO: 0844 248 5075
Email: info@shaw-theatre.com
Web Site: www.shaw-theatre.com
ADMINISTRATION:
Props: The Accor Group
Artistic Director and Theatre Manager: Issy Fitzgerald
Completed in 1999, the new Shaw Theatre is a comfortable 450 seat theatre ideally suited to musicals, plays and events. There are 4 large dressing rooms which can accomodate up to 80 people. Part of the Novotel London Euston and within 5 minutes walk of Kings Cross and Euston Stations, it has excellent transport links. The Shaw Theatre is available for short/medium runs, one off events and is a perfect London base for shows transferring from the provinces or overseas.
Capacity: 446
TECHNICAL:
STAGE: Grid Height 9.8m, Stage width 16.31m, Stage depth 6.71m, Prosc width 12.40m, Apron width 12.40m, Apron depth 3.92m, get in: door height 4.4m, door width 2.4m.
Power: 125amp 3 phase supply, 16amp and 13amp single phase sockets at various locations. 5 x 24way CCT dimmer racks, hard wired for 1 to 1, 108 ways of dimming.
Flying: 11 flying bars, 8 on ratchet winches (SWL 250kg evenly laden) and 3 on 5 strand hemp lines (SWL 25kg evenly laden).
SOUND: Yamaha GA 24/12 Mixing Desk. Denon DN77R single casette player, Denon 2600F Pro. dual CD player, Tascam mini disc deck, Rane MQ302s equaliser unit. 2 x electrovoice P2000 full range amplifiers, 1 x electrovoice P1200 paging amplifier, 1 x electrovoice P3000 sub bass amplifier, Canford audio rack monitor, 2 x martin audio speakers F12 and 4 x F10, Denon DN-720R CD player, Yamaha SPX990 effects processor, Sony CDP-D11 CD player, 2 x 600w sub bass speakers. 2 x microphone (proscenium right and left high), 2 x microphone (in centre control room and on prompt desk).
LIGHTING: Compulite Photon 120 channel desk, DMX 512 channel analogue signal converter. Alto fresnels 6 x 2k, Starlette PC 6 x 1k, Starlette Fresnel 3 x 1k, various minuettes 500w, Minuette Cyc floods (3 cell) 4 x 6650w, ETC Source 4 15/30 Profile 11 x 575w, ETC Source 4 25/50 Profile 2 x 575w, Parcan CP64 4 x 1K.

SHEPHERD'S BUSH EMPIRE

Shepherds Bush Green, London W12 8TT
Mgt: 020 8354 3300 Mgt Fax: 020 8743 3218 BO (Ticket sales): 0844 477 2000
Email: mail@o2shepherdsbushempire.co.uk
Web Site: www.o2shepherdsbushempire.co.uk
ADMINISTRATION:
Theatre Manager: Bill Marshall
Technical Manager: Jim Boyle
Capacity: 2,000

SHOESTRING THEATRE

Oakley Road, South Norwood London SE25 4XG
BO/ Mgt: 020 8655 1098
Email: mail@cyto.org.uk
Web Site: www.cyto.org.uk
ADMINISTRATION:
Policy: Home of C.Y.T.O.. Theatre, rehearsal room and dance studio available for hire at very reasonable rates subject to availability.
Theatre Cap: 85, smaller spaces also available (cap: 40-60 max. seated).

SOHO THEATRE & WRITERS STUDIO

21 Dean Street, London W1D 3NE
BO: 020 7478 0100 Admin: 020 7287 5060
Email: hires@sohotheatre.com, amy-smith@sohotheatre.com
Web Site: www.sohotheatre.com
ADMINISTRATION:
Artistic Director: Steve Marmion
Executive Director: Mark Godfrey
Writers' Centre Director: Nina Steiger
General Manager: Catherine McKinney
Front of House and Events Manager: Amy Smith
Policy: New Writing. Hires suitable for; rehearsed readings, conferences, filming, press launches and lectures or meetings
Theatre available for hire, subject to availability.
Rehearsal rooms available for hire. (Contact Amy Smith)
Theatre Capacity: 144 Seats
Studio Capacity: 85 seats
TECHNICAL:
Full wheelchair access. Infra-red system for the hard of hearing. Signed and audio described performances.
For technical details contact: Production

Manager and Senior Technician, Nick blount on:
Tel: 020 7478 0120

SOUTHBANK STUDENTS UNION

Keyworth Street, London SE1 6NG
Switchboard: 0207 815 6060 Fax: 020 7815 6061 Conferences: 0207 815 7000
Email: su.general@lsbu.ac.uk
Web Site: www.londonsouthbanksu.com
ADMINISTRATION:
President: Nordin Jahar
Vice President Communications: Eric Barcatali
Vice President Societies and Activities: Halima Chitalya
Capacity: 1,200 (approx)

ST JOHN'S

Smith Square, Westminster, London SW1P 3HA
Mgt: 020 7222 2168 BO: 020 7222 1061
Email: info@sjss.org.uk, boxoffice@sjss.org.uk
Web Site: www.sjss.org.uk
ADMINISTRATION:
Props: St.John's, Smith Square Charitable Trust
Registered Charity No: 1045390
Registered in England Co.No: 3028678
Policy: Concert Hall available for hire for concerts, choral & orchestral recitals, chamber opera, etc. Art exhibitions in The Footstool restaurant gallery. Open for lunch on weekdays and at all concerts. Fully licensed. Special functions also catered for.
Perfs: Normally 1.00 or 7.00-7.30; all performances end before 10.00.
Seats: 764 max.
To apply for a concert date, please contact the admin department
TECHNICAL:
Unusually-adaptable stage incorporating 6 variable orchestra/choral risers. Max. no of performers 100, but also suitable for recitals. Stage-lighting 24 x 1kw operated by 12-channel fader.
Dressing Rooms: 4 plus changing area.
In addition to public concerts, St. John's is used for recording and by the BBC and major record companies on account of its exceptional acoustics.

ST MARTIN IN THE FIELDS

St. Martins Place, Trafalgar Square, London WC2N 4JJ
BO/ Admin: 020 7766 1100
Email: info@smitf.org,
Web Site: www.smitf.org
ADMINISTRATION:
Chief Executive: Allyson Hargreaves
Email: allyson.hargreaves@smitf.org
Events and Sales Executive: Vanya Cunningham Azoro
Cafe and Events Manager: Ladka Cervena
Email: ladka.cervena@smitf.org
Policy: Primarily Baroque music
Capacity: 825
For more information on Events and Venue Hire Tel: 020 7766 1165 or Email: events@smitf.org

ST MARTIN'S THEATRE

West Street, Cambridge Circus, London WC2H 9NZ
SD: 020 7836 1086 BO: 020 7836 1433
Mgt Tel: 020 7497 0578 Admin Tel: 020 7828 0600 Fax: 020 7379 8699
Email: enquiries@stmartinstheatre.co.uk
Web Site: www.the-mousetrap.co.uk
ADMINISTRATION:
Mousetrap Productions Limited.
General Manager: Andrew Mills.
Policy: West End Runs of Plays.
Perfs: Mon-Sat 8.00; Mats: Tues. 2.45; Sat. 5.00.
Seats: 552. Bars. Air conditioning.
TECHNICAL:
STAGE: Proscenium Stage, practically flat; Pros. Opening 7.92m; Ht. of Pros. 7.77m; Depth of S/Line 7.01m P.S., 7.62m O.P.; Ht. of Grid 15.24m US, 18.29m DS, 28 lines, 23 C/W, 5 Hemp; Scenery Flying Ht. 7.32m; Flying Bars 10.97m; W/Widths P.S. 4.57m. O.P. 2.44m; Prompt Cnr. O.P.
LIGHTING: Switchboard: Strand Electric Compact 80 ways; F.O.H. Spots 26 10 1000w, 16 500w; 4 Battens; Floats; Dips 11 each side; 4 Spot Bars.
SOUND: Cue Call.
OTHER: Dressing Rooms 10, accom. 25; Orchestra Pit 8.
Membership: SOLT

ST. MARY'S CHURCH HALLS

York Street, London W1H 1PQ
Tel: 020 7258 5040
Email: contact@stmaryslondon.com
Web Site: www.stmaryslondon.com
ADMINISTRATION:
Rector/ General Manager: John Peters
Services & Events Administrator: Lisa Trundle
Tel: 020 7258 5040,
Policy: Not available for hire on Sundays. No events later than 10.30pm due to local restrictions.
Capacity: Main Auditorium; 500 Theatre Style, 300 Cabaret, 600+ Standing. Lower Floor; 250 Theatre Style, 400 Standing.
TECHNICAL:
Main Auditorium: Wooden floors. 24 m length x 19 m width.
Lower Floor: 29m x 11m. Moveable, soundproof wall to divide the room.
Additional facilities: Large, modern and professionally equipped kitchen. 2 small syndicate rooms. AV equipment, including 40 channel sound desk and DVD/video projection. 8 lighting trusses. 63 amp, 3 phase power supply. Telephone and ISDN lines, and Wi-Fi internet access.
Disabled access.

STANLEY HALLS

12 South Norwood Hill London SE25 6AB
Mgt: 020 8253 1038 Fax: 020 8253 1032
Email: arts@croydon.gov.uk
Web Site: www.stanleyhalls.org.uk
ADMINISTRATION:
Props: London Borough of Croydon
Operations Manager: Mr. Fran Mcelory
Policy: Available for Hire
Perfs: As required.
Capacity: Concert Hall: 150 seated/weddings/functions, 320 audiences/theatre, 250 buffet style. Upper and lower assembly halls: 65 seated, 100 buffet-style.
Committee room: 15.
TECHNICAL:
STAGE: Proscenium stage, Flat; Pros. opening 6.71m; Ht. of Pros. 4.57m; Depth of S/Line 6.10m; Scenery Flying Ht. 6.10m; 6/7 lines, Hemp; W.Widths P.S. 2.44m, O.P. 2.44m; Prompts Cnr. O.P.
LIGHTING: Switchboard: Strand Master, 24 ways; F.O.H. Spots 4 Patt. 253; 1 Batten; 1 Float; Dips 2 each side; 2 Spot Bars. Cyc Float and Ground Row.
SOUND: Speakers House P.A. + Amp. Twin tape deck & microphones available for hire.
OTHER: Dressing Rooms 3, accom. 36. Orchestra Pit 10. Available with other room attached as excellent rehearsal or audition rooms.
Membership: TMA

STEINER THEATRE

Anthroposophical Society in Great Britain, Rudolf Steiner House, 35 Park Road, London NW1 6XT
Tel: 020 7723 4400
Email: rsh-office@anth.org.uk
Web Site: www.rsh.anth.org.uk
ADMINISTRATION:
Props: Anthroposophical Association Ltd.
Theatre bookings: Doris Bailiss, 020 7723 4400
In the face of increasing global challenges, Dr. Rudolf Steiner (1861 - 1925) pointed to the need for a spiritual renewal of western culture, in areas including education, agriculture, medicine, economics, the sciences, religion and the arts.
Capacity: 228 Theatre Style

STOKE NEWINGTON ASSEMBLY HALL

Stoke Newington Church, Stoke Newington Church Street, London N16 7UK
Tel: 020 8356 5505 Event Tel: 020 8356 5505
Email: stokenewingtonvenuehire@hackney.gov.uk
Web Site: www.hackney.gov.uk/snth.htm
ADMINISTRATION:
Contact: Kirsten Patterson
Props: London Borough of Hackney
Capacity: 500 Standing, Theatre Style 420, Banquet 300. Additional Balcony Area; 94, permanent Theatre Style seating.

STRATFORD CIRCUS

Theatre Square, Stratford, London E15 1BX
BO: 0844 357 2625 Tel: 020 8279 1015
Email: alison@stratford-circus.com
Web Site: www.stratford-circus.com
ADMINISTRATION:
Operations Manager: Alison Darren
Direct Tel: 020 8279 1010, or Email: alison@stratford-circus.com
Events and Creative Producer: Paula Van Hagen
Email: paula@stratford-circus.com
Events and Hires: Vanessa Dalton
Policy: A wide range of presented and produced drama, dance, music and multimedia together with arts education work.
Capacity: Main Auditorium: 298 seated, 512 mixture of seated & standing, 650 Standing. Studio: 93 Seated, 160 Standing. Rehearsal Room: 120 Standing.
For more information on venue hire contact the Events team on: bookings@stratford-circus.com.
TECHNICAL:

CIRCUS ONE:
Seating configuration is based around a courtyard shaped auditorium consisting of retractable stalls seating, and a lower and upper balcony. Other seating configurations are available subject to council approval and public licensing laws.
STAGE: Dimensions; Wall to wall: width 15.27.m, depth 11.91m. Prosc.: Minimum: w 8.60m, h 4.90m, Maximum: w 10.50m, h 6.00m. Wing widths: Minimum: SR 3.34m, SL 3.34m, US nil, Maximum: SR 2.39m, SL 2.39m, US nil. Forestage dimensions: Width 10.30m max, depth 3.00m located on pit elevator, up position. Orchestra pit dimensions: Width 10.3m, depth 4.50m - located on pit elevator, down position. Clearance: Height of grid: 10.00m. Floor: Hardwood strip on ply. No rake, flat level: standard configuration. The stage area is black Confidence 12m wide x 10m deep. Get-in facilities: through dock located MSL. Dock is located at street level. Stage is at street level. Get-in doors: width 3.7m, height 4.5m. Load-in doors: width 2.7m, height 4.5m.
LIGHTING: Lighting board: STRAND 520i CONSOLE, 200 channels of Genius Pro software, 200 attribute channels, Tracker Moving Light software, Networker system software. Dimmers: 160 saturated configuration, 152 x 2.4kw, 8 x 5kw, 3 Phase, (LD90). Operation: Control room located centre back of 2nd balcony. Luminaires: 9 x Strand SL 10 (GKV, 600w), 40 x Strand SL 15/32 (GKV, 600w), 10 x Strand SL 23/50 (GKV, 600w), 18 x Strand Cantata PC (T/29, 1200w), 8 x Strand Alto PC (CP91, 2500w), 30 x Thomas Par64 (CP62, 1000w), 6 x Strand Iris 3 pole operated (P2/12, 1250w), 2 x Strand Coda 500/3 ground-row (K/1, 500w), 4 x Floor stand, Manfroto 4' 6" c/w spigots, 4 x 11.2m, IWB (18 circuit) for over head stage, 8 x 3.0m, IWB (6 circuit) for over head or FOH.
SOUND: Mixing Consoles: Midas Venice 320: Mono-Inputs (Mic/Line) with Inserts 24 , Stereo-Line/Mono-Mic-Input Channels 4/4, Stereo-Effect-Returns (Line) 4, Stereo-Tape-Return (Line) 1 left/right
Playback and Effects: Mini-Disc Record/Player, Citronic Dual CD/MP3 player, DAT Recorder, Digital Effects Processor, Digital Reveberator, Dual 1/3 Octave Graphic Equaliser, Dynamics Processors. Amplifiers: 6 Inter-M, MA-430 100W/ch, 8 Inter-M, MA-930 250W/ch. Speakers: 4 Tannoy Main system, T12, 4 Tannoy Small, CPA5, 2 Tannoy Subbase, T40, 4 x JBL VRX 932LA, 2 x JBL VRX 918S, 4 x RCF ART 310A Monitors, HK Projector system (please check for availability). AV Equipment: Sanyo PLC-XP200L 7000 Lumens Projector, Datavideo 4 input vision mixer.
ADDITIONAL: 16 x 8 ft x 4 ft Alideck various height legs available. 12 x 2m x 1m Revostage lightweight staging with 1ft risers.

CIRCUS TWO:
STAGE: Stage/floor Dimensions; 10.30m wide, 6m deep. Height of grid: 5.60m. Get-in facilities: loading door located on wall SR to outside ground level
LIGHTING: Lighting Board; Strand 300 series, 125ch, Attribute software. Dimmers;6 x Act 6 (24 x 2.4kw). Temporary Power supply; 2 x 3 phase, 32 amps per phase, (control room). Luminaires: 11 x Strand SL 15/32 GKV, 600w ; 12 x Strand Quartet PC T/26, 650w ; 8 x Cantata PC T/29, 1200w ; 10 x Thomas Par64 CP61, 1000w ; 2 x Strand Coda 500/1 K/1, 500w. Rigging: suspension lighting grid fixed, 64 x patchable outlets.
SOUND: Allen & Heath GL2200 16 input channels, 2 stereo channels, 4 group channels, 6 Aux. Speakers: 2 x Tannoy T12, 2 x Tannoy T40 Subs. Playback: Citronic Dual CD/MP3 player
ADDITIONAL: HK Projector system (please check for availability), Sanyo PLC-XP21E 2500 ANSI Lumens XGA (1024 x 768) Projector.

CIRCUS THREE:
This bright dance studio / rehearsal studio space comes with a sprung floor, adjustable shading, mirrors and bars.
STAGE: Floor Dimensions: 15m wide, 15m deep. Highest point: 5m
SOUND: Mixer; RCF PR4092. CD Player; DAP Audio DS8606. Speakers; RCF ART310
ADDITIONAL; HK Projector system (please check for availability), Citronic Dual CD/MP3 player.

THE TABERNACLE

35 Powis Square, Talbot Road London W11 2AY
Tel: 0207 221 9700
Email: niki@tabernaclew11.com
Web Site: www.tabernaclew11.com
ADMINISTRATION:
General Manager: Matthew Phillip
Operations Manager: Niki Kudar
Email: niki@tabernaclew11.com
Policy: Concerts, Corporate Events, Film Screenings, Cabaret, Private Functions, Dinner & Dance, Stand-Up, Conferences, Meetings & Lectures, Ballroom Dancing, Awards Ceremonies, Fashion Shows & Galas, Film and TV location shoots, Theatre Performances.
The newly renovated building is fully accessible and houses a theatre, a contempory art gallery and well equiped dance, digital arts and sound studios.
Capacity: 499 Standing, 260 Theatre Style

TARA STUDIO

Under construction until Autumn 2015
356 Garratt Lane, Earlsfield London SW18 4ES
Tel: 020 8333 4457 (information/BO/hire line)
Email: admin@tara-arts.com
Web Site: www.tara-arts.com
ADMINISTRATION:
Studio Theatre Space.
Artistic Director: Jatinder Verma
Executive Director: Jonathan Kennedy
General Manager: Alex Wyatt

THE AMBASSADORS THEATRE

West Street, London WC2H 9ND
Mgt: 020 7395 5410 BO: 08448 112 334
SD: 020 7395 5400 Admin Fax: 020 7395 5411
Email: enquiries@theambassadorstheatre.co.uk
Web Site: www.theambassadorstheatre.co.uk
ADMINISTRATION:
Props: Sir Stephen Waley-Cohen
Contact: Andrew Mills
Capacity: 388 Seated
TECHNICAL:
STAGE AND LIGHTING: Please contact venue.
SOUND: Soundcraft Spirit Folio 1482, 1 x Denon minidisc, 1 x CD, 1 x reverb, 2 x electrovoice speakers.

THE BRIDGE LEISURE CENTRE

Kangley Bridge Road, Lower Sydenham London SE26 5AQ
Tel: 020 8778 7158
Email: mark.penny@fusion-lifestyle.co.uk
Web Site: www.fusion-lifestyle.com
ADMINISTRATION:
Centre Manager: Mark Penny
Sports Hall available for concerts, theatre productions, sports events and conferences.
Cap: 300
Stage & Lighting available on request.

THE DUBLIN CASTLE

94 Parkway, London NW1 7AN
Tel: 020 7485 1773 Office Tel: 0207 700 0550 / 0880
Email: info@bugbearbookings.com
Web Site: www.bugbearbookings.com
ADMINISTRATION:
Licensee/Owner: Henry Conlon
Contact: Tony Gleed, Jim Mattison
Promoter: Bugbear Promotions,
Capacity: 1st Bar - 118; 2nd Bar - 122
Policy: Up and Coming Bands
TECHNICAL:
SOUND: Speaker system Tri-amped 5.4KW. 2 x JBL 1.5kw mid high speakers, 4 x 600w 118 sub bass, 1 x Pulse 2200w power amp, 2 x QSC 1200W power amps,1 x DBX Driverack 260 processor. Monitor system on 4 mixes; 2 x 800w side fills, 1 x 400w drum fill, 2 x Martin LE400 bi amped stage monitors, 2 x C Audio 600w amps, 1 x QSC 1200w amp, 1 x BSS 360 crossover, 1 x 4 way mix w/4ch compression control. Control system; 1 x Yamaha LS9/16 Digital mixer 16ch + 8 mic/line inputs. Mixer has comps/gates for all channels, onboard FX and comprehensive EQ. 1 x CD player. Mics; SM57A, SM58, SM57, E604 , Beta 91, D112 and Dis. Disco; 2 x Technics 1210, 1 x Numark Twin CD / mixer.
LIGHTING: 10 x Visage LED Par 375 lamps, 1 x Programmed mixer w/ chase and scene options, 2 x Martin Raptor / 1 Abstract Twister IV / 1 ministar FX Lighting.

THE LINCOLN LOUNGE

52 York Way, Kings Cross, London N1 9AB
Tel: 020 7837 9339
ADMINISTRATION:
Manager: Joyce Whelan
Exhibitions, live music events, cabaret and a laid back bohemian crowd.
Capacity: 130

THE MAGIC CIRCLE HEADQUARTERS

12 Stephenson Way, London NW1 2HD
Admin: 020 7387 2222
Email: mail@magiccirclevenue.co.uk
Web Site: www.themagiccirclevenue.co.uk
ADMINISTRATION:
Props: The Magic Circle Headquarters
Sales Manager: Jackson Baugh
Capacity: Theatre; 162. Devant Room; 80 Theatre Style/ Dining, 100 Reception. Club Room; 50 Theatre Style/ Dining, 65 Reception.
Policy: In addition to seasonal shows the building is available for hire seven days a week. Ideal for a wide range of events and meetings - from conferences to product launches and promotions to corporate entertainment.
Located in Central London, next to Euston station, the venue has excellent national travel links and is easily accessible by public transport. Modern facilities include a fully equipped purpose built theatre, flexible meeting, dining and function rooms, a clubroom and bar; perfect for receptions and meetings and a magic museum showcasing one of the largest magic collections in Europe. There is a lift to all floors, induction loop in the theatre and disabled access throughout the building.
TECHNICAL:
Modern purpose built building including the theatre with very extensive lighting and sound systems and comprehensive AV equipment.
Technical Specifications available on request.

THE NEW WIMBLEDON THEATRE

The Broadway, Wimbledon, London SW19 1QG
SD: 020 8545 7900 Fax: 020 8543 6637
BO: 0844 871 7646
Email: callumkemp@theambassadors.com
Web Site: www.atgtickets.com/wimbledon
ADMINISTRATION:
General Manager: Callum Kemp
Administration & Events Manager: Emma Brack
House Manager: Ross Hodges, Lara Harding
Technical Manager: Stuart Graham
Executive Marketing Manager London: Damien Hewitt
Press Officer: Stacey Pedder
Email: staceypedder@theambassadors.com
Capacity: Approx 1600 seats over 3 levels. Studio theatre 50-80 seats.
TECHNICAL:
Main Stage approx 42' x 71', Proscenium 34' wide. Studio theatre stage area 22' x 16'. Full technical specifications for both spaces available on request.

THE PORCHESTER HALL

Porchester Road, Bayswater, London W2 5HS
Tel: 020 7792 2823
Email: Charlotte.Oakes@gll.org
Web Site: www.porchesterhall.co.uk
ADMINISTRATION:
Events Administrator: Charlotte Oakes
Policy: Wedding receptions, record label showcases, award ceremony's, dinner dancers, school plays, fashion shows, recitals.
Capacity: 450 Dinner/ Theatre Style, 400 Cabaret.
TECHNICAL:
DIMENSIONS: Length 30.3m, Width 15.15m, Height 7.5m, Stage Width 9.7m, Stage Depth 5.75m.
LIGHTING: Controls in room/ chandeliers on dimmers.
POWER: Numerous 13 amp sockets in the main hall and on stage. 100 amp 3 phase power. Microphone outlet sockets.

THE ROCKET COMPLEX

London Metropolitan Universit 166-220 Holloway Road London N7 8DB
Events Info Line: 020 7133 3717
Switchboard: 020 7423 0000
Email: entertainment@londonmet.ac.uk
Web Site: www.londonmet.ac.uk/about/the-rocket.cfm
ADMINISTRATION:
Marketing Officer: Madeline Edmonds-Brown
Direct: 020 7133 2134
Email: m.edmonds-brown@londonmet.ac.uk
Venue Bookings Co-Ordinator: Alex Massey
Direct: 020 7133 2765
Email: alex.massey@londonmet.ac.uk
A large Victorian theatre/multi-purpose venue with an emphasis on music and dance. It accommodates 350 seated and 1000 standing. It is also suitable for conferences and educational activities.

THE SOUTH BANK CENTRE

Belvedere Road London SE1 8XX
Switchboard: 020 7960 4200 BO: 0844 875 0073
Email: customer@southbankcentre.co.uk
Web Site: www.southbankcentre.co.uk
ADMINISTRATION:
Props: South Bank Board
Artistic Director: Jude Kelly OBE
Chairman: Rick Haythornthwaite
Chief Executive: Alan Bishop
Policy: The space is used for classical concerts, jazz, world, folk, mime/theatre, dance, talks, conferences,etc. It is flexible and multi-purpose. When the extended stage is in, the seating capacity is reduced.
For more information on Venue Hire, Tel: 020 7921 0702, or Email: events@southbankcentre.co.uk.

THE SSE ARENA WEMBLEY

Arena Square Wembley Middlesex HA9 0DW
Tel: 020 8782 5500 BO: 0844 815 0815
Fax: 020 8782 5501
Email: customerservices@ssearena.co.uk
Web Site: www.ssearena.co.uk
ADMINISTRATION:
Props: AEG Facilities
General Manager: John Drury
Marketing Manager: Robert Lieveseley
Box Office Manager: Emily Thorpe
Technical Manager: Peter Fewings
Cap: Concert - 12,500; Conference - 5,000 - 12,500
Facilities: Bar & Restaurant, Hospitality Suite.
TECHNICAL:
STAGE: Sico folding set providing variable stage sizes and heights.
LIGHTING: Fully dimmable tungsten halogen house lighting.
SOUND: Central speaker cluster array,

suitable for small scale events or where background music and PA is required.
RIGGING: Motorised mother grid providing straight forward safe rigging in end stage format.
DRESSING ROOMS: 9 Dressing Rooms all equipped with en-suite WC and Shower, telephone and Wi-Fi. Additional offices available for Promoter and Production.
OUTSIDE BROADCAST: 2 x dedicated OB truck bays with broadcast fibre and power.
PARKING/ LOAD IN: Undercover load-in service yard with parking for 15 x 40' trucks.
CREW CATERING: Kitchen and dining area with commercial cooking and refrigeration facilities.

THE VENUE

Students Union, Borough Road, London, SE1 6OG
Tel: 020 7815 6060 Fax: 020 7815 6061
Email: robsonpw@lsbu.ac.uk
Web Site: www.lsbsu.org
ADMINISTRATION:
Bar/Venue Manager: Paul Robson
Cap: 300 Cabaret Style, 600 Standing

THEATRE 503

The Latchmere, 503 Battersea Park Road, Battersea, London SW11 3BW
BO/Admin: 020 7978 7040
Email: info@theatre503.com
Web Site: www.theatre503.com
ADMINISTRATION:
Artistic Directors: Paul Robinson
Executive Director: Jeremy Woodhouse
Origins: Purpose built above the Latchmere Public House, the theatre opened in 1982.
Policy: Fearless new theatre that pushes at the boundaries of the medium.
Capacity: 63

THEATRE ROYAL, STRATFORD EAST

Gerry Raffles Square, Stratford, London E15 1BN
Mgt: 020 8534 7374 BO: 020 8534 0310
Press Office: 020 8279 1110 Fax: 020 8534 8381
Email: theatreroyal@stratfordeast.com
Web Site: www.stratfordeast.com
ADMINISTRATION:
Executive Director: Mary Caws
Artistic Director: Kerry Michael
General Manager: Lee Henderson
Press Department contact: fmussell@stratfordeast.com
Policy: The bulk of the year is taken up with own productions of new plays. No permanent company and a minimum technical and administrative staff. Play choice ranges from family shows like pantomimes, musicals, melodramas and farces through to controversial modern work, particularly with appeal to young audiences.
Occasional Sunday events, including variety and comedy nights.
7 day a week entertainment programme in the bar.
Seats: 450
TECHNICAL:
LIGHTING: Equipment: Board; Arri Impulse 2.
Dimmers: 112 x 2K, 12 x 5K. Lanterns: 150 various.
Follows spots: 2 x 1K CSI.
SOUND: Equipment: Board; Hill Audio 4400 (24-8-2). Good FOH amplification and speakers and FX. 2 Revox and CDE. Misc. mics and stage speakers.
Musical Equipment: 1 piano.
OTHER: Limited hemp flying, stock masking including 20' x 20' soft black box, stage braces and weights. Limited video equipment. Two Licensed Bars
BACKSTAGE FACILITIES: Dressing Rooms 6, accom. 20; Showers. Orchestra Pit 6.
Membership: TMA.
Seating Capacity: 446

THEATRE ROYAL, DRURY LANE

Catherine Street, London WC2B 5JF
Mgt: 020 7850 8793 SD: 020 7850 8790
Email: rupert.bielby@reallyuseful.co.uk
Web Site: www.reallyuseful.co.uk
ADMINISTRATION:
Props: Really Useful Theatres Ltd
Policy: Plays, Musicals, Comedy, Concerts.
Chief Executive: André Ptaszynski
Theatre Manager: Rupert Bielby
For all bookings and production enquiries, contact: Michael Townsend (Concerts & Hirings Manager). Facilities may be made available for day time, late night and weekend use for private and press receptions, conferences and meetings - Contact Michael Townsend - Tel: 020 7240 0880
Fax: 020 7240 1292
Seats: 2,220 approx. Varied according to production.
6 Bars, Entertainment Suites, Theatre Tours.
TECHNICAL:
STAGE: Raked 1:24; Pros. Opening 12.95m; Ht of Pros. 7.92m; Depth of Stage 24.69m; Ht of Grid 21.34m; 120 lines, C/W; Prompt Cnr. P.S.
LIGHTING: Lighting Board: Strand Galaxy II, 360 circuits.
Situated Rear of Grand Circle.
OTHER: Dressing rooms: 22
Membership: SOLT

THEATRE ROYAL, HAYMARKET

18 Suffolk Street, London SW1Y 4HT
Tel/SD: 020 7930 8890 BO: 0845 481 1870 Mgmt Fax: 020 7389 9661
Email: boxoffice@trh.co.uk, info@trh.co.uk
Web Site: www.trh.co.uk
ADMINISTRATION:
Props: Crown Estates
Lessees: Theatre Royal Haymarket Ltd, Chairman: Arnold M. Crook
General Manager: Nigel Everett
Theatre Manager: Mark Stradling. Tel: 020 7930 8890
Chief Electrician: Steve MacGuire
Box Office Manager: Matthew Palin
Stage Door Manager: Brian Russell
Policy: Plays.
Seats: 880. Bars.
TECHNICAL:
For capacities, dimensions, details of prompt desk and communications, lighting, sound, load bays and electrics, please contact Steve MacGuire, Chief LX on steve@trh.co.uk
STAGE: Proscenium Stage, Raked 1 in 20; Pros. Opening 8.23m; Ht. of Pros. 7.62m; Depth of S/Line 8.69m to 12.60m; Ht. of Grid 15.85m; 23 lines, 15 C/W; Scenery Flying Ht. 7.62m; Flying Bars 11.28m; W/Widths P.S. 2.05m O.P. 4.27m; Prompt Cnr. P.S.
LIGHTING: Switchboard: Gemini 120 way, P.S. Perch; F.O.H. Spots 26 Patt. T645, 2 Patt. 23N 500w; 3 Battens; Dips 10 each side, 22 Flys; 1 Spot Bar 16 Patt. 23, 4 Patt. 123.
SOUND: Please contact venue.
OTHER: Dressing Rooms 10, accom. 30-35; 1 Shower; Orchestra Pit 10 plus extension.
Membership: SOLT

TOOTING LEISURE CENTRE

Greaves Place, Garratt Lane, Tooting, London SW17 0NE
Tel: 020 8333 7555 Fax: 020 8333 7711
Email: enquiries@pfpleisure.org
Web Site: www.tootingleisurecentre.co.uk
ADMINISTRATION:
Props: London Borough of Wandsworth
Capacity: Lola Jones Hall seated capacity - 300
Small Lola Jones Hall seated capacity - 40
Manager: Paul Duffell

TRAFALGAR STUDIOS

14 Whitehall, London SW1A 2DY
Mgt: 020 7321 5410 BO: 0844 871 7632
SD: 020 7321 5400 Fax: 020 7321 5411
Email: trafalgartheatremanagement@theambassadors.com
Web Site: www.atgtickets.com
ADMINISTRATION:
Props: The Ambassador Theatre Group Limited
Head of Operations London: Richard Wingate
Theatre Manager: Martin Scorer
Technical Manager: James Naish
Box Office Manager: Joseph Webb
Policy: Plays
Seats: 400. Two bars

TECHNICAL:
STAGE: Pros. Stage Flat. Pros. Opening

8.46m; Ht. of Pros. 6.40m; Depth of Setting Line 4.10m; Ht. of Grid 14.93m; No. of Lines 20 C/W; Electric Act Drop; Scenery Flying Ht. 13.72m; Width of Flying Bars 13.72m; W/Widths O.P. 1.52m, P.S. 2.13m; Prompt Cnr. P.S.
LIGHTING: Switchboard: Dress Circle level, Gemini, Softpatch 180 ways 15 2360 dimmers, with disc storage 2 x 100 amp. Special effect on PS perch; 3 x Colour wheel controllers.
OTHER: Dressing Rooms 8, accom. 30; 2 Showers. Dock Doors 2.40m high x 1.50m wide 3.96m above stage.

TRICYCLE THEATRE

269 Kilburn High Road, London NW6 7JR
Mgt: 020 7372 6611 BO: 020 7328 1000
Fax: 020 7328 0795
Email: info@tricycle.co.uk
Web Site: www.tricycle.co.uk
ADMINISTRATION:
Props: Tricycle Theatre Co. Ltd
Executive Director: Kate Devey
Artistic Director: Indhu Rubasingham
Company Secretary: Trish McElhill
Technical Manager: Shaz McGee
Policy: Presentation of new plays. Adult programme generally for 6-9 week runs. Childrens shows on Saturdays. Plays both by Tricycle Co. and by other production companies.
Seats: 235
TECHNICAL:
Full technical information from management on 0171 372 6611.
LIGHTING: ETC 125 LX desk + Emphasis system, 60 Rank Strand Permus Dimmers, 40 Strand LD 90 dimmers, 18 Source 4 Zooms 25/50, 5 Source 4 36 degree, 6 Source 4 26 degree, 15 16/30 prelude, 10 minuette profile 650 w, 30 Par cans (mainly CP62), Numerous birdies with transformers, 6 Alto 2Kw fresnels, 10 743 fresnels, 10 1.2Kw Cantata fresnels, 6 1Kw Cantata PC, 8 Prelude F 650w fresnels, 10 minuette fresnels 650w, 6 Short nose Par cans, 10 Coda 1Kw floods, 6 coda 500w floods.
SOUND: 2 Denon cassette players, 2 Denon CD players, 4 Sony MD players, O2R 96 Yamaha desk, SPX 1000 effects processor, 4 E9 D&B speakers (2 fixed in rig), 4 E3 D&B speakers, 2 E15 D&B subs (Fixed under seating), 6 E1 D&B speakers, ALL D&B's POWERED BY E-PACS, OR P600 AMPS, 8 Galaxy hotspots, 1 Amcron DC 300 WPC amps, x1 Crown 250W amp. A selection of microphones and DI's available, An SFX unit is available at a cost of £ 100.00 per week to hire.
GENERAL: Soft Cue System with 12 out stations, Tecpro cans system, DF50 Hazer machine/DMX controlled smoke machine/Mini Mist.

TRISTAN BATES THEATRE

The Actors Professional Centre 14 Tower Street, London WC2H 9NP
Tel: 020 7632 8010 BO: 020 7240 6283
Tech: 020 7632 8010
Email: act@actorscentre.co.uk
Web Site: www.tristanbatestheatre.co.uk
ADMINISTRATION:
Creative Producer: Laura Kriefman
Artistic Director: Matthew Lloyd
General Manager: Toma Dim
Development Director: Michelle Bennett
Finance Manager: Roberto Salvatore
Operations Manager: Rachel Roberts
Capacity: 58
TECHNICAL:
STAGE: Dimensions: Width: 6m 40, Depth: 6m 80. Fully sprung floor (skim covered)
LIGHTING: Stand 300, 24 ways of hard wired dimming, Sound Desk 6 channel Folio Spirit 102. 2 CD players. 1 Minidisk player with auto pause function and a dual tape deck. 2 speakers.
BACKSTAGE: Dressing Rooms: 2
For further information, please contact Technical Manager:
Roger Walpole (Tel: 020 7240 3940 ext 210)
Email: tbt@actorscentre.co.uk

TROXY

490 Commercial Road, London E1 0HX
Tel: 020 7790 9000
Email: enquiries@troxy.co.uk
Web Site: www.troxy.co.uk
ADMINISTRATION:
Proprietor: Ashburn Estates
Policy: Live Music
Capacity: Theatre Style, 300-2,200
3 permanent bars. Canopy smoking area. The venue offers flat floor access from street level to the front of the Upper Level of the Grand Hall. A ramp can be installed between the Upper and Lower levels of the Grand Hall if required (held onsite). Disabled toilet and baby change facilities are located in the Foyer.
TECHNICAL:
For full technical specifications visit the venue website.
STAGE: 9.6mx 8.4m - height from dance floor, 90cm or 150cm.
LIGHTING: Desk; Avolites Pearl 2004
BACKSTAGE FACILITIES: 6 backstage rooms with furnishing, wi-fi, a fridge and mirrors. Production office, with Internet access and a direct dial telephone line. 3 front of house dressing rooms available.

THE UNDERWORLD

174 Camden High Street Camden London NW1 0NE
Tel: 020 7482 1932 Fax: 020 7482 1955
Email: contact@theunderworldcamden.co.uk
Web Site: www.theunderworldcamden.co.uk
ADMINISTRATION:
Operations Manager: Jon Vyner
Capacity: 500

UNICORN THEATRE

147 Tooley Street, Southwark, London SE1 2HZ
BO: 020 7645 0560 SD: 020 7645 0500
Email: admin@unicorntheatre.com
Web Site: www.unicorntheatre.com
ADMINISTRATION:
Box Office Manager: James Orr
Production Manager: Phil Bentley
Programme Producer: Carolyn Forsyth
Executive Director: Anneliese Davidsen
The Unicorn Theatre offers two performance spaces, the Weston Theatre (320 max) and the Clore Studio Theatre (100 max), plus the John Lyon Conference Room (25), the Foyle Education Studio (40), the Judi Dench Rehearsal Studio and our Broccoli Foyer (200).
TECHNICAL:
For more information contact the Production Team. Tel: 020 7645 0500.
Email: production@unicorntheatre.com.

UPSTAIRS AT THE GATEHOUSE

The Gatehouse, Highgate Village, London N6 4BD
Manager Tel: 020 8340 3477 BO Tel: 020 8340 3488 Admin: 020 8340 4256
Email: events@ovationproductions.com
Web Site: www.upstairsatthegatehouse.com
ADMINISTRATION:
Upstairs at The Gatehouse is a large London Fringe Theatre situated in a refurbished Victorian Music Hall. It is administered by Ovation Theatres Ltd (020 7387 2342).
Contacts: John and Katie Plews
Policy: Open. New plays, revivals and occasional one-off cabaret and comedy nights. Ideal for Festival previews.
Terms: Rental, Box office splits or Co-productions.
Capacity: Theatre style: 128 (on three sides). Cabaret: 140 using a combination of tiered seating and pub style tables and chairs.
Location: Junction of Hampstead Lane and North Road, N6. Nearest tube: Highgate, Buses: 143, 214, 210, 271. Easy street parking.
TECHNICAL:
STAGE: Thrust stage with audience seated on three sides. Tiered seating in blocks of 74/27/27. Playing area 8.7m wide x 5.8m deep. Height to grid 4.35m. No rake. No flying facilities. Crossover behind tabs. Theatre situated on first floor, no lift, wide staircase. Doors to stage 1.8m wide, 2m high. Four Alistage 8'x4' units available with 16 x 200mm, 16 x 400mm, 8 x 600mm and 8 x 800mm legs. Three front projection screens: 72" x 54" (1829 x 1372mm), 80" x 60" (2032 x 1524mm), 96" x 72" (2438 x 1829mm).
LIGHTING: Fat Frog lighting board (48 way with memory) 72 outlets, 48 way mini racks. Operator position above stage right on Gallery. No follow spots. On Extras List: Two moving disco lights, Rotaflash police lights (3), Fibre Optic Star Cloth with seperate control unit, Mirror Ball and one speed motor

SOUND: Soundcraft Spirit 4 12 + 2:4:2 desk. Excellent acoustics for spoken word and musicals. Operator position above stage right on Gallery. Extras: Foldback system (amp and two JBL speakers), Radio mics (4 x Trantec S4000), 4 x Yamaha Hydraulic Easy Grip.
STAGE MANAGEMENT: No prompt corner. Headsets available. Show relay to Dressing Room / Box Office.
BACKSTAGE FACILITIES: Good size dressing room with hanging space, accommodates 8 - 10. 2 toilets, 2 hand wash basins and a fridge. Iron and ironing board. Washing Machine & Tumble Dryer.
ADDITIONAL: No construction or painting facilities. Small kitchen for tea / coffee etc. Good pub food and cheap drinks downstairs.

VAUDEVILLE THEATRE

404 Strand, London WC2R 0NH
Mgt: 020 7836 1820 BO: 0844 412 4663
SD: 020 7836 3191
Email: alistair.sutherland@nimaxtheatres.com
Web Site: www.nimaxtheatres.com
ADMINISTRATION:
Props: Nimax Theatres Ltd, 1 Lumley Court, Off 402 Strand, London, WC2R 0NB
Chief Executive: Nica Burns
Theatre Manager: Alistair Sutherland
Technical Manager: Ricky McCulloch
Policy: West End Presentation
Perfs: Times of performances vary according to production.
Seats: 694; 3 bars.
Location: Parking: NCP at Upper St Martins Lane, Masterpark at Trafalgar Square. Public Transportation: Nearest Underground: Charing Cross (Northern, Bakerloo), Embankment (District, Circle). Bus Routes: 1, 4 , 6, 9, 11, 13 , 15, 68, 76, 171, 176, 188
For more information on Venue Hire, contact Laurence Miller on Tel: 020 7395 0794.
TECHNICAL:
STAGE: Proscenium stage, pros opening 7.26m, height of pros 5.03m, rake 1:24, depth of stage from pros 9.54m, forestage 0.54m, height of grid 14.33m, 50 lines, 12 counterweights, 38 hemp, wing widths P/S 1.83m, OP 2.29 D/S, 3.20 U/S. Prompt corner P.S.
LIGHTING: Board: Rank Strand Mini Light Palette 90 - 100 ways.
OTHER: Dressing rooms 9, accom. 27; 9 Showers. Additional Rooms for Company Manager and Wardrobe. Air conditioned.
Membership: SOLT

THE VENUE

2a Clifton Rise, New Cross London SE14 6JP
Mgt/BO: 020 8692 4077 Fax: 020 8694 8208
Email: dance@thevenuelondon.com
Web Site: www.thevenuelondon.com
ADMINISTRATOR:
General Manager: Jimmy Cristy
Promoter: Richard Evans (richard@thevenuelondon.com)
Capacity: 1,500 (nightclub).
5 Floors, 7 bars.

VICTORIA PALACE THEATRE

Victoria Street, London, SW1E 5EA
Admin/SD: 020 7834 2781 BO: 0844 248 5000
Email: enquiries@victoriapalace.co.uk
Web Site: www.delfontmackintosh.co.uk
ADMINISTRATION:
Props: Delfont Mackintosh
Theatre Manager: Kylie Shaw
Policy: Musicals, Variety, Revue, Plays, Sunday Concerts.
Perfs: Once nightly. Mats. twice weekly: Mon-Sat 7.30; Thurs. & Sat. 2.30.
Seats: 1,550. Six Licensed Bars.
TECHNICAL:
STAGE: Proscenium Stage, Raked 12.7mm to 25.4mm; Pros. opening 10.77m; Ht. of Pros. 9.22m; Depth of s/Line 9.45m; Ht. of Grid 16.76m; 38 lines; C/W Scenery Flying Height 7.32m; Flying Bars 12.19m; O.P. 5.49m; Prompt Cnr.; O.P. W/Widths P.S. 12.19m.
LIGHTING: Switchboard: ARRI, 110 Memories; 140 circuits; 36 F.O.H.; 16 Stage dips, Flys 88, Spot Bars as required.
SOUNDt: Details available direct from Theatre.
BACKSTAGE FACILITIES: Dressing Rooms 12, accom. 75; 6 Showers; Orchestra Pit 24. Easy get-in direct to stage from street level.
Other: Membership: SOLT

WALTHAMSTOW ASSEMBLY HALL

Forest Road London E17 4JD
Hall Bookings Tel: 020 8496 8018
Email: assemblyhall.bookings@walthamforest.gov.uk
Web Site: www.walthamforest.gov.uk
ADMINISTRATION:
Props: London Borough of Waltham Forest
Hall Manager: Diana Grover
Halls Co-ordinator: Nicola McGibbon
Email: assemblyhall.bookings@walthamforest.gov.uk
Policy: Available Monday - Sunday, 9am-1am. Minimum hire period 8 hours. Concert Hall, Music, Pop, Jazz, Opera, Ballet, Dances, Conferences, Boxing, Exhibitions, Recordings, Touring Shows.
Capacity: Concerts, large meetings, 1150. Dancing (open floor, no tables minimal seating), 800. Dancing (with minimal tables and chair layout and large dance floor), 450. Dinner, weddings and buffets (with small dance floor), 450.
TECHNICAL:
STAGE: Dimensions: Dimensions of main hall 97'-6" x 68'-5", Dimensions of Antler bar 60' x 27', Dimensions of stage 24' x 36''.
LIGHTING: Control: Strand MX console 48 way (32 Ways available). (Minimum) 10 x 1000 watt Powercans, 8 x 1000 watt T spots 4 x 1000 watt Area floods, Syke Lighting 8 x 500 watt Fresnels 2 x 2000 watt CSI follow spots (operators not supplied).
SOUND: Desk: Studio Master 24 way, 17 line inputs (all XLR) Tape deck/Record player, 2 x Wedge monitors Talk back from stage to lighting, sound controls & dressing rooms 3 Cabaret microphones SM48.
BACKSTAGE FACILITIES: Dressing Rooms, 2.

WANDLE RECREATION CENTRE

Mapleton Road, Wandsworth, London SW18 4DN
Tel: 020 8871 1149 Fax: 020 8870 4134
Email: enquiries@wandlerecreationcentre.co.uk
Web Site: www.wandlerecreationcentre.co.uk
ADMINISTRATION:
Props: London Borough of Wandsworth
Manager: Natasha Gurney
Membership Manager: Lisa Sayers
lisasayers@pfpleisure.org
Bookings Manager: Spiros Lakonitis
Sports Hall Cap: 50 (seated). Caters for children's parties. dance studio for hire, with 20-30 capacity.

WANDSWORTH CIVIC SUITE

High Street, Wandsworth, London SW18 2PU
Bookings Tel: 020 8871 6394/5
Email: phalls@wandsworth.gov.uk
Web Site: www.wandsworth.gov.uk
ADMINISTRATION:
Props: London Borough of Wandsworth
Capacity: Civic Suite, Theatre Style - 428. Civic Hall: With wooden floor and stage. Can be adjusted accordingly. Situated next to the Banquet Hall which caters for weddings, parties. Total capacity: 500 (seated).
Manager: Peter Tracy

THE WAREHOUSE

13 Theed Street, South Bank, London SE1 8ST
Tel: 020 7928 9251 Fax: 020 7928 9252
Email: the.warehouse@lfo.co.uk
Web Site: www.thewarehouselondon.co.uk
ADMINISTRATION:
For further information on studio availability and hire charges, please contact Executive Director: Elizabeth Szücs
Email: easzucs@lfo.co.uk
Capacity: Standing Cap: Studio 1: 100, Studio 2: 50. Seated: Studio 1: 100, Studio 2: 40. Orchestral/Rehearsal Setup: 85 max.

WATERMANS

40 High Street, Brentford, Middlesex TW8 0DS
Admin: 020 8232 1019 BO: 020 8232 1010
Email: info@watermans.org.uk
Web Site: www.watermans.org.uk
ADMINISTRATION:
Director: Jan Lennox
General Manager: Rachel Francis
Marketing Director: Erica Weston
Programme Administrator: Jason, Tel: 020 8232 1031 or email jason@watermans.org.uk.
Capacity: Theatre: 239; Foyer Downstairs: 300-400; Studio 1: 80; Studio 2: 20; Cinema: 125; Gallery space: 80. All Available for public hire.
For more information about availability and prices contact the Customer Relationship Managers in charge of hiring:
Day: Mirko Petrovich.
Tel: 020 8232 1019 or mirko@watermans.org.uk
Evening: Edoardo Zollo.
Tel: 020 8232 1019 or edoardo@watermans.org.uk
TECHNICAL:
STAGE: Proscenium arch with small thrust. No rake. Suitable for dance. 1 baby grand piano available for performance, good. Smoke machine.
STAGE MANAGEMENT: PA and tannoy to the dressing rooms
BACKSTAGE FACILITIES: 2 dressing rooms accommodate 10, Green Room, wardrobe with washing machine.
STAFF: Technical staff - 3 technicians, ushers available
Technical specs and lighting plans available. Contact Technical Manager: Ryan Beattie, tel: 020 8232 1042 or ryan@watermans.org.uk.

WEMBLEY STADIUM

Wembley National Stadium, Wembley, Middlesex HA9 0WS
Tel: 0800 169 2007 Special Events Tel: 020 8795 9660
Email: info@wembleystadium.com
Web Site: www.wembleystadium.com
ADMINISTRATION:
Managing Director: Roger Maslin
Group Events Director: David Thomson
Head of Sales: Ruth Kaye
Cap: 90,000

WIGMORE HALL

36 Wigmore Street, London W1U 2BP
Mgt: 020 7258 8200 BO: 020 7935 2141
Mgt Fax: 020 7258 8201
Email: info@wigmore-hall.org.uk
Web Site: www.wigmore-hall.org.uk
ADMINISTRATION:
Director: John Gilhooly
Senior House Manager/Head of Operations: David King
Registered Charity No: 1024838
Policy: Concerts and Education projects.
Performances: Mondays to Sunday, 7.30pm, Lunchtime & coffee concert every Sunday at 11.30 am. Concert recital for BBC Radio 3 every Monday lunchtime.
Auditorium, Restaurant, Bars, Cloakroom, Function Room.
Cap: 537 (seated).
TECHNICAL:
STAGE: Concert Platform. no Pros. Flat.
DRESSING ROOMS: 2.
ADDITIONAL: Excellent acoustics - often used for recording sessions by BBC and all Record Companies. The Hall is equipped with an induction loop for hearing aid use.

WINDMILL BRIXTON

Available for hiring
22 Blenheim Gardens London SW2 5BZ
Tel: 020 8671 0700 Mob Tel: 07931 351 971
Email: windmillbrixton@yahoo.co.uk
Web Site: http://windmillbrixton.co.uk
ADMINISTRATION:
Bookings Manager: Tim Perry
Cap: 130

WOOLWICH PUBLIC HALL

Hall not available for hire after 6 pm and on Sundays
Wellington Street, London SE18 6PW
Tel: 020 8921 5022 Fax: 020 8921 6427
Hall Bookings: 0208 921 5009
Email: townhallbookings@greenwich.gov.uk
Web Site: www.greenwich.gov.uk
ADMINISTRATION:
Props: London Borough of Greenwich
Hall Bookings Officer: Janet Smith: Tel 020 8921 5022
The Public Hall can be used for wedding or civil partnership receptions and parties. It accommodates up to 250 people and can be hired Monday to Saturday from 9am to 6pm.
A variety of smaller committee rooms are also available to hire for meetings upon request.
These consist of two small rooms seating a maximum of 15, two larger rooms seating 20 and another seating 35 maximum. The Council Chamber can accommodate theatre-style meetings of up to 70.

WYNDHAMS THEATRE

Charing Cross Road, London WC2H 0DA
BO Tel: 0844 482 5120 Mgt Tel: 020 7759 8077
Email: wyndhamsmanagers@delmack.co.uk
Web Site: www.delfontmackintosh.co.uk
ADMINISTRATION:
Props: Delfont Mackingtosh
London Operations Manager: Billy Differ
Theatre Manager: Emma Whelan
Master Carpenter: Arthur Turner
Policy: Plays, Musicals etc.
Perfs: Variable according to production.
Seats: 789. Licensed Bars.
TECHNICAL:
STAGE: Proscenium Stage, Flat; Pros. opening 8.31m; Ht. of Pros. 6.40m; Depth of S/Line 8.00m; Ht. of Grid 14.78m; 30 lines, Hemp; Scenery Flying Ht. 14.02m; Flying Bars 10.06m; W/Widths P.S. 6.52m; O.P. 3.40m; Prompt Cnr. as required.
LIGHTING: Switchboard: Arri Imagine board installed. Circuit distribution. F.O.H. 42, Flys 54, Stage 34, 60A 3 phase available for additional dimmers. Control Desk rear of Royal Circle; Remote Terminal Prompt Cnr. F.O.H. Spots 16 Patt. 264; 3 circuits; Floats & Dips as required. Air Conditioned (Auditorium).
SOUND: As required.
OTHER: Dressing Rooms 8, accom. 30
Membership: SOLT

YORK HALL LEISURE CENTRE

5- 15 Old Ford Road, Bethnal Green London E2 9PJ
Tel: 020 8980 2243
Email: yorkhall@gll.org
Web Site: www.better.org
ADMINISTRATION:
Event Manager: Mohamed Gutale
Email: yorkhallevents@gll.org
Large Hall used for concerts, theatre productions, conferences
and sports events.
Cap: 300 - seated.
Full power and stage available. Please contact venue for further details.

YOUNG VIC THEATRE

66 The Cut, London SE1 8LZ
Mgt: 020 7922 2800 / 2805 BO: 020 7922 2922 Fax: 020 7820 2805
Email: info@youngvic.org
Web Site: www.youngvic.org
ADMINISTRATION:
Artistic Director: David Lan
Executive Director: Lucy Woollatt
General Manager: David Fletcher
Policy: Theatre.
Perfs: Phone or write or see Press for details.
Seats: 500- 600; Studio Space number 1: up to 160; Studio Space number 2: 80
Bar and restaurant.
TECHNICAL:
STAGE: Thrust/in the round Stage, Flat; Ht. of Grid 8.23m; Prompt Cnr. O.P. audit.
LIGHTING: Switchboard: Gemini Memory Control System for 132 and capacity of 192 cues. dips 5 patchable each side; Spot Bar, Open Grid; 36 Patt. 264, 10 Patt. 23.
SOUND: Soundcraft K3, 16-8-2 with 8X8 matrix, Alcai 3000 sampler, 2 Cds, 1 Minidisc, 1 SPX1000, Assorted microphones, Meyer speaker system.
OTHER: Dressing Rooms 4, accom. 20; Showers.
Entrance from dressing rooms to S.R. and round back of auditorium to SL and SR stairs removable to acting balcony. Bridges to connect balconies.

FRINGE THEATRES

THE ALBANY
Theatre and community centre. Douglas Way, Deptford, London SE8 4AG
Admin: 020 8692 0231 BO: 020 8692 4446 Fax: 020 8469 2253
Email: senay.gaul@thealbany.org.uk
Web Site: www.thealbany.org.uk
ADMINISTRATION:
The Albany is a lively, intimate and friendly venue with an exciting programme of the very best in theatre, live music, cabaret, family shows, club nights and multimedia events in informal cabaret-style seating.
CEO/Artistic Director: Gavin Barlow
Operations & Administration: Senay Gaul
Room Bookings & Venue Hires: Lily Hannell
Production & Events: Ben Stephens
Head of Communications: Amber Massie-Bloomfield
Box Office: Vicky Harrison
Front of House: Kate Miners (reception@thealbany.org.uk)
Policy: Variety of events, including music, theatre, dance, spoken word, clubs and family events.
Capacity: Main Auditorium: 300 seated/ 500 standing. Studio/ Conference Rooms: 12 - 100.

BARRON THEATRE
North Street, St. Andrews, Fife KY16
Tel: 01334 461701
Email: barron@st-andrews.ac.uk
Web Site: www.barrontheatre.co.uk
ADMINISTRATION:
Contact: Julie Amphlett
Capacity: 60 Seats.

Since the Theatre cannot accept mail, all post should be directed to: Barron Theatre, c/o Students Association, St Mary's Place, St Andrews, Fife KY16 9UZ
The Barron Theatre is located on North Street in between the Cinema and St Salvator's Chapel, and opposite the Police Station. It is a 10 minute walk from St Andrews Bus Station.

BATTERSEA ARTS CENTRE
Venue undergoing restoration, capacity unknown until 2016 Lavender Hill, London SW11 5TN
Mgt: 020 7223 6557 BO: 020 7223 2223
Fax: 020 7978 5207 Admin: 020 7326 8239
Email: boxoffice@bac.org.uk, mailbox@bac.org.uk
Web Site: www.bac.org.uk
ADMINISTRATION:
Artistic Director: David Jubb
Executive Manager: Rebecca Holt
Technical Manager: Kevin Miles
Theatre: Multi-purpose performance space. Capacity: 200 +
Lower Hall Capacity: 100 - 200
Recreation Room Capacity: 50 - 100
Policy: To work with artists and audiences towards the development of innovative forms of theatre.
For venue hire contact the theatre on: venues@bac.org.uk.
TECHNICAL:
STAGE (Theatre): The playing area (on floor) is normally 27 feet x 21 feet.
LIGHTING: 6 X Harmony 1k Fresnels all with Barndoors, 10 X Cantata 1.2k Fresnels all with Barndoors, 10 X Cantata 1.2k Profiles 18/32 with Rotary Gobo Gate, 15 X 650w Prelude Fresnels all with Barndoors, 8 X Thomas Pars all CP 62.
LX Desk: ETC Express:- 120 Channels 2k per way Digital.
SOUND: Soundcraft K1 Sound Desk 16-4, 1 X Denon DCD -425 single C.D. Programmable, 1 X Denon DRM 550 single cassette unit, 2X EV P1250 PWR Amps, 1 X EV XP200 Cross Over, 4 X EV S x 200 Midd and Top Speakers, 2 X EV Sb 120 Bass Speakers, 1 X Alesis Quadravert, Relevant Cables, Patch Bay.
Please contact the Technical Manager for full technical specifications.

BLUE ELEPHANT THEATRE
59a Bethwin Road, Camberwell, London SE5 0XT
Tel: 020 7701 0100
Email: info@blueelephanttheatre.co.uk
Web Site: www.blueelephanttheatre.co.uk
ADMINISTRATION:
Artistic Director: Naimh Valera and Jo Sadler-Lovett
Policy: Physical and dance theatre, and new writing and classics.
Capacity: 50 Theatre Style
TECHNICAL:
STUDIO THEATRE SPACE:
LIGHTING: 1 x ETC Smartfade Lighting desk (48 Channel), 4 x ACT 6 Dimmers, 7 x Minuette 35/42 650w Profile, 7 x Minuette 650w Fresnel , 5 x Minuette 650w PC, 3 x 1Kw Starlette Fresnel (only 1 barndoors), 2 x 1Kw Harmony Fresnel (no barndoors), 2 x CCT Sil 30 1.2 Kw, 1 x Par 64 (CP62), 11 x Grelcos, 1 x Par 36 (VNS), 1 x Par 16 (MF), 3 x Floor Stands, Max. Load per channel 2Kw.
SOUND: 1 x Peavey PV6 mixer, 4 channel, 6 input mixer, 1 x Sony MDS-JE520 mini disc player, 1 x Sony CD player, 1 x DVD player, 3 x SM58 Microphones, 2 x Mic Stands.
OTHER: 1 x Talkback Master Station, 2 x Tec Pro Headsets

BRICK LANE MUSIC HALL
443 North Woolwich Road, Silvertown, London E16 2DA
Tel: 020 7511 6655
Email: admin@bricklanemusichall.co.uk
Web Site: www.bricklanemusichall.co.uk
ADMINISTRATION:
Props: London Borough of Newham
Capacity: 180 theatre style
Theatre Director: Vincent Hayes
Manager: Zara Kattan
Technical Manager: Oliver Savage
All correspondence through the Theatre Director.

BRIDEWELL THEATRE
Bride Lane, off Fleet Street, London EC4Y 8EQ
Tel: 020 7353 3331 Fax: 020 7353 1547
Email: info@sbf.org.uk
Web Site: www.sbf.org.uk
ADMINISTRATION:
Props: St. Bride Foundation.
Theatre Manager: Mikey Palmer
Capacity: 134 Theatre Style, 200 Standing.
TECHNICAL:
DIMENSIONS: Depth 4.0m, Width 7.8m, Height 3.6m, Area 31.2m2, Door width 1.0m.
LIGHTING; Natural daylight, blinds for full black out, full lighting rig available.
COMMUNICATIONS; Wireless broadband available on request.

BROADGATE ARENA
Broadgate Estates
Exchange House 12 Exchange Square Primrose Street London EC2A 2BQ
Tel: 020 7505 4100 Fax: 020 7382 9854
Email: arena@broadgatesestates.co.uk
Web Site: www.broadgateinfo.net
ADMINISTRATION:
Estate Manager: Ross McQuillan
Deputy Events Manager: Lee Jones
Open Air Amphitheatre hosting free week-day lunchtime entertainment, all year round.
TECHNICAL:
Performing area 80' diameter max.
Canopy available - written notice required.
More details at www.broadgateinfo.net

BROMLEY LITTLE THEATRE
North Street, Bromley, Kent BR4 1SB
BO: 07917 853621 Membership: 01689 825107 Artistic Team: 07984 722308
Email: paulj@bromleylittletheatre.org
Web Site: www.bromleylittletheatre.com
ADMINISTRATION:
Props: Bromley Little Theatre Ltd.
Contact: Paul Johnson
General: playgoers@bromleylittletheatre.org
Board: board@bromleylittletheatre.org
Membership: membership@bromleylittletheatre.org
Box Office: boxoffice@bromleylittlethe-

atre.org
Artistic Director: artistic@bromleylittletheatre.org
Seats: 113
TECHNICAL:
STAGE: Proscenium, Flat; Pros. Opening 4.88m; Ht. of Pros. 2.59m; Depth of S/Line 6.40m; Ht. of Grid 6.10m.
BACKSTAGE FACILITIES: Dressing rooms: 2, accom. 24 approx.
Club Theatre. Resident Company. Established 1937. Season January to December.

CANAL CAFE THEATRE

Canal Café Theatre,
The Bridge House, Delamere Terrace, London W2 6ND
Tel: 020 7289 6056 BO: 020 7289 6054
Email: mail@canalcafetheatre.com
Web Site: www.canalcafetheatre.com
ADMINISTRATION:
Theatre Manager: Annie Biddlecombe
Artistic Director: Emma Taylor
Theatre Technician: Stuart Glover
Fringe Pub Theatre specialising in stand-up and farcical acts and productions, in cafe-style layout with bar and food.
Capacity: 60

CHATS PALACE

42-44 Brooksby's Walk, Homerton, Hackney, London E9 6DF
Tel: 020 8533 0227
Email: info@chatspalace.com
Web Site: www.chatspalace.com
ADMINISTRATION:
Capacity; Seated: 100. Standing: 200.
TECHNICAL:
STAGE: Floor area 5.5m x 6m deep, pros opening 5.5m x 3m. Rubberised dance-floor available. Black curtains / white cyclorama / black brick wall. Backstage crossover - just! Stage units form raked seating or can make 5m x 4m stage for music, etc. Traverse, round, other variations possible.
LIGHTS: Zero 88 Fat Frog programmable board. 18 circuit @2kw, operated from back balcony. 50 various fresnels, profiles, PCs and floods, and follow spot.
SOUND: 16.4.2 sound mixing desk operated from back of hall OR 20.2 mixing desk operated from back balcony. 2kW turbosound rig with 1kW monitoring.10 mics, 4 DI boxes, 2xCD, MD, DA, MC.
Also available - projector (video/DVD/etc) and screen, 2 x slide projector, turntables and mixer, upright piano (good).
Acoustic suitable for music and spoken word.
BACKSTAGE FACILITIES: One dressing room, stage right. Some wing space both sides.

THE CHELSEA THEATRE

7 World's End Place, King's Road, London SW10 0DR
Admin Tel: 020 7352 1967
Email: admin@chelseatheatre.org.uk
Web Site: www.chelseatheatre.org.uk
ADMINISTRATION:
Artistic Director: Francis Alexander
Marketing and Advertisment
Management: Kathryn Stephens-Berry
Policy: In-house producing and Small scale touring.
Committed to the presentation of new work. Also workshops & full youth arts programme..
Seats: 110 Adults, 140 Children
TECHNICAL:
STAGE: Depth of stage from setting line to back wall 6600mm, Depth from front of seats to back wall 7200mm, Width of stage 9600mm, Grid height 3800mm.
MASKING: 7 x Black wool stage drapes 3900mm drop x 2500mm wide, 1 x Black wool stage drape 4800mm drop x 2700mm wide, Assorted black wool masking flats, 1 x Roll of black harlequin dance floor, black/white reversible, 2 x 8 foot Zarges ladders.
LIGHTING Control; ETC Express 24/48 Lighting Desk, 48 Ways Digital Dimming, 48 Circuits direct to dimmers (one to one) Including house lights. Lanterns: Profiles; 5 x SL, 15/32, 600W, 9 x SL, 23/50, 600W, 2 x SIL 30, 1K, 2 x T-Spot, 1K, 5 x Cantata 18/32 1K. Fresnels; 6 x CANTATA, 1.2K, 13 x Quartet, 650W, 4 x 743, 1K, 7 x PATT 123, 500W, 3 x MINUETTE, 650W. Other: 6 x Parcan CP62, 4 x MR16 (Birdies) 2 transformers only, 4 x ADB, Cyc (ACP 1001, 2 of which usually house lights). 6 x SL GOBO HOLDERS, Assorted 15A TRS (EXTENSION CABLE), Limited 13A extension cable, Limited grelcos.
SOUND: 1 x 24 Channel MX 24/4/2 Euro Desk, 1 x Yamaha P3200 amp, 1 x Sony MD JE480 Single Mini-Disk Player, 1 x Denon DRM-595 Single Cassette Player, 2 x Cambridge Azur 540 CD player, 2 x DVD Players, 2 x Control 1 Speakers, 2 x Control 5 Speakers, 4 x Mosquito Dynacord Speakers, 2 x Mackie Art2000a Powered Speakers, 1 x SM58 Vocal Microphone and boom stand, 2 x Cans headsets (1 at control desks, 1 backstage), 4 x Microphone outlets onstage, 6 x Speaker outlets onstage, Limited XLR and speaker cable
ADDITIONAL: Show relay to backstage and dressing rooms.

COCKPIT THEATRE

Gateforth Street Off Church Street
London NW8 8EH
Admin: 020 7258 2920 BO/Reservations: 020 7258 2925
Email: dave@thecockpit.org.uk, mail@thecockpit.org.uk
Web Site: www.thecockpit.org.uk
ADMINISTRATION:
Props: City of Westminster College.
Theatre Manager: Dave Wybrow
Technical Co-ordinator and Theatre Technician: Deb Jones
Policy: Incoming companies/shows & exhibitions.
Seats: In the Round 220; Thrust 180.
Upstairs Rehearsal Studios for Hire.
Bar, Large dressing rooms, workshop, foyer capacity 240. Large loading dock doors. Hire rates £300-£400 per show day.
Disabled Access at street level to auditorium and disabled toilets.
TECHNICAL:
STAGE: Adaptable stage, Round/Thrusts/End.
LIGHTING: Switchboard: Strand 60 way, 3 x 3 preset; F.O.H. Spots 19 Patt. 223, 27 Patt. 264, 4 Patt. 123, 12 Patt. 23.
SOUND: 2 Ferrograph, 1 Garrard in Lighting/ Control Box above stage; Speakers 4 floating 12 in Axion 7 positions.
OTHER: Dressing Rooms 2; accom. 20; 2 Showers.
For full technical specifications contact Theatre Technician,
deb@thecockpit.org.uk

CORBETT THEATRE

Rectory Lane, Loughton, Essex IG10 3RY
Admin/BO: 020 8508 5983 Fax: 020 8508 7521
Email: east15@essex.ac.uk
Web Site: www.east15.ac.uk
ADMINISTRATION:
Technical Manager: Phil Webb
Email: pjwebb@essex.ac.uk
Excellent small theatre with extensive parking facilities set in 5 acres of gardens with lake - periodically for hire. 12 miles east from Central London, 4 miles off M25; 1 mile off M11; access also by tube to Debden, Central Line.
Seats 125

EMBASSY THEATRE

The Royal Central School of Speech & Drama, 64 Eton Avenue, Swiss Cottage, London NW3 3HY
Tel: 020 7722 8183 Fax: 020 7722 4132
Email: enquiries@cssd.ac.uk
Web Site: www.cssd.ac.uk
ADMINSTRATION:
Marketing Manager: Susan Emmanuel, ext. 2262
Capacity: Theatre; 250 Theatre Style. Studio: 100.
For more information on the Technical Specifications, contact the Technical Department, ext. 516.

ETCETERA THEATRE CLUB

Oxford Arms,
265 Camden High Street, London NW1 7BU
Admin Tel: 020 7482 4857 BO: 020 7482 4857
Email: admin@etceteratheatre.com
Web Site: www.etceteratheatre.com
ADMINISTRATION:
Management: Maude Madlyn
Policy: To continue our current successful two shows a night policy, as well as a Monday night slot for 'one-off' perform-

ances, presenting a popular and varied programme with an emphasis on new work. To maintain and enhance the theatre's high media profile and to continue to provide the opportunity for small theatre companies, with limited finances, to stage productions in Central London. Studio theatre with seating capacity of 42.
TECHNICAL:
STAGE: Flat; 5.40m (w) x 4.00m (d) to back wall, 5.40m (w) x 3.70m (d) to chimney breast. Grid Height: 3.25m. Clearance Height: 2.75m. Get-In; ground floor side entrance, Door Dimensions approx 1.10m (w) x 1.80m (h). Staircase width approx 1.10m (w). Double Door Dimensions approx 2.20m (w) x 1.80m (h).
LIGHTING: Lighting console located in control room. Console: Zero 88 Level 12. 12 way analogue 2 preset lighting desk with timed fades. House lights controlled via an independent dimmer in the control room. Dimming; 2 x Green Ginger, 6 channels, 24 x 15a outlets. Patchable via 38 overhead 15a outlets. Independent Power. 4 x 13a adaptable outlets on US wall. Lantern Stock: Fresnels; 3 x Minuette Fresnel 500w, 6 x Pattern 123 Fresnel 500w, 4 x Parcans PAR64, 2 x Parcans PAR64 SN, 4 x Pinspot PAR36 with int. Transformer, 2 x Sun Flood. Profiles; 1 x Strand SL 23/50 600w, 3 x Strand Quartet 22/40 500w, 2 x Patten 23 30o 500w, 1 x Minuette Profile 500w. Limited birdies, cables, grelcos, gobos and holders etc. (please ring for availability). Visiting companies must supply their own gel although a small stock of pre-cut colour is available FOC.
SOUND: Audio Tie Lines, 12 XLR tie lines USL terminating in the control room. Control: Yamaha MG12/4. 12 input channels, capable of taking XLR, TRS Phone Jack and RCA line input. Installed Loudspeaker System. 2 x JBL Control 1 mounted SL & SR powered by Samson Servo 260 amplifier Outboard Equipment. 1 x Tascam 122 Cassette Deck. 1 x Sony Mini-disc Player/Recorder. 1 x Sony CD Player. All of the above are housed in a rack located in the control room. Microphones; 3 x Shure Beta 58 (equivalent), 2 x Microphone stands, Cables, connectors etc. please contact us for more information.
BACKSTAGE FACILTIES: 1 Dressing Rooms, accomm. 5 people. Additional space in the technical room, opposite the dressing room, accomm. 2 people. Audio show relay system; Full show relay system to dressing rooms and control box.

FAIRKYTES ARTS CENTRE
51 Billet Lane, Hornchurch, Essex RM11 1AX
Tel: 01708 456 308 Fax: 01708 475 286
Email: fairkytes@havering.gov.uk
Web Site: www.havering.gov.uk
ADMINISTRATION:
Arts Co-ordinator: Mark Etherington
Supervisor: John Shadwell
Converted Georgian house seating 40, used for many kinds of arts and crafts activities. Also small studio theatre seating 100. Spacious garden is suitable for drama performances if a company tours all its own equipment.

FINBOROUGH THEATRE
118 Finborough Road,
London SW10 9ED
Tel: 020 7244 7439 BO: 0844 847 1652
Email: admin@finboroughtheatre.co.uk
Web Site: www.finboroughtheatre.co.uk
ADMINISTRATION:
Artistic Director: Neil McPherson.
Policy: New writing and neglected plays from the last 150 years.
Cap: 50

GATE THEATRE
Above The Prince Albert
11 Pembridge Road London W11 3HQ
Admin: 020 7229 5387 BO: 020 7229 0706 Fax: 020 7221 6055
Email: gate@gatetheatre.co.uk
Web Site: www.gatetheatre.co.uk
ADMINISTRATION:
Artistic Director: Christopher Haydon
General Manager: Steve Sargeant
Technical Manager: Andy Rungen
Seating: 70

GREENWICH & LEWISHAM YOUNG PEOPLES THEATRE
The Tramshed,
51 - 53 Woolwich New Road, London SE18 6ES
Tel: 020 8854 1316
Email: info@glypt.co.uk, zoe.bateman@glypt.co.uk
Web Site: www.glypt.co.uk
ADMINISTRATION:
Artistic Director: Jeremy James. Email: jeremy@glypt.co.uk
General Manager: Zoë Lally. Email: zoe@glypt.co.uk
Administrator: Zoe Bateman
Capacity: 110 Theatre Style. Studio Capacity 40
TECHNICAL:
Acting space: 27' x 21'.
Lighting Equipment: Details of other equipment available on application. Studio workshop also available. Access for wheelchairs.

HEN AND CHICKENS THEATRE
Hen and Chickens Theatre
109 St Pauls Road, London N1 2NA
Tel: 020 7704 2001
Email: henandchickens@aol.com
Web Site: www.henandchickens.com
ADMINISTRATION:
Capacity: 54
For more information on venue hire contact Felicity Wren on henandchickens@aol.com

HOXTON HALL THEATRE & ARTS CENTRE
Undergoing refurbishment until February 2015 130 Hoxton Street, London N1 6SH
Tel: 020 7684 0060
Email: info@hoxtonhall.co.uk
Web Site: www.hoxtonhall.co.uk
ADMINISTRATION:
Original victorian music hall theatre built in 1863 and designed by Sir James Mortimer. Venue & Youth Arts training organisation. Cap: 270 seat theatre (venue available for hire).
TECHNICAL:
STAGE: 5.10m wide x 3.9m. Apron: 4.88m wide x 1.06m with a possible 4.88m wide x 0.9m extension. Height to rig; Main stage: 5.15m, Apron: 5.8m, Floor: 6.5m, Stage blocks 1.2m x 0.9m. Get in: Main entrance 2.03m x1.15m, Rear entrance 2.04m x1.13m.
LIGHTING: Zero 88 DEMUX into 24 10A dimmed channels, 7 x PAR 64, 2 x vision 1200 fresnels - no Barn doors, 6 x Patt 123, 6 x Minuet PC's, 4 x Minuet Fresnels, 2 x Teatro 1K Zoom Profiles, 2 x Minuet Zoom Profiles, 5 x Quartet Profiles, 3 x Minuet Floods, 2 x Pattern 23 Profiles.
SOUND: 2 x Spirit FX16 16:4 mixer with internal FX processor, CD, MC, MD players, Ring intercom system. Amps: Peavey 4C 200w per channel, Peavey 8.5C 400w per channel, Peavey CS1000 500w per channel, Sound Tech PL602 300W per channel, Samson servo 170 85w per channel. Speakers: 1 x Pair Peavey SYS 4 700w per speaker, 1 x Pair Peavey SYS2 350w per speaker, 3 x HISYS2M 350w per speaker, 1 x Pair 150 w per speakers.
DRESSING ROOMS: 2, accommodating 10. Washing and toilet facilities.

ICA THEATRE
Institute of Contemporary Arts
The Mall, London SW1Y 5AH
Tel: 020 7930 0493 BO: 020 7930 0493
Email: events@ica.org.uk
Web Site: www.ica.org.uk
ADMINISTRATION:
Executive Director: Gregor Muir
Head of Events: Emilia Bromiley
Technical Manager: Sam Martin
Capacity: 350 standing, 180 theatre style.
TECHNICAL:
STAGE: Ply floor 74' x 33' Grid over whole area 14'6". Seating primarily on four movable bleachers enabling various endstage traverse thrust and round layouts up to a maximum capacity of 206 seats.
LIGHTING: 48 way Micron. Switch patching 3 ways on 12 channels. 174 Grid outlets. Lanterns: 12 x Patt. 23, 12 x Sil 30, 18 x Cantata Fres., 6 x harmony Fres., 14 x Parcans (1K), 2 x 15/28 Profiles, 2 x 22/40 Profiles.
SOUND: 2 x Revox B77; 1 x Revox A77; 1 x Tascam 8 x 4 x 1 Mixer. Bose Speaker System.

JACK STUDIO THEATRE

410 Brockley Road, London SE4 2DH
Admin: 020 8291 6354 BO: 0844 8700 887
Email: admin@brockleyjack.co.uk
Web Site: www.brockleyjack.co.uk
ADMINISTRATION:
Artistic Director: Kate Bannister
Theatre Manager: Karl Swinyard
Policy: Performance of plays, film, comedy and poetry. Available on a weekly basis. Priority given to three-four week runs.
Perfs: Tuesday to Saturday. No performances on Mondays.
Capacity: 50
TECHNICAL:
STAGE: 7 mts wide x 5 mts deep. Two entrances either side of the stage. Rig height: 3.3 mts.
LIGHTING: 1 x Zero 88 Jester 24/48 programmable desk /DMX, 1 x Sirus 24 Programmable desk DMX/Analogue, 4 x Beta Pack, 2 x Plus Dimmer Racks DMX (10 amps per channel); 24 x Channels for lx on rig. Lantern: 4 xADB Fresnels 500w, 2 x ADB Fresnels 1Kw, 6 x Quartet PC 650w, 10 x Quartet PC Zooms 650w, 1 x CCT Minuette Fresnel 650w, 2 x Minuette Fresnel 500w, 3 x CCT Starlette Fresnel 1kw, 1 x Harmony 15/28 Profile 1K, 3 x Patt 223/743 1kw/650w, 3 x Patt 23 500/650w, 6 x Patt 123 500/650w, 4 x Furse Floods 500w, 10 x Par 16 Mains voltage, 1 x Jem Martin 800 Fog Machine, 1 x Acme Haze machine, 21 x Grelcos, 60 x Various 15 Amp cables 1mt to 10mts, 30 x Gobos.
SOUND: 1 x 24 Channel Berhringer mixing Desk 24-4-2 (4 submasters), 1 x Phonic Max 1500w 2 Channel, 2 x Carlsbro Gamma 12/250P watt speaker cabinets, 2 x Carlsbro Gamma 10/250P watt speaker cabinets, 1 x Carlsbro Equinox 12 Channel mixer/amp; 300w Stereo. 4 x Microphones and 3 stands, 1 x Sony Multi CD Player, 1 x Cambridge Audio CD Player, 1 x KAM Professional Twin Cd Player auto/cue pause, 2 x Sony MD Players with auto pause, 1 x Sony MD Playerswithout auto pause, 1 x Show relay.
BACKSTAGE FACILITIES: Large dressing room / rehearsal facilities (6 mts wide x 11 mts deep) above the theatre.

JACKSONS LANE

Opp Highgate Tube,
269a Archway Road, London N6 5AA
Admin: 020 8340 5226 BO: 020 8341 4421
Email: admin@jacksonslane.org.uk
Web Site: www.jacksonslane.org.uk
ADMINISTRATION:
Props: Haringey Borough Council
Artistic Director: Adrian Berry
General Manager: Ruth Turner
Theatre Technician: Nick Waddel
Email: technical@jacksonslane.org.uk
Policy: To provide a programme of music, drama, dance, mime and cabaret, representing multi-cultural interests. Training will play a large part in our programme, and many of our staff are trainees and volunteers.
Location: Alongside the Archway Road (A1), opposite Highgate tube. Served by buses 43, 134, X43, 263. Terms: Hire of theatre (negotiable); box office split.
Seats/Capacity: 166
Bars: one in foyer, one in auditorium.
TECHNICAL:
STAGE: End on, flat stage, semi-sprung wood floor, raked. 11m x 8m deep (without wing masking/ black tabs). 8m x 7m deep APPROX. (with wing masking/ black tabs). Grid Height: 6.2m. Get-In: Via 1.5m x 3.5m stage door from Archway Road (A1 facing north). Red route restrictions apply; parking for one hour between 10am and 4pm. Unrestricted parking after 7pm. Underground station car park charges £3 per day.
LIGHTING: Control: Strand 91703 300 Console 125ch 24sub. Lanterns: 10 x 1k Starlette fresnels, 6 x Par 64 (assorted lenses - please check with us), 2 x 650 w Minuette profiles, 6 x 1k Compact 6 fresnels, 12 x 1.2k ETC Source 4, 15/30 zoom profiles, 7 x 1.2k ETC Source 4, 25/50 zoom profiles, 4 x 500w Quartet fresnels, 2 x 3 cell 500w flood units. All lanterns are compete with barn doors, gel frames and shutters as appropriate.
SOUND: Allen and Heath GL 3300. Playback; Numark CDn22 Dual CD Player, 2x RCF Art 315a Powered speakers (Fixed Position). Various Microphones available.
ADDITIONAL: Infrared hearing systems fitted, 1x FXlab Small Hazer, 1x Martin magnum 650 Smoke Machine, 1x 30cm Mirror ball. Video Projector; NEC NP100 2000 lumen Projector. Projection Screen; Matt white front projection screen surface. 9m wide x 5.95m drop.
DRESSING ROOMS; 3, accomm. 20. Iron and ironing board available.
For more information contact Joe Boxshall on joe@jacksonslane.org.uk.

LION & UNICORN PUB THEATRE

42-44 Gaisford Street, Kentish Town, London NW5 2ED
Tek: 0207 267 2304 BO: 08444 771 000
Email: info@lionandunicorntheatre.com
Web Site: www.lionandunicorntheatre.co m
ADMINISTRATION:
Props: Giant Olive Theatre Company Ltd.
Contact: Tamzin Paskins
The Lion actively seeks companies for short and long term theatre productions. Competitive rental rates available.
Capacity: 50

MENIER CHOCOLATE FACTORY

53 Southwark Street, London SE1 1RU
Admin: 020 7378 1712
Email: office@menierchocolatefactory.com
Web Site: www.menierchocolatefactory.c om
ADMINISTRATION:
Artistic Director: David Babani
General Manager: Thomas Siracusa
Associate Producer: Lucy McNally
The Menier Chocolate Factory has been a full time producing house since 2004, and comprises a theatre, restaurant, bar and large rehearsal space.
Capacity: 200

THE MISKIN THEATRE

Oakfield Lane, Dartford, Kent DA1 2JT
Admin: 01322 629 472 BO: 01322 629 422 Fax: 01322 629 469 Tech Tel: 01322 629 492
Email: miskintheatre@nwkcollege.ac.uk
Web Site: www.miskintheatre.co.uk
ADMINISTRATION
Manager: Hannah More
Artistic Director: Robbie McGovan
Stage Manager: Rebecca Cummins
Administrator: Nikki Morre
Policy: In House Theatre, Music and Dance plus suited touring.
Cap: Main Theatre; 160, depending on configuration. Studio Theatre; 120.
Licensed bar and tuckshop.
TECHNICAL:
STAGE: Main Auditorium; 12m X 21.2m with adaptable seating, scene dock, 4.2m x 5.1m door, grid height of 5.3, 17.3m x 10.2m. Studio Space: with 35mm cinema projector and Motorised Full Academy Cinema Projection Screen. Harlequin Activity Sprung Dance Floor in both spaces.
LIGHTING: Strand Light Pallette 72 dimmers, full range of current lamps plus stock of lee filters
SOUND: Mackie SR40/8 mixing desk, full range of equipment including 6 Sennheiser E835 radio mic's, x 2 recording studios, fully fitted with; 32 & 16 channel Sound Craft mixing desk, multi track logic audio recording equipment.
AV: LCD projector (4000 lumens), Video Mixer and Monitors, 2x glass Projector Screens
DRESSING ROOMS: x2, capacity 50 plus, ensuite toilets, sinks and showers
DANCE STUDIOS: Studio 1: 7m x 10m; Mirrors, Barrs 5 channel mixer and CD player; Studio 2: 11m x 9m, Mirrors, Barrs 10 Channel Mixer and CD player; Studio 3: 12m x 9m, Mirror, 6 Channel Mixer and CD player.

OLD RED LION THEATRE CLUB

418 St. John Street, Islington, London EC1V 4NJ
Admin Tel: 020 7833 3053 BO: 0844 412 4307
Email: info@oldredliontheatre.co.uk
Web Site: www.oldredliontheatre.co.uk
ADMINISTRATION:
Managing Director: Helen Devine
Artistic Director: Stewart Pringle

Performance area approx. 20' square.
Policy: New British writing, London Premieres of North American Plays.
Capacity: 60 Theatre Style.
Infomation can be found on the theatre's website: www.oldredliontheatre.co.uk

ORANGE TREE THEATRE

1 Clarence Street, Richmond, Surrey TW9 2SA
Mngt: 020 8940 0141 BO: 020 8940 3633 Fax: 020 8332 0369
Email: admin@orangetreetheatre.co.uk
Web Site: www.orangetreetheatre.co.uk
ADMINISTRATION:
Artistic Director: Paul Miller
Administrative Director: Sarah Nicholson
Stage Manager: Stuart Burgess
Policy: New, classics, revivals, musicals, schools and children's work. All home produced.
Perfs: Mon-Sat 7.45pm, Mats Thursdays 2.30pm, Saturdays 3.00pm.
Seats: 170, fully licensed theatre bar.
TECHNICAL:
Theatre-in-the-round. Stage 4.85m X 5.70m, height to grid 4.75m.
LIGTING: Strand 300 series, 72w of Dimmers, 52 x 650w Profiles, 18 x 650w Fresnels, 6 x 1000w profiles, 16 x 1200w fresnels, 16 x par 64, 6 source 4 par.
SOUND: Soundcraft 12-4-2, 3 power-amps/ 4 Jbl1, 4 misc speakers, Vocal and radio.
OTHER: 2 dressing rooms, green room, shower, wardrobe with Iron, washing machine, dryer.
STAFF: 3 stage, 2 technical,casuals available.

OVAL HOUSE THEATRE

52-54 Kennington Oval, London SE11 5SW
Admin: 020 7582 0080 BO: 020 7582 7680 Fax: 020 7820 0990
Email: info@ovalhouse.com
Web Site: www.ovalhouse.com
ADMINISTRATION:
Props: Christ Church (Oxford) University Clubs
Lessees: C.C.O.U.C.
General Manager: Wendy Dempsey
Email: wendy.dempseyt@ovalhouse.com
Head of Press and Marketing: Debbie Vannozzi
Email: debbie.vannozzi@ovalhouse.com
Policy: New work, emerging companies, women's, lesbian & gay, black and Asian, work relevant to local audiences.
Performance and Rehearsal space.
Two performance spaces, upstairs and downstairs 50 and 100 capacity respectively.New cafe & cabaret space; extra dance studio and rehearsal space.

OXFORD HOUSE THEATRE

Derbyshire Street, Bethnal Green, London E2 6HG
Tel: 020 7739 9001
Email: info@oxfordhouse.org.uk
Web Site: www.oxfordhouse.org.uk
ADMINISTRATION:
Policy: Drama, musical or dance performances and rehearsals.
Theatre Capacity: 120 Theatre Style, 80 Cabaret, 200 Standing.
For more information on hiring the venue, contact Room Bookings on: 020 7739 9001or email: room.bookings@oxfordhouse.org.uk

PEOPLE SHOW

Brady Arts Centre
192-196 Hanbury Street London E1 5HU
Tel: 020 7729 1841
Email: people@peopleshow.co.uk
Web Site: www.peopleshow.co.uk
ADMINISTRATION:
Cap: Seating: 80

PLEASANCE THEATRE

Carpenters Mews, North Road, London N7 9EF
Admin: 020 7619 6868 BO: 020 7609 1800
Email: info@pleasance.co.uk
Web Site: www.pleasance.co.uk
ADMINISTRATION:
Director: Anthony Alderson. Email: anthony@pleasance.co.uk
General Manager: Haimish Morrow
Email: haimish@pleasance.co.uk
Status: National Touring House & Producing Theatre. Designed by Christopher Richardson, this 280 raked, flexible seater is housed in the General Omnibus Company's timber store in Carpenters Mews. Overlooking a cobbled courtyard and the splendid Shillibeer's Brasserie, the venue is run by the same management team as the Pleasance venue at the Edinburgh Festival. The Venue is self financing but we acknowledge the support given to its construction by the National Lottery through the Arts Council of England and the Foundation for Sports and the Arts.
Performances: Tuesdays to Sundays, times vary. Morning, afternoon and evening performances. Bookings: Guarantee and box office split by negotiation.
Policy: Sister theatre, Edinburgh Pleasance, has a reputation for showcasing some of the most imaginative theatre in Europe and providing a breeding ground for a new generation of writers, directors, designers and performers. In London, performances are mainly an invited programme of new writing, classical revivals and musicals. We are also available for conference hire, TV and radio recordings, weddings and parties.
Capacity: 200
1 licensed bar. Facilities and access for the disabled.
For further information on the facilities we have on offer or to arrange a site visit please contact Dan O'Neill at dan@pleasance.co.uk
TECHNICAL:
STAGE: Stage elevated at 220mm, Stage depth 7.8m, Stage width 7.6m, Height from stage to roof beams 4m, Restricted flying height 6.5m, 6m MetScene revolve motor or hand winch driven (detailed specs available on request), 5 Hemp Handline Flying sets, 4 fixed IWB Lighting bars, 1 fixed position bar, Full perimeter blacks available, 4 pairs of 1.2m x 3.9m Black Masking Flats, Access is a 10 rung Zargees. Control room is above the auditorium leading to the technical gantries and dimmers. Get In: The stage is on the first floor of the building with access up two flights of stairs. Large items can be lifted through a set of double doors at stage level.
LIGHTING: Power Supply, Control and Dimming: Zero88 ORB Lighting Desk, 59 ways of Zero 88 Rack 6/ ID12/Beta Pack 2 dimming. 70 Socapex circuits available for gantries and onstage (including IWB's). Lighting bars and technical gantries at 5m. 32amp stage level additional power. Lanterns: 5 x Selecon 1000W cond Profile 24/40, 1 x Selecon 1000W cond Profile 18/34, 2 x Source four Jr Zooms, 2 x Selecon 500W Profiles 24/44, 6 x Selecon 1000W PC, 3 x Selecon 1000W Fresnel, 6 x CCT Starlette 1000W Fresnels, 8 x Patt 734 1000W Fresnel, 8 x Par64 (CP 62 Lamps), 8 x Selecon 500W Fresnel, 8 x Selecon 500W Pc, 4 x Strand Quartet 500w Fresnel, 6 x Pin Spots, 6 x Par 16 Birdies.
SOUND: Soundcraft K1 16+2:4:2 Mixing Desk, 1 x pair D&B 902 loudspeakers, 1 x pair D&B E3 loudspeakers, 1 x D&B P1200L amplifiers, 1 x pair Ohm 300w loudspeakers, 1 x Peavy CS800 amplifier, 1 x Behringer Crossover Unit, 1 x Behringer Effects Unit (used as FOH Delay), 2 x Minidisc players, 1 x Double CD player, 2 x SM58 Microphones, 2 x Fully adjustable Microphone stands, 1 x 2 channel DI. Sound is operated from either the control room above the auditorium or the back left corner of the auditorium
BACKSTAGE FACILITIES: Dressing Rooms; 2. A small stage level dressing room can be made available. Washing machine, tumble dryer and iron.

POLKA THEATRE FOR CHILDREN

240 The Broadway, Wimbledon, London SW19 1SB
Admin: 020 8545 8325 BO: 020 8543 4888
Email: info@polkatheatre.com
Web Site: www.polkatheatre.com
ADMINISTRATION:
Prop: Polka Children's Theatre Ltd.
Artistic Director: Peter Glanville
Email: peter@polkatheatre.com
Head of Finance and Administration: Bernadette Cava
Email: bernadette@polkatheatre.com

Technical Manager: Chris Randall
Email: chris@polkatheatre.com
Policy: Children's Theatre Repertoire and visiting Children's Theatre Companies.
Seats: Main Theatre; 300. Adventure Theatre; 60-70
Children's Restaurant, Exhibitions, Playground.
TECHNICAL:
Proscenium stage. Area: 6.77m width, 6.33m depth. Full details on request.

THE RED HEDGEHOG

255 - 7 Archway Road, Highgate London N6 5BS
Tel: 020 8348 8485 BO: 0208 348 5050
Fax: 020 7900 3350
Email: clare.f@theredhedgehog.co.uk
Web Site: www.theredhedgehog.co.uk
ADMINISTRATION:
Fringe theatre, music and visual arts.
Artistic Director: Clare Fisher
Specialist Events Organiser: Natasha Graham.
Contact: eventhire [AT] theredhedgehog.co.uk
For more information on hiring the venue email: theatrehire@theredhedgehog.co.uk

ROSEMARY BRANCH THEATRE

2 Shepperton Road, London N1 3DT
Bar: 020 7704 2730 Theatre & BO: 020 7704 6665
Email: rosemarybranchtheatre@googlemail.com
Web Site: www.rosemarybranch.co.uk
We present an eclectic mix of drama, opera and music, most suitable for casts of ten or less. Shows usually run for 3 weeks, with tryout slots occasionally available. Straight hire fee, box office splits negotiable. Good local following.
Rehearsal space available.
Capacity: 59, and can take 65 with an extra row at the front.
Contact: Cecilia Darker
Stage area 6m wide by 5.7m. Contact for full technical details.

TABARD THEATRE

2 Bath Road, Turnham Green, Chiswick, London W4 1LW
Tel: 020 8995 6035
Email: info@tabardtheatre.co.uk
Web Site: www.tabardweb.co.uk
ADMINISTRATION:
General Manager: Simon Reilly
Policy: Plays, musicals, comedy gigs, music recitals, workshops and rehearsals.
Capacity: 96

THE AFRICA CENTRE

Richmix Culture Foundation
35-47 Bethnal Green Road London E1 6LA
Tel: 020 7836 1973
Email: info@africacentre.org.uk
Web Site: www.africacentre.org.uk
ADMINISTRATION:
Administrator: Kojo Akuffo

THE BUSH THEATRE

7 Uxbridge Road London W12 8LJ
Admin: 020 8743 3584 BO: 020 8743 5050
Email: info@bushtheatre.co.uk
Web Site: www.bushtheatre.co.uk
ADMINISTRATION:
Leessees: Alternative Theatre Company Ltd Trading as The Bush Theatre
Artistic Director: Madani Younis
Marketing Manager: Lauren Clancy
Technical Manager: Neil Hobbs
Policy: Producing new writing, some receiving of productions.
Perfs: 8.00pm Mon. to Sat.
Seats: Licensed to seat 144. Bar and Buffet in pub.
TECHNICAL:
STAGE: 10m x 7m with a grid height of 3.35m.
LIGHTING: Control is by an ETC Element console with 48 ways of dimming by an Avolites ART 2000 rack. For the most up to date lantern list please contact the production office.
The Bush has rehearsal space, workshops and a small props, costume and furniture store all very close to the theatre.
For enquiries relating to any of the above please contact the production office production@bushtheatre.co.uk

THE COURTYARD THEATRE

Bowling Green Walk, 40 Pitfield Street, London N1 6EU
Tel: 020 7729 2202 BO: 0844 477 1000
Email: info@thecourtyard.org.uk
Web Site: www.thecourtyard.org.uk
ADMINISTRATION:
Co Artistic Directors: June Abbott and Tim Gill
Production Manager: John Bell
Theatres Manager: Rupert Holloway
Venue Manager: Mikel Krumins
Administrator: Joanna Kazmierska
The resident companies, the Court Theatre Company and the Court Theatre Training Company, together with visiting productions present both new and classical works.
Performances usually 8pm. Tuesdays to Sundays.
Capacity: Main Theatre, 150 Seated. Studio, 80 Seated.
Dressing room accommodates 15.
TECHNICAL:
MAIN THEATRE STAGE: Room Size: 7.8m x 20m, Ceiling Height: 4.5m.
STUDIO STAGE: Dance Floor Size: 11.3m x 7.9, Ceiling Height: 3.2m, Room Size: 16.1m x 6.9, Ceiling Height: 3.2m, Stage to ceiling height: 2.4m, Stage Size: 7.6m x 4.7m.
AV EQUIPMENT: Technics SL-PG380A - CD Deck (with Auto-Pause), Yamaha MG-166C-USB - Mixing Desk, Peavey 2600 - Powered Amplifier, 2x BOSE 801 Series II - Professional PA Speakers, Tannoy - Professional Sub-Woofer Unit.
STAGE LIGHTING: Zero88 Jester 12/24, 24 Dimming Channels, 2x Light Processor 1210 Dimension - Dimmer Racks. Lanterns: Theatre can provide general cover plus a range of specials upon request.

THE NEW DIORAMA THEATRE

15-16 Triton Street, Regent's Place, London NW1 3BF
Tel: 020 7419 2000 BO: 020 7383 9034
Hires: 020 7383 9036
Email: hello@newdiorama.com
Web Site: www.newdiorama.com
ADMINISTRATION:
Policy: Theatre, comedy, opera.
To hire the space or to make further enquires please ring the admin line or email: hires@newdiorama.com.
Capacity: 80 Theatre Style. 60 raked.

THE OLD COURTHOUSE

Market Square, Antrim BT41 4AW
Tel: 028 9446 3113
Email: info@antrim.gov.uk
Web Site: www.antrim.gov.uk/oldcourthouse
ADMINISTRATION:
Cultural Services Manager: Gary Shaw
Tel: 028 9448 1338. Email: gary.shaw@antrim.gov.uk
Props: Antrim Borough Council
Capacity: Seated 188

THEATRE 503

The Latchmere,
503 Battersea Park Road, Battersea, London SW11 3BW
BO/Admin: 020 7978 7040
Email: info@theatre503.com
Web Site: www.theatre503.com
ADMINISTRATION:
Artistic Directors: Paul Robinson
Executive Director: Jeremy Woodhouse
Origins: Purpose built above the Latchmere Public House, the theatre opened in 1982.
Policy: Fearless new theatre that pushes at the boundaries of the medium.
Capacity: 63

THEATRO TECHNIS

26 Crowndale Road, London NW1 1TT
Tel: 020 7387 6617
Email: info@theatrotechnis.com
Web Site: www.theatrotechnis.com
ADMINISTRATION:
Director: George Eugeniou
Policy: The studio is available to theatre, film and TV companies, offering a bar and foyer, an amphitheatre performing space, dressing rooms.
Seating Capacity: 105 Fixed, Max 120.
Disabled access for the audience and for the companies.
TECHNICAL:
STAGE: Amphitheatre dimensions: Height

to grid is 3 metres.
Stage area: Length 7 metres; Width 3 metres
LIGHTING: An up to date system with a 72 way 15 Amp Patch Bay, lighting rig that consists of 4 wall bars, 3 main bars (full length of the theatre) and 5 cross bars all mounted on a new grid. A Zero 88 illusion, 120 lighting board and 4 x Zero 88 Betapack Dimmer (8 x 15 amp DMX), 6 x Selection Zoom , Profile Spots and 10 x Acclaim F's all 650W.
SOUND: An up to date system with 4 x Renius-Heinz Qube-12 speakers, a Denon CD player, 2 x Denon Professional Mini-Disc players, an Alesis Midiverb-4, a Mackie 1604 Pro Mixer, a Crown CE series amplifier, a Behringer Ultracurve Pro Digital Graphic Equaliser and a total of 10 Pro-Mics (Audio-technica , Sennheiser) are provided.

TRICYCLE THEATRE

269 Kilburn High Road, London NW6 7JR
Mgt: 020 7372 6611 BO: 020 7328 1000
Fax: 020 7328 0795
Email: info@tricycle.co.uk
Web Site: www.tricycle.co.uk
ADMINISTRATION:
Props: Tricycle Theatre Co. Ltd
Executive Director: Kate Devey
Artistic Director: Indhu Rubasingham
Company Secretary: Trish McElhill
Technical Manager: Shaz McGee
Policy: Presentation of new plays. Adult programme generally for 6-9 week runs. Childrens shows on Saturdays. Plays both by Tricycle Co. and by other production companies.
Seats: 235

UPSTAIRS AT THE GATEHOUSE

The Gatehouse, Highgate Village, London N6 4BD
Manager Tel: 020 8340 3477 BO Tel: 020 8340 3488 Admin: 020 8340 4256
Email: events@ovationproductions.com
Web Site: www.upstairsatthegatehouse.com
ADMINISTRATION:
Upstairs at The Gatehouse is a large London Fringe Theatre situated in a refurbished Victorian Music Hall. It is administered by Ovation Theatres Ltd (020 7387 2342).
Contacts: John and Katie Plews
Policy: Open. New plays, revivals and occasional one-off cabaret and comedy nights. Ideal for Festival previews.
Terms: Rental, Box office splits or Co-productions.
Capacity: Theatre style: 128 (on three sides). Cabaret: 140 using a combination of tiered seating and pub style tables and chairs.
Location: Junction of Hampstead Lane and North Road, N6. Nearest tube: Highgate, Buses: 143, 214, 210, 271.
Easy street parking.
TECHNICAL:
STAGE: Thrust stage with audience seated on three sides. Tiered seating in blocks of 74/27/27. Playing area 8.7m wide x 5.8m deep. Height to grid 4.35m. No rake. No flying facilities. Crossover behind tabs. Theatre situated on first floor, no lift, wide staircase. Doors to stage 1.8m wide, 2m high. Four Alistage 8'x4' units available with 16 x 200mm, 16 x 400mm, 8 x 600mm and 8 x 800mm legs. Three front projection screens: 72" x 54" (1829 x 1372mm), 80" x 60" (2032 x 1524mm), 96" x 72" (2438 x 1829mm).
LIGHTING: Fat Frog lighting board (48 way with memory) 72 outlets, 48 way mini racks. Operator position above stage right on Gallery. No follow spots. On Extras List: Two moving disco lights, Rotaflash police lights (3), Fibre Optic Star Cloth with seperate control unit, Mirror Ball and one speed motor
SOUND: Soundcraft Spirit 4 12 + 2:4:2 desk. Excellent acoustics for spoken word and musicals. Operator position above stage right on Gallery. Extras: Foldback system (amp and two JBL speakers), Radio mics (4 x Trantec S4000), 4 x Yamaha Hydraulic Easy Grip.
STAGE MANAGEMENT: No prompt corner. Headsets available. Show relay to Dressing Room / Box Office.
BACKSTAGE FACILITIES: Good size dressing room with hanging space, accommodates 8 - 10. 2 toilets, 2 hand wash basins and a fridge. Iron and ironing board. Washing Machine & Tumble Dryer.
ADDITIONAL: No construction or painting facilities. Small kitchen for tea / coffee etc. Good pub food and cheap drinks downstairs.

WACARTS

Hampstead Town Hall Centre
213 Haverstock Hill, London NW3 4QP
Tel: 020 7692 5800 Events: 020 7692 5809
Email: events@wacarts.co.uk
Web Site: www.wacarts.co.uk
ADMINISTRATION:
Events Manager: Craig Huxley
Email: craig.huxley@wacarts.co.uk
Cap: Council Chamber Room 120, Main Hall 250, Smaller Hall 120 Standing. Dance Studios and smaller rooms available to hire.

WIMBLEDON STUDIO

The Broadway Wimbledon London SW19 1QG
Mgmt/SD Tel: 020 8545 7900 BO: 0844 871 7646 Fax: 020 8543 6637
Email: wimbledonadmin@theambassadors.com
Web Site: www.atgtickets.com/wimbledon
Exciting fringe venue located in the New Wimbledon Theatre.
Capacity: 50-80 seats
Executive General Manager: Callum Kemp
Technical Manager: Stuart Graham

THE WORKHOUSE THEATRE

242 Pentonville Road London N1 9JY
Tel: 020 7837 6030
Email: acting@thepoorschool.com
Web Site: www.thepoorschool.com
ADMINISTRATION:
Contact: Paul Caister
Seating: 50 - 80 max. Licensed.

YAA ASANTEWAA ARTS AND COMMUNITY CENTRE

1 Chippenham Mews, London W9 2AN
Tel: 020 7286 1656
Email: admin@yaaasantewaa.com
Web Site: www.yaaasantewaa.com
ADMINISTRATION:
Community arts and social centre, providing cultural, artistic, educational and recreational activities relevant to the needs of the local population.
TECHNICAL:
Small studio theatre (60 seats) with adequate light and sound. Large hall for music show, cabarets. Seats 200 with adequate lighting and sound, also disabled access.

YORK HOUSE

Richmond Road, Twickenham, Middlesex TW1 3AA
Tel: 020 8831 6108 Fax: 020 8891 7939
Email: halls@richmond.gov.uk
Web Site: www.richmond.gov.uk
ADMINISTRATION:
Props: London Borough of Richmond on Thames.
Large Hall, with stage facilities. Contact the Lettings Office for venue hire.
Capacity: Clarendon Hall - 250 Theatre Style, 150 Banquet;
Hyde Room- 60 Dinner, 70 Theatre Style.

PROVINCIAL VENUES

Abercynon, Mid Glamorgan

ABERCYNON SPORTS CENTRE
Parc Road, Abercynon, Mid Glamorgan CF45 4UY Wales
Admin/Mgt: 01443 740 141 Admin/Mgt Fax: 01443 743 000
Email: brent.bennett@rhondda-cynon-taff.gov.uk
Web: www.rhondda-cynon-taff.gov.uk
ADMINISTRATION:
Props: Rhondda Cynon Taff County Borough Council
Manager: Brent Bennett
Capacity: Main Hall - 600 (function room setup); Hall 2 - 190.
Total Capacity: 790

Aberdare, Mid Glamorgan

Pop: 64,500. Newspapers: Western Mail (daily); Cynon Valley Leader (weekly). Local commercial radio: Red Dragon. Local television station: HTV Wales. STD Code 01685

THE COLISEUM
Mount Pleasant Street, Trecynon, Aberdare, Mid Glamorgan CF44 8NG Wales
Mgt: 01685 882 380 BO: 08000 147111
Email: adrian.p.williams@rctcbc.gov.uk
Web Site: www.rct-arts.co.uk
ADMINISTRATION
Props: Rhondda Cynon Taff County Borough Council
Policy: Mixed Programme
Seats: 588 (seated).
TECHNICAL:
STAGE: Proscenium stage, very slight rake. Pros. opening 7.8m; Width (wall to wall 9.9m; Depth (Iron to back wall) 5.85m; Fore-stage Depth 2.85m; Height (below flyfloor) 6.6m. Flying system; 5 x winch bars, 12 x hemp bars.
LIGHTING: Switchboard: Strand Lightboard (72 way, with 24 submasters, and 199 memories); Strand Act-6 Dimmers - 72 channels in all.
SOUND: Desk; Allen & Heath SC series 16:4:2 - feeding Left/centre/right clusters. 1 Denon DRM 510 cassette deck. 1 Yamaha CDX550E CD player.
BACKSTAGE FACILITIES: Dressing Rooms: 3, Accom. seating 27. 2 Showers, orchestra pit 24.
ADDITIONAL: 35 mm full projection facilities. Bar/Function Rooms. Car parking for 75 cars adjacent to theatre.

MICHAEL SOBELL SPORTS CENTRE
The Ynys, Aberdare, Mid Glamorgan CF44 7RP Wales
Admin/Mgt Tel: 01685 870 111
Email: mark.griffiths@rctcbc.gov.uk
ADMINISTRATION
Props: Rhondda Cynon Taf County Borough Council
Capacity: 1,250-1,500 (Stage available)

Aberdeen, Aberdeenshire

Pop 204,000. London 543 miles. Newspapers: Evening Express (ntly); The Press & Journal (dly). Local commercial radio: Northsound. Local television station: Grampian. STD Code 01224

ABERDEEN EXHIBITION & CONFERENCE CENTRE
Exhibition Avenue, Bridge of Don, Aberdeen AB23 8BL Scotland
Tel: 01224 824 824 Fax: 01224 825 276
Email: aecc@aecc.co.uk
Web Site: www.aecc.co.uk
ADMINISTRATION:
Props: Aberdeen Exhibition & Conference Centre Ltd
Managing Director: Brian Horsburgh
PR Manager: Victoria Withy
For bookings contact: Sales Department.
Policy: Modern complex used for concert, sporting and arena events, conferences and exhibitions.
Capacity: 4,700 seated; 8,500 standing.
TECHNICAL:
Electrical: 300, 200 and 100 amp 3 phase supplies . Also single phase.
Access: 5m x 5m shutter door from car park direct into arena. Fork lift on site.
Staging, lighting, backstage, arrangements according to requirements.
Excellent flying capability.

HIS MAJESTY'S THEATRE
Rosemount Viaduct, Aberdeen AB25 1GL Scotland
Mgt: 01224 337 650 BO: 01224 641 122
SD: 01224 337 650 Fax: 01244 337 690
Email: info@aberdeenperformingarts.com
Web Site: www.hmtheatre.com
ADMINISTRATION:
Props: Aberdeen Performing Arts
Head of Operations: Martin Latham
Email: martin.latham@aberdeenperformingarts.com
Chief Executive: Jane Spiers
Head of Corporate Services: Gary Craig
Head of Customer Servuces, Sales & Marketing: Lynne Hackett
Policy: Opera, Ballet, Plays, Summer Revues, Pantomime and Touring.
Perfs: Variable.
Cap: 1,446. Two Bars. Cafe & Restaurant.
TECHNICAL:
Contact graeme.shepherd@aberdeenperformingarts.com or greig.dempster@aberdeenperformingarts.com for new tech. specs. & plans.

MUSIC HALL
Union Street, Aberdeen AB10 1QS Scotland
Mgt: 01224 632 080 BO: 01224 641 122
Fax: 01224 632 400
Email: doug.taylor@aberdeenperformingarts.com
Web Site: www.boxofficeaberdeen.com
ADMINISTRATION:
Props: Aberdeen Performing Arts
Programming Manager: Doug Taylor
Senior Technician: Dougie Hay
Email: dougie.hay@aberdeenperformingarts.com
For all hiring enquires, please contact the Programme Manager: Doug Taylor (Tel: 01224 337 662)
Director of Marketing and Communications: Lauren Taylor
Policy: Multi purpose auditorium, concerts,exhibitions and conferences. Full license and full catering facilities.
Main Hall capacity: Stalls 1000 standing; 775 seated; Balcony 506
The Music Hall has a room for hire for meetings, seminars, training courses and market research.
Capacity: 50 - theatre style.
TECHNICAL:
STAGE:
Permanent with wooden surface and a rake of approx 1 in 40
13.6m wide at front (17.8m max.) x 10.6m deep x 1.4m high Clearance 13.6m (ie Stage to Ceiling). Designed for a superimposed loading of 5.0kN/m2.
DRAPES: 8 x Sico multi-height (max. 4.2m) black drape frame, 2 x black tab each 6m x 9.1m, 2 x sound drape each 9.1m x 3m. ROSTRA: Sico 1.2m x 2.4m rostra with treads and guardrails: 20 x 77cm or 97cm high, 8 x 37cm or 57cm high, 6 x 27cm or 42cm high
HOUSE BARS/GROUND SUPPORT: House bars each, 13 x 2.5kW circuits, per bar, max capacity 300kg. FOH bar 5.4m from downstage edge, 12m long. Bar 1 = 60cm down stage from stage line, 12m long. Bar 2 is 3.1m upstage 14m long. Bar 3 is 7.45m upstage, 14m long. Drape Bar 200kg 8.35m upstage 12m long. max flying height 13m from stage. 2 booms on balcony with 5 x 2.5k circuits each. 4 dips on stage with 6 x 2.5k circuits each. All outlets are 15 Amp.

6 x FLYING STRONG POINTS 1 TON EACH POINT. 2 x upstage, 7.95m upstage, 10.75m between points. 2 x midstage, 4.4m upstage, 10.5m between points. 2 x advanced 2m from stage line, 10.5m between points. SOUND FLYING POINTS 750kg x2. On stage line 4 x 400kg chain hoists. 2 x points per side 1.5m apart
Stalls floor designed for a superimposed loading of 5.0kN/m2.
POWER: Stage: General Single phase, 230V, 13A. Lighting: 3 phase, 415V, 125A. 3 phase, 415V, 63A. 3 phase, 415V, 32A. Single phase, 230V, 32A. 4 x Single phase, 230V, 16A.
Sound: 3 phase, 415V, 63A. 3 phase, 415V, 32A. Single phase, 230V, 63A. 2 x Single phase, 230V, 16A. 13A sockets are distributed around the stage with lighting and sound power located under Stage Right. 13A or CEEform connectors - NO bare ends, lugs or camlocks. RCD protection is essential
Power will be cut automatically on activation of the Fire Alarm.
LIGHTING:
Follow spot; 2 x Pani HMI 1200 (platform in each corner of rear balcony). Lighting house rig; 72 x 1K Parcan, 2 x 2.5K Stand Alto 14/32 profile, 4 x 2K Strand 19/32 Cadenza profile, 4 x 1K Strand Cadenza profile, 16 x 2K Strand nocturne flood, 6 x 2k Strand Alto F fresnel, 10 x Martin Mac 600 NT (E) - (by request only).
Control; Avolite Sapphire 2000, Strand Permus dimmers - 76 x 2.5K & 8 x 5K, 2 x Zero 88, Demux 48.
See 'House Bars / Ground Support' section above
SOUND:
4 x JBL 4892 mid / high speakers (2 flown per side), 6 x JBL 4892 mid / high speakers, 2 x JBL 4893 bass speakers, 4 x C-Audio SR707, 3 x C-Audio SR606, C-Audio SR404, 2 x C-Audio EQ312, C-Audio EQ311, 2 x JBL system controller dBx 166 limiter, BSS TCS-803 time corrector, 4 x JBL MR series monitors, Yamaha 03D, Ashley Stereo 6 band para EQ, Ashley 4 Ch noise gate, Yamaha SPX90, Denon CD player / recorder, Denon cassette deck, 6 x Shure SM58, Shure SM57, 2 x AKG C568, AKG D12, 2 x Beyer CK703, 3 x Shure UHF SM87, 2 x Shure UHF Tie clip, EMO DI boxes, 10 x long boom stands, 3 x short boom stands, 4 x small table top stands.

Abergavenny, Monmouthshire

Pop: 12,500 (Catchment 30,000). London 147 miles. Nespapers: Abergavenny Chronicle. STD Code 01873

BOROUGH THEATRE

Cross Street, Abergavenny,
Monmouthshire NP7 5HD Wales
Mgt: 01873 735 830 BO: 01873 850 805
Tech: 01873 735824
Email: boroughtheatre@monmouthshire.gov.uk
Web Site: www.boroughtheatreabergavenny.co.uk
ADMINISTRATION:
Theatre Manager: Nick Banwell
Technical Manager: Nathan Long
Email:
nathanlong@monmouthshire.gov.uk
Marketing Department: Lynsey Wheeler / Marion Morden
Status: Bricks and Mortar. Theatre situated on top (3rd) floor of town hall, built late 1800s, renovated 1990, central local.
Venue funded by Monmouth County Council. RAA Arts Council of Wales.
Policy: All forms of music, dance, drama and opera. Can negotiate fees, split, first call etc. Theatre not available for hire to commercial managements. Non-performance activities: Occasional functions, exhibitions and conferences.
Capacity: Seating 338; raked cinema seats. Catering, Bar and light refreshments available.
Access car park: adjacent, nearest railway station: 1 mile, nearest coach terminal: 5 mins' walk, bus routes: local buses.
For the disabled 5 wheelchair spaces - deaf loop system - lift - assistance available contact box office- parking - level access - all house facilities fully accessible except bar.

For details on hiring the Theatre to local amateur performance groups and to organisations based in Monmouthshire for fundraising events, contact the Theatre Manager, Nick Banwell on 01873 735 830 or email: boroughtheatre@monmouthshire.gov.uk
TECHNICAL:
STAGE: Dimensions; Procenium Opening 8.6m. Depth from tab line to rear wall 6.7m. Depth of apron 1.5m. Depth of stage left wing 1.4m. Depth of stage right wing 1.5m. Rigging and Staging: 2 lx bars front of house with 6 ways of patching on each bar, 3 lx bars on stage with 12 ways of patching on each bar, 4 lx perch positions (2 stage left and 2 stage right) with 6 ways of patching on each perch, 6 boom bases and 2m scaffold, 2 t bar lighting stands, various number of floor stands available, 7 fly bars controlled on electric winches on stage (max load 125kg per bar) recommended depth of clothes if flown should not be more that 18ft, 1 tallescope and 1 'a' frame ladder for focusing on stage, 1 extending ladder for focusing front of house, 1 starcloth, 1 cyclorama, 3 triple 'e' wipe tracks, 2 sets of black tabs and tracks for their use, 2 pairs of black legs and 2 pairs of white legs, 1 set of house tabs, numerous stage braces, 19 stage weights, 12 8ft x 3ft staging units in heights of 1ft, 18" and 2ft high (4 units of each), 1 pretrof grand piano, 1 jem techno smoke machine.
Orchestra Pit: The front 2 rows of stalls seating are removed. the pit is approx 1ft below the next level of seating.
Accommodates 14 max. 14 rat stands and 1 petrof upright piano available on request.
LIGHTING: Lantern Stock; martin mac250+ moving lanterns x 4, 1.2kw cantata 18/32 profiles x 12, 650w prelude 16/30 profiles x 9, 575w source 4 jnr profiles 25/50 x 6, 650w prelude fresnels x 12, 650w quartet fresnels x 40, 1kw thomas parcans x 24, 1kw thomas floor cans x 2, 500w coda 4 floods x 4, 500w coda 3 floods x 3, 2kw robert juliet 'margot' follow spots x 2, various lengths of 13amp and 15amp cables and 2 way adaptors. Control: ETC Congor INR lighting console. This includes the fader wing of 2 x 20 faders. Strand act 6 d54 dimmers x 5. Zero 88 chilli 24-10i dimmers x 2. Total number of dimming chanels available - 78.
SOUND: FOH: 1 allen & heath gl2200 40 channel mixing console, 3 bss opal 31 band graphic equalizers, 2 drawmer dl241xlr dual compressors, 1 yamaha spx2000 multi effects processor, 1 denon dcd825 cd players, 1 sony mini disk players. Amplification and speakers: 2 turbosound txd-118 single 18" bass speakers, 6 turbosound txd-151 15" loudspeakers, 4 turbosound txd 12m floor monitors, 3 turbosound t1000 mc2 power amps 500wpc/4ohm (2 for monitors 1 for foh), 1 turbosound lms-d4 tq310-315 controller, 1 turbosound t2000 mc2 amplifer 2x1000w microphones, cables and stands, 15 shure sm58-lc microphones, 6 shure sm57-lc microphones, 1 set of sure drum microphones, 2 akg se300b & ck91 combination microphones, 16 beyerdynamic gst500 tall boom mic stands, 6 beyerdynamic gst590 short boom mic stands, 3 emo d.i boxes, 200m of speaker cable in various lengths, 150m of microphone cable in 10m lengths, 1 30m 24 send 8 return multicore. A small sound system available containing allen & heath gl2 mixer, a pair of jbl4716a speakers, a pair of peavey hisys monitor, cs400 amplifier and a jbl mpa400 amplifier.
STAGE COMMUNICATIONS: Full paging facilities from stage right to dressing room 1, 2 and corn exchange with full show relay in operation. Full intercom facilities with outlets at stage left x 2, stage right x 2, orchestra pit, rear of balcony (left, centre and right), rear of stalls (centre) and conrol box.
BACKSTAGE FACILITIES: Dressing Rooms, 2, with wash basin and toilets available in both. The corn exchange room also available on 1st floor, with toilet facilites.

Aberlour, Morayshire

FLEMING HALL
Queens Road, Aberlour, Morayshire AB38 9PR Scotland
Tel: 01340 871 853 Mob: 07765 503 414
ADMINISTRATION:
Props: The Aberlour Community Association
Cap: Seated 180; Dancing 128
Contact Hall Secretary: Mrs Pamela Winchester, 128 High Street, Aberlour, AB38 9NX

SPEYSIDE COMMUNITY CENTRE
Mary Avenue, Aberlour, Morayshire AB38 9QN Scotland
Tel/Fax: 01340 871 641
Email: grant.gallagher@moray.gov.uk
Web Site: www.moray.gov.uk
ADMINISTRATION:
The Moray Council, High Street, Elgin, Morayshire IV30 1BX
Props: Moray Council
For bookings contact Grant Gallagher
Function Room Cap: 300 seated.
Available for hire. Mainly used for theatre or music performances.

Aberystwyth,Ceredigion
Pop: 10,650. London 212 miles.
Newspapers: Cambrian News (wed). STD Code 01970

ABERYSTWYTH ARTS CENTRE
Penglais, Aberystwyth, Ceredigion SY23 3DE Wales
Tel: 01970 622 882 BO: 01970 623 232
Stage Mgr: 01970 628774 Fax: 01970 622 883
Email: gar21@aber.ac.uk
Web Site: www.aberystwythartscentre.co.uk
ADMINISTRATION:
Props: University of Wales, Aberystwyth
Director: Gareth Lloyd Roberts
Administrator: Maris Davies
Technical Manager: Nick Bache (Tel: 01970 628774)
Email: nbb@aber.ac.uk
Front of House Manager: Auriel Martin
Policy: Drama, Ballet, Concerts, Recitals, Exhibitions, Courses, conferences and Films plus special events.
Touring professionals/local amateurs. Arts Centre comprises Theatr Y Werin (321 seats) plus Concert Hall (900 seats), Art Galleries, 100 Seat Studio, Cinema, and 3 Dance Studios.
TECHNICAL:
Theatr Y Werin
STAGE: open end or proscenium, flat with thrust or Orchestra Pit. Pros. opening 14.6m/12.7/11.0/9.75m; Ht. of Pros. and fly floors 6m; distance between fly floors 11m; Depth of Stage from Pros 8.93m (with thrust 12.9m); Ht to Grid 15.4m; 22 lines C/W double purchases; Bars 9.5m; Prompt Cnr. S.L. or rear auditorium.
LIGHTING: Switchboard: Rank Strand Gemini 2 rear auditorium.
OTHER: Dressing Rooms 6; Accom. 21; Chorus Room Accom. 30; 2 Shower suites.

Accrington, Lancashire

HYNDBURN SPORTS CENTRE
Henry Street, Church, Accrington, Lancashire BB5 4EP
Tel/ Fax: 01254 385 945
Email: hyndburn@leisure.co.uk
Web Site: www.hyndburnleisure.co.uk
ADMINISTRATION
Props: Hyndburn Leisure
Sports Hall Cap: 1,200
Manager: Steve Canti

OSWALDTWISTLE CIVIC THEATRE
Union Road, Oswaldtwistle, Accrington, Lancashire BB5 3DF
Tel: 01254 380295 BO: 01254 380293
Email: kerry.smith@hyndburnleisure.co.uk
Web Site: www.hyndburnentertainment.com
Contact: Kerry Smith
Capacity: 470

TOWN HALL
Blackburn Road, Accrington, Lancashire BB5 1LA
Bookings Tel: 01254 380 293
Email: kerry.smith@hyndburnleisure.co.uk
Web Site: www.hyndburnentertainment.com
ADMINISTRATION
Props: Hyndburn Leisure
Capacity: 400
Hall Bookings Officers: Kerry Smith, Judith Singleton
The venue is available to hire by businesses, charity groups, voluntary groups and private individuals for a variety of uses. Rooms can be booked either individually or in any combination to suit.
Capacities and uses:
- THE BALLROOM:
400 Theatre style for Concerts, Seminars
180 Dinner Dances (large circular tables & dance floor)
200 Dances (small casual tables & dance floor)
200 Fashion Show (2 catwalk sizes: 28' x 12' or 28' x 8')
Wedding Receptions: Up to 240 depending on layout style
- THE SUPPER ROOM: Can be used in conjunction with the Ballroom for larger events or on its own. 60 Theatre style for lectures, meetings, seminars & training. 50 Café style for a more casual layout suitable for informal meetings and fundraising activities. 30 Boardroom layout for meetings, seminars & training.
- THE CONFERENCE ROOM: 40 Theatre style for lectures, meetings, seminars & training. 24 Café style for a more casual layout suitable for informal meetings and fundraising activities
22 Boardroom layout for meetings, seminars & training.
THE COUNCIL CHAMBER: 60 The fixed seating is set with a long top table facing tables & chairs in a semi-circular arrangement.

Aldeburgh, Suffolk
Pop 2,670. London 97 miles. STD Code 01728

SNAPE MALTINGS CONCERT HALL
Aldeburgh Music and Britten-Pears Young Artist Programme
Aldeburgh Music, Snape Maltings Concert Hall, Snape, Suffolk IP17 1SP
Mgt Tel: 01728 687 100 BO Tel: 01728 687 110 Fax: 01728 687 120
Email: enquiries@aldeburgh.co.uk
Web Site: www.aldeburgh.co.uk
ADMINISTRATION:
Props: Aldeburgh Music
Chief Executive: Roger Wright
Policy: Concerts, Opera, Ballet, Master Classes,
Jazz/Folk/Dance.
Seating: 827 (280 on level rows A-K; 547 raked rows L-ZF). Catering: Restaurant overlooking River Alde and marshes, special parties catered for, full bar. Ticket outlets: Aldeburgh Box Office, telephone (01728) 451500. Access car park: on site, nearest railway station: Saxmundham, 4 miles; nearest coach terminal: Saxmundham, 4 miles; bus routes: 081 Aldeburgh-London. For the disabled: 6 wheelchair spaces - parking - level access - lifts to the bar and restaurant. Other facilities: Rehearsal rooms, practice studios, seminar room.
TECHNICAL:
Stage: End Stage. Performing area 17.68m wide x 12.2m deep x 6.1m (height at sides). Stage can be raked (jack system for raking stage, understage) - floor gurjun strip, suitable for dance, lino available, no crossover, stage heated. No tab track - 200kg permitted on 7 bars - maximum flying height 6.1m - black and brown masking. 6 single RCD 13A sockets. Forestage 14.63m x 2.7m, 2 entrances. Orchestra pit accommodates 50 in forestage and understage area. Get-in via SL side - height 2.3m x width 2.3m. Tallescope. Scale stage and light-

ing plans available.
Lighting: 5 winched trusses (Max. 540kg each). Desk - Strand 503i, 350 channels, 250 attributes. Dimmers: 192. Lanterns: 103 various.
Sound: Recording room and comprehensive mic. sockets and tie lines for recording and editing - sound reinforcement system by prior arrangement. Acoustics ideally suitable for music.
Stage Management: Show relay& calls to dressing rooms, portable SM desk with Q lights and calls, video patching system.
Backstage: 10 dressing rooms, 2 chorus rooms, 1 wardrobe room, access by artist's entrance - green room/band room - double socket in each dressing room.
Refreshments by arrangement with caterers. Advice given on accommodation.
Staff - 2 stage - casuals available - no security personnel. Backstage facilities not fully accessible to disabled performers and staff. Additional Information:
Chamber Organ: Hindmarsh, built 1971; transposing keyboard (A = 415 and A = 440), tracker action, 6 speaking stops, 1 manual, 336 pipes, very good condition.
2 Steinway D Grand pianos also available.

Aldershot, Hampshire

Pop: Rushmoor 81,400. London 36 miles. Newspapers: Aldershot News and Mail; Star. STD Code 01252

PRINCES HALL

Princes Way, Aldershot, Hampshire GU11 1NX
Admin: 01252 327 671 BO: 01252 329 155 Fax: 01252 320 269
Email: sian.alden@rushmoor.gov.uk
Web Site: www.princeshall.com
ADMINISTRATION:
Props. Rushmoor Borough Council
General Manager: David F Phillips
Email: david.phillips@rushmoor.gov.uk
Marketing: Edward Haversham
Email:
edward.haversham@rushmoor.gov.uk
Senior Technician: Kevin Andrew.
Contact: 01252 327 671 or
kevin.andrew@rushmoor.gov.uk
Policy: One night stands, concerts - m.o.r., variety, middle range pop, ballet, opera, amateurs, conferences, rallies, exhibitions, children's entertainment and pantomime.
Perfs: Usually 8p.m., but by arrangement.
Seats: 600. Fully licensed bars.
For hall hire contact:
amanda.stallard@rushmoor.gov.uk
TECHNICAL:
STAGE: Soft proscenium stage; Flat wooden floor; Pros. opening variable up to 15.24 metres; Pros. Height 4.57 metres; Depth of sight line 6.10 metres; Height of grid 7.32 metres; Stage depth 6.40 metres; 5 x 12 metre long hemp lines - 5 line bars; 5 x PCMs Unibar 12 metre motorised standard plain aluminium barrels; 3 x manually operated hand winch with 12 metre 12 way 15 amp IWB for in-house lighting equipment only.
Apron blocks 10 x 1.22 meters x 1.22 metres (always used unless required to be removed). Rostra blocks available on request in the following sizes: 10 x 2ft high by 8ft by 4ft, 3 x 1ft high by 8ft by 4ft. Extension option on 5 of the 2ft high blocks can go up to 3ft high. Get In/Access; Main access area at rear of the building. Level access onto a large lift going to main hall and stage levels. Lift is 2m27(7½ft) wide x 3m34 (11ft)death. Door height 3m57 (11ft 9).
LIGHTING: Control; 1 x Avolites Peal running 2004 software with two strings of DMX (1) 5pin (2) 3pin. Fully dimmable house lights controlled through the above lighting desk. Dimming; 120 channels of 10 amp Zero 88 Chilli Pro dimmers; 6 channels of 20 amp Zero; 88 Chilli Pro dimmers (1 hard wired for the house lights); 3 x 6 way Zero 88 Beta pack2 - DMX available if required. FOH; Advance 3 metre LX bar (1 way + 1 Indi); Fixed 16 metre truss (25 ways in centre 12 metres + Indi); Horizontal Side SR & SL Slips (3 ways each side); Booms SR & SL (6 ways each side); Apron Truss (8 ways + 2 Indi). Stage; LX 1 Hand Winch (12 ways); LX 2 Hand Winch (12 ways); LX 3 Hemp bar (6 ways); LX 4 Hand Winch (18 ways); SL Rear wall Dips (6 ways); SR Rear wall Dips (6 ways); Dips Through traps in floor (7 ways paired across stage). Effects lighting; 4 x Source flame effects; 1 x Strobe with variable output; 1 x 18" mirror ball Fixed in FOH position. Various Followspots, fresnels, and pars available.
SPECIAL EFFECTS; 2 x Antari Z 3000 haze machine, 1 x Unique Haze machine. - DMX, 1 x Antari Z - 80 smoke machine, 1 x Magnum Pro 2000 Smoke machine. - DMX, 1 x Antari snow machine, 2 x Source Glacier low fog machines. - DMX, 3 x High out put source bubble machines, 1 x 2 way Pyro System. Inc: 4 x Single flat basic pyro pods, 1 x Large angle pyro pod.
SOUND: 1 x 24 channel Alen & Heath GL2200 desk with 2 way monitor mix, 1 x 16 channel sound mixer with 2 aux sends & returns, 2 x Sound lab Graphic EQ units - Speq 131, 2 x LTO 4 way Compressors - CLE4.0, 1 x Yamaha SPX 90 Special FX unit amps, 2 x Soundlab SP8 amp, 1 x Soundlab SP12 amp, 1 x Jucie amp, 1 x Behringer suppressor - DE200, 1 x Behringer feedback destroyer DSP1100. 4 x Soundlab monitors. 150 w. Speakers; 2 x TOA monitors. 240 w, 6 x Bose 802's speakers. Plus Bose Control Units, 2 x Bose bass bins. Plus Bose Control Units.
Playback Media: 2 x Phillips CD player's - CD610 & AK630, 3 x Sony Mini disk recorder/players, 1 x Yamaha single deck tape recorder/players - K 340, 1 x Kenwood single deck tape recorder/players - KX 550hx, 4 x DI boxes.
DRESSING ROOMS: 5; Accomm 40. All dressing rooms have fitted mirrors, mirror lights and fitted sinks. Green Room - Same level as the stage, has an iron, ironing board, fridge, kettle and microwave oven.

Alloa, Clackmannanshire

ALLOA TOWN HALL

Marshill, Alloa, Clackmannanshire FK10 1AB Scotland
Tel/Fax: 01259 216 904
Email: smorrison@clacks.gov.uk
Web Site: www.clacksleisure.co.uk
ADMINISTRATION:
Props: Clackmannanshire Council
Bookings Officer: Stephen Morrison
Cap: Concert 500; Dance (without tables) 300; Dance (with tables) 192; Cabaret 192; Fashion Show (with catwalk) 420.
For bookings tel: 01259 213131 Fax: 01259 721313
Fully fitted and well equipped kitchen is located off the main hall. A fully fitted and furnished bar is located on the first floor. Also available for functions is the Tommy Downs Room.
TECHNICAL:
Hall 19.5m x 14.6m. Stage 9m x 9m fitted with modern computerised stage lighting, house lights and modern sound equipment all of which are operated by the council's own technicians at an additional cost. There are 4 modern and well equipped dressing rooms together with toilet and shower facilities.

BOWMAR COMMUNITY CENTRE

Scott Crescent, Alloa, Clackmannanshire FK10 1BT Scotland
Tel: 01259 215 150
Email: info@clacksleisure.co.uk
Web Site: www.clacksleisure.co.uk
ADMINISTRATION:
Props: Clackmannanshire Leisure
For bookings enquiries, contact the library on Tel: 01259 213 131
Bookings Officer: Francis McClaren
Lounge area & kitchen with coffee bar. Large and small committee rooms, small hall, medium hall with stage, large sports hall.
Cap: 130

Alsager, Cheshire

CIVIC CENTRE

Lawton Road, Alsager, Stoke-on-Trent, South Cheshire ST7 2AE
01270 879 711
Email: pamevans@congleton.gov.uk
Web Site: www.congleton.gov.uk
ADMINISTRATION:
Props: Congleton Borough Council

Capacity: Concert 360 Banquet 200, Dance 180 + Access for disabled persons.
For bookings contact Mrs Pam Evans.
Main Hall with stage, bar, lounge and meeting room, kitchen etc.

Altrincham, Cheshire

Pop: 41,140. London 178 miles.
Newspapers: Sale & Altrincham Messenger (thurs). STD Code 0161

ALTRINCHAM LEISURE CENTRE

Oakfield Road, Altrincham, Cheshire WA15 8EW
Tel: 0161 926 3255
Email: jonathan.francis@traffordleisure.co.uk
Web Site: www.traffordleisure.co.uk
Centre Manager: Jonathan Francis
Large arena available for functions, concerts, theatre productions and sports events.
Available on request.

GARRICK PLAYHOUSE

Barrington Road, Altrincham, Cheshire WA14 1HZ
BO: 0161 928 1677 Option 1 Mktg: 0161 925 5133 Theatre Manager Tel: 0161 925 5133 Fax: 0161 928 7407
Email: admin@altrinchamgarrick.co.uk
Web Site: www.altrinchamgarrick.co.uk
ADMINISTRATION:
Administrators: Neville Roby
Theatre Manager: Neville Roby
Email: n.roby@altrinchamgarrick.co.uk
Policy: Repertory
Perfs: Mon. to Sat. 7.30. Seats 401.
Public Bar and Coffee Bar; Private Bar.
Seats: 401
TECHNICAL:
Stage: Proscenium Stage, Flat; Pros. Opening 9.14m; Ht. of Pros. 4.57m; Depth of S/Line 7.92m; Ht. of Grid 6.50m; 24 Flying lines; Prompt Cnr. P.S.
Lighting: Eurolight Applause computerised lighting desk. 100 channels of dimming. 3 LX bars over stage. Side & Cyclorama lighting available. 70 Channels on stage. 30 Channels F.O.H. A vast variety of lanterns - in excess of 100. 2 x 1kw F/Spots in control box.
Sound Equip: Seck12:8 mixer. Open Reel, cartridge & cassette machines. Amps 2 x Quad 405. 2 x Quad 202 and others. F.O.H. speakers Martin CX2. Foldback stage Pro-Ac Stabs. 12 mic lines to box. Various mic inc 5 x Sennheiser 803. Beyer M201. AKG D190. Live musicals can be mixed from rear of auditorium.
Studio Theatre: Rear rehearsal room (35' x 25') can double as a 50 seater studio theatre. Please discuss your requirements with the administrators. Any technical queries can be answered by the stage director. Extra equipment can be hired in to suit.
A full size theatre run entirely by amateurs and its membership. Employing professional producers and workshop staff, box office, marketing director, bar steward.

Alva, Clackmannanshire

COCHRANE HALL

West Stirling Street, Alva, Clackmannanshire FK12 5LJ Scotland
Tel: 01259 760 208 Bkg: 01259 213 131
Fax: 01259 721 313
Email: leisurebookings@clacks.gov.uk
Web Site: www.clacksweb.org.uk
ADMINISTRATION:
Props: Clackmannanshire Council
Cap: Concert 300; Dinner Dance 180; Public Dance (without tables) 300; Fashion Show (with catwalk) 264; Cabaret 200
Hall 19.6m x 13m. Stage 2.74 x 8m.
Two small dressing rooms are available for use by performers. Bar facilities and a fully fitted kitchen is located off the main hall.

Ammanford, Carmarthenshire

AMMAN CENTRE

Margaret Street, Ammanford, Carmarthenshire SA18 2NP Wales
Tel: 01269 598705
Email: john.evans@zen.co.uk
Web Site: www.treforiscatering.co.uk
Contact: John Evans
Seats: 180

AMMANFORD MINERS' THEATRE

Wind Street, Ammanford, Dyfed SA18 3DN
Tel: 0845 226 3510
Email: theatres@carmarthenshire.gov.uk
Web Site: www.theatrausirgar.co.uk
Props: Carmarthenshire County Council
Contact: Nick Stevenson
Capacity: 156

Andover, Hampshire

Pop: 35,000. London 74 miles.
Newspapers: Andover Advertiser (fri); Southern Evening Echo (daily). STD Code 01264

THE LIGHTS ANDOVER

West Street Andover Hampshire SP10 1AH
Tel: 01264 368368
Email: stop@thelights.org.uk
Web Site: www.thelights.org.uk
Director: Heather Wittam
Capacity: 242

Annan, Dumfries & Galloway

VICTORIA HALLS COMPLEX

Downies Wynd, Annan, Dumfriesshire DG12 6EE
Tel: 0303 333 3000
Email: lgoannan@dumgal.gov.uk
Web Site: www.dumgal.gov.uk
ADMINISTRATION:
Props: Dumfries & Galloway Council
Cap: Main Hall Seated 200; Seated with tables 160; Dancing 270.
Market Hall Seated 250; Seated with tables 200; Dancing 200. NB: Some seats are restricted view behind pillars.
Lesser Hall Seated 50; Dancing 50
Meeting Room Seated 40
For bookings Tel: 0303 333 3000 xt. 67249
Visit website for more information

Arbroath, Angus

ARBROATH SPORTS & COMMUNITY CENTRE

Keptie Road, Arbroath, Angus DD11 3EW Scotland
Tel: 01241 438 190
Email: mallarkeyg@angus.gov.uk
Web Site: www.angus.gov.uk
ADMINISTRATION:
Props: Angus Council
Cap: Main Hall Max 600; Upper Room Max 90; Lower Room Max 90.
For bookings enquiries, contact: Gail Mallarkey

SALTIRE LEISURE CENTRE

58 Montrose Road, Arbroath, Angus DD11 5JN Scotland
Tel: 01241 431 060
Email: consaltlc@angus.gov.uk
Web Site: www.angus.gov.uk
ADMINISTRATION:
Props: Angus Council
Manager: Kathleen Hutchison

WEBSTER MEMORIAL THEATRE

64 High Street, Arbroath, Angus DD11 1AW Scotland
Tel: 01241 435 805 Fax: 01241 435 801
BO: 01241 435 800
Email: info@webstertheatre.co.uk

Web Site: www.webstertheatre.co.uk
ADMINISTRATION:
Theatre Manager: Audrey Hood
Props: Angus Council
Cap: 500 with wheelchair access

Ardrossan, Ayrshire

ARDROSSAN CIVIC CENTRE
Glasgow Street, Ardrossan, Ayrshire KA22 8EV Scotland
Tel: 01294 607 295
Email: communityfacilities@north-ayrshire.gov.uk
Web Site: www.north-ayrshire.gov.uk
Central Booking Number: 0845 2301325
ADMINISTRATION:
Props: North Ayrshire Council
Cap: 200

Armagh, County Armagh

MARKET PLACE THEATRE AND ARTS CENTRE
Market Street, Armagh, County Armagh BT61 7BW Northern Ireland
Tel: 028 3752 1820 BO: 028 3752 1821
Fax: 028 3752 1822
Email: admin@marketplacearmagh.com
Web Site: www.marketplacearmagh.com
Theatre Director: Jill McEneaney
Operations Manager: Vincent McCann
Technical Manager: Rodney Ellis (Direct Tel: 028 3752 1825)
The Market Place presents an annual programme of performing, visual and creative arts events and activities.
Main Auditorium - 397 seats. The main house is the perfect space for performing arts, conferences and commercial hires.
Studio Theatre - 128 seats (retractable seating makes this space suitable for dance, workshops, and smaller meetings, conferences and presentations.
Bistro-Style Restaurant - Our acclaimed restaurant presents a full a la carte menu, serving business lunches, as well as meals before or after the programme.
Coffee House - Serving snacks throughout the day as well as a comprehensive lunch menu and coffees

Ashford, Kent

THE STOUR CENTRE
Station Approach Ashford, Kent TN23 1ET
Admin/Mgt Tel: 01233 663503
Email: enquiries@ashfordleisuretrust.co.uk
Web Site: www.ashfordleisuretrust.co.uk
ADMINISTRATION
Contact: The Booking Office
Props: Ashford Leisure Trust
Cap: Main Hall: 1000

Ashington, Northumberland

ASHINGTON LEISURE CENTRE
Institute Road, Ashington, Northumberland NE63 8HP
Reception: 01670 532 380 Admin/Mgt Tel: 01670 622 144 Admin/Mgt Fax: 01670 857 189
Email: ncandlish@activenorthumberland.gov.uk
Web Site: www.northumberland.gov.uk
ADMINISTRATION
Props: Northumberland County Council
Manager: Richard Calvert
Capacity: Sports Hall 900, Community Hall 180

Atherstone, Warwickshire

ATHERSTONE LEISURE COMPLEX
Long Street, Atherstone, Warwickshire CV9 1AX
Tel: 01827 722 198
Email: clairelodge@northwarks.gov.uk
Web Site: www.nwbc.gov.uk
ADMINISTRATION
Props: North Warwickshire Borough Council
Capacity of Memorial Hall: Cinema Style/Live Music - 200; Sit down Dinner - 140.
Manager: Claire Lodge

Axminster, Devon

THE I.E. THEATRE
Units 1 & 2 St George's, Victoria Place, Axminster, Devon EX13 5NQ
Tel: 01297 631 607
Email: ietheatre@fsmail.net
Artistic Director: Steve Black

Aylesbury, Buckinghamshire

LIMELIGHT THEATRE
Queens Park Arts Centre, Queens Park, Aylesbury, Buckinghamshire HP21 7RT
Tel: 01296 431 272
Email: info@qpc.org
Web Site: www.qpc.org
Artistic Director: Sarah Lewis
Capacity: 120

WATERSIDE THEATRE
Exchange Street, Aylesbury, Buckinghamshire HP20 1UG
Admin: 01296 745111 BO: 01296 745122 /3 /4 SD: 01296 745100
Email: emmahenderson@theambassadors.com
Web Site: www.atgtickets.com/aylesbury
ADMINISTRATION:
Props: Ambassadors Theatre Group
Chief Executive: Elizabeth Adlington
Technical Manager: Colin Ashman
Theatre Administrator: Emma Henderson
Policy: Major musicals.
Capacity: 1200 seating, 1800 standing.

Ayr, Ayrshire
Pop: 50,000. London 390 miles.
Newspapers: Ayr Advertiser (thurs); Ayrshire Post (fri); Ayr Free Press (thurs).
STD Code 01292

AYR TOWN HALL
New Bridge Street, Ayr KA7 1LX Scotland
Council: 0300 123 0900 Tel: 01292 617 660 Fax: 01292 612 143
Email: alison.kenny@south-ayrshire.gov.uk
Web Site: www.whatsonayrshire.com/ayr-townhallevents
Bookings Contact: Alison Kenny or Jean Young, email jean.young@south-ayrshire.gov.uk
Seats: 700. Stalls stack, balcony fixed.

GAIETY THEATRE
Carrick Street, Ayr KA7 1NU Scotland
Tel: 01292 288 235
Email: info@ayrgaiety.co.uk
Web Site: www.airgaiety.co.uk
ADMINISTRATION:
Props: South Ayrshire Council
Operations Manager: Sally Rennie
Marketing Manager: Suzanne McLellan
Front of House Manager: Michael Stewart
Technical & Stage Manager: Doug Paisley
Policy: Pantomime, Variety, Touring Productions, Summer Shows.
Seats: 584

Bacup, Lancashire

BACUP HUB
Burnley Road, Bacup, Lancashire OL13 8AG
Tel: 01706 875 550
Email: enquiries@bacuphub.co.uk
Web Site: www.bacuphub.co.uk
ADMINISTRATION
Hall Capacity: 450-500
Centre Manager: Catherine Chadwick

Bala, Gwynedd

NEUADD BUDDUG THEATRE
Pensarn Road, Bala, Gwynedd LL23 7SR
Mgt Tel: 01758 704 088
Email: annrowenajones@gwynedd.gov.uk
Web Site: www.gwynedd.gov.uk/neuad-dbuddug
ADMINISTRATION
Props: Gwynedd County Council
Theatre Manager: Ann Rowena-Jones
Capacity: 285 Seated

Ballymena, County Antrim

THE BRAID ARTS CENTRE
1-29 Bridge Street Ballymena, County Antrim BT43 5EJ Northern Ireland
Tel: 028 2565 7161
Email: rosalind.lowry@ballymena.gov.uk
Web Site: www.thebraid.com

Main contact plus booking enquiries: Rosalind Lowry - ArtsDevelopment Officer, Ballymena Borough Council
Capacity: Main concert Hall 400 - full lights and sound, full flytower; Studio Theatre: 100 - stage lifts.

Ballynahinch, County Down

BALLYNAHINCH CENTRE
55 Windmill Street, Ballynahinch, County Down BT24 8HB Northern Ireland
Tel: 028 9756 1950 Fax: 028 9756 5606
Email: blc.reception@downdc.gov.uk
Web Site: www.downdc.gov.uk
Bookings Officer: Mrs E Rooney
Props: Down District Council
Main Hall S/Cap: 400. Stage and audio-visual facilities.
Meeting Room S/Cap: 18.

Bangor, Gwynedd

Pop: 10,700. London 235 miles. STD Code 01248

JOHN PHILLIPS HALL
Bangor University School of Creative Studies and Media John Phillips Hall College Road Bangor, Gwynedd LL57 2DG Wales
Tel: 01248 388560/383215 Fax: 01248 383 239
Email: scsm@bangor.ac.uk
Web Site: www.bangor.ac.uk
Contact School Administrator: Emma Thomas

PRICHARD JONES HALL
Main Arts Building, Bangor University, College Road, Bangor, Gwynedd LL57 2DG Wales
Tel: 01248 388088/ 382795 Fax: 01248 660 335
Email: conferences@bangor.ac.uk
Web Site: www.bangor.ac.uk/conference_office
ADMINISTRATION:
For bookings enquiries, contact conference office team
Contact: Conference office : 01248 388088
Seats: Prichard Jones Hall: 400 (inc balcony 126). Powis Hall: 160
Please enquire.

Barnard Castle, County Durham

TEESDALE SPORTS CENTRE
Strathmore Road, Barnard Castle, County Durham DL12 8DS
Tel: 0300 026 0862
Email: leisure-teesdale@durham.gov.uk
Web Site: www.durham.gov.uk/tessdaleleisurecentres
ADMINISTRATION
Props: Durhan County Council
Manager: Ben Kelsey
Cap: 400
TEHCNICAL
Main Hall: 33m x 18m

Barnsley, South Yorkshire

Pop: 224,000. London 172 miles. Newspapers: Barnsley Chronicle (fri). STD Code 01226

PENISTONE PARAMOUNT
Shrewsbury Road Penistone South Yorkshire S36 6DY
Admin: 01226 762004 BO: 01226 767532
Email: info@penistoneparamount.co.uk
Web Site: www.penistoneparamount.co.uk
Props: Barnsley Metropolitan Council
Manager: Brian Barnsley
Administrator: Kath Jones
Capacity: 351

Barnstaple, Devon

Pop: 32,000. London 195 miles. Newspapers: North Devon Journal - Herald (thurs); North Devon Gazette (wed); North Devon Advertiser (thurs). STD Code 01271

NORTH DEVON LEISURE CENTRE
7 Brethren Bank, Sticklepath, Barnstaple, Devon EX31 2AP
Tel: 01271 373 361 Fax: 01271 373234
Email: northdevon@parkwood-leisure.co.uk
Web Site: www.leisure-centre.com
Large arena, used for concerts, theatre productions, sports events and conferences.
Cap: 800
Available on request

QUEEN'S THEATRE
Boutport Street, Barnstaple, Devon EX31 1SY
Mgt/Admin: 01271 327 357 BO: 01271 324 242 Fax: 01271 326 412
Email: info@northdevontheatres.org.uk
Web Site: www.northdevontheatres.org.uk
ADMINISTRATION:
Traditional theatre design, built 1952. Extensively renovated in 1993. Venue financed by North Devon District Council, RAB SWA, the local authority.
Director: Alan Dodd
Contact (PA): claire.thomson@northdevontheatres.org.uk
Technical Services Manager: Glyn Allen. Contact: glyn.allen@northdevontheatres.org.uk
Publicity Officer: Sarah Anderson
Development Manager: Jo Griffiths
Programme Director: Alan Dodd
Seats: 683 Raked Stalls plus circle.
Policy: Varied programme of entertainment including educational and cultural events, with the emphasis on diversity and quality. Willing to premiere show.
Performance schedule: Evening performances start at 7.30-8pm. Booking terms: hire, box office split, guarantee & split, guarantee, co-production, by negotiation.
Other activities exhibition, educational projects.
Other Facilities: Café bar, 2 licensed bars, Access car park; adjacent; railway station: 0.75 mile; coach terminal: 0.5 mile. For the disabled up to 8 wheelchair spaces - assistance available - deaf loop system - ramp - all house facilities fully accessible. Lift to all floors.
TECHNICAL:
STAGE: Pros. Width 29' 10" 9.09m, Height 17'10" 5.44m, Height to Steel Grid 37'10" 11.53m, Depth (From Apron) 25'04 7.72m, (From Iron) 22'07" 6.88m, Wing Width S.L. 11'01" 3.38m, S.R 10'03" 3.12m, Apron to Box 58'10" 17.10m, Apron to FOH, Sound 44'00" 13.41m, (Box to FOH Sound) 14'10" 4.52m, Height to Apron: 3'053/4 1.05m. Get-In: Length from Street to Stage 32'00" 9.75m.
LIGHTING: Board & Control ETC Eos or Strand 530i series. DMX out to dimmer room via 2 tie-lines. 1 direct to dimmers, 1 to DMX buffer. Dimming: 96 ways Strand SLD96 (Channels 1 - 96). 48 ways

Strand Chilli (Channels 97 - 144). 12 way Strand Act 6 (Channels 145-152 On Bridge - Universe 2). Follow Spots; FOH Bridge; 2 Robert Juliat 'Marius' 1200w MSR Followspots 6 way colour magazine and dimmer. Luminaries: 30 x Cantata Fresnel; 8 x Cantata 11/26 (4 @ FOH Bridge); 8 x Cantata 18/32 (FOH Bridge); 20 x Cantata 26/44; 48 x PAR 64 (CP62); 6 x Floor Can (CP62); 27 x Source 4 PAR (Narrow/Med/Wide); 4 x Source 4 - 26 Degree; 1 x Source 4 - 50 Degree; 8 x Source 4 - 15/30 Zoom (FOH Bridge); 8 x SL 15/30; 2 x SL 25/50; 4 x Coda 4 Cell. Extras (Charges may Apply): 4 x Martin Mac 250; 4 x Martin MAC 500; 4 x Martin MAC 600; 8 Chroma Q-16 Frame Scroller, Power Supply & Cabling.
EXTRAS: Various smoke/haze machines. Lemaitre pyro firing system. Power 200A Three-Phase Bus-Bar with Distribution unit S/R. (100A if used in conjunction with in house dimming.) 3PH/N 125A CeeForm rated to 100A Us/R Stands 2 Telescopic stands 1.25m - 2.5m high. 4 x Doughty 4M Stands. Rigging 4 x I.W.B. on winches overhead stage. FOH Bridge and perch boom positions (Side and front) We have various lengths of mains multicore: - Socapex & Electriflex. Plus a large pile of TRS.
SOUND: Sound Desk: Sound Craft MH2; 32 Mono channels; 4 Stereo channels; 8 Audio Groups; 8 VCA's; 10 Aux sends. Crown CE1000 (FoH Full range); Crown CE2000 (Sub); Crown CE1000 (Circle); Crown CE1000 (Under Balcony); Crown CE1000 (Upper Circle). F.O.H. Speakers: 2x Announcement Audio 15" + 2"; Compression Driver (Full Range); 2x FBT Maxx 12" (Circle); 3x FBT Maxx 10" (Upper Circle); 4x EV i6.2 (Under Balcony Fill). F/B Amps: Yamaha 3200. F/B Speakers: 2 EAW DS1222 HP Full Range. Tie Lines: 18 Stage to Box, 6 Box to Stage. Mixing Positions: Mixing Positions in the Rear of Stalls, 5 Seats Wide. Wider Spaces by Request. Outboard FX & 1 Yamaha REV 500. Processing: 1 Yamaha REV 100; 6 Channel of Compression; 4 Channels of EQ for Monitors; 2 SONY MiniDisc; 1 Technics CD Player; Extra Mics (Various) DI Boxes, Wedge Monitors (Yamaha 12"+HORN X4), 4 X Gates are available on request.
COMMUNICATIONS: Tecpro Head Sets to all areas.
DRESSING ROOMS: 4, accommodates 90, access by stage entrance.

Barrow-In-Furness, Cumbria

Pop: 72,635. London 278 miles.
Newspapers: North Western Evening Mail (ntly); West Cumberland Advertiser (thurs). STD Code 01229

THE FORUM

28 Duke Street, Barrow-in-Furness, Cumbria LA14 1HH
Mgt: 01229 876 482 BO: 01229 820 000
Email: theforum@barrowbc.gov.uk
Web Site: www.theforumbarrow.co.uk
ADMINISTRATION:
Manager: Sandra Baines
Policy: Multi-purpose theatre.
Seats: 529. Licensed Bars and Restaurant.

Barry, Vale Of Glamorgan

MEMO ARTS CENTRE

Gladstone Road, Barry, Vale Of Glamorgan CF62 8NA
Admin/Mgt Tel: 01446 400 111 BO Office: 01446 738 622
Email: enquiries@barrymemo.co.uk
Web Site: www.memoartscentre.co.uk
ADMINISTRATION
Props: M.H.T Management Committee
Capacity: Seats 886 or 1,300 in concert format.
General Manager: Kate Long
Policy: Live music concerts, theatre performances, business meetings, conferences, weddings and special occasions, banquets and dances etc. The venue also benefits from multiple spaces ideal for pre-production, technical rehearsals, TV and filming.
TECHNICAL
Full Stage Facilities.
Proscenium flat; proscenium opening 10m long, 6m wide; fire curtain to back wall 7.1m; forestage to back wall (cyc) 10.3m; stage width wing to wing 11.9m, forestagewidth 12.7m, height 3m; backstage crossover 18 hemp flying lines, 150kg per set; three winch-lifted LX bars.
Disabled Access: Ramp access into the building, two lifts to all levels and induction loop system in the Main Hall.
Dressing Rooms: 8 dressing rooms, and facilities include toilets and showers.
Other: Power sockets throughout the area for large exhibitions and presentations. On-site specialist equipment including; sound, audio visual, Wi-Fi, projectors and screens, as well as hospitality facilities and services.

Basildon, Essex

Pop: 134,330. London 29 miles.
Newspapers: Basildon Standard Recorder (fri); Evening Echo (ntly); Yellow Advertiser (fri). STD Code 01268

TOWNGATE THEATRE & CONFERENCE CENTRE

St Martins Square Basildon, Essex SS14 1DL
Tel: 01268 465 465 Fax: 01268 465 468
Email: towngate@basildon.gov.uk
Web Site: www.towngatetheatre.co.uk
ADMINISTRATION:
All enquiries to Basildon District Council
Main: 544 theatre style Studio: 186 theatre style
Room Hiring, Please contact: Ann-Marie Woodley
TECHNICAL:
Please contact Tim Lloyd, Tel: 01268 465 461.

Basingstoke, Hampshire

Pop. 91,000. London 47 miles.
Newspapers: Reading Post (dly); Basingstoke Gazette (mon/wed/fri). STD code 01256

THE ANVIL

Churchill Way, Basingstoke, Hampshire RG21 7QR
Admin/SD: 01256 819 797 BO: 01256 844 244 Fax: 01256 331 733 BO Fax: 01256 366 900
Email: ann.dickson@anvilarts.org.uk
Web Site: www.anvilarts.org.uk
ADMINISTRATION:
Chief Executive: Christine Bradwell
Marketing Director: Matthew Cleaver
Technical Manager: Ian Jones
Two licenced bars
Proscenium Format
Seats: 1,060 (without orchestra pit) 992 (with orchestra pit) upto 6 wheelchair spaces depending on format.
1,400 in the round with choir stalls; black box and flat floor formats also available.
TECHNICAL:
Stage: Demountable Proscenium 10 metres wide x 7 metres high, stage front to setting line 2 metres, setting line to rear wall 9.5 metres, width at setting line 17 metres, width at rear wall 11 metres, flying height 20 metres, 7 motorised bars (500 kilo SWL), 19 hemp sets. Four 500 kg. rigging points F.O.H. for advance truss, flying bar lengths vary from 16m downstage to 10m upstage. Prompt corner D.S.L.
Lighting: Equipment: Control desk Strand 550, dimmers 168 x 2.5kw, 12 x 5 kw, Luminaires: 12 2k profiles 9/15, 24 1.2k profiles 10/26, 16 1.2k fresnels, 16 1.2k P.C, 60 Par cans, 4 4 x 1k cyc floods, 2 Pani followspots, 4 x Robe 500 moving lights.
Sound: Equipment: Audient Aztec 32 into 10 into 4 into 2, Tascam minidisc player, Dennon DN 2000F twin quick start CD player, Tascam DA30 DAT machine, Tascam 122Mk II cassette machine, Yamaha SPX 900 multi effects processor, Rane 1/3 octave graphic equaliser, various mics and stands, 48 input and 12 return tie lines from stage/control room.
Loudspeaker System: Powered by Amron Amplifiers via Yamaha D2040.
Programmable controllers, portable loudspeakers; 2 x EV FM1202 wedge moni-

tors 3xEV S1503 side fill/effects speakers, 2 x EV S200 speakers.
Other: Dressing room facilities: stage level 3 en suite rooms and 4 with sinks, visiting managers office with phone. First floor level 4 rooms, laundry room and showers.
Power Supplies: Visiting lighting supply 200 amp 3 phase U.S.L. Buss Bar, visiting sound supply 100 amp 1 phase D.S.L. Buss Bar, 4 x 32 amp C form sockets, visiting O.B. supply 300 amp 1 phase.
Communications: Stage Managers Desk D.S.L. c/w cue lights, ring intercom c/w 12 x headsets and packs,LX 200amp 3 phase, 2 channel infra red system, paging & show relay, video show relay, computer tie lines.
Get In: The get in is all at stage level via loading bay and corridor minimum width 2.3 metres.
Auditorium: The Auditorium has a variety of different layouts offering up to 1400 seats.
Orchestra pit: The Orchestra pit is available in the certain format and is approx. 4 metres x 18 metres. The venue has 65 RAT music stands.
Stage Equipment: The venue has a complete set of black masking, white cyclorama, house tabs. Assorted weights braces, and sand bags.
Forge Sound and Lighting:
Lighting control: Strand MX 24
Dimmers: 24 x 2.5 kw
Sound: As required from main auditorium stock

CENTRAL STUDIO

Queen Mary's College, Cliddesden Road, Basingstoke, Hampshire RG21 3HF
Tel: 01256 417 511 BO: 01256 418 318
Fax: 01256 417 501
Email: steph.monger@qmc.ac.uk
Web Site: www.centralstudio.co.uk
ADMINISTRATION:
Theatre Manager: Stephanie Monger
Marketing & Publicity: Jodie Cooper
130 seater auditorium with audience seated on 3 sides (thrust).
Programming small scale touring theatre, live music, dance, film and children's theatre. The venue and its equipment is also available for hire. Central Studio also has access to a 400 seater proscenium arch theatre for larger events.
TECHNICAL:
Please contact Theatre Technician -Ryan Messer

HAYMARKET THEATRE

Wote Street, Basingstoke, Hampshire RG21 7NW
Anvil BO: 01256 844 244 Admin Tel: 01256 819797 BO Fax: 01256 366 900
Email: alison.goodall@anvilarts.org.uk
Web Site: www.anvilarts.org.uk
ADMINISTRATION:
Lessees: The Anvil Arts Trust
Chief Executive and Programme Director: Christine Bradwell
Policy: Producing theatre - up to 8 in house shows +3 or 4 visiting shows.
Season: September to June. Shows run between 1 and 4 weeks. Developing community and education programme.
Perfs: usually 7.45p.m.
Seats: 426, Circle and Stalls, Licensed & Coffee Bars, Theatre Restaurant.
TECHNICAL:
Please contact The Anvil for further information as Theatre is currently undergoing refurbishment.

Bath, Somerset

Pop. 85,000. London 106 miles.
Newspapers; Bath & West Evening Chronicle (ntly); Western Daily Press (dly); Evening Post (ntly); Keynsham Weekly Chronicle; Chippenham News/Wiltshire Times, Somerset Guardian/Standard, Wiltshire Gazette & Herald (wkly). STD code 01225

BATH PAVILION

Bath Pavilion North Parade Road Bath BA2 4EU
Tel: 01225 486902
Email: jenny.jacob@aquaterra.org
Web Site: www.bathpavilion.org
ADMINISTRATION:
General Manager: Jenny Jacob
Cafe and Bar facilities (unspecified catering)
Seats: 1,000
TECHNICAL:
50' x 26'9" stage, (110A TP & N3 phase supply), 90' x 70' hall.

GUILDHALL

The High Street, Bath, Somerset BA1 5AW
Reception: 01225 477 793
Email: guildhall_roombookings@bathnes.gov.uk
ADMINISTRATION:
Props: Bath & North East Somerset Council, Heritage Services, Pump Room, Stall Street, Bath, BA1 1LZ
Venue Manager: Rosie Legg
Seats: 360

KOMEDIA BATH

22-23 Westgate Street, Bath BA1 1EP
Mgmt: 01225 489 070 BO: 0845 293 8480 Mkting: 01225 489 070
Programming: 01273 647 111
Email: infobath@komedia.co.uk
Web Site: www.komedia.co.uk/bath
ADMINISTRATION:
Props: Komedia Bath HQ Brighton
Policy: Cabaret, Music, Comedy, Club Nights, Food, Drink
Venue Manager: Stephen Rees (stephenrees@komedia.co.uk)
Marketing Manager: Erica Pease (erica@komedia.co.uk)
Box Office Manager: Lucy Springthorpe (lucyspringthorpe@komedia.co.uk)
Programming: Marina Kobler (marina@komedia.co.uk)

Capacity: Small stage cabaret style, 463. Large stage cabaret style, 450. Theatre Style, 486. Standing, 684.
TECHNICAL:
STAGE: Movable stage 8m wide x 4m deep full and 8m wide and 3m deep without extension.
LIGHTING & SOUND: Comprehensive sound and lighting system installed. Contact Technical Director Richard Daws for more information, rich@komedia.co.uk.
BACKSTAGE FACILITIES: 1 back stage room with toilet, sofa, iron & board, full mirror, fridge and hot drinks facilities, prep space and mirror at back of stage.

MOLES CLUB

14 George Street, Bath, Somerset BA1 2EN
Tel/BO: 01225 404 445
Email: info@moles.co.uk
Web Site: www.moles.co.uk
ADMINISTRATION:
Prop: Philip Andrews; Studio: Jon Walker; Club: Phil Andrews
Capacity: 250

THE RONDO THEATRE

St Saviours Road, Bath, Somerset BA1 6RT
Admin: 01225 444 003 BO: 01225 463 362
Email: director@rondotheatre.co.uk
Web Site: www.rondotheatre.co.uk
ADMINSTRATION:
Theatre Director: Ian McGlynn
Marketing Administration: Alison Farina
Seats: 105
TECHNICAL:
STAGE: 7.9m wide to tab line or 5.5m to the audience. Height is 3.6m to tad line border, approx 4m at side walls and 6m to ceiling for the centre 4m width of the stage. A set of soft black borders and legs are available for masking, and all stage walls are painted black. A dance floor is available in black..
LIGHTING: supply 100 single phase.
Dimmers: 5 racks each 6#2kw & 3#1kw for house and control room lighting. Distribution 42 patch circuits. All outlets at ceiling height; boxes marked on plan.
Desk: Arri Image. Lanterns: 8 X Patt 743 1kw fresnel, 6 X Berkey 1kw fresnel, 2 X Cantata PC 1kw PC, 2 X Patt 814 1kw PC, 4 X Patt 764 1kw profile, 4 X Sill 40 1.2kw profile, 4 X Patt 123 500 fresnel, 12 X Patt 23 500 fresnel, 2 X Raylight 1kw, 4 X Cycfloods 1kw, 1 X Sil 12 1kw follow spot.
SOUND: 2offNAD 602 cassette, Revox B77, Philips CD player, 12 into 4 mixer, Quad 303 and Quad 606 amps, EV 200 speakers front of Tabs, Yamaha rear stage speakers. Show relay: Stereo mics

to control room, with feed to dressing room. Clearcom intercom headsets 3 sets.

THE FORUM
Forum Buildings, St James's Parade, Bath BA1 1UG
Tel: 01225 443 114 Fax: 01225 460 651
Email: enquiries@bathforum.co.uk
Web Site: www.bathforum.co.uk
A unique conference and concert venue.

THEATRE ROYAL
Sawclose, Bath, Somerset BA1 1ET
Mgt/SD: 01225 448 815 BO: 01225 448 844 Fax: 01225 444 080 Technical: 01225 823 474
Email: firstname.surname@theatreroyal.org.uk
Web Site: www.theatreroyal.org.uk
ADMINISTRATION:
Props: The Theatre Royal Bath Limited
Director: Danny Moar
Finance Director: Gabby Akbar
General Manager: Eugene Hibbert
Technical Manager: Joe Wright
Artistic Director (Ustinov Studio): Laurence Boswell
Policy: Wide and Varied visiting programme of Opera, Ballet, Dance, Musicals and Drama. Also own productions with view to touring and West End transfer.
Perfs: (usual) Mon-Wed 7.30pm; Thurs-Sat 8.00pm; Mats: Wed & Sat 2.30pm
2 Restaurant's
Private catering suite
Main House Seats: 870
Ustinov Studio Seats: 145
TECHNICAL:
For further technical information, please contact the Technical Manager - Joe Wright Email: joe.wright@theatreroyal.org.uk
Stage:
Proscenium stage, flat; Pros. Opening 8.35 m; Height of Pros.7.70 m; Depth of stage 13.0 m; Height of Grid 18.3 m; Distance between fly floors 12.6 m; Height under fly floor 7.35 m; Wing Space O.P. 1.95 m, P.S. 2.95 m; Crossover under stage.
Flying System: 51 single purchase counterweight bars; maximum counterweight load 340 kg per set.
Tabs on bar 3 diverted.
Prompt Corner: Prompt side on perch above stage entrance.
Stage Manager's desk with full cue lights to all usual stations, plus others if required. CCTV monitor, paging station for R.O.H./F.O.H calls 6 way satellite cue light desk for stage level cueing position.
Orchestra Pit: Rows A and B on lift with under-stage area. Rows C, D and E on removable rostra.
Dressing Rooms: 12 accommodating 43. M.D.'s room, 2 Band rooms, Company Manager's office, Wardrobe and Laundry.
Lighting:
Control: Rank Strand 550i. 400 channels, 400 attributes. Rank Strand 510i tracking backup. Rank Strand R120 riggers. Rank Strand 520i Stalls console - available by prior arrangement. DMX buffered distribution system. Ethernet distribution system with 2 portable SN102 nodes. Dimming equipment; Rank Strand LD90 dimmer racks. 240 ways of 2.5 kw, 24 ways of 5 kw. Temporary mains: 63 amp clean sound power DSR. 200 amp 3-phase power lock/cam lock distribution panel in scene dock. Loose lantern stock information available on website.
Communications: Clear-com 2-channel master station; Clear-com 6-pin, 2-channel belt packs x 14; single muff headsets for above. Motorola GP300 radios x 6 complete with headsets.
Sound: Sound control position at the rear of Royal Circle with 16 pair multi-core to stage. Meyer UPA1c Front of house speaker system. NEXO ps10 on-stage speakers. Other outboard equipment and mixing desks available by request.
Ustinov Studio
TECHNICAL:
This studio is a fully air-conditioned 145 seat space. It is a non-smoking area. Flat plywood stage with 6 mm hardboard skin. Width 6.83 m Depth S/L 6.39m. S/R 7.13 m. Dressing Rooms x 2 each with four stations and ensuite WC and shower. Control area at rear of auditorium on mezzanine. Open plan.
Lighting:
Control: Rank Strand 520i with 72 ways of LD90 dimming. Loose lantern stock information available on website.
Sound: Midas Venice 24-channel mixing desk. Martin EM75 speaker system. GPO jack field patch system. Other outboard equipment available by request.
General: 1xStage Management desk with 6 cue lights, 4 TecPro belt packs and headsets.

Bathgate, West Lothian

REGAL COMMUNITY THEATRE
24-34 North Bridge Street Bathgate West Lothian EH48 4PS
Tel: 01506 632558 BO: 01506 630085
Email: scott.j.kyle@hotmail.com
Web Site: www.bathgateregal.org
Artistic Director: Scott Kyle
Bar, 5 attractive spaces available to hire for parties, functions. meetings, rehearsals and workshops.
Capacity 206

Batley, West Yorkshire

TOWN HALL
Market Place, Batley, West Yorkshire, WF17 5DA
Tel: 01924 326002 Mktg: 01484 221 902 Bkg: 01484 221 947 / 913 Bkg Fax: 01484 221 541
Email: townhallbookings.cs@kirkleesmc.gov.uk
ADMINISTRATION
Props: Kirklees Metropolitan Borough Council
Assistant Manager: David Roach
Superintendent: Graham Clements
Booking Contacts: Gary Ellis, David Roach
Capacity: 300

Beaconsfield, Buckinghamshire

BEACON THEATRE AND LEISURE CENTRE
Holtspur Way, Beaconsfield, Buckinghamshire HP9 1RJ
Tel/Fax: 01494 677 764
Email: sam.parker@gll.org
Web Site: www.better.org.uk
ADMINISTRATION
Capacity: Approx 209 (theatre style)
Centre Manager: Steve O'Reilly
Props. Better
N.B. Managed by Greenwich Leisure Ltd on behalf of South Buckinghamshire District Council.

Bearsdon, Dunbartonshire

BEARSDON HALL
69 Drymen Road, Bearsdon, Dunbartonshire G61 3QT Scotland
PCB Tel: 0141 942 0868 Bkgs: 0141 574 5730
Email: halls@eastdunbarton.gov.uk
Web Site: www.eastdunbarton.gov.uk
ADMINISTRATION:
Props: East Dunbartonshire Council
Main Hall 400; Lesser Hall (upstairs) 100; Small Lesser Hall 40.

KESSINGTON HALL
58 Milngavie Road, Bearsdon, Dunbartonshire G61 2DP
PCB Tel: 0141 942 7266
Email: jook_b@hotmail.com
ADMINISTRATION:
Props: XS Kessington Hall Ltd
Cap: Main Hall 350; Larger Lesser Hall

70; Smaller Lesser Hall 45.
For bookings Tel: 0141 942 7266
Contact Bookings Supervisor: Marie Mcaneny

WESTERTON HALL
82 Maxwell Avenue, Bearsdon, Dunbartonshire G61 1NZ
Tel: 0141 942 2679 BO: 0141 574 5730
Email: halls@eastdunbarton.gov.uk
Web Site: www.eastdunbarton.gov.uk
ADMINISTRATION:
Props: East Dunbartonshire Council
Cap: Main hall 200; Lesser Hall 35.
To make a booking, please call 0141 574 5730.
Contact Caretaker: William Molloy

Beaumaris, Isle of Anglesey

BEAUMARIS LEISURE CENTRE
Canolfan Beaumaris, Rating Row, Beaumaris, Isle of Anglesey LL58 8AL
Admin/Mgt Tel: 01248 811 200
Admin/Mgt Fax: 01248 811 040
Email: Canolsanhamddenbeaumaris@btconnect.com
Web Site: www.canolsanbeaumaris.org.uk
ADMINISTRATION
Main Auditorium Capacity: 374
Manager: Warren Jones
Technical/Duty Manager: Warren Jones

Bebington, Wirral

BEBINGTON CIVIC CENTRE
Civic Way, Bebington, Wirral, Merseyside CH63 7PN
Tel: 0151 643 7237 Bkg Tel: 0151 643 7239 Bkg Fax: 0151 643 7231
Email: bebcc@wirral.gov.uk
ADMINISTRATION
Props: Wirral Borough Council
Capacity: Civic Suite 80, Phoenix Suite 80
Manager: Graham Knowles
For bookings contact: Suzanne Woo

VICTORIA HALL
Acorn Close, Higher Bebington, Wirral CH63 8PT
Tel: 0151 608 1527
Email: bebcc@wirral.gov.uk
ADMINISTRATION
Props: Wirral Borough Council
Capacity: Large Hall 180, Small Hall 80
Manager: Graham Knowles
For bookings, contact: Suzanne Woo

Beccles, Suffolk

BECCLES PUBLIC HALL
Smallgate, Beccles, Suffolk NR34 9AD
Tel: 01502 712 808 Bkg Tel: 01502 713 113
Web Site: www.becclespublichall.co.uk
ADMINISTRATION:
Available for hire from Waveney District Council's local office at: 6 Market Street, Beccles
The Hall can accommodate 150 people seated at tables, closely seated 200, dancing 250, mixed occupancy 150 and in the balcony 70. There is a small stage on which amateur dramatic productions are held.
Extensive refurbishment has recently taken place with improved toilets and access.

Bedford, Bedfordshire

Pop: 74,000. London 60 miles.
Newspapers: Times & Citizen (Wkly); Beds on Sunday (Wkly). STD Code 01234

THE BEDFORD CORN EXCHANGE
St Paul's Square, Bedford MK40 1SL
Admin: 01234 718 044 BO: 01234 718 044 Fax: 01234 325 358
Email: cornexchange@bedford.gov.uk
Web Site: www.bedfordcornexchange.co.uk
ADMINISTRATION:
Props: Bedford Borough Council
Cap: 830
General Manager: Andy Pidgen
Operations Manager: Andy Pidgen
Full bar, technical and catering services. Includes Miller and Bunyan Rooms (capacity 25 each). Also includes Howard Room (capacity 100); Harpur Suite (capacity 200)
TECHNICAL:
Main Auditorium: Multi-Purpose venue with staging accommodating up 830. Offers complete sound and flexible stage lighting systems.

BEDFORD THEATRE
Bedford School, De Parys Avenue, Bedford MK40 2TU
Admin Tel: 01234 362 269 BO: 01234 718 112
Email: admin@bedfordtheatre.co.uk
Web Site: www.bedfordtheatre.co.uk
ADMINISTRATION:
Props: Bedford School
Theatre Manager: James Pharaoh
Policy: To facilitate education and encourage new writing and to offer the local community a professional arts resource and venue.
Perfs: Normally 7.30pm
Bedford School Theatre has two main seating formats giving seating to 278 or 170 audience members. The 170 seat arrangement is favourable to smaller/intimate shows whereas, the 278 capacity will require the use of the main stage.
TECHNICAL:
The stage is a fixed proscenium with a height of aprox 90mm (3 feet) from the theatre floor. The apron depth is 2.5m, proscenium opening is 8m and height is 3.6m. Beyond this is the main stage area which is aporximately 8m deep and 10.5m wide. The floor area in front of the raised stage is 6m deep and 11.5m wide. The lighting grid is hardwired and is equipped with 60 circuits on a three phase supply. Six 200watt speakers are the foundation of the sound system controlled by a computer enabling surround sound and quick/easy access to thousands of sound effects. The mixing desk is a Behringer MX9000. Please contact us for more details.
We have a good supply of lanterns. These include:
Strand Quartet Zoom Profile x4; ETC Source Four Juniors x6
Sillhouette Zoom Profile x6; Strand Cantata Profile x2; CCT Minuet Pebble Convex x8; Starlette Fresnel x6; Cantata Fresnel x6; Strand Quartet Fresnel x10; CCT Minuet Fresnel x17;
Thomas Parcans x5; Parcans Long Nose x6; 4x1 Coda Batten Floods x4; Our lighting control desk is a Strand 300 Series.

Bedlington, Northumberland

BEDLINGTON COMMUNITY CENTRE
Front Street West, Bedlington, Northumberland NE22 5TT
Tel: 01670 824 141
Email: bedlingtoncommunitycentre@hotmail.co.uk
Web Site: www.bedlingtoncommunitycentre.co.uk
ADMINISTRATION
Props: West Bedlington Town Council
Main Hall Cap: 200
For booking enquiries, contact: Enid Dunbar

Bedworth, Warwickshire

Pop. 40,000 London 99 miles.
Newspapers: Tribune (thurs); Coventry Evening Telegraph. STD code 01203

CIVIC HALL IN BEDWORTH
High Street, Bedworth, Warwickshire CV12 8NF

Mgt: 024 7637 6705 BO: 024 7637 6707
Fax: 024 7637 6730
Email: civic.hall@nuneatonandbedworth.gov.uk
Web Site: www.civichallinbedworth.co.uk
ADMINISTRATION:
70's style municipal multi-purpose venue, well equipped with good facilities.
Props: Nuneaton & Bedworth Borough Council
General Manager: Tim Norton
Contact: tim.norton@nuneatonandbedworth.gov.uk
Technical Manager: Simon Farndon
Contact:simon.farndon@nuneatonandbedworth.gov.uk
Administrator: Lisa Redhead
Policy: Multi-purpose.
Perfs: Variable.
Seats: 745 approx. Bar, Bistro, Coffee Bar, Small Hall, Meeting Rooms and Gallery.
TECHNICAL:
STAGE: Concert platform, flat, solid construction, 0.45m high (18ins), Total width with wings: 20.9m (68ft), Pros. width: 10.97m (36ft), can be masked. Depth of stage: 7.63m (25ft), Depth to Cyc: 7.17m (23ft 7 inches), Height: Stage to bottom of borders 4.74m (15ft 6inches), Height to Grid: 7.93m (26ft) NOTE: No fly tower. 3 x lighting bars on hand winches (250 Kg). 12 x hemp lines (125Kg) hand pull, No1 always house border. Stage access height maximum 2.03m (8ft 6in) X 2.70m (8ft 10in). Get in: loading bay 1.3m (approx.) high, flat loading dock with ramp to stage.
LIGHTING: Control; Congo Avab by ETC with 2 monitors, ELC Focus Brain remote riggers control. 72 Channel of ADB Eurotrack, 24 Ch of Permus Dimmers (powered from 125A Cee-form) Colour Changes and special effects (S/E 1-4) switch from control box. Lamps: 4 x LED UV Cannons, 6 x Scrollers, 2 x Tiger scan 575 watt, 2 x VL1000 1000watt, 10 x ETC Source 4 Fixed profile 2 with standard gobos, 8-x ETC Source 4 profile zoom 750watt, 4 x ETC Source 4 Junior 575watt, 16 x Cantata F 1000watt, 8 x Cantata PC 1000watt, 8 x Selecon Rama F 1000watt, 10 x Prelude F 650watt, 4 x Selecon F 650w, 10 x Cantata 18/32 4 with colour changer 1200watt, 7 x Prelude 28/40 with standard gobos 650watt, 4 x Par 64 with top hat 1000watt, 5 x Coda Batten 4s 500watt each Ch, 6 x Coda 500watt, 4 x Teatro flood 500watt. Additional Lamps available. Additional Equipment; Smoke Machine (extra cost), Haze Machine (extra cost), Mirror Ball located in Main Hall with 2 xs pat 123 500watt. Follow spot, 2 x Robert Juliat Super Korrigan, 1200 HMI lamps, fixed position rear of auditorium.

SOUND: Mixer Position: Rear of Hall, 45m multi-core required. Control: 1 x Allen & Heath GL3300, 1 x Roland V 400 Digital Mixer, 1 x Yamaha Q2031B Graphic, 2 x DBX 231 Graphic, 1 x Yamaha SPX990, 1 x Roclab DDL, 24 mic lines from stage into control box. Also available Sound craft Delta Theatre 24-4-2, Sound craft Spirit 16-4-2, Spirit E6. Speakers: 2 x GAE 2x15 Bins 4 x GAE mid tops 2 x GAE fills (stalls) all flown. Fold back: 2 x GAE 15" wedges 2 x GAE 10" wedges with Chevin amps 2 x 200 EV wedges, 2 x Allan Gordon wedges, 1 x Carlsboro PM 50-90 powered monitor with 1 x Carlsboro slave unit. DI. Various Microphones available. Effects: 1 x Sony Multi-effect DPS-V55M, 1 x T C Electronic M.one effects unit, 2 x DBX Graphic 231,1 x DBX Compressor/Gate 166XL, 1 x DBX QuadGate 1074, 1 x Roclab DDL (extra cost).
BACKSTAGE FACILITIES: Dressing Rooms: 2 x Dressing Rooms with en-suite shower and toilet (accommodates 6 in each). 2 x "Band" Dressing Rooms, accommodating 20 and 6 with shared toilet facilities. Green Room (Kettle, Micro Wave, fridge seats 14). Small Hall may be used as a Large Dressing Room (accommodates 30+ available at extra cost).
Staff: 3 x full time technicians, 10 x experienced casual technicians/humpers/follow
spot operators.
ADDITIONAL: Pianos: Steinway Concert Grand, Welmar Baby Grand, Welmar Upright (available at extra cost).

Belfast, County Antrim

Pop. 500,000 Newspapers: Irish News (dly); News Letter (dly); Belfast Telegraph (dly). STD code 028 90

THE BELFAST EMPIRE

42 Botanic Avenue, Belfast, County Antrim Northern Ireland
Tel: 028 9024 9276 BO: 0844 2774455
Head Office Tel: 028 9074 6274
Email: kerrie@wineinns.com
Web Site: www.thebelfastempire.com
Props: Wine Inns Ltd
Marketing & Promotions Manager: Kerrie Malone
Bar Manager: Mark Mateer
Empire Basemant: 450
Empire Music Hall: 200
Regular gigs include The Empire Laughs Back. From The Abba Experience to The Asian Dub Foundation, The Belfast Empire and Music Hall has something to meet every musical taste!

BELFAST WATERFRONT HALL CONFERENCE & CONCERT CENTRE

2 Lanyon Place Belfast, County Antrim BT1 3WH Northern Ireland
Admin Tel: 028 9033 4400 BO Tel: 028 9033 4455 Fax: 028 9033 4456 / 7
Email: boxoffice@waterfront.co.uk
Web Site: www.waterfront.co.uk
Production & Stage Manager: Danielle Noble
Tel: 028 9033 4406 Fax: 028 9033 4458
Email: nobled@waterfront.co.uk
The Belfast Waterfront Hall is designed as a multi-functional venue offering state fo the art facilities for all required uses. Comprises two halls - a main auditorium seating from 450 to 2,235 and 2,750 standing; the studio seating up to 360 front of stage.
TECHNICAL:
For further information, please contact: Danielle Noble - Technical Services Manager on: Tel - 028 9033 4406
Email: nobled@waterfront.co.uk
Stage: 20m W x 14m D half moon orchestral. 10 adjustable elevators. Choir terrace. Deployable soft proscenium 10m H x 14m W. Grid 21m optional orchestra pit.
Lighting: ETC & Avolite consols, large range of ETC and Robert Juliet Luminares, Four Aramis Follow Spots. 8 Cyberlights.
Sound: Midas & Soundcraft consols, D+B Audiotechnik speakers.
Other: 12 Dressing rooms, 10 showers, laundry room, 3 loading bays.

DUNDONALD INTERNATIONAL ICE BOWL

111 Old Dundonald Road, Dundonald, Belfast, County Antrim BT16 1XT Northern Ireland
Reception Tel: 028 9080 9100 Fax: 028 9048 9604
Email: sales@castlereagh.gov.uk
Web Site: www.theicebowl.com
Corporate Booking & Sales Officer: Joanne Best
Email: joannebest@castlereagh.gov.uk
For further information on our corporate packages, or our external catering facilities, please contact a member of our sales team on 028 9080 9123.
Function Suite Cap: 200 max.

GRAND OPERA HOUSE

Great Victoria Street, Belfast, County Antrim BT2 7HR Northern Ireland
Mgt/SD: 028 9024 0411 BO: 028 9024 1919 Fax: 028 9023 6842
Email: info@goh.co.uk
Web Site: www.goh.co.uk
ADMINISTRATION:
Chief Executive: Mary Dean
Theatre Administrator: Susy Millar
Email: smillar@goh.co.uk
Head of Sales and Marketing: Sian Mawhinney
Technical Manager: Paula Mcgeptrick
Policy: No. 1 Touring plus some local productions - Drama, Opera, Ballet, Musicals, Celebrity Shows and Variety, Concerts and Recitals, Pantomime, Children's Shows.
Baby Grand seats up to 150 - used for smaller productions, rehearsal space,

conferences and workshops.
Perfs: Normally Mon to Sat 7.30. Mats. variable. Occasionally twice nightly.
Seats: 1,060 on three levels. Three licensed bars and a restaurant.
TECHNICAL:
STAGE: Proscenium:Height 10.07m (33ft)
Stage level to Pelmet : At lowest point 6.36m (20.8ft At highest point 7.35m (24.1ft)
Safety Curtain Width: From centre line: Stage Left 9.450m (31.00ft); Stage Right 9.450m (31.00ft) Wing widths: Stage Left 3.430m (11.2ft); Stage Right 3.430m (11.2ft)
Depth: Rear of Proscenium to back wall 14.110m (46.2ft) (not including stage pocket) Forestage and orchestra lift 4.040.m (13.2ft) Height: To underside of grid 18.72m (61.4ft; To under fly floor 7.75m (25.4ft) Scenery flying height 9.000m(29.5ft)
Floor: Flat stage extended to rear; There are two Get in areas both on O.P. side New dock doors: At street level 6.14m (20.1ft) high; 4.68m (15.3ft) width.
Secondary dock doors: At street level 2.450m wide (8ft); 5.490m high (18ft)
Stage pocket: Height 9.275m (30.4ft); Width 13m (42.6ft); Length 7m (22.9ft)
Flying System: 50 sets of double purchase counterweights at 0.200m (0.6ft) centres. Last line 11.430m (37.5ft) from tabs. Bar capacity 380kg (836lbs). Counterweight bars 14.63m (47.9ft) except for first four sets which are 12.819m (42.ft) wide. Prompt corner: P.S.
Storage: Stage Left 35.3m2; Stage Right 35.3m2
ELECTRICAL: Control: Strand 550i; Remote Designer Control R120 on stage. Dimmers: ETC sensors; 100 x 2.55; 44 x 5K
Front of House: Bridge: 14 x Robert Juliat 2k Profiles Lower Slips: Positions can be rigged to your requirements. 5 circuits per side. Lamp Stock: 50 x 1.2k Cantata Fresnel; 16 x Source 4 Profile; (16 x 36 Degree, + spare lens tubes; 4 x 19 and 8 x 26 degree.); 4 x Coda 3 Battens (500W); 6 x Thomas 4 cell 1K; 6 x 2.5k Selecon Fresnels; 36 x Parcan (CP61 or CP62); 1 x Hazer (Unique) Sound Equipment: Allen&Heath GL2400 16 channel sound desk 4 x JBL 4825; 2 x Community wedges CSX 38-S2; 2 x Carver PM 1400 amps 1 x Yamaha 990 Processor; 1 x Sony Mini Disc player; 1 x Sony CD Player; 1 x TEAC cassette player; 2 x Shure SM 58 mics (please check first); 4 x Sennheiser boom stands; Multi run from stage to operating position in back of stalls. Auxillary power on stage: Stage right: 400 amps 3 phase with cam locks/power locks
63 cee form - 3 phase; 32 amp cee form - 3 phase Stage Left: 63 amp cee form outlet - single phase; 32 amp cee form outlet - 3 phase. Other: 1 x Cyc; 2 x Mirror Balls 500mm; 6 x 18 way 15 amp IWB. Other: Artistes' Accommodation: 13 Dressing Rooms accommodate 106 artistes on 2 floors above stage level; 20 Showers, 1 Conductor's Room; 1 Bandroom; Green Room.Rehersal room available if needed. Orchestra Accommodation: 60 players.

KING'S HALL CONFERENCE CENTRE

Lisburn Road, Balmoral, Belfast, County Antrim BT9 6GW Northern Ireland
Tel: 028 9066 5225 Fax: 028 9066 1264
Email: info@kingshall.co.uk
Web Site: www.kingshall.co.uk
ADMINISTRATION:
Marketing & Sales Manager: Kathryn Williamson
Events Manager: Colim Graham
Conference Centre Cap: Octagon space 580 - theatre style.
King's Hall Cap: 6000 - theatre style.

LYRIC THEATRE

55 Ridgeway Street, Stranmillis Embankment Belfast, County Antrim BT9 5FB Northern Ireland
Mgt: 028 9038 5684 / 5671 BO: 028 9038 1081 Fax: 028 9038 1395
Email: info@lyrictheatre.co.uk
Web Site: www.lyrictheatre.co.uk
ADMINISTRATION:
Props: Lyric Players Theatre Productions
Executive Producer: Jimmy Fay
Chief Operating Officer: Kieran Mcauley
Production & Technical Manager: Keith Ginty
Administration Manager: Clare Gault
Policy: Subsidised Repertory.
Perfs: 8.00p.m. Monday to Saturday (inclusive). Matinees and Sunday performances optional.
Seats: 389. Studio: 153.One Bar, Coffee Bar.

QUEEN'S UNIVERSITY CONCERT HALLS

University Road, Belfast, County Antrim BT7 1NN Northern Ireland
Tel: 028 9097 5185 Fax: 028 9097 1462
Switchboard: 028 9024 5133
Email: heather.stewart@qub.ac.uk
Web Site: www.qub.ac.uk
ADMINISTRATION:
Whitla Hall 1,250
Elmwood Hall: 478
Harty Room: 120
External Bookings Officer: Heather Stewart

ULSTER HALL

Home of the Ulster Orchestra.
Bedford Street, Belfast, County Antrim BT2 7FF Northern Ireland
Tel: 028 9033 4400 Fax: 028 9024 7199
Email: ulsterhall@belfastcity.gov.uk
Web Site: www.ulsterhall.co.uk
ADMINISTRATION:
Props: Belfast City Council
Managing Director: Jacqui Owens
OwensJ@waterfront.co.uk
Stage Technician: Mr. P Byrne
Policy: For Hire
Seats/Capacity: 1200 - 1500
TECHNICAL:
Venue currently undergoing major refurbishment. Due to reopen late 2008. Open Half-moon stage 38ft wide, 23ft depth, 5ft height. Mulholland Grand Organ. For details of technical facilities please contact the above.

Benfleet, Essex

RUNNYMEDE HALL

Kiln Road, Thundersley, South Benfleet, Essex SS7 1TF
Bookings Direct Tel: 01268 882 200
Bookings Fax: 01268 882 464
Email: halls@castlepoint.gov.uk
Web Site: www.castlepoint.gov.uk
ADMINISTRATION
Props: Castle Point District Council
Main Hall Cap: 300
For bookings contact the Community Halls Manager

Berkhamsted, Hertfordshire

BERKHAMSTED CIVIC CENTRE

High Street, Berkhamsted, Hertfordshire HP4 3HD
Tel: 01442 228 925
Email: gary.macdonald@dacorum.gov.uk
ADMINISTRATION
Props: Dacorum Borough Council
Cap: 250 for Shows, dances, rehearsal rooms, Weddings and Parties.
Bookings Officer: Gary Macdonald
Private Hiring - dances, meetings, exhibitions, etc.
TECHNICAL
Pros. arch stage.

Bexhill-on-Sea, East Sussex

Pop. 40,000. London 65 miles.
Newspapers: Bexhill News (wed). STD code 01424

DE LA WARR PAVILION

Marina, Bexhill-on-Sea, East Sussex TN40 1DP
Admin Tel: 01424 229 100
BO/Reservations: 01424 229 111 Mgt: 01424 229 110 Fax: 01424 229 101
Catering: 01424 229 136
Email: info@dlwp.com / firstname.surname@dlwp.com
Web Site: www.dlwp.com
ADMINISTRATION:

Props: De La Warr Pavilion Charitable Trust
Policy: Plays, Conferences, Concerts, Ballet, Opera, Festivals, Dancing, Variety, One Night Stands, Orchestra etc.
General Manager: Patricia Lochans
Front of House Managers
Head of Marketing: Sally Ann Lycett
Director: Stewart Drew
Perfs: As required.
Cap: Main Auditorium (1000); Restaurant (100), rooftop foyer (100) & meeting room (20) & second floor foyer (40).
Lounge and Theatre Bars, Café and Party Catering.
TECHNICAL:
For further information, please contact the Technical Manager: Tony Williams - Email: tony.williams@dwlp.com
Stage: Proscenium Stage and Large Apron, Flat floor; Pros opening 28'; Ht. of Pros. 14', Depth of Apron 8'6" and removable 3' extension. Depth from setting line to cyc - 28'. 16 Hemp Set; Flying Ht. 20'; Flying Bars width 30'.
Lighting: Switchboard: Lee Colortran Prestige 1000 located in lighting box at rear of balcony. Lee Colourtran Status 24/48 located in S.M. Corner. F.O.H. Spots: 8 Windsor 11-26 Profile (1KW), 4CCT Sil 15 (1KW), Advance Bar: 6 743 Fresnels (1KW), 4 Windsor 24-48 Profiles (1KW). On stage no.1 bar: 8 743 Fresnels (1KW); On stage no.2 bar: 6 743 Fresnels (1KW); Cyc Bar: 6 1KW Iris Floods; Side lighting FOH 4 1kw Parcan, Downstage 4 1KW Parcan, Midstage 4 1KW Parcan.
Followspots: 2 Lycian Followspots with integral 6 colourchangers. (In Lighting Box); Additional Lamps 6 Minim PC (500W); Various additional floods, Stands etc.
Sound: Seck 12 into 8 Studio Mixer; Twin Channel 10 Band Graphic Equaliser; Stereo 400W MOS - FET Amplifier; 4 x 150W Celestion Speakers FOH. Show relay talkback to six stations.
Other: Dressing Rooms 7; Accom: 60; Orchestra Pit 20.

Bexleyheath, Kent

CIVIC CENTRE
2 Watling Street Bexleyheath, Kent DA6 7AT
Tel: 020 8303 7777 Bookings Fax: 020 8319 9651
Email: tina.bates@bexley.gov.uk
Web Site: www.bexley.gov.uk
ADMINISTRATION
Props: London Borough of Bexley
Cap: 220
Bookings Contact: Tina Bates

CROOK LOG SPORTS CENTRE
Brampton Road, Bexleyheath, Kent DA7 4HH
Tel: 020 8304 9090 Fax: 020 8304 4604
Email: crooklog@parkwood-leisure.co.uk
Web Site: www.leisure-centre.com
ADMINISTRATION
Props: Parkwood Leisure Ltd
Cap: 1000 (portable seating and staging)
For bookings contact: Kenny Oliver

Bideford, Devon

BIDEFORD ARTS CENTRE
The Quay, Bideford, Devon EX39 2EY
Tel: 01237 472 462 Fax: 01237 425 665
Email: aclbideford-mailbox@devon.gov.uk
Web Site: www.learndevon.co.uk
ADMINISTRATION
8 rooms available for hire.
Cap: 181 (Floor Stage)
Bookings Administrator: Mrs Sandra Coates

BIDEFORD COLLEGE THEATRE
Bideford College, Abbotsham Road, Bideford, Devon EX39 3AR
Reception Tel: 01237 477 611
Email: mail@bideford.devon.sch.uk
Web Site: www.bideford.devon.sch.uk
Business Manager: Mr Paul Ryder
Cap: 181 seats
Hirings will vary depending on the type of use

Biggar, South Lanarkshire

BIGGAR PUPPET THEATRE
Puppet Tree House, Broughton Road, Biggar, South Lanarkshire ML12 6HA Scotland
Mgt/BO: 01899 220 631
Email: admin@purvespuppets.com
Web Site: www.purvespuppets.com
ADMINISTRATION:
Company Directors: Jill & Ian Purves
Technical Manager: Ian Purves
Policy: Puppetry, Pantomime, plays, private hiring by negotiation. Craft fairs, receptions, film, educational projects, in-service courses, workshops and youth theatre.
Performances: Variable
Facilities: Up to 6 wheelchair spaces, deaf loop system, assistance available parking - level acces, special toilet - all house facilities fully accessible.
Cap: 90
TECHNICAL:
Proscenium arch. Performing area 6.5m x 4m - pros opening 4m x 2.5m - wing widths 1m SR, 1m SL. No rake - floor wood sections, suitable for all dance, lino available, backstage crossover, stage heated. Height grid 7.5m - 10 hemp seats, 20cm apart - tab track - 100kg permitted on bars - maximum flying height 4.2m - black velvet legs and traverse - back wall used as cyclorama - red velvet house tabs, drawn. Seven 13 amp sockets. Traps in centre of stage. Get-in via rear of side entrances, 2 steps up, large double doors. Scale stage, fly and light plans available.
Lighting: Strand Tempus 12 board, 12 circuits, operated from back-stage or rear of auditorium - no supply available for temporary board. 12 lanterns.
Sound: Operated from various positions. Music by arrangement - Revox B7 reel-to-reel; cassette tape systems - small recording studio. Acoustics suitable for music and spoken word.

Billingham, Cleveland

Pop. 35,900. London 240 miles.
Newspapers: Evening Gazette; Northern Echo (dly). STD code 01642

FORUM THEATRE
Town Centre, Billingham, Cleveland TS23 2LJ
Mgt: 01642 551 389 BO: 01642 552 663
Fax: 01642 533 367
Email: forumtheatre@btconnect.com
Web Site: www.forumtheatrebillingham.co.uk
ADMINISTRATION:
Props: Riverside Leisure Promotions Ltd
General Manager: Derek Cooper
Stage/Technical Manager: Liam Devlin
Policy: Mixed Programme - touring, Opera, Ballet, Pantomime, Concerts, Films.
Perfs: 8.00 Evenings. 2.30 Matinee (Saturdays)
Seats: 649 including 12 wheelchair positions. Bar, VIP Lounge
Now on facebook
TECHNICAL:
Stage : Proscenium Arch, Width: 12.9m, Height: 6.4m
Stage dimensions: Centre line to stage left wall 10.6m, Centre line to stage right wall 10.6m, Width between fly rails 17m, Stage floor to underside of grid 18m, clear working height under fly gallery 7m, prosc. to back wall 11m, prosc. to front of stage 0.5m, stalls floor to stage 0.9m.
Stage floor: Rake of stage none, Surfaced with Canadian Maple.
Orchestra pit: Area 31.5 sq. m, stage front to pit rail 2.74m (max) 1.52m (min), Stage level to orchestra pit 1.47m.
Flying: 29 Double purchase C/W sets, length of counterweight bars 15.2m, maximum C/W bar weight 225kg, 1 Single purchase C/W set (house tabs), 13 Hemp Sets, maximum hemp bar weight 100kg.
Access: Height of stage above street 0.15m, dock door in cul-de-sack at rear of theatre, dock area 75 sq. m.
Lighting: Strand 300 lighting desk, 250 channels. 125 circuits, 40 FOH, 24 Stage, 61 Fly floor. Equipment - 20 Source 4 zoom profiles, 18 Strand SL zoom Profiles, 6 2kw Fresnels, 40 1kw

Fresnels, 6 650w Fresnels, 16 cyc Floods, 10 groundrow Floods, 36 ass. beam Parcans. 2 Follow spots Selecon 1200w MSR performer.
Sound: Equipment list available from stage manager.
Masking: 2 sets gathered black tabs, 1 set flat black tabs, 4 sets black legs, 4 black borders plus house border, 1 set reds tabs,2 sets red legs, 2 red borders, white cyclorama, white guaze, black guaze and various hard masking flats.
Accommodation: 11 dressing rooms, including 2 company dressing rooms, 9 with showers. Showers in male and female toilets. Company office available with metered telephone line. Band room in basement. Wardrobe in basement with washing machine, 2 tumble driers, iron and ironing board. Small green room in basement.

Bingley, Yorkshire

BINGLEY ARTS CENTRE

Main Street, Bingley, West Yorkshire
BD16 2LZ
Tel: 01274 519814
Email: office@bingleyartscentre.co.uk
Web Site: www.bingleyartscentre.co.uk
ADMINISTRATION
Props: Bingley Arts Centre
Main Auditorium Cap: 359

HARDEN MEMORIAL HALL

Wilsden Road, Harden, Bingley, West Yorkshire BD16 1JP
Tel: 01943 436 224 Fax: 01943 436 224
Email: christopher.ashton@bradford.gov.uk
Props: City of Bradford Metropolitan Council
Contact: Christopher Ashton
Capacity: 100

Birkenhead, Wirral

Pop. 15,743. London 200 miles.
Newpapers: Daily Post; Liverpool Echo (ntly); Wirral Globe (wkly); Wirral Newspapers (free). STD code 0151

TOWN HALL

Hamilton Square, Birkenhead, Wirral
CH41 5BR
Town Hall Tel: 01516 663 995 Tel: 01516 663 888
Email: joannehorn@wirral.gov.uk
Web Site: www.wirral.gov.uk
ADMINISTRATION
Props: Wirral Borough Council
Cap: 284; Raked seating 222; balcony seating 62
Bkgs Contact: June Brundrett or Sheila Machias

Birmingham, West Midlands

Pop. 1,076,760. London 110 miles.
Newspapers: Birmingham Evening Mail (ntly); The Birmingham Post (dly); Metro News (dly). STD code 0121

ASTON STUDENTS' GUILD

Students' Guild, Aston University, The Triangle, Birmingham B4 7ES
Mgt Tel: 0121 204 4855 Fax: 0121 333 4218
Email: l.b.cook@aston.ac.uk
Web Site: www.astonguild.org.uk
Marketing Manager: George Dowding
Bar Manager: Lisa Knight
City Centre venue. Hall with stage and capacity of 940

THE ASYLUM

38-43 Hampton Street, Hockley, Birmingham B19 3LS
Tel: 0121 233 1109 Fax: 0121 233 1286
Email: roy@theasylumvenue.co.uk
Web Site: www.theasylumvenue.co.uk
Manager: Roy Davis
Promoter: Rich Stanton
Capacity: 410

BIRMINGHAM HIPPODROME

Hurst Street, Birmingham B5 4TB
Gen Enq: 0844 338 5020 Box Office: 0844 338 5000 Group Bookings: 0844 338 7000
Email: admin@birminghamhippodrome.com
Web Site: www.birminghamhippodrome.com
ADMINISTRATION:
Props: Birmingham Hippodrome Theatre Trust Ltd
Chief Executive: Stuart Griffiths
Head of Sales, Marketing & Development: Rob MacPherson
Head of Technical Services: Mike Bradford
Head of Conference & Events: Ros Wilson
Head of Finance: Helen Bates
Administrator: Sarah Boran & Grace Morgan
Email: sarahboran@birminghamhippodrome.com
TECHNICAL:
Main Auditorium
Stage: Procinium arch. Performing area 18.89m x 22.72m - pros opening 12.79m x 7.92m - wing widths 2.5m SR, 3m SL. No rake - floor lino on ply, sprung, suitable for all dance, under stage crossover, stage heated.
Lighting: Strand 550 and 520 lighting boards. 400 circuits. 2 x 200A, 1 x 400A 3 phase power supplies (SR). 3 x Limelight 2kw Xenon followspots, operated from rear of circle.
Sound: Operated from rear of stalls. Delay speakers installed.
Backstage: 24 dressing rooms (inc band rooms), access by Thorpe Street entrance - Green Room. Rehearsal piano. Casual's available. 11 dressing rooms and stage accessible to wheelchairs.
Orchestra: Orchestra pit available, accommodates 50-100.
Seats: Auditorium seats circa 1847

Patrick Centre
Stage: Studio Theatre, with retractable bleacher seating. Nominal performing area of 9 x 9m (with seats extended).
Lighting: Strand 300 lighting board. 110 circuits. Stage Power 1 x 125A, 1 x 63A 3 phase Cee Form & 1 x 32A single phase Cee Form.
Backstage: 3 dressing rooms.
Seats: Auditorium seats 206.

Facilities
10 x well appointed conference suites
Leith's Restaurant - 100 covers
3 x bars
Membership: TMA

The Birmingham Hippodrome is the base for Birmingham Royal Ballet and DanceXchange.

BIRMINGHAM REPERTORY THEATRE

Centenary Square Broad Street
Birmingham B1 2EP
Mgt: 0121 245 2000 BO: 0121 236 4455
SD: 0121 245 2000 Fax: 0121 245 2182
Email: ticketservices@birmingham-rep.co.uk
Web Site: www.birmingham-rep.co.uk
ADMINISTRATION:
Props: Birmingham Repertory Theatre Ltd
Executive Director: Stuart Rogers
Artistic Director: Roxana Silbert
Head Of Production: Tomas Wright
Head of Stage: Adrian Bradley
Head of Marketing and Communications: Paul Reece
Policy: Repertory
Perfs: Variable
Seats: 824.

TECHNICAL:
For further information, email: adrian.bradley@birmingham-rep.co.uk
Stage: Proscenium Stage, Flat; Pros. Opening 15m; Ht. of Pros. 8m; Depth of S/Line 15m; Ht. of Grid 23m; Fly 56 C/W sets, Flying Bars 17m; W/Widths P.S. US 4m, DS 10m, O.P. 3.2m DS 6m.
Lighting: Strand 530i, 324 ways@2.5kw, 72 ways @ 5kw.
Other: 10 dressing rooms + 2 chorus, accommodating approx 60. Orchestra Pit 15.

Studio Theatre ('The Door'): Variable space. Seating minimun 140.
Lighting: Strand 520i 80 x 2.5kw
Dimmers 4 x 5kw, Spots variable;
Sound:DDA C53 16 x 4 desk.

Membership: TMA, NCA.
The Studio, available in conjunction with the library. Seats 290.

CRESCENT THEATRE
Sheepcote Street, Brindleyplace, Birmingham B16 8AE
Mgt/Admin: 0121 643 5858 BO: 0121 643 5858 Fax: 0121 643 5860
Email: boxoffice@crescent-theatre.co.uk
Web Site: www.crescent-theatre.co.uk
ADMINISTRATION:
General Manager: Barry Dudley
Assistant theatre Manager: Sosia Binnie Baines
Policy: The Crescent Theatre Company stages a wide variety of productions each season, including studio and touring shows, in addition to approximately 10 main productions each year. The Theatre is available for hire by touring groups, conference organisers and others.
Seats: 340
Studio Theatre Max. Cap:110
TECHNICAL:
For full technical details apply to the Theatre.

LG ARENA
National Exhibition Centre, Birmingham B40 1NT
Tel: 0121 780 4141 BO: 0844 338 8000
Email: lgarena@necgroup.co.uk
Web Site: www.lgarena.co.uk
Director of Arenas: Phil Mead
Seating Capacity: 4,000 - 16,000
Technical operations manager: Alan Goodman 0121 644 7122
Email alan.goodman@necgroup.co.uk

MIDLANDS ARTS CENTRE
Cannon Hill Park, Birmingham B12 9QH
Admin: 0121 446 3200 BO: 0121 446 3232 Fax: 0121 446 3201
Email: info@macbirmingham.co.uk
Web Site: www.macbirmingham.co.uk
ADMINISTRATION:
Props: Midlands Arts Centre
Chief Executive: Dorothy Wilson
Head of Administration: Sue Longfils
Head of Communications: Lindsey Cook
Operations Director: Michelle Smith
Policy: Concerts, Films, Visiting Companies, Festivals, Professional Music, Theatre, Literature Events, Education and Comedy Programmes, Exhibitions.
Perfs: Various, 10.30, 13.00, 14.30, 20.00, 19.30.
Seating: the Theatre: 220 (The Theatre can be adapted to suit particular type of play.); the Hexagon: 86; the Open Air Arena Theatre: 470; the Cinema: 150.
Dressing Rooms: the Theatre: 2, the Hexagon: 2; Showers.
Cafe and Bar.
Membership: TMA, ACA

NEW ALEXANDRA THEATRE
Station Street, Birmingham B5 4DS
Admin: 0121 230 9082 BO: 0844 871 3011 Tech: 0121 230 9088 Fax: 0121 632 6841
Email: birminghamoffice@theambassadors.com
Web Site: www.atgtickets.com/Birmingham
ADMINISTRATION:
Prop: Ambassadors Theatre Group (Venue) Ltd.
Policy: Mixed Programme.
General Manager: Andrew Lister
Box Office Manager: Michele Thomas
Marketing Manager: Hannah Brooks
Contact: hannahbrooks@theambassadors.com
Capacity: 1,397

TECHNICAL:
STAGE: Flat. Pros. Width 12m, Pros. Height 7.20m, Stage Depth (to back of Iron) 9.70m, Stage Depth including Forestage 10.50m, Width of SL wing 5.80m, Width of SR Wing 6.20m, Height of Grid from Stage 16.80m. Flying/ Rigging: 53 bars each with a maximum 250kg evenly distributed S. W. L. Fly Floor is situated SL. Over-Stage Rigging is from a series of 500kg RSJ Clamps (we currently have 5) situated approx 1.50m above the grid. FOH Rigging is from 5 x 500kg points 3.80m from the Iron, one on centre then each 3m apart. 15.50m drop from these points to the Auditorium floor. Get- In Access; via a goods lift (Approx 1.75m height difference) with a S.W.L. of 3500kg emerging at USL. The auditorium is accessible through a side wheelchair access.
LIGHTING: ETC Ion console with additional 20 way fader wing. 136 ways LD90 Dimmers (including 8 x 5k): 001 - 030 FOH, 031 - 074 Flys SR, 075 - 126 Stage, 127 - 136 Pit. Control: Manual or via DMX as circuits 501 - 503. FOH Fixed Rig - Grand Circle Front: 1.2k Cantata 18/32 x 14, 1.2k Canata 12/26 x 4. Stage Rig: 1k Cantata Fresnels x 9, 1k Cantata PC x 9, Par64 x 20 (We stock CP62 but may have a few CP61), Source 4 x 6 (4 x 19 & 2 x 36). Followspots: 2 x Robert Juliat Foxies (750MSR) behind the Dress Circle.
SOUND: Control; Allen & Heath GL2200 - 424 - 24/4/2 Mixer. PA; OHM BR - 15 x 12, OHM BR218B Dual 18" Subs x 2, OHM BR-12 x 2, OHM BR-6 x 6, W2 Monitors x 2. Ancilliary; Yamaha SPX 900 FX Unit x 1, MiniDisc Player/ Recorder x 1, CD Player x 1. Tie Lines; Control Room x 32, Rear Stalls x 32, Stage DSL x 16 (1 - 16), Stage DSR x 16 (17-32), All patch bays also include L+R and 4 x Aux outs.
STAGE MANAGEMENT: TechPro 2 channel system. Hard-wired connections at Prompt Corner, Flys, Spots, Control Room. We have 2 additional packs for other stage/FoH positions. Cue Lights - 12 way 4 pin system controlled from the Prompt Desk; we currently carry 6 boxes.
BACKSTAGE FACILITIES: 11 dressing rooms; accomm approximately 63.
Facilities: Shower, toilets, basins, T.V. and video, fridge, portable fan, B.T. 'phone line. Wardrobe; 1 x washer, 1 x dryer, 1 x ironing board, there is plumbing for x3 touring washing machines, plenty of adaptable shelving, large sink, internal 'phone. Orchestra Pit; approx. 50.4 sq. metres (166 sq.ft.). - Stalls rows A and B removed, up to approx. 45 capacity (dep. On instruments/equipment)-approx. 70.8 sq. metres (232 sq. ft.). Resident Crew Room; Vending machine and microwave for general use.

NIA ACADEMY
NEC Group Ltd, King Edwards Road, Birmingham B1 2AA
Sales: 0121 767 3981 BO: 0844 338 0338
Email: arena-sales@necgroup.co.uk
Web Site: www.nia.co.uk
ADMINISTRATION:
Director of Arenas: Phil Mead
Technical Manager: Alan Goodman
Marketing Manager: Claire Considine
Bookings Contacts: Guy Dunstan (general), Peter Monks (theatre)
Capacity: 3,500 - 4,500 (flexible)
TECHNICAL:
Stage: 60' x 4' flat stage with PA wings, DR flat floor area (max) 32m x 17m. Clear height fo 19m. House flying system rigged as required.
Dressing Rooms: 8 (sub-divisible) and offices.

THE OLD REP THEATRE, BIRMINGHAM
Station Street, Birmingham B5 4DY
Mgt/Admin: 0121 359 9440 BO: 0121 359 9444 SD: 0121 359 9445 Techl Office: 0121 359 9448
Email: info@oldreptheatre.co.uk
Web Site: www.oldreptheatre.co.uk
ADMINISTRATION:
Theatre Director: David Edmunds
Stage Technician: Andrew Drayton
385 seat theatre staging professional and amateur theatre productions, stand-up comedy, dance productions and small concerts.
TECHNICAL:
Stage: Proscenium arch; Performing Area 7.2m X 7m (excluding thrust; Width Stage Left Wing: 1.6m; Width Stage Right Wing: 2.6m; Stage slightly raked; Floor: timber;
Dance: suitable for dance.
Access: dock door 1900mm above street level (no lift)
Heating: stage is not heated
Grid: 13000mm
Flying: 22 hemp sets, 7 winch bars
Orchestra pit: can be covered by thrust, accommodates 12 musicians (approx.)
Safety Curtain: Yes
Plans: 1:25 plans available
Lighting: ETC ION with 2 universes (operated from rear stalls); 132 LD90 dimmers; 125A 3 phase, 63A Single phase supplies available at side of stage; 14 X SL 19

degree profiles; 09 X SL 15/32 Zoom Profiles; 08 X SL 23/50 Zoom Profiles; 18 X Cantata 18/32 Zoom Profiles; 06 X Cantata 11/26 Zoom Profiles; 23 X Cantata Fresnels; 12 X ETC S4 Fresnels; 04 X Cantata PC; 14 X Prelude 16/30 Zoom Profiles; 11 X Prelude 28/40 Zoom Profile; 04 X Prelude 500W Fresnel; 50 X Par 64; 04 X Par 64 Floorcan; 04 X Howie Battens; 12 X Coda 4 cell cyc floods; 02 X Solo CSI Followspots; 02 X Mac 700; 04 X Mac 250 Entour; 04 X Mac 250+; 02 X Mac 300; 08 X Chauvet Colour Dash accent 2 LED Birdies.

SYMPHONY HALL

Broad Street, Birmingham B1 2EA
Mgt: 0121 644 6200 BO: 0121 345 0600
Fax: 0121 212 1982
Email: concerts@thsh.co.uk
Web Site: www.thsh.co.uk
ADMINISTRATION:
Prop: National Exhibition Centre Ltd.
Director, Symphony Hall: Andrew Jowett
Director of Performances: Chris Baldock
Marketing Manager: Joanna Sigsworth
Development Manager: Karen Daw
Policy: Broad and varied programme includIng British and overseas orchestras, solo recitals, contemporary and early music, semi-staged opera, pop, jazz, choral concerts, folk, cabaret, conferences and lectures. CBSO, resident orchestra.
Seating/Capacity: 2,260 on 4 levels, including choir.
Perfs: Normally 7.30 or 8.00pm, matinees as required.
Coffee terrace, bar area on each foyer level, shop/sales area. Facilities for people with disabilities including easy access, toilets and infra-red hearing system.
TECHNICAL:
Stage: Semi-circular concert platform, 23m wide x 15m deep. With pit lift raised, depth increased to 18m. Platform height 1.2m. Orchestra/choir risers on air castors for use as required (in left/right and upper/lower sections). No rake - timber floor, suitable for dance.
Access: Flat access to platform area via loading door 8m wide x 4.5m high. Covered loading bay area approx. 24m long, 8m wide, 4.5m high.
Suspension: Approx. 90% of platform covered by movable acoustic canopy, containing dedicated concert lighting (N.B. cannot tilt). Around and to the rear of the canopy provision for point hoists and curved bar set for masking drapes. Ceiling height 18.75m above platform level. Point hoists can be rigged by ICC staff at various points in auditorium ceiling. Rigging plan available.
Lighting: Concert - Dedicated permanent lighting rig mounted in canopy and ceiling around it, independent of main production lighting. Stage - Arri imagine 250 control with 400 cue capacity, rigging controls, designers remote, full tracking backup. By prior arrangement control can be exchanged for either a Celco 90 Gold with Connexions soft patch to 512 circuits or a Celco 60 major with Connexions soft patch to 512 circuits.
Circuits: 222 x 2.5kw and 8 x 5kw.
Luminaires: 24 x 2kw profile spots, 30 x 2kw Fresnel PC spots; 12 x 1kw profile spots; 42 x 1kw Lekolites 72 x Par.64; 2 x 2.5kw HMI follow spots and 2 x 1.2kw HMI spots. Full circuit layout and standard rig drawing available.
Sound: Acoustic adjustments within the auditorium rely on physical means and no electronics are used. Reverberation chambers behind auditorium walls contain a volume of approx. 50% of the hall itself. The reverberation time of the hall is affected by a series of hydraulically operated doors opening onto the chambers. Acoustic banners and curtains can reduce reverberance. Acoustics suitable for live music and amplified sound.
Amplification: 3 suspended loudspeaker array's, one central within the acoustic canopy and one on each side of the front of the canopy. All units d + b audiotechnik 402 - 1200A amps 10k. Additional d + b 402 - 1200A amps ground fill 5k. sound consoles; DDA D series 24:8:8 in control room; DDA D series 40:8:8 in FOH cockpit; Cockpit desk can be removed to accommodate artists' own equipment. All consoles supported by comprehensive effect racks. Cassette and open reel tape record/replay facilities available including 4 track open reel and 3 track cassette for AV plus CD player. DAT digital tape recorder/player .
Comprehensive stock of microphones.
Communications: Hall and foyers covered by main ICC PA system divided into zones as required. Telecommunication and Datacom circuits available. Radio communication system with dialling access to and from telephone system. Performance communications via Clear Com mainstations and hardwired unit with TECHPRO portable outstations. All industry standard audio visual equipment available for hire on request.
Temporary Power Supplies: 2 x 250amp TPN & E at rear stage. Permanent power supplies: 200 amp TPN & E stage right (LX), 100 amp TPN & E stage left (Sound).
Cable Access: With advance notice, cable pass-through available to link all areas.
Other: Backstage: 4 orchestra rooms, artists lounge, 6 dressing rooms, 2 offices, rehearsal piano. Backstage facilities accessible to disabled performers and staff.
Full selection of concert Grand Pianos available (Steinway and Yamaha).

TOWN HALL BIRMINGHAM

Reopened October 2007 after £35m renovation.
Victoria Square, Birmingham B3 3DQ
Tel: 0121 644 6157 BO: 0121 780 3333BO: 0121 345 0600 Fax: 0121 212 1982
Email: concerts@thsh.co.uk
Web Site: www.thsh.co.uk
ADMINISTRATION:
Props: Birmingham City Council
Management: Symphony Hall Trust
Director of Performances: Chris Baldock
Programme Coordinator: Chris Proctor
For booking or hiring enquiries, please email:
concerts@thsh.co.uk
Hall capacity: 1,100 including choir benches, 850 for most shows.

Bishop Auckland, County Durham

BISHOP AUCKLAND TOWN HALL

Marketplace, Bishop Auckland, County Durham DL14 7NP
Tel: 03000 269 524 Fax: 01388 604 960
Email: janet.strong@durham.gov.uk
Web Site: www.bishopaucklandtownhall.org.uk
ADMINISTRATION
Props: Durham County Council
Cap: 210. 2 meeting rooms.
Centre Manager: Janet Strong
Bar. Stage sound and lighting facilities.

STANHOPE TOWN HALL

Front Street, Stanhope, Bishop Auckland, County Durham DL13 2TS
Caretaker Mob Tel: 07879 867 117
Email: ken.elgey@durham.gov.uk
ADMINISTRATION
Props: Durham County Council
Cap: 200 Stage facilities
For bookings contact: Kenneth Elgey

Bishopbriggs, Dunbartonshire

WAR MEMORIAL HALL

1 Balmuildy Road, Bishopbriggs, East Dunbartonshire G64 3BS
BO: 0141 574 5730
Email: halls@eastdunbarton.gov.uk
Web Site: www.eastdunbarton.gov.uk
ADMINISTRATION:
Props: East Dunbartonshire Council
Cap: Main Hall 130; Lesser Hall 20
For bookings Tel: 0141 574 5730

Blaby, Leicestershire

ELMESTHORPE VILLAGE HALL

Wilkinson Lane, Elmesthorpe, Leicestershire LE9 7SP
Tel: 07528077240

Email: clerk.elmesthorpe@hotmail.com
ADMINISTRATION
Props: Parish Council
Management: Village Hall Association
Cap: 120
For booking enquiries, contact the Clerk to the Council: Michael Cattell - Address: 8 Ayrshire Close, Barwell, Leicester LE9 8HQ
Bookings may be made for private parties, weddings etc. as well as regular meetings for your club or society.

ENDERBY CIVIC CENTRE
King Street, Enderby, Leicester LE19 4NT
Tel: 0116 275 3711
Email: enderbyparish@btconnect.com
ADMINISTRATION
Props: Enderby Parish Council
Cap: 200
For bookings, contact Glenise Lee

ENDERBY LEISURE CENTRE
Mill Lane, Enderby, Leicestershire LE19 4LX
Tel: 0116 275 0234 Fax: 0116 286 1256
Web Site: www.everyoneactive.com
ADMINISTRATION:
Props: Sport and Leisure Management
Manager: Dean Randell
Cap: Main Hall Seated 500; Dance Studio; Bowls Hall with 6 rinks.

THE PAVILION AT HUNCOTE
Sportsfield Lane, Huncote, Leicestershire LE9 3BN
Tel: 0116 275 0246
Email: enquiries@blaby.gov.uk
Web Site: www.blaby.gov.uk
ADMINISTRATION
Props: Blaby District Council
Contact Reception for further booking information.
Cap: Main Hall 300 Standing, Social and Bar Area 120 Seated; Meeting Room 40-50.

Blackburn, Lancashire

Pop. 143,000. London 215 miles.
Newspapers: Lancashire Evening Telegraph (ntly); The Citizen (thurs). STD code 01254

KING GEORGE'S HALL
Northgate, Blackburn, Lancashire BB2 1AA
Mgt: 01254 582 579 BO: 01254 582 582
Fax: 01254 667 277 Admin: 01254 582 579 Prod: 01254 582 579
Email: steve.burch@blackburn.gov.uk
Web Site: www.kinggeorgeshall.com
ADMINISTRATION:
General Manager: Anne Macksmith
Entertainments Bookings: Steve Burch
Seating: 1,853; Seating/Standing: 2,200

Technical Specifications on Request.

THWAITES THEATRE
Aqueduct Road, Blackburn, Lancashire BB2 4HT
Mngt: 01254 680 137
Email: thwaitestheatre@yahoo.co.uk
Web Site: www.thwaitestheatre.co.uk
ADMINISTRATION:
Owners: Blackburn Theatre Trust Ltd
Chief Executive: Harriet Roberts
Policy: touring, variety shows, opera, ballet, concerts and amateurs.
Seats: 350

THE WINDSOR SUITE, KING GEORGE'S HALL
Northgate, Blackburn, Lancashire BB2 1AA
Contact King George's Hall. Admin: 01254 582 579 BO: 01254 582 582
Production: 01254 582 579
Email: steve.burch@blackburn.gov.uk
Web Site: www.kinggeorgeshall.com
ADMINSTRATION:
General Manager: Neil Dagnall
Ents Bookings: Steve Burch
Seats: 550

Blackpool, Lancashire

Pop. 150,000. London 228 miles.
Newspapers: West Lancashire Evening Gazette (ntly); Blackpool Herald (fri)

ARENA
Pleasure Beach, Blackpool, FY4 1EZ
Tel: 01253 342 426 or 01253 336 341
BO: 0871 222 9090
Email: info@stageworkswwp.com
Web Site: www.pleasurebeachblackpool.com
ADMINISTRATION:
Props: Blackpool Pleasure Beach Ltd.
Capacity: theatre 1800, concert 2400
A unique and versatile complex, ideal for conferences, product launches and presentations as well as concerts, sporting events and theatrical events. Its ice floor may be covered when required.

ATTIC
Pleasure Beach, Blackpool FY4 1EZ
Stageworks Worldwide Productions Tel 01253 342 426 or 01253 336 341
Email: info@stageworkswwp.com
Web Site: www.pleasurebeachblackpool.com
Capacity: reception standing 250, buffet 200
A perfect late night venue for all occasions with a delightfully different Moroccan theme and open air roof terrace with spectacular views.

CENTRAL PIER
Promenade, Blackpool, Lancashire FY1 5BB
Mgt: 01253 623 422
Email: info@sixpiers.co.uk
Web Site: www.centralpierblackpool.co.uk
ADMINISTRATION:
Props: Six Piers Ltd
Family Bar: 350
Legends Cabaret Bar: 424
General Manager: Rob Jones
Administrator: Mark Boden

GLOBE THEATRE
Pleasure Beach, Blackpool FY4 1EZ
Stageworks Worldwide Productions Tel 01253 342 426 or 01253 336 341
Email: info@stageworkswwp.com
Web Site: www.pleasurebeachblackpool.com
Capacity: theatre 850 reception 1000
A stunning venue with a translucent elliptical stage backed by a fibre-optic star cloth. Ideal for presentations, conferences, product launches or theatrical productions.

GRAND THEATRE
33 Church Street, Blackpool, Lancashire FY1 1HT
Admin: 01253 290 111 SD: 01253 743 218 BO: 01253 290 190 Fax: 01253 751 767
Email: boxoffice@blackpoolgrand.co.uk
Web Site: www.blackpoolgrand.co.uk
ADMINISTRATION:
Prop: Blackpool Grand Theatre Trust Ltd
General Manager: Ruth Eastwood
Technical Manager: Max Allatt
Financial Manager: David Cass
Head of Marketing: Andrew Howard
Theatre Administrator: Robert Kearton
Policy: Mixed programme Touring House, Summer Season, Plays, Dance, Musicals, Concerts.
Capacity: 1,053. 4 Licensed Bars (Matchams Bar open during the day).
TECHNICAL:
For further information, email: stage@blackpoolgrand.co.uk
STAGE: Proscenium Stage, rake 1 in 48, Hardwood, Pros. Opening 9.35m; Depth of Stage Safety curtain to rear wall 8.9m; Safety curtain to edge of stage 1.2m; Ht. of Grid 15.24m; 50 line C/W. Flying Bars 11.58m Wing Width P.S. 5.4 - 6.3m O.P. 5.4m; Scene Dock P.S.; Prompt Cnr. P.S.
DISABLED FACILITIES: Induction loop system fitted in Lawrence House Studio and main auditorium. Assisted dogs welcome. Lawrence House Studio fully accessible to wheelchair patrons via lift. Accessible washroom.
OTHER: Dressing Rooms 12; showers: 6; plus wardrobe with washer and dryer; bandroom. Studio space available for hire.

HORSESHOE
Pleasure Beach, Blackpool FY4 1EZ
Stageworks Worldwide Productions Tel 01253 342 426 or 01253 336 341
Email: info@stageworkswwp.com
Web: www.pleasurebeachblackpool.com
Capacity: theatre 500, classroom 250, dinner cabaret 250-350
Offers the latest sound and lighting plus an elevating stage which transforms into a dance floor.

NORTH PIER THEATRE
North Pier, Promenade, Blackpool, Lancashire FY1 1NE
Mgt/SD: 01253 621 452 BO: 01253 623 304
Email: admin@northpierblackpool.co.uk
Web Site: www.northpierblackpool.co.uk
ADMINISTRATION:
Props: Premier Pier (Blackpool) Ltd
General Manager: Dominic Herdman
Unit Controller: Martine Hagel
Policy: Summer Show
Perfs: Once Nightly
Seats: 1,500
TECHNICAL:
Stage: Proscenium Stage: Pros. Opening 10.49m; Ht. of Pros. 3.86m; Depth of S/Line 9.30m; Ht. of Grid 8.99m; 20 lines Hemp, 9 lines C/W; Scenery Flying Ht. 4.27m; Flying Bars 12.19m; W/Widths P.S. 2.59m, O.P. 2.59m; Prompt Cnr. P.S.
Lighting: Switchboard: ETL Lightmaster 500; 60 off 2kw dimmers fitted, provision for a further 30 dimmers; 500 cue capacity without disc; Disco facility included.
Sound Equip: Mixer is now Soundcraft 200B 16/4/2; Turbo Sound Speakers; Stereo sound in auditorium.
Other: Dressing Rooms 16; Accom. 30, 4 Bathrooms.

PARADISE ROOM
Blackpool FY4 1EZ
Stageworks Worldwide Productions Tel: 01253 342 426 or 01253 336 341
Email: info@stageworkswwp.com
Web Site: www.pleasurebeachblackpool.com
Capacity: theatre 600, classroom 350, dinner/cabaret 430, reception standing 700
State of the art sound and lighting systems and a rising stage. Panoramic views across the Blackpool promenade. Licensed for weddings and civil partnerships.

THE BRICK WORKSHOP THEATRE
The University Centre Bennett Avenue
Blackpool FY1 4EE
Tel: 01253 352 352
Email: ucreception@blackpool.ac.uk
Web Site: www.blackpool.ac.uk
Theatre Manager: Nigel Brown
Cap: 120

THE WINTER GARDENS COMPLEX
Incorporating The Empress Ballroom, Opera House, The Arena, The Pavilion Theatre, The Olympia, Spanish Hall.
Church Street, Blackpool, Lancashire FY1 1HW
Mgt: 01253 625 252 BO: 0844 856 1111
Fax: 01253 629 700 Marketing: 01253 629 811
Email: events@wintergardensblackpool.co.uk
Web: www.wintergardensblackpool.co.uk
ADMINISTRATION:
Props: Blackpool Borough Council, run by CC Ltd
General Manager: Kathy Smith
Theatre Manager: Linda Baker
Stage Manager: Duncan Jump
Policy: All types of Productions
Opera House Cap: 2,876 Seated
Empress Ballroom Cap: Reception up to 3000; Theatre 2700;
Inc. balconies 3000; School room 800; Buffet dance 2000; Banquet 1000.
Interlinking offices, bars, refreshment areas and presentation rooms.
Arena Cap: Reception 600; Theatre 400; Banquet 300; Dinner Dance 220
The Pavilion Theatre Cap: Theatre 600; Reception 700
The Olympia Cap: Banquet 400-1000; Caberet 200-1000; Classroom 200-800; Standing/Concert 1000-3500; Theatre 50-1000; Exhibition 50-300 stalls.
Spanish Hall Cap: Theatre 600; Banquet 500; Dinner dance 400
TECHNICAL:
OPERA HOUSE:
Stage: Proscenium Stage, Raked; Pros. opening 13.72m; Ht. of Pros. 9.14m; Depth of S/Line 13.41m; Ht. of Grid 21.34m; 94 lines, C/W Scenery Flying Ht. 9.14m P.S., O.P.; Flying Bars 17.68m; W/Widths P.S. 6.10m, O.P. 3.05m; Prompt Cnr. P.S.
Lighting: Switchboard: Galaxie II Rearstalls Control Room.
Other: Dressing Rooms 16; Accom. 100; 6 Backstage Showers; Orchestra Pit 22.
EMPRESS BALLROOM: L 49m x W 24m x H 19m.
General lighting, stereo sound with 16 mic, line inputs & mixing.
THE ARENA: L 35m x W 16m x H 11.7m.
General lighting with blackout; 4 inputs on stage, 100 watt amplifier & mixing; Direct exterior access
THE PAVILION THEATRE: Exhibition space - 1435 square metres.

Blackwood, Gwent

BLACKWOOD LITTLE THEATRE
Woodbine Road, Blackwood, Gwent NP2 1QJ Wales
Tel 01495 223 485
Email: blackwoodtheatre@googlemail.com
Web Site: www.blackwoodlt.org.uk
Technical Manager: Aneurin Brown
Publicity Manager: Huw Rosser
Main Auditorium Cap: 140

BLACKWOOD MINERS INSTITUTE
High Street, Blackwood, Gwent NP12 1BB Wales
BO: 01495 227 206 Fax: 01495 226 457
Email: bmi@caerphilly.gov.uk
Web Site: www.blackwoodminersinstitute.com
ADMINISTRATION
Props: Caerphilly County Borough Council
General Manager (Programming): Sharon Casey
Email: caseys@caerphilly.gov.uk
Technical Manager: Robin Bainbridge.
Email: bainbr@caerphilly.gov.uk
Cap: Auditorium; Floor level 156 seats, Rake 187 seats, Balcony 56 seats. Total: 399. Abingdon Studio, 20-30.
TECHNICAL:
STAGE: Proscenium arch opening 7.18m x 4.2m. Performance area 8.1m x 6m (including apron). Wing space 1.3m (SR/SL). Height to grid 5.04m at rear of stage, no flying. Tab tracks US, MS, DS. Stage raked 1:24, hardboard, suitable for dance (not barefoot). Dock Doors 2m x 2.5m. 'Flat' - Floor Space Performance Area; Floor space 14m x 9m (with rake & balcony seating only). Floor space 14m x 20m (fully retracted seating). Get-in; via car park at rear of building - double doors into the auditorium. White Cyclorama Cloth. Backstage crossover. Red House Tabs - operated from SR or control room. Orchestra area available by removing 4 rows of seats, accommodates 30. Petrof Baby Grand Piano, 7 Octave (lives on flat). 2 pairs of black legs available (4 in total). 6 of 10 x 6 Hard Black Maskers available. 12 stage weights & braces available. 12 of 6 x 4 steeldeck staging available. 9 of 8 x 4 steeldeck staging available. Various quantities of legs for steeldeck available (sizes 15', 30', 45').
LIGHTING: 3 colour wash & specials, 1 ETC Congo Jnr Lighting desk. Please contact the technical department for more information.
SOUND: Sound system available. Please contact the technical department for more information.
STAGE MANAGEMENT: Prompt positions SL & SR (SR in auditorium)
DRESSING ROOMS; 2, accommodating 34. Access by stairs. (Unfortunately backstage is not accessible for wheelchair users)

Blandford Forum, Dorset

THE COADE HALL THEATRE
The Coade Hall, Bryanston School, Blandford Forum, Dorset DT11 0PX
Box Office Tel: 01258 484 623
Email: clt@bryanston.co.uk
Web Site: www.bryanston.co.uk/theatre
Contact: Mark Humphris

Bletchley, Buckinghamshire

BLETCHLEY LEISURE CENTRE
Princes Way, Bletchley, Milton Keynes, Buckinghamshire MK2 2HQ
Tel 01908 377 251
Email: bletchley@miltonkeynesleisure.co.uk
Web Site: www.leisureconnection.co.uk
Manager: Sarah Davies
Main Hall Seating Capacity: 850 max.

WILTON HALL
Wilton Avenue, Bletchley, Buckinghamshire MK3 6BN
Tel: 01908 372 277 Fax: 01908 372 852
Email: info@wiltonhall.co.uk
Web Site: www.wiltonhall.co.uk
ADMINISTRATION
Props: Tony Manni
Cap: 300 Theatre style
For bookings contact Tony on Tel: 01908 372 277

Blyth, Northumberland

BLYTH SPORTS CENTRE
Bolam Avenue, Blyth, Northumberland NE24 5BT
Tel: 01670 542 222 Fax: 01670 368 384
Email: ADixon@activenorthumberland.org.uk
Web: www.activenorthumberland.org.uk
ADMINISTRATION
Props: Blyth Valley Borough Council
Cap: 800
Manager: Adam Dixon

CONCORDIA LEISURE CENTRE
Forum Way, Cramlington, Northumberland NE23 6YB
Tel: 01670 542 222 Fax: 01670 590 648
Email: cwinfield@activenorthumberland.org.uk
Web Site: www.activenorthumberland.org.uk
ADMINISTRATION
Props: Blyth Valler Arts and Leisure
Manager: Colin Winfield
2 Dance Studios, 2 Function rooms

PHOENIX THEATRE
37A Beaconsfield Street, Blyth, Northumberland NE24 2DS
BO: 01670 367 228 Admin: 01670 540 668 Fax: 01670 366 446
Email: admin@thephoenixtheatre.org.uk
Web Site: www.thephoenixtheatre.org.uk
ADMINISTRATION:
Manager: Richie Ross
Technical Manager: Paul Worth
Phoenix Theatre is a new small scale venue catering for community theatre (non professional) and a full scale professional touring programme. The theatre is fully equipped with sound and lighting systems and a manual, hemp flying system. The programme is varied and seeks to introduce various arts and mixed media events to the town.
Main Auditorium/Studio and Bar are available for hire. To enquire about booking the Phoenix, please contact Richie Ross.
Capacity: 299
TECHNICAL DETAILS
Contact Technical Manager

Bognor Regis, West Sussex

Pop. 33,910. London 65 miles.
Newspapers: B R Observer (thurs); Promoter (wed); Journal (wed); Guardian (thurs). STD code 01243

THE REGIS CENTRE
Belmont Street, Bognor Regis, West Sussex PO21 1BL
Admin: 01243 867 676 BO Tel/Fax: 01243 861 010
Email: mike.stevens@regiscentre.co.uk
Web Site: www.regiscentre.co.uk
ADMINISTRATION:
Centre Manager: Mike Stevens
Senior Technician: Andy
Administrator: Jane Goldstein
The Alexandra Theatre, Studio, Gallery are all available for hire.
Theatre Cap: 357 (194 in the stalls & 163 in the circle). This capacity is reduced to 334 when using the Orchestra pit or apron
Studio Cap: 100 seated theatre style
Gallery Cap: 60 Seated
TECHNICAL:
Stage: Proscenium arch. Performing area 9.14m x 9.14m; Pros. opening 9.14m x 5.49m; wing widths 4.57m S.R., 4.57m S.L., no rake; Floor - plywood on battens, suitable for dance (not barefoot); backstage crossover; stage heated; height of grid to lowest block 7.4m; 10 hemp sets at 250 Kg. each, 6 winches at 500 Kg. each, 1 winch at 250 Kg.; 4 sets black legs & borders; 1 set black tabs; 1 set silver tabs; 1 set orange/red house tabs. Back wall used as Cyclorama. 7 x 13 Amp. & 8 x 15 Amp. independant circuits. Forestage entrance in front of Pros. Orchestra pit on hydraulic lift. Get in via doors from car park. Tallescope. Safety curtain. Plans available.
Lighting: Zero 88 Frog Board, 88 x 2 Kw. & 8 x 5 Kw. circuits.
Other: Stage management: Prompt corner S.R. cue lights & headsets; show relays to all rooms. 5 dressing rooms, access by stage door. Iron, washing machine & tumble dryer available.
Perfs: as required.
Seats: 364 capacity, 4 wheelchair spaces, induction loop.
Equipment (Theatre)
For Tech. Spec. please contact venue.

Bolton, Lancashire

Pop. 261,000. London 195 miles.
Newspapers: Evening News (ntly); Metro News (thurs). STD code 01204

ALBERT HALLS
Victoria Square, Bolton, Lancashire BL1 1RU
Tel: 01204 334 306 Fax: 01204 523 945
BO: 01204 334 400 Mgt: 01204 334 305
Email: info@alberthalls-bolton.co.uk
Web Site: www.alberthalls-bolton.co.uk
ADMINISTRATION:
Props: Bolton Council
General Manager: Christine Forster
Business Development Manager: Chris Cordingley. Tel: 01204 334366
Technical Manager: Alan Flatley
Email: alan.flatley@bolton.gov.uk
Policy: Concert hall used for concerts, recitals, opera, ballet, fashion shows, exhibitions, children's entertainment, pantomime. Booking Terms: Hire, box office split, guarantee and split, guarantee by negotiation.
Seating/Capacity: Full Theatre 673; Theatre + 2m stage extension 592; Standing & balcony 850; Cabaret & balcony 356; Wrestling & Boxing 566
For room hire contact the Sales Office on 01204 334301.
TECHNICAL:
Alan Flatley - Technical Manager
Telephone: 01204 334308 Fax: 01204 399928
E-Mail: alan.flatley@bolton.gov.uk
STAGE: Thrust. Performing area 16m x 6m, wing widths dependant on masking. No rake, floor sprung wood, suitable for all dance, backstage crossover, 6 stage heated or cooled. 8 Lx Bars 750 Kg Max. permitted on bar, very flexible rig more bars can be added or removed. Black masking, white cyclorama. Proscenium Arch and black fibre optic starcloth available at no extra cost. 13 x 30A ring mains. Piano hoist, centre stage. 2m x 14m Stage extension available. Orchestra pit, dimensions variable according to number of seats removed. Get in via ground floor. Scale stage plans available.
LIGHTING: Bar 1-2 channels 01 - 24

location: FOH 15Amp sockets; Bar 3 -10 channels 25 - 72 location: Stage15Amp sockets; Stage boxes channels 73 - 90 location: flexible 15Amp sockets; Practical channels P1 - P6 location: flexible; Channels 60 - 70 are patchable to either stage or the rig.
LIGHTING DESK: Zero88 bullfrog
SOUND: Nexo P515's, P510's and subs, Bose 802 and 803, 4 foldback monitors, 3 x 1 K Mos fet amps, graphic equaliser/digital delay AKG, 1 cassette tape deck/CD, basic facilities for recording and editing. Acoustics suitable for music and spoken word.
OTHER: Stage management: Show relay/Tannoy to dressing rooms. Talk-back system. Backstage: 5 dressing rooms, band room, quick change rooms. Refreshments available, tea/coffee/sandwiches if requested beforehand. Steinway Grand piano on stage only 2 Rehearsal pianos can be placed in any rooms. 3 TVs & Videos, 4 OHPs, 2 Slide Projectors, 5 Portable Front Progection Screens, 1 Front & Back Projection Screen 10"

OCTAGON THEATRE

Howell Croft South, Bolton, Lancashire BL1 1SB
Admin: 01204 529 407 BO: 01204 520 661 Fax: 01204 556 502
Email: info@octagonbolton.co.uk
Web Site: www.octagonbolton.co.uk
ADMINISTRATION:
Props: Octagon Theatre Trust Ltd
Executive Director: Roddy Gould
Artistic Director: David Thacker
Technical Manager: Andy Smith
Production Manager: Oliver Seviour
Head of Marketing: Helen Jones
Policy: Repertory (4-weekly)
Perfs: Evenings 7.30, Matinees 2.00pm.
Seats on average: 389
Bar, Coffee Bar, Pre-Theatre Dining
TECHNICAL:
Octagon Theatre:
Stage: Flexible Stage hence variation in seating. Round 7.95m x 5.4m; Thrust 7.95m x 8.00m; Open 17.00m x 7.20m; Ht. of Grid 7.00m; Prompt Cnr. F.O.H. Control Box.
Lighting: Switchboard: Compulite Applause 286 with back-up. 64 x 2.5 Kw Lee Dimmers: Circs 1-20 Patchable: Circs 21-64 Hardwired, Lanterns: 8 x T84, 2 x T64, 10 x 16/30, 6 x 764, 6 x 264, 22 x 23, 2 x Sil 15, 2 x 23N, 10 x Starlette, 10 x MFR, 24 x 123, 4 x 804, 8 Parcans, 2 x Coda 4, 1 x 252, 16 Parcans.
Sound Equip: 16 Way Soundcraft Delta 2 x B77, 1 x A77, 1 x ADC Disc, 2 x H + H M900 AMB, 8 way speaker patch, 10 x 8" Cabs, 2 x JUC 15" Cabs, 1 x SM58, 1 x 14L, 2 x 803 + ME40.
Communications: Full F.O.H. and B/S Paging Relay, 16 way Q Light System (all installed) 5 Belt Packs.
Bill Naughton Theatre:
Flexible seating for 80.

Lighting: Switchboard: Tempus M24 + Tempus 24 Way 2 G: 4 x 6 way Tempus 15A Racks: 56 way 15 amp patch.Lanterns: Shared with main house. Speak to Chief LX.
Sound Equipment: 1 x Revox 377, 1 x Studio Master - 2 - 1, 1 x Stella Amp, 2 x 8" cabs, 8 x XLR TIE Lines, 4 way speaker patch.
Other: Communications: Full F.O.H. and B/S Paging, 3 Belt Packs.
Dressing Rooms 2; Accom. 8; 1 Shower.
Membership: TMA

Boston, Lincolnshire

Pop. 26,230. London 116 miles.
Newspapers; see Lincoln. STD code 01205

BLACKFRIARS ARTS CENTRE

Spain Lane, Boston, Lincolnshire PE21 6HP
Mgt :01205 363 075 BO: 01205 363 108
Email: director@blackfriars.uk.com
Web Site: www.blackfriarsartscentre.co.uk
ADMINISTRATION:
Props: Blackfriars Arts Centre Ltd
Technical Manager: Megan Rodgers
Policy: Touring, Amateurs, Outreach and Community Arts Development
Auditorium Seats: 229 constant raked.
Fully licensed bar.
TECHNICAL:
Stage: Proscenium Stage with 0.91m apron, Flat: Pros. Opening 7.32m; Ht. of Pros. 3.96m; Depth of S/Line 7.32m; Ht. of Grid 9.14m; 17 lines, 20 stage weights. 10 braces; Scenery Flying Ht. 9.14m; Flying Bars 6.40m; W/Widths P.S. 2.05m, O.P. 1.44m; Prompt Cnr. P.S. Vinyl dance floor available with advanced notice.
Lighting: Switchboard: ETC Express 48 Channels; Control Box at rear of Auditorium; 8 1000w Sil 15 with attached Croma-Q Scrollers permanent FOH ;8 Selacon Pacific Profiles FOH; 10 Selacon Cyc. Floods ; 18 650 watt Fresnels ; 36 IWB channels as follow 12 FOH, 2 perch, 10 bar 1, 6 bar 2, 6 bar 3 ; 12 channels as floor dips
Sound Equipment: 1 Spirit Digital 328 Desk, 2 EV sx500 speakers installed in pros., 2 EV sx300 speakers+ 2 EV sx200 speakers for foldback, 2 sm58 mics, 4 AKG C1000s mics, 3 Crown Plate mics, 5 Tie-clip radio mics, 1 Twin Cassette deck, 2 mini disc decks, 2 CD Players with autopause.
Other: Dressing Rooms 3; Accom. 20, Please note no showers. Washing machine & Tumble dryer; Show Relay.

Bourne, Lincolnshire

BOURNE LEISURE CENTRE

Queens Road, Bourne, Lincolnshire PE10 9DX
Tel: 01778 421 435 Fax: 01778 394 528
Email: bourne@1life.co.uk
Web Site: www.1life.co.uk/bourneleisure-centre
ADMINISTRATION
Props: Leisure Connection Ltd
Hall Cap: 600 (stage facilities)
Business Manager: David Downs
Duty Manager: Bobby Blow

THE CORN EXCHANGE

Abbey Road, Bourne, Lincolnshire PE10 9EF
Bkgs: 01778 423 579
Email: i.bland@bournecornexchange.co.uk
Web Site: www.southkesteven.gov.uk
ADMINISTRATION:
Props: South Kesteven District Council
Site Manager: Ian Bland
Bkg Contact: Ian Bland
Cap: Theatre - seated 200
The main hall features a small stage with sound and lighting facilities. The hall is excellent for large conferences up to 300 delegates or can easily be partitioned for smaller events.
The venue can be hired year round by all members of the community.

Bournemouth & Boscombe, Dorset

Pop. 153,000. London 104 miles.
Newspapers: Evening Echo (ntly); Bournemouth Times (fri). STD code 01202

BOURNEMOUTH INTERNATIONAL CENTRE

Exeter Road, Bournemouth, Dorset BH2 5BH
Tel: 01202 456 400 BO: 0844 576 3000
Fax: 01202 456 500 Party Bookings Tel: 01202 451865
Email: steve.turner@bhlive.co.uk
Web Site: www.bic.co.uk
ADMINISTRATION:
Props: Borough of Bournemouth
Managing Director: Peter Gunn.
Technical Coordinator: Christian Knighton (Tel: 01202 451891)
Stage Manager: Simon Bagnell (Tel: 01202 451899)
Entertainments Mgt: Steve Turner (Tel: 01202 456400)
Policy: 4 Multipurpose halls used for concerts, entertainment, sporting and special events, conferences and exhibitions.
Seating/Capacity: Windsor Hall 4,000 seated, 6,500 standing. Seated and

Standing 4,750.
Solent Hall - Cap: Seated 1,300, Standing 2,500
Tregonwell Hall - Cap 1,100 Seated
Purbeck Hall - Cap 1000 seated, Standing 2000
TECHNICAL:
Windsor Hall
Stage: Sico portable staging available - Maximum size 64' X 40'
Lighting: Control ETC Express - 120 ETC Dimmers
Sound: Yamaha DM1000 Digital Mixer feeding D&B Line array System.
Full specification on request

Solent Hall
Stage: Steeldeck stage maximum size 40' X 28'
Lighting: Strand GSX - 96 Permus Dimmers
Sound: Allen & Heath Mixer - into D&B sound system
Full Specification on request

Tregonwell Hall
Stage fixed - 38' Wide X 28'
Lighting: Strand GSX - 66 Dimmers
Sound: Soundcraft 24/4/2 Spirit Live into Bose speaker system
Full specification on request

Purbeck Hall
Stage: Steeldeck built size to suit the event
Lighting: Strand GSX - 48 Dimmers
Sound: Soundcraft 12/2/2 Spirit Live into Bose speaker system

PAVILION THEATRE & BALLROOM

Westover Road, Bournemouth, Dorset BH1 2BU
Mgt: 01202 451 869 BO: 0844 576 3000
Ents Dep: 01202 456 436 Fax: 01202 451 024 Party Bookings Tel: 01202 451 865
Email: steve.turner@bhlive.co.uk
Web Site: www.bic.co.uk
ADMINISTRATION:
PAVILION THEATRE:
Props: BH Live
Chief Executive: Peter Gunn
Entertainments Programming Manager: Steve Turner Tel: 01202 456499
General Manager: Paul Griffiths
Technical Coordinator: Christian Knighton Tel: 01202 451 891
Stage Manager: Simon Bagnall Tel: 01202 451 899
Policy: Plays, Ballet, Opera, Musicals, Comedy, Pantomime, Summer Spectaculars, one night stand concerts, pop, rock, MOR.
Perfs: Vary with type of attraction.
Capacity: 1458. Bars and Restaurants.
PAVILION BALLROOM: 1053m2
Capacity: 600 (theatre style); 600 (banquet style); 900 (reception style).
TECHNICAL:
Pavilion Theatre:
STAGE: Proscenium Stage, Flat mahogany Hard-wood; 13.51m x 6.5m x 12.33m. Height of grid 14.76m, 50 lines c/w, scenery flying height 14.02, Flying bars 13.41, W/widths P.S. 4.87m, O.P. 6.10m, Prompt Corner S.L. Orchestra Pit 15.24m x 2.74m.
LIGHTING:ETC Congo 300 x 3kw Dimmers,. Two 2kw Xenon Limelight follow spots.
SOUND: Soundcraft Spirit Live 24/4/2, Bose Speakers FOH, 2 X JBL Bass Bins, 2 x Bose 802 Foldback. Various Mics
DRESSING ROOMS: 17, accommodating 150.

Pavilion Ballroom:
STAGE: Concert Platform Stage - w 11.26m x d 5m x h 3m; 22" high off the ground apron; plus additional Steeldeck stage units available on request.
SOUND - Soundcraft Spirit Folio 12/4/2 mixer with CD and Mini Disk Player in a portable rack. Various amplifiers and speakers throughout.
LIGHTS - House lighting by chandeliers. Small rig of stage lighting suspended over dancefloor.

Bracknell, Berkshire

Pop. 80,000 (district). Newspapers: Reading Evening Post (dly); Bracknell News; Bracknell Times. STD code 01344

BRACKNELL SPORT & LEISURE CENTRE

Bagshot Road, Bracknell, Berkshire RG12 9SE
Tel: 01344 404 791 Fax: 01344 868 511
Email: bslc.enquiries@bracknell-forest.gov.uk
Web Site: www.bracknell-forest.gov.uk/be
ADMINISTRATION
Props: Bracknell Forest Borough Council
Cap: Main Hall 1000; Function Suite 450
Sport Centre Manager: Gareth Jones (Tel: 01344 355 444)
For bookings, contact: Caroline Smith, Maureen Selvon

SOUTH HILL PARK ARTS CENTRE

Ringmead, Bracknell, Berkshire RG12 7PA
Admin: 01344 484 858 BO: 01344 484 123 Fax: 01344 411 427
Email: enquiries@southhillpark.org.uk
Web Site: www.southhillpark.org.uk
ADMINISTRATION:
The Wilde Theatre is part of the Arts Centre complex, which also includes a cinema, recital room, gallery, art and craft studios, workshops, rehearsal rooms, 50 seat studio theatre, and two bars.
Props: Bracknell Forest Borough Council
Chief Executive: Ron McAllister
Technical Manager: Joe Malyan
Tel: 01344 413 531 Email: joe.malyan@southhillpark.org.uk
Policy: In-house theatre and music theatre productions, mid-scale theatre, music theatre and dance tours, concerts, amateur companies.
Seats: 328 (plus 70 standing) or 300 (with orchestra pit).
TECHNICAL:
Wilde Theatre:
STAGE: Stage width; 49', 16m. Prosc. Width; 27'6", 8.4m. Dock Doors - 2390mm x 3920mm. Stage Depth; 30'9", 9.38m. Stage Height, Floor to Grid; 26', 8m. Flying: 14 x Single purchase counterweight sets, 8 x Four line hemp sets, 1 x Separate counterweight set for house tabs. Operated from stage DSL, 1 x Motorised bar for cyclorama, blacks etc.
LIGHTING: Control; ETC Ion, 1000 channels. Dimmers; ETC Sensor dimmers, 130 x 3kW, 6 x 5Kw. Lanterns; 28 x Robert Juliat 310 fresnel 1.2 kW. 8 x Strand Harmony Fresnels 1kW. 4 x Strand Prelude Fresnels 650W. 22 x ETC Source 4 zooms 15/30 750W. 24 x ETC Source 4 zooms 22/50 750W. 4 x Strand Harmony Profiles 1kW. 30 x Parcan CP62 ONLY 1kW. 12 x Strand Iris 1 Floods 1kW. 5 x Strand coda 4 (4 x 500W floods). 2 x UV Canon 300W. 1 x Robert Juliat Marius followspot (1.2kW MSR).
SOUND: Mixer #1, 32 mono/8 VCA / 8 Audio/2 (+4 stereo) Soundcraft MH3. Mixer #2, 12 channel Soundcraft Spirit Folio. Graphics; Clarke Teknik DN360; Also 1 x BSS and 1 x Rane. Effects; 1 x SPX900, 1 x SPX990. Compressor; 8 channel Klark Teknik Square One. CD Player: Denon C630. Minidisc: Denon DNM 2000r. Amps: QSC RMX 5050, Crown Macrotech 2402, Crown 460 CSL. Speakers: 4 x Nexo PS15, 2 x Nexo LS1200, 4 x EV SX300.
STAGE COMMUNICATIONS: Prompt desk is DSR (can be moved into LX box for theatre in-the-round). Cuelight and headset facility. Backstage and foyer tannoy. Show relay to dressing rooms, green room.
Headsets: 5 x single muff. One channel. Flash button. 1 x double muff. One channel. Flash button.
BACKSTAGE FACILITIES: 3, accommodating; 32. 1 x Washing machine, 1 x Tumble dryer, 3 x Toilets, 2 x Showers. Show relay; To all dressing rooms, green room.

Bradford, West Yorkshire

Pop. 483,000. London 195 miles. Newspapers: Telegraph & Argus (ntly). STD code 01274

ALHAMBRA THEATRE AND STUDIO

Morley Street, Bradford, West Yorkshire BD7 1AJ
Mgt/SD: 01274 432 375 BO: 01274 432 000 Fax: 01274 742 736
Email: adam.renton@bradford.gov.uk
Web Site: www.bradford-theatres.co.uk
ADMINISTRATION:
Props: City of Bradford Metropolitan District Council
Seats: 1,453. 3 Bars & Bistro
Manager: Adam Renton
Programme Manager: Laura Wood
Deputy General Manager: Laura Wood
Theatre Operations Admin Officer: Bev Barnes
Stage Manager: Martin Small
Senior Marketing Officer: Liz Hall
Policy: Touring Opera, Ballet, Drama, Musicals, Pantomime and Concerts.
TECHNICAL:
Stage: Proscenium Stage, Flat; Pros Opening 10.8m; Pros Height 7.5m; Pros Height to bottom of pelment 7.0m; Depth of S/Line to B/wall 15m; Height of Grid 18m; 88 c/w lines plus two up and down bars each side, flying bars 15.7m; W widths P.S. 4.5m; O.P. 4m; Orchestra Pit seats 30-60; Scene dock 13.3m x 10.6m. Technical Workshop facilities, wardrobe facilities including 4 extra washer/drier points.
Lighting Equipment: Lighting Board - RSE Gemini 2 + 360 way; F.O.H. Lighting Circuits - 38; Stage Lighting Circuits - 112 (+40 extras). Circuits - 1.132: 2.5kw; 133.150 : 5kw; 151.190 : 2.5kw; 6 internally wired bars - 5 x 18 way; 1 x 12 way. Lanterns - F.O.H. - 8 pairs of 1.2kw optiques. Loose Equipment: 20 x 1k axial sil 15, 10 x 1k sil 15. Harmony 15.28 Profile x 14; Harmony 22.40 Profile x 20; Harmony F Fresnel 1kw x 48; Cadenza Fresnel 2kw x 2; Iris 1 - 1kw Flood x 26; 4 Circuit Thomas Groundrow x 5; Follow Spots - RSE Solo x 3; Pan Can 64's x 40, Ancillary Power - 250A TPNE located on stage level DSR, 400 TPNE Located on fly floor D.S.R. - Down Stage Right. 12 x 6 way 20m Multicore. Bradford Centre Theatres will provide within reason all F.O.H. colour in LEE filter.
Sound: Desk & Stage: A & H Saber Desk with 24 into 8 into 8. 72 Mic inputs around stage area including 2 x 19 way stage-box - All appearing on Jack Field in control room. 8 Tie line sockets around the stage area plus 24 in control room - All appearing on Jack Field in control room. 2 x B77 Revox reel to reel tape machine 15/17.5 i.p.s. 2 x Technics Cassette Machine; 1 x Technics CD Player 1 x Denon cassette player, 1 x Pioneer CD player (6 disc), 2 x 31 band graphic equaliser, 1 x spx 1000, 1 x DMPX; 1 x Yamaha DMD7.
AMPS: Yamaha PZ2002 main amps drive pros left (2) - right (2) - cluster (2) - subbass L&R (1) plus 2 floating for foldback. Main PA operating with Meyer Limiters.
Speaker System: All Meyer UPA1 (4 x pros. L & R) (4 x centre top Cluster) with back up re-inforcement on digital delay in rear Stalls, Circle, Balcony, 2 x Sub bass units (Meyer) USW/1; Foldback 2 x Yamaha Wedge S2115 HZ; 2 x Yamaha S3115H (general work); 2 x EV Eliminatir 10. 2 x DVB Audiotechnik HON 15 wedger Patchable Speaker Outlets EP3's; 8 on Stage; 4 Orchesta; 12 Auditorium; 2 Flys; 2 Understage. Apply to the theatre for further details.
DRESSING ROOMS:
Dressing room accommodation: 72 places, company office, technical office.

ALHAMBRA STUDIO:
Small performance/ rehearsal area, 15.7m x 25.5m including 2 dressing rooms (accommodating up to 20 people), which can also be used in conjunction with those for the main house. The rehearsal area's dimensions corresponds with the working area of the main stage. Seats up to 200 in theatre style.
Technical:
6 x 8m motorised Flying Bars (S.W.L. 300kg each).
Lighting Board R.S.E. Lightboard M; Lighting Circuits: 72 appearing as 12 per electric flying bar or patchable to floor area; Ancillary Power - 100A TPNE located at stage level.
Membership: TMA

DENHOLME MECHANICS INSTITUTE

Main Road, Denholme, Bradford, West Yorkshire BD13 4BL
Hall Bkgs Tel: 01943 436 224 Tel: 01274 833 613
Email: christopher.ashton@bradford.gov.uk
Web Site: www.bradford.gov.uk
ADMINISTRATION
Props: City of Bradford Metropolitan District Council
Cap: 300
Denholme Mechanics Institute offers various rooms and facilities for hire.
Cap: Main Hall 200 - ideal for parties and social functions;
Blue Room 100; Reading Room 25 - ideal for small meetings.
Bookings contact: Chris Ashton

ST GEORGE'S CONCERT HALL

Bridge Street, Bradford, West Yorkshire BD1 1JT
Mgt: 01274 432 374 BO: 01274 432 000
Tech: 01274 431 963 Hiring: 01274 433 626 SD: 01274 432 375
Email: administration@bradford-theatres.co.uk
Web Site: www.bradford-theatres.co.uk
ADMINISTRATION:
Props: City of Bradford Metropolitan District Council
Manager: Adam Renton
Stage Manager: Martin Small.
Email: martin.small@bradford.gov.uk
Contact (Venue Hire): Helen Green or Caroline Fellows
Email: helen.green@bradford.gov.uk
Capacity: 1790 Standing, 1490 Seated.
Policy: Comedy; Rock and Pop; Children's; Ballet; Orchestral Season
Four bars and Restaurant/Buffet.
TECHNICAL:
STAGE: Plywood finish with nil rake.
Dimensions: Total width of stage: 47' 5'' (14.5 m). Total width-flying: 41' (12.5 m). Total depth of stage: 37' (11.5 m). Height to truss 1 out dead: 39' 9'' (12.10m). Height to truss 2 out dead: 38' 1'' (11.60m). Height to truss 3 out dead: 33' (10.06m). Height to Box truss out-Dead: 35'8" (10.87m). Height to ceiling: 49' (15.0 m). Height from stage to hanging points in roof: 51' (15.54m). Height from stalls floor to hanging points in roof: 54' 8" (16.66m). Height from auditorium floor to lip of stage: 4' ½" (1.24m). Height of overhang above stage: 6'3" (1.90m). 15 stage weights and various braces are available. Back stage exits from stage up stage left and right. Cross over via back stage load in area. Get in Doors: Width 4'5½" (1.36m), Height 7'11" (2.41m).
Choir Stalls: 98 Bench seats at rear of stage 6'10½" 2 m above stage. A variety of drapes available. Flying Trusses: Electrically Operated Winches, 3 x Custom built triangular steel truss - S.W.L. 1000kg evenly spread from 4 hanging points.
LIGHTING: Control: Avolite Pearl 2008 positioned in Rear of Stalls in Private Room with View of Stage. Lx Rig: 36 x Black 1kw Parcans (Cp62 Lamps) Limited Other Lamps Available Cp60 x 6, Cp61 x 6, 6 x Black Floor Parcans, 6 x Source Four Profiles 36 degree + 4 x 19 degree lens tubes, 12 Source 4 15/30 Profiles (F.O.H) Centre of Grand Tier Level, 2 x 6 way IWB's with 6 chrome Par 64s on each, 2 x 6 way IWB's with 6 Black Par 64s on each, 2 X Ivanhoe 2.5K Follow-Spots at Centre Rear of Grand Tier, 36 Dimmers Overhead (12 per triangular truss), 12 Dimmers (F.O.H), 7 Dimmers On Stage. Large Stock of Lee Gel. House Lights DMX
SOUND: 1 x Allen & Heath GL3300 24-8-2 Mixer, 1 x Yamaha SPX 1000 Multi-Effects Processor, 1 x Denon DCD 615 Compact Disc Player, 2 x Denon DRM 540 Cassette Players, 1 x Sony MDS JE530 Minidisc Player/Recorder.
Speakers: 2 x Bose 302's (Bass Bins) In Stalls, 4 x Bose 802's In Stalls, 4 x Bose 802's Cluster (On Front Truss), 2 x Bose 802's In Dress Circle, 2 x Turbo Sound Txd 530's In Grand Tier, 4 x D+B Monitor Wedges. Amplifiers: 5 x Crest FA 90i-300+300 Amps, 1 x Bose 1800-400+400 Amps. Microphones: 4 x SM 58, 1 x Shure SM58 Switched Mic, 4 x C451, 2 x PCC 160, 2 x BSS DI Boxes, Various Other Mics, DI's, On Request.
STAGE COMMUNICATIONS: Show Relay & Paging System to All Dressing Rooms. 5 Way Tech Pro Headset Communication

To Stage L & R Lighting, Soundbox And Followspots
DRESSING ROOMS: 8 with w/basin, accommodating 30. Orchestra Room / Catering, accommodating 60. 1 x Sink 2 x electric cookers, 1 x microwave, 1 x fridge, 1x freezer. Show relay and paging facilities to all rooms. 2 x showers in the male toilets & 2 self contained (Female). A washing machine and dryer is available in the orchestra room / catering.
ADDITIONAL: Orchestra Equipment: 97 Red plush chairs and a conductor's rostrum are also available, 10 Illuminated R.A.T. music stands available on request, 1 Illuminated Conductors R.A.T music stand. Pianos: 1 x Steinway Model B Grand Piano, 1 x Upright Rehearsal Piano.

THEATRE IN THE MILL
University of Bradford, Shearbridge Road, Bradford, West Yorkshire BD7 1DP
Tech: 01274 233 190 BO: 01274 233 200 General: 01274 233 185
Email: theatre@bradford.ac.uk
Web Site: www.bradford.ac.uk/theatre
ADMINISTRATION:
Props: University of Bradford
Artistic Director & Programming: Iain Bloomfield
Administrator: Ruth Prendergast
Email: r.prendergast@bradford.ac.uk
Technical Director: Ivan Mack (Tel: 01274 233 190)
Policy: Commissioning and support for the development of new work and practice. Hosts regular theatre workshop events. New Writing & Emerging Artists. Home to the University of Bradford Theatre Group.
Perfs: Variable. Three annual seasons.
Cap: Flexible Seating from 0-100. Theatre Bar.
TECHNICAL:
Stage: Great Flexibility of both stage and lighting.
Lighting: Tempus M24 & M24 FX plus Tempus 24 & Tempus 6-way desks, 4 Patt.23, 12 Patt.123, 4 Patt.743, 3 Battens, 6 flood, 26 minuet fresnels, 2 Sil - 30 profiles, 8 prelude 28/40 profiles, 6 prelude 16/30 profiles, 10 prelude P.C., 4 Patt.264s, 8 Patt.223s.
Sound Equip: Studiomaster 16/4/2 Mixing desk; Teac 0.25 Track Reel to Reel; Revox A77 DENON DRM 400, Yamaha KX 330 Cassette Deck, Cassette Deck; Garrard 401 Record Deck; 2 Bose 802, 2 Bose 402, 2Bose 101 Speaker; Mosfet 600 W & Mosefet 300 W Amps; 2 Quod 303 Amps; 1 HH Echo & Reverb. Unit; 1 Technical Projects 2 Circuit Communication System with 3 portable headset stations, and show relay/paging to dressing rooms and FOH; 6 mics. with flexible Mic. and speaker line system. Additional equipment available if requested in advance.
Other: 1 Dressing Room, Max. Accom. 12, Shower.

VICTORIA HALL
Station Road, Queensbury, Bradford, West Yorkshire BD13 1AB
Tel: 01274 883 978
Web Site: www.bradford.gov.uk
ADMINISTRATION
Props: City of Bradford Metropolitan District Council
Hall Cap: 250
Dance Studio also available for hire.
Bookings Contact: Josie Mamood, Philip Haley

VICTORIA HALL
Victoria Road, Saltaire, West Yorkshire BD18 3JS
Tel: 01274 327 305
Email: hello@victoriahallsaltaire.co.uk
Web Site: www.victoriahallsaltaire.co.uk
ADMINISTRATION
Props: Shipley College
Cap: Main Hall 300; Ancilliary Rooms 140, 80, 140, 40
For Bookings, contact: Vicky Summers

Bradford-on-Avon, Wiltshire

ST MARGARET'S HALL
St Margaret's Street, Bradford-on-Avon, Wiltshire BA15 1DE
Tel: 01225 864 240
Email: townclerk@bradfordonavontown-council.gov.uk
Web Site: www.bradfordonavontown-council.gov.uk
ADMINISTRATION
Props: Bradford on Avon Town Council
Cap: Standing 380; Seated 190
For bookings enquiries, contact: Tim Yeomans (01225 309 210)

Braintree, Essex

BRAINTREE LEISURE CENTRE
Panfield Lane, Braintree, Essex CM7 1FF
Tel: 01376 552 585 Fax: 01376 344 195
Email: enquiries@braintreeleisurecentre.co.uk
Web Site: www.dcleisurecentres.co.uk
ADMINISTRATION
Props: Braintree District Council
Manager: Greg Sandridge
Private Function Hire in the Terrace Rooms & Gallery Bar.

HIGH BARN
Currently closed as up for sale.
28 the Bardfield Centre Great Bardfield Braintree, Essex CM7 4SL
Tel: 01371 811 291
Email: info@high-barn.com
Web Site: www.high-barn.com
Cap. 200 standing
110 seated plus 60 standing
Manager: Paul Boon

Brechin, Angus

BRECHIN CITY HALL
9 Swan Street, Brechin, Angus DD9 6EE Scotland
Tel: 01356 623088 Council Tel: 01307 461 460 Bkg Fax: 01307 462 590
Email: haddenl@angus.gov.uk
Web Site: www.angus.gov.uk
ADMINISTRATION:
Props: Angus Council
Cap: Main Hall 360; Lesser Hall (ideal for meetings and conferences) 90
Hall Bookings Administrator: Barry Stirling

BRECHIN LEISURE CENTRE
Inch Park, Brechin, Angus DD9 7EQ Scotland
Tel: 01356 623 088
Email: conberclc@angus.gov.uk
Web Site: www.angus.gov.uk
ADMINISTRATION:
Props: Angus Council
Manager: Barry Stirling
Main Hall Cap: 160 plus. Ideal for birthday parties. Also 1 meeting room available for hire.

Brecon, Powys

THEATR BRYCHEINIOG
Canal Wharf, Brecon, Powys LD3 7EW
Tel: 01874 622 838 BO: 01874 611 622
Email: heidi@brycheiniog.co.uk
Web Site: www.theatrbrycheiniog.co.uk
Director: Paula Redway
Theatr Brycheiniog provides multi-purpose spaces for use by professional touring companies, the community and voluntary groups. Theatr Brycheiniog presents quality theatre, dance, opera, concerts, exhibitions, conferences and is one of the venues for the very successful Brecon Jazz Festival.
Cap: 477 seated.
Stage dimensions:
Width 14.5m, depth 12.3m (with orchestra pit 15.3m)
Height: 11.1m (not a full height fly tower)
disabled resources Level access and lifts to all public areas. Disabled toilets. Spaces for wheelchair users in the stalls and balcony. Infra red system for the hard of hearing. Guide dogs welcome. Reserved parking. Information about events available in large print.
notes Two get-ins, one at street level via workshop, the other at lorry height straight on to the stage
4 dressing rooms plus a rehearsal studio / conference room holding up to 150 people

Brentwood, Essex

THE BRENTWOOD CENTRE
Doddinghurst Road, Pilgrims Hatch, Brentwood, Essex CM15 9NN
Bkg: 01277 215 151 BO: 0871 2241113
Email: enquiries@brentwoodleisure.co.uk
Web Site: www.brentwood-centre.co.uk
Events Manager: Phil Thomas
Props: Brentwood Leisure Trust
2,000 seater Event Hall, Cafeteria, Bar, 3 meeting rooms and 1 gallery room.

BRENTWOOD THEATRE
15 Shenfield Road, Brentwood, Essex CM15 8AG
BO: 01277 200 305 Admin: 01277 230 833 Stage door: 01277 226 658
Email: david@brentwood-theatre.org
Web Site: www.brentwood-theatre.org
ADMINISTRATION:
Props: Brentwood Theatre Trust
Cap: Seated 80-170; Standing 270
Production Manager: David Zelly
Email: david@brentwood-theatre.org

Brentwood Theatre is a professional, community theatre based in the town centre, giving access to professional and non-professional performers. Musicals, plays, recitals, drama, comedy and children's shows are all represented at this unique and friendly venue, with a different show nearly every week.
TECHNICAL:
Full lighting and sound rig, jands LX desk soundcraft spirit sound desk 10m x 7m acting area. Flat floor stage. Tiered moveable seating. F.O.H and licensed bar.

Bridgend, Mid Glamorgan

BLAENGARW WORKMEN'S HALL
Blaengarw Road, Blaengarw, Bridgend, Mid Glamorgan CF32 8AW Wales
Tel: 07989506154
Web Site: www.bridgend.gov.uk
ADMINISTRATION
Props: Bridgend County Borough Council
Cap: Hall 220; dance studio 40 seated
Manager: Donald Sage
Proscenium arch. Performing area 9.45m x 6.4m - pros.
Opening 7.01m x 4.88m - wing widths 1.22m SR, 1.22m SL.
Stage slightly raked - floor timber on joists, suitable for all dance, no crossover, stage heated. Height to grid 9.45m approx. - no flying facilities - tab track - black legs and borders, 1 set black tabs - white cloth cyclorama - blue house tabs, drawn. Several 13a sockets.
Forestage 7.01m x 0.95, entrances SR and SL. Get-in via rear of stage, 9.15 drop to ground level (no hoist), or via auditorium doors and through FOH, flat access. Paint frame.
Lighting - Strand MX board, 36 circuits, operated from projection room at real of balcony - 14 spots, 12 fresnels - followspot operated from balcony.
Sound - TOA 16 channel mixer, operated from projection room on balcony - 4 speakers - 1 mc - cassette tape system - PA system. Acoustics suitable for music and spoken word.

BRIDGEND RECREATION CENTRE
Angel Street, Bridgend, Mid Glamorgan CF31 4AH Wales
Tel: 0300 012 1223 (Option 1)
Web Site: www.haloleisure.org.uk
Centre Manager: Karl Patison
Facilities: 2 meeting rooms and 1 dance studio
TECHNICAL:
Stage dimensions 35' x 16' (width can be extended with portable staging units).
2 separate artists changing rooms with en suite facilities.
Lighting: 18 flood lights, 16 spot lights and follow spot.
Catering facilities: licenced bar available.

Bridgnorth, Shropshire

BRIDGNORTH LEISURE CENTRE
Northgate, Bridgnorth, Shropshire WV16 4ER
Tel: 01746 761 541
Email: debbie.swales@shropshire.gov.uk
Web Site: www.shropshire.gov.uk
ADMINISTRATION
Props: Bridgnorth District Council
Cap: Main Hall 650; Small Hall 200
Manager: Debbie Swales
Technical Manager: Paul Evans
Lounge bar available.

Bridgwater, Somerset

TOWN HALL
High Street, Bridgwater, Somerset TA6 3AS
Tel: 01278 427 692
Email: townclerk@bridgwatertowncouncil.gov.uk
Web Site: www.bridgwatertowncouncil.gov.uk
ADMINISTRATION
Props: Bridgwater Town Council
Cap: 400
Bookings Contact: Alan Hurford

Bridlington, East Yorkshire

Pop. 28,590. London 221 miles.
Newspapers: Bridlington Free Press (thurs); Hull Daily Mail (dly). STD code 01262

SPA ROYAL HALL & THEATRE
South Marine Drive, Bridlington, East Yorkshire YO15 3JH
Tel: 01262 401400 BO: 01262 678258
Email: andrew.aldis@eastriding.gov.uk
Web Site: www.thespabridlington.com
ADMINISTRATION:
Props: East Riding of Yorkshire Council
Senior Facility Manager: Andrew Aldis
Stage Manager: Nige Harrison
Policy: All-year-round professional entertainment plus local amateur use. Also conference and concert hall use.
Spa Royal Hall Cap: Able to hold concerts with audiences of up to 3800 people. New and refurbished rooms of different sizes are available for hire for events, conferences, exhibitions, weddings and meetings.
Spa Theatre: Seats: 677. Stalls Bar.
TECHNICAL:
For further information contact Paul Groves

Brierley Hill, West Midlands

CIVIC HALL
Bank Street, Brierley Hill, West Midlands DY5 3DA
Tel: 01384 815 577
Email: borough.halls@dudley.gov.uk
Web Site: www.dudley.gov.uk/entertainment
ADMINISTRATION
Props: Dudley Metropolitan Borough Council
Cap: 695
Halls & Entertainments Manager: Peter Jordan
Meetings & Events Co-ordinator for Dudley Hall & Brierley Civic Hall: Kath Drew
Email: kathleen.drew@dudley.gov.uk

Brighton, East Sussex

Pop. 163,710. London 53 miles.
Newspapers: Evening Argus (ntly); Brighton & Hove Leader (free wed). STD code 01273

THE BASEMENT
Argus Lofts, 24 Kensington Street, Brighton, East Sussex BN1 4AJ

Tel: 01273 699 733
Email: info@thebasement.uk.com
Web Site: www.thebasement.uk.com
Year round arts production, resource and support centre for performing, visual and live arts groups. Also have large underground venue suitable for performance, showcase and rehearsal. The Basement has recently undergone refurbishment to provide three new workable arts spaces for devising, rehearsal and professional development including study room and intimate amphitheatre. We will have disabled access and an increased capacity of 250.

BRIGHTON CENTRE

Kings Road, Brighton, East Sussex BN1 2GR
Mgt: 01273 290 131 BO: 0844 847 1538 (Ticketmaster)
Email: brightoncentre@brighton-hove.gov.uk
Web Site: www.brightoncentre.co.uk
ADMINISTRATION:
Business & Operations Manager: Carrie Walsh
Premises Manager: Ian Hardy
Capacity: Main Hall 5127 (Standing/Seated), 4,500 (Fully Seated), Syndicate Wing 600 (Standing), Auditorium '2' 600-800.

THE BRIGHTON DOME

12a Pavilion Buildings, Castle Square, Brighton, East Sussex BN1 1EE
Admin: 01273 700 747 BO: 01273 709 709 Hiring: 01273 260 815
Email: info@brightondome.org
Web Site: www.brightondome.org, www.brightonfestival.org
ADMINISTRATION:
Props: Brighton Dome Ltd.
General Manager: Maxine Hort
Policy: Concerts, Symphony Concerts, One Night Stands, Summer Entertainments Conferences, Pop, Jazz Shows, etc.
Perfs: Variable
Seats: 1,800
Art-Deco concert hall. Lyric, promenade or proscenium stage.
Licensed Bar and Catering Services.
The Dome, The Pavillion Theatre and The Corn Exchange are all part of the same complex. They are programmed all year round with all kinds of arts activities, fairs, conferences, etc. A very high level of technical equipment and supervision applies throughout.
Studio Theatre available seats 241 to 350 standing

THE CORN EXCHANGE

12a Pavilion Buildings, Castle Square, Brighton, East Sussex BN1 1EE
Admin: 01273 700 747 BO: 01273 709 709 Fax: 01273 707 505
Email: info@brightondome.org
Web Site: www.brightondome.org
ADMINISTRATION:
Props: Brighton Dome Ltd
Operations Manager: Maxine Hort
Seats: 57—1,100
17m wide and 53m long room with optional theatre, seating and staging. Very versatile.
The Dome, The Pavillion Theatre and The Corn Exchange are all part of the same complex. They are programmed all year round with all kinds of arts activities, fairs, conferences, etc. A very high level of technical equipment and supervision applies throughout.
TECHNICAL:
Please contact The Brighton Dome for full technical specifications.

KOMEDIA BRIGHTON

44-47 Gardner Street, North Laine, Brighton, East Sussex BN1 1UN
Box Office: 0845 293 8480 Admin: 01273 647 101
Email: info@komedia.co.uk
Web Site: www.komedia.co.uk/brighton
ADMINISTRATION:
Props: Komedia Productions Ltd
MD: Colin Granger
Programming: Marina Kobler, Lex Hollingworth
Administrator: Sarah Rowe
Press Manager: Emily Coleman
Head of Marketing & Box Office Manager: Cassie Ledger
Box Office Supervisor: Lawry Tilbury
Operations Manager: Paul Musselwhite
Cap: Seats up to 350, (290 with tables/chairs and stools). New Studio Bar Cap; 90 (theatre/cabaret/music)

Policy:
THEATRE: Presenting, producing and promoting new theatre work and comedy by local, regional, national and internation small-scale touring companies and performers. Komedia also promotes new writing, carries out a comprehensive theatre-in-education programme and presents high quality theatre for children and young people.
CABARET BAR: Promoting and presenting the best in live music across a wide range of sound: jazz, soul, world, funk, blues, folk, acoustic, songwriting, classical and pop. Also a venue for top quality comedy, cabaret, spoken word and workshops.
TECHNICAL:
Please contact Lex (Technical Manager) to discuss any specific needs your event requires. Tel: 01273 647116
Email: technical@komedia.co.uk

Komedia Downstairs:

STAGE: 5m wide x 2m deep x 30cm high. Maximum stage size is approx. 5m wide x 3m deep x 30cm high. Metrodeck Staging Units.
LIGHTING: Lighting Desk: Zero88 Frog. 6 x 650w Fresnels, 1 x 650w Profiles, 2 x Robe 300 CT's, 3 x Birdies, 2 x Parabeam 300's. Martin Starcloth. Various Sound-to-Light Disco Lights.
AV Equipment: Projector: Sharp XG-PH50x 4000 Lumens with geometric adjustment. Screen: 83 inches / 210 cm operated by remote control (4:3). Plasma Screens: 2 x 40inch NEC Screens - flown to the sides of FOH Speakers. Edirol 4 Channel V4 Vision Mixer. 2 Sony D70 Remote Cameras and controller DVD Player. DVD Player.
SOUND: Soundcraft Series 2 Mixer. 32 Mono Channels and 2 stereo. 8 Groups and 8 auxiliaries. 24 channels on the stage box; 8 returns - 6 permanently wired for foh sends and aux sends. Aux 1 - 4 permanently wired for Monitor Mixes. Aux 5 - 7 permanently wired for Effects Sends. Aux 8 - Unused. 4 channels of Behringer Multigate. 4 channels of DBX 1066 Compressor/Limiter. SPX990 Effects Unit - mono sends and returns. SPX1000 Effects Unit - mono sends and returns. Sony Mini Disc Player. Sony CD Player. Speakers: 4 Noise Control mpm1518b mid/top speakers (flown). Powered by C-Audio Pulse 2650 Amps. 2 Noise Control nc215 Bass Bins. Powered by FFA 5000 Amp. Monitors: 4 mixes available. Powered by 2 stereo QSC RMX2450 Amps.

Komedia Upstairs:

STAGE: 8m wide x 4m deep x 1metre high. Dimensions: Lighting rig to stage: 417cm. Ceiling to stage: 447cm. Lighting rig to floor 517cm. Ceiling to floor: 547cm. Theatre bars (low rig) to Mezzanine: 370cm. Low Ceiling to Mezzanine: 408cm. Theatre bars (low rig) to floor 375cm. Low Ceiling to Floor 413cm. Stage to Mazzanine 870cm. Mezzanine: 8m x 10m approx.
LIGHTING: Desk: Zero88 Fat Frog 48 channel. 1 Mac250 Moving Lights (with Gobos). 2 Mac 500 Moving Lights. 4 Robe 300 CT Moving Lights. 9 Source4 Profiles. 7 Source 4 Junior Profiles. 2 1.2Kw Cantatas (fresnels). 6 Selecon 1Kw Fresnels. 4 1K Harmony Fresnel. 8 650 Quartet F's (4 in rig 4 on floor). 4 Source 4 Par Cans. 6 Par 64. 6 Pin Spots. 1 patt 23 with Mirrorball. House lights operated through the lighting desk and require the use of 2 desk channels.
SOUND: Desk: MIDAS Verona 560, 48 mono channel. FOH Racks: 2 of BSS Quad Gates DPR 504 (8 channels), 2 of BSS Quad Compressors DPR 404 (8 channels), 2 of Yamaha SPX2000 Effects Units (mono sends), 4 of BSS FCS 966 Graphic Eq's. Noise Control Audio NFA I-Fly Series: 4 x TMT 600F 1 x 10? + 1 x 1.4? Mid /Hi Enclosure (Neodymium), 4 x RGW 112F 1 x 12? Bass Enclosure (Neodymium), 2 x VSB 218 2 x 18? Sub Enclosure (Neodymium), Amplifiers + Processors. Noise Control Audio Full Frequency Series: 1 x FF 408D (XTA 448 digital speaker management), 2 x FF 6.0

(6000 watts @ 2 ohms), 2 x FF 3.6 (3600 watts @ 2 ohms), Monitors, Noise Control Audio SM / ASYM Series. Stage wedge monitors: 5 x SM 15P passive 1 x 15? + 1 x 1.4? (Neodymium). Drum Fill: 1 x ASYM 2.5 2 x 15? + 1 x 1.4? (Neodymium)
ADDITIONAL: AV; Projector: Sharp XG-PH50x 4000 Lumens with geometric adjustment - Screen 1: 105 inches/267cm diagonal (16:9), Screen 2: 174 inches/442 cm diagnol (16:9). Edirol V8 Vision Mixer. DVD Player

Komedia Studio:

Capacity: 80 seated, 120 standing.
STAGE: 2.5m deep x 4m wide. Draped in black wool serge curtains.
SOUND: FOH rig: D&b C690 Full range speakers on Stands powered by E-Pac Amps. 2 mixes of monitors through a pair of powered MSR400 Wedges. FOH desk: 16 Channel Spirit Folio 16l with inbuilt Lexicon Effects Unit, CD and Mini DIsc.
LIGHTING: 2 colour stage wash, spot light and sound to light disco light via Manual 2 preset 6 channel mixer. 3 x f 300w Par Cans and 1 650 Fresnel as Backlight. 2 x 650W PC's as G/C. 1 x Single Spot. 1 Par 64 audience. 1 pin spot and mirror ball. Numerous RCD protected double 13amp power sockets available at the rear of the stage.
ADDITIONAL: AV: Projector: Sony VPL-ES3, Screen: 105 inches / 267 cm (16:9). Piano available at additional cost.

OCEANA CLUB
Kingswest, West Street, Brighton, East Sussex BN1 2RE
Tel: 08452 968590 Fax: 01273 208 996
Email: oceana-brighton@luminar.co.uk
Web Site: www.luminar.co.uk/brighton
Nightclub Capacity: 2600
General Manager: Tony Buck
Currently unavailable for public hire.

SALLIS BENNEY THEATRE
University of Brighton, College of Arts and Humanities, Grand Parade, Brighton, East Sussex BN2 0JY
Mgt: 01273 643 010 BO: 01273 709 709
Fax: 01273 643 038
Email: g.wilson@brighton.ac.uk
Web Site: www.bton.ac.uk/gallery-theatre/
Theatre situated within University of Brighton in the centre of town near Brighton Pavilion. At the junctions of Lewes Road (A27) and London Road (A23).
ADMINISTRATION:
Props: University of Brighton
Theatre & Gallery Manager: Gez Wilson
Technical Technician: Graham Rees
Administrator: Clari Little
There is a maximum capacity of 272 seated or 400 standing. In addition to staging the University Cultural Programme and lectures, the theatre can be used to stage concerts, workshops, film and conferences. Catering services are available on request including a licensed bar. Gallery space can be used as an alternative meeting room or for functions and is available for hire whilst certain exhibitions are on.
TECHNICAL:
For further information contact the Theatre Technician: Graham Rees on Tel: 01273 643 011 or visit the website: http://www.bton.ac.uk/gallery-theatre/venuehires.html

UNIVERSITY OF SUSSEX STUDENTS' UNION
Mandela Hall, Falmer House, Falmer, Brighton, East Sussex BN1 9QF
Tel: 01273 678 152 Fax: 01273 873 892
Email: paul.n@sussexstudent.com
Web Site: www.sussexstudent.com
ADMINISTRATION:
Union Director: Paul Newton
Cap: Seated: 400, Standing: 600.

THE BARN THEATRE
Run by Volunteers For bookings or ticket enquiries please phone after 7pm
24 Southwick Street, Southwick, West Sussex BN42 4TE
Admin Tel: 01273 592 819 BO: 01273 597 094
Email: enquiries@southwickcommunity-centre.org.uk
Web Site: www.southwickcommunitycentre.org.uk
Barn Theatre part of the Southwick Community Centre
Run by volunteers

THEATRE ROYAL
New Road, Brighton, East Sussex BN1 1SD
Admin: 01273 764 405 BO: 0844 871 7650 SD: 01273 764 400 Fax: 01273 764 404
Email: bridiewilliams@theambassadors.com
Web Site: www.ambassadortickets.com/Theatre-Royal-Brighton
ADMINISTRATION:
Props: Ambassador Theatre Group Ltd
General Manager: John Baldock
Technical Manager: Tom Hitchins
Head of Marketing & Development: Michelle Shipley
Administrator: Bridie Williams
Policy: No. 1 Touring / Production
Perfs: Mon-Sat 7.45; Mats 2.30 Thurs and Sat.
Seats: 969. Six Licensed Bars. Corporate Entertainment Facilities.
TECHNICAL:
STAGE: Proscenium Stage, Racked 1 in 48; Pros. Opening 8.99m; Ht. Of Pros. 9.14m; Depth of S/Line 8.99m; Ht. of Grid 15.24m; Approx 50 Hemp Sets (40 Bars). 3 temp assist; scenery flying ht. 9.14m; Flying Bars 10.82m; W/Widths P.S. 4.57m, O.P. 4.06m; Prompt Cnr. P.S. Orchestra Pit approx. 20. Scene Dock PS. Large Dock O.P. Wardrobe.
LIGHTING: Strand 520i running system 2.6ci; rear of gallery, 29x Source4 19deg in fixed front of house rig, 117 circuits on strand STM dimmers (including 5x 5KW).
Other: Dressing Rooms: 13; 2 Showers.

Bristol
Pop. 376,148. London 126 miles.
Newspapers: Evening Post; Bristol Journal. STD code 0117

BRISTOL BIERKELLER
All Saints Street, Bristol, Avon BS1 2NA
Tel: 0117 926 8514
Email: bs1bierkeller@gmail.com
Web Site: www.bristolbierkeller.co.uk
ADMINISTRATION:
Seating/Capacity: 500 seated, 750 standing.
Contact General Manager: Austin Mockeridge
Policy: Concerts, Gigs, Comedy, Private Hire
TECHNICAL:
Stage: 7.5m x 5.5m, PA 7-14K, Dressing Rooms, 1 Main + 1 Secondary accommodating 15 and shower.

BRISTOL HIPPODROME
10 St. Augustines Parade, Bristol, Avon BS1 4UZ
Admin: 0117 302 3310 BO: 0844 871 3012 SD: 0117 302 3251 Fax: 0117 925 1661
Email: bristoladmin@theambassadors.com
Web Site: www.atgtickets.com/bristol
ADMINISTRATION:
Props: Ambassadors Theatre Group Ltd
Policy: West End shows, Opera, Ballet, Comedy, Childrens' Shows, Concerts, Circus acts, Dance shows.
General Manager: Lisa Chew
Stage Manager: Paul Birch
Contact: paulbirch@theambassadors.com or 0117 302 3239
Box Office Manager: Ian Kennedy
Marketing Manager: Steve Jones
Customer Services Managers: Maria Pike, Helen Jaffer
Capacity: 1951
TECHNICAL:
STAGE: Proscenium Stage; Pros. Opening 14.63m; Ht. of Pros. 9.14m; Depth of S/Line 18.28m, last line 14.63m; Ht. of Grid 18.28m; 65 lines including 5 elec., C/W; Scenery Flying 9.14m; Flying Bars 16.61m; W/Widths P.S. 8.53m, O.P. 8.53m; Prompt Cnr. Right. Orchestra Pit with access to the band room.
LIGHTING: Switchboard: Eurolight Ovation. F.O.H. Spots; 2 x Lycian, 12 T84s, 16 T-Spot Box Booms, 8 Patt.263, Pros. Booms, 2 Battens, 1 Float, Spot Bar 2 x 12 Patt.743s.

SOUND: Equipment for sound is locally hired.
DRESSING ROOMS: 21 over various floors; Accom. 90; 3 star dressing rooms, with en-suite facilities, TV, fridge, phone and settee, and separate dressing area. Laundry room, which offers both washing and drying facilities. 10 toilet cubicles and 7 shower cubicles available.
DISABLED FACILITIES: Two disabled lifts allowing patrons access to the Auditorium and to the Stalls bar.

BRISTOL OLD VIC

King Street, Bristol, Avon BS1 4ED
Mgt: 0117 949 3993 BO: 0117 987 7877
SD: 0117 949 3993 Fax: 0117 949 3996
Email: admin@bristoloIdvic.org.uk
Web Site: www.bristoloIdvic.org.uk
ADMINISTRATION:
Props: Theatre Royal Trustees
Lessees: The Bristol Old Vic Trust Ltd
Executive Director: Emma Stenning
Artistic Director: Tom Morris
Director of Production & Operations: Jason Barnes
Marketing Director: Jonathan Harper
Policy: Repertory, Visting Companies
Perfs: Mon-Sat 7.30p.m, Studio times vary
Mats: Thurs & Sat 2.00 p.m.
Seats: Main house 550, Studio 145
TECHNICAL:
For further information, please contact Jason Barnes
production@bristoloIdvic.org.uk

CIRCOMEDIA

St Paul's Church, Portland Square, Bristol, Avon, BS2 8SJ
Admin Tel: 0117 924 7615
Email: info@circomedia.com
Web Site: www.circomedia.com
Props: The Churches Conservation Trust
Lessees: Circomedia
Creative Director: Bim Mason
Chief Executive: Chris Humphrey
Centre Manager: Jude Hutchins
Technical Manager: Joe Mapsom
Performer/Agency Manager: Rebecca Fitzgerald
Policy: Contemporary circus and physical theatre training, rehearsal and performance. Suitable for for cabaret, dance, exhibitions etc.
Cap: 264 performance style; 164 when alcohol served.
Perfs: Variable
Full size flying trapeze rig and range of aerial equipment. Sprung dance floor. Further details on application.
Other: Dressing rooms; Accom.; 12; 3 showers
Catering facilities: Café and bar service can be arranged.

COLSTON HALL

Colston Street, Bristol, Avon BS1 5AR
Mgt: 0117 204 7115 BO: 0844 887 1500
Email: hello@colstonhall.org
Web Site: www.colstonhall.org
ADMINISTRATION:
Props: Bristol Music Trust
Chief Executive: Louise Mitchell
Technical Manager: Andy Collins
Marketing Manager: Sarah Robertson
Operations Manager: Nick Craney
Policy: Concert Hall available for hire for all musical events with some joint promotions.
Seating/Capacity: 1,834 or 2,069 with choir and boxes (fully seated or partiallly standing.)
TECHNICAL:
For further information, please contact the Technical Manager: Andy Collins
Email: a.collins@colstonhall.org
Stage: Concert platform, performing area 14.9m x 7.62m, floor sprung wood. Variable height grid - 3 tonnes permitted on each of bars 1 & 2, 2 tonnes on bar 3. Get-in via ramped entrance at stalls level. Scale stage and lighting plans available.
Lighting: Celco major 30 lighting board operated from front of house or from control room overlooking platform. 41 x 1kw downlighters over platform. 30 x Par 64. 2 x CSI follow spots.
Sound: TAC Bullet 12:4:2 board operated from control room or DDA 32:8:2 operated from mid stalls FOH. Stalls speakers: 2 x Turbosound TXD 580. Balcony speakers: 4 x Turbosound TSE 111, 4 x Turbosound TSE 118. Central cluster: 4 x Turbosound TSE 111, 2 x Turbosound TSE 118. Microphones: 11 x Beyer 201, 2 x AKG 321, 2 x SM 58, 4 x AKG 451 + CK 8, 4 x DI Boxes. CD and cassette players. Acoustics suitable for music and spoken word.
Other: Backstage: 6 dressing rooms, band room, irons, etc. as required. Refreshments available. Advice given on accommodation. Staff: 2 lighting/sound; casuals available; security personnel as required. Backstage facilities available to disabled performers and staff. Additional information on application.

THE REDGRAVE THEATRE

2 Percival Road, Clifton, Bristol, BS8 3LE
Admin: 0117 315 7602 Tech: 0117 315 7605 For Hiring Enq: 0117 315 7602
Email: david@redgravetheatre.com
Web Site: www.redgravetheatre.com
ADMINISTRATION:
Props: Clifton College
Contact for hiring: David Fells
Technical Manager: Sam Hollis-Pack
Policy: Educational venue.
Drama , Dance, Film, Lectures, Concerts, Small Scale Opera, Local & Touring, Amateur and Professional. Willing to Premiere show.
Seats: 315, disabled access.
Facilities: Licensed foyer bar.

TECHNICAL:
Stage: Proscenium Arch. Pros. opening 10m, tapering to 8.5m x 7.5m. Pros. Arch 10m x 4.1m. Wing width 1.5m. Height of grid 6.4m. Orchestra pit 5m x 4m on split level. Dock doors, SL, 1.8m x 3.8m. Green House Tabs, flown.
Lighting: ARRI Mirage with colour monitor, 48ch. Strand LX 24, 2 preset, 4 group manual board. 126 Patch channels. Control room at rear of auditorium. 31 spots, 32 Fresnels, 12 PC's, 10 Pars, 5 Cyc battens; All Strand.
Sound: Soundcraft Spirit Live 4 2 (24 Channel). 2 x Bose 802, 2x Bose 101, 2x ATC Bass Bins, 2x Community CSX 35. PPX Amps. AKG & Beyer Mics. Tape deck, CD player, Revox B77. Acoustics suitable for music & spoken word. Tecpro Talkback system. Foyer & backstage show relay system.
Other: 2 x Dressing rooms, 1 x Green room.
2 x Technicians, Casuals available.

ST GEORGE'S BRISTOL

Great George Street, Off Park Street, Bristol, BS1 5RR
Admin Tel: 0117 929 4929 BO: 0845 4024 001 Fax: 0117 927 6537
Email: administration@stgeorgesbristol.co.uk
Web Site: www.stgeorgesbristol.co.uk
For bookings contact the Event's Manager
Auditorium Seating/Capacity: 562 (stalls, gallery combined)

THORNBURY LEISURE CENTRE

Alveston Hill, Thornbury, Bristol, Avon BS35 3JB
Tel: 0300 333 0300 Fax: 01454 865775
Email: simon.cowdery@circadiantrust.org
Web Site: www.circadiantrust.org
ADMINISTRATION:
Props: Circadian Trust
Cap: Main Hall 150; Sevenfife Hall: 800
Manager: Simon Cowdery
Policy: Concerts, dances, exhibitions, etc.
TECHNICAL:
Portable Stage

YATE LEISURE CENTRE

Kennedy Way, Yate, Bristol, Avon BS37 4DQ
Tel: 0300 333 0300 Fax: 01454 865 805
Email: ylc@circadiantrust.org
Web Site: www.circadiantrust.org
ADMINISTRATION
Props: Circadian Trust
Main Hall Cap: 600
Centre Manager: Matt Simmons
Policy: Concerts, dances, exhibitions, etc.
3 Meeting Rooms available for hire. The Courtside Suite is situated on the ground floor and and caters for up to 40 people. The Rowling Suite is based on our ground floor. The room caters for up to 40 people and can benefit from an adjacent bar if requested.

TECHNICAL: Portable Stage

Broadstairs, Kent

PAVILION GARDEN ON THE SANDS
Harbout Street, Broadstairs, Kent CT10 1EU
Tel: 01843 600 999 Fax: 01843 600888
Email: enquiry@pavilion-broadstairs.co.uk
Web Site: www.pavilion-broadstairs.co.uk
ADMINISTRATION
Theatre Cap: 275 seated; 350 standing
Manager: Mac Towe

Bromborough, Wirral

BROMBOROUGH CIVIC HALL
Allport Lane, Bromborough, Wirral CH62 7HR
Halls Manager Tel: 0151 643 7237 Bkg Tel: 0151 643 7239 Bkg Fax: 0151 643 7235
Email: bebcc@wirral.gov.uk
ADMINISTRATION
Props: Wirral Borough Council
Cap: Large Hall: 300; Small Hall: 80
Manager: Graham Knowles
For bookings contact Susanne Woo

Bromley, Kent

CHURCHILL THEATRE
High Street, Bromley, Kent BR1 1HA
Admin/SD: 020 8464 7131 BO: 0844 871 7620 Fax: 020 8290 6968
Email: bromleystagedoor@theambassadors.com
Web Site: www.atgtickets.com
ADMINISTRATION:
Props: Ambassadors Theatre Group Ltd
Marketing Manager: Jamie Leadbeatter
Head of Creative Learning: Kiaran Hall
Technical Manager: Ed Brimley
Theatre Manager: Gavin Schuman
Policy: Co-Productions are combined with touring shows to provide a comprehensive mix of plays, musicals, opera, dance, pantomime, family shows and concerts.
Extensive Education Programme: contact the Education Officer, Liam Shea, for more details.
Perfs: Evenings Monday-Saturday 7.45. Thursday and Saturday matinees 2.30.
Seats: 785 (760 when orchestra pit used). Two Bars.
TECHNICAL:
STAGE: Apron; Flat; Pros. opening 9.15m-13.7m variable; ht. of Pros. 7.01m; Depth of S/Line 15.09m; Ht. of Grid 14.46m; 50 (47-50 storage only) lines c/w, Scenery Flying Ht. 5.49m; Flying Bars 16.4m; W/Widths P.S. 10.87m, O.P. 10.67m; Prompt Cnr. P.S. or O.P.
LIGHTING: Strand 520i with 350 channels 350 attributes. Radio remote. Fully networked. 4 streams of DMX512 available on stage, control box, dimmer room and auditorium. XTBA DMX available on stage. Dimmers; 144 x 2.5kw, 24 x 5kw patchable to 350 circuits. Temp supplies; 200A TPN+E USL, 100 TPN+E DSR, 3 63A single sound supply DSL. Lanterns; 97 profiles, 64 fresnel/PC, 100 parcans, 6 iris 4, 10 Coda 4, 2 Robert Julia + Korrigan follow-spots. Some of the equipment is on a chargable use basis.
SOUND: Soundcraft Venue 32:8:2 desk with 8-way matrix, operated from back of stalls, CD player, 3 minidisc. Acoustics suitable for music and spoken word.
ADDITIONAL: Dressing Rooms 12, accom. 135 inc. Band and Chorus; 6 Showers; Orchestra Pit :15 plus.

Bromsgrove

ARTRIX
Slideslow Drive Bromsgrove B60 1PQ
Tel: 01527 577330
Email: artrixadmin@ne-worcs.ac.uk
Web Site: www.artrix.co.uk
Capacity: 300

Broxbourne, Hertfordshire

BROXBOURNE CIVIC HALL
High Street, Hoddesdon, Hertfordshire EN11 8BE
Admin: 01992 444 504 BO: 01992 441 946
Email: civichall.bookings@broxbourne.gov.uk
Web Site: www.broxbourne.gov.uk/leisure_and_culture/halls_for_hire.aspx
ADMINISTRATION:
Props: Broxbourne Borough Council
Manager: Tony Driver
Senior Technician: Mark Goode
Contact:
Mg.civic.leisure@broxbourne.gov.uk
Policy: Adaptable rooms for formal or informal events.lectures, presentations, exhibitions, social meetings, concerts, craft fayres, and dinner dances.
Capacity: Main Auditorium Hall; 566 theatre style (350 dinner); Bar Lounge; 60; The Dinant Room; 40.
TECHNICAL:
STAGE: Proscenium flat; pros opening, 52'8"; Stage Depth 26'6"; Width Stage Right 13'5". Get in doors via Stage Right Height 11'6", Width 6'8". Height of Grid 36'. Orchestra Pit; 28' w, 5'7" h, 9'8" d; Access via dressing room corridor.
LIGHTING: Zero 88 Leap Frog 96 control desk; Dimmers 92 Repatchable Circuits, 2.5kw per channel; 4 Cyc bar Circuits, 5kw per channel; Lighting Bars 4 x onstage 500kg electric Winches; DMX Points, Control Room. Onstage lighting 4 colour wash, 8 onstage fresnels in each colour,. 24 x 1.2kw Cantata with Barn doors. 12 x 1kw Aurora Flood Lights. 28 x 1kw Par cans P64 Cp62 Lamps. Foh Lighting 14 x source 4s 16 x par cans(8 per side - 2 in each colour) 10 moving lights in stock (subject to hire charge)Additional lanterns available.
SOUND: 1x Allen and Heath GL4800 (32-8- 2), 3x Behringer 31 Band Graphic Equalisers, 1x Tascam Cd160 CD Player, 1x Tascam MD350 Mini Disc Player, 1x Alesis Midi verb 4 - For delay Lines, 1x Lexicon MX200, 1x Yamaha SPX 900, 12x Sennheiser EW300 Receivers + Compressors, 4 x Studio spares Speakers 1200w RMS (2 left 2 Right), 4 x Studio spares Sub Woofer 800w RMS (2 Left 2 Right), 4 x EV SPX 300w RMS Rear fill for terrace seating. Various Microphones available.
COMMUNICATIONS: 4 x Coloured Monitors in dressing rooms for show relay; paging system from prompt corner and control. F.O.H calls run from the control room. Communication headsets located in control room.stage left and right, fly floor and 2 followspot posistions
OTHER: 1 x Mirror ball and lights fixed in auditorium. 1 x Steinway baby grand (On stage). 1 x Upright piano (In auditorium)
DRESSING ROOMS: 4 dressing rooms with basins, accomm. 46; 2 showers. Washing Machine and dryer available. Central heating, video and audio show relay.
DISABLED FACILITIES: Disabled parking. Wheelchair access to building - automatic doors. Disabled toilet. Hearing Loop system. Limited wheelchair spaces in auditorium.

Buckhaven, Fife

Pop. 6,500. Newspapers: East Fife Mail (wkly); Dundee Courier (dly); Scotsman (dly). STD code 01592

BUCKHAVEN PARISH CHURCH THEATRE
Lawrence Street, Buckhaven, Leven, Fife KY8 1BQ Scotland
Mgt/BO: 01592 715 577
Email: ally@levenmouthymca.com
ADMINISTRATION:
Props: Buckhaven Parish Church
Stage Manager: Alan Dingwall
Box Office Manager: Fred Pullar
Policy: Community theatre with commitment to professional theatre training. Regular professional productions - own company, ARK - with Christmas pantomime. Additional touring productions by own community company, local amateur companies, professional concerts, youth & children's theatre. Aims to give training and experience to theatre personnel and

to recreate an 'old-style' repertory theatre within the local community. Welcomes small professional touring companies.
Perfs: Mon-Sat 7.30p.m. Mats. Saturday and by arrangement.
Seats: Auditorium 102 raked plus boxes accommodating 10-30 (depending on staging). Foyer: 30-40, moveable seating.
TECHNICAL:
Stage: Proscenium width 7.25m opening to 12m with some restricted view. Stage depth 7.5m within proscenium width.
Forestage: Removeable extension. Width 7.10m. Depth 2.20m. Overall stage depth 9.80m Proscenium height 4m, grid height 4.5m, masking height 3.5m. Prompt on stage right. Workshop on stage right 11.1m x 4.2m x 4.9m high. Complete black masking. Stage Equip: 5 tab tracks plus house tabs. 8 x 3m braces. 8 x 2m braces. 20 x 28-lb stage weights.
Lighting: Lighting board M24 plus effects panel. 72 circuits. 12 prelude 16/30. 8 prelude 28/40. 18 prelude F. 10 prelude PC. 5 coda 500/4. 2 Patt.23. 4 T-84. 2 T-64. 1 Cantata 11/26 (F-Spot). 4 Code 500/1. 35mm slide projection facilities available. 4 stage stands.
Sound equip: Studiomaster 8 into 4 mixer. 3 Studiomaster Mosfet 500 amplifiers. 2 x 300w OHM FOH speakers. 2 x 70w Peavey wedges. 3 SM58 mics. 1 Teac cassette deck. 1 Sharp cassette deck. 1 Revox B77, 2 M69, 1 M201. 1 AKG 451. Headset communication points throughout auditorium.
Other: Dressing Room call system. F.O.H. call system. Cue lights x headsets x 6.
Projection: 1 Fumeo HL 2000 16mm projector, with 1800m spool capacity.
Video facilities: Hi8 Sony Camera and playback facilities.
Dressing Rooms: 4 with comfortable accom. for 50 people plus utilitiy room. 6 showers. Orchestra pit for 36 musicians with 24 stands. Green Room.
Non Performance Activities: Conferences, art & craft exhibitions, youth theatre (Sat. mornings), film club.
Catering: Restaurant & Coffee/snack bar open daily at lunch time and in the evenings. Suppers/full meals can be booked in Theatre restaurant.
Access: Own car parks and other free parking spaces available. Nearest station: Kirkcaldy. Bus service. Free transport often available for early block bookings.
Facilities for the Disabled: Up to 8 wheelchair spaces; lift; toilets; auditorium and front-of-house fully accessible.
Other Facilities: Conference rooms, audio/visual equip., Yamaha and clavinova, superb condition. Smoke machine, large costume hire department.

Buckie, Morayshire

BUCKIE COMMUNITY CENTRE
West Cathcart Street, Buckie, Morayshire AB56 1QB Scotland
Tel: 01542 832 841
Email: keith.cc@moray.gov.uk
Web Site: www.moray.gov.uk
ADMINISTRATION:
Props: Moray Council
Leisure Assistant: Susan Bell (Tel: 01542 882222)
Area Leisure Supervisor: Mark Bruce
Cap: 3 rooms. 1 - craft room, seats 20 round tables; 2 - mini hall max. 80; 3 - 50 max. Access to school assembly hall and coffee bar (60) and social area (100 max).

BUCKIE TOWN HOUSE
Cluny Place, Buckie, Morayshire AB56 1PZ
Caretaker Tel: 01542 836 490 Bookings: 01542 832 691 01542 831 150
Email: alan.taylor@moray.gov.uk
Web Site: www.moray.gov.uk
ADMINISTRATION:
Props: Moray Council
Cap: Seated 140; Dancing 160; Dancing/Seated at tables 120; Seated at tables 110.
For bookings Tel: 01542 832691 Fax: 01542 833384
If you require further information please contact:
Educational Services, Council Office, High Street, Elgin IV30 1BX

FISHERMEN'S HALL
16 Pringle Street, Buckie, Morayshire AB56 1PZ Scotland
Bookings Tel: 01542 832 691 Hallkeeper Tel: 01542 833 273
Email: marian.ogg@moray.gov.uk
Web Site: www.moray.gov.uk
ADMINISTRATION:
Props: Moray Council
Cap: Seated 336; Dancing 310
If you require further information please contact:
Educational Services, Council Office, High Street, Elgin IV30 1BX
Tel: 01343 563396 Email alan.taylor@moray.gov.uk
Contact Assistant Resources Officer: Marian Ogg Tel: 01343 563 206

LADY CATHCART COMMUNITY CENTRE
High Street, Buckie, Morayshire AB56 1AZ Scotland
Tel: 01542 882222
Email: buckie.cc@moray.gov.uk
Web Site: www.moray.gov.uk
ADMINISTRATION:
Props: Moray Council
Centre Co-ordinator: Mark Bruce

PORTGORDON COMMUNITY CENTRE
Richmond Terrace, Portgordon, Morayshire AB56 2BT
Tel: 01542 832 841
Email: buckie.cc@moray.gov.uk
Web Site: www.moray.gov.uk
ADMINISTRATION:
Props: Moray Council
Centre Co-ordinator: Mark Bruce

Builth Wells, Powys

Pop. 1,600. London 173 miles.
Newspapers: Brecon & Radnor Express (wed); County Times and Express (sat); Mid-Wales Journal (fri). STD code 01982

STRAND HALL
Strand Street, Builth Wells, Powys LD2 3AA
Tel: 01982 551 568
Email: builthwellstowncouncil@ymail.com
Web Site: www.builthwellstowncouncil.org.uk
ADMINISTRATION
Props: Powys County Council
Run by: Strand Hall Management Group
Strand Hall Commitee Booking Clerk: Geraint Evans

WYESIDE ARTS CENTRE
Castle Street, Builth Wells, Powys LD2 3BN Wales
Mgt: 01982 553 668 BO: 01982 552 555
Email: boxoffice@wyeside.co.uk
Web Site: www.wyeside.co.uk
ADMINISTRATION:
Props: Wyeside Arts Centre Ltd
Marketing Manager: Miriam Hall
FOH /Technical Manager: Tim Serrett
For bookings contact Dilwyn Davies
Cap: Theatre: 154; Cinema: 180
Multi use Arts Centre - 2 Auditoria, Gallery.
Disabled access, symbols for wheelchairs and hard of hearing (infra red & lift now installed).
TECHNICAL:
For more information, contact Ian Andrews
Email: housewyeside@powys.org.uk
Market Theatre Unique performance area 19m x 10m, flat floor, stone finished interior with alcoves on 3 sides. Usual use: end stage 7m x 10m with raked seating. Sprung Stage, suitable for dance. M24 Lighting Board into 70 ways hard wired. 6'6" Bechstein Grand.
Castle Theatre/Stereo Cinema End stage 9m x 7m, no wing space, limited height. Fixed seating max. 212. Two-level projection/control room auditorium rear - 2 x Westrex 35mm projectors. Thorn SM40

3-Preset board, limited lighting facilities.
5'8" Bechstein grand.
Available between 2 theatres:
Lighting: 16 x 1K Profiles; 26 x 1K Fresnels, 10 x 650w Fresnels.
Sound: 12/2 Studiomaster mixer; 1 x B77 Revox reel-to-reel tape deck; 1 x Teac Stereo Cassette deck; 1 x HZ DPX1000 power amp, Driving Kudos, full range cabs (1/2 k per side approx.).

Burgess Hill, West Sussex

MARTLETS HALL

Martlets Hall, Civic Way, Burgess Hill, West Sussex RH15 9NN
Tel: 01444 242 888
Email: martletshallenquiries@pfpleisure.org
Web Site: www.martletshalls.org
ADMINISTRATION
Props: Places for People
Run by: Places for People
Manager: Michael McGinley
Capacity: 362 seated, 450 standing

Burnham-on-Sea, Somerset

THE PRINCESS THEATRE AND ARTS CENTRE

Princess Street, Burnham-on-Sea, Somerset TA8 1EH
Admin: 01278 793 099 BO: 01278 784464
Email: info@theprincesstheatre.co.uk
Web Site: www.theprincesstheatre.co.uk
ADMINISTRATION
Props: Burnham & Highbridge Town Council
Cap: 200 theatre style; 120 sitdown dinner
For bookings contact Sam Nicol

Burnley, Lancashire

Pop. 94,000. Newspapers: Burnley Express (tue-fri); Burnley Citizen (wkly); Lancs Evening Telegraph (ntly). STD code 01282

BURNLEY MECHANICS

Manchester Road, Burnley, Lancashire BB11 1BH
BO: 01282 664 400 Fax: 01282 664431
Email: boxoffice@burnley.gov.uk
Web Site: www.burnleymechanics.co.uk
ADMINISTRATION:
Props: Burnley Council
Technical Manager: Lee Rothwell. Mob: 07980 152920, Email: LRothwell@burnley.gov.uk
Policy: Amateur and Professional drama, music and dance plus resource base for community out-reach programme.
Capacity: 493 seated, 600 standing, Cabaret 300.
TECHNICAL:
STAGE: 7.0m d x 8.4m w x 4.5m h. Auditorium floor to stage 1.2m. Wooden stage: 1" ply overlaid with oil resistant hardboard. Painted matt black. Not raked. Stage right: Space is limited. Apex Roof: No fly tower. Safety curtain: Immediately behind pros. Flys: 15 hemp bars rated at 25kg each 10.2m long. Cross Over: Across back of stage: Under stage - Steps to be negotiated. House Tabs: Operated from SM position or control room Red. Cyc: White or Black. Legs: Black. Borders: Black. Get-in: via a lift that is capable of carrying 20 people or 2250 kg. Internal dimensions are: Height 2.30m, Width 1.70m, Depth 2.60m.
STAGE COMMUNICATIONS: Show Relay All dressing room areas & Tudor Room. TV Monitor: A static TV camera is focused on the stage from LX slot 3 is viewable at the prompt
position. (Picture is also relayed to dressing rooms area). Talk-back facilities: Canford TecPro single channel head set and belt pack points are located at; Stage: prompt corner (D/S left, U/S left, U/S right, D/S right; at Control Room: LX and Sound Operator Positions; at Follow Spot positions S/L & S/R; at Auditorium control positions to top and bottom of tiered seating.
LIGHTING: Lighting Board: Chamsys MagicQ MQ100 Pro Lighting Console, 5000 Cues, 1000 Cue Stacks, 4 x DMX Universes, Built-in Fixture Editor, FX and Gel Library, Arkaos Media Server, Wireless focussing remote, ETC Unison Architectural DMX controller. ETC Sensor Racks Dimmer circuits 140, each rated at 10amps. Independent circuits: 18, each rated at 20amps. Stage: LX1 thru LX4: 4 x 9m box trusses, on Lodestar winches All with hot power and DMX. Distances From Pros: Truss 1 (15 circuits) 0.70m, Truss 2 (15 circuits) 2.20m, Truss 3 (10 circuits) 3.70m, Truss 4 (14 circuits) 5.90m. FOH LX 3 x Fixed Bars located above auditorium in roof slots. Lantern stock: 1kw Harmony PC 30, 1kw Harmony Profiles 8, 750w Source 4 Zoom 15/30 6, 650w Prelude 16/30 Profiles 10, 650w Prelude Fresnels 6, 500w Par64 (mixture of lamps available) 40, 500w Par64 (short) floor cans 20, 500w/3-way Coda floods 5. Robe 250AT Spots 4, Robe 250XT Washes 2. Follow Spots: Robert Juliat, Manon MSR1200w 2, 1 x located in control room, stage left, 1 x top of aisle in auditorium, stage right (Seats X 26 & 27 are not available when in use). Gel stock: Most popular colours. Details on request. Truss Access: Zarges & 'A' Frame ladders.
SOUND: FOH Mixer: Allen & Heath GL3000 32 - 4 - 2. FOH Rack: Comprising of: 1 x DBX 260 Speaker Management System, 2 x 31 band graphic equalizers. Speakers: Auditorium L & R 2 x Kling & Freitag 12" & Horn (400w). Auditorium centre fill 2 x Kling & Freitag 6" & Horn (165w). Auditorium rear delay 2 x Kling & Freitag 6" & Horn (165w).
Amplifiers: Location: Stage & Control Room 3 x Amcron 1201. Monitor Amplifiers: Up to a 4 way send Each with 31 band graphic equalizer. Monitors: Kling & Freitag Cabinets 4 x 12" & Horn 400w monitor wedges. Microphone Channels: Tie lines, stage to control room. 10 stage left behind pros, 10 stage right behind pros. Microphones / D.I. Boxes: A comprehensive selection. Play Back Equipment: 1 x Dennon CD, 1 X Dennon Double tape deck, 1 x Sony Mini Disc Player/Recorder. FX Rack: 1 x Lexicon digital FX unit, 1 x TC Electronic M-One digital FX unit, 1 x noise gate unit, 1 x compressor unit. xing:
DRESSING ROOMS: 5, accommodating 28. (Dressing room 4 accessible to wheelchair users). Facilities: Clothes rails, wash basins, illuminated make-up mirrors, central heating, forced air ventilation and air conditioning available in dressing rooms 1,2,3,&4. Adjacent facilities: Ladies & gents toilets, 2 showers and access to the control room. Wardrobe facilities: Iron & Board available. NO Laundry or dying facilities. Catering facilities: Refrigerators in dressing rooms 1 & 3, Sink in dressing room 3. NO microwave or other cooking facilities available. Access to stage: From dressing rooms and other areas. All via steps. All dressing rooms are lockable, keys provided on request.ng facilities:
ADDITIONAL: Piano: Steinway C Grand. Data Projector.

Burton-on-Trent, Staffordshire

BREWHOUSE

Union Street Burton Upon Trent Staffordshire DE14 1EB
Admin: 01283 508350 BO: 01283 508100
Email: info@brewhouse.co.uk
Web Site: www.brewhouse.co.uk
Props: East Staffordshire Borough Council
Manager: Lynne Edwards
Technical Manager: Matt Bancroft
Capacity: 242

TOWN HALL

Civic Functyion Suite King Edward Place, Burton-on-Trent, Staffordshire DE14 2EB
Tel: 01283 508 548 / 7 Fax: 01283 535412
Email: cheryl.maxim@eaststaffsbc.gov.uk
Web Site: www.eaststaffsbc.gov.uk
ADMINISTRATION

Props: East Staffordshire Borough Council
Cap: 557 (concerts); 400 stalls downstairs with seperate stage; 157 balcony.
For bookings contact: Cheryl Maxim
Tel: 01283 508 549
Also available for weddings, dinner dances, exhibitions and seminars.
Separate facilities are available in the Lingen Room and The Dove Room. Ideal for family gatherings, seminars and meetings. Approx. 80 capacity.
TECHNICAL:
No resident technician; Technical specifications on request

Bury St Edmunds, Suffolk

Pop. 30,000. London 75 miles.
Newspapers: Bury Free Press (fri); East Anglian Daily Times. STD code 01284

THE APEX

Charter Square, Bury St. Edmunds, Suffolk IP33 3FD
Tel: 01284 758 000
Email: enquiries@theapex.co.uk
Web Site: www.theapex.co.uk
Marketing Co-ordinator: Tim Clark
Props: St Edmundsbury Borough Council.
Capacity: Auditorium 516 seated, 650 standing. Studio 1, 60. Studio 2, 80. Studio 2a, 40. Studio 2b, 40. Full upstairs bar: 300 - 350 (standing). Half bar, 175 (standing).

THEATRE ROYAL BURY ST EDMUNDS

Westgate Street, Bury St Edmunds, Suffolk IP33 1QR
Mgt: 01284 755 127 BO: 01284 769 505
General Enquiries Tel: 01284 755 127
Fax: 01284 706 035
Email: admin@theatreroyal.org
Web Site: www.theatreroyal.org
ADMINISTRATION:
Props: The National Trust
Lessees: Bury St. Edmunds Theatre Management
Director: Karen Simpson
Marketing Manager: Emma Martin
Production Manager: Adrian Grady
Policy: Touring, Opera & Ballet, Concerts, Pantomime, Amateurs
Perfs: (usual) 7.30
Seats: 360. 2 Bars. Foyer Coffee (Restaurant)
The Theatre Royal recently underwent a Capital Restoration and Development project and reopened on the 11th of September 2007.
If you have any questions concerning the Restoration of the Theatre Royal, please contact 01284 755 127.
TECHNICAL:
For further information, please contact: Lawrence Chicon
Email: lawrence@theatreroyal.org

TECHNICAL:
Stage: Proscenium Stage, Flat with either Forestage or Orch. Pit; Pros. Opening 7.32m; Ht. of Pros. 4.82m (variable); Depth of S/Line 9.75m; Ht. of Grid 6.09m; 12 Hemp sets, 10 Winch sets; Flying Bars 9.75m; W/Widths P.S. 1.52m, O.P. 1.52m; Prompt Cnr. P.S.
Lighting Control ECT Congo Jnr The control room is located in the gallery. There are 108 ways of dimming.
96 x 2.5k - 24 FOH, 72 on stage, all 16 amp c-form. 12 x 5k - 12 onstage, all 32 amp c-form.
Lanterns in stock: Fresnel: Patt 123 x 8, Minuette x 9, Patt 743 x 20, CCT Fresnels x 20, Cantata F x 8, Patt 243 2k x 7, Alto 2k x 4.
Profile: Patt 23 x 19, Prelude 16/30 x 4, Prelude 28/40 x 2, Source 4 Junior 25/50 x 12, Cantata 18/32 x 12, FOH gallery position, Source Four 19 degree x 16.
Par Can 64: Tom Cat x 23, CCT x 7
Floods: CCT Starlet floods x 12, S Batten 3-way X 4. Note, the theatre mixing desk is usually located at the lighting box side of the gallery. It can be moved to other parts of the auditorium or stage as required, but there is no room in the lighting box for sound equipment. If a different position for the mixing desk is required, that involves the blocking off of seats. This must be negotiated with the theatre management at time of booking.
1 x Allen & Heath GL4000 840 Mixing Console 40 Channels,8 Groups. 1 x Soundcraft Folio FX 8: 8 mic/line inputs with EQ, 4 stereo inputs, 4 aux inputs, lexicon effects.
Other: Dressing Rooms 7; Accom. 35 excl Band accommodation; 2 Shower, Orchestra Pit up to 25.
Get-in limited by gate 1.22m x 2.59m.
Parking difficult.
Membership: TMA

Bury, Lancashire

BURY VENUES

Knowsley Street, Bury, Lancashire BL9 0SW
Tel: 0161 253 5903
Email: buryvenues@bury.gov.uk
Web Site: www.buryvenues.co.uk
Bury Venues are proud of our long established tradition of providing excellent facilities, good quality food, a high standard of service from friendly and efficient staff and value for money packages.
Central Bookings contact: Christine Eaton

ELIZABETHAN SUITE

Town Hall, Knowsley Street, Bury, Lancashire BL9 0SW
Tel: 0161 253 5196 Central Booking Office: 0161 253 5903
Email: elizabethansuite@bury.gov.uk
Web Site: www.bury.gov.uk/elizabethansuite

ADMINISTRATION
Props: Bury Metropolitan Borough Council
For a full brochure or to make a booking contact: Christine Eaton or Sarah Fitchett at Bury Venues Central Bookings on Tel: 0161 253 5903 Email: buryvenues@bury.gov.uk
Cap: 300 theatre style
The spacious Main Hall can accommodate up to 300, and has an open platform stage. The Peel and Lancaster Rooms are both very comfortably furnished and are excellent settings for smaller events of 50 to 70 people. Licensed bars are situated in the Main Hall, Lancaster Room and Balcony area

RAMSBOTTOM CIVIC HALL

Market Place, Ramsbottom, Lancashire BL0 9AJ
Tel: 0161 253 5513
Email: ramsbottomcivichall@bury.gov.uk
Web Site: www.bury.gov.uk
ADMINISTRATION
Props: Bury Council
Cap: 160 Theatre Style
Hall Manager: Simon Green

Buxton, Derbyshire

Pop. 20,000. London 159 miles.
Newspapers: Buxton Advertiser (thurs).
STD code 01298

OPERA HOUSE

Water Street, Buxton, Derbyshire SK17 6XN
BO: 0845 1272 190 SD: 01298 72524
Admin: 01298 72050 Fax: 01298 27563
Tech: 01298 72050 / 72524
Email: rtaylor@boh.org.uk
Web Site: www.buxtonoperahouse.org.uk
ADMINISTRATION:
Props: High Peak Theatre Trust Ltd and Arts Council England.
Chief Executive: Simon Glinn.
House Manager: Rachel Taylor.
Theatre Secretary: Pat Russell.
Contact: theatresecretary@boh.org.uk
Technical Manager: Guy Dunk. Contact: technical@boh.org.uk
Policy: Professional and Amateur Productions, One Night Stands, Conferences, Filming, Festival July/August.
Perfs: Variable (usually 7.30p.m.; Mats, Thurs & Sat)
Capacity: 903 seated. 3 Bars.
Arts Centre available for hire.
Cap: 360, Studio: 93.
TECHNICAL:
STAGE: Proscenium Stage, raked with removable forestage over orchestra pit, to seat 50 Musicians. Pros opening 9.06m x 6m high. Pros wall to back wall 12m. Grid Ht. (downstage) 14.75m. Flying; 37 lines, 'Hemp' from OP flyfloor. 4 lighting winch-

es. Prompt corner PS. Get-in: Get-in Doors on DSL, 4.2m high, 3.m wide approx. opening. 2.25 tonne Scissor Lift 2.9m x 1.5m wide. Also 13 steps from street down to stage. Visiting Managers are strongly advised to provide high visibility clothing for any of their staff or contractors loading or unloading vehicles in Water Street. Get in doors 3m wide x 4.25m high. Large orchestra pit available by removing sections of forestage. 40 RAT lit music stands 1 RAT conductor stand 11 Doughty lit music stands 50 padded seat and back chairs.
LIGHTING: Control: Strand Lighting 520i, 250 channels. Strand Lighting R120 BIM2 radio remote. Dimmers: 174 ETC Sensor Dimmers 3K, 4 ETC Sensor Dimmers 5K, 8 non-dim. Flyfloor power: 125amp TPN C-form and 63amp TPN C-form. Stage power (mid stage left) 125amp TPN C-form socket, 63amp TPN C-form and Power lock outlets. Luminaires: Standard rig: 14 Cantata 11/26 on gallery bar. 6 SL15/32 on SL upper circle boom. 6 SL15/32 on SR upper circle boom. 3 Prelude 28/40 on SL proscenium boom. 3 Prelude 28/40 on SR proscenium boom. 12 Cantata PC, with barn doors, on winch 1. 12 Cantata PC, with barn doors on winch 2. 12 Cantata PC, with barn doors, on winch 3. 16 Iris 1000/1 floodlights (4 washes) on winch 4. 4 Prelude PC on Seecol stands, on stage. 2 Solo CSI in follow spot box, in gallery. 2 Furse MPR tab warmers, on gallery bar. 2 Minim PC conductor specials, on proscenium booms. Additional rig: (stored understage): 12 Cantata 26/44. 2 Cantata PC. 8 Coda 500/1. Other equipment: 1 Topdeck telescope, platform height adjustable from 3.9m to 5.9m high.1 Zarges 41000, 5.5m maximum height as A-frame. 2 Zarges 40227, 3m maximum height as A-frame. Selection of TRS and 6-way multicores. The following luminaires are available for hire: 50 Thomas PAR 64 CP62/61/60. 4 Cadenza F, with barn doors. 2 Cadenza PC, with barn doors 12 Cantata 18/32.
SOUND: Proscenium PA 4 Martin Audio WT2 400w AES, 2 Martin Audio MA1400, 2 x 700w at 4 ohms.2 Martin Audio S15+ sub bass 750w,1 Martin Audio MA1400, 2 x 700w at 4 ohms. Upper Circle & Gallery PA 2 Martin Audio WT2 400w AES, 1 Martin Audio MA1400, 2 x 700w at 4 ohms. Audio Management 1 Allen & Heath iDR-8 Audio Management System. Monitors 6 Martin Audio F12+, 12" + 1" Wedge 300w AES 3 Martin Audio MA1400, 2 x 700w at 4 ohms, 3 Martin audio M3+ blackline system controller. Mixers: 1 Allen & Heath GL2800-24 Audio Console, 1 Soundcraft Spirit Live 42 mixer 12-4-2. 1 Soundcraft Spirit Live 32 mixer 8-2-1. Outboard 4 XTA GQ600 Dual 30 Band EQ, 1 TC Electronic D-TWO Multitap Rhythm Delay, 2 BSS DPR404 Quad Compressor / De-Esser, 2 BSS DPR504 Quad Noise Gate, 1 TC Electronic M3000 Studio Reverb Processor, 1 Yamaha SPX2000 Multi Effects Processor, 1 Yamaha SPX-90 effects unit. Playback:1 Tascam MD-350 Minidisc player. 1 Denon DN-C630 CD player. Microphones 1 AKG D112, 2 Shure SM57, 4 Sennheiser E604, 5 AKG C 391B, 6 Shure SM58 microphones, 4 BSS AR133 Active DI Box, 2 BSS AR116 DI boxes. Stands: 6 K&M Telescopic Mic Stand/Boom Black, 2 AKG H 85 Universal shock mount, 3 K&M Telescopic Low Boom Mic Stand Black 18cm high, 6 Boom stands, 5 Banquet stands. Radio Mics for hire: 1 Trantec S5.3 4-Way Racked & Ready System, 1 Lavalier & 3 handhelds - Hire charge £10 plus VAT per day, £30 per week each.
COMMUNICATIONS: Headset system: Single channel, 8 belt packs and headsets available. Cue light system: 6 available to all usual technical areas. Loudspeakers in all dressing rooms.
DRESSING ROOMS: All dressing rooms have at least one sink with hot and cold water supply. 8 dressing rooms, or 7 dressing rooms & company office. The theatre does NOT have a band room or a green room - please allow for this when allocating dressing rooms. There are 2 separate unisex toilets and showers. 70 dressing room chairs available.
OTHER: Wardrobe room: 1 front loading washing machine. 1 tumble drier. 1 Steam iron & ironing board. Piano: Schimmel 6' 9" Grand is stored on its legs, in the SR wing, for use on stage only.

PAVILION GARDENS

St John's Road, Buxton, Derbyshire SK17 6XN
Tel: 01298 23114 Fax: 01298 27622
Email: paviliongardens@highpeak.gov.uk
Web Site: www.paviliongardens.co.uk
ADMINISTRATION:
Props: High Peak Borough Council
Bookings Manager: Paul Kelsall
Octagon Hall: Seating/Cap: 1,000 (flexible)

Camberley, Surrey

Pop. 44,967. London 30 miles.
Newspapers: Camberley Mail (tues); Camberley Courier (fri); Star (thurs); Camberley News (fri). STD code 01276

THE CAMBERLEY THEATRE

Knoll Road, Camberley, Surrey GU15 3SY
Mgt: 01276 707 603 / 7 BO: 01276 707 600 Fax: 01276 707 644
Email: camberley.theatre@surreyheath.gov.uk
Web Site: www.camberleytheatre.biz
ADMINISTRATION:
Props: Surrey Heath Borough Council
Operations & Technical Manager: Simon Spearing
General Manager: Ben Roberts
Policy: Pantomime, Variety Shows, Opera, Ballet, One Night Stands, Amateur Productions, cinema and conferences, exhibitions, etc. Full A.V and conference facilities.
Perfs: Variable
Seats: Auditorium 408 max. Licensed Bar, Cafe/Bar, Full Catering services. 16 x 16m flat floor available.
TECHNICAL:
STAGE:
Proscenium stage: Opening 8.75m, apron 1.90m; height of prosc. 3.81m, full depth 8.5m. wing width 3m(approx) Backstage crossover; stage floor black. 11 hemp lines, 6 electric winch bars. Prosc to grid 1m(approx). Bar length 11m. 5 Triple E tracks. House tabs (Gold, blue and 2 sets of black tabs). 4 sets of black legs, 4 black borders. Orchestra Pit; length 9.2m width 1.8m. Depth .50 or .20m, accomodates 12. Get in doors at rear of stage 2.44m high. Tallescope and Zarges. Scale stage Plan available.
LIGHTING:
Strand 530i, 76 dimmers, 2 followspots, 32 profiles, 50 fresnels, 4 x 4 Cyc Floods, 6 birdies, 24 Parcans, 10 Source 4 Par's, 10 1K floods, 16 Chroma Q colour Scrollers.
SOUND:
Martin Audio Stereo System. Sound console: Soundcraft Series 2 32-8-2. Central cluster 2 x EM76, Prosc R & L 2 x EM76, 2 WS2A Bass Bins, 4 EM 26 delay speakers, 4 x EM15 front Fills. Playback 1 Denon Cassette Deck, 2 Tascam Mini Disc, 1 Denon CD player, 1 CD and Mini Disc Deck, 1 Yamaha SPX990. Microphones 11 SM58, 8 SM57, various condensors, 8 Audio Technica Radio Mics.
STAGE MANAGEMENT:
Prompt corner SL - TechPro talkback system - show relay/tannoy to dressing rooms.
BACKSTAGE:
5 Dressing rooms, access by stage door. Rehearsal piano, good. Advice given on accommodation. No security personnel. Backstage facilities fully accessible to disable performers and staff.
STUDIO:
Width 6.4m length 10.36m
Lighting: Sirius Zero 88 24 way, 24 dimmers, 14 fresnels, 8 profiles. Portable sound system. Scale plan available.
MEDIA SUITE:
Mackie D8B, Mackie HDR 24/96. PC Running CuBase, Cooleditpro and Sibelius. Media 100 AV Edit suite, 2 x JVC Minidv cams Panasonic vision mixer.

Cambridge, Cambridgeshire

Pop. 100,250. London 54 miles.
Newspapers: Cambridge Evening News (ntly); Cambridge Weekly News (thurs); Town Crier (thurs). STD code 01223

ADC THEATRE

Park Street, Cambridge CB5 8AS
Mgt: 01223 359 547 BO: 01223 300 085
Email: info@adctheatre.com
Web Site: www.adctheatre.com
ADMINISTRATION:
Props: Amateur Dramatic Club
Lessees: University of Cambridge
Manager: Florence Carr
Operations Manager: Oli Rew
Production Manager: Mitchell Clarke
Technical Manager: Iain Harvey
Office Administrator: Rhys Fraser
Box Office Administrator: Ella Bucklow
Policy: Amateur productions by University and local groups, occasional small professional touring groups (no fees given).
Perfs: 7.45pm + 11pm. Tues-Sat and late nights
Seats: 228. Licensed Bar.
TECHNICAL:
For further information contact the Technical Manager: Iain Harvey
Email: iain@adctheatre.com
Stage: Proscenium Stage with flat forestage, stepped apron or orchestra pit. Flat Pros. Opening 6.63m; Ht. of Pros. 3.96m; Depth of S/L 8.53m; Ht. of Grid 12m; 40 lines (26 Hemp, 14 cwt). Flying width 9.5m; W/widths PS 4.27m, OP 2.89m; prompt corner P.S.
Lighting: Switchboard Rank Strand 520 with effects unit controls 92 fixed 2.5kw & 8 fixed 5kw dimmers & 5 Act 6 dimmer racks located around stage area. Space for follow spot in lighting box. Lanterns: 20 1kw Silhouette 30, 2 1kw Silhouette 15, 24 1kw Starlette Fresnels, 8 2kw Patt. 243, 24 120V Par 64, 15 500W Minuette Profiles, various 500W fresnels, 12 Coda 1000, 1 2kw Silhouette 15 follow spot, 6 kw starlette PC, 5 Coda 3 Groudrow, 8 240v par 64.
Sound Equip: Mixers - 1 Soundcraft, Power amps; 1 C Audio RA3000, 1 Bose 1800 dual channel (425w), 1 Quad 606 Dual channel (150w); Speakers: 6 Bose 802, 2 A & R CS62 100w columns; Sources: 1 Ferrograph Logic 7 Reel to Reel, 1 Denon DN990R minidisc, 1 Denon DN770 Twin Casssette Deck, 3 CD players, 1 Yamaha REV100 reverb unit, 1 stereo 30 band EQ; Mics: 3 Shure SM58, 3 AKG D190, 3 Beyer M201. TecPro Talkback ring (10 station); 2 x 35mm Carousel slide projectors (250w) with dissolve unit.
Scenery and lighting service available during vacations.
Other: Dressing Rooms - 2; Accom. 25; Washing machine, irons and drier; Orchestra Pit 10
Winch motor installed..
Membership CEA.

CAMBRIDGE ARTS THEATRE

6 St Edwards Passage, Cambridge CB2 3PJ
BO: 01223 503 333
Email: info@cambridgeartstheatre.com
Web: www.cambridgeartstheatre.com
ADMINISTRATION:
Executive Director: Dave Murphy
Head of Programming: Chloe Ireland
Head of Marketing: Al Morley
Front of House Manager: Grace Hadley
Technical Manager: Mark Passey
Box Office Manager: Kat Andrews
Status: National Touring House. City centre venue founded by John Maynard Keynes in 1936, designed by C Kennedy. Reopened in December 1996 after major refurbishment. Currently funded by Arts Council England East and Cambridge City Council. Membership of TMA.
Policy: Drama, Dance, Opera, Music, Film, Pantomime and Revue. Willing to premiere show. Terms by negotiation. Also workshops, conferences, trade shows, lectures, films.
Seating: Raked on two levels. Capacity 666.
Catering: restaurant and bars with new facilities.
Access: Nearby car parks, 20 mins from Cambridge rail station, 5 mins from Cambridge coach station.
Facilities for disabled: fully accessible to audience, staff & performers. Wheelchair spaces, accessible toilets on every floor, hearing loop, facilities for signed performances and audio description, accessible dressing room space including shower. Lift to all floors.
TECHNICAL:
For further information please contact the Technical Manager: Mark Passey
Email: tech@cambridgeartstheatre.com
Stage: Proscenium arch. Performing area 10.2m x 10.2m pros opening 7.72m x 4.8m. wing widths 3.5m SR, 4.5m SL with 12.5m flat scene dock. No rake - floor lino on wood, suitable for dance. Understage crossover, stage heated. Height of grid 14.4m 47 counterweight lines. House tabs flown. Forestage apron extensions 1.5m or 2.5m, entrances in front of pros. Orchestra pit in two sizes, maximum depth 6m, width 11.5m. Get-in via alleyway doors SL. Tallescope. Safety Curtain. Scale stage and lighting plans available.
Lighting and Sound: Please contact venue for details.
Other: Backstage: space for 50 understage. 5 rooms with ensuite facilities. Accessible room at stage level. 15 band changing spaces. Crew changing rooms and kitchens. Wardrobe and laundry.
The Arts Theatre is owned and managed by Cambridge Arts Theatre Trust.

THE CAMBRIDGE CORN EXCHANGE

Wheeler Street, Cambridge CB2 3QE
Mgt: 01223 457 280 BO: 01223 357 851
Fax: 01223 457 559
Email: admin.cornex@cambridge.gov.uk
Web Site: www.cornex.co.uk
ADMINISTRATION:
Props: Cambridge City Council
General Manager: Steve Bagnall
Business and Marketing Manager: Neil Jones
Contact: neil.jones@cambridge.gov.uk
Senior Business Officer: Anthony Delaney
Finance Officer: Anthony Delaney
Technical Manager: Chris Norton
Contact: chris.norton@cambridge.gov.uk
House Manager: Jeff Charnock
Programme Officers: Megan Charnock, Roisin McManus
Policy: Rock, Jazz, Classical concerts, Theatre Productions, Musicals, Opera, Dance, Spectator Sports. Also lectures and private bookings.
Capacity Range: 1256 - 1462 seated; 1849 standing.
TECHNICAL:
Please visit the website www.cornex.co.uk and then follow the technical links to access full spec.
STAGE: Dimensions: Full stage (two extensions) Width 15.8m Depth 9.5m; With one extension Width 15.8m Depth 7m; Fixed stage Width 15.8m Depth 4.9m; Stage Height 1m. Stage size affects the audience capacity. Clearance: Stage to grid 7.8m, Stage to gantry 6.3m, Smallest dimensions; Width 2.1m. Get in: Smallest dimensions; Width 2.16m; Height 2.42m.
LIGHTING: Control: Strand 530i control desk with remote on-stage access; House lights under separate control from same positions. Dimmers; 144 x 2.5kw Strand LD 90; DMX breakouts available for installation of additional equipment. Lanterns: 54 x 1K Fresnels, 24 x CCT Freedom, 15/32 zoom profiles (N.B. 12 normally rigged on FOH bridge.), 4 x CCT Freedom 28/58 zoom profiles, 4 x Cantata 18/32 zoom profiles, 92 x Par 64 (CP62), 6 x Par 64 floorcans (CP60), 8 x Par 56 floorcans, 5 x CCT Cyc. lights (4 x 1K), Irises and gobo holders available for profiles. Barn doors on all fresnels. Follow Spots: 2 x Pani HMI 1200 Follow spots rigged; 8m under FOH bridge. Please note restricted to use by house operators only. Other: Unique 2 hazer. 2 x 50cm Mirror Balls.
SOUND: 6 x Martin CT2 powered by 2 x C Audio RA3001 in 2 x 3 clusters; 2 x Martin CTX powered by 1 x C Audio RA3001; 1 x Martin MX2 System controller; Opus AT1000 3 Way Active Array Technology Cabinets; Opus 5B118 Sub Bass Cabinets; Opus x234 Loudspeaker Management System + Opus HD High Definition Power Amps; 3 x C Audio/Crown Pulse Amps Flightcased to make a small portable system with Martin speakers. Control and processors: Midas Venice 24/4/2 - 16 Mono inputs, 4 stereo inputs;Soundcraft Delta SR 8/4/2; 1 x C Audio EQ312 Graphic (Stage system); 1 x DBX Drive Rack; 1 x C Audio EQ311 Graphic (Delay system - centre); 1 x Yamaha Q2031 Graphic (Delay system - L&R); 1 x Yamaha Q2031 Graphic (inserts / sub groups); 2 x Klark Teknik DN700 delay line (L&R); 1 x Klark Teknik DN710 delay line (Centre); 1 x Sabine FBX900

Feedback exterminator; 1 x Ability DA210E Summed mono device; 1 x SPX 990 multi effects processor; 1 x Rev 500 (digital reverb); 1 x dbx 266xl Compressor (Twin Channel); 2 x BSS Opal EQ.
Replay/recording; 1 x Denon DN770R Twin cassette deck; 1 x Denon DRM540 Cassette deck; 1 x Denon DCD315 CD player; 1 x Sony MDS E-10 Minidisc.
Various Microphones Available.
DRESSING ROOM: Accomm. 50; production office; fully equipped kitchen.
STAGE MANAGEMENT: Metro Audio base station, 6 x Metro or tec-pro belt-packs/headsets.

GUILDHALL
The Guildhall, Market Street, Cambridge CB2 3QJ
Tel: 01223 457 000 Cambridge City Council Admin Tel: 01223 457 000
Email: concierge@cambridge.gov.uk
Web Site: www.cambridge.gov.uk
ADMINISTRATION:
For booking enquiries, please contact the Arts & Entertainment Department, Cambridge City Council on Tel: 01223 457 555
Cap: Large Hall: 576 Theatre style; with seated balcony 646; 400 standing; Small Hall: 200 Seated; 150 standing plus buffet; 100 theatre style.

KELSEY KERRIDGE SPORTS CENTRE
Queen Anne Terrace, Gonville Place, Cambridge CB1 1NA
Tel: 01223 462 226 Fax: 01223 363 889
Email: info@kelseykerridge.co.uk
Web Site: www.kelseykerridge.co.uk
ADMINISTRATION
Props: Cambridge Sports Hall Trust
Main Hall Cap: 1500
Manager: Liane Shadrack

MARCH TOWN HALL
Market Place, March, Cambridgeshire PE15 9JF
Tel: 01354 652 769
Email: info@marchtownhallevents.co.uk
Web Site: www.marchtownhallevents.co.uk
Props: The March Civic Trust
Management: 20 Twenty Productions
The Town Hall is a fully accessible venue situated in the centre of the market town of March. A very versatile space with removable seating and staging. When not in use for performances/workshops, the space is also used as an exhibition gallery. Please contact the venue or check out the website for more details.
Cap: 120

THE JUNCTION
Clifton Way, Cambridge CB1 7GX
Admin Tel: 01223 578 000 Box Office Tel: 01223 511 511
Email: info@junction.co.uk
Web Site: www.junction.co.uk
General Director: Daniel Brine
Technical Manager: Simon Talbot simon@junction.co.uk
- Venue Capacity
Large Venue: 850 all standing; Theatre Venue: 220 seated
The Junction is one of the eastern region's premier multi-arts centres and has been presenting the very best in theatre, dance, clubs, music, comedy, children's and participation events since opening in 1990. A registered charity, the venue underwent major re-development in 2004/5 through £7.5 million of lottery funding secured through Arts Council England. As well as upgrading existing facilities, the development also included the opening of a brand new 220-capacity theatre and a dedicated education and rehearsal space. All spaces are available for hire for performance and/or conferences with a difference!
All areas have full disabled access.
TECHNICAL:
For further information please contact The Operations Manager
THEATRE SPEC -
Stage: 10m wide x 8.6m deep of a sprung wooden construction, ideal for dance. Flexible seating arrangements mean various stage designs (thrust, in the round, etc).
Load In: Direct on the flat, through dock doors Rigging - tension wire grid over theatre + Genie AWP 25 powered access personnel lift for work below grid.
Lighting: 30x 1.2K sellecon HP fresnels, 6x 2K HP sellecon arena fresnels, 20x 1K sellecon pacific 14-30 deg zooms, 10x 1K sellecon pacific 25-50 deg zoom, 8x ETC source
4 jnr (575W) 25-50 deg, 4x Thomas 1K cyc floods, 18x Par 64 (CP60, 61, 62 stocked), 10x strand prelude fresnels (650W). 60 channels of ETC sensor dimmers, 2.5K in 2x 96 way racks, various dim, non dims and independent power outlets.
Sound: 2x Tascam CD 160, 1x Tascam MD 350, 1x Tascam MD 801, 1x soundcraft spirit live 24 ch, 4 sub, 6 aux, 4x Martin black line F8 balcony front speakers powered from Yamaha P3500S, Control room monitoring from a pair of Tanoy Reveal, Multi effects/outboard units on request (advance notice essential), Further sound reinforcement and monitoring may available on request, 2 x Hand Held Radio Microphones (ch69 frequencies), 2 x Lapel Radio Microphones (ch69 frequencies), Extensive microphone line and tie line system.
Drapes: Upstage tab, black wool surge, running width of stage, floor to grid. White filled cloth Cyc, running width of dance floor, floor to grid. 4 bays each side of the stage achieved with soft masking (black wool surge).

Cannock, Staffordshire
Pop. 63,210. London 31 miles.
Newspapers: Cannock Express & Star; Cannock Chronicle; Chase Post; Mercury.
STD code 01543

CHASE LEISURE CENTRE
Stafford Road, Cannock, Staffordshire WS11 2AL
Tel: 01543 504 065 Fax: 01543 502 655
Web Site: www.wlct.org
ADMINISTRATION
Props: Wigan Leisure and Culture Trust
Cap: 1250
Manager: Terry Simms

CIVIC SUITE
Beecroft Road, Cannock, Staffordshire WS11 1BG
Bkgs Tel: 01543 462 621 Fax: 01543 462 317
Email: customerservices@cannockchasedc.gov.uk
Web Site: www.cannockchasedc.gov.uk
ADMINISTRATION
Props: Cannock Chase District Council
Cap: 140
Bookings Manager: Tracie Clarke
Email: tracieclarke@cannockchasedc.gov.uk

HAYES GREEN COMMUNITY CENTRE
23 School Road, Norton Canes, Cannock, Staffordshire WS11 9SQ
Tel: 01543 448 614
Email: janine_arm@hotmail.com
ADMINISTRATION
Props: Heath Hayes & Wimblebury Parish Council
Main Room Cap: 150 seated 250 standing; 1 meeting room
Bookings Scretary: Janine Arm

PRINCE OF WALES CENTRE
Church Street, Cannock, Staffordshire WS11 1DE
Mgt: 01543 466 453 BO: 01543 578 762
Fax: 01543 574 439
Email: princeofwales@cannockchasedc.gov.uk
Web Site: www.cannockchasedc.gov.uk
ADMINISTRATION:
Theatre Manager: Richard Kay
Technical Manager: Andrew Kennerley
Status: Multi-purpose centre. A modern building, situated in the town centre, a multi-purpose entertainments complex, built in 1984. Venue funded by Cannock Chase District Council; Local Authority Cannock Chase District Council. RAA WMA.
Policy: Complete range of entertainment including music (classical, jazz, folk, popular), dance, drama, variety and rock music.

Perfs: Usually open 7 days a week.
Booking terms box office split, guarantee & split, guarantee, by negotiation.
Non-performance activities: Snooker, wrestling, darts, exhibitions, craft fairs, sales and conferences.
Seating: 428; half flat floor, half retractable.
Catering: 2 Licensed bars.
Ticket outlets: Box Office only.
Access car park: Adjacent, nearest railway station: Cannock, nearest coach terminal: adjacent, bus routes: adjacent.
For the disabled: Wheelchair spaces provided as required - assistance available, contact Duty Manager - lift - parking - level access - ramp at entrance - all house facilities fully accessible.
TECHNICAL:
Stage: Proscenium arch. Performing area 9m x 6.65m - pros. opening 9m x 5.82m - wing widths 1.83m SR, 1.06m SL. Stage raked, 1 in 50 - floor sprung wood, suitable for all dance, no crossover, stage heated. Height of grid 2m - 16 hemp sets, 10cm apart - tab track - maximum flying height 4.57m - black borders, legs and book wings - white cyclorama - red house tabs, drawn - 8 x 13A, plus 60A independent circuits. Forestage 1m. Orchestra pit can be formed by removing front seats. Get-in via dock doors SL - dock doors 1.9m x 2.1m. Tallescope. Scale stage, fly and lighting plans available.
Lighting: Rank Strand Duet 2 Memory System board, 96 circuits @ 10A, 3 phase, operated from back of auditorium or SL - 28 spots, 32 fresnels, Rank/Harmony - followspots operated from back of auditorium.
Sound: Oval 12:2 series 3 desk, operated from back of auditorium - 4 x 250w output FOH, 2 x 100w output foldback, reverb unit - 3 radio, 5 x Shure, 5 x AKG, 2 x Rifle mics - cassette tape systems. Acoustics suitable for music and spoken word.
Other: Stage Management: Prompt corner SL - Technical Projects cue system, 6 outstations - show relay to dressing rooms.
Backstage: 1 x SR, 2 x SL dressing rooms, access by stage door. No wardrobe, but iron and board available, 4 x 13A sockets. Refreshments available during the day from the cafe until 3.00p.m. Piano, moderate. Advice given on accommodation. Staff - 2 technicians - casuals available - no security personnel. Backstage facilities not accessible to disabled performers/staff.

Canterbury, Kent

Pop. 36,290. London 56 miles.
Newspapers: Kentish Gazette (fri); Adscene (tues); Canterbury Extra (tues).
STD code 01227

GULBENKIAN THEATRE

Gulbenkian, University of Kent, Canterbury, Kent CT2 7NB
Admin: 01227 769 075 Marketing: 01227 827 956 Cinema: 01227 823 491 Café Bar: 01227 823 842 Technical: 01227 823 430 Bookings: 01227 769 075
Email: boxoffice@kent.ac.uk
Web Site: www.thegulbenkian.co.uk
ADMINISTRATION:
Props: University of Kent
Director: Liz Moran
Technical Manager: Jake Taylor
Head of Marketing: David Yard
Ticket and Informations Manager: Lianna Macari
Located on the University Campus, purpose built in 1969 and refurbished in 1997. Part of a complex incorporating cinema, licensed café bar and exhibition area.
Policy: Mixed programme, middle scale touring and one-nighters with some student, amateur and in-house productions. Also concerts, comedy, opera, drama, dance, children's shows, festivals and events. Frequently used to premiere shows and for pre London warm ups. Also available for conferences and private hire.
Seats: 340. Raked auditorium. Large, newly extended licensed café/bar with exhibition area.
(Nearest BR station: Canterbury West)
Free Public Car Park adjacent. All areas fully accesible.
TECHNICAL:
Stage: Open thrust Flat stage raised 0.6m above auditorium floor - hardboard on sprung wood. Reversible Harlequin dance floor available. D.S. width of thrust 4.95m widening to 10.97m at max. Depth 10.13m, Ht. of grid 5.64m. W/widths S.L. 6.4m. Stage right wing now available (from Oct 2005) . Prompt corner S.L. No Flying. Fixed scaffolding grid. Soft black masking. White cyc available. Hand winched blue house tabs S.L. Get-in dock doors 5m x 3m S.L. at stage level. Scale plans available - downloadable from website. Upright and Bechstein grand pianos available. CCTV in S.L. wing.
Lighting: Strand 520i LX board in control room at rear of auditorium. F.O.H: 12 sil 30 1kw, 6 patt 264, 12 patt 743, 4 Prelude 16/30. On stage: 2 patt 243, 18 patt 743, 5 patt 263, 8 patt 23, 6 patt 123, 4 Prelude PC, 6 Iris 1, 4 patt 60, 2 patt 252,
8 par 64 (CP61), 8 Par 64 (CP62), 8 source 4 (36o),2 freedom Sil, 1 2kw Sil 30, 1 patt 293 followspot in control room. F.O.H. outlets 18 x 2kw. 2 auditorium booms 1 x 1kw and 1 x 2kw per side. Advance bar 16 x 1kw. Overstage 24 x 2kw and 4 x 5kw patchable. Dips 8 x 2kw U.S.L, 3 x 5kw U.S.R. Open fixed grid. 60A single phase supply SL. Mobile tower.
Sound: adjacent to LX board in control room (rear of auditorium). Mackie TT24 digital console in lighting box. 2 x PSL2402 amps(for F.O.H. & sub bass) 1 x QUAD 405 (for EV Sx200s) 4 x Community RS220 (front of house, 2 wall L and R, 2 centre) 2 x Community LFC215 sub bass speakers (on stage) 2 x EV SX200 wedges (on stage) 1 NAD C451 CD player. 1 x Yamaha KX580 SE single cassette deck, 1 x Kenwood KT 1010L stereo tuner, 1 x Technics SL - PG500A CD player, 1 x NAD C451 CD player, 1 x SONY JB930 minidisc recorder, 1 x Yamaha SPX 900, various mikes, 24 mike tie lines to lighting box. Accoustics suitable for music and the spoken word. Mixing position in auditorium - advance notice required.
Other: Stage Management: Techpro show relay and paging system to all areas.
Dressing rooms: 3 accomm. 30. Also one laundry/green room equipped with washing machine, tumble dryer, iron and board, fridge and microwave. No showers.
Staff: 3 technical. Casuals available.
Disabled access: backstage and F.O.H. areas fully accessible to performers and public. Infra-red audio system.

THE MARLOWE THEATRE

The Friars, Canterbury, Kent CT1 2AS
SD: 01227 862268 Tel: 01227 787 787
Email: info@marlowetheatre.com
Web Site: www.marlowetheatre.com
ADMINISTRATION:
Props: Canterbury City Council
Theatre Director: Mark Everett
Head of Operations: Paula Gillespie
Head of Marketing & Communications: John Baker
Policy: Top touring venue. Programme: Musicals, Drama, Dance, Comedy, Concerts of all types, Ballet, Opera and Light Entertainment (Main House). Wide-ranging policy of performance, new commissions, creative collaborations and education projects (Second Space).
Seats: 1200 (Main House) 150 Seating/300 Standing (Second Space)

TECHNICAL:
MAIN STAGE; Stage floor loading is 7.5.kN/m2-this extends fully into the wings and onto lifts 1 & 2. Prosc. Dimensions: Structual Opening Height: 7.5m (unmasked, not suitable for live flying); Masked Opening Height: 6m (header/pelmet in place, required for live flying); Full Opening Width: 13m. Dimensions: Playing area: 13m x 12m (prosc width x depth from setting line to up stage wall); Stage Left Wing: 3.7m; Stage Right Wing: 4.25m (to front edge of flying frame); Stage Left Dock: 32.52m2 (accessed via a 3.5m wide by 5m high opening in the centre of the stage left wall). The stage edge is 1m down stage of the setting line. Manually operated counterweight flying system in place.
PROMPT DESK: custom built: Venue wide paging facilities; Colour and B&W

monitors from FOH Cameras; 20 x way Q light Outstation system; Can be located stage left or right.
ORCHESTRA PIT: There are three orchestra pit lifts which enable the formation of three different sized pits. All pit sizes include an area of 16m2 usable space immediately under the stage edge. Pit Lift 1 - 29m2 (small pit total size 45m2) Loses 43 seats; Pit Lift 2 - 30m2 (medium pit total size 75m2) Loses a further 61 seats; Pit Lift 3 - 15.5m2 (large pit total size 90.5m2) Loses a further 32 seats. Pit fully accessible. 20 x Lit Rat Stands, 40 x Unlit Music Stands, 1 x Yamaha C7 Grand Piano. 60 orchestra chairs.
Lighting: Strand 5201 Lighting Board 250 channel with com pro, network and track software; strand 301 Backup.
FOH DESK & OUTBOARD: 1 x Allen & Heath GL2800 Mixing Desk; 1 x Yamaha SPX2000; 1 x DBX2231 Stereo EQ Unit; 1 x Yamaha Stereo EQ Unit; 1 x Tascam; CDR900 CD Recorder; 3 x Technics/Denon/Philips CD Player; 1 x Sony MD Recorder.
GREEN ROOM: Located stage level stage right. Kitchen with fridge and microwave available. All back stage areas have wifi coverage.
Dressing Rooms: located under stage and at stage level. Toilets and showers available, some ensuite.
Wardrobe: Wardrobe dept located stage right. Facilities for plumbing touring machines and numerous power outlets available.
AV: 1 x High Resolution colour camera with manual zoom; 1 x B&W camera with manual zoom.

Canvey Island, Essex

THE PADDOCKS COMMUNITY CENTRE
Long Road, Canvey Island, Essex SS8 0JA
Caretaker Tel: 01268 695271
Admin/Bookings: 01268 882465
Email: halls@castlepoint.gov.uk
Web Site: www.castlepoint.gov.uk
ADMINISTRATION
Props: Castle Point District Council
Cap: Main Hall 400; Hall Two 175

Cardiff, South Glamorgan

Pop. 278,400. London 154 miles.
Newspapers: South Wales Echo (ntly); Western Mail (dly); South Wales Argus (dly). STD code 029 20

BUTE THEATRE
Castle Grounds Cathays Park Cardiff CF10 3ER
Tel: 029 20391376 Fax: 029 20391304
Email: janet.smith@rwcmd.ac.uk
Web Site: www.rwcmd.ac.uk
Venue Manager: Janet Smith
Cap: 160

CHAPTER ARTS CENTRE
Market Road, Canton, Cardiff, South Glamorgan CF5 1QE Wales
Tel: 029 2031 1050 BO: 029 2030 4400
Email: enquiry@chapter.org
Web Site: www.chapter.org
ADMINISTRATION:
Theatre Manager: Cathy Boyce
Email: cathy.boyce@chapter.org
At our main site in Canton, west of Cardiff City Centre you'll find 3 theatres, 2 cinemas, a gallery, studios, 2 bars, a cafe, over 60 cultural workspaces and more! We're open 7 days a week from 10.00am to 11.00pm (often later) and admission is free, so just drop in and check out what's happening. Chapter Gallery and Shop is open (during exhibitions) from Tues - Sunday, 11am - 8pm.
Cap: 120
For more information on Venue Hire, telephone: 029 2031 1058, or email: nicky.keeping@chapter.org

CLWB IFOR BACH
11 Womanby Street, Cardiff CF10 1BR
Tel: 029 2023 2199 Fax: 029 2030 1113
Email: press@clwb.net
Web Site: www.clwb.net
ADMINSTRATION:
Contact: Richard Hawkins
Policy: Hire and self-promote
Capacity: 220

DORA STOUTZKER CONCERT HALL
Castle Grounds Cathays Park Cardiff CF10 3ER
Tel: 029 2039 1376 Fax: 029 2039 1304
Email: janet.smith@rwcmd.ac.uk
Web Site: www.rwcmd.ac.uk
Venue Manager: Janet Smith
Cap: 395

GREAT HALL,CARDIFF UNIVERSITY STUDENTS' UNION
Park Place, Cardiff CF10 3QN
Tel: 029 2078 1400
Email: studentsunion@cardiff.ac.uk
Web Site: www.cardiffstudents.com
ADMINISTRATION:
Contact : Tracey Bishop
Policy: Hire and Self-promote
Capacity: 1,500

MILLENNIUM STADIUM
Westgate Street, Cardiff CF10 1NS
Tel: 029 2082 2467
Email: alexluff@millenniumstadium.com
Web Site: www.millenniumstadium.com
ADMINISTRATION
Contact: Alex Luff, Venue Sales Manager
Policy: Hire and self-promote
Capacity: 65,000, 20,000-30,000 (arena configuration).

MOTORPOINT ARENA CARDIFF
Mary Ann Street, Cardiff, South Glamorgan CF10 2EQ Wales
Tel: 029 2023 4500 BO: 029 2022 4488
Group Bookings (10 people+): 029 2023 4510 Fax: 029 2023 4501
Email: motorpointarenacardiff.sales@livenation.co.uk
Web Site: www.livenation.co.uk/cardiff
ADMINISTRATION:
General Manager: Phil Sheeran
Technical Manager: Glyn Cornelius
Props: Live Nation (Venues) UK Ltd
Main arena facilities: 7,500 Entertainment and Convention Seating Capacity, 5,000 Banqueting Seating Capacity.
Exhibition Area: 4,000 sq.m.
For all booking information and further details, please contact: Alexandra Otley or Joanna McKay at Live Nation (Venues) UK Ltd, address to arena.
E-mail: venue.bookings@livenation.co.uk
TECHNICAL:
Stage: Steel deck stage, 2 x 300amp 3 phase stage power. Exhibition services via floor ducts. 12K Sherman Performance Sound System. Extensive Conference Services, Barco 5,000 Projector.
350 Delegate conference suite, 36 executive suites, press suite with dedicated facilities, function suites for up to 500 persons.
Also includes: Cardiff World Trade Centre - trade research, business secretariat and communications centre, video conference suite, boardrooms, meeting rooms and offices, private dining rooms, Langleys restaurant and World Trade Centre club lounge.

NEW THEATRE
Park Place, Cardiff, CF10 3LN Wales
Mgt: 029 2087 8787 Mgt Fax: 029 2087 8788 BO: 029 2087 8889 SD: 029 2087 8900
Email: gmcfarlane@cardiff.gov.uk
Web Site: www.newtheatrecardiff.co.uk
ADMINISTRATION:
Props: Cardiff County Council
Marketing Manager: Matt Smith
Theatre Manager: Grant McFarlane
House Manager: Philip Sage, Caroline Hirst
Chief Technician: Julian Maxwell
Box Office Manager: Dave Mcateer
Policy: Touring, Drama, Opera, Ballet, Pantomime, Children's Shows, Musicals
Perfs: Variable, but usually Mon-Sat 7.30, Sat.Mat. 2.30 or 3.00
Seats: 1,144 seated
TECHNICAL:

Stage: Proscenium Stage, cantilevered over orchestra pit. No traps available. Rake 1 in 24. Dock door R.S.L. at street level. Understage crossover possible. House Tabs can be operated from stage or fly floor. Height under fly floor, downstage 7.5m, upstage 7m. Height under grid 16.15m; Pros. Opening 9.14m; 6.4m to border; Depth of setting line 12.19m; Wing widths, P.S. 5.18m, O.P. 4.42m; Prompt corner O.P. (stage right); 45 X counterweight sets, 15 X double purchase @ 300kg, 30 X single purchase @ 400kg, All bars 12.05m. Power on stgae, 200A TPN bus-bar with RCD set 300mA @ 200ms delay; 3 X 125A BS4343 socket outlets; 3 X 200A SPN speed clamps. power on fly floor S.L., 200A TPN camlocks with RCD set 300mA @ 200ms delay.Orchestra Pit/Forestage: On three hydraulic scissors lifts 3.05 X 9.11m each. Full large pit 9.11 X 9.54m, & extends 5.49m under stage, to accommodate 75 musicians.
Lighting: 550i sited in control room at rear of stalls, with 168 X 10A Permus ways & 12 X 25A Permus ways. 2 X Theatro 1200w MSR follow spots; 27 X Cantata F, 13 X Patt 743, 12 X Furse MPR, 4 X Sil 30, 6 X Patt 23, 49 X Parcans, 5 X Iris 4; FOH 24 X Cadenza, 12 X Cantata 11/26, 10 X Cantata 18/32.
Sound: Soundcraft 500 mixer 24-8-2 sited in control room; Central cluster with Renkus-Heinz speakers fed by 2 X "C" Audio SR 404 amps, Renkus-Heinz speakers at stalls level fed 1 X "C" Audio RA 2000 amp, BES speakers in 2 X delay rings for rear stalls & rear circle fed by 1 X "C" Audio SR 202 amp, Misc. Shure & Kudos speakers for on stage foldback etc.; Klark- Teknic & Harrison 1/3 outave graphics, Yamaha SPX1000 processor, Revox B226 CD, Denon DRM-540 cassette, 2 X Revox B77 R-R; 5 X PCC160, Selection AKG mics, Selection Shure mics.
General: 13 dressing rooms for 77 people; Wardrobe, Wig room, & Laundry equipped with 1 washing m/c & 1 tumble dryer; Company Office, Visiting Dtage Manager, Conductor, Band room for 60 persons, Band room for 10 persons. Telephones in all general & dressing rooms; fax points in Company Office, Stage Manager, Dressing room 1 & 1A, & fax m/c at stage door. Show relay, voice & video communication to all parts of theatre.
Signed and audio described performances on selected shows.

RICHARD BURTON THEATRE

Castle Grounds Cathays Park Cardiff CF10 3ER
Tel: 029 2039 1376 Fax: 029 2039 1304
Email: janet.smith@rwcmd.ac.uk
Web Site: www.rwcmd.ac.uk
Venue Manager: Janet Smith
Cap: 180

SHERMAN THEATRE

Senghenydd Road, Cardiff, South Glamorgan CF24 4YE South Wales
Tel: 029 206 46900 Admin: 029 2064 6901
Email: elin.partridge@shermancymru.co.uk
Web Site: www.shermancymru.co.uk
ADMINISTRATION:
Props and Lessees: Sherman Theatre Ltd
Director: Chris Ricketts
General Manager: Margaret Jones
Head of Development: Emma Goad
Literary Manager: Sian Summers
Administrator: Elin Partridge
Policy: Theatre for young people with 2 auditoria centering around productions of resident Sherman Theatre Company. Venue for visiting large and small scale professional drama, dance, opera and concerts; also host to local amateur and operatic companies. Programme includes Saturday children's shows and touring of own children's and young people's productions. Facilities for conferences.
Perfs: Morning, lunchtime, afternoon, evening, late night.
Seats: Sherman main auditorium 450 plus space for 6 wheelchairs. Studio Theatre flexible units giving up to 100 seats depending on arrangement. Public bar, restaurant.
TECHNICAL:
MAIN THEATRE:
STAGE: Unstressed proscenium opening 11.66m x 5.53m. Depth of stage excluding apron 10.64m. Max depth of semi-circular apron (orchestra lift) 3m Grid Ht. 14.4m; Wing Space 4m (PS) 7m(OP); Single Purchase Counterweights 34. Bar length 15.85m. Get in door 2.7m x 3.5m, 1.6m above road level.
LIGHTING: A.D.B Vision 10 plus full tracking backup.m 250 ways fitted. 3 F.O.H. bridges, and two side auditorium lighting slots. O.P. and P.S.
SOUND: Soundcraft venue 2.40 into 10 into 7 mixer, 8 off meyer UPA1 .4 Matin W3's, 8 Matin Em 26's crown amps minidiscs, CD.
ADDITIONAL: Screen overall 11.15m x 5.49m (picture size 31ft x 13.5ft), 2 x 35mm, 1 x 16mm projectors. Stereo optical sound.
STUDIO:
Octagonal with all round balcony at 1.98m. Max width of floor 11.89m. Width of clear floor with seating in the round 6.4m. Get in doors 1.7m x 1.93m at road level. Lighting bridges over stage. Arri Image Control, 80 ways overhead. 12 ways on stage.
SOUND:Yamaha 02R 24 into 8, 8 matin W3 (central cluster) mini disc and CD.
GENERAL:
COMMUNICATIONS: Full SM facilities, F.O.H. calls ring intercom, cue lights, show relay. Closed circuit TV.
DRESSING ROOMS: 5 on 2 floors accommodating 12, 16,4, 7, 17 Showers
ORCHESTRA PIT: 20 musicians.
RECORDING STUDIO:
Yamaha 02R and full facilities. cassette decks. 1 compact disc player. 1 Tascam DA 30 DAT, 1 Tascam DA 88 DAT, 1 Akai 53200 Sampler. Assorted effects.
To rear of stage is a large paint shop extending the full width of stage including PS and OP wing. Paint frame fitted. Wardrobe and laundry are situated on the first floor. Rehearsal Room, and Dance Studio are accommodated in the basement.

ST DAVID'S HALL

The National Concert Hall of Wales, The Hayes, Cardiff, South Glamorgan CF10 1AH Wales
Mgt: 029 2087 8500 BO: 029 2087 8444
Fax: 029 2087 8599
Email: sdhreception@cardiff.gov.uk
Web Site: www.stdavidshallcardiff.co.uk
ADMINISTRATION:
Props: Cardiff County Council
Operations Manager: Rodger Hopwood
Programme Manager: Susan King
Technical Contact: Dave Walker
Contact: dwalker@cardiff.gov.uk
Policy: Classical and popular music, conferences, film and fashion shows, lectures.
Capacity: 1,956.
TECHNICAL:
STAGE: Open platform in 10 hydraulic lifts, standard platform size 10.8m x 17.3, maximum platform size 16.6m x 17.3m; Suspension facilities over stage. Get-in; Goods lift 2.8m x 2.1m to platform level. Plus direct access via external hoist.
LIGHTING: 250 Channel Rank Strand 550i control 2.5k 5k and 10k dimmers; 2 x 2kw Strong Supertroopers.
SOUND: P.A. 40 channel Midas Sienna mixer, 18 mic points in auditorium, 32 on platform.
STAGE COMMUNICATIONS: Full S.M. desk facilities, ring intercom and cue light. Dressing room calls and show relay. CCTV system. Loop aerials throughout stalls area for deaf aids and translation.
ADDITIONAL: TV facilities; Power supplies and cable ducts to vehicle parking bay. Auxiliary power supplies available on platform. 1 x 200 amp TPN, 2 x 100amp TPN 1 x 32amp TPN, 1 x 60 amp SP. Film Projection; 35mm and 16mm film projectors. Full size roll-up cinemascope screen. 35mm Slide projection facility with dissolve.
DRESSING ROOMS: 7; with toilet and shower facilities. 8; changing rooms with different capacities and toilet and shower facilities. Green Room; with licensed bar and refreshment facilities; one other small rest room.
MEMBERSHIP: TMA

THE GLOBE

125 Albany Road, Roath Cardiff CF24 3NS
Tel: 07590 471888
Email: theglobevenue@gmail.com

Web Site: www.globecardiffmusic.com
ADMINISTRATION:
Contact: Tuan Duong, Bing Wu
Policy: Hire and self-promote
Capacity: 350

WALES MILLENNIUM CENTRE
Bute Place, Cardiff CF10 5AL
Box Office: 029 2063 6464 Admin Tel: 02920 636400 Marketing Tel: 029 2063 4667 Admin Fax: 02920 636401
Email: chris.carter@wmc.org.uk
Web Site: www.wmc.org.uk
Chief Executive - Matthew Milsom
Head of Marketing and Communication: Dylan Tozer
Programming Director - Graeme Farrow
Venue Operations Director - Jonathon Poyner
Cap: 1,800

Y PLAS, CARDIFF UNIVERSITY STUDENTS' UNION
Cardiff Student's Union, Park Place, Cardiff CF10 3QN
Tel: 029 2078 1456
Email: suevents@cardiff.ac.uk
Web Site: www.cardiffstudents.com, www.cardiffboxoffice.com
ADMINISTRAION:
Contact Venues Department
Policy: Hire and self-promote
Capacity: 1,000

Cardigan, Ceredigion

THEATR MWLDAN
Bath House Road, Cardigan, Ceredigion, SA43 1JY
Tel: 01239 621 200
Email: boxoffice@mwldan.co.uk
Web Site: www.mwldan.co.uk
Multi Artform presenting venue, two auditoria presenting own promotions, producing own shows, third party hire and cinema part of the Arts Council of Wales' Regional Centres Network.
Full technical details available at www.mwldan.co.uk

Carlisle, Cumbria

Pop. 71,000. London 307 miles.
Newspapers: Cumberland News (fri); Courier Gazette (wed); Weekly Group.
STD code 01228

SANDS CENTRE
The Sands, Carlisle, Cumbria CA1 1JQ
Mgt: 01228 633 767 BO: 01228 633 766
Fax: 01228 625 666
Email: sandscentre@carlisleleisure.com
Web Site: www.thesandscentre.co.uk
ADMINISTRATION:
Props: Carlisle Leisure Ltd
Events Manager: Jonathan Higgins
Technical Manager: Richard Lloyd
Email: sandstechnical@carlisleleisure.com
Policy: This extremely versatile venue can house classical and popular music concerts, comedy, opera, ballet, dance, plays, pantomime, spectator sports, conferences, exhibitions.
Capacity: Main Hall Up to 1400 seated; 1800 standing. Secondary Hall 252.
Full disabled facilities. Two licensed bars, restaurant, riverside terrace.
TECHNICAL:
STAGE: Hall Dimensions; Height from floor to lower grid, 9m (29'6"), Stage to lower grid, 7.7m (25'6"), Hall Dimensions (Floor space without stage), 36m (118') x 26m (85'). Versatile stage size from 1.2m/8ft sq. up to 9.7m (32ft) x 21.9(72ft), average height of 1.2m (4ft). Load-In Access door: w 3.5m (11'4"), h 3.5m (11' 4").
LIGHTING: Control; Strand 520i (250ch). 3 x 4 500w Cell Codas, 16 x 1K Fresnels, 44 x par 64's, 6 x 2K alto Fresnels, 8 x 1K Selecon pacific profiles, 18 x 1.2K 11/26 cantatas'. Followspots; 2 x Robert Juliat 1200w followspots. Dimmers; 108 Dimmers- 60 ways of 2K (Control: Green ginger), 48 ways of 2K (Control: Zero 88 ID1216)
SOUND: Foh rack; CD/MD/FOH EQ/Mon EQ/Delays EQ/Peavey FX unit. Mixer; Allen & Heath GL3300. Delays; 12 x Bose 802 (3 lines separately timed and amplified). Foh speakers; DB Audiotechnic DVA LINE ARRAY comprising, 4x T4 modules per side plus 1x S20 2x18" sub, 2 x Martin Audio F10's - centre fill. Monitors; 2 x Martin Audio F12's. Mics; a selection of mics are available.
STAGE MANAGEMENT: Comms, show relay and backstage paging. No cue lights or any kind of camera/monitor system.
ADDITIONAL: 1 Steinway Concert Grand model D, (please specify tuning pitch), 1 Steinway Baby grand model A, UV lighting, Laser, Strobes, Pyrotechnics, Smoke/Haze/Fog, Naked flame.
BACKSTAGE FACILITIES: Dressing Rooms; 5, with Hot & cold water, Power points, Mirrors, Clothes hooks and Showers. Wardrobe; Automatic washing machine, Tumble dryer, Ironing board + Iron. Production/Company Manager room with internet access. Adequate parking free of charge for most size productions.

Carmarthen, Carmarthenshire

ST PETER'S CIVIC HALL
Nott Square, Carmarthen SA31 1PG Wales
Tel: 01267 235 199 Fax: 01267 221 607
Email: eleri@carmarthentowncouncil.gov.uk
Web Site: www.carmarthentowncouncil.gov.uk
Contact: Eleri James
Seating/Capacity: 392 (284 downstairs, 108 upstairs). Hall available for hire only.

THE LYRIC THEATRE
King Street, Carmarthen, Dyfed SA31 1BD
Tel: 0845 226 3510
Email: theatres@carmarthenshire.gov.uk
Web Site: www.theatrausirgar.co.uk
Props: Carmarthenshire County Council
Contact Nick Stevenson
Capacity: 665

Carnoustie Angus

CARNOUSTIE LEISURE CENTRE
Links Parade, Carnoustie, Angus DD7 7JB Scotland
Tel: 01241 803 590
Email: concarnlc@angus.gov.uk
Web Site: www.angus.gov.uk
ADMINISTRATION:
Props: Angus Council
Manager: Derek Whamond

Carrickfergus, County Antrim

CARRICKFERGUS LEISURE CENTRE
Prince William Way, Carrickfergus, County Antrim BT38 7HP Northern Ireland
Tel: 028 9335 8888
Email: amphitheatre@carrickfergus.org
Web Site: www.carrickfergus.org
ADMINISTRATION:
S/Cap: 900

JOYMOUNT TOWN HALL
Museum & Civic Centre 11 Antrim Street Carrickfergus, County Antrim BT38 7DG Northern Ireland
Tel: 028 9335 8000 Fax: 028 9336 6676
Email: linda.telsair@carrickfergus.org
Web Site: www.carrickfergus.org
Community Officer: Linda Telsair

Carshalton, Surrey

London 17 miles. STD code 020 8

THE CHARLES CRYER STUDIO THEATRE
39 High Street, Carshalton, Surrey SM5 3BB
Mgt: 020 8770 6984 BO: 020 8770 6990
Email: boxoffice@sutton.gov.uk
Web Site: www.suttontheatres.co.uk

Contact: Gina Gillam
Hire only small scale studio theatre - dance, cabaret, music, plays.
Performance arts programme running through Carshalten College.
Intergrated thai restaurant & bar
Seats: 80-110
TECHNICAL:
Stage: Open flexible performance space suitable for end on: In the round etc.
Lighting: Zero 88 Sirius 48 desk; 50 lanterns + 12 parcans
Sound: Soundtracs FM 12:4:2 sound desk + revox, cassette, CD + turntable. 12 mics, 7 stands, 2 X mini disc players.
Other: Dressing Rooms: 2. Disabled access to control room. Rehearsal room available. Adjacent scenery workshop with full facilities for building, painting, scenery for hire, commercial & educational projects, tuition, school parties, visits etc. Outdoor paved area for craft, street performers etc.

WESTCROFT LEISURE CENTRE
Westcroft Road, Carshalton, Surrey SM5 2TG
Tel: 020 8669 8666
Email: westcroftinfo@everyoneactive.com
Web Site: www.everyoneactive.com
ADMINISTRATION:
Props: Everyone Active on behalf of London Borough of Sutton
Manager: Mark Bednarczyk
Cap: 250 Tiered seats, theatre style plus 100 movable seats

Castle Douglas, Kirkcudbrighshire

CASTLE DOUGLAS TOWN HALL
5 St Andrew Street, Castle Douglas, Kirkcudbrightshire DG7 1DE Scotland
Tel: 0303 333 3000
Web Site: www.dumgal.gov.uk
For Bookings Contact: Agnes Neale (01556 505260 Ext. 60322 or 60168
Seating/Capacity: 296 (Main Hall).

Castleford, West Yorkshire

CASTLEFORD CIVIC CENTRE
Ferrybridge Road, Castleford, West Yorkshire WF10 4JH
Tel: 01977 727015
Email: eventsandfunctions@wakefield.gov.uk
Web Site: www.wakefield.gov.uk
ADMINISTRATION
Props: Wakefield Metropolitan District Council
Cap: 600

Chatham, Kent

Pop. 59,060. London 31 miles.
Newspapers: Chatham News; Chatham Stand (fri/tues); Kent Today (mon-fri); Adscene. STD code 01634 (Medway)

THE CENTRAL THEATRE
170 High Street, Chatham, Kent ME4 4AS
Mgt: 01634 338 300 BO: 01634 338 338
Mktg: 01634 338 309 Fax: 01634 827 711
Email: arts@medway.gov.uk
Web Site: www.medway.gov.uk/theatres
ADMINISTRATION:
Props: Medway Council
Technical Manager: Chris Stevens
Policy: One night stands and weekly productions; Orchestral; Pop; Folk; Big Band; Jazz; Country; Panto.
Perfs: Varies
Seats: 966. Licensed Bar and full catering services.
TECHNICAL:
STAGE: Proscenium (with 3.66m apron stage), Flat; Grid; Width 9.09m; C. Line 7.47m curved back wall; 2 (door width) entrances; Prompt Cnr. O.P.; (apply to management for full technical specification). 15 Hemp Flying Barrels. CCTV to all areas.
LIGHTING: Switchboard: ETC Congo, 6 Colour Par Can (80 units) Wash, 6 x MAC 500, 2 x MAC 300, 40 profiles, 20 Fresnels, Star Cloth, Haze Blinders Howies etc, 2 x HMI Follow spots, 1 x Electric winch bar 16 feet from edge of stage.
SOUND: Allen & Heath GL4 32-8-2 with complete effects rack (patchable to Cinema Dolby Stereo).
Projection: 35mm Projector with full Dolby Stereo.
OTHER: Dressing Rooms 5; Accom. 40 persons: 3 Showers; Band Room for 80 persons.

SPOTLITES @ KINGS THEATRE
Spotlites @ Kings Theatre 338 High Street, Chatham, Kent ME4 4NR
Admin: 01634 829468 BO: 01634 829 468 Fax: 01634 829 468
Email: office@spotlites.co.uk
Web Site: www.spotlites.co.uk
ADMINISTRATION:
General Manager & Artistic Director: Rachel Thomson-King
Capacity: 110 Studio: 50
Policy: Provide innovative performing arts and theatre and training for children and young people, aged 5-30 years.
TECHNICAL:
Full LX & SD (Fat Frog, Mini Disc etc) SFX

THE BROOK THEATRE
The Brook Theatre, Old Town Hall, Chatham, Kent ME4 4SE
Admin: 01634 338 300 Box Office: 01634 338 338 Marketing: 01634 33 8310/ 2782
Email: thelma.talty@medway.gov.uk
Web Site: www.medwayticketslive.co.uk
Sales and Booking Manager: Deborah Pinder
Administration Assistant: Thelma Talty
There is also a Studio Theatre with a capacity of 60.

Chelmsford, Essex

Pop. 58,000. London 32 miles.
Newspapers: Chelmsford Weekly News (thurs); Essex Chronicle (fri). STD code 01245

CIVIC THEATRE
Fairfield Road, Chelmsford, Essex CM1 1JG
Mgt: 01245 606 752 BO: 01245 606 505
Duty Mgr: 01245 606 950 Admin: 01245 606 974
Email: tom.johnson@chelmsford.gov.uk
Web Site: www.chelmsford.gov.uk/theatres
ADMINISTRATION:
Props: Chelmsford City Council
Cultural Events Manager: John Gower
Production/ Technical Manager: David Digby
Contact: david.digby@chelmsford.gov.uk
Policy: Professional repertory/touring theatre, with occasional opera, ballet, concerts, panto and childrens' shows. professional concerts, amateur productions, childrens' shows, touring theatre/dance. Non-performance activities, Sep-July. Seminars, workshops.
Perfs: Open 7 days - evening shows starting at 7.45p.m. and 8.00p.m. Sat.mat. start at 2.30, 3.30 or 5.00p.m.
Booking terms: Hire, Box Office split, guarantee & split, guarantee, co-production, by negotiation.
Seating: 505, raked.
Catering: Coffee, ice cream, sweets etc. available, buffets can be arranged, bar with theatre licence.
Access car park: adjacent, nearest railway station: Chelmsford, adjacent, nearest coach terminal: Chelmsford, adjacent, bus routes: adjacent.
Disabled Access: Wheelchair spaces available - infra red assistive listening system and signed performances on selected performances - level access - all house facilities fully accessible, except balcony. Audio described performances on selected performances.
For venue hire contact Amy Shorey. Tel: 01245 606974.

TECHNICAL:
STAGE: Proscenium arch. Wooden, painted black, No rake. Performing area: 12.2m x 7.00m (40ft x 22ft 11.5in). Pros opening: 11.17m x 4.11m (36ft 8in x 13ft 6in). Forestage depth: 2.14m (7ft). Wing widths S/R 3.66m (12ft). S/L 1.83m (6ft). Dock doors: 1.53m x 4.85m (5ft x 15ft 10in). Height to grid: 10m (33ft).

Orchestra Pit: 19 X Doughty lit music stands, 1 x Doughty lit conductors music stand, 1 x Knight Upright Piano (tuning by request)
LIGHTING: FOH; Advance Bar: 26 Circuits, 3 x Cantata Strand PC with colour scrollers (1.2kw) - not to be moved, 16 x CCT Starlette (1.2kw Fresnels), 6 x Source 4 15/30 zoom profiles, No.1 PERCH 7 Circuits (each side), 5 x paired Par-Cans (each side), 1 x Tab warmers (each side), 1 x Strand Cantata 22/44 Profile (1.2kw), No.2 PERCH 4 Circuits (each side), 3 x Source 4 15/30 zoom profiles, No.3 PERCH 3 Circuits (each side), 3 x Source 4 15/30 zoom profiles, 2 x Cormar Popilota Follow spot (1200w). Stage;14 x Strand Cantata F (1.2kw), 13 x Strand Cantata 18/32 Profiles (1.2kw), 6 x Strand Cantata 22/44 Profiles (1.2kw), 15 x Strand Cantata PC (1.2kw), 6 x CCT Starlette F (1kw), 4 x CCT Starlette F (2kw), 2 x Strand Alto F (2kw), 6 x Strand Coda 4 (4 x 500w ea.), 15 x Strand Patt 743 (1kw), 4 x Strand Prelude 16/30 Profiles (650w), 4 x Strand Quartet F (650w), 50 x Par 64 fitted with CP62 (1kw), 24 circuits (4 x Socapex) per side for 4 booms (per side) on stage, 3 x 18 way pre-wired bar (3 x Socapex) on electric winches 500kg, 4 way socapex 25A for cyc circuits on electric winch 500kg, Assorted 15A cable in 1,5,10,15 and 20m lengths, 2 way and 3 way 15A splitters, Various Bars of six, Various Socapex multicores with spiders.
Dimming and Lighting Control: 1 x ETC sensor dimmer rack containing; 182 x 15A dimmers (MCB protected), 12 x 25A dimmers (MCB protected), 12 x 15A Switch circuits (MCB protected), 8 x houselight circuits. 1 x ETC Insight 2 x Control desk with; (512 Channels, 600 Groups, 10 pages of 108 subs, 600 cues & 5 moving light jog wheels), 3 separate DMX 512 outputs (on one DMX Universe), Riggers remote, Designers work tablet.
EFFECTS: 1 x White Lightning Strobe, 4 x Par 36 240v Pinspots, 2 x DHA effects disks with ripple effect, 2 x Martin Magnum Pro2000 Smoke machine, 1 x Nuetron star Hazer, 1 x Gobo rotator, 1 x Mirrorball, 1 x Starcloth 30ft wide x 15ft 6in drop, 1 x Sanyo portable data projector (4000 ANSI Luments) (subject to availability).
FLYING SYSTEM: 21 x Double purchase counterweight system (3 point pick up), (swl 250kg), 4 x Electric Winch systems (5 point pick up) (swl)
SOUND: Control: Soundcraft GB8 48 (+ 4 stereo):8:2:1 (+ 4 way matrix) 8 aux. FOH: 6 x Martin Audio EM75 (365w PMPO), 2 x JBL Bass bins (650w PMPO), 2 x Martin Audio WT15 (75w PMPO) Flown from FOH Truss, 4 x Boston Acoustics 325 (50w PMPO) mounted in pit panels. Centerfills: 4 x JBL Control 1 (110w PMPO), Rear fill/Surround. Stage: 6 x Martin Audio Blackline F15 monitors (400w PMPO). Amplification; 4 x CAudio RA1001 (250w at 8ohms), 4 x CAudio RA1000 (250w at 8ohms), 1 x CAudio RA3001 (650w at 4ohms), 1 x Yamaha P4050 quad amp (75w at 4ohms).
Various microphones available.
Processing and Effects: 2 x Yamaha SPX2000 Stereo effects processor, 4 x BSS FCS 966 30 band stereo graphic EQ, 1 x 2ch Behringer Composer Compressor /Liniter /Expander /gate, 1 x Sabine FBX 2020 Feedback Exterminator, 1 x Yamaha D1030 Delay unit.
STAGE COMMUNICATIONS: 8 cue lights available with four sockets S/L and S/R; 1 x Tecpro dual circuit power supply; 1 x Speaker station (LX Box); 1 x Master station (Prompt desk); 6 x Tecpro BP111 Belt packs with single muff headsets; (2 x followspot, Flys, Sound, S/L and S/R)
DRESSING ROOMS: 3; accomm. 38; WC and shower facilities. Green room under the stage with a sink, refrigerator, microwave and TV/Stage monitor. All dressing rooms, green room and workshop receive show relay and stage manager calls. Disabled Access.

CRAMPHORN THEATRE

Fairfield Road, Chelmsford, Essex CM1 1JG
Mgt: 01245 606 752 BO: 01245 606 505
Duty Mgr: 01245 606 950
Email: tom.johnson@chelmsford.gov.uk
Web: www.chelmsford.gov.uk/theatres
ADMINISTRATION:
Props: Chelmsford Borough Council
Policy: Small Scale Touring Theatre & Dance, Concerts and Recitals, Workshops, Cabaret. Independent Cinema.
Box Office and bar in foyer, plus publicity display space and pay-phone.
Capacity: 145 seats; 170 seats with no stage; seating is raked with a central aisle. It is strongly advised that in view of sightlines, all productions make use of staging.
TECHNICAL:
Stage: The overall size is 16' deep x 36' wide, made up of modular units of 8' x 4', plus 4 units of 8' x 3'. Please note the maximum playing depth is 14', allowing for 2' of the stage which is lost beneath the projection screen. The stage is 800mm high. Stage Drapes - everything is in a matching matt dark black fabric. There is one set of tabs on tab track running immediately in front of film screen (see plan). Plus two drapes of adjustable height for either masking stage right and left, or midstage or downstage tabs.
Lighting: Fluorescents for working lights. Dimmable spot houselights. Stage lanterns available -6 x Harmony 22/40's, 12 Harmony F's. if requested in advance, further lamps are available. Stage lighting control in control room at rear of auditorium and comprises of a ETC Express 48/96 memory board. There is a patch circuiting system comprising of 62 hard wired plugs into 36 dimmer channels. Please note that there is no access to control room via auditorium for any cables from stage area (window does not open). There are 4 x 13 amp sockets at floor level.
Projection: 35mm + 16mm Cine Projection; 2 x Kodak Carousels.
Sound: Bose 2 x Bose 802 and 2 x 402 with crest amps. Soundcraft K1 8 + 2: 2 + 1 mixing desk. 1 x sony minidisc + Tascam CD/casette combi.
Other: Dressing Rooms: Male & female dressing rooms each accommodating 10 people, plus toilets and one shower. No wardrobe facilities at present and there is limited backstage storage. Infra red assistive listening system.

Cheltenham, Glocestershire

Pop. 85,000. London 98 miles. STD code 01242

CHELTENHAM TOWN HALL

Imperial Square, Cheltenham, Gloucestershire GL50 1QA
Mgt/BO: 0844 5762210 Fax: 01242 573902
Email: boxoffice@cheltenhamtrust.org.uk
Web Site: www.cheltenhamtownhall.org.u k
ADMINISTRATION:
Props: The Cheltenham Trust
Entertainments and Business Manager: Gary Nejrup
Policy: Concert Hall. Concerts, shows, exhibitions, lectures, banquets, dinner dances, balls, fashion shows, corporate presentations, conferences, sales, discos, boxing, wrestling, AGMs, ceremonies, wedding receptions, large meetings. Broad-ranging music and light entertainments programme.
Main Hall Capacity: 1,000 . Side rooms also available with a capacity of 15 - 300.
Full catering service and licensed bar.
Computerised box office Infx.
Disabled Access: Parking spaces in rear car park; ramped access; suitably adapted toilet and telephone; level access to all facilities, but no lift to balcony. Assistance available. Guide dogs admitted.
To hire the hall contact Laura Bryon on 01242 264231 or email boxoffice@cheltenhamtrust.org.uk. Booking terms: hire, box office split, guarantee, co-production by negotiation.
TECHNICAL:
STAGE: Open concert platform, performing area 15.85 x 6.7m. Wood - very gentle rake, suitable for dance. Permanent red festoon tabs at rear. Width: 52 feet. Depth: 16 feet or 24 feet with forestage extension. 160A 3 phase independent circuits. 6 choir risers and organ at rear of stage. Orchestra pit/stage lift. Hydraulic forestage doubles as lift and pit for four musicians. Get-in via rear, dock doors 1.83m x 2.13m. Additional portable staging available.

LIGHTING: House lights control located in balcony stage left. 2 Solo CSI follow spots operated from rear gallery. Stage lighting: 20 Par 64 and 4 Fresnels. Q24 Lighting board. Portable lighting system comprising: 6 Par56, 8 Nova, 2 Minuet, a 6 channel desk and 2 stands.
SOUND: Soundcraft Spirit desk, portable operating position, 2 channel, 16 graphic splits, 2 time zones, gated system. Various mics. Pioneer double tape deck. Technics CD Player. Carlsbro CDX, 8 channel, reverb. Show relay and Tannoy. House PA system. Acoustics suitable for music.
COMMUNICATION: Intercom positioned at the house lighting board (balcony AA), follow spots, stage right, rear of hall and roof.
DRESSING ROOMS: 3 permanent; 7 toilets; 4 unisex showers. Other rooms available on request.
OTHER: Steinway "D" concert grand, baby grand and upright pianos. Advice given on accommodation. No permanent stage staff but casuals available.
Backstage facilities accessible to disabled performers and staff. Restricted on-site car parking, to liaise with Event Managers

EVERYMAN THEATRE

Regent Street, Cheltenham, Gloucestershire GL50 1HQ
SD: 01242 512 515 Press Office: 01242 236 700 BO: 01242 572 573 Fax: 01242 224 305
Email: admin@everymantheatre.org.uk
Web Site: www.everymantheatre.org.uk
ADMINISTRATION:
Props: Cheltenham Borough Council
Lessees: Gloucestershire Everyman Theatre Co Ltd.
Chief Executive: Geoffrey Rowe
Technical Manager: Graham Williams
Policy: Producing and presenting theatre and Saturday children's shows and Sunday night concerts. Education and Community department.
Main House capacity: 672, Studio theatre capacity: 60 (variable).
Perfs: (usual) Mon-Sat 7.45pm. Mats. Thurs, Sat 2.00pm.
Cafe and Bars 01242 572 532.
TECHNICAL: (Main House)
Flat stage prosc. opening 7.36m, height 8.8m, depth from setting line 9.7m; setting line to apron 1.6m; orchestra pit 2.8m deep x 12.2m wide; hydraulic pit, 20 musicians; height of grid 17.7m; counterweight lines 34, scenery flying height 9m; flying bars 10m + 2m extensions; wing widths SR 8.3m, SL 5.4m; prompt corner SR; LX control room rear dress circle.
Lighting: LX board strand 430, Genius software; 2 FOH follow spots Solo CSIs.
Sound Equipment: 32 into 4 into 2 mixer; 6 FOH tannoy speakers; 2 Revox A77 tape decks; 2 cassette decks.
TECHNICAL (Studio)
Length 9.8m; depth 6m; LX grid height 5m; restricted get in/out; limited suspension; LX board: Strand GSX 24 channels; 12 into 4 into 2 sound mixer; cassette deck; gallery at one end.
Dressing Rooms: 6, accom. 50; 10 showers, 2 baths.

PITTVILLE PUMP ROOM

Pittville Park, East Approach Drive, Cheltenham, Gloucestershire GL52 3JE
Mgt/BO: 0844 5762210 Fax: 01242 573902
Email: boxoffice@cheltenhamtrust.org.uk
Web Site: www.cheltenhamtownhall.org.uk
ADMINISTRATION:
Props: The Cheltenham Trust
Capacity: 400 seated or standing.
Fine Regency building in the grounds of Pittville Park. Available for hire for any suitable function or event. Usually open 7 days a week. Booking terms: hire, co-production, box office split, guarantee and split by negotiation. Full catering facilities, 1 licensed bar, computerised box office Infx
3 other rooms available for hire.
Oval Room, Cap 50, West Room, Cap 50, East Room, Cap 50.
150 Parking spaces adjacent to front doors; level access to all facilities; suitably adapted toilet. Dressing rooms not accessible to wheelchair users. Assistance available. Guide dogs permitted.
TECHNICAL:
Flexible performance area. Flat floor, suitable for dance. Portable staging. 30A 3 phase supply. Basic lighting. House PA. Acoustics suitable for music and speech, if amplified.
Dressing rooms: 2. Upright piano and steinway grand piano.

THE BACON THEATRE

Hatherley Road entrance.
Dean Close School, Cheltenham, Gloucestershire GL51 6HE
Tel: 01242 258 002 Fax: 01242 258 007
Email: team@bacontheatre.co.uk
Web Site: www.bacontheatre.co.uk
ADMINISTRATION:
Theatre Administrator: Nicholas Tobias
Policy: To provide a well equipped stage for Dean Close School, local amateur productions, and professional entertainment; drama groups, opera and dance companies, touring professional companies.
Seats: 566 Licensed bar/teas/coffees/catering facilities.
Also Tuckwell Amphitheatre, Open-Air Theatre Festival in July.
TECHNICAL:
Stage: 20m wide x 10m; Scenery flying facilities; Orchestra pit 9m wide x 2.5m; Steinway 9ft grand piano with lift.
Lighting: 96-way Bullfrog and 12 ZERO 88 beta packs with twin 15 amp outlets. 100 assorted lanterns.
Sound: 24 Channel Eurodesk; Carver PM900 amplifier; 2 pairs of Bose 802 speakers/ Tech pro communications systems.
Other: Green room and changing facilities for up to 50.

Chertsey, Surrey

CHERTSEY HALL

Heriot Road, Chertsey, Surrey KT16 9DR
Tel: 01932 566 645 Bkg: 01932 425 684/7
Email: halls@runnymede.gov.uk
Web Site: www.runnymede.gov.uk
ADMINISTRATION
Props: Runnymede Borough Council
To view the hall only contact the duty manager: 01932 566645
Cap: 230 Auditiorium Style ; Small Hall 40 Seated

THORPE VILLAGE HALL

Coldharbour Lane, Thorpe, Surrey TW20 8TE
Admin: 07539 528654
Email: info@thorpevillagehall.org
Web Site: www.thorpevillagehall.org
ADMINISTRATION
Props: Thorpe Village Hall Trust
Cap: 90
For bookings contact Bookings Co-ordinator Sue Hurst

Chesham, Buckinghamshire

London 28 miles. Newspapers: Chesham Advertiser and Bucks Examiner. STD code 01494

THE ELGIVA

St. Marys Way, Chesham, Buckinghamshire HP5 1HR
BO: 01494 582 900
Email: manager@elgiva.com
Web Site: www.elgiva.com
ADMINISTRATION:
Props: Chesham Town Council
Theatre Manager: Mark Barnes
Technical Manager: Tristan Collett
Policy: Mixed programme, all touring arts and entertainment, cinema, conferences, exhibitions, banquets.
Seats: Seats: variable up to 300 retractable seating, disabled access.
Catering: Bar Cafe in foyer. Fully licensed.
TECHNICAL:
Stage: Proscenium stage (flat) - 7m 82 cm deep (25ft 8inch) x 10m wide, Mechanical thrust/pit lift - 1m 94cm (6ft 4inch) x 7m 92cm (26ft), Pros. opening 9m 50cm (31ft 2inch); Ht of pros. 4m 87cm (16ft), 11 x manual hempline flybars - 11m (36ft 1inch); scenery flying height 4m 87cm (16ft), height of fly tower 11.5m (37ft 9inch), 1 x white cyclorama cloth -

6m 47cm (21ft 3inch) 10m 54cm (34ft 7inch), scene dock - 4m 57cm (15ft) x 4m 11cm (13ft 6inch), orchestra pit dimensions - 3m 92cm (12ft 10inch) x 7m 92cm (26ft), 2 x 63amp power supplies (single and 3-phase)
Lighting: Jands Hog 500 digital lighting console
Other: Disabled access, Box Office Intercom System, Deaf-Aid System - Williams Sound TIRX 10 95khz infrared transmission system, auditorium 17m squared. Zero 88 Sirius 48 Lighting Console, ADB Eurorack dimmer system, 8 x Miniscan HPE moving lights, P292 follow spot, Testa 1200w MSR follow spot, 8 x Cantata 1 Kw profiles, 6 x ADB 1kw fresnels, 2 x p264 1 kw profiles, 10 x 1kw Parcans, 2 x P23 500w, 6 x p123 500w fresnels, 12 x Minuette 650w fresnels, 13 x Prelude 650w fresnels.
Sound: Soundcraft Delta 16-4-2, Yamaha SPX 900 Digital Effects PRocessor, Yamaha QA2031A Graphic Equaliser (foldback), Denon CD, Casette, Tuner amplifier, 2 x JBL control 1 monitor speakers, Tecpro intercom system. On stage/FOH: 4 x JBL 4726 speakers, 2 x JBL G731 monitor speakers, 1 x Proart 31 + 31 band stereo graphic equaliser, BSS-FDF360 electronic crossover, 5 x vocal mics, 3 x rifle mics, 7 radio mics, 2 x DI boxes. Full Dolby Digital 35mm cinema equipment, Yamaha C7 Grand Piano. 3 Dressing rooms, maximum accommodation; Albany Room 20; Drury Lane Room 8; Shaftsbury Room 1 also has shower. Male/Female backstage toilets plus shower facilities, Show relay.

Chester, Cheshire

Pop. 62,320. London 182 miles.
Newspapers: Chester Chronicle (fri). STD code 01244

ALEXANDER'S JAZZ THEATRE

2 Rufus Court, Chester, Cheshire CH1 2JW
Box Office: 01244 340 005 Booking Agency: 01244 400414
Email: info@alexanderslive.com
Web Site: www.alexanderslive.com
Contact: Ms Thompson
Live entertainment venue specialising in Jazz, Blues, acoustic and comedy.
Available for hire by independant promoters and bands.
Cap: 150

THE FORUM STUDIO THEATRE

Hamilton Place, Chester, Cheshire CH1 2BH
Tel: 01244 341296
Email: info@tiptopproductions.co.uk
Web Site: www.chestertheatre.co.uk
ADMINISTRATION:
Props: Tip Top Productions
Theatre Manager: Steve Davies
Technical Manager: Ian Jones
Policy: Concerts, Tours, Amateurs, Community
Perfs: 7.30pm Mat. 2.30p.m. Sat.
Seats: 145. Bar
TECHNICAL:
Stage: Proscenium Stage with 3m deep removable forestage. Flat. Pros. opening 9.75m, Ht. of Pros. 4.88m. S/Line to limit of flying 11.17m. Ht. of Grid 12.19m. 30 lines C/W. Flying Bars 10.36m, W/Widths. S.L. Minimal S.R. Dock 4.88m Ht. x 4.5m square. Rear Dock 9.7m x 2.8m x 5.5m Ht. Prompt Cnr. S.L. Get-in 5.4m above ground.
Lighting: Switchboard: Strand 520i, 132 ways 2 x F.O.H. Bridges Stage Spot Bars variable.
Sound: 1 x Allen Heath 24-8-2, 3 x mini disc, 1 x cd player, 1 x cassette, 2 x SPX 990, 2 x ultra curve, 2 x EQ's, 4 x Meyer Upa Speakers, 4 x Crown Micro Tech 1200 Amps, 4 x Crown Power Tech Amps.
Further details on request.
Other: Dressing Rooms 4; Accom. 35; 2 Showers; Orchestra Pit.
Membership: TMA

Chesterfield, Derbyshire

Pop. 95,000. London 149 miles.
Newspapers: Derbyshire Times (fri); Sheffield Star (dly). STD code 01246

POMEGRANATE THEATRE

Corporation Street, Chesterfield, Derbyshire S41 7TX
Mgt: 01246 345 220 BO: 01246 345 222
Email: box.office@chesterfield.gov.uk
Web Site: www.chesterfieldtheatres.co.uk
ADMINISTRATION:
Props: Chesterfield Borough Council
Arts and Venues Manager: Anthony Radford
Stage Manager: Stuart Basson
Chief Technician: Stuart Basson
Policy: Touring, Pantomime, Plays, Musicals, Variety, Sunday Concerts.
Perfs: to suit production.
Seats: 546. Licensed Bar in Stalls; Coffee bar.
TECHNICAL:
Stage: Proscenium Stage, Raked; Pros. opening 7.92m; Ht. of Pros. 6.71m; Depth of S/Line 9.10m; Ht. of Grid 13.41m; 22 lines; Hemp. Flying Ht. 7.32; Flying Bars 9.14; W/Width 2.44m; Prompt Cnr. O.P.; Get-in Street Level.
Lighting: Switchboard: Rank Strand Duet 2 or 60 x 10, Duet Pin Matrix. remote from rear stalls; FOH Spots 6 T84, 14 Patt.763, 4 Patt.23; Stage 3 Patt.23, 7 Patt.23S, 14 Patt.123, 3 Patt.23N, 6 Patt.223, 7 Patt.243, 2 Patt.252, 10 Iris 1, 2 Patt.43B, 2 Patt 765 Follow Spots.
Sound Equip: 1 Revox B77 Tape deck 2 Tandberg 0.50 track Tape Decks; H/H Amplifier.
Other: Dressing Rooms 8; Accom 30; Orchestra Pit 25.
Membership: TMA

THE WINDING WHEEL

13 Holywell Street, Chesterfield, Derbyshire S41 7SA
Tel: 01246 345 333 BO: 01246 345 222
Fax: 01246 345 330
Email: box.office@chesterfield.gov.uk
Web Site: www.chesterfieldtheatres.co.uk
ADMINISTRATION:
Arts and Venues Manager: Anthony Radford
Front of House Manager/ Operations: Keith Tuttle, Matthew Rimmington
Auditorium: 700 Seated, 1000 standing.
Ballroom: 200 Function Room: 120

Chichester, West Sussex

Pop. 21,000. London 163 miles.
Newspapers: Chichester Observer (fri); Chichester Promoter (thurs). STD code 01243

CHICHESTER COLLEGE OF ARTS

Westgate Fields, Chichester, West Sussex PO19 1SB
Tel: 01243 786 321 Fax: 01243 539 481
Email: mark.warwick@chichester.ac.uk
Web Site: www.chichester.ac.uk
ADMINISTRATION:
Contact: Barry Jarvis
Directorate Administrator for Music and Drama: Mark Warwick
Studio Theatre (seats 90, retractable) to form large studio or exhibition area.
Workshop, Dressing Rooms
2 dance studios - sprung floors, mirrors
5 drama studios - showers, toilets
Lighting and sound control room, recording facilities.
Administration and Box office, coffee bar area.
TECHNICAL:
Pre wired grid - 106way soft patch. 24 x 2Kw Dimming, Mx24 Light Control Board, Spirt F1 14 -2 Sound Desk, CD/Minidisk/Cassette, HT to grid 4m, selection of soft masking, 1 pair black running tabs, max performance width 8.7m depth 6.3m.

CHICHESTER FESTIVAL THEATRE AND MINERVA THEATRE

Summer Festival Season of Plays runs from late Spring to early Autumn
Festival Theatre, Oaklands Park, Chichester, West Sussex PO19 6AP
Mgt/SD: 01243 784 437 BO: 01243 781 312 Fax: 01243 787 288
Email: admin@cft.org.uk
Web Site: www.cft.org.uk
ADMINISTRATION:

Props: Chichester Festival Theatre
Artistic Director: Jonathan Church
Executive Director: Alan Finch
Theatre Manager: Janet Bakose
Technical Co-ordinator: Sam Garner-Gibbons
Policy: The main season runs from late Spring to early Autumn.
Perfs: 7.30pm evenings:, Mats. Wed and Thurs 2.15pm
Seats: 1,307 and 283. Three Bars, One Snack Bar.
TECHNICAL:
Stage: Thrust. Performing area 9.34m x 9.65m. No Rake. Floor Canadian Maple (not sprung), suitable for dance. Understage crossover. Stage heated. Height to rods 6.4m, no flying, hanging only - Black flats and soft masking, tab track. Forestage entrances and backstage. Get-in via platform lift. Dock door 3.05m x 2.64m. Scenery lift. Scale stage and lighting plans available.
Lighting: ETC Eos and Ion lighting desks with RPU backup, 168 circuits @ 10A, 24 circuits @ 25A, 3 phase, control room rear auditorium - 200A 3 phase supply available from temporary board up centre - 2 followspots. Sound: 1 x Yamaha PM5D, operated from auditorium /FOH - Various amps - Meyer UPA, D&B, Bose speakers - limited facilities for recording and editing. Acoustics suitable for both music and the spoken word.
Other: Stage Management: prompt corner auditorium/FOH Tecpro, Clearcom and radio comms system, show relay/video relay/Tannoy to dressing rooms.
Backstage: Various dressing rooms, showers, access by backstage. Green Room. Band Room. Quick Change Room. Wardrobe backstage with laundry facilities and various sockets.
Refreshments available include hot drinks, snacks. Upright rehearsal Piano OK.
Advice given on accommodation.
Some Backstage facilities accessible to disabled performers and staff.

MINERVA THEATRE
at the Chichester Festival Theatre
ADMINISTRATION:
See the Chichester Festival Theatre.
Policy: Theatre which offers one of the most adventurous programmes during the year in the south. Minerva Theatre season runs in conjunction with the main house. Conference facilities.
Perfs: 7.45pm eves, Mats 2.30pm.
Seats: 283
Brasserie in the Park Restaurant (Tel 01243 782219); Brasserie Upstairs, Bar.
TECHNICAL:
Stage: Thrust. Performing area 9.7m x 7.3m. No Rake. Wooden floor. Black flats and soft masking track. Height to lighting bars 5.6m - tab track. No flying, hanging only. Platform lift 4.8m x 2m from get-in to stage level. Scale stage and lighting plans available on request.
Lighting: ETC Ion desk, 144 circuits @ 10 amps. 6 ways @ 25 amps, control room rear auditorium - 63A 3 phase supply available from temporary supply upstage right - 2 followspots.
Sound: DM1000 in either control box or auditorium. UPA, D&B and Bose speakers.
Stage Management: prompt corner auditorium/FOH Tecpro and radio comms system. Show relay/video relay and tannoy to dressing rooms.
Backstage: 2 dressing rooms - accommodates 20. Wardrobe area, Stage Management office, small kitchen. Showers.

THE COUNCIL HOUSE
North Street, Chichester, West Sussex PO19 1LQ
Tel: 01243 788 502 Fax: 01243 773 022
Email: clerk@chichestercity.gov.uk
Web Site: www.chichestercity.gov.uk
ADMINISTRATION
Props: Chichester City Council
Cap: Assembly Room: 180; Courtroom: 60
The Council House has now been granted a licence to hold Civil Wedding Ceremonies. The venue is also available for hire for wedding receptions, shows, craft fairs, exhibitions, fund-raising events, sales etc. Disabled facilities. Induction loop system fitted.

WESTGATE LEISURE CENTRE
Viva Ravenna, Chichester, West Sussex PO19 1RJ
Tel: 01243 785 651 Fax: 01243 533849
Email: kmccoy@chichester.gov.uk
Web Site: www.westgateleisure.co.uk
ADMINISTRATION
Props: Chichester District Council
Manager: Kevin McCoy

Chipping Norton, Oxfordshire

Pop. 5,500. London 74 miles.
Newspapers: Oxford Times; Cotswold Standard; Banbury Guardian. STD code 01608

THE THEATRE
2 Spring Street, Chipping Norton, Oxfordshire OX7 5NL
Mgt: 01608 642349 BO: 01608 642350
Fax: 01608 642324
Email: admin@chippingnortontheatre.com
Web Site: www.chippingnortontheatre.com
ADMINISTRATION:
Props: Council of Company
Stage Manager: Chris Hoad
Email: stage@chippingnortontheatre.com
General Manager: Jo Ludford
Email: operations@chippingnortontheatre.com
Policy: Touring Theatre (including Children's), concerts, films, opera, dance, occasional own productions, including yearly pantomime.
Perfs: Variable
Seats: 213, 4 wheelchairs. Bar, Art Gallery
TECHNICAL:
STAGE: Proscenium Stage, Flat; Width of Pros 5.34m; Ht. of Pros. 3.46m; Depth of Stage 7.9m; W/Widths 1.22m; Ht. of Grid 3.6m. Flying facilities: 15 hemp sets, 4 winched LX bars. Prompt Cnr. P.
LIGHTING: Control: 72 ways. Dressing Rooms 3; Accom. 16.
Membership: TMA

Chorley, Lancashire

ASTLEY COMMUNITY CENTRE
Hallgate, Astley Village, Chorley, Lancashire PR7 1XA
Tel: 01257 515811
Email: community.centres@chorley.gov.uk
Web Site: www.chorley.gov.uk
ADMINISTRATION
Props: Chorley Borough Council
Leisure and Cultural Buildings Officer: Carol Gore
Cap: 100

EAVES GREEN COMMUNITY CENTRE
Lower Burgh Way, Chorley, Lancashire PR7 3QE
Tel: 01257 515811
Email: contact@chorley.gov.uk
Web Site: www.chorley.gov.uk
ADMINISTRATION
Props: Chorley Borough Council
Cap: 100
BOOKINGS: CSCDEV Unit, Civic Offices, Union Street,
Chorley PR7 1AL

LANCASTRIAN SUITE
Town Hall, Market Street, Chorley, Lancashire PR7 1DP
Tel: 01257 515 151 Bkg: 01257 515 144
Email: paula.brindle@chorley.gov.uk
Web Site: www.chorley.gov.uk
ADMINISTRATION
Props: Chorley Borough Council
Cap: 400 Concert style
Bookings Contact: Paula Brindle

TATTON COMMUNITY CENTRE
Silverdale Road, Chorley, Lancashire PR6 0PR
Tel: 01257 411677 Fax: 01257 411677
Email: centrebookings@tattoncommunity-centre.org
Web: www.tattoncommunitycentre.org
ADMINISTRATION
Props: Chorley Borough Council
Cap: 100

For bookings and all enquiries contact CSCDEV, Civic Offices, Union St. Chorley PR7 1AL
Tel. 01257 235826
FAX: 01257 235827

Christchurch, Dorset

THE REGENT CENTRE

51 High Street, Christchurch, Dorset BH23 1AS
BO: 01202 499199
Email: admin@regentcentre.co.uk
Web Site: www.regentcentre.co.uk
Manager: Greg Rawlings
Technical Manager: Shaun Luckly
Film, Amateur, Professional, One-Night Stands.
Guarantee / Split / Hire Available.
Main Auditorium Cap: 484
Dolby 35mm Projection
Proj opening 9.2m; 100 Lanterns
ADB Cantor 96 Desk.
Soundcraft LX7 Desk , Cassette, CD, Minidisc

Cirencester, Gloucestershire

THE CORN HALL

Market Place, Cirencester, Gloucestershire GL7 2NY
Tel: 07970 859703 Bkgs: 01285 700 900
Email: augustawreay@hotmail.com
Web Site: www.cornhallcirencester.org.uk
ADMINISTRATION:
Props: Wildmoor Properties
Events Manager: Sian Pirone
Cap: 400 (Theatre Style)

COTSWOLD LEISURE CENTRE

Tetbury Road, Cirencester, Gloucestershire GL7 1US
Tel: 01285 654057
Email: cotswoldleisurecentre@cotswold.gov.uk
Web Site: www.cotswold.gov.uk
ADMINISTRATION
Centre Manager: Andrea North
Props: Cotswold District Council
Cap: 600

SUNDIAL THEATRE

Cirencester College, Stroud Road, Cirencester, Gloucestershire GL7 1XA
Admin: 01285 626184 BO: 01285 654228 Fax: 01285 644 171
Email: boxoffice@cirencester.ac.uk
Web Site: www.sundial-theatre.co.uk
ADMINISTRATION:
Theatre Manager: Joe Beardsmore
Technician: Alex Cresswell
Artistic Adviser: Duncan Walthew
Policy: To further the partnership between the professional arts, education and the community.
Status: Arts Centre on the Fosse Way Campus of Cirencester College.
Seats: 212-300 raked, retractable, fully upholstered One bar, full licence, variable hours College Refectory, variable hours. Disable access and toilet. Car park in College grounds. Nearest station: Kemble.
TECHNICAL:
Stage: Performing area sizes overload. End platform stage. Wings defined by curtains. Entrance via side doors or main entrance. Height of grid from stage 3.92m. Height of grid from floor 4.85m.
Lighting: Zero 88 Fat Frog Desk; 36 channels using Act 6 Dimmer Racks, operated from control box box at rear of Auditorium. 4 x Strand SL Profile spots; 4 x Prelude 16/30; 4 x Cantata 18/32 zoom spots; 4 x Cantata PC; 2 x Cantata Fresnels; 6 x Quartet PC; 6 x Nova 500w Fresnels; 10 x Par 64; 4 x Coda 3 way cyc battern. 12 x CCT 1k Starlette Fresnel, 12 x Par 64, 2 x Robe MSZOOM 250 x T Moving Head, 4 x Robe Wash 250 x T Moving Head Fixture.
Sound: Mackie 16/4, 16 channel Live desk, including digital effects processor. DB technology amplifier 500w per Channel. Pair of JBL 15EON Speakers. FX Rack comprising of: 1 x Sony Mini Disk machine; 2 x Denon CD players; 1 x Denon cassette deck; 1 x Peavey graphic equalizer. 3 x AKG Voval mics; 1 x AKG UHF Radio mic (Handheld); 1 x AKG UHF Radio (Lapel). Standby PA to dressing rooms and/or bar area. 5-way headset intercom system available, operated from control box at rear of auditorium. Acoustics suitable for music and spoken word. Wooden floor suitable for dance. Bechstein grand piano tuned regularly.
Audio Facilities: A variety of connecting cables are available. Please call for details. There are 6 x Tie lines running from stage right to main facility panel in control room. There are 6 x NL4 speakon tie lines which runj to pros wall and 1 no. appearing at each corner of the LX grid. 2 x Audio tie lines for stage returns from control room to stage right position. show relay and paging is available on request.
Lighting Equipment: A variet of connecting cables are available. Please call for details. Act 6 Dimmers, 6 x 2K channel and DMX512. Patch facilities available in control room, cables terminate at various points around the room (on Auditorium right) at ceiling height on Lectriflex connectors, which can be connected to different lighting bars depending on the configuration required.
General: Large dressing room with power points and sink. Large workshop area with excellent access to stage. Solid moveable partition between workshop and stage.
Hearing loop system

Clackmannan, Clackmannanshire

THE CLACKMANNAN TOWN HALL

Main Street, Clackmannan FK10 4JA Scotland
Tel: 07944 566068
Email: enquiry@clackmannantownhall-trust.co.uk
Props: The Clackmannan Town Hall Trust
Zetland Room: Unseated 300, Seated (without tables) 200, Seated (with tables) 110
Craigrie Room: Seated (without tables) 90, Seated (with tables) 50
Brucefield Room: Seated (without tables) 25
Watermill Room: Seated (with tables) 30

Clacton-on-Sea, Essex

Pop. 50,000. London 69 miles.
Newspapers: Clacton Gazette (fri). STD code 01255

PRINCES THEATRE

Station Road, Clacton-on-Sea, Essex CO15 1SE
Tel: 01255 686653 BO: 01255 686633
Email: princestheatreclacton@tendringdc.gov.uk
Web Site: www.tendringdc.gov.uk
ADMINISTRATION:
Props: Tendring D.C.
Technical Manager: Kai Aberdeen.
Tel: 01255 686652. Email: kaberdeen@tendringdc.gov.uk
Marketing Manager: Melissa Leek
Tel: 01255 686653. Email: mleek@tendringdc.gov.uk
Policy: All year attractions (mainly One Night Stands), Band and Orchestral Concerts, Dances, Wrestling, Conferences, Professional Pantomimes, Weddings
Seats: 820. Bar.
TECHNICAL:
STAGE: Rake; Pros. Opening 9.75m; Ht. of Pros. 5.49m; Depth of S/Line 6.10m; 20 lines, C/W; Flying Bars 10.97m.
LIGHTING: Switchboard: Sirius 48 channel zero 88, 16 Dip Points, 3 Battens, Floats, 10 F.O.H. x 1000w Spots, 8 Cabaret Floods, Mirror Ball with 4 x 500 Spots; 2 x 2000 Follow Spots. Full technical talk back system.
SOUND EQUIPMENT: Soundcraft 200SR Mixer Desk 16-4-2. Hill amplifiers LC1200 and LC400. Bose speaker system and fold backs. 12 x Shure SM58 microphones. 4 x Sennheiser Rifle microphones. 4 x Sennheiser Diversity Clip-on microphones.

WEST CLIFF THEATRE

Tower Road, Clacton-on-Sea, Essex CO15 1LE
Mgt: 01255 474 000 BO: 01255 433 344
Email: admin@westcliffclacton.org
Web Site: www.westcliffclacton.co.uk
ADMINISTRATION:
Props: West Cliff (Tendring) Trust Ltd
Manager: Paul George
Technical Manager: Keith Harris
Policy: Medium-scale touring productions & concerts, amateur drama and panto; professional summer show July-Sept.
Perfs: vary with event.
Seats: 590 + 3 wheelchairs. Bar/coffee bar. Foyers used for small exhibitions.
TECHNICAL:
Stage: Raked (2°) stage with thrust, 8.5m wide, 9m deep, working height 5.5m, max flying height 7.5m. possible within thrust. Rope flying with 17 barrels.
Lighting: Avolites Pearl 2000 desk, 60 dimmers, plus Eltec Sceptre computer; usual lanterns plus 2 Strand 765 follow-spots.
Sound: Soundcraft Delta SR mixing desk, Quad 606 amp feeds Bose 802 speakers. Cassette, selection AKG & Shure microphones. Yamaha Clavinova 550 electric piano (no grand).
Dressing Rooms: 6, Accom. 27

Clay Cross, Derbyshire

SHARLEY PARK LEISURE CENTRE

Market Street, Clay Cross, Derbyshire S45 9LX
Tel: 01246 217 277
Email: malcolm.reed@ne-derbyshire.gov.uk
ADMINISTRATION
Props: North East Derbyshire District Council
Cap: 800
Manager: Malcolm Reed

Cleckheaton, West Yorkshire

TOWN HALL

Bradford Road, Cleckheaton, West Yorkshire BD19 3RH
Tel: 01274 335 003 Bkg: 01484 223 200
Web Site: www.kirklees.gov.uk
ADMINISTRATION
Props: Kirklees Metropolitan Borough Council
Cap: 500 (Stage Facilities)
Town Hall Manager: David Roche
Superintendent: Dean Rounding

Clydebank, Dunbartonshire

CLYDEBANK TOWN HALL

49 Dumbarton Road, Clydebank, West Dunbartonshire G81 1TX Scotland
Tel: 0141 562 2406/8 Bkg: 01389 738 762 Bkg Fax: 01389 941 0932
Email: marie.wright@west-dunbarton.gov.uk
Web Site: www.wdcweb.info
ADMINISTRATION:
Props: West Dunbartonshire Council
Cap: Main Hall Seated 522; Stalls 370; Balcony 152.
Lesser Hall Seated 170; Seated with tables 100.
For hiring info contact: Environmental Services Events and Halls Section, West Dunbartonshire Council, Rosebery Place, Clydebank, G81 1TG. Tel: 01389 738762
Fax: 0141 9410932
Email:Protective.Services@west-dunbarton.gov.uk

Coalville, Leicestershire

CENTURY THEATRE

Snibston Discovery Museum, Ashby Road, Coalville, Leicestershire LE67 3LN
Tel: 01530 278 444
Email: snibston@leics.gov.uk
Web Site: www.centurytheatre.co.uk
ADMINISTRATION:
The Century Theatre was built as a travelling theatre in 1952. It now has a permanent site in its home county. The Theatre is managed by Leicester County Council, assisted by a dedicated group of volunteers. It hosts regular events in all types of performing arts. Please contact the main box office on the number above for further details on Theatre activities.
TECHNICAL:
Stage 7m(w) x 6m(d) x 3m(h). Adequate lighting and sound equipment for its size. Licenced bar. Dressing rooms, plus toilets with wash basins and kitchen.

Colchester, Essex

Pop. 145,100. London 54 miles.
Newspapers: East Anglian Daily Times; Evening Gazette (ntly); Colchester Express (thurs); Essex County Standard (fri). STD code 01206

CHARTER HALL

Colchester Leisure World, Cowdray Avenue, Colchester, Essex CO1 1YH
Tel: 01206 282 946 BO: 01206 282020
Fax: 01206 282024
Email: frank.turmel@colchester.gov.uk
Web Site: www.charter-hall.co.uk
ADMINISTRATION
Props: Colchester Borough Council
Cap: 1200
Event Manager: Frank Turmel
Event Officers: Sarah Castleton, Stephanie Ward & Katie O'Sullivan
Modern multi-purpose venue. Extensive backstage
facilities. Up to 1200 capacity. Concert PA and Lighting. Dedicated team on-site. Free parking.
Hospitality suites. Easy access.
TECHNICAL:
SOUND:
GENERAL DESCRIPTION: A fully mixed, comprehensive sound system is linked from the stage to the Upper Gallery situated at a high level to the rear of Charter Hall. The system includes full sound effects and high limit cut off at 120 dba. STAGE BOXES 20 Channel stage boxes, one mounted either side of the stage, incorporating 4 outputs and 16 inputs. Patchable at Upper Gallery. MIXING DESK: Sound Craft Spirit 8. 16 POWER AMPLIFIERS: 1 x 707 SR C Audio. 2 x E Pack 2500 Amps. 2 x RA 3001 300 Watt per channel Stage Monitors SPECIAL EFFECTS. SPEAKER CONNECTS. RECORDING PLAYBACK 1 x Yamaha SPX x 900 Professional multi effect processor. 1 x DBX PA Drive Unit. 1 x Pioneer DVD 575A. 1 x Dennon tape deck. 1 x Dennon Tuner. MICROPHONES: 2 x Bayer microphones consisting 5 TG300 with stands. 1 x AKG. 3 x TG700. 4 x choir mics at 853A condensor. 5 x Trantec Radio Mics S3500 MTX. 2 x Astatic CTM 92. PA SYSTEM: Flown cluster centre stage 4 x JBL 4726. Compact Bi-radial speakers. 4 x JBL 7228 Bi-radial stage monitor speakers 2 x KV2 ES1.0 Full range speakers.
POWER SUPPLY STAGE LEFT SPN - 125amp, 63amp, 32amp, 16amp C-form sockets for sound. STAGE RIGHT TPN # 125 amp and 63 amp C-form sockets for lighting system. FINISHES FLOOR: Herringbone granwood flooring. WALLS: Beech veneer acoustic panelling above curtained pink facing block work. CEILING Acoustic tiles above stage and over centre section of hall.
STAGE:
TYPE OF STAGE Sico multiple height modular mobile folding stage.
PERFORMING AREA: Total area: 190.2metres square. 22 units x 2.97 square metres. Adjustable height capacity: 0.75m, 0.90m, 1.05m and 1.20m. 6 units x 2.97 square metres and 24 units x 4.6 square metres. Adjustable height capacity: 1.20m, 1.35m, 1.50m, 1.65 and 1.80m. BASIC MASKING 48# wide black back drop suspended off motorised truss. Star cloth. Stage tabs. SKIRT CURTAIN Multi-height stage skirt curtains in #Hercules# flame retardant fabric.
LIGHTING:
POWER SUPPLY : 3 phase 100 amp. LIGHTING BOARD: Sirius 088, 48

way control desk. Situated in Upper Gallery. COMMUNICATION SYSTEM: 1 x Tecpro PS711 power supply unit. 3 channel and overload protection. 4 x Tecpro BP111 Belt Pack, with volume control, latching push-to-talk button and call light
4 x Tecpro SMH210 single muff headset. 2x Senheisor Headsets. 2x Metro Belt Packs. LIGHTING GRID: 4 x 18m 20 way internally wired bars running across the stage area 40# Motorised back truss. All internally wired bars to be wired back to a 15amp patch system located in the Upper Gallery. LANTERNS: 40 x Par 64 cans; 36 x Strand Cantata PC. 12 x Strand Cantata 18/32 profile spot. 8 x Strand Coda. 2 x Strand Solo CSI follow spots. 4 x Predator intelligent lights.

UNIVERSITY OF ESSEX LAKESIDE THEATRE

Wivenhoe Park, Colchester, Essex CO4 3SQ
Mgt: 01206 873 261
Email: arts@essex.ac.uk
Web Site: www.lakesidetheatre.org.uk
ADMINISTRATION:
Props: University of Essex
Arts Officer: Jessica Kenny
Technical Manager: Harry Harris
Artistic Director: Barbra Peirson
Policy: To run a season of Wednesday night theatre programming a selection of the best small-scale touring companies. The theatre has a strong commitment to student productions with 12 productions a year.
Theatre available for hire during vacation.
Perfs: Variable
Seats: 200. Bars. Coffee Bars and Restaurant available on campus.
TECHNICAL:
Stage: Flexible, normally Proscenium with apron, but licensed and easily used as Open form with small thrust. Stage floor flat. Permanent curved Cyc. Pros. opening 9.38m; Ht. 4.51m; Depth of S/Line 7.74m; Ht. of grid 6.32 - 7.23m; W/Widths P.S. 2.43m; O.P. 2.68m; Prompt Cnr. P.S.
Lighting: Board: Ovation 96 ways fitted, 2 x SP60/III backup. Control room at rear audit; 16 x Patt.264, 6 x Patt.T64, 8 x Sil 25, 9 x Patt.23 ('N' noses available), 15 x Patt. 243, 30 x Patt.743, 7 x Patt.123, 2 x Patt.750, 12 x Parblazer 4, 12 x AC1001L, 5 x Pallas 4, 2 x Patt.230C, 4 x Patt.252, 1 x Sil. 10, follow spots: 3 x Patt.765; Dips 15 each side; 2 F.O.H. Spot Bars (access via catwalks), 5 Stage Bars, 4 F.O.H. Perches, 2 Pros booms.
Sound Equip: Thorens/SME/V15 Record deck, Revox PR99, Tascam BR20 (7.5/15ips), Denon DN77OR cassette, Panasonic SV3700, Denon CD, Libra 10 modular mixer (12 mic/line in, 10 groups out), 6 x JBL Control 10, 2 x Stagesound ST2/115, 2X Mission 770 speakers with individual associated power amps; Signal Processing: 2 x Roland SDE 3000 Digital Delays, 2 x Dod 31 Band Graphic Equalisers, 6 x Rebis Compressor/Limiters. 8 x Rebis Parametrics, 6 x Rebis Gate/Expanders, G.B.S. Yamaha SPX1000 Reverberation Unit; D.B.X. (Simultaneous) on tape machines, Computerised recording a playback on hard disc, 4 F.O.H., 4 Stage, 2 Foyer speaker outlets. 10 mic inputs P and O.P. 2 mic inputs control room. 5 undedicated tielines P and O.P. to control room. A.K.G. microphones and stands. Show Relay, S.M. Call, ring headsets and cue-lights to all locations.
Dressing Rooms 4, Accom 29 min, 2 showers, Wardrobe Room. Fully equipped Workshop/Paintshop. Small Rehearsal Room. Get-in at stage/street level, direct access to service road - Dock doors 4.78m x 1.35m. No fly tower, but height and equipment to fly smaller items.
Membership: TMA, ABT.

MERCURY THEATRE

Balkerne Gate, Colchester, Essex CO1 1PT
Mgt: 01206 577 006 BO: 01206 573 948
Fax: 01206 769 607
Email: info@mercurytheatre.co.uk
Web Site: www.mercurytheatre.co.uk
ADMINISTRATION:
Lessees: Colchester Mercury Theatre Ltd
Marketing Manager: Robin Fenwick
Production Manager: Christine Piper
Policy: Ensemble company.
Performances: Mon, Tues, Wed, Thurs, Fri & Sat 7.30 pm; Mat. Thurs & Sat 2.30 pm.
Seats: 499 Open stage. 409 Pros. Licensed Bar, Restaurant, Lift, Wheelchair Spaces 4. 1 Signed performance per run. Studio - Maximum seating 75
TECHNICAL:
Stage:Main house: Adaptable proscenium/Open semi-thrust stage flat, hexagonal; Pros. Opening min. 8.53m; Max. open width 12.19m; Ht. of Pros. 5.73m; Working stage depth 8.84m plus 1.52m apron; Ht. of grid 13m; 14 double-purchase C/W lines, 1 single purchase C/W for house tabs;W/Widths P.S. irregular 1.40m min. 4.88m max., O.P. regular 1.40m max. some room in scene dock adjacent P.S. Prompt cnr. P.S.
Lighting: F.O.H: - 3 bridges with catwalks over auditorium, side positions in audit. walls. Main house: Strand 530 desk and 501 syncronised backup desk operated from control room at rear of auditorium, 166 circuts @ 2.5kw, 15 independent channels. 63A 3 phase supply for temporary equipment. Stock - 70 profiles, 45 fresnels, 36 pars, 24 floods. 2 followspots operated from control room.
Sound: Soundcraft K3 24:8:4:2 and 328 Digital desks, operated from control room or rear auditorium. 2 x 5 Meyer M1D miniature curvelinear arrays, 5 Meyer UPM1 front fills, 2 USW1P Subs. 2 crest V650 and 4 PM700 amps, various speakers, mics and stands, Akai hard disk recorder, 2 MD players, 2 CD players, 2 tape players, 4 graphic equalisers, 2 effects units.
Studio: Variable performance area - 5m - 7m approx. No rake - floor sprung wood. Height to ceiling 5.5m. Get in via double crash doors - 1.45m x 1.9m.
Lighting: Strand LBX board, 24 circuits @ 2.5kw, operated from control room or catwalk. Stock - 25 profiles, 20 fresnels, 8 pars. Sound: Soundcraft Spirit Folio F1 16:2 desk, operated from control room or catwalk, Crest V650 amp, 2 community speakers, 2 MD players, CD player, tape player. Accoustics suitable for music and spoken word.

Coleraine, County Londonderry

Pop. 25,000. Newspapers: Coleraine Times (wed); Coleraine Chronicle (thurs); Northern Constitution (fri). STD code 028 70

RIVERSIDE THEATRE

The University of Ulster, Cromore Road, Coleraine, County Londonderry BT52 1SA Northern Ireland
Admin: 028 7032 4459 BO: 028 7032 3232 Marketing: 028 7032 3037 Tech: 028 7032 4456 Fax: 028 7032 4924
Email: riversidetheatre@ulster.ac.uk
Web Site: www.riversidetheatre.org.uk
ADMINISTRATION:
Artistic Director: Andrea Montgomery
Technical Supervisor: David Coyle
Marketing Manager: Sharon Kirk
Box Office Supervisor: Louise Geddis
Policy: Touring & in-house production, also opera and dance.
Perfs: Mon-Sat 8.00p.m.; Occasional Schools Mat. 10.30a.m. or 1.30 p.m.
Seats: Thrust 358, Pros. 274, bar, Foyer Art Gallery.
TECHNICAL:
Variable Auditorium.
Stage: Thrust stage flat; Height of grid 7.60m; 18 lines suspension only. Prompt corner variable P.S. O.P. or Control Box; Pros. stage flat; stage 9.12m depth 8.51m opening; Wings 2.89m max. Flat Height 4.86m Easy get-in 7.60m x 3.65m.
Lighting Equip: Strand Light Board M, 84 way, all circuits 2kw + 45kw; 5 ind. non-dim 2kw circuits; Lamps 14CCT SIL30 profile, 15 strand contata, 30 fresnels; 2 x Sil. 15 follow spots, 2 Pani BP 15, 30 Harmony P.C.S. Lighting bridges wrap around, and centre crossover. Control room rear auditorium.
Sound Equip: 1 Total Audio Concepts 16-8-2 mixer, 2 Amcron DC300A amps, 1 Amcron D150A amp, 4 Profley 200 speakers, 2 foldback wedges, 4 FX speakers, 12 mic lines, 6 speaker lines, all fully patchable via 260-point patch field and local tie lines; 2 Revox B55 track stereo tapes, 1 Garard 401 deck; 1 Technics RST33R cassette. All speaker

connections 4 Pin XLR all mics 3 Pin XLR. SM Control 16 out station ring intercom. 10 way patchable Q Light system. 6 x 12 volt AC and DC supplies.
Dressing Rooms: 4; Accom. 30 plus Quick Change room op. (2); 2 showers; 1 large rehearsal room; Orchestra Pit varies 5 to 30.
Membership: TMA, ART N1

Colne, Lancashire

THE MUNI THEATRE

Albert Road, Colne, Lancashire BB8 0AE
BO: 01282 661 234 Bkgs: 01282 661 220 Hires: 01282 661 234 Fax: 01282 661 221
Email: alison.goode@pendleleisuretrust.co .uk
Web Site: www.themuni.co.uk
ADMINISTRATION
Props: Pendle Leisure
Executive Manager: Alison Goode
Cap: 611 Seated, 800 Cabaret

Colwyn Bay, Conwy

Pop. 25,470. London 221 miles. Newspapers: North Wales Weekly News (thurs); Abergele Visitor (fri); Llandudno Advertiser (fri); Colwyn Bay Pioneer (sat). STD code 01492

THEATR COLWYN

Abergele Road, Colwyn Bay, Conwy LL29 7RU North Wales
BO: 01492 577888 Marketing: 01492 577886
Email: joann.rae@conwy.gov.uk, theatr-colwyn@conwy.gov.uk
Web Site: www.theatrcolwyn.co.uk
ADMINISTRATION:
Manager: Philip Batty
Props: Conwy County Borough Council.
For promotion or hire email phil.batty@conwy.gov.uk
Policy: Small-scale Tours//Winter Openings
Seats: 329. One Bar.

Congleton, Cheshire

Pop. 25,000. London 140 miles. Newspaper: The Congleton Chronicle. STD code 01260

DANESIDE THEATRE

Park Road, Congleton, Cheshire CW12 1DP
Tel 01260 278481 BO: 01260 271095
Email: info@danesidetheatre.co.uk
Web Site: www.danesidetheatre.co.uk
ADMINISTRATION:
Technical Manager: Phil Drage
Props: Daneside Theatre Trust Ltd
Bookings Manager: Mrs Nicky Evans Tel: 07962 170378, email: nicky@livelife-lovedance.co.uk
Policy: Multi-use. Mostly amateur, but available for hire by professional companies for shows and rehearsal.
Perfs: Vary according to show
Seats: 300 raked auditorium. Bar.
TECHNICAL:
Stage: Proscenium, Pros. opening 30ft. Height of pros. 14ft, depth of stage 20ft. Stage width 50ft. Loading doors 6ft hight, 8ft wide. Height to grid 18ft. Workshop same size as stage. 6 Minin Fresnel, Sirius 48 Desk.
Lighting: Switchboard: 40 x 2.5Kw; 12 Harmony 22/40, 12 Patt.137, 10 Patt.23, 4 Patt.223, 2 Prelude PC, 24 way cyc. batten.
Sound Equip: Seck 1282 mixing desk, feeds onstage and FOH speakers and dressing room feed, 9 AKG microphones. TEAC 3440 tape deck.
Dressing Rooms 4; accom 40. Orchestra Pit area 2m x 15m.

TOWN HALL

High Street, Congleton, Cheshire CW12 1BN
Tel: 01260 270350 Fax: 01260 280357
Email: st@@congletontowncouncil.co.uk
Web Site: www.congletontowncouncil.co.uk
ADMINISTRATION
Props: Congleton Town Council
Main Hall:
Cap: 220 - concert style
Bridestones Suite
Cinema Style 100-Boardroom Style 150
Spencer Suite
Cap: 20 -30 cinema style, 12 Boardroom style
Tapas Bar
Bookings Contact Halls Officer: sc@congletontowncouncil.co.uk or st@congletontowncouncil.co.uk

Connah's Quay, Flintshire

CIVIC HALL

Wepre Drive, Connah's Quay, Deeside, Flintshire CH5 4HA
Hall: 01244 811 102 Council Offices: 01244 819 420
Email: info@connahs-quay.co.uk
Web Site: www.connahs-quaytowncouncil.co.uk
ADMINISTRATION:
Props: Connah's Quay Town Council
Cap: 350
Correspondence Address: Connah`s Quay Town Council Offices, Quay Buildings, Fron Road, Connah's Quay, CH5 4PJ.
Controlled by Connah's Quay Town Council; full catering/bars facilities by arrangement with on-site Lessees.
Contact: Mr Ian Jones, Clerk + Financial Officer
Policy: Tours, Variety, Dances all Catering Functions, Conferences.
Licensed Bar and Cafe facilities available.
Dressing Rooms 3. Separate Lounge available. S/Cap 50.
TECHNICAL:
Stage Width 7.32m, Ht. 5.49m, Stage Left 3.66m, Stage Right 5.49m. Electrics: Voltage 230-250 with additional source of supply. 28 Circuits; Wattage 10,000; F.O.H. Spot Bars 4; Batten Floods on Batten Bar 9; Batten Floods on back stage reserve 3; Wing Floods 2.

Cork, Eire

Pop. 133,000. Newspapers: The Examiner; Evening Echo. STD code 00 353 21

CORK OPERA HOUSE

Emmet Place, Cork, Eire
Admin: 00 353 21 427 4308 Mktg: 00 353 21 4905 213 BO: 00 353 21 427 0022 Admin Fax: 00 353 21 427 6357 Mktg Fax: 00 353 21 427 6357 BO Fax: 00 353 21 427 0960
Email: info@corkoperahouse.ie
Web Site: www.corkoperahouse.ie
ADMINISTRATION:
Props: Cork Opera House Plc
Executive Director: Mary Hickson
Financial Controller: Dermot O'Driscoll
Executive Assistant: Ashley Keating
Marketing Manager: Siobhan Brennan
Marketing Assistant: Laura Hart
Box Office Manager: Heather Murphy
Policy: Used for Musicals, Concerts, Plays, Grand Opera, Ballet, Conferences and Exhibitions. Front of House equipped with Bars, Coffee Kiosk & Shop.
Seating Capacity: 920
TECHNICAL:
Stage: 40' wide, 30' deep; stage clearance 17' each side and 15' back of cyclorama; computer Lighting Board: T.V. Luminaries.
Backstage: Green room with Bar, 9 Dressing Rooms plus rehearsal rooms.
The Half Moon Theatre which is situated at the rear of Cork Opera House opened in December 1997 following redevelopment as a multi-purpose entertainment venue with an audience capacity from 150 to 450.

Corwen, Denbighshire

CORWEN LEISURE CENTRE

Carrog Road, Corwen, Denbighshire LL21 9RW
Tel/Fax: 01490 412600

Email: dcc_leisure@denbighshire.gov.uk
Web Site: www.denbighshire.gov.uk
ADMINISTRATION
Props: Denbighshire County Council
Manager: Hayden Jones
Duty Officer: Justin Jones

Coventry, West Midlands

Pop. 336,370. London 92 miles.
Newspapers: Coventry Evening Telegraph; Birmingham Post and Mail; Leamington Spa Courier. STD code 024 76

BELGRADE THEATRE

Belgrade Square, Coventry, Warwickshire CV1 1GS
Tel: 024 7625 6431 BO: 024 7655 3055
Fax: 024 7655 0680
Email: admin@belgrade.co.uk
Web Site: www.belgrade.co.uk
ADMINISTRATION:
Lessees: Belgrade Theatre Trust (Coventry) Ltd;
Artistic Director and Chief Executive: Hamish Glen
Executive Director: Joanna Reid
Director of Communications: Nicola Young
Operations Manager: Eamonn Finnerty
Head Of Production: Adrian Sweeney
Policy: Repertory, Pantomime with occasional Tours - 3 weekly Rep, one off concerts.
Perfs: Mon-Thurs 7.30; Fri 8.00; Sat 8.00; Mat 2.45.
Capacity: 866.
Studio Capacity 230
2 Licensed Bars, Licensed Restaurant, Snack and Coffee Bar.
TECHNICAL:
STAGE: Proscenium, Flat; Pros. opening to 10.90m; Ht. of Pros. 5.79m; Depth of S/Line 8.24m; Ht. of Grid 12.50m; 37 lines, C/W; 2 wing bars over aprom W/Widths PS TM op 1.5m. Scenery Flying Ht. 6.00m; Flying Bars 13.26m; W/Widths P.S.
LIGHTING: 120 Way Galaxy 2 Arena, Rear of Stalls 100 x 2kw circuits; 20 x 5kw circuits; 2CCS.S15, 2kw, 20 CCT S30 1kw, 10 CCT S25 1kw, 18 Patt.264, 20 Patt.223, 10 Patt.243, 29 ADB 1k, 6 Harmony 1, 5 Iris 4, 14 T84, 6 S63 G/rows, 2 CCT CS1 Follow Spots.
SOUND EQUIP: DDA 24/8/2 D Series in Control Room rear of Stalls, 5HH V500; 4 Amcron D150; 8 Bose 802; 2 Bose 302; and other speakers, various mics; Prompt Corner PS or Control Room.
DRESSING ROOMS: 7; Accom. 30 approx; 4 showers; Orchestra Pit 12-14 max.
ADDITIONAL: Permanent Plaster cyc. white Forestage approx. 2.8m. Height under Fly Floors approx. 5.9m, Flys Operating Gallery O.P.
MEMBERSHIP: TMA

WARWICK ARTS CENTRE

University of Warwick, Coventry, Warwickshire CV4 7AL
Admin: 024 7652 3734 Tech: 024 7652 3793 Stage Door: 024 7652 2442
Mrkting: 024 7652 4669 Fax: 024 7652 4525
Email: arts.centre@warwick.ac.uk
Web Site: www.warwickartscentre.co.uk
ADMINISTRATION:
Props: University of Warwick
Director: Alan Rivett
Events Manager: Laura Elliot Tel: 024 7652 4439
Policy: A mixed programme of middle scale touring; opera; concerts; dance and drama with an independent film programme. The Arts Centre has five auditoria: Concert Hall, Theatre, Studio, Conference Room and Film Theatre, also art gallery, a bookshop, restaurant and shop.
Perfs: Nightly (theatre) 7.30p.m. Occasional mid-week/Sat.Mats. 2.30 & 5.00p.m.
Capacity: Theatre 543/573. Studio Theatre, max. 200, (flexible bleachers seating), Cinema 226, Concert Hall 1300. Cafe Bar, Restaurant open Mon-Sat 9.00a.m. - 8.00p.m.; two licensed bars, large foyer accommodating 2,000. Bookshop open Monday to Saturday.
TECHNICAL:

Main Auditorium:
STAGE: Adjustable pros. arch. Performing area 27.32m x 12.2m - pros. opening 10.98m x 5.35m - 6.4m - wing widths 7.31m SR, 7.31m SL. No rake - floor hardboard over birch ply/demountable, suitable for dance, lino available, backstage crossover, stage heated. Grid height 18.28m - 36 counterweight sets, double purchase, 0.22m apart - no tab track - 250kg permitted on bars - maximum flying height 16.75m. White plaster back wall used as cyclorama - blue house tabs, flown. Forestage 2.74m x 10.98m. Orchestra pit forestage lift/understage area, accommodates 70. Get-in via step 0.91m - dock doors 2.28m x 7.01m. Tallescope. Large paintframe and workshop facilities available.
LIGHTING: Switchboard: Strand 530i; 99 dimmers; 93 at 2kw, 6 at 5kw. Lanterns: 10 SIL 15, 24 SIL 30, 36 1 kw Fresnels, 8 2kw PCs, 5 CCT 4 compartment floods. 4 x SIL 15, 24 x SIL 30, 12 x ADB Europe, 44 x 1kw Fresnel, 8 x 2kw PC, 5 x CCT 4 compartment floods.
SOUND: Turbosound speakers with crest amps: 2 Denon 1050 Minidisk, Soundcraft K3 desk 32/8, Screen.
DRESSING ROOMS: 6, plus large chorus room; 8 showers; Orchestra Pit 30-40.

Studio Theatre:
Lighting switchboard Strand 530; 46 2kw dimmers. Sound: DDA desk 16-8, tannoy CPA 15 + CPA 12 speakers, HH Amps.

Membership: TMA. Association of British Concert Promoters.

Craigavon, County Amagh

CRAIGAVON CIVIC CENTRE

Lake View Road, Craigavon, County Armagh BT64 1AL
Tel: 028 3831 2400 Fax: 028 3831 2444
Email: info@craigavon.gov.uk
Web Site: www.craigavon.gov.uk
Manager: Denise McCluskey
Cap: 620 Flat Floor
For bookings please contact June Guy on 028 3831 2423.
Conferences, Meetings, Seminars, Banquets and Weddings, Concerts, Plays and Shows, Exhibitions, Fashion Shows, Product Launches, Charity Events, Private Functions / Dinner Dances.

LURGAN TOWN HALL

Union Street, Lurgan, Craigavon, County Armagh BT66 8DY Northern Ireland
Tel: 028 3832 2422 Fax: 028 3834 8298
Email: lurgan.town.hall@craigavon.gov.uk
Web Site: www.craigavon.gov.uk
Manager: Kate Freeburn
Cap: 200 Flat seating, 50 Balcony
For bookings please contact Manager on above number or Janet Hart on 028 3831 2584

PORTADOWN TOWN HALL THEATRE

Edward Street, Portadown, Craigavon, County Armagh BT62 3LX Northern Ireland
Tel: 028 3833 5264 Fax: 028 3836 1987
Email: conrad.wilson@craigavon.gov.uk
Web Site: www.craigavon.gov.uk
Portadown Town Hall is a victorian building which houses a theatre with the most modern lighting and sound facilities, fly tower and orchestra pit. Well worth a visit.
Cap: Tiered Seating 275, Flat 319

Crawley, West Sussex

Pop. 93,000. London 31 miles.
Newspapers: Crawley News, Crawley Observer (wed); Evening Argus (ntly). STD code 01293

CRAWLEY LEISURE CENTRE

Pease Pottage Hill Crawley, West Sussex RH11 9BQ
Tel: 01293 585300 Fax: 01293 585301
Email: k2enquiries@freedom-leisure.co.uk
Web Site: www.freedomleisure.co.uk
ADMINISTRATION
Props: Freedom Leisure
Cap: 1700 (seated concert) 3000 (standing concert)
Bookings Cali Stanton Tel: 01293 585309

Fax: 01293 585301
Fully equipped, large capacity venue. Available for one night stands, concerts, rock concerts, light entertainments, major sporting events, fairs, exhibitions, etc.

HAWTH THEATRE

Hawth Avenue, Crawley, West Sussex RH10 6YZ
Mgt: 01293 552 941 BO: 01293 553 636
Press: 01293 859953 Tech: 01293 859957
Email: dave.watmore@parkwoodtheatres.co.uk
Web Site: www.hawth.co.uk
ADMINISTRATION:
Props: Parkwood Community Leisure
General Manager: Dave Watmore
House Manager: Ben Manning
Technical Manager: Quentin Whitaker
Marketing Officer: Steve Crane
Policy: Broadmix programme - professional Touring Drama, traditional and contemporary arts, light entertainment, rock, pop, childrens shows and pantomime. Willing to premier show. Film, exhibitions, trade shows, conferences, banquets. Studio - small scale performances including theatre, cabaret, dance, jazz, folk, country, lectures, workshops, exhibitions etc. Summer programme possible in grounds. Amphitheatre available.
Perfs: 7.30p.m. to 8.30p.m. including Sundays 2.30p.m. Usually open 7 days a week.
Capacity: Main House: 862 raked. Portable /retractable/ground. Studio: Max 146 raked.
Additional Facilities: 5 spaces for wheelchairs, disabled parking area, level access. Induction loop system for the hard of hearing. Regular audio described and signed performances.
TECHNICAL:
STAGE (Main House): Variable - proscenium, thrust in the round. Performance area 13m x 12m. Proscenium opening 13m x 8.5m. Flying height 17.5m 49 c/w sets, single and double purchase. Auditorium/Front-stage access S.R. 100 seat choir stalls. Extensive range of rostra units. Tallescope. Steinway grand piano. Yamaha upright piano. 3-phase 200A USL, 100A DSI. 1:25 plans available on request.
LIGHTING: Strand 550 lighting control. 178 Strand LD90 2.5kw 8 LD90 5kw dimmers. 2 x 1Kw Solo CID Follow Spots with Dimmer shutters and 6-way Colour Magazines. 8 x 2Kw Cadenza 12/22 Profiles with Iris and Gobo holders. 22 x 1.2kw Cantata 11/26 Profiles. 30 x 1.2kw Cantata 18/32 Profiles. 6 x 2kw Cadenza PC's with Barn Doors. 4 x 2kw Cadenza F's with Barn Doors. 24 x 1.2kw Cantata Pc's with Barn Doors. 20 x 1.2kw Cantata F's with Barn Doors. 30 x 1kw Punchlite Parcans. 8 x 1.25kw Iris 3 flood battens. 8 x Coda 4 flood battens/groundrow.
SOUND: Allen & Heath Sabre 40-8-8-2 Matrix Mixing Desk. 2 x Shure handheld radio mics. 8 x beltpack radio mics. 11 x Shure SM 58.8 x AKG C 451 EB. 6 x AKG CK 1 Mic. Capsules. 4 x AKG CK 3 Mic. Capsules. 6 x AKG CK 8 Mic. Capsules. 1 x AKG D 112.2 x AKG C 567E Tie-Clip Mics. 2 x AKG VR2 extension tubes. 6 x AKG VR1 extension tubes. 7 x EMO passive DI boxes. 2 x Yamaha SPX 900 effects units. 2 x Yamaha SPX90 II Effects Units. 2 x TOA310D Digital Delay Units, 1 x Peavey Autograph analyser and Equaliser Unit, 4 x Peavey Automate Equalisers Units. 4 x TOA E11 31 Band Graphic Equalisers. 2 Yamaha 2031 Graphic Equalisers. 1 x Bose CSC-1 Cinema Sound Controller, with output to Bose Cannon Bass Units. 1 x Yamaha GC2020B Compressor/Limiter. 1 x Tascam GE20B Graphic Equaliser. 5 x Bose 802C Control Units, 1 x Bose 402C Control Unit.. 3 x Revox B77 Tape Decks. On wheeled stand. 1 x Tascam 122 Cassette Deck. 1 x Tascam 112 Cassette Deck. 1 x TEAC V550X Cassette Deck. 1 x Tascam 388 8-track mixer/recorder. 1 x Revox B226 Compact Disc player. 1 x Denon DCD-1500 Compact Disk player. Sound Effects Discs. 4 x TOA P300D 2-Channel amplifiers. 1 x TOA P75D 2-Channel amplifier. 2 x HILL LC1200 amplifiers. 2 x H.HM900 2-Channel amplifiers. 1 x Quad 306 2-Channel amplifier. 4 x Q.S.C.2 chan. amps1 x LIC Audio XL 2500 Induction-loop amplifier. 6 x TOA 380SE rull-range cabinets. 2 x Bose Cannon Bass Units. 12 x Bose 802 Units. 2 x Bose 402 Units. 1 x Dolby 4-channel sound de-coder. 2 x TOA SM-25M powered monitor speakers. 1 x Fostex self-powered monitors. 10 x TOA F150 speakers in Delay System. 2 x Yamaha NS10M monitors. 2 x JBL control one monitors. 2 x BOJ double-ported monitors. Canford Tecpro. Acoustics suitable for music and the spoken word.
STAGE MANAGEMENT: Intercom Outstation, 10 way cuelight system. 10 x Canford Tecpro Single Muff Headsets. 2 x Canford Tecpro Double Muff Headsets. Stage-Door paging to dressing rooms. Full show-relay to all back-stage areas. With Stage Manager over-ride. CCTV System: camera focussed on stage, with 6-way video BNC Patchfield to outlets on stage and in the auditorium.
DRESSING ROOMS: 7 dressing rooms, Green Room, company office. Rehearsal room by prior arrangement. 2 quick change rooms. Accommodation 70. Full B.T. connection in all dressing rooms and company office.

Crediton, Devon

LORDS MEADOW LEISURE CENTRE

Commercial Road, Crediton, Devon EX17 1ER
Tel: 01884 234 970
Email: lordmead@middevon.gov.uk
Web Site: www.middevonleisure.co.uk
ADMINISTRATION
Props: Mid Devon District Council
For bookings contact Lee Chester

Crewe, Cheshire

Pop. 103,164 (Crewe and Nantwich Borough). London 161 miles.
Newspapers: Crewe Chronicle (wed); The Guardian (wed). STD code 01270

COPPENHALL LEISURE CENTRE

Coronation Street, Coppenhall, Crewe, Cheshire CW1 4DJ
Tel: 01270 685 560 Fax: 01270 250681
Email: coppenhall@crewe-nantwich.gov.uk
Web Site: www.crewe-nantwich.gov.uk
ADMINISTRATION
Props: Crewe & Nantwich Borough Council
Manager: Brian Tebbutt
Drama hall

LYCEUM THEATRE

Heath Street, Crewe, Cheshire CW1 2DA
Mgt: 01270 537321 BO: 01270 368 242
Tech: 01270 537336 Fax: 01270 537 322
Email: lyceumtheatre@cheshireeast.gov.uk
Web Site: www.lyceumtheatre.net
ADMINISTRATION:
Props: Cheshire East Council
Refurbished in 1994 to provide completely new front of house facilities, the Lyceum is now a first class presenting venue. A wide-ranging policy of quality work embraces drama, dance, opera, concerts, children's theatre and a traditional pantomime.
General Manager: Jane Ashcroft
Marketing Manager: Phillippa Unett
Technical Manager: David Thomas
Contact:
david.thomas@cheshireeast.gov.uk
Perfs: Variable
Capacity: 677, seating.
Disabled: Seats in stalls, lift and toilets on all floors, infra red hearing system.
Membership: TMA
TECHNICAL:
STAGE: Proscenium, Raked (1:18) with removable forestage (1.35m) to reveal orchestra pit; W 7.39m, L 2.14m, H 1.85m. Pros opening 8.55m x 5.6m; Depth from front of stage to last fly bar 10.36m (C.L.).Ht of grid (upstage): 13.08m. Fly floor height (u/s) 6.1m. Hemp lines x 24, counterwieght lines 4 + 1 for house tabs, winches x 4 (lx). Hemps & winches grid at 12.8m. Counterweights at 11.4m. Get-in; DSR through 3 dock doors; outer:H2.7m x W1.8m central:H2.4m x 1.78m inner:H3.5m x 1.55m.

LIGHTING: Control Desk; ETC Congo Lighting consol with 99 pages of 20 sub-masters, 3 universes each with 512 DMX channels. Lamp and other Technical Stock; (not including permanent F.O.H Rig); 32 x 19 Degree Source 4 Profile 575 w, 14 x 26 Degree Source 4 Profile 575 w, 8 x 36 Degree Source 4 Profile 575 w, 4 x 50 Degree Source 4 Profile 575 w, 6 x source 4 jnr, 48 x Selecon 1200 w Rama Fresnel, 48 x Selecon 1000 w Compact Fresnel, 24 x Thomas 1000 w Par cans (CP 62), 14 x Coda Floods 1K, 16 x Selecon Lui Floods 1K, 8 x Thomas Howie Battens (20 cell), 2 x 18inch Mirror Balls, 1 Mini Mist Smoke Machine (Fluid Contra as used), 2 Jem Haze Machine (Fluid Contra as used), 1 sweep fog haze machine (Fluid Contra as used), 1 6 x 4 Le Maitre Pyrotechnic Firing box system (Contra per use), 8 Le Maitre angle pods, 12 single straight pods. Dimmers; 104 x 2.5Kw on Stage Outlets, 48 x 2.5Kw FOH Outlets. Additional; Assorted cabling and Converters, Barn Doors, Colour frames, Various Go-Bo's and holders, Irises, 4 x Apollo DMX smart moves, 1 x Apollo Right arm, Sanyo PLC xt25 with Hanging Bracket, 8 x Ballet boom
SOUND: Mackie TT24 Digital Live Console. 2 x C7 D&B Subs. 2 x C6 D&B Speakers (Stalls). 4 x C7 D&B Speakers (Circle, Gallery). 4 x E3 D&B Front Fills. 8 x D12 Digital D&B Amps. 1 x Tascam MD-CD1 CD/MD player. 1 x Tascam MD 350 M.D Player. Furman HD56 Pit Headphone System (6 Base Stations with 12 Headphones). 24 x Tie Lines XLR Sends at Desk End - Male. 8 x Tie Lines XRL Returns at Desk End - Female. 24 x Tie Lines XLR Sends at Stage Multi D/S/L - Female. 8 x Tie Lines XRL Returns at Stage Multi D/S/L - Male. 18 x Tie Lines XRL to Pit. 2 x Martin LE400 Monitors. 2 x HK Audio PR:O 12M Monitors. 8 x Yamaha MS8. 6 x Monitor Points (2 D/S/L, 2 U/S/L, 2 D/S/R) all return to desk on XLR. Various Microphones available. Radio coverage all over stage and auditorium. 1 x 12 Way Van-Dam Multi Stage Box. Various Jumpers leads and Sound Cables.
STAGE MANAGEMENT: Metro Audio intercom Call Facility to All Dressing Rooms, Technical Office, Crew Room, Green Room, Band Position Under Stage, Rehearsal Room. Metro Audio Communications System (CANS). HME DX200 Wireless Intercom System giving an extra 9 intercom sets. Metro Audio Cue-light system. (8 Fully Patchable ways). Monitor for Pit Camera which shows Musical Director in the Pit. (Black & White Picture). Monitor for the Infra-Red Camera. Camera is Positioned on the Gallery F.O.H Lighting Rail which shows all of the Stage - Pros to Pros (Colour Picture).
DRESSING ROOMS: 7; Accomm.17 artistes (1 optional as company office). Shower, Toilet, and Wash Basin facilities. Green Room with Kettle, Washing Machine, Dryer and Kitchen sink.
FACILITIES FOR THE DISABLED: Toilets on all floors. There are currently no toilets for disabled people back stage. 2 x lifts giving access to the F.O.H area and to ground floor only back stage. Wheelchair spaces available at stalls level. Infrared system for people with hearing impairments.

SHAVINGTON LEISURE CENTRE

Rope Lane, Shavington, Cheshire CW2 5DJ
Tel: 01270 685551
Email: shavington@everybody.org.uk
Web Site: www.everybody.org.uk
ADMINISTRATION
Props: Cheshire East Council
Contact: Gerard Baldwin

VICTORIA COMMUNITY CENTRE

West Street, Crewe, Cheshire CW1 2PZ
Tel: 01270 685571
Email: vcc@everybody.org.uk
Web Site: www.everybody.org.uk
ADMINISTRATION:
Props: Cheshire East Council
Gerard Baldwin - Manager
Cap: Sports Hall, flat 4-500.

Criccieth, Gwynedd

CRICCIETH MEMORIAL HALL

20 Gwaen Ganol, Criccieth, Gwynedd LL52 0TB
Tel: 01766 523 672
Email: bookings@cricciethmemorialhall.co m
Web Site: www.cricciethmemorialhall.com
ADMINISTRATION:
Contact: David Thomas
Seats: 500.
Contact Hall Booking keeper
TECHNICAL:
LBX Board. Sound up to Broadcasting Standard.
Lighting: 3 Pirouetts; 16 Parcans; 6 Cantatas; 12 Harmonys; 6 764s; 12 T60s; 4 Cods; 3 Coda cyclights; 6 743s.
Sound: 2 Radio mics; 4 tin clip mics; 3 Bayers; 2 Sanhyser; 3 AKG; Cassette player - mini disc player; cans.

Cromer, Norfolk

Pop. 5,380. London 133 miles.
Newspapers: North Norfolk News (thurs); Eastern Daily Press (dly). STD code 01263

PAVILION THEATRE

Cromer Pier, Cromer, Norfolk NR27 9HE
Mgt: 01263 512 281 BO: 01263 512 495
Email: rwass@thecromerpier.com
Web Site: www.cromer-pier.com
ADMINISTRATION:
Props: Pier and theatre operation managed by Openwide Coastal in conjunction with North Norfolk District Council.
General Manager: Rebecca Wass
Policy: Early-Late season attractions. Sunday Celebrity Concerts, Children's Shows.
Perfs: 7.30
Seats: 510. Licensed Bar, Coffee shop and Restaurant, Gift Shop
For Technical Specifications please contact the Theatre.

Crook, County Durham

SPECTRUM LEISURE CENTRE

Hunwick Lane, Willington, Crook, County Durham DL15 0JA
Tel: 01388 747000 Fax: 01388 747098
Email: bouldd@slamcdt.co.uk
ADMINISTRATION
Prop: Ian Hirst
Cap: 600 (stage facilities)
Contact Centre Manager: Dan Boulton

Crowngate, Worcester

HUNTINGDON HALL

Crowngate Worcester WR1 3LD
Tel: 01905 611 427
Email: liz@worcesterlive.co.uk
Web Site: www.worcesterlive.co.uk
Props. Worcester City Council
Contact: Liz Grand
Capacity 330

Croydon, Surrey

FAIRFIELD HALLS

Park Lane, Croydon, Surrey CR9 1DG
Mgt/SD: 020 8681 0821 BO: 020 8688 9291 Marketing Fax: 020 8603 3862
Admin Fax: 020 8603 3838
Email: info@fairfield.co.uk
Web Site: www.fairfield.co.uk
ADMINISTRATION:
Props: Fairfield (Croydon) Ltd
Chief Executive: Simon Thomsett
Technical Manager: Chris Whybrow
Head of Operations: John Bartliff
Policy: Concert Hall, Music, Films, Pop, Jazz, Opera, Comedy, Conferences, Ballet.
Capacity: Seats: 1998 max.
Foyer, Coffee shop, Restaurant, Bars, Banqueting & Conference Rooms.
TECHNICAL:

STAGE: Concert Platform, mechanical variable sections.
LIGHTING: Switchboard: Strand Lightboard 'M' commanding 120 channels 200amp 3 phase and 60 amp single phase power supplies available for temporary supply; F.O.H. spots 42 CCT profiles. 2 spot bars available on electric hoist. Selection of lamps; P.A.R. cans and fresnels.
Get-in via platform lift, Direct Access & Parking. No flying facilities, but good grid provision and soft blacks for upstage masking.
SOUND EQUIPMENT: 7kw fully integrated Meyer sound system with permanent mixing position.
OTHER: Dressing Rooms: 7, accom. 200; 3 showers; Orchestra Pit 28.90 orch. music stands, 2 Steinway concert D type Grand Pianos; seats 120 orch. max 250 choir seats.
Staff: 5 Technicians - Casual Crew.
A registered charity.

Cullen, Morayshire

CULLEN COMMUNITY CENTRE
Seafield Road, Cullen, Morayshire AB56 4AF
Tel: 01542 840701
Email: cullen.cc@moray.gov.uk
Web Site: www.moray.gov.uk
ADMINISTRATION:
Props: Moray Council
For Bookings call: 01542 840 701

CULLEN TOWN HALL
11 The Square, Cullen, Morayshire AB56 2RR
Tel: 01542 831150
Email: thecullen@hotmail.com
Web Site: www.cullentownhall.co.uk
ADMINISTRATION:
Props: Moray Council
Cap: Main Hall Seated 220; Dancing 225; Dancing seated at tables 175; Seated at tables 158.
Memorial Hall: Seated 100; Dancing 100; Dancing seated at tables 75; Seated at tables 72.
For bookings Tel: 01542 831150
Contact Bookings Officer: Lissa Allardyce

Cullumpton, Devon

CULM VALLEY SPORTS CENTRE
Meadow Lane, Callumpton, Devon EX15 1LL
Tel: 01884 234 320
Email: culmval@middevon.gov.uk
Web Site: www.middevonleisure.org.uk
ADMINISTRATION
Props: Mid Devon District Council
Cap: 500
For bookings contact Kelly Lee

Cumbernauld, Strathclyde

Pop. 55,000. Glasgow 12 miles.
Newspapers: Cumbernauld News (wkly); Glasgow Herald; Evening Times (dly). STD code 01236

CUMBERNAULD THEATRE
Cumbernauld Theatre, Kildrum, Cumbernauld, Glasgow, North Lanarkshire G67 2BN Scotland
Admin: 01236 737 235 BO: 01236 732 887
Email: info@cumbernauldtheatre.co.uk
Web: www.cumbernauldtheatre.co.uk
ADMINISTRATION:
Artistic Director: Ed Robson
Venue Technician: Sean Smith
Administration and Resources Manager: Jean Cairns
Policy: Home productions. Touring Theatre Companies, Music, Mime, Theatre in Education, Dance, Exhibitions, Films, Workshops
Seats: 258 (main auditorium): 60 (studio)
TECHNICAL:
For more information contact the Technical Department on: technical@cumbernauldtheatre.co.uk
STAGE: Permanent Thrust Stage, adaptable to be 'in the round'. 6.9m wide x 13.5m deep x 5.53m to grid; Control Room at back of auditorium.
LLIGHTING: Arri Imagine II memory desk, Arri smartracks 96 x 2.5kw; 14 x T64, 6 x T84, 26 x Patt.73, 18 x Patt.23, 19 x Patt.123 12HD; 6 ind. circuits all 2k; All connections 15 amp 3 pin round.
SOUND: Revox B77 .DAT. CD., Dennon cass; Garrard SO25; Mixer:Soundtracks 24:4:2.
DRESSING ROOMS; 2.
STUDIO: Performing space 7.1m x 4.19m x 2.7m to grid. Pulsar MS4 72 way board, Racks 2k dimmers. All connections 15 amp round pin.
Membership: TMA, FST

Cumnock, Ayrshire

CUMNOCK TOWN HALL
62 Glaisnock Street, Cumnock, Ayrshire KA18 1BY
Tel: 01290 421028
Email: lynn.morrison@east-ayrshire.gov.uk
Web Site: www.east-ayrshire.gov.uk
ADMINISTRATION:
Props: East Ayrshire Leisure
Cap: 300
Lesser Hall: 120
Manager: Janice Gilmore
On the ground floor there is a very large hall with stage and integral bar with adjoining kitchen offering the full range of catering facilities. Having a full PA system with Loop, this is a popular venue for Weddings, Dances, Concerts and Conferences. It also offers a tabled meeting room on the ground floor and a lesser hall on the first floor which also has kitchen facilities. Easily accessible from all surrounding areas, this facility is one of the best in the area.

Cwmbran, Torfaen

Pop. 48,000. London 147 miles.
Newspapers: S.W. Argus and S.W. Echo (ntly); Western Mail (dly); News and Free Press (wkly). STD code 01633

CONGRESS THEATRE
50 Gwent Square, Cwmbran, Torfaen NP44 1PL Wales
Admin/BO: 01633 868 239
Email: info@congresstheatre.net
Web Site: www.congresstheatrecwmbran.co.uk
ADMINISTRATION:
Props: Congress Theatre Board
Registered charity No. 1019104
Manager: Martin Redwood
Policy: Touring, Community Theatre, Children's Shows, One-Night Stands, Jazz and Classical Concerts, Conferences and Meetings, Amateur Productions, Seminars
Perfs: As required
Lounge Bar.
Seats: 312
TECHNICAL:
Stage: Fixed timber stage, flat; Opening 12.20m, Ht. to Lighting Battens 5.18m; Depth of Stage 7.52m; No Flying Facilities; Prompt Cnr. O.P.; small storage area, get-in 4.57m above pavement.
Lighting:: 6 Patt.15-28 Harmony, 6 Patt Harmony 'F', 3 Batten, 12 x Patt 264, 2 x Cantata Profiles, 6 x Cantata Fresnels, 6 x Thomas Profiles, 6 x Thomas Fresnels, 6 x Par Cans, 2 x ACT 6.
Switchboard: Strand SP60, 3 Preset plus M24 48 Channel.
Sound: 8 mics. Mixer Studiomaster 16-2 Stereo. 3 x 300 watt Marshall Amps. Revox B77.150w RCF Speakers and Monitors, 1 x Technics Graphic, 2 x Technics Cassette, 1 x Technics C.D., 1 x Alesis Midi Verb III, 4 Foldback Monitors.
Dressing Rooms: 4; Accom. 21; 2 showers; green room.

Dagenham, Essex

BECONTREE HEATH LEISURE CENTRE
Althorne Way Dagenham RM10 7FH
Tel: 020 8227 3338
Email: 3000direct@lbbd.gov.uk
Web Site: www.lbbd.gov.uk

Props: Barking and Dagenham Council
Centre Manager: Marcus Downham
Bookings: Fiona Heneghan

Dalbeattie, Kirkcudbrightshire

DALBEATTIE TOWN HALL

High Street, Dalbeattie, Kirkcudbrightshire DG5 4AD Scotland
Tel/Fax: 01556 503 806
Web Site: www.dumgal.gov.uk
Contact: Louise Wilson
Seating capacity: 250

Darlington, County Durham

Pop. 100,000. London 242 miles. Newspapers: The Northern Echo (dly); The Evening Gazette; Darlington & Stockton Times (sat). STD code 01325

DARLINGTON CIVIC THEATRE

Parkgate, Darlington, County Durham DL1 1RR
Mgt: 01325 387775 BO: 01325 486 555
Fax: 01325 368 278
Email: artscentre.info@darlington.gov.uk
Web Site: www.darlingtonarts.co.uk
-ADMINISTRATION:
Props: Borough of Darlington
Theatre Director: Linda Winstanley
Financial & Admin Manager: Hazel Watson
Marketing Manager: Sue Wilson
Technical Manager: Adam Nix
Policy: Major touring of plays, ballet, opera, musicals. Variety and major pantomime season. Conference facilities.
Perfs: variable
Seats: 893, 3 Licensed bars and 2 coffee bars. 6 wheelchair spaces at rear of Stalls. Disabled persons toilet. Infra red hearing system and loop.
TECHNICAL:
Stage: Pros. Stage Raked. Pros width 8.68m. Ht. to house border 5.5m. Ht. to grid 13.3m. Depth of Stage 8.8m. 30 sets of lines in hemphouse. Flying bars 11m. Flys working side S/R. W/widths S/L. 3.05m. S/R 2.44m. Prompt Cnr. S/R.
Lighting: Switchboard: 430 (150 channels) rear of stalls. Stage 14 x 5kw. 72 x 2.5kw. F.O.H. (via patch panel). 34 x 2.5kw 300 amp TPN supply on stage; F.O.H. lanterns; 16 x 1kw. sil 15; stage lanterns: 30 x starlette 1kw Fresnel, 6 x sil 30, 11 x Patt.264, 20 Parcans. 12 x Iris 1. Four electric bars on motorised winches.
Sound Equip: located at rear of Stalls. 2 Revox tape machines; Hill 18 x 8 x 2 mixer. 6 x float mics. Speakers: 4 x Bose 802 + delays. Full head set system around theatre.
Dressing Rooms: 11; showers 3; Orchestra Pit. Fire Curtain. Wardrobe; 8 music stands, plus conductor stand.
Membership: TMA

THE DOLPHIN CENTRE

Horse Market Darlington County Durham DL1 5RP
Tel: 01325 388 410
Email: paul.soderman@darlington.gov.uk
Web Site: www.darlington.gov.uk
ADMINISTRATION:
Props: Darlington Borough Council
Centre Manager: Mike Crawshaw
Contact: Paul Soderman , Susan Minto
Seating/Capacity: Main Sports Hall: 1,250 seated; Central Hall: 500 seated (theatre style seating).

Dartford, Kent

Pop. 76,000. London 17 miles. Newspapers: Kentish Times Group (thurs); Kent Messenger Group (fri); Kent Today (dly); News Shopper (wed); Mercury Group (thurs). STD code 01322

THE ORCHARD THEATRE

Home Gardens, Dartford, Kent DA1 1ED
Mgt: 01322 220 099 BO: 01322 220 000
Fax: 01322 227 122
Email: info@orchardtheatre.co.uk
Web Site: www.orchardtheatre.co.uk
ADMINISTRATION:
Props: HQ Theatres Ltd
Theatre Director: Chris Glover
Ticket Office Manager: Jan Rogers
Customer Services Manager: Zelda Kitto
Contact: zkitto@orchardtheatre.co.uk
Buildings and Technical Manager:: Will West
Contact: wwest@orchardtheatre.co.uk
Policy: Touring plays and musicals, Opera, Ballet, Concerts (rock, popular and classical), Children's entertainment, Variety, Conferences and Banquets.
Perfs: Three seasons - Autumn (September to December), Winter/Spring (January to April) and Summer (May to August).
Seats: 956. Two licenced bars; pre-show catering (Mon-Sat).
TECHNICAL:
STAGE: Proscenium, flat, grey lino covered. Pros. Opening 13.8m; Pros. ht 6.00m; stage depth 10.60m; stage width (inc. wings) 21.33m; forestage/orchestra lift 3.30m extra; ht. of grid 15.10m; ht. of fly floors 8.00m; width between fly floors 16.00m; 44 single purchase C/W sets x 200mm centres; length of bars 15.25m, max bar weight 453kg; Prompt Cnr. PS; Scene store 3.45m on OP - get-in direct on stage OP at tailboard height.
Orchestra Pit: 25, 65 extended. 1 conductor's and 20 music stands.
LIGHTING: Strand 550 (v2.6b); Strand STM dimmers (D54) 107 x 2.5kw, 13 x 5kw; 36.1.2w Cantata fresnel, 26 x 750w Source 4 zoom 15/40 profile, 54 x Par 64 (60, 61 & 62), 8 x Par 64 floorcan, 4 x Iris 4 floods, 8 x 500w Coda one flood, 6 x 1kw Coda flood.
SOUND: Soundcraft 24 (8 subs/8 aux), 5 x Crown MA-3600VZ, 3 x QSC EX 1250, 6 x Nexo PS15, 2 x Nexo LS1200 sub-bass (main PA), 3 x Nexo PS8 (delay cluster), 2 x Nexo PS15, 2 x Nexo LS1200 sub-bass (portable), 4 x Martin F12 monitor, 4 x Yamaha MS101 power monitor, 3 x Sabine graphic equaliser, 1 x Alesis Microverb, 1 x Marantz SD4050 twin cassette deck, 1 x marantz SD4000 CD, 1 x Sony MJE-440 minidisk, 1 x Sony MDS JE730 minidisk, 4 x Trantec S4000L lapel radio mic, 2 x Trabtec S4000L handheld radio mic, 8 x SM58, 5 x AKG 451 EB (CK1/CK8), 3 x AKG D224 E, 3 x AKGD330 BT, 6 x Crown PCC 160, 2 x 12-way stage box.
STAGE MANAGEMENT: SM desk (prompt side); 12 way cue light system, paging to dressing rooms, bar bells, technical ring intercom linked to Motorola base station.
DRESSING ROOMS: 14; accommodates 65. 6 showers and toilets (3 male, 3 female). Wardrobe at stage level with washing machine, tumble dryer, and ironing facilities.
ADDITIONAL: Piano; 9' Blüthner Concert Grand; Welmar Upright.
Membership: TMA/IEAMM/ ABTT

THE MICK JAGGER CENTRE

Shepherds Lane Dartford Kent DA1 2JZ
Tel: 01322 291100
Email: mail@themickjaggercentre.com
Web Site: www.themickjaggercentre.com
ADMINISTRATION:
Contact: Manager Nicola Bowden
Capacity: 600 standing, 350 seating with optional pit

Dartington, Devon

SPACE AT DARTINGTON

Dartington Hall, Totnes, Devon TQ9 6EN
Admin: 01803 847074 BO: 01803 847070
Email: arts@dartington.org
Web Site: www.dartington.org/arts
ADMINISTRATION:
Senior Technical Manager: Jim Macaulay
Executive Producer: Kate Farmery
The Great Hall: Cap: 320 - Seated Concerts and recitals. No blackout.
The Barn Theatre: Cap: 160 - Used for cinema and touring theatre and small scale opera and jazz. Large stage.
Range of studio spaces available: Cap: 4 -120

Dartmouth, Devon

THE FLAVEL

Flavel Place Dartmouth Devon TQ6 9ND

Tel: 01803 839530
Email: boxoffice@theflavel.org.uk
Web Site: www.theflavel.org.uk
General Manager: Sid Davis
Artistic Director: Sarah Hackford
Programme & Marketing Manager: Lisa Chandler
Capacity: Main Hall: 220 seated, 265 standing
Studio: 40

Darvel, Ayrshire

DARVEL TOWN HALL

10/12 West Main Street, Darvel, Ayrshire KA17 0AQ Scotland
Tel: 01560 322 437 Admin Tel: 01563 554 026 Fax: 01563 554 030
Email: darveltownhall@east-ayrshire.gov.uk
Web Site: www.east-ayrshire.gov.uk
ADMINISTRATION:
Props: East Ayrshire Leisure Trust
Cap: 360
There is a very large hall with stage, dressing rooms and small kitchen on the ground floor as well as a small hall and adjacent kitchen located on the first floor. This offers a wide variety of facilities that can accommodate wedding receptions, Dances, Concerts, Parties and Conferences.
Contact Caretaker: David Boyd

Darwen, Lancashire

DARWEN LIBRARY THEATRE

Knott Street, Darwen, Lancashire BB3 3BU
Admin: 01254 774 684 BO: 01254 706 006
Email: dlt@blackburn.gov.uk
Web Site: www.darwenlibrarytheatre.com
Prop: Blackburn With Darwen Borough Council
General Manager: Steve Burch
Capacity: 214
Sound Equipment: 1 x Allan and Heath 24 channel sound desk,
1 x Studiomaster Club Series 12 channel mixing desk, 1 x Denon CD/Cassette Combi Deck, 1 x Denon Mini Disc Player, 1 x Sony MDS Mini Disc Player/Recorder, 1 x S100 DigiTech Studio Effects Unit, 2 x EQ-9231 Graphic Equaliser's, 2 x Studiomaster 700D amplifiers, (Use with Monitor speakers).
2 x Behringer FOH amplifiers, 4 x OHM RW3 speakers, FOH sound, 2 x OHM RW Sub Bass speakers, 2 x Shermmam MX200 Monitor Wedges, 2 x Audio-technica MB 1000L, 2 x Audio-technica MB 2000L, 3 x Audio-technica Pro 45 Choir Mics,
2 x Audio-technica AT815b Shotgun Mics, 3 x Behringer XM 2000 cardiod microphones, 1 x Set Drum microphones (Comprising 1 x Kick Drum mics, 4 x Clip on Tom mics, 2 x Condenser mics),
2 x Hand held radio mics and receivers, 12 x mic stands, 2 x speaker stands, 1 x 16 way multi core, 3 x Passive DI Boxes, Additional FX Rack (Available on Request), Incl : Drawmer Gates, Compressors, Reverb Unit
Lighting Desk: 1 x Strand GSX Lighting Desk. Dimmers Packs: 3 x Strand LD90 dimmer packs (75 ways of dimming).
Lantern Stock: 8 x Strand Cantata Fresnels 1200w + barn doors, 6 x Strand Cantata PC 1200w + barn doors, 2 x Iris (Source 4),
8 x Gobo Holders (Source 4 M Size), ETC Source 4 profiles - 4 x 50 degrees, 5 x 36 degrees, 2 x 26 degrees, Par Cans: 24 x Par 64's. Refurbished stock: 16 x single floodlights, 12 x Patten 23 profiles, 5 x Strand Patten 123 Fresnels 1x 4-colour flood batten,
3 x 8 colour flood batten (3 circuit, 8 Compartments), 4 x Furs SPK 500 watt Fresnel's. A/V Equipment: 1 x Desktop Projector,
1 x DVD Player, 1 x Projector Screen (5x6).

Daventry, Northamptonshire

DAVENTRY LEISURE CENTRE

Lodge Road, Daventry, Northamptonshire NN11 4FP
Tel: 01327 871 144
Email: jamiebrightwell@everyoneactive.com
Web Site: www.everyoneactive.com
ADMINISTRATION
Props: Daventry District Council
Cap: Saxon Suite: 320
Manager: Jamie Brightwell

Dawlish, Devon

DAWLISH LEISURE CENTRE

Sandy Lane, Dawlish, Devon EX7 0AF
Tel: 01626 215 620
Email: dawlishlc@teignbridge.gov.uk
Web Site: www.teignbridge.gov.uk
ADMINISTRATION:
Props: Teignbridge District Council
Cap: 450-500 Seated

Derby, Derbyshire

Pop. 219,910. London 125 miles.
Newspapers: Derby Evening Telegraph (ntly). STD code 01332

ASSEMBLY ROOMS

Market Place, Derby DE1 3AH
BO: 01332 255 800 Mgt: 01332 255443
Programming: 01332 287361 Mktg: 01332 287360 Operations: 01332 255 433 Technical: 01332 255421 Fax: 01332 255 788
Email: derbylive@derby.gov.uk
Web Site: www.derbylive.co.uk
ADMINISTRATION:
Props: Derby City Council
Policy: Multi Form Auditorium that can meet a variety of staging configurations, Stage Shows, Orchestral Concerts, Rock & Pop, One-Night Stands, Exhibitions, Conferences, Dinners etc.
Capacity: Concerts up to 1720, Theatre up to 1200, Standing up to 2000.
Director: Peter Ireson.
Creative Producer. Pete Meakin
Programme Manager: Bob Rushton
Production & Technical Manager: Gareth Chell.

TECHNICAL:
THE GREAT HALL;- rectangular, with a balcony all round. Proscenium arch can be created using soft legs for theatre format shows.
STAGE: Wood effect linoleum on concrete floor or black wooden floor (laid on top of the wood effect to enable screwing down of set); Can be up to 15.45m wide (depending on masking requirements). Depth 6.85m; Ht. 7.30m; 12 lines motorised; Demountable Stage 2m wide each side; No wings, but space under side balconies. Orchestra lift can be moved to 4 levels: Get-in, Orchestra Pit, Auditorium - floor level, Stage level.
LIGHTING: ETC EOS lighting desk; Zero 88 Chili-Pro dimmers (144 dims, plus 24 houes light dims - all DMX512) wide variety of lanterns including parcans, one and two KW profile spots, floods and stands etc. 2 x Xenon followspots, A variety of intelligent and LED lights are also available.
SOUND EQUIP: Yamaha M7CL or Allen and Heath GL4000 are available. Meyer M1D speaker system configured as LCR + fills. Monitors - Martin LE400C / H3 system outboard racks inc BSS EQ; Yamaha, Tc, Lexicon FX; Drawmer dynamics. Assorted Mic / DI stock.
DRESSING ROOMS: 4; Band room; Production office; Showers in all dressing rooms.
ADDITIONAL: Canford Tech Pro ring intercom. Piano; Steinway 'D' type concert grand; Bechstein 10' grand; Steinway model B grand. Power Supplies: 3 phase 300 amp, 3 phase 100 qamp, single phase 60 amp.

THE DARWIN SUITE;- seating 300-500 available for conferences, recitals, rock shows, etc. Flat Floor. Small installed vocal PA - additional by arrangement; Fixed grid lighting rig with mix of fresnels, profiles and pars 1kW Followspot

THE '45 SUITE & RECEPTION SUITE;- seating 150 & 70 respectively, available

for wedding parties, meetings, etc. Full facilities.

DERBY THEATRE

15 Theatre Walk St Peters Quarter Derby DE1 2NF
SD: 01332 593900 BO: 01332 593939
Mktg: 01332 593955 Technical: 01332 593985
Email: tickets@derbytheatre.co.uk
Web Site: www.derbytheatre.co.uk
ADMINISTRATION:
Props: University of Derby Theatre Ltd
Theatre Manager: Gary Johnson Tel: 01332 593911
Production Manager: Jay BridgesTel: 01332 593945
Marketing & Audience Development Manager: Sarah Cockburn Tel: 01332 593921
Artistic Director: Sarah Brigham
Formerly Derby Playhouse, the venue was re-opened in October 2009 by the University of Derby as a learning theatre (part of Derby City Council)
Policy: Produced theatre for around 22 weeks each year, plus a mixed programme of touring plays and musicals, comedy, dance, concerts, children's entertainment, conferences, community theatre and amateur productions. The University of Derby Theatre Arts productions are presented for 4 weeks of the year. Main Theatre managed in partnership with Derby LIVE. Studio presentations and small scale touring theatre presented by the University of Derby.
Seats: 535 (Main Theatre) 110 (Studio). licensed bar and Costa Coffee cafe.
TECHNICAL:
Stage (Main House): Pros opening 10.4m wide x 5.65m high - Wing widths 4.92m SR, 14.68m SL. Performing area 10m x 10m - flat floor, wooden, suitable for all dance. Height of grid 15.25m - 28 counterweight sets, 0.2m apart - max flying height 14.7m. Curved forestage/orchestra pit on elevator 10m x 2.7m max. Accommodates 17. Get in via back of building, 1 floor up in lift, 5.1m high, 1.8m wide, 2.7m deep.
Lighting: ETC Eos and ion back up. DMX and Ethernet network. 180 2.5k Dimmer circuits with 15A outlet, 12 5K dimmer circuit with 32Sa CEEform outlets, 32 2.5K Non-Dim circuits with 15A outlets. 250Amp power lock touring power in SL wing. 100 Profile lanterns, 64 Fresnels, 60 parcans and beamlights, cyc floods, scrollers and colour wheels. 6 Clay Paky Alpha Wash Halo wash lights.
Sound: Yamaha M7CL 48 channel sound desk, d&b Audiotechnik Q7, Qsub, E12 D, Max12 and E3 speakers, CD and minidisc players, Sennheiser ew300 G3 radio mics, Shure sm57/58 microphones.
Accessories: Smoke and dry ice machines, UV, mirror balls and strobe.

GUILDHALL THEATRE

Market Place, Derby DE1 3AE
Mgt: 01332 255443 Programming: 01332 287361 Mktg: 01332 287360 Operations: 01332 255433 Technical: 01332 255421 BO: 01332 255800 Fax: 01332 255788
Email: derbylive@derby.gov.uk
Web Site: www.derbylive.co.uk
ADMINISTRATION:
Props: Derby City Council
Director: Peter Ireson
Creative Producer. Pete Meakin
Programme Manager: Bob Rushton
Production Manager: Gareth Chell
Audience Engagement Manager: Ed Green
Policy:
The Guildhall Theatre is situated in the centre of Derby and currently stages an expanding programme of alternative comedy, recitals, concerts, an Arts Festival, musicals and small/mid scale theatre companies - this being an area the venue would like to build on.
TECHNICAL:
Stage: proscenium, has an opening of 25', a depth of 18' (22' with forestage), and a grid height of 15'. The raked auditorium seats 179 plus three wheelchair spaces, with 60 in the balcony - total capacity 242. It has a licensed bar and coffee bar.
Lighting: ETC ION lighting desk, controlling a variety of lanterns.
Sound: GL2200 Desk, FOH consists of a HK powered rig augmented with a pair of Meyer UPM speakers for Balcony fill. Limited/shared mic. stock. CD/MD playback and assorted EQ/Effects.
Piano: An upright piano is kept in the bar area and is available for the stage.

Derry, Londonderry

Local Newspapers: Derry Journal (Tues & Fri); Londonderry Sentinel (Wednesday); Belfast Telegraph (daily) STD Code: 028 71

THE MILLENNIUM FORUM

Newmarket Street, Londonderry BT48 6EB Northern Ireland
Admin Tel: 028 7126 4426 Fax: 028 7127 2799 BO Tel: 028 7126 4455
Email: info@milleniumforum.co.uk
Web Site: www.milleniumforum.co.uk
ADMINISTRATION
Props: Derry Theatre Trust
Chief Executive: David McLaughlin
Technical Manager: Lorcan McLaughlin 02871 272 781
Policy: Mixed programme - own productions, touring plays and musicals, ballet, dance, concerts (rock, popular & classical), children's entertainment, one night stands, community theatre and amateur productions.
TECHNICAL:
MAIN THEATRE - THE MILLENNIUM COMPLEX
Adaptable scale theatre from 367 (including 4 wheelchairs) with an 8.55 metre proscenium and small theatre acoustic or 716 seats including 6 wheelchairs with 11.00m pros. and medium scale theatre acoustic. The largest form is 1,020 seats including 10 wheelchair positions, a 11.00m pros. with large scale theatre acoustic. The theatre also has concert hall acoustic form and film projection facilities with Dolby and surround sound.
Pros. width: 11.00m reducing to 8.55m for smaller seating arrangements. Pros. height: 7.00m (max). Setting line to back wall 11.85m (rear crossover behind stage).
Wing widths: SR: 7.8m downstage tapering to 6.0m upstage. SL: 6.9m downstage tapering to 5.4m upstage. Flying height: 16.5m travel on bars 12m long with 1m extensions provided each end.
Flying: 38 counterweight sets (double purchase) with 500kg flying load plus up/downstage sets either side of stage. 12 hemp sets.
Lighting: 208 ways computer control desk. 194 x 2.5kW and 24 x 5kW dimmers. New luminaires in theatre rig - 134. Temporary dimmer supply - Z-wing:200A 3ph downstage right.
Sound: Mixer - Soundcraft live 8 26 mono + 2 stereo channels, 8 group, 6 aux.
Sound sources: cassette, DAT, mini-disc, CD, 4 radion mics. Loudspeakers - Tannoy@: 5 No. T300, 2 No. B475, 2 No T12. Temporary sound supply - 63A 3ph.downstage left.
Orchestra pit formed by two lifts. Maximum capacity 50.
Dressing Rooms: 2 quick change at stage level. First floor 1 for 3 persons, second floor 2 for 2 persons, 4 for 4, 1 for 9, 2 for 12, third floor 2 for 3 (beside studio). All dressing rooms have en-suite toilets and showers.
STUDIO THEATRE:
Studio theatre/rehearsal room 12 x 12m. Fitted with lighting grid. Flexible form seating up to 100. Stage lighting: 24 way memory control desk, 24 x 2.5 kW dimmers, 28 luminaires in rig. Sound Spirit Folio SX mixer with cassette, DAT & CD sound sources.
FOYER PLATFORM PERFORMANCE AREA:
Stage lighting 24 memory control with 24 x 2.5kW dimmers and 24 luminaires in rig. Sound uses studio portable desk when required.

Dewsbury, West Yorkshire

DEWSBURY TOWN HALL

Old Wakefield Road, Dewsbury, West Yorkshire WF12 8DQ
Tel: 01924 324 501

Email: dewsbury.boxoffice@kirklees.gov.uk
Web Site: www.kirklees.gov.uk/townhalls
ADMINISTRATION:
Assistant Venue Manager: Richard Batterby
For bookings Tel: 01484 221 947/221 913 or fax 01484 221 541
Seating: 685(stage facilities)

Didcot, Oxfordshire

DIDCOT LEISURE CENTRE

Mereland Road, Didcot, Oxfordshire OX11 8AY
Tel: 01235 811 250 Fax: 01235 816 356
Email: wendy.hill@gll.org
Web Site: www.better.org
ADMINISTRATION:
Props: South Oxfordshire District Council
Cap of Main Hall: 400
Manager: Wendy Hill

Dollar, Clackmannanshire

DOLLAR CIVIC CENTRE

Park Place, Dollar, Clackmannanshire FK14 7AA
Tel: 01259 743253 Bkgs Tel : 01259 213131 Fax: 01259 743328
Email: fmclaren@clacks.gov.uk
Web Site: www.clacksweb.co.uk
ADMINISTRATION:
Props: Clackmannanshire Council
3 meeting rooms, opened to one large area with seating capacities of 100 for theatre, dances, concerts.
For bookings Tel: 01259 213131 Fax: 01259 721313
Contact Frances Mclaren

Doncaster, South Yorkshire

BIRCOTES LEISURE CENTRE

off Whitehouse Road, Bircotes, Nr Doncaster DN11 8EF
Tel: 01302 743 979
Email: nicola.north@bpl.org.uk
Web Site: www.barnsleypremierleisure.org.uk
ADMINISTRATION:
Props: Barnsley Premier Leisure
Cap: 300
Area Manager: Glyn Davies

THE DOME

Doncaster Lakeside Bawtry Road, Doncaster, South Yorkshire DN4 7PD
Admin: 01302 379 156 BO: 01302 537704
Email: steven.parker@dclt.co.uk
Web Site: www.the-dome.co.uk
Entertainment & Events Manager: Steve Parker
Marketing Manager: Carl Lewis
Capacity: 1,856 Seated
3,658 standing

DONCASTER CIVIC THEATRE

Waterdale, Doncaster, South Yorkshire DN1 3ET
BO: 01302 342 349 Admin: 01302 735 600 Fax: 01302 367 223
Email: kevin.johnson@doncaster.gov.uk
Web Site: www.doncastercivic.co.uk
ADMINISTRATION:
Theatre available for Hire.
Props: Doncaster Metropolitan Borough Council
Perfs: Presentation of Local Voluntary Arts, Professional Entertainment, Artistic Performances, Presentations, Workshops and Meetings.
Manager: Kevin Johnson
Technical Manager: Lee Walker
Contact: lee.walker@doncaster.gov.uk
Capacity: 495 Proscenium

Dorking, Surrey

DORKING HALLS

Reigate Road, Dorking, Surrey RH4 1SG
Mgt: 01306 879 200 BO: 01306 881 717
Fax: 01306 877 277
Email: dorking.halls@mole-valley.gov.uk
Web Site: www.dorkinghalls.co.uk
ADMINISTRATION:
Props: Mole Valley District Council
General Manager: Keith Garrow
Technical Manager: Michael Knight
FOH Co-Ordinator: Nicola Jenks
Policy: Extensively refurbished in 1997; includes three Halls, function rooms, Coffee Shop and Bars. Wide range of one night stands, split and full weeks, conferences, fairs and private functions. Flexible deals from guarantees to hires. Also full time cinema.
Seating:
Grand Hall: 791 (302 stalls, 281 bleacher, 208 balcony), 1,118 standing, 247 sq. metres exhibition space.
Martineau Hall: 176 (raked)
Masonic Hall: 66 (raked)
TECHNICAL:
Stage: Proscenium, raked 1 in 44. Pros opening 15.5m, tormentors to 12m or 8.2m. Height to grid 7.4m. Depth from apron 11m. No fly gallery. SM desk SL. Orchestra Pit: 13.4m x 1.9m. Maximum 14 musicians.
Lighting: House desk ETC, Express 250 with V3 software.
Over 100 lanterns, Patt 765, 1k CSI follow spot and Teatro 1.2k MSR follow spot.
On stage power: Situated DSR 1 x 63 amp 3 phase, 1 x 63 amp single and 3 x 32 amp single. Back line power: six 2 x 13 amp. Orchestra pit: two 6 x 13 amp and 200 amp 3 phase.
Sound: Allen and Heath GL 3300, 32-8-2 plus matrix. FOH speakers: 2 x EAW FL 103 on L & R of pros and 2 x EAW, JF 80 on delay for balc. 5 x Sennheiser MD 735, 2 x SM 58, 2 x Sennheiser K6, AKG SE 300 and AKG 190. 2 x dual DI box, Dennon CD player, double tape player, Alesis midi verb, 27 way multicore.
Dressing Rooms: Five rooms (2 x principal, 3 x chorus), Male and female WCs with 2 showers each. Payphone available. Wheelchair access to Main Hall.
Piano: Kawai 6' 4".
Parking: Ample dedicated parking for trucks, etc, with direct access to stage.

Douglas, Isle of Man

Pop. 72,000. Newspapers: Isle of Man Examiner (tue); Isle of Man Independent (fri); Isle of Man Courier (thurs). STD code 01624

GAIETY THEATRE

Harris Promenade, Douglas, Isle of Man IM1 2HN
Tel: 01624 686703
Email: dawn.maddrell@gov.im
Web Site: www.villagaiety.com
ADMINISTRATION:
General Manger: Dawn Maddrell
Technical Manager: Seamus Shea
Front of House Manager: Neill Cowin, John Foster
Policy: Musicals, straight plays, opera, ballet, concerts - pop, jazz and classical. Performance schedule Open 7 days - no performances Christmas Day - evening shows start at 8.00p.m., matinees on various days at 2.30p.m.
Booking terms hire, box office split, guarantee & split, guarantee, by negotiation.
Facilities: Seating 898; raked. Catering: 2 licensed bars, 2 private entertaining suites. Facilities for the disabled 12 wheelchair spaces - deaf loop system - assistance available, contact Box Office - level access - toilets at lower stalls level accessible by electric chair lift.
TECHNICAL:
Stage: Proscenium arch. Performing area 8.68m x 12.2m - pros opening 8.68m x 9.4m - wing widths 2.3m SR, 3.96m SL, 6.1m US. Stage raked, 1 in 36 - floor sprung wood covered in lino, suitable for all dance, backstage crossover, stag heated. Height of grid 14.63m - 29 Counterweight, 0.6m apart - tab tracks - 250kg permitted on bars - maximum flying height 13.71m - full set black masking - white linen weave cyclorama - green house tabs, tableau Victorian Act Drop Curtain. Orchestra pit 10.21m x 2.21, accommodates 15. Get-in via dock doors, 2.14m x 3.05m. Safety curtain.

Scale stage and fly plans available.
Lighting: Strand 520 desk. 120 Circuits. Operated from rear dress circle. 100 amp 3 phase supply available on stage. 29 profiles. 45 Fresnels. 10 Parcans. 2 Follow Spots 2kw.
Sound: Soundcraft K2 32ch. Peavey Miniframe 208 Media Matrix control system, Denon mini disc, Denon CD player SPX990, 4 X EV system 200 stage monitors, rev 7 reverb. Various Crown & Sure mics with boom stands. Full Range P.A. System. Cassette decks + Revox reel to reel tape recorders. Operated from rear of upper circle. Basic recording and editing facilities. Acoustics suitable for music and spoken word.
Backstage: 8 dressing rooms, modern shower rooms access by rear of stage. No wardrobe, but washer, tumble dryer, spin dryer available, ample power points. Pianos: Stage, new Rehearsal Piano and 6'8" Danemann Grand (Concert work only) Orchestra Pit: New Matched Pair of Good Upright Pianos. Advice given on accommodation. Staff - 4 stage - casuals available - no security personnel. Backstage facilities not accessible to disabled performers and staff.
Stage management Prompt corner SL - cueing via headsets x 6 - show relay to dressing rooms.

VILLA MARINA ROYAL HALL

Harris Promenade, The Colonnade, Douglas, Isle of Man IM1 2HP
BO: 01624 600555 Private Hire Tel: 01624 694 566
Email: dawn.maddrell@gov.im
Web Site: www.villagaiety.com
ADMINISTRATION:
Props: Isle of Man Government
General Manager: Dawn Maddrell
Technical Manager: Seamus Shea
Box Office Manager: Philip Greene
Cap: 1626 Standing, 1360 Seated

Dover, Kent

DOVER TOWN HALL

Biggin Street, Dover, Kent CT16 1DL
Tel/Fax: 01304 201200
Email: dover@yourleisure.uk.com
Web Site: www.dovertownhall.co.uk
ADMINISTRATION
Props: Your Leisure Kent Ltd.
Cap: 600
Manager: Val Leadbetter

Downham Market, Norfolk

TOWN HALL

Bridge Street Downham Market, Norfolk PE38 9JS
Tel: 01366 382 329 Bkg: 01366 387 770
Email: info@downhammarkettc.co.uk
Web Site: www.downhammarkettown-council.org.uk
ADMINISTRATION:
Props: Downham Market Town Council
Cap: 260
Booking Contact: Nikki Hannan Tel: 01366 387770
Address: Downham Market Town Council, 15 Paradise Road, Downham Market, Norfolk PE38 9HS

Downpatrick, County Down

THE BRIDGE CENTRE

27 Braeside Gardens, Killyleagh, Downpatrick, County Down BT30 9QE Northern Ireland
Tel: 028 4482 8648 Fax: 028 4482 8615
Email: bridgecentre@downdc.gov.uk
Web Site: www.downdc.gov.uk
Props: Down District Council
Manager: Roy Kelly
Cap: 400

DOWN LEISURE CENTRE

114 Market Street, Downpatrick, County Down BT30 6LZ
Tel: 028 4461 3426 Fax: 028 4461 6905
Email: joseph.degan@downdc.gov.uk
Web Site: www.downdc.gov.uk
General Manager: Joseph Degan
Props: Down District Council
S/Cap: 600. Stage and audio-visual facilities. Meeting rooms, Conference facilities.

Dublin, Eire

Pop. 1,024,000. Newspapers: Evening Herald (ntly); Evening Press (ntly); Irish Independent (dly); The Irish Times (dly); The Irish Press (dly); Sunday Independent, Sunday Press, Sunday Tribune, Sunday World. STD code 00 353 1

3 ARENA

Northwall Quay, Dublin 1 Eire
Mgt: 00 353 1 819 8888 Fax: 00 353 1 866 3401 Ireland BO: 0818 719 3000 International BO: 00 353 1485 0810 NI/UK BO: 0870 2434 455 Ireland Group Bkgs: 08187 19 371
Email: enquiries@3arena.ie
Web Site: www.3arena.ie
ADMINISTRATION:
Props: Live Nation
Director and Chief Executive: Mike Adamson
Finance Director: Eimear McMahon
Theatre Manager: Cormac Rennick
Assistant Manager: John Johnson or Roslyn Long
Secretary: Cathriona Smith
Cap: 13,000
For all booking information and further details, please contact: Cormac Rennick on Tel: 003531 866 3412 or email: cormac.rennick@3arena.ie
TECHNICAL:
Please contact venue for further details.

BORD GAIS ENERGY THEATRE

Grand Canal Square, Docklands, Dublin Dublin 2 Ireland
Tel: 00353 1677 7999
Email: justask@bgetheatre.ie
Web Site: www.bgetheatre.ie
ADMINISTRATION:
General Manager: Stephen Faloon
Press and Marketing Manager: Claire Whelan
Technical Manager: Liam Fitzgerald
Policy: National and International Theatre, Musicals, Drama, Opera, Ballet, Family Shows & Classical Concerts
Capacity: 2,111 seated

DUBLIN GATE THEATRE

1 Cavendish Row, Dublin 1 Ireland
Mgt: 00 353 1 874 4368 BO: 00 353 1 874 4045 Admin: 00 353 1 874 4085
Fax: 00 353 1 874 5373
Email: info@gate-theatre.ie
Web Site: www.gate-theatre.ie
ADMINISTRATION:
Props: Edwards-MacLiammóir, Dublin Gate Theatre Productions
Director: Michael Colgan
Theatre Manager: David Quinlan
Production Manager: Jim McConnell
Policy: Arts Theatre
Perfs: 7.30 pm
Seats: 371. Cafe serving coffee, minerals and confectionary; licensed bar.
TECHNICAL:
Stage: Please contact venue for specific details.
Lighting: Control: Strand GSX Genius version 1.2, 72 x 2kw dimmers, 8 cantata 18/32, 6 x P264, 1 x T84, 4 x T64, 1 x P243, 12 x Prelude 16/30, 8 x Minuette V.B Profile, 4 x P23, 18 x P223, 5 x P123, 16 x Minuette Fresnel, 4 x Berkey 6" Fresnel, 4 x Coda 4 Floods, 25 x Par 64, 9 X Source 36 degrees..
Sound: Sound room at rear of auditorium studiomaster 12:4:2 desk. 3 stereo amps s/master and bose. 1 monitor amp. FOH: 2 EV Motor Vator 2R speakers. 2 bose speakers at rear of auditorium. Stage: 6 speaker lines. TOA speakers. 1 Tascam tape deck. 1 JVC twin tape deck. 1 Sony CD player. 1 Yamaha SPX 90 II 1 mixer 31 band graphic equaliser. 4 AKG rifle mics. 2 Denon Mini Disc players. Full speaker and amp patch facility. Acoustics suitable for spoken word. Tannoy to green room and dressing rooms. Talk back between auditorium, stage and control room.
Dressing Rooms 4. Full Wardrobe facility.

GAIETY THEATRE

South King Street Dublin 2 Eire

SD: 00 353 1 679 5622 BO: 00 353 1 456 9569
Email: alan@gaietytheatre.com
Web Site: www.gaietytheatre.ie
ADMINISTRATION:
Managing Director: Caroline Downey
PA to MD: Aoife
Marketing Manager: Justin Green
Theatre Manager: Alan McQuillan
Deputy Manager: Carol Partridge
Box Office Manager: Liz Gannon
Accounts: Teresa Flannery
Stage Manager: Pawel Nieworaj
Technical Manager: Dan Egan
Policy: Touring Companies, Musicals, Drama, Opera, Pantomime, Revue.
Perfs: Nightly 7.30pm, Matinee Sat 2.30pm (may vary).
Seats: 1,166; 4 Fully Licensed Bars; Corporate Hospitality.
Technical:
Stage: Proscenium Stage - no rake; Pros. opening 8.40m; Ht. of Pros. 7.10m; Depth of s/line 9.50m; Ht of Grid 14.564; 34 counter weight; 3 hemp lines; Scenery flying Ht. 6.20m; Flying Bars 10.90m; Scene Docks P.S. 4m X 12m; Prompt Cnr. O.P.; 3 full black curtains; 10 soft black legs; 2 full borders; 10 hark black masking flats.
Lighting: Switchboard: Strand Gemini 166 Channel Control; 200 laterns of various types, beams and angles including 18 FOH, 2 boom bars each side of pros. and 2 CSI follow spots.
Backstage: Green room with bar; Dressing rooms 11, Accom. 40 (coms and show relay to all); Showers 5.
Other: Orchestra Pit 20.

KATHERINE BRENNAN HALL

Royal Irish Academy of Music 36-38 Westland Row Dublin 2 Republic of Ireland
Tel: 00 353 1 676 4412 Fax: 00 353 1 662 2798
Email: info@riam.ie
Web Site: www.riam.ie
Contact: Eoin Dwyer
Katherine Brennan Hall: 150-seater
Recital Hall: 60-seater

LIBERTY HALL

Eden Quay, Dublin 1 Eire
Tel: 00 353 872291887
Email: psterling@siptu.ie
ADMINISTRATION:
Manager: Philip Sterling
Cap: 411

NATIONAL CONCERT HALL

Earlsfort Terrace, Dublin 2 Eire
Admin: 00 353 1 417 0077 BO: 00 353 1 417 0000 Admin Fax: 00 353 1 417 0078 BO Fax: 00 353 1 475 1507
Email: info@nch.ie
Web Site: www.nch.ie
CEO: Simon Taylor
Capacity: Main auditorium 1,200 seated; John Field Room 250 seated

NATIONAL GALLERY OF IRELAND

Merrion Square (West), Dublin 2 Eire
Tel: 00 353 1 661 5133 Fax: 00 353 1 661 5372
Email: info@ngi.ie
Web Site: www.nationalgallery.ie
Capacity: Shaw Room 320 seated; Lecture Theatre 250 seated

NATIONAL STADIUM

145 South Circular Road Dublin 8 Eire
Tel: 00 353 1 453 3371 Fax: 00 353 1 454 0777
Email: iaba@eircom.net
Web Site: www.iaba.ie
Chief Executive Officer: Fergal Carruth
Capacity: 2,200 seated, max

NATIONAL THEATRE (ABBEY THEATRE)

26 Lower Abbey Street, Dublin 1 Eire
Mgt: 00 353 1 887 2200 BO / Credit Card Booking: 00 353 1 878 7222 Fax: 00 353 1 872 9177
Email: promotions@abbeytheatre.ie
Web Site: www.abbeytheatre.ie
ADMINISTRATION:
Props: National Theatre Society Ltd
Managing Director: Declan Cantwell
Artistic Director: Fiach Macconghail
Policy: Irish plays and international classics. Resident year round Repertory Company.
Perfs: 7.30 nightly except Sunday.
Seats: 435. Bar. Portrait Gallery.
TECHNICAL:
Stage: Proscenium with Thrust, Flat, but with 3 Lifts to alter levels; Pros. opening 12.19m; Ht. of Pros. 9.75m; Depth of S/Line 8.53m; Ht. of Grid 18.90m; 39 lines, C/W; Scenery Flying Ht. 8.53m; Flying Bars 14.63m; W/Widths P.S. 3.96m, O.P. 3.96m; Prompt Cnr. P.S.
Lighting: Switchboard: Rank Strand Galaxy 240 channel memory board with electronic back-up system and ancillary equipment; FOH Spots 55 Patt.264, Dips 12 PS, 17 OP; 4 Spots Bars Patts.223, 264, 243 plus CCT profile and fresnel spots.
Sound Equip: DDA Q Series Mixer 16/8/2; 2 Revox B77 HS; 1 Sony D.A.T.; 1 Sony CD; 1 ALESS15 MIDIVERB 11; 1 8 track Tascam; 1 Roland W30 Sampler/Sequencer/Keyboard; 1 Roland U110 sound module; 1 Techniks twin cassette deck; 1 C-Audio RA-1000 amp; 2 Quad 405 Amp; 8 Loudspeaker positions. Back Stage; 2 FOH PROS; 2 Back Auditorium.
Dressing Rooms 6; Accom 36; Showers in all. Orchestra pit 28.
F.O.H. Light is fixed to ceiling panels which are variable in height (motorised to suit scenery).
1.52m permanent Forestage with additional forestage (lifts) 2.74m.

NATIONAL THEATRE (PEACOCK THEATRE)

26 Lower Abbey Street, Dublin 1 Eire
Mgt: 00 353 1 887 2200 BO / Credit Card Booking: 00 353 1 878 7222 Fax: 00 353 1 872 9177
Email: promotions@abbeytheatre.ie
Web Site: www.abbeytheatre.ie
ADMINISTRATION:
Props: National Theatre Society Ltd
Artistic Director: Fiach Macconghail
Managing Director: Declan Cantwell
Policy: New Work and Experimental Theatre.
Perfs: Mon-Sat 8.00p.m.
Seats: 157. Bar
TECHNICAL:
Stage: Convertable stage to 6 different positions. Flat in proscenium; pros opening 8.43m; Ht of pros 3.73m; depth of S/line 5.79m; ht of grid 12.04m, 20 lines, c/w double purchase; scenery flying ht 457m; flying bars 8.53m; w/widths P.S. 2.74m, O.P. 4.42m; prompt Cnr. O.S.
Lighting: Switchboard: Rank Strand Gemini 160 Channel Dips - P Side 15; O.P. Side 15; Spot Bars - Patt 23, Pat 123, Patt 223, Prelude 16/30, Prelude 28/40 Quartet F.
Sound Equipment: 1 Spirit Auto 16-8-2 and Atari Ste and Steinberg prog, 2 Revox B77 H.S.; 1 Harrison 6001 Amp; 2 Quad 303 Amps; 6 Loudspeaker positions; 4 on stage; 2 FOH; 2 Back Aud; 1 Technics twin Cassette deck. 1 Alesis Quadraverb II, Intercom -4 Channel Clearcom Headset system.
Other: Dressing rooms 4, Accom 24, showers in all dressing rooms.
Permanent forestage 1:52m with entrance on at Actors Left. It is possible to convert to Theatre-in-Round (almost) in four hours approx. Permanent Forestage 1.52m with entrance on at Actors Left.

OLYMPIA THEATRE

72 Dame Street, Dublin 2 Eire
Gen Enq: 00 353 1 672 5883 BO: 00353 1 679 3323
Email: info@olympia.ie
Web Site: www.olympia.ie
ADMINISTRATION:
Props: Olympia Productions Ltd
CEO: Brian Whitehead
General Manager: Jimmy Grant
Policy: Touring Companies, Revue, Drama, Pantomime, Opera, Musicals, Ballet
Perfs: Nightly at 8.00, Matinee Sat. 3.00
Seats: 1,621 Standing, 1,241 Seated.4 Bars
TECHNICAL:
Stage: Proscenium, Raked 1 in 48; Pros. Opening 10.46m; Ht. of Pros. 7.32m; Depth of s/line 8.38m; Ht. of Grid 16.50m 15 Counter weight. 12 Hemp lines. Scenery Flying Ht. 7.32m; Flying Bars 11.73m; W/Widths P.S. 3.96m, O.P. 4.09m; Prompt Cnr. O.P.
Lighting: Switchboard: Arri Imagine 150 Channel Control. Total of 120 various

lanterns including 20 FOH, 1 Boom Bar each side of pros. arch and 2 Follow Spots CSI/CCT.
Sound Equip: Deltamax 1152 full range system with delay lines and cluster driven by Amcron Amps. TAC Scorpion 30. 12 desk FOH and Stage mix. FOH effects Rack and EV mikes.
Other: Dressing Rooms 8, Accom. 40. 3 Showers.
Orchestra Pit 20 (extendable).
Membership: Irish Theatre Management Assn.

ROTUNDA PILLAR ROOM

The Rotunda Hospital, Dublin 1 Eire
Tel: 00 353 1 872 2377
Email: friends@rotunda.ie
Web Site: www.for.ie
ADMINISTRATION:
Manager: Sheila Thompson
Seating/Capacity: 300

ROYAL DUBLIN SOCIETY CONCERT HALL

Merrion Road, Ballsbridge, Dublin 4 Eire
Tel: 00 353 1 668 0866 Fax: 00 353 1 660 4014
Email: reception@rds.ie
Web Site: www.rds.ie
ADMINISTRATION:
Props: The Royal Dublin Society
Contact: Michael Duffy
Seating/Capacity: 1,000 retractable tiered seating

SIMMONSCOURT PAVILION

Ballsbridge, Dublin 4 Eire
Tel: 00 353 1 668 0866 Fax: 00 353 1 660 4014
Email: sales@rds.ie
Web Site: www.rds.ie
ADMINISTRATION:
Contact: Olivia O'Reilly
Props: Royal Dublin Society
Seating/Capacity: Leinster Hall 6,500 Theatre Style

THE HELIX

DCU Collins Avenue, Glasnevin, Dublin 9
SD: +353 1 700 7077 BO: +353 1 700 7000
Email: info@thehelix.ie
Web Site: www.thehelix.ie
Contact: Programming: Tara Walsh Tel: 700 7112
The Mahony Hall - Capacity: 1260
The Space - Capacity: 145
The Theatre - Capacity: 450

For technical information please see website.

Dudley, West Midlands

Pop. 304,615. London 115 miles.
Newspapers: Express and Star (dly); Chronicle (fri). STD code 01384

DUDLEY CONCERT HALL

St James's Road, Dudley, West Midlands DY1 1HP
Tel: 01384 815 577 BO: 01384 812 812
BO Administrator: 01384 815 591
Email: patricia.round@dudley.gov.uk
Web Site: www.dudley.gov.uk/entertainment
ADMINISTRATION:
Props: Dudley Metropolitan Borough Council
Operations Manager: Patricia Round
Halls Technician: Martin Jones (Tel: 01384 815 539)
Box Office Administrator: Nick Holloway
Multi purpose concert hall, wide range of music, light entertainment, jazz, one night stands.
Seats: 1,008
TECHNICAL:
Sound: Soundcraft K2 24:8:2 desk; EAW & RCF Speakers, EV Foldback, Yamaha & Cloud Amplification; MD, CD, Cassette.
Lighting: Strand M x 48 board, 30 Circuits @ 10amp, 4 profiles, 16 fresnels, 10 pcs, 20 PAR64, 2 CID followspots. Additional 60amp 3 phase supply available.

NETHERTON ARTS CENTRE

Northfield Road, Netherton, Dudley, West Midlands DY2 9ER
Tel: 01384 812846
Email: nicki.bainbridge@dudley.gov.uk
Web Site: www.dudley.gov.uk/dpa
ADMINISTRATION:
Props: Dudley M.B.C.
Manager: Nicki Bainbridge
Policy: touring drama, children's theatre, educational activities, local amateur groups, available for hire.
Cap: 322 seated, stalls flat, balcony raked
TECHNICAL:
Stage: Proscenium arch. Performing area 10.97m x 6.87m - pros opening 7.01m x 3.43m - wing widths 1.97 SR, 1.97m SL. Stage very slightly raked - floor wood, suitable for dance (not barefoot), lino not available, no crossover, stage heated. Height of grid 6.7m - 7 hemp sets, 280mm apart - tab track - 35kg permitted on bars - 4 borders, 4 pairs legs, black/grey, 2 sets of tabs in black and blue - gold house tabs, drawn. 12 x 13A independent circuits. Trap, centre stage. Get-in via doors SL or through auditorium - dock doors 1.48m wide. Safety curtain. Scale stage and lighting plans available.
Lighting: Furse 2 present board, 36 circuits @ 10A, 3 phase, operated from control room at rear of stalls - no supply for temporary board - 8 spots, 14 fresnels, 3 floods, Strand - 2 followspots can be operated from rear of balcony.
Sound: Seck 16:8:2 desk - 2 foldback speakers - 4 mics, radio mics by arrangement - 2 cassette tape systems - CD player. Acoustics suitable for music and spoken word. Fully dedicated sound recording facility.
Backstage: 3 dressing rooms, access by SR - quick change room. Refreshments can be provided by prior arrangement. Piano, poor. Advice given on accommodation. Staff - 1 technician - casuals by arrangement - security personnel by arrangement. Backstage facilities not accessible to disabled performers and staff.
Stage management: Techpro headset system. 8 sets, show relay and paging.

Dufftown, Morayshire

DUFFTOWN COMMUNITY CENTRE

Church Street, Dufftown, Morayshire AB55 4AR Scotland
Tel: 01340 871641
Email: grant.gallagher@moray.gov.uk
ADMINISTRATION:
Props: Moray Council
Sports and Leisure Supervisor: Grant Gallagher
Please send any letters etc to: Speyside CC, Mary Avenue, Aberlour, AB38 9QN

Dumbarton, Dunbartonshire

BURGH HALL

Burgh Hall Castle Street Dumbarton Dumbartonshire G82 1JY Scotland
Tel: 01389 731 281 Bkgs Tel: 01389 737 073
ADMINISTRATION:
Props: West Dumbartonshire Leisure Trust
Cap: Main Hall 300; Small Hall 40; 2 Committee Rooms seating 10 people each room.
Please contact: Cameron Taylor, West Dumbartonshire Council
Commercial and Technical Services, Halls and Events Section, Richmond Street, Clydebank G81 1RF

DENNY CIVIC THEATRE

St Mary's Way, Dumbarton, Dunbartonshire G82 1NL Scotland
Tel/Fax: 01389 602 575
Web Site: www.west-dunbarton.gov.uk
ADMINISTRATION:
Props: West Dunbartonshire Leisure Trust
Cap: 340
For bookings Tel: 01389 757 806
Admin/Contact Address: Events & Hall Section, Richmond Street Depot, Clydebank G82 1RF Scotland

Dumfries

THEATRE ROYAL

Closed for refurbishment till July 2015
Shakespeare Street, Dumfries, DG1 2JH Scotland
Tel: 01387 254209
Email: shielah4@btinternet.com
Web Site: www.guildofplayers.co.uk
Prop: Dumfries Guild of Players
Contact: Master of Guild Players - Anne Aldridge, Tel: 01387 257136

Dundee, Angus

Pop. 181,842. London 428 miles. Newspapers: Courier & Advertiser (dly); Evening Telegraph (ntly). STD code 01382

BONAR HALL

University of Dundee, Park Place, Dundee, Tayside DD1 4HN Scotland
Tel: 01382 227 684
Email: emoore@dundeereptheatre.co.uk
Web Site: www.dundeerep.co.uk
Seating/Capacity: Main Hall 458, Ustinov Room Capacity: 160
Events Manager: Eve Moore

CAIRD HALL COMPLEX

City Square, Dundee, Tayside DD1 3BB Scotland
Tel: 01382 434 030 BO: 01382 434940
Email: susan.gillan@leisureandculture-dundee.com
Web Site: www.cairdhall.co.uk
ADMINISTRATION:
Manager: Susan Gillan
Technical Manager: Allan Bruce
Props: Dundee City Council
Policy: Concert Hall used for concerts, exhibitions, conferences.
Seating/Capacity: Caird Hall 2,000; Marryat Hall 350; Ashton Hall 60.
TECHNICAL:
Further details from above number.

DUNDEE REPERTORY THEATRE

Tay Square, Dundee, Tayside DD1 1PB Scotland
Mgt: 01382 227 684 BO: 01382 223 530
Fax: 01382 228 609
Email: vbegg@dundeereptheatre.co.uk
Web Site: www.dundeerep.co.uk
ADMINISTRATION:
Props: Dundee Repertory Theatre Ltd
Artistic Directors: Philip Howard, Jemmima Levick
Executive Director: Philip Howard
Head of Business Development and PR: Susie Crawford
Head of Production: Nils Denhertog
Policy: Repertory, 4 week run interspersed with visiting productions.
Perfs: Tues.-Sat. 7.30; Mats Sat 2.30p.m.
Seats: 455. 2 Bars and Restaurant
TECHNICAL:
Stage: Adaptable Proscenium/Open Flat; Pros. Opening width variable to 13.00m max, Ht. variable 5.00m to 9.00m; Depth, Setting Line to Back Wall 9.60m, Setting Line to front of apron (centre stage only) 1.75m; Width, Centre Line to PS Wall 9.17m, to OP Wall 9.17m; Ht. to underside of grid 15m, to underside of fly floors 6m; Flying equipment 20 Hemp sets (adjustable as required), 8 Double purchase C/W sets 200kg capacity; Length of Bars 13.5m; Prompt Crn. P.S.
Lighting: Switchboard: Rank ARRI Imagine 120 way, situated at rear of auditorium; FOH 40 circuits (patchable), Flys 66 circuits, Dips 14 circuits; 2 FOH Bridges and 2 Slots.
Equipment: 12 CCT 1K Floods. 36 1K SIL 30, 12 Minuette 500W Floods, 3 2K Fresnels, 18 par 64, 48 1k Fresnels, 20 Patt.23, 6 Minuette Fresnels, 10 Minuette Profiles. 1.2 kw SIL15 Follow Spot
Sound Equip: Control situated with lighting control equipment. Soundtracs Solo Live 16:4:2 Mixer; 3 HH V800 Power Amplifier; 2 Revox B77 Tape Decks, 1 Technics Cassette Deck 1 x Sony CD Player, 1 Technics Turntable; FOH P.S. 4 x BOSE 802 Loudspeakers; 2 HH Unit system 3 Effects Speakers; 30 Mic lines, 20 L/S lines. Equipment list available.
Dressing Rooms: 8 with showers to accommodate 26. Green Room.
Orchestra: Front 3 rows of seating removable for orchestra space approx. 30 sq. metres at 600mm below stage level.
Get-in at street level, rear of Stage; clock door 3.00m wide; Door 3.00m wide x 5.5m high.
Membership: TMA. Fed. of Scottish Theatres

GARDYNE THEATRE

Gardyne Road Broughty Ferry Dundee DD5 1NY
Admin: 01382 448874 BO: 01382 434940
Email: info@gardynetheatre.org.uk
Web Site: www.gardynetheatre.org.uk
General Manager: Alan Dear
Technical Manager: Jim Taylor
Administrator: Sharon Nicholl
Capacity: Seated 370, Standing 404
Full Technical spec at: www.gardynetheatre.org.uk/technical/

WHITEHALL THEATRE

Bellfield Street, Dundee, Tayside DD1 5JA
Mgt: 01382 322684 Mob: 07897455069
Email: manager@whitehalltheatre.com
Web Site: www.whitehalltheatre.com
ADMINISTRATION:
Props: Whitehall Theatre Trust
General Manager: Scott McRuvie
Contact: manager@whitehalldundee.co.uk
Policy: Touring shows, one-night stands, plus local operatic and musical societies. Willing to premiere show.
Built in 1928 as Alhambra Cinema, with a stage for acts between the films; the stage was extended in 1984. Venue is self-financing.
Performance Schedule: Open 52 weeks a year; evening performances start at 7.30pm, matinees on Saturdays at 2.15pm. Booking terms: hire percentage.
Facilities: Seats: 700, 4 wheelchair spaces, raked. Coffee bar, licensed bar. Car park adjacent, station: Dundee, coach terminal, bus route: 21. Deaf loop system - assistance available. Parking & level access. Small rehearsal hall, large workshop and storage area.
TECHNICAL:

STAGE: Proscenium Arch 17' high x 34' wide; Stage depth 28' from the Proscenium Arch; Apron depth 10' in front of the Proscenium Arch; 22 counter-weighted fly bars. Scene dock doors; 3300mm x 1600mm.
LIGHTING: Desk; ETC expression 256. Front of house (mid auditorium); 8 ETC Source 4 zoom (25-50), 4 CCT Silhouette (15-32). Advanced bar (above the orchestra pit); 6 Strand 743 (1k Fresnel), 6 CCT Silhouette (15-32). Side slots (above the orchestra pit); 2 Pars 64, 2 Strand 743, 2 Strand 803. Auditorium booms, 4 Strand 264, 2 Pars 64. Stage: Stage booms; 4 CCT minuette profiles (500w). 12 CCT / zero 88 minuete (500w). Front lx (stage bar 3); 9 CCT starlette (1k Fresnel), 2 Strand 743 (1k Fresnel). Mid-bar lx (stage bar 15); 5 CCT starlette (1k Fresnel), 4 Strand 743 (1k Fresnel). Cyc lx (stage bar 20); 6 diluvio (1k cyc lights), 8 Strand P60 (500 w). Dimming; 12 Zero 88 Install 6 2k dimmers. 2 additional racks can be installed at 1k per channel. An addition dmx line is run over the roof which can be used for movers ect.
SOUND: YAMAHA O1V Digital Mixing Desk (16 ch; 12mic, 2 stereo, 4 aux), Behringer CX2300 Crossover (2 way), 1x CROWN POWERTECH 3 Amp, 1x PPX 900 Amp, JBL 4771A Concert Series Speakers, 2x Mackie SRM350 Monitors (active), 1x IMQ Stageline 400w Amp, 2x Peavey ProSys 15 (side fills), 1x Amcron Geodyne I Amp, 20 ch Multicore with 4 returns installed S/L Pros to sound position (10 extra sends and 2 returns also available), 8 ch snake x 20m, 8 ch stagebox x 15m, approx 100m XLR. Various mics available. DENNON CD Player, 3 x SONY Minidisk.
ADDITIONAL: Comms system between Stage Manager and all positions. 7 Dressing Rooms, Accomm. 106 (with hot water); Rehearsal room; 2 shower rooms (currently not in use); Kitchen with laundry and cooking facilities.

Dunfermline, Fife

ALHAMBRA THEATRE

33 Canmore Street, Dunfermline, Fife

KY12 7NX
BO/Mgt: 01383 740 384
Email: info@alhambradunfermline.com
Web Site: www.alhambradunfermline.com
ADMINISTRATION:
A unique and atmospheric venue for events and functions.
Policy: Musical theatre, Dance, Drama, Orchestral Concerts, Comedy.
General Manager: Simon Fletcher
Capacity: Main auditorium, 250 -2100 (600 ground floor seating, standing 1400); Alhambra 2, 140 (seated) 300 (standing).

CARNEGIE HALL

East Port, Dunfermline, Fife KY12 7JA
Tel: 01383 602302
Email: verdi.clark@onfife.com
Web Site: www.onfife.com
Theatre Manager & Artistic Director: Verdi Clark
Marketing and Audience Delopment Manager: Laura Crielly
Cap: 520

Dunlop, Ayrshire

DUNLOP VILLAGE HALL

48 Main Street, Dunlop, Ayrshire KA3 4AG
Tel: 01560 486608
Email: dunlophall@gmail.com
Web Site: www.dunlopvillage.org.uk
ADMINISTRATION:
Props: Dunlop & District Community Company
For bookings contact: Linda Pinkerton (07956018428)
The hall can accommodate Functions, Parties, Concerts, Shows and meetings.

Dunoon, Argyll

QUEEN'S HALL

9 Argyll Street, Dunoon, Argyll PA23 7HH
Tel: 01369 702800 Fax: 01369 705370
Email: lorna.whyte@argyll-bute.gov.uk
Contact: Lorna Whyte
Capacity: 650 Seated, 1000 Standing

Dunstable, Bedfordshire

GROVE THEATRE

Grove Park Court Drive Dunstable Bedfordshire LU5 4GP
Admin: 01582 609351 BO: 01582 602080 Fax: 01582 661787
Email: grovetheatre@1Life.co.uk
Web Site: www.grovetheatre.co.uk
Contact General Manager: Jo Ditch
Market Dept Email: marketing.grove@1Life.co.uk
Props: 1 Life on behalf of Central Beds Council.
Capacity: 780 Seats, and 1000 for stand up concerts.

Durham, County Durham

GALA THEATRE

Millennium Place, Durham, County Durham DH1 1WA
Admin: 03000 266601 BO: 03000 266600
Email: info@galadurham.co.uk
Web Site: www.galadurham.co.uk
Programme Manager: Robin Byers
Admin & Finance Officer: Joanne Alexander
Technical Manager: Brian Dunn
Front of House Manager: Catherine Ditchburn and Stacey Forsyth
Hospitallity Manager: Carol Scullion
Cap: 500
The venue has performance spaces ranging from a capacity of 70 to 880 both seated and standing, and has all the state-of-the-art sound and lighting equiptment you would expect from a fully equipt modern theatre.

LAMPLIGHT ARTS CENTRE

Lamplight Arts Centre Front Street, Stanley, Co. Durham DH9 0NA
Tel: 01207 218893 BO: 01207 218899
Email: lamplight@leisureworksonline.co.uk
Web Site: www.leisureworksonline.co.uk/lamplightarts.cfm
ADMINISTRATION:
General Manager: Louise Strong
Capacity: 410 Theatre Style

TECHNICAL:
STAGE: Get-in: Street level. A large roller-shutter dock door is located at the left-hand end of the building, with access via a small service road directly in front. Width between pros. Arch, 7.5m, Width behind pros. Arch, 9m, Depth from front edge to cyclorama wall, 7.5m. Stage lift at S/L, connecting the stage to auditorium level and other facilities, to assist disabled performers. Flying facilities; fly tower over the stage, with a hauling gantry positioned S/R. A number of scenery bars, hauled by hemp ropes, which are suitable for flying light-weight scenery.
LIGHTING: Control Desk: Zero 88 "Fat Frog". Power: The venue has an optional 125A, 3-phase cee-form touring socket at S/L. Dimmers: 6 No. 6 x 10A channel Strand Tempus dimmers, analogue-controlled, Via 2 No. demux units. A comprehensive patch-bay is located below the dimmers. An additional 2 No. 63A sockets to facilitate extra dimmers. Lantern Stock: 3 x Cantata Profile 18/32; 3 x Cantata Profile 11/26; 8 x assorted 500W profiles; 12 x 1kw Par cans; 5 x 200W floods; 20 x 1kw fresnels; 4 x 4 x 500w codas, rigged LX4; an assortment of 15A and 13A cables are available.
SOUND: Mixing desk: Midas Venice 32:4:2. Multicore: The multi-core has 12 stage sends, 2 FOH sends, 4 aux. Sends, and 4 talkback sends. Power: an optional 63A single-phase touring socket (cee-form) is located S/L. FOH: 4 x Bose 802 mounted in pairs either side of the proscenium arch. Powered by Yamaha and DVS power amps rack-mounted at S/L. Monitors: 2 x EV 300 cabs powered by a Citronic PPX 450 amp. Maestro induction-loop for hearing-impaired. Ultra-Curve Pro 31 band digital graphic equalizer. Marantz twin cassette deck. Marantz C.D. player. Denon mini-disc player. Yamaha reverb unit Rev500. A small selection of microphones and stands, XLR cables and other connections, is available.
DRESSING ROOMS: 1, with two small integral private rooms, at the rear of the stage, and a green room next door.

East Grinstead, West Sussex

CHEQUER MEAD

Community Arts Centre, De La Warr Road, East Grinstead, West Sussex RH19 3BS
Admin: 01342 325 577 BO: 01342 302 000
Email: tickets@chequermead.org.uk
Web Site: www.chequermead.org.uk
Full Administration details are available on our website.
Full Technical details are available on our website.

East Kilbride, Glasgow

Pop. 85,000. London 397 miles.
Newspapers: East Kilbride News (thurs).
STD code 01355

THE VILLAGE THEATRE

Maxwell Drive, East Kilbride, Glasgow, Strathclyde G74 4HG
Tel: 01355 248 669 Fax: 01355 248 677
Email: village.theatre@southlanarkshireleisure.co.uk
Web Site: www.sllcboxoffice.co.uk
ADMINISTRATION:
Props: South Lanarkshire Leisure and Culture Ltd
Venues Manager: Lyn McDougall
Theatre Techical Officer: Kenny Sarquherson
Policy: Tours, One Night Stands, Hire, Amateur
Perfs: Usually 7.30pm

Seats: 318 (on one raked tier) 298 if orchestra pit used. Rehearsal room with kitchen, bar, Coffee Bar.
TECHNICAL:
Stage: Proscenium, Flat; opening 7.31m; Pros. Ht. 5m; Depth of S/Line 8.08m; W/Widths P.S.4.95m, O.P. 2.89m; Grid Ht. 11.31m; Ht. to under fly floor 6.23m; Flying Bars C/W (16 of) 18.08m, Hemp (6 of) 10.06m. 18 C/W flylines. (3.05m extension available).
Lighting: Switchboard: "Eurolight Micron" Memory System (60 way), plus "Thorn TGM" Manual System (60 way) Control Room is at rear of auditorium. FOH Lighting: 8 @ CCT Sil.30; FOH Alcoves: 2 @ Par 64 and 2 @ Sil. 30 per side. 4 Sils and the 4 Par 64 have "Chromatic" Colour-Wheels; Perches: 2 @ 1kw Fresnels per side; Footlights: 3 Circs (S-Type Battens); No.1 Bar: 12 @ Pat.743; No.2 Bar: 8 @ Pat.743 extra spot-bars can be rigged as required. Flood Bar: 12 @ CCT. 500w Minuette Floods (3 Circs) Flys and stage area have Dips and independent Skts. 10 Non-Dim Skts controlled form Switchboard. Headset/Cue Light Skts in most areas.
Sound Equip: "Electrosonic" 10 channel/3 Group Mixer. 100w per Group. "PAN" Facility (100V Line) 1 Revox A77; 2 @ Cassette Decks; 1C Record Deck. (situated in Control Room); Various monitors available. 24 @ Show Relay/Paging Speakers situated around the Theatre at strategic points. Tech communication - Headset "Ring" system or Cue Lights. Induction Loop System fitted. Land-Line installed for "Live" transmission to local hospital radio network.
Dressing Rooms 6; with comfortable accommodation for 4 in each. 1 auxillary room 4 showers. Orchestra Pit: Front row of seats must be removed. Accommodated 8-10.

East Molesey, Surrey

VINE HALL

Vine Road, East Molesey, Surrey KT8 9LF
Tel: 01932 254750
Email: elmbridgehalls@dcleisure.co.uk
Web Site: www.elmbridge.gov.uk
ADMINISTRATION
Props: Elmbridge Borough Council
Cap: 200 standing, 90 seated
For bookings contact the lettings officer on 01932 254750

Eastbourne, East Sussex

Pop. 80,000. London 64 miles.
Newspapers: Eastbourne Gazette (wed); Eastbourne Herald (sat). STD code 01323

THE CONGRESS THEATRE

Carlisle Road, Eastbourne, East Sussex BN21 4BP
Mgt: 01323 415 500 BO: 01323 412 000 SD: 01323 410 048 Fax: 01323 727 369
Correspondence to Winter Garden, 14 Compton Street, Eastborne, East Sussex BN21 4BP
Email: theatres@eastbourne.gov.uk
Web Site: www.eastbournetheatres.co.uk
ADMINISTRATION:
Props: Eastbourne Borough Council
Artistic Director: Chris Jordan
General Manager: Gavin Davis Tel: 01323 415529
Marketing & Sales Manager: Suzanne Hopp. Tel: 01323 415525
Stage Manager: Chris Robinson. Contact: 01323 415516 or chris.robinson@eastbourne.gov.uk
Box Office Manager: Zoe Bourne. Contact: 01323 415531 or boxoffice@eastbourne.gov.uk
Policy: All Class (Except Rep)
Perfs: Variable, depending on production.
Seats: 1,689. Two Licensed Bars, Licensed Restaurant (organised party catering).
TECHNICAL:
STAGE: Proscenium, Flat; Pros. opening 13.72m; Ht. of Pros. 6.40m; Depth of S/Line 10.97m; Ht. of Grid 16.00m; 56 lines, 42 C/W, 14 Hemp; Flying Bars 15.24m; W/Widths P.S. 3.96m average (variable), O.P. 9.14m; Prompt Cnr. P.S. False sprung floor available for Ballet presentation. Direct on stage Get-in facilities. Electrically operated orchestra lift. Tallescope. Orchestra Pit acomm. 25 (average).
LIGHTING: 1 x Strand 530I, 350 Channels. 100 x ETC Sensor 2 Dimmers. FOH Rig: 10 x Strand SL Zooms 18/32°, 10 x Source 4 - 26°, 2 x PAR 64 (CP 62), 2 x Robert Juiliet Cyrano Follow Spots. Stage Rig: 30 x Strand Cantata F, 12 x Strand Alto F, 10 x Source 4 - 26°, 50 x PAR 64, 6 x PAR64 Short Nosed Floor cans, 4 x Iris 4 Cyc Floods.
SOUND EQUIP: Allen & Heath ML 4000 Mixing Desk. PPX 1200 w Amp FoH System, PPX 1600 w Amp FoH System, VS 1100 w Amp Monitors, Altec 9849 Speakers FoH System, 4 x Tannoy Cougar Wedges, 1 x Mini Disc Player, 2 x CD Player, 1 x Twin Cassette Player, 2 x DI Boxes, 4 x S M 5 8 M i c r o p h o n e s, 1 x Shure 839 Cond. Lavalier, 2 x AKG CK8 Shotgun Heads, Various Stands 6 x AKG 747.
STAGE MANAGEMENT: 'Clear Com' Talk Back to all out stations & belt packs. Cue lights to all out stations.
DRESSING ROOMS: 11; Accom. 100; 5 Showers. Large wardrobe room with washing machine and tumble dryer.
MEMBERSHIP: TMA

DEVONSHIRE PARK THEATRE

Compton Street, Eastbourne, East Sussex BN21 4BP
Mgt: 01323 415 500 BO: 01323 412 000 SD: 01323 410 074 Fax: 01323 727 369
Correspondence to Winter Garden, 14 Compton Street Eastbourne, East Sussex BN21 4BP
Email: theatres@eastbourne.gov.uk
Web Site: www.eastbournetheatres.co.uk
ADMINISTRATION:
Props: Eastbourne Borough Council
Artistic Director: Chris Jordan
General Manager: Gavin Davis
Stage Manager: Paul Debreczeny
Marketing & Sales Manager: Suzanne Hopp
Box Office Manager: Zoe Bourne
Policy: Major Touring Plays
Perfs: Variable, depending upon production
Seats: 936, Licensed Bar.
TECHNICAL:
Stage: Proscenium. Raked 1 in 24; Pros. Opening 8.04m; Ht. of Pros. 4.27m to border; Depth of S/Line 7.32m; Ht. of Grid 10.05m - 30.36m; 26 lines, Hemp. 2 C/W, 4 winch sets; Scenery Flying Ht. 9.75m; Flying Bars 10.97m; W/Widths P.S. 3.66m, O.P. 3.66m; Prompt Cnr. P.S.
Direct on stage Get-in facilities, P.S. scene-dock with 4.88m headroom.
Lighting: Switchboard: Strand Duet, 80 ways, sited rear of dress circle; Lanterns; Grand Circle level 14 x 264's, 2 x T64's; Box 1 Spot Bar; 12 x 743's. Additional Equipment: 14 x 743's, 10 x Quartet Fresnels, 16 x Par 64's, 4 x 243 (2 ks) 6 x Berkey 1k Floods. 4 x 3-way ground row, 4 x 4-Way Way cyc. battens; 8 x 4' 6" stands.
Circuits: 25 x 2kw in O.P. Flys; Stage: 13 x 2kw O.P. 10 x 2kw P.S., plus 4 x 2kw linked across.
Sound Equip: Sound Desk situated rear dress circle. Soundcraft 200B mixer 16 into 4 into 2 + 2 foldback. 2 x Revox B77's. 1 Gram Deck. 1 x Cassette. 4 Electrovoice mid/high cabinets on prosc. - 300 watts each. 6 Shure SM 58 Microphones, 3 AKG D190 microphone, 6 floor stands with Boom arms.
Dressing Rooms 9, Accom 25-30. 2 showers. Orchestra Pit.
Membership: TMA

ROYAL HIPPODROME

108 - 112 Seaside Road, Eastbourne, East Sussex BN21 3PF
BO: 01323 412 000 Tel: 01323 726 756
Email: enquiries@royalhippordrome.com
Web Site: www.royalhippodrome.com
ADMINISTRATION:
Stage Manager: Ben Cooper
Policy: Summer Variety Shows
Perfs: Evening 8.15p.m., Mats Tues & Thurs 2.30p.m.
Seats: 599, Licensed Bar and Coffee Shop.
TECHNICAL:
Stage: Proscenium, Raked; Pros. Opening 7.62m; Ht. of Pros. 5.18m; Depth of S/Line 6.71m; Ht. of Grid

14.5m; 25 line; Hemp; 3 C/W. Scenery
Flying Ht. 7m; Flying Bars 9.14m.
W/Widths P.S. 2.50m, O.P. 2.50m;
Prompt Cnr. P.S. Scene Dock U/S P.S.
9.75m x 3.66m x 5.49m high; Prop Room
U/S O.P. 5.49m x 3.66m x 2.74m high.
Lighting: Switchboard: Strand Threeset,
40 ways, situated rear of Grand Circle;
Lanterns: Follow Spots 2 x Patt.293 2kw;
FOH 6 Patt.T84 plus colour wheels,
Stage 11 Patt.223, 8 Patt.264, 9
Patt.123, 7 Patt.23; 5 AC1001 Floods. 2
Patt.243, 2 Patt.137; 2 x 4 Circuit
Battens; 6 Booms.
Sound Equipment: RH Sound Allen &
Heath SR 12 way mixing desk; PPX 900
Citronic Amplifier; PPX450 Citronic
Amplifier;
Denon Cassette machine; Show Relay;
Talk Back System; various microphones.
Dressing Rooms 8 plus
Wardrobe; Accom. 22;
Band facilities below Stage. Orchestra Pit
8.
Membership: TMA

WINTER GARDEN
14 Compton Street, Eastbourne, East
Sussex BN21 4BP
Mgt: 01323 415 500 BO: 01323 412 000
Fax: 01323 727 369
Email: theatres@eastbourne.gov.uk
Web Site: www.eastbournetheatres.co.uk
ADMINISTRATION:
Props: Eastbourne Borough Council
Artistic Director: Chris Jordan
General Manager: Gavin Davis
Marketing & Publicity Manager: Suzanne
Hopp
Stage Managers: Chris Robinson and
Paul Debreczemy
Box Office Manager: Zoe Bourne
Perfs: Variable
Membership: TMA
FLORAL HALL
Seats: 900 Theatre, 600 Cabaret, 842
Wrestling,
2 Licensed Bars.
Lighting: Strand SP 40 Board, 40 circuits,
operated from SR on stage level - 100A 3
phase supply available for temporary
board - various pats, spots and fresnels,
2 follow spots operated from gantry at
rear of auditorium.
Dressing Rooms: 3 large dressing rooms
near stage level plus one above, accommodating 24
Backstage facilities not accessible to disabled performers and staff.

GOLD ROOM:
Above Floral Hall.
Multi-purpose flat-floor hall.
Seats: 400. Licensed Bar.
Stage: 6m deep x 13m wide (variable).
Lighting: Thorn 20/2 switchboard.
Sound Equipment: 12 Channel Sect mixing desk, twin cassette deck, 4 x FOH
speakers.

Eastgate, Peebles

EASTGATE THEATRE & ARTS CENTRE
Eastgate, Peebles EH45 8AD
Admin Tel: 01721 725 785 BO Tel:
01721 725 777
Email: caroline@eastgatearts.com
Web Site: www.eastgatearts.com
Programmer: Caroline Adam
Finance & Administation Manager: Jen
Knight
Cap: 200

Eastleigh, Hampshire

FLEMING PARK LEISURE CENTRE
Passfield Avenue, Eastleigh, Hampshire
SO50 9NL
Tel: 023 8068 4800 Fax: 023 8062 9248
Email: enquiry@flemingparkleisurecentre.c
o.uk
Web: www.flemingparkleisurecentre.co.uk
ADMINISTRATION:
Props: Eastleigh Borough Council/DC
Leisure Ltd
Cap: 980
Manager: Jo Parker

THE POINT DANCE & ARTS CENTRE
The Point, Leigh Road, Eastleigh,
Hampshire S050 9DE
Tel: 023 8065 2333 Admin Fax: 02380
651123
Email: thepoint@eastleigh.gov.uk
Web Site: www.thepointeastleigh.co.uk
ADMINISTRATION
Props: Eastleigh Borough Council
Cap: 318
Director: Owen Calvert-Lyons
General Manager: Donna Reeves
Technical Manager: Tim Slater
TECHNICAL:
Sprung dance floor, 10 x 10m. flexible
space, retractable seating.

Ebbw Vale, Gwent

THE BEAUFORT THEATRE & BALLROOM
Beaufort Road, Beaufort Hill, Ebbw Vale,
Blaenau Gwent NP23 5QQ
BO: 01495 355 800 Admin Tel: 01495
355 945
Email: beaufort.theatre@virgin.net
Web Site: www.blaenaugwentvenues.co
m
ADMINISTRATION
Props: Life Leisure Trust
Cap: Auditorium 314; Ballroom 150

Venues Manager: Susanne Allen

Edinburgh, Mid Lothian
Pop. 439,721. London 373 miles.
Newspapers: Evening News (ntly); The
Scotsman (dly). STD code 0131

CHURCH HILL THEATRE
33 Morningside Road, Edinburgh, Mid
Lothian EH10 4DR Scotland
Admin: 0131 447 7597 Head Office:
0131 220 4348
Email: churchhilltheatre@assembly-roomsedinburgh.co.uk
Web Site: www.assemblyroomsedin-burgh.co.uk
ADMINISTRATION:
Props: City of Edinburgh Council
Policy: Mostly amateur but professional in
Summer and odd weeks in Winter.
Perfs: Vary according to show
Seats: 353. Coffee Bar and Rehearsal
Rooms
TECHNICAL:
Stage: Proscenium, Flat; Pros. opening
8.53m wide by 3.81m high; Depth of
S/Line 7.62m; Forestage 1m; Grid none;
8 Hemp Sets; Paint Dock; Scene Dock;
Bars 10.36m wide; Wings P.S. 2.13m,
O.P. 2.29m; Prompt Cnr. P.S.; One
Wardrobe Room; Get-in; Dock Doors
3.50m by 1.19m; Difference in level
0.91m.
Lighting: Switchboard: Situated at back of
auditorium. (44 x 1kw, 10 x 2kw); 3
Battens, 4 Patt.263 (with colour change),
10 Patt.23, 16 Patt.123, 34 Patt.60 3 x
1.83m Patt. S Groundrow. Can be augmented by equipment from other theatres
(C.S.I.'s etc.) Rank Strand lightboard
(m)3 Junior. Dimmers (80) way.
Sound Equip: 4 mics and amplifier;
Speakers F.O.H. Tape input.
Dressing Rooms: 4 with Showers and toilets; 24 persons. Orchestra Pit: Area 18
sq.m., rail 1.83m in front of stage.
Disabled toilet - unisex.

THE EDINBURGH CORN EXCHANGE
11 Newmarket Road, Edinburgh, Mid
Lothian EH14 1RJ Scotland
Tel: 0131 477 3500 Fax: 0131 443 9022
Email: info@ece.uk.com
Web Site: www.ece.uk.com
Contact: Neil Rudram
Capacity: 3000 (standing), 1500 (seated)
Stage: 8m x 15m

EDINBURGH FESTIVAL THEATRE
13-29 Nicolson Street, Edinburgh, Mid
Lothian EH8 9FT Scotland
SD: 0131 662 1112 Fax: 0131 667 0744
BO: 0131 529 6000 Fax: 0131 662 1199
Email: enquiries@edtheatres.com

Web Site: www.edtheatres.com
ADMINISTRATION:
Props: Festival City Theatres Trust
General Manager: Duncan Hendry
Theatre Manger: Brian Loudon
Marketing Manager: Nick Parr
Technical Manager: Jim Clark
Seating Capacity: 1,900
Please contact the theatre for full technical details.

EDINBURGH INTERNATIONAL CONFERENCE CENTRE - EICC

The Exchange, 150 Morrison Street, Edinburgh, Mid Lothian EH3 8EE Scotland
Tel: 0131 300 3000 Fax: 0131 300 3030
The Cromdale Exhibition Hall, The Strathblane Hall, The Lomond Suite and The Galloway Suite, Breakout Rooms & The Pentland Suite,
Email: sales@eicc.co.uk
Web Site: www.eicc.co.uk
ADMINISTRATION:
Capacity: 1200
Recently expanded with additional space: see website for details
TECHNICAL:
THE CROMDALE EXHIBITION HALL
750 sq.m.net 1185 sq.m/12 738 sq.ft. gross. Suitable for banquets of up to 800, exhibitions & receptions.
Under floor ducts on 6.5m./24ft.centres, including high powered electrical outlets, telephone points, water & waste. Closed circuit television and PA systems. Disable access. A 5000kg capacity goods lift serves all floors.
THE STRATHBLANE HALL
1128 sq.m. net/12 128 sq.ft net.
Capacity 1000.
THE LOMOND SUITE AND THE GALLOWAY SUITE, BREAK OUT ROOMS AND THE PENTLAND SUITE
Further details available on request.

EDINBURGH PLAYHOUSE

18-22 Greenside Place, Edinburgh, Mid Lothian EH1 3AA Scotland
Admin: 0131 524 3333 BO: 0131 524 3353 Fax: 0131 524 3350 SD: 0131 524 3324
Email: garyroden@theambassadors.com
Web: www.edinburghplayhouse.org.uk
ADMINISTRATION:
Props: Ambassadors Theatre Group Ltd
General Manager: Gary Roden
Sales & Marketing Manager: Sarah Heney
Box Office Manager: Barbara Callard
Technical Manager: Graham Wade
grahamwade@theambassadors.com
Policy: Multi-use; Opera, Ballet, Rock and Pop Concerts, Variety, Cinema, Musicals etc.
Seats: 3,056. 5 Bars.
TECHNICAL:
STAGE: Proscenium width 14.87m, Pros Height 8.5m, Full stage width 22.8m, Full stage Depth - Propmt Side 12.17m, OP side 13.60m, Width between Fly Floors 18.25m, Flying width 15.24m, Flying Depth (from tabs) 10.70m, Height to Grid 18.13m, Height to underside fly floor 8.50m, Height to bar - Out Dead 17.20m, Height to Beams in grid 20.12m, Flat Stage, Prompt Corner Stage Right.
FLYS: Operated from fly flor Stage Right, Counterweight Sets: Single Purchase x 26 (1-26) Double Purchase x 26 (27-52), House Tabs on Bar 1, Double Purchase bars are Gas Pipe Diameter. MAXIMUM Set 1-26 weight loading spread over 4 lines 500kg, Set27-52 weight loading spread over 4 lines 450kg, Bar Lengths Set 1-26 - 50', Set 27-52 Varies.
ORCHESTRA PIT: Basic Small Pit 30 musicians no seats removed, Medium Pit 80 musicians rows A,B removed, Large Pit 120 musicians rows A-D removed.
Temporary Power Distribution; it should be noted that the building sincoming mains is only rated at 3 x 600 amps.
There is also a selection of 13 x 15 amp independants around the stage area.
Stage Left: 1 x 3 x 300Amps (fitted with Powerlocks); 1 x 3 x 200 Amps (fitted with single & 3 phase 63A CEE-Form, Single & 3 Phase 125A CEE form); 1 x 3 x 63 Amps (fitted with 3 phase CEE-form); 2 x 3 x 32 Amps (fitted with phase 3 CEE-forms). Lx Gallery S/L 1 x 3 x 32 Amps (fitted 3 phase CEE-form). S/R 1 x 3 x 32 Amps (fitted 3 phase CEE-form). Grid 3 x 3 x 32 amps (fitted 3 phase CEE-form), Sub Stage S/R 1 x 3 x 32 amps (fitted 3 phase CEE-form), Sub Stage U/S 1 x 3 x 63 amps (fitted 3 phase CEE-form), 1 x 3 x 32 amps (fitted 3 phase CEE-form), Rear Circle Mixer Platform 1 x 3 x 32 amps (fitted 3 phase CEE-form). Multicore Run to front of house mixer position (rear circle) 65 metres. This can be run from either side of the stage. Balcony Front has scaf bar running the full width, Circle Front has 19' of aluminium scaf bar at centre, Balcony Slips have scaf frames. Dome bridge has space for 8 x 2k profile's up to 18 leco's. Both the LX gallery and the fly floor have scaf bar running the full depth of the stage. 2 x follow spots: Lycean Long throw 2K xenon. 12 x 20 10 circuits internally wired bars. NO HOUSE LIGHTING STOCK, No in house Q light system, Intercom system available. TECPRO 3 channel PSU, single channel ring 8 x in packs 7 H/sets. Lighting desk is a Strand Lighting Gemini 2+ with D54 mux out only. There are 240 Dimmers, JTM/STM type. Laser Water Supply; Feed up stage centre, Drain usually toilet off stage left, Pressure approx 80 psi.

HERIOT-WATT UNIVERSITY STUDENT'S UNION

The Union, Riccarton, Currie, Edinburgh, Mid Lothian EH14 4AS Scotland
Tel: 0131 451 5333 Fax: 0131 451 5344
Email: g.j.fortune@hw.ac.uk
Web Site: www.hwunion.com
President: Jessie Nelms.
Cap: 455

KING'S THEATRE

(All Correspondence to go to the Festival Theatre)
2 Leven Street, Edinburgh, Mid Lothian EH3 9LQ Scotland
Admin: 0131 662 1112 Fax: 0131 667 0744 BO: 0131 529 6000 BO Fax: 0131 662 1199
Email: enquiries@edtheatres.com
Web Site: www.edtheatres.com
ADMINISTRATION:
Props: Festival City Theatres Trust
General Manager: Duncan Hendry
Theatre Manager: Brian Loudon
Marketing Manager: Nick Parr
Technical Manager: Jim Clark
Policy: Drama, Pantomime, etc.
Perfs: Variable depending on production
Seats: 1,340.
TECHNICAL:
Stage: Proscenium, Raked 1 in 24; Pros. opening 9.75m; Ht. of Pros. 6.55m; Depth of S/Line 15.24m; Ht. of Grid 15.24m; 57 lines, Fly Floor, C/W; Scenery Flying Ht. 14.63m; Flying Bars 12.04m; W/Widths P.S. 3.50m; O.P. 4.27m; Prompt Cnr. P.S. One Wardrobe Room, Dock Door 1.83m from street level; Paint Frame back door; 2 Traps.
Lighting: Switchboard: Strand Galaxy 150 ways (upper circle). Lanterns: 200 Assorted mostly strand, 4 x 4 circuit battens, 4 x 4 circuit footlight/groundrow 4 x 5 way flood bar, 2 x 12 I.W. Spot Bars, 4 x 4 way ladders each side of track.
F.O.H. positions on centre front of both circles and top tier of side boxes.
Sound: Full PA system including 20 way Alice Mixer 2 Revox B77 tape decks and an assortment of microphones. Full sound and lighting details on application.
Dressing Rooms 13; Accom. 96; 6 Showers; Orchestra Pit partially under forestage.

THE QUEEN'S HALL

Clerk Street, Edinburgh, Mid Lothian EH8 9JG Scotland
Mgt: 0131 668 3456 BO: 0131 668 2019
Fax: 0131 668 2656
Email: info@queenshalledinburgh.org
Web Site: www.thequeenshall.net
ADMINISTRATION:
Contact: Iain McQueen
A converted Georgian church with the flexibility and acoustic to accommodate the Scottish Chamber Orchestra, Courtney Pine and Sophie Ellis-Bextor. Central location. Venue is self financed.
Local Authority: City of Edinburgh Council.
Membership: Edinburgh Arts & Entertainment, Music Venues Association
Policy: The Queen's Hall is committed to the presentation, promotion and production of live music in all its forms. The Hall seeks to to present work of the highest quality across all musical genres and

styles and to create opportunities for audiences from all sectors of society to access this work. Willing to premiere shows.
Performance schedule: usually open 7 days. Booking terms hire.
Booking terms:own promotions, splits, hires - as long as it makes financial sense.
Capacity: 900 standing / 850 seats
For disabled persons: Up to 299 wheelchair spaces - infra red sound system and induction loop - ramp at entrance - assistance available - all house facilities fully accessible - special toilet, low telephone.
Other Facilities: The Lothian Room, The Hope Scott Room and John Tunnell Room, suitable for meetings and receptions.
TECHNICAL:
Stage: Thrust 0.6m high, flexible. Performing area 9.75m x 7.92. No rake - floor part wood, rest moveable platforms, suitable for dance, no lino available, backstage cross-over, stage not heated. 1 operational set - no tab track - 120kg permitted on bars. Get-in via front or back. Scale stage plans available.
Lighting: 200A 3 phase supply. Also 63A 3 phase supply. Tango 48 Board. 1 x 12 channel front of house bar, 2 x 6 channel side bars, 6 Fresnels, 8 Preludes, 4 Profiles.
Sound: Integrated public address and show relay system with facility for background music in foyers and auditorium. Suitable for speech . A motorised bar with black backdrop. Acoustics suitable for music and spoken word.
Stage Management: Show relay/Tannoy to dressing rooms.
Backstage: 3 dressing rooms, access from front or back - 2 band rooms. Facilities include iron with board and numerous power points. Refreshments available from FOH. Two Steinway concert grand pianos. Advice given on accommodation. Staff - casuals available - security personnel. Backstage facilities accessible to disabled performers and staff.

REID CONCERT HALL, UNIVERSITY OF EDINBURGH

14 Bristo Square, Teviot Place, Edinburgh, Mid Lothian EH8 9AH Scotland
Mgt: 0131 650 2427 Mgt Fax: 0131 650 2425
Email: music@ed.ac.uk
Web Site: www.ed.ac.uk
ADMINISTRATION:
Seating/Capacity: 300; raked.
Contact: Moira Landels, Tel: 0131 651 3212

ROYAL HIGHLAND CENTRE

Ingliston, Edinburgh EH28 8NB
Tel: 0131 335 6210/ 6273 Fax: 0131 333 5236
Email: francesd@rhass.org.uk
Web Site: www.royalhighlandcentre.co.uk
Sales Manager: Frances Davidson, Lynne Haining
Capacity: 10,500

ROYAL LYCEUM

Grindlay Street, Edinburgh, Mid Lothian EH3 9AX Scotland
Admin: 0131 248 4800 BO: 0131 248 4848 Fax: 0131 228 3955
Email: info@lyceum.org.uk
Web Site: www.lyceum.org.uk
ADMINISTRATION:
Props: City of Edinburgh Council
Lessees: The Royal Lyceum Theatre Company Ltd
Artistic Director: Mark Thomson
Development Director: Zuleika Brett
General Manager: Ruth Butterworth
Theatre Manager: Jackqui Nagib
Management Accountant: Fiona Semple
Head of Production: David Butterworth
Major repertory theatre, built 1883; architect C.J. Phipps. Listed grade A; major refurbishment finished September 1996 base for Royal Lyceum Theatre Company Limited; funded by Scottish Arts Council, The City of Edinburgh Council.
Membership: TMA, Federation of Scottish Theatres, ABTT, S4T.
Policy: Repertory seasons of major world classics and production of new Scottish writing. 8-9 productions per year. Willing to premiere show. Occasional visiting productions. Performance schedule: open Tuesday to Saturday; 7:45pm evening performances (8:00pm during summer); 2.30pm matinees (1 or 2 per month).
Non-performance activities: Conferences, receptions, meetings, exhibitions.
Facilities: Seating - Theatre 658. Catering - Restaurant and three bars licensed until 1:00am. Access/car park: NCP Castle Terrace; nearest railway station Haymarket/Waverley, nearest coach St Andrew Square. For People with disabilities: Designated orange badge parking within 50m, 9 wheelchair spaces in Stalls level adjacent to other seats, lifts to all areas, level at entrance, induction loop all levels + infra-red system, adapted toilet, low level public telephones, restaurant seating not fixed, staff training. Any specific requirements contact Theatre Manager/House Manager.
TECHNICAL:
Stage: Proscenium arch. Pros opening 8.46m x 7.16m, 7.47 pelmet, wing widths 2.44m SR, 112.78 sq m SL, stage raked 1:24, floor hardboard over wood, suitable for dance, no lino available, understage cross-over, stage heated. Height of grid 20m. 55 single purchase counterweight including 2 up/down stage SWL 450kg. Spot hemps as required. Full black masking. White Cyc. Red/gold house tabs flown No. 1 bar. Removable forestage 12.6m x 1.6m. Orchestra pit 12.6m x 1.5m or 12.6m 3.7m accommodates 12/40. Get-in via lift 4.6m from street, SWL 5000kg. Lift depth 6.8m , width 2.9m, height 3.07m. Tallescopes. Safety Curtain. Scale stage, fly and lighting plans available 1:25.
Lighting: Control Box situated in Gallery. Board: Strand 550 with Genius Software. Circuits: 208@2.5kw & 16@5kw. 100A 3 phase supply for Temp Board/on-stage. FOH Rig: Upper Circle: Single circuits PS+OPS, 10@Source 4 zoom 15/30deg. per side. Gallery: Single circuits from PS to OPS, 20@Robert Juliat 710SX 10/25deg 2k profile. Stock Lanterns: 30@Source 4. Profile body; 18@Source 4. 50 deg. lens tubes; 10@Source 4. 19 deg. lens tube; 10@Source 4. 26 deg. lens tube; 10@Source 4. 36 deg. lens tube;6@Source 4 10 deg. lens tube; 10@Source 4 A size Gobo holder; 10@Source 4 B size Gobo holder; 6@Source 4 Donut 10 deg; 20@Source 4. Donut 19-50 deg; 4@Cantata 11/26 1.2k; 8@Cantata 18/32 1.2k; 8@Cantata 26/44 1.2k; 5@Harmony 12 1k; 12@Harmony 15/28 1K; 8@Quartet 22/40 650w; 4@T64; 4@T84; 4@243; 34@223; 22@803 - no barn doors; 16@123; 14@264; 18@764; 10@23N MK1; 14@23 MK2; 10@PAR CANS; 15@Coda; 10@Birdies; 4@10 way Howie battens; 2@ Robert Juliat hot strike Korrigan Follow Spot operated from Gallery.
Sound: Operated from box rear of Upper Circle. Option of operating from Gallery or rear of Stalls available. Mixer: Soundcraft K3 Theatre, Soundcraft 200B 24-4-2. Playback: 1 x Tascam MD802R Mini-disc Player/Recorder; 1 x Tascam MD801P Mini-disc Players with BU-801 random buffer Teac Dap20 Player/Recorder; 3 x Revox B77 (1 x low speed 2 x high speed); 1 x Dennon CD; 1 x Pioneer Cassette Deck; 1 x Yamaha SPX 90 II; 1 x dbx 120XP sub processor; 5 x Roland EQ231 graphic Eq; 3 x Yamaha Q2031A graphic Eq; 8 x Shermann GXcub/401 (2 used as source for Gallery operation); 2 x Shermann GXB 110/300 (Stalls in-fill); 2 x Shermann GXB 118 Sub Bass; 6 x Bose 802 (on-stage playback); 4 x Bose 101 (2 used as Control room Monitors); 5 x Roland SRA Power amps; 4 x Carver PM 900 amps (3 used as on-stage playback). Mics: 1 x SM58; 5 x AKG CK451E; 2 x AKG 568; 1 x AKG D1200 E; 3 x ADR D113 DI box; 1 x ADR D116 DI box; 7 x mic stands.
Stage Management: Prompt corner SL - headsets, 10 outstations - show relay/tannoy to dressing rooms, backstage work areas and FOH.
Backstage: 10 Dressing rooms accommodating 24, access by stairs and lift - green room - wardrobe on level 5 with iron, laundry. Advice given on accommodation. Staff - 3 Stage, 3LX, casuals available, security personnel.

ST CECILIA'S HALL

Closed for refurbishment until early 2016

Niddry Street, Cowgate, Edinburgh, Mid Lothian EH1 1NQ Scotland
Mgt: 0131 650 2427 Hall Direct Line: 0131 650 2805
Email: Anne.McCrae@ed.ac.uk
Web Site: www.ed.ac.uk
ADMINISTRATION:
Seating/Capacity: 200; flat.
Contact: Anne McCrae Tel: 0131 651 2196

TRAVERSE THEATRE

Cambridge Street, Edinburgh, Mid Lothain EH1 2ED Scotland
Admin: 0131 228 3223 BO: 0131 228 1404 Fax: 0131 229 8443 Traverse Bar Cafe: 0131 228 5383
Email: admin@traverse.co.uk
Web Site: www.traverse.co.uk
ADMINISTRATION:
Artistic Director: Orla O'louthlin
Executive Producer: Linda Crook
Chief Electrician: Renny Robertson
Policy: The Traverse produces new and innovative writing of the highest quality plus visiting companies.
Perfs: Traverse 1 Tues-Sun 8.00pm. Traverse 2 Tues-Sun 7.30pm (various times)
Seats: Traverse 1 from 216 up to 270 depending on configuration. Traverse 2 up to 110
TECHNICAL:
TRAVERSE 1
Stage: Flexible seating system, 9 configurations. 3 proscenium, Pros to back wall 7.50, Pros 8.50 wide. 1 U-shaped ,10.70 x 6.20. 3 in round, 6.20 x 6.20. 1 Traverse, 13.60 x 4.70. 1 Thrust, 10.60 x 6.30. Seats from 240 up to 328 depending on configuration. 5 counterweight fly bar in pros arch. 8 hemp fly bars. Height to Grid 6.40. Tab track masking all round the auditorium.
Lighting: Strand 520 350 channels 250 attributes; 24 submasters, operated from soundproof control room at back of auditorium. Strand EC90 dimmers, 120-10amp, 24-25amp, 30 x Strand Cantata Fresnels, 10 x Strand Cantata PCs, 12 x Cantata 11/26 profiles, 16 x Cantata 18/32 profiles, 12 x Cantata 26/44 profiles, 6 x SL 15/32 profiles, 6 x SL 23/50 profiles, 16 x Par 64, 6 x Strand Quartet Fresnels, 6 x Quartet PCs, 8 x Quartet 22/40 profiles, 6 x Strand Coda Floods, 5 x Coda 4 floods. All Cantata with 1.2kW lamps, all Quartet with 650w lamps. Small selection of stands and bases, availability must be checked in advance. 100amp 3 phase temporary supply Stage left, please advise in advance.
Sound: Soundcraft K2 24:8:2 mixer. In control room at back of auditorium, 24 mono channels plus 4 stereo. 4 x D&B E9 full range cabinets (flown), 2 x D&B 1801 sub bass cabinets, 3 x D&B p1200A amplifiers, 2 x Sony MD players, 1 x Phillips CD player, 1 x Denon cassette deck. 6 x Shure SM58 microphones, 4 x AKG 190 microphones, 1 x AKG 568 condenser microphone. Please note microphones are shared between both theatres and availability must be checked in advance.
TRAVERSE 2
Stage: Flexible 3 row seating in 8 moveable modules. 5 configurations approx. stage space 5m x 5m. Grid height 4.50. No flys. Tab track masking all around perimeter. Get-in door 2.40 x 5.00.
Lighting: ETC Express 24/48 96 channels 24 submasters. Operated from control room situated stage right. Strand EC90 dimmers, 46 x 10amp, 2 x 25amp. 10 x Strand 743 Fresnels, 8 x Strand Quartet Fresnels, 15 x Strand Quartet Fresnels, 6 x Minuette PCs, 10 x Quartet 22/40 profiles, 2 x Strand Prelude 28/40 profiles, 4 x Minuette profiles (very scabby). Temporary 64 Amp 3 phase supply Stage right - Please advise in advance.
Sound: Soundtracs Topaz 18:4:1 Mixer. Operated from control room situated stage right. 2 x C-Audio RA2001 Amplifiers, 4 x Bose 802 full range cabinets, 2 x Bose 302 bass bins, 2 x Sony MD players, 1 x Aiwa CD player, 1 x Denon cassette deck. Shared microphone stock with Traverse 1.
BOTH THEATRES
Communications: Full switchable show relay system to all dressing rooms and green room. Prompt desks with cuelights and calls Not normally in use, so please advise in advance.
Get-in: scenic lift 4m x 2m from Ground floor loading bay. Direct from lift into workshop 14 x 9 through scenic corridor to Auditorium. Workshop suitable to build sets, not fitted out with heavy machinery.
Dressing rooms 4-6 people per room, showers and washbasins in each. There are 3 backstage toilets and a green room with microwave, kettle and television.

USHER HALL

Lothian Road Edinburgh, Mid Lothian EH1 2EA Scotland
Tel: 0131 221 6335 BO: 0131 228 1155
Email: linda.alexander@usherhall.co.uk
Web Site: www.usherhall.co.uk
ADMINISTRATION:
Props: Edinburgh Council
Events Co-Ordinator: Linda Alexander
Capacity: 2,900 standing / 2,200 seated

Edzell, Angus

INGLIS MEMORIAL HALL

High Street, Edzell, Angus DD9 7TF Scotland
Tel: 01356 623088
Email: hooda@angus.gov.uk
Web Site: www.angus.gov.uk
ADMINISTRATION:
Props: Angus Council
Cap: 180

Egham, Surrey

HYTHE CENTRE

Thorpe Lea Road, Egham, Surrey TW20 8BN
Tel: 01932 425684
Email: halls@runnymede.gov.uk
Web Site: www.runnymede.gov.uk
ADMINISTRATION
Props: Runnymede Borough Council
For bookings contact The Hall Booking Clerk on 01932 425 684
For viewing contact the Duty Manager on 01784 456102

LITERARY INSTITUTE

51 High Street, Egham, Surrey TW20 9EW
Tel: 01784 471116
Email: shampton@strodes.ac.uk
Web Site: www.strodes.ac.uk
ADMINISTRATION
Props: Strode's College
Cap: 100
For bookings contact Sandra Hampton

Elgin, Morayshire

ELGIN COMMUNITY CENTRE

Trinity Road, Elgin, Morayshire IV30 1UE Scotland
Tel: 01343 543 736 Fax: 01343 550 543
Email: ecec@moray.gov.uk
Web Site: www.moray.gov.uk
ADMINISTRATION:
Props: Moray Council
For bookings, call the Council on Tel: 01343 543 736
Fax: 01343 550 543
Centre Co-Ordinator: Nicola Nash
Cap: 90 Seated

ELGIN TOWN HALL

Elgin Town Hall, 1 Trinity Place, Elgin, Morayshire IV30 1UL Scotland
Tel/Fax: 01343 547 767
Email: elgin.townhall@technleisure.moray.co.uk
ADMINISTRATION:
Props: Moray Council
Cap: Main Hall Seated 504 + 148 in gallery; Dancing 367; Dancing/Seated at tables 311; Seated at tables 257; Supper Room Seated 225; Dancing 250; Dancing/Seated at tables 238; Seated at tables 180
For bookings Tel: 01343 562600 / 542746 Fax: 01343 563610
Caretaker: William McCook
Office details: Educational Services, Council Office, High Street, Elgin, Morayshire IV30 1BX Scotland

Ellesmere Port, Cheshire

CIVIC HALL

Hinderton Road, Neston, Cheshire CH64 9PE
Tel: 0151 336 1077 Fax: 0151 353 8223
Email: doreen.vickers@brioleisure.org
Web Site: www.brioleisure.org
ADMINISTRATION:
Props: Brio Leisure
Cap: 220
Manager: Doreen Vickers

ELLESMERE PORT CIVIC HALL

Civic Way, Ellesmere Port, Cheshire CH65 0AZ
Tel: 0151 356 6890
Email: debbie.ankers@brioleisure.org
Web Site: www.brioleisure.org
ADMINISTRATION
Props: Brio Leisure
Cap: 636
Manager: Debbie Ankers

THE GRANGE THEATRE

The Grange Centre, Sutton Way, Ellesmere Port, South Wirral CH65 8EJ
Tel: Fax: 01244 670 380
Email: d.sherlock@west-cheshire.ac.uk
Web Site: www.west-cheshire.ac.uk
Props: West Cheshire College
Theatre & Technical Manager: Dave Sherlock
Cap: 150 in college seating

TOWN HALL

High Street, Neston, Cheshire CH64 9TR
Tel: 0151 336 3840
Email: support@nestontowncouncil.org.uk
Web Site: www.nestontowncouncil.org.uk
ADMINISTRATION:
Props: Neston Town Council
Cap: 70-100 theatre style
Manager: Alison Kunaj

Ellesmere, Shropshire

ELLESMERE TOWN HALL

1-3 Willow Street, Ellesmere, Shropshire SY12 0AL
Tel: 01691 622 689
Email: clerk.ellesmeretc@btinternet.com
Web Site: www.ellesmere.info
ADMINISTRATION:
Props: Ellesmere Town Council
Cap: 250
For bookings contact Joanne Butterworth on 01691 622 188.

Ely, Cambridgeshire

THE MALTINGS PUBLIC HALL CONFERENCE & BANQUETING CENTRE

Ship Lane, Ely, Cambridgeshire CB7 4BB
Tel: 01353 662633
Email: themaltingsely@compass-group.co.uk
Web Site: www.themaltingsely.com
ADMINISTRATION:
Props: Compass Group
Cap: 240
Contact: Alice Sibley

THE BROOK THEATRE

49 Brook Street, Soham, Ely, Cambridgeshire CB7 5AD
Tel: 01353 721748 Mob: 07974 303464
Email: info@brookentertainment.co.uk
Web Site: www.brookentertainment.co.uk
ADMINISTRATION:
Executive/ Artistic Director: Daniel Schumann
For more information on Venue Hire, please contact the venue on: 07974 303 464 or email dan@brookentertainment.co.uk
Capacity: 10 to 350 (depending on seating arrangements).
TECHNICAL:
STAGE: Dimensions: 4m deep x 7.3m wide (9m including wings) x 0.55m high. Thrust stage extension 2.4m deep x 5.3m long x 0.42m high. Get in: double doors to either side of the stage and a moveable ramp which is normally set on stage left.
LIGHTING: 1 x Fat Frog lighting desk. 1 x 24ch DMX Dimmer Rack with patch bay. 12 x Par64. 8 x Par56 short nose. 4 x 1Kw Starlette Fresnel. 6 x 650w Fresnel. 4 x 500w Flood. 4 x Source4 Jr. 2 x Source4 Zoom 15/30. 13amp Non-Dimmed power and DMX are available on both wall bars FOH1 and LX1 bars.
Power: A large number of 13 amp sockets on the back wall of the stage along with 1 x 32amp 3 phase socket. A second 3 phase socket is available if the in house dimmer packs are not being used.
SOUND: 1 x Allen & Heath GL2400 32ch mixing desk . 2 x FBT HiMaxX60a 900w RMS active PA speaker. 2 x FBT HiMaxX100Sa 900w RMS 133Db Sub. 1 x Numark CDN22 Double CD Player. 1 x DBX twin 31band EQ. 1 x DBX Compressor Limiter. 32/8 multicore from the rear of the space split 16/4 to each side of the stage. Connecting cables to link the mixing desk into the multicore and to link all outboard equipment.

Enfield, Middlesex

FORTY HALL BANQUETING SUITE

Forty Hill, Enfield, Middlesex EN2 9HA
Tel: 020 8363 4774 Fax: 020 8363 8252
Email: info@fortyhallbanqueting.co.uk
Web Site: www.fortyhallbanqueting.co.uk
ADMINISTRATION:
Props: Enfield Council
Two rooms (250 standing, 180 seated and 160 standing, 70 seated)
Contact: Abbie Dix

Enniskillen, County Fermanagh

Pop. 15,000. Belfast 90 miles. Dublin 105 miles. Newspapers: News Letter, Irish News (dly); Belfast Telegraph (ntly); Fermanagh Herald; STD Code 028 66

ARDHOWEN THEATRE

97 Dublin Road, Derrychara Enniskillen, Co Fermanagh BT74 6FZ Northern Ireland
Admin: 028 6632 3233 BO: 028 6632 5440 Fax: 028 6632 7102
Email: ardhowen.theatre@fermanagh.gov.uk
Web Site: www.ardhowentheatre.com
ADMINISTRATION:
Props: Fermanagh District Council - After April 1st 2015: Fermanagh & Omagh District Council
Technician: Mick McLoughlin
Policy: Mixed programme, touring drama, music, opera, dance, films, exhibitions, concerts, pantomimes and amateur productions. Available for private functions, including trade shows and conferences. Theatre By The Lakes: Seats 290. Two bars, restaurant, lakeview terrace and marina.
TECHNICAL:
Stage: Proscenium, flat and level with optional thrust apron over orchestra pit, pros. 8700 wide, 5300 high to fixed pelmet. c.st-s right 4900, c.st-s left 5900. depth-rear of pros. wall to back wall - 8700, to x-over gallery 7475. Height (beneath fly floors) 4900, beneath roof beams - 7484. Flying: 12 installed sets, (capacity 33), single purchase, 400Kg per bar. Bar length 13000. S.M. sl corner (can be removed to s.r.) scenery store s.l. (capacity 79m2) Orchestra Pit 30m2, 2600m below stage.
Lighting: 120 way Gemini II, with full back-up and disc storage, Dimmers Rank-Strand permus II, (24 5k, 96 2.5k). Additional power 2 200A tpn situated USL.
1 roll drum projection screen.
Sound: 16/4/2 mixer by Audix Ltd., 27 mic inputs, 19 loudspeaker outlets, 2 MD

players, 1 CD player, 1 stereo cassette deck.
Desk by Audix Ltd., c/w paging, show relay, twin ring intercom, cue lights and effects circuits.
Dressing Rooms: 6 rooms for 50 persons, on 3 floors. S.M. office, green room, showers.

Studio Theatre:
Seats: 45-50
Policy: Rehearsal room and readings.
Facility for electrics (24 circuits 2.5k) and sound size: 7900 by 7850.

Epsom, Surrey

Pop. 70,000. London 19 miles.
Newspapers: Epsom Herald; Epsom & Ewell Advertiser (thurs); Epsom Guardian; Epsom News; Epsom Planet. STD code 01372

EPSOM PLAYHOUSE

Ashley Avenue, Epsom, Surrey KT18 5AL
Mgt: 01372 742 226 BO: 01372 742 555
Tech: 01372 728 887 Mrkt: 01372 740 371
Email: eteague@epsom-ewell.gov.uk
Web Site: www.epsomplayhouse.co.uk
ADMINISTRATION:
Props: Borough of Epsom & Ewell
Playhouse Assistant Manager: Elayne Teague
Contact: eteague@epsom-ewell.gov.uk
Production/Technical Manager: Simon Banks
Contact: playhousetech@epsom-ewell.gov.uk
Policy: Touring - opera, dance, drama, concerts, films pantomime, jazz and rock music, amateur productions, conferences and trade shows.
Perfs: Variable
Capacity: Main auditorium 450; 432 with Orchestra Pit; 396 with forestage in place. Studio 80. 2 Bars/Coffee Bar/Restaurant.
TECHNICAL:
STAGE: End-on proscenium theatre, with a courtyard-style auditorium. Pros; Width 11.5m 37' 9", Width (between tormentors) 9.1m 29'9", Height 4.97m 16' 4". Back wall to; Safety Curtain 6.85m 22' 5", Pros. 7.83m 25' 3", Stage edge 9.35m 30' 8", Forestage edge 11.87m 38' 11". Width between; Fly floors 11.2m 35' 9", Columns 14.35m 47' 1", Wing Depth : SR 3.2m 10' 6", SL 1.64m 5' 4". Height; Grid 10.88m 35' 8", Under fly floor 5.18m 16' 9", Into wings 2.1m 6' 10". Get - In Width 1.5m 4' 11", Height 2.9m 9' 6".
LIGHTING: Standard rig of fresnels and profiles overhead, profiles FoH, and source four PARs on booms. Booms cannot be moved. LX bars on electric winches, 5 of 300kg each. Onstage bars are 10m wide ladder bars, advance bars are 8.5m wide standard barrel. Small stock of lanterns additional to those in the standard rig. Stock of Lee filters (101-205), cables, grelcos, gobos, gobo holders etc. 138 x 2.4kW dimmers. 6 x 4.8kW dimmers. ETC 'Impression 2' memory desk (600 cues, 24 subs). DMX control. Facility to patch touring desks to DMX in control room, auditorium or at prompt desk. 2 x DMX lines from control room to dimmer room, patchable via splitters to both fly floors, both wings (US and DS), onstage LX bars (all bars on 1 feed), each advance bar (individually), LX bridges and pit. Either DMX universe may appear at any point, but not both universes. 2 x Pani HMI 1200 followspots on perch at rear of auditorium, with view of whole stage (but max height of 2m above floor upstage). Production desk position in mid stalls with mains power, 2 x DMX line, comms, cuelight, houselight control, working light control and audio tieline.
SOUND: FOH; 2 x QSC RMX 1450 amps drive 3 x Martin CX2 per channel - 1 flown at pros height, 2 at gallery floor height. 1 x QSC RMX 1850 amp drives 1 x Martin BX2 bass unit per channel Combined system power 1200 Watts per channel FOH system is permanent and not movable. Dual 31-band eq. Foldback; 3 x 350 W / channel amps, 2 x Martin F12, 2 x JBL 15" + horn wedge, 2 x Martin CX2, 2 x EV S200. Mixing; Allen & Heath GL3300 24:8:2, permanently situated in a control room. Soundcraft LX7ii 24:4:2. Various Microphones available. Playback / Signal Processing; 2 x CD, 2 x Cassette, 2 x Minidisc, 2 x effects unit (Yamaha / Alesis), 4 x dual 31-band graphic (Yamaha / Behringer), 2 x Alesis 3630 Dual channel compressor/limiter, *1 x MD,CD,FX unit available at FoH position. All other equipment in control room only.
TOURING POWER: 63A single phase supply in stage left wing. 63A or 32A Ceeform connectors. 100A 3-phase supply in stage left wing. 125A Ceeform connector (No facility to 'tail in').
STAGE COMMUNICATIONS: Prompt desk stage right. Audio show relay and calls to dressing rooms. Comms to SL, lighting, sound, flys, followspots. CCTV show relay and pit/conductor relay to prompt desk, SL and SR wings, flys.
ORCHESTRA PIT: 11m x 3m, 2m deep (ie floor 2m beneath stage level). Conductor's rostrum 0.2 or 0.4m high, 1.2m square. Illuminated conductors music stand. 13 x illuminated music stands on dimmer feed, controlled from prompt desk. CCTV camera to show conductor on monitors in wings and at prompt desk. Access to pit through auditorium only. Use of pit removes requires removal of first row of auditorium seating (18 seats).
DRESSING ROOMS: 5; Capacity 86 persons. Domestic washing machine & tumble dryer. Iron & board.
Full Technical Specifications available on www.epsomplayhouse.co.uk.

Ewell, Surrey

BOURNE HALL

Spring Street, Ewell, Surrey KT17 1UF
Tel: 020 8393 9571 Fax: 020 8786 7265
Email: bournehall@epsom-ewell.gov.uk
Web Site: www.epsom-ewell.gov.uk
ADMINISTRATION:
Props: Epsom & Ewell Borough Council
Cap: 360
Manager: Bul Bul Mohammed
Multi-purpose venue. Available for Hire for concerts, recitals, conferences, dinner dances and weddings. The venue also houses a museum, library, gym and 3 banqueting suites and a minor hall that seats 90.
TECHNICAL:
Stage 30' Width x 20' Depth X 15' Height. Limited stage lighting and sound.

EWELL COURT HOUSE

Lakehurst Road, Ewell, Surrey KT19 0EB
Tel: 020 8786 7400 Council: 01372 732000
Email: ewellcourthouse@epsom-ewell.gov.uk
Web Site: www.epsom-ewell.gov.uk
ADMINISTRATION:
Props: Epsom & Ewell Borough Council
Lessee: Crown Catering Group

Exeter, Devon

Pop. 105,000. London 170 miles.
Newspapers: Express & Echo (dly); Western Morning News (dly). STD code 01392

EXETER UNIVERSITY GREAT HALL

Reed Hall Streatham Drive Exeter, Devon EX4 4QR
Tel: 0844 472 2001 Fax: 01392 263 512
Email: eventexeter@exeter.ac.uk
Web Site: www.eventexeter.com
Seating/Capacity: 1,435

NORTHCOTT THEATRE

Stocker Road, Exeter, Devon EX4 4QB
Mgt: 01392 223 999 BO: 01392 493 493
Fax: 01392 223 996
Email: info@exeternorthcott.co.uk
Web Site: www.exeternorthcott.co.uk
ADMINISTRATION:
Executive Director: Kate Tyrrell
Perfs: Variable
Seats: 460. Licensed Bar and Food Bar
TECHNICAL:
Stage: Proscenium, Flat; Pros. opening 15.85m; Ht. of Pros. 6.55m; Depth of S/Line 9.14m; Ht. of Grid 14.33m; 23 lines, C/W Scenery Flying Ht. 7.01m; Flying Bars 16.17m; W/Widths P.S. 2.74m. O.P. 2.74m; Prompt Cnr. mobile P.S. Electrics.
Lighting: Strand 530 & 140 dimmers

Sound: Soundcraft Series 2; 3 mini Disc Recorder/Player; 1 Rexl/Reel 7.5 15 IPS. Current Details on Lighting & Sound, on request.
Dressing Rooms 4; Accom. 36; 2 Showers; Orchestra Pit Semi-Circle approx. 3.66m radius, 18 persons.

THE RIVERSIDE LEISURE CENTRE

The Plaza, Cowick Street, Exeter, Devon EX4 1AF
Tel: 01392 221 771 Fax: 01392 499 676
Email: riversideexeter@parkwood-leisure.co.uk
Web Site: www.parkwood-leisure.co.uk
ADMINISTRATION:
Props: City Centre Leisure
Duty Manager: Daryl Cole
Deputy Manager: Darren Parrot
Policy: large sports hall arena used for Concerts, Theatre Productions, Cap: 1250 seated
TECHNICAL:
Arena West: Stage: Platform stage made from units 1.83m x 2.44m. Performing area 9.75m x 7.31m. No rake - Merrick Sico units, not suitable for dance, possible backstage crossover, stage not heated. Height of grid 10m - several fixing points - 1 tonne per point permitted - 2 flats, blue tabs - black screen at rear - back wall panelled. Several 13A independent circuits. Get-in via rear of stage, ground level, drive-in doors 3.5m x 2.6m. Cherry picker. Scale stage and lighting plans available.
Lighting: 16 channel manual board, 16 circuits, operated from rear of auditorium or front of stage area - 1 x 60A 3 phase, 1 x 160A 3 phase, 3 x 32A single phase supplies available for temporary board, 12 spots, 4 fresnels, 12 pars, 4 x 4 circuit battens, 2 x CSI followspots, operated from side balcony.
Sound: Third Generation 24 channel mixer, flexible operating position, 6 speakers - 2 x 1000w amps, 1 x 675w amp - 24 channel graphic equaliser, foldback sound, compensator limiter, 6 x SMB58 mics, 1 x Citronic cassette deck, disco deck, Citronic twin record decks, PA system. Acoustics suitable for music and spoken word.

THE CORN EXCHANGE

Formerly St George's Hall
Market Street, Exeter EX1 1BW
Tel: 01392 665 866 Fax: 01392 665 940
Correspondance Address: Exeter Corn Exchange Office, 1 George Street, Exeter, EX1 1BU
Email: cornexchange@exeter.gov.uk
Web Site: www.exeter.gov.uk/cornexchange
ADMINISTRATION:
Seating/Capacity: 500 Theatre Style.
Manager: David Lewis
Fully licensed bar and catering services available.
TECHNICAL:
STAGE: Dimensions: Pros. Width: 9.1m, Height: 4.2m, Depth from Iron: 7.4m, Depth from Apron: 8.6m, Apron Depth: 1.2m, Stage height from hall floor: 1.2m, Apron to FOH Sound position: 29.0m. Portable staging. 9 no Sico stage units 2400mm length x 1200mm width x 600mm height. Get-In: 1440mm x 1955mm.
LIGHTING: Desk: Strand 200 Lighting Desk 48 Channel. Strand s72 Demultiplexer. 1 x permus 24 x 10amp dimmer. 1 x Permus 12 x 10amp dimmer. Stage Lighting: 1st LX Bar: 8 x Cantata F 1 Fresnel with barndoors. 2nd LX Bar: 4 x Nocturne 500 Symmetrical Floods & 2 Strand PAT 23. 3rd LX Bar: 4 x 500/ 4 Quad Cyc Flood. Side Stage: 2 x Strand Pat 50 (1 either side). FOH Lighting: Bar One, 6 x Par cans each side (in pairs 3 x 2) ; Bar Two, 3 x Cantana 11/26.
SOUND: Allen & Heath Mix Wizard WZ3 16:2 Mix Wizard. 2 x Yamaha XP Amplifiers. 2 Martin Audio Blackline F15+ speakers facing into main hall. 6 x Turbosound Impact 50 delay speakers down side of hall (3 each side). Denon CD/ MP3 Player. 3 chrome mic stands. 3 Shure 565SD Unisphere mics. 1 Shure SM58. 1 Shure C606. 1 Gemini UX1600 radio mic. Various leads. Induction loop in the main hall.

WESTPOINT ARENA AND EXHIBITION CENTRE

Westpoint, Clyst St. Mary, Exeter, Devon EX5 1DJ UK
Tel: 01392 446000 Fax: 01392 445843
Email: info@westpoint-devonshow.co.uk
Web Site: www.westpoint-devonshow.co.uk
ADMINISTRATION:
Events Manager: Sarah Toms
Contact: Jo Blaby
Policy: Exhibitions and concerts
Seating capacity: 5,500 seated 7,500 standing
Stage and seating are not provided.
TECHNICAL:
Stage: Length: 85 metres. Width: 54 metres. Gross usable area: 4,590 square metres. Clear height: Eaves: 7 metres. Apex: 13 metres. Height of goods doors: 6 metres (Direct access to stage). Width of goods doors: 6 metres (Direct access to stage). Floor surface: Asphalt. Floor loading: 100KN/square metre. Roof loading: 3.2 tonnes per frame evenly distributed, frames at 6.6 metre centres. Power: 400 amp high level bus bar and 600 amp single point supply. House lighting: Adjustable to 500 lux maximum. Heating and ventilation: By air handling units at roof level. Box Office.

Exmouth, Devon

THE PAVILION

The Esplanade, Exmouth, Devon EX8 2AZ
Tel: 01395 222477 BO: 01395 222477
Email: exmouthpavilion@ledleisure.co.uk
Web Site: www.ledtickets.co.uk
ADMINISTRATION
Props: LED Leisure Management Ltd.
Cap: 550
Manager: Jannette Cass

Falkirk

FALKIRK TOWN HALL

West Bridge Street, Falkirk, Stirlingshire FK1 5RS Scotland
BO: 01324 506 850 Mgt: 01324 506 174
SD: 01324 506 192
Email: venue@falkirkcommunitytrust.org
Web Site: www.falkirkcommunitytrust.org
ADMINISTRATION:
Props: Falkirk Community Trust
Capacity: 604-1,124 (depending on layout)
General Manager: Julia Harkness
Technical Contact: Colin Proudfoot
Tehnicians: Brian Duff, Keith Stevenston, Greig Shankland
Arts Development Officers: Hazel Beattie and Alison Strauss
Film Officer: Alison Strauss
Stage: Proscenium stage, slight rake pros opening 34ft: height of pros 14ft. Fly tower with 28 counterweight fly bars. House Lighting: Strand LBX desk with genius software. 102 circuits. 2 FOH trusses flown by 1 tonne motors. Selection of parcans profiles fresnels floods. 2 CSI F/Spots rear of balcony. Sound. 3K rig soundcraft Delta, 24 Channel desk. Selection mics / radio mics.
Dressing Rooms: 2 chorus size, 3 performer dressing rooms. Showers. Disabled access backstage.

Falmouth, Cornwall

PRINCESS PAVILION

Melvill Road, Falmouth, Cornwall TR11 4AR
BO: 01326 211222
Email: astairmand@tempusleisure.org.uk
Web Site: www.princesspavilion.org.uk
ADMINISTRATION
Props: Tempus Leisure
Cap: 400 seated, 600 standing
Manager: Anna Stairmand
A multipurpose venue that caters for a wide variety of Theatre, live music concerts and shows. The venue can be

arranged as all seating, cabaret and all standing. Excellent vehicular access to backstage entrance. A wide range of lighting and sound needs catered for.

THE POLY
Church Street, Falmouth, Cornwall TR11 3EG
Admin: 01326 319 461 BO: 01326 319 461
Email: info@thepoly.org
Web Site: www.thepoly.org
Programme Director: Dot Peryer
Cap: 180 Seated

Fareham, Hampshire
Pop. 92,6000. London 70 miles.
Newspapers: Southern Evening Echo (Southampton); The News (Portsmouth) - both ntly. STD code 01329

FERNEHAM HALL
Osborn Road, Fareham, Hampshire PO16 7DB
Mgt: 01329 824 864 BO: 01329 231 942
Email: rcameron@fareham.gov.uk
Web Site: www.fernehamhall.co.uk
ADMINISTRATION:
Props: Fareham Borough Council
Ferneham Hall Manager: Rod Cameron
Marketing contact 01329 824863
A prestigious multi purpose venue conveniently situated mid-way between Portsmouth and Southampton.
Policy: Mixed programme of entertainment with use for international variety artistes, cinema, classical and popular music, cabaret, dances, exhibitions, theatre and wrestling.
Seats: 752
Octagon Lounge 120; Bar, Coffee Lounge/Restaurant.
TECHNICAL:
Stage: Proscenium arch. Performing area 16m x 6m - pros opening 14m x 5.5m - wing width 2m SR, 2m SL, 2m US. No rake with Harlequin lino, suitable for all dance. Forestage 14m x 2m, entrance SR and SL. No pit, but could be constructed. Backstage crossover, stage not heated. Height of grid 6.5m - 3 hemp sets, 25kg permitted on bars - maximum flying height 7.5m, 1m and 2m apart - 2 x Wipe track, - 3 sets of runners - silver, blue and black - white wall used as cyclorama - green house tabs drawn. 5 x 13A independent circuits. Get-in via backstage dock doors, 2.5m x 3.5m. Various scale plans available.
Lighting: Celco Ventura 242 way, 150 circuits @ 10A operated from control room - 3 phase, 1 x 200A an 1 63A single phase available for temporary supplies - 12 profiles, 120 parcans and 36 fresnels Thomas and Teatro - 2 x 1.2HMI followspots.
Sound: Allen & Heath 32:4:2 desk, operated from control room - Amcron amps - 6 x Bose 802, 1 x 302 subs 4 x Bose 802 foldback speakers - Shure mics *x Radio Mics - Denon CD, Tape and DAT. Acoustics suitable for music and spoken word.
Stage Management: Prompt corner SL - ring intercom, 8 outstations, show relay to dressing rooms.
Backstage: 3 dressing rooms, access by stairs backstage - Green Room - 2 power points in dressing rooms, 8 in Green Room. Staff - 3 Technicians - casuals available.
Backstage facilities not accessible to disabled performers and staff.

Farnham, Surrey
Pop. 32,000. London 40 miles.
Newspapers: Farnham Herald (fri). STD code 01252

FARNHAM MALTINGS
Bridge Square, Farnham, Surrey GU9 7QR
Tel: 01252 745444 Fax: 01252 718 177
Email: boxoffice@farnhammaltings.com
Web Site: www.farnhammaltings.com
Chief Executive: Gavin Stride
General Manager: Nikki Small

Felixstowe, Suffolk
Pop. 35,000. London 83 miles. STD code 01394

FELIXSTOWE LEISURE CENTRE
Undercliff Road West, Felixstowe, Suffolk IP11 2AE
Tel: 01394 670 411 Fax: 01394 277 456
Email: enquiries@felixstoweleisurecentre.co.uk
Web: www.felixstoweleisurecentre.co.uk
ADMINISTRATION
Props: Suffolk Coastal District Council
Bookings Manager: Alice Palmer
Cap: 250

SPA PAVILION THEATRE
The Sea Front, Undercliff Road West, Felixstowe, Suffolk IP11 2DX
Mgt: 01394 288 052
Email: info@thespapavilion.com
Web Site: www.thespapavilion.com
Closed until Further Notice.

Fenwick, Ayrshire

FULTON HALL
91 Main Road, Fenwick, Ayrshire KA3 4AG Scotland
Tel/Fax: 01560 600 809
ADMINISTRATION:
Props: East Ayrshire Leisure
Caretaker: Mrs Haggerty
Cap: 120

Ffestiniog, Gwynedd

FFESTINIOG VILLAGE HALL
6 Moyl Gwyl Ffestiniog, Gwynedd LL41 4PB Wales
Tel: 01766 762313
ADMINISTRATION:
Cap: Downstairs 120; Gallery 50
For bookings contact:
Basic stage facilities with some lighting and amplification available. Ground floor access to disabled persons. No reception or permanent staff. Several stage lights and hearing induction loop system.

Findochty, Morayshire

FINDOCHTY TOWN HALL
Station Rd, Findochty, Morayshire AB56 4SG Scotland
ADMINISTRATION:
Props: Moray Council
Cap: Seated 140; Dancing 160; Dancing/Seated at tables 136; Seated at tables 112.

Fishguard, Pembrokeshire

THEATR GWAUN
West Street, Fishguard, Pembrokeshire SA65 9AD
Tel: 01348 873421
Email: theatrgwaun@gmail.com
Web Site: www.theatrgwaun.com
ADMINISTRATION
Props: Theatr Gwaun Community Trust
Cap: 179
For bookings contact Box Office 01348 873421

Fleet, Hampshire

THE HARLINGTON
Fleet Road, Fleet, Hampshire GU51 4BY
Tel: 01252 811 009
Email: customerservices@fleet-tc.gov.uk
Web Site: www.theharlington.co.uk
ADMINISTRATION:
Props: Fleet Town Council
Cap: 400
Manager: Alex Robins

Fleetwood, Lancashire

Pop. 29,530. London 234 miles. Newspapers: Evening Gazette (6 days per week); Fleetwood Weekly News (fri). STD code 01253

MARINE HALL

The Esplanade, Fleetwood, Lancashire FY7 6HF
Mgt: 01253 887693 BO: 01253 887693
Email: marinehall@wyre.gov.uk
Web Site: www.marinehall.co.uk
ADMINISTRATION:
Props: Wyre Borough Council
Hall Manager: Gary Bullen
Policy: Corporation Multi-purpose Hall. Seats: 685. Restaurant with Bar. Wyre Lounge and Beer Garden.
TECHNICAL:
Stage: Proscenium, Raked; Pros. opening 8.53m; Ht. of Pros. 4.27m; Depth of S/Line 7.01m; Ht. of Grid 4.88m; W/Widths P.S. 2.59m, O.P. 2.59m.
Lighting: Switchboard: Eurolight-Ovation 240 CH. C105 output - standard back up computer 96 channels - 10V output demux rigger control. F.O.H. No. 1 Spot Bar 12 circuits, No. 2 Spot Bar 6 circuits, Arena 8 circuits; Stage: 5 x 10 x 2kw, Dips 4 x 2kw, 2 x 1kw Follow Spots CSI, 6 Patt.743 1kw, 6 Patt.763 1kw, 10 16/30 Profiles, 12 Patt. 60 Flood, 8 Patt.749 1kw Flood, 75 x 500w Fresnels/Profiles, 1 Batten Floats.
Sound: 1 Soundcraft Venue II 24:8:2 Feeding Audio low-mid-high. Yamaha SPX 900. Graphic GQ mics various, Shure AKG, 4 radio mics.

Folkestone, Kent

Pop. 45,490. London 70 miles. Newspapers: Folkestone, Hythe & District Herald (thurs); Folkestone & Hythe Extra (wed). STD code 01303

LEAS CLIFF HALL

The Leas, Folkestone, Kent CT20 2DZ
BO: 0844 8713015 Admin: 01303 228 600
Email: clivewatson@theambassadors.com
Web Site: www.atgtickets.com/folkestone
ADMINISTRATION:
Props: ATG Venues Ltd
General Manager: Clive Watson
Marketing Manager: Dave Cameron
Box Office Manager: Karen Hamilton
Technical Manager: Roy Hamilton
Policy: Concerts, Rock Concerts, Comedy, Exhibitions, Conferencing and Functions etc.
Perfs: From 7.00p.m. and 8p.m.
Seats: 825-1,004 - standing concerts 1,514.
Three Licensed Bars, one Cafe.
TECHNICAL:
STAGE: Proscenium, Flat; Pros. opening 6.70m; Ht. of Pros. 6.10m; W/Widths P.S. 3.5m, O.P. 3.5m + 12 x mobile extensions giving additional 48' x 12'.
LIGHTING: ETC Express 250 (24 subs plus memory - DMX) - 72 Circuits at 2.5kw operated from F.O.H. Control box. 25 T 84's, 12 Patt.123's, 10 CCT 1.2kw Fresnel, 4 Patt 743 1kw Fresnels, 2 Patt 243 2kw, 15 Pulsar 650w PC. 3 follow spots 1 operated from control box 2 from side balcony
SOUND: Soundcraft Spirit Live 4-2 24 Channel Desk, Digital delay, 4 TOA 380 SD speakers (plus circle infill) 1.1kw P.A. 5 Shure SM 58's, 5 Shure SM 57's, 1 AKG C451 E, 1 AKG CK1, 3 B55 AR 116 Active DI Boxes, 20 Assorted microphone stands.
BACKSTAGE FACILITIES: 6 dressing rooms, External phone available, broadband availble in 5 rooms, free satalite TV, access by side of stage - green room - band room.
Steinway Grand Piano available. Advice given on accommodation.
STAFF: stage, lighting, sound as required - casuals available - SIA security personnel from outside supplier.

QUARTERHOUSE

Mill Bay, Folkestone, Kent CT20 1BN
BO: 01303 760 750
Email: info@quarterhouse.co.uk
Web Site: www.quarterhouse.co.uk
ADMINISTRATION:
Props: Creative Foundation Trading Ltd
Capacity: 250 seated, 450 standing.
Contact: Allegra Galbin
For venue hire and meeting room enquiries please contact Sally Otteson on email
sallyotteson@creativefoundation.org.uk

Forfar, Angus

LOCHSIDE LEISURE CENTRE

Lochside Country Park, Craig O'Loch Road, Forfar, Angus DD8 1BT
Tel: 01307 464201
Email: conforlc@angus.gov.uk
ADMINISTRATION:
Props: Angus Council
Manager: Mark Nisbet
Cap: 192

REID HALL

Castle Street, Forfar, Angus DD8 5JX Scotland
Tel: 01307 464 201
Email: cultural@angus.gov.uk
Web Site: www.angus.gov.uk
To hire contact: Leisure Services, Angus Council, County Buildings, Forfar DD8 3WF
Tel: 01307 461460
Fax: 01307 462590
Main Hall: 520 Theatre style, 240 dinner dance
Lesser Hall: 90

Forres, Morayshire

FORRES HOUSE COMMUNITY CENTRE

High Street, Forres, Morayshire IV36 1BU
Tel: 01309 672838
Email: forres.house@moray.gov.uk
Web Site: www.moray.gov.uk
ADMINISTRATION:
Props: Moray Council
Manager: Douglas Cowie

TOWN HALL

51 High Street, Forres, Morayshire IV36 1PB
Tel: 01309 694002
Email: alan.taylor@moray.gov.uk
Web Site: www.moray.gov.uk
ADMINISTRATION:
Props: Moray Council
Cap: Main Hall Seated 250; Dancing 275; Dancing/Seated at tables 250; Seating at tables 200.
Lesser Hall Seated 100; Dancing 130; Dancing/Seated at tables 100; Seated at tables 90.
If you require further information please contact
Educational Services, Council Office, High Street, Elgin IV30 1BX
Tel: 01343 563396

Fort William

THE NEVIS CENTRE

Anaird, Fort William, Scottish Highlands PH33 6AN Scotland
Tel: 01397 700 707
Email: kenny@neviscentre.co.uk
Web Site: www.neviscentre.co.uk
ADMINISTRATION:
Props: Highland Council
Cap: 1,500
Manager: Kenny McLaughlin

Frinton-on-Sea, Essex

Pop. (Frinton & Walton) 12,710. London 71 miles. Newspapers: East Essex Gazette (fri); Essex County Standard (fri); East Anglian Daily Times. STD code 01255

SUMMER THEATRE

Frinton-on-Sea, Essex
Tel: 01255 674 443
ADMINISTRATION:
Write to: 21 Queens Road, Frinton, Essex CO13 9BL
Policy: One play per week, July-September

Seats: 230
Proscenium Stage.

Frome, Somerset

Pop. 20,000. London 105 miles. STD 01373

FROME MEMORIAL THEATRE

Christchurch Street West, Frome, Somerset BA11 1EB
Mgt: 01373 463 427 BO: 01373 462 795 Publicity: 07846 640496 Stage Mgr Tel/Fax: 01373 466254 Stage Mgr Mobile: 07974 716001 Hire of Assembley Rooms: 07575706092
Web Site: www.fromememorialtheatre.org.uk
ADMINISTRATION:
Entertainments Manager: Dawn Phillamore
Chairman: Humphrey Barnes
FOH Manager: Simon Plenty, Tel: 01373 466897
Secretary: Sandra Elmer
Stage Manager: Will Davis
Publicity Director: Humphrey Barnes
Box Office Manager: Judy Smith
Company Secretary: Roger Hatherell
Capacity: 536
Status: National touring house. Also home of Frome Amateur Operatic Society (founded 1906). Built by public subscription and opened in 1924. Owners: Frome Memorial Hall Trust. Self-financing and operated by volunteer staff.
Local Authority: Mendip District Council
Membership: IEAM, NODA
Policy: Variety, big bands, ballet, comedy, jazz, rock, amateur musicals and pantomime. Willing to premiere shows.
Performance Schedule: evening shows start at 7.30pm. Matinees at 2.30pm as required.
Booking Terms: Box Office split, first-call, hiring, by negotiation.
Other Activities: The management also operates the modern Assembly Rooms adjoining the theatre, which has full catering facilities and licensed bar.
Assembly Rooms
Cap: 150 for wedding receptions and recitals, 250 for dances. Resident managers and full staff. Car park adjoining.
Theatre
Facilities: Seats 536 in raked stalls and balcony. Catering: confectionery, ices and coffee; licensed bars in stalls and balcony. Snacks for artistes by arrangement.
Access: Car parks to rear of theatre and off Park Road, opposite. Station: Frome (from Paddington), 0.5 miles. Bus and coach routes: Frome Market Place and Frome Station approach.
For the Disabled: Four wheelchair spaces in stalls (contact FOH manager); Deaf loop system. Assistance available. New balcony bar not accessible to diabled.
Pros. arch. Performing area 7.2m x 7.32m, plus 2 aprons of 2m, tapering. Pros. opening 7.31m x 4.88m. Height of stage from floor 1.3m. Wing widths 2.75m SR, 2.75m SL. Border from stage 3.65m. Stage rake, 1 in 19.2. Floor hardwood, suitable for all dance, under stage crossover. No grid, lines fixed to roof 7.92m downstage, reducing to 5.79m upstage. 28 Polyester sets, single purchase, 0.23m apart, 30kgs. SWL each. Permanent legs at sets 4, 9, 15, 20, & 22. Two half tab sets on sets 5, & 11. Red house tabs, drawn. Orchestra pit acc. 20. Pit is 0.38m below floor level. Scale stage, fly & lighting plans available.
Prompt position: stage right. Access ramp from stalls. Get in from lane at side of theatre.
Lighting: 300amp three phase supply to permanent installation. including 1-125amp C form 3 phase & neutral socket, 1-63amp C form single phase socket & 1-32amp C form single phase socket clean supply for sound. All for visitors use. 72 -10 amp dimmable circuits with DMX 512 control. Strand 300 series 48/96 desk with colour VDU. 4 - Strand patt. 223 fresnel. 8 - Strand patt. 123 fresnel. 2 - Strand patt. 60 flood. 8 - Strand Cantata 26/44 degree profile on front of house bar. 4 - Strand Cantata fresnel with barn doors on front of house bar. 4 - Strand Quartet fresnel with barn doors on front of house bar. 10 - Strand backdrop cyclight Coda 500/4 - 66 degree. 1 - 3 circuit footlight (each circuit 7 x 100 watt lamps.) 2 Strand 1000 watt Solo CSI follow spots.
Sound: 1 - 200w amplifier & 2 - Speakers (main aud.). 2 - Peavey Q231 - 31 band stereo graphic equaliser (1 - main aud., 1 - balcony). 2 - Peavey CS200 stereo power amp - 110w x 2 & 2 speakers (balcony). 1 - Soundcraft Spirit LX7, 24 channel mixer. 2 - Shure SM58 microphones & boom stands. 2 - Proel active di Box - Model DBA1CH. 1 - Sony CD & minidisc unit - Model MXD-D3. 1 - Canford audio talkback system, comprising; 1 - Tecpro PS711 power supply, 5 - Tecpro single-muff headsets SMH210 & 5 - Tecpro beltpack outstations. 1 - Technics digital piano - Model SX-PX201M, with fully weighted keyboard. 1 - Induction loop system for the deaf. Accoustics suitable for music and the spoken word.
Backstage: Four dressing rooms (3 plus chorus, acc. 25), quick-change room by arrangement, access by backstage. Iron and ironingboard. Hot and cold beverages by arrangement. Advice given on accommodation. Staff - 1 stage, 1 lighting, casuals available. Stairs from dressing rooms to stage (L&R), not accessible to disabled performers and staff.

MERLIN THEATRE

Bath Road, Frome, Somerset BA11 2HG
Admin Tel/Fax: 01373 461 360 BO: 01373 465 949
Email: claudia@merlintheatre.co.uk
Web Site: www.merlintheatre.co.uk
ADMINISTRATION:
Props:Merlin Theatre Trust Ltd.
Director: Claudia Pepler
Technical Manager: Matthew Tipper
Marketing Officer: Claudia Pepler
Policy: The theatre promotes visits by touring companies - drama, ballet, mime and music. It is available for hire. It is a community theatre (drama workshop and college facility during school hours).
Perfs: 7.45 (Mats. variable)
Seats: 240. Bar, Coffee Bar, Ice Cream.
TECHNICAL:
Stage: Adaptable. Open, Proscenium, Round; Flat; Pros. Opening 9.00m; Ht. of Pros. 5.50m; Depth of S/Line 10.50m; Ht. of Grid 5.50m; W/Widths P.S. 4.00m, O.P. 4.00m; Prompt Cnr. P.S.
Lighting: 6 x T Spots (T84 1000w); 4 Patt.23; 6 SPR Profile 500w, 8 MFR Fresnel 1,000w TH: 4 Cantata PC 1,200w, 4 MFL 500w Flood Lights, Cyc. Lighting: 3 6B Lengths of Batten 3 x 6CY Trough Groundrows; 4 colour circuits, 900w per circuit above, 900w per circuit below. Total 1,800w per colour; Voltage 240; Max. Load of control board 200 amps; 57 circuits; 24 Dimmers, (Action 24 Computerised), wattage 2,000. Most sockets can be paired.
Sound Equip: Please contact venue for details.
Dressing Rooms: 2; Accom. 20; 2 Showers.

Gatehead, Ayrshire

GATEHEAD VILLAGE HALL

2a Fairlie View, Gatehead, Ayrshire KA2 0AU Scotland
Tel: 01563 554 940
Web Site: www.eastayrshireleisure.com
ADMINISTRATION:
Props: East Ayrshire Leisure
For bookings contact Halls Officer: Alison Kerr

Gateshead, Tyne and Wear

CAEDMON HALL

Central Library, Prince Consort Road, Gateshead, Tyne and Wear NE8 4LN
Tel: 0191 433 8480
Email: privatehires@gateshead.gov.uk
Web Site: www.gateshead.gov.uk
ADMINISTRATION
Props: Gateshead Council
Cap: 240 theatre style
For bookings contact Janice Holmes
Full sound and lighting rig.

THE SAGE GATESHEAD

The Royal Northern Sinfonia is the orchestra for The Sage

St. Marys Square, Gateshead Quays, Gateshead, Tyne and Wear NE8 2JR
Switchboard: 0191 443 4666 Bookings: 0191 443 4661
Email: corin.mcewan@sagegateshead.co m
Web Site: www.sagegateshead.com
Cap: Hall 1 - 1,700, Hall 2 - 400
Performance Programme Manager: Tamsin Austin

Glasgow, Strathclyde

Pop. 861,898. London 394 miles.
Newspapers: Daily Record (dly); Evening Times (ntly); Herald (dly); The Scotsman (dly). STD code 0141

BARROWLAND

244 Gallowgate, Glasgow, Strathclyde G4 0TT Scotland
Tel: 0141 552 4601 Fax: 0141 552 4997
Email: info@glasgow-barrowland.com
Web Site: www.glasgow-barrowland.com
Manager: Tom Joyes
Capacity: 1,900

BRAEHEAD ARENA

Unit 25 Braehead Shopping Centre Kings Inch Road, Glasgow, Strathclyde G51 4BP Scotland
Mgt: 0141 886 8300 BO: 0141 886 8300
Fax: 0141 885 4620
Email: scott-martin@capshop.co.uk
Web Site: www.braehead-arena.co.uk
ADMINISTRATION:
Operations Director: Lauren Little
Marketing Director: Christine McDonald
Finance Manager: Amanda Clark
Policy: Multi-purpose arena that can meet a variety of staging configurations, pop concerts, sports arena, exhibitions, conferences, product launches and banquetting etc. Also other areas including curling rink and bar and smaller ice skating rink.
Facilities: Foyer Bar.
Cap: 3,900 tiered fixed seats. Can accommodate up to 5,200 when in concert mode.
For Bookings and Enquiries: Scott Martin
TECHNICAL:
In-house stage and sound system.
Motorised mothergrid; multi-vapour lighting system. Power: 1000kva, 1400 amps, 3 phase. Height 12.8m maximum trim height.

CITIZENS THEATRE

119 Gorbals Street, Glasgow, Strathclyde G5 9DS Scotland
Mgt/SD: 0141 429 5561 BO: 0141 429 0022 Fax: 0141 429 7374
Email: info@citz.co.uk
Web Site: www.citz.co.uk
ADMINISTRATION:
Props: Glasgow City Council
Lessees: Citizens' Theatre Ltd
Director: Dominic Hill
Company Manager: Jacqueline Muir
Technical Manager: Jimmy Hayes
Marketing Manager: Alison Mertin
General Manager: Judith Kilvington
Policy: Repertory of Plays, Christmas Show and Seasons of Visiting Companies
Perfs: 7.30pm
Seats: Three theatres (600, 60, 40). Two bars
TECHNICAL:
Stage: Proscenium, Raked 25/500mm; Pros. Opening 7.75m; Ht. of Pros. 6.10m; Depth of S/Line 11.00m; Ht. of Grid 16.35m; Flying: 39 counterweight sets Ht. 6.10m; Flying Width 9.20m; W/Widths P.S. 4.27m; O.P. 4.27m; Prompt Cnr. P.S.; 39 counterweight sets; LX - Arri Imagine 250/210 way Lighting Board.
Lighting: On Stage - No.1 Spot Bar, 15 circuits, PS/OP Boom Poles, 10 circuits (linked), Fly Floor - 3 patch panels, each 10 circuits (7 x 2kw + 3 x 5kw), FOH - Gallery Front, 9 circuits, No. 1 Spot Bar, 12 circuits, No. 2 Spot Bar, 12 circuits, Box Booms PS/OP, 8 circuits (4 pairs), Circle Ends PS/OP, Each 12 circuits.
Dressing Rooms: 7; Accom. 21; 3 Showers.
Membership: TMA

CITY HALL

Candleriggs, Glasgow, Strathclyde G1 1NQ Scotland
Tel: 0141 353 8000 BO: 0141 353 8000
Fax: 0141 352 8006
Email: info@glasgowlife.org.uk
Web Site: www.glasgowconcerthalls.com
ADMINISTRATION:
Props: Glasgow Life
Seating/Capacity: 1,121 Plus 4 Wheelchair Spaces

GLASGOW PAVILION

121 Renfield Street, Glasgow, Strathclyde G2 3AX Scotland
Mgt: 0141 332 7579 BO: 0141 332 1846
Party Bkgs: 0141 333 1791
Email: manager@pavilliontheatre.co.uk
Web Site: www.paviliontheatre.co.uk
ADMINISTRATION:
Fully computerised Box Office.
Props: George Martin Associates
Manager & Licensee: Iain J Gordon
Administrator: Marie Donnelly
Policy: Plays, Variety & Pantomime, Rock and Pop, Conference
Perfs: Variable depending on show
Capacity: 1,449, seating (677 stalls, 341 circle, 413 balcony and 18 box seats)
TECHNICAL:
STAGE: Proscenium, Raked; Pros. Opening 10.97m; Ht. of Pros. 7.62m centre arch; Depth of S/Line 5.49m; Ht. of Grid 15.24m; 28 lines, C/W; Scenery Flying Ht. 7.62m; Flying Bars 10.36m; W/Widths P.S. 2.74m, O.P. 4.88m; Prompt Cnr. O.P.; Stage extension available to cover Orchestra Pit.
LIGHTING: Switchboard: Lightboard M 96 ways, Stage: No.1 Bar 20 Par 64, 3 Sil 40; No. 2 Bar 1 Batten 4 colour; No. 3 Bar 1 Batten 4 colour; No. 4 Bar 20 Par 64, 4 Patt.23, 2 Sil; No. 5 Bar 8 Iris IS; No. 6 Bar 1 Batten 4 colour; Ladders 16 Par 64; FOH: 10 Par 64, 4 Sil 40; Follow Spots 2 1kw CSI; Special effects available.
DRESSING ROOMS: 11; Accom. 30; 2 Showers; Orchestra Pit 9 plus M.D.

GLASGOW ROYAL CONCERT HALL

2 Sauchiehall Street Glasgow, Strathclyde G2 3NY Scotland
BO: 0141 353 8000 BO Fax: 0141 353 8006 Tel: 0141 353 8080 0141 287 4833
Email: events@glasgowconcerthalls.com
Web Site: www.glasgowconcerthalls.com
ADMINISTRATION:
Props: Glasgow Life
Concert Hall Bookings Contact: Alan Dickson
Capacity: 2,500 seated, including choir. 8 wheelchairs spaces.
Also Strathclyde Suite seating 500.

UNIVERSITY OF GLASGOW STUDENT'S UNION

32 University Avenue Glasgow, Strathclyde G12 8LX Scotland
Tel: 0141 339 8697 Fax: 0141 341 1066
Email: honsec@guu.co.uk
Web Site: www.guu.co.uk
ADMINISTRATION:
Capacity: 450
Contact: Gemma Higgins

KING'S THEATRE

297 Bath Street, Glasgow, Strathclyde G2 4JN Scotland
Mgt: 0141 352 8206 BO: 0844 8717648
SD: 0141 240 1300 Fax: 0141 240 1301
Tech: 0141 352 8201
Email: glasgowtheatremanager@theambassadors.com
Web Site: www.ambassadortickets.com
ADMINISTRATION:
Props: Ambassador Theatre Group Ltd
Head of Admin & Projects: Chris Evans
Marketing Manager: Yvonne Elliott
Technical Manager: Graeme Miller
Policy: All purpose
Performances vary from week to week.
Seats: 1,785 with provision for five wheelchairs. Disabled access to stalls. There is a licenced bar on each of the four floors - stalls, grand circle, upper circle & gallery.
TECHNICAL:
STAGE: Proscenium arch. Performing area 21m wide, pros opening 9.14m x 6.4m (mean height), Stage raked, 1 in 24, floor suitable for all dance, crossover, stage heated. Height of grid 16m (mean height), 52 counterweight sets, 0.2m & 0.18m apart, tab track, black box masking, 4 soft black legs, 4 soft black borders

(3.6m drop), 2 soft black borders (7.3m drop), Gerriets 'Opera' cyclorama, neutral, red house tabs, Slider trap SL & CS. Tallescope. Safety curtain. Scale stage, fly and lighting plans available.
LIGHTING: Strand 530i desk controlling 183 ETC Sensor [protocol DMX], allocated as follows; 2.5k - 46 circuits FOH; 54 circuits PS Fly Floor, 19 circuits OP Fly Floor; 4 a side Perches; 18 a side Stage Dips; 5k - 5circuits PS Fly Floor, 1 circuit OP Fly Floor, 2 a side Stage Dips. 10 x source 4 zooms; 8 x Source 4 [50 deg]; 2 x Source 4 [36 deg]; 6 xSource 4 [26 deg]; 6 x Source 4 [19 deg]; 12 x Brio [25/50 deg]; 8 x Brio [18/32 deg]; 8 x Harmony [15/30 deg]; 6 x Harmony [12 deg]; 6 x Harmony PC; 48 x Parcans; 12 x Cantata F; 24 Patt 743 [1k]; 24 Patt 243 [2k]; 4 x UV guns. 2 x Peasouper dry ice machines;2 x JEM fog machines; 2 x Minimist smoke machines; assorted telescopic floor and bench stands; 2 x 8-way pyrotechnic control units. STAGE MANAGEMENT: Prompt corner desk using cue lights to LX, Sound, Flys, Pit and six other outstations. Talkback via Tecpro headset system.
NB The King's has no sound installation. Stage management cue lights to all technical areasssss. Show relay/Tannoy to dressing rooms/FOH.

BACKSTAGE FACILITIES: 14 dressing rooms (one can be used as a company office), some ensuite/with own shower. 2 green rooms (1 with cooking facilities). Band room (understage), laundry room (basement), rehearsal piano available on request. Advice given on accommodation. Staff - 4 stage, 3 LX.
Membership: TMA

MITCHELL THEATRE

6 Granville Street, Glasgow, Strathclyde G3 7DR Scotland
Tickets available from computerised Box Office at the Ticket Centre, Candleriggs, Tel: 0141 287 4855 Theatre & Library: 0141 287 2999 Mktg: 01412 870 163
Email: maggie.macdonald@cls.glasgow.gov.uk
ADMINISTRATION:
Props: Glasgow City Council, Department of Cultural & Leisure Services
Bookings Officer for the Mitchell Theatre: Maggie Mcdonald
Community Facilities and Events Manager: Susan Dighan
Theatre Operations Manager: Stephen Kelly
Policy: Mixed programme, mainly drama and dance. Amateur and professional use. Conferences, exhibitions and social events.
Perfs: Variable, week to week
Seats: 418, with accommodation for up to five invalid wheelchairs;
Lecture/Exhibition Hall - 400. Coffee Bar, Licensed Bar Services, Coffee/Snack Bar also open 10.30 - 4.30 and at perf. times.
TECHNICAL:
Stage: Proscenium, Flat; Pros. opening 10.10m; Pros. Height 4.10m; Depth of S/Line 12.5m; 25 bars including tab tracks and electric bars; Scenery flying height 3.65m, flying bar area 10.2m; W/Widths P.S. and O.P. 2.8m av.; Prompt Cnr. P.S.
Lighting: Switchboard: AMC 80 way with M24, 3 preset FOH; FOH No.1 bridge 12 T64, No. 2 bridge 8 T64; Alcoves 3 T54 aside; No. 1 Spot Bar 12 Patt.743, 3 T64; No.2 Spot Bar 12 Patt.743, 3 T64; Floodbar 16 Patt.60; Portable Equipment: 6 x 4'6" Tele stands, 4 Patt.123, 4 Patt.23, 2 Follow Spots.
Full 16mm Film Projection and A.V. facilities. Show relay, paging.
Sound Equip: Soundcraft Delta 24 into 4 into 2; 4 Tannoy speakers - 3 MOS FET V800 amps; 2 Tannoy speakers - 2 EV 9000 amps; 5 TOA Radio Mics. 4 Foldback H/H Pro 200; 2 Cassette Decks Various Shure, AKG, Beyer Mics. 14 in total; 1 CD Player; Boss Reverb effect unit
Dressing Rooms: 4; Accommodation 40 approx; 2 Showers; No Orchestra Pit but accommodation for small orchestra in front of stage.

ORAN MOR

Top of Byres Road Glasgow G12 8QX
Tel: 0141 357 6200 Fax: 0141 357 6201
Email: info@oran-mor.co.uk
Web Site: www.oran-mor.co.uk, www.playpiepint.com
General Manager: Sandy Gourlay
Capacity: 120-230 seated, 500-600 Standing.

SCOTTISH EXHIBITION & CONFERENCE CENTRE

Exhibition Way, Glasgow, G3 8WY Scotland
Tel: 0141 248 3000 Fax: 0141 226 3423
Email: info@secc.co.uk
Web Site: www.secc.co.uk
ADMINISTRATION:
Props: Scottish Exhibition Centre Ltd
Director - Marketing: Sean Murray
Technical Manager: Tony Edwards
Seating/Capacity: 12,000 Hall 4: 9,276, Clyde Auditorium: 3000 and Lomond Auditorium: 620

THEATRE ROYAL

282 Hope Street, Glasgow, Strathclyde G2 3QA Scotland
Mgt: 0141 352 8203 SD: 0141 332 3321
BO: 0844 871 7647 Fax: 0141 332 4477
Email: pauldundas@theambassadors.com
Web Site: www.atgtickets.com
ADMINISTRATION:
Props: Scottish Opera Theatre Royal Ltd
Managed by the Ambassador Theatre Group
General Manager: James Haworth
Technical Manager: Graeme Miller
Administrator: Paul Dundas, Robin Davis
Policy: Scottish Opera Home Season. Visiting ballet and drama companies, classical, light concerts and Scottish Ballet Glasgow Season.
Perfs: 7.30
Seats: 1,547. Four Bars. 3 Buffets, cafe bar.
TECHNICAL:
STAGE: Proscenium, Flat. Pros. opening 10.362m; Ht. of 8.53m; Depth of S/Line 13.563m; Ht. of Grid 17.678m; 47 lines, c/weight; Flying Ht. 17.373m; Flying bars 15.849m; W/Widths P.S. 2.438m, O.P. 2, 133m; Prompt. Cnr. P.S.
LIGHTING: Switchboard: Galaxy - 1st Circle 240 ways; spots as required; dips as rig requires; spot bars as required.
SOUND: 10 chan. Mixer; 2 x Revox.
DRESSING ROOMS: 10; max accom. 69; Showers to all rooms.
BACKSTAGE FACILITIES: Orchestra pit for 110 (60 below stage).
Dock storage - inner dock. 100 sq.m., outer 50 sq.m. Staff restaurant (green room) - Snacks 10.00a.m. to end of interval.
Coaching room 24ft sq. (or extra wardrobe or dressing room). (24).
Front of pit on lift to form apron.
Membership: TMA

TRAMWAY

25 Albert Drive, Glasgow, Strathclyde G41 2PE Scotland
Tel: 0141 276 0950 BO: 0845 330 3501
Fax: 0141 276 0954
Email: claire.jackson@glasgowlife.org.uk
Web Site: www.tramway.org
ADMINISTRATION:
Props: Glasgow Life
Project Funding: Trust Foundations Sponsorship, Foreign Sources
Director: Sarah Munro
Senior Producer: Tim Nunn
Visual Arts: Claire Jackson
Policy: Producing, coproducing; international performance visual arts space with an emphasis on innovative, challenging and radical work in three disciplines. The programe is artist-centred and provides appropriate public contexts for completed or developing work by artists of all nationalities. Other emphases include cross-border exchange and co-operation. Touring productions occasionally hosted.
Perfs: Vary from week to week. Open 6 days
Capacity Tramway 1: 600
TECHNICAL:
Stage (Area One): Dimensions 40m x 26m. Performing area 26m (10m between side pillars) x 16m. No rake - floor concrete, suitable for dance only if stage provided, backstage crossover, stage heated. Height of grid 7.7m - fixing points as required - tab track - black tabs at rear - red plaster back wall can be used a cyclorama. 13A independent circuits. Get-in via rear of stage through small scene dock, stage level - dock doors

2.7m x 3.2m. Tallescope. Scale stage plans and full technical schedule available. Lighting: Strand Gemini board, 100 circuits, operated from lighting box at rear of auditorium.
Sound: No equipment. Operating position in lighting box or at rear of floor area. PA system. Acoustics suitable for music and spoken word.
Stage Management: Prompt corner position variable - cue lights and headsets. Show relay/Tannoy to dressing rooms.
Backstage: 6 dressing rooms accommodating 60 plus by side of stage - area can be made available for green room - wardrobe at stage level, washing machine, drier, drying room, several 13A sockets. Advice given on accommodation by Greater Glasgow Tourist Board. No permanent technical staff, but casuals available - security personnel. Backstage facilities accessible to disabled performers and staff.

Stage (Area Two): Dimensions 57m x 27m - height to ceiling 7.7m. Concrete floor. No lighting or sound equipment - supply available for temporary lighting - equipment may be borrowed from Area One. Backstage details as for Area One.

Stage (Area Three): Small performance gallery. Total dimensions 8m x 32m, height 3.5m. No lighting or sound equipment.

Stage (Area Four): Small performance gallery. Dimensions as Area Three. 36-way manual lighting board available.

TRON THEATRE

63 Trongate, Glasgow, Strathclyde G1 5HB Scotland
Admin: 0141 552 3748 BO: 0141 552 4267 Bar: 0141 552 8587 Fax: 0141 552 6657 Delivery and Get-In Address: 38 Parnie Street, Glasgow, G1 5LS
Email: info@tron.co.uk
Web Site: www.tron.co.uk
ADMINISTRATION:
Props: Tron Theatre Ltd
Artistic Director: Andy Arnold
General Manager: Lesley Renton
Production Manager: Dave Shea
Policy: Theatre, Dance and Music from the UK and Abroad, plus 2/3 productions a year by Tron Theatre Co.
Perfs: 7.45 pm
Capacity: Theatre 230. Raked fixed seating. Wheelchair positions - front row and upper auditorium right. Changing house studio - 70. Two cafe/bar spaces. Bar open all day.
TECHNICAL:
STAGE: 9.45m wide x 7.5m deep to setting line, 7m to front of auditorium stairs, 3m to underside of Tech Gallery. Prompt corner SL; Entrances - USL, USC, USR, DSL, DSR. Rigging: Bar Height from Stage 7940mm, 11 Double purchase Counterweight sets (200kg payload). Operated from SR Tech Gallery; 10 Hemp sets (2, 4 & 7 operated from SR remainder from SL), 2 Motorised hoists (250kg payload), Tension Wire Grid over seating with LX bars, 8 portable 4.3m internally wired bars - 6 circuits each. Masking Standard set-up - black traveller curtain along back wall, Side wipes under galleries SL & SR. Also available assorted borders & legs. Black masking flats - 1500 x 3000 & 750 x 3000. White PVC screen 9m x 7.4m. Misc: Braces and weights (10). Tallescope, Zarges & Ladders, Limited storage and workshop facilities.
LIGHTING: Desk: ETC ION (1024) with 1 x fader wing, Dimmers: 168 ways of Zero 88 Chili dimming, Power: 3 Phase supply. 63 amp - 3 Phase supply - SL. 32amp supply - SL. 63 amp Supply for O.B. at Get-in. Fresnels: 15 x 1k Harmony F, 10 x 1k Cantata F, 4 x 650w Quartet F. Profiles: 5 x 575w Source 4 19°, 10 x 575w Source 4 36°, 8 x 750w Source 4 25/50°, 9 x 750w Source 4 15/30°, 8 x 600w Strand SL 15/32°, 5 x 600w Strand SL 23/50°, 5 x 650w Strand Prelude 16/30° Pro Spot, 4 x 650w Strand Prelude 28/40° Pro Spot. Floods: 18 x 1Kw Starlette Floods, 2 x 1k Nocturne Floods, 1 x 1k Coda Flood. Pars: 30 x 1k Parcans. LX misc: 1 x 2k Strand Solo Follow Spot (in control room), 8 x Boom Bases, 2 x DHA Gobo Rotators RTR002 (fixed speed @ 5rpm) to fit, S.L. stock only, Iris's - 5 x strand and 4 x Source 4 stock, Selection of Gobos and Irises, 4 x lighting stands.
SOUND: Desk: Allen & Heath 2200. 24+ Channel, (Also Available. Yamaha LS9 - 32). Playback: 2 x Tascam MD 350 Minidisc player, 1 x JB Systems 560 Twin CD player, 1 x Yamaha SPX 2000 Reverb unit, Extra playback subject to availability. EQ: 2 x Yamaha EQ Racks (Set up for FOH Speakers), Extra EQ racks subject to availability. Amps: 3 x T&M 800 Pro (used for FOH and subs), 3 x QSC PLX1804. 600 watts per channel, Extra amps subject to availability. FOH: 2 x GAE 152TM loudspeakers (Permanently Rigged FOH). Speakers: 2 x GAE 1001F loudspeakers (Permanently Rigged FOH), Subs - subject to availability (2x T&M 215 Subs). Foldback: 2 x T&M 122 Loudspeaker, 2 x DAS 12 loudspeakers, 4 x Bose 101 loudspeakers (subject to availability). Microphones: We have a selection of mics - stock numbers and availability on enquiry. Shure SM 58's, Shure SM 57's, Audio Technica AT 857A, Audio Technica AT 195QMRX/ML AKG C391B, AKG 419 (clip mic), PZM's. Sound misc: Stock numbers on enquiry. Emo e520 Passive DI boxes. Telescopic mic stands, Boom arm mic stands, Banquet Stands. Music Stands, Keyboard Stands. Assorted Cables XLR, ¼ Jack, Speakon etc.
BACKSTAGE FACILITIES: Dressing Rooms: 6, with showers (2 Disabled Dressing-rooms.) Capacity varies. Laundry: 2 washing machines, 2 tumble dryers, drying cabinet. Facilities iron and board.

Glenrothes, Fife

ROTHES HALLS

Rothes Square, The Kingdom Centre, Glenrothes, Fife KY7 5NX Scotland
Tel: 01592 612 121 BO: 01592 611 101
Fax: 01592 612 220
Email: enquiries.rotheshalls@onfife.com
Web Site: www.onfife.com
ADMINISTRATION:
Theatre Manager: Anna Darmody
A theatre, entertainment and conference venue with two halls, adaptable stage and theatre seating, dance floors and full catering.
Main hall capacity 616 theatre style. Hall B: 204
Located 30 minutes by car from Edinburgh and St. Andrews.
TECHNICAL:
Stage (Hall A): A modular Sico staging system total 96 sq metres at variable heights of 750, 900, 1050 and 1200 mm provides conference use staging. For heavier duty, 33 sections of steeldeck are available (heights as for sico). Ramp available on request. Retractactable and mobile tiered seating with further rows of linked stalls seats available depending on stage layout. All seating removable for flat floor space of 825sq metres.
Full catwalk system 8.4m above floor height. Number of half tonne hanging points. Fixed lighting bars at 9.2m above floor height accessible from catwalk. House tabs on minibeam trussing are located as required to form false proscenium. 12 way remote control motor with additional chain hoists available. Main lighting grid flown above stage, 48' x 24' on chain hoists. Lighting: Strand 300 v2.6d lightboard and EC90 dimmers (120 @ 2.5kw, 24 @ 5kw). 24 dips split between prompt side and O/P, 16@ 2.5kw 4@ 5kw. Selecon Performer MSR 1200 Followspots available incl 6 colour changer. Lighting available - 18 x 1kw Cantata Fresnels, 18 x 1kw Cantata PC's, 56 x Par 64 (40x CP60 and 16 CP62), 8 x 1kw Cantata 18-32 profiles, 8 x 1kw Cantata 11-26 profiles, 10 x 575w ETC Source four zooms 15/30, 6 x Mac 250+ moving heads, 12 x 2kw Alto Fresnels. DMX ports located on catwalk and prompt side running to a splitter located in the control room. All DMX ports are 5-pin although we do have 3->5 pin converters.We have a standard lighting rig, plot available on request. If you intend to use our in-house lighting then we must receive all plots at least two weeks before the event. If no specific lighting plot is received we will use our standard rig.
Sound: Versatile Crest X8 32:8:4:2 desk and modular d&b sound system for conference and concert use. Cassette, Revox, MD, CD available. Induction loops

are fitted in Halls A&B and in meeting rooms 5, 10 & 11.
Backstage: Fully fitted dressing rooms. Cars and vans may be driven into the scenedock for unloading.
Stage (Hall B): Permanent alcove stage. Units as required, to form thrust stage, models catwalk, in-the-round or other configurations on request. Mobile tiered seating used normally but can be removed leaving flat floorspace of 225 sq metres.
Lighting: Strand MX board and EC90 dimmers. Lighting available. Shared stock with Hall A.
Sound: Versatile Yamaha 32CH Desk d&b sound system for conference and concert use. Cassette, Revox, MD, CD available. An induction loop system is fitted.

Glossop, Derbyshire

THE GLOBE

144 High Street West Glossop Derbyshire SK13 8HJ
Tel: 01457 852 417
Bookings Manager: Diana Virgo
Live music venue.
Capacity: 80 seated; 90 standing.

Gloucester, Gloucestershire

GLOUCESTER GUILDHALL

Gloucester Guildhall, 23 Eastgate Street, Gloucester GL1 1NS
BO: 01452 503 050 Admin Tel: 01452 396 382
Email: guildhall.boxoffice@gloucester.gov.uk
Web Site: www.gloucesterguildhall.co.uk
ADMINISTRATION:
Programme and Marketing Manager: Dan Charles
Email: dan.charles@gloucester.gov.uk
Props: Gloucester City Council
Cap: 250 seated, 380 dancing, Cinema 100, Blue Coat Room 60.
Bar, Workshops and Gallery.
TECHNICAL:
Flat floor performing area 30' x 40'; fixed platform 40'/15'.

Glyndebourne, East Sussex

London 52 miles. Newspapers: Sussex Express & County Herald (fri); Evening Argus (Brighton) mon-sat. STD code 01273

GLYNDEBOURNE FESTIVAL OPERA

Glyndebourne, New Road, Ringmer, Lewes, East Sussex BN8 5UU
Mgt/SD: 01273 812 321 BO: 01273 813 813
Email: info@glyndebourne.com
Web Site: www.glyndebourne.com
ADMINISTRATION:
Box Office and Customer Service Manager: Donna Marsh, email: donna.marsh@glyndebourne.com
Head of Communications: Laura Jukes, email: laura.jukes@glyndebourne.com
Production Managers: Tom Harrison email: tom.harrison@glyndebourne.com
Policy: Festival Opera Season
New Opera House opened in May 1994. Please contact venue for further details.
Cap: 1200

Grange-over-Sands. Cumbria

VICTORIA HALL

Main Street, Grange-over-Sands, Cumbria LA11 6DP
Tel: 01539 532 375
Email: contactus@grangeoversands.net
Web Site: www.grangeoversandstown-council.gov.uk
ADMINISTRATION
Props: Grange Over Sands Town Council
Cap: 300
For bookings contact Town Clerk

Grantham, Lincolnshire

GRANTHAM GUILDHALL ARTS CENTRE

St Peters Hill, Grantham, Lincolnshire NG31 6PZ
Tel: 01476 406159 BO: 01476 406158
Email: granthamtic@southkesteven.gov.uk
Web Site: www.guildhallartscentre.com
ADMINISTRATION
Props: South Kesteven District Council
Manager: Graham Burley
Cap: 210
Raked auditorium, full stage facilities. Function hall, studio space & gallery.

GRANTHAM MERES LEISURE CENTRE

Trent Road, Grantham, Lincolnshire NG31 7XQ
Tel: 01476 581 930
Email: Grantham@1Life.co.uk
Web Site: www.1life.co.uk
ADMINISTRATION
Props: 1Life and South Kesteven Council
Cap: Balcony (fixed seating) 350; Tiered seating 490; Floor seating 597; Total 1387
Manager: James Cole
The hall has been purposebuilt for concerts with top quality acoustics.
TECHNICAL:
Dimension: 35m x 28m x 9m
There are 50 staging units. Back stage area is 18m x 18m.

Gravesend, Kent

Pop. 88,000. London 22 miles.
Newspapers: Gravesend & Dartford Reporter (fri); Dartford Times (fri); (Kentish Times); Kent Today (mon-fri); Kent Messenger; New Shopper (wed). STD code 01474

WOODVILLE THEATRE

Woodville Place, Gravesend, Kent DA12 1DD
Mgt: 01474 33 74 56 BO: 01474 33 77 74 Marketing: 01474 33 7718
Email: woodville.halls@gravesham.gov.uk
Web Site: www.woodville.co.uk
ADMINISTRATION:
Props: Gravesham Borough Council
General Manager: Neil Chandler
Technical Manager: Stuart Labran stuart.labran@gravesham.gov.uk or telephone 01474 33 7456
Capacity: 810 seats with 50 standing or 1000 standing or up to 514 dining.
Policy: Mixed programme, musicals, plays, concerts, films. Available for private functions throughout the year. Perfect location for your events including, weddings, dinner-dances, conferences and exhibitions.
For hire contact:
hallhire@gravesham.gov.uk
TECHNICAL:
STAGE: Proscenium. Overall size 36 ft x 38 ft x 28 ft, Safety Curtain 36 feet high x 27 ft wide. Proscenium opening - min 12 ft high x 24 ft wide max 18 ft high x 30 ft wide. 20 x counterweight flybars. Dock doors onto loading bay - 10 ft wide x 16 ft high Height to grid - 50 ft. Orchestra pit - 26 ft long x 8 ft wide. Prompt corner - stage left.
SOUND: Four x RCF Event 1000 x 600w horns, two mounted permanently each side of proscenium arch, powered by RCF 1200MCF amplifier 1200w per channel. Four x Fane 1 x 15 200w floor wedge monitors/foldback driven by a Harrison 900w amplifier. Two x TOA control 160w infills powered by TOA 1300 amplifier 1200w per channel.
SOUND DESK: Sound craft 24 channel spirit live sound console. Call over system to all dressing rooms with show relay. Two Denon cassette players. One Tascam tape deck. One Denon CD player. One Yamaha SPX 90 Effects unit. Headset intercom system to stage flys spots, control box. One Pioneer minidisc player
LIGHTING: 1 Celco Venturer desk 72 channels. 2kw dimmer circuit racks.

Coemar 1kw follow spots. Six cell floods. 1000w Fresnels with barn doors. 42000w Fresnels. Eight 650w Profile spots. 20 1000w Profile spots. Two 400w U V Cannons. 48 Parcan Raylite. Six Martin Robo Scans. Two Strobes. One Mirror ball. Four flash boxes & firer.
DRESSING ROOMS: 8 dressing rooms for max 50 people. Orchestra room for 70 people. Four showers & toilet facilities. Relay & Cue call system.
DISABLED FACILITIES: 6 wheelchair spaces in main auditorium (with an adjacent companion seat) and an infrared hearing system for selected seats (headsets can be reserved at the time of booking or requested before the performance begins, subject to availability). An electric stair lift is installed in the foyer and one toilet facility is available at the rear of the auditorium.

Grays, Essex

Pop. (Borough) 127,000. Newspapers: Thurrock Gazette; Yellow Advertiser (both Friday). STD code 01375

CIVIC HALL

Blackshots Lane, Grays, Essex RM16 2JU
Tel: 01375 401 234 Fax: 01375 394463
Email: civic.hall@impulseleisure.co.uk
Web Site: www.impulseleisure.co.uk
ADMINISTRATION:
Props: Impulse Leisure
Manager: Mark Jennings
Technical Manager: Michael Rixson
Policy: Dance hall, catering, hires, trade shows, stage shows on any deal.
Seats: 747. 996 standing, 432 dance/dinner.
TECHNICAL:
Stage: Proscenium, flat with apron. Pros height: 4.8m, width: 12.1m, depth 0.5m. Stage depth: 10.3m. Wing width: 1.5m (max) OP & PS. Apron width: 13.8m, depth: 1.9m. Apron height from dance-floor: 0.9m. Stage height from apron: 0.2m. BP Screen (centre stage) dimensions: height: 5.5m, width 10.5m.
Dance Floor: 21.5m x 23.4m.
Electrics: 4x 13a sockets on stage. 1x 125A 3 phase, 1x CEE form 63a mains sockets on stage: 1 portable sound mains (max load = 63a). 3 phase portable LX mains (man load 100a).
Lighting: Desk: Strand 300 (360 channels). 84 Strand permus dimmers. 2 CCT silhouette follow spots (Iris, Dimmer, Colour change).
Disco rig control. Mac 500's & light jockey
Sound: Desk: Soundcraft 200B (16:4:2). 2 PPX 900 amps, 1 H&H power amp. 4 Bose 802's, 2 Bose 301's, 2 tannoy lynx monitors. 2 Technics CD Players. 1 Double Kenwood cassette player. 10 AKG Mics (D321S). Mini Disc.
Other: 1 Chapell Grand Piano. 1 Chapell Upright piano. 9 Sico stage extensions 2.45m x 1.22m.
Dressing room1 large splits into 3 with Marley doors. Shower and toilets.

THAMESIDE THEATRE

Thameside Complex, Orsett Road, Grays, Essex RM17 5DX
Admin: 01375 413 980 BO: 0845 300 5264
Email: thameside.theatre@thurrock.gov.uk
Web Site: www.thurrock.gov.uk/theatre
ADMINISTRATION:
Props: Thurrock Borough Council
Arts Manager: Mark Allinson
Technical Manager: Graham Robinson
Policy: Small scale tours, Pantomime, Amateurs, Films, Concerts, Conferences, Lectures, One Night Stands.
Seats: 315. Licensed Bar, Coffee Lounge
THAMESIDE TWO:
40 seat meeting room.
TECHNICAL:
Theatre is situated on third floor, stage loading via lift from side street to stage. Maximum flat size that fits in lift 3.2m x 1.8m. Collection of weights and braces. Scenery height Maximum of 3.2m on stage(no clearance fixed LX bars and borders) No flying space, backcloths and wipes drop 4.37m.
Stage: Proscenium, Flat; Pros. opening 9.07m; Ht. of Pros. 2.97m; Depth of S/Line 7.01m; W/Widths P.S. 1.83m, O.P. 0.61m; Stage Manager position S/R. Curved Stage Apron. Cushioned, light coloured, wood effect Harlequin dance floor. Crossover behind CYC. Lighting Desk AVO.SAP.2000 in LX box/projection room; Two F/Spots. Good range of profile and wash lanterns. Also Eighteen moving head lanterns. All LX bars are pre-rigged and fully populated. Black Drapes and gold house tabs. Roll down cinema screen.
Equipped for Digital Cinema Projection also 35mm Slide Projection. Video playback facilities on DVD, SVHS.
Sound Equip: CD, MiniDisc and Tape, JBL speakers, Allen & Heath auditorium mixer. Radio Mics. Eight way wireless talkback system. Below stage: Four dressing rooms have audio & video stage relay. Four showers. No Orchestra Pit but can accom. approx. 7 musicians by removing seats.

Great Yarmouth, Norfolk

Pop. 49,830. London 126 miles. Newspapers: Yarmouth Mercury (fri). STD code 01493

BRITANNIA THEATRE

Britannia Pier, Marine Parade, Great Yarmouth, Norfolk NR30 2EH
Mgt: 01493 842 914 BO: 01493 842 209
Fax: 01493 858 807
Email: info@britannia-pier.co.uk
Web Site: www.britannia-pier.co.uk
ADMINISTRATION:
Props: Family Amusements Ltd
On-Site Director: Darren Threadwell
Theatre/Pier Manager: Elaine Thompson
Policy: Closed October-March
Perfs: To suit show.
Seats: 1,270. Long John Silvers Bar adjoining and Lounge Bar
TECHNICAL:
Stage: Proscenium, Raked 1 in 26; Pros. opening 11.89m; Ht. of Pros. 4.72m at centre; Depth of S/Line 9.14m; Ht. of Grid 10.36m; 17 C/Ws 7 Hemp; Scenery Flying Ht. 5.18m; Flying Bars 12.19m; W/Widths P.S. 1.52, O.P. 1.52; Prompt Cnr. P.S. 4 Futore Scans plus smoke.
Lighting: Switchboard: Rank Strand M24 Memory board. F.X. Effects board; 12 F.O.H. Spots; 4 Battens 4 circuits; 1 Float 4 circuits; 4 Dips 3 circuits; 1 Floodbar; 2 Spot Bars; 2 Follow Spots.
Sound Equip: Studio Master Series 5 16 way mixer, 2 banks speakers F.O.H. Foldback Monitors on stage, 1 Foldback Monitors pit, Mixing Unit; 2 Bans Speakers 40w.
Dressing Rooms 10; Accom 37.
Orchestra Pit.

HIPPODROME CIRCUS

St George's Road, Great Yarmouth, Norfolk NR30 2EU
BO: 01493 844 172 Tel: 01493 780223
Email: chrisjay@btconnect.com
Web Site: www.hippodromecircus.co.uk
Circus building in the round with 32ft diameter drop-down water facilities (swimming pool standard).
Contact: Peter Jay
Capacity: 950

THE PAVILION THEATRE GORLESTON

Pier Gardens, Gorleston, Great Yarmouth, Norfolk NR31 6PP
BO: 01493 662 832
Email: info@gorlestonpavilion.co.uk
Web Site: www.gorlestonpavilion.co.uk
ADMINISTRATION:
Props: Great Yarmouth Borough Council
Publicity and Entertainments Officer: Stuart Malkovich
Cap: Cabaret Style 300
TECHNICAL:
Stage:
Proscenium, Raked; Pros. Opening 7.26m; Ht. of Pros. 4.52m; Depth of S/Line 4.80m; W/Widths P.S. 3.66m, O.P. 2.28m; Prompt Cnr. O.P. Max flying height 16ft 6", Bar length 26ft 8". 13xHemp fly Bars. 100kg max per Bar.
Lighting:
GSX Strand console, 50 channel DMX, 36 ways, 3 phase; FOH 18 par 64, 6 x 650w fresnels, 2 pre-focus spots. Follow spots 2.5kw.
Sound:
2 x 1200w amps, (1 sub), 32 channel Behringer Sound desk, (Eurodesk

MX3282A), 4 speakers Audit (25 sub, 2 full range), 2 x stage monitors, 16 channel stage box (16 XLRR, 4 stereo jack), 2 x mini disc, 1 x CD deck.
General: 4 Dressing Rooms ; Accom 10.

Greenford, Middlesex

GREENFORD HALL

Greenford Broadway, Greenford, Middlesex UB6 9QN
Tel: 020 8578 1076 Booking no: 0208 825 6060 / 7217
Email: halls@ealing.gov.uk
Web Site: www.ealing.gov.uk/halls
ADMINISTRATION:
Props: London Borough of Ealing
Manager: Fiona Elliot
Cap: Seated 542, Small Hall 117

Greenock, Inverclyde

BEACON ARTS CENTRE

Custom House Quay Greenock, Inverclyde PA15 1HJ Scotland
Tel: 01475 723 723
Email: info@beaconartscentre.co.uk
Web Site: www.beaconartscentre.co.uk
CEO: Julie Ellen
General Manager: Pauline Kane
Cap: 500

Grimsby, North East Lincolnshire

GRIMSBY AUDITORIUM

Cromwell Road, Grimsby, North East Lincolnshire DN31 2BH
Tel: 01472 311 300 BO: 0844 871 3016
Email: claire.williams@lincsinspire.com
Web Site: www.atgtickets.com/grimsby
ADMINISTRATION:
Props: Lincs Inspire Ltd.
General Manager: Claire Williams
Marketing/Press Manager: Sharon Daulton
Box Office Manager: Julie Gerard
Technical Manager: Ed Turrell
Max Seating Capacity: 1224 (incl. 12 wheel Chairs) Max Standing Capacity: 2040
TECHNICAL:
AUDITORIUM:
Length 36m; Width 26m; Height 9.1m (floor to underside of catwalks), 8.1m (floor to underside of truss), 8.1m (stage to underside of catwalks), 7.1m (stage to underside of truss), Floor Granwood (sports hall floor).
Access: Floor level access into loading bay at rear of stage, doors 3 m (w) x 2.2 m (h), distance to stage approx. 10 m. Equipment needs to be ramped on to the stage as there is no stage lift.
STAGE:
Stage: Steeldeck 74 units at 8' x 4', 6 units at 4' x 4', 4 sets of treads.
Standard stage dimensions: 22m (w) x 8.5m (d) x 1m (h). Usual performance area: 14m (w) x 7.5 m (d), with 4 m (w) x 6 m (d) wings either side and a 0.75m, (d) crossover at rear. The standard stage layout uses 60 units at 8' x 4' and 4 units of 4', remaining units can be used as risers etc. The stage can be removed completely or re-built in different configurations if required (please consult technical department for details).
No set or scenery to be fixed to the stage. NOTE: any costs associated with altering the stage from our standard layout will be recharged to the Promoter / hirer.
Proscenium: A false proscenium is created with the house border, legs and house tabs. The opening is variable (usually 14m). Height from stage to house border 6.1m.
Rigging Positions: 0.00 m d/s of back wall - Hemp bar 3 (usually used for eye and star cloth); 0.75 m d/s of back wall - Tab track rigged with full blacks; 1.00 m d/s of back wall - Back edge of house truss; 1.55 m d/s of back wall - Black legs; 2.00 m d/s of back wall - Hemp bar 2; 3.35 m d/s of back wall - Black legs; 3.85 m d/s of back wall -; 5.10 m d/s of back wall - black legs; 6.00 m d/s of back wall - Front edge of truss 6.50 m d/s of back wall - House tabs; 7.00 m d/s of back wall - House boarder; Front of House - 3 lighting bridges with 15 amp socket outlets. NOTE: The house box truss measures 21 m x 5 m with 5 up and down stage spans 2 m apart (see separate plan) and it is rigged over stage on 10 Liftket 1 tonne motor hoists. The hemp sets can be used with the truss rigged but the lines have to be dropped through the truss and the bars re-attached underneath. NOTE: There is a 15 m (w) front of house truss rigged on 4 Verlinde 1 tonne motor hoists (NOTE: this truss is 12" box section and is therefore unsuitable for walking on).
Additional Rigging: There are girders in the roof, which can be rigged on using span sets or girder clamps. Capacity 1000 kg per bay, up and down the hall. Capacity 2000 kg per bay, across the hall.
Tab Tracks: 4 triple E tracks 21 m wide with pulleys for rope work. 1 track can be used as a crossover track.
Dance Floor: 12 rolls of reversible black / grey vinyl flooring (10m x 1.5m) - please check availability with technical department.
SEATING:
Stalls (flat) - 266 seats; Circle (raked) - 630 seats; Balcony (raked) - 196 seats; Side Balconies (raked) - 2 x 66 seats; Max Seated - 1224 seats (inc up to 12 wheel chairs); Max Stand - 2040
LIGHTING:
96 ways of ADB Eurorack 60 3Kw dimmers; 96 channel Jands Event Plus Lighting Desk; 30 ADB F101 1.2Kw fresnels c/w barndoors; 16 ADB DS101 1.2Kw profiles (12 permanently rigged in F.O.H. bridges); 66 PAR 64 cans; 24 PAR 64 cans - rigged on 6 ways Socapex bars;; 2 lighting stands - height up to 3 m; 8 tank trap bases c/w 3 m high booms; 9 floor stands; 2 Selecon Performer 1200w MSR Follow Spots. All dimmer outlets are 15 amp and are hardwired in groups around the building - there is no hard patch. We stock Socapex multicores and spiders to run feeds from truss and stage to dimmer outlets, we also stock a selection of T.R.S.
SOUND: The P.A. System consists of: Yamaha M7CL - 48 ch, D&B C4 Speakers and P1200 Amplifiers (2 Subs and 2 Tops per side), 48 Way send - 16 Way return Multicore, Tascam MD 350 MiniDisc Player, Tascam CD 101 CD player, 2 x D&B Max 12 Monitors.
Balcony Fills: 2 pairs of EV SX200 Speakers mounted in the roof and 1 pair mounted covering the side balconies.
Microphones and Accessories: 3 x Sm58, 3 x Crown PCC Boundry Microphones, 2 x EV ND 308 Dynamic Cardioid Mics, 2 x Sennheiser 300 Series Radio Mic Systems (Handheld & Lavalier), 1 x Trantec Lavalier System, 1x Shure VHF Handheld Radio System, 2 x Radial Di Boxes, 8 x Boom Stands, 6 x Vertical Pump Stands, 5 x Table Mounted Stands. Infra-red hard of hearing system - there is no induction loop. Other equipment including radio microphones, monitor systems and complete p.a. systems can be hired from our suppliers - please contact the Technical Department for detail and prices.
TOURED SOUND & LIGHTING:
There are 2 x 200 amp three phase supplies for toured lighting and sound. Power is available either from Powerlock or a full range of CEE 17 single and three phase connectors (except 16 amp). Mains cables run to stage approx. 10m. Temporary mixer position is at the back of the stalls on a flat floor, maximum size 2 rows of 12 seats, multicore run approx. 50m.
ORCHESTRA EQUIPMENT:
Steinway Model D grand piano - can only be tuned to A =440 Hz, if other tuning settings required an alternative piano must be hired in. Piano tunings are charged at £30.00 each 59 Rat illuminated music stands. 1 Rat conductors stand. Conductors podium. 70 Orchestra Chairs. Orchestra Rail - makes an area suitable for approx. 5 musicians (there is no pit).
MISCELLANEOUS EQUPMENT:
Stage Managers desk c/w 6 way cue light

system; Le Maitre 6/24 pyro firing box & 4 x double firing pods - we do not stock cartridges. Le Maitre G300 Smoke Machine - hire charge £15.00
Pea Souper dry ice machine - dry ice is recharged to the Promoter / Hirer.
Lecturn. White cyclorama cloth 40' x 25'; Black Star Cloth 40' x 25'; 300 x banquet chairs; 42 x 6' tables; 25 x 2'6" tables.
DRESSING ROOMS:
There are 4 dressing rooms located on the first floor, each with it own toilet and shower facilities. 2 x star dressing rooms - 3m x 2.75m, 1 x mirror; 2 x chorus dressing rooms - 8.75 x 5m, 4 x mirrors.
NOTE: The chorus rooms can be opened into one communal area if required.

Guernsey, Channel Islands

Pop. 60,000. Newspapers: Evening Press & Star (ntly); Guernsey Weekly Press (sat); Guernsey Globe (thurs). STD code 01481

BEAU SEJOUR CENTRE

Amherst Road, St Peter Port, Guernsey GY1 2DL Channel Islands
Mgt: 01481 747215 BO: 01481 747200
Email: cultureleisure@gov.gg
Web Site: www.beausejour.gg
ADMINISTRATION:
Props: States of Guernsey Culture and Leisure Dept.
Centre Manager: Martyn Bourgaize
Policy: Theatre, Films, Conferences, Concerts.
Seats: 400 raked. Theatre Bar and other facilities of the Centre available.
TECHNICAL:
Stage: Area - 58'4" x 28'9"; Pros. opening 39'8"; Height of Pros. 12'1"; Orchestra Pit 30' x 4'.
Lighting: Switchboard: LBX 36 Way.
Sound Equip:16 mic lines to a Sound System; 16 x 4 TOA desk; various tape/CD.
Projection Equip: The Theatre has a projection room equipped with 2 - 35mm projectors, 1 - 16mm projector, 35mm slide, front projection screens - 10'6" x 24'.
Dressing Rooms: 6 plus showers.

Guildford, Surrey

Pop. 124,700. London 29 miles.
Newspapers: Surrey Advertiser (wkly); Surrey Times (wkly). STD code 01483

ELECTRIC THEATRE

Onslow Street, Guildford, Surrey GU1 4SZ
BO: 01483 444 789 Admin Tel: 01483 444 788 Admin Fax: 01483 563 913
Email: electrictheatre@guildford.gov.uk
Web Site: www.electrictheatre.co.uk
ADMINISTRATION:
Props: Guildford Borough Council
Audience Capacity: Balcony, bleacher and orchestra pit: 210
With orchestra pit in use:180
Manager: Amanda Hargreaves
Technical Manager: Darren Carrig
Steward/Usher Seats: 3
Wheelchair Spaces: Any seats in the front row of the bleacher units (row C) may be removed for up to six wheelchair users (one wheelchair takes out two seats).
TECHNICAL:
Stage: Proscenium: width with doors set in 7.20m, width with doors out 10.90m, height (structural) 6.00m, height (visual) adjustable down to 4.50m. Depth from stage edge: to upstage flying bar 9.10m, to back wall 10.40m, Width between stage walls 12.20m, zypo - bar flying downstage 8.10m, bar flying upstage 4.30m, Overall area 118m.sq. Flying adjustable pelmet and No.1 LX bar on hand winches, 31 handline sets, capacity 150kg, distance between bars 0.25m, bar length (including extensions) 9.00m.
Rostra: 11 - 2.4 x 1.2m (8x4) & 2 - 1.2 x 1.2m (4x4) Adjustable to four hieghts - 6", 12", 18", 24" designed to be compatible with 'Steeldeck' staging sections.
Floor: flat and level - tongue and groove maple, semi-sprung
Get-in: tailboard height above roadway in private yard into stage right wing: width 2.90m, height 3.00m. Scene Store: None
Auditorium: Normal use of Theatre is as a single tier of seats facing a proscenium arch formed by folding zypo and an adjustable height pelmet. With the seating retracted and proscenium doors folded back a flat floor hall is formed. Fixed stage edge to balcony front 11.80m, fixed stage edge to back wall 10.10m, Clear length of flat floor 'hall', inc. stage 21.90m, Width between walls 12.20m, Width between proscenium doors folded out 10.90m, Height-floor to side ceiling 9.30m
Orchestra Pit: Front two rows retract under fixed floor to provide facilities for an orchestra pit. Orchestra pit - total area 14.40m.sq, Orchestra rail to stage edge 1.80m, Max depth of pit below stage 1.40m.
Lighting: Control room in rear of auditorium above fixed balcony. Alternative position in row C or back of stalls.
Control system: Strand 520i (250 channel DMX) / Strand GSX(75 channel DMX)
Dimmed channels: 48 no. @10a in 2 no Strand LD-90 racks. 2no. Strand Act 6 portable dimmers. Lighting equipment: 6 no. Cantata 11/26 2 no. Cantata 18/32; 12 no. Cantata F, 18 no. Starlette F, 18 no. Prelude F, 8 no Prelude 16/0, 6 no. 19 dg source 4 spotlights, 2 no. 25-50 dg source 4 zoom spotlights, 28 no par 64/CP62 parcans; 8 no par 64/CP95-EXG scrollercans, 12 no Par-56 MFL; 27 no. Birdies, 10 no Coda 500/4 /4 no Nocturn 500w floods; 8 no CromaQ scrollers 11 no CCT Minuette fresnels
2 no 700w MSR 'Foxie' Followspots.
Smoke Machines: 2 no Jem ZR31 smoke machines - DMX / remote control. 2 no LeMaitre Neutron Star Hazer; Sound: Control position in control room, in the back, or in row C of stalls, as above. 32 Microphone lines, 16 Loudspeaker lines.
Vocal mic - 4 Beyer BDM88TG, 3 SM 58
Instrument mic - 4 SM 57 Float mic - 3 Audio Technica AT835B
3 K6/ ME67 'Long Gun' mics 5 x passive Di boxes /1 x Active Di box 1 x dual input passive Di box 10 boom mic stands
Mixing desk Soundcraft K3 24 Channel (control rO;om position only) Soundcraft K1 16/4/2; Effects playback 1 Tascam 102 Cassette Deck 1 Sony CD Player 1 Sony Mini-Disc player/recorder 1 Dennon Mini-Disc player/recorder 1 Yamaha SPX1000 digital reverb processor. 2 x Yamaha Q2031 Stereo graphic equalizer 3 x Crown 800 CSL stereo amplifiers 1 x RMX 2450 amplifier 1 Yamaha EMX 640 mixer/amplifier 2x Behringer stereo feedback destroyers
Loudspeakers 4 x Electrovoice Sx200 with Xp200 processor (FoH) 2 x Celestion QX122 foldback wedge 2 x Electrovoice Sx200 fold back/effects speakers 4 x Wedges Communications: Full facilities on SM desk includes single-Channel intercom by Metro Audio, 8-station cue light system show relay and paging system Radios 4 x Motorolla 2 way radios
Assisted listening: Sennheiser infra-red system, single channel Induction loop at Box Office counter 8 Backstage Dressing rooms: 2 on first floor fitted out, each for 8 to 12. Toilet and showers: ensuite to each dressing room Video system Relaying stage to dressing rooms and box office.

G LIVE

London Road, Guildford, Surrey GU1 2AA
Tel: 01483 739040 BO: 08447 701797
Email: info@glive.co.uk
Web Site: www.glive.co.uk
ADMINISTRATION:
Props: HQ Theatre
Venue Manager: Alvin Hargreaves
Programme Manager: Fran Everist
Marketing Manager: Fran Everist
Cap: 1700 (standing) 1031 seated
Stage & Technical:
Max width 22.1m (72ft) Max depth 15.5m (50.85ft) including extension lift. Width of lift 17.3m (57ft) Standard depth 10.6m (34.8ft).
Enclosed mixer position. 3x FOH auditorium LX bridges. Auditorium rigging points for further FOH trusses. Control desk Avolites Pearl Expert 80 Submasters.
Contact for full technical details.

GUILDFORD SPECTRUM

Parkway, Guildford, Surrey GU1 1UP
Tel: 01483 443322
Email: info@guildfordspectrum.co.uk
Web Site: www.guildfordspectrum.co.uk

ADMINISTRATION
Props: Freedom Leisure
Area Manager: Steve May
Cap: Arena - 1,500 Seated.

MAMBO
2-5 The Quadrant Bridge Street Guildford, Surrey GU1 4SG
Tel: 01483 440900 Casino: 01483 865 780
Email: amank@staroyster.com
Web Site: www.barmambo.co.uk
ADMINISTRATION:
Capacity: 350 standing

YVONNE ARNAUD THEATRE
Millbrook, Guildford, Surrey GU1 3UX
Mgt/SD: 01483 44 00 77 BO: 01483 44 00 00 Fax: 01483 564 071
Email: yat@yvonne-arnaud.co.uk
Web Site: www.yvonne-arnaud.co.uk
ADMINISTRATION:
Props: Yvonne Arnaud Theatre Trust;
Lessees: Yvonne Arnaud Theatre Management Ltd;
Director: James Barber
General Manager: Brian Kirk
Commercial Operations: Dave Palmer
Box Office Manager: Tim Slater
Head of Marketing: Dan McWilliam
Press Officer: Laura Butler
Technical Stage Manager: Liza Cheal
Capacity: 590
Policy: Mainly 2-3 week runs of No. 1 tours and pre-West End shows. Also mounts own in-house productions with view to subsequent touring and possible West End transfer.
Perfs: Mon-Thurs 7.45; Fri & Sat 8.00; Mats: Thurs and Sat. 2.30.
All catering facilities open to theatregoers and non-theatregoers alike. The Riverbank Restaurant, a la carte and table d'hote, open for lunch before, during and after performances; Figaro's piano bar and restaurant; Riverbank Cafe open from 10.00a.m. until the end of the last interval, serving hot and cold snacks; foyer bar open for normal theatre hours.
TECHNICAL:
STAGE: Proscenium, Flat; Pros. opening 10.06m; Ht. of Pros. variable 4.57m - 5.49m; Depth of S/Line 8.92m; Ht. of Grid 11.78m; 31 C/W lines, Hemp rigged as necessary; Scenery Flying Ht. 5.48m; Flying Bars 9.75m with extn. 12.19m; W/Widths P.S. 7.92m, O.P. 7.92m; Prompt Cnr. P.S.
LIGHTING: Strand 520i. For full specifications visit the company website.
DRESSING ROOMS: 10; Accom. 48; 4 Shower, 4 Bathrooms; Orchestra Pit up to 18.
Membership: TMA

Hailsham, East Sussex

HAILSHAM PAVILION
George Street, Hailsham, East Sussex BN27 1AE
Tel: 01323 841 414
Email: info@hailshampavilion.co.uk
Web Site: www.pavilionhailsham.co.uk
TECHNICAL:
Stage: Proscenium, Raked 1 in 24; Pros. opening 9.75m; Ht. of Pros. 6.55m; Depth of S/Line 15.24m; Ht. of Grid 15.24m; 57 lines, Fly Floor, C/W; Scenery Flying Ht. 14.63m; Flying Bars 12.04m; W/Widths P.S. 3.50m; O.P. 4.27m; Prompt Cnr. P.S. One Wardrobe Room, Dock Door 1.83m from street level; Paint Frame back door; 2 Traps.
Lighting: Switchboard: Strand Galaxy 150 ways (upper circle). Lanterns: 200 Assorted mostly strand, 4 x 4 circuit battens, 4 x 4 circuit footlight/groundrow 4 x 5 way flood bar, 2 x 12 I.W. Spot Bars, 4 x 4 way ladders each side of track. F.O.H. positions on centre front of both circles and top tier of side boxes.
Sound: Full PA system including 20 way Alice Mixer 2 Revox B77 tape decks and an assortment of microphones. Full sound and lighting details on application.
Dressing Rooms 13; Accom. 96; 6 Showers; Orchestra Pit partially under forestage.
Lighting equipment:3 x lighting bars, each with 6-way 15amp plugs, 6 x 500 watt Fresnel lanterns, 6 x 500 watt PC lanterns, 6 x miscellaneous lanterns, 1 x Alcora Zero 88 dimmer unit, operated from a control room at the rear of the auditorium.
Sound equipment: 8 (2 x 4) microphone inputs at the rear of the stage (Note: 4 of these inputs are also connected in tandem to inputs fitted at the front of the stage area), 2 x Peavey Impulse 200 speakers at rear of stage, 2 x microphone inputs at the rear of the auditorium, 2 x speaker connections on jack fixings at rear of auditorium, connected to similar sockets at rear of stage (All the above are connected to a Folio SX console int he control room). 1 x Marantz Cd player, 1 x Marantz cassette deck, 1 x compressor, 1 x 31-band graphic equaliser, 2 x Samson S12 microphones, 1 x Audio Technica ATM33A condenser microphone, 3 x floor-standing microphone stands, miscellaneous microphone cables etc.
The loop induction system (for film presentations only) follows the inner perimeter of the main seating area and crosses the front of the stage.

Halesowen, West Midlands

CORNBOW HALL
Hagley Street, Halesowen, West Midlands B63 3AT
Tel: 01384 812 960
Email: borough.halls@dudley.gov.uk
Web Site: www.dudley.gov.uk
ADMINISTRATION
Props: Dudley Metropolitan Borough Council
Cap: 384
For bookings contact Suzy Cadman
Tel: 01384 812 960

Halesworth, Suffolk

HALESWORTH RIFLE HALL
London Road, Halesworth, Suffolk IP19 8LW
Tel: 07585 963 963
ADMINISTRATION:
Props: Waveney District Council
Contact: Ollie Platt

Halifax, West Yorkshire

Pop. 90,320. London 193 miles. Newspapers: Evening Courier (ntly). STD code 014225

BRIGHOUSE CIVIC HALL
Bradford Road, Brighouse, West Yorkshire HD6 1RS
Tel: 01422 392601
Email: tracy.ambler-vinco@calderdale.gov.uk
Web Site: www.calderdale.gov.uk
ADMINISTRATION:
Public Halls Centre Manager: Tracy Ambler-Vinco
Props: Metropolitan Borough of Calderdale
Capacity: Main Hall 300

CLAY HOUSE
Clay House Park, Greetland, Halifax, West Yorkshire HX4 8AN
Tel: 01422 392601
Email: tracy.ambler-vinco@calderdale.gov.uk
Web Site: www.calderdale.gov.uk
ADMINISTRATION:
Props: Metropolitan Borough of Calderdale
Capacity: Main Hall 100; Ante Room 50.

PIECE HALL

Closed for renovation, reopening Spring 2016
Halifax, West Yorkshire HX1 1RE
Tel: 01422 321002 Fax: 01422 349 310
Web Site: www.thepiecehall.co.uk
ADMINISTRATION
Props: Calderdale Metropolitan Borough Council
Capacity: 4,100
Contact: Dawn Mitchell
Exhibitions, outdoor entertainments - theatre, bands, etc.
Licensed restaurant, cafeteria, meeting room, art gallery & tourist information centre.
Outdoor arena in eighteenth century courtyard 110m x 110m. Concert platform stage 24' x 24', covered and with extensions. Excellent for outdoor concerts.

SHELF VILLAGE HALL

Halifax Road, Shelf, Halifax, West Yorkshire HX3 7NT
Tel: 01422 288091 Bookings: 01422 392601
Email: tracy.ambler-vinco@calderdale.gov.uk
Web Site: www.calderdale.gov.uk
ADMINISTRATION:
Props: Metropolitan Borough of Calderdale
Manager: Tracy Ambler-Vinco
Capacity: Main Hall 225

TODMORDEN TOWN HALL

Bridge Street Todmorden, Lancashire OL14 7AB
Tel/Fax: 01706 813597
Email: tracy.ambler-vinco@calderdale.gov.uk
Web Site: www.calderdale.gov.uk
ADMINISTRATION:
Props: Metropolitan Borough of Calderdale
Manager: Damion Priestley
Capacity: Main Hall 300; Room 'A' 36; Room 'B' 20; Room 'C' 40.
For Bookings - Halls Letting Section Tel: 01422 392601

THE VICTORIA THEATRE

Fountain Street, Halifax, West Yorkshire HX1 1BP
Mgt: 01422 351 156 BO: 01422 351 158
Email: victoriatheatre@calderdale.gov.uk
Web Site: www.victoriatheatre.co.uk
ADMINISTRATION:
Props: Calderdale Metropolitan Borough Council
General Manager: Tim Fagan
Technical Manager: Mark Jennens, email: mark.jennens@calderdale.gov.uk
Policy: Concerts, Shows, Amateur Societies, Exhibitions, Conferences, Rock, Pop, Opera, Dance.
Perfs: As required
Capacity: 1,568 seating / part standing: 1860
Two Bars, coffee lounge.
TECHNICAL:
STAGE: Proscenium, Flat; Pros. opening 13.71m wide x 8.29m high; Stage Depth 9.09m. Rear of safety curtain to back wall 7.60m, Grid height 14.33m; 33 c/w lines, Flying height 6.8m; Bar width 12.19m; Prompt corner stage left.
LIGHTING: Lighting control: ADB Vision 10. Dimmers: 156x3kW, 6x5K, 2 x 6 way Zero 88 packs, DMX control, 2 x 1kW CSI Followspots, lantern stocklist on request.
ADDITIONAL POWER: Stage left 200A 3 phase (camlock/powerlock) no tails; 63 A 3 single phase DSL; 16A Cee Form. Dimmer room above stage left wing 100A 3 phase tails only. Front Truss on 2 points at 750 kg/point swl.
SOUND: House Turbo Sound system, 24 channel desk, microphone and monitor stock. No Orchestra pit. Orchestra plays on stalls floor. Call venue for further details.
DRESSING ROOMS: 8 can accommodate up to 80.
OUTSIDE ACCESS: Powell Street loading door, large 5t UDL platform lift from street to stage level.

WAINWRIGHT HALL

Jepson Lane, Elland, West Yorkshire HX5 0PY
Hall Lettings Tel: 01422 392601
Email: tracy.ambler-vinco@calderdale.gov.uk
Web Site: www.calderdale.gov.uk
ADMINISTRATION:
Props: Metropolitan Borough of Calderdale
Manager: Tracy Ambler-Vinco
Capacity: 100

Hanley, Stoke-on-Trent

VICTORIA HALL

Bagnall Street, Cultural Quarter, Hanley, Stoke-on-Trent, Staffordshire ST1 3AD
SD: 01782 213 808 BO: 0844 871 7649
Fax: 01782 214 738
Email: stokestagedoor@theambassadors.com
Web Site: www.atgtickets.com
ADMINISTRATION:
Props: Ambassadors Theatre Group (Venues) Ltd
General Manger: Andrew Nicklin
Marketing Manager: Victoria Power
Contact: victoriapower@theambassadors.com
Technical Manager: Martin Lund
Contact: martinlund@theambassadors.com
Cap: 1467 Seated. 1685 Standing
TECHNICAL:
STAGE: Rectangular concert platform curved at rear. Flat, Polished Hardwood Floor. Lower side balconies impinge on stage at front corners. Height, 12.8m; Distance from stage surface to chandeliers, 10m. Width, 19m. Depth of stage at centre, 9m. Depth of stage at sides, 7m. Stage extension options. Additional depth, 1.2m or 2.4. NB. Stage extension 1.2m looses 2 rows of chairs and 2.4m extension looses 4 rows of chairs in auditorium. Platform Depth can be increased using Steeldeck platforms with consequent loss of stalls seating. 2 sets of treads (removable) for access to stalls from stage. 80 Orchestra chairs and conductors rostrum. 3 sets of permanent, retractable bleachers. Organ and console center stage in choir stalls. Principle artists entrance DSR, other entrances USL and USR.
LIGHTING: Dimmers; ADB Eurorack 60, 96 x 3KW, 12 x 5KW, 20 x Non Dim Circuits all 15A, 5 x Music Stand outlets - all 15A Sockets (on dimmable circuit), 2SL, 2SR, and 1 CS (In trap), All Hardwired Circuits. Control; ETC ION and remote, ETC Express 125 - 24 submasters - programmable, Riggers remote - outlets on SL and SR, Control room at rear of circle, Patchable DMX rings to most lighting positions including stage. Lanterns; Fixed Parcan rig comprising 5 colour wash over 4 bridges; A selection of Source four zoom 15-30 deg Profiles - 575W to be used as specials; 48 x 110V parcans (permanently focused concert lighting); 2 x Pani long throw followspots (HMI 1200W) - on bridge 5.
SOUND; Control; Soundcraft Spirit 16-4-2. 4 D&B 1801 subs, 4 D&B 902 mid/high cabs (moveable stacks on stage), 9 Communitys (4x920's and 8x915's) in the roof - all fixed positions. 22 EAW JF60's delay speakers (fixed positions) and 6 x D&B E3 fill speakers (for front of stage fill). The system has various settings for different situations and is fully patchable. Suitable for speech and music, not large concerts. 2 x 915's and 1 x 920 for general purpose cover (side fill/extra house cover if required). 40 mic lines and 10 speaker outputs available on stage. 2 spare amplifier channels for monitors etc. Outboard Equipment; CD , Mini Disc , EQ , Yamaha SPX.
STAGE MANAGEMENT: Platform Managers corner is situated off stage right. Cue lights permanently wired at choir and orchestra entrances (4 in total - one control). Techpro Dual channel system. 25 comms outputs around the building. 4 Beltpacks and Headsets available, plus one headset at platform manager. Show relay and paging to all dressing rooms. Backstage and foyer paging operated from Platform Managers corner and control room. Video patch system with BNC type outputs in the building and a Camera on the upper circle complete with a show relay microphone. There is a monitor in Platform Managers corner. 4 Video Monitors with sound in the foyer

area. Ethernet links Running from stalls, circle and control room mixing positions to comms room and amp room (BNC type).
RIGGING; Each Lighting Bridge has 4 Rigging Points - SWL - 500Kg's each. Maximum Load on any bridge in 1500Kg. 2 additional rigging points situated above the Platform. 8 motors rigged on bridge 2 & 3 and a 16 way controller. 10m clearance below Chandeliers on stage and 12.8m to bridges from stage.
7 line winch carries curved truss for acoustic black drapes in front of choir stalls. Max Payload 400Kg. UDL. From stage to upper circle hand rail 12.6m. From stage to circle hand rail 5.7m.
ACCESS: Flat access to platform from undercover loading area via double door USR. Space for 2 Trucks (55ft) to unload and park. Cable ducts for Outside Broadcast above get in doors.
Backstage storage and crossover area. Get in doors 6ft ,1 inch W x 7ft , 1 inch H.
ADDITIONAL: Steinway Grand Piano available. Equipment for hire; 6 pieces of Medium Duty Box Truss, 500mm x 500mm (12ft length); 14 Steeldeck Platforms (2.4x1.2m); Portable PA System comprising of Mixing Desk, 5 Disc CD Changer and Speakers; Video Projector capable of projecting images from composite video source, RGB or PC.; Projector throws.
DRESSING ROOMS; 10, accomm.118 People total; Green Room; Backstage assembly area.

Harlech, Gwynedd

Pop. 2,000. STD code 01766

THEATR HARLECH

Harlech, Gwynedd LL46 2PU Wales
BO: 01766 780 667
Email: post@theatrharlech.com
Web Site: www.theatrharlech.com
ADMINISTRATION:
Director: Andrew Orton
Status: National Touring House
Purpose-built theatre opened in 1972 - attached to Coleg Harlech (Residential College).
Funding: Venue funded by Arts Council of Wales, Gwynedd Council
Policy: Receiving theatre for professional companies performing in Welsh and English. Willing to premiere show.
Perfs: performances on approx.3-4 days a week - evening shows regularly start at 7.30p.m. - matinees held at 1.00p.m. on weekdays, 2.30p.m. on Saturdays.
Booking terms: Box Office split, guarantee and split.
Non-performance activities: Film, hire to community, snooker, art exhibitions, craft exhibitions, conferences, workshops.
Facilities: seating 260; raked. Catering: Bar and coffee shop/sales area. Access: theatre car park, railway station Harlech.
Facilities for the disabled: assistance available for disabled, ramped entrance, disabled lift. Other facilities: showers in dressing rooms.
TECHNICAL:
Stage: open stage with centre thrust, 'token' proscenium. Performing area 13.10m (apron 3.5m) x 9.90m (inc. apron) - pros. opening 13.10m x 4.72m (min) - 5.63 (max) - wing widths 1.52m. SR, 1.52m. SL No rake - floor sapele timber on joists, suitable for all dance, lino available, crossover, stage heated. 10 hemp sets plus 5 winch sets, tab track. 2 borders, 1 set tabs, surround, 4 tormentors, all black. 4 x 15A independent circuits. Forestage (apron) 3.50m x 13.5m. Get-in via dock door, 3.05m hjigh. Manual scenery hoist. Tallescope. Technical information sheets available.
Lighting: Strand M24 memory board, 60 circuits, 58 @ 2kw, 2 @ 5kw, 160A, 3 phase, operated from Control Room at rear of auditorium - 60A single phase supply stage right - 15 x Sil 30 1k Profiles, 19 x 1k Fresnels (9 x Patt.743, 6 x Harmony F, 4 x ADB0), 6 x Patt.123, 3 x Patt.23, 5 x 6ft battens, 1 x 2kw follow spot.
Sound: Operated from Control Room - Soundcraft Delta 200B 8-4-2 mixer, 2 x Carver 1.5 amps, 4 x Tannoy Puma speakers, 1 x Revox A77, 1 x Phillips CD, 2 x Casette Decks, 3 x Shure SM 58, mics, 3 x Shure 545F.

Harlow, Essex

Pop. 84,000. London 25 miles.
Newspapers: Harlow Citizen (wed); Harlow Star (thurs); Herts and Essex Observer (thurs). STD code 01279

THE PLAYHOUSE

Playhouse Square, Harlow, Essex CM20 1LS
Admin: 01279 446 704 BO: 01279 431 945 Mrkting: 01279 446 739 Tech: 01279 446 747 Fax: 01279 424 391
Email: playhouse@harlow.gov.uk
Web Site: www.playhouseharlow.com
ADMINISTRATION:
Props: Harlow Council
Director: Scott Ramsay
Administration: Germaine Knight
Marketing Manager: Leigh Hesketh
FOH Manager: Brian Palmer
Policy: In-house theatre and musical theatre productions. Available for all kinds of touring productions.
Capacity: 409 Seated. Studio Theatre 120.
TECHNICAL:
STAGE: Black box set, consisting of: 8 x 18'Black Masking Flats 4 either side, 4 x Black Borders on (Cwts 1,5,18,29), Blacks Backdrop (2x Half Tabs Cwt 33) with 2 x 22'Black Book Flats either side.
Fly Floor; 33 Double Purchase Counterweight system. Dimensions Pros Width - 9.75M (32') - 12.20M(40'), Pros Height - 5.48M (18'). Stage Depth; To Cwt 33 - 10.60M (34'), To Back wall - 11.20M (37'), Grid Height - 13.40M (44'), Fly Floor Height - 7.30M (24').
LIGHTING: Control; Strand 550. Dimmers; Light Processor Paradime. Permanent rig; F.O.H. No1 Bridge - 18x Strand SL, Advance Bar - 12x Strand Cantata F, LX 1 Cwt 9 - 12x Stand Cantata F, LX 2 Cwt 20 - 12x Strand Cantata F, Back Light Cwt 28 - 20x Par64 (CP62), CYC Bar Cwt 29 - 16x CCT Starlette 1k Floods. Follow Spots; 2x LDR Canto 1200 MSD/MSR MKII Follow Spots (with LDR Colour commanders and scrollers containing LDR's standard 16 frame colour string. Colour as follows). Other Lanterns are available on request.
SOUND: Desk; Yamaha M7CL 48 Channel (Digital Desk). 32 Mic tie lines from the stage to the F.O.H. desk. Tie lines 1 - 20 appear both D.S. left and D.S.Right Tie Lines 21 - 32 appear only D.S. Left 8 Returns Appear D.S.L. F.O.H. P.A; 2x d&b C190's as Left and right, 2x d&b C190's and 2x d&b C160's as Vocal cluster, 4x E0 as front fills across front of stage, 2x E3's as side fills under pearch's for side seats.Playback; 1x 10way computer playback (CSC), 2x Miranze C.D. Players, 1x Tascam M.D. Player, 1x Sony M.D. Player.Fold Back; 4 Aux's Mix's (4 more mix's available subject to charge), 4x D&B Max12's, 4x EV Sx200, 2x JBL JRX112M.
STAGE COMMUNICATIONS: Tecpro comms system with headset points feeding all of the technical areas but at present limited to 8 headsets and belt packs. Metro Audio Cue light system. Variable Prompt desk, SR wing equipped with a 12" monitor showing an infrared picture of the stage.
DRESSING ROOMS: 9, Accomm. 88. All have show relay and calls, which can be switched from the studio and main house.

Harpenden, Hertfordshire

HARPENDEN PUBLIC HALLS

Southdown Road, Harpenden, Hertfordshire AL5 1PD
Tel: 01582 762 880 Box Office: 01582 767 525
Email: hphmarketing@1life.co.uk
Web Site: www.harpendenpublichalls.co.uk
ADMINISTRATION
Manager: Glenn Povey
Props: 1 Life Ltd
Cap: 400
Mainly private functions, theatrical performances and craft fairs.

Harrogate, North Yorkshire

Pop. 64,000. London 204 miles.
Newspapers: Harrogate Advertiser (fri).
STD code 01423

HARROGATE INTERNATIONAL CENTRE

Kings Road, Harrogate, North Yorkshire HG1 5LA
Mgt: 01423 500 500 SD: 01423 537 222
Fax: 01423 537 210 Tourist Information: 01423 537 200
Email: sales@harrogateinternationalcentre.co.uk
Web Site: www.harrogateinternational-centre.co.uk
ADMINISTRATION:
Props: Harrogate Borough Council
Director: Simon Kent
Policy: Conferences, Commercial and Trade Presentations, Product Launches, Popular and Classical Concerts, TV Shows, Sports Events
Perfs: Various. Interlinked to Exhibition Centre and Royal Hall.
Seats: 2000 over 3 tiers (578 removable from main arena). Licensed Bar and banqueting Hall adjacent for up to 900. Can cater for banquets up to 1,800. VIP/Press suites and simultaneous interpretation booths overlooking auditorium.
TECHNICAL:
Stage: Concert platform style, overall size to walls 15m wide x 7.2m deep x 0.975m high, tapered at front. Central section in three screw jack lifts each 10m wide x 2.4m deep, travels from arena floor to 1m above normal stage level. Stage extendable to 0.975m height to maximum 15m wide x 24m deep (with loss of seats). Total floor area of lowered stage plus cleared arena 350 sq.m. approx. Access to stage and arena via 10 tonne car lift 6.2m long x 3.00m wide x 3.7m high. Up to nine electric hoist bars (250 kg - 750 kg) for drapes, lighting etc. 10 fixed 300 kg electric point hoists over arena. 6 x 1000kg mobile electric chain hoists plus rigging equipment.
Lighting: Strand 550 board, 220 circuits@ 2.5kW and 5kW, 3 phase, operated from rear of auditorium - 200A 3 phase and 100A 3 phase supplied available for temporary board - 80 spots, 60 fresnels, 100 parcans, CCT/Strand/Thomas - 2 1200W Pani HMI followspots.
Sound: Soundcraft series 5, 48 channel matrixed desk, operated from rear or centre of auditorium - Electrovoice 5.6k central cluster - 10kW Meyer MSL3/DS2 system flown in permanent position - Shure, AKG mics - Tascam cassette tape systems, Tascam DAT player, twin CD players, Tascam minidiscs. Acoustics suitable for spoken word.
Stage Management: Prompt corner position SR, Technical Projects cue system, up to 20 outstations. Show relay/Tannoy to dressing rooms. Colour CCTV to stage, foyers and principal dressing rooms.
Backstage: Dressing room accommodates 42, access by lift - green-room. Refreshments available. Rehearsal piano, Steinway Model D full concert grand. Advice given on accommodation. Staff - 1 stage, 1 lighting, 1 sound and additional technical crew as required - casuals available - security personnel. Backstage facilities accessible to disabled performers and staff.
Additional information: Special facilities for television outside broadcast or recordings. VHS (all PAL/SECAM/NTSC). Cinema screen max 11m x 4.7m with variable masking. Colour CCTV system with tie lines to Royal Hall and Exhibition Halls. Staff radio pagers. Induction loop for hard of hearing.
Dressing Rooms: Principal - 2 x 2 person, 2 x 1 person. Chorus - 2 x 24 person. Additional accommodation available.

HARROGATE THEATRE

Oxford Street, Harrogate, North Yorkshire HG1 1QF
Admin: 01423 502 710 BO: 01423 502 116
Email: emma.mcdowell@harrogatetheatre.co.uk
Web Site: www.harrogatetheatre.co.uk
ADMINISTRATION:
Props: Harrogate District Council
Lessees: Harrogate (White Rose) Theatre Trust Ltd
Marketing Manager: Emma McDowell
Production Manager: Richard Bielby
Finance Manager: Andrew Robinson
Policy: Full mix of the performing arts - drama, dance, music, mime, children's shows etc., one night to whole weeks.
Perfs: Evenings 7.30p.m.; Sat Mat.2.30p.m.
Seats: Main Theatre 500. Studio Theatre 69. Licensed Bars.
TECHNICAL:
STAGE: Proscenium arch 7.9m x 6.5m, soft header height 5.6m. Stage 7m x 11m. Height to fly floor 6m, max flying height 6.86m, height to grid 13.72m, stage rake 01:24.
Additional Information: Martin Stage Hazer. DMX or remote control, Jem Sharkie 650w smoke machines, Comar Tas Windy high output fans, Chroma Q scrollers, PAR Can back plate for scrollers, Source 4 Junior back plates for scrollers, Cantata fresnel back plates for scrollers, DHA Vari speed Gobo Rotators for Cantata Profile Spots, Le Maitre 2-Way Pyro Flash Control System, Le Maitre Flash Pods, Spotlight Blackgun 400w UV Guns.
LIGHTING:
Main House: ETC Expression with Emphasis. 1000 Channels. 3 x DMX outputs, DMX Distribution via ETC net 2 system and scroller Power Distribution. Submasters. Moving light control.
Dimmers: 288 Channels of ETC Sensor Intelligent Dimming. All are 3Kw except, 10 x 5 Kw circuits and 12 interchangeable switching modules. Channel number locations TBC.
Studio: Zero 88 Fat Frog with moving light control. Dimmers 36 Channels Comprising of 24 x 1k & 12 x 2k circuits. Switching circuits 6-DMX controlled from desk. Studio space has 36 x Ways all patchable to any of the above dimmers or swicthpack or 13A power. 12 x 575W source four Parnels C/W barn doors. 5 x 650W Strabd Prelude 28/40 Profiles. 2 x 650W Strand quartet Profiles.
SOUND:
Main House: Mixer Desk: Allen and Heath GL2000 32 channels / 4 groups/6 Aux. Main PA; Stalls: 2 x Nexo PS10 600w, 2 x 350w Sub base bins, 4 x work studio 3 fills (for rear stalls). Circle: 2 x Nexo PS10 600w, 4 x work studio 3 fills (for rear circle). Balcony: 2 x 300w mid range speakers, 2 x 350w sub bass bins. On Stage; Moveable: 4 x Qmax 300w FS115 monitor wedges, 2 x Dynamax 500w cabinets. Powered by: 2 x Yamaha 350XS stereo power amps, 1 x MOS-FET M400 matrix power amp.
Tie LInes; 20 ways from rear stalls to orchestra pit (16 ways/ 4 returns)
Equipment: 1 x Marantz CD52 CD player, 1 x Sony MDS JE510 mini disc recorder, 1 x Sony MDS JE640 mini disc recorder, 1 x Lexicon Multi FX LXP-15, 1 x DOD SR 231 stereo graphic equaliser, 1 x Behringer feedback destroyer pro, 1 x AKG D65 S Mic, 1 x Stageline DM-2500 Dynamic Studio Mic, 1 x Audio Technica PRO 29HE Dynamic Mic, 1 x Audio TechnicaATM 89R Condenser Mic, 3 x Audio Technica AT 835B Riflle Mics, 8 x Audio Technica ATW-T51 UHF Belt-pack Radio Mics (with headband and lapel mics), 2 x Audio Technica ATW-T36HE VHF hand held radio Mics, 4 x Behringer Autocom Pro Stereo Audio Processors, 2 x Stageline LTR100 DI Boxes with Phase Reverser, 2 x Stageline DIB100 DI Boxes, we also carry a large stock of XLR of various lengths and various adapters.
Studio: Mixer Desk; Spirit Folio SX with 12 Mic Inputs & 2 x Stereo Inputs, Outputs L + R, Sub L + R and 3 Aux. Amplifier; Quad QD-4480 4 x 80w Channel Amplifier. Speakers; 2 x D.A.S 8 150w RMS through 8 Ohms. Playback; 1 x Marantz CD4000 CD Player, 2 x Tascam MD - 350 Minidisc Recorder/Players. Tie Lines; 8 Mic Lines and 4 Sends TO rear of studio, 6 x Speaker Outputs around studio space.

ROYAL HALL

Harrogate International Centre Ripon Road, Harrogate, North Yorkshire, HG1 2RD
Switchboard: 01423 500 500 (24 Hrs)
SD: 01423 537222 Fax: 01423 537210
Email: simon.kent@hicyorkshire.co.uk
Web Site: www.royalhall.co.uk

ADMINISTRATION:
Props: Harrogate Borough Council
Director: Simon Kent
Policy: Conferences, Trade and Commercial Presentations, Popular and Classical Concerts, Touring Shows, Pantomime etc.
Perfs: Variable
Seats: 868 on two levels plus boxes. Licensed Bar and Buffet. Stalls seats (527) removable to fully sprung maple dance floor.
Interlinked to Harrogate Conference and Exhibition Centres.
TECHNICAL:
Stage: Proscenium - Raked 1 in 40; Pros. opening 9.7m; Ht. of Pros 5.3; Depth - from S/Line 7.4m, from stage from 10.4m; Ht. of Grid 11m; Double purchase counterweight system - 19 bars at 200mm centres. House tabs on one additional set controlled from SR prompt or fly floor. Main fly floor located SL. Maximum loading on any bar 300kg. Bar length: 10m. 3 line hemp sets are available US of bar 18; W/Widths P.S. 1.5m; O.P. 1.5m; Prompt corner SR. Stage side walls taper to rear.
Lighting: Strand 430 control desk and 175 ways of dmx dimming. Lanterns - 36 Starlettes, 12 Sil 30, 8 Sil 15, 4-way cyc bar, 20 x 1kw PAR 64, 2 Pani Followspots; extra equipment on request.
Sound: Meyer 4kw system with delays, effects etc., and Soundcraft K3 48 channel mixing desk. Revox PR99 or A77 tape decks, Tascam 112 cassette decks, AKG/Beyer/Shure microphones. Technical Projects intercom. Induction loop for hard of hearing.
Other: AV facilities: 35mm slides. Conference set with large screen for side by side 7.2m x 3.6m.
Video and audio tielines to Conference Centre and Exhibition Halls.
Sound and Lighting controls located in control room at the rear of the Grand Circle.
Dressing Rooms: 8; Accom. 52; Orchestra Pit 30.

Harrow, Middlesex

CEDARS YOUTH CENTRE

Chichley Road, Harrow Weald, Middlesex HA3 6QH
Tel: 020 8421 4676
Email: reception@cedarsycc.org
Web Site: www.cedarsycc.org
ADMINISTRATION:
Props: London Borough of Harrow
S/Cap: 200
Manager: Steve Williams

Hartlepool, Cleveland

Pop. 90,000. Newspapers: The Hartlepool Mail (ntly). STD code 01429

BOROUGH HALL

Middlegate, Headland, Hartlepool, Cleveland TS24 0JD
Mgt: 01429 266 269 BO: 01429 890 000
Email: jackysullivan@hartlepool.co.uk
Web Site: www.hartlepool.co.uk
ADMINISTRATION:
Technical Manager: Jacky Sullivan
Props: Hartlepool Borough Council
Capacity: 1,200
Regularly hired for cabaret and pop one-nighters.
TECHNICAL:
Stage: Equipment entrance - W 6' H 6' 6". Stage - D 48' W 21'. Drop - 4'. Position - Middle of 105' wall. Dressing rooms - 2. Accoustics 0.5secs. Power Supply - 3 phase 100 amp. 13 Amp on stage. Off stage - 6/N.
Lighting: Fully computerised rig. Number of Banks - N/A 36 par cans, 6 profiles, 2 battens. Console - Sirius zero 88 24 channel. Position - N/A F.O.H. Other information
Sound: House P.A. - Peavey Mono. Wattage & Impedance - 1600 watts. Speakers - 4. Mics - 4/5 + radio mic shure 58, 2 x AKG C451. Connections - N/A XLB. Mic Stands - 4.5. Monitors - No. Position - F.O.H. Mixer - Yes TASCAM 1016. Channels - 8 x LR mic inputs 6 stereo inputs.

TOWN HALL THEATRE

Raby Road, Hartlepool, Cleveland TS24 8AH
Mgt: 01429 523 409 BO: 01429 890 000
Tech : 01492 523 607 Mktg: 01429 523 451 Council: 01429 266522
Email: clare.irvine@hartlepool.gov.uk
Web Site: www.hartlepooltownhalltheatre.com
ADMINISTRATION:
Props: Hartlepool Borough Council
Theatre Manager: Clare Irvine
Technical Manager: Garry Marshall
Marketing Officer: Jamie Kelly
Seats: 406 (theatre style); can convert to flat floor/cabaret

TECHNICAL:
Stage: Flat, pros. opening 8.3m, pros height 4.97m (from stage), stage height 1.23m. Apron depth 2.7m, stage depth 5.25m, SL wing/w 3m, SR wing/w 1.6m. House tabs and full black box masking, 3 sets of black tabs on travellers (DS, MS & US), 5 x US hemp sets (restricted height). Equipment access 2.25m(w) x 2.8m(h). Parking available, 4 station TechPro comms, 2 large dressing rooms with video/audio show relay, close to stage.
Lighting: Control desk: Strand GFX 72 channel, control room at rear of auditorium.
Dimmers: 5 x Strand Mini-2 (5 amp), 6 channel packs, 5 x Strand Tempus (15 amp), 6 channel packs.
FOH. Stage left and right horizontal side boom (each bar) 4 x Strand Prelude Freshnels c/w barndoors (650W). 6 x Parcans (1000W). 4 x Strand Prelude 28/40 Profiles (1000W). 2 x Strand T/2 Profiles (100W). FOH Advance Bar, 8 x Strand Fresnels c/w barndoors (1200W), 1 x UV flood, 1 x strobe light. FOH Rear Bar, 6 x Profiles (100W), 4 x Profiles (650W). On stage bar #1 (DS), 8 x Fresnels (500W), 8 x floods (200W). On stage bar #2, 8 x Fresnels (500W), 6 x floods (200W). On stage bar #3, 3 x magazine battens (each 8/200W). On stage bar #4 (U.S.), 4 x 4Coda/4 (each 4/200W). On stage DIPs, 3 x DSL (5 amp), 2 x DSR (5 amp), 3 x USL (5 amp).
Sound equipment: Mixer, Soundraft Spirit Live 24:2. Effects, Peavey digital effects processor. Loudspeakers, Peavey International (total power 1.6 KW). Microphones, 22 assorted with assorted stands, operated from sound control room at rear of auditorium.
Other: Auditorium on two levels. Bluthner grand piano, Challenor upright piano.

Hastings, East Sussex

Pop. 76,000. London 63 miles.
Newspapers: Hastings & St. Leonards Observer (fri); Hastings News (wed). STD code 01424

SUMMERFIELDS LEISURE CENTRE

Bohemia Road, Hastings, East Sussex TN34 1ET
Tel: 01424 457691 Fax: 01424 203083
Email: summerfieldsenquiries@freedom-leisure.co.uk
Web Site: www.freedom-leisure.co.uk
ADMINISTRATION:
Props: Hastings Borough Council
Lessees: Freedom Leisure
Operations Manager: Paul Wilson
Cap: Max. 450

WHITE ROCK THEATRE

White Rock, Hastings, East Sussex TN34 1JX
Admin: 01424 462 280 Ticket Office: 01424 462 288 Marketing: 01424 462 284 Hospitality: 01424 462 291 Fax: 01424 462 289
Email: enquiries@whiterocktheatre.org.uk
Web Site: www.whiterocktheatre.org.uk
ADMINISTRATION:
Props: HQ Theatres Ltd.
Stage Manager: Adam Harkin
Policy: All purpose Theatre
Seats: 1,066. Two Bars, cafe/restaurant.
SUSSEX HALL:.200 seated 300 standing 3090 sq.ft
TECHNICAL:
STAGE: Proscenium, Raked 1 in 48; Pros. opening 9.14m; Ht. of Pros. 5.49m; Depth of S/Line 5.79m; Ht. of Grid

9.75m; 15 lines C/W, 21 Hemp; Scenery Flying. Ht. 4.88m; Flying Bars 12.19m; W/Widths PS 2.25m, US 4.57m, DS OP 8.97m, US 4.57m DS. Stage Extension 10m wide 2m deep. Prompt Cnr. PS.
LIGHTING: Avolight Pearl Expert, dimmers ETC Sensor 96 x 2.5kw circuits, lighting stock - 12 source 4 junior 26 Patt. Harmony 15/28 48 PAR 64 10 Harmony F, Cyc 10 Coda 500/3 (plan available).
SOUND: Soundcraft Spirit live 24/4/2 F.O.H. mixer position. 4 JBL full range speakers, 2 Sony MD players, 2 Denon CD and cassette decks. Echo and reverb. Units selection of AKG and Shure microphones,8 Trantec S5.5 Radio mics. Show relay and call system to all dressing rooms. Rank Strand intercom system.
DRESSING ROOMS: 4 stage right, 4 stage left; Accom. Up to 100 . 5 Showers.
DISABILITY ACCESS: Entry via ramp or lift. Space for up to 3 wheelchair users per performance. Infra-red hearing system. Assistance dogs are welcome.
MEMBERSHIP: TMA

Hatfield, Hertfordshire

Pop. 29,000. London 27 miles.
Newspapers: Welwyn TImes (thurs); The Review (thurs); Herald and Post (thurs).
STD code 01707

HATFIELD LEISURE CENTRE

Travellers Lane, Hatfield, Hertfordshire AL10 8TJ
Tel: 01707 268769 Fax: 01707 267500
Email: council.services@welhat.gov.uk
Web Site: www.finesseleisure.com
ADMINISTRATION:
Props: Welwyn Hatfield Council
Manager: Mike Barlow

UH ARTS

University of Hertfordshire, College Lane, Hatfield, Hertfordshire AL10 9AB
Tel: 01707 281127 BO: 01707 281127
Email: uharts@herts.ac.uk
Web Site: www.herts.ac.uk/uharts
ADMINISTRATION:
Aim to raise the cultural profile of the University within the community through the provision of high quality, affordable arts events.
Seating/Capacity: 460; stalls/circle
The Weston Auditorium, University of Hertfordshire, De Havilland Campus, Hatfield, Hertfordshire AL10 9EU
TECHNICAL:
Stage: stage height 790mm - arch width 11m 700mm - total stage depth 9m 600mm - total stage width 16m 850mm. Allowance to underside of bridges for lighting: 25kg/m - allowance to side of bridge balustrade: 25kg/m.
Lighting/Sound: please contact venue technical manager for further information.
Dressing rooms: 2 dressing rooms, access by backstage corridor, both with shower, good light and full size mirror - additional rooms available on request - green room and others in vicinity to the auditorium.
Disabled Access: Wheelchair seating, disabled parking, induction loop system installed, guide dogs welcome, backstage facilities accessible to disabled performers and staff.

Haverhill, Suffolk

HAVERHILL ARTS CENTRE

High Street, Haverhill, Suffolk CB9 8AR
BO: 01440 714 140 Admin: 01440 710 174 Fax: 01440 718 930
Email: boxoffice@haverhillartscentre.co.uk
Web Site: www.haverhillartscentre.co.uk
ADMINISTRATION
Props: Haverhill Town Council
Programming Manager: Nick Keeble
Admin: Mary Argent
Cap: 210
Flexible performance space offering raked theatre seating or cabaret style. Facilities available for conferences and meetings. Full disabled access to all public areas. Bar. 2 dressing rooms.

Hayes, Middlesex

BECK THEATRE

Grange Road, Hayes, Middlesex UB3 2UE
Mgt/Admin: 020 8561 7506 BO: 020 8561 8371 Fax: 020 8569 1072
Email: enquiries@becktheatre.org.uk
Web Site: www.becktheatre.org.uk
ADMINISTRATION:
Props: HQ Theatres Ltd.
Theatre Director: Louise Clifford
Operations Manager: Jack Schofield
Contact: jack@becktheatre.org.uk
Theatre Administrator: Kay Grover
Perfs: Open 7 days per week. Variable, generally 8.00 p.m. for plays and single performance concerts.
Policy: Major theatre tours and concerts, children's shows, pantomime, films, plus local amateur and daytime conference hirings. Cabaret performances, dance evenings, folk, jazz, dance workshop, fringe theatre, etc.
Capacity:
Theatre: Deluxe tiered, fixed auditorium seats: 600. With orchestra pit/thrust stage: 564.
Second Performance Area: Foyer area seating up to 120 around central performance floor of semi-sprung Canadian maple, dimensions up to 30' x 30'.
Extra: Licensed bar, kiosk, coffee shop. Rooms available for private functions and meetings of up to 70; in-house catering.
Exhibition areas in foyer and function rooms.

Haywards Heath, West Sussex

CLAIR HALL

Perrymount Road, Haywards Heath, West Sussex RH16 3DN
Tel: 01444 455 440
Email: enquiries@clairhall.org
Web Site: www.clairhall.org
ADMINISTRATION
Props: Places for People Leisure Ltd.
Cap: 360 Seats; 400 Dances
Events Manager: Erica Martin
Entertainments & Art's Venue/Conference/meeting facilities

Hednesford, Staffordshire

PYE GREEN COMMUNITY CENTRE

Bradbury Lane, Kings Bromley, Hednesford, Staffordshire DE13 7JT
Tel: 01543 424872 / 495630 Fax: 01543 495630
Email: rbiqircls@lycos.com
ADMINISTRATION
Contact: Laurie Bowman
Cap: 100 Seated

RUGELEY ROAD PAVILION

Rugeley Road, Hednesford, Staffordshire
Email: eddieclarke@cannockchasedc.gov.uk
ADMINISTRATION
Props: Cannock Chase District Council
Cap: 50
Halls Manager: Arthur Ralls
For bookings contact Jo Smith
Tel: 01543 462621 Fax: 01543 462317

Helensburgh, Dumbartonshire

VICTORIA HALLS

Sinclair Street, Helensburgh, Dunbartonshire G84 8TU
Tel: 01436 673 275 Fax: 01436 672 308
Email: victoriahallhelensburgh@argyll-bute.gov.uk
Web Site: www.argyll-bute.gov.uk
ADMINISTRATION:
Contact: Lorna Whyte
Seating/Capacity: 387 seated

Hemel Hempstead, Hertfordshire

THE OLD TOWN HALL THEATRE

High Street, Hemel Hempstead, Hertfordshire HP1 3AE
Tel: 01442 228 090 BO: 01442 228 091
Email: othadmin@dacorum.gov.uk
Web Site: www.oldtownhall.co.uk
Props: Dacorum Borough Council
Capacity: 120
Raked audit. Flat performance area 25' x 25'. Full stage lighting available.

Henley-On-Thames, Oxfordshire

Pop. 11,780. London 36 miles. Newspapers: Henley Standard (fri). STD code 01491

HENLEY INDOOR SPORTS CENTRE

Gillotts Lane, Henley-on-Thames, Oxfordshire RG9 1PA
Tel: 01491 577909
Email: henley@gll.org
Web Site: www.better.org.uk
ADMINISTRATION
Props: Better
Manager: Ashley Debell

KENTON THEATRE

New Street, Henley-on-Thames, Oxfordshire RG9 2BT
BO: 01491 575 698 MD: 07850756856
Email: bookings@kentontheatre.co.uk
Web Site: www.kentontheatre.co.uk
ADMINISTRATION:
Props: Kenton Theatre (Henley-on-Thames Management Society) Ltd.
For bookings contact Mrs Laura Poulton
Policy: For hire to Touring & Repertory, Concerts and Amateur Productions. Cinema in between live stage productions. 4th oldest working Theatre in the country.
Cap: 234 Seated
TECHNICAL:
Technical Contact: Tom Smith 01491 412 347

Hereford, Herefordshire

Pop. 47,500. London 138 miles. Newspapers: Evening News (dly); Hereford Times (thurs). STD code 01432

THE COURTYARD

Herefordshire's Centre for the Arts.
Edgar Street, Hereford, Herefordshire HR4 9JR
Admin: 01432 346 500 BO: 01432 340 555 Front of House: 01432 346 530
Email: foh@courtyard.org.uk
Web Site: www.courtyard.org.uk
ADMINISTRATION:
Head of Sales & Marketing: Curtis Fulcher (curtis.fulcher@courtyard.org.uk)
Operations Manager: Alex Green (alex.green@courtyard.org.uk)
Front of House Manager: Phil Pearcy (phil.pearcy@courtyard.org.uk)
Production Manager: Carl Hulme (carl.hulme@courtyard.org.uk)
Policy: Multi-arts, including touring theatre, comedy, dance, music, film and visual arts; plus own productions inc. pantomimes.
Capacity: Seats 418 (main house) + 130 (studio theatre). Café-bar and restaurant in building plus rehearsal/meeting spaces.
TECHNICAL:
STAGE: W: 10M x H: 7.6M x D: 11M. Pit Capacity: 10+ (please call to discuss configurations). Prompt desk in Prompt Corner (Stage Left): Show Relay, Video Monitor and Cueing System. Prompt Side Wing Width: 7.6M. O.P. Wing Width: 5.2M. Access via dock doors: Height 5M, Width 3M. Dock and stage are flat to outside car park; Transit vans can be backed directly into dock. Backstage crossover via dock. Soft Black Marking: 4 x Legs, 4 x Borders, 2 x Sets of Full Blacks. Hard Masking: 8 x Black Masking Flats, White Cyclorama, White Gauze. Stage Weights: Approx. 20. Ballet Booms: 8 c/w 4 x Boom Arms.
LIGHTING: Strand 520i Lighting Desk - 250 channels and up to 2000 attributes c/w 2 TFT Monitors and Keyboard. Strand 301 Backup Lighting Desk. Stage Electrics R120 Wired Strand Focus Remote. 164 ADB Dimmers - Consisting of 160 x 2.5K and 4 x 5K. 8 x ADB 1K 11/23 Profiles. 8 x ADB 1K 15/31 Profiles. 10 x 15/30 Source 4 Zoom Profiles. 4 x 25/50 Source 4 Zoom Profiles. 2 x Fixed 50 Source 4 Profiles. 2 x Cantata 18/32 Profiles. 4 x Cantata 26/44 Profiles. 20 x ADB 1k Fresnels (10 without barn doors). 10 x ADB 1k PC c/w barn doors. 5 x Strand 2k Fresnel (4 c/w barn doors). 42 x Thomas Par 64 Par Can. 4 x Thomas Floor Can. 4 x 4 unit ADB Circuit Cyc top light floods. 6 x Iris single unit floods. 2 x Robert Juliat Buxies Followspot c/w Colour changer. 2 x Source 4 Iris'. 8 x ADB Gobo Holders. 8 x Source 4 Gobo Holders. 6 x Cantata Gobo Holders.
SOUND: Allen and Heath GL4000 40 channel Mixing Desk. 2 x Sony MDSJE510 Mini Disk Players. 1 x Sony CDP - XE330 CD Player. 1 x Yamaha SPX900 Professional Digital Multi-Effects Unit. 1 x Yamaha REV500 Digital Reverberator. 2 x Yamaha Q2031B 1/3 Octave 2 Channel Graphic Equaliser. 1 x Yamaha GQ1031C 1/3 Octave 1 Channel Graphic Equaliser. 1 x Behringer Composer Pro MDX2200 2-Channel Compressor/Limiter/Expander/Gate and Peak Limiter. 1 x Behringer Multicom Pro MDX4400 4-Channel Compressor/Limiter and Peak Limiter. 4 x XTA DP200 DSP Multiprocessor. 5 x Crest VS1100 Power Amplifiers. 1 x Crest VS1500 Power Amplifier. 2 x Crest VS650 Power Amplifiers. 2 x Mackie Fussion 3000 Active Full Range Loudspeakers. 2 x Mackie Fussion 1800 Active Sub Bass Loudspeakers. 2 x Mackie Fussion 1800S Passive Sub Bass Loudspeakers. 19 x JBL Control 1AT Small Fill Speakers. 2 x Community CSX28 - S2 Fold Back Monitor Speakers. 2 x EAW (replica) 15" Wedges. Hearing Impaired System / Audio Show Relay / Video Show Relay. Canford/Tecpro Ring Intercom Communications System
DRESSING ROOMS: 4 over 3 levels. Accommodating 33. Toilet and shower facilities and show relay and calls via the SM desk in all dressing rooms. Green Room - Fridge, Microwave, Kettle, Washing Machine and Dryer. Iron and Ironing Board available on request. Strictly non-smoking.

Herne Bay, Kent

KINGS HALL

Beacon Hill, The Downs, Herne Bay, Kent CT6 6BA
Tel: 01227 374 188
Email: thekingshall@canterbury.gov.uk
Web Site: www.thekingshall.com
ADMINISTRATION
Props: Canterbury City Council
Cap: 500 Theatre Style
Manager: Amanda Jones

Hertford, Hertfordshire

HERTFORD THEATRE

The Wash, Hertford, Hertfordshire SG14 1PS
Admin: 01992 504 537 BO: 01992 531 500
Email: box.office@hertfordtheatre.com
Web Site: www.hertfordtheatre.com
ADMINISTRATION
Props: East Hertfordshire District Council
Cap: 600 (standing) 400 (seating)
Theare Director: Rhys Thomas
TECHNICAL
Full stage facilities. Pros. Width 10.23m. Ht. 4.86m. Depth of stage 9m. Ht to grid 11.96m, 3-level lift - stage level (apron). Floor level or as Orchestra Pit. Own scenery dock. Zero Illuston DMX. Memory control desk. 4 dressing rooms.

Heswall, Wirral

HESWALL HALL
Telegraph Road, Heswall, Wirral CH60 0AF
Tel: 0151 342 2614
Email: trudi@heswallhall.co.uk
Web Site: www.heswallhall.co.uk
ADMINISTRATION:
Props: Heswall Hall Community Trust
Cap: 252
Manager: Trudi Harris

High Wycombe, Buckinghamshire
STD code 01494

WYCOMBE SWAN
St Mary Street, High Wycombe, Buckinghamshire HP11 2XE
Mgt: 01494 514444 BO: 01494 512 000
Fax: 01494 538 080
Email: enquiries@wycombeswan.co.uk
Web Site: www.wycombeswan.co.uk
ADMINISTRATION:
Proprietors: HQ Theatres Ltd
Theatre Director: Simon Stallworthy
Building & Technical Manager: Richard Muirhead
Marketing & Sales Manager: Sam Matthews
Status: National Touring House. Opened in November 1992. Red brick building, designed by county architects. Central location.
Policy: Major theatre tours, comedians, concerts, children's shows, pantomime, local amateur shows, community events.
Performance Schedule: Open 7 days . Booking terms by negotiation.
Non-performance activities: Conferences, trade shows, functions, exhibitions.
Seating: Swan Theatre 1,076, raked. Town Hall: 600 standing, 400 theatre-style or 250 cabaret. Oak Room: 130, loose chairs. Catering: 4 licensed bars - hot food available. Transport/Access: Adjacent public car park. High Wycombe railway station, 5 minutes walk. Local bus routes. Facilities for people with disabilities: 12 wheelchair spaces, infra-red hearing enhancement system, lift, level access to car park-all house facilities fully accessible. Level access to all floors of the auditorium, disabled toilets on ground and first floor.
Cap: 1076
TECHNICAL:
STAGE: Proscenium arch and forestage. Stage area 23.6m x 11m - pros opening 13.6m x 7.2m. No rake - floor timber suspended on concrete frame, suitable for all dance, Marley dance floor available, backstage crossover, stage heated. Height to grid 18m - 51 counterweight sets, single purchase, 200mm apart - 500kg permitted on bars - black legs and borders, 2 sets tabs (black), - white filled gauze cyclorama - red house tabs, flown. Several 13A sockets. Forestage 13.6m x 3m. Orchestra pit on screwjack lift (doubles as forestage), accommodates 48. Get-in via ramp to scene dock SL, large shutter lift 8m high. Tallescope. Safety curtain. Scale stage, Plans available from Modelbox.
LIGHTING: Strand 520i and rigger control, 200 circuits, 164 @ 2Kw, 36 @ 5Kw, operated from control room at rear of stalls - 400A 3 phase supply available for temporary board - 60 spots, 40 fresnels, 24 Source 4 pars, 6 x 4-circuit cyc battens, 2x Robert Juliat Aramis followspots, operated from upper circle.
SOUND: Soundcraft MH4 mixer, operated from control room at rear of stalls - 8 amps - graphic equalisers - 8 x JBL speakers as infill, 10 x JBL speakers as infill, 4 effects speakers, 2 foldback, 2 crossover units - 20 Shure & AKG mics - -2 Tascam CD player - record deck - Acoustics suitable for music and spoken word.
STAGE MANAGEMENT: Prompt corner SR or SL - cue lights and intercom, 8 outstations - show relay/Tannoy to dressing rooms. Colour and Infrared cctv.
OTHER: 7 dressing rooms + Bandroom, access by lift and stairs, accommodates 50 - band room - possible quick change rooms - wardrobe SR, equipment washing machine and dryer. Refreshments available from FOH on performance days. Advice given on accommodation. Staff - 6 technicians - casuals available. Backstage facilities accessible to disabled performers and staff. Steinway D grand and 2 Boston upright pianos plus one Boston Baby Grand available.

TOWN HALL:
Adjacent to main Theatre.
STAGE: composed of Steeldeck units, variable size, maximum performing area 12.2m x 6.1m. Floor modules on carpet, dance floor available. Height to ceiling 8m from floor, 7.5m to trusses. Several 13A sockets. Get-in via ramp at side of stage.
LIGHTING: Congo Junior - 20 x S4 profiles 750w - 20 1.2k fresnel - 40 x parcans 1,000w. Fixed lighting rig.
SOUND: Allen & Heath 24:4:2 mixer. JBL speaker system 4K (Including Foldback).
DRESSING ROOMS: 2.

OAK ROOM:
Above Town Hall - used for small events. Performing area 4.57m x 6.1m - floor flat wood. Height to ceiling 3.6m. Several 13A sockets. No lighting or sound equipment.

Holyhead, Gwynedd

HOLYHEAD CONCERT HALL
Town Hall, Newry Street, Holyhead, Gwynedd LL65 1HN North Wales
Tel (office hrs): 01407 764 608
Email: townclerk@holyheadcouncil.co.uk
Web Site: www.holyheadtowncouncil.co m
ADMINISTRATION:
Cap: Dancing 200, Functions Seating 150, Concert 200, Standing 250.
Small kitchen and Bar facilities
Contact: C.L. Everett

Holywell, Flintshire

HOLYWELL LEISURE CENTRE
Fron Park, Holywell, Flintshire CH8 7UZ
Tel: 01352 704 460
Email: chris.travers@flintshire.gov.uk
Web Site: www.flintshire.gov.uk
ADMINISTRATION:
Props: Flintshire County Council
For bookings contact Sue Reece
Tel: 01352 702 442
Email: sue.reece@flintshire.gov.uk
Contact Centre Manager: Chris Travers

Hornchurch, Essex
Pop. 134,000. London 17 miles.
Newspapers: Romford Recorder; Havering Post Extra; Yellow Advertisers; Brentwood Gazette. STD code 01708

DUKES HALL
May Green Crescent, off Park Lane, Hornchurch, Essex RM11 1EJ
Council: 01708 434343 Hall: 01708447766
Email: grant.aitken@havering.gov.uk
Web Site: www.havering.gov.uk
ADMINISTRATION:
Props: London Borough of Havering
Cap: 250
For bookings contact Grant Aitken

QUEEN'S THEATRE
Billet Lane, Hornchurch, Essex RM11 1QT
Mgt: 01708 462 362 BO: 01708 443 333
SD: 01708 462 362 Fax: 01708 462 363
Email: daveg@queens-theatre.co.uk
Web Site: www.queens-theatre.co.uk
ADMINISTRATION:
Props: Borough of Havering
Lessees: Havering Theatre Trust Ltd
Administrative Director: Thom Stanbury
Artistic Director: Bob Carlton
Production Manager: Dave Godin

Marketing Manager: Chris O'Kelly
Education Manager: Beth Flatley
Policy: Four weekly repertory, concerts, Sunday lunchtime jazz, children's events, comedy club, unplugged sessions and venue hire.
Seats: 503. Large Bar (Licensed); Coffee Bar - Buffet (lunch and evening). Access for the disabled, signed and audio described performances. Induction loop.
TECHNICAL:
Stage: Proscenium, Flat; Pros. opening 10.4m; Ht. of Pros. 6.2m; depth of S/Line 9.14m; Ht. of Grid 17.68m; Lines 30, 20 C/W, 1 Hemp, 3 Winch; Scenery Flying Ht. 5.49m; Flying Bars 12.4m; W/Widths P.S. 9.07m, O.P. 7.32m; Prompt Cnr. stage right.
Lighting: Switchboard: Rear Auditorium Compulite Ovation 40. 102 dimmers; F.O.H. Spots approx. 30; Dips 10 each side; 3 Spot Bars.
Sound Equip: Yamahah DM2000 Mixer, 2 minidisks, 6 radio mics, 2 x F/Spots, Full stereo control rear of Auditorium; Speakers General P.A. and Music Auditorium plus misc. effects speakers.
Dressing Rooms 6; Accom. 30; 2 Showers; Orchestra Pit 16 musicians.
Membership: TMA

Hornsea, East Yorkshire

HORNSEA FLORAL HALL

The Esplanade, Hornsea, East Yorkshire HU18 1NQ
Tel/Fax: 01964 532919
Email: alanbrooks@floralhall.org
Web Site: www.eastriding.gov.uk
ADMINISTRATION:
Manager: Mr Alan Brooks
Capacity: 500 standing, Seated 370.

Horsham, West Sussex

Pop.26,830. London 38 miles.
Newspapers: West Sussex County Times (fri). STD code 01403

THE CAPITOL

North Street, Horsham, West Sussex RH12 1RG
Admin: 01403 756 095 BO: 01403 750 220
Email: nick.mowat@horsham.gov.uk
Web Site: www.thecapitolhorsham.com
ADMINISTRATION:
Props: Horsham District Council
Manager: Nick Mowat
Operations Manager: Jon Simpson
Sales and Marketing Manager: Nigel Fitzsimmons
Policy: Number one, middle and small-scale touring drama, opera, music, dance and film. Available for private functions.
Seats: 420 available with orchestra pit/apron stage; 2 Wheelchair spaces.

TECHNICAL:
For more details contact: jason.ashdown@horsham.gov.uk
STAGE: Pros. Opening: H 4.8m 15.75', W 10.1m 33'. Stage Width: 11m (36') - 15m (49.2'). Depth: 7.85m (29.75') - 9.5m (31'). Height to underside of Grid 12.6m (41'); Height to underside of fly floors 6.5m (21')
LIGHTING: 520i & 136 ways of Compulite Dimming
SOUND: Yamaha M7CL; 4 no. Martin Wavefront WT3 plus 2 x WS2A subs, Bi-amplified by QSC PLX Series amplifiers; 4 no. Martin EM15 frontfills/FX speakers, 2 no. Bose 802 loudspeakers (Centre Cluster fixed in the roof void)

Houghton-le-Spring, Tyne and Wear

RAINTON MEADOWS ARENA

Rainton Business Park Mercantile Road Houghton le Spring, Tyne and Wear DH4 5PH
Tel: 0191 584 8630 Fax: 0191 584 6323
Email: karol.carter@raintonmeadowsarena.co.uk
Web Site: www.raintonmeadowsarena.co.uk
ADMINISTRATION:
Sales & Marketing Executive: Karol Carter
Policy: All types of events including conferences and live entertainment
Capacity: 2000 , 1200 seated

Hounslow, Middlesex

PAUL ROBESON THEATRE

Centrespace, Treaty Centre, High Street, Hounslow, MIddlesex TW3 1ES
Hire Enquiries: 0845 456 2796 (Option 7)
Email: hounslow-info@laing.com
Web Site: www.hounslow.info
ADMINISTRATION:
Props: London Borough of Hounslow
Press Officer: Michelle Morley
For Admin Enquiries please contact: Jason Sykes, 1st Floor, Centrespca, Treaty Centre, High Street, Hounslow, TW3 1ES
Policy: Mixed programme of evening performances including theatre, dance, multicultural events, music and children`s shows. Daytime activities include youth workshops, children`s events and senior citizen events. The theatre is also available for commercial and community hire.
Closed Sundays.
Seats: 20-280
Community Room - adjacent to the theatre, can be used as Green Room or as a separate facility.
TECHNICAL:
STAGE: No actual stage. Performance space same level as row A; Performance Space: 39ft x 18ft (inc. cross over and tab bunching); Performance Area: 25ft x 14ft; Height to Grid: 30ft; Flying Lines: None, 3 x Wipe Tracks D.S./C.S./U.S.; Tabs: Black tabs at rear & mid stage, plus legs and borders; House Tabs: Blue/Green (Motorised); Cinema Screen: Picture Size 18ft x 9ft max (C.S.); Cinema Projector: Elmo Lx 2200 16mm; Slide Projector: Elmo Omnigraphic 552 Xenon; Power Supply: One 32A Cee Form (P.S.) 16 x 13A sockets (S.R.).
LIGHTING: Lighting Desk: Zero 88, Sirius 48; Dimmers: Electrosonic ES6000 series 2kw/chan also 4 x Non dim circuits (1kw each); Stage Bars: 3, 1 x 12 way, 1 x 10 way, 1 x 6 way (all internally wired); Stage Dips: 4 (U.S.L.), (All stage bars and dips are patchable across 22 circuits); F.O.H. Bridges: 2 each 6 way (both paired and internally wired); Follow Spot: 1 x Strand Solo 1kw CSI; Lanterns: Various types of luminaries are available.
SOUND: Sound Desk: Yamaha MC2404 II 24 Chn. Main Amps: Harrison Xi 600 (300w/chn) Mustang 200 (100w/chn); House Speakers: 4 x Tannoy Puma (Flown above pros), 2 x Yamaha S2 15ES (floor level); Foldback System: A basic 2 mix monitor system is available; Yamaha CDX480 CD player. Tape Decks: Revox B77 (1/2 Track 1/4 inch) JVC TD-X502, Denon M12 XR (Cassette Decks); Effect Units: Alesis Midiverb II; EMP100; Yamaha Comp/LIM. Equalisation: Citronic SPX 7-21 Graphic (Pre Set). Mics: Various types of vocal and instrument mics are available along with 5 passive D.I.s.
BACKSTAGE FACILITIES: Dressing Room, 2. Shower facilities available.

Hove, East Sussex

HOVE TOWN HALL

Closed for refurbishment
Norton Road, Hove, East Sussex BN3 4AH

PORTSLADE TOWN HALL

Victoria Road, Portslade, East Sussex BN41 1YF
Tel: 01273 292922
Email: premisesteamhelpdesk@brighton-hove.gov.uk
ADMINISTRATION
Props: Brighton & Hove Borough Council
Caretaker: A P Security (0844 371 5434)
For bookings contact Premises Team Helpdesk
Tel: 01273 292081

Cap: 150 + 2 committee rooms

Hucknall, Nottinghamshire

HUCKNALL LEISURE CENTRE

Linby Road, Hucknall, Nottinghamshire NG15 7TX
Tel: 0115 956 8750 Fax: 0115 956 8760
Email: hucknallfm@slm-ltd.co.uk
Web Site: www.everyoneactive.com
ADMINISTRATION
Props: Ashfield District Council
Cap: 400
Centre Manager: Richard Chatwin
Duty Manager: Robert Onion

Huddersfield, West Yorkshire

LAWRENCE BATLEY THEATRE

Queen's Square, Queen Street, Huddersfield, West Yorkshire HD1 2SP
Tel: 01484 425 282 BO: 01484 430 528
Technical: 01484 484 414 Fax: 01484 425 336
Email: theatre@thelbt.org
Web Site: www.thelbt.org
Artistic Director: Victoria Firth
S/Cap: 477. Cellar Theatre: S/Cap: 120
Attic Theatre S/Cap: 60
Contact Technical Manager for full details.

CIVIC HALL

Huddersfield Road, Holmfirth, West Yorkshire HD9 3AS
Tel: 01484 222 452 Bkg: 01484 226 325
Email: premises.cs@kirklees.gov.uk
Web Site: www.kirklees.gov.uk
ADMINISTRATION
Props: Kirklees Metropolitan Borough Council
Cap: 320 (large hall) 120 (small hall).
Stage facilities.
Caretaker: Sharon Baxter
Bookings Contact: Pat Peart

HONLEY COMMUNITY CENTRE

Stoney Lane, Honley, West Yorkshire HD7 2DY
Tel: 01484 226325
Email: amy.mann@kirklees.gov.uk
Web Site: www.kirklees.gov.uk
ADMINISTRATION
Props: Kirklees Metropolitan Council
Cap: 120
For bookings contact Amy Mann
Tel: 01484 226325

HUDDERSFIELD TOWN HALL

Ramsden Street, Huddersfield, W Yorks HD1 2TA
Tel: 01484 221 900 BO: 01484 223 200
Email: amy.mann@kirklees.gov.uk
Web Site: www.kirklees.gov.uk/townhalls
ADMINISTRATION:
Seating/Capacity: 1,200.
Venue Manager: David Roache

MELTHAM CIVIC HALL

Carlile Institute, Carlile Street, Meltham, West Yorkshire HD9 4AE
Tel: 01484 852 249
Email: bookings@carlileinstitute.co.uk
Web Site: www.carlileinstitute.co.uk
ADMINISTRATION
Props: Meltham Carlile CIC
Cap: 80 Theatre, 70 Dance

SLAITHWAITE CIVIC HALL

New Street, Slaithwaite, Huddersfield, West Yorkshire HD7 5AB
Tel: 01484 226325
Email: amy.mann@kirklees.gov.uk
Web Site: www.kirklees.gov.uk
ADMINISTRATION:
Props: Kirklees Council
Cap: 200 (stage facilities)
For bookings contact Amy Mann
TECHNICAL:
Proscenium arch stage, sprung floor

ST PAUL'S HALL

The University of Huddersfield
Queensgate, Huddersfield, W Yorks HD1 3DH
Tel: 01484 472 130
Email: r.moorw@hud.ac.uk
Web Site: www.hud.ac.uk
ADMINISTRATION:
Contact: Rachel Moore
Seating/Capacity: 400
St Paul's Hall is a converted church and has very limited technical, and no dressing room facilities.

Hull, East Yorkshire

THE DONALD ROY THEATRE

(Gulbenkian Centre), University of Hull, Cottingham Road, Hull, East Yorkshire HU6 7RX
Admin: 01482 466 141 BO: 01482 466 607 Production office: 01482 465 617
Email: gulbenkian@hull.ac.uk
Web Site: www.drama.hull.ac.uk
ADMINISTRATION:
Props: University of Hull
Head of Drama and Music: Alastair Borthwick
Policy: Adaptable Teaching Theatre for Drama Department Productions and Classes. Accepts Touring Professional Companies, Experimental work, Films etc. by arrangement.
Seats: 168. Coffee Bar.
Perfs: 7.30p.m. Normally
TECHNICAL:
Stage: Adaptable, Flat; Pros. opening 8.31m; Ht. of Pros. 4.88m; Depth of S/Line 10.51m; Ht. of Grid 12.80m; 30 lines C/W, Scenery Flying Ht. 6.10m; Flying Bars 10.36m; W/Widths P.S. 4.50m; O.P. 3.81m; Prompt desk (with cameras) back of auditorium.
Lighting: Switchboard: Lightpalette 90 - LD90 Dimmers, 144 ways to Socapex outlets. Cantatas, Patt.223, Patt.243, Patt.264, Sil 30, SL26, Parcans, Codas, Beamlights, lee Colourtran 2K.
Sound: Mixer: Soundcraft studio 24-8-2, Pro Series Pentium IV Audio Workstation, two CD players, mini-disk, cassette, 10 mic lines, 4 radio mics, 2 effects units, 2 graphic EQ, 2 feedvack destroyers, 8 Ramsa speakers (6 variable positions).
Dressing Rooms: 3; Accom. 30; Orchestra Pit small 4-6. Get-in off road through 4.88m x 2.44m doors. Stage trapped over basement (area 58m2).
Check website for more information

HALTEMPRICE LEISURE CENTRE

Springfield Way, Anlaby, Hull, East Yorkshire HU10 6QJ
Tel: 01482 652501 Fax: 01482 650577
Email: info@haltempriceleisurecentre.co.uk
Web Site: www.haltempriceleisurecentre.co.uk
ADMINISTRATION:
Centre Manager: Tony Clarkson
Cap: 200-250 Seated

THE HULL ARENA

Kingston Street, Hull, East Yorkshire HU1 2DZ
Tel: 01482 325 252 Fax: 01482 216 066
Web Site: www.hullcc.gov.uk
ADMINISTRATION:
Proprietor: Kingston upon Hull City Council
Capacity: Seated 3,150, Standing and seated 3,750
TECHNICAL:
Stage: Stage area: 60feet wide by 40 feet deep.
Lighting: Broadcast-quality sports lighting system.
Sound: Public address type sound clusters located over centre of main floor.
Dimensions and Floor size: 6.9m from floor to rigging grid. 1,800 square metres available. 60m long by 30m wide.
Electric Services: 1x 200 amp 3 phase + N + E, 1 x 100 amp phase + N + E.
Facilities/Loading: 1 x zip-up Platform, forklift trucks hired in to your requirements, entrance 8 feet wide by 8 feet high.
Facilities/Performers: Four dressing rooms with shower facilities, VIP room for parties, receptions etc, production office, fully equipped cafeteria.
Facilities/Public: Two fully exuipped con-

cession stands, on-site first aid room, disabled facilities - lift/toilets/wheelchair stand, licensed bar.

HULL CITY HALL
Queen Victoria Square, Hull, East Yorkshire HU1 3RQ
Admin: 01482 613 817 Fax: 01482 613 961 BO: 01482 300 300 (Option 2)
Email: janice.wincott@hullcc.gov.uk
Web Site: www.hullcc.gov.uk/hullcityhall
ADMINISTRATION:
Props: Kingston upon Hull City Council
City Hall Manager: Janice Wincott
Marketing Manager: Joanna Baines, Tel 01482 613812
Stage Manager: Tony Evans
House Manager: Lorna Weston
Capacity: 1,767 seating and standing (concerts)
Victoria Bar 80 theatre style, Mortimer Suite Cap: Theatre style 200
Stage: Width 52ft, depth 21ft, height 4ft 3 1/2"
Flying: Maximum weight 2 tonnes suspended evenly across four points, front, back, two middle.
Please note the flying points and limits are under review - please telephone for update.
Distance from stage to points is 58ft.
Access to Hall: All access to the City Hall before 9am is subject to contract.
For large get-ins, a goods' hoist is available.
Lift door - Width 5ft height 8ft
Lift size - 11ft X 9ft
Black Backcloth: Comes in two sections - height 25ft, width 27ft pair section.
Six small black stage flats are also available - height 7ft X 6ft.
Piano: Small Concert Steinway is free. Full concert Grand Piano is available for hire £95.00. Piano tuner is also extra £25.00.
Organ: Details available upon request.
Conductors Rostrum & Stand: Large, brass.
Chairs: Orchestral - 130 black, Choir - 130 small red, General - 100 various.
Tables: Trestle - 35 X 7ft 6" in length / 2ft 6" in width. Round - 25 X 5ft.
Gypsy - 72 X 2ft 6" square.
Changing rooms: 1 Best Room, 2 Large Band Rooms, 1 Production Office. the Mortimer Suite maybe available for changing subject to booking.
Raisers: Only one 8ft X 8ft, height 1ft.
Treads: One set to stage height.

HULL NEW THEATRE
Kingston Square, Jarratt Street, Hull, East Yorkshire HU1 3HF
Admin: 01482 613 818 Admin Fax: 01482 613 961 BO: 01482 300 300 SD: 01482 318 300
Email: theatre.admin@hullcc.gov.uk
Web Site: www.hullcc.gov.uk/hullnewtheatre
ADMINISTRATION:
Props: Kingston Upon Hull City Council
Manager: Janice Wincott
Marketing Officer: Claire Balfour
Technical Manager: Allan Green
Policy: Major touring Plays, Ballet, Opera, Musicals, Variety, Concerts and Pantomime season.
Seats: Flexible between 1104 - 1160
Stalls Bar/Restaurant and Circle Bar.
TECHNICAL:
For specifications of new systems please ring the chief electrician (01482) 313 800.
STAGE: Proscenium with apron if required; flat. Pros. Opening 10.98m; ht of pros. 7.01m; depth of S/Line 12m: Ht of Grid 14.78m: 45 lines C/W, 7 of which are double purchase. Scenery flying ht 14.63m: Flying bars 12.19m. W/Widths PS 4.88m. OP 5.18m. Prompt Cnr. PS.
Orchestra pit: Flexible seven - 70.
LIGHTING: Control board; Compulite Spark situated at the rear of the circle.
Circuit distribution; F.O.H 36 Circuits Stage 78 Circuits (including 12 5Ks.).
Follow spots; 2 Super Corrigan situated in the lighting box at the rear of the circle.
Lanterns; 20 Starlette 1Kw fresnels, 5 Starlette 2Kw fresnels, 11 Floods, 12 Par Cans
SOUND: Soundcraft 24-4-4 Mixing Desk. One CD Player. Sony Mini-disc Player. Four Shure SM58 Vocal Mics. D + B amps + speakers.
COMMUNICATIONS: All dressing rooms have both show relay and call speakers. 11 headsets for distribution as required.
Cue lights: 12 sets are available for use as required.
DRESSING ROOMS: 15, accommodates 80. 10 showers within the dressing room, plus two separate showers.
Membership: TMA

HULL TRUCK THEATRE
Hull Truck Theatre Company
Hull Truck Theatre, 50 Ferensway, Hull HU2 8LB
Admin: 01482 224 800 BO: 01482 323 638 Publicity: 01482 325 012
Email: kate.denby@hulltruck.co.uk
Web Site: www.hulltruck.co.uk
ADMINISTRATION:
Artistic Director: Mark Babych
Executive Director: Janthi Mills-Ward
General Manager: Ian Archer
Head of Production: Fran Maskell
Membership: TMA (Touring)
Policy: Resident productions; comedy and jazz nights; incoming productions; jazz and literature festivals; education and outreach activity; youth theatre activity.
Capacity: 437 Maximum, Studio Capacity 134
For more information on hiring, email: events@hulltruck.co.uk.
TECHNICAL:
STAGE: Thrust Stage: Area 8.1m x 7.5m, no rake, floor ply on concrete, lino not available. Height of grid: 3.5m, black box masking. Get-in at rear, stage level. Back Doors 1.4m x 2.6m. Scale stage, fly + LX plans available 1:50 and 1:25 metric.
Electrics: operated from control room overlooking stage on S.R. side of auditorium
LIGHTING: Lee Colortran Prestige 1000 board, 55 circuits @ 10A, 30 x 1kw fresnels; 20 x 650w PC's; 6 x Sil 30's. Full list on demand. 3 phase operated SR of auditorium (20 spots Berkley/Strand 30 fresnals).
SOUND: Soundcraft 16:4: 2 desk, Revox, cassette, quadreverb and assorted mics. (contact theatre for more information).
DRESSING ROOMS: 2. Accom: 20

THE MIDDLETON HALL
The University of Hull, Cottingham Road, Hull, East Yorkshire HU6 7RX
Tel: 01482 465 341 Fax: 01482 466922
Email: yourevents@hull.ac.uk
Web Site: www.hull.ac.uk/yourevents
ADMINISTRATION:
Props & Lessees: The University of Hull
Contact: Jenny Potts
Facilities Directorate: Tel 01482 465 341
Policy: Hire out only.
Seats: 514. Catering available by arrangement.
TECHNICAL:
Stage: Proscenium and Thrust, Flat; Pros. opening 11.28m; Ht. of Pros. 6.71m; Depth of S/Line 8.15m; Ht. of Grid 8.99m; 8 Hanging Bars 13.11m, W/Widths P.S. 3.05m, O.P. 5.49m; Prompt Cnr. O.P.
Lighting: Desk light board M 78 channels., F.O.H. 32 circuits; stage 46 circuits.
Lamps: 16 Cantata 26/44; 10 18/32; 4 CCT Minuettes; 25 Strand 743; 3 Strand Patt 23; 2 Strand Patt 123; 5 Patt S/64 Battens; 21 Patt 500w floods; 8 Par 64 Par Cans; 11 Strand Patt 264; 30 RAT music stands.
Sound Equip: C Audio RA 2000 amp, Crest VS 450 amp; Soundcraft Spirit Live 16-4-2 mixer; 2 RCF Art800 AS speakers, 4 RCF Art 300 speakers; 4 Martin EM15s; Dressing relay system. CD player, mini disk player, cassette player, Pro-Tech communication system. Facilities for slide and video projection.
Dressing Rooms 2; Accom 20; 2 Showers. additional room(s) if required.

Hunstanton, Norfolk
Pop. 4,500. London 124 miles.
Newspapers: Eastern Daily Press & Lynn News & Advertiser. STD code 01485

PRINCESS THEATRE
13 The Green, Hunstanton, Norfolk PE36 5AH
BO: 01485 532252
Email: boxoffice@princesshunstanton.co.uk
Web Site: www.princesshunstanton.co.uk
ADMINISTRATION:

Technical Manager: Ian Larkin
Admin Manager: Helen Baxter
Policy: Plays, dance, music, films throughout the year.
Theatre bar
Seating Capacity: 464
TECHNICAL:
Stage: Proscenium raked stage (1:40), wings 4.1m, grid height 10.10m, 8 motorised, 5 drill/hand, 4 hemp flying bars.
Lighting: Zero 88 Bull Frog Control Desk, 48 ways of DMX @ 10A. Assorted lanterns.
Sound: Soundcraft LX7 16/4/2 Mixer, 2 x Crest CA6 Amps to 4 x Renkus Heinz FOH Speakers & 2 x Yamaha Amps to 2 x Renkus & 2 x Yamaha Monitors, 1 x Behringer ultra curve digital EQ, 2 x Behringer ultra graph EQ, 1 x BSS Opal DPR422 compressor, 1 x Behringer multi-gate, 1 x ART multiverb, 1 x Denon DCD685 CD Player, 1 x Sony MDS JB940 Minidisc: Assorted microphones and kit.
Dressing Rooms: 4 to accomodate 24
Other: 63 A TPNE LX Power Supply, 63 A SPNE Sound Power Supply
Grotrian Steinweg Concert Grand

Huntly, Aberdeenshire

STEWART'S HALL

Gordon Street, Huntly, Aberdeenshire AB54 8AJ Scotland
Tel: 01466 792 779
Email: john.greer22@btinternet.com
Hall keeper: John Greer
Seating/Capacity: 350

Ickenham, Middlesex

COMPASS THEATRE AND ARTS CENTRE

Glebe Avenue, Ickenham, Uxbridge, Middlesex UB10 8PD
Admin: 01895 632 488
BO: 01895 673 200
Email: boxoffice@hgfl.org.uk
Web Site: www.compasstheatre.co.uk
Administration:
Theatre Manager: Tim Saward
Arts Programming Officer: Tim Saward
Technical Manager: Tom Peters
Box Office & Marketing: Fjola Stenning
Purpose built theatre with retractable seating for 158, refurbished in 1990.
Policy: Plays, musicals, concerts, children's performances. Willing to premiere a show.
TECHNICAL:
Stage: Proscenium arch, stage extensions available. No rake. Basic performing area: 6.1m x 6.1m. Pros opening: 6.1m x 3.2m. Wing widths: 3.05m SR, SL. Forestage: 6.1m x 1.37m, entrance from auditorium. Height of grid: 7.01m
Lighting: Sirius 48 way lighting board, 100 amp three phase power supply. Operated from control box at rear of auditorium. Temporary three phase power supply to grounds and cafe. 26 profiles, 32 fresnels, source fours and codas available. Scaffolding tower available. 1 fixed position lighting bar, 3 hemp flown lighting bars, cyc flood bar plus 2 FOH bars.
Sound: Soundcraft Spirit Folio 10 operated from control box. Main amp switch PL500. Peavey Eurosys 350w speakers. Second amp revox B251 for effects and foldback. 2 cassette tape system, 1 reel to reel. CD player.
Stage Management: Prompt corner DSL. Show relay to dressing rooms and green room. Tech relay with 6 outstations.
Backstage: 2 permanent dressing rooms, accom. for 30 performers. Large green room, catering available. Washing, drying facilities. Workshop space for set maintenance, fully equipped. Large studio available backstage for rehearsal. 2 pianos available. 1 Yamaha Grand Piano and 1 upright.

Ilfracombe, Devon

Pop. 9,140. London 203 miles.
Newspapers: North Devon Journal-Herald (thurs). STD code 01271

THE LANDMARK THEATRE

The Seafront, Wilder Road, Ilfracombe, Devon EX34 9BZ
Tel: 01271 865 655 Fax: 01271 867 707
Email: foh.lm@northdevontheatres.org.uk
Web: www.northdevontheatres.org.uk
ADMINISTRATION:
Manager: Alan Dodd
Props: North Devon Theatres Trust
Cap: 483

Ilkley, West Yorkshire

KINGS HALL/WINTER GARDEN

22 Station Road, Ilkley, West Yorkshire LS29 8HB
Tel: 01943 436 224
Email: christopher.ashton@bradford.gov.uk
Web Site: www.bradford-theatres.co.uk
ADMINISTRATION:
Props: City of Bradford Metropolitan District Council
Cap: 500 Theatre Style
For bookings contact Chris Ashton
Tel: 01943 436 224

KIRKLANDS COMMUNITY CENTRE

119 Main Street, Menston, Ilkley, West Yorkshire LS29 6HT
Bookings: 01943 436 224 Tel: 01943 874335
Email: christopher.ashton@bradford.gov.uk
Web Site: www.bradford.gov.uk
ADMINISTRATION
Props: City of Bradford Metropolitan District Council
Cap: 150

QUEENS HALL

Main Street, Burley-in-Wharfedale, Ilkley, West Yorkshire LS29 7BT
Tel: 01943 864062 Bookings: 01943 436 224
Email: christopher.ashton@bradford.gov.uk
Web Site: www.bradford.gov.uk
ADMINISTRATION
Props: City of Bradford Metropolitan District Council
Cap: 150

Inverness, Highland

Pop. 37,000. London 529 miles.
Newspapers: Highland News (thurs); Inverness Courier (tues/fri); Press and Journal. STD code 01463

EDEN COURT THEATRE

Eden Court, Bishops Road, Inverness IV3 5SA Scotland
Admin: 01463 239 841 BO: 01463 234 234
Email: admin@eden-court.co.uk
Web Site: www.eden-court.co.uk
ADMINISTRATION:
Director: Colin Marr
Policy: Open all year housing all forms of touring entertainment from opera to popular music, concerts, ballet, modern dance, drama and films. Full Conference facilities.
Seats: 840 on three levels. Three Foyer Bars, Restaurant and Cocktail Bar, Exhibitions in the stalls foyer and in additional adjacent rooms. 2 cinemas
TECHNICAL:
For further details of Eden Court's technical specifications email: bshanks@eden-court.co.uk

ONE TOUCH THEATRE

Bishops Road, Inverness IV3 5SA Scotland
Admin: 01463 239841 BO: 01463 234234
Email: admin@eden-court.co.uk
Web Site: www.eden-court.co.uk
Director: Colin Marr
Tech: Bob Shanks
bshanks@eden-court.co.uk
Capacity: 250

THE IRONWORKS
122b Academy Street, Inverness IV1 1LX Scotland
Tel: 01463 718555 BO: 0871 7894173
Email: office@ironworksvenue.com
Web Site: www.ironworksvenue.com
ADMINISTRATION:
Venue Manager: Caroline Campbell
Tour Booking: Robert Hicks
Capacity: 200-1000 standing, 400 theatre style, 250 cabaret style.

Ipswich, Suffolk

Pop. 123.070. London 72 miles.
Newspapers: East Anglian Daily Times; Evening Star (ntly); Suffolk Mercury (thurs); Suffolk Extra (fri). STD code 01473

IPSWICH REGENT AND CORN EXCHANGE
3 St. Helens Street, Ipswich, Suffolk IP4 1HE
Mgt: 01473 433 555 BO: 01473 433 100
Tech: 01473 433 695 Mgt Fax: 01473 433 727
Email: info@ipswichregent.com
Web Site: www.ipswichregent.com
ADMINISTRATION:
Props: Ipswich Borough Council
Policy: Live entertainment, single nights or week runs.
General Manager: David Mansfield.
Contact: david.mansfield@ipswich.gov.uk
Show Manager: Shelley Rook
Operations Manager: Mark Whiting
Technical Manager: Chris Last and Julian Smith. Contact: chris.last@ipswich.gov.uk or julian.smith@ipswich.gov.uk
Box Office Manager: Linda Wines
3 bars, hospitality lounge
Seating capacity: 1,535 (Including 6 Wheelchair spaces)
TECHNICAL:
STAGE: Depth 8.7 Metres + Ext 2.3 m (Orchestra Pit), Width 16.8m. Clearance: 11.5m to grid. Proscenium; Width 11.9m, Height 7.0m. Equipment: Full black masking, Stage RostRA. Flying Points: 3 x 1 ton U/S, 3 x 1 ton D/S, + 2 ton FOH + 16 x 250kg Fly Bars (3 of which are counter weight). 4 c 500kg LX Bars (hand winched)
STAGE POWER: 400A 3ph - Assorted Cee form & power locks + dedicated 63a single phase sound power.
LIGHTING: Dimmable - 168 ways, Avolites pearl 2000 control desk, 45 x Thomas Par 64 Parcans (CP60's and CP62's), 20 x Selecon "Rama" 1kw Fresnell, 10 x Selecon "Arena" 2kw Fresnell, 35 x Strand Patt 223 1kw Fresnell, 16 x Strand Patt 243 2kw Fresnell, 20 x Source 4 Zoom (15°-30°) Spot, 6 x Sil 30, 9 x CCT 1kw Flood, 2 x Followspot - Robert Juliat Korrigan 1200, 1 x DF-50 haze machine
SOUND: Hired by arrangement
DRESSING ROOMS: 8 to accommodate 60. 3 Showers.

THE NEW WOLSEY THEATRE
Civic Drive, Ipswich, Suffolk IP1 2AS
Mgmt: 01473 295912 BO: 01473 295900
Email: info@wolseytheatre.co.uk
Web Site: www.wolseytheatre.co.uk
ADMINISTRATION:
Lessees: Wolsey Theatre Co. Ltd
Artistic Director: Peter Rowe
Chief Executive: Sarah Holmes
Duty Manager: Kelly Kirkbride
Policy: Touring venue with three or four productions per year in-house.
Perfs: 7.45; Mat 2.30
Seats: 400. Bar open during performances and normal licensing hours.
TECHNICAL:
Stage: Open (Thrust) Stage and Rear Stage. Flat; Thrust Stage Depth 12.25m; Max Width 14.20m; Width at Opening to Rear Stage 8.25m; Rear Stage Depth 6m; Width 8.25m; Wing Space P.S. 10.33m; O.P. 3.70m; Ht. over Thrust Stage 8.5m. Ht. over Rear Stage 7.5m; Prompt Cnr. O.P. (mobile to Control Room F.O.H.) No Fly Tower.
Lighting: Switchboard: Rank Strand Galaxy III 120 ways, 60 Profiles, 50 Fresnels, 7 x 5kw circuits.
Sound: DDA 24/8/2 mixer inc. theatre matrix. 3 Revox B77, 1 TEAC 4 track, 1 cassette, 1 CD, Bose 802/302 system.
Dressing Rooms 5; Accom. 25. Showers 3.
Membership: TMA

WOLSEY STUDIO
St. George's Street, Ipswich, Suffolk IP1 3NF
Mgt: 01473 295912 BO: 01473 295900
Email: info@wolseytheatre.co.uk
Web Site: www.wolseytheatre.co.uk
ADMINISTRATION:
Lessees: Wolsey Theatre Co. Ltd
Artistic Associate: Peter Rowe
Chief Executive: Sarah Holmes
Seats: Flexible 95-120. Bar open during performances only.
TECHNICAL:
Stage: Stage area flexible. Minimum 6.20m x 5.10m; maximum 10.70m x 7.80m.
Lighting: Board: ADB Cantor 36 way; 25 x 650w PCs + 10 x 650W zoom profiles; 6 x 1K Fresnels.
Sound: Allen Heath SC + 6 Mong 3 stereo input; 4 x 4 matrix output; 6 channel C audio amp outputs; 1 Revox B77, 1 cassette, 1 CD.
Dressing Rooms: 2, accommodation 10.

Irvine, North Ayrshire

Pop. 58,000. Glasgow 26 miles. London 417 miles. STD code 01294

MAGNUM THEATRE
Magnum Leisure Centre, Harbourside, Irvine, Ayrshire, KA12 8PP Scotland
BO: 01294 313010 Fax: 01294 317461
Email: info@kaleisure.com
Web Site: www.kaleisure.com
ADMINISTRATION:
Props: KA Leisure
Policy: Magnum Theatre is a combined theatre and all types of entertainments are presented in the widest possible range.
Perfs: Variable
Cap/Seats: 317. Cafeteria
Main Hall Cap: 1164 seated 1500 standing
TECHNICAL:
Stage: Proscenium, opening 32ft; rear wall (drapes) 21ft, rear wall to sky cloth 20ft, depth of stage (without FOH) 20ft; depth of stage (using FOH) 27ft; Height of flats 16ft.
Lighting: Tempus M24 Lighting Board, Tempus M24 Effects Board, 60 channels & 185 memories.
Sound: TOA 12 channel mixing console, TOA front of House speakers, Talk Back system (wireless). Twin cassette deck, CD player, Alesis Midiverb Unit, Shure SM58 microphones, on stage monitors.
Other: 2 x 35mm projectors, 24ft x 12ft cinema screen, remote control slide carousel projector, overhead projector, portable screens, lectern, VHS video & monitor, portable PA systems, flip charts and black board.

MAGNUM MAIN HALL:
Capacity 1,200 seated, 1,800 standing.
Size: 115ft x 102ft, height 40ft.
Stage: 40ft wide, 24ft deep, 4ft high (plus 16ft x 16ft PA wings.)

VOLUNTEER ROOMS
19 High Street, Irvine, Ayrshire KA12 0BA
Tel: 01294 278390
Email: communityfacilities@north-ayrshire.gov.uk
Web Site: www.north-ayrshire.gov.uk
ADMINISTRATION:
Props: North Ayrshire Council
S/Cap: 400, 230 seated
For Bookings: Tel 0845 2301325
Caretaker: David McManus
Head of Community Facilities: Donna Morrison

Irvinestown, County Fermanagh

BAWNACRE CENTRE
Castle Street, Irvinestown, Enniskillen, County Fermanagh, BT94 1EE Northern Ireland
Tel: 028 6862 1177 Fax: 028 6862 8082
Email: george.beacom@fermanagh.gov.uk
Web Site: www.bawnacrecentre.com
ADMINISTRATION:

Centre Manager: George Beacom
Seating: 900 in main hall. Purpose built stage with full lights and curtains. Minor hall: seating for 320. Small hall: seating for 100. Excellent workshop, exhibition & cafe facilities available.
TECHNICAL:
Full lights, curtains and P.A. system

Isle of Arran

BRODICK HALL
Isle of Arran, Ayrshire KA27 8DL Scotland
Tel: 01770 302 065 Bkg Tel: 01770 302231
Email: john_sillars@talktalk.net
ADMINISTRATION:
Props: North Ayrshire Council
Cap: 200
Contact: John Sillars

Ivybridge, Devon

THE WATERMARK
Erme Court Leonards Road, Ivybridge, Devon PL21 0SZ
Tel: 01752 892220
Email: info@ivybridgewatermark.co.uk
Web Site: www.ivybridgewatermark.co.uk
Conference Centre/Cinema/Coffee Shop/Bar
Capacity: 210 seated
Henlake Suite/bar, Capacity: 60
Stowford Hall, Capacity 280 standing
Manager: Jonathan Parsons

Jersey, Channel Islands

Pop. 84,082. Newspapers: Jersey Evening Post (dly). STD code 01534

FORT REGENT LEISURE CENTRE
St Helier, Jersey JE2 4UX Channel Islands
Mgt: 01534 449600
Email: t.lesueur@gov.je
Web Site: www.gov.je
ADMINSTRATION:
Props: States of Jersey
Events Officer: Tom Le Sueur
Policy: Multi-purpose
Seats: Variable from 660 to max 1,974
TECHNICAL:
Stage: Concert platform in acoustically correct bowl. 12.80m deep x 17.07m wide.
Lighting: Strand GSX 75 full theatre lighting system available.
Sound Equip: Combination of Bose loudspeakers with a Soundcraft 400B 32 channels.

JERSEY OPERA HOUSE
Gloucester Street, St Helier, Jersey JE2 3QR Channel Islands
Management Tel: 01534 511 100 BO: 01534 511 115 Marketing: 01534 511 109
Email: admin@jerseyoperahouse.co.uk
Web Site: www.jerseyoperahouse.co.uk
ADMINISTRATION:
Theatre Director: Jasmin Hendry
Technical Manager: Chris Wink
Theatre Manager: Forbes Mann
Marketing Manager: Abi Nance
Status: National Touring House
History: Traditional proscenium arch theatre, listed building built in 1900 and reconstructed in 1921, near town centre. Opened in July 2000 aftter major refurbishment.
Local Authority: Baliwick of Jersey
Policy: All types of production, both professional and amateur. Programme includes drama, dance, music, opera, ballet, musicals, comedy. Theatre tours. Willing to premier shows.
Jersey Opera House is a producing Theatre as well as a receiving venue.
Perfs: Open 7 days, shows start 7 - 8.30pm; matinees as required.
Other activities: Workshops as requested. Full Outreach programme.
Facilities: Seats; 625 raked, Upper Circle, Dress Circle, Stalls. 3 licensed bars. 14 wheelchair spaces, induction loop system, level access, toilet.
Other facilities; bar gallery space, rehearsal rooms. Venue available for filming, photgraphic sesions and conferences outside of performance times.
TECHNICAL:
Stage: Proscenium arch. Performing area 8.5m x 8.4m - pros opening 8.5m x 5.5m - wing widths 3.4m SR, 5m SL. No rake - floor suitable for dance, backstage crossover. Height to grid 14m - 33 counterweight sets - 2 tab tracks. Forestage 4m deep. Orchestra pit accomodates 30. Get-in via door - 4.5m x 2.2m. Safety curtain. Scale stage, fly and lighting plans available.
Lighting; Strand 520i lighting desk, 136 channels @ 2.5kW plus 4 channels @ 5kW dimming - 55 1kW profiles, 66 fresnels - 200A 3 phase touring supply. HIre items: 8 x mac 250's; x 18 scroller units; various smoke effects.
Sound; Soundcraft 24:8:2 K2 sound desk - 8 D&B 690 speakers, 2 D&B bass speakers - minidisc, CD and cassette playback. Hire items: 14 x radio mic channels:- x 12 belt packs; 4 hand-held; various stage monitors.
Stage Management; SM desk, DSL - cue lights and headset available - show relay to all dressingrooms.
Backstage; Maximum 5 dressingrooms accomodate approx 50 - wardrobe, with irons and laundry facilities and prop store on ground floor. Showers and toilets.
Additional Information; Steinway Grand piano and upright. Theatre is leasing s/c flats for use by visiting companies.

Keighly, West Yorkshire

HOLDEN HALL
Colne Road, Oakworth, Keighley, West Yorkshire BD22 7PB
Tel: 01535 644197
Email: lynn.middleton@bradford.gov.uk
ADMINISTRATION
Props: City of Bradford Metropolitan District Council
Cap: 130
For bookings contact Lynn Middleton, Tel: 01274 431576, Fax: 01274 431523

SILSDEN TOWN HALL
Kirkgate, Silsden, Keighley, West Yorkshire BD20 0PB
Tel: 01535 652 466 Booking Enq: 01274 431576
Email: lynn.middleton@bradford.gov.uk
ADMINISTRATION:
Props: City of Bradford Metropolitan District Council
Cap: 200
For bookings contact Lynn Middleton

VICTORIA HALL
Victoria Park, Hard Ings Road, Keighley, West Yorkshire BD21 3JN
Tel: 01535 681763
Email: louise.newton@bradford.gov.uk
ADMINISTRATION
Props: City of Bradford Metropolitan District Council
Cap: 550
For bookings contact Louise Newton
Tel: 01535 681763 Fax: 01535 690454

Keith, Morayshire

KEITH COMMUNITY CENTRE
Banff Road, Keith, Morayshire AB55 5GT Scotland
Tel: 01542 882 222 Fax: 01542 886 735
Email: keith.cc@moray.gov.uk
Web Site: www.moray.gov.uk
ADMINISTRATION:
Props: Moray Council
Manager: Ken Brown

LONGMORE HALL
Church Road, Keith, Morayshire AB55 3BR
PCB Tel: 01542 886712
Email: keith.access@moray.gov.uk
ADMINISTRATION:
Props: Moray Council
Cap: Main Hall Seated 325; Dancing 300; Dancing/Seated at tables 240; Seated at tables 213.
Lesser Hall Seated 200; Dancing 200; Dancing/Seated at tables 150; Seated at

tables 138.
For bookings Tel: 01343 543 451 Fax: 01542 885523

Kelso, Roxburghshire

TAIT HALL

Edenside Road, Kelso, Roxburghshire
TD5 7BS Scotland
Tel 01573 224 233
Email: alan.scott@scotborders.gov.uk
Web Site: www.scotborders.gov.uk
ADMINISTRATION:
Manager: Frank Dutch
Seating/Capacity: 600; balcony fixed, loose stacked in stalls.

Kendal, Cumbria

KENDAL TOWN HALL

Highgate, Kendal, Cumbria LA9 4DL
Tel: 01539 793 102 0755 792 0857
Email: d.mckee@southlakeland.gov.uk
Web Site: www.southlakeland.gov.uk
ADMINISTRATION
Props: South Lakeland District Council
Cap: Assembly Hall 370. Dance without tables or Maximum Seating, 190 with extended stage and cabaret style seating
For bookings contact: Debbie Mckee
Dressing rooms, catering, bar, concerts, shows.

NORTH COUNTRY LEISURE KENDAL

Burton Road, Kendal, Cumbria LA9 7HX
Tel: 01539 729 511 BO: 01539 729 702
Fax: 01539 731 135
Email: derek.jones@northcountryleisure.org.uk
Web Site: www.northcountryleisure.org.uk
Recreation Officer For Events: Derek Jones
Seating/Capacity: 893 max.

Kerry, Eire

INEC

Muckross Road, Killarney, Kerry Ireland
Tel: 00 353 64 66 71 555
Email: shaneod@inec.ie
Web Site: www.inec.ie
General manager: John Dolan
Capacity: 2000
The INEC is located in Ireland's South West. It is the second largest in-door venue in Ireland. It has a catchment area of 600,000 people all within a two hour drive. Cork & Limerick cities are both within a one hour drive. It has three international airports within it's catchment area (Kerry 20min - Cork 1hour - Shannon 90min).

Keswick, Cumbria

Pop. 5,169. London 283 miles.
Newspapers: Keswick Reminder (fri); Times & Star; News & Star; Lake District Herald; Cumberland News. STD code 017687

THEATRE BY THE LAKE

Lakeside, Keswick, Cumbria CA12 5DJ
Mgt: 01768 772 282 BO: 01768 774 411
Email: enquiries@theatrebythelake.com
Web Site: www.theatrebythelake.com
ADMINISTRATION:
Props: Cumbria Theatre Trust Ltd.
Executive Director: Patric Gilchrist
Head of Production: Matt Hall
Technical Manager: Andrew J Lindsay
Policy: Professional repertoire of plays, June-October. Also functions as a receiving venue for small-scale drama, opera and ballet.
TECHNICAL:
Main Stage: Flexible space 16.6m wide x 10.5m deep with proscenium opening. No rake, timber floor. Crossover via Backstage corridor. Heat and ventilation to stage area. Pros height 5.5m, height to grid 13m. Double purchase counterweight flying. Approx 40 sets 12m bars plus up and down bars for side masking. Drapes black velour, size tba. Flexible rostra to form centre area of stage and forestage. Forstage 9m x 2m. Orchestra pit. Get-in: flat access to 5.5m doors UL. Scale plans available.
Lighting: 1 Strand 520i lighting console, 1 strand 510 backup console, 138 x 2.5 K, b x 5k dimming, 12 non-dim circuits. Operating position control room centre rear stall. 200A three phase supply for touring. Lantern stock attached.
Sound: Mackie 24-8-2 mixing console in control room centre rear of stalls or at positions onstage or in auditorium. 5 Meyer UPA1-P, 2 Meyer USW1, 4 Nexo PS10, 16 JBL Control, 2 Lab1200c, 6 SM58, 4 SM57, 1 AKG D112, 4 AKG SE300B power modules + CK91 mic-heads, 4 Audio Tech AT961R boundary mic.s, 12 K&M 10/9 mic stands, 4 25/9 mic stands, 4 BSS Audio AR133 D.I boxes, 2 Tascam MD501R mini disc, 1 Denon DN1000F Cd player, 1 Denon DN720R cassette desk, 1 Yamaha SPX990 effects processor, 1 Yamaha REV500 reverb, 2 Yamaha Q2031 graphic equalisers, Soundweb 9088, 2 Sennheiser infra-red modulators/radiators, 18 Sennheiser HD91 single channel receivers.
Stage Management: Prompt corner SL. 10 way cue light system, 1 Metro dual channel masterstation, 12 Metro single channel beltpacks & headsets, 48 comms positions, show relay and tannoy to dressing rooms.
Studio Theatre: 9m x 9m. Equipment tba. Lighting: 1 Strand 520i lighting console, 40 x 2.5K dimming. Lantern stock attached.
Sound: 1 Mackie 1402 mixing console, 1 Tascam MD501R mini-disc recorder, Denon T620 CD player/Cassette deck, 1 Metro CCU4 portable masterstation, 3 comms position, 6 way cue light system. Amplification and loudspeakers are subject to availability of Main stage sound stock.
Studio Theatre: 9m x 9m, Strand 520 lighting console, Mackie 1402ymixing console sound
Backstage: 4 dressing rooms, (total capacity 15), rehearsal room, studio dressing room. Wardrobe, with washer, dryer and ironing facilities. Paintstore. Green Room with fridge, kettle etc. All backstage areas including basement and flies fully accessible to disabled people.

Kettering, Northamptonshire

THE LIGHTHOUSE THEATRE

Thurston Drive, Kettering, Northamptonshire NN15 6PB
BO: 01536 414 141 Fax: 01536 414 334
Email: enquiries@lighthousetheatre.co.uk
Web Site: www.lighthousetheatre.co.uk
ADMINISTRATION:
General Manager: Paul Hammond
Stage Manager: James Dainty
Props: Phoenix Leisure Management
Policy: Music, Drama, Dance and Comedy.
Capacity: 567. 424 tiered seats at ground floor level and a further 143 in the balcony. Disabled seating: 8 wheelchairs max.
TECHNICAL:
STAGE: 16m (incl wings) x 10.15m. Proscenium arch: 11.7m wide x 5.9m high (10.5 x 5.1 with tormentors & border). Fly grid: 11.9m above stage floor fitted with 20 fly barrels each with a swl of 200kg. Rear five barrels restricted flying height. Stage access: By external door 4.5m high x 3.5m wide via 9m x 4.5m scene dock. Personnel access from auditorium left and right. Power supply: 63amp 3phase plus 32amp 3phase travelling supply on stage. Orchestra Pit: 9.0m x 3.0m floor 2.5m below stage. Internet access on stage. Auditorium fitted with induction loop for the hard of hearing
LIGHTING: Controls: 72 Chilli Pro dimmers and Zero 88 Leap Frog desk. Various lights available including fesnel lanterns, floods, profile lanterns and parcans. House lighting in two systems, one for general and conference lighting, providing 300lux, one fully dimmable.
SOUND: Soundcraft Live 8 (40 channel) desk linked to a Peavey sound system comprising of 4 No. ILS1564V speakers together with other linked speakers in dressing rooms and bar areas.
DRESSING ROOMS: 5, 6.5m x 3.5m with associated toilets and showers.

Kidderminster, Worcestershire

GLADES ARENA
Wyre Forest Glades Leisure Centre, Bromsgrove Street, Kidderminster, Worcestershire DY10 1PP
Tel: 01562 515 151 Fax: 01562 861 458
Email: stuartbooton@dcleisure.co.uk
Web Site: www.dcleisurecentres.co.uk
Centre & Events Manager: Stuart Booton
Capacity: 1,350 seated; 1,800 standing.

Kilbirnie, Ayrshire

WALKER HALL
39 - 45 Main Street, Kilbirnie, Ayrshire KA25 7BX Scotland
Tel: 01505 683 652
ADMINISTRATION:
Props: North Ayrshire Council
Cap: 150
Contact: Managing Supervisor Donna Morrison or Hall Supervisor Heather Lynn

Kilmarnock, Ayrshire

Pop. 48,785. London 391 miles. Newspapers: Kilmarnock Standard (thurs). STD code 01563

BELLFIELD COMMUNITY CENTRE
193b Whatriggs Road, Kilmarnock, Ayrshire KA1 3SZ Scotland
Tel/Fax: 01563 572 832
ADMINISTRATION:
Props: East Ayrshire Leisure Trust
Cap: 200

BONNYTON COMMUNITY CENTRE
51 Garrier Place, Kilmarnock, Ayrshire KA1 2NG Scotland
Mob: 0777 3647601
ADMINISTRATION:
Props: East Ayrshire Council
Cap: 90

GRAND HALL
1a London Road, Kilmarnock, Ayrshire KA3 7AA Scotland
Caretaker Tel: 01563 576 750 Bookings: 01563 554940
Email: EAleisureletting@east-ayrshire.gov.uk
Web Site: www.east-ayrshire.gov.uk
ADMINISTRATION:
Props: East Ayrshire Leisure
Cap: Main Hall 900; Pillared Hall 250(Theatre); Arts Room (1) 200; Arts Room (2) 200; Reception Room 50.
For bookings contact Palace Theatre on 01563 578156

NEW FARM LOCH COMMUNITY CENTRE
2a Fraser Walk, Kilmarnock, Ayrshire KA3 7NT
Tel: 01563 535333
ADMINISTRATION:
Props: East Ayrshire Council
Contact: Bookings: Craig Montgomery Tel 01563 531256

PALACE THEATRE
9 Green Street, Kilmarnock, Ayrshire KA1 3BU
BO: 01563 554900 Mktg: 01563 554 330
Email: janice.gilmour@east-ayrshire.gov.uk
Web Site: www.eastayrshireleisure.com
ADMINISTRATION:
Props: East Ayrshire Council
Theatre Manager: Janice Gilmour
Audience Development Officer: Louise Kyle
Operations Officer: Andy Gale
Policy: Professional & Amateur Drama, Music, Comedy, Opera, Ballet, Concerts and Variety etc.
Perfs: Varied.
Seats: 497
Bars: 1
TECHNICAL:
Stage: Pros, slight rake; Pros. opening 7.47m; Ht. of Pros. 4.88m; Depth of S/Line 7.32m; Ht. to Grid 10.06m; 20 Hemp sets.
Lighting: Please contact management.
Sound Equip: Fully professional sound system. Upgraded 2001. Please apply to management for details.
Dressing Rooms 7.

RICCARTON COMMUNITY CENTRE
23 Campbell Street, Kilmarnock, Ayrshire KA1 4HL
Tel: 01563 571138
Web Site: www.east-ayrshire.gov.uk
ADMINISTRATION:
Props: East Ayrshire Council
Centre Supervisor: Colin Paton
Capacity: 80

King's Lynn, Norfolk

Pop. 30,220. London 98 miles. Newspapers: Lynn News & Advertiser (tues/fri); Eastern Daily (dly). STD code 01553

ASSEMBLY ROOMS
Saturday Market Place, King's Lynn, Norfolk PE30 5DQ
Tel: 01553 775 839 Fax: 01553 772 361
Email: sandy.lea@west-norfolk.gov.uk
ADMINISTRATION:
Props: Kings Lynn & West Norfolk Borough Council
Booking Enquiry: Mrs Lea
Cap: 180 (Portable stage available)

THE CORN EXCHANGE
Tuesday Market Place, King's Lynn, Norfolk PE30 1JW
Admin: 01553 765 565 BO: 01553 764 864 Fax: 01553 762 141
Email: cornexchangeadmin@aliveleisure.co.uk
Web: www.kingslynncornexchange.co.uk
ADMINISTRATION:
Props: Alive Leisure
Venue Manager: Philip Bayfield
Contact: philip.bayfield@alivemanagement.co.uk
Senior Technician: Jason Barker.
Contact: 01553 779103
Policy: Plays, Dance, Music.
Capacity: 738 seated, 1,200 standing
TECHNICAL:
STAGE: Open flat stage 12m x 8m (extends 10.5m). Wing width 1.75m each side, grid height 8m. 2 of 11.5 truss, 6 winched double barrels.
LIGHTING: ETC Impression 2 Control desk (250 channels) 80 dimmers 66 @ 10A, 12 @ 25A, hard wired to socket outlets. 60 x par 64, 30 x 1.2k fresnels, 12 x 1.2k 22/40 profiles, 8 x 1.2k 15/28 profiles: 2 x 1200 MSR followspots.
SOUND: Crest century GT 24 channel mixer, 7 crest amplifiers, 8 community FOH speakers, 6 peavey wedges, Yamaha SPX 990, 6 x compressors, 4 x noise gates, 6 channels of graphic EQ, 2 Tascam 112 cassette decks, 1 Tascam CD 401 CD player, 1 Denon Mini Disc Player, 6 shure SM58, 4 AKG SE 300B c/w CK91, 3 Sennheiser MD421, 2 AKG D112, 1 Shure SM58.
DRESSING ROOMS: 5, accomodating up to 70.
OTHER: 160A TPN Stage LX power supply, 160A SPN stage sound. Intercom systems. Portable staging. Piano available, 19 music stands.

KING'S LYNN ARTS CENTRE
29 King Street, King's Lynn, Norfolk PE30 1HA
Admin: 01553 779 095 BO: 01553 764 864
Web Site: www.kingslynnarts.co.uk
ADMINISTRATION:
General Manager: Liz Falconbridge (liz.falconbridge@kingslynnarts.co.uk)
Senior Technician: Jason Barker
Policy: Plays, Dance, Music, Films throughout year.
Seats: 349. Theatre Bar.
TECHNICAL:
Stage: End on Proscenium opening 6.67m; ht. of Pros.3.36m; Depth of stage 6.8m; Flying bars 15 lines Hemp.
Lighting: Strand 40 way manual switchboard hard wired in prompt side: 10 x Patt.23, 8 x Patt.743, 10 x Patt.123, 4 x

Patt.60, 8 Minims.
Sound: 16 channel soundcraft studio, renkus-heine speakers on Pros.arch; 4 Peavey monitor wedges; ,CD, Twin cassette; SPX 990.
Dressing Rooms: 4, Accom. 30, Orchestra Pit 16.
Max. height of Flats 3.66m; Max, width of Flats 1.91m.

TOWN HALL
Saturday Market Place, King's Lynn, Norfolk PE30 5DQ
Tel: 01553 775 839 Fax: 01553 772 361
Email: sandy.lea@westnorfolk.gov.uk
Web Site: www.westnorfolk.gov.uk
ADMINISTRATION:
Props: Kings Lynn & West Norfolk Borough Council
Booking Enquiry: Mrs Lea
Cap: 180 (Portable stage available)

Kingsbridge, Devon

QUAYSIDE LEISURE CENTRE
Rope Walk, Kingsbridge, Devon TQ7 1HH
01548 857 100
Email: m.green@toneleisure.com
Web Site: www.toneleisure.co.uk
ADMINISTRATION:
Props: Tone Leisure
Cap: 750 (Main Hall) plus Dance (rehearsal) Studio and ancilliary changing faciliites.
Licenced bar.
Manager: Matt Green
Disabled Access.

Kingston-Upon-Thames, Surrey

ROSE THEATRE
24-26 High Street Kingston KT1 1HL
Tel: 020 8546 6983 Fax: 020 8546 8783
BO: 020 8174 0090
Email: admin@rosetheatrekingston.org
Web Site: www.rosetheatrekingston.org
ADMINISTRATION:
Executive Producer: Jerry Gunn
Emeritus Director: Sir Peter Hall
Chief Executive: Robert O'Dowd
Assistant Producer: Naomi Webb
Director of Marketing and Communications: Sarah Lowry
Head of Production: Wayne Parry
Theatre Manager: Lesley Rowden
Policy: The Rose is a producing theatre that also presents a wide range of drama, music, comedy, dance, and events.
The Main Auditorium (capacity for 900, including cushion area)
The design of the auditorium took its inspiration from the Elizabethan Rose Theatre, situated on London's Bankside and has the same lozenge shaped stage, semi-circular seating configuration and pit area, where audiences can sit on cushions to watch performances.
The Gallery (capacity for 60 people, no fixed seating)
Cafe and Bar

THE THEATRE AT KINGSTON GRAMMAR
Performing Arts Centre.
Queen Elizabeth II Building, London Road, Kingston upon Thames, Surrey KT2 6PY
Tel: 020 8939 8821Tel: 020 8546 5875
Email: enquiries@kgs.org.uk
Web Site: www.kgs.org.uk
Technical Manager: Simon Gray
Policy: During term time after 4pm only, School holidays and weekends it is available to hire for any art form, professional or amateur. Booking terms by negotiation.
Capacity: 216 max seated. 400 Standing, 160 Cabaret style. Seating can be retracted to make a 16m by 14m Rehearsal room or Dance Studio (whole floor is sprung) also functions, art exhibitions, youth theatre.
Facilities: Licensed bar with large foyer
Transport: 5min walk from Kingston Train Station, 20min to Waterloo, NCP car park 2 min walk from venue. Disabled access.
Stage: Proscenium Arch. Performing Area 10m x 6m Pros opening is adjustable max with 13 m. Wing widths 2m SL & SR. No rake, Harlequin Sprung Floor covered with Rosco twin black / grey dance floor, suitable for all dance, backstage crossover, stage heated. Height to grid 7m, No fly tower. 14 bars with a mixture of winched and hemp. 3 pairs of leg, 3 borders, 2 sets of black half tabs, cloth white Cyc, permanent Rosco plastic white Cyc, House border and House Tabs in Plum. 8 Double 13amp sockets on stage. Get in via 2 sets of double doors street level. 3 section Zarges Skymaster and a 2 person electric driveable Scissor Lift. Sennheiser inferred loop system.
Lighting: Zero 88 Frog II running 46 Chill Pro dimmers @ 2.5k operated from large control room built into rear of theatre - no supply for temporary dimmers. 32 Fresnels 20 spots, 20 S4 Pars, 4-4 cell Cyc lights, 16 Scrollers, 4 - 574 w Moving Lights.
Sound: 24:8:2 desk operated from large control room built into rear of theatre, 3 amps, 8 Tannoy V8s 2 graphic EQ's, Omnidive speaker management unit.
8 SM58, 8 SM57 4 MD players 2 CD player & 4 Radio Mics.
Stage Management: Prompt corner SL or SR , 6 Beltpacks and Cans, Show relay and tannoy to dressing room also tannoy to FOH.
Backstage: One large dressing room or two smaller dressing rooms divided with an acoustic wall, 4 other rooms can be used to hold more cast all have show relay and tannoy.
Other: Staff - Technical Manager - casual's available but will be recharged.
Backstage accessible to disabled performers.

Kirkby-in-Ashfield, Nottinghamshire

FESTIVAL HALL
Festival Hall Leisure Centre, Hodgkinson Road, Kirkby-in-Ashfield, Nottingham NG17 7DJ
Tel: 01623 457 100 Fax: 01623 457 099
Email: alanjones@slm-ltd.co.uk
Web Site: www.ashfield-dc.gov.uk
Manager: Katie Roberts
Leisure Centres Liaison Officer: Joy Elmer
Seating/Capacity: 400

Kirkcaldy, Fife
Pop. 150,000. London 398 miles.
Newspapers: Fife Free Press (fri). STD code 01592

THE ADAM SMITH THEATRE
Bennochy Road, Kirkcaldy, Fife KY1 1ET Scotland
BO: 01592 583302
Email: boxoffice.adamsmith@onfife.com
Web Site: www.onfife.com
ADMINISTRATION:
Props: On Fife
Programming Manager: Evan Henderson
Operations Manager: Mark Wheelwright
Policy: All forms of touring entertainment including plays, musicals, ballet, opera, concerts, jazz, rock, country, folk etc. Regional Film Theatre. Stereo Dolby Sound System.
Perfs: 7.30p.m.
Seating: 475 on one raked tier. Licensed Bar. Restaurant. Three Functions Suites.
TECHNICAL:
Stage: Proscenium Arch; width 10.00m; height 6.00m. Level Stage. Curved Apron extends over Orchestra Pit. Depth - Prosc. to back wall 7.40m. Prosc. to Apron edge, Centre 2.5m. Ends 1.5m. Curved orchestra pit extension 2.0m. Stage width between dip traps 13.0m. Grid height 8.60m. 30 sets 3 line polyester ropes on 48mm. O.D. alloy barrels, length 12.19m. One counterweighted set and steel barrel. Ten motor winches with 4 line sets and steel barrels. Stage plan available. Fly floor S.L. only. Full black masking available. Get-in by 3.00m. square lift (O.P. stage) from ground level 5.00m below stage level. 6 dressing rooms on three levels accom. 55. Wardrobe room, 2 washing machines, ironing board, 2 tumble dryers. Deep sink. Car Park. House tabs. Manual winch (drawn across) grand piano, also upright. One large and one small Tallescope.

Orchestra pit seats 34 approx.
Lighting: Control Room rear auditorium projection suite. 156 dimmer channels. 2 lighting bridges: 2 vertical slot booms (Apron sides), bars hung to order. ETC desk. For list of lanterns available apply to theatre. Auxillary mains supply (S.L.) 100 amps, 3 phase AC supply. 2 pole booms, permanent d.S.L+R.
Sound: Control from rear of auditorium or stage. Selection of Shure and AKG microphones. Headset inter-comm. to all work stations. Paging and relay to dressing rooms. For further information apply to theatre.

Kirkcudbright, Kirkcudbrightshire

KIRKCUDBRIGHT TOWN HALL
St Mary Street, Kirkcudbright, DG6 4AA
Tel: 01556 503806
Email: louise.wilson@dumgal.gov.uk
Web Site: www.d&gcouncil.gov.uk
Cap: 250 Seated

Kirkwall, Orkney

THE PICKAQUOY CENTRE
Muddisdale Road, Kirkwall, Orkney KW15 1LR Scotland
Tel: 01856 879 900 Fax: 01856 879 901
Email: enquiries@pickaquoy.co.uk
Web Site: www.pickaquoy.co.uk

Kirriemuir, Angus

TOWN HALL
28-30 Reform Street, Kirriemuir, Angus DD8 4BS Scotland
Tel: 01575 577 177
Email: conkirrsc@angus.gov
Web Site: www.angus.gov.uk/leisure
ADMINISTRATION:
Props: Angus Council
Facilities Manager: Grant Donaldson
Cap: 368

Knighton, Powys

KNIGHTON COMMUNITY CENTRE
Community Centre Management Committee, Bowling Green Lane
Knighton Powys LD7 1DR Wales
Mob: 07751 221487
Email: knightoncomm@googlemail.com
Web Site: www.knightoncommunitycentre.com
ADMINISTRATION:
Props: Knighton and District Community Centre Management Committee
Cap: 500 approx. Stage facilities available.
Contact: Chris Plant

Lancaster, Lancashire

Pop. 49,820. London 223 miles.
Newspapers: Lancaster Guardian (fri).
STD code 01524

ASHTON HALL
Dalton Square, Lancaster, Lancashire LA1 1PJ
Tel: 01524 582 512 Admin: 01524 582 000
Email: roombookings@lancaster.gov.uk
Web Site: www.lancaster.gov.uk
ADMINISTRATION:
General Theatre Bookings: Michelle Shorrock
Municipal Buildings Manager: Sheila Hall
Capacity: 800 Theatre style

THE DUKES THEATRE & CINEMA
Moor Lane, Lancaster, Lancashire LA1 1QE
Mgt: 01524 598 505 BO: 01524 598 500
Fax: 01524 598 519
Email: info@dukes-lancaster.org
Web Site: www.dukes-lancaster.org
ADMINISTRATION:
Props: Lancaster City Council
Lessees: Duke's Playhouse Ltd
Theatre Director: Joe Sumsion
Production Manager: Phil Clark
Chief Technician: Brent Lees
Policy: Repertory, outdoor site specific work, regional film theatre, education, community and outreach work.
2 auditoria. End Stage (313 seats). In-the-round (236 seats) stage approx 5.3m x 6.1m.
TECHNICAL: End Stage
Proscenium Stage with apron, Flat; Pros. opening 10.67; Ht. of Pros. 5.79m; Depth of Line 9.14m; Ht. of Grid 6.10m; Winch No. 1 Bar, other bars hemp as required; Flying Bars 11.89m W/Widths P.S. 2.47m, O.P. 2.47m; Prompt Cnr. Portable prompt desk.
Computerised Box Office.
Sound Equip: Revox Tapes Goldring Pan & Bose 80L; Speakers as required. Dolby 35 + 16mm film sound track. Soundcraft Mixing Desk.
Dressing Rooms 3 Accom. 12; 3 showers.
Membership: TMA

GRAND THEATRE
St. Leonard's Gate, Lancaster, Lancashire LA1 1NL
BO: 01524 64 695
Email: ellie@lancastergrand.co.uk
Web Site: www.lancastergrand.co.uk
ADMINISTRATION:
Props: Lancaster Footlights Club
Manager: Ellie Singleton
Policy: Available for hire.
Perfs: Variable according to production.
Mixed amateur and professional.
Seats: 460. Licensed Bar.
Toilets and limited access for the disabled installed. Hearing Loop.
TECHNICAL:
STAGE: Proscenium Raked. Pros. opening 6.4m; Ht. of Pros. 5.2m; Stage depth 6.4m; Ht. of grid 12.2m; 30 lines hemp; W/widths PS 2.4m; OP 1.8-4.8m
LIGHTING: Switchboard: Fat Frog 72 channels, rear of auditorium; circuit distribution F.O.H. 16 Stage 56. Spots 24, Freznel 24, Par 64=18, Par 64 Floor=4 Flood 5=9.
SOUND: A+H Sound Desk to circle and PA.
DRESSING ROOMS: 5; accom. 40.
Orchestra Pit 12. Costume hire.
Membership: Little Theatre Guild of Great Britain, NODA.

NUFFIELD THEATRE
University of Lancaster, Bailrigg, Lancaster, Lancashire LA1 4YW
Tel: 01524 593777 BO: 01524 594151
Email: julia@liveatlica.org
Web Site: www.liveatlica.org
ADMINISTRATION:
Props: University of Lancaster
Director: Jamie Eastman
Administrator: Julia Carradus
Policy: Multi-Purpose Theatre accepts Touring Professional Theatre, Experimental Theatre Lab. Work, Dance, Mime, adapted classics.
Seats: 250 (max). Licensed Bar.
TECHNICAL:
Stage: Open Studio 22.86m.sq., Flat; Depth of S/Line depends on Stage Form; Ht. of Grid 5.18m; Lines as required, Hemp; Scenery Flying Ht. 3.05m; W/Widths adaptable; Prompt Cnr. either.
Lighting: Switchboard: Gemini or Jands ESP II 24 way, 124 way board; 24 way sirius; 124 dimmers; F.O.H. Spots as required; Dips as required; Full range of lanterns.
Sound Equip: Professional Mixing Desk, 8 channel 3 group; Speakers 4 Tannoy York etc.
Dressing Room: 1, large (can be divided); Accom. 20; Bathrooms; Orchestra Pit as required.
Very Flexible Studio 22.86m centre pit 1.52m deep, 15.24m.sq. Stage/s adaptable to any part of Studio. Seating can be tiered or flat, 6.71m. Wheelchair access and disabled toilets.

Langholm, Dumfries & Galloway

BUCCLEUCH CENTRE

Buccleuch Square, Langholm, Dumfries & Galloway DG13 0AW Scotland
Tel: 01387 381196
Email: info@beccleuchcentre.com
Web Site: www.beccleuchcentre.com
ADMINISTRATION:
Props: Dumfries & Galloway Council
Manager: Jill Graham
Cap: 280

Leamington Spa, Warwickshire

Pop. 42,300. London 90 miles. STD code 01926

ROYAL PUMP ROOMS

The Parade, Leamington Spa, Warwickshire CV32 4AA
Tel: 01926 742700 Fax: 01926 742705
Email: prooms@warwickdc.gov.uk
Web Site: www.warwickdc.gov.uk/royalpumprooms
ADMINISTRATION:
Props: Warwick District Council
Cap: Concerts - 250; Dinners - 200
For bookings contact Qdos: 0770346188 or 01926 742751
An elegant Assembly Room suitable for a wide range of events.

ROYAL SPA CENTRE

Newbold Terrace, Leamington Spa, Warwickshire CV32 4EA
Mktg: 01926 737 154 BO: 01926 334 418 Hirings: 01926 737 160
Email: spa.hirings@warwickdc.gov.uk
Web Site: www.royalspacentreandtownhall.gov.uk
ADMINISTRATION:
Props: Warwick District Council
Marketing: Jo Lewis. Email: jo.lewis@warwickdc.gov.uk
Technical manager: John Greet
Contact:
spa.technical@warwickdc.gov.uk
Capacity:
The Main Stage: Seating 668. 2 Licensed bars. 2 coffee bars.
The Studio: Seating 188, raked conference style.
TECHNICAL:
THE MAIN STAGE:
POLICY: Comedy, ballet, rock, opera, jazz, big bands, children's shows, variety, dance competitions and a recognised talent competition. Ideal for conferences and seminars, exhibitions and fairs.
Perfs: Regularly 7.30
STAGE: 3'9" high from hall floor. Main proscenium giving stage working area 34'w x 26'd. Soft black masking - fixed. Tabs and runners. Limited wing space. Understage crossover. Blue painted back wall cyclorama. Full motorised flying facilities, 18'h x 40'w clothsize. 15'6" clearance height to lighting bars (permanent). 100A 3 phase and 60A single phase power supply available for temporary rigs. Orchestra pit available. 4'deep apron available. Limited rostrums available. Entrance to stage level via dock (to rear of stage). Plan available.
LIGHTING: Grand Ma desk to 168 dimmers. Rig consists of various parcans, fresnels, pro 400s and limited spots in fixed focus washes. 2 x Clay Paky Shadow HM1 1200 follow spots
SOUND: Soundcraft series II desk 40:8:3. 10kw Turbosound flash/flood/TSC (all flown). Various FX, microphones and stands.
STAGE COMMICATION: Techpro headset communication system linked to sound, lights, followspots, flys and additional capacity. Tannoy and show relay to dressing rooms.
DRESSING ROOMS: 5 rooms; 2 showers. Accommodating 25.
STAFF AVAILABILITY: 3 full time Technicians. Casuals available.

THE STUDIO:
POLICY: Conferences and meetings. Film shows.
STAGE: No stage, flat floor area with curved cinema screen behind, with associated masking and tabs. No flying facility.

THE ASSEMBLY

Spencer Street, Leamington Spa, Warwickshire CV31 3NF
Tel: 01926 311311
Email: info@leamingtonassembly.com
Web Site: www.leamingtonassembly.com
Capacity: 400 Seated, 1000 standing.
Private Hires: Chris Lynch, chris@leamingtonassembly.com
General Manager: Chris Lynch
Marketing & Media: Will Dee

Leatherhead, Surrey

Pop. 41,160. London 20 miles.
Newspapers: Leatherhead Advertiser (thurs). STD code 01372

THE LEATHERHEAD THEATRE

Church Street Leatherhead Surrey KT22 8DN
Admin: 01372 365121 BO: 01372 365141
Email: admin@the-theatre.org
Web Site: www.the-theatre.org
Technical Production Manager: Paul Ashcroft
Capacity: 520 seats

LEATHERHEAD LEISURE CENTRE

Guildford Road, Leatherhead, Surrey KT22 9BL
Tel: 01372 377 674 Fax: 01372 386 749
Email: mike.silence@fusion-lifestyle.com
Web Site: www.fusion-lifestyle.com
ADMINISTRATION:
Props: Mole Valley District Council & Fusion Lifestyle
Cap: 2 Halls - 1,200 & 350
Bookings Contact:
Mike Silence

Leeds, West Yorkshire

THE CARRIAGEWORKS THEATRE

3 Millenium Square, Leeds LS2 3AD
Marketing: 0113 224 3139 BO: 0113 224 3801
Email: carriageworks@leeds.gov.uk
Web Site: www.carriageworkstheatre.org.uk
ADMINISTRATION:
Props: Leeds City Council
Press and Promotions Officer: Gwen Marie Ewing
Chief Technician: Peter Waddicor
Policy: Mixed programme professional and amateur productions of drama, dance concerts, opera, pantomime, children's shows, light entertainment, touring theatre companies, community arts.
The Carriageworks is a community theatre available for hire, housed in the electric press development in the heart of Leeds.
Separate additional rehearsal rooms available.
Main Capacity: 349
Studio Capacity: 55 (Maximum dependent on configuration)
TECHNICAL:
Pros. Opening 9.6m; Ht. of Pros. Normally 5.5 m can be raised to a maximum of 8.2m; Total Depth 9m; Ht. of Grid 10m.
Removable orchestra pit to seat 35.
Flexible theatre, full flying equipment, removable curtain, full disabled access. 6 rehearsal/workshop rooms.
Dressing Rooms 6; 2 Showers.

CITY VARIETIES MUSIC HALL

Swan Street, Leeds, West Yorkshire LS1 6LW
Mgt: 0113 391 7777 BO: 0113 243 0808
Fax: 0113 234 1800
Email: info@cityvarieties.co.uk
Web Site: www.cityvarieties.co.uk
ADMINISTRATION:
Props: Leeds Grand Theatre & Opera House Ltd
General Manager: Ian Sime
Chief Technician: Charles Phillipson

Policy: Music Hall, Pantomime, Variety, Tours, Celebrity Concerts, Conferences, and available for hire.
Perfs: Various, according to performance.
Seats: 467, Stalls, Circles, Upper Circle and Boxes.
TECHNICAL:
Stage: Proscenium, Rakes; Pros. opening 6.10m; Ht of Pros 5.18m; Depth of S/Line 4.88m; Ht of Grid 9.75m; 16 lines, Hemp; Flying Bars 6.71m; Prompt Cnr P.S.
Lighting: Switchboard: 48 way Bullfrog 12 Profiles, 10 Fresnels, 10 Pebble Convex, 12 x single Cell Floods, 2 x Clay Paky Followspots.
Sound: Sound Desk, 24 Channel Sound Craft, 2 Nexo PS15 speakers, 2 Nexo PS10 speakers, 1 Nexo 1000 Sub bass, 1 crown 2400 amplifier to PS15, 1 Crown 1200 Amplifier to PS10, 1 crown 1200 amplifier to sub bass. 6 x 31 band graphic equalisers. HH 450w and 200w foldback amps. 2 mini disk player. 2 CD Players. 1 Yamaha Upright Piano. 1 Yamaha Gran Touch Digital Piano.

LEEDS GRAND THEATRE AND OPERA HOUSE

46 New Briggate, Leeds, West Yorkshire LS1 6NZ
Mgt: 0113 2456014 BO: 0844 848 2700
Fax: 0113 2977049 Opera North (Switchboard) 0113 243 9999
Email: ian.sime@leedsgrandtheatre.com
Web Site: www.leedsgrandtheatre.com
ADMINISTRATION:
Props: Leeds Grand Theatre and Opera House Ltd
General Manager: Ian Sime
Head of Technical: Alan Dawson
Chief Electrician: Nick Stelmach
Stage Door: Steve Rushman
Policy: Touring plays, musicals, ballet, dance, concerts, home of Opera North, licensed catering centre. Facilities: Main theatre, 5 tier, seats 1400 + 84 stand. Conference, exhibition, concert reception, rehearsal rooms, 7 licensed Bars, 4 Coffee Lounges, 1 Sponsors Bar - Linacre Room.
Studios: Seats 192 stands 250. Dimensions 10m x 14m x 5m _ two side Studios each 4.9m. x 12m x 2.43m.
Grand Hall: Seats 100 stands 160. Dimensions 8.2m x 13.4m x 6.1m.
Assembly Rooms: Dimensions 13m x 22.75m x 2.95m minimum for rehearsals only.
Advanced Booking Office with ENTA computer ticket issuing system plus 120 booking agents.
TECHNICAL:
Stage. Rake 1 in 24, Pros. opening 9.90m, Pros. Ht. 8.23m; Depth from setting line 13.61m; Grid Ht. 18.29m; 60 Double purchase Counterweight lines; P.S. Wings 3.76m; O.P. Wings 2.66m; Prompt Cnr. Control P.S.; 2 Stage and conductor TV cover cameras, 2 Portable TV monitor; Rank Strand 520 control board; Get-in: for ordinary scenery etc via single deck hoist (.89m x 4.5m x 7m high) 1000kg; for baggage etc via passenger lift (2.50m x .95m x 2m); for large bulk via steel roller shutter doors 5.41m above street level using swing jib and push travel trolley with electric chain hoist 500kg; cloth shute from stage to street; stage 2 floors up (5.41m from street).
Lighting: Switchboard: 160 operative ways + 36 unconnected; 200 rehearsal and plotting remote control board. LX equip: 12 X Alto; 8 X Cantata 11/26; 6 X Cantata 18/32; 6 X Cantata Fresnels; 6 X Cantata 26/44; 8 X Source 4's; 25 X 223's; 12 X IRS floods; 8 X 20' 11w barrels; Stands 2 X 8'6"; 8 X 4'6", 2 x 1000 watt CSI follow spots; 5 battens x 4 circuits, floats 4 circuits; dips 8 circuits per side; 2 tallescope ladders; 3 ph supply 240/415 Ex.sup 150 amp.
Sound Equip: MCM Series 12 input; 6 output channels, plus metal cassette deck; P.S. control; 1 Revox tape deck; 15 Ass.Mics.; Speakers - 6 Bose 802, Auditorium; 2 stage; + delay line to balcony and rear stalls show calls and relay to all backstage areas.
Dressing Rooms 14; Accom. 80 persons; 12 shower rooms; orchestra pit 25-70 musicians; music stands 20; 2 band rooms. Instrument store, music library, 3 rehearsal rooms. Wardrobe, backstage bar and canteen. Digs, technical and press lists and stage plans available on request.
Membership: TMA, Yorkshire Tourist Board, Audiences Yorkshire.

LEEDS PLAYHOUSE

Please refer to the West Yorkshire Playhouse

LEEDS UNIVERSITY UNION

PO Box 157, Leeds, West Yorkshire LS1 1UH
Tel: 0113 380 1234 BO: 0113 380 1372
Fax: 0113 380 1416
Email: luuhelpdesk@leeds.ac.uk
Web Site: www.luu.org.uk
ADMINISTRATION:
Entertainments Manager: Steve Keeble (Tel: 0113 380 1334)
Capacity: 1,800

WEST YORKSHIRE PLAYHOUSE

Playhouse Square, Quarry Hill, Leeds LS2 7UP
Admin: 0113 213 7800 BO: 0113 213 7700 Press: 0113 213 7273 Minicom: 0113 213 7299
Email: info@wyp.org.uk
Web Site: www.wyp.org.uk
ADMINISTRATION:
Chief Executive: Sheena Wrigley
Artistic Director: James Brining
Producer: Mark Rosenblatt
Financal Director: Helen Makhwul
Director of Communications: Nick Hallam
Head of Arts Development: Sam Perkins
Technical Stage Manager: Mick Cassidy
Producing Theatre. Two auditoria seating 350 & 750.
Policy: Subsidised Repertory, year round programme; touring welcome National and Regional Drama and Dance. Young People's Theatre programme and black arts events: concerts, foyer events, cabaret and late night shows, Schools Company. It also includes community work in its artistic policy. Restaurant, bar, shop, rehearsal room, function & entertainment facilities, full workshops. Facilities for the disabled.
Seats: 750
QUARRY THEATRE:

STAGE: 15m wide x 7.5m deep, SL wing 6.5m wide, SR wing 7.5m wide. Get-in SR via 7.4m high x 4m wide scene dock door. Fly galleries: 9m above stage level. Clearance below fly galleries: 7.5m. Intermediate galleries: 13.5m above stage level. Loading gallery (stage left): 18m above stage level. Fore-Stage: 15m wide x 7.5m deep, Maximum suspension height 10m, Winch/Pin rail located on stage left at grid level, Pulley steels installed suitable for hand winch and rope sets. Rear-Stage: 26m wide x 9.5m deep, Maximum suspension height: 8m, Maximum 10 No. winches, Height of opening between main stage and rear stage: 7.4m. Stage Floor Surface: 6mm oil tempered hardboard on 25mm ply. Cross over via backstage corridor. Several tallescopes. Full black masking.
LIGHTING: Strand Galaxy 3 lighting board - 240 channels. Act 3 and Act 6 temporary dimmer packs available. Full lighting rig comprising 120 No. profiles, 30 No. plano convex, 52 No. fresnels, 65 No. parcans. Cyc lighting, follow spots and effects projectors also available. Control room at rear auditorium.
SOUND: Operating position at rear of auditorium. Separate recording studio. Acoustics suitable for music and spoken word.
STAGE MANAGEMENT: SM control position at rear of auditorium (in lighting control room). 20 Circuit cue light control patchable to 44 outlets. 2 Channel Tecpro headset system. Maxom transceivers for SM. CCTV and CATV system with low light infra red and colour cameras. Show replay and paging system to all FOH, artists and staff areas. Northern Light system 2000 working light control system.
BACKSTAGE FACILITIES: 9 Dressing rooms accommodating 31 persons. Facilities for disabled performers. Maintenance laundry available by arrangement. Installed with washers, dryers, drying cabinets and industrial irons. Grand piano and upright piano.

COURTYARD THEATRE

STAGE: Floor surface of 6mm oil tem-

pered hardboard on 25mm ply. Modular end stage floor system comprising 29 No. 1200mm x 1200mm and 4 No. 1200mm x 1670mm modules. 4 No. 1200mm x 1200mm removable floor modules located in auditorium area for 'Theatre in the Round' use.
SEATING: 350. Courtyard Theatre. Air-conditioned. 2 Audience Galleries and end stage. Retractable bleacher seating is provided for 'end on' stage use, The first three rows of seating are lowered on a lift 11.74m x 2.85m, 5 No. removable floor modules are located in the seating lift surface.
END STAGE GRID: Max flying height 9.8 m, Fly galleries 5.5m above stage level. Upper (Technical) galleries 8.0m above stage level. Operating gallery Stage left. 9m long winch rail, on outer stage wall, drilled for winches at 500mm centres.12 No. 250kg cross stage self sustaining hand winch sets fitted with 12.5m single 50mm O/D bars. 2 No. 250kg up/down stage self sustaining hand winch sets (1 No Stage left, 1No Stage right) fitted with single 50mm O/D bars.
LIGHTING: Control: 1 x strand 550i 450 channel (back up 510i), 1 x strand 510 back up 450 channel, 1 x strand sn102 ethernet node, 1x designers laptop c/w designers remote. Profiles: 30 x strand sl's 600w 15/32°, 10 x strand sl's 600w 23/50°, 6 x etc source 4 575w (fixed) 50°, 6 x etc source 4 zoom 15/30°. Fresnels: 36 x selecon compact 6 1.2kw c/w barn doors, 10 x selecon arena 2.0kw c/w barn doors, 1 x strand bambino 5kw c/w barndoors, 1 x polux 5kw c/w barndoors. Par cans: 40+ x thomas par64 1kw (any head). Scrollers: 16 x chroma q cq1d (adaptors to fit parcans & sl's), 2 x chroma q 8 way psu. Dimmers: 120 x 10a dimmers (green ginger wall mount 90), 12 x 20a dimmers (green ginger wall mount 90), 12 x 10a non dims (contactors), 2 x 10a strand act 6 packs
SOUND: Controls: Midas Heritage 1000 Console, Yamaha DM1000 Digital Console. Loudspeakers: FOH L; 2 x Tannoy CPA12, 1 x Tannoy B50 (Fill), FOH R; 2 x Tannoy CPA12, 1 x Tannoy B50 (Fill), FOH Centre; 3 x Tannoy CPA12, Subs; 2 x d&b E15X, ROH; 2 x Tannoy CPA12, On stage FX; 4 x Martin F15, 6 x d&b E3 (subject to availability). Amplifiers: 4 x Yamaha H5000, 4 x Yamaha H3000, 1 x d&b D6 (House Subs), 6 x d&b E-Pac (subject to availability). Playback: 1 x Denon DN1050R Minidisc, 1 x Tascam MD-350 Minidisc, 1 x Denon DN-C635 CD Player, 1 x Cassette Tape Player, 1 x Akai S6000 Sampler, 1 x Show Control PC (Windows XP). Software: G-Type for Windows, SFX Pro Audio 5.6 & 6.1, SCS Professional Plus 10, Yamaha Studio Manager V2.
Control Position: Control Room at rear of auditorium (top seating gallery) with sliding/removable glass panels.
STAGE COMMUNICATIONS: Tecpro wired comms system with interface to Motorola Radio's (number available may vary)
BACKSTAGE FACILITIES: Dressing Rooms; 5 over 2 levels, accommodating 14 - 16 persons. Sink, shower, and toilet facilities. Phone lines.

Leicester, Leicestershire

Pop.281,440. London 100 miles. STD code 0116

ATHENA

Queen Street, Leicester LE1 1QD
Tel: 0116 262 6556 Fax: 0116 2513 442
Email: contact@athenacb.co.uk
Web Site: www.athenacb.co.uk

CURVE THEATRE

Cultural Quarter, 60 Rutland Street, Leicester LE1 1SB
Reception: +44 (0)116 2423560 Ticket Office: +44 (0)116 2423595
Email: enquiries@curvetheatre.co.uk
Web Site: www.curveonline.co.uk
Props: Leicester Theatre Trust Ltd
Leicester's state of the art theatre, designed by world renowned architect Rafael Viñoly is based in the heart of the new Cultural Quarter on Rutland Street.

Curve features two auditoria, one with 750 fixed seats while a 350 seat auditorium will provide a versatile smaller space. When the 32 tonne steel walls separating the stage and the foyer are lifted, the stage will be visible from street level.

Additional rooms for hire: Three rehearsal rooms with capacities ranging from 60-110; Mezzanine offering reception space for up to 400; Seminar Rooms accommodating up to 200.

DE MONTFORT HALL

Granville Road, Leicester LE1 7RU
BO: 0116 233 3111 Fax: 0116 233 3182
Email: pete.mitchell@leicester.gov.uk
Web Site: www.demontforthall.co.uk
ADMINISTRATION:
Props: Leicester City Council
Manager: Mr Flint
House Manager: Andy Gillespie
Box Office Manager: Robbie Kerr
Marketing Development Manager: Emma Dezelu
Technical Manager: Jim O'Mahoney
Contact: jim.o'mahoney@leicester.gov.uk
Policy: One Night Concerts, Dances, Conferences,
Weekly shows for children and Musicals
Seating/Capacity: 1,973 seated, 1,600 tiered, 2,200 standing, Outdoor up to 9000.
TECHNICAL:
STAGE: Height 11.25m (Centre) 8.60m (Side), Width 23.60m, Depth 8.30m, with Extention: Width 22.80m, Depth 11.80m.
Pros: Variable, Rigging: 12x Motorised bars (500 Kg UDL Max) 20x1 Ton Verlind Chainhoist, 125Mx GP trussing (assorted lengths), Full rigging plan available on application.
POWER: Temp supplies - Lighting 400A Powerlock @ St R with local isolation and step down rubber box, Sound 125A3pne, 63 3pne, 63A1pne, 32A1pne Cform, 200A powerlock or Tails.
LIGHTING: Avolite Diamond 4 or Avo Saphire 2000, 204 Way dimming (DMX Controlled), 30 Way 10A Non-Dim(DMX Controlled), DMX Distrobution 2 x DMX to stage from control, 500K + Generic Lighting rig, 2 Followspots (xenospot 2k, telrads and frost), 6 x ClayPaky 1200 stage zoom, 6 Robe AT 575 wash. Full equipment list on application.
SOUND: Yamaha M7CL48, D&B Loudspeaker System, 6x Eaw Jfx260I. Monitors,64/32 Way Multi System With Broadcast Splits, IR System (Hearing Loops), Portable small scale P.A. Full equipment list on application.
AV: NEC NP4100- 6.2k Projector, 10'/8' Fast Fold Screen + Front/Rear Surface, Rolland V8 Mixing Surface, Various Data Video Preview Screens. Various camera options.
OTHER: Capable of dealing with 2 artics on doors + 2 tour bus stands, all with power point available if notified in advance. (All parking is on private grounds under security cameras.)

LITTLE THEATRE

Dover Street, Leicester LE1 6PW
Admin: 0116 254 2266 BO: 0116 255 1302 Wardrobe Hire: 0116 254 0472
Email: admin@lds-mail.net
Web Site: www.thelittletheatre.net
ADMINSTRATION:
Manager: Philip Royley
Seats: 349
TECHNICAL: Please contact venue for details.

NEW WALK MUSEUM

53 New Walk, Leicester LE1 7EA
Tel: 0116 225 4900
Email: museums@leicester.gov.uk
Web Site: www.leicester.gov.uk
Head of Marketing: James Hickford (Tel: 0116 374 284)

PHOENIX SQUARE: FILM AND DIGITAL MEDIA

4 Midland Street, Leicester LE1 1TG
Mgt: 0116 242 2835 BO: 0116 242 2800
Email: ros.hill@phoenix.org.uk
Web Site: www.phoenix.org.uk
ADMINISTRATION:
Partnership Initiative: De Montfort University & Leicester City Council
Lessees: Leicester Arts Centre Ltd
CEO: John Rande
Operations Manager: Ros Hill

Policy: Broad based arts centre promoting the best film and multi-cultural arts exhibitions.
Perfs: Eves 7 days a week, Saturday Family Film Matinees.
Seats: Screens; (1) 220, (2) 120, (3) 30. Courtyard Suite; Standing 100, Theatre Style 70. Recording Studio. Screen Lounge Cafe Bar Licensed open 9am - 11p.m. Building open 7 days a week.

THE Y
7 East Street, Leicester LE1 6EY
BO: 0116 255 7066
Admin: 0116 255 6507
Email: theatre@leicesterymca.co.uk
Web Site: www.leicesterymca.co.uk
ADMINISTRATION:
Technical Co-Ordinator: Martyn Pole
Theatre Programmer/Producer: Amy Christer
Policy: A presenting venue with a multi art form programme. Music leads the programme followed by comedy, theatre, variety and dance. The venue also runs community and education courses and events. The venue is available for whole or split weeks and one night stands and aims to support new artists.
Seats: Balcony with flexible seating in stalls - seating can be in rows, in the round, cabaret, or standing, Variable capacity from 100 to 300
TECHNICAL:
Proscenium Stage with flat floor flexible stalls & Balcony with fixed seating. Pros wall has been built out over original line of balcony to create deeper stage. Door USL to dressing rooms. Limited wing space both sides, with partially limited headroom. No fly tower, but 6 hemp sets on which cloths etc can be hung.
Stage: Fixed stage, Pros opening 6.95m Forestage 6.95m x 1.1m Maximum stage depth including forestage 6.6m at centre, 4.5m at pros. 1m stage extension available, can be reconfigured as catwalk etc in 2mx1m sections. Fixed red velour house tabs with winder SL. 2xmovable tab tracks, 1 full width wipe track. Various Drapes.
Get-in: Street level through stalls double doors.
Lighting: LSC maxim XXL desk. 60 dimmers controlled via DMX. Various lanterns including Parcans, Profiles, Fresnels & Cyc Floods. 2x 2kW followspots. Various FX including Smoke m/c, Hazer, UV, Strobe.
Sound: Soundcraft Spirit Folio 10+2 ch desk. 2kW PA. Digitech DSP256 FX unit. Denon CD player. Denon twin Cassette deck. Small number of mics, DIs etc. Tecpro comms system with calls to dressing rooms. Induction Loop to stalls & balcony.
Control/Mix position variable, dependant on stalls seating format.
2 Dressing rooms beside stage, others available elsewhere in building.
Piano: Reid-Sohn grand, can be used on stage or on stalls floor.

Leigh, Lancashire

DERBY ROOM
Leigh Library, The Turnpike Centre, Civic Square, Leigh, Lancashire WN7 1EB
Tel: 01942 404 469
Email: wayne.reedman@trustinleigh.org
Web Site: www.creativeleigh.org
ADMINISTRATION:
Props: Trust in Leigh
Cap: Max 120
For bookings contact Wayne Reedman

Leighton Buzzard, Bedfordshire

Pop.33,000. London 40 miles.
Newspapers: Leighton Buzzard Observer (thurs). STD code 01525

LEIGHTON BUZZARD THEATRE
Lake Street, Leighton Buzzard, Bedfordshire LU7 1RX
Mgt: 0300 300 8130 BO: 0300 300 8125
Email: hazel.kerr@centralbedfordshire.gov.uk
Web: www.leightonbuzzardtheatre.co.uk
ADMINISTRATION:
Props: Central Bedfordshire Council
Theatre Manager: Hazel Kerr
Arts Development Officer: Victoria Abrahams
Centre Facilitator: Carole Perham
Technician: Phil Pattinson
Funded by Beds Central Bedfordshire
Policy: Mixed programme of film, professional small scale touring drama, music recitals, plus performance by local amateurs. Childrens films, drama shows and workshops. Exhibitions. Performing arts workshops. Perfs: Mon-Sat 8.00, mats. 1.30p.m
Hire, box office split, guarantee & split, guarantee by negotiation.
Seats: 170, raked.
Daytime coffee bar. Licensed bar on performance nights. Foyer coffee servery Limited wheelchair space, lift-assistance available, contact Manager, level access.
TECHNICAL:
STAGE: Proscenium arch with 0.85m apron. Performing area 8.25m x 5.65m - pros. opening 7.15m x 4.6m - wing widths 1.38m SR, 1.38m SL. No rake - floor sprung wood, suitable for dance, backstage crossover, stage heated.
Grid:4.9m. Tab track - black tabs - white cloth cyclorama - turquoise house tabs, electrically drawn. Get-in via public lift.
LIGHTING: Rank Strand MX48 board, operated from projection room or wings - 51 lanterns.
SOUND: Diamond Studiomaster Pro 12-3 mixerdesk. RevoxB77mk2 reel-to-reel, TEAC W-750 R double cassette system, TEAC CD-P3200, PA system. Operated from projection room. Paging - 100w power amplifier and 100v line transformer - speakers in various locations. 6 inputs - foldback facility - 4 mics and stands.
Acoustics suitable for music and spoken word.
STAGE MANAGEMENT: Prompt corner position SL - phone/intercom cue system, 6 outstations - show relay/Tannoy to dressing rooms. Backstage: 2 dressing rooms, access by lift and stairs - band room - quick change rooms - 4 power points in each room. Coffee bar which is open limited hours daytime only and evening licensed bar. Rehearsal rooms, piano, good. Staff - 1 part-time lighting/sound - casuals not available - security personnel. Backstage facilities not accessible to disabled performers and staff.

Lennoxtown, Dunbartonshire

CAMPSIE MEMORIAL HALL
2 Main Street, Lennoxtown, Dunbartonshire G66 7HA
Tel: 01360 238002
Email: bookings@campsiehall.org.uk
Web Site: www.campsiehall.org.uk
ADMINISTRATION:
Props: East Dunbartonshire Council
Cap: Main Hall 200; Lesser Hall 40; Committee Rooms 10.

Lenzie, Dunbartonshire

LENZIE PUBLIC HALL
61 Kirkintilloch Road, Lenzie, Dunbartonshire G66 4LD
Tel: 0141 775 2902 Fax: 0141 574 5555
Email: halls@eastdunbarton.gov.uk
Web Site: www.eastdunbarton.gov.uk
ADMINISTRATION:
Props: East Dunbartonshire Council
Cap: Main Hall 215; Lower Hall 63; Committee Room 18

Leominster, Herefordshire

COMMUNITY CENTRE
School Road, Leominster, Herefordshire HR6 8NJ
Tel: 01568 616411
Email: enquiries@leominstercommunitycentre.com
Web Site: www.leominstercommunitycentre.com
ADMINISTRATION:
Capacity: 90
Manager: Jennifer Gough

LEOMINSTER LEISURE CENTRE
Coningsby Road, Leominster,
Herefordshire HR6 8LL
Tel: 01568 612 540
Email: matt.smith@haloleisure.org.uk
Web Site: www.haloleisure.org.uk
ADMINISTRATION:
Props: Herefordshire Council.
Cap: 900
Manager: Matt Smith

Lerwick, Shetland Islands

GARRISON THEATRE
Market Street, Lerwick, Shetland ZE1 0HD Scotland
Tel: 01595 743843 Fax: 01595 694001
Email: info@shetlandarts.org
Web Site: www.shetlandarts.org
ADMINISTRATION:
Props: Shetland Arts
Manager: Graeme Howell
Booking/Enquiries: Shetlands Arts
Policy: Local & Touring Drama, concerts, recitals, films, opera, ballet & pantomime.
Perfs: 7.30 / variable.
Seats: 280 max. (250 raked, up to 30 removable to increase orchestra space).
Provision for disabled patrons: level access, toilet, inductive loop, 4 wheelchair bays.
TECHNICAL:
Stage: Proscenium Stage: Pros. opening 6.7m; Ht. of Pros. 2.9m; Stage Depth 5.5m plus apron 0.9m; Split height grid from Pros. extending up stage 1.8m, height 6.45m, remaining US grid to stage rear 4.2m, height 3.65m.
Wing widths - SR 1.3m, SL 1.2m, rear crossover. Stage floor - no rake, sprung wood, suitable for dance, lino available. Stage heated. 7 hemp sets - tab track - black or grey legs & borders - black or grey curtain as cyclorama - wine house tabs, drawn. 16 x 13A independent circuits, 6 x 15A independent circuits controlled from control room. Scale stage plans available. Get-in via rear double doors, off Market Street. Show relay and paging to dressing rooms & Control Room, 2 channel 12 station intercom system (six belt packs and 4 fixed stations), 6 cue light stations. SM Desk SL.
Lighting: 48 x 2.5kw channels controlled by ETC Express 48/96 desk normally situated in control room at rear of auditorium but can be used from SL next to SM desk. F.O.H. bar - 10 circuits & 2 x 15A independents, 4 x T84 c/w colour wheels, 2 x Harmony, 2 x Patt.263 and 2 x Patt.23. Access from above auditorium. Followspots - 2 x Rank Strand Cantata operated from positions above either side of auditorium, 1 x dimmer circuit & 1 x 15A independent circuit in each position. Access from above auditorium. No. 1 Stage LX bar - 10 circuits & 2 x 15A independents, Electrical winch. No. 2 Stage LX bar - 7 circuits & 2 x 15A independents. No. 3 Stage LX bar - 6 circuits & 2 x 15A independent. No. 4 Stage LX bar - 4 circuits. All attached to rear grid, height 3.65m. Boom - SL & SR 1 circuit & 1 independent each. Dips - 7 circuits; Stage perimeter - 7 circuits. 60A Single Phase Temporary Supply SL, 32A Three Phase Temporary Supply SL. 6 x Coda Flood, 8 x Patt.60 Flood, 10 x Patt.23 profile, 5 x Patt.123 Fresnel, 4 x minum F, 2 x 4 circ., 8 comp. Battens, UV fittings, Le Maitre Pyroflash system & Rosco Fog machine.
Video Equip: 2 remotely controlled Panasonic F10 cameras wall mounted either side of the auditorium linked to Panasonic MX10 Production Mixer & Pioneer Titling computer located in control room at rear of auditorium. Sony video projector.
Sound Equip: An extremely versatile system with limited control from side of stage or full control facilities from control room at rear of auditorium. On-stage control; 6 channel Tascam mixer into 400w stereo audio system, patch panel, line amps, 20 stage inputs, cassette deck. Control room operation; 16/2 Allan & Heath mixer, inputs from stage at line level, 20 stage inputs. 400w auditorium stereo audio system & 2 x 200w per channel stage monitors. Tape playback, cassette, CD, Minidisk or reel to reel. Recording facility 8 track 1/2" with 6 channel premix, 2 track Tascam mastering & cassette. 20 stage inputs. 7 headphone monitors on stage, 2 x 200w stage monitors. Access for external P.A. system.
Dressing Rooms: Accommodating 20 each, two showers, two toilets, refreshments from kitchen, access by stairs. Prop room/quick change room at rear of stage, Workshop off prop room. Staff - casual available from community centre - security personnel. Backstage facilities presently not accessible to disabled.

Lewes, East Sussex

ALL SAINTS CENTRE (ARTS & YOUTH)
Friars Walk, Lewes, East Sussex BN7 2LE
Tel: 01273 486391
Email: alewes@lewes-tc.gov.uk
Web Site: www.lewes-tc.gov.uk
Capacity: Seated 220
Venue Manager: Lizzie Zeyfert

TOWN HALL
High Street, Lewes, East Sussex BN7 2QS
Tel: 01273 471 469 Fax: 01273 480 919
Email: lewestowncouncil@hotmail.com
Web Site: www.lewes-town.co.uk
ADMINISTRATION:
Props: Lewes Town Council
Assembly Hall: Cap with audience and performers: 400 (max), Audience Cap: 340(max). Portable stage facilities available.
Corn Exchange: No fixed stage, but portable stage available. Cap: 400 (max), 340(max).
Lecture Room: No stage. Cap: 80
For bookings contact Mr L Symons.

Lichfield, Staffordshire

Pop. 30,000. London 112 miles.
Newspapers: Lichfield Mercury. STD code 01543

LICHFIELD GARRICK THEATRE
Castle Dyke, Lichfield, Staffordshire WS13 6HR
Admin: 01543 412 110 Fax: 01543 412 120 BO: 01543 412 121
Email: garrick@lichfieldgarrick.com
Web Site: www.lichfieldgarrick.com
ADMINISTRATION:
Props: Lichfield Garrick Theatre Ltd
Chief Executive and Artistic Director: Adrian Jackson
Deputy Head of Sales and Marketing: Daniel Ingleby
Head of Marketing and Operations: Chris Moore
A modern 525 seat theatre with an additional studio facility of 200 seats.

Limerick

UNIVERSITY CONCERT HALL
University of Limerick Limerick Ireland
BO: 00353 61 331549 Fax: 00353 61 331585
Email: sharon.quilligan@uch.ie
Web Site: www.uch.ie
Director: Sinead Hope
Marketing Manager: Emma Foote
Technical Manager: Paul Boland
Capacity: 1000

Lincoln, Lincolnshire

Pop. 73,810. London 132 miles.
Newspapers: Lincolnshire Echo (ntly); Lincoln, Rutland & Stamford Mercury (fri); Lincolnshire Chronicle (fri); Lincolnshire Free Press (tue); Lincolnshire Standard (fri). STD code 01522

THE LAWN IN LINCOLN
Union Road, Lincoln LN1 3BL
Tel: 01522 568 080 Fax: 01522 516 061
Email: enquiries@thelawninlincoln.co.uk
Web Site: www.thelawninlincoln.com

ADMINISTRATION:
Props: Lincoln City Council
Cap: Main Hall seats 400, stage portable. Small theatre seats 100. Stage permanent.

LINCOLN DRILL HALL
Freeschool Lane, Lincoln, Lincolnshire LN2 1EY
Box Office: 01522 873 894 Admin: 01522 873 891 Fax: 01522 873 890
Email: boxoffice@lincolndrillhall.com
Web Site: www.lincolndrillhall.com
Owned by Lincoln Arts Trust.
A multi purpose flexible arts and community venue, refurbished in 2004.
Contact: Chris Kirkwood
Seated: 370. Standing: 550
Stage: open flat stage 10m x 5m.
Lighting: switchboard Strand 520i control room, good range of profile, fresnel, flood and beam lights including mac 300's.
Sound: ML 3000 ans wizard 16 desks turbosound speakers, 1 DR-8 control system, fully equiped effects rack.
No orchestra pit. Dance base by Harlequin. Steinway piano.
Disabled access to stage.

LINCOLN PERFORMING ARTS CENTRE
University of Lincoln Brayford Pool Lincoln LN6 7TS
Tel: 01522 837600 BO: 01522 837616
Email: bookings@lpac.co.uk
Web Site: www.lpac.co.uk
Artistic Director: Craig Morrow
Technical Manager: Mike Hoyle, Tel: 01522 837617
Policy: Mixed programme Touring House, Summer Season, Plays, Dance Musicals, Concerts.
Capacity: 446

LINCOLN THEATRE ROYAL
Clasketgate, Lincoln LN2 1JJ
Tel: 01522 545490
Email: boxoffice@lincolntheatreroyal.com
Web Site: www.lincolntheatreroyal.com
ADMINISTRATION:
Lessees: Ian Dickens
Artistic Director and CEO: Ian Dickens.
Contact: iand@lincolntheatreroyal.com
Operations Director - Ian Marston
House Manager - Maggie Kershaw
Policy: Touring shows, drama films, concerts, amateur, productions.
Perfs: Nightly 7.30. Saturdays usually 6.15pm & 9pm.
Seats: 482. 2 Bars.
TECHNICAL:
STAGE: Proscenium arch. Performing area 9.5m x 7m slight rake; Pros. opening 6.55m x 5.49m wing widths 3.66m SR, 3.66m SL. Stage raked, 1 to 72 - floor plywood with hardboard top, suitable for all dance, understage crossover, stage heated. Height of grid 12.8 - 36 hemp sets, 0.2m apart, 2 tab tracks, 350/400kg permitted on bars. Max flying height 12.6 black masking, white sharkstooth filled gauze cyclorama, maroon house tabs, flown. 10 x15A independent circuits. Forestage 7.5m x 2m entrances both sides. Orchestra pit 6.55m x 2m, accommodates 14. Get-in via dock doors 1m above street level, 2.5m x 4.7m. Tallescope, safety curtain. Scale stage, fly and lighting plans available.
LIGHTING: Switchboard: Rank Strand Gemini 2+ 100 circuits, 90 x 2kw, 10 x 5kw, operated from SL perch: 2 x 60A 3-phase supplies for temporary board. F.O.H. 16 x cantata 18/32 and pattern 23's. No.1 Spot bar 12 x Patt.743's. Flood bar 12 x 500w coda CYC floods. Extra equipment: 20 x 1kw profiles, 24 x 1kw Fresnels, 12 x 1000w Parcans, 8 x Patt 243's, 14 x patt.23's. 9 Lengths S. Type Batten. Follow Spots - 2 x 2kw Solos in Upper Circle.
SOUND: Soundcraft 200 16 into 4 into 2 desk, operated from prompt corner, basic system outline suitable for all sound reinforcement, 5 x Sennheiser K3 U with ME40 and ME80 heads, 2 x SM58, 2 x Revox B77 tape decks, 1 x Sansui D100 cassette deck. P.A. system. Facilities for recording and editing. Acoustics suitable for music and the spoken word.
STAGE MANAGEMENT: Prompt corner SL headphones, 6 outstations, CCTV system to P.C. and other outstations, show relay/Tannoy to dressing rooms.
Backstage 9 dressing rooms, access by stairs from stage level. Rehearsal piano, advice given on accommodation.
DISABLED FACILITIES: 2 wheelchair spaces. Contact House Manager.

THE ENGINE SHED
University of Lincoln Brayford Pool Lincoln LN6 7TS
Tel: 01522 837 400 BO: 0844 888 87 66
Email: bars@lincoln.ac.uk
Web Site: www.engineshed.co.uk
Capacity: 1,640

YARBOROUGH LEISURE CENTRE
Riseholme Road, Lincoln LN1 3SP
Tel: 01522 873 600 Fax: 01522 873 603
Email: ylc.lincoln@communityleisure.co.uk
Web Site: www.activenation.org.uk
ADMINISTRATION:
Props: Lincoln City Council
Cap: 900
Manager: Kerry O'Neill

Lisburn, County Antrim

ISLAND ARTS CENTRE
Island Arts Centre, Lagan Valley Island, Lisburn, County Antrim BT27 4RL Northern Ireland
Tel: 028 92 509 509 BO: 028 92 509 254
Textphone: 028 92 509 508
Email: arts.info@island.lisburn.gov.uk
Web Site: www.islandartscentre.com
ADMINSTRATION:
Island Arts Centre provides a balanced and accessible programme of Arts-related activities. It encourages active participation from the community by producing and promoting the Arts, and increasing the level of opportunities for the local community to participate in the arts.
Props: Lisburn City Council
Community Arts Officer: Lesley Wilson
Email: lesley.wilson@island.lisburn.gov.uk
Technical Contacts: Cathal (028 92 509 515) Email: cathal@island.lisburn.gov.uk
Capacity: Main Auditorium, Seats 430. Studio Theatre: 110 Theatre Style, 70 Cabaret Style, 150 Standing.
TECHNICAL:
Studio Theatre;
STAGE: 10m W x 6m 40cm D. Height to the upstage bar of grid of 3.5m and 3.9m to rest of grid. Curtain Tracks: 1 x 30m perimeter curtain track covering three sides of the theatre. Stage drapes : 8 x 3m x 3.5m drop drapes in black wool surge creating a perimeter curtain of 30m in total. Drapes have Velcro to edges and tab hooks to top with chain at base.
LIGHTING: Desk: 1 x Strand 300 with 520 software, 1 x Avolites Tiger. Lighting grid is 10m by 10m made from alloy. 40 x Socket outlets are positioned within the grid. 8 x Floor Sockets. 4 USL & 4 USR. Dimmers: 3 x Act 6 dimmer racks 10amp per channel with twin socket outlets, 2 x ETC Smartpack (12 ways per pack), 1 x 48 way patch panel. (42 ways of dimming). Luminaries: 12 x ETC Source 4 25-50 zoom profiles, 20 x Strand Quartet Fresnels 650w (12 with barn doors), 6 x Strand Coda 500w, 8 x Robe 240 AT colour wash.
SOUND: 1 x Camco Q6 Power amplifier, 1 x AP 30 induction loop amplifier, 1 x Talk back power supply, 1 x Yamaha LS9 16 channel mixing desk, 4 x Martin Audio F15+ suspended from ceiling. (Floor to bottom of speakers is 3.3m), 1 x CD player, 1 x Mini Disc player.

Littlehampton, West Sussex

THE WINDMILL ENTERTAINMENT CENTRE
The Green, Windmill Road, Littlehampton, West Sussex BN17 5LM
Tel: 01903 724929 BO: 01903 722224
Mgt: 01903 890310
Email: windmill@inspireleisure.co.uk
Web Site: www.inspireleisure.co.uk
ADMINISTRATION:
Props: Arun District Council
Cap: 213
Centre Manager: Carrie Reynolds

Amateur shows, community events, one-night stands, theatres own craft fairs, first run feature films, conferences and seminars.

Liverpool, Merseyside

Pop. 588,600. London 167 miles.
Newspapers: Liverpool Daily Post; Liverpool Echo (ntly); Liverpool Weekly News (thurs). STD code 0151

THE EPSTEIN THEATRE

Hanover House 85 Hanover Street, Liverpool, Merseyside L1 3DZ
Tel: 0151 709 4044
Email: info@epsteinliverpool.co.uk
Web Site: www.epsteinliverpool.co.uk
ADMINISTRATION:
Lessees: Liverpool City Council
Manager: Rebekah Pichilingi
Stage Manager: Jordan Hewitt
Policy: VIsiting Amateur & Professional Companies.
Perfs: Various Times.
Seats: 388. Bar (evenings).
Theatre closed at moment for refurbishment
TECHNICAL:
Stage: Proscenium Stage with apron. Raked; Pros. Opening 8.33m; Ht. of Pros. 4.5m; Depth of Stage: a) including apron 10.3m, b) with orchestra pit open 7.80m, c) from setting line 7.10m, d) restricted sightlines max. depth 3.3m centre stage; Ht. 4.27m; Flying Bars 8.99m; W/Widths P.S. 2.74m; O.P. 2.59m; Prompt Cnr.O.P.
Lighting: Switchboard in circle: 66 ways; F.O.H. spots, 22 x 1k, Dips 5 each side, spot bars, patt 23 and 123, pat 743 and par cans.
Sound Equipment: 12-2 Revox, B77, Cassette and C.D, D.R. relay system.
Dressing Rooms 5; Accom. 40; 2 Showers; Orchestra Pit 18-25.

KNOWSLEY VILLAGE HALL

School Lane, Knowsley Village, Merseyside L34 9EN
Tel 0151 546 3412
Email: knowsleyparishcouncil@knowsley.gov.uk
Web Site: www.knowsleyparishcouncil.gov.uk
ADMINISTRATION:
Props: Knowsley Parish Council
Cap: 174 with stage facilities
For bookings contact Heather Weightman, clerk to the council on Tel: 0151 548 4545

LIVERPOOL EMPIRE

Lime Street, Liverpool, Merseyside L1 1JE
BO: 0844 871 3017 Group Booking: 0844 871 3037 Admin: 0151 702 7320
Fax: 0151 702 7349
Email: info@theambassadors.com
Web Site: www.liverpoolempire.org.uk
ADMINISTRATION:
Props: Ambassadors Theatre Group Ltd
General Manager: Diane Belding
Box Office Manager: Peter O'Brien
Sales & Marketing Manager: Stephen Ainsworth
Administrator: Theresa Morgan
Policy: Touring - Opera, Ballet, Variety, Plays, Concerts and Pantomime
Perfs: Eve. 7.30. Mat. 2.30
Seats: 2,381. 3 Bars.

TECHNICAL:
STAGE: Proscenium. Pros. Opening 14.1m; Ht. of Pros. 7m; Depth of S/Line 11.58m; Ht. of Grid 22.2m; 57 c/w lines, 840lbs single purchase, C/W Scenery Flying ht. 7.62m; Flying Bars 18.29m; W/Widths P.S. 4.57m; O.P. 6m; Prompt Corner P.S.
LIGHTING: Gemini +2; (52 F.O.H.); Follow Spots Teatro MSR. 1 Ton Advance Truss (18 ways); 25 x T64s; 25 x 1k Fresnels (Berkey); No. 1 Bar 12 x 743s; 8 x Iris Is; 6 x Sil 15s (2k).
SOUND: Communication: 6 Outstation Strand Intercom.
Dressing Rooms 17; Accom. 105; Showers; Orchestra Pit 84.

LIVERPOOL EVERYMAN AND PLAYHOUSE THEATRE

5-11 Hope Street Liverpool, Merseyside L1 9BH
Admin: 0151 708 3700 BO: 0151 709 4776 Fax: 0151 708 3701
Email: info@everymanplayhouse.com
Web Site: www.everymanplayhouse.com
ADMINISTRATION:
Props: The Liverpool & Merseyside Theatres Trust
Executive Director: Deborah Aydon
Communications and Sales Director: Sarah Ogle
The Everyman and Playhouse Theatres have come together under the Liverpool & Merseyside Theatres Trust. Both venues have a commitment to providing quality theatre.
The Playhouse Capacity: 681+ 5 wheelchair places

LIVERPOOL OLYMPIA

West Derby Road, Liverpool, Merseyside L6 9BY
Tel: 0151 263 6633 Fax: 0151 263 4985
Email: czorbaolympia@hotmail.com
Web Site: www.liverpoololympia.com
ADMINISTRATION:
Director and Marketing Manager: Chris Zorba
Policy: Concert Hall, shows, musical revue, popconcerts, comedy, sporting events.
Booking terms hire / % deals
Capacity: Seated 1535; Standing 1300 / Seated 700
TECHNICAL:
Load in address: Boaler Street, Liverpool. Back of Venue.
Stage: 40ft x 40ft retractable to 20ft x 20ft
Lights: Lighting Grid - 3 PHASE 65 AMP. 6 Lighting bars. Numerous flying points, 2 tonne per point, 90k Dimmer Lights.
House Monitors: Pearl 2000 desk. Special Effects: 4 Mac 500's
Sound: In House PA: "Turbo Sounds" 8k 16 Channel desk. Mixer position: Back of house.
Power: PA / Lights: 3 PHASE 63 AMP
Dressing Rooms: 10 with shower and toilet facilities.
Catering: restaurant + Full catering services.
Parking: 250+ ample street parking.

UNIVERSITY OF LIVERPOOL

Guild Of Students, 160 Mount Pleasant, Liverpool, Merseyside L3 5TR
Tel: 0151 794 6868 Fax: 0151 794 4174
Email: guild@liv.ac.uk
Web Site: www.liverpoolguildofstudents.org
ADMINISTRATION:
Cap: Mountford - 900 seated - 2300 standing; Stanley Theatre - 320 seated 400 standing.

PHILHARMONIC HALL

Hope Street, Liverpool, Merseyside L1 9BP
Mgt: 0151 210 2895 BO: 0151 709 3789
Mrkt: 0151 210 2895 Fax: 0151 210 2902
Email: info@liverpoolphil.com
Web Site: www.liverpoolphil.com
ADMINISTRATION:
Props: Liverpool City Council.
Chief Executive: Michael Eakin
Technical Manager: Steve Burke
Head of Communications & Corporate Affairs: Jayne Garrity.
Built in 1939, original architect Herbert Rowse. Refurbished 1991-95, architect Peter Carmichael. Renowned art deco concert hall famous for its acoustics and wall reliefs. Central location, between the two cathedrals and both universities. Owned and managed by RLPS. Underwent major refurbishment (open 1995) giving it vastly expanded facilities and programme. Winner of 1996 RICS Building Conservation Award. The venue is funded by Arts Council of England, Local Authorities in Merseyside, Lancashire and Cheshire.
RAA: NWAB
Policy: Wide ranging international programme, including resident and visiting orchestras, solo recitals, pop, jazz, choral concerts, cinema, cabaret, comedy. Venue is home to the Royal Liverpool Philharmonic Orchestra, Principal Conductor. Promotions by the Royal Liverpool Philharmonic Society, joint promotions, hires. Willing to premiere show. Performance times vary, normally

7.30pm.
Booking terms: Hire, box office split, by negotiation.
Ticket Outlets: on site box office. 25 agencies throughout Merseyside. Shop and sales area.
Access: Car parks close by, very convenient for central train and bus terminals, also airport and motorway links.
Catering: Rubato Restaurant 70 covers. Open every event evening. Substantial hospitality and event catering facilities. Banqueting for up to 100 people.
Facilities for the disabled: Level access and ramps, assistance available. 10 wheelchair spaces. Grand foyer bars, bistro, infra red system.
Seating: 1682 fixed, slightly raked, plus 102 platform seats.
TECHNICAL:
STAGE: Width - useable 18.5m, max 20m. Depth useable 11m, max 12m. High 0.86m. Both front and rear platforms are curved. Get in with goods lift available width min 1.03m height min 2.04m. 24 X 1 ton flying points(eye bolt fixed to steel above concert ceiling). 15 positions over platform, 9 positions FoH allowing Left/Right PA clusters to be flown separately from main FoH truss. Temporary motor supply can be run to platform on 3 phase 32amp 'C' form. 3 phase 16amp 'C' form motor connector @ 11 flying points. Flying can only be done from official, designated points.
LIGHTING: In house concert and theatre lighting systems. Control: Strand 430 - 250 ways active 134 ways connected. Dimmers 4 x 24 way 2.5kw Strand LD90 - 2 x 24 way 2,5 kw ADB. Outlets all single 15 amp - one outlet per dimmer. 32 ways of production lighting, 42 ways of concert lighting, 60 ways of house lighting, 6 x 16amp non dim - 2 used for follow spots. Lanterns 12 x 2kw Alto zoom 28/38 (second roof slot in front of platform), 40 x 1kw 240v PAR64 (24 nearest roof slot to stage - 12 inside slots), 2 x PANI HMI standard throw follow spots in roof space, 60 x 1kw 110v PAR64 over platform for concert lighting. Concert lighting cannot be coloured, refocused or units moved elsewhere.
SOUND: Mixing Desk Allen & Heath 24:4:2:1, six Aux sends. Outboard, Alesis Reverb, Sabine Dual Channel Feedback Suppressor, 2 Channels of Behhringer Composer compressor/limiter/gate. Amplifiers deliver approx 3.6kw distributed - mixture of Amcron and Ramsa. Loudspeakers Nexo. Microphones, 3 x Beyer M88, 1 Shure SM58, 4 x Calrec 1050, 2 x Calrec 1051, 4 x Trantec radio mics (2x handhed, 2x lav). BBC facility in rack with feed to o/p panel with BBC compatible connection system. Surround loudspeakers, suitable for cinema sound. Multi microphone positions to stage. Dolby cinema system.
STAGE MANAGEMENTt: CCTV to auditorium with monitor locations front and back of house. Public address to all areas with microphone locations at front and back of house. Show relay to all performers and to public areas. Cue system with out-stations, loop intercom system.
BACKSTAGE: Dressing/soloists/green rooms available. Rehearsal piano in green room. Refreshments available. Backstage fully accessible to wheelchair users. In-house stage and lighting sound and casual technical and get in staff available.
ADDITIONAL: Organ - Rushworth and Dreaper 1939, refurbished 1983 by Rushworth and Dreaper, 3 chambers behind grilles at side and rear of concert platforms; electro-pneumatic action with solid state switching; 70 speaking stops, 15 couplers, 3 manuals and pedal, 2930 pipes, very good condition; console on electrically raised lifts CS - can swivel to face audience, face the rear of the platform or sideways; the console can be played under stage as well as at stage level. Pianos: two stage pianos, to include at least one Steinway D, excellent condition.

ROYAL COURT THEATRE

1Roe Street, Liverpool, Merseyside L1 1HL
Tel: 0870 787 1240 BO: 0870 787 1866
Fax: 0870 787 1241
Email: kevin@royalcourtliverpool.com
Web Site: www.royalcourtliverpool.co.uk
Programmer: Jessice Bolger
Assistant Theatre Producer : Jessica Bolger
Marketing Manager: Iain Christie
Policy: Touring Shows - Music & Comedy, seating in circle and balcony
Seating - 1200

Stage:
The stage is non raked and is 16.6m wide by a maximum of 15m deep, however upstage area is used for storage of stalls seating, this reduces upstage depth to 11.5m. The proscenium width is 9.60m. Our standard Black Box blacks in their current configuration provide a 3.6m deep stage which is raised from the original stage level by 0.7m and measures 7.3m by 2.4m deep. This raised platform can be easily removed and the blacks adjusted to meet your requirements. There are 6 x 3.5m by 9.2m black legs and 2 x 12m by 1.2m borders. There is one full black cloth, which is 12m by 9.2m. There are two staircases from the auditorium which lead directly beneath the stage. These are used for quick access for waitress service during Rawhide. Get in is via Roe Street, through roller shutter (2.45m x 2.75m) in up stage wall, note: shutter is 0.75m above stage level and so access is via a ramp. Alternatively access to stage directly through stage door (immediate of SR access doors). Door dimensions 2.34m x 1.12m. Stage door is unmanned, if you require stage door to be manned this will incur a charge. The safety curtain is not in operation but will lower in the event of an emergency. Due to the age of the theatre and without a full overhaul of all bars, we have very restricted flying. DISCLAIMER If you wish to use flying please let us know well in advance. There is no technical support area and tools etc are limited.
Lighting:
FOH Tri LiteTruss suspended on 3 x Lodestar 1 tonne motors. On stage Box Truss suspended on two Lodestar 1 tonne motors from counterweight 3. Third lx bar is counterweight 23. 4m Truss on centre of circle front and two 1m lengths either end of circle front. These are currently used for Disco lighting for Rawhide; please let us know if you wish to use these trusses.
We have a stock of additional Tri Lite Truss pieces (3 x 3m lengths and 2 x 2m lengths). The lighting rig is a standard stage wash and there are few spare fixtures. Follow spots are not owned however we can aquire them at a cost to the touring management.
Power, Dimming and Control:
All fixtures run on 16A socapex. 32A, power to Truss motor control board. 63A power unit outputs: 4 x 13 amp sockets, 12 x 16 amp outlets and 4 x 32A outlets (which power 3 x Zero 88 Betapack 6 way dimmers and 1 x Pulsar 6 x 10 amp switch panel (all located stage right). ETC Express 48/96 lighting control desk with monitor is situated at rear of stalls (auditorium left, under canopy). Houselights for stalls are controlled via the desk (dmx). Houselights for the Circle and Balcony are controlled from the stage right Perch. We have additional lighting desks and switch dimmer racks available. There is a single channel comms system from SR to lighting and sound control. Additional comm sets can be added to additional locations if required. There are no cue lights.
Lantern Schedule:
Currently on rig: 2 x Source 4 Zoom 15/30; 20 x Source 4 Par; 3 x Coemar 650w fresnels (used as house lights); 12 x par 56; 10 x Par 36 pinspot; 4 x Thomas chrome floor cans 4 x Martin Mac 500; 2 x 500w floods (workers)
Additional Kit:
3 x Source 4 Par; 2 x Coemar 650w fresnel; 5 x 500w fresnel; 4 x Thomas groundrows (4 x 1000w); 3 x 8 Lamp Molefay
4 x Par 36 pinspot; 2 x Source 4 zoom 15/30; Sound System Control is from rear of stalls, Auditorium left (under canopy). Stage Box is located Down Stage Right. 1 x Soundcraft Spirit Lx7, 16 channel, 4 Submasters and stereo out Mixing Console; 2 x QSC Audio PLX 300c Amps; 2 x SRX 3801 Amps (Subs); 1 x Omnidrive Loudspeaker Management System; 2 x Mk2 Nexxo PS 15; 4 x Nexxo Speakers; 2 x DF321 750w Bass Bins. Monitors are not supported but we have speakers we can use for that purpose. Additional Kit: 4 x AA12 600w Speakers; 2 x JBL Speakers; System

Inputs; 3 x Sony Mini Disk Players; 1 x 7 Disk changer CD Player; 1 x DI Box; 2 x SM58 Microphones. All with Mic Stands. Audio Visual (hire fee applicable): 1 projector screen flown on counterweight bar. 1 projector. Special Effects: 1 x le maitre Mini Mist Smoke Machine: 1 x Vision 200 Hazer: 2 x G300 Smoke Machines; 2 x 12" Mirror Balls; 2 x DHA Animation Disks (with controller and PSU).

THE CAVERN CLUB LIVERPOOL

10 Mathew Street, Liverpool L2 6RE
Day Tel: 0151 236 9091 Evening Tel: 0151 236 1965 Fax: 0151 236 8081
Email: office@thecavernliverpool.com
Web Site: www.cavernclub.org
Props: Cavern City Tours Limited
General Manager: Billy Irwin
Capacity: 400

THE VENUE

Civic Way, Poplar Bank, Huyton, Merseyside L36 9GD
Tel: 0151 443 3761
Email: huytonsuite@knowsley.gov.uk
Web Site: www.thevenuehuyton.co.uk
ADMINISTRATION
Props: Knowsley Borough Council
Cap: Main Hall: 400 with stage facilities

UNITY THEATRE

1 Hope Place, Liverpool L1 9BG
Admin Tel: 0151 709 6502 BO Tel: 0844 873 2888 Fax: 0151 709 7182
Email: marketing@unitytheatre.co.uk
Web Site: www.unitytheatreliverpool.co.uk
Marketing Manager: Sam Freeman
Marketing Assistant: Paul Dunbar
Artistic Director: Graeme Phillips
Technical Manager: Phil Saunders
Executive Director: Sue Williams
Unity 1: Capacity: 150
Unity 2: Capacity: 88

Llandrindod Wells, Powys

Pop. 3,470. London 170 miles.
Newspaper: Radnor Express (wed); Shropshire Journal (fri); County Times & Gazette (sat). STD code 01597

THE ALBERT HALL

Built in 1896
Ithon Road Llandrindod Wells, Powys LD1 6AS Wales
Tel: 01597 822 703
Email: golf098765@hotmail.com
ADMINISTRATION:
Props: Committee of Management
Contact: Secretary: Howard Nixon
Physical Address:
Caehof
Ithon Road
Llandrindod Wells
Policy: Stage Plays, Concerts, Repertory, Pantomime, Meetings, etc. Hiring only. No promotion.
Perfs: as required.
Seats: 430 approx. Kitchen and Refreshment Room in Lower Hall.
TECHNICAL:
Stage: Proscenium, Flat; Pros. opening 7.82m; Ht. of Pros. 4.88m; Depth of S/Line 5.49m plus 3.05m Apron; Ht. of Grid 7.32m; W/Widths P.S. 3.66m approx. O.P. 0.91m.
Lighting: Switchboard: 3 Strand Dimmer Packs each of 12 x 1000w capacity with provision for another pack. Movable console 2 x 24; F.O.H. Spots 8 x 1000w profile plus 2 x 500w Follow Spots; 2 Battens; Front 8 x 500w. Back 6 x 300w.
Sound Equipment: Available if required. Speakers above P.S.
Dressing Rooms 4; Orchestra Pit 6.

THE PAVILION

Spa Road, Llandrindod Wells, Powys LD1 5EY Wales
Tel: 01597 823 532 Fax: 01597 824 413
Email: pavilion@powys.gov.uk
Web Site: www.pavilionmidwales.co.uk
Seating/Capacity: 499
Contact: Val James

POWYS DANCE

Powys Dance Centre, Arlais Road, Llandrindod Wells, Powys LD1 5HE Wales
Tel: 01597 824 370
Email: powys.dance@powys.gov.uk
Web Site: www.dawnspowysdance.org
Contact: Amanda Griffkin
Capacity: 120

Llandudno, Conwy

Pop. 17,620. London 226 miles.
Newspapers: Llandudno Advertiser (fri); North Wales Weekly Press (thurs); North Wales Pioneer (wed). STD code 01492

VENUE CYMRU

The Promenade, Penrhyn Crescent, Llandudno, Conwy LL30 1BB Wales
Tel: 01492 879771 BO: 01492 872000
Fax: 01492 860790 Tech: 01492 879771 EXT: 1205
Email: info@venuecymru.co.uk
Web Site: www.venuecymru.co.uk
ADMINISTRATION:
Props: Conwy County Borough Council
General Manager: Sarah Ecob.
Contact: sarah.ecob@venuecymru.co.uk
Technical Manager: John Owen.
Contact: john.owen@venuecymru.co.uk
Marketing Manager: Richard P Jones
Policy: Orchestral Concerts, Touring Companies, One-nighters, Conferences, Exhibitions, Fairs, Television Studios etc.
Perfs: usually 8.00p.m.
Capacity:
Arena; Theatre, 1800. Reception, 1500. Banquet, 1000.
Theatre; 1500.
Conference Centre; Various, 8 - 800.
TECHNICAL:
STAGE: Proscenium Opening 14m wide x 8m high. No rake. Stage floor - Lino over oil-tempered hardboard. Stage width 14.45m. Front of stage to s/line 0.95m, S/line to back pillars 12.75m. Orchestra pit lift at stage level adds 2.1m fore-stage. Height: Stalls floor to stage floor - 0.95m ; Stage floor to grid - 20m ; grid to rigging points - 2m. Get-in from car park directly into scene dock - tailgate height, 3.5m high x 4.5m wide
STAGE MANAGEMENT: Show relay and tannoy to dressing rooms and backstage areas. Prompt corner normally Stage Right. Cue lights and Comms available.
LIGHTING: Strand 530i 350 Channel Lighting Desk. 204 x 2.5Kw Dimmers. 36 x 5Kw Dimmers 19 Switched Non-Dim Outlets. DMX Tie Lines from control room to all areas. Lighting stock consists of PARS, Fresnels, Profiles etc. 2 x Selecon Performer 1200w MSR Follow Spots (Central at rear of circle).
SOUND: 1 x Allen & Heath GL4000 32 Channel mixing desk - situated in control room or rear of stalls. 1 x Portable FX rack containing: Tascam 122 cassette deck, Sony CD machine, Denon 2000R Minidisc & Tascam 301 Minidisc, Yamaha SPX990 multi-effects unit, B.S.S FCS960 dual 31-band graphic equaliser (patchable). Auditorium sound system configuration: Centre speaker cluster (3 x community RS220, 2 x Community RS Jr.), Stereo Speaker System (4 x Martin Audio EM 75 Per Side), Balcony / Circle delay system (4 x Community RS220, 9 x JBL Control 1), Sub-bass cabinet (2 x Community CSX).
DRESSING ROOMS: 7 over 3 levels, acomm. 68. Various toilets, showers, and basins on all levels. 3 band rooms acomm. 10. Wig Room, Laundry Room, Make Up Room. Industrial washing machine and domestic dryer.
DISABLED ACCESS: reduced price tickets for wheelchair users and other disabled patrons. Dedicated parking spaces. Unisex accessible toilet. Working / Guide dogs welcome. Selected Audio described and signed/ stage text performances on weekly/long running shows. Infra Red loop system.

Llanelli, Carmarthenshire

FFWRNES

Park Street Llanelli SA15 3YE
Tel: 0845 226 3510
Email: theatres@carmarthenshire.gov.uk
Web Site: www.theatrausirgar.co.uk
Props: Carmarthenshire County Council
Contact: Nick Stevenson
Capacity: Main Theatre 504, Studio 100

Llangollen, Denbighshire

ROYAL INTERNATIONAL PAVILION
Abbey Road, Llangollen, Denbighshire LL20 8SW Wales
Tel: 01978 860 111 Fax: 01978 860 046
Email: enquiries@llangollenpavilion.co.uk
Web Site: www.llangollenpavilion.co.uk
ADMINISTRATION:
Spectacular venue which can seat 1,500 to 4,500 in a semi-outdoor arena or 400 in a heated indoor hall.
Venue Manager: Haydn Jones
Full technical specification available on request

Llantrisant, Mid Glamorgan

LLANTRISANT LEISURE CENTRE
Southgate Park, Llantrisant, Mid Glamorgan CF72 8DJ
Tel: 01443 228538 Fax: 01443 229727
Email: gary.d.dalton@rhondda-cynon-taff.gov.uk
Web Site: www.rctcbc.gov.uk/leisure
ADMINISTRATION:
Props: Rhondda Cynon Taff County Borough Council
Cap: Sports Hall 900, Functions Hall 300
Manager: Gary Dalton
Administrative Assistant: Collette Davies

Lochgelly, Fife

LOCHGELLY CENTRE THEATRE
Bank Street, Lochgelly, Fife KY5 9RD Scotland
Tel: 01592 583 367
Email: william.gibson@onfife.com
Web Site: www.onfife.com
Facility Manager: William Gibson
Capacity: 379 + 15 Wheelchairs

Lockerbie, Dumfries & Galloway

TOWN HALL
High Street, Lockerbie, Dumfries & Galloway DG11 2ES Scotland
Tel: 01576 202632 Fax: 01576 203 789
Email: enquiries@lockerbietownhall.org
ADMINISTRATION:
Props: Dumfries & Galloway Council
Cap: 230 max
Contact Bookings Officer: Carol

Longton, Staffordshire

ALBERT HALL
Longton Town Hall, Times Square, Longton, Staffordshire ST3 1BZ
Tel: 01782 232 732
Email: david.powell@civic1.stoke.gov.uk
Web Site: www.stoke.gov.uk
ADMINISTRATION:
Props: City of Stoke on Trent Council
Contact: Business Development Manager - David Powell
Cap: 240

Lossiemouth, Morayshire

LOSSIEMOUTH COMMUNITY CENTRE
Coulardbank Road, Lossiemouth, Morayshire IV31 6JW
Tel: 01343 815299 Fax: 01343 810149
Email: lossiemouth.cc@moray.gov.uk
ADMINISTRATION:
Props: Moray Council
For bookings contact Hall Letting Department at Moray Council
New Hall Capacity 200

LOSSIEMOUTH TOWN HALL
High Street, Lossiemouth, Morayshire IV31 6AA
Hall Bkgs Tel: 01343 813327
Email: katiebung@hotmail.com
ADMINISTRATION:
Props: Lossiemouth Town Hall Management Committee
Cap: Main Hall Seated 200+ 40 in balcony; Dancing 250; Dancing/Seated at tables 150; Seated at tables 150.
Seaview Suite for small meetings, Capacity 30
Mezanine Floor, Capacity 50

Loughborough, Leicestershire

Pop. 146,800. London 114 miles.
Newspapers: Loughborough Echo (wkly); Loughborough News (free wkly); Herald & Trader (free wkly); Echo Extra (free wkly); Leicester Mercury (wkly). STD code 01509

LOUGHBOROUGH TOWN HALL
Market Place, Loughborough, Leicestershire LE11 3EB
BO: 01509 231 914 Fax: 01509 634 914
Theatre Programming & Mktg: 01509 634 913 Room Hire: 01509 634 775 Theatre Marketing: 01509 634 915
Email: townhall@charnwood.gov.uk
Web: www.loughboroughtownhall.co.uk
ADMINISTRATION:
Manager: Nigel Strong, Tel. 01509 634 700
Loughborough Town Hall was refurbished during 2004. The venue includes a restaurant, cafe and bars andhas two theatres; the main auditorium seating up to 500 and the Victoria Room seating 150. The theatre offers a balnaced programme of entertainment. Rooms are available for hire for a variety of events, including weddings, shows and conferences.

Lowestoft, Suffolk

Pop. 58,000. London 116 miles.
Newspapers: Lowestoft Journal (fri); Eastern Daily Press. Freesheets: Waveney Advertiser (fri). STD code 01502

MARINA THEATRE
The Marina, Lowestoft, Suffolk NR32 1HH
Admin: 01502 533202 BO: 01502 533 200 Chief Executive: 01502 533201 Tech Mgr: 01502 533203
Email: info@marinatheatre.co.uk
Web Site: www.marinatheatre.co.uk
ADMINISTRATION:
Props: Marina Theatre Trust
Perfs: Variable
Seats: 786. Fixed and raked. Bars and cafe/teashop in theatre.
TECHNICAL:
Lighting: Switchboard: Compulite Ovation, 40 controller 386, 1000 mem, 96 circs.
4 pars 56, 10 Prelude 16/30, 6 Cant 11.26, 5 Prelude 28/40, 5 Cant 18.32, 8 X ADB F, 10 X CCT F, 6 X CCT PC, Theatre Fresnels, 18 Prelude F, 3 Cant F, 12 Prelude PC, 12 Coda 500/1, 4 Parblazer, 8 Iris 1, Barndoors.
Followspots: 2 Strand Solo 2k C/W 6 colour magazines. F/S operated from rear sides of circles.
Cinema 35mm x 16m. Projection Equip: 1 Prevost Westar P 93, flown screen projection surface 7.88mm (wide) x 4.5m (height), manual draw tabs. 2 x elf 16mm projectors, mobile screens. Fully Dolby sound.
Sound Equip: Venue theatre 24-8-2. Effects SP x 900. FOH tannoy and EV SPCIS, ROH, tannoy 20 ass mikes. 2 cassette deck, Revox B77Hs, CD. Control room at rear stalls. Talkback: 6 headsets/ outstations, FOH & ROH calls and show relay.
Other: 1 Grotrain Steinway Grand Piano, 1 Upright overstrung Knight Piano.
Theatre operating and security staff available as required.

PLAYERS THEATRE
The Bethel Battery Green Whapload Road Lowestoft Suffolk NR32 1DL
Tel: 01502 563614 BO: 01502 770020

Email: stephenartwizard@aol.com
Web Site: www.lowestoftplayers.co.uk
Props: The Lowestoft Players Ltd
Registered Charity 130421
Bookings: Bernie Gooch
Tel: 07752 807302
On Line box office available.
Capacity: 200
Adjustible seating styles can be used
Cabaret style with tables
Bar and Coffee Bar
Stage: Proscenium arch, level stage.Performing area 8.2mx6m
Thrust stage available.
Fixed grid 4.6m Barrel height 4.3m
Ongoing improvements to technical equipment.
Lighting/stage technician available.
72 ways of hardwired 3ph dimming 1-24 FOH, 25-72 on stage.
DMX on all bars. Cats on all bars
Additional equipment by arrangement
Sound Equipment available
Upright piano and other keyboards available
Lighting and sound operated from back of auditorium
Backstage 3 Dressing Rooms available.
No Orchestra pit.

SEAGULL THEATRE

Morton Road, Lowestoft, Suffolk NR33 0JH
BO: 01502 589726
Email: info@theseagull.co.uk
Web Site: www.theseagull.co.uk
ADMINISTRATION:
Voluntary run theatre for the community
Manager: Paul Amer
Cap: 110

Ludlow, Shropshire

LUDLOW ASSEMBLY ROOMS

1 Mill Street, Ludlow, Shropshire SY8 1AZ
Admin: 01584 873 229 BO: 01584 878 141 Bar & Catering: 01584 874 041
Email: admin@ludlowassemblyrooms.co.uk
Web: www.ludlowassemblyrooms.co.uk
ADMINISTRATION
Props: The Ludlow and District Community Association
Director: Helen Hughes
Head of Sales and Marketing: Tony Johnston
Technical Manager: Simon Nicholls
The main auditorium seats 291 people, and is used for cinema, theatre, music and talks. The lower floor is called OSCARS and has room for 200 people. It is used for dinners, lectures, discos, parties etc. The upper floor known as 'The Studio' is a similar space and is used for workshops and dance.
Gallery for exhibitions

Luton, Bedfordshire

Pop. 162,930. London 32 miles.
Newspapers: The Luton News (wed); The Herald (thurs). STD code 01582

THE LIBRARY THEATRE

Central Library, St George's Street Luton, Bedfordshire LU1 2NG
Mgt: 01582 547477 BO: 01582 878 100
Email: venues@lutonculture.com
Web Site: www.lutonlibrarytheatre.com
ADMINISTRATION:
Manager: Vicki Richmond
Technical Manager: Jenni Jackson
Props: Luton Culture
Policy: Small Touring Companies. One Night Stands, Theatre, Recitals, Amateur Lessees.
Perfs: times variable.
Seats: 238. Bar and Coffee Bar.
TECHNICAL:
Stage: Proscenium, Flat: Pros. opening 7.62m; Ht. of Pros. 3.66m; Depth of S/Line 5m; W/Widths P.S. 2.44m; O.P. 1.22m; Prompt Cnr. P.S.
Lighting: Switchboard: In projection box, Sirius 48 board memory and manual. 8 Spots; 2 Battens; 1 Float; Dips 2 each side; 4 Spot Bars. 8 Fresnel, 8 Stage Spots.
Sound Equip: Record Player, CD player, Cassette deck, Revox Tape eck, 30w amp P.S.: Speakers either side of stage.
Dressing Rooms: 4; Accom.25.

Lyme Regis, Dorset

MARINE THEATRE

Church Street, Lyme Regis, Dorset DT7 3QB
BO Tel: 01297 442 138
Mgmt: 01297 442394
Email: admin@marinetheatre.com
Web Site: www.marinetheatre.com
ADMINISTRATION:
Props: Lyme Arts Community Trust
Theatre Directors: Harry Long, Tim Bell
Seating/Cap: 220
TECHNICAL:
Stage: Proscenium arch, performing area 9.45m x 4.6m, pros opening 6.7m x 2.95m. Stage slightly raked. Height 3.66m.
Lighting: Lighting technician available. Sirius Level 12 - 12 channel, 2 preset; 4 x 650w Pebble Convex; 8 x 650w Fresnel; 2 x T64 Profile 1000. Additional equipment by arrangement.
Sound: Spirit Folio 14 channel mixer; 500w stereo amp - Technics CD and Cassette; 5 x Sure SM 58 Mics & Strands. Lighting and Sound operated from box at back of auditorium.
Other: Backstage: 2 dressing rooms. Piano. Two permanent staff and casuals available.

Lymington, Hampshire

LYMINGTON COMMUNITY CENTRE

New Street, Lymington, Hampshire SO41 9BQ
Tel: 01590 672337 Fax: 01590 678147
Email: lymcomass@aol.com
Web www.lymingtoncommunitycentre.org.uk
Venue available for small touring or amateur companies.
Cap: 110
Small stage with lighting. Fixed audience seating.

Lytham St Anne's, Lancashire

LOWTHER PAVILION

West Beach, Lytham St Anne's, Lancashire FY8 5QQ
Tel: 01253 794221
Email: boxoffice@lowtherpavilion.co.uk
Web Site: www.lowtherpavilion.co.uk
ADMINISTRATION
Props: Lowther Trust
Capacity: 457
For Bookings Contact: Roger McCann

Mablethorpe, Lincolnshire

Pop. 6,340. London 149 miles.
Newspapers: see Lincoln. STD code 01507

DUNES FAMILY ENTERTAINMENT CENTRE

Central Promenade, Mablethorpe, Lincolnshire LN12 1RG
Tel: 01507 479 999
Email: paddyprin@ic24.net
Web Site: www.dunescomplex.co.uk
ADMINISTRATION:
Props: Paddy Prince
Seats: 220. Licensed Bar
The Dunes offers excellent entertainment throughout the year. The entertainment ranges from competitions to bands, family variety shows, musical shows, talent shows, pantomimes and comedians.
TECHNICAL:
Stage: Proscenium, Raked; Pros. Opening 7.32m; Ht. of Pros. 3.66m; Depth of S/Line 2.08m; Ht. of Grid 3.74m; W/Widths P.S. 1.11m, O.P. 1.11m; Prompt Cnr. P.S.
Lighting: Zero 88XLS board, 24 circuits, operated backstage/front of house; F.O.H. Spots 14; 2 Battens; 6 Dimmers; 2 Spot Bars. 1 followspot operated from the rear of the theatre.

Sound Equip: 1 Amplifier, 2 Speakers, 5 Microphones.
Dressing Rooms: 3.

Macclesfield, Cheshire

MACCLESFIELD LEISURE CENTRE

Priory Lane, Upton Priory, Macclesfield, Cheshire SK10 4AF
Tel: 01625 383 981
Email: mlc@everybody.org.uk
Web Site: www.everybody.org.uk
Policy: Multi-purpose Hall with stage facilities.
Manager: Maria Tatters
Seating/Capacity: Main Hall: 1200

Maesteg, Mid Glamorgan

TOWN HALL

Talbot Street, Maesteg, Bridgend CF34 9DA Wales
Tel: 01656 733 269 BO: 01656 733 700
Email: info@maestegtownhall.com
Web Site: www.maestegtownhall.com
ADMINISTRATION:
Seating/Capacity: 550
Manager: Louise Ralph
Events Coordinator: Paula Torrance

Maidenhead, Berkshire

MAGNET LEISURE CENTRE

Holmanleaze, Maidenhead, Berkshire SL6 8AW
Mgmt: 01628 685314 BO: 01628 685333
Email: magnet@rbwm.gov.uk
Web Site: www.rbwm.gov.uk
ADMINISTRATION
Props: Royal Borough of Windsor and Maidenhead
Manager: Mark Camp-Overy
Cap: Pearce Suite 1,000 Seated; Main Hall Seated 1,400

TOWN HALL

St. Ives Road Maidenhead, Berkshire SL6 1RF
Tel: 01628 683800 ext 6409 Fax: 01628 685757
Email: facilities@rbwm.gov.uk
Web Site: www.rbwm.gov.uk
ADMINISTRATION:
Props: Royal Borough of Windsor and Maidenhead
Astor Suite: Cap 70, no stage facilities.
Desborough Suite: Cap 282, stage facilities
For bookings contact Dean Graham, facilities team extension 6409

Maidstone, Kent

Pop. 130,000. London 37 miles.
Newspapers: Kent Messenger (fri), KM Extra (wed). STD code 01622

MAIDSTONE LEISURE CENTRE-MOTE HALL

Mote Park, Willow Way, Maidstone, Kent ME15 7RN
Mgt: 01622 220 210 BO: 08451 552 277
Fax: 01622 672462
Email: joyce.veal@leisure.serco.com
Web Site: www.maidstoneleisure.com/events
ADMINISTRATION:
Events/Live Entertainment Manager: Joyce Veal
Policy: Full range of performing arts, musicals and variety productions. This versatile venue is perfect for concerts, exhibitions, wedding receptions and conferences.
Auditorium: The Mote Hall
Seats: 1,200. Licensed Bar and Cafe.
TECHNICAL:
Multi-function hall. Stage fully demountable to maximum size of 14m x 8m. Pros. arch created using Drapes. Full front tabs and mid stage tabs. Rear cyc. screen. Power available 3 x 200 amp, 1 x 150 amp.
Lighting: In-house lighting controlled by Strand M24. 60 x 10 amp circuits. Limited range of lamps. Followspot available.
Sound: In-house sound Ramsa speaker, AHB 12 channel mixer; Selection of mics and stands.
Dressing Rooms: 2 large Artistes dressing rooms, one with private toilet and wash, large amount of sports changing available

THE HAZLITT THEATRE

Earl Street, Maidstone, Kent ME14 1PL
Admin: 01622 753 922 BO: 01622 758 611
Email: natalie.price@parkwoodtheatres.co.uk
Web Site: www.hazlitttheatre.com
ADMINISTRATION:
Props: Parkwood Leisure Ltd
Technical Manager: Sam Ray
Commercial Manager: Natalie Price
Policy: For hire; all types of stage shows, pantomimes, films, guaranteed split, 1st call & % deals.
Seats: Up to 389, Bar, Coffee Lounge.
The Corn Exchange: Capacity 200/148 Seated
The Fourth Wall: Capacity 75 standing
TECHNICAL:
Seating and stage flexible within hall, 10m x 27m. Floor Canadian maple, suitable for all dance, no crossover, area heated.
Various 13A/15A independent circuits.
Get-in via Rose Yard. Tallescope.
Lighting: Sirus 24 Programmable, 36 circuits, operated from balcony or floor - various lanterns - 1 followspot, operated from balcony.
Sound: Soundcraft 16:4:2 desk operated from balcony - various mics - 1 cassette deck. Acoustics suitable for music and spoken word. 1 CD.
Backstage: 3 dressing rooms, Piano, upright. Advice given on accommodation.
Staff - 1 stage, 1 lighting - casuals available - security personnel.

Malton, North Yorkshire

THE MILTON ROOMS

The Market Place, Malton, North Yorkshire YO17 7LX
Tel: 01653 696240
Email: info@themiltonrooms.com
Web Site: www.themiltonrooms.com
ADMINISTRATION:
Capacity: 300 + 40 seated, 400 standing
TMR is run by Milton Rooms Management Committee (MRMC).
Registered charity number - 1026109
Chairman: Stephen Shaw

Fixed sound and light for drama, dance, PA etc.

Malvern, Worcester

Pop. 31,000. London 119 miles.
Newspapers: Malvern Gazette (fri). STD code 01684

MALVERN THEATRES

Grange Road, Malvern, Worcestershire WR14 3HB
Mgt: 01684 569 256 BO: 01684 892 277
Fax: 01684 893 300
Email: post@malvern-theatres.co.uk
Web Site: www.malvern-theatres.co.uk
ADMINISTRATION:
Props: Malvern Theatre Trust Ltd
Chief Executive: Nicolas Lloyd
Technical Manager: Matt Cox
Policy: Plays, Variety, Ballet, Opera, One Nighters, Pantomime, Variety, Ballet, Dance, Music, Film, Exhibitions and Conferences.
Perfs:
Festival Theatre 8.00pm, Mat 2.30pm
Forum Theatre 7.30pm, Mat 2.00pm
Seats: Festival Theatre 844, Forum Theatre variable up to 840
Complex includes Two Theatres, Cinema, Restaurant, Bar, Circle Bar, Exhibition Space and Hospitality Suites.

FESTIVAL THEATRE
Policy: No 1 Tours, pre west end shows. Co-productions, Variety, Opera, Dance, One Night Stands.

Also in forum we have a back projection cinema screen for art house films.
TECHNICAL:
Stage: Proscenium, raked 1.24, pros opening 9.20m, Ht of pros, 5.98m. Depth of s/line 7.85m, Ht of Grid 15.70m. 36 counterweight sets plus 2 up and down stage sets. Max. flying Ht. 14.7m. flying bars 9.20 ext. to 11.00m.
Lighting: Control: Arri Imagine 2 120 ways (Control Room rear of auditorium).
Dimmers: LD90s, various profile and fresnel luminairs.
Sound: Soundcraft 6000, Tascam tape machines, Teac CD and cassette machines. Operate from control room or rear of stalls. Comprehensive tie lines and speaker outlets to stage and F.O.H. Good selection of mics and speakers.
General: Communications: Intercom and telephones to all key areas. Paging to F.O.H., Auditorium and backstage.
Dressing Rooms: 9 plus wardrobe, bathrooms and showers. Orchestra pit: accommodates 20.

FORUM THEATRE
Policy: Concerts, Variety, Opera, Dance, Jazz, Conferences, Exhibitions, Film.
Seats: Balcony - 217 seats, flat floor - 500sqm, or raked seating and flat floor seating 640 seats. Cafe bar, circle etc.
TECHNICAL:
Stage: Thrust, flat, modular type, size from 7.32m X 17m to 9,76m X 17m. A truss type grid suspends over the whole stage area.
Lighting: ETC expression from control room, at side of auditorium or operated from rear of auditorium. Assorted Profile and Fresnel Lanterns.
Sound: Tascam 312B, Sherman speaker clusters surround sound speakers with Dolby processer for 35mm film projection. Operated from control room or rear of auditorium or projection room. Comprehensive TIE lines and speaker outlets.
General: Communications: Intercom and telephone to all key areas. Paging to F.O.H., auditorium and backstage areas.
Dressing Rooms: 5 plus band room.

THE CINEMA
Policy: First run films, Special Screenings 7 days a week, day time conferences, lectures, seminars.
Seats: 371 with balcony.
TECHNICAL:
Stage: Flat, size 7.95m X 3.08m.
Lighting: Srius 24 way desk - rear of circle. Assorted Profile and Fresnel Lanterns.
Sound: 312B, Tannoy speakers, surround sound speakers with Dolby proccesor. Audio TIE lines and speaker outlets.
General: 35mm & 16mm projection with full Dolby stereo sound. Screen - 7.42m X 3.8m. Full satalite facilities with video projection. Full 35mm slide projection facilities.

Manchester, Gtr. Manchester

Pop. 531,270. London 184 miles.
Newspapers: Manchester Evening News (fri). Other regional papers monthly. STD code 0161

THE BRIDGEWATER HALL

Lower Mosley Street, Manchester M2 3WS
Tel: 0161 950 0000 BO: 0161 907 9000 Fax: 0161 950 0001 BO Fax: 0161 907 9001
Email: admin@bridgewater-hall.co.uk
Web Site: www.bridgewater-hall.co.uk
ADMINISTRATION:
Operated and managed: SMG Europe Holdings Ltd
Chief Executive: Nick Reed
Head of Marketing: Dawn Yates
Operations Manager: Sandra Perrott
Technical Manager: Jonathon Rowland
Programming Manager: Amy Ward
Seats: 2,330 over four levels (24 wheelchair seats).
TECHNICAL:
Stage: Open concert platform, 19m wide at the front, tapering 12.3m at rear. Built in stage lifts, the first at 5.5m from front of stage with a total depth of 12.8m allow for total flexibility on the platform. Platform is 1m high from stalls floor.
Lighting:Strand 550 and 300 desks and Avolite Pearl. 200 production circuits, full production lighting rig in addition to concert platform lighting. 2 x 2500w follow spots. Power source: 400a 3 phase + neutral Camlocks, or 3 x 125a sockets, 3 phase + neutral, located stage left.
Sound: Midas Heritage 2000 desk and Allen and Heath ML 3000. Meyer M2D Line Array System. Cable traps and runs to most parts of the auditorium on all levels. Sennheiser infra-red hard of hearing system. Power sources: 100 amp single phase located stage right. Independent: various 15a & 13a non-dim circuits.
General: Rigging: 57 x 2 ton fixed points with 6 x 1 ton lodestar motors available to hire. Clearance above stage approximately 13m. Pyrotechnics and smoke effects by prior arrangement only. Production office with telephone available. Dressing Rooms: Four ensuite changing rooms on platform level to accommodate 25-30 each. Guest Conductor and five solo ensuite dressing rooms on first floor level. Lift access to all levels..

THE COMEDY STORE MANCHESTER

Arches 3 & 4 Deansgate Locks, Whitworth Street West, Manchester M1 5LH
Tel: 0161 839 9595 Fax: 0161 839 9696
Email: manchester@comedy-store.net
Web Site: www.thecomedystore.co.uk
Contact: Emilie Jones
Seats: 500

CONTACT THEATRE

(Manchester Young People's Theatre Ltd.)
Oxford Road, Manchester M15 6JA
BO: 0161 274 0600 Mktg: 0161 274 0604 Tech: 0161 274 0632
Email: info@contact-theatre.org.uk
Web Site: www.contactmcr.com
ADMINISTRATION:
Chief Executive: Matt Fenton
Technical Manager: Jack Dale
Contact is a registered charity.
Focus on young people (target ages 13-30) and programming aims to combine an innovative mix of productions, touring and participatory projects. Art, Word, Music, Dance, Comedy, Debate, Drama, Club events, Mixed Media.
Cap: 350
TECHNICAL:
Space One - End on theatre playing area 12m wide and 7.5m deep, which may be augmented by use of forestage lifts by arrangement. Full black masking and cyclorama available. 20 electrically winched flying bars at 12m long, S.W.L. 180kg each. Lighting: ETC expression board: 48 profiles; 41 fresnels; 38 beam lights, 18 floods. Sound: Minidisc & CD players; Soundcraft 32:8 mixer; Mackie amps with 9 Community speakers, opportunity for monitoring, Shure SM58 microphones.
Space Two- Flexible Studio with dimensions 11mx11m. Fixed grid. Lighting: 12 profiles; 15 fresnels; 12 PCs; 9 Parcans. Sound: Minidisc and CD players, Mackie 1604 mixer, Mackie M1400 amps with 4 Community Speakers.
Space 3 - Rehearsal and workshop studio with dimensions 15mx9.5m.

DANCEHOUSE THEATRE

10 Oxford Road, Manchester M1 5QA
Mgt/SD/Mktg: 0161 237 1413 BO: 0161 237 9753
Email: dancehousedave@googlemail.com
Web Site: www.thedancehouse.co.uk
ADMINISTRATION:
Theatre Manager: Crispin Radcliffe, Dave Crook
Seats: 433, raked, retractable and moveable.
TECHNICAL:
Stage: Performing area 13.7m wide + 2 side aisles 2m wide each x 12.55m depth. Backstage area 16m x 6m, 2.47m to rear balcony. No rake, floor sprung wood, suitable for all dance. Height to ceiling 6.3m at apex, sloping sides.
Lighting: Arri Mirage DMX 512 board, 125 channels, 48@2.5kw, 6@5kw, operated from control box by auditorium rear -

200A 3 phase supply available 20IT Profile 10 500w profile, 24 fresnels, 12 pars, 12 floods, 8 x Dance Booms.
Sound: Spirit LX7 from audio-visual room next to LX control room - 2 x H&H amps - 2 x Bosc 802, 2 x Tannoy Speakers. 1 mic, 1 x Revox B77 reel-to-reel, 1 x Denon, PA system. Acoustics suitable for music and spoken word.
Backstage: Changing facilties in Green Room, accommodates 30; other rooms available. Wardrobe adjacent to Green Room, iron and board, washing machine and dryer, sewing machine.
Technics electric piano. Backstage facilties accessible to disabled performers and staff with difficulty. Help needed.

FORMBY HALL

Alder Street, Atherton, Manchester M46 9EY
Tel: 01942 256 903
Email: formby@roseleisure.com
Web Site: www.roseleisure.com
ADMINISTRATION:
Props: Rose Leisure Group
Formby's large main hall can comfortably accommodate up to 350 people. The adjoining smaller hall holds up to 150 people and a lounge room is available for smaller functions.
Manager: Mr T Manniex

HOME

2 Tony Wilson Place First Street
Manchester M15 4FN
Admin: 0161 236 5086
Web Site: www.homemcr.org
ADMINISTRATION:
Props: Greater Manchester Arts Centre Ltd
Artistic Director: Walter Meierjohann
Technical Director: Jasper Gilbert
Policy: Repertory
Capacity: Main theatr, 500 (Seated)

LONGFIELD SUITE

Longfield Centre, Rectory Lane
Manchester M25 1AY
Tel: 0161 253 7227 Fax: 0161 773 9395
Email: longfieldsuite@bury.gov.uk
ADMINISTRATION:
Props: Bury Metropolitan Borough Council
Cap: 500
Venue Manager: Paul Haywood

MANCHESTER ACADEMY

Oxford Road, Manchester M13 9PR
Admin/BO: 0161 275 2930
Email: annlouise.elliott@manchester.ac.uk
Web Site: www.manchesteracademy.net
Contact: Ann Louise Elliott
Capacity Manchester Academy: 2,400
Academy 2, Capacity 810
Academy 3, Capacity 450
Club Academy, 500

MANCHESTER CENTRAL

Windmill Street, Manchester M2 3GX
Tel: 0161 834 2700
Email: sales@manchestercentral.co.uk
Web Site: www.manchestercentral.co.uk
Contact: Elizabeth Convoy
Seating/Capacity: 10,000

MANCHESTER METROPOLITAN UNIVERSITY STUDENTS' UNION

Changed building's in December 2014
21 Higher Cambridge Street Manchester M15 6AD
Tel: 0161 247 1162 Fax: 0161 247 6423
Email: mmsu@mmu.ac.uk
Web Site: www.mmunion.co.uk
Entertainments Manager: James Charleson

MIDDLETON ARENA

Joe Halliwell Way Middleton, Manchester M24 1AG
Tel: 0161 662 4000 BO: 0844 855 4020
Email: middleton.civic@rochdale.gov.uk
Web Site: www.link4life.org
ADMINISTRATION:
Props: Rochdale Borough Council
Cap: Dancing 600, General purpose hall.
Manager: Claire Costigan
SOUND:
2 clusters of 3 mackie PA151 cabinets flown in a vertical array L+R of Pros, 1 mackie PA121 flown as mezzanine Delayed fill,
4 PSS Custom designed bass cabinets 1x18" driver 1Kw Rms sunk into stage, 4 Behringer Eurolive monitors 1x15"+ 1.5" comp driver, 2 Peavey Hisis 2XT cabs (drum Fill), 3 QSC RMX 2450 amps 1 for L+R tops 2 Bridged for subs L+R, 2 QSC RMX 1450 amps for 4way mon mix, 1 QSC RMX 850 for delayed fill, 2 x Behringer Ultra curves, 2 x Behringer Ultra graphs 3rd octave srereo eq, 4 x Behringer Composer pros compressor/gates, 2 x Alesis Midiverb 4 FX Units, 1 x allen and heath GL3300 24chn (all mono) desk, 1 x Behringer SuperX pro, 11 x double boom mic stands, 1 x short boom stand, 7 x SM58, 2 x sm57, 3 x e604,
1 x 504, 2 x M201, 1 x ME66+K1, 1 x d112, 1 x short rifal, 5 x behringer Active DI boxs, 2 x EMO dual DI boxs.
various length xlr leads and all speaker cabling etc
2 x 12 sends and 4 reterns stage L+R which can be patched to 3 mix positions in the audatorium, 1 x 12 way 20m multicore,
Also available 2 PSS MR12's 1x12" + 1x 2" comp Driver + QSC RMX 2450 for front fill etc.

O2 APOLLO MANCHESTER

Stockport Road, Ardwick Green,
Manchester M12 6AP
Mgt: 0161 273 6921 BO: 08444 777677
SD: 0161 273 2958 Fax: 0870 749 0779
Email: O2apollomanchester@livenation.co.uk
Web Site: www.livenation.co.uk
ADMINISTRATION:
Props: Live Nation (Venues) UK Ltd
Theatre Manager: Phil Rogers
Chief Technician: Rob Lloyd
Policy: International Concerts, Live Shows, Pantomime & Cinema
Seats: 2,700 Standing capacity: 3,500
Licensed Bar and Catering
For all booking information and further details, please contact: E-mail: phil.rogers@livenation.co.uk
TECHNICAL:
Stage: Thrust, Raked; Pros. opening 14.02m; Ht. of Pros. 7.62m; Depth of S/Line 1.83m; Ht. of Grid 19.81m; 19 lines, 5 C/W, 14 Hemp; Scenery Flying Ht. 19.81m; Flying Bars 13.72m; W/Widths P.S. 8.53m, O.P. 8.53m; Prompt Cnr. O.P.
Dressing Rooms 16; Accom. 19. No Orchestra Pit.

OPERA HOUSE MANCHESTER

Quay Street, Manchester M3 3HP
BO: 0844 871 3018 SD: 0161 828 1700
Admin: 0161 828 1708
Fax: 0161 833 2421
Email: sarahbleasdale@theambassadors.com
Web: www.atgtickets.com/manchester
ADMINISTRATION:
Props: Ambassadors Theatre Group (Venues) Ltd.
General Manager: Sarah Bleasdale
Deputy Manager: Joanne Whiteley
Stage Manager: Anis Khan
Policy: No.1 Touring Theatre presenting extended runs of major musicals.
Seats: 1,915. 7 Licensed Bars.
TECHNICAL:
STAGE: Proscenium, Pros. Opening 11.24m. Ht. of pros. 7.6m. Stage depth, working 12.8m. ht. of Grid: 17.6m. bar length 12.19m. 60 lines.
LIGHTING: Control: Eurolite 200 Way. Dimmers: 176 at 2kw, 24 at 5kw. Patch panel to Front of House proscenium booms, circle front and gallery front.
SOUND: Control: 60amp single phase clean feed provided. Permanent mixing position at rear of stalls, powered by 8 x 13 amp outlets fed from the above.
Orchestra Pit: 10.6m wide x 2.64m deep in the centre and 2.13m deep at the ends. 3 stage lifts - Nos. 1 & 2 travel to 0.8m above stage and 2.54m below stage. No. 3 to 1.83m above and 1.22m below.
STAGE MANAGEMENT: Controlled from stage manager's portable desk, stage left. Ring intercom and cue light stations serving all key technical working areas.
Paging to all dressing rooms, band room, workshop and office areas.
DRESSING ROOMS: 45 positions plus Co. Managers office, Band Room, Wig Room, Wardrobe.

PALACE THEATRE

97 Oxford Street, Manchester M1 6FT
BO: 0844 871 3019 SD: 0161 245 6600
Admin: 0161 245 6604 Admin Fax: 0161 245 6645
Email: staceybroadmeadow@theambassadors.com
Web Site: www.manchesterpalace.org.uk
ADMINISTRATION:
Props: Ambassador Theatre Group
Theatre Manager: Stacey Broadmeadow
Stage Manager: Mike Hall
Email: mikehall@theambassadors.com
Chief Electrician: John Mace
Head of Marketing: Emma Cureton
Policy: No. 1 Touring Theatre (Opera, Musicals etc)
Seats: 2,000. Seven licensed bars. Theatre pub 'The Stage Door'.
TECHNICAL:
STAGE: Proscenium, Pros. opening 12.95m; Ht. of Pros. 7.95m; Stage Depth, working 17.07m; Ht. of Grid 21.95m; Bar Length (downstage) 18.29m, (upstage) 17.07m, centred at 0.17m; 73 lines. Orchestra pit accomodating 120 musicians.
LIGHTING: Strand 520i Desk; Dimmers - 250 capacity. 48 x Par Can Lamps. 18 Source 4 - 15/30 zoom Lamps. 12 Source 4 - 10 degree Lamps. 2 Robert Juliat Cyrano 2.5KW HMI Follow Spots.
SOUND: 6 x D&B Ci90. 2 x D&B Q-Sub. 4 x D&B E3. 2 x D&B Max 15 Wedge. 10 x E-Pac Amplifiers. 1 x Yamaha P7000s. Midas Verona 32 Channel Desk. 1 x CD/Mini Disk Player. 1 x Quad Gate Compressor. 2 x BSS Opal Stereo Graphic EQ. 32 Channel Multi-core & Stage Box.
COMMUNICATIONS: 12 way cue light system, twin ring intercom system, paging to dressing rooms, office, annexe. Controlled from Stage Manager's portable desk. The stage door can also page selectively if the SM is not doing so.
DRESSING ROOMS: accommodates 150 artistes

PHONES 4 U ARENA

Victoria Station Manchester M3 1AR
Tel: 0161 950 5000 BO: 0844 847 8000
Email: maxine.price@smg-europe.com
Web Site: www.phones4uarena.co.uk
Props: SMG (Europe) Ltd
General Manager: John Knight
Commercial Director: Ben Williams
For Booking Enquiries:
sarah.hodson@smg-europe.com
Capacity: 19,500

RADCLIFFE CIVIC SUITE

Thomas Street, Radcliffe, Manchester M26 2UH
Tel: 0161 253 7812 Fax: 0161 724 4897
Email: radcliffecivicsuite@bury.gov.uk
Web Site: www.bury.gov.uk/radcliffecivicsuite
ADMINISTRATION:
Props: Bury Metropolitan Borough Council
Cap: 400 Seated
Venue Manager: David Catterall

ROYAL EXCHANGE THEATRE

St. Ann's Square Manchester M2 7DH
SD: 0161 833 9333 BO: 0161 833 9833
Fax: 0161 832 0881
Email: marketing@royalexchange.co.uk
Web Site: www.royalexchange.co.uk
ADMINISTRATION:
Funded by NWAB; Association of Greater Manchester
Local Authority: Manchester City Council
Artistic Director: Sarah Frankcom
Executive Director: Fiona Gasper
Producer (Studio): Richard Morgan
Marketing Director: Clare Will
Senior Press Officer: John Goodfellow
History: Largest theatre-in-the-round in the country, opened in 1976. Auditorium is futuristic steel and glass structure built within the Great Hall (now a vast foyer) of Manchester's former Cotton Exchange (present building dates from 1921). Theatre architects were Levitt Bernstein Associates (in collaboration with Richard Negri). Royal Exchange is situated in city centre, entrances in Cross Street and St. Ann's Square. The Theatre was completely refurbished in 1998 following extensive bomb damage, with Studio theatre added.
For the Disabled: Up to 8 wheelchair spaces - sound reinforcement system - Braille performances, audio description. Studio fully accessible with 6 wheelchair spaces.
Seats: 750 raked on three levels. Studio 120 on flat floor, flexible.
Catering: Self-service, fully licensed Café Exchange 12.00pm. Evening restaurant 5.30pm - curtain up. Bar Exchange 9.30am - 11.00pm. 4 interval bars. Group catering for pre-show refreshments on request. Function rooms for hire.
TECHNICAL:
STAGE: In the round. Performance area 8.5m diameter with 7 entrances and 7 banks of seating. Floor oak planks with no rake and no substage. Height to central lighting 'basket' 5.5m. Height to trusses 7.5m. Automated flying system with 28 axes of
control driving 125 kg swl point hoists. Spot hemp lines also available. 63 amp 3 phase power available at stage and grid levels. Tallescope and genie tower. Lift to stage level 1.9m wide 3.85m long 2.0m high. Otherwise, 27 steps from street through doors 1.5m wide 2.2m high. 1:25 scale plans available.
Studio: Clear space approximately 14m long 8m wide. Clear height 3m. Central area of 5m long 7m wide with clear height 7.5m and fly floors on long sides. Tubular steel grid. Automated flying system with 12 axes of control driving 125kg swl point hoists. 3 x 250kg swl, 3 line hand winches. 4 x 3 line hemp sets. Tallescope and genie tower. Lift to stage level through get-in doors. 120 seats of different heights to form flexible seating layouts. Mobile SM, SND and LX control can be positioned on floor. 1:25 scale plans available.
LIGHTING: Main Theatre: Strand Dual 530icontrol desk with 405 dimmers; 160 profiles, 78 fresnels, 80 parcans, various moving lights, scrollers, floods.
Studio: Strand Dual 530icontrol desk with 78 dimmers; 40 profiles, 56 fresnels, 40 parcans 6x8"scrollers. Full list available from the Theatre LX Department.
SOUND: Custom made CADAC desk, operated from 2nd gallery with LX and SM, also Soundcraft 24/8/2 K3 Theatre, Soundcraft Folio and Mackie 8 bus desks. Lab Gruppen and HH amplification. Meyer UPM1, UPA1, USW, MSL2, EV Sx300, ProAc, and JBL speakers. FX playback through Denon Minidisc, CD machines and Akai S6000 samplers controlled by Timax level control and matrix system or G-type software. Lexicon PCM80 reverbs, Yamaha SPX990 multiFX, Klark Technik graphic EQ's. Full recording and editing facilities include Protools, Tascam DA88, Cubase and Vision sequencing, DAT and Yamaha 02R desk. Various Neumann, Sennheiser, Shure and AKG microphones. Trantec S5000 lapel and hand held radio microphones. BSS DI boxes. 3 channel RTS/Telecom and rx communications. Extensive microphone, speaker, CCTV and communications tie lines covering all areas. Sennheiser infrared listening system. Acoustics suitable for spoken word and music.
STAGE MANAGEMENT: Control position 2nd gallery with LX, sound and 20 way cue lights - show relay/tannoy to dressing rooms.
BACKSTAGE FACILITIES: 2 x single, 2 for two, 3 for three, 2 for four, 1 for five dressing rooms, access by stage door, green room, band room, quick change rooms built as required, washing, drying, ironing facilities available. Tea, coffee, snacks available. 2x rehearsal rooms available, 2 x pianos. All facilities accessible to performers and staff who are disabled. 1x3 person dressing room with suitable turning circle for wheelchair users. Accommodation lists available. Visiting company technical office available.
ADDITIONAL: Main piano - Steinway Model D concert grand. Two Schimmel upright pianos.

ROYAL NORTHERN COLLEGE OF MUSIC

124 Oxford Road, Manchester M13 9RD
Hiring: 0161 907 5289 BO: 0161 907 5555
Email: info@rncm.ac.uk
Web Site: www.rncm.ac.uk
ADMINISTRATION:
Props: Royal Northern College of Music
Events Manager: Tom Besford, Email:

tom.besford@rncm.ac.uk
Policy: Productions of Opera and Drama. Available for hire by Opera and Ballet and Theatre Companies.
Perfs: 7.15 or 7.45
Capacity: Theatre; 607 (+ 50 in orchestra pit if not used).Concert Hall; Level 1- 445 Fully open with balcony 610, Small ensemble layout 730. Carol Nash Recital Room - 100. Studio Theatre - 120. Coffee Bar and Licensed Bar.
TECHNICAL:
Theatre:
STAGE: Pros. Opening 13.72 m, Pros. Height 6.10 m, Depth of Stage 8.53 m, Depth of Rear stage 9.84 m
LIGHTING: 530i Strand control console, 350 Channels.
SOUND: For recording: 20XLR lines which run back to the Recording Department. A permanent PA system which is suitable for speech and some music. There is also a 4.5 KW Martin PA rig.

Studio Theatre:
STAGE: Dimensions; 7.5m x 7.5m.
LIGHTING: Strand Lighting 300 Series. 60 circuits
SOUND: Same as above.

TALIA THEATRE

1 Hoscar Drive, Manchester M19 2LS
Tel: 0161 249 0564
Email: info@taliatheatre.com
Web Site: www.taliatheatre.com
Talia Theatre was founded in 1997 by James Beale and Chloe Whitehead, with the intention of developing high quality, dynamic theatre. We work with community institutions, schools and theatres in an attempt to produce art that can communicate across language and cultural barriers.
Since 2000 we have created and toured a new piece of theatre each year. We are unusual in that we are one of the only companies in Europe to specialise in Meyerhold's Biomechanics, a system of movement training for actors resulting in dynamic and unique visual theatre. Talia Theatre's Associate Director, Gennadi Bogdanov is an internationally acclaimed Russian director and world renowned Biomechanics expert, who directed 7 Assilon Place, An Evening Of Chekov's Vaudevilles and The Life of Moliere.

Mansfield, Nottinghamshire

Pop. 97,000. London 173 miles.
Newspapers: The Chad (thurs). STD code 01623

OAK TREE LEISURE CENTRE

Oak Tree Leisure Centre, Jubilee Way South, Mansfield, Nottinghamshire NG18 3RT United Kingdom
Tel: 0345 0000 231
Email: info.oaktree@serco.com
Web Site: www.mansfieldleisure.com
ADMINISTRATION:
Props: Serco
Cap: Up to 400
Facility Manager: Darren Kissane

THE PALACE THEATRE

Leeming Street, Mansfield, Nottinghamshire NG18 1NG
Mgt: 01623 412 950 Fax: 01623 412 922
BO: 01623 633 133 Tech Mgt: 01623 412 952
Email: atucker@mansfield.gov.uk
Web Site: www.mansfield.gov.uk/palacetheatre
ADMINISTRATION:
Props: Mansfield District Council
Cultural Services Manager: Andrew Tucker
Technical Manager: Dai Evans
Policy: Midscale Touring, Pantomime, Amateur, Dance, Ballets, Operatic, Orchestral, Workshops.
Perfs: As required.
Seats: 534. Foyer Bar, Coffee Lounge.
TECHNICAL:
Stage: Proscenium, 8.5m wide by 5.5m high, stage depth; max. 10m, flat stage; scenery flying height 7m; 27 counterweight sets @ 500kg each; flying bars 10.5m, wide upstage to 14m downstage; height of grid 14.7m, wing widths P.S. 6.5m O.P. 6m (approx); Intercom, cue light and calls systems. SM desk P.S. Full orchestra pit with lift; loading bay at rear of stage - level access.1:25 plan available.
Lighting: ETC. Impession 300 + Remote Focus Unit. 120 ways ETC. Smartrack dimming; 9 X 15A independent circuits. DMX network. 28 x 1kwF, 8 x Alto F, 8 x T84, 10 x Cantata 18/32, 4x Quartet F, 21 x Coda 1kw, 42 x Par 64, 36 x ETC Source 4 (Variety of lenses available 19º-50º), 2 x HMI 1200 F/Spots.
Sound: Allen & Heath ML3000 32 ch; CD Player, Mini Disc recorder/player,2 X cassette player: 2 FX units, graphic eq; Assorted microphones inc. SM58, Crown PCC 160. 4 Bose 802 for monitor use. F.O.H. speakers d&b full range; delay system above and below balcony. 12 x Sennheiser Radio mics (Lavalier).
General: 10 Dressing Rooms; 3 Showers (1 of which has access for disabled). Access for disabled to all areas. Other Facilities: Rehearsal room, dance studio, function/conference room, bar and restaurant, computerised box office.

Margate, Kent

Pop. 52,000. London 74 miles.
Newspapers: Isle of Thanet Gazette (fri); Thanet Times (tues); Freepapers: Adscene (tues); Thanet Extra (thurs). STD code 01843

THEATRE ROYAL MARGATE

Addington Street, Margate, Kent CT9 1PW
Admin: 01843 296 111
BO: 01843 292 795
Email: lynne.boyd@yourleisure.uk.com
Web Site: www.theatreroyalmargate.com
ADMINISTRATION:
The Theatre Royal is managed by a charity trust. It is open all year round for both professional & amateur productions on either percentage deals or hires. All enquiries should be addessed to Lynne Boyd at the theatre.
Capacity: 466 seated
TECHNICAL:
All technical details email: technical@theatreroyalmargate.com

WINTER GARDENS

Fort Crescent, Margate, Kent CT9 1HX
Tel: 01843 296 111 BO: 01843 292 795
Email: boxoffice@yourleisure.uk.com
Web: www.margatewintergardens.co.uk
ADMINISTRATION:
Props: Your Leisure Ltd
General Manager: Steve J Davis
Contact: 01843 868302 or steve.davies@yourleisure.uk.com
Technical Manager: Mike Baines
Contact: mike.baines@yourleisure.uk.com
Policy: Summer Shows, Conferences, Dances, Banquets, Pop Concerts, Variety Shows, Cabaret style shows, Fashion Shows, Speech days, Jobs Fairs, Exhibitions.
Perfs: Vary.
Main Hall: 1420 (1900 standing)
Queens Hall: 100 - 350
TECHNICAL:
MAIN HALL:
STAGE: Proscenium, Flat; opening 10.2m; Ht. of Pros. 5.6m; Depth of S/Line 1.2m; Ht. to Grid 7.625m; depth 7.625m.
LIGHTING: Strand lightboard. 60 x faders & 24 x submaster; 1 x spotbar; 3 x 500 w lighting bars with dimmable colours. F.O.H; 6 x cantatas; 24 x quartets; 6 x T64.
SOUND: 1 x soundcraft K1 24/2/4 mixer; 1 x Yamaha Q2031 31 Band Stereo Equalizer; 1 x Yamaha SPX90 effects machine; 1 x twin cassette deck; various amplifiers; various F.O.H. speakers; Shure, SM58, AKG D190E Microphones, 1 x denon CD player; 1 x mini disc player. Communications system from prompt corner to follow spot. Sound and lights controlled from prompt corner.
DRESSING ROOMS: 6 x dressing rooms; 4 x showers; 5 x WC.

QUEEN'S HALL:
STAGE: Proscenium, Flat; Pros. opening 8.53m; Ht. of Pros. 3.35m; Depth of S/Line 2.13m; Ht. of Grid 3.66m; Prompt Corner P.S. Orchestra Pit, accom. 5. Stage extension 1.22m permanent Run out 2.44m.
LIGHTING: Switchboard: Strand MX 24, 18 - X650 prelude, 6 x 1200W cantanas

with colour changers. 1 x 1K C.I.D. follow spot, stage 2 x battens - codas.
SOUND: 1 x 16-4-2 Soundcraft 200B, 4 x Martin wall speakers 6 x JBL 1 speakers, amps - Mxf's & 200s, monitors - available, radio mics - available.
DRESSING ROOMS: 6; Accom. 12.
OTHER: Access for wheelchairs and deliveries. Parking on promenade at rear of building.

Market Drayton, Shropshire

FESTIVAL DRAYTON CENTRE

Frogmore Road, Market Drayton, Shropshire TF9 3AX
Tel: 01630 654444 BO: 01630 654444
Fax: 01630 655967
Email: info@festivaldraytoncentre.com
Web Site: www.festivaldraytoncentre.com
Chairman: Geoff Vernon
Centre Manager: Glynn Jackson
Sound & Lighting: Peter Morris
Chief Projectionist: Graham Saul
Policy: Mutipurpose facility used for Live events, Cinema, Leisure Activities, Conferences and Exhibitions.
Capacity: 200 raked-seating.
Stage: Proscenium arch 6.5m wide x 5m high, stage depth 7m to curtain, 8m overall. Portable staging available in unit sizes 2.4m x 1.2m.
Lighting: Fat Frog, 78 channels dimming.
Sound: 16 ch mixer, Speakers 2 x FOH.
Power 32A Single Phase + 32A Three Phase Stage Left.

Marlow, Buckinghamshire

SHELLEY THEATRE

Court Garden Leisure Complex, Pound Lane, Marlow, Buckingshamshire SL7 2AE
Tel: 01628 405200 Fax: 01628 473277
Email: enquiries@pspleisure.org
Web Site: www.courtgardenleisurecomplex.org
ADMINISTRATION
Props: Places for People Leisure
Contact April Miller for bookings.
Cap: 250 seat flat floor hall, flat stage.
Stage lighting and sound facilities.
Dressing rooms, projection room, bar, restaurant and sporting facilities adjoining.
Suitable for Dancing, Theatre, Exhibitions, Conferences and social events.

Melksham, Wiltshire

THE ASSEMBLY HALL

Market Place, Melksham, Wiltshire SN12 6ES
Tel/Fax: 01225 709 887
Email: assemblyhall@melkshamtown.co.uk
Web: www.melkshamassemblyhall.com
Capacity: 320 dining and dancing, 400 concert style seating.
Bar and lounge.
Proscenium Arch stage. Lighting, PA, Loop sysytem.
3 dressing rooms.

Melton Mowbray, Leicestershire

Pop. 157,200. London 247 miles.
Newspapers: Northern Echo (dly); Evening Gazette (ntly). STD code 01642

MELTON THEATRE

Asfordby Road, Melton Mowbray, Leicestershire LE13 0HJ
BO: 01664 851 111 Fax: 01664 855 455
Email: boxoffice@brooksbymelton.ac.uk
Web Site: www.meltontheatre.co.uk
ADMINISTRATION:
Contact: W Crawford, M Harris
Technical: Andrew Edwards
Policy: Touring, Pantomime, Concerts, Films, Amateur shows.
Small foyer venue - stand-up comedy, acoustic
Seats Theatre: 340-480 raked with room for 3 wheelchairs. Bars and refectory.
Seats Foyer Venue: 100 with bar.
STAGE: Proscenium opening 10.6m, Depth of stage 11.75m, height of proscenium 4.5m, height of grid 11.8m, max flying height 11m.
SOUND:
2 x RCF ART500 500w powered speakers proscenium arch house left and right, 1 x RCF 800w active bass bin proscenium arch house left and right, 3 x RCF ART300 300w powered speakers proscenium arch centre. 4 x (12 + 4) stage boxes situated SL and SR. Citronic Z-5DM Zone mixer. Outboard; 1 x Digitech DSP16 signal processor (reverbs, delays), 2 x Alesis 2 channel, 48 band graphic equaliser, 1 x Behringer DSP1400p Ultramiser (stereo sound maximiser).
Playback; 2 x Denon DCD695 CD player, 1 x Sony JE330 Minidisc player/recorder, 1 x Tascam DRW585 dual cassette deck.
LIGHTING:
Dimmers; 72 x 2.4kW across 3 Strand Tempus racks hardwired to 100A 3 phase supply. 28 to FOH lighting positions. Control; Strand Series 300 control desk. Zero88 in desk. Lanterns; Fresnel/Pebble Convex:- 12 x Selecon Compact 1.2kW with Barn Doors, 8 x Strand Harmony 1kW with Barn Doors, 8 x Strand Pattern 743 1kW with barn Doors, 2 x Furse MFR 1 kW with Barn Doors, 2 x Strand Harmony PC. Profile Lanterns:- 6 x CCT Silhouette 1.2kW, 4 x Strand Cantata 1kW, 4 x Strand Pattern 264, 4 x Strand Harmony 1kW, 6 x Furse SPR 500w. Floods:- 4 x Thomas Asymmetrical 1kW, 3 x Furse LFL Asymmetrical 1kW, 3 x Strand pattern 60 300w. Parcans:- 26 x Par 64 various lamps. Followspot:- Strand pattern 793 2kW colour changer (dediacted electronic dimmer). Additional Equipment (at extra cost):- 12 x silver Par64 with CP62 lamp, 12 x Silver Par 64 with CP88 500w lamp, 6 x Black Par56 with P56M lamp, 2 x Zero 88 Betapack6ch. Dimmer with DMX/analogue control, 4 x Robe Spot250 XT moving heads witha selection of gobos, 1 x LeMaitre Neutron STAR hazer.
POWER:
1 x single phase CEE 32A, 3 x CEE 63A single phase (one of each), 1 x CEE 63A three phase.

Middlesbrough, Cleveland

MIDDLESBROUGH THEATRE

The Avenue, Linthorpe, Middlesbrough, Cleveland TS5 6SA
Admin: 01642 824490 BO: 01642 815 181
Email: david_lindsey@middlesbrough.gov.uk
Web: www.middlesbroughtheatre.co.uk
ADMINISTRATION:
Props: Middlesbrough Borough Council
Theatre Manager: David Lindsey
Stage Manager: Andrew Charlesworth
Policy: All types of events especially drama, dance, classical and folk music, jazz, poetry. Full/split weeks, single nights. Will premiere Childrens, producing house.
Perfs: Usually 7.30
Seats: 484. Licensed Bar and Coffee Bar above Foyer.
TECHNICAL:
Stage: Proscenium width - 25'9" (7.86m); Proscenium height - 14'0" (4.28m); Depth of stage - 39'0" (11.12m); Grid height - 25'5" (6.75m); Wing width - 14'5" (4.4m); Orchestra Pit - 25'9" x 8'8" accommodating approx. 20; Prompt Desk - Stage Left; Flying system - 23 x 3 fall hemp sets; Fly floor Stage Left; All fly bars 40'0" width x 1 7/8" O.D; SWL 150kg each, evenly distributed. Stage floor - Black hardboard, no rake. Loading doors - Stage Right at 1'9" above road level (Ramp available), Opening 14'6" x 8'6". Ample turning room for articulated vehicles.
Backstage Accommodation: Green Room, 5 Dressing Rooms.
Lighting and Sound control rooms, and follow spot positions, are located behind the rear circle.

A rear-stalls position (not central) is available, with coms and DMX lines only, no sound tie lines. Multicore run to this position is 25 metres. Please advise when booking if this position is required so those seats can be taken off sale.
Fobs are available for access between backstage and FOH and the lighting and sound control rooms. These must be returned at the end of each performance, or the cost of replacements will be recharged to the visiting company.
The fire safety curtain is fully automatic, linked to the detection and alarm system. Stage and auditorium detection can be isolated during performances to allow for use of smoke, haze and pyros.
Lighting: Control - ETC Ion with 2 x 20 Fader Wing and Net3 Radio Focus Remote, controlling 96 ways of Strand LD90 dimming, on one DMX universe. Circuit distribution: LX Bar 1 - 12 Circuits - Yellow Phase; LX Bar 2 - 12 Circuits - Yellow Phase; LX Bar 3 - 12 Circuits - Yellow Phase; LX Bar 4 - 12 Circuits - Yellow Phase; LX Bar 5 - 12 Circuits - Blue Phase; LX Bar 6 - 12 Circuits - Blue Phase; Advance Bar - 10 Circuits - Red Phase; FOH Bar - 14 Circuits - Red Phase; FOH Perches - 10 Circuits - Red Phase; Dips - 24 Circuits (12 S/L, 12 S/R) - Yellow Phase; Booms - 6 Circuits (3 S/L, 3 S/R) - Blue Phase; Orchestra Pit - 1 Circuit - Red Phase; Circle Front Bar - 3 Circuits - Red Phase. Lanterns normally available: 36 x Stand Patt743 1Kw; 6 x Strand Patt243 1Kw; 36 x Thomas Parcan 1Kw (CP62 only); 4 x Strand Cantata 18/32 1.2Kw; 12 x Strand Coda Floods 1Kw; 6 x Short-Nose Floor can (CP62 only); 14 x ETC Source Four 15/30 Zoom (On FOH Bar only); 12 x Selecon Acclaim Axial 18/34 Zoom; 8 x Selecon Acclaim Axial 22/44 Zoom (Please note Selecon profiles take a size M gobo only).
Sound: Control - Allen & Heath GL2400 32ch, Soundcraft Spirit LX7 24ch. FOH speakers - 2 x Turbosound TQ 310 DP 700W Powered Speakers; 2 x Turbosound TQ 308 DP 500W Powered Speakers; 2 x Turbosound TQ 425 DP 1600W Powered Subs; 2 x Nexo PS 10 as circle fill only. Stage monitors - 4 x Martin Audio LE400; 2 x HK Audio Pro12M 800w. Amps - 2 x Channels Phonic MCX2500 (Nexo PS10's only); 4 x Channels Crown Xli2500; 2 x Channels Crown XLS602. Playback - 2 x Tascam 301 Mk II Mini Disc Player; 2 x Denon DNC615 CD player. Outboard - 1 x Yamaha SPX 900; 1 x Sabine FBX 901 Feedback Exterminator; 2 x Behringer Multicom Pro XL 4 Way. Compressors - 2 x Behringer Ultragraph Pro 31 band EQ; 2 x Rane ME30B 30 band EQ (FOH). Microphones normally available: 6 x Sennheiser E845; 4 x Shure SM 58; 2 x Shure SM 57; 3 x Audio Technica Pro 27 HE; 1 x Shure PG58; 2 x Crown PCC 160 Boundary; 1 x JTS NX2; 1 x JTS NX7; 2 x Rode NT5; 1 x Shure PGDMK4 drum kit set. No Radio Microphones.
Mic inputs: 8 each side, rear of proscenium wall and 10 in orchestra pit. Various speaker tie lines onstage and in the auditorium. Line level inputs on stage and orchestra pit.
Stage Power: Stage right - 14 x 13A Sockets; Stage left - 16 x 13A Sockets; Prompt Corner: 3 x 32A Single Phase, 1 x 63A Three Phase, 1 x 125A Three Phase. The supplies at prompt corner are RCD protected and are set to trip at 300mA. Please note that the RCD WILL NOT be by-passed under any circumstances.
Communications: Show relay to all dressing rooms, Green Room, lighting and sound control rooms. Techpro beltpacks and headsets between stage desk, stage right, sound control room, lighting control room, fly floor, follow spots and rear of stalls. Telephone between stage desk, box office, company office, manager's office, sound control room, lighting control room, green room and bar.
Stock scenery and equipment: 5 no. 40' x 6' Black wool serge borders for top masking; 8 no. 16' x 8' Black wool serge flats for side masking. Hard masking only, no legs available; 2 pairs 18'6" drop x 20' wide Black wool serge Tabs; Various adjustable braces and stage weights; Various straight and boom mic stands; 20 no. RAT lit music stands; 20 no. Black orchestra chairs.
Additional equipment available to hire: Bechstein Grand piano; Broadwood Upright piano; 2 x LDR Canto 1200MSR Follow Spots; 20' x 40' Fibre optic Star Cloth; Various sizes of Steeldeck and legs; Hazer; Smoke machine; Mirror Ball; Projector & Screen; UV cannons.

TOWN HALL

Albert Road Middlesbrough, TS1 2QQ
Tel: 01642 729 652 BO: 01642 729 729
Fax: 01642 221 866
Email: patfysh@middlesbrough.gov.uk
Web Site: www.middlesbrough.gov.uk
Main County Hall:
Props: Middlesbrough Council
Business and Development Office: Rob Guest
Manager: Pat Fysh
Capacity: 1,198 seated; 1,352 standing.
All types of events, especially classical and popular music, rock, jazz, comedy, variety, craft fairs and exhibitions, conferences.
Crypt:
Capacity: 300 seated; 600 standing
All types of events including popular music, rock, jazz, comedy, dances, craft fairs and exhibitions.

Middlewich, Cheshire

CIVIC HALL

Civic Hall, Lenin Street, Middlewich, Cheshire CW10 9AT
Tel: 01606 837 175 Council: 01606 833 434
Email: robert.nightingale@congleton.gov.uk
Props: congleton Borough Council
Cap: 300 Concert, 200 Banquet, 180 Dance
For bookings contact: Dave McFarlane
Tel: 01270 763261 Fax: 01270 768460
Access for disabled persons.
Contact Bookings Officer: Robert Nightingale

Milford Haven, Pembrokeshire

Pop. 13,960. London 250 miles. STD code 01646

THE TORCH THEATRE

St Peter's Road, Milford Haven, Pembrokeshire SA73 2BU Wales
Mgt: 01646 694 192 BO: 01646 695 267
Email: info@torchtheatre.co.uk
Web Site: www.torchtheatre.co.uk
ADMINISTRATION:
Artistic Director: Peter Doran
Finance Director: Tim Cockburn
Technical Manager: Andrew Sturley
Policy: Mixed programme theatre with in house repertory company 3/4 times a year. Also visiting companies, opera, dance, music, children's shows, choirs, variety, films, exhibitions.
Perfs: Vary. Mon -Sun 7.30 pm.
Seats: 295. Bar
Studio: Seats 100
Cinema
Cap: 295
The Torch Theatre, a not-for-profit, registered charity, was founded in 1977 and is one of only three building-based producing theatres in the whole of Wales. The Theatre has provided a consistent annual programme of Drama and Performing Arts for the community of, and visitors to, Pembrokeshire. The Torch also offers the Joanna Field Art Gallery and provides cinema facilities for Milford Haven and Pembrokeshire.
TECHNICAL:
Stage: Proscenium, Flat; Pros. Opening 10m; Ht. 4.85m; Depth of S/Line 9m; Ht. of Grid 14m; 9 C/W lines: 10 hemp lines; Flying Ht. 13.5m; Length Flying Bars 13m; 1 L/X Winches; W/Widths 3-4m; apron Thrust/Pit 1.9m.
Lighting: Strand 430 80 circuits, 28 T-spots, 13 ADB's 1kw, 25 cantata 11/26 (2000w), 4 strand Prelude F (650w), 6 Cantata Fresnels, 10 Coda 1's/10 Mint Iris, 10 Cantata PC (1200w), 12 743's, 4

243's, 10 Par Cans. 1 35mm Projectors with Tower System. 1 16mm projector.
Sound: Soundcraft Spirit, Ultra Mic 24-4-2 Mixer,1 TASCAM 8 Track, 2 Sony Mini Disk Player, 2 SM57 Microphones, 4 SM58 MIcrophones, Revox B77, 1 SPX990, 1 Denon Cassette Player, 1 Denon CD Player. All stage boxes 3 pin XLR Mic Line Speakers all Speakon plugs.
Dressing Rooms: 3 to accommodate 16; 3 Showers; Orchestra Pit 12-15. Films: The theatre is fully equipped for all types of 35mm presentations.
Membership: TMA, WAPA, PAG, Creu Cymru.

Millport, Ayrshire

DA HALL
Garrison Grounds Millport, Ayrshire KA28 0DG
Tel: 0845 230 1325
Email: communityfacilities@north-ayrshire.gov.uk
Web Site: www.north-ayrshire.gov.uk
ADMINISTRATION:
Props: North Ayrshire Council
Cap: 100

MILLPORT TOWN HALL
Clifton Street, Millport, Ayrshire KA28 0AZ
Tel: 0845 230 1325
Email: communityfacilities@north-ayrshire.gov.uk
Web Site: www.north-ayrshire.gov.uk
ADMINISTRATION:
Props: North Ayrshire Council
Cap: 100

Milngavie, Dunbartonshire

TOWN HALL
71 Station Road, Milngavie, Glasgow G62 8BZ
Tel: 0141 956 3132 Bkg: 0141 574 5730
Bkg Fax: 0141 574 5555
Email: halls@eastdunbarton.gov.uk
Web Site: www.eastdunbarton.gov.uk
ADMINISTRATION:
Props: East Dunbartonshire Council
Cap: Main Hall 350 seated; 200 for an event. Lesser Hall 60
Contact: Elaine Kennedy, Gail Siddons, Catherine Rae

Milton Keynes, Buckinghamshire

Pop. 185,000. London 55 miles.
Newspapers: Milton Keynes Herald; Milton Keynes Citizen; Chronicle and Echo. STD code 01908

MILTON KEYNES THEATRE
500 Marlborough Gate, Central Milton Keynes, Milton Keynes, Buckinghamshire MK9 3NZ
BO Tel: 0844 871 7652 SD: 01908 547500 SD Fax: 01908 547 647 Tech: 01908 547611
Email: jaidebirch@theambassadors.com
Web: www.atgtickets.com/miltonkeynes
ADMINISTRATION:
Proprietors: Ambassadors Theatre Group (Venues) Ltd
Lessees: Ambassador Theatre Group Ltd
General Manager: Emma Sullivan
Technical Manager: Jason Wright
Administrator: Jaide Birch
Capactity: 2-Tier Format: 1,080 3-Tier Format: 1,376
TECHNICAL:
STAGE: Proscenium Arch: Grid height 23000mm; Prosc. width variable 11000 - 14000mm; width of Stage: CL to SL 12450mm; width of Stage CL to SR 18800mm; distance between Fly Galleries 22460mm; rear of Safety Curtain to Back Wall 15000mm. 73 single purchase counterweight bars SWL 500kg length 15600mm (with 1 .5m extensions each end); 2 motorised bars; 2 up and down stage motorised bars; 2 counterweight & 2 hemp up and down stage bars; 3 motorised bars above Forestage. 3 independent Orchestra Pit lifts can accommodate up to 100 players or form 7000mm Forestage. Get-in direct onto Stage SR; 3 trailers can unload simultaneously at Dock doors.
LIGHTING: Switchboard: Strand 520i. 336-2.5kw, 62-5kw, 6-10kw, 20 non-dims. F.O.H.: 40-2kw profiles, 2 Robert Juliat Aramis 2.5kw HMI Followspots; Lantern Stock: 20-1.2kw profiles, 30-1.2kw fresnels, 6-2kw fresnels, 6-2kw p.c., 38 par cans, 8-4 square cyc floods, 8-4 in line groundrows.
SOUND: Soundcraft K2 40:8:2; Community SLS920s Cluster & Prosc. driven & EQ'd by Peavey Media Matrix processor; 175 mic sockets; 60 audio tie lines; 6 foldback speakers. S.M. desk movable SL, SR, Stalls & Circle. Twin ring intercom. Infra-red hard of hearing & audio description. Audio & video to all areas.
ADDITIONAL: Accommodation: 11 Dressing Rooms on 2 levels, all with showers (capacity 97); 3 Band Rooms (capacity 70); Visiting Manager & Visiting Staff offices; Wardrobe & Laundry; lifts to all floors.

THE NATIONAL BOWL
Watling Street, Milton Keynes, Buckinghamshire
Tel: 01173 292 400
Email: chris.beard@hca.gsi.gov.uk
Web Site: www.hca.gsi.gov.uk
ADMINISTRATION:
Contact: Helen Smith at English Partnerships on Tel no. listed.
Policy: Venue for major concerts.
Car parking for 12,000 cars.
1000 KVA power available.
Booking on a daily or weekly basis.
Capacity: 65,000.
Gaming International Ltd: 0117 902 9255

STANTONBURY THEATRE
Purbeck, Stantonbury, Milton Keynes, Buckinghamshire MK14 6BN
Admin: 01908 324 422 Fax: 01908 324 401 BO: 01908 324 466
Email: theatre@stantonbury.org.uk
Web Site: www.stantonburytheatre.co.uk
ADMINISTRATION:
Props: Stantonbury Arts and Leisure
Development Manager: Hilary Rhodes
Technical Manager: James Tearle
Professional theatre, dance, opera, classical and other music, community theatre, pantomime, folk/popular concerts, youth theatre, brass bands, children's theatre, exhibitions/conferences.
Perfs. To suit each performance.
Seats 198 - 250. Bar facilities.
TECHNICAL:
Stage: Round, Thrust or Proscenium, Flat (Audience Raked); Pros. opening 15.35m max; Ht of Pros Tab Track 5.35m. Depth of S/Line 79.75m - 10.97m. W/Widths P.S. 2.44m; Prompt Cnr. Mobile.
Lighting: ETC Express 125 with 72 ways of dimming, 22 spots, 34 fresnels, 1CCT follow spot (from rear), 6 x 3 way coda floods, 12 CP62 Parcans.
Sound: 16:4:2 Yamaha MX400 mixer operated from rear CD/Tape/Minidisk/microphones.
Switchboard control room back of auditorium. White cyc and grand piano.
Dressing rooms 4, accom 20, orchestra pit 18 max.

THE STABLES
The Stables Theatre Ltd
The Laine Dankworth Centre, Stockwell Lane, Wavendon, Milton Keynes, Buckinghamshire MK17 8LU
Mgmt: 01908 280 814 BO: 01908 280 800 Fax: 01908 280 825
Email: stables@stables.org
Web Site: www.stables.org
ADMINISTRATION:
Chief Executive: Monica Ferguson
Technical: Martin Chammings
Capacity: 398
TECHNICAL:
Get In - under cover loading bay for one truck. Bay dimensions; width 2.70m, height 3.90m, step-in 0.75m.
Stage Area - main stage; width 8.50m, length 5.50m, height 5.00m. Full front thrust; width 6.00m, length 5.40m.
Seating - 400 seated (with full front thrust); 450 standing (with full front thrust).
Control Platform - located at the third floor with access to lighting bridges.
Lighting control. Stage manager's desk and follow-spots also located here if required. Sound position in auditorium.

Backstage Accommodation - dressing rooms; stage room 4 x four person; dressing rooms can be extended to make 2 large rooms with a shower in each. Rehearsal room; backstage green-room at stage level.
Masking - there are no House Curtains or legs. There are; 4 - borders 10m(w) x 2m(d), 4 - flat panels 2m(w) x 5m(d), 1 - sound wall 8m(w) x 5m(d) which can be moved from front to back of stage.
Temporary electrical supplies - 63A TPN BS 4343 sockets & 63A SPN BS 4343 socket located stage left and in recording studio and stage right. Clean earth supplies - 13A SPN BS 4343 technical earth sockets. Located stage left and right and on catwalks.
Lighting: Control - lighting located on the control platform, central at third floor. Console; Strand LBX with Genius software, 125 channel. Displays; VDU 14" for console. Dimmers - ADB 36 x 3kw, 6 x 5kw. DMX distribution system and patch. Ethernet distribution system and patch. Lantern stock - Profiles; 10 - ADB DS105 15 to 59 degrees @ 1kw. 10 - Treatro Tratto 12 19 - 40 degrees @ 1kw. 9 - Patt 23 17 degrees @ 500w. Fresnels; 11 - ADB F101 13 - 59 degrees @ 1kw. 9 - Preludes 9 - 53 degrees @ 650w. 9 - Patt 123 8 - 36 degrees @ 500w. Parcans; 19 - Par 63 CP/62 wide @ 1kw.
Sound & Communications: Audio Tie Line Infrastructure - audio tie lines terminating on control platform patch. 32 way audio tie line microphone splitter terminated on a multi-pin socket located stage left, stage right and the recording studio for recording or monitor desk (monitors can be mixed from the sound position or on stage.
Loudspeaker Line Infrastructure - loudspeaker lines on NL4 sockets terminated on audio rack loudspeaker patch.
Sound Mixing Console - Midas Heritage 1000 32 inputs/10 aux/10 group/8 matrix out. Console is located centrally at rear of the auditorium. Toured console's may also be located here, subject to management agreement.
Monitor Mixing Console - Allen & Heath GL4000 32 inputs/8 aux/8 gropus, console is located stage left. toured monitor console's may also be located here, subject to management agreement.
Loudspeaker System - 8 - Martin W8C. 6 - Martin W2. 4 - Martin W8S. They have been set-up as specified Martin Audio. 8 - Martin LE400C (foldback).
Amplifiers - QSC PLX 3402, 3002, 2402.
Outboard Equipment - 1 - BSS FCS960 dual band equaliser (FOH). 4 - BSS FCS960 dual band equaliser (foldback). 1 - Lexicon PCM91 digital reverberator. 1 - Yamaha SPX990 multi effects. 1 - BSS DPR504 quad noise gate. 1 - BSS DPR404 quad compressor/de-esser. 1 - Tascam MD501 minidisc player/recorder. 1 - Tascam CD450 pro compact disc player. 1 - Tascam 122 MkIII cassette recorder. All housed in a rolling rack.
Microphones - 6 - Shure SM58. 6 - Shure Beta SM57A. 4 - Shure SM98A. 4 - Calrec CM1050. 1 - Beyer M88 TG hypercardioid. 10 - BSS ARR-133 di boxes. Stands, cables, connectors etc.
Radio Microphones - 4 - Shure SM 58 Handheld UHF. 2 - Shure Body Pack UHF. 4 - Shure receivers.
Stage Manager's Desk: Mobile desk connects either stage left, sound position and/or on the control platform. Paging control and two-channel intercom master station.
Ring Intercom - clear-com 2 channel with outlets on sound boxes. 12 two-channel belt packs and headsets.
Video System - Video tie lines with central patching in the amp room. Colour camera with manual control lens mounted on control platform. Portable colour video monitor.
Intraref Listening System - Two channel Sennheiser infrared listening system suitable for use by hearing-impaired persons and for providing an audio descriptive commentary or language translation.
Audio Show Relay System - Auditorium microphones patchable via theatre tie line infrastructure to show relay mixer.

Moffat, Dumfries & Galloway

TOWN HALL

High Street, Moffat, Dumfries & Galloway DG10 9HF Scotland
Tel: 01683 220536 Fax: 01683 221489
Email: maggie.thorpe@dumgal.gov.uk
Web Site: www.dumgal.gov.uk
ADMINISTRATION:
Props: Dumfries & Galloway Council
Cap: Main Hall 140 close seated, 110 table seated and 160 dancing. Reception Room 48, 20 table and 50 dancing.
For bookings Tel: 01683 220536 Fax: 01683 221489

Mold, Flintshire

Pop. 8,180. London 191 miles. STD code 01352

CLWYD THEATR CYMRU

Rake's Lane Mold, Clwyd CH7 1YA
Admin Tel: 01352 756 331 Box Office Tel: 0845 330 3565 Admin Fax: 01352 701558 Box Office Fax: 01352 701529
Email: william.mcmillan@clywd-theatr-cymru.co.uk
Web Site: www.clwyd-theatr-cymru.co.uk
General Manager: Julia Grime
Assistant to General Manager: William McMillan
Associate Director: Plays & Touring William James
Casting Manager: Leigh-Ann Regan
Box Office Manager: Marie Thorpe
Marketing Officer: Morwenna Honan
Technical Stage Manager: Jayson Noble
Technical Manager: Pat Nelder
Capacity: 550-560 (Depending on sound/light desks)
Anthony Hopkins Theatre: Capacity 520-580
Emlyn Williams Theatre: Capacity 147-240

Monmouth, Monmouthshire

SAVOY THEATRE

Church Street Monmouth Monmouthshire NP25 3BU Wales
Tel: 01600 772467
Email: monmouthsavoy@hotmail.com
Web Site: www.monmouth-savoy.co.uk
ADMINISTRATION
Props: The Monmouth Savoy Trust Ltd
Director and General Manager: Christopher Ryde
Technical Manager: Paul Halpin
Cinema Manager: Mike Harrold
Capacity: 370
Policy: Commercial cinema and concert and live event venue. Available for hire as well as promotions.

Montrose, Angus

TOWN HALL

Melville Gardens, Montrose, Angus DD10 8HG Scotland
Tel: 01674 662666
Email: conmontsc@angus.gov.uk
Web Site: www.anguscouncil.gov.uk
ADMINISTRATION:
Props: Angus Council
Arts Officer: Patricia McGowan
Cap: 663 theatre style
Leisure Services, Angus Council, County Buildings,
Forfar DD8 3WF
Tel: 01307 461 460
Fax: 01307 462 590

Morecambe, Lancashire

THE PLATFORM

Station Buildings Central Promenade Morecambe Lancashire LA4 4DB
Tel: 01524 582 803 Fax: 01524 831 704
Email: jmills@lancaster.gov.uk
Web Site: www.lancaster.gov.uk/platform
ADMINISTRATION:
Props: Lancaster City Council
General Manager: Jason Mills
Marketing Manager: Emma Jones
Unique multipurpose venue for exhibitions, conferences, Community Arts, Jazz

and live music. Newly restored former Edwardian Railway Station. Capacity 350 seated, 1000 standing. Private & commercial hire.

Morpeth, Northumberland

RIVERSIDE LEISURE CENTRE
Newmarket, Morpeth, Northumberland
NE61 1PR
Tel: 01670 514665
Email: riverside@leisureconnection.co.uk
Web Site: www.leisureconnection.co.uk
ADMINISTRATION:
Props: Leisure Connections
Cap: 1,000 Seated, 500 tables
Duty Managers John Peverley

ST JAMES COMMUNITY CENTRE
Wellway, Morpeth, Northumberland NE61 1BN
Tel: 01670 514314
Email: gillian.turner@morpeth-tc.gov.uk
Web Site: www.morpeth-tc.gov.uk
ADMINISTRATION:
Props: Morpeth Town Council
Cap: 100
For bookings contact Tel:01670 514314

STOREY PARK COMMUNITY CENTRE
St Mary's Field Morpeth NE61 2QE
Tel: 01670 514314
Email: dee.cota@morpeth-tc.gov.uk
Web Site: www.morpeth-tc.gov.uk
Props: Morpeth Town Council
Capacity: 100

TOWN HALL
Market Place, Morpeth, Northumberland
NE61 1LZ
Tel: 01670 514314
Email: dee.cota@morpeth-tc.gov.uk
Web Site: www.morpeth-tc.gov.uk
ADMINISTRATION:
Props: Morpeth Town Council
Cap: Ballroom 100 seats, Corn Exchange 100
For bookings please contact: Morpeth Town Council, Market Place, Morpeth NE61 1LZ
Tel: 01670 514314

Motherwell, Lanarkshire

Pop. 149,000. London 379 miles.
Newspapers: Motherwell Times; Wishaw Press. STD code 01698

MOTHERWELL CONCERT HALL
Civic Centre, Motherwell, Lanarkshire
ML1 1AB Scotland
Admin/BO: 01698 274545 Fax: 01698 302992
Email: motherwellconcerthall@culturenl.co.uk
Web Site: www.northlanarkshire.gov.uk/entertainment
ADMINISTRATION:
Prop: Culture NL Ltd
Arts and Venues Manager: Jillian Ferrie
Theatre Manager: Craig Smart
Technical Manager: Stephen Ellis
Cap: 1,008 Seated, Flat; 883 Seated, Tiered; 1,600 Standing.
TECHNICAL:
Stage: Proscenium. Pros. opening 15.09m; Ht. of Pros. 4.95m; Depth of S/Line 7.92m; Ht. of Grid 5.99m; 20 lines; W/Widths P.S. 2.90m, O.P. 2.90m; Prompt Cnr. P.S.
Lighting: - Strand Gemini 2.71 2kw circuits - full range of lanterns, smoke, strobe and dry ice.
Sound Equip: 16 channel, mixing desk - full range of microphones including radio mics.
Dressing rooms - 8 Theatre/concert hall)

MOTHERWELL THEATRE
Civic Centre, Motherwell, Lanarkshire
ML1 1TW
Admin/BO: 01698 274545 Fax: 01698 302992
Email: motherwellconcerthall@culturenl.co.uk
Web Site: www.northlanarkshire.gov.uk/entertainment
ADMINISTRATION:
Theatre Manager: Craig Smart
Technical Manager: Stephen Ellis
Seats: 395
TECHNICAL:
Lighting:strand Gemini 96 2Kw circuits - fulll range of lanterns. Smoke, strobe and dry ice.
Sound Equipment: Channel Soundcraft, Venue II - full range of microphones including radio mics.
Dressing rooms: Theatre/Concert Hall - 8.

Mull, Argyll

COMAR
Druimfin Tobermory Isle of Mull Argyll
PA75 6QB Scotland
BO: 01688 302 211 Admin: 01688 302 673
Email: info@comar.co.uk
Web Site: www.comar.co.uk
ADMINISTRATION:
Artistic Director: Alasdair McCrone
Chairman: Norman Quirk
Finance Manager: Lesley Hastie
Policy: Repertory and Touring
Perfs: April-Sept, various dates, 8.00pm; Matinees various.
Seats: 100

TECHNICAL:
Stage: Removeable Proscenium Stage, Flat; Pros. Opening 3.05m; Ht. of Pros. 2.74m; Depth of S/Line 1.83m; W/Widths P.S. 0.30m, Hearing Loop Installed.
Audio Equipment: 1 Nad Stereo Amplifier Model No. 3020E, 1 Alesis Stereo Amplifier Matica 900, 1 Yamaha Mixer MX200, 1 Maplin Mixer MQC 6100, 2 Peavey Loudspeakers Eurosys-3, 4 Canford Loudspeakers, 2 Microphones TOA DM 605, 2 microphones Samson S12, 1 Hearing Loop Amplifier Talisman II, 4 Loud Speaker Leads, 6 Microphone leads, 1 Microphone Lead for Hearing Loop Amplifier, 2 Loudspeaker stands proel, 1 Microphone stand TOA, 2 Aiwa Cassette Recorders Model No. ADF 410, 1 Headset for Mixer, 2 Loop Listening Units, 4 assorted audio leads, 1 Large loudspeaker (above stage) 2 Mini-Disc Recorderer.
Dressing Rooms 1.
Membership: ITC and FST

Musselburgh, Mid Lothian

Pop. 17,249. London 369 miles.
Newspapers: Musselburgh News, East Lothian News, East Lothian Courier (fri).
STD code 0131

BRUNTON THEATRE
Ladywell Way, Musselburgh, East Lothian
EH21 6AF Scotland
Admin: 0131 665 9900 BO: 0131 665 2240 Fax: 0131 653 5264
Email: info@thebrunton.co.uk
Web Site: www.thebrunton.co.uk
ADMINISTRATION:
Props: Brunton Theatre Trust
General Manager: Lesley Smith
Programme Policy: Touring plays, opera, dance, concerts, variety, films, lectures etc.
Perfs: 7.30; matinees 10a.m., 2.30p.m.
Seats: Theatre 296. Venue 1 - Multi purpose max 500 seated. Exhibition area. Bar and Buffet facilities.
TECHNICAL:
Stage: Octagonal/Thrust, Flat; Pros. opening 10.2m; Ht. of Pros. 4.62m; Ht. of grid 5.63m; Depth of S/Line 6.40m; wrape around cyc.; induction loop.
Lighting: Switchboard: Rank Strand SP40/2 and R.S. Memory Board M24 + Duet; 40 ways; 12 harmony profiles, 10 263 (fresnel lens), 4 263 (P.C. lens), 4 23, 16 743, 8 Harmony fresnel, 4 min. fresnel, 2 min. profile, 2 coda 4 500w battens (4 comp. 2 circuit), 6 cada 1 500w flood, 5 stype battens (8 comp. 4 circuit), 4 500w floods.
Sound: Talkback: Bantam Headsets - various outlets. 16/4/2 Soundcraft Series 200B Mixing Console; 4 Tannoy Pumas F.O.H.; 2 Tannoy Pumas (moveable); 4 C Audio SR202 Amplifiers; 3 Yamaha Q2031 A Graphic Equalisers; 1 Revox

B77 Tape Recorder, 1 Kenwood KX54 Cassette Recorder; 36 mic lines (12 Pit, 6 USC, 6 PSL, 6 DSR, 6 Catwalk). Technics SLP 777 CD Player; Revox B77 Mark II; Tape Deck Kenwood KX 54; BBC collection sound effects on compact disc; 3 AKG 451 microphones.

Nantwich, Cheshire

CIVIC HALL

Market Street, Nantwich, Cheshire CW5 5DG
Tel: 01270 628 633
Email: nantwichcivic@cheshireeast.gov.uk
Web Site: www.cheshireeast.gov.uk
ADMINISTRATION:
Props: Nantwich Town Council
Cap: 640 standing; 500 seated
Contact: David Thomas

Neath & Port Talbot, West Glamorgan

GWYN HALL

6 Orchard Street, Neath, West Glamorgan SA11 1DU
Tel: 0300 3656677
Email: gwynhall@celticleisure.org
Web Site: www.gwynhall.com
ADMINISTRATION:
Capacity: 393 Tiered (Main Hall)
Studio and Cinema pod (Capacity 73)

THE PRINCESS ROYAL THEATRE

Civic Centre, Port Talbot, West Glamorgan SA13 1PJ Wales
BO Tel: 01639 763 214 Fax: 01639 763 134
Email: l.dennis@npt.gov.uk
Web Site: www.npt.gov.uk/theatres
ADMINISTRATION:
Props: Neath Port Talbot District Council
Cap: 798 (max)
Manager: Leigh Dennis
Multi-purpose hall, fully air conditioned. 11.5 x 6.5m stage, orchestra pit and comprehensive lighting and sound facilities.

Nelson, Lancashire

BARNOLDSWICK CIVIC HALL

Station Road, Barnoldswick, Lancashire BB18 5NA
Tel: 01282 818 253
Email: barnoldswicktowncouncil@gmail.com
ADMINISTRATION:
Props: Barnoldswick Town Council
Bookings Contact: Joanne Geldard
Cap: 100
Lounge: 50
2 rooms upstairs, Room 1: 15, Room 2 :25

THE ACE CENTRE

Cross Street, Nelson, Lancashire BB9 7NN
Tel: 01282 661080
Email: bookings@acecentre.co.uk
Web Site: www.acecentre.co.uk
Props: Pendle Leisure Trust
Operations Manager: Beverly McKiernan
Policy: Arts, Culture and Enterprise Centre
Capacity: 194

New Brighton, Merseyside

Pop. 70,000. London 199 miles.
Newspapers: Liverpool Echo (ntly); Daily Post (dly). STD code 0151

FLORAL PAVILION THEATRE AND CONFERENCE CENTRE

Marine Promenade New Brighton, Wirral, Merseyside CH45 2JS
Admin: 0151 606 2963 BO: 0151 666 0000
Email: davidmackenzie@wirral.gov.uk
Web Site: www.floralpavilion.com
ADMINISTRATION:
Props: Metropolitan Borough of Wirral
General Manager: David Mackenzie
Technical Manager: David Sherlock
Policy: Bands, One Night Concerts, Pantomime, Various Amateur Productions.
Perfs: Variable.
Seats: 810. Bar and Buffet.
TECHNICAL:
Stage: Proscenium stage flat; Pros. Opening 8.5m; Ht. of Pros. 3.66m; Depth of Stage 6.40m; Ht. of Grid 4.88m 14 lines; W/Widths P.S. 6.10m.
Lighting: Switchboard: Strand Sirrius 30 way. 10 T-spots, 4 Harmony, 8 Parcans, 2 Patt 123; 6 Harmony, 2 Iris, 4 Patt 137, 8 Fresnel, 8 Patt 123.
Sound: Allen & Heath 24 channel GL3 mixer, 2-4 monitor lines, Digital Effects unit, Tape Deck.
General: Dressing Rooms 7; Showers 3; Orchestra Pit (Capacity) 16.

New Galloway, Dumfries & Galloway

TOWN HALL

High Street, New Galloway, Dumfries & Galloway DG7 3RN Scotland
Tel: 01644 420 214
Web Site: www.dumgal.gov.uk
ADMINISTRATION:
Manager: Karen Brownlie
Seats: 153.

Newark, Nottinghamshire

Pop. 24,646. London 125 miles.
Newspapers: Newark Advertiser and Herald; Nottingham Evening Post (ntly); Lincolnshire Echo. STD code 01636

PALACE THEATRE

Appleton Gate, Newark, Nottinghamshire NG24 1JY
Admin: 01636 655 750 BO: 01636 655 755
Email: palace@nsdc.info
Web Site: www.palacenewark.com
ADMINISTRATION:
Props: Newark & Sherwood District Council.
Theatre Director: Carys Coulton-Jones
Technical Manager: Mark Noutch
Policy: Mixed programme of Professional and Amateur Productions: Drama, Ballet, Popular Music, Orchestral and Classical Music, Musicals, Concerts and Films.
Seats: 616. Licensed Bar, Coffee Bar, Room hire and rehearsal facilities.
TECHNICAL:
STAGE: Proscenium. Flat; Pros. opening 8.47m; Ht. of Pros. 6.68m; Depth of S/Line 9.34m; HT. of Grid 13m; 18 lines, C/W Hemp; Scenery Flying Ht. 12m; Flying Bars 10m; W/Widths P.S. 4.98m, O.P. 3.70m; Prompt Cnr. O.P. Stage painted satin black on 25mm marine ply. Dock Door at street level. Access to stage via shallow ramp. Orchestra pit accomm. 16 musicians.
LIGHTING: Avolites Sapphire 2000 lighting control situated in control room. Dimmers; 96 ways of ADB Euro Rack (3kw per channel) on 300amp 3 phase mains. 3 x Permanent winched bars on stage (SWL 500kg), 2 x Bridges FOH (situated at 45 degree's and 55 degree's to the setting line. 2 x Fixed proscenium booms from stage level to underside of fly floor (6.7m). 2 x FOH slip positions at 7m running from pros wall to rear bridge position. Follow Spot: 2 x CCT Sil 8's 2500w. Additional lanterns available.
SOUND: 1 x Soundcraft MH2; 32 + 4 stereo / 8 / 3 channel. 10 Auxiliaries + 8Vca (Front of House). 1 x Soundcraft

200SR; 16 channels 16 / 4 / 2 + 4 aux (Control Room). 1 x Soundcraft Folio, 6 channels + 1 Aux (Mobile). Speakers; 3 x Bose 802's; 1 pair Martin BX2 Bins; 2 Logic System 15" x 2" wedges; 2 Logic System 12" x 1" wedges; 2 JBL control 1. FOH Control; 4 Klark Technic square one 31 band stereo graphic; 2 Klark Technic square one 8 channel dynamics / compressor / gates; 2 spx 2000 effects processors; 1 Tascam MD - 350 Minidisk player; 1 Denon DN - C630 CD player. Various microphones available.
DRESSING ROOMS: 6; Accom. 60; Showers and toilets adjacent. Provides apron stage, when not in use 3m x 8m.
ADDITIONAL: 1 x Broadwood Upright piano (in pit), 1 x Allison Boudoir Grand piano (on stage).

Newbiggin-by-the-Sea, Northumberland

NEWBIGGIN SPORTS & COMMUNITY CENTRE

Woodhorn Road, Newbiggin-by-the-Sea Northumberland NE64 6HG
Tel: 01670 532348
Email: a.douglas@activenorthumberland.org.uk
Web: www.activenorthumberland.org.uk
ADMINISTRATION:
Props: Northumberland County Council
Cap: Sports Hall 475, Small Hall 182
For bookings contact Andrew Douglas

Newbury, Berkshire

London 56 miles. Newspapers: Newbury Weekly News (thurs); Newbury & Thateham Chronicle (fri). STD code 01635

THE CORN EXCHANGE

Market Place, Newbury, Berkshire RG14 5BD
Admin/Mktg: 01635 582 666 BO: 08455 218 218 Fax: 01635 582 223
Email: admin@cornexchangenew.co.uk
Web Site: www.cornexchangenew.com
ADMINISTRATION:
Director: Katy Griffiths
Technical Manager: Guy Dickens
Policy: Mixed programme of performing arts, visual art, flm and conferences.
Operates 7 days a week, all year.
Performances: Evenings, 7.45pm. Matinees, variable.
Seats: 380, 500 standing; retractable raked seating, variable stage/seating layouts. Also a meeting room; 63 seats, theatre style; variable layouts.
Public Cafe/Bar in main foyer, open all day. Private catering available.
Also manage New Greenham Arts Theatre, see venue listing for details.
TECHNICAL:
Stage: 40 x Steeldeck Units to a maximum of 100 sq.m. Stage at 1m height from auditorium floor. In normal Prosc. arch format performance area is 9.5m x 8.2m: wings SR 3.2m, SL 3m. No Rake. Grey Harlequin Studio floor available. Height to grid from stage level 9.2m, 13 winches, SWL 250kg, 10 Hemp sets, SWL 150kg, 1 set House Tabs on hand drawn track, 3 pr. black legs, 3 black borders, white cyc 11m x 7m, black travellers US.
Lighting: Strand 520 Board, 140 Dimmers. 50 Profile spots, 40 Fresnels, 30 Pars, 4 x4 cell cyc units, 2 x Pani 1202 Follow Spots.
Sound: Allen and Heath GL3300 24 channels (8 Groups, 8 Aux) Mixing desk, operated from control room or auditorium. 7 x JBL M 330 speakers with crest amplification. Denon CD Player, Sony Minidisc Player. Assorted mics and D.I's. Tecpro 2 channel intercom talkback system. Show relay and paging facilities to F.O.H & Backstage. Induction Loop System.
Dressing Room: 4, accommodates 20 people, showers in all dressing rooms, meeting room can double as band room.
Other: 35mm film projection system.
Steinway D Concert Grand Piano.
Membership: TMA

NEW GREENHAM ARTS

Managed by The Corn Exchange, Newbury
113 Lindenmuth Way, New Greenham Park, Newbury, Berkshire, RG19 6HN
Tel Admin: 01635 517 964 BO: 08455 218 218
Email: admin@cornexchangenew.co.uk
Web Site: www.cornexchangenew.com
ADMINISTRATION:
Director: Katy Griffiths
Technical Manager: Guy Dickens
Contact at: The Corn Exchange, Market Place, Newbury RG14 5BD
Policy: Mixed programme of performing arts, visual art and conferences.
Operates 7 days a week, all year.
Performances: Evenings, 8pm. Matinees, variable.
Seats: 100-150, 300 standing; variable stage/seating layouts. Also a meeting room; 12 seats.
Tandori restaurant open 7 days a week lunch and evening. Private catering available.
STAGE:
Venue: 16.5m long x 13.2m wide
Performance area: 6.4m deep x 8m wide (at opposite end to fixed stage). Height to grid: 3.3m. Flexible 'studio theatre' layout, with lighting grid over the space at approx 2.5m centres. Small permanent raised stage at one end, but performances can play at either end. Floating wooden floor, suitable for dance.
EQUIPMENT:
1 x White cyc (on wipe track), 1 x Black back cloth (on wipe track), 8 x Black (wool serge) Flats 8' x 4' (with french braces, can be used as masking legs), 10 x stage weights, 5 x 8mx1.6m rosco black/grey reversible dance floor, 1 x Yamaha upright piano, 8 x 8' x 1m wooden rostra (4@ 8", 4@16" heights) - used for seating, 4 x 8' x 5' Sisco rostra (2@ 16", 2 @ 24" height) with handrails, 2 x 8 tread A frame ladders.
LIGHTING:
Strand 1 BX control desk (with 24 subs - DMX protocol), 24 channels Zero 88 Betapack dimming (all 10A with 15A outlets), 6 x FTC Source 4 Junior wide Zoom (20 degree - 50 degree), 4 x Sil 30 1kw profile, 2 x Strand Patt 23, 6 x Strand quartet F(all with barndoors),6 x ADB 1kw Fresnel (only 3 x barndoors), 2 x Strand Patt 123, 6 x Thomas asymmetric 500w flood, 6 x 1.8m tripod Stands, 4 x gobo holders for Source 4's ("M" size gobos), N.B House lights use up one of the 24 dimming channels.
SOUND:
Soundcraft Folio 14/2 mixer, 1 x Tascam cd150CD player, 1 x Tascam md301 Mini Disc player, 2 x Crest CPX 1500 amps, 4 x JBl M330 (2 rigged from grid, 2 wall mounted), 1 x Sennheiser vocal mic, 1 x Boom mic stand.
Dressing rooms: 2 accomodates 8 people.

NORTHCROFT LEISURE CENTRE

Northcroft Lane, Newbury, Berkshire RG14 5BT
Tel: (01635) 31199
Email: northcroft@parkwood-leisure.co.uk
Web Site: www.leisurecentre.com
Large arena used for concerts, theatre productions, events and conferences.
Capacity: 1,000
Full power and stage available. please apply to venue for further details.

WATERMILL, WEST BERKSHIRE PLAYHOUSE

Watermill Theatre Bagnor, Newbury, Berkshire RG20 8AE
Admin: 01635 45834 BO: 01635 46044
Fax: 01635 523726 Restaurant: 01635 570 920
Email: admin@watermill.org.uk
Web Site: www.watermill.org.uk
ADMINISTRATION:
Artistic/Executive Director: Hedda Bebby
General Manager: Clare Lindsay
Production Manager: T. Doyle Laurence
Policy: February to January
Perfs: 7.30 Mon-Sat,Thur & Sat 2.30 matinees.
Seats: 216/230
Bar and Restaurant open until 11.30
TECHNICAL:
Stage: Proscenium/Thrust, Flat; Pros. opening 4.88m; Ht. of Pros. 4.88m; Depth of S/Line 3.96m; Ht. of Grid

8.53m; Scenery Flying Ht. 3.66m; Flying Bars 4.88m; W/Widths P.S. 1.83m, O.P. 1.83m; Prompt Cnr. back of auditorium.
Lighting: Switchboard: At the rear of Auditorium central; Lighting Board with optional FX panel. Spot Bars 8; Various Lanterns. Lighting control Rankstad 300 series. 60 Channel dimming. 250 Channel dimming.Various ETC Lanterns. Chroma Q Scrollers.
Sound Equip: Variable as needed. Mackie into 4 mixer. Amcron power Amps. Mayer upm speakers. Infra red hearing system.
Dressing Rooms 3; Accom. 10 persons. Actors live in theatre houses whilst rehearsing and performing.
Membership: TMA

Newcastle, County Down

NEWCASTLE CENTRE
Central Promenade, Newcastle, County Down BT33 0AA Northern Ireland
Tel: 028 4372 5034
Email: karen.halliday@downdc.gov.uk
Web Site: www.downdc.gov.uk
Props: Down District Council

Newcastle-upon-Tyne, Tyne and Wear

Pop. 217,220. London 274 miles. Newspapers: Evening Chronicle (ntly); The Journal (dly). STD code 0191

CITY HALL
Northumberland Road, Newcastle-upon-Tyne, Tyne and Wear NE1 8SF
Tel: 0191 277 8037 BO: 0191 277 8030
Email: cityhall@newcastle.gov.uk
Web Site: www.newcastlecityhall.org
Manager: Peter Brennan
Technical Manager: Derek Hawkins Tel: 0191 277 8038
Marketing Officer: Miranda Robertson Tel: 0191 211 6283
Seating/Capacity: 2,135

LIVE THEATRE
Broad Chare, Quayside Newcastle upon Tyne NE1 3DQ
Admin: 0191 261 2694 BO: 0191 232 1232
Email: tickets@live.org.uk, wendy@live.org.uk
Web Site: www.live.org.uk
ADMINISTRATION:
Chief Executive: Jim Beirne
Artistic Director: Max Roberts
Operations Director: Wendy Barnfather
Marketing & Press Officer: Emma Hall
Technical Manager: Dave Flynn
Capacity: Main Theatre, 160. Studio Theatre, 60. Additional Rehearsal Room available.
Resident company Live Theatre Co.
For more information on hiring the venue, contact Events & Venue Hire Administrator, Chris Foley, on 0191 229 2376.

METRO RADIO ARENA
Arena Way, Newcastle-upon-Tyne, Tyne and Wear NE4 7NA
Tel: 0191 260 5000 Booking Tel: 0844 4936666 Fax: 0844 4933313
Email: john.sutherland@smg-europe.com
Web Site: www.metroradioarena.co.uk
Executive Director: Paul Tappenden
Marketing Manager: Nichola McKenna
Capacity: 11,000

NORTHERN STAGE
Barras Bridge, Newcastle-upon-Tyne, Tyne and Wear NE1 7RH
Admin: 0191 232 3366 BO: 0191 230 5151 Fax: 0191 242 7257
Email: info@northernstage.co.uk
Web Site: www.northernstage.co.uk
ADMINISTRATION:
Chief Executive:
Artistic Director: Lorne Campbell
Director of Theatre Operations: Edmund Nickols
Administrative Director: Susan Coffer
Professional middle-scale venue with up to 15 weeks per year devoted to festivals, touring theatre and middle-scale dance. The theatre is now the home for core work for Northern Stage. Other activities include daytime conferences/seminars, foyer installations, exhibitions and participatory workshops.
TECHNICAL:
STAGE 1
Capacity: 447
Stage: Platform stage. Performing area 16.80m x 10.33m. No rake. Height of stage from auditorium floor 0.80m. Height from stage to 1st lighting bridge 6.50m. Height from stage to grid 12.17m. Setting line from front of stage 1.20m. Tormentors SL & SR (each up to 2m wide). Dock door onto stage left. Maximum flying height 11.70m. Length of flying bars 18.00m. 28 single purchase cross stage counterweight flying bars (max load 400kg per bar evenly spread). 4 single purchase up and down counterweight flying bars (2 SL and 2 SR) - (max load 400kg per bar evenly spread). Under certain circumstances forestage can be added. Dance floor available. Ground plan and technical specifications available on request.
Lighting: Avab Congo 1500ch Lighting Console with full tracking Backup. Comprehensive Ethernet system throughout the theatre. Profile, Fresnel, floods and beam lights. Full kit list available on request.
Sound: Yamaha DM1000 with 8 analogue in and 8 in + 8 out ADAT card and/or A&H Mixwizard 14:4:2 analogue desk. Show relay, paging system and assisted listening system is installed. Clearcom head-set comms system is available. Full kit list available on request.
Stage Management: Prompt corner - DSL, DSR or Rear Auditorium (Control Room) position. 24 Way Howard Eaton Softcue System-can be used from D/S/R, D/S/L, Auditorium or Control Room. Show relay/paging to dressing rooms.
Backstage: 5 dressing rooms. Wardrobe facilities available. Green Room with internet access. Company office with internet access. Wi-Fi available for a charge. Casuals available. Fully accessible to disabled performers and staff.

STAGE 2
Capacity: 160
Stage: End on, thrust and traverse available by negotiation. Max performing area approx 11.5m x 12m with no wings or crossover. No rake, wood floor. Dance floor available. Height of grid approx 7m. Get-in via dock loading bay backstage. Ground plan and technical specifications available on request.
Lighting: Avab Congo 1000ch Lighting Console + Backup. Source, Alto, Cantata and Iris. Full kit list available on request.
Sound: A&H desk 14:4:2 mixer with 10 mic channels, 2 x stereo line inputs and 2 x stereo unbalanced inputs. Show relay, paging system and assisted listening system is installed. Clearcom head-set comms system is available. Full kit list available on request.
Stage Management: Prompt from control room. 12 Way Howard Eaton Softcue System-can be run from the Control Room or Auditorium.
Backstage: 2 dressing rooms. Wardrobe facilities available. Green Room with internet access. Company office with internet access. Wi-Fi available for a charge. Casuals available. Fully accessible to disabled performers and staff.

STAGE 3
Capacity: 90
Stage: Max performing area 5m x 6m x 5m high approx. Raised stage area available on request. Ground plan and technical specifications available on request.
Lighting: Avab Congo 1000ch Lighting Console. Prelude and par lanterns. Full kit list available on request.
Sound: Spirit SX 14:2:2 mixer desk with 12 mic channels, 2 x stereo line inputs and 1 x stereo unbalanced input. Full kit list available on request.
Backstage: 1 dressing room. Wardrobe facilities available. Green Room with internet access. Company office with internet access. Wi-Fi available for a charge. Casuals available. Fully accessible to disabled performers and staff.

PEOPLE'S THEATRE

Stephenson Road, Newcastle-upon-Tyne, Tyne and Wear NE6 5QF
Tel: 0191 265 5020 op 2 (BO)
Email: peoplesvenuemanager@hotmail.com
Web Site: www.peoplestheatre.co.uk
ADMINISTRATION:
Props. & Lessees: Peoples Theatre Arts Group Ltd
Policy: Repertory, Arts Centre, Amateur.
Venue Manager: Steven Robertson
Technical Manager: Peter Harrison
Perfs: Evenings 7.30
Seats: Variable up to 514, Studio 90. Two Bars.
TECHNICAL:
STAGE: Proscenium, Flat; Pros. Opening 10.36m; Ht. of Pros. 4.27m - 6.10m; Depth of S/Line 10.36m + 4.60m thrust forestage; Ht. of Grid 10.67m; 10 lines, Hemp; Scenery Flying Ht. 4.87m; Flying Bars 9.14m; W/Widths P.S. 5.49m, P.O. 1.83m; Prompt Cnr. P.S.
LIGHTING: Switchboard: Strand GSX, 96 ways; 22 F.O.H. Spots, all 1k various Flats 3 circuits; Cyc. 4 circuits; Dips 8 each side; 2 Perches; 3 Spot Bars, 30 Spots Patts.243,223,123; Bridge 12 circuits T-spots (12) + Patt.93's.
SOUND: Uher 5 channel stereo mixer; Stereo amplifier 200w (Pioneer 8500); Mono R.A. Amplifier; 2 Akai 4000 DS Stereo tape decks; Pioneer PC112D turntable; Shure cartridge M75D; 4 Moving coil mics (AKG - 2 hand, 2 shotgun); 4 mic stands; 2 stage speakers; 2 F.O.H. speakers (tannoy); 2 Overhead speakers; 4 channel microphone mixer Shure M68FCE; 4 point low impedance microphone system.
DRESSING ROOMS: 3; Accom. 40; 2 Showers; 1 Bathroom; 3 lavatories; 5 hand basins; Orchestra Pit 20.

THE MILL VOLVO TYNE THEATRE

Westgate Road, Newcastle-upon-Tyne, Tyne and Wear NE1 4AG
BO: 0844 493 9999 Admin Tel: 0191 243 1172 Fax: 0191 243 1170
Email: phil.smith@smgnewcastle.co.uk
Web Site: www.themillvolvotynetheatre.co.uk
ADMINISTRATION:
Props: SMG Europe
Director: Phil Smith
Capacity: 1,100

THEATRE ROYAL

100 Grey Street, Newcastle-upon-Tyne, Tyne & Wear NE1 6BR
SD: 0191 244 2500 BO: 08448 11 2121
Fax: 0191 244 2512
Email: jo.tomkins@theatreroyal.co.uk
Web Site: www.theatreroyal.co.uk
ADMINISTRATION:
Chief Executive: Philip Bernays
Director of Finance: Pamela Dowds
Director of Marketing and Sales: Jo Kirby
Director of Operations: Dawn Taylor
Stage Manager: Steve White
Chief Electrician: Nathan Reynard
Policy: No.1 Touring, Children's Shows, Concerts and Pantomime & RSC's third home
Perfs: Variable. Computerised Box Office (Databox).
Seats: 1,294. 9 Bars, Coffee Shop/ Bistro, Restaurant-Pasqualinos. 10 Wheelchair spaces available.
TECHNICAL:
STAGE: Raked of wooden construction. Rake:1:24. Depth from setting line exc. Back Dock, 11.40m. Depth from riser to setting line, 1.00m. Back Dock, 15.50m wide x 5.04m deep. Proscenium Dimensions, 9.01m wide x 9.53m high. Height to permanent Proscenium Pelmet @ 7.90m. Height to underside Safety curtain @ 7.50m. Wing depth, P.S. 4.38m OP. 1.83m. Height to fly floor, 7.90m. Distance between fly floors, 11.90m. Length of flying bar: 10.94m. Flying height 17.200m @ Bar 1. Flying height 16.700m @ Bar 5. Max. Lifting Capacity: 400Kg. Get-ins Dimensions. 3.935m high x 2.995m wide. Orchestra Pit: Pit on 2 lifts able to accommodate up to 75 musicians.
LIGHTING: Control Room Console: ETC Eos. Auditorium / Designers Console: ETC Ion. 336 x 3k ETC Sensor+ Dimmers, 38 x 5k ETC Sensor+ Dimmers, 24 x 3k Sine-wave Dimmers, 50 x 3k ETC Sensor+ Relays, 8 x Double ETC Sensor+ relay modules. FOH: 24 x Source 4 15/30 750W profiles on Gallery Circle Front, 12 x 14degree Source 4 750W profiles on Gallery Circle Front,12 x Strand Cadenza 2kW profiles on Gallery Ceiling Bridge, 10 x Source 4 15/30 750W profiles on Upper Circle Front, 2 x 26degree Source 4 750W profiles in each Grand Circle Turret.
STAGE EQUIP: 16 x Strand Harmony F 1kW Fresnel, 26 x Strand Patt 743, 12 x Source 4 15/30 or 25/50 750W profiles, 12 x Strand Cadenza PC, 48 x Source 4 750w heads with the selection of 4 x 19o, 12 x 26o, 33 x 36 o and 28 x 50 o lens tubes, 44 x Strand Punchlites (Parcans), 106 x Thomas type Parcans, 12 x Strand Prelude F, 24x CCT Starlette Fresnels. Cyclorama: Flood bar: 20 x CCT 1kW Asymmetric Floods and 6x Thomas 4 cell 1k battens, Flood Bar/Groundrows: 23 x Strand Coda 500/4. Follow Spots: 2 x 1.2 kW HMI Robert Juliat Korrigan
SPECIAL EFFECTS: 1 x JEM ZR22 DMX smoke machine, 2 x Unique Hazel, 1 x Look Solutions Tiny Compact cordless smoke machine, 1 x Look Solutions Power Tiny handheld smoke machine, 2 x Atomic 3000 strobes.
SOUND EQUIPMENT: Control: 48ch. DigiDesign Venue D-Show Profile mixing desk. 2 x MD recorders, 1 x DAT recorder, 1 x Yamaha SPX 1000 FX, 1 x Yamaha Rev 500, 2 x CD Player, 4 x Stereo Graphics. Main P.A.: 8x D&B Q7i. Permanently rigged. Subs: 2x D&B B2s, 4x D&B Q1s. Foldback: 4x D&B E12s, 4 x Sherman wedge monitors. 4x JBL Control 1s. Frontfills: 4x D&B E3s. Delays: 16x D&B E0s. Permanently rigged. Amps: 11x D&B D6 for main PA, foldback and delays and 2x D&B D12 for Subs. Also 3x Yamaha P7000, 3x Yamaha P3500.
Microphones: A large selection available.
STAGE COMMUNICATIONS: 4 Channel RTS ring intercom 15 wired & 6 radio headsets, 18 x Cuelights (First 8 fixed position on Cue desk, next 10 patchable), FOH and M.D. Video, 4 x B/W Monitors. 1x Colour monitor.
BACKSTAGE FACILITIES: 14 with 31 showers and 2 bathrooms, accommodating up to 86 performers. Principal dressing rooms 1-6 have televisions. All floors served by 16 person / goods lift. Band Rooms: 2 in basement. Can also double as studio for sound, & has audio, video, comms and speaker lines installed.
Wardrobe, Laundry & Wigs: 2 Heubsh top-loading washing machines, 2 Heubsh drier, 1 Ironing board, 1 Steam iron.
Rehearsal Room: 13.7m.x 9.1m.
ADDITIONAL: 1 Harlequin Black Dance Floor to cover performing area of 15m x 15m.1 Upright piano for use onstage and rehearsal room.

Newmilns, Ayreshire

MORTON HALL

123 Main Street, Newmilns, Ayrshire KA16 9DG
Tel/Fax: 01560 320071
Email: shona.mcaulay@east-ayrshire.gov.uk
Web Site: www.east-ayrshire.gov.uk
ADMINISTRATION:
Props: East Ayrshire Council
Cap: 250 Seated

Newport, Gwent

Pop. 135,000. London 130 miles. STD code 01633

NEWPORT LEISURE CENTRE

Kingsway, Newport, Gwent NP20 1UH South Wales
Tel 01633 656656
Email: info@newport.gov.uk
Web Site: www.newport.gov
ADMINISTRATION:
Head of Leisure: Steve Ward, Civic Centre, Newport, Gwent NP20 4UR
Events Manager: Sarah Williams
Policy: Mixed programme of entertainments, and sports events.
Seats: Up to 2,024 in multi-purpose main hall. Easy access for disabled. Fully licensed bar and full catering service available. 7 function suites.
TECHNICAL:
Stage: Main Hall: Height adjustable 0 - 2m. Dimensions - 17m x 7m (extendable).

Floor: Material - Granwood. Area - 1,250m. Max loading 9kn/m. Lighting: 24 lighting barrels (16 winched, 8 fixed). 60 channel, 3 pre-set lighting control console with 3 independent groups per pre-set. Full mastering with automatic dipless crossfade. Power: 300 amp 3 phase supply and 60 amp single phase clean supply backstage.
Sound: Ring intercom system. Audio deaf-aid induction loop. Broadcasting Facilities: Power - 300kw (3-phase) for specialist lighting. 50kw (single) for control vehicles. Communication lines. Comprehensive high level catwalk. 24 lighting barrels.
Access and Parking: 2.65m x 3.71m elephant door giving direct access for get-ins. On site parking for event vehicles; adjacent car parks for 2,000.
Dressing Rooms: Function suite adjacent to stage has been designed specifically to double as artistes' dressing rooms (2).

THE RIVERFRONT THEATRE & ARTS CENTRE

Kingsway, Newport, Gwent NP20 1HG
Tel: 01633 656757 BO: 01633 656757
Admin: 01633 656677
Email: theriverfront@newport.gov.uk
Web Site: www.newport.gov.uk
Contact: Sarah Williams
Capacity: 489

Newport, Isle of Wight

Pop. 22,430. London 91 miles. (inc. ferry). Newspapers: Isle of Wight County Press (fri). STD code 01983

MEDINA THEATRE

Fairlee Road, Newport PO30 2DX Isle of Wight
Tel: 01983 823 884
Email: paul.broome@iow.gov.uk
Web Site: www.medinatheatre.co.uk
ADMINISTRATION:
Props: Isle of Wight Council
Manager: Paul Broome
Secretary: Leanne Grafham
Theatre Technician: Duncan Lockhart
Policy: Professional and touring performances and events encouraging school and community involvements. Music concerts, recitals, variety, theatre, mime, meetings, lectures includes Local Amateur Societies etc.
Perfs: Flexible
Seats: 419 (Extended stage), plus facilities for disabled.
TECHNICAL:
Please see our website.

Newry, County Down

NEWRY TOWN HALL

Bank Parade, Newry, County Down BT35 6HR Northern Ireland
Tel: 028 3031 3180
Email: jacqueline.turley@newryand-mourne.gov.uk
Web Site: www.newryandmourne.gov.uk
ADMINISTRATION:
Props: Newry & Mourne District Council
For bookings contact the Administrative Director, Jacqueline Turley, Newry Arts Centre, 1A Bank Parade, Newry, County Down BT35 6HP Northern Ireland
Fax: 028 3076 6839
Policy - Musicals, Theatre, Pantomime
Seating: 150 Balcony, 300 Main Hall
TECHNICAL:
Stage: Stage Area - depth 5 metres, width 7 metres. Wing space 35 metres each side. Total Stage Depth 8.5 metres (to Cyc Cloth). Pros Arch Height 4.25 metres.
Lighting: Rank Strand AMC St Lighting system with 60 Circuits (58 wired).
Other: Dressing Rooms 5,(1 quick change). Passenger lift to Main Hall, Dressing Rooms and Back Stage. Intercom to all areas.

SEAN HOLLYWOOD ARTS CENTRE

1a Bank Parade, Newry, County Down BT35 6HP Northern Ireland
Tel: 028 3031 3180 Fax: 028 30266839
Email: jacqueline.turley@newryand-mourne.gov.uk
Web Site: www.newryandmourne.gov.uk
ADMINISTRATION:
Props: Newry & Mourne District Council
Facilities manager: Jacqueline Turley
Policy: To promote good Theatre and Arts in the Newry and Mourne area.
Seating: Auditorium; 150 seats.
TECHNICAL:
STAGE: Area: Flat stage with Proscenium Arch. Width 6.28m, Depth 6.28m, Height 6.5m. Passenger lift to all floors. House intercom system.
LIGHTING: Rank Strand AMC System with 60 No. circuits.
ADDITIONAL: Rooms: Auditorum. 2 Dressing Rooms. Green Room. Exhibition Areas. Coffee Bar. Photographic Studio etc. Rehearsal room.

Newton Aycliffe, County Durham

NEWTON AYCLIFFE LEISURE CENTRE

Beveridge Arcade, Newton Aycliffe, County Durham DL5 4EH
Tel: 0300 026 6446
Email: leisure-newton-aycliffe@durham.gov.uk
Web Site: www.durham.gov.uk
ADMINISTRATION:
Props: Durham County Council
Cap: 3 Halls - 900, 180 & 80
Manager: Lesley Tindale
Full licensed, portable stage, lighting and PA available.

Newtown, Powys

THEATR HAFREN

Llanidloes Road, Newtown, Powys SY16 4HU Wales
Admin: 01686 614565 Mktg: 01686 614556 BO: 01686 614555
Email: admin@theatrhafren.co.uk
Web Site: www.thehafren.co.uk
ADMINISTRATION:
Props: Powys County Council
Administrator: Sara Clutton
Marketing Manager: Del Thomas
A venue/arts centre in Mid Wales, approximately 35 minutes drive from Shrewsbury.
Cap: 568 Seated
Receiving theatre - broad-based programme ranging from community use to national tours of dramas, comedian and pop stars/bands.
TECHNICAL:
See website for detailed technical specifications, or email: tech@theatrhafren.co.uk.

Newtownabbey, County Antrim

THE COURTYARD THEATRE AT BALLYEARL

Ballyearl Arts and Leisure Cen 585 Doagh Road Newtownabbey, County Antrim BT36 5RZ Northern Ireland
Tel: 028 9084 8287
Email: bclarkson@newtownabbey.gov.uk
Web Site: www.newtownabbey.gov.uk
Theatre Seats: 180 also smaller rooms and exhibition areas.
Manager: Bernard Clarkson
Duty Manager: Alister Bell

Newtyle, Angus

WHARNCLIFFE HALL

Kinpurnie Estate manages the halls bookings
North Street, Newtyle, Blairgowrie, Perthshire PH12 8TT
Tel: 01828 650 500
Email: denise.cassell@kinpurnie.co.uk

ADMINISTRATION:
Props: Angus Council
Cap: 120
Contact Manager: Denise Cassell

Northallerton, North Yorkshire

HAMBLETONFORUM

Bullamoor Road, Northallerton, North Yorkshire DL6 1LP
Tel: 01609 776230
Email: info@forumnorthallerton.org.uk
Web Site: www.forumnorthallerton.org.uk
ADMINISTRATION:
Cap: 400
Manager: Dan Brookes

Northampton, Northamptonshire

Pop. 127,460. London 66 miles. Newspapers: Chronicle & Echo (ntly); The Mercury (thurs). STD code 01604

ROYAL & DERNGATE

19/21 Guildhall Road, Northampton NN1 1DP
Mgt: 01604 626 222 BO: 01604 624 811
SD: 01604 626 289 Fax: 01604 250 901
Email: box.office@royalandderngate.co.uk
Web Site: www.royalandderngate.co.uk
ADMINISTRATION:
Props: Northampton Theatres Trust Limited.
Chief Executive: Martin Sutherland
Technical Manager: Dave Reeve
Contact:
david.reeve@royalandderngate.co.uk
Director of Finance: Lorraine Kaye
Director of Marketing & Sales: Jo Gordon
Artistic Director: Laurie Sansom
Programming Manager: Steve Scrivens
Head Of Customer Service: Steve Joyce
Operations Manager: Richard Clinton
Policy: Multi-purpose entertainment centre. Wide programme including ballet, opera and all forms of touring theatre, big band concerts, orchestral concerts, spectator sports and conferences. Large concourse area for exhibitions and special events. Bars, meeting rooms and restaurant.
Capacity:
The Royal Theatre; 460 Seating, 583 standing.
The Derngate Auditorium; 1550 arena style,1200 as Lyric theatre, 1450 as concert hall, or flat floor area of 600 sq.m. for exhibitions, banqueting and dinners with cabaret.
TECHNICAL:
THE ROYAL THEATRE:
STAGE: Rake 1:23 (approx), Stage Height Auditorium floor to stage 1000mm, Depth Rear of Iron to back wall 11000mm, Front of stage to back wall 11700mm, Width Pros. Opening 6320mm, Fly floor to fly floor 9800mm, Centre line to SR wall 7100mm, Centre line to SL wall 14000mm, Height Pros. 6630mm To Grid 15000mm, To underside of SR fly floor DS 5500mm, US 5300mm, To underside of SL fly floor DS 5400mm, US 5300mm, Back Bridge 8000mm. Get in: Door 2500mm H x 1700mm W, 2700mm above stage level. Lift to stage level 5000mm x 2000mm, 3000 Kg SWL.
Orchestra Pit: Length 8700mm, Width 1600mm, Pit floor to stage floor 1450mm, Pit can be covered.
LIGHTING: Control; Strand 530i, ver2.5e networked to PC backup. Located in control room at rear of stalls. Lantern Stock: Wattage, 14 x Minuette F 500, 24 x Starlette F 1000, 8 x Harmony F 1000, 1 x Patt 743 1200, 2 x 828 F 2000, 2 x ADB F 2000, 4 x Starlette F 2000, 4 x Patt 814 PC 1000, 4 x Starlette PC 1000, 8 x Source 4 15/30 750, 6 x Source 4 25/50 750, 6 x Sil 30 1000, 20 x Sil 15/30 Turbo 1200 (rigged FOH), 6 x sil 19/45 Turbo 1200, 10 x Prelude 16/30 500/650, 2 x Patt 23/23N 500, 14 x Brio 25/50 600, 5 x Alto 8/16 2500 (rigged FOH), 38 x Parcans - mixed head 1000 (10 scroller cans), 4 x short nose PARS 1000, 12 x Birdies (12v) 75, 2 x Minuette floods 500, 5 x Starlette 4 cell battens 1000, 10 x Starlette floods 1000, 5 x Minuette 3 cell battens 500, 6 x Birdie floods (microflood) 75, 6 x Iris 1 1000. Followspots and dimmers available.
SOUND: Control; Yamaha M7CL 48 console (including 1 Auvitran AVY16-ES card), 2 AD8HR mic pre-amps at stage giving 16 digital channels to M7 console. Remaining tie lines are analogue patched via control room. Record/Playback; 1 SFX sound effects computer, 16 Outputs, 1 twin cassette deck, 1 CD Player, 2 Denon record/play mini-disc player. Extra; 2 Shure SM58, 2 EW 100 Sennheiser radio mics UHF, 10 EW 300 Sennheiser radio mics UHF, 1 EW 300 Sennheiser hand held radio mic, 6 Sennheiser rifle mics, 4 AKG CS6EB rifle mics, 2 AKG D321, 2 Shure SM57, 3 EMO DI boxes, 4 Sennheiser 406, 1 Sennheiser 402
STAGE MANAGEMENT: Single channel Tec-Pro style comms to all permanent stations plus dual ring between sound and Lighting control positions; 8 single channel belt packs and headsets; 3 dual channel belt packs and headsets. Cue lights to flys and control room plus up to 4 additional cue lights. Prompt desk is situated SL. Full volume controlled show relay to all rear stage rooms and dressing rooms with over-ride paging from prompt corner.
DRESSING ROOMS: 6, accomm. 16, with en-suite shower facilities, including access to a disabled shower. Wardrobe facilities by prior arrangement only, subject to availability and cost. Contact Technical Manager.
STAFFING: There are 5 full time technical staff comprising Head of Stage, Head of Lighting and Sound, Senior Technician Stage, Senior Technician LX/sound plus a Technician, augmented by casual staff as required by performance and contract. Hours of work are totally flexible, subject to contract.

DERNGATE AUDITORIUM:
STAGE: Wing Wall to Wing Wall 28 metres (91.86ft) (Lyric Theatre Format), 18.5 - 19 metres approx (Concert Format), Stage Depth 12.6 metres (41.33 ft), Height to Grid 22 metres (72.17 ft), Pros. Width 14 metres (45.93 ft) (Lyric Theatre Format), Pros. Height 11.4 metres (37.4 ft), Flying Bar Width 17 metres (55.77 ft) (see "FLYING" below). Performance area; 12.19 metres (40 ft) wide and 9.625 metres (31.57 ft) deep, setting from house tabs. Floor covering is linoleum over plywood mounted on rubber dampers. The wings are linoleum over concrete. The stage is not raked.
Orchestra pit; Length 16m, Width 4m for 4m either side of centre, narrowing to 2m, Height to Stage Variable. Get-in; Roller shutter door at stage right, 5.48 metres (18 ft) x 2.59 metres (8.6 ft) into tower storage area/scene dock 11.58 metres (38 ft) from side stage. Flat floor to stage.
LIGHTING: FOH: 30 x 1kw Starlette Fresnel, 10 x 1kw Sil 30° profile, 12 x Source 4 Profile (15°-30°), 6 x 2kw ADB Fresnel, 50 x 1kw Par cans - mixed head, 2 x Limelight 2kz Zenon Follow Spots.
Control: 1 x ETC Avab Congo, 192 x Circuits - 11 5kw, 181 2.5kw, split into:2.5kw 5 kw, 60 FOH 3 FOH, 10 stage 3 stage, 50 S.L Fly Floor 5 S.L. Fly Floor 72 S.R. Fly Floor.
SOUND: House System; Yamaha M7CL48 - fitted with 3x Auvitran Ethersound cards, Stage Box - 40 sends via 5x AD8HR, 16 returns via 2x Yamaha DME8io-ES. Stage box can be located anywhere there is a network patch point. Stage box has capability for stage splits. 2x Meyer MTS-4A full range cabinets as Left & Right Ground stacks, 1x Central hang of 1 x Meyer 600HP plus 8x Meyer M'elodie Line Array, plus 4x UPJ-1P to cover sides and rear when 'in the round'. 3x Meyer UPJ-1P for upper circle delays. Controlled via a Yamaha DME network over standard ethernet infrastructure, and can be operated from the control room via tie-lines and hardwired MIDAS Venice 32. Extra: 8x L'accoustics 112P powered wedge monitors, Various mics - Shure/AKG/Sennheiser, BSS D/I's, Various mic stands
STAGE MANAGEMENT: 6 wired and 2 radio TELEX RTS Dual Channel comms sets, plus Master Station at prompt desk. Please note that house comms are not compatible with Tec-Pro type systems. Cue lights to all permanent stations plus up to 4 additional cue lights. Prompt desk either S.L. or S.R. (In Lyric Theatre format only, no prompt desk in Concert format). Full volume controlled show relay to all

rear stage rooms with over-ride paging from prompt corner and U.S.R.
DRESSING ROOMS; 14, accomm. 64, with disabled access, toilets and showers, 1 x Green Room. 1 x Company Office. All Dressing Rooms fitted with lights, power, mirrors. 2 x rooms understage close to Orchestra pit entrance, accomm. 50. Small Wardrobe Room, up 4 steps from stage level (Ramp available) containing Professional top loading Washing Machine, Front Loading Tumble Drier. Sink, plus ironing board. Towels are NOT available
STAFFING: 6 full time technical staff comprising Head of Stage, Head of Lighting and Sound, Senior Technician Stage, Senior Technician LX/sound plus two Technicians, augmented by casual staff as required by performance and contract. Hours of work are flexible, subject to contract.

Norwich, Norfolk

Pop. 119,600. London 111 miles.
Newspapers: Eastern Daily Press (dly); Eastern Evening News (ntly); Norwich Mercury; Norwich Advertiser (fri). STD code 01603

MADDERMARKET THEATRE

St. Johns Alley, Norwich, Norfolk NR2 1DR
Mgt: 01603 626560 BO: 01603 620917
SD: 01603 626560 Fax: 01603 661357
Email: office@maddermarket.org
Web Site: www.maddermarket.co.uk
ADMINISTRATION:
Props: Maddermarket Theatre Trust Ltd
Creative Directors: Stash Kirkbride and Peter Beck
Technical Stage Manager: Rhett Davies
Policy: Amateur - 12 productions per year, visiting companies and one night stands.
Perfs: Nightly 7.30, Mat. 2.30.
Seats: 310 with Stewards. Exhibition Space. Licensed Bar.
TECHNICAL:
Stage: Open neo Elizabethan, Flat with Thrust, Overall Pros. Width 9.75m; Max. Ht. 4.88m; Total Depth 7.8m.
Lighting: Switchboard: 48 way Strand GSX; F.O.H. Front and Rear.
Dressing Rooms: 2, accom. 40.

NORWICH PLAYHOUSE

42-58 St George's Street, Norwich, Norfolk NR3 1AB
Mgt 01603 612 580 BO: 01603 598 598
Mktg: 01603 612 580 Education: 01603 612 580 Fax 01603 617 728
Email: info@norwichplayhouse.co.uk
Web Site: www.norwichplayhouse.co.uk
ADMINISTRATION:
Director: Caroline Richardson
Technical Manager: Peter Wright
Marketing Manager: Caz Slota
Receiving house. 3 main seasons, autumn and spring and Summer. Takes drama, comedy, music and dance, including one night stands and hires.
Theatre bar with riverside terrace.
Conference facilities.
Capacity 300
TECHNICAL:
Stage: Width 14.4m, Depth 6.8m, Grid Height 5.4m.
Sound: Allen & Heath GL3 16/4/2.; amps 1 x C Audio 2000; 1 x Denon CD; 2 x SM58; 1 x Denon Tape; 2 x SM57; Strand 520 & Rigers Remote 96 Channels; 12 x Cantata 18/J2; 20 x Cantata PC; 12 x Cantata Fresnels; 24 x Par; 2 x Cantata 26/44; 1 x 600mm Mirror Ball; 4 x 2k Fresnels; 6 x 16/30 Preludes; 2 x Quartet F; 4 x Stands (2 x for Followspots); 4 x Yamaha Wedge Monitors

NORWICH PUPPET THEATRE

St James, Whitefriars, Norwich, Norfolk NR3 1TN
Mgt: 01603 615 564 BO: 01603 629 921
Fax: 01603 617 578
Email: info@puppettheatre.co.uk
Web Site: www.puppettheatre.co.uk
ADMINISTRATION:
General Manager: Ian Woods
Marketing Coordinator: Kerry Leathley
Workshop Coordinator: Denise Hargrave
Director: Joy Haynes
Education and Outreach: Rosie Walker
Status: Puppet Theatre
Policy: Norwich Puppet Theatre is a touring company with almost unique benefit of own home theatre base with raked auditorium, studio performance space and workshops. Produces work for all ages from 3 years upwards which tours throughout the UK and Europe. Where possible live music is included in productions. Willing to premiere show.
Facilities: Seating in main house 185 raked. 4 wheelchair spaces, level access - all house facilities fully accessible. Induction loop system.
Studio theatre 50 informal, level access. The Octagon exhibition gallery. Licensed bar. Food brought in for specific functions.
TECHNICAL:
STAGE: Proscenium arch. Performing area 5m x 6m - pros opening 5.5m x 5.5m wing width 5.3m US. No rake - floor sprung wood composition, suitable for dance (not barefoot) backstage crossover, trench DS. Height of grid 3.05m - variable hemp sets - tab track - maximum flying height 5.5m. Black masking - black house tabs, drawn. 10 x 13A, 16 x 15A sockets. Get-in via road to stage area - dock doors 1m x 2m. Scale stage plan available.
LIGHTING: Jands ESP + circuits @ 2.5K, can be moved and operated from various positions - 21 spots, 25 fresnels, CCT/Rank Strand followspots could be operated from various positions.
SOUND: Alesis equaliser - Amcron amp - 2 x JBL speakers - 3 mics. Technics double cassette tape systems, AKAI CD Decks.. Acoustics suitable for music and spoken word. Stage management Prompt Corner available.
BACKSTAGE FACILITIES: 1 green room, doubling as dressing room with shower. Iron, 4 power points available. Advice given on accommodation. No permanent staff - casuals
available - no security personnel.
Backstage facilities partially accessible to disabled performers and staff. Rehearsal rooms, piano fairly good.

Technical Studio Theatre - Flat wooden floor with informal seating 5m x 3m - no masking. In house lighting facility 18 x 15a socket outlets, Lighting equipment borrowed from main theatre - 8 x 13A socket outlets. No sound equipment.

ST ANDREW'S & BLACKFRIARS HALLS

St Andrews Hall Plain, Norwich, Norfolk NR3 1AU
Tel: 01603 628 477 Fax: 01603 762 182
Email: thehalls@norwich.gov.uk
Web Site: www.thehallsnorwich.co.uk
Contact: Matthew White
Seating/Capacity: St. Andrews Hall: 900; Blackfriars Hall: 300
Hire only venue.

THEATRE ROYAL

Theatre Street, Norwich, Norfolk NR2 1RL
Mgt: 01603 598 500 BO: 01603 630 000
Mktg: 01603 598 529 SD: 01603 598 500 Mgt Fax: 01603 598 501 BO Fax: 01603 622 777
Email: admin / technical @theatreroyalnorwich.co.uk
Web Site: www.theatreroyalnorwich.co.uk
ADMINISTRATION:
Chief Executive: Peter Wilson
General Manager: Jane Claridge
Press & Programming: Jane Walsh
Marketing & Publicity Director: Mark Hazell
Technical Manager: Will Hill
Chief Electrician: Ian Greeves
Seats: 1,311. 3 Licensed Bars. 3 Licensed Corporate Rooms. Coffee Bar. Full catering facilities. Full disabled facilities.
TECHNICAL:
Stage: Proscenium stage 'flat'.
Proscenium opening 9.68m x 6.63m high.
Flys C/W 52 lines plus 2 lateral bars.
Modelbox ground plan.
Lighting: Strand 550, 180 way.
Sound: Reinforcement system.
Dressing Rooms: 9 (6 en suite), 3 Chorus (2 en suite).
Orchestra Dressing room facilities:
Orchestra pit particulars on application.
Workshop facilities.
Specialists in scenery and costume hire, scenery design. Scenic Artist. Building facilities.

Full technical specification available on application.

Nottingham, Nottinghamshire

Pop. 294,420. London 123 miles.
Newspapers: Nottingham Evening Post (ntly). STD code 0115

BONINGTON THEATRE

High Street, Arnold, Nottingham NG5 7EE
Mgt/BO: 0115 967 0114 / 901 3640 Fax: 0115 956 0731
Email: arnold@gedling.gov.uk
Web Site: www.bonington-theatre.co.uk
ADMINISTRATION:
Props: Gedling Borough Council
Theatre Manager: David Popple
Policy: Mixed amateur and professional programme of drama, music, light opera, ballet.
Perfs: 7.30 or 8.00, Matinees 2pm
Seats: 176. Theatre Bar.
TECHNICAL:
Stage: Proscenium, flat area 7.4m x 7.4m, including 1.5m forming apron. Small wing space.
Lighting: Switchboard: Eclipse 72ct board. 250 memories. 125 lantern rig on 3 phase. Fixed bars over stage, grid in auditorium.
Sound: Allen & Heath 16CN mixer, 4 fold-back ch. 10 mike lines to stage, 4 tie lines. Mini-disk, cassette player, CD player.
SM; full stage manager system
Dressing Rooms: 2 with capacity for ten people. Extra room with capacity for 20 also available.
Full details on website.

NOTTINGHAM ARTS THEATRE

George Street, Nottingham NG1 3BE
Admin Tel: 0115 947 5925 Fax: 0115 947 5925 BO: 0115 947 6096
Email: peter@artstheatre.org.uk
Web Site: www.nottingham-theatre.co.uk
ADMINISTRATION:
Thetare Administrator & Licensee: Peter Mayall
Business Manager & Licensee: Raymond Wright
Receiving house for amateur and professional visiting companies and charitable foundation for educational facilities. Has daily box office open on site.
Capacity: 300
Studio Theatre cap 50
Rehearsal facilities
TECHNICAL:
Traditional pros. arch theatre, fixed seating, good dressing rooms, rehearsal space etc. Short-term hire available. Spec on request.

NOTTINGHAM PLAYHOUSE

Wellington Circus, East Circus Street, Nottingham NG1 5AF
Mgt: 0115 947 4361 BO: 0115 941 9419
SD: 0115 947 4361 Fax: 0115 947 5759
Email: rebeccad@nottinghamplayhouse.co.uk
Web Site: www.nottinghamplayhouse.co.uk
ADMINISTRATION:
Props. & Lessees: Nottingham Theatre Trust Ltd
Chief Executive: Stephanie Sirr
Artistic Director: Giles Croft
Theatre Manager: Rebecca Dallman
Policy: All year round Repertory with occasional visiting companies, concerts and late-night events.
Perfs: 7.45 Mon - Sat
Seats: 685-766 (adaptable). Licensed bars, coffee bars and adjoining Restaurant and Bars.
TECHNICAL:
Stage: Proscenium with two forestages (3.96m in all). Flat; Pros. opening 9.75m; Ht. of Pros. 6.71m; Depth of S/Line 9.75m; Ht. of Grid 18.58m; 32 lines, C/W; Scenery Flying Ht. 7.18m; Flying Bars 12.19m; Widths P.S. 3.66m, O.P. 7.32m;Lighting: 3 rear of stalls; 192 ways inc. 24 5kw. LX Equipment: 70 x Profiles. 50 x 1k Fresnels & 20 x 2k Fresnels, 60 Parcan, 2 Follow Spots, 20 x Iris 1. Lighting Board Strand 530I, 10 x colour call scrollers.
Sound Equipment: Soundcraft 32-8-2 Main Mixer; 3 x Rainbow 15" scrollers; 2 x cassette decks; assorted mics and stands. Main installed speaker system Meyer UPA and USW system front of house, Bose 802's on stage. 2 X Denon 990R mini disks. 2 x Yamaha O3D desks. E4 emo and E6400 samplers. Power Mac G3 with logic audio gold 3.5 sequencing package. 2 DAT players.
Dressing Rooms: 10, accom. 39, showers, Orchestra Pit 3.96m x 10.67m.
Membership: TMA ABTT

ROCK CITY

8 Talbot Street, Nottingham NG1 5GG
Tel: 0845 413 4444
Email: bart@dhpgroup.co.uk
Web Site: www.rock-city.co.uk
ADMINISTRATION:
Managers & Promoters: Bart Easter, George Akins Jnr.
Policy: Concert venue, club and disco, Venue for live bands, Thur student night, Fri floor fillers, Sat alternative night. Venue consists of a ground floor, balcony and smaller disco room, four drinks bars and a fast food bar. Sunday - available for bands.
Seating/Capacity: 1,900 standing.
TECHNICAL:
Stage: dimensions 31ft (10m) wide x 19ft (6m) deep x 3ft (1m) high, fully carpeted. P.A. Risers: Stage Left 2 (4ft x 3ft); Stage Right 1 (4ft x 3ft) - due to Fire Exit on this side. Stage to ceiling clearance - Stage Rear: 12ft (4m); Front truss clearance - 22ft - with house flying chains. Power: Lights 3 x 100 amp - 3 phase. Sound: 3 x 60 amp - 3 phase.
Mixing Point: on raised area 40ft from stage centre - 4ft x 3ft. Rostra available on raised dais - 4ft x 8ft.
Backstage: catering facilities available.

ROYAL CENTRE

See the Theatre Royal and the Royal Concert Hall

ROYAL CONCERT HALL

Theatre Square, Nottingham NG1 5ND
Mgt: 0115 989 5500 / Fax: 0115 947 4218 BO: 0115 989 5555 / Fax: 0115 950 3476 Tech: 0115 9895595 / Fax 0115 9153798
Email: robert.sanderson@nottinghamcity.gov.uk
Web Site: www.trch.co.uk
ADMINISTRATION:
Props: Nottingham City Council
The Royal Concert Hall is on the main touring circuit for the world's leading orchestras, major contemporary bands and solo stars and as a major conference venue. Clients include Shell and the Liberal Democrats.
Managing Director : Robert Sanderson.
Head of Marketing: Jonathan Saville
Conference and Events Manager: Kate Collins
Technical Director: Dave Guy.
Contact: dave.guy@nottinghamcity.gov.uk
Catering Mgr: Qdos Catering, Tel 0115 989 5569
Policy: Classical concerts. Popular music and variety concerts, Conferences, Films, Ballet.
Seats: 2,294. Two large bars and buffet.
TECHNICAL:
STAGE: Platform - polished hardwood finish. With choir stall seating retracted - width at front 19.10m. Width at rear 14.30m, Depth 10.8m, Area 206 sq.m.; With 4 levels of choir stall seating - width at front 19.10m, width at rear 12.10m, depth 8.80m, area 137 sq.m.; Platform equipment includes 3 levels of Orchestra Rostra and Conductor's podium.
Suspension point hoists. 25 positions. 37-ton adjustable acoustic canopy. Get In: Dock Door 12ft wide by 11.5ft high.
Orchestra Pit; Max Area: 990 sq.ft (92 sq.metres). Depth: 2.25m from stage, 1.25m from floor. NB. Pit reduces overall seating capacity.
LIGHTING: Control; Strand 520i 250 channels. 24 subs. DMX to house dimmers. F.O.H Lighting; 12 x Selecon: 5.5 /13° profile spots, 18 x Selecon: 12 / 30° profile spots, 10 x Source 4: 36° profile spots. Canopy Lighting Bridges; 28-x 110 volt Par 64 cans, 6 x 240 volt Ray lamps. Side/Perch Lighting; 32-x 110 volt Par 64 cans. Additional Lighting: 10 x Source 4 / 36 degree profile spots, CCT 1 and 2Kw Fresnels available if required. Follow Spots: 2 x Robert Juliat "Aramis" HMI 2.5Kw situated rear of Tier 2.

SOUND: Mixing Console: Soundcraft MH3 32 Channel. Flown centre array of 8 L'Acoustics Arcs (180 degree coverage). Stage left + right stacks of 2 L'Acoustics SB 218 subs, and 3 Arcs. Also 2 MTD 108 compacts. 2 MTD 108 compacts mounted left and right on lower box level. Processing for main stage and flown array is by XTA DP226, and for MTD 108's is L'Acoustics LLCa processor. 2 x XTA GQ 600 dual EQ. 2 x BSS DPR 422 dual compressor. 1 x BSS DPR522 dual gate. 1 x BSS DPR 944 dual comp/gate. 2 x Yamaha SPX 2000 multi FX. Sony pro CD player and MD recorder / player. Sony CD writer. 10 x Shure SM58 mics. 1 x Shure Beta 87a mic. 4 X Shure SM 57 mics. 8 x AKG 451 mics.
ADDITIONAL: Pianos; 1 x Bosendorfer Grand Pianos. 1 x Steinway. Projection Equipment; Sony VPL PX31 data projector for presentation text or graphics. Front or Rear projection format on to a 12' X 9' screen.
DRESSING ROOMS: 6; with en-suite washbasin, WC and shower unit. 3 dressing rooms, for orchestral use; 1 containing an electric cooker, fridge, freezer and sink, and can be used as a catering preparation area, Total Capacity; 119.

THEATRE ROYAL

Theatre Square, Nottingham NG1 5ND
Mgt: 0115 989 5500 BO: 0115 989 5555
SD: 0115 989 5500 Mgt Fax: 0115 947 4218 BO Fax: 0115 950 3476 SD Fax: 0115 979 9145
Email: enquiry@trch.co.uk
Web Site: www.royalcentre-nottingham.co.uk
ADMINISTRATION:
Props: Nottingham City Council
Managing Director: Robert Sanderson
Head of Marketing: Jonathan Saville
Conference and Events Manager: Kate Collins
Technical Manager: Dave Guy
Catering: Qdos Catering. Tel: 0115 989 5569
Policy: Touring Opera, Ballet, Drama, Variety, Pantomime and Concerts.
Seats: 1,186. Three Bars, Buffet and Restaurant
The modernised Victorian Theatre Royal is on the No 1 Touring Circuit and plays host to Companies such as the Royal Shakespeare Company, Royal National Theate, Opera North, Northern Ballet and pre and post West End Tours.
TECHNICAL:
Stage: Proscenium, Raked 1/25. Pros. opening 9.10m; Ht. of Pros. 8.5m; Depth of S/Line 13.15m; Ht. of Grid 18.90m; D/S 18.3m; 55 lines C/W 1 up and downstage C/W set each side; Scenery Flying Ht. 18.00m, Flying Bars 12.55m, 50mm diam; W/Widths PS 3.10m, OP 3.95m. Scene Dock OP 9.8m x 13.00m; Rear stage area 17.3m x 6.3m; Prompt desk OP can be PS. Tabs swagged by motor. Forestage elevator forms pit size for 25 musicians. Larger Orchestra Pit with 5 rows of seats removed accommodates 65 musicians.
Lighting: Switchboard: Rank Strand Galaxy 3 174 ways, 154 2kw, 20 5kw dimmers positioned at rear of Upper Circle. 12 x 1200 Watt Cantata in ceiling slots; Gallery front 10 source 4; Circle sides 16 T spots; Pros Booms 12 Patt.23/123; Flood bar 6 Iris 4 units; Additional lantern stock available; 3 internally wired spotbars; 4 6way ladders on tracks; Limes 2 x PANI 1200.
Sound Equip: Hill Audio 16:8:2 desk; Revox A77 tape deck, Technics cassette player, Yamaha SPX 90, 10 AKG and shure mics, installed speaker system in proscenium boxes - Martin CT2 speakers with Amcron MA600 amplifiers.
Dressing Rooms: 16 accommodating 120, with showers and bathrooms, bandroom and wardrobe with automatic washing machine and tumble drier, 20 music stands, Yamaha 6'6" grand piano.

Oban, Argyll

Pop. 8,134. London 506 miles.
Newspapers: The Oban Times. STD code 01631

CORRAN HALL

Corran Esplanade, Oban, Argyll PA34 5AB Scotland
Tel: 01631 567 333
Email: lorna.whyte@argyll-bute.gov.uk
Web Site: www.argyll-bute.gov.uk
Manager: Lorna White
Seating/Capacity: 600; stacking chairs.

Oldbury, West Midlands

OLDBURY REP

Box office open
Spring Walk, Langley, Oldbury, West Midlands B69 4SP
Tel: 0121 552 2761
Email: admin@oldburyrep.org
Web Site: www.oldburyrep.org

Oldham, Lancashire

Pop. 227,000. London 185 miles.
Newspapers: Oldham Evening Chronicle (ntly); Weekend (free wkly); Advertiser (free wkly). STD code 0161

COLISEUM THEATRE

Fairbottom Street, Oldham, Lancashire OL1 3SW
Admin: 0161 624 1731 BO: 0161 624 2829
Email: mail@coliseum.org.uk, boxoffice@coliseum.org.uk
Web Site: www.coliseum.org.uk
ADMINISTRATION:
Props: Oldham Coliseum Theatre Ltd
Chief Executive: Kevin Shaw
Production Manager: Lesley Chenery
Head of Participation: Richard Hall
Policy: Four weekly Repertory + tours + one nighters.
Perfs: Mon-Sat 7.30p.m, Two Sat Mat. per run 2.30p.m.
One nighters: Monday - Saturday - 7.30pm
Seats: 524. 2 Bars.
TECHNICAL:
Stage: Proscenium, Flat; Pros. opening 8.90m; Ht. of Pros. 4.27m; Stage Depth 13.10m; Depth from S/Line 9.75m; Ht. of Grid 10.66m; 30 lines; Scenery Flying Ht. 5.25m; Flying Bars 9.8m; W/Widths P.S. 4.88m, O.P. 6.40m; Prompt Cnr. P.S.
Lighting and Sound: Control: F.O.H.: Switchboard: ADB Phoenix 5; 204 Dimmers 27 x 1k Profiles, 16.5k Profiles. 22 1k Fresnels, 19 x .5k Fresnels 3 x 2k Fresnels, 38 Par64, 12 Floods, 1 x CSI F/S.
Sound Equip: 24-8-2 Soundcraft Ghost, 6 x Bose 802E, 4 x Pro 100's, 5 x Poweramps, 7 Rifles, 8 vocals, 10 Radio/mics. 2 x B77, 1 record desk. 1 x cass. Minidisk.
Dressing Rooms 6; Accom. 20; 4 Showers.
Orchestra Pit.

GRANGE ARTS CENTRE

Rochdale Road, Oldham, Lancashire OL9 6EA
Admin 0161 785 4238 BO 0161 785 4239 Tech 0161 785 4239
Email: grangearts@oldham.ac.uk / joanne.draper@oldham.ac.uk
Web: www.oldham.ac.uk/grangetheatre
ADMINISTRATION:
Props: Oldham College Corp.
Director: Veronica Conlon
Manager: Joanne Draper
Policy: Amateur and Professional programme of drama, music, and dance, often with special educational performances.
Perfs: Usually 7.30p.m. Mats. various.
Seats: 84 - 434. One Bar. Exhibition facilities in two foyer areas.
TECHNICAL:
Stage: The main performance area is cruciform in design with 4 bleachers of 84 seats and capable of accommodating any form of staging (round, arena, traverse, thrust, 2 pros. sets of varying dimensions and auditoria).
Lighting: A lighting bridge surrounds the performance area and a 48mm modular Grid is suspended 5.5m above the acting area and continued into the seating bays in the form of ornamental balustrading. Control by Strand 520 memory board with integral sub-masters and Effects Generator controlling 140 fixed circuits through 120 dimmers, all terminated in 15

amp 3 pin sockets distributed at grid and floor level. In addition to the above there are 8 independent 5 amp circuits. Lanterns available (all Rank Strand): 30 .5kw and 1kw Profile Lanterns. 65 .5kw, 1kw and 2kw Fresnels C/W barndoors. 30 .5kw and 1kw floods. 2 Follow spots C/W integral colour change and Iris. Specific requirements for incoming shows can be rigged by prior arrangement. The Centre is also equipped with 2-30 amp auxiliary power supplies.
Sound Equip: Main P.A.: 4 Bose 802 Speakers; 1 Citronics PPX 900 Stereo Amplifier 280w per channel into 8 ohms. Bay Reinforcement: 4 JBL Control 1, 1 Quad 405-5 Stereo into 4-16 ohms. Mixing/Effects: 1 Studiomaster Series 2 16/8/2, 1 Steven Digital Reverb. Amplifiers: 1 Quad 405-5 100w stereo into 4-16 ohms. Speakers available for Spot Sound and Foldback: 4 Toa F-300 8 ohm cabinets (150w). Microphones: 40 various inc. Diversity Radio Hand Held and lavalier. Tape Decks: 1 Memorex Cassette Deck (Dolby B & C). The Centre carries a full range of Microphone Stands and an Induction Loop System is installed for the benefit of the hard of hearing.
Backstage: Talkback and Cue Lights are available at any point within the Auditorium and Backstage, with Show Relay and Communication to all Dressing Rooms.
The Centre is equipped with colour C.C.T.V. equipment, which is used as a stage management aid.
Rostra: 34 Sico Stage units with elevators and 18 King Cole units.
Access: At tail-gate height via Scene Dock Door 5.5m high x 2.5m wide with similar aperture into Auditorium. Full technical details are available on request.

HEYWOOD CIVIC CENTRE
Church Street Heywood, Lancashire OL10 1LW
Tel: 01706 368130
Email: graham.duckworth@link4life.org
ADMINISTRATION:
Props: Link for Life
Cap: Cabaret Style 450; Theatre 393
Manager: Graham Duckworth
General Purpose Hall

OLDHAM THEATRE WORKSHOP
Old Museum, Greaves Street, Oldham, Lancashire OL1 1DN
Mgt/BO: 0161 911 3240
Email: otw@oldham.gov.uk
Web Site: www.oldhamtheatreworkshop.co.uk
ADMINISTRATION:
Props: Oldham Metropolitan Borough Council
Artistic Director: James Atherton
Policy: Own Productions; Touring productions; Summer Schools; Workshops.
Cap: 80

THE RIVERSIDE
Whitworth Civic Hall Market Street, Whitworth, Rochdale, Lancashire OL12 8DP
Telephone: 01706 854130
Email: riverside-whitworth@zen.co.uk
Web Site: www.whitworthriverside.co.uk
ADMINISTRATION:
Props: Rossendale Borough Council
Cap: 250

Ormskirk, Lancashire

CIVIC HALL
Southport Road, Ormskirk, Lancashire L39 1LN
Tel: 01695 554 154
Email: matt.orr@engine-rooms.co.uk
Web Site: www.ormskirkcivichall.info
ADMINISTRATION:
Props: The Engine Rooms
Cap: 320
Contact: Matt Orr

Oundle, Northamptonshire
Pop.3,500. London 83 miles.
Newspapers: See Peterborough. STD code 01832

STAHL THEATRE
West Street, Oundle, Peterborough, PE8 4EJ
Tel/Fax 01832 273 930
Email: ajhb@oundleschool.org.uk
Web Site: www.oundleschool.org.uk
ADMINISTRATION:
Props: Oundle School
Director: Alistair Boag
Policy: To provide a well-equipped stage for Oundle School and other local productions, and professional entertainment: the best of small drama groups, small opera and dance companies, mime, puppets, children's theatre, revue, readings. Occasionally whole week, mainly half-week or one-night bookings.
Seats: 264 on single raked tier.
TECHNICAL:
Stage: End stage wing space and optional forestage/ orchestra pit; Width 7.5m, Depth 8.1m (max) 3.3m (min); Typical flying bar ht. 5.7m. 2 winches and 4 hemp sets, Wing Widths P.S. 4m O.P. 1.5m.
Lighting: Switchboard: Avab Pronto with 62 Dimmers. Two lighting bridges acros auditorium, and follow spot positions. Approx. 80 lanterns (various).
Sound Equip: Spirit mkII 12-4-2 mixer, Crown amplifiers, EV and Tannoy speakers. 2 x minidisk, 2 x CD, 1 x cassette and 1 x Revox B77.
Dressing Rooms 1-6, 2-4; Green room. 2 Showers, 2 WCs. Orchestra Pit 12 sq.m. approx. 12 players.
Get-in door 1.8m wide by 4.2m high into scene dock of 20 sq.m. by 4.3m high.
Workshop/scene store 60 sq.m. by 4.3m high.

Oxford, Oxfordshire
Pop. 111,680. London 57 miles.
Newspapers: Oxford Mail (ntly); Oxford Times (fri). STD code 01865

ARTS AT THE OLD FIRE STATION
40 George Street, Oxford OX1 2AQ
Tel: 01865 263980
Email: jeremy.spafford@oldfirestation.org.uk
Web Site: www.oldfirestation.org.uk
ADMINISTRATION:
Props: Arts at the Old Fire Station Oxford and Crisis Skylight Oxford
Director: Jeremy Spafford
Technical Manager: Josh Tomalin
Bookings: Sam Scott
Seats: 124 seated, 200 standing
TECHNICAL:
Stage: Removable. Width 7320mm; depth 5150mm
Lighting: 100 channel ARRI Image desk with DMX512 protocol to the racks, 92 ways Green Ginger/Eurolight dimmers. Stands and Cabling available.
Sound: Soundcraft Spirit Live 4 Mark II 16:4:2 mixing desk, 1 x AB 1200 stereo amplifier, 2 x Bose 800 full-range speakers (with hook clamps) and equaliser. Denon cassette deck. Mics etc available.
For full technical details please contact the venue.

THE NEW THEATRE
George Street, Oxford OX1 2AG
Admin/ SD: 01865 320 760 BO: 0844 871 3020
Email: deanstewart@theambassadors.com
Web Site: www.atgtickets.com/oxford
ADMINISTRATION:
Props: Ambassadors Theatre Group (Venues) Ltd
General Manager: Dean Stewart
Stage Manager: Sarah Ripley
Contact: oxfordstagemgmt@theambassadors.com
Box Office Manager: Tim Nicholls, contact: 01865 320765
Policy: Touring Plays, Ballet, Opera, Musical, Comedy, Concerts, Pantomime.
Seats: 1,800. Four Bars. (Stalls 831, Circle 556, Balcony 413)
TECHNICAL:
STAGE: Proscenium Stage, Flat; Pros. opening 13.72m; Ht. of Pros. 7.32m; Depth of S/Line 12.19m; Ht. of Grid 18.29m; 62 lines, C/W, Scenery Flying Ht. 17.68m; Flying Bars 15.24m, 63mm dia., W/Widths P.S. 12.19m x 4.27m plus

Scene Dock 2.44m x 12.19m, O.P. 4.57m x 5.49m plus 6.10m x 2.44m; Prompt Cnr. O.P.
LIGHTING: Switchboard: ETC Express 250, 132 ways (12 x 5kw), 12 Source 4, 12 1200w starlett fresnels + sils + stock etc. Rear of Circle; F.O.H. House Boom 6 Sil 30 each side, Balcony 18 Sil 15.12 x source 4. Lantern stocks available. Limes: 2 Teatros, rear of Balcony. Local supplier of additional equipment exists also.
PROJECTION: 2 Gaumont Kalee 35mm, rear of Circle.
DRESSING ROOMS: One suite, 11 rooms accommodating seventy +; Showers. Orchestra Pit 24; Accom. 2 rooms plus washing facilities. Artiste's call box at the stage door 245691.
OTHER: Piano available.

OXFORD PLAYHOUSE

Beaumont Street, Oxford OX1 2LW
Admin: 01865 305 305 BO: 01865 305 305 SD: 01865 305 301 Mktg: 01865 305 399 Press: 01865 305 388 Admin Fax: 01865 305 333 BO Fax: 01865 305 335
Email: admin@oxfordplayhouse.com
Web Site: www.oxfordplayhouse.com
ADMINISTRATION:
Props: Oxford Playhouse Trust
Theatre Director: Louise Chantal
Senior Front of House Manager: Gemma Somerfield
Operations Manager: Stewart Smith
Technical Manager: Tim Boyd
Policy: Drama, Dance, Opera, Music, Concerts
Perfs: 7.30p.m., Fri 8.00p.m Matinee: Thurs & Sat 2.30p.m.
Seats: 600. Licensed cafe, bar.
TECHNICAL:
Stage: Proscenium with forestage, Flat; Pros. opening 8.38m; Ht. of Pros. 4.88m; Depth of S/Line 7.77m; Ht. of Grid 12.04m; 25 lines C/W, Scenery Flying Ht. 5.33m; Flying Bars 11.28m; W/Widths P.S. 1.52m, O.P. 2.44m; Prompt Cnr. S.R. 6x motorised flying bars.
Lighting: Lanterns: Profiles; 40x Juliat 15 / 38 1200w, 12x Source Four 12x19, 8x26, 4x36, 12x Selecon 650w 12x 18/32, 4x 24/44. Fresnel; 40x Juliat 1200w, 12x Juliat 2000w, 6x Selecon 650w PCs. Parcans; 20x par 64 120v 1000w 2'(narrow) & 5's (med/flood), 12x par 64 240v 1000w CP61 (narrow) & CP62 (med/flood). Floods; 12x irs 1s 1000w. Control: Lighting Board; Strand 520i and ETC Insight X2. Racks; Strand E.C. 90, 132 ways (120x2.5, 12x5K)
Sound: Mixer; Soundcraft K3 31-8-3 with 11x8 Matrix 128 mute groups. With Midi Control. Amps; 1x D&B 1200A For C6s, 2xD&B 1200A For E9s, 1x D&B 1200A for E18s, 3x C Audio RA 3001, 2x E PACS. Speakers; 4x D&B E9, 2x D&B C6, 4x D&B E3s, 4x Community CSX 35s, 2x D&B E18s. Playback; 1x Revox B77 (15 and 71/2ips), 1x Denon 770 Cassette deck, 1x Denon 1000N CD Player,2x Sony Mini Disc MDS E12, 1x Tascam DAT. F/X; 2x BSS 31 band St Graphic Equaliser, 1x Lexicon PCM 91 Digital Reverb, 2x BSS DPR 402 (4 channels of compressor / limiters), 1x DPR 504 (4 channels of noise gates), 1x Yamaha SPX 1000, 1x XTA DP 200. Mics; 3x Beyer M88, 4x Beyer 201, 2x Neuman KN1, 5x Shure Sm58, 1x Sennheiser 421, 2x Active BSS DI Boxes, 3x Passive EMO DI Boxes, 3x Crown PCC160, 2x 4 channel BSS AR 204 Line Balancing Unit. Stands; 8x boom stands.
Dressing Rooms: 7; Showers 4.
Orchestra pit - 30 musicians when forestage lowered below auditorium level.
Membership: TMA

OXFORD TOWN HALL

St Aldate's, Oxford OX1 1BX
Tel: 01865 252351
Email: townhall@oxford.gov.uk
Web Site: www.oxford.gov.uk
ADMINISTRATION:
Props: Oxford City Council
Cap: Main Hall 500 upstairs; 242 Gallery; Assembly Room 200; Old Library 120
For bookings contact Town Hall Management Office
Tel: 01865 252195 Fax: 01865 252388

PEGASUS THEATRE

Magdalen Road, Oxford OX4 1RE
Admin: 01865 812160 BO: 01865 812150 Fax: 01865 812170
Email: info@pegasustheatre.org.uk
Web Site: www.pegasustheatre.org.uk
ADMINISTRATION:
Policy: Small scale touring venue. Home of the Oxford Youth Theatre
Perfs: Approx. evenings 8.00pm
CEO/ Artistic Director: Jonathan Lloyd
Office Manager: Jessica McHugh
Head of Technical and Production: Dave Thwaites
TECHNICAL:
STAGE: Floor level. Performing area 9.5m x 7.2m - wing width 3m SR. No rake - floor sprung wood with optional double-sided Harlequin Dance Lino, suitable for dance, backstage crossover possible, stage heated. Height of grid 5.2m. Get in direct to stage - back doors 1.3m x 3m. Tallescope + Ext Ladder.
LIGHTING: Sirius 48 board, 100 patch circuits.6 x independents, suitable lantern stock.
SOUND: Soundcraft Delta 16:4:2 Mixer, 16 way mic patch 1 x 100W per channel amp, 2 x cassette deck, 1 x Revox B77 reel-to-reel , Alesis Quadroverb, 1 CD player, 1 Graphic Equaliser (31 band stereo). 2 x Meyers and 2 x JBL control 10, cans comms. Acoustics suitable for music and spoken word. Basic mic stock.Details and plans available on request.
BACKSTAGE: 1 Dressing room, accom. up to 10 people; access by stairs; iron and board; 6 power points. Rehearsal rooms. Advice given on accommodation. Staff - casuals available. Backstage facilities are partially accessible to disabled performers and staff - dressing room can be arranged in adjacent building.

SHELDONIAN THEATRE

Broad Street, Oxford OX1 3AZ
Tel 01865 277 299
Email: enquiries@sheldon.ox.ac.uk
Web Site: www.sheldon.ox.ac.uk
Manager: Maggie Vurge
Seating/Capacity: 900
Ceremonial Hall of University of Oxford - Concerts of serious music (no stage)

Paisley, Renfrewshire

PAISLEY ARTS CENTRE

New Street, Paisley, Renfrewshire PA1 1EZ Scotland
Tel: 0300 300 1210
Email: ram.els@renfrewshire.gov.uk
Web Site: www.renfrewshire.gov.uk
ADMINISTRATION:
Arts and Museum Manager: Mhairi Cross
Paisley Arts Centre and Paisley Town Hall are managed by Renfrewshire Arts, part of Renfrewshire Council's department of Education and Leisure Services. Paisley Arts Centre houses a 151 seat theatre and programmes all year round with drama, dance, comedy and music events. Paisley Arts Centre also has a workshop space available for hire. Paisley Town Hall is a magnificent Victorian building which programmes large scale music events and is available to hire for weddings, conferences, meetings and social events. Renfrewshire Council also has numerous other community halls available for hire. For more information on hiring the venue, email: eventhires@renfrewshire.gov.uk
TECHNICAL:
Paisley Arts Centre and Paisley Town Hall are fully technically equiped and serviced buildings.

PAISLEY MUSEUM

High Street, Paisley, Renfrewshire PA1 2BA Scotland
Tel: 0300 300 1210
Email: arts.els@renfrewshire.gov.uk
Web Site: www.renfrewshire.gov.uk
Arts and Museum Manager: Mhairi Cross

Pembroke Dock, Pembrokeshire

PATER HALL

Lewis Street, Pembroke Dock, Pembrokeshire SA72 6DD Wales

Tel: 01646 622 788
Email: i.s.jones@lineone.net
ADMINISTRATION:
Props: The Pater Hall Community Trust
Main Hall: Capacity 255 seated, 300 standing, dance hall with tabled seating 180.
Warrior Room: Seated 50
Sunderland Room: Seated 50
Meyrick Owen Suite: Seated 50
For bookings contact Mr Ian Jones
Dance hall, conference hall, limited theatre license, plays, social functions, concerts, etc, catering facilities. Adjoining rooms for smaller functions.

Penarth, South Glamorgan

THE PAGET ROOMS

Victoria Road, Penarth, South Glamorgan CF64 3EG Wales
Tel: 029 2070 0721 Fax: 029 2071 2574
Email: enquiries@penarthtowncouncil.gov.uk
Web: www.penarthtowncouncil.gov.uk
ADMINISTRATION:
Props: Penarth Town Council
Cap: 398
For bookings contact the Town Clerk, Penarth Town Council, West House, Stanwell Road, Penarth, South Glamorgan CF64 2YG. Tel: 029 2070 0721 Fax: 029 2071 2574

Penzance, Cornwall

Pop.19,110. London 281 miles.
Newspapers: The Cornishman (thurs).
STD code 01736

ACORN THEATRE

Parade Street, Penzance, Cornwall TR18 4BU
Tel: 01736 363545
Email: admin@theacornpenzance.co.uk
Web Site: www.theacornpenzance.com
ADMINISTRATION:
Contact: Vanessa Jackson
Technician: Steve Warhurst
Tel: 01736 363545
Capacity:
Main Auditorium; Standing, 170, Balcony, 53, Closely seated, 170. Cabaret, 100.
Small downstairs auditorium: Capacity 80 max.
Basement Bar; Standing, 80. Cabaret, 60. Seated, 80., dressing room.
TECHNICAL:
STAGE: Performing area; 8m x 6m (total 42m2). Black box masking - back wall used as cyclorama. Access to a grey harlequin dance floor. Baby Grand piano (there is a charge to have this tuned). Get In; Access via ramp in Union Street carpark. One parking permit is available for carpark behind venue.
LIGHTING: Desk; ZERO 88 FROG with screen. Dimmers; STRAND ACT 6, ZERO 88 BETA PACKS. 4 permanently set up giving 24 channels. 2 more can be added giving 36 channels running the FROG in wide mode. Lanterns; 10 x Quartete profiles, 12 x Quartete frenels, 6 x Par64, 10 x Par 36 pin spots, 4 x ADB profiles, 8 x ADB frenels, 5 x Patt 23, 2 x Strand 833.
SOUND: Main Auditorium; Soundcraft K2 24 channelAlesis HD24, Alesis Masterlink ml9000, Tascam MD305, Denon DN-T620 cd/cassette, Bheringer DEQ9624, Bheringer GEQ3102 x 3, Bheringer Composer x 2, Bheringer Multiygate x 2, Lexicon MPX1, Alesis Midiverb 4. F.O.H speakers and amps. Martin EM75, EV SB180, Bheringer CX3400 crossover, Yamaha PC2602 amp, EV P3000 amp.
Lower Auditorium; Soundcraft Powerstation 600, Denon DN-T620 cd/cassette, Martin EM75. Monitors; Viscount Base 12 self powered x 2, DAS 15A selfpowered x 2, Bose 802 pair.
Microphones; AKG C1000 x 4, AKG C416 x 2, AKG C411 x 2, AKG D770 x 2, AKG D3700 x 3, AKG Full drumset, Shure SM58 x 6, Shure SM57 x 6, Shure SM58 radio mics x 2, AudioTechnica AT804 x 2, Sennhiser 602E
DRESSING ROOMS; 2, limited washing facilities.

MINACK THEATRE

On the Open Cliff-side, Porthcurno, Churchtown, St. Levan, Penzance, Cornwall TR19 6JU
BO 01736 810181 Fax 01736 810779
Email: info@minack.com
Web Site: www.minack.com
ADMINISTRATION:
Prop: The Minack Theatre Trust
Theatre Manager: Philip Jackson
Policy: Weekly change of Company and production through season of seventeen weeks May - September.
Perfs: Five evenings at 8.00, usually two Mats. at 2.00.
Seats: 700. Coffee and Light Refreshments served in interval and before performance.
TECHNICAL:
Stage: Adverse Rake Stage
Lighting: Frog, 36 dimmers.
Sound: Allen and Heath GL2 16:4:2 control desk with graphic equaliser etc., connected to amplifiers. 16 channels. CD, DAT and cassette available.
Dressing Rooms: Accommodate up to 40.

ST JOHN'S HALL

Alverton Street, Penzance, Cornwall TR18 2QR
Foyer Tel: 01736 363244
Email: david.frost@penwith.gov.uk
ADMINISTRATION:
Props: Penwith District Council
Cap: 399
For bookings contact Mrs Clare James
Tel: 01209 615050 Fax: 01

Perth, Perth & Kinross

Pop. 42,583. London 417 miles.
Newspapers: Perthshire Advertiser (tues/fri). Dundee Courier (dly). STD code 01738

PERTH CONCERT HALL

Admin Address: Mill Street Perth PH1 5HZ
Admin: 01738 472 700 Fax: 01738 624 576 Stage Door: North Port, Perth, PH1 5HZ
Email: info@horsecross.co.uk
Web Site: www.horsecross.co.uk
ADMINISTRATION:
Marketing Manager: Hollie Wegner-Jaszkin
Conference and Events Manager: Michaela Ruff
Capacity: 1186 seated, 1622 with standing room

GANNOCHY AUDITORIUM:
STAGE: 20m (65') wide @ front, 15m (49') wide @ rear, 10m (32') deep
BACKSTAGE FACILTIES: Dressing Rooms: 6, accommodating 223 maximum. Laundry Facilities: 1 x washing machine 5kg load capacity, 1 x tumble Dryer (Condenser) 7kg load capacity, 2 x ironing boards, 2 x steam irons.
Visit the website for full technical specifications.

PERTH THEATRE

Closed till 2017
185 High Street, Perth, Perth & Kinross PH1 5UW Scotland
Mgt: 01738 472 700 BO: 01738 621 031
SD: 01738 621 435 Fax: 01738 62 4576
Email: info@horsecross.co.uk
Web Site: www.horsecross.co.uk
ADMINISTRATION:
Props: Perth Repertory Theatre Co Ltd
General Manager: Graeme Wallace
Technical Manager: Gavin Johnston
Policy: Repertory Season and Tours in.
Perfs: 7.30. Mats Sat. 2.30
Seats: 490. Licensed Bar, Coffee Bar, Restaurant, Exhibition Area.
TECHNICAL:
Stage: Proscenium arch. Performing area 9.6m x 8.23m - pros opening 7.35m x 6.1m - wing widths 5.2m front, 4m rear SR, 3.45m front, 2.6m rear SL. Stage raked, 1 in 24 - floor hardboard on hardwood, sprung, suitable for dance, backstage crossover, stage heated. Height of grid 13.41m - 37 counterweight sets, single purchase (plus 1 hemp set for cyc), 35 x 0.15m apart, 3 x 0.38m apart - maximum flying height 12.3m (no. 15 is 12m only) - black legs and borders - brown and gold house tabs, flown. 6 x 15A sockets. Flexible trap openings midstage, DSR and DSL. Forestage 7.35m x 1.2m. Orchestra pit variable, accommodates up

to 46. Get-in via service area off Mill Street, dock doors 3.5m x 3.28m. Safety curtain. Scale stage plan available, 1:25.
Lighting: GSX board, 94 circuits, operated from control room at rear of circle - 100A 3 phase supply available for temporary board - 18 profiles, 26 fresnels, 18 floods, 12 pars - 2 followspots operated from gallery.
Sound: Soundcraft 3.24 Digital 32:16 Mixer - 4 x C-Audio amps - 4 x Turbosound TMS, 8 x Yamaha, 4 x d&b MAX speakers - 2 x Shure SM58, 4 x Sennheiser MKH 416, 2 x Neuman KM84i, 5 x Crown PCC 160 mics - Revox CD player, 3 x Tascam minidiscs. Acoustics suitable for music and spoken word. K1 16:4 Analogue Mixers, TEAC Cassette Player.
Stage Management: Prompt corner SR - show relay/Tannoy to dressing rooms.
Backstage: 6 dressing rooms, 43 places, access by stair - green room - quick change rooms as required - wardrobe above dressing rooms, with irons, industrial washing machine, dryer and dry cleaner, lots of power points. Access to FOH catering plus hot and cold drinks machine. Rehearsal room and piano, excellent. Advice given on accommodation. Staff - 3 stage, 2 lighting, 1 sound, 1 wardrobe - casuals available - security personnel. Backstage facilities accessible to disabled performers and staff.
Additional Information: Steinway Model B grand piano available for concert hire.
STUDIO THEATRE
Stage: Performing Area 14.75m x 10.65m including variable seating area. Floor sprung composition, suitable for dance. Height of grid 5.4m (6m to roof). Get-in as main theatre.
Lighting: BBC Micro-pulsar software, 36 channels @ 10A, operated from gallery.
Sound: Acoustics suitable for music and spoken word. Stage management tannoy to dressing rooms.
Backstage: Facilities shared with Main Theatre.
Studio Theatre: 7m x 5m, seating: 110 max
Membership: Federation of Scottish Theatres, Ltd. Salvo.

Peterborough, Cambridgeshire

Pop. 124,000. London 81 miles.
Newspapers: Peterborough Citizen (thurs); Peterborough Evening Telegraph (nlty); Peterborough Herald & Post (fri).
STD code 01733

BUSHFIELD SPORTS CENTRE

Orton Centre Bushfield, Peterborough, Cambridgeshire PE2 5RQ
Tel: 01733 864 656
Email: bushfieldsports@vivacity-peterborough.com
Web Site: www.vivacity-peterbough.com
ADMINISTRATION:
Props: Vivacity
Manager: Ben Chan
Capacity: 800

CRESSET THEATRE

Rightwell Bretton Centre Peterborough Cambridgeshire PE3 8DX
Tel: 01733 265705
Email: pbanham@cresset.co.uk
Web Site: www.cresset.co.uk
Props:
General Manager: Phil Parker
Technical Manager: Darren Buckman
Bookings: Pam Banham
Capacity: 860

DEEPINGS LEISURE CENTRE

Park Road, Deeping St James, Peterborough, Cambridgeshire PE6 8NF
Tel: 01778 344 072
Email: deepings@litc.co.uk
Web Site: www.litc.co.uk
ADMINISTRATION:
Props: South Kesteven District Council
Cap: 600 (stage facilities)
Manager: Michael Chester

KEY THEATRE

Embankment Road, Peterborough, Cambridgeshire PE1 1EF
Mgt: 01733 552 437 BO: 01733 207 239
Email: maggie.saxon@vivacity-peterborough.com
Web Site: www.vivacity-peterborough.com
ADMINISTRATION:
Props: Vivacity
Artistic Director: Maggie Saxon
Policy: Touring in-house productions and concerts
Seats: 354
One Bar. Riva Restaurant
TECHNICAL:
Stage: Thrust stage with easy access between stage and auditorium. No safety curtain. Auditorium and stage share a common roof; there is no ceiling and no physical proscenium arch, the upper limit of the audience's aspect being defined rather by the exposed lighting grid and black painted structural ironwork.
Stage Dimensions: Overall width including wings: 20.7m (68ft). Overall depth including 2.4m (8ft) thrust: 10.6m (35ft).
Approx depth from setting line if tabs used: 7.2m (23ft 6ins). Pros opening: 13.1m (43ft) wide can be reduced to a minimum of 9.7m (32ft) by semi-permanent black tormentors). Minimum overhead clearance on stage is dictated by the roll-up cinema screen at 5.5m (18ft), structural ironwork at 5.9m (19ft 4ins) and fixed LX bars at 6.4m (21ft). Overall height stage floor to roof: 8.2m (27ft).
Hemp Lines - 2 sets, 0.48m o.d. barrels, max height of bar 8m (26ft 3ins) above stage floor (ie approx 2.1m (7ft) above grid height). One additional set, light duty only, against back wall (max flying height 5.4m (17ft 10ins).
Stage floor - Black hardboard. No rake.
Masking - Complete black masking (except top masking) as follows:-
Midstage - black screen-masking tabs. These tabs can be fully closed if required, reducing depth of stage to 4.9m (16ft), including thrust. Upstage - 5.5m (18ft) black legs on wrap-around track to give full or partial rear masking.
Cyclorama - Canvas cyc 14.6m (48ft) wide x 5.5m (18ft) high on straight track immediately upstage of black masking track. Cyc track is approx. 9m (3ft) downstage from back wall.
House tabs - Cherry coloured draw-tabs operated by hand-drum OP. Not recommended for fast curtain calls.
Orchestra pit - 9.1m (30ft) wide x 3m (10ft) deep, accommodates up to 18 musicians. All or part of the front row of seating is lost (ie up to 26 seats), depending on size of pit required. Please advise as early as possible if the orchestra pit is required.
Get-in - Good access for lorries up to get-in doors 2m (6ft 6ins) wide x 3m (10ft) hight. Doors open directly on to stage (OP side), with a loading height of .8m (2ft 8ins) above outside ground level.
Scene dock - adjacent to stage, PS.
Usable storage space approx 3m x 1.83m (10ft x 6ft) for props, wardrobe etc. Access from stage via doors 6.1m (20ft) high x 2m (6ft 6ins) wide.
Wardrobe area - in scene dock.
Equipment comprising washing machine, tumble dryer, iron and ironing board.
Dressing rooms - No1. 4 seats, No 2. 4 seats, No 3. 8 seats (all on stage level), Nos 4-7 all at rear of theatre in well appointed Portakabins(attached to main building). Special arrangements for large companies if necessary. All dressing rooms have wash basins, power points, mirror (with lights) and costume rails.
Shower and WC at stage level (Gents) and 1st floor (Ladies).
Cueing system - SM desk on PS.
Headset intercom system is provided.
Paging facility to dressing rooms and foyers; show relay to dressing rooms.
Lighting: Positions - Two bridges FOH, with 0.48m o.d. hanging rail at 6.7m (22ft) above stage level. 5 LX bars on stage at a fixed height of 6.4m (21ft). 4 telescopic stands. For further details see stage plan.
Lighting control - ETC Insight 3X (8 x 5kw, 124 x 2kw, 18 non-dim).
Lanterns - 24 x 54 15-30 degrees; 24 x Patt 743 with barndoors, 4 x 4 cell Cyc floods, 24 x 54 par.
Colour - Lee.
Lime positions - with LX and sound control. 2 x solo C.I.D.
Sound: Control position rear of auditorium in same room as LX.
8 x Shur SM58, 2 x Beyer 201, 1 x Soundcraft Venue 32-8-2 mixer, 1 x SPX-90 11.
5 x mic stands, Soundcraft 40-8-2 spirit live, 8 x SM 58 (shure), 2 x Mini Disc play-

ers, 1 x CD player, 6 x AKG C1000, 1 x Sennheiser E602, 4 x Sennheiser E604, 4 x Crown PCC 160. For companies touring large sound rigs a FOH mixing position is available, centre back row, at the expense of up to 16 seats. Please advise as early as possible if this is required. length of multicore needed to reach the stage is approx 100ft.
Ground Plans - 1:24 scale ground plans are available on request

WERRINGTON SPORTS CENTRE

Staniland Way, Werrington, Peterborough, Cambridgeshire PE4 6JT
Tel: 01733 576 606 Fax: 01733 320 053
Email: werringtonsportscentre@vivacity-peterborough.com
Web Site: www.vivacity-peterborough.com
ADMINISTRATION:
Props: Vivacity Peterborough Culture and Leisure
Manager: Jamie Fenton
Capacity: 300

Peterlee, County Durham

PETERLEE LEISURE CENTRE

St Cuthbert's Road, Peterlee, County Durham SR8 1AF
Tel: 0191 586 2400 Fax: 0191 586 5479
Email: peterlee@leisureconnection.co.uk
Web Site: www.leisureconnection.co.uk
ADMINISTRATION:
Props: One Life
Manager: Malcolm Grinstead
Cap: 1,500 Standing
Multi-use leisure centre. Conferences, exhibitions, dances, sporting events.

Pitlochry, Perth & Kinross

Pop. 2,419. London 444 miles. STD code 01796

PITLOCHRY FESTIVAL THEATRE

Port-Na-Craig, Pitlochry, Perthshire PH16 5DR Scotland
Admin: 01796 484 600 BO: 01796 484 626 Fax: 01796 484 616
Email: admin@pitlochryfestivaltheatre.com
Web Site: www.pitlochryfestivaltheatre.com
ADMINISTRATION:
Administered by Pitlochry Festival Theatre
Chief Executive: John Durnin
Artistic Director: John Durnin
Theatre Manager: Margaret Pirnie
Head of Production & Resources: Steve Carlin
Commercial Director: Derek Allan
Policy: Festival of plays in repertoire (May-October); Sunday Concerts, Art Exhibitions, Conferences. Winter Season (Nov-Apr).
Perfs: Eves. 8.00; Mats. 2.00. (Winter 8pm)
Seats: 540 + 4 wheelchair spaces.
Restaurant & Bars open daily (inc. Sunday) Parking for 120 cars and disabled 10.
TECHNICAL:
Stage: Proscenium, Flat; Pros. opening 10.47m; Max Ht. to adjustable house border 6.80m; Depth: Setting line to back wall; 13.10m; Curved forestage 2.00m deep (max), Width: Centre line to P.S. wall 10.80m; Centre line to O.P. C/W frame 8.80m; Height: to underside Grid 9.15m; to underside fly floor O.P. 7.64m; Flying: 22 Hemp, 5 line sets; 15 sets single purchase C/W. Max Bar load 250 kg. All bar lengths 13.50m. Prompt Cnr.
Variable Storage: Scene dock P.S. 140 sq.m. Scene dock O.P. 132 sq.m.; Get-in in P.S. scene dock. Door with 0.20 step, 3.37m x 6.95m high.
Lighting: Control: Rank Strand 139 way Gemini situated in Control Suite above rear stalls; Circuits: F.O.H. 44 (3 slots each side paired across, and 2 bridges), Grid. 54, Dips. 28 (iincluding 3 ladders on track each side); Equipment: 34, Sil 30, 12. Starlett, 18. Minuette, 2 Patt.243, 40 Patt.743, 23 Patt.123, 26 Patt.264, 18 Patt 23II, 23 Patt. 23, 14 1001 Flood, 4 (3 circuit) PAR batten, 8 (4 circuit) Pallas groundrow 2 Sil 15.
Sound Equip: Soundcraft 24-16, 3 x Revox B77, 2 x Cassette Decks, 1 x CD player, all situated in Control Suite above rear stalls; 15 balanced microphone inputs, 3JBL speakers each side of pros.; 4 portable speakers.
Artistes' Accommodation: 6 Dressing Rooms capable of taking 5 artistes each. 4 Showers. With financial assistance from Scottish Arts Council and Perth & Kinross Council.
Membership: Federation of Scottish Theatre.

Plymouth, Devon

Pop. 257,900. London 211 miles.
Newspapers: Western Evening Herald (ntly); The Western Morning News (dly); South Devon Times (fri); Sunday Independent. STD code 01752

THE BARBICAN THEATRE

Castle Street, Plymouth, Devon PL1 2NJ
Tel: 01752 267 131
Email: info@barbicantheatre.co.uk
Web Site: www.barbicantheatre.co.uk
ADMINISTRATION:
Director: Sheila Snellgrove
Artistic Director: Mark Laville
Theatre Administration and Box Office: Dan Baker
Technician: Jamie Smith (01752) 242015
Policy: Young People's Theatre Centre, small scale touring venue for Dance and experimental/new work. Producer of TIE touring issue-based work.
Cap: 140
TECHNICAL:
STAGE: A semi sprung wooden floor, with black/grey performance/dance floor available. Stage front lifts out to reveal stepped pit beneath (see plans); open stage with flexible black drape surround, legs and cyclorama (see plans). Stage Dimensions - Width 10.20m, Depth 8.90m depth (7.15 with pit open), Height to LX line 5.50m, 7.90m to highest point of ceiling.
LIGHTING: Distribution - 96 circuits (15amp). Dimming - 48 ways DMX (Anytronics) in 3 phases. Control - Sirius 48 programmable. Riggers - Zero88 Linebacker. Lantern Stock - P743 Fresnels (1000w) 4 no +B/D; Ianero Fresnel (1000w) 2 no +B/D; Thomas Fresnel (500w) 2 no; Prelude F (650w) 1 no +B/D; Pat 123 (500w) 3 no +B/D; Cantata PC (1200w) 4 no +B/D; Quartet PC (650w) 10 no +B/D; Prelude PC (650w) 5 no +B/D; Minim PC (500w) 4 no; Sil 30 profile (1000w) 3 no; SL 23/50 (600w) 3 no; Quartet 22/40 (650w) 6 no; Prelude 16/30 (650w) 5 no; Milano 16/30 (650w) 1 no; Pat 23 Profile (500w) 1 no; Minim F (300/500w) 4 no - used as houselights; Parcan (1000w) 8 no; Coda 1 (500w) 9 no; Pat 60 Flood (500w) 4 no.
Ceiling: The ceiling is beamed and vaulted above the lighting bar line.
SOUND: Speakers - 2 x Ohm RW3 300w full range; Foldback - 2 x Peavey powered 100w; Amp - Peavey CS800 Stereo power 800w; Desk - Allen & Heath Sc series 24 channel; Playback - CD, MD, Cass (analogue and digital; Tielines - Box to stage/stage to box - 12 x XLR, 4 x 0.25" jack; Comms - Box/USL/USR/DSL/Rehearsal studio.
ACCESS: The theatre building, auditorium, backstage areas and stage have good disabled and wheelchair access. The lighting control box and upper dressing room have difficult access.
Seating - 110 fixed seats in a raked auditorium, other 145 seats with stepped pit open as seating area, both end - on.
DRESSING ROOMS: 2 dressing rooms, washing facilities and shower (shower has difficult disabled access)
Piano: An upright is available.
Any queries or further information: Contact Production & Facilities Manager.

PLYMOUTH PAVILIONS

Millbay Road, Plymouth, Devon PL1 3LF
Tel: 0845 146 1460
Email: enquiries@plymouthpavilions.com
Web Site: www.plymouthpavilions.com
ADMINISTRATION:
Props: Plymouth Pavilions Ltd.
Chief Executive: James Brent
General Manager: Gavin Marshall
Events Bookings: Pippa Reigate

Policy: Concert Venue opened summer 1991, also available to host conferences, exhibitions and major sporting events. Full light and sound system, large scale in-house catering service, seven meeting/green rooms plus dressing rooms. City Centre based.
Seating/Capacity: 2,542 seated, 3,800 standing/seated; 1,600 recital format, seated.

THEATRE ROYAL

Royal Parade Plymouth, Devon PL1 2TR
Mgt/SD: 01752 668 282 BO: 01752 267 222 Mgt Fax: 01752 230506 BO Fax: 01752 230 502 Mktg Fax: 01752 230506
Tech Fax: 01752 230506
Email: info@theatreroyal.com
Web Site: www.theatreroyal.com
ADMINISTRATION:
Props: Theatre Royal (Plymouth) Ltd
Chief Executive: Adrian Vinken
Artistic Director: Simon Stokes
Acting Director of Production: David Miller
Technical Manager: Mark Hawker
Marketing & Sales Director: Marianne Locatori
Finance Director: Helen Costello
Creative Learning Director: Victoria Allen
Capacity: 1320/175
Policy: Theatre Royal; Own productions of large-scale musicals and plays, usually with partner theatres or producers, either transferring to London or touring nationally. A wide and varied visiting programme of opera, ballet, dance, musicals and drama. Drum Theatre; An extensive range of new writing drama and education-based work, both produced and visiting.
Seats: Main House Auditorium 1,320 max - adjustable ceiling reduces seating to 768. Drum Theatre - studio theatre with variable seating and staging a max of 250 seats. Two Bars, Coffee Bar, Restaurant, Sponsor's Bar, Function Room and Mezzanine Art Gallery with work by local artists. Facilities for disabled patrons include internal wheelchair lift, audio described and signed performances.
TECHNICAL:
Stage: Proscenium with thrust fly tower over stage and forestage. Flat stage, Modular, total of 40 (2.4m x 1.2m) removable sections 2 orchestra pit lifts; Pros. opening 12.5m; Ht. of Pros. (Max) 8.5m; Stage depth from front of stage to back wall 14m (from US of orchestra); Depth of forestage 3.15m; Grid 25m; 78 single purchase counterweight sets at 200mm centres; 4 motor sets over forestage; Flying bars 14.5m (extendable to 18.5m); 1 up and downstage counterweight set each side; 2 motor up and downstage sets each side (Each half depth of stage); Stage manager's desk P.S.
Lighting: 3 supplies 200A per phase TP&N plus others. Control: Strand 530.Control room at rear of stalls; 350 channels Genius Pro full software; 185 2.5kw circuits; 347 ways of LD90, (258x2.5kw circuits; 81x5kw circuits; 8x10kw circuits) supplied by 800A TP&N. 3DMX Tie lines + RJ45 tie line infrastructure. Powerlock in. Further information on www.theatreroyal.com.asp
Sound: Sound control position rear of stalls. Sound tie line system. Meyer UPAs and adequate playback systems.
Yamaha 02R Digital Desk, 10 buss, 6 aux 2 inboard fx, adat card Soundcraft FX16, 4 buss, 3 aux, 1 inboard fx. DDA interface 20 ch, 6 buss, 6 aux, Comms system.
Dressing Rooms 20; accom. 113 (rooms shared with Drum Theatre). Most rooms with Showers.
Orchestra Pit to accommodate 76 musicians. 4 Band Rooms.
DRUM THEATRE
The Drum Theatre is based on an end stage form (usually accommodating 175 seats) but can be re-arranged in various formats.
Stage: Clear height beneath lighting catwalks 5.75m. Set of black flats for a black box Lighting: Control is a Strand 430 control desk with 150 channels Genius Pro spftware (3 x DMX 1 x D54 outputs) & Riggers control on stage. Backup control is Strand System Wide Control 99 mem with times only. The desk will take show disks from Strand GSX, LBX, 430, 520, 530, 550 desks. 144 x 2.5kw Strand LD90 Digital Dimming Supplied by a 600 amp SP&N supply. Temp supply of 100 amps TP&N at stage level. ELECTRICS RIG: 8 x Selecon Acclaim 18/34 degree (600w axial-'M'size gobo) 10 x 26 degree Source fours 10 x 36 dregree Source fours 24 x 1kw CCT Sil 30 degree Profiles 12x 650w Selecon Acclaim Fresnels 24 x 1kw Starlette Fresnel 2 x 1.2kw Selecon Fresnel 2 x 2kw A.D.B. Fresnel 2 x 2kw Strand Bambino Fresnel 24x 240v Parcans SOUND RIG 1 x Sound Craft FX16 Sound desk (16 inputs, 4 outputs, 3 Aux, Onboard FX) 4 x Meyer UPA Speakers with flying frames. 2Subs 2Tascam Minidisc Recorders 2Numark CD Players.
Lighting: Control room at gallery level. Alternative position for desk available; Control, Rank Strand 430, 144 X 2.5kw dimmers
Sound: Control room side gallery. 16 microphone and 20 loudspeaker sockets located at all levels.

Pontefract, West Yorkshire

PONTEFRACT TOWN HALL

Bridge Street, Pontefract, West Yorkshire WF8 1PG
Tel: 01977 723420 Bookings: 01924 305830
Email: eventsandfunctions@wakefield.gov.uk
Web Site: www.wakefield.gov.uk
ADMINISTRATION:
Props: Wakefield Metropolitan District Council
Capacity: 274

Pontypridd, Rhondda Cynon Taff

HAWTHORN LEISURE AND RECREATIONAL CENTRE

Fairfield Lane, Pontypridd, Rhondda Cynon Taff CF37 5LN Wales
Tel: 01443 843 406 Fax: 01443 841 880
Email: phillip.n.owen@rctcbc.gov.uk
Web Site: www.rctcbc.gov.uk
ADMINISTRATION:
Props: Rhondda Cynon Taff County Borough Council
Cap: Multi-purpose sports hall 750; modern concert hall 250
Senior Assistant Manager: Dan Godfrey
For bookings contact Phillip Owen

Poole, Dorset

Pop. 125,000. London 112 miles.
Newspapers: Poole & Dorset Advertiser; Bournemouth Evening Echo. STD code 01202

LIGHTHOUSE, POOLE'S CENTRE FOR THE ARTS

21 Kingland Road, Poole, Dorset BH15 1UG
BO: 0844 406 8666
Email: info@lighthousepoole.co.uk
Web Site: www.lighthousepoole.co.uk
ADMINISTRATION:
Props: Poole Arts Trust Ltd
Lessees: Poole Arts Trust Ltd
Policy: Mixed programme with Concert Hall used for classical and popular music and in its flat floor mode for rock, cabaret, dances and exhibitions. Theatre used for touring repertory company, opera and ballet. Full-time cinema, studio, art gallery and function rooms.
Capacity: Concert Hall, 1473, Rock, 2459. Theatre, 669. Cinema, 103. Function Rooms, 240. Studio, 135.
Foyer Bars and Cafe Bar.
TECHNICAL:
Concert Hall:
STAGE: Orchestra seating for 120 and choir seating for 140. Details available on request. Steinway 'D' concert piano available.
DRESSING ROOMS: 4 Guest Artiste Rooms each with shower.
3 chorus changing rooms (approx. 25 each).
Theatre:
STAGE: Proscenium: Width 9900mm, Ht. 5400mm; Max. Width 19880mm; between Flyrails 13899mm; Depth 9900mm. Orchestra Pit: Approx 25 per-

sons, on lift. Converts to forestage.
Other technical information available on request.

Porthcawl, Mid Glamorgan

GRAND PAVILION

The Esplanade, Porthcawl, Mid Glamorgan CF36 3YW Wales
Tel: 01656 815995 Fax: 01656 815990
Email: pavillion@bridgend.gov.uk
Web Site: www.grandpavilion.co.uk
ADMINISTRATION:
Props: Bridgend County Borough Council
Cap: Theatre 643; Stage Door 100
Manager: Mark Phillips

Portsmouth, Hampshire

Pop. 187,000. London 71 miles.
Newspapers: The News (ntly); Streetlife (wkly); Journal (wkly). STD code 023 92

GUILDHALL

Guildhall Square, Portsmouth, Hampshire PO1 2AB
Tel: 023 93870 200 BO: 023 9282 4355
Fax: 023 9283 4177
Email: sharonhammond@portsmouthguildhall.org.uk
Web: www.portsmouthguildhall.org.uk
ADMINISTRATION:
Managed by Portsmouth Cultural Trust
General Manager: Andy Grays
Stage Manager: Nick Coles
Stage Productions Office: 023 9283 4162
Policy: Rock/Pop Concerts, live shows, major conferences, exhibitions, orchestral concerts, dinners, dances, product launches, sporting events.
Capacity: 2,228 Standing. 2,017 seated.
Cafe Guildhall, Full catering service and bars service available.
TECHNICAL:
Stage: Concert Hall (no proscenium arch), Flat; pros opening 21.78m x 8.9m high. Depth of stage 10.84m. stage width reduces to 10.64m at rear clearance 7.2m. 3 rows of 6 flying points (500 kg each).
PA & Lighting: PA System Turbosound TSE central cluster plus 6 bose 101s underneath balcony (upper stalls area) with fixed delay. Feed Mono; Graphic Klark Technic DN300 (settings fixed); Limiter Klark Technic DN500 (settings fixed) Desk Soundtracs Solo 32/4/2 Desk Input/Output Via BPO patch bay located at rear of effects rack. Tie Lines 20 balanced tie lines (fixed position) 4 rear auditorium 9 front stage 6 rear of stage 1 off stage right 8 tie line mobile stage box; Foldback 4 foldback lines controlled from desk 3 Turbosound TMW 212s Effects Rack 2 Denon Cassette Decks 1 Denon CD Player SPX 90. Front of House 12 x 1k pars (basic down light, covers front 10ft of stage) Front Truss 15 circuits 15amp x 3 32 amp x 1 Mid Truss 15 circuits 15amp x 3, 32amp x 1 Back Truss 15 circuits 15amp x 3 32amp x 1; Lamps 10 x 2k sils (without iris) 2 x 1k sils (without iris) 8 x 1k floods (working lights) 8 x 1k fresnels 8 x 2k fresnels 3 x bars of 6, Par 64 narrow beam 15 x par 64 narrow beam Spot Lights
2 x Pani 1200.
Microphones; 4 Micron hand held mics, 4 radio lapel mics.
Dressing Rooms 5; Accom. 150; 2 with showers. Open stage option or mobile staging units available to provide orchestra risers and/or Stage extensions.

NEW THEATRE ROYAL

20-24 Guildhall Walk, Portsmouth, Hampshire PO1 2DD
Mgmt: 023 9284 3979/ 023 9264 6477
BO: 023 9264 9000
Email: caroline@newtheatreroyal.com
Web Site: www.newtheatreroyal.com
ADMINISTRATION:
Props: The New Theatre Royal (Portsmouth) Trustees Ltd
Head of Marketing and Communications: Bradley Eccleshare
Policy: Busy and varied programme of professional touring theatre, concerts, dance events and community theatre.
Cap: 700

Potters Bar, Hertfordshire

THE WYLLYOTTS THEATRE

Darkes Lane, Potters Bar, Hertfordshire EN6 2HN
BO: 01707 645 005 Admin: 01707 660067 Fax: 01707 649 849
Email: ginny.williams@hertsmereleisure.co.uk
Web Site: www.wyllyottstheatre.co.uk
ADMINISTRATION:
Props: Hertsmere Leisure
Theatre Manager: Ginny Williams
Cap: 421 for stage shows, 120 for diners, exhibitions, art gallery, museum, 3 conference rooms, cafe and bar. Also used as part time Cinema

Preston, Lancashire

Pop. 95,450. London 212 miles.
Newspapers: Lancashire Evening Post (dly). STD code 01772

CHARTER THEATRE

Guild Hall Ltd Lancaster Road, Preston, Lancashire PR1 1HT
Tel: 01772 804 440 BO: 01772 804 444
Email: info@prestonguildhall.co.uk
Web Site: www.prestonguildhall.com
ADMINISTRATION:
Props: The Villa Group
General Manager: Melanie Hutchings
Contact: 01772 440 266 or melanie.hutchings@prestonguildhall.co.uk
Marketing Manager: Hannah Slater
Contact: 01772 440 263 or hannah.slater@prestonguildhall.co.uk
Senior Technician: James Hubbard
Contact: 01772 440 269 or james.hubbard@prestonguildhall.co.uk
Policy: Various
Seats: 780. (Stalls: 578, Circle: 202)Bars, Restaurant, Lounge Bar
TECHNICAL:
STAGE: Proscenium Arch - Orchestra pit used as thrust. Performing area 12.2m x 10.5m - pros opening 9.4m x 4.88m - wing widths 2.44m SL, 9.75m SR. No rake - floor lino on wood, semi sprung, suitable for all dance, backstage crossover, stage heated. Height of grid 15.07m - 3 hemp, 33 counterweight sets, single purchase - 2 tab tracks - 500kg permitted on bars - maximum flying height 7.3m - black and white legs and borderes - white filcloth gauze cyclorama - purplehouse tabs, flown. 2 x 13 amp ring mains. Orchestra pit (electrical) 3 levels front stage 10.25m x 2.35m entrance from under stage in lowest position. Auditorium level can be used to accommodate 40 musicians, entrance from side stage pass door. Get-in via lift and scenery hoist 3.05m x 2.44m. Tallescope. Scale stage, fly and lighting plans available.
LIGHTING: Ovation board with macro wing and moving light wing, Arri smart rack dimmers 150 circuits, 144 @ 2.5kw, operated from rear of auditorium - 100A 3 phase and 200A 3 phase supplies available on stage for temporary board - 52 profiles, 46 fresnels, 40 pars, 2 x Strand CSI followspots, operated from FOH.
SOUND: DDA 24:8:2 desk, operated from FOH - FOH and FX turbo speakers, 1 Kw PA system - 10 various mics _ Revox B77 reel -to-reel, Tascam DAT, Tascam Minidisc, Cassette tape systems - facilities for recording and editing. Acoustics suitable for music and spoken word.
STAGE MANAGEMENT: Prompt corner SL, cue lights and headsets, 8 outstations - show relay to dressing rooms.
BACKSTAGE: 7 dressing rooms, accommodating 34, 16 showers, facilities for disabled performers, access to stage by stairs and lift - green room - band room - quick change rooms - wardrobe in dressing room area with washing machine and dryers, 4 x 13amp sockets. Refreshments from front of house. Piano, Bechstein grand, excellent - stage doorkeeper and security personnel. Advice given on accommodation. Staff - 2 stage, 1 lighting, 1 sound casuals available.
ADDITIONAL: 35mm film projection, wide

screen and cinemascope. Dolby stereo sound with surround.

GUILD HALL

Lancaster Road, Preston, Lancashire PR1 1HT
Tel: 01772 804 440 BO: 01772 804 444
Email: info@prestonguildhall.co.uk
Web Site: www.prestonguildhall.com
ADMINISTRATION:
Props: The Villa Group
General Manager: Melanie Hutchings
Policy: Concert Hall, mixed use.
Seats: 2,020. Bars.
TECHNICAL:
Stage: Concert Stage - 6 piece hydraulic stage - 0.76m x 7.60m x 18.24m, plus choir area. Various positions for flying trusses available.
Lighting: Switchboard: Jands Event 40 x 2k fresnels, 12 x 2k profiles. Advance truss with 48 parcans. All round spot rail and sockets.
Sound Equip: 16:4:2 mixer, 1 Akai Reel, 2 Denon Cassette Decks, 1 Marantz CD Player. Speakers stage only. Turbosound P.A. + foot monitors. Dressing room relay.
Dressing Rooms: 6 + large Band Room. 2 showers and shared dressing room and shower facilities with Theatre, when available.

Pwllheli, Gwnedd

NEUADD DWYFOR

Stryd Penlan, Pwllheli, Gwynedd LL53 5DE Wales
Tel: 01758 704 088
Email: annrowenajones@gwynedd.gov.uk
Web Site: www.gwynedd.gov.uk/neuadd-dwyfor
ADMINISTRATION:
Props: Gwynedd County Council
Cap: 354
Manager: Ann Rowena
Technical Manager: Endaf Williams
Access: From Penlan St, side door (12ft X 15ft) via goods lift on to stage (lifft load capacity 2000kg)
Stage: Wood Flooring : Suitable for Dance; Proscenum Arch Stage: Pros opening 9.14m x 5.8m; Perfforming Area: 9.14m x 7.6m; Wing width: 5.2m; Height of Grid: 10m; Crossover available
Stage Dressing: Blue House Tabs on pulley, Red House Tabs on motor for the cinema, Black Tabs upstage, 4x White legs, 4x Black legs, 2x Borders. Stage loading: Maximum Point load to main stage area 0.63kn. Any loading in excess of this figure, should be place upon spreader members transferring load directly to longitudinal timbers. Capacity of longitudinal timbers should be 1.10km/m2. Futher information available if required.
Lighting control: Zero88 frog 48 channels, 12 subs, 2 x LD90, Dimmer racks, DMX point. Power: 48 channels, 62 + 32 amp 5 pin, 3 phase appliance on SL and SR, Access to grid via tallescope
Lamp Stock: 10 x Par64 (1k), 10 x Prelude 16/30 profiles (650w)
10 x Quartet Fresnels (650w), 6 x SL 15/32 (600w), 6 x Cantata Fresnels (1200w), 3 x strand coda 500/3 compartment floods
Sound: Mixing Console Soundcraft Spirit Lx7 24 channels, 4 x Yamaha SM 121v monitors, Re-verb 18 effects, 1 x CD Player
1 x MD Player, 3 x DI Box, 2 x Sure 57, 5 X Sure 58, 4 x Talkback System, Call system for dressing rooms and FOH
Baby Grand Piano can be supplied through in house technicians. Cost of tuning subject to terms and conditions.
Dressing Rooms: There are 2 principle dressing rooms SL & SR with en -suite wash basins. Shower and W.C available only in SL dressing room.

Queensferry, Flintshire

DEESIDE LEISURE CENTRE

Chester Road West, Queensferry, Flintshire CH5 1SA Wales
Tel: 01352 704 200
Email: deeside_leisure_centre@flintshire.gov.uk
Web Site: www.flintshire.gov.uk
ADMINISTRATION:
Props: Flintshire County Council
Cap: 2,300
For bookings contact Mike Welch

Radlett, Herts

THE RADLETT CENTRE

1 Aldenham Avenue, Radlett, Hertfordshire WD7 8HL
Admin/Tech: 01923 857 546 Fax: 01923 857 592 BO: 01923 859291
Email: admin@radlettcentre.com
Web Site: www.radlettcentre.co.uk
ADMINISTRATION:
General Manager: Greg Dexter
Technical Manager: Paul Foskett
Capacity: 300

Ramsgate, Kent

Pop. 40,070. London 74 miles.
Newspapers: Thanet Times (tues); Isle of Thanet Gazette (fri). STD code 01843 (Thanet)

GRANVILLE THEATRE

Victoria Parade, Ramsgate, Kent CT11 8DG
BO: 01843 591750 Admin: 01843 855 000
Email: granvilletheatre@btconnect.com
Web Site: www.granvilletheatre.com
ADMINISTRATION:
Props: Granville Theatre Ltd
Policy: Summer Show, Repertory, Panto, Operatic, Arts, Films, Hiring, etc.
Seats: Theatre: 240, Cinema: 120.
Licensed Bar.
TECHNICAL:
Stage: Proscenium, Raked; Pros. opening 9.75m; Ht. of Pros. 5.49m; Depth of S/Line 7.32m; Ht. of Grid 10.97m; 21 lines, various; W/Widths P.S. 6.10m. O.P. 4.27m. 35mm Proj. Dolby sound.
Lighting: Switchboard: Strand Major; 48 ways; F.O.H. Spots 6 Fresnels Patt.243; 4 Battens; 3 circuits; Dips up to 4 each side; 4 Spot bars 10AA's 6A 23.
Sound: Speakers: Column 4 (sides of stage).
Dressing Rooms 6; Accom. 32; Orchestra Pit 20 max.
Membership: TMA

Rayleigh, Essex

THE MILL HALL

Bellingham Lane, Rayleigh, Essex SS6 7ED
Tel: 01268 778171 Fax: 01268 778737
Email: info@millhall1.fsnet.co.uk
Web Site: www.themillhall.co.uk
ADMINISTRATION:
General Manager: Martin Downs
Managed by Fusion Lifestyle
Capacity: 500, Main hall 400 plus and the bar lounge 100 max.

Reading, Berkshire

Pop. 143,100.London 48 miles.
Newspapers: Reading Post (Weds): Reading Chronicle (Fri): STD code 0118

THE HEXAGON THEATRE

Queen's Walk, Reading, Berkshire RG1 7UA
Admin Tel: 01189 372 123 BO: 01189 606 060 Tech: 01189 390 001
Email: boxoffice@readingarts.com
Web Site: www.readingarts.com
ADMINISTRATION:
Props: Reading Borough Council
Theatre Manager: Sarah Cox
Programme Manager: Charity Gordon.
BO Manager: Jacqui Barnett
Finance Manager: Sam Sweeney
Technical Manager: Rick Bull
Contact: rick.bull@reading.gov.uk
Policy: Adaptable Venue, Touring Productions, Concerts and Comedy, Music, Dance and Theatre.
Perfs: by arrangement.
Capacity: 517 to 1686 depending upon format.
The auditorium is equipped with Sennheiser hard of hearing infra-red sys-

tem.
TECHNICAL:
As some of this equipment is in other Theatres Division venues, please consult the Technical Department for full availability.
STAGE: Entrance: 1.88m wide, 2.56m high, 3.15m on the diagonal. Dimensions: Depth of Stage - 10.06m, Back Wall Width - 11.22m, Front Edge (normal Prosc opening) - 11.96m, Total Width - 21.11m, Height from Stage to underside of RSJ, Downstage of Hemp bar 1 10m. Upstage of Hemp bar 1 11.71m, 19 Hemp bars sets, 5 Motorised bars & 4 dedicated LX bars, For Flying heights of bars see section. Height from auditorium floor. Stage up 0.952m. Stage down (Get in height) 0.66m. Access: Loading bay for one 45' Artic. Load in through scene dock stage left. Stage entrance: 1.88m wide, 2.56m high, 3.15m on the diagonal.
LIGHTING: Lighting Control Desk: Rank Strand 550 with 510 backup. Controlling 118 x 3kW circuits and 46 x kW circuits. 23 x 3kW non-dim independents. ELC riggers control, accesses all dimming circuits. 12 Strand SL 23/50 600w profile. 16 Strand Prelude 16/30 650w profile. 8 Strand Cadenza 2kw F. 8 Strand Alto 2.5kw. F. 48 Strand patt.743. 72 Thomas Par 64 Parcan. 8 Thomas Par 64 Floorcan. 8 Iris 2 cyc units. 8 Strand Alto 8/16 2.5kw (rigged on FOH galleries). 8 CCT Sil 15 2kw (rigged on FOH galleries).16 Strand Cantata 11/26 1200w (rigged in FOH bridge 3). 12 Strand SL 15/32 600W profile (rigged in FOH bridge 2). 10 CCT Par 64 Rockette (rigged FOH bridge 1). 2 Robert Juliat Korrigan 1200 HMI Follow Spot.
SOUND: Mixing Desk; Soundcraft Vienna 2, 48 channel with 8 VCA's and 12 x 8 matrix situated audience right of centre in the balcony. There is also a Soundcraft 200B 16 channel desk, normally used in the control room but can be used in other positions if required. Outboard equipment; - at the mixing position there are 8 klark Technic DN 300 mono 30 band one-third octave graphic equalisers, patchable as required. There are also 1 Yamaha SPX 990, 1 Yamaha SPX 2000, a Yamaha Rev 5, a Tascam 122 cassette, a domestic Sony MDSGE 510 mini disc player. We have a Revox A77 3 3/4 / 7 1/2 i.p.s and 2 Revox B77's 7 1/2 / 15 i.p.s available when required. We also have 6 ways of compression and 2 Drawmer quad gates. Flown P.A.,- Consists of 2 clusters hung permanently below ceiling level 13 metres apart, each cluster consisting of an upper layer of four Turbosound TSE 111's, a middle layer of three Turbosound TSE 115's, and a lower layer of a further three Turbosound TSE 111's. Choir fill is catered for by three Turbosound TSE 111's and two Turbosound TSE 115's mounted to the rear of each cluster. The choir fill is only switched in when required - it does not run all the time. Arena P.A. - Consists of two stacks, one either side of stage, each consisting of two Turbosound TSE 218's one on top of the other, supporting two Turbosound TSE 111's. The on-stage P.A. is removed when not required. The system is normally run in stereo. All amplifiers are Crest. 8001's driving the stage bass and sub-bass, 4001's otherwise. Separate Klark Technic DN 360 Dual 30 band one-third octave graphic equalisers are provided for flown P.A., on-stage P.A. and choir system equalisation. A single Klark Technic DN 300 mono 30 band one-third octave graphic equaliser is provided for sub-base equalisation. Loudspeaker management including crossovers comes from 3 XTA DP226. Graphics and crossovers are non-adjustable by outside personnel. There are 40 mic lines and 8 returns off stage left. We have two 16 way stage boxes, each with 4 returns plus an 8 way stage box for lines 33-40.
Monitors - There is a mobile amp rack containing 3 MC2 T1000 amplifiers, which can be used on or off stage or in the orchestra pit, as required. We have up to 6 Turbosound TMW 212 wedges, 2 Turbosound TCS59's, 1 Turbosound TXD530's, and 2 Bose panaray speakers for foldback, also 8 Ramsa A10'a which can be used as pit monitors etc. We have a selection of microphones available including: 2 Shure SM58, 4 AKG 414 EB, 8 Shure SM57 Beta, 2 Sennheiser MD421, 2 Sennheiser E609, 2 AKG D 80, 5 AKG C 451 EB & the following capsules:- 5 CK1, 1 CK5, 5 AKG SE300B Powering modules & the following Capsules:- 5 CK98, 5 CK91, 2 AKG D112. Plus a variety of stands and accessories to suit the above. We also hold 4 BSS AR 116 and 6 BSS AR133 active D.I. boxes. Should you require radio microphones please contact the technical department in advance.
ORCHESTRA PIT: (available as Pit, Auditorium floor or Thrust) Width 3.5m, Length 11.96m, Depth to Auditorium 1.56m, Depth to Stage (up) 2.51m, Chairs 120 max, Accommodation 48, Music Stands (lit) 25 max, Music Stands (unlit) 72 max, Steinway model D (tuned to A440hz), Upright Piano.
DRESSING ROOMS: 9 Dressing rooms plus Chorus and Band room and/or Wardrobe. 10 Backstage showers. Laundry room with 2 Washing Machines & 2 Tumble/Spin dryers, with facilities to plumb in a Twin tub.

THE MILL AT SONNING THEATRE

Sonning Eye, Reading, Berkshire RG4 6TY
Mgt: 0118 969 6039 BO: 0118 969 8000
Email: sallysonningmill@btconnect.com
Web Site: www.millatsonning.com
ADMINISTRATION:
Managing/Artistic Director: Sally Hughes
Assistant Administrator: Ian Southgate
Policy: 6/5 weekly repertory
Perfs: Tues-Sat 8.15p.m. Mat Sat. 2.15p.m.
Restaurant opens 6.30p.m. Sats 12.30p.m.
Capacity: 215
TECHNICAL:
Stage: Thrust stage, semi-circular. Depth of stage 5.40m width at centre 9.42m, width at US line 10.44m, width at DS line 3.95m; max setting depth (for box sets) 1.37m, max height 3.50m.
Lighting: Strand GSX lighting desk. 60 2kw circuits.
Sound Equipment: 2 x teac 2 track reel-to-reel tape decks; 1 x 8 channel mixer; 4 x 100w Bose speakers.
Dressing Rooms: 5, Accom. 12.

READING TOWN HALL

Blagrave Street, Reading, Berkshire RG1 1QH
Tel: 0118 937 3400 BO: 0118 960 6060
Email: townhall.admin@reading.gov.uk
Web Site: www.readingarts.com
ADMINISTRATION:
Props: Reading Borough Council
Manager: Rhodri Thomas
Rhodri.thomas@reading.gov.uk
Programme Manager: Charity Gordon
Conference, function and arts venue, comprising:
Concert Hall: Up to 780 Theatre Style
Victoria Hall: Comfortable elegant room, 220 sq.m., seating up to 200 for concerts, performances, conferences, exhibitions, dinners, etc. High level audio-visual equipment, including video, full sound equipment, film projection, etc. Rostra stage; piano; basic theatre lighting.
Meeting Rooms: Four ancillary rooms for meetings, conferences and functions. Waterhouse Chamber - 70 sq.m. Seating for up to 60 theatre style with bar facilities. Silverthorne Room - 40 sq.m. Seating for up to 40. Oscar Wilde Room - 20 sq.m. Seating for up to 20. Jane Austen Room - 20 sq.m. Seating for up to 20.
TECHNICAL:
Stage: Thrust stage 9m x 6m x 1.17m. Get-in at street level. Goods lift to stage; Father Willis organ. No piano - hired by arrangement.
Lighting: Fixed rig flown on truss; 6 x Mac 500; 10 x Strand SL; 6 x Mac 600; 16 x Par 64 (CP62); 12 x Par 64 with Chroma Q Scrollers.
Desk: Strand 520; Sound D + B system; Flown cluster of 2C7 and 4C6. Ground system IC7 and IC7 Sub. Front fill of 4E3 units. 6 Martin LE 400C monitors fed from mobile monitor rack. Desk Soundcraft K3 32-8-4; Parametric EQ; BSS Soundweb. Please note there is no partking at The Concert Hall.

RIVERMEAD LEISURE COMPLEX

Richfield Avenue, Reading, Berkshire RG1

8EQ
Tel: 0118 901 5000
Email: warren.higgins@gll.org
Web Site: www.better.org
ADMINISTRATION:
Props: Reading Borough Council
Manager: Warren Higgins
Policy: Leisure centre with concert facilities. Car parking facilities for 650, 3 phase power supply.
Seating/Capacity, Main Hall: 2,400 seated, 3,000 standing.

SHINFIELD PLAYERS THEATRE & ARTS CENTRE

Whitley Wood Lane, Shinfield Park, Reading, Berkshire RG2 9DF
BO: 0118 975 8880
Email: graham@shinfieldplayers.co.uk
Web Site: www.shinfieldplayers.org.uk
ADMINISTRATION:
Licensee: Mrs E Denny
Cap: 156 Wheelchair facilities.
For bookings contact Jim Taylor, Secretary: 18 Keswick Close, Tile Hurst, Reading RG30 4SD Tel: 0118 942 4606

Redcar, Cleveland

COATHAM MEMORIAL HALL

Coatham Road, Redcar, Cleveland TS10 1RH
Tel: 01642 483263
Email: info@redcardevelopmenttrust.com
Web: www.redcardevelopmenttrust.com
ADMINISTRATION:
Props: Redcar Development Trust
Cap: 250
For bookings telephone 01642 483263

Redditch, Worcestershire

Pop. 75,000. London 126 miles. Newspapers: Redditch Advertiser; Birmingham Evening Mail; Redditch Standard; Bromsgrove Messenger. STD code 01527

PALACE THEATRE

Alcester Street, Redditch, Worcestershire B98 8AE
Admin: 01527 61544 BO: 01527 65203
Email: tim.mackrill@bromsgroveandredditch.gov.uk
Web Site: www.redditchpalacetheatre.co.uk
ADMINISTRATION:
Props: Redditch Borough Council;
Lessees: Palace Theatre Redditch Ltd
Theatre Manager: Tim Mackrill
Cultural Arts Manager: Jonathan Cochrane
Technical Manager: Tim Mackrill and Carl Phillips
Press & PR: Paul Hughes
Theatre Administration: Natasha Parker
Policy: Professional and amateur productions; brought-in one/two night stand music, theatre, dance, exhibitions, youth theatre and holiday youth activities. Policy of community involvement and access to the arts, Conferences.
Perfs: Normally 7.30.
Capacity: 420. 10 Wheelchair Spaces.
Bar Facilities.
Studio capacity 64.
TECHNICAL:
STAGE: Proscenium Stage, Raked; Pros Opening 6.7m (22'). Pros Height to Tabs 3.8m (12'6"). Depth of Stage 6m (19'6"). Extension over orchestra pit, 1.60m (5'3"). Wing Widths SR 2m (6'6"). Wing Widths SL 1.52m (5'). Stage Width Wall to Wall 14.2m (46'6"). The Stage has a rake of 25 mm in 1m (1 in 40). Get-In doors via Stage Right. Width: 2.16m (7'1"). Height: 3.25m (10'8"). For all lorry access and Luton vans access via a dedicated load in platform from the car park (stage left side) flat out from the vehicle through the scene doc onto the stage. Complete level access.
LIGHTING: Desk; ADB Phoenix 5, 360 channel with Isis + software. Dimmers: Strand Permus 96 Circuits. 2.5K (10 amps) per channel. 3 x 7.15m IWB. (On stage) 250 Kg each hand winch. 6 x DMX points: Dimmer room (SL), DSR, DSL, CSL, CSR, USl, USR, LX 1, LX 3, front of Circle bar & FOH Booms. Fresnels; 20 x 1.2k CANTATA, With barn doors. Profiles; 4 x 1.2k Cantata 11/26, 4 x 1.2k Cantata 18/32, 6 x 575w Source 4 26 , 6 x 650w Prelude 16/30, 5 x 600w Brio 18/30. Other: 8 x 3 x 36 watt LED fine art moving heads for all stage colour washes, 5 x 500w Coda 3, 14 x 1k Parcans P64 CP62 Lamp, 2 x 1k Parcans P64 CP61 Lamp, 1 x Black light U V Gun, 4 x MAC 250+. Accessories; 2 x Iris to fit Cantata, Prelude & Brio Profiles, 6 x B Size Gobo holders (GH06), 6 x A Size Gobo holders (GH40). FollowSpots; 2 x Robert Juliet Foxie MSR 750 Lamp. (Complete with Sights & Colour Magazine loaded as per standard lighting Rig). Additional Lanterns Available.
SOUND: 4 x Martin Audio AQ10's (Circle) - 1,200w RMS (2 left & 2 right), 4 x Martin Audio AQ10's (Stalls) - 1,200w RMS (2 left & 2 right), 2 x Martin Audio AQ5's (1 x Box A & 1 x Box B mono sum of PA), 2 x Sub Bass Martin Audio S18's (Both in Orchestra pit) - 1000w RMS, 1 x Sub Bass Martin Audio ICTS (Box A) flooding into circle, 2 x Martin Audio AQ5's Rear Circle Surround sound, 2 x Tanoy Lynx rear stalls Surround sound, 1 x Martin Audio DX1 Digital System Controller/ Crossover, 2 x H & H 300 watt RMS speakers (Permanent side fills on stage), 6 x Channels of fold back via Martin Audio 4 x F10 & 1 x F12 full range cabinets & ICTS Base bin. Main Mix: 1 x Yamaha M7CL sound desk. 1 x Behringer Composer. 2 x Alesis M-EQ 230 30 Band Graphic Equalizer, 1 x Tascam MD 301 Mini Disc Player/Recorder, 1 x Tascam CD player 160, 1 x Audio Media player. Plays direct from USB memory sticks & card readers, 1 x PC dedicated to Audio play back, 1 x DVD / CD player with 5.1. Extra Equipment: Various Microphones.
ADDITIONAL: 1 x Mirror ball and motor. Multimedia; 1 x Video projector Optoma EP727 DLP on Front of circle LX Bar, 1 x DVD player located in sound position, 1 x VGA Lead for Power Point presentations located in prompt corner and control room, 1 x Colour Camera on front of circle LX Bar for video relay to wings, 1 x Black and White Camera in Pit also links to video relay system including monitor on front circle, 3 x 14" Colour TV'S (Stage Left, Stage Right & Fly floor), Channel 1 stage view, channel 2 pit. Star cloth available at additional cost.
STAGE MANAGEMENT: Full show relay to all dressing rooms with paging system via prompt corner & Control Room. FOH calls done from the control room or Stage by the technician on duty.
Communication head sets at lighting, Control room mix position, main mix position, follow spot 1 & 2, prompt corner, opposite prompt and fly floor.
DRESSING ROOMS: 7 over 2 floors, with basin, toilet, and shower facilities; Accomm. 60. 1 x Disable toilet and shower combined. 1 x Laundry Room / Kitchen with Auto Washer, Dryer, Steam Iron and Ironing Board and tea and coffee making facilities. All dressing rooms have central heating, show relay and back stage call system.
BACKSTAGE: Orchestra pit; Accomm. 16; 14 x Lit music stands, 1 x Lit conductors stand, 14 x folding chairs, 1 x Steinbeck Upright Piano (subject to tuning charge); 1 x Yamaha Clavinova CLP 550 (subject to hire charge). Second floor (FOH) Studio; Accomm 50. Stage; Accomm. 120.

Redhill, Surrey

Pop. 55,000. London 18 miles. Newspapers: Surrey Mirror (thurs); Independent (fri). STD code 01737

THE HARLEQUIN THEATRE AND CINEMA

Warwick Quadrant, London Road, Redhill, Surrey RH1 1NN
Admin: 01737 276 830 BO: 01737 276 500 Fax: 01737 765 549
Email: harlequin@reigate-banstead.gov.uk
Web Site: www.harlequintheatre.co.uk
ADMINISTRATION:
Props: Reigate & Banstead Borough Council
Manager: Elizabeth Smith
Sales & Marketing Manager: Christopher O'Brien
Technical Manager: Phillip Bashford
House Manager: Ian Orrick
Seating: 17 800mm wide x 24 500mm

long together with a balcony at one end with four rows of permanently installed seats. Proscenium panels are hinged and fold flat against stage walls. Retractable bleachers store beneath balcony; tiered seating on orchestra pit may be rolled away beneath auditorium floor to provide large or small pit giving:- full config. 494, small pit: 470, large pit: 422.
Standing & Seated: 764
TECHNICAL:
Stage: Proscenium - 11 950 wide x 7600 high to fixed pelmet. Height may be reduced with flown header. Width - Centreline to St. Right 8900; Centreline to St. Left 8900. Distance between Fly Floors 14 000. Depth - Rear of House Curtain to stage edge 400. Height - Clear beneath Fly Floors 8335; beneath u/side of Grid 10 337. Floor - Flat and level, covered in 'Harlequin' dance flooring. Flying System - 30 installed hemp sets, generally 200mm centres. Maximum bar capacity 150 kg. 9 electrically operated winch bars max. capacity 250 kg. Bar length 13000. Stage manager working corner on Stg. left. Mobile control desk with extension cable. Get-in: from servce loading bay 1 floor below stage with lift access to stage level upstage R. Max. dimensions of lift 5740 x 2290 x 2450 high. Access to stage 2175 x 2075 high. Orchestra: Pit - 45 m.sq. on lift. Maximum depth below stage/auditorium level 1050mm. Access to Pit via auditorium.
Lighting: 120 way 550 by Strand in control room at rear of Balcony. Dimmers - 24 x 5kw (to 32a CEE 17 s/o with changeover to 4 x 15a 3-pin s/o). 96 x 2.5kw (to 15a 3-pin s/o). Dimmer Room one floor above stage, upstage left. Additional Power - 200a TPN designated 'Special Effects' situated downstage Actors' left. Projection Equipment: Single 16/35mm projector by Kineton. Rolled projection screen on electrically powered winch bar. Full Dolby stereo. Sound and Communications. Allen & Heath 32/8/2 Soundcraft 400B 20/4/2 mixer desk, Patchfield with 38 microphone inputs, 20 tielines from Prompt corner facilities panel to jackfield in control room.
2 Revox B77 tape recorders, 2 Cassette Recorders, 1 record deck, 1 C.D. player, Yamaha SPX 90 2 Peavey Autograph Eq, Drawmer Compresser/
Limiter, Alesis Quadraverb, Digital Sampler. 5 31 band Yamaha graphic equalisers. Microphones: 3 Shure SM58s, 3 AKG 321s, 3 224s, 9 AKG C451 bodies, 7 AKG CK8 heads, 4 AKG CK1 heads, 2 AKG CK22 heads. Various Microphone floor stands. Full P.A. with Bose P.A. with separate monitor mix. Contact theatre for full spec. Infra-red hearing aid system in auditorium.
Stage Management: SM desk by Showstrand incorporates paging and show relay, twin-ring intercom, cue lights and effects circuits. Induction loop. Yamaha Grand and upright pianos and Roland D50. Accommodation: 5 rooms for 39 artists at stage level. Green Room at stage level St. left. 4 showers (2 each sex). Detailed equipment list and drawings from the technical manager.

Retford, Nottinghamshire

MAJESTIC THEATRE
Coronation Street, Retford, Nottinghamshire DN22 6DX
Tel: 01777 706 866
Email: majesticbox@talktalkbusiness.net
Web Site: www.majesticretford.com
ADMINISTRATION:
Bookings contact Elaine Shaw Tel: 07702 302 303
Proprietors: Retford Theatre Trust
Capacity: 652

RETFORD LEISURE CENTRE
Old Hall Drive Retford, Nottinghamshire DN22 7EA
Tel: 01777 706500
Email: tom.ramsey@bpl.org.uk
Web Site: www.bpl.org.uk
ADMINISTRATION:
Props: Barnsley Premier Leisure
Centre Manager: Simon Ferrarelli
Capacity: 100, up to 400 school sights.

RETFORD TOWN HALL
17b The Square, Retford, Nottinghamshire DN22 6DB
Tel: 01909 533111/ 533414
Email: karen.kelk@bassetlaw.gov.uk
Web Site: www.bassetlaw.gov.uk
ADMINISTRATION:
Props: Bassetlaw District Council
Cap: Ballroom 350; Council Chamber 100; Butter Market 230 (for exhibitions).

Rhayader, Powys

RHAYADER LEISURE CENTRE
North Street, Rhayader, Powys LD6 5BU
Tel: 01597 811013
Email: rlc@powys.gov.uk
Web Site: www.powys.gov.uk
ADMINISTRATION:
Props: Powys County Council
Cap: 400
Manager: Tim Davies

Rhyl, Denbighshire

Pop. 22,000. London 211 miles.
Newspapers: Rhyl Journal; Prestatyn Weekly (thurs); Rhyl & Prestatyn Visitor.
STD code 01745

LITTLE THEATRE
Vale Road, Rhyl, Clwyd LL18 2BS Wales
Mgt/BO: 01745 342229
Email: rhyllittletheatre@yahoo.co.uk
ADMINISTRATION:
Contact: Mr G Willams
Policy: Repertory (Amateur and Professional), Pantomime and Variety
Perfs: Usually 7.30 (occasional Saturday Matinees 2.30)
Seats: 192 + 3 wheelchair spaces.
Access for disabled. Coffee Bar.
TECHNICAL:
Stage: Proscenium stage with removable Apron, Flat; Pros. Opening 6.71m; Ht. of Pros. 3.35m; Depth of S/Line 7.45m; Ht. of Grid 6.71m; 16 sets, Hemp; Scenery Flying Ht. 6.50m; W/Widths P.S. 2.83m, O.P. 3.76m; Prompt Cnr. P Side (R).
Lighting: Switchboard: Strand JSN24 (Control Room Rear of House, Single Phase); 24 ways (patch panel); F.O.H. Spots 12 Patts.243, 23, 263; 2 Battens plus Cyc.; Dips 2 P, 3 O.P. (11 way); 3 Spot Bars Patts.23 & 123.
Sound Equip: 2 Turntables, Tape Recorder (Control Room); Westrex Speakers Pros. and Stage.
Dressing Rooms 2; Accom. 12 - 15.
Orchestra Pit 6.
Apron Stage 5.53m x 1.47m. Dock Doors 1.98m x 1.52m. Car Park at rear of Theatre - Railway Station 200 yards away.

PAVILION THEATRE
Promenade, East Parade, Rhyl, Denbighshire LL18 3AQ Wales
Mgt: 01745 332 414 BO: 01745 330 000
Tech: 01745 360 088 Fax: 01745 339 819
Email: gareth.owen@denbighshire.gov.uk
Web Site: www.rhylpavilion.co.uk
ADMINISTRATION:
Props: Denbighshire County Council
Theatre Manager: Gareth Owen
Marketing Officer: Sian Williams
Technical Manager: Andy Hughes
Theatre Administrator: Val Simmons
Policy: Professional and amateur productions; brought-in one/two night stand music, theatre, dance, concerts etc. Also available for conferences.
Perfs: 7.30 or 8.00p.m.
Seats: 1,032. Coffee Bar, Licensed Bars.
TECHNICAL:
Stage: Proscenium, raked (1:35).
Proscenium Width 12.9m; Pros. Ht. 6.2m; Max. Stage Width 25m; Max. Stage Depth (to front forestage) 10.9m (13.2m); Orchestra Pit: 50 sq.m. - to seat 30 maximum, can be covered. Stage Surface Grey Flecked hardboard; 44 single purchase counter-weight sets; 500 kg maximum loading per bar; Bar Length 16.25m; Distance between bar centres 200mm; Grid Height 16.5m.
Lighting: Gemini 2+ 156 Channels; Assortment of Strand Lanterns; 2 CSI Follow Spots; 5 Martin Roboscans; 2 Front of House Bridges; 2 Front of House

Booms ; 4 Internally Wired Bars.
Sound: 24.4.2. Sound Tracs, Desk; SPX 900 and ART FX Units; Mini-disc Revox; CD; Cassette; Selection of Microphones & radio mics.
Dressing Rooms: 12; Accom. 70.
Membership: TMA

RHYL TOWN HALL

Wellington Road, Rhyl, Denbighshire WL18 1AB
Tel/Fax: 01745 337 480
Email: rhyltownhall@denbighshire.gov.uk
Web Site: www.denbighshirecountycouncil.gov.uk
ADMINISTRATION:
Props: Denbighshire County Council
Manager: Steve Ward
Cap: 400

Richmond, North Yorkshire

Pop. 7,260. London 234 miles.
Newspapers: Darlington & Stockton Times (sat); Northern Echo. STD code 01748

GEORGIAN THEATRE ROYAL

Victoria Road, Richmond, North Yorkshire DL10 4DW
Mgt: 01748 823 710 BO: 01748 825 252
Email: admin@georgiantheatreroyal.co.uk
Web Site: www.georgiantheatreroyal.co.uk
ADMINISTRATION:
Manager: Warnock Kerr
PA: Jo Mawhinney
Stage Manager: Tony Wilcock
Policy: Professional Drama and Concerts, Local Amateur Societies.
Seats: 214
TECHNICAL:
Stage: Proscenium, Raked; Pros. opening 4.72m; Ht. of Pros. 3.50m; Depth of S/Line 6.40m; Ht. of Grid 5.18m; 15 lines, Hemp; Prompt Cnr. P.S.
Stage Plan available.
Lighting: Switchboard: Tempus 2G36 in Pros. box P.S.; Circuits: 10 FOH on barrels, 4 Pros. Box, 3 Dips, 1 Footlights, 4 battels - 43 circuits. Lamps: 34 Patt.23, 2 Patt.23N, 24 Patt.123 11 Patt.137.
Sound: Please contact venue.
Other: Dressing Rooms 4; Accom. 20.
Membership: TMA

Richmond, Surrey

RICHMOND THEATRE

The Green, Richmond, Surrey TW9 1QJ
Mgt: 020 8332 4500 BO: 0844 871 7651
SD: 020 8332 4500 SD Fax: 020 8332 4509 Tech: 020 8332 4500
Email: christiaandevilliers@theambassadors.com
Web Site: www.atgtickets.com/richmond
ADMINISTRATION:
Props: Ambassadors Theatre Group (Venues) Ltd
General Manager: Christiaan Devilliers
Marketing Manager: Samantha Preston
Technical Manager: Ken Savva
Policy: Touring Drama, Opera and Ballet, Concerts and Pantomime.
Perfs: Evenings at 7.45 pm, Matinees Wed and Sat.
Seats: 818 on three levels. Three licensed bars and entertaining suite.
TECHNICAL:
STAGE: Proscenium raked 1:24. Pros opening 8.16m. Ht. of Pros. 7.0m. Depth of Stage 9.1m. Ht. to Grid 14.0m. Wings 5.5m. P.S. 3.0m O.P. x over stage level. Flying system 35 sets single purchase counterweight 350kg S.W.C., bars 10m long. Get-in street level P.S. Removable rostra (row A) over orchestra pit 10m x 2m approx.
LIGHTING: Control: Strand 520i at rear of stalls. Dimmers 168 x 2.5kw and 12 x 5kw. Lanterns. Full permanent F.O.H. rig - details on application.
SOUND : Full wiring infrastructure for sound control on stage or by prior arrangement at rear of stalls. Details of equipment on application. Full cuelight system, ring intercom and paging to all the usual areas.
ADDITIONAL: Dressing Rooms 9, accom. 26 on 3 floors; 8 Showers; Green Room; Bandroom; Wardrobe and Laundry.

Rickmansworth, Hertfordshire

Pop. 78,000. London 20 miles.
Newspapers: Watford Observer; Focus.
STD code 01923

WATERSMEET THEATRE

High Street, Rickmansworth, Hertfordshire WD3 1EH
Tel: 01923 711 063
Email: watersmeet@threerivers.gov.uk
Web Site: www.watersmeet.co.uk
ADMINISTRATION:
Props: Three Rivers District Council
Capacity: 515

Rochdale, Gtr Manchester

Pop. 91,454. London 221 miles.
Newspapers: Rochdale Observer (wed/sat); and Manchester newspapers.
STD code 01706

GRACIE FIELDS THEATRE

The Gracie Fields Theatre Oulder Hill Leisure Complex, Hudsons Walk, Rochdale, Lancashire OL11 5EF
Admin: 01706 716 689 BO: 0843 208 1835
Email: enquiries@graciefieldstheatre.com
Web Site: www.graciefieldstheatre.com
ADMINISTRATION:
Props: Rochdale M.B.C.
Assistant Theatre Manager: Nikki Jackson
Technical Manager: Emily Clegg
Email: emily@graciefieldstheatre.com
Policy: Available for hire and some promotions.
Seats: 688. Licensed Bar and Coffee Bar.
TECHNICAL:

Auditorium:

STAGE: Fully raked auditorium to a flat floor black box 'end on' stage. Small selection of wire and shackles available for flying. Stage Weights: 14, French Braces: 14, Black Bolton Twill Border: 3, Black Wool Serge Legs: 4 Pairs, Black Bolton Twill Tabs: 2 Pairs, Black Serge Tabs: 1 Pair, White Cyclorama: 1. Orchestra pit accommodating 10 musicians (including percussion).
STAGE COMMUNICATIONS: Technical Projects PS711: 1, Technical Projects Beltpack and Headset: 6, Technical Projects Alert Strobe: 1.
LIGHTING: Desk: ETC Express 48/96 / Zero88 Demux. Profiles: Strand Patt 23, 3. Strand T-Spot, 25. Strand Harmony 12, 2. Strand Quartet 25, 1. ETC Source 4 15/30, 16. Fresneals: ETC Source4 Parnel, 8. CCT Minuette, 4. Strand Patt 743, 28. Floods: Strand Patt 60, 16. Strand Patt 137, 2. Others: ETC Source 4 Par, 8. Par 64, 8. Strand Patt 814 (PC), 6. UV Fluorescent, 9. Strand Mirror Ball, 1.
SOUND: Martin Audio CX2, 8. Martin Audio EX-2 System Controller, 3. HK Audio PR:O 12M, 2. Soundcraft Spirit Live (16+2:4:2), 1. Tascam CD-01U (CD Player), 1. Tascam MD-301 (Mini Disk Player), 1. Klark Teknik DN360 Graphic Equaliser, 1. BSS FC2-960 Graphic Equaliser, 1. Yamaha SPX90 Effects Processor, 1. Yamaha REV500 Reverb Unit, 1. Microphones, DI Boxes, Stands: Shure SM58, 4. Shure SM57, 2. Sennheiser ME80, 4. AKG D112, 1. AKG C1000s, 2. Sennheiser e604, 3. Audio Tecnica AT815B, 2. BSS Active DI, 2. Pump action straight stand, 4. Boom Stand, 6. Portable System: OHM TRS 212 Mid High, 2. OHM TRS 218 Sub Bass, 2. OHM Cred Controller, 1. OHM Amplifiers, 2. EV SX300, 2. QSC RMX1450, 1. Soundcraft Spirit Live (24:2), 1.
DRESSING ROOMS: 2, accommodating 10 people, with mirrors, power, hand basins and toilets. Additional facilities available for larger casts. Laundry Facilities: iron and ironing board.

Studio Theatre:

Raked auditorium. Flexible removable seating arrangement. Soft proscenium formed by black tabs and a border. All technical details are the same as for the main auditorium.

Romford, Essex

TWEEDWAY HALL
Tweed Way, Rise Park, Romford, Essex RM1 4AZ
Tel: 01708 765 235
Email: tweedwayhall@gmail.com
Web Site: www.tweedwayhall.com
ADMINISTRATION:
Props: London Borough Havering
Cap: 150 Theatre Style
Contact Halls Lettings Manager: Lisa Gleed

Romsey, Hampshire

PLAZA THEATRE
Winchester Road, Romsey, Hampshire SO51 8JA
BO: 01794 512 987 (Tourist Information Centre) Admin Tel: 01794 523 054
Email: postmaster@plazatheatre.com
Web Site: www.plazatheatre.co.uk
ADMINISTRATION:
Props: Romsey Amateur Operatic & Dramatic Society
Cap: 240 Seated + 6 wheelchair spaces
Plays, musicals, Shakespeare, youth productions, Pantomime, visiting productions/concerts (amateur and professional). Available for hire (subject to availability) - Contact Bookings Manager at above address or via email address given above. Green Room and fully stocked licensed bar. Car Park (approx 40 Spaces.)
See website for tech spec/info

Rotherham, South Yorkshire

Pop. 250,000. London 161 miles.
Newspapers: South Yorkshire & Rotherham Advertiser (fri). STD code 01709

ROTHERHAM CIVIC THEATRE
Catherine Street, Rotherham, South Yorkshire S65 1EB
Mgt: 01709 823 641 BO: 01709 823 640/01709 823621
Email: mark.scott@rotherham.gov.uk
Web Site: www.rotherham.gov.uk
ADMINISTRATION:
Props: Rotherham Borough Council
Principal Arts Officer: Mark Scott
Policy: Plays, Opera, Ballet, Musicals, Orchestral & Band Concerts, Celebrity Nights, Revue, etc.
Perfs: Nightly at 7.15. (Sunday 7.30).
Seats: 356. Coffee Lounge and Licensed Bar.
TECHNICAL:
STAGE: Proscenium, Flat; Pros. Opening 8.07m; Ht. of Pros. 4.27m; Depth of S/Line 11.89m; Ht. of Grid 7.62m; 20 lines; Flying Bars 8.53m; W/Widths P.S. 9.14m, O.P. 2.44m; Prompt Cnr. P.S.
LIGHTING: Switchboard - Strand LBX 72 channel, rear of auditorium; Strand LD90 dimmers; FOH lighting 12 x Strand Cantatas; 4 bars on Stage with mix of 16 x Patt. 743 Fresnel; 6 x CCT Frebels; 20 x Selecon Acclaim 500w floods; 12 x Source 4 Junior zoom; 20 x Parcans; 8 x Floorcans; Cyc bar (4) has 8 x 1k Codas; Dips 4 each side.
SOUND: Spitit Soundcraft; 1200 Powerstation Speakers FOH; 2 x Peavey HI-SYS2; Foldback on stage; 4 x Shure SM58 mics; 2 x mini-disc players; 1 x cd player; 2 x cassette decks; Techpro belt-pack system. Dressing Room Show Relay & Call System.
DRESSING ROOMS: 5; Accom. 40; Orchestra Pit 12

Rugby, Warwickshire

THE BENN HALL
Newbold Road, Rugby, Warwickshire CV21 2LN
Tel: 01788 533 719
Email: bennhall@rugby.gov.uk
Web Site: www.thebennhall.co.uk
ADMINISTRATION:
Cap: 430; 120 (Rokeby Room)
Manager: Julie Booker
Stage and dressing rooms
Bar, full catering facilities, easy access from motorways, ample parking.
Brochures and details available from the Manager.

Rugeley, Staffordshire

RUGELEY ROSE THEATRE
Taylors Lane, Rugeley, Staffordshire WS15 2AA
Tel: 01889 584036
Email: theatre@rugeleytowncouncil.gov.uk
Web Site: www.rugeleytowncouncil.gov.uk
ADMINISTRATION:
Props: Rugeley Town Council
Cap: 210 Seated, 300 Standing
Managers on Site:Mrs Glenis Turner, Mrs Chris Panter-Hood

Ruislip, Middlesex

WINSTON CHURCHILL HALL
Pinn Way, Ruislip, Middlesex HA4 7QL
Tel: 01895 277643
Email: artsvenues@hillingdon.gov.uk
Web Site: www.compasstheatre.co.uk
ADMINISTRATION:
Props: London Borough of Hillingdon
Cap: 351 Multi-purpose Hall

Salford

THE LOWRY
The Quays, Pier 8, Salford Quays M50 3AZ
Admin: 0843 208 6001 BO: 0843 208 6000 BO Fax: 0161 876 2001 Groups: 0843 208 6003
Email: info@thelowry.com
Web Site: www.thelowry.com
The Lowry includes The Lyric and Quays Theatres and the Studio space as well. The Lyric Theatre has the largest stage in England outside London. Plus Galleries, shops, cafés and restaurants.
Chief Executive: Julia Fawcett
Technical Manager: Dave Woodward
Marketing Director: Jonathan Harper
Head of Ticketing Services: Keith Kelly
Capacity: Lyric Theatre 1743, Quays Theatre 479

Salisbury, Wiltshire

Pop. 35,890. London 84 miles.
Newspapers: Salisbury Journal (thurs).
STD code 01722

CITY HALL
Malthouse Lane, Salisbury, Wiltshire SP2 7TU
Mgt: 01722 434 726 BO: 01722 434 434
Mrkting: 01722 434721 Fax: 01722 337 059
Email: cityhall@wiltshire.gov.uk
Web Site: www.cityhallsalisbury.co.uk
ADMINISTRATION:
Props: Wiltshire Council
Policy: Meetings, Conferences, Exhibitions, Corporate Functions, Fundraisers, Workshops, Craft Fairs, Presentations,
Venue Manager: Phillip Smith
Senior Technician: Phillip Manning.
Contact: 01722 434720 or phil.manning@wiltshire.gov.uk
Finance & Administration Officer: Yvonne Amor.
Contact: yvonne.amor@wiltshire.gov.uk
Auditorium Capacity: 1255 standing; 953 theatre seating; 350 dinner dance; 86 exhibition stalls.
TECHNICAL:
STAGE: Proscenium arch, max width 12.5m, max height 4m (5.7m max). Stage Width 15.5m, Depth 7m, Height 8.5m.
LIGHTING: Avolite Pearl 2000 Lighting Desk, Graphic Tablet and Riggers Remote, ELC focus HAND radio riggers remote; XTBA Smartlink 2, DMX512/ D54 Converter. 1 x Line of DMX 512 accessed

from Control Room. 6 x Strand LD90 Dimmer Racks, 24 x 2.5 KW, giving total of 144 channels. 12 x CCT Starlettes Fresnel (1KW). 72 x PAR 64 Parcans (1kw). 8 x PAR 64 Floorcans (1kw). 9 x CCT Minuette Fresnel (500watts). 6 x CCT Minuette TT profiles (500watts). 10 x Strand SL 15/30 Zoom Profiles. 4 x Strand Cantata 18/32 Profiles. 4 x Strand Cantata 26/ 44 Profiles (1kw). 2 x Strand Solo CS1 1K Followspots. 3x Motorised Lighting Bars over stage. Downstage 20x 3.2kW outlets, midstage 18x 3.2kW outlets, upstage 18x 3.2kW outlets.
SOUND: Allen and Heath GL 2200 24/4/2 Mixing Console. 1 x Rane ME 60 2 x 30 Band Graphic Equaliser, 1 x Samson 2030 2 x 31 Band Graphic Equaliser, 2 x DN - C635, 1 x Tascam Min Disk Player, 1 x Yamaha GC 2020C Compressor/ Limiter, 1 x Yamaha SPX 990 Digital Effects Processor. Stage monitoring/ Portable PA system: 1 x Soudcraft Spirit Folio 12/2 Mixing Desk, 1 x Peavey EQ-215 Graphic Equaliser, 1 x Peavey CS200X Power Amplifier. 2 x Eurosys IM Monitor Speakers, 4 x Tannoy Power V12. Wide range of Microphones available. 4x Tannoy V15 speakers fixed as 2x Pair on Pros Arch. 4x Tannoy V18 Sub-bass speakers.
ADDITIONAL: AV Equipment; 2 x Dell Laptop Computers, 1 x EIZO FlexScan IM421M Data Projector; 1 x Plus US - 532h Data Projector; 1 x Integrated plug and play AV system; 1 x Daewoo 28" Colour TV Monitor; 1 x Micro DVD player; 1 x 12 x 9 Easi-rect Projection Screen.
STAGE MANAGEMENT: Paging System to backstage and dressing rooms operated from prompt corner, control room and front of house. 6 x Tec Pro SHM 210 Headsets, 6 x Tec Pro BH111 Beltpacks, 1 x Tec Pro PS 7113 Circuit Power Supply Terminating in: 3 x control room sockets, 1 x prompt corner socket, 1 x flytower socket.
DRESSING ROOMS: 6; with washbasin, toilet, and shower facilities. Wireless internet access available.

THE MEDIEVAL HALL

Sarum St Michael, Cathedral Close, Salisbury, Wiltshire SP1 2EY
Tel: 01722 324 731 Mob: 07814 970945
Email: info@medieval-hall.co.uk
Web Site: www.medieval-hall.co.uk
ADMINISTRATION:
Props: John and Jane Waddington
Policy: Music, theatre, exhibitions etc.
Capacity: 140
Perfs:Any time, not after 10.30 pm.
Seats: 140 (comfortable stacking chairs & padded wall benches).
TECHNICAL:
Stage: Flat stage 14ft x 31ft, with wooden rostrum available. Flat york stone floor; 150ft. of linear hanging space.
Lighting: Purpose designed picture lighting; stage lighting with 18 channel dimmer circuit.
Sound: PA and sound equipment available.
Other: Limited catering facilities.
For further technical details apply to John or Jane Waddington at 10 Shady Bower, Salisbury SP1 2RG

SALISBURY GUILDHALL

Market Place, Salisbury, Wiltshire SP1 1JH
Tel: 01722 342860
Email: guildhall@salisbury.gov.uk
Web Site: www.salisburyguildhall.co.uk
ADMINISTRATION:
Props: Salisbury City Council
Cap: 300 Flexible/seating facilities.
Contact Julia Tregellas for bookings.

SALISBURY PLAYHOUSE

Malthouse Lane, Salisbury, Wiltshire SP2 7RA
Admin: 01722 320 117
BO: 01722 320 333
Email: info@salisburyplayhouse.com
Web Site: www.salisburyplayhouse.com
ADMINISTRATION:
Props: Salisbury Arts Theatre Ltd
Artistic Director: Gareth Machin
Production Manager: John Titcombe
Policy:Repertory, Studio, Touring and education work.
Perfs: Mon, Tues, Wed 7.30; Thurs 2.30 & 8.00; Fri 8.00. Sat 2.30 & 8.00.
Seats: 517 (open stage)
TECHNICAL:
Stage: Hexagon shape, max width 12.2m; Max Depth 12.2m (incl forestage); Ht. of Pros. 5.8m; Ht. to Grid 13.0m; Ht. to Fly Gallery 5.3m; Ht. understage 2.1m; Ht. of stage riser 0.86m; Stage flat; side Stage left 6.7m x 6.4m.
Machinery: 19 Double Purchase CW sets (No. 0 used for house tab, No. 1 used for LX Bar), Cradle. Modular trapped forestage, full width 3m (forms small orchestra pit); modular trapped floor in centre 3m section of stage.
Lighting: 2 Auditorium Bridges, 1 Pros Bridge. Auditorium slot positions within tower walls. Internally wired bars (1 x 12 way, 1 x 16 way).
Control: Strand Lighting 520: 116 ways (72 x 2kw, 36 x 2.5kw, 8 x 5kw). 12 independent circuits. All circuits fed to 129 outlets via 2 patch-panels. Auditorium bridges and towers; red phase; stage and fly tower, yellow phase. 60 amp 3 phase supply on stage.
Luminaires: profile 40 x T64 (1kw) 2 x Patt 264 (1kw), 10 x CCT Silhouette 30 (1kw), 12 x Patt 23 (500w), 6 x Model 823 (650w), 12 x Prelude 16/30 (650w), 24 x Strand Cantata 18/32 (1.2kw).
Fresnel: 4 x Minim F(500w), 27 x Patt 743 (1kw), 10 x Patt 243 (2kw). Floods: 12 x ADB AC1001 (1kw), 20 x Patt 60 (500w), 6 x Patt 137 (150w), 6 x S/63 Batten.
Other: 18 x Cantata PC (1.2kw), 24 x Par can (All CP61 lamps). Followspots: 2 x Patt 765 (1kw CSI).
Sound: Soundcraft K3. Also 2 mini disc players. 2 x Yamaha Q2031A Graphic Equalisers. Dynacord DDL204 Delay Unit. Yamaha SPX 900 Effects Processor, Technics RS-B655 Cassette Deck, Sony CDP-M50 Compact Disc Player, Technics SL-D202 Record Deck, 2 x Revox A77 Tape Decks (7.5ips). 2 x Carver PM900 Power Amplifiers, 1 x Carver PM300 Power Amplifier, 3 x HH TPA 100D Power Amplifiers (Mono), 4 x EV S200 Loudspeakers (Permanently installed in Auditorium Roof), 4 x Altec 604-8G Speakers for onstage use. 2 x A & R Column Speakers in Auditorium.
Microphone and Loudspeaker points in all areas of auditorium. Communications: SM Desk situated DSR corner on 10m multicore cable. 20 x Q lights to all parts of stage and auditorium. Ring Intercom. FX-Bell and telephone ringing circuits. Paging to dressing rooms, foyers and stage. Show relay to dressing rooms and backstage areas. Production desk in stalls with complete comms. facilities.

Studio Theatre
Seating: Variable depending upon layout. Maximum 149.
Stage: Dimensions: 13.4m x 10.9m. Ht. to underside of roof steels: 5m. Ht. to underside of gallery: 2.9m. No stage rake. No stock masking.
Machinery: None.
Lighting: Control: LBX 150 - 2kw per channel. 6 x independent outlets. All circuits fed to outlets around studio via patch panel from 48 dimmers.
Luminaries: 17 x Patt 23 (500w), 12 x Prelude 16/30 (650w), 23 x Patt 123, (500w), 4 x Patt 743 (1kw), 2 x Prelude PC (650w).
Sound: Soundcraft Spirit Folio Mixer (10/2), Revox A77 tape deck, 2 x HH TPA 100D power amplifiers, 2 x Tannoy 15" speakers.
Communications: Show relay, paging to backstage and foyers. Ring intercom.

Sandbach, Cheshire

TOWN HALL

High Street, Sandbach, Cheshire East CW11 1AX
Tel: 01270 600 835
Web Site: www.sandbach.gov.uk/sandbach-town-hall.htm
ADMINISTRATION:
Props: Sandbach Town Council
Cap: 240 (200 with stage extensions)
For bookings contact: Tel 01270 375349

Sanquhar, Dumfries & Galloway

SANQUHAR TOWN HALL

High Street, Sanquhar, Dumfries & Galloway DG4 6BN Scotland
Bkg: 01659 50347 Bkg Fax: 01659 50697
Web Site: www.dumgal.gov.uk
ADMINISTRATION:
Props: Dumfries & Galloway Council
Cap: 180 seated; 250 standing

Sauchie, Clackmannanshire

SAUCHIE HALL

Mar Place, Sauchie, Clackmannanshire FK10 3AE Scotland
Tel/Fax: 01259 720 948 Bkg: 01259 213 131
Email: leisurebookings@clacks.gov.uk
Web Site: www.clacksweb.gov
ADMINISTRATION:
Props: Clackmannanshire Council
Cap: Concert 200; Public Dance (without tables) 200; Dance (with tables) 150; Cabaret 150.

Scarborough, North Yorkshire

Pop. 43,080. London 231 miles.
Newspapers: Scarborough Evening News (dly); Scarborough Mercury (sat); Trader & Weekly News (thurs). STD code 01723

SPA GRAND HALL

The Spa Complex, South Bay, Scarborough, North Yorkshire YO11 2HD
Mgt: 01723 376 774 Fax: 08701 911324
Email: spaenquiries@sivltd.com
Web Site: www.scarboroughspa.co.uk
ADMINISTRATION:
Props: Scarborough Borough Council
General Manager: Jo Ager
Policy: Light orchestral concerts Summer Season, Conferences; Occasional One-night stands.
Seats: Seating: Theatre style seats - Ground floor - 1225; balcony - 745; ground floor seats removable; disabled access.
Bar and Restaurant.
TECHNICAL:
Stage: Width - 16.61m; Full Depth - 9.14m; Depth - Centre of curved frontage to steps 3.66m; 5 steps - 0.91m depth x 0.31m rising. Stage columns - from s/r 4.27m x 4.27m from stage front, from s/l 3.66m x 4.27m from stage front. Front tabs behind columns, drawn; 2 hemp sets, 2 winch LX bars, 2 fixed tab tracks; 2 pair gold tabs; get-in through auditorium - doors 2.43m x 1.52m; Stage entrance s/l, s/r.
Lighting: Strand 60 Channel 2 preset manual board; 16 1KW floods, 14 Parcans, 6 Cantatas; 8 Strand T84; 1 2KW follow spot.
Visual Aids: 1 overhead projector, 2 slide projectors.
Sound: 14 Audio Technica mics; 3 hand held radio mics; 1 tie mic radio; 16 channel soundcraft Sound Desk; 8 Bose 802 speakers, 2 Bose 402 speakers, 2 Twin cassette desks.
Backstage: 4 dressing rooms; 1 band room (with partition).
Piano: 1 Steinway Model D - full size concert grand.

SPA THEATRE

The Spa Complex, South Bay, Scarborough, North Yorkshire YO11 2HD
Mgt; 01723 376 774 Fax: 08701 911324
BO: 01723 357 869
Email: spaenquiries@sivltd.co.uk
Web Site: www.scarboroughspa.co.uk
ADMINISTRATION:
Props: Scarborough Borough Council
General Manager: Jo Ager
Policy: Resident Summer Show and occasional one-night stands and amateur shows out of season plus Christmas Panto.
Auditorium: Theatre style seats -Ground Floor: 1175 (removable), Balcony: 260, Disabled access and wheelchair spaces.
Buffet and Bar.
TECHNICAL:
Stage (concert Platform): Width 16.61m. Full Depth: 9.14m.
Front tabs behind columns, drawn, 2 pairs gold tabs, 1 hemp set, 2 winch LX bars, Stage entrance - stage left / stage right.
Sound: Soundsystem consisting of 8 Bosa 802 and 2 Bose 402 controlled through a Bose 802e System Controller. 16 channel Soundcraft 'Spirit' Live 4squared Sound Mixer. 4 Mustang amplifiers VX2500, 1 C audio RA1001, Induction Loop. Twin Cassette deck (installed on request), 1 CD player (installed on request), Tec Pro Talkback system consisting of Base unit and 3 'Canford' comm packs with headsets (installed on request).
Lighting: Zero 88 Fat Frog Lighting Console (48 channel) with Demux, Strand STM Dimmers, 1 x 1K CSI Strand follow spot, 10 Par 64 Cans, 4 x Cantanas, 3 x Strand T84, 6 x Iris 1 kW Floods. 2 Lighting bars run down the sides of the hall. Inputs are on 5 Amp sockets not 15 Amp.
General: Get in through auditorium - doors 2.43m x 1.52m. Power Supply - 63Amp 3 phase (200 Amp is available on request, tailed onto Bus Bar). Piano.
Backstage: 4 dressing rooms, 1 band room with partition.

STEPHEN JOSEPH THEATRE

Westborough, Scarborough, North Yorkshire YO11 1JW
Mgt/SD: 01723 370 540 BO: 01723 370 541 Fax: 01723 360 506
Email: enquiries@sjt.uk.com
Web Site: www.sjt.uk.com
ADMINISTRATION:
Props: Scarborough Theatre Trust Ltd
Artistic Director: Chris Monks
Finance Director: Ian Wyatt
Theatre Manager: Paul Vaines
Production Manager: Densil Hebditch
Press & Marketing Manager: Georgette Donoghue
Policy: Repertory. April to January. New plays every season.
Restaurant, Bar.
THE ROUND
Perfs: 7.30p.m.; (Sat. 2.30pm & 7.30pm)
Seats: 404 max.
THE McCARTHY
Perfs: 7.45pm.; (Sat. 2.45pm & 7.45pm)
Seats: McCarthy 165 max.
Also doubles as a cinema.
THE RESTAURANT
Seats: 64 for lunchtime and late night plays and music.
THE BODEN ROOM
Seats: 75 for conferences and meetings.
TECHNICAL:
THE ROUND
Stage: Performing area 6070mm x 6495mm; 3 Vom entrances (each 1220mm wide). Stage to mesh 5400mm (stage to LX bars 6400mm).
Lighting: Compulite Micron 4D; 210 x 10A Grid Circuits; 27 x 10A Dip Circuits; 3 x House Light circuits controlled by lighting desk. Lanterns - wide selection of Selecon Fresnels and Profiles. 12 x Compulite Whisper 16 colour Scrollers.
Sound: Soundcraft 6000 24/16/2; Chevin Quad 6 amplifiers; EAW JF100:P speakers. Mini disk player; Akai DR4 hard disc recorder; S3200I sampler.
THE McCARTHY
Stage: Performing area 13260mm x 5500mm (@C). Stage to Grid c5000mm (clearance under Cinema Screen Box - 3700mm). Various Black masking - hard & soft.
Lighting: Compulite Spark 4D; 96 x 12A dimmers. Lanterns - wide selection of ADB and CCT Fresnels and Profiles.
Sound: DDA D Series 16/8/2 with 8way matrix. Pevey cinema amps and speakers. Mini disc and CD players.

For definitive equipment list, please contact theatre.

Scunthorpe, North Lincolnshire

Pop. 70,330. London 160 miles.
Newspapers: Scunthorpe Star (fri); Scunthorpe Evening Telegraph. STD code 01724

THE BATHS HALL

Doncaster Road, Scunthorpe, North Lincolnshire DN15 7RG
Tel: 0844 854 2776
Web Site: www.scunthorpetheatres.co.uk
ADMINISTRATION:
Props; North Lincolnshire Council
Manager: Dan Harris
Policy: Multi-purpose Hall hosting diverse events, cabaret, dance, concerts, opera, etc. Stage, conference and seminar facilities.
Seating/Capacity: Main Hall with upstairs, 1,200, 2000 standing

PLOWRIGHT THEATRE

Laneham Street, Scunthorpe, North Lincolnshire DN15 6JP
Mgt: 01724 297 862 BO: 0844 8542776
Email: plowright.theatre@northlincs.gov.uk
Web Site: www.scunthorpetheatres.co.uk
ADMINISTRATION:
Props: North Lincolnshire Council
Licensee/Manager: Dan Harris
Contact: dan.harris@smg-europe.com
Policy: Touring, Mixed programme.
Perfs: Normally 7.30.
Seats: 354. Licensed Bar, Tea and Coffee Bar, Restaurant
Disabled access to most parts of building.
TECHNICAL:
STAGE: Chipboard and painted black. Proscenium width 23' 9". Proscenium height 11' 10". Grid height 22' 9". Depth of stage 22' + 7' 3" (apron). Prompt corner Stage Right. 14 hemplines with 48mm OD bars SWL 70Kg. Orchestra pit; in the auditorium and is obtained by removing rows A, B and C. Ample 13A sockets are available on the front of the apron.
LIGHTING: Lanterns: 11 x 1Kw Starlettes. 9 x 500W Patt 23's. 6 x 500W Patt 123's. 6 x 1Kw T84's (Permanently fixed on FOH bars). 6 x 1Kw Punchlite Parcans. 11 x 1Kw Par 64 Parcans. 2 x 500W Par 56 Parcans. 2 x 500W Patt 23N. 6 x 650W Prelude 16/30. 6 x 500W Minim PC. 5 x Patt 60 floods. 1 x 4 circuit "S" type cyc batten. 4 x Furse 4 circuit Groundrow. Control Desk: Strand LBX memory desk with Genius software and designers remote control. Dimmer protocol is D54 and a softpatch facility is available. FOH; 5 circuits available (1-5 & 7-11) each side of the auditorium and can be patched on the Fly floor. Follow Spot; Strand 818 2Kw follow spot & 1Kw CCT CSI follow spot located in the LX box at the rear of the auditorium.
SOUND: Standard System: FOH Speaker: Ultrasonics custom 15" + 1' Horn 2 way passive 400W per side mounted next to apron booms. FOH Amp: Ramsa 300W + 300W. Mixer: Behringer UB12-4 (12 input 2/2 bus). CD Player: Goodmans single disc. Tape Deck: Aiwa twin deck. Speakers: 2 off Ultrasonics 150W 10" + horn speakers, 2 off Acoustec 200W 12" + horn speakers. Larger system available, for more information visit: www.northlincs.gov.uk/NorthLincs/Leisure/theatres.
STAGE COMMUNICATIONS: Stage show relay system to all dressing rooms and the lighting box. The stage desk also has a call facility to all dressing rooms. 6 x sets of sets of Tech Pro Cansets - sockets stage left, stage right, lighting box, auditorium front and rear, fly floor. Internal phones used between the stage desk, technical box, box office, auditorium, FOH office, managers office and bar. CCTV screens installed.
BACKSTAGE FACILITIES: Dressing room; 4, accomm. 10 people. They are all heated and have mirrors. 3 toilets, 2 showers, and basin facilities. Dressing room one is designed for disabled use and has disabled toilet facilities. Washing machine: Automatic washer & tumble dryer dressing room 4. Closed Circuit TV: All Dressing rooms & each dock. Show relay: All Dressing rooms, Lx box. Calls: All Dressing rooms, Separate F.O.H. calls. Piano: Grand Piano & Upright. Canset: 6 sets Techpro available. 4 outlets in LX box, 3 on-stage, 2 auditorium, 1 flys.
DISABLED FACILITIES; Access available from the dressing rooms to stage via a chair lift and from stage to front of house via a ramp. Disabled toilets situated at rear of the auditorium and in dressing room 1. Induction loop system fitted and a visual fire alarm system installed. Lift available from the foyer to the 1st floor bar.

Seaham, County Durham

SEAHAM LEISURE CENTRE

Deneside Recreation Ground, Deneside, Seaham, County Durham SR7 8NP
Tel: 0191 581 6366 / 0191 581 6788
Fax: 0191 581 6852
Email: seaham@leisureconnection.co.uk
Web Site: www.onelife.com
ADMINISTRATION:
Props: One Life
Cap: 300
Manager: Wayne Adamson
Multi-use leisure centre. Conferences, exhibitions, dances, sporting events.

Seaton, Devon

THE GATEWAY

Fore Street, Seaton, Devon EX12 2LD
Tel: 01297 625699
Email: seatonsvoice@btinternet.co.uk
Web Site: www.seatongateway.co.uk
ADMINISTRATION:
Props: Seatons Voice
Caretaker: Carol Manley
Cap: 226 seated, 500 dancing
Stage productions, concerts, exhibitions, dances, excellent stage and auditorium facilities.

Selby, North Yorkshire

SELBY LEISURE CENTRE

Openinmg March 2015
Scott Road, Selby, North Yorkshire YO8 4BL
Tel: 01757 213 758
ADMINISTRATION:
Props: Selby District Council
Run by Wigan Leisure and Cultural Trust
Manager: Paul Hirst

Settle, North Yorkshire

SETTLE VICTORIA HALL

Kirkgate, Settle, North Yorkshire BD24 9DZ
Tel: 01729 825718
Email: info@settlevictoriahall.org.uk
Web Site: www.settlevictoriahall.org.uk
An exciting professional venue for all performing art forms. Comprehensive box office facilities, credit cards accepted
Seating capacity: 234 (variable)
Traditional theatre-style seating (with balcony) or cabaret layout
Monthly "What's On" Leaflet and active mailing list
Traditional pros. arch stage
Proscenium width 17'6", height 11'0". Stage depth 21'0". Wings (prompt and op) 3'0". Height to fly floor 12'0". Height to grid 20'0". Lighting: Sirius 48 zero 88 board. Sound: Inter-M powered mixer (basic PR system suitable for theatre). 12 tie-lines stage to LCR.
Fully maintained lighting rig and sound system
Full front of house and backstage suppor
Full tech. spec. available on request

Sevenoaks, Kent

Pop. 105,931. London 25 miles.
Newspapers: Sevenoaks Chronicle (thur); Focus (tue); Kentish Times Leader (tues).
STD code 01732

STAG COMMUNITY ARTS CENTRE

London Road, Sevenoaks, Kent TN13 1ZZ
Mgt: 01732 451 548
BO/Info: 01732 450 175
Email: enquiries@stagsevenoaks.co.uk
Web Site: www.stagsevenoaks.co.uk
ADMINISTRATION:
Props: Stag Community Arts Centre
General Manager & Company Secretary: Andrew Eyre
Technical Manager: Rod Henderson

Marketing Manager: Rebecca Harrison
Policy: Producing and receiving house for professional productions. Drama, musicals, dance and opera. Amateur productions.
Perfs: Usually 7.30/8.00pm
Seats - Theatre:454, Studio:up to 150, Cinemas x 2: 126 and 107
General Facilities: Wheelchair access to all auditoria, 2 spaces in theatre and 3 in each cinema, flexible arrangements in studio. Large bar and foyer. Bar and studio available for hire as meeting rooms. Toddler facilities. Fully computerised box office.
TECHNICAL:
Stage: Size 60ft x 60ft performing area, 120 way dimmers, Arri Image lighting board. Manual lighting board, two lighting control boxes, Tech Pro headset system, full sound system/mixing desk, radio mic etc.
Lighting: Large in house lighting rig - inc 24 x Starlette fres. 36 x Cantata profile 14 x P743 Fres. Parcans, Codas, Minuettes and 2 x 1k csi followspots. 65 amp 3 phase supply on stage. 2 x 65 amp single phase supply on stage. Large scenery truck (horizontal flying system) 20ft x 20ft in 10ft x 5ft sections. Dressing rooms: 2 principals with en-suite showers, wash basin etc. Large chorus room for up to 70 with shower block, WC's etc. Orchestra pit for up to 50 musicians, removal lid on forestage. Prompt corner usually p.s. Baby grand and rehearsal pianos available. Large vehicle hoist to lift level with stage for get in (up to 7 ton short wheel base lorry).Large public car park at rear. Full technical support by our 4 in house technicians, casuals available.

Shanklin, Isle of Wight

SHANKLIN THEATRE

Prospect Road, Shanklin, Isle of Wight PO37 6AJ
Mgt: 01983 862 739 BO: 01983 868 000
Email: bookings@shanklintheatre.com
Web Site: www.shanklintheatre.com
ADMINISTRATION:
Props: Shanklin Theatre Ltd
Bookings Manager: Vic Farrow
Technical Manager: Chris Gardner
Policy: Touring - Concerts, Drama, Dance, Opera, Ballet, Comedy, One Night Stands and Amateur Productions
Seats 615
TECHNICAL:
Stage: Proscenium, raked. Proscenium opening 8.99m. Height of proscenium 5.50m. Depth of S/Line 8.99m. Height of grid 9.90m. 20 lined hemp. W/widths P.S. 2.5m, O.P. 1.5m. Prompt corner P.S.
Lighting: Switchboard: Compulite Vector Orange. Memory Board normally operated FOH stalls. 32aamp 3 phase supply available for temp. board.
Switched independents in flys, stage and F.O.H. Large lamp stock available.
Sound: Soundcraft K2 24.8.2 Martin W8C with QSC amps. Assorted mics AKG CMS system Acoustics suitable for music or spoken word.
Stage management: Dressing room call and relay. Intercom and Q lights to all technical stations.
Backstage: 7 dressing rooms accommodating 40-100
Staff: stage Manager, casuals.

Sheffield, South Yorkshire

Pop. 513,310. London 160 miles.
Newspapers: The Star (ntly); Telegraph (wkly). STD code 0114

CRUCIBLE THEATRE

Norfolk Street, Sheffield, South Yorkshire S1 1DA
Mgt: 0114 249 5999 BO: 0114 249 6000
Email: info@sheffieldtheatres.co.uk
Web Site: www.sheffieldtheatres.co.uk
ADMINISTRATION:
Props: Sheffield Theatres Trust
Chief Executive: Dan Bates
Artistic Director: Daniel Evans
Business Resources Director: Bookey Oshin
Sales and Communications Director: Claire Murray
Policy: Producing Theatre with full education team.
Perfs: Eves. 7.30 (Studio 7.45)
Seats: 1,000 approx.
Studio for hire
Licensed Bar, Cafe, and frequent foyer exhibitions.
TECHNICAL:
Please contact venue for full listings.

DRONFIELD SPORTS CENTRE

Civic Centre, Dronfield, Sheffield S18 1PD
Tel: 01246 217217
Email: paul.newton@ne-derbyshire.gov.uk
Web Site: www.ne-derbyshire.gov.uk
ADMINISTRATION:
Props: North East Derbyshire District Council
Area Manager: Chris Mills
Capacity: 600

LIBRARY THEATRE

Central Library, Surrey Street, Sheffield, South Yorkshire S1 1XZ
Tel: 0114 273 4102 Fax: 0114 273 5009
Email: philip.repper@sheffield.gov.uk
Web Site: www.sheffield.gov.uk/libraries/librarytheatre
ADMINISTRATION:
Props: Sheffield City Council
Cap: 260
For bookings contact: Philip Repper

LYCEUM THEATRE

Tudor Square, Sheffield, South Yorkshire S1 1DA
Mgt: 0114 249 5999 BO: 0114 249 6000
Email: info@sheffieldtheatres.co.uk
Web Site: www.sheffieldtheatres.co.uk
ADMINISTRATION:
Props: Sheffield Theatres Trust
Chief Executive: Dan Bates
Artistic Director: Daniel Evans
Business Resources Director: Bookey Oshin
Sales and Communications Director: Claire Murray
Perfs: Eves. 7.30 (Studio 7.45)
Seats: 1,000 approx.
Lyceum seats 1,100 on three levels. No 1 touring theatre, ballet, opera, musicals, drama, and pantomime. 3 bars.
TECHNICAL:
Please contact venue for full listings.

MOTORPOINT ARENA, SHEFFIELD

Broughton Lane, Sheffield, South Yorkshire S9 2DF
Tel: 0114 256 2002 BO: 0114 256 5656
Fax: 0114 256 5520
Email: joe.waldron@livenation.co.uk
Web Site: www.motorpointarenasheffield.co.uk/ www.livenation.co.uk
ADMINISTRATION:
Props: Live Nation
General Manager: Rob O'Shea
Hiring Manager: Lynda Cliffe
Staging major sporting events, exhibitions and conferences for the 13,000 seat capacity venue.
For all booking information and further details, please contact: Joe Waldron, Motorpoint Arena Sheffield, Broughton Lane, Sheffield S9 2DF: Joe.Waldron@livenation.co.uk

SHEFFIELD CITY HALL

Barker's Pool Sheffield S1 2JA
Enquiries/Bookings: 0114 223 3740
Marketing/Press: 0114 223 3714 Box Office: 0114 278 9789 Box Office Admin: 0114 223 3750 Fax: 0114 223 3765
Email: info@sheffieldcityhall.co.uk
Web Site: www.sheffieldcityhall.co.uk
ADMINISTRATION:
Props: Sheffield International Venues
General Manager: Richard Hunter
Bookings Administrator: Lesley Charlesworth. Contact: 0114 223 3746
Marketing: Ruth Proctor. Contact: 0114 223 3715
Box Office Administrator: Peter Sporne, 0114 223 3750
Irwin Mitchell Oval Hall: 2,272
Memorial Hall: 500 (Stalls 350, Balcony 150)
Ballroom: 800 (500 seating with tables)
TECHNICAL: Irwin Mitchell Oval Hall
STAGE: Open stage / No fire curtain. 19m x 8.5m (60'6" x 27'6"). Height of stage 1020mm (40"). Stage extension 15.5m x 2.15m (50'6" x 7'0"). PA wings

4m x 2.8m (13'. 00" x 9.'00"). Stage load 5kn/m2 (104lb/ft2). Blacks and pros arch if required at a cost.
LIGHTING: Stage: Celco Pathfinder Board, Celco Dimmers (7). 22 x 1 kw par cans (floods). 28 x 1kw rank strand fresnells. 4 x 1kw rank strand profiles. 6 x 1kw source four. 2 x 1200w follow spots.at a cost of £60 each. House lights: Full or part blackout controlled from side stage.
DRESSING ROOMS: 10 dressing rooms; 8 toilets; 5 showers; localised air conditioning in 4.

THE OCTAGON CENTRE
University of Sheffield Western Bank
Sheffield S10 2TQ
Tel: 0114 222 8888
Email: octagon@sheffield.ac.uk
Web Site: www.shef.ac.uk/cics/octagon
ADMINISTRATION:
Seating/Capacity: 1,200, retractable. 1,500 standing.
TECHNICAL:
Full range of equipment available for hire along with support staff

Sheringham, Norfolk
Pop. 4,770. London 130 miles.
Newspapers: North Norfolk News (fri); Eastern Daily Press (dly). STD code 01263

SHERINGHAM LITTLE THEATRE
2 Station Road, Sheringham, Norfolk NR26 8RE
Admin: 01263 822117 BO: 01263 822347 10am-4pm (Mon-Sat)
Email: boxoffice@sheringhamlittletheatre.com
Web Site: www.sheringhamlittletheatre.com
ADMINISTRATION:
Props: Sheringham Little Theatre Society
Policy: Summer repertory - rest of year on hire; Professional Panto produced, also cinema.
Perfs: 7.30 pm normal
Cap: 180
TECHNICAL:
Stage: Proscenium, Pros. Opening 5.26m; Ht. of Pros. 3.20m; Ht. of Grid 3.74m; Prompt Cnr. O.P. Width, 7.3m, depyh, 4.6m, height, pros.
Lighting: Switchboard: Sirius 48.
Sound: Speakers: 2 - one each side of Pros.
Film: Twin 35mm.
Dressing Rooms 2; Accom. 9 Male, 10 Female.

Shildon, County Durham

SHILDON SUNNYDALE LEISURE CENTRE
Midridge Lane, Shildon, County Durham DL4 2EP
Tel: 01388 728866
Email: ssic@durham.gov.uk
Web Site: www.durham.gov.uk
ADMINISTRATION:
Props: Durham County Council
Cap: 300 max. Portable stages
Manager: Ben Kelsey

STADIUM 2000
Shildon Sunnydale Leisure Centre, Midridge Lane Shildon, County Durham DL4 2EP
Tel: 01388 728866
Email: peter.boddy@durham.gov.uk
Web Site: www.durham.gov.uk
ADMINISTRATION:
Props: Durham County Council
Manager: Ben Kelsey
Capacity: 800/1,000
Athletics events/open air concerts/social events/Rugby/football pitchers

Shipley, West Yorkshire

IAN CLOUGH HALL
Hall Cliffe, Baildon, Shipley, West Yorkshire BD17 6ND
Tel: 01274 531 465 Hire: 01943 436 224
Email: community-hall@bradford.gov.uk
Web Site: www.bradford.gov.uk
ADMINISTRATION:
Props: City of Bradford Metropolitan District Council
Cap: 160 Theatre Style
For bookings contact Chris Ashton.

Shrewsbury, Shropshire
Pop. 57,300. London 148 miles.
Newspapers: Shropshire Star (btly); Shrewsbury Chronicle (thurs); Shrewsbury Ad-Mag (thurs). STD code 01743

THEATRE SEVERN
Frankwell Quay Shrewsbury Shropshire SY3 8HQ
Admin: 01743 281 282 BO: 01743 281 281
Email: peter.nicholson@shropshire.gov.uk
Web Site: www.theatresevern.co.uk
ADMINISTRATION:
Props: Shropshire Council
General Manager: Peter Nicholson
Venue and Programme Manager: David Jack
Technical Manager: Grant Wilson
Marketing Manager: Craig Reeves
Policy: Week, Part-week and single performances of Drama, Dance, Opera, Variety, Concerts etc.
2 Auditoria: 683 seats fixed, The Walker Theatre: 250 retractable seats, 500 standing.
Dance Studio and Function Room.
Licensed bars, restaurant, function catering facilities.
TECHNICAL:
Stage: Proscenium, width 10m depth 9m. Upstage crossover. Flat floor wood on joists. Burgundy House Tabs. Black wool serge masking. White Cyc. Star cloth. Black/White gauze. Stage Management prompt side. 6 Dressing rooms. Showers. Laundry facilities.
Lighting: ADB phoenix 10 desk. Euro rack dimmers. DMX link to stage/FOH. 2x mac500. 4x Roboscan 918. Wide selection of generics. 2x Korrigan 1.2k HMI Followspots.
Sound: 5k Rig. Soundcraft K3 Standard. Martin W3/W2. Foldback LE350/400. Mixing position centre rear auditorium.

Sidmouth, Devon
Pop. 12,500. London 163 miles.
Newspapers: Sidmouth Herald (sat). STD code 013958

MANOR PAVILION THEATRE
Manor Road, Sidmouth, Devon EX10 8RP
Mgt 01395 576798 BO: 01395 514413
Mgt Bookings: 01395 576798 (Graham Whitlock)
Email: gwhitlock@eastdevon.gov.uk
Web Site: www.manorpavilion.com
ADMINISTRATION:
Props: East Devon District Council
Bookings Manager: Graham Whitlock
Policy: Summer Repertory July to September inclusive. Also Professional and Amateur and Concert Recitals throughout the year.
Seats: 277

Skegness, Lincolnshire
Pop. 15,000. London 139 miles.
Newspapers: Skegness Standard (fri); Skegness News (wed). STD code 01754

EMBASSY CENTRE
Grand Parade, Skegness, Lincolnshire PE25 2UG
BO: 0845 674 0505 Admin: 01754 897 670
Email: trish.wiles@e-lindsey.gov.uk
Web Site: www.embassytheatre.co.uk
ADMINISTRATION:

Props: Magnavitea Trust for Leisure and Culture
Theatre Manager: Trish Wiles
The Embassy Centre Theatre, centrally situated on the Skegness seafront, is a modern multi-purpose venue which is available for private hire and can host conferences, exhibitions, trade fairs and alike. The Theatre plays host to many of the top stars throughout the year including Ken Dodd, Billy Pearce, The Nolans, Joe Brown, The Chuckle Brothers, Joe Pasquale, Chas 'n' Dave, Joe Longthorne as well as summer and Christmas pantomimes and Duggie Chapman's Good Olde Days.
Capacity: 1168 in theatre style. Lower level 760 seats (332 loose, 428 retractable); balcony seats fixed. Catering facilities. Licensed Bar.
TECHNICAL:
STAGE: Proscenium with fixed apron; Proscenium opening 7.00m; Ht. of Pros. 3.5m; Depth 4m curved. Vario's available for stage extensions. Soundcraft 200 sound desk.
LIGHTING: Avolites pearl board, 48 dimmer channels, Martin moving heads, par can rig, profiles and 2 follow spots.
SOUND: Allen and Heath desk, 4k sound system plus foldback, xps 990 effects and full range of Mics inc Radio Mics.
DRESSING ROOMS: 4 Dressing rooms with toilets and showers, access by stage door. Quick change space available.
Please apply to Centre for full technical specification.

Skipton, North Yorkshire

TOWN HALL

High Street, Skipton, North Yorkshire BD23 1AH
Caretaker Tel: 01756 706 322 Bkg: 01756 706 395
Email: jriley@cravendc.gov.uk
Web Site: www.cravendc.gov.uk
ADMINISTRATION:
Props: Craven District Council
Cap: 350 with Stage Facilities.
Caretaker: Steven Brane
Bookings Contact: Judith Riley

Solihull, West Midlands

Pop. 198,700. London 110 miles.
Newspapers: Solihull News (thurs); Solihull Times (fri). Plus Birmingham Newspapers. STD code 0121

SOLIHULL ARTS COMPLEX - THEATRE & STUDIO

Homer Road, Solihull, West Midlands B91 3RG
Mgt: 0121 704 6961 BO: 0121 704 6962
Fax: 0121 704 6991
Email: artscomplex@solihull.gov.uk
Web Site: www.solihull.gov.uk
ADMINISTRATION:
Props: Solihull MBC
Arts & Tourism Manager: Lawrence Smith
Policy: Mixed use
Seats: 340 (theatre), 200 (studio)
Cafe bar, boxoffice and gallery attached to main Solihull Central Library.
TECHNICAL:
Stage: Pros. opening 9.00m; Ht. of pros 4.00m (permanent with safety curtain); Stage 13m wide between galleries; 17.37m wall to wall; Ht. of Stage 11.75m to grid, 5.7m to underside of galleries; Stage surface soft wood boarding, Cyc permanent; 15 hemp fly lines.
Lighting: Strand 72 channel LBX LX board; Stage Managers control desk (working corner SL) operating house tabs; intercom to FOH, Backstage show relay FOH; Backstage cue light system.
Sound Equip: Soundcraft K3 32-8-2-1; Denon Cassette deck; Bose 802-302 speaker; C Audio amps DN360 Graphics.
Projection facilities: Elmo 16mm Kodak SAV2010.
Dressing Rooms: 2 principal, shower/wash basin/wc; 2 chorus with 2 wash basins and wc; Wardrobe Green Room.
Get-in: 5.75m high x 3.00m wide dock door direct off carpark, drop to road .80m.
Also in complex , studio, art gallery, Chapter and Verse cafe bar adjacent to Solihull Central Library.

South Shields, Tyne and Wear

THE CUSTOMS HOUSE

Mill Dam, South Shields, Tyne and Wear NE33 1ES
BO Tel: 0191 454 1234 Admin: 0191 427 3749 Fax: 0191 456 5979
Email: mail@customshouse.co.uk
Web Site: www.customshouse.co.uk
ADMINISTRATION:
Executive Director: Raymond Spencer MBE
Technical Manager: Alison Hickman
Marketing and Programming Manager: Sally Hoban
Capacity 439 (main theatre) ; 145 (studio).
Policy: Broad mix of music, drama, dance and film.

TEMPLE PARK CENTRE

Temple Memorial Park, John Reid Road, South Shields, Tyne and Wear NE34 8QN
Tel: 0191 456 9119 Fax: 0191 456 6621
Email: harry.blackett@southtyneside.gov.uk
Web Site: www.s-tyneside-mbc.gov.uk
ADMINISTRATION:
Props: South Tyneside Metropolitan Borough Council;
Centre Manager: H. Blackett.
Policy: Multi-purpose Hall used for concerts, shows, sporting and special events, conferences and exhibitions.
Seating/Capacity: 1,800 seated; 3,000 standing.
TECHNICAL:
Main Hall: 155' x 119' (47.5m x 36.5m); Height 36' (11.0m); Total Area 18,445 sq. ft. (1,733 sq.m.).
Power: 100 amp 3 phase; 60 amp 3 phase; backstage
external generator feed point.
Sound and Lighting: In-house P.A. and full sound system. Strand lighting system with control room.
Flying Facilities: 15 suspension points at 11.0 metres. Overall loading of 4 tons.
Other: Backstage: dressing rooms (private and communal); showers, w.c.; laundry and ironing.
Catering: Separate crew catering and dining fully equipped.
Changing: Large communal areas all with showers, hairdryers and w.c.
Production: Offices available with metered telephone, fax etc.
Access and Loading: Direct points adjacent to Main Hall.

Southampton, Hampshire

Pop. 213,710. London 77 miles.
Newspapers: Southern Evening Echo (ntly); Southampton Advertiser (thurs).
STD code 023 80

MAYFLOWER THEATRE

Commercial Road, Southampton Hampshire SO15 1GE
Mgt: 023 8071 1815 BO: 023 8071 1811
SD: 023 8071 1800 Fax: 023 8071 1801
Email: margarita.mifsud@mayflower.org.uk
Web Site: www.mayflower.org.uk
ADMINISTRATION:
Props: Mayflower Theatre Trust
Chief Executive: Michael Ockwell
Director of Finance: Alison Harrison
EA to Chief Exec: Margarita Mifsud
Head of Marketing: Sarah Lomas
Technical Manager: Rachel Fox
Stage Manager: Steve Jarrett
House Managers: Gareth Carr & Alice Banet
Box Office Manager: Christine Ward
Policy: No. 1 Touring Companies including National Ballet and Opera, Musicals (Pre/Post West End), Concerts, One Nighters, Conferences etc.
Seats: 2,194 plus 130 standing - total capacity 2,324.
TECHNICAL:
Stage: Pros. opening 13.5m; Ht. 7m, depth 12m P.S. 3.7m, O.P. 5.1m, stage width overall 22.6m.
Lighting: Control 300 channel Strand 530.

Dimmers 5kw. Dimmer 48 2kw Dimmer 252. Stage management control desk has full dual queueing system of lights and head-set communication video cameras can monitor orchestral pit and stage.
Dressing Rooms: 18 (accommodating up to 120 persons) all on individual call system, plus show relay facility. Band rooms; situated under the stage with direct access to orchestra pit, 2 rooms with accommodation for approx. 20 in each.
Lifting front of Proscenium 6 x 1 tonne Points Stage Grid 16 x 1 tonne Scene height 6.4m Dock, Width 4.3m; Depth 16.2m;
Touring Managers Office.
Power: 3 x 3ph 200 amp.

NUFFIELD THEATRE

University Road, Southampton, Hampshire SO17 1TR
Admin: 023 8031 5500 BO: 023 8067 1771
Email: info@nuffieldtheatre.co.uk
Web Site: www.nuffieldtheatre.co.uk
ADMINISTRATION:
Props: The Nuffield Theatre Trust
Director: Sam Hodges
Administrative Director: James Gough
FOH Manager: Clare White
Chief Technician: Neil Stark
Policy: 3/4 weekly repertory (Sept-May) occasional tours and amateur hire.
Perfs: Mon-Sat Eve 7.30 pm; Mats: occasionally Mid-Week & Saturday.
Seats: 481 (varies according to stage).
Fully licensed Theatre Bar, Restaurant.
Audio Description on last Saturday matinee of professional run. Signed performance on last Saturday matinee of professional run.
TECHNICAL:
Stage: Proscenium arch with thrust. Pros.opening 9.1m x 4.5m. Depth 7m 21. wing widths 4.11m SR, 4.11 SL. No rake - floor hardboard covered, backstage crossover. Height of grid 9.57m - 20 hemp sets, 4 cw's, 0.2m apart - tab track - maximum flying height 4.5m - black serge legs and tabs - white filled cotton cloth cyclorama - house tabs flown on c/w. Forestage (not rectangular) in 2 parts, 1st forestage: 2m 60 x 7m 50, 2nd forestage 2m 30 x 7m 90. Tensioned wired grid above the foredtage. Orchestra pit accommodates 15 with single forestage or 25 if double. 12 lit music stands available. Get-in via doors 2100 x 3000. Tallescope. Safety curtain. Scaled 1.25 plans available.

LIGHTS:
Dimming and Control: ETC Expression 3, 400 Channel Lighting Console. Strand LD90 Dimmer Racks, 228 Channels (216 x 2.5kw, 12 x 5kw). Focus Brain Radio DMX Remote. DMX Controlled House Lights. 36 Non-Dim Circuits. (Not DMX, controlled from LX Box).
Stage Power: Three Phase Supply DSR (3L, + N + E), 1 x 32A, 1 x 63A, 1 x 125A, Three Phase Supply USL (3L, + N + E), 1 x 32A, 1 x 63A, 1 x 125A, 13A Sockets Around Stage
Power Distribution: 5A TRS (Varying Lengths), 13A TRS (Varying Lengths), 15A TRS (Varying Lengths), 15A Splitters, Grelcos And Trelcos, Socapex (Varying Lengths), Socapex Male Spiders, Socapex Female Spiders (Some staggered), Socapex Female Boxes.
LX Bars and Positions: 5 x Onstage Counterweight LX Bars
2 x Booms Inside Pros, 4 x Booms Outside Pros, 1 x Motorised FOH Advance Bar, 2 x LX Catwalks FOH, 1 x SL and 1 x SR Slips Catwalk, 1 x SL and 1 x SR Curved Bars FOH, 2 x Followspot Position House L and House R.
Profile Lanterns: (shutters supplied unless stated), 4 x ETC Source 4 Zoom 25-50° 575w, 12 x ETC Source 4, Interchangeable Lens 575w, 9 x 50° lens, 7 x 36° lens, 4 x 26° lens, 2 x 19° lens. 49 x CCT Silhouette 30 1k, 4 x CCT Silhouette 40 1k, 2 x CCT Minuette 650w, 1 x Selecon Pacific 90° 800w, 3 x Tulla Lito 650w
Fresnel Lanterns: (Barndoors supplied unless stated), 32 x Strand Patt 743 1k, 10 x Tulla Lito 1k, 9 x Strand Patt 243 2k 8 x Coemar 2k, 2 x CCT Minuette 650w (w/o Barndoors).
Flood Lanterns: 5 x Strand Iris 4 1k, 6 x Strand Iris 1 1k, 6 x Strand Coda 4 500w, 4 x Minuette 500w, 2 x 16 Cell Floodbanks 800w.
Par Lanterns: 6 x Pulsar Par 36 Pinspot, 16 x Par 30, 2 x Par 64 Floorcan, 4 x Par 64 Short-nose, 54 x Par 64 Standard, (CP60, CP61 and CP62 lamps available as requested)
Other Lanterns & Accessories: 2 x Strand 2k Followspot, 1 x Coemar Pilotta 1200 Followspot, 3 x Strand Beamlight, 10 x Iris for Silhouette 30 / 40, 2 x Iris for Source 4, 25 x B Gobo Holder for S4 Profile, (12 x Metal, 13 x Glass), 38 x A Gobo Holder for Sil Profile, (35 x Metal, 3 x Glass), 1 x M Gobo Holder For Minuette Profile, (Limited gobo stock available on request), 4 x Top Hat for Par 64, 1 x Rainbow Scroller PSU, 6 x Rainbow 16 Colour Scrollers for Par 64, (Adaptor plates for other lanterns are available on request).
Smoke & Effects: 5 x Diablo DFX-1 Flame Effect, 2 x UV Cannon
2 x Martin Atomic 3000 Strobe (DMX), 1 x Bubblestream Bubble Machine, 1 x Le Maitre Neutron Star Hazer (DMX), 1 x Rosco 1700 Smoke Machine (DMX), 1 x Unique Hazer (DMX), Projection: 1 x Eiki Video Projector 3200 lumens

SOUND:
Mixers: 2x 24 Channel Behringer MX9000 24:8:6, 1x Yamaha 02R Digital Console, 1x Soundcraft Spirit4 12:4:2.
Speakers: 2x Bose 802 + Controller, 2x Ohm Wedges 150w, 2x Bose 101, 2x JBL Control1, 2x TOA Full Range Speakers, 2x Tannoy Mecury (Control Room Monitors), 4 Ramsa A10.
Amps: 1x Quad 306 (Control Room Monitors), 1x Quad 520, 1x Toa, 1x Amcron, 1x Crown CSL 460.
Main PA: 4x TOA Hi-Mid (spx), 2x TOA Sub-Bass (spx), 1x TOA OP A-800amp (HI) + Controller, 1x TOA OP A-1200amp (MID) + Controller, 1x TOA OP A-2000amp (BASS) + Controller.
Recorders & Players: 2x Tascam MD801R, 1x Akai S3000XL Midi Stereo Digital Sampler & Opti Driver 230MB, 1x Akai OR4VR Hard Disk Recorder 2GB, 1x Denon Twin Cassette Recorder, 1x Denon CD Player, 1x Technics Record Player, 3x Revox Recorders/Players.
Processors: 1x Alesis Microverb4, 1x Yamaha SPX 50D, 1x TOA Digital Signal Processor OPO204, 1x Alesis G-EQ, 1x BSS Opal EQ.
Microphones: 3x RS Dynamic Microphones, 3x Crown PCC160, 1x AKG 0955, 4x Audio Technica Rifle Mic, 1x Sennheiser MD421 Dynamic Mic + Stand (Describing Mic), 3x Shure SM58, 10x Sennheiser EW300 RadioMics.
Accessories: 1x Round Base Mic Stand, 3x Chrome Boom Arm Mic Stands (Chrome) 2x Adjustable Small Mic Stands, 4x Dual DI Boxes, 1x Single DI Box, 2x 16 way XLR->XLR Multicore.

Stage Management: Prompt corner SL - cue system, 10 outstations, Stage monitor screen, show relay / tannoy to dressing rooms. Backstage: 2 dressing rooms - green room - wardrobe rear of stage with iron, washing machine, dryer and 3 power points. Rehearsal areas by arrangement, piano good. Advice given on accommodation. Staff - 1 stage, 2 lighting - casuals available - no security personnel. Backstage facilities accessible to disabled performers and staff.

O2 GUILDHALL SOUTHAMPTON

Civic Centre, West Marlands Road, Southampton, Hants SO14 7LP
Gen Mngr: 023 8083 2775 Operations Mngr: 023 8083 2289 Technical: 023 8083 2286 BO Mngr: 023 8083 2611 Mktg Mngr: 023 8083 3112 Bars Mngr: 023 8083 2622 Admin: 023 8083 2453 BO: 023 8063 2601 Fax: 0870 094 9177
Email: judy.amandini@livenation.co.uk
Web Site: www.livenation.co.uk/southampton
ADMINISTRATION:
Southampton Guildhall comprises of three multi-purpose auditoriums.
Props: Livenation (Venues) UK Ltd
Area General Manager: Mandy Fields
Assistant General Manager: Les Turner
Box Office Manager: Carolynn Freeman
Marketing Manager: Leah Lloyd
Senior Technician: Simon Williams
Administrator: Judy Amandini
Policy: Rock Concerts, Conferences, Dinners, Dances, Exhibitions, Weddings.
Capacities: Guildhall: 1,749 standing/balcony seating, 1,271 seated; 600 Dinner.

Solent Suite: 200 standing; Lecture Theatre 118.
Bar and Catering facilities.
TECHNICAL:
GUILDHALL:-
STAGE: Proscenium with 1.24 rake. Main stage 48'W x 27'D x 3'6"H (fixed). Stage height 28'. Black walls, ceiling, flooring, backdrop and truss boarders. Additional staging; up to 12 x 6' x 4' Steeldeck, 6 x 8' x 4' Steeldeck. Organ; Compton double console pipe organ.
LIGHTING: Dimming - 156 circuits Avolites ART 4000; Control - Chamsys MQ100 + wing, Zero 88 Jester 24/48; Colour medium - various colours in stock from LEE. Luminaires; About 200 Par64 cans, 16 x 1kw single cyc units, 6 x Source 4 15-30 zooms, 4 x 4 lite DWE blinders, 6 x Bars of ACL's, 4 x Atomic strobes, 6 x 400w UV gun's. Other; 32" Mirror Ball, smoke and haze machines. Followspots; 2 x Robert Juliat 'Korrigan' 5° - 9° 1200w HMI.
SOUND: Main PA; L'Acoustics dV DOSC. Mixing; Midas Venice 240, Yamaha O1V. Muilticore; 40ch send 20ch return. Outboard; Behringer, Rane, Dynacord and Yamaha
Mic's - Shure SM58, SM57, BETA 52A, Shure Premier radio system, AKG 747, C1000's. Playback; Tape, CD, Minidisk, Tascam and Denon. PA; 12 x L'Acoustics dV-DOSC, 4 x DV subs + in fill's.
DRESSING ROOMS: 6; 2 with shower and toilet, one with washer/ dryer
DISABLED FACILITIES: Full level access to the Guildhall made via purpose built ramp to the right of the Main Entrance. Viewing platform and auditorium space for wheelchair users. Full level toilet facilities located on ground floor of the auditorium. Motorised lift available on stage on request. Limited parking spaces available at venue car park for concert attendees with disable badges. Guide Dogs welcome. Infra red system. Please inform the box office of your request at the time of booking.
SOLENT SUITE:-
STAGE: 31.5m X 8.78m, Permanent dance floor.
LECTURE THEATRE:-
STAGE: Pros opening 4.3m, 2.57m H, 4.66m D; full stage 9m W.
General: Induction loop hearing system.

SOUTHAMPTON UNIVERSITY

University Road, Highfield, Southampton, Hants SO17 1BJ
Tel: 023 8059 5213
Email: j.boyce@soton.ac.uk
Web Site: www.southampton.ac.uk
ADMINISTRATION:
Contact: Jenna Boyce
Main venue: seating/capacity: 800 (but only available for hire on weds. and sat.)
Other venues: Seating/Capacities: 500 and 400 (Both are available for hire throughout the week.)

THE BERRY THEATRE

Wildern Lane, Hedge End, Southampton Hants SO30 4EJ
Tel: 01489 799499 BO: 02380 352333
Email: theberrytheatre@eastleigh.gov.uk
Web Site: www.theberrytheatre.co.uk
Administration:
Props: Eastleigh Borough Council
Cap: 276
Director: Owen Calvert-Lyons
General Manager: Donna Reeves
Technical Manager: Tim Slater

TURNER SIMS CONCERT HALL

University of Southampton, University Road, Southampton, Hampshire SO17 1BJ
Mgt: 023 8059 2223 BO: 023 8059 5151
Fax: 023 8059 2505
Email: info@turnersims.co.uk
Web Site: www.turnersims.co.uk
ADMINSTRATION:
Concert Hall Manager: Kevin Appleby
Seating/Capacity: 372 max, raked.

Southend-On-Sea, Essex

Pop. 175,300. London 40 miles.
Newspapers: Evening Echo (ntly); Standard Recorder (wkly); Yellow Advertiser (wkly). STD code 01702

PALACE THEATRE

Palace Theatre, 430, London Road, Westcliff-on-Sea, Essex SS0 9LA
BO 01702 351135 Fax 01702 335518
Email: georgiep@southendtheatres.org.uk
Web Site: www.southendtheatres.org.uk
ADMINISTRATION:
Props: HQ Theatres Ltd
General Manager: Ellen McPhillips
Policy: Repertory. Infra-red audio/description system.
Perfs: Nightly 8.00; Mats 2.30 Sat Mats.2.30pm
Bar.
Cap: Main House: 603, Studio: 100
TECHNICAL:
Stage: Proscenium Arch: 8m wide, 5.5m high. 4.9m depth @ Centre Line (NB: Back wall does not run parallel). Alcove at rear, understage crossover. Rake 1:18. Grid 16.76m. 13 Lines hemp. 6 Lines CWT. Flying bars 9m long. Orchestra pit (coverd when not in use) accom. 12.
MAIN HOUSE
Sound: Soundcraft K3 24 channel, RCF Vision 152 + processing speakers, Yamaha amps,1 amp spare for on stage. 1 crown ma1202
Lighting: Strand 430 with Genius+ Version 2.8, working dimmers. Harmony 15/28, Harmony 22/40, Cantata 26/44, Prelude 16/30, Harmony PC, Harmony F, ADB F, Prelude F, Minuette PC, Prelude PC, PAR 64, Nocturne flood, AC1001L floods, Coda battens.
STUDIO
Sound: The Studio has a basic sound system.
Lighting: Strand action 24 way board dimmers. SIL 30 (AXIAL), PAT 803 F, T64, PAT 743, PAT 813 PC.
Playback: Revox B77, CD players, cassette deck. Mics: AKG D330BT, Shure SM58, Sennhiser K6 (ME66 Capsules).
General: Dressing rooms: 4, accommodates 20. Wardrobe with full laundry facilities. Workshop. Paintshop. Complex also incorporates the Dixon Studio with its own LX and Sound systems, Cueing facilities and Show Relay.

SOUTHEND THEATRES LTD

Cliffs Pavilion The Palace Theatre
Station Road, Southend-on-Sea, Essex SS0 7RA
Mgt: 01702 331 852 BO: 01702 351 135
SD: 01702 350456 Admin: 01702 390 657 Mktg: 01702 390 472 Fax: 01702 391573
Email: kateh@southendtheatres.org.uk
Web Site: www.southendtheatres.org.uk
ADMINISTRATION:
Props: HQ Theatres Ltd
Managing Director: Ellen McPhillips
Stage & Events Manager: Paul Seed
Stage and Technical Manager: Paul Seed
Contact: paulse@southendtheatres.org.uk
Cliffs Pavilion: The largest purpose-built performing arts centre east of London and in East Anglia! With a capacity of 1657 for seated performances and 2,268 for mixed seated events, the Cliffs Pavilion regularly presents the complete range of live entertainment from Ballet, Opera and Ice Dance, through top-name comedians and singers, to major West End musicals, big name rock bands, top children's shows and the largest pantomime in the South-East.
The Palace Theatre: An Edwardian listed building with a seating capacity of 603, the Palace Theatre is ideal for smaller scale touring productions and regularly presents drama and comedy. It's intimate atmosphere lends itself to "Audience with..." evenings as well as comedians and live music. The main auditorium is complemented by the 100 seat Dixon Studio which is perfect for small-scale productions and ideal for rehearsal and workshop space.
Capacity:
Cliffs Pavilion; 1,000 Arena Events; 1,657 Concerts, Shows; 2,268 Standing. Palace Theatre; 603 seats. Dixon Studio; 100 seats.
Licenced Bars.Full Conference Facilities.
TECHNICAL:
CLIFFS PAVILION:-
STAGE: Rake, 1 To 25, Pros. Width 9.92m to 14.17m, Pros. Height, 5.33m (17'6), Stage Depth, 9.5m.Height to Grid, 11.62m. Height to Fly Floor; 6.4m (21'). Control Room to Stage Front; 25.45m (83'6').
ROSTRA; 22 Merricks Sico Wheeled Rostra; Surface Area, 2.4m x 1.2m

(8'x4'). Height; 8 x 45cm (19'), 4 x 60cm (2'), 4 x 75cm (2'6'), 6 x 90cm (3').
FLYING : Flying Height 5.3m (17'6), Flying Height to Fly Floor 6.4m (21'). 27 sets of counterweight flying lines. Weight capacity per cradle: 400Kg (873lb). Flying Bar Lengths; 16.45m (54')
Masking: Black masking, comprising:- 1 x set of full black tabs 18 ft high, 1 x set of full black tabs 25 ft high, 3 x 2 metre high black borders, 5 x 15 ft black borders, 8 x 2 metre wide black legs, 8 x 12 ft wide x 25 ft high black legs, 1 x Set of scarlet and gold house tabs.
VISITING SOUND SUPPLY: 100 amp, 3 phase:- 1 x 1 phase 32 amp Ceeform, 1 x 1 phase 63 amp Ceeform, 1 x 3 phase 63 amp Ceeform.
VISITING LIGHTING SUPPLY: situated down stage right. Supply: 400 amp, 3 phase. The distribution outlets are as follows: 15 amp - 1 - 2; 16 amp Ceeform - 1- 6; 32 amp ceeform - 3 - 1; 63 amp Ceeform 1 - 2; 63 amp Ceeform 3 - 1; 125 amp Ceeform 3 - 1; 200 amp Power Locks 3 - 1 Set; 200 amp Power locks - 3 - 1 set; 400 amp Power locks 3 - 1 set; 1 set Power Lock to Cam Lock jumpers.
LIGHTING: 8 x E.T.C Source 4 25 / 50 575w / 750w, 18 x E.T.C Source 4 Zooms 15 /30 750w, 2 x E.T.C Source 4 19 750w, 6 x E.T.C Source 4 36 750w, 1 x E.T.C Source 4 50 750w, 2 x E.T.C Source 4 Lens Tube 5, 1 x E.T.C Source 4 Lens Tube 10. Fresnels: 10 x C.C.T Starlette 1k No barn doors, 24 x Stand cantata F 1k With barn doors, 3 x Strand2k F Alto With barn doors. Floods and par cans: 50 x Thomas Par 64 CP62, 4 x Thomas Floor Can CP62, 10 x Rank Strand Iris 1 Flood 1k, 6 x Coda 4s 500w. Follow Spots: 2 x Pani 1202 situated on bridge three.

THE PALACE THEATRE:
STAGE: Height 1.03m (3'5'), Stage Rake 1 to 18, Pros. Width 8m, Pros. Height 6m (19'8'). Stage Depth; Back wall to tab line, 4.57m (15'), Tab line to stage front, 3.2m (10'6'). Height to Grid 15m, Scenery Flying Height 6m (19'8'), Height to Fly Floor 7.23m D/S, Height to Fly Floor 7.14m U/S.
POWER: Visiting Lighting Power Supply; 200 amps, 3 phases. Visiting Sound Power Supply; 63amps single phase. Sound Power Supply in Orchestra Pit; 63amps single phase. Each out put is fused at 20amps.
LIGHTING: Control; MA GRAND MASTER LIGHT, 999 channels of control. 4 x Cantata 26/40 1000watts. 16 x E.T.C Source 4 Zooms 15 /30 750watts. 40 x Cantata F with barn door 1000watts. 20 x Thomas Par 64 with CP62 1000watts. 4 x Coda 4s with socapex connection. 500watts each compartment. Follow Spots: 2 x strand Solo CSI follow spots with six way colour magazine. FOH Lighting Positions; FOH 1 - 2nd top balcony Throw to edge of stage 12.20m; FOH 2 - 1st balcony Throw to edge of stage 8.40m. On Stage; 3 x 12 way bars with15amp sockets. Each bar fed with 2 six way socapex cables and out-puts with a 15 amp socket. Dimming; 5 racks of Rank Strand LD90, giving 120 ways of 2.5kw dimmers; 26 to FOH - 12 to Booms - 24 to Dips - 4 to orchestra pit. - 54 high level stage. Flying system; Max SWL lighting 200k per bar including bar, Max SWL hemp 100k per bar.
SOUND: Mixer in control room; Soundcraft K3 12 mono & 4 stereo into 8 into 2, 4 way matrix control, Twin mini disk Denon DN-M2300R, Twin C/D Denon DN-1800F, Cassette deck Denon DRM-555. Mixer in Auditorium: Soundcraft K3 22 mono & 2 stereo into 8 into 2, Twin mini disk Denon DN-M2300R, Twin C/D Gemini CDX-802. Amplifiers Main PA; 6 x EV 1200RL Precision controlled DSP controlled, 1 x EV P3000RL Precision controlled DSP controlled. Various FOH Speakers.
STAGE MANAGEMENT: 8 x Tech Pro Belt packs and head sets available. Various comms points. Cue Lights; 8 way Q-Light base station with 3 Q-lights.
ADDITIONAL: Rostra: 2 x wooden rostra/risers 8' x 4' suitable as a drum riser. Masking; 1 x Set of scarlet and gold house tabs. Piano; Full size concert Steinway.

THE CLIFFTOWN THEATRE

Nelson Street, Southend-on-Sea Essex SS1 1EF
Tel: 01702 328 335
Email: clifftown@essex.ac.uk
Web Site: www.clifftowntheatre.co.uk
Contact: Teressa Zoers or Megan Hung
Capacity: 150-200 Theatre Style

Southport, Merseyside

Pop. 89,400. London 210 miles.
Newspapers: Southport Midweek Visitor (wed); Southampton Champion (wed); Southport Visitor (fri). STD code 01704

FLORAL HALL

Promenade, Southport, Merseyside PR9 0DZ
Admin: 01704 540 454 BO: 0844 871 3021 SD: 01704 540 454 Fax: 01704 536 841
Email: wendylucas@theambassadors.com
Web Site: www.atgtickets.com/southporttheatre
ADMINISTRATION:
Props: Sefton Metropolitan Borough Council
Managed by Ambassador Theatre Group
General Manager: Lisa Chu
Resident Technicians: J. Hopper, Vinny Whalley
Seats: 900

TECHNICAL:
Stage: Proscenium. Pros. opening 10.9m x 4.4m. Stage depth 6.24m. Forestage 1.8m. 10 Hemp. Lighting: Switchboard: Rank Strand Memory System 46 way GSX.
Sound: Soundcraft mixer, 16 channel, Rowland Spale Echo. Speakers Proscenium Side.
Dressing Rooms: 3 Showers 1.

SOUTHPORT THEATRE AND CONVENTION CENTRE

The Promenade, Southport, Merseyside PR9 0DZ
Admin Tel: 01704 540 454 Fax: 01704 536 841 BO Tel: 0844 871 3021
Group/Access Bookings: 01704 500036
Email: lisachu@theambassadors.com
Web Site: www.atgtickets.com/southporttheatre
ADMINISTRATION:
Props: Ambassadors Theatre Group (Venues) Ltd.
Managed by: Ambassador Theatre Group
General Manager: Lisa Chu
Marketing Manager: Emma Baldwin
Operations Manager: Darren James
Email: DarrenJames@theambassadors.com
Policy: Pantomime, Summer Season, Concerts, Touring.
Seats: 1,631. Four Bars & Four Function Suites.
TECHNICAL:
STAGE: Proscenium with 3.35m deep thrust. Flat; Pros. Opening 13.41m; Ht. of Pros. 5.18m; Depth of S/Line 7.32m; Ht. of Grid 9.14m; 20 lines, Hemp; Scenery Flying Ht. 5.18m, O.P. 5.18m; Prompt Cnr. P.S.
LIGHTING: Switchboard: Lightboard M 96 channels, Projection Room; 80 ways; F.O.H. Spots 12 Patt.763; 2 Dips 6 P.S. 6 O.P.; 3 Spot Bars, 28 Patt.743, 2: Pani 1200 follow spots.
SOUND EQUIPMENT: 18 channel Soundcraft desk Mosfet & H/H Power amps. H/H Power amps projection room; Speakers Pros. side walls.
DRESSING ROOMS: 9; Showers 4; Orchestra Pit 10.
OTHER: Film Equipment fitted for 70mm, 35mm and 16mm with optical or magnetic sound - Dolby Stereo Sound.

THE ATKINSON

Lord Street, Southport, Merseyside PR8 1DB
BO Tel: 01704 533 333
Email: info@theatkinson.co.uk
Web Site: www.theatkinson.co.uk
ADMINISTRATION:
Props: Sefton Metropolitan B.C.
Administration: Julie Farrell
Director: Emma Anderson
Perfs: Small/mid scale touring productions, film, dance, all kinds of music, exhibitions etc.
Capacity:
Theatre: 400; Studio: 260 . Bar/Buffet.

All venues available for hire at competitive rates.
TECHNICAL:
TECHNICAL:
Please see website for technical information.

Southsea, Hampshire

(see Portsmouth for information). STD code 01705

THE KING'S THEATRE

Albert Road, Southsea, Hampshire PO5 2QJ
BO: 02392 828 282 Admin: 02392 852 205
Email: admin@kings-southsea.com
Web Site: www.kingsportsmouth.co.uk
ADMINISTRATION:
CEO: David Cooper
Operations Manager: Louise Birchall
Marketing Manager: Kelly Haswell
Contact: 02392 852236 or kelly.haswell@kings-southsea.com
Technical Manager: Nick Benjamin
Contact: lnick.benjamin@kings-southsea.com
Policy: Weekly Tours, Season, Pantomime, Plays, Ballet, Opera and one night stands.
Perfs: Variable. 7.30pm. Matinee Variable
Seats: 1,600 max.
Two Bars. Three Function Rooms.
TECHNICAL:
STAGE: Proscenium arch 9.14m x 7.92m; Bottom of tabs 5.26m; Stage Depth 11.5m; Wing Width SL 4.27m, SR 4.27m; Scene Dock SR. Stage raked 1:24, surface hardboard on sprung wood suitable for dance (no linoleum); stage heated. Backstage crossover, get in off-street- SL wing 1.22m above street. Dock doors 3.66m x 3.05m. Height of grid 16.76m max, flying height 8.23m. 45 Hemp House, (50 sets lines),5 winch bars, 14 power bars 130/140mm apart, 12m long (Bars +/-0.18m apart; Bars +/- 10m to 11.5 long). Max load/bar Hemp 200kg Winch 250 kgs 400kg power bar. House tabs flown - red with gold trim. 1 Tab track, 3 sets of black legs and borders, 1 complete Pink Swag, 1 Black 1 white cyclorama. Orchestra pit 10.76m x 2.4m, accommodated 20. Can extend by taking out the first 2 rows of seats
STAGE MANAGEMENT: position - downstage right. Cue lights and headsets available. Show relay and tannoy to dressing rooms.
LIGHTING: Board Strand 520i; 160 circuits, 8 @ 5kW, rest @ 2.5kW/circuit; lanterns 40 x spots; 44 x Fresnels; 22 x Parcans and 4 Circuit Floats.
SOUND: Acoustics suitable for music and spoken word; 1 Yamaha upright piano, 1 Yamaha grand piano
POWER: Onstage - 200 amp 3 phase; 63 amp single phase DSR; Lighting and sound operated from rear centre of stalls..
BACKSTAGE: 11 dressing rooms (no company office); 1 band room under stage with direct access to orchestra pit; wardrobe on ground floor; showers available.
Technical Specifications can be downloaded from www.kings-southsea.com

Southwold, Suffolk

Pop. 2,010. London 107 miles. STD code 01502

SOUTHWOLD SUMMER THEATRE

St Edmunds Hall Cumberland Road, Southwold, Suffolk IP18 6JP
BO Evenings(Mid July-Sept 5-9 pm): 07527 228657 BO Daytime(June-Sept) 01502 724441 Admin 01502 724462
Email: enquiries@southwoldtheatre.org
Web Site: www.southwoldtheatre.org
ADMINISTRATION:
Props: Church Council
Lessee: Suffolk Summer Theatres
Policy: Available for Repertory, Summer Season, Pantomime
Perfs: As required (ex. Sunday)
Seats: 240
TECHNICAL:
Proscenium Stage, Flat
Sound Equip: 2 F.O.H. Speakers
Dressing Rooms 2; Accom. up to 12.

Spennymoor, County Durham

SPENNYMOOR LEISURE CENTRE

The High Street, Spennymoor, County Durham DL16 6DB
Tel: 03000 261161
Email: sportandleisure@durham.gov.uk
Web Site: www.durham.gov.uk
ADMINISTRATION:
Props: Durham County Council
Cap: 1,198
Centre Manager: Mark Lee
Stage facilities. Lighting and PA available, fully licensed.

St Albans, Hertfordshire

Pop. 53,000. London 21 miles.
Newspapers: Herts Advertiser (fri). STD code 01727

ABBEY THEATRE & STUDIO

Westminster Lodge, Holywell Hill, St Albans, Hertfordshire AL1 2DL
Mgt: 01727 847 472 BO: 01727 857 861
Fax: 01727 812 742
Email: manager@abbeytheatre.org.uk
Web Site: www.abbeytheatre.org.uk
ADMINISTRATION:
Props: Abbey Theatre Trust (St. Albans) Ltd
Manager: Tina Swain
Policy: Own amateur use; also occasional touring companies and other local society use.
Perfs: 8.00
Main Theatre: 230, Studio Theatre 78, Bar and Coffee.
TECHNICAL:
Main Theatre:
STAGE: Stage is 3ft above ground level. White cyc wall at rear. Proscenium arch 24 ft wide. 11ft 6in high. Stage depth 22 ft. Full plan and section available on request. Full height fly tower. 6 counter-weight lines plus front tabs, 13 hand lines, three winched lighting bars. Well equipped stage managers desk. Black drape traverse, legs and borders. Soundproof control room for sound and lighting at the back of the auditorium.
LIGHTING: 96 Channel desk, 2DMX universes. Variety of Profile, Fresnel, Par Can and Floods available.
SOUND: 16 Channel desk, Minidisc and CD player/recorder, 6 speakers.
BACKSTAGE FACILITIES: Dressing Rooms; 4, accomm. 5 - 6. Green room. The club room is sometimes available, by arrangement, as an extra dressing room for large cast productions.

Studio:
STAGE: Black drapes on three walls. Basic stage managers desk. Techpro communication. Normally separate control rooms for sound and lighting.
LIGHTING: 48 Channel desk, 1DMX universe. Grid of scaffold tubing across the ceiling 14ft above ground level. Variety of Profile, Fresnel, Par Cans and Floods available.
SOUND: 16 channel desk, Minidisc and CD player/recorder,4 speakers.
BACKSTAGE FACILITIES: 3-4 entrances for actors, near each corner. An adjacent room for use as a dressing room or meeting room. Screens can be used to partition this room.

THE ALBAN ARENA

Civic Centre, St Peters Street, St Albans, Hertfordshire AL1 3LD
Mgt: 01727 861 078 BO: 01727 844 488
Email: alban.arena@1life.co.uk
Web Site: www.alban-arena.co.uk
ADMINISTRATION:
Props: 1 Life
Manager: Frank Leclezio
Box Office Manager: Davina Lines
Technical Manager Contact: 01727 861078 or aatechnical@1life.co.uk
Policy: Mainly one night stands, professional concerts, touring productions, shows and amateur productions, conferences, films and dances. General pur-

pose venue also used for exhibitions etc. Seats: 856, standing: 1150. Retractable stalls, fixed circle. 3 Licensed Bars and 1 Coffee Bar.
TECHNICAL:
STAGE: Proscenium, Flat; Pros. Opening 12.01m; Grid height 10.08m. Prompt corner stage left. Apron 15.2m x 2.6m. deep. Orchestra pit 13.7m x 3.04m x 0.3m deep. Flying: 23 c/w bars. 6 LX Winch bars. Loading bay door 6.5ft x 13.8ft/2m x 4.2m. Dock Lift 2.5m x 1.5m, Travel from road level to stage level 1.7m. Multicore length to FOH position minimum 50m.
LIGHTING: Control from projection room. Zero 88 eclipse, 72 channel, extended level memory, programmable chasers and cartridge fx. 2 x 1kw CSI followspots. FOH 12 1kw TH furse, 12 patt 263 (TH) 8 parcans. Stage No.1 bar 6 x 1kw TH furse. 4 Cantata, 6 x parcans (booms). Stage No.2 bar 6 x 1kw fresnel, 4 x parcans, 2 Cantata, Coda 3's. Stage No.3 bar 6 x Coda 3's (3CCT) 4 x patt 23's, 6 x patt 123's. Stage floor 3 CCT's D/S, 3 CCT's Mid Stage, 3 CCT's U/S. Stage Power - 2 x 13 amp rings (30 amp loading each). Prompt Cnr - 1 x 100 amp 3 phase supply and 60 amp single phase supply. (N.B. The above lamps may not always be in the position allocated).
SOUND: Mixers - Allen & Heath 16:2 Mixwizard in control room. Soundcraft K3; 28 theatre + 4st + matrix O/P stalls. Processors: BSS Varicurve + Omnidrive, on main; + KT Graphics on monitors. Amplifiers: C Audio on main; H/H mosfet on monitors. Speakers: Turbosound TCS system with sub/base - main JBL Tannoy - side fill + wedges + personal monitors. Effects: Yahama SPX 990, Roland 201. Mics: 19; 6 AKG D310, 5 AKG Tri Power, 4 Crown PCC's, 4 SM58, assorted AKG C451s + accessories.
OTHER: Denon Mini Disc, Denon DAT, Denon CD, TEAC 122 cassette, Revox A77 H/S, Technics t/table; Sennheiser Infra Red System for hard of hearing; S.I.A.P. Acoustic system. Film Equip: 2 x Westrex 7000 35mm, Dolby surround, Opt/sound/silent speeds: 1 x fumero x 900 16mm Opt/mag/sound/silent. Harkness flown screen opening to 3.56mm high x 7.3m wide (5 ratios, inc scope). One baby grand piano: Moutrie C3. Haze and smoke machines with hire fee.
DRESSING ROOMS: Rear stage 6; Accom. 32, 2 Showers. Washing machine, condenser tumble dryer, iron.
DISABLED FACILITIES: Wheelchair access throughout ground floor. Limited wheelchair spaces in the Auditorium. Disabled toilets on ground floor. Limited parking for blue badge holders.

MALTINGS ARTS THEATRE

Level 2 The Maltings, St Albans, Hertfordshire AL1 3HL
Tel: 07807 521436
Web Site: www.ovotheatre.org.uk
ADMINISTRATION:
Manager: Liz Widdowson
Capacity: 140
TECHNICAL:
Stage: The Studio Theatre has end-on playing on the level, with black drapes and legs. Raked seating maximum audience 140/200. The flat floor playing area can be adjusted to any size (maximum 37 feet wide, 30 feet deep) the usual format being 25 by 25 feet square, providing 6 feet wing space at either side and access behind the black drape to both sides. Maximum height of the theatre is 11 feet 6 inches.
Lighting: 48 way ETC Express; 30 x Selecon 650 Fresnel; 12 x 650w Profile-Selecton/Minuette; 8 x 1kw Profile-Selecon/Sil 30; 6 x 500w Floods; 6 x Par Cans.
Sound: 16 Channel Soundcraft 'Spirit' desk, 6 Shure mic with stands, twin cassette. Mini Disc, CD, Yamaha Grand Piano (5).
Dressing room, toilet and shower available.

TRESTLE THEATRE COMPANY

Trestle Arts Base, Russet Drive, St Albans, Hertfordshire AL4 0JQ
Tel: 01727 850 950
Email: admin@trestle.org.uk
Web Site: www.trestle.org.uk
ADMINISTRATION:
Artistic Director: Emily Gray
Buildings and Finance Manager: Clare Winter
Trestle Theatre Company was founded in 1981 and has enjoyed 30 successful years of touring mask and Physical led theatre. Trestle creates and tours theatrical productions and operates Trestle Arts Base as a performance venue. Trestle also produces international residencies and tours and delivers education programmes across the UK and abroad. The Company aims to engage audiences and participants in an interactive, inclusive and inventive experience of theatre.
Trestle Arts Base - Fully equipped studio theatre,rehearsal room and meeting room, all available for hire to professional and amateur companies for previews and runs
Capacity: 80 - 125
TECHNICAL:
Studio Theatre:
8m depth x 7.5m width at full height, 2.5m width stage right to outside wall under sloping ceiling and pipe work, 2.5 width stage left to outside wall under walkway. Height of grid 5m. 2.54m high double doors at rear of stage area, 2.25m wide. Door to lobby outside dressing rooms stage right. Scenery Storage 5.5m by 2m by 5m. 8 x 3m by 5m serge drapes. 20m x tab track in 6 x 3m lengths, 2 x 2m lengths. Strand 3001X Board, 96 channels.
Scenery Workshop 6.5m by 4m by 2.2m equipped with various machines.
Dressing rooms; 2, accommodating 10 in total.

St Andrews, Fife

Pop. 11,633. London 422 miles.
Newspapers: The Courier (dly); East Fife Mail (wed); St. Andrew's Citizen (fri); Fife Herald (wed); Fife News (fri); Fife Free Press (fri). STD code 01334

BYRE THEATRE

Abbey Street, St Andrews, Fife KY16 9LA Scotland
Tel: 01334 475 000
Web Site: www.byretheatre.com
ADMINISTRATION:
Artistic Director: Michael Downs
General Manager: Stephen Sinclair
Box Office and Promotions Manager: Mary McKenzie
The Byre Theatre presents a varied programme of contemporary and classic drama, dance, concerts, opera, comedy and film supported by professional touring companies and local amateur societies. There is also a cafe bar and restaurant run by Kingarroch at the Byre, and conference facilities.
Cap: 216
TECHNICAL:
Stage: Proscenium Opening (max.) 9.16m, Pros. height (variable with header) 5m-5.75m, Stage depth(forestage to rear wall) 8.5m at centre, stage depth (setting line to back wall) 6.7m (rear of pros to front of back wall), stage width(wing to wing) 15.30m, SL wing 3m (max), SR wing 2.7m, width of opening to dock 8m, Depth of dock (squared off to stage) 5.2m (4.7m behind wall), Height to u/s of grid 13.25m, Heght to u/s of side catwalks 5.75m, counterweight sets (single purchase) 12, Hemp sets 6, FOH lighting bridges(direct access to control room and fly floor) 2, control room(combined lighting/sound projection) - rear of auditorium, follow spot positions(either side of controlroom) 2, house tabs(optional) Flown, othertabs and hard and soft masking available (detailed spec. on request). All measurements should be regarded as approximate and subject to final confirmation.
Please contact Stephen Sinclair for full technical details.

YOUNGER GRADUATION HALL

University of St Andrews North Street, St Andrews, Fife KY16 9AJ Scotland
Tel: 01334 462 226 Fax: 01334 462 228
Email: music@st-andrews.ac.uk
Web Site: www.st-andrews.ac.uk/music
Contact: Helen Gregory for Hall bookings during term time (01334 462226).
Contact: Ann Martin (01334 462501) for Hall bookings outside term time.
Conference and Group Services, 79 North Street, 81 Andrews, Fife KY16 9AL

Scotland
Seating/Capacity: 968

St Helens, Merseyside

Pop. 104,430. London 191 miles.
Newspapers: St.Helens Reporter (fri); Star. STD code 01744

BROADWAY COMMUNITY LEISURE CENTRE

Broadway, Grange Park, St Helens, Merseyside WA10 3RY
Tel: 01744 675407
Email: broadway@sthelens.org.uk
ADMINISTRATION:
Props: St Helens Metropolitan Borough Council
Bookings Contact Terry Bates

THE CITADEL ARTS CENTRE

Waterloo Street, St Helens, Merseyside WA10 1PX
Tel: 01744 735 436
Email: info@citadel.org.uk
Web Site: www.citadel.org.uk
Chief Executive: Fay Lamb
Capacity: 161 Seated, 307 Standing and Seated

SUTTON COMMUNITY LEISURE CENTRE

Eltonhead Road, St Helens, Merseyside WA9 5AU
Tel: 01744 677375
Email: iangrace@sthelens.gov.uk
Web Site: www.sthelens.gov.uk
ADMINISTRATION:
Props: St Helen's Metropolitan Borough Council
Cap: 1000
For bookings contact Andy North, Ian Grace, Sean Ahearn Duty Managers.
Large hall 33m x 36m. Stage available.

THEATRE ROYAL

Corporation Street, St Helens, Merseyside WA10 1LQ
BO: 01744 756 000 Admin: 01744 756 333 Admin Fax: 01744 756 777
Email: info@sthelenstheatreroyal.co.uk
Web Site: www.sthelenstheatreroyal.com
ADMINISTRATION:
Props: Theatre Royal St. Helens Trust
Theatre Manager: Chantelle Nolan
Stage Manager: Mike Randolph
Marketing contact Bill Elms Associates 0151 708 5158
Policy: Touring Companies, childrens prods, Ballet, Pantomimes, Concerts, Pop, Classic, Brass Bands, Small & Large scale musicals.
Perfs: By mutual agreement Morn/Mat/Eve.
Seats: 708. Licensed Bar & Coffee Bar.
TECHNICAL:
Stage: Proscenium, Raked; Pros. opening 8.30m; Ht. of Pros. 7.01m; Depth of S/Line 10.36m; Ht. of Grid 14.63m; 42 lines Hemp; Scenery flying Bars 11.28m; W/Widths P.S. 3.35m, O.P. 3.66m; Prompt Cnr. P.S.
Lighting: Switchboard: Rank Strand 3 set 80 way board; 27 circuits to F.O.H.; 34 circuits in hanging positions over stage and 19 independent Dips. 75 of the ways are 2kw and 5 are 5kw.
Soundcraft spirit live 8 channel. 1 Aiwa tape deck, 1 OMP MXF 200 power amp, 1 OMP MXF 400 power amp, 5 Sm 58 Shure mics, 2 Calrec rifle mics, 1 realistic/shure highball mic.Facilities for playing F.O.H. and 5 backstage outlets. Playback to dressing rooms, Talk back between Prompt Cnr. files, switchboard and limes. Sound and Lighting: Control Rear Stalls. 35mm Film Projection. Independent 100 amp 3 phase supply set of lines over the auditorium for extra lighting (pop groups, etc.).
Dressing Rooms 6; Accom. 109; Showers Back Stage. Orchestra Pit 19 plus M.D.

St Ives, Cambridgeshire

ONE LEISURE ST IVES

Westwood Road, St Ives, Huntingdon, Cambridgeshire PE27 6WU
Tel: 01480 388500 Fax: 01480 388513
Email: oneleisurestives@huntingdonshire.gov.uk
Web Site: www.oneleisure.net
ADMINISTRATION:
Props: Huntingdonshire District Council
Cap: Burgess Hall with S/Cap of 700.
Stage facilities.
Manager: John Clark

St Ives, Cornwall

ST IVES CONCERT HALL

The Guild Hall Street An pol, St Ives, Cornwall TR26 2DS
Tel: 01736 797840
Email: admin.stivestowncouncil@googlemail.com
Web Site: www.stivestowncouncil.com
ADMINISTRATION:
Props: St Ives Town Council
Cap: 490
For bookings contact Jeremy Ward

St Just, Cornwall

TOWN HALL

Chapel Road St Just, Cornwall TR19 7HT
Tel: 01736 788928
Email: dave@davesyl.plus.com
ADMINISTRATION:
Props: St Just Community and Business Centre
Cap: 200

St Leonards-on-Sea, East Sussex

AZUR AT THE MARINA PAVILION

Lower Promenade, Marina, St Leonard's-on-Sea, East Sussex TN38 0BU
Tel: 01424 447461
Email: enquiries@azurmarinapavilion.com
Web Site: www.azurmarinapavilion.com
ADMINISTRATION:
Chief Executive: David Thorpe-Tracey
Props: Hastings Borough Council
Capacity: 800

St Neots, Cambridgeshire

THE PRIORY CENTRE

Priory Lane, St Neots, Cambridgeshire PE19 2BH
Tel: 01480 388922 Fax: 01480 388915
Email: priory.centre@stneots-tc.gov.uk
Web Site: www.theprioryCentre.com
ADMINISTRATION:
Props: St Neots Town Council
Cap: 400 Theatre Style 318
Manager: Steven Barrett

Stafford, Staffordshire

Pop. 55,000. London 140 miles.
Newspapers: Stafford Newsletter (fri); Express & Star (ntly); Evening Sentinel.
STD code 01785

STAFFORD GATEHOUSE THEATRE

Eastgate Street, Stafford, Staffordshire ST16 2LT
Tel: 01785 619 080
Email: gatehouse@staffordbc.gov.uk
Web Site: www.staffordgatehousetheatre.co.uk
ADMINISTRATION:
The Gatehouse is a complete Arts and Entertainments complex, with theatre/concert hall, studio theatre, and performance space.
Props: Stafford Borough Council
Manager: Derrick Gask
Operations Manager: Stuart Boyd
Technical Manager: Matt Glass
Contact: mglass@staffordbc.gov.uk
Policy: Professional and amateur use.One-nighters, pantomime, ballet,

drama, opera, variety, comedy, music, exhibitions, conferences, weddings, banqueting, films, educational projects, youth theatre, recording studio.
Perfs: Usually open 7 days. Evening shows at 7.30/8pm; matinees at 2.30pm.
Capacity: 564 in one raked tier (reduces to 490 when orchestra pit fully extended). MET Studio; 120, 116 in the round, 96 End Stage.
TECHNICAL:
STAGE; Proscenium arch. Performing area 15.24m x 7.1m - adjustable pros opening, 9-12m x 4.6-6m - wing widths 3.1m SR/SL. No rake - floor wood covered with hardboard, suitable for all dance, lino available, backstage crossover, stage not heated. Height of grid 10.4m - 22 4 line hemp sets, 0.22m apart - 7 winches - 2 tab tracks - 100kg permitted on bars, 300kg on winches - legs, tabs, borders in black, gold or pink, other drapes available - white plaster back wall used as cyclorama - red house tabs, drawn. Several 13A sockets. Orchestra pit 9.14m x 1.06m, accommodates 25. Get-in via service yard, lift 2.7m x 2m or stairs - dock doors 1.83m x 2m. Scenery lift. Tallescope. Scale stage, fly and lighting plans available, also full technical specification sheets.
LIGHTING; ETC Ion control board, 112 circuits, operated from control box at rear of auditorium - 200A 3 phase supply available for temporary board - Fresnels - 48, Profiles - 46 (24 x CCT sils, 10 x Cantatas, 10 x etc sils, 2 x wide angle sils), Parcans - 91, Source 4 pars - 13, Source 4 Juniors - 14, Floorcans -20 (10 x black, 10 x chrome), 3 x 1000w Iris - 4, 500w Coda 4 - 4, Rainbow Scrollers - 8, Apollo Scrollers - 16, Studio Spot 250's - 2, Qmaxz 700 profiles - 2, Qmaxz 575 washes - 3, Qmaxz 575 profiles - 3, Qmaxz 250 profiles - 4, Birdies - 20 (chrome), robert juliat followspots 2 (operated from above control room at rear of stalls), UV cannons -2.
SOUND; Yamaha LS9 - 40 channel digital desk, operated from rear centre of auditorium - KV2 PA system comprising 4 ES 1.0 and 4 ES 2.5 speakers and 2 EX10 in delay position, 4 EPAK 2500R amplifiers. 8 powered monitors - 16 lavelier radio mics (12 Audio technica AEW 5000, 2 Sennheizer EW 300 and 2 Sennheizer 3032) 3 handheld radio mics (all Sennheizer EW100) -Assorted mics including Sure-SM58(8) SM57(5) SM87(2) AKG -414(2) 321(2) D112(2) Audio Technica AT4040(2) Sennheizer E604(3) facilities for recording and editing using digitaland analogue methods.
PROJECTION: film projector - 35mm 1kw lamp, perforated screen. Sanyo xf46 projector (with hanging bracket) STAGE
STAGE MANAGEMENT: Prompt corner SL - TechPro cue system, 12 outstations, cue lights, 9 outstations 12 way communications headsets (including 4 wireless) - show relay/Tannoy to dressing rooms and for FOH calls BACKSTAGE; 4 dressing rooms, accomm. 24, access by rear of stage; 2 other rooms available if needed; crew room; wardrobe above stage level with washer, dryer and 2 power points. Refreshments as requested. Rehearsal room, piano. Advice given on accommodation. Staff; 4 technicians; casuals available; no security personnel. Backstage facilities accessible to disabled performers and staff.
ORCHESTRA PIT: 27 square metres, 9 metres x 3 metres x 1metre.
ADDITIONAL: Equipment for hire; Grand Piano, Upright Piano, Multimedia Projector, Slide Projector, Projector Screens, Overhead Projector, TV and DVD, Flipchart Stand, Photocopying.

MALCOLM EDWARDS THEATRE:-
LIGHTING: Strand 520i 72 circuits 30 500w fresnels 10 650w profiles use of stock from main house
PROJECTION: 1200 lumin multimedia projector, 4000 x 1900 matt white perforated roller screen.
SOUND: Yamaha LS9 - 16, 2x bose 802 FOH speakers, use of stock from main house.
STAGE MANAGEMENT: Open ring intercom (Compac M) 6 stations; Cue lights 6 outstations; paging/show relay to dressing rooms.
DRESSING ROOMS: 2 each for 6 (each with shower) (can be increased by upper level dressing rooms).
GET-IN: Ground Floor - domestic size doors).

Staines, Middlesex

SPELTHORNE LEISURE CENTRE

Knowle Green, Staines, Middlesex TW18 1AJ
Tel: 01784 493 493 Fax: 01784 496 605
Email: spelthorneinfo@slm-ltd.co.uk
Web Site: www.everyoneactive.com
ADMINISTRATION:
Props: Everyone Active
Cap: 750
General Manager: Karl Miles

Stamford, Lincolnshire

Pop. 18,000. London 92 miles.
Newspapers: Stamford (fri). STD code 01780

STAMFORD ARTS CENTRE

27 St. Marys Street, Stamford, Lincolnshire PE9 2DL
Mgt/ Admin: 01780 480846 BO: 01780 763203
Email: emma@stamfordartscentre.com
Web Site: www.stamfordartscentre.com
ADMINISTRATION:
Props: South Kesteven District Council
Programming: Graham Burley
Technical Manager: Adrian Hill
Policy: Integral part of Stamford Arts Centre. Theatre is used by touring professional companies/artistes and is available for hire by amateur groups. Drama, dance, mime and music presented. Induction loop and lift for disabled.
Seats: 166. Bar and catering facilities available.
TECHNICAL:
STAGE: Proscenium flat; Pros. opening 8.27m. Ht. of Pros. 3.35m; W/Widths P.S. 0.91m, O.P. 0.91m
LIGHTING: Switchboard: Sirius 24. Control room rear of auditorium; F.O.H. spots. Lanterns: 10 CCT Minuette Profile 650w, 6 Strand Patt 813 Profile 500w, 2 Patt 23 Profile 500w, 17 Patt 803 Fresnels 650w, 8 CCT Minuette Fresnels 650w.
SOUND: Speakers either side of pros. arch. Hill LC 400 Amplifier, Technics Cassette Player, Denon CD player, 8 channel mixer desk.
DRESSING ROOMS: 2; Accom. 24; Basins and toilets. No Orchestra Pit

STAMFORD CORN EXCHANGE THEATRE

Broad Street Stamford Lincs PE9 1PX
Tel: 01780 766455
Email: stamfordcetc@hotmail.co.uk
Web Site: www.stamford-corn-exchange.co.uk
Props: The Cornish Exchange Theatre Company, charity run organisation.
Manager: Judith Mackie
Capacity: 399

Stevenage, Hertfordshire

Pop. 77,000. London 31 miles.
Newspapers: Stevenage Comet; Stevenage Gazette; Stevenage Herald.
STD code 01438

GORDON CRAIG THEATRE

Stevenage Arts & Leisure Centre, Lytton Way, Stevenage, Hertfordshire SG1 1LZ
Admin: 01438 363 200 BO: 01438 363 200 Tech: 01438 242 612
Email: gordoncraig@stevenage-leisure.co.uk
Web Site: www.gordon-craig.co.uk
ADMINISTRATION:
Props: Stevenage Leisure Ltd
Arts Programming, Marketing and Sales Manager: Paul Ruff
Marketing Manager: Claire Salisbury
Cheif Technician: Dave Nott.
Contact: 01438 242612 or Dave.Nott@stevenage-leisure.co.uk
Policy: Mixed Programme
Perfs: 7.45
Seats: 506. Bar, Restaurant.
TECHNICAL:

STAGE: Proscenium Stage, Flat; Pros. opening adjustable 9.15m - 12.2m; Black Harlequin Dance Floor. Ht. of Pros. 5.38m; Depth of S/Line 9.15m; Ht. of Grid 15.04m; width 25.30m; Flying Bars 13.41m; 29 Double Purchase Counterweight Bars total. Prompt Cnr. P.S. Various drapes and masking available. Orchestra pit accommodates 20.
LIGHTING: Strand 430 control desk, storage to 3.5" disk. Strand LD90 Dimmers, 136 x 2.5kw + 36 x 5kw, 24 x non-dim. 400a Three phase power. Operated from control suite rear of auditorium. Temporary/Touring supply 2 x 63a Three Phase supply SL. 72 x 1kw Profile spots, 64 x 1kw fresnels. 2 x 1kw CSI followspots operated from control suite rear of auditorium. Full range of LEE Filters Colours 101 - 206 available.
SOUND: main mixer desk; Allen & Heath GL4000 40/8/L, R, M. Sub mixer desk; Soundcraft Delta SR 24/4/2, operated from control suite near rear of auditorium. D&B audiotechnik full range speaker system, 4 x foldback monitors. 5 x PCC160, 5 x SM58, 2 x SM57, DI Boxes, CD, Revox 7.5"/15ips, graphics and processing available. ACS Acoustic Control System. Variable acoustics for music and drama.
OTHER: Steinway Concert and Kwai Baby Grand pianos; Christie ten-rank 3-manual theatre organ. Pyrotechnics, smoke, firearms, strobe lighting etc. available (28 days written notice required). 35mm Film projector with two-sided film tower and projection screen.
STAGE COMMUNICATIONS: Prompt desk/corner SL, full cue light intercom with 12 outstations. Full headset intercom. Show/Conductors view monitor screens. Show relay and tannoy to all dressing rooms/backstage areas.
DRESSING ROOMS: 14 over 2 floors, accom. 70. Showers. Wardrobe room with automatic washing machine and tumble dryer. Green Room on ground floor with fridge, kettle, eating area, TV. Video Show Relay to this room. Rehearsal Room with mirrors to one wall, practice bars.

STEVENAGE ARTS AND LEISURE CENTRE

Lytton Way, Stevenage, Hertfordshire SG1 1LZ
Tel: 01438 363200 BO: 01438 363200
Tech: 01438 242629 Fax: 01438 242 342 Tech Fax: 01438 242 615
Email: BOR@stevenage-leisure.co.uk
Web Site: www.stevenage-leisure.co.uk
ADMINISTRATION:
Props: Stevenage Leisure Ltd
Arts & Entertainments Manager: Paul Ruff
Technical/Stage Manager: Dave Nott
Contact: dave.nott@stevenage-leisure.co.uk or backstage@stevenage-leisure.co.uk
Marketing Manager: Jon Stone
Conference Co-ordinator: Christine Green
Contact: christine.green@stevenage-leisure.co.uk
Capacity: 2000 (Reception), 1,200 (Theatre Style), 600 (Dinner)
TECHNICAL: Main Hall
STAGE: Floor space 35m x 35m, height 10m. Staging 6 x Sico 'Roll and Set' units. Various Stage configurations possible unto 40' x 20'. Get In via car park to side at floor level through double width doors. Floor sprung maple sports floor. Flying points available. 1X Star dressing room and 1x band room.
LIGHTING: 300a Three Phase Supply. (Powerlock/Ceeform/Tails) available for toured lighting and sound equipment. Basic 6 colour in house lighting. 2x follow spots
SOUND: No equipment.

Stevenston, Ayrshire

HAYOCKS HALL

Hyslop Road, Stevenston, Ayrshire KA20 4HS Scotland
Admin Tel: 0845 230 1325 Tel: 01294 607 297
Email: communityfacilities@north-ayrshire.gov.uk
Web Site: www.north-ayrshire.gov.uk
ADMINISTRATION:
Props: North Ayrshire Council
Cap: 140

Stirling, Stirling

Pop. 30,047. London 410 miles. Newspapers: Stirling Observer (wed/fri). STD code 01786

THE ALBERT HALLS

Albert Place, Dumbarton Road, Stirling SK8 2QL Scotland
Tel: 01786 473 544
Email: alberthalls@stirling.gov.uk
Web Site: www.stirling.gov.uk/alberthalls
ADMINISTRATION:
Prop: Stirling Council.
General Manager: Eddy White
Technical Manager: Christobel Wandless
Contact: wandlessc@stirling.gov.uk
Policy: Private functions, Weddings, Productions, Shows,Fairs, Conferences, Fashion Shows.
Capacity: 10 - 500

Stockport, Cheshire

Pop. 138,750. London 177 miles. Newspapers: The Messenger (thurs); Manchester Evening News; Stockport Express (thurs). STD code 0161

PLAZA THEATRE

Mersey Square, Stockport, Cheshire SK1 1SP
BO: 0161 477 7779 Tel: 0161 480 3818
Email: boxoffice@stockportplaza.co.uk
Web Site: www.stockportplaza.co.uk
ADMINISTRATION
Props: Stockport Plaza Trust
General Manager: Ted Doan
Contact: ted.doan@stockportplaza.co.uk
Technical Manager: Rosie Holdaway
Contact: rosie.holdaway@stockport-plaza.co.uk
Box Office and Deputy Manager: Peter Johnson
Box Office Supervisor: Joyce Smith
Policy: Mixed Programme, Touring Productions, Pantomime, Plays, Dance, Musicals, Concerts, Films, Amateurs, Theatre Organ Concerts.
Capacity: 1300 plus Wheelchair accommodation.
The Plaza is in a prime position in Stockport town centre with an audience catchment of 500,000 in the immediate area.
Licensed bar/cafe serving stalls and circle.
TECHNICAL:
STAGE: Pros. Arch 50ft wide, 23ft deep; 6 ft deep full flytower upstage of housetab line. Masking legs typically set at 40 feet across stage but can be increased or decreased to suit. 12 counterweight sets, SWL 290kg each. (5 in flytower). 12 hemp sets, SWL 160kg each. (3 in flytower). Limited wing space - around 10 feet each side. Access to dressing rooms from both sides of stage. Orchestra Pit; accomm.20 musicians max. 1.5t capacity scissor lift in orchestra pit.
ADDITIONAL: Up to 900 square feet perforated cinema screen on electric winch situated at rear of fly tower masked to accommodate all film formats. In/Out time of screen under 1 minute. Weight around 250kg. Cinema speakers for movie use providing 3 channels & sub-bass. Projection Box: 35mm projection facilities with mono, stereo and Dolby Digital sound formats. Get-Ins & Get-Outs; Via front of building due to most of building being underground. Care must be taken lifting heavy equipment up steps onto stage. 1932 Compton cinema organ of 11 pipe ranks on electrically operated lift, centre auditorium in front of stage. Induction Loop in Stalls - permanently installed, in use for all shows.
LIGHTING: DMX 512 control via Zero 88 Bullfrog desk situated at rear of stalls. 72 channels. Circuits spread over 3 phases with 6 x suitable modern trip protection. Portable dimmers can be added to increase circuits by 12 if necessary. 16A & 13A non-dimmed outlets available above stage and on stage. Standard LX rig consists of generic lighting in an even full stage wash of blue, red, amber and one of blue-green, pink, lavender. In House Lanterns: Depending on state of repair, but normally to include not less

than- 12 x Patt 264 1kW profile spots, 12 x ETC Source 4 19o profile spots, 8 x T-84 zoom 1kW profile spots, 6 x Lekolite 1kW profile spots, 6 x axial profile spots, 24 x 1kW Fresnels, 12 x PAR64 PARcans (CP60, CP62, EXG & CP95 lamps available), 12 x PAR64 short PARcans (floorcans) (CP60, CP62, EXG & CP95 lamps available), 4 x 1kW cyclights, 4 x 4 circuit, 8 lamp compartment battens for footlight use, 6 x 4 foot u. v. fittings providing full stage u.v, 2 x 1200W HMI follow spots at rear of circle. Lanterns & other electrical devices may be brought into the building subject to current PAT certificate and approval by TSM/RSM.
SOUND: In house sound system and operator may be available by negotiation. Clean supply 32A Ceeform single phase socket outlet provided for sound equipment. 24 channel (+ 2 stereo) into 8 into 2 modern sound control board. Graphic Equalisers & Digital Sound Processors. MD/CD/Tape can be provided. Various mics/DI boxes can be provided. 24 x mic outlets situated on stage. Tie lines to Sx position. Main speakers situated on stage left & stage right. Subwoofers situated in orchestra pit. Circle speakers (6) situated in circle ceiling on manual winches. All powered by appropriate power amplifiers with delays & signal processors as required.
BACKSTAGE FACILITIES: 9 dressing rooms; accomm. up to 135 performers. Performer controlled fans in all dressing rooms. Audio show relay with individual dressing room volume control. Mirror lights (tungsten balanced) with local control in all dressing rooms except DR3. Overhead cool white fluorescent lighting.

ROMILEY FORUM

SMBC, The Precinct, Compstall Road, Romiley, Stockport, Cheshire SK6 4EA
BO: 0161 430 6570
Email: darren@nktheatrearts.org.uk
Web Site: www.nktheatrearts.co.uk
ADMINISTRATION:
Props & Lessees: Met.Borough Stockport. Community Services Division.
Manager: Darren Stannade
Policy: Touring, Repertory, Dance, Music, Comedy.
Perfs: 7.30pm, Mats. 2.30pm
Seats: 410. 1 Bar, Theatre Cafe.
TECHNICAL:
Stage: Proscenium arch, flat. Pros opening 11.58m, Ht. of Pros. 4.27m, Depth of S/Line 3.96m; Ht. of Grid 5.49m; apron depth 2.44m, 10 lines, hemp. W/Widths 3.05m S.R., 3.05m S.L.; Prompt Cnr S.L.; backstage crossover; Tab track - black masking - blue house tabs, safety curtain.
Lighting: Zero 88 Sirius 48 way board. 84 circuits. 64 amp socket available for touring systems - 24 1.2k profiles, 8 1.2k PC's, 14 650w fresnels, 12 650w PC's, 17 1k parcans CP62 beam angle, 5 x 4 circuit battens, 2 followspots.
Projection facilities 16mm.
Sound: Soundcraft Studio 24 channel, Spirit Folio 16 channel, 4 Bose 802, 2 bass driver speakers, foldback system, 1 Yamaha SPX90 effects unit, 1 Bose RE 1000 reverb unit, 1 Alesis Noisegate, 1 Harrison 600, 1 H&H 600 amps, 19 mics, cassette tape system, CD/MD player, PA system.
Other: Backstage: 2 dressing rooms, accom 5, 2 Showers/toilets. Band/chorus accom 20+, Scenery hoist and lift, tallescope, rehearsal piano, show relay/tannoy to dressing rooms.

STOCKPORT TOWN HALL

Wellington Road South, Stockport, Cheshire SK1 3XE
Events Team Tel: 0161 474 3451 Fax: 0161 474 7698
Email: venue.management@stockport.gov.uk
Web Site: www.stockport.gov.uk/services/leisureculture/townhall
ADMINISTRATION:
Props: Stockport Metropolitan Borough Council
Cap: 600
For bookings contact The Events Team

Stockton-on-Tees, Cleveland

GEORGIAN THEATRE

Green Dragon Yard, Stockton-on-Tees, Cleveland TS18 1AT
Tel: 01642 674 115
Email: info@teesmusicalliance.org.uk
Web Site: www.georgiantheatre.co.uk
ADMINISTRATION:
Props: Stockton On Tees Borough Council
Lessees: Tees Music Alliance: Georgian Theatre, Unit 5, Calvin House, Green Dragon Yard, Stockton-on-Tees TS18 1AE
Concert Hall for minority arts seating 200.

THORNABY PAVILION

New Town Centre, Thornaby, Stockton-on-Tees, Cleveland TS17 9EW
Tel: 01642 760971
Email: thornaby.pavilion@stockton.gov.uk
Web Site: www.stockton.gov.uk
ADMINISTRATION:
Props: Stockton On Tees Borough Council
Run by Tees Active
Cap: Main Hall: 1500 including 384 fixed seats in balcony and approximately 1,100 on floor according to size of staging.
Watson Hall Cap: 200
Manager: David Seller

Stoke-on-Trent, Staffordshire

Pop. 262,120. London 147 miles.
Newspapers: Staffordshire Sentinel (daily); Staffordshire Advertiser (thurs). STD code 01782

THE NEW VIC

Etruria Road, Newcastle-under-Lyme, Staffordshire ST5 0JG
Mgt: 01782 717 954 BO: 01782 717 962
Mktg: 01782 717 539 Fax: 01782 712 885
Email: admin@newvictheatre.org.uk / marketing@newvictheatre.org.uk
Web Site: www.newvictheatre.org.uk
ADMINISTRATION:
Props: Stoke on Trent and North Staffordshire Theatre Trust Ltd
Artistic Director: Theresa Heskins
Executive Director: Fiona Wallace
Production Manager: Steve O'Brien
Policy: In-house productions, tours and concerts.
Perfs: Normally Mon-Sat 7.30pm, many mats in summer, Xmas.
Capacity: Audiorium: 597 seated. Studio: 100 seated.
Restaurant, Coffee Bar, Two Bars, Craftshop, Exhibition space.
TECHNICAL:
Theatre in the Round (Perm).
Lighting: Switchboard: Rank Strand Gemini; 120 channels, Lanterns: 12 Harmony 15/28, 15 Harmony F, 20 Patt.23, 25 Patt.123, 2 Patt.223, 12 Patt.264, 4 ADB 1000 TNH, 17 Patt.23N, 2 Patt.774, 48 Prelude 16/30, 6 Cadenza, 2 Fresnel + 55 Parcans.
Sound Equipment: DDA (D Series) Mixing Console, 12, channels. 4 x Martin CX2 speakers. 5 Revox Tape Decks, 4 Quad Amps. Induction Loop Rehearsal Room (flex open space). Projection facility.
Dressing Rooms: 4; 20m, 6m, 10f, 4f.
Membership: TMA, MVA

REGENT THEATRE

Stoke-on-Trent Theatres Ltd, 35 - 37 Piccadilly, Stoke-on-Trent ST1 1AP
Mgt: 01782 211 208 SD: 01782 213 808
BO: 0844 871 7649 Fax: 01782 214 738
Email: andrewnicklin@theambassadors.com
Web Site: www.regenttheatre.co.uk
ADMINISTRATION:
Props: Ambassadors Theatre Group (Venues) Ltd
General Manager: Andrew Nicklin
Technical Manager: Martin Lund
Marketing Manager: Victoria Power
Policy: Plays, Musicals etc
Cap: 1615
TECHNICAL:
STAGE: Proscenium 12.63m W x 8.55m H, Depth from back of Iron Stage left 16.5m, Stage right 13.6m, Depth from back of iron to stage front 0.6m, Depth

from back of iron to forestage elevator front 3.7m in centre, Height to underside of grid 21m, Clearance under flyfloors 8.5m, Height to flybars (out dead) 19.8m except bars, 7-15 @ 17.55m, Length of bars 1-3 15m, Length of standard fly bars 17.5m, Distance between fly bars 19.7m, Stage surface Tempered hardboard on doublke 18mm ply on timber bearers, House curtain manually operated from stage or fly gallkery, Traps Downstage Centre area accessible for cutting traps, Crossovers Across rear of stage of understage, Drainage Downstage right (wing) or Trap room, Water, Downstage right (wing) or Upstage left offstage, Pass door Downstage left.
Access: Street slops down SR to SL (one way street SL to SR), Stage 1.1m above street level - get in via elevator, Trap for ice plant pipes/outside broadcast cables - USR
BACKSTAGE FACILITIES: Dressing Rooms 13, Band Rooms 2, Green Room (Second floor), Company Office (adjacent to stage door), Wardrobe (understage)
LIGHTING: Dimmers; ADB Eurorack 60, 288 x 3kw, 24 x 5kw, 40 x non dim circuits all 15A, All hardwired circuits. Outlets 3kw & non dims - 15A, 5kw - 32A subfused to 2 x 15A sockets, DMX 512 - XLR 5 pin. Control; Strand 550, Wireless Riggers remote, Houselights controllable from Lighting Board or Stage Desk (S/L or S/R) (control room at rear of stalls), Patchable DMX rings at all lighting positions - links for touring dimmers and controls. DMX backup facility, Non Dims switchable from panel in control room, Lanterns 35 x Strand SL Zooms 15-32 deg profiles 600W, 24 x Strand SL 10 deg profiles 600W, 20 x Strand Cantata F fresnels 1200W, 49 x Par 64 (mainly CP61's) 1000W, 14 x Strand patt 243's 2000W, 8 x Strand quartzcolour groundrows (orion 4 cells) 625W, 5 x Thomas cyc lights (4 cell) 1000W, 2 x Robert Juliat HMI 2500 installed in dome space for 2 additional followspots (16A Ceeform) and site for advance spots (32 x 15A Sockets) on auditorium side top galleries. Also a reasonable amount of cable, grelcos, multicore and male spiders available.
SOUND: The in house system comprises of 4 D&B 1801 subs, 13 D&B 902 mid/high cabs and 24 EAW JF60 delays. The system has various setting for different situations and is fully patchable. The auditorium's acousitc can be varied by using absorbent shutters. There are 66 Mic lines on stage, 22 Orchestra pit , all have both sexes available. 22 Speaker outputs and 4 amplifiers for additional speakers, 2 of which are bridged mono. Mic lines are fully patchable at GPO patch rack in control room. Control 24-4-2 with matrix, Outboard Equipment 2 x Yamaha SPX 1000, Autoquad 2400 Expander/gate, BSS DPR404 4ch comp de-esser, Drawmer Dual auto compressor, 2 x Tascam MD-801 R (mini disc player), Tascam DA-30Mk 2 (DAT player), Tascam CD-401Mk 2 (CD player). Mixer positions (touring or in house) can be situated at rear of stalls in open fronted booth. Mics 2 handheld radiu, 2 lapel radio, 4 beyer dynamic TG-X80 (Vocal), 4 BEyer Dynamic M88 TG (Vocal instrumental), 3 Astatic Plate Mics 901, 1 Audio Technic ATM25, 2 Audio Technic AT4041, 1 Audio Technic AT4050. Misc 4 BSS Audio AR 133 Active DI Box, 6 Mic Stands with detachable booms, 5 Floor Stands. There is a 2 channel infra red system for hard of hearing and audio described performances. A comprehensive duct system allows for temporary cables to be easily installed, i.e. productions, outside broadcasts, etc.
Rigging/Suspensions: Counterweights 500kg single purchase 6 line sets, 60 sets @ 200mm centers, 4 sets up and down stage. Fly and intermediate galleries SL and SR and cross rear of stage. 2 Loading galleries SL. Automation; extra groove on head and return pulleys and power on intermediate gallery SL.
Forestage suspensions: 3 rows of 5 x 500kg points. Sleeved holes through roof allow for chains. There are 10 chain hoists in the forestage roof void - operate from SL.

STOKE TOWN HALL

Glebe Street, Stoke-on-Trent,
Staffordshire ST4 1RT
Mgt: 01782 232 631
Email: venuesandcatering@stoke.gov.uk
Web Site: www.stoke.gov.uk
ADMINISTRATION:
Props: Stoke on Trent City Council
Facilities Manager: David Powell
the Jubilee Lounge, for up to 45 people;
the Windsor Room, for up to 70 people with bar and full Audio Visual facilities, ISDN lines;
the Council Chamber, for up to 150 people;
the Jubilee Hall, for up to 200 people with ornate ceilings, stained glass windows and large dance floor;
the Kings Hall, for up to 450 dining, 1140 theatre style, with ornate ceilings, stained glass windows, bar and large dance floor, lift access to stage from the auditorium; and
smaller meeting rooms and suites for more intimate meetings and events, which will accommodate up to 15, 20 or 30 people.

Stonehaven, Aberdeenshire

STONEHAVEN TOWN HALL

36 Allardice Street, Stonehaven
Aberdeenshire AB39 2BU
Tel: 01569 765 341
Email: admin@stonehaventownhall.org
Web: www.stonehaventownhall.org.uk
ADMINISTRATION:
Props: Aberdeenshire Council
Cap: 175
For bookings contact
Shirley Grubb on 07780227529

Stourbridge, West Midlands

TOWN HALL

Crown Centre, Stourbridge, West Midlands DY8 1YE
Tel: 01384 812 948 Fax: 01384 812 963
Email: stourbridge.townhall@dudley.gov.uk
Web Site: www.dudley.gov.uk/entertainment
ADMINISTRATION:
Dudley Metropolitan Borough Council
Cap: 520
Manager: Wayne Corfield

Stowmarket, Suffolk

REGAL THEATRE

Ipswich Street, Stowmarket, Ipswich
Suffolk IP14 1AY
Tel: 01449 612 825
Email: mail@regalstowmarket.co.uk
Web Site: www.regalstowmarket.co.uk
ADMINISTRATION:
Manager: David Marsh
Props: Stowmarket Town Council
Cap: 200
Large open stage, no drapes, with dressing accommodation. Theatre available for daytime conferences.
Bar and refreshment facilities.

Stranraer, Wigtownshire

THE RYAN CENTRE

Fairhurst Road, Stranraer, Wigtownshire
DG9 7AP Scotland
Tel: 01776 703 535
Email: ryancentre@dumgal.gov.uk
Web Site: www.dumgal.gov.uk/ryancentretheatre
ADMINISTRATION:
Arts Officer: Alison Mcauley
Technician: Eric McCune
Status: Leisure Centre and Theatre
Architects Dumfries and Galloway Council.
Venue financed by Galloway Council.
Props: Dumfires and Galloway Council
Policy: To provide the widest range of performing arts, both professional and community based, side by side with sports and leisure provision. Willing to

premiere show. Performance schedule open 7 days; performance times by arrangement. Booking terms by negotiation.
Facilities: Seats: Theatre 263, Games Hall 600, catering cafeteria, bar, entertainment licence. Access car park, at centre, station Stranraer, 1km; coach terminal: Stagecoach, Lewis Street, 40m; bus routes, none for the disabled 4 wheelchair spaces - lift chair/stair lift - assistance available, level access, all house facilities fully accessible. Other facilities: rehearsal dance studio, sprung wood floor, ballet barre and mirrors.
TECHNICAL:
Stage: Proscenium arch. Performing area 18.5m x 7.7m - pros opening 10m x 6m - wing widths 4.2m SR, 4m SL. No rake - floor soft wood, suitable for all dance, backstage crossover, stage heated. Height to grid 10.37m, 13 counterweight double purchase sets - maximum flying height 4.27m - tab track - 3 set black legs and borders - white cyclorama - claret house tabs, flown. 3 phase power supply. Orchestra pit 9m wide, 2m deep, accommodates 12. Get-in via dock doors on Fairhurst Road, 3.5m x 3.5m. Tallescope. Scale stage, fly and lighting plans available.
Lighting: Strand MX manual/memory board, 48 circuits at 2kw at present, 3 phase, operated from projection room at rear of auditorium - 2 x 32A supplies available for temporary board - 10 spots, 10 fresnels, 10 650 watt preludes, 10 300 watt, parcans, 4 side stands. Follow spot (Strand 2kw).
Cinema Facilties: Cinemactor Projector CX20H Dolby surround (digital).
Sound: Allen & Heath: 16:2 desk - 2 x Yamaha P2150 amps - 2 x Yamaha Q2031A graphic equalisers - 4 x Shure SM58, 8 x AKG D190E mics, 3 radio mics - tape deck and CD player. Acoustics suitable for music and spoken word. Stage management Prompt corner SR - Canford Audio cue system, belt-packs and headsets, 4 outstations.
Backstage - 2 dressing rooms, accommodate 25, access via passage from Leisure Centre foyer. Rehearsal room and pianos, Collard & Collard, upright new and Yamaha baby grand. Advice given on accommodation.
Staff: 2 technicians - casuals not available. No security personnel. Backstage facilities accessible to disabled performers and staff.
Games Hall - Open space 36m x 18m. Floor sprung wood. Height to ceiling 9.14m. 20 x 16A 3 phase supplies available for lighting, 32A supply for sound - equipment from theatre.

Stratford-Upon-Avon, Warwicks

Pop. 19,760. London 92 miles.
Newspapers: Stratford-upon-Avon Herald (fri). STD code 01789

ROYAL SHAKESPEARE THEATRE, SWAN THEATRE, COURTYARD THEATRE

Waterside, Stratford-upon-Avon, Warwickshire CV37 6BB
Mgt: 01789 296 655 BO: 0844 8001110
Mgt Fax: 01789 294 810 BO Fax: 01789 403 413
Email: info@rsc.org.uk
Web Site: www.rsc.org.uk
ADMINISTRATION:
Artistic Director: Michael Boyd
Licensee & Manager: Liz Wainwright
Technical Manager: Geoff Locker
Policy: Royal Shakespeare Company's own seasons from Nov to Oct. Occasional Sunday concerts and local drama groups.
Perfs: Evening 7.30, Mats. Thurs & Sat variable
Seats: RST 1,000, Swan 464, Courtyard 1,000. Restaurants. Cafe Bar, Rooftop restaurant, 3 other bars.
TECHNICAL:
ROYAL SHAKESPEARE THEATRE
Stage: Proscenium, Flat; Pros. Opening 8.94m; Ht. of Pros. 9.20m; Depth from S/Line 13.60m; Ht. of Grid 19.81m; 60 lines, C/W; Flying Bars 12.19m; W/Widths P.S. 12.19m, O.P. 12.19m; Prompt Cnr. P.S.
Lighting: Switchboard: Rank Strand Galaxy 240 way, rear of Dress Circle, F.O.H. Spots as required; Spot Bars as required.
Sound Equipment: Tape built to specification; Speakers as required.
Dressing Rooms 14; Accom. 60; 9 Bathrooms.
NB: Technical information above relates to Winter Season conditions. During RSC's Shakespeare Seasons there is an apron stage, steeply raked, no orchestra pit, and many other changes from the information given.
Membership: SWET, TMA
SWAN THEATRE
FACILITIES:
Seating: 464; on 2 galleries and ground level.
Catering: Wide range available in adjacent Royal Shakespeare Theatre. 1 bar sells all range of drinks and has theatre licence.
Ticket outlets: Own box office and usual agents.
Computerised box office system: RITA.
Shop/sales area.
Access: Nearest public car park: in front of RST; railway station: Stratford upon Avon; coach terminal: Stratford upon Avon.
Facilities for the disabled: 4 wheelchair spaces available, but have prior warning - deaf loop system - assistance available, contact Attendant - parking - ramp at entrance - all house facilities fully accessible.
TECHNICAL:
Stage: Thrust, gallery, 3 sides. Performing area 5.81m x 13.09m - pros opening 7.04m x 5.24m. No rake - floor plywood, suitable for dance, no lino available. Backstage crossover, stage heated. No tab track - back wall used as cyclorama. 4 x 15A independent circuits. Lift, centre stage, entrances DS. Scenery lift. Scale stage and lighting plans available, 1 to 25.
Lighting: Strand Galaxy board, 288 circuits, 300A, 3 phase, operated from 2nd gallery DS - no supply for temporary board - 100 profiles, 35 fresnels, 60 pars, 40 pc's, Strand - 2 followspots operated from centre technical gallery DS.
Sound: DDA 16 into 10 into 10 desk, operated from 2nd gallery DS - Harrison amps driving Tannoy Lynx and Puma speakers - AKG, Beyer mics - ASC dart replay machines - dubbing room available. Acoustics suitable for music and spoken word.
Stage management: Prompt corner SR - show relay/Tannoy to dressing rooms.
Backstage: Various dressing rooms, access by backstage - green room - wardrobe backstage with irons, washing machines, dryers. Refreshments from green room serving snacks and main meals. Rehearsal rooms, piano, good. Advice given on accommodation. Staff - 1 stage, 2 lighting, 1 sound, 1 wardrobe - casuals available - security personnel.

Street, Somerset

Pop. 11,000. London 130 miles.
Newspapers: Central Somerset Gazette (thurs); Shepton Mallet Journal (fri); Bridgewater Mercury (tues); Wells Journal (fri); Western Gazette (thurs). STD code 01458

STRODE THEATRE

Strode College, Church Road, Street, Somerset BA16 0AB
Admin: 01458 446 529 BO: 01458 442 846
Email: theatre@strode-college.ac.uk
Web Site: www.strodetheatre.org.uk
ADMINISTRATION:
Props: Strode College
Manager: Liz Leyshon
Technician: Dominic Sandford
Policy: Mixed programme, professional tours, mostly one nighters but some split weeks. Also amateur and educational users and Regional Film Theatre. Film, Live Professional, Amateur, Small Scale Touring, Music, Alternative content.
Seats: 343. Bar and refreshments.
Disabled facilities: 3 wheelchair spaces - deaf loop system - parking - level access - adjacent disabled toilet on ground floor.
TECHNICAL:
Stage: Proscenium arch. Performing area 13.41m x 6.4m - pros opening 9.75m x 5.5m. No rake - floor wood covered in black vinyl, suitable for dance, vinyl floor available, backstage and sub-stage crossovers, stage heated. Height to grid

9.14m - 14 hemp sets - tab track - black legs - white painted wall used as cyclorama - red drawn house tabs. Several 13 amp sockets. De-mountable Apron stage - 12m x 1.2m., Orchestra pit - accommodates 30, Get-in S.R. 1.7m x 2.4m - tailboard height - stage and lighting plans available.
Lighting: Lighting Control - Strand, 530 situated in control room rear of stalls. Dimming - 3 x LD90, 72 circuits @ 2.5kW; 26 circuits allocated FOH. Lanterns - Permanent FOH/H rig; 8 x Cantata 11/26; 4 Sil 30; 8 T84; 2 x Coemar followspots. Stage Lanterns - 25 x 1kW fresnels, 12 x parcans (6 CP62 and 6 CP61); 4 x Coda 3, 6 x Prelude 16/30.
Sound: (situated at rear of stalls) Allen & Heath GL3800. 1 x BSS dual graphics; Alessi compressor with gate; Alessi midiverb; Tascam CD player; Tascam minidisc; Dynacord PA speakers.
Stage Management: Prompt corner S.L. talkback - show relay tannoy to dressing rooms and FOH. Casual staff available by arrangement.
Backstage: 4 dressing rooms, accommodates 25, band room - below stage.
Piano: Steinway B7 grand.

Stroud, Gloucestershire

STRATFORD PARK LEISURE CENTRE

Stratford Road, Stroud, Gloucestershire GL5 4AF
Tel: 01453 766771 Fax: 01453 764585
Email: clarehamptonneale@everyoneactive.com
Web Site: www.everyoneactive.com
Centre Manager: Dan Coleman
Large arena available for functions, concerts, theatre productions and sports events.
Available on request.

SUBSCRIPTION ROOMS

George Street, Stroud, Gloucestershire GL5 1AE
Tel: 01453 760999 BO: 01453 760900
Email: subscription.rooms@stroud.gov.uk
Web Site: www.stroud.gov.uk
ADMINISTRATION:
Props: Stroud District Council
Cap: 400 seated, 450 standing
For bookings contact Kay Tanner
Local authority venue, hired for community and professional use; limited number of own promotions.
Policy: concerts, opera, dance, comedy and drama. 2 bars.
TECHNICAL:
Stage: flexible modular rostra up to 40 sq.metres.
Lighting: Celco Pathfinder desk 48 way
Dressing Rooms: 1 dressing room, 2 band rooms with access to toilets and washbasin.

Sudbury, Suffolk

Pop. 17,911. London 50 miles.
Newspapers: Suffolk Free Press (wkly); Mercury (wkly). East Anglian Daily Times.
STD code 01787

THE QUAY THEATRE

Quay Lane, Sudbury, Suffolk CO10 2AN
Admin: 01787 374 745
BO: 01787 374 745
Email: admin@quaytheatre.org.uk
Web Site: www.quaytheatre.org.uk
ADMINISTRATION:
Co-Ordinator: Sharon Buckler
Policy: Touring plays; childrens' theatre, music (jazz, folk, classical and popular); amateur dramatic, light operatic, jazz, and youth groups.
Perfs: Mon-Sun evenings and occasional days. Box Office open 10am - 9.30pm performance nights/ 10am - 6.00pm non show nights Mon-Sat
Seats: 125. Licenced Bar
TECHNICAL:
Stage: Open stage, end on. Raked auditorium. Stage width 6.1m. Depth 8 m. Wing space and get-in SR only.
Lighting: Zero 88 Eclipse 36 way 250 memory, 36 x 2Kw dimmers.
Sound: Peavey MD-II 12-2 mixer desk. Technics cassette deck. 6 independent speakers, mono or stereo. Teac X-7 spool tape deck + remote.
Dressing Rooms: 2; accommodating 12 and 6.

Sunbury-on-Thames, Middlesex

RIVERSIDE ARTS CENTRE

Run by voluntary community association
59 Thames Street, Sunbury, Middlesex TW16 5QF
Tel: 01932 789249 Tel: 01932 782850 (Eric Champion)
Web Site: www.riversidearts.co.uk
ADMINISTRATION:
Cap: 150
Manager: Eric Champion
For bookings contact Peter Anderson, bookings secretary
Tel: 020 8890 6586
Props: Spelthorne Borough Council

SUNBURY LEISURE CENTRE

Nursery Road, Sunbury-on-Thames, Middlesex TW16 6LG
Tel: 01932 772 287
Email: SunburyGM@slm-ltd.co.uk
Web Site: www.everyoneactive.co.uk
ADMINISTRATION:
Props: Everyone Active
S/Cap: 400+
Manager: Debbie Hazell

Sunderland, Tyne and Wear

Pop. 215,280. London 269 miles.
Newspapers: Echo (ntly); Sunderland Star (wkly). STD code 0191

EMPIRE THEATRE

High Street West, Sunderland, SR1 3EX
Tel: 0191 566 1040 BO: 0844 871 3022
SD: 0191 566 1057 Fax: 0191 566 1065
Email: benphillips@theambassadors.com
Web Site: www.atgtickets.com/sunderland
ADMINISTRATION:
Props: Ambassadors Theatre Group (Venues) Ltd
General Manager: Ben Phillips
Technical Manager: Mikey Smith
Box Office Manager: Susan Baillie
Policy: Touring, Opera, Ballet, Pantomime, etc.
Perfs: 2.30 & 7.30
Seats: 2,014. Stalls Bar , Dress Circle Bar
TECHNICAL:
STAGE: Proscenium arch. Performing area 13.72m x 12.8m, pros. opening 10.5m x 5.9m. Stage raked, 1 in 19.5", floor sprung wood covered with ply, suitable for all dance, backstage crossover, stage heated. Height of grid 18.34m - 2 hemp sets, 35 counterweight, double purchase sets 0.15m - 0.22m apart tab track, max flying height 19.8m, black masking. White cyclorama, brown house tabs, flown. Forestage 9.75 x 2.13m entrances from stage. Orchestra pit 12.5 x 2.13m x 1.3m deep, accommodates up to 100. Get-in via street level. Tallescope, safety curtain. Scale stage and fly plans available.
LIGHTING: Rank Strand Gemini board, 120 circuits, operated from box at back of circle - 200A 3 phase supply available for temporary board, OP side - 34 Profiles, 36 Fresnels, Rank Strand 2 follow spots operated from front of Gallery; single phase 60 amps for sound P.S. . Stage management Prompt corner can be OP or PS. Cue lights, 10 permanent show relay/Tannoy to dressing rooms. Backstage Green room, band room, wardrobe on 2nd floor with industrial washing machine & drier, coin-op, iron and 5 double 13A sockets. Piano. Advice given on accommodation. Staff, 2 stage, 2 lighting, casuals available, security personnel. Backstage facilities not accessible to disabled performers and staff.
SOUND: Soundcraft 500 40 channel desk, operated from rear of circle - 10k FOH Apogee speakers - 11 x SM58, 6 x Beyer 86, 10 x radio mics - 2 x Revox

Reel-to-reel, 1 x Denon cassette tape systems - 1 x Denon CD player.
Acoustics suitable for music and spoken word.
Studio (Films): 35mm optical sound; Projector Victoria 5 Cinemaccanica.
For further information please contact: Melvyn P James (Technical Manager) on 0191 566 1057.

SEABURN CENTRE

Whitburn Road, Seaburn, Sunderland SR6 8AA
Tel: 0191 529 4872
Email: seaburn@sunderland.gov.uk
Web Site: www.sunderland.gov.uk
ADMINISTRATION:
Props: City of Sunderland Council
Manager: John Emery
Cap: 600 Seated, 800 Standing

Sunninghill, Berkshire

NOVELLO THEATRE

High Street, Sunninghill, Ascot, Berks SL5 9NE
Tel: 01344 620 881
Email: junemrose@me.com
Web Site: www.novello-jackandthe-beanstalk.eventbrite.co.uk
ADMINISTRATION:
Contact: June Rose
Stage Manager: Rob Carr-Grant
Independently owned, specialises in work for children and young people - resident company and some visiting touring companies doing similar work. mainly morning and afternoon performances also weekends.
Available for occasional lettings.
Licensed bar. Coffee bar.
Seats 158 raked Auditorium.
Wheelchair access. No stairs.
TECHNICAL:
Proscenium stage. Opening 28ft depth. No flying, 3 traps, lighting box at back of auditorium. Full PA sound system/2 tape decks. Board - Zero 88 Sirius 24 Twenty four channel 2 pre-set, 99 programmable memories. Cue lights, strobe, UV lights, smoke and dry ice machine, 24 lanterns. Orchestra pit. 1 piano, 1 keyboard. Get-in at street level. 2 dressing rooms seat 5/6 in each. Scene dock/workshop. Washing machine etc.

Sutton Coldfield, West Midlands

Pop. 84,160. London 112 miles.
Newspapers: Sutton Observer (fri); Sutton Coldfield News (fri); Metro News (thurs).
STD code 0121

HIGHBURY THEATRE CENTRE

Sheffield Road, Sutton Coldfield, West Midlands B73 5HD
Admin/BO: 0121 373 2761 SD/Mgt: 0121 382 5214
Email: admin1@highburytheatre.co.uk
Web Site: www.highburytheatre.co.uk
ADMINISTRATION:
Props: Highbury Theatre Centre Ltd
Chairman: Steve Bowyer
For Technical Information Contact: Steve Bowyer
Policy: Amateur Little theatre presenting 7 plays per season for 10 performances each and Studio productions 3 a year (6 nights) and touring professional companies (one-night stands).
Box Office open from 7.30pm until 9.30pm
Perfs: 7.30
Seats: 138. Coffee Bar and Licensed Club Bar.
Disabled access, toilets and lifts.
TECHNICAL:
STAGE: Proscenium, Flat; Pros. opening 4.72m; Ht. of Pros. 3.50m; Depth of S/Line 6.55m; Ht. of Grid 7.62m; 42 lines, Hemp; Scenery Flying Ht. 3.66m; Flying Bars 5.49m; W/Widths P.S. 1.83m, O.P. 0.61m; Prompt Cnr. O.P.
LIGHTING: Please contact venue.
SOUND: 2 x tape disks, 1 x mini disk, 1 x CD. Speakers auditorium and stage. Induction loop.
DRESSING ROOMS: 3; Accom. 24.
Private Membership Theatre.
Membership: L.T.G.B.

Sutton In Ashfield, Nottinghamshire

HUTHWAITE LEISURE CENTRE

New Street, Huthwaite, Sutton-in-Ashfield, Nottinghamshire NG17 2LR
Tel: 01623 457 130 Fax: 01623 457 131
Email: huthwaitegm@sln-ltd.co.uk
Web Site: www.everyoneactive.com
ADMINISTRATION:
Props:Everyone Active
Manager: Laura Raynham
Cap: 100

SUTTON CENTRE THEATRE

High Pavement, Sutton-in-Ashfield, Nottinghamshire NG17 1EE
Tel: 01623 405513
Email: chris.metcalf@suttonacademy.attrust.org.uk
Web: www.suttonacademy.attrust.org.uk
ADMINISTRATION:
Props: Sutton Community Academy
Cap: 227
Centre Manager: Chris Metcalf

Sutton, Surrey

SECOMBE THEATRE

42 Cheam Road, Sutton, Surrey SM1 2SS
Mgt: 020 8770 6988 BO: 020 8770 6990
Tech: 020 8770 6989
Email: gina.gillam@sutton.gov.uk, diane.cash@sutton.gov.uk
Web Site: www.suttontheatres.co.uk
ADMINISTRATION:
Props: London Borough of Sutton
Press & Publicity: Kate Puleston
Theatre and Arts Services Manager: Gina Gillam
Marketing Manager: Kate Puleston
Tel: 020 8770 6987, Email: kate.puleston@sutton.gov.uk
Venues Administration: Diane Cash
Policy: Mixed programme, professional one nighters, drama, tours, variety, dance, cinema, children's shows, pantomime, annual talent show, amateur theatre, lettings.
Seats: 341 (Max. 390). Foyer Bar, Foyer Buffet. Second performance space/letting room available.
TECHNICAL:
For more information, contact the Technical Team on: theatretechnicians@sutton.gov.uk
STAGE: Prosc. Opening: Width: 8.23 metres (27'), Height: 4.52 metres (14' 10"), Depth: 8.54 metres (28'), Depth from tab line: 7.31 metres (24'). Height to grid: 9.15 metres (30'), Wing space S/R (O.P.): 5.35 metres (17' 7"), Wing space S/L (P.S.): 3.28 metres (10' 9"), Height of stage from floor: 1.17 metres (3' 10").
LIGHTING: ETC Express 96/144 Lighting Desk, 66 circuits (48 onstage, 18 FOH) + 6 independents, All circuits rated at 2.5kw.
FOH Lighting Rig is permanent consisting of: 12 ETC Source four zoom Juniors 25-50, 12 Source four Par EA, and 3 S4 zooms 25-50. On stage: 13 ETC Source four zoom Juniors 25-50, 30 ETC Parnell, 22 ETC source four Par MCM, 2 RJ cricket Follow spots and stands, 4 internally wired bars over stage (hand winched), 6-wheeled boom bases, 8 Chroma Q Scrollers inc power to fit ETC Pars.
SOUND: Allen & Heath GL2800 48-8-3 Mixing Desk, 2 x C Audio 1000w per channel amplifiers, Behringer Crossover, CS 400X Peavey Power Amp, Studiomaster 800c power amplifier, Drawmer LX20 expander/compressor, Art Alpha Multi Fx Processor, Yamaha, Rev 500 Digital Reverb unit, CD Player, Minidisc Player, Cassette Player, DAT Player, 2 x Logic Systems LS152A 800w fixed position FOH speakers, 2 x Logic Systems LS218A 1600w FOH Bass speakers, 2 x Bose 802 fixed position FOH speakers, 2 x Bose 802 mobile stage speakers, 2 x Peavey 112 Ti Stage Monitor wedges - SM58's, AKG CS1000's and 3 Float/floor microphones,

Various microphones Stands, Various microphones XLR cables, 1 x 8 way XLR stage box with 15' TAIL.
ADDITIONAL (By prior arrangement): Le Maitre pyroflash system with 2 pods, 2 follow spots - Silhouette 15 - (2kw), 4 x Genius Micro Scanners, 1 x Strobe, 1 x Black Night U.V., 1 x Gem Mini Smoke Machine, Snow machine. 1x Glitter ball, 12 Silhouette 1000w Profiles, 12 Par Cans, 6 pairs - usually 3 colour wash, 4x Silhouette 30 (1kw), 10x Starlette Fresnel (1kw), 3x Starlette P.C. (1kw), 24x Parcans 240v (1kw), 15x Minuette Flood (500w). Other sound equipment available on request; Spirit Folio F1 Mixing Desk, Digital Sound control from PC.

Swanage, Dorset

Pop. 7,660. London 123 miles.
Newspapers: Purbeck Advertiser. STD code 01929

THE MOWLEM THEATRE

Opening Booking Times: 10 am - 1 pm Mon-Sat
The Mowlem, Shore Road, Swanage, Dorset BH19 1DD
Mgt: 01929 422 229 BO: 01929 422 239
Email: mowlemtheatre@gmail.com
Web Site: www.mowlemtheatre.com
ADMINISTRATION:
Props: Mowlem Theatre
Policy: Touring, Repertory and Film Shows
Production Manager: Thomas Curtis, thomascurtistechnician@gmail.com.
Administration: David Bale
Seats: 379
TECHNICAL:
Stage: Proscenium, Flat; Pros. opening 9.14m; Ht. of Pros. 4.88m; Depth of S/Line 6.55m; W/Widths P.S. 1.52m, O.P. 2.89m.
Lighting: Switchboard: 24 way Zero 88 'Sirius'
Sound: "Custom Sound" speakers; "Any-Tronics" amplifiers; 35mm projectors. JBL Speakers, Soundcraft Spirit Folio Sound Desk, CD PLayer, Mini Disc Player, Twin Cassette Player.
Dressing Rooms: 2.
Lift to all floors.

Swanley, Kent

THE WOODLANDS

Hilda May Avenue, Swanley, Kent BR8 7BT
Tel: 01322 613900 Fax: 01322 664 739
Email: swanleybanqueting@swanley.org.uk
Web Site: www.swanley.org.uk
ADMINISTRATION:
Props: Swanley Town Council
Cap: 160 seated + two smaller rooms available

Policy: Local shows including ballet.
Available for conferences and banquets.
Large car park.

Swansea, West Glamorgan

Pop. 171,520. London 192 miles.
Newspapers: South Wales Evening Post 9ntly); Western Mail (dly); Herald of Wales (thurs for sat). STD code 01792

BRANGWYN HALL

The Guildhall, Swansea SA1 4PE South Wales
Tel: 01792 635 432 Fax: 01792 635 434
Email: tracy.ellicott@swansea.gov.uk
Web Site: www.swansea.gov.uk
Brangwyn Hall Manager: Tracy Ellicott
Capacity 1,070
Available for hire, concerts, recordings, conferences, functions, dinner.

DYLAN THOMAS THEATRE

Gloucester Place, Maritime Quarter, Swansea SA1 1TY
Tel 01792 473238
Email: info@dylanthomastheatre.org.uk
Web Site: www.dylanthomastheatre.org.uk
ADMINISTRATION:
Contact:: Dreena Morgan-Harvey
Cap: 160 Seated
Disabled Access and 8 Wheelchair spaces
Policy: Annual Under Milkwood Performance and selection of amateur plays. Theatre for hire.

PATTI PAVILION

Gorse Lane, Swansea, West Glamorgan SA1 4PQ Wales
Tel: 07773 784944
Email: mabs@pattipavilion.co.uk
Web Site: www.pattipavilion.co.uk
Contact: Mabs Noor
Caps: Standing 900, Seating on tables 400.

PENYRHEOL THEATRE

Penyrheol Leisure Centre, Pontardulais Road, Gorseinon, Swansea, West Glamorgan SA4 4FG Wales
Mgt/BO: 01792 897 039 Fax: 01792 894 931
Email: emma.evans@swansea.gov.uk
Web Site: www.swansea.gov.uk
ADMINISTRATION:
Owner: City & County of Swansea
Manager: Emma Evans
Policy: Arts. Mixed and balanced Arts and Entertainments programmes of professional productions and available for hire.
Seats: Max. 500; Balcony 160; (seating is retractable). Main auditorium - 340 seats maximum. The seating in the main auditorium is not a fixed arrangement and can be arranged according to the function/production within the maximum seating.
TECHNICAL:
Stage: Width: (Wall to wall) - 14.2m.
Proscenium: 10.6m wide, 4.7m high.
Stage Depth: 7.0m to front tabs; Stage Apron: 1.0m; Stage Rake: None; Stage Height: To hangers - 7.1m; To lighting Grid - 6.0m. Cyclorama: The stage is equipped with full cyclorama measuring 10.9m wide x 6.0m high. Curtains: One pair front tabs (red in colour); 2 pairs black traverse tabs; 3 pairs black legs; 3 black borders.
Machinery: None.
Green Rooms: Two (1 male, 1 female) situated behind the stage on stage left.
Dance Studio: Situated at the rear of the stage with access onto stage from both sides.
Lighting: Control: Furse EDRC 36 way electric switchboard. Each dimmer is rated at 2kw; 48 way patch panel.
Control Desk: 36 way 2 preset control desk with master sliders and blackout switches. Location: In control room front of house. A remote control point is switched in the wing stage right.
Intercom: 7 stations provided - 4 front of house. 4 on stage.
Sound Equip: One TOA 12 channel mixer & TOA Power Amp (300 watt) fitted Bose speakers & Equaliser, 3 Shure microphones + 2 audio technica. Prompt Corner. Get-in: Stage left or stage right; Main access through foyer at ground floor level and door No. 7 for very long equipment.
Other: Access Equipment: Tallescope.
Piano. 1 Danemann Baby Grand.
Stage Manager's Desk: Located stage wings.
Power: The theatre also has a three phase electrical supply at 100 amps per phase. Each supply is at 220/240 volts per phase. Fifty cycles are fused/switch junction box and the power is supplied by a 5 wire system (3 positive), 1 neutral return and 1 earth and one additional isolated phase of sixty amps to be available for sound.

PONTARDAWE ARTS CENTRE

Pontardawe Arts Centre, Herbert Street, Pontardawe, Swansea, SA8 4ED Wales
Tel: 01792 863 722
Email: a.dickinson@neath-porttalbot.gov.uk
Web Site: www.nptartsandents.co.uk
ADMINISTRATION:
Props: Neath Port Talbot Borough Council
Cap: 420 theatre style, 320 cabaret, 500 standing.
For bookings contact Venue Manager: Angie Dickinson
Operations Manager: Meirion Gittins
Space is available for cabaret settings.

SWANSEA GRAND THEATRE

Singleton Street, Swansea, SA1 3QJ
South Wales
Mgt: 01792 475242 BO: 01792 475715
SD: 01792 478535
Email: gerald.morris@swansea.gov.uk
Web Site: www.swanseagrand.co.uk
ADMINISTRATION:
Owners: The City and County of Swansea
Strategic Finance & Operations Manager: Gerald Morris
Email: gerald.morris@swansea.gov.uk
Programme,Marketing & Development Manager: Paul Hopkins
Marketing Manager: Helen Dalling
Senior Front of House Managers: Louise Evans & Caroline Davies
Box Office Manager: Rob David
Stage Manager: Steve Miles
Chief LX : Chris Barrett
Policy: Touring, Opera, Ballet, Drama, Children's Shows, Pantomime, Sunday Concerts. Various in-house productions plus Co. Productions with commercial producers.
Perfs: Variable depending upon attraction.
Seats: 1,021
Bars and Coffee Bars at all levels.
Exhibition Areas.
Two restaurants. Studio space
TECHNICAL:
STAGE: Proscenium, flat; Pros. opening 8.80m; Ht. of Pros. 8.00m; Depth of S/Line 14.00m; Working widths PS 7.80m, OP 12.00m; Ht. of Grid 21.50m; Flying Lines: 70 single purchase 400k sets at 200m centres, 8 motorised sets; all 13m long, with 2m extensions each side. On each side of stage 1 up and down hemp set, 1 full length and half length up (2 nr.) and down motorised sets; motorised cloth hoist; Prompt Cnr. normally PS, alternative OP.
LIGHTING: Switchboard: Rank Strand Galaxy 3 184 channel rear of gallery; 4 x 10kx 36 x 5k, 144 x 2.5k dimmers.
SOUND: As per sound spec
BACKSTAGE FACILITIEs: Dressing Rooms; 15, accom. 100, most with showers. 1 Dance Studio, 1 Rehearsal Studio. Orchestra Pit to accommodate 90 in two independent lifts adjusted to stage floor or pit level. 2 Band Rooms and Music Store.
Membership: ILAM, IEAM

TALIESIN ARTS CENTRE

Swansea University Singleton Park
Swansea SA2 8PZ Wales
Admin: 01792 29 52 38 Tech: 01792 295 492 BO: 01792 602 060
Email: office@taliesinartscentre.co.uk
Web Site: www.taliesinartscentre.co.uk
ADMINISTRATION:
Props: University College of Swansea
Manager: Sybil Crouch. Email: s.e.crouch@swansea.ac.uk
Technical Management Team: Dave Palmer
Email: d.palmer@swansea.ac.uk
Policy: Drama, dance, opera, concerts, films. Mixed programme touring and in-house productions.
Perfs: 7.30 nightly
Seats: 330 Theatre Style, Space for 2 wheelchairs. Bar, Foyer, Ceri Richards Art Gallery, Bookshop.
TECHNICAL:
STAGE: Flat floored stage with adjustable proscenium walls; forestage lift to pit; wood floor covered hardboard.
Proscenium opening 9.6m to 15.9m. Max stage width 20m. Depth 9.3m, with thrust 11.6m. Floor to roof beams 10.5m. Floor to fly galleries 6.0m. 16 4 line hemp sets rated at 250Kg s.w.l. 6 I.W.B. winch sets. 4 pairs black legs. 3 black borders. Motorised F.o.h. Tabs - Gold, 1 cyclorama, 1 set of Black Travellers, walls brown painted brick.
LIGHTING: 4 FOH lighting bridges plus booms on adjustable side walls, 6 on stage internally wired lighting bars on power winches, 4 Side lighting stands, Desk: Strand 530, 150 channels - 138 x 2.5kw and 12x 5kw dimmers. Control to rear of auditorium. Lanterns: 10 x SL Zoom 15/32, 20 x SL Zoom 23/50. 10 x Cantata PC's, 20 x Cantata Fresnels, 6 Alto 2kw Fresnels (all with barn doors). 10 Prelude 16/30. 10 Prelude fresnels. 10 x 500w Coda Floods. 16 x 1kw Coda floods permanently hung on cyc bar, 24 Par Cans. Film: 2 x Century 35mm film projectors, 1 x fumeo 16mm film projector, 2 x Kodak 2010 slide projectors, 2 x Simda 3040 slide projectors with dissolve.
SOUND: 24/8/1 Soundcraft Series 2 mixer. F.O.H. speakers: 4 x Sherman. Portable monitors 4 x JBL (M330) MK2. 4 x JBL Monitor wedges. 2 x Sherman stacks for main PA. Microphones 4 x shure beta 58 radio mics, 6 x shure beta 58, 2 x SM58, 4 x shure beta 57, 2 x AKG D3600 Cardiod Instrument mics, 3 x crown p.c.c. 1 x denon twin cassette deck, 1 x denon cd player, 2 denon DN-1100 minidisc machine, 1 tascam DA20 DAT machine, 2 Yamaha SPX 990, 3 x Yamaha 2301 equalisers. Drawmer 4 ch Compressor.
STAGE COMMUNICATIONS: Stage managers desk (prompt), rehearsal desk auditorium/control room, intercom and cue lights to all areas, 4 x dressing rooms for 28 artists at stage level. Green room, laundry, showers, access to workshop and scene dock at stage level from roadway.

Swindon, Wiltshire

Pop. 175,000. London 79 miles.
Newspapers: Evening Advertiser (ntly); Wiltshire Gazette & Herald (thurs); Wiltshire Star (thurs); Swindon Messenger (thurs). STD code 01793

LEVEL 3

73 Commercial Road, Swindon, Wiltshire SN1 5NX
Tel: 01793 534 238
Email: level3_therolleston@yahoo.com
Web Site: www.level3club.co.uk
ADMINISTRATION:
Contact: Bill Adams, Omar Khamkhami
Swindon's purpose-built live venue.
Cap: 350
TECHNICAL:
Brand new 5k rig with on-stage facilities. Full lighting rig, experienced honest promoter. Advance ticket facility. Licenced until 2am. Booking Wednesdays & Thursdays. Dressing Room. Easy In/Out Parking. In-house catering. Good Security.

OASIS LEISURE CENTRE

North Star Avenue, Swindon Wiltshire SN2 1EP
Tel: 01793 507 110
Email: michelle.jones1@gll.org
Web Site: www.better.org
ADMINISTRATION:
Props: GLL
Manager: Paul Sherman
Event Programme Manager: Michelle Jones
Policy: Leisure centre with multi-purpose used for concerts, sporting and social events, conferences and exhibitions.
Seating/Capacity: 1,640 seated: 3000 standing
TECHNICAL:
Dimensions of concert hall 126' x 108'; height 29'; no flying facilities.
Power: Lighting - 300 Amp 3 phase; Sound - 60 Amp 3 phase. Lighting basic white or colour spots only. Stage: standard layout 40' x 24', multi-height 2'6'-4,20 units 8' x 6' available. Access ground floor direct from car park.

TOWN HALL STUDIOS

Regent Circus, Swindon, Wiltshire SN1 1QF
Tel: 01793 601700
Email: info@swindondance.org.uk
Web Site: www.swindondance.org.uk
ADMINISTRATION:
Props: Swindon Dance
Cap: 98, raked.
Bookings Contact: Marie McClusky
Studio theatre for small scale productions. Multi-purpose lighting and sound equipment. Disabled access. Dressing room facilities. Bar facilities.

WYVERN THEATRE & ARTS CENTRE

Sixth Sense Theatre Company
Theatre Square, Swindon, Wiltshire SN1 1QN
SD: 01793 535534 BO: 01793 524481
Fax: 01793 480278
Email: info@wyverntheatre.org.uk
Web Site: www.wyverntheatre.org.uk
ADMINISTRATION:
Props: HQ Theatres Ltd
Theatre Director: Derek Aldridge. (Tel 01793 509035)

Publicity & Marketing Manager: Richard Loftus
Technical Manager: Simon Francklin
Contact: sfrancklin@wyverntheatre.org.uk
Policy: Touring Drama, Opera and Dance, Concerts, Children's Theatre, Mixed Programme, Exhibitions.
Perfs: Variable.
Capacity: 635. Wyvern Restaurant, Stalls Licensed Bar, Refreshments Bar.
TECHNICAL:
STAGE: Proscenium Fully Trapped Stage, Flat; Apron 1.22m plus Orch. Lift 1.83m; Pros. opening 10.77m; Ht. of Pros. 5.90m; Depth of S/Line 9.24m; Ht. of Grid 17.30m; 35 C/W (33x double purchase; 2x single purchase), Scenery Flying Ht. 8.23m; Flying Bars 12.19m; W/Widths P.S. 6.40m, O.P. 6.40m; Prompt Cnr. O.P.
STAGE MANAGEMENT: 12 way cue light system, controlled from the Prompt Desk. Technicians' ring intercom; 8 Tec Pro Belt Packs available in the following positions: stage usl, usr, dsl, dsr, prompt, flys, f/spot x2, lx, sound, auditorium. Access equipment; 1 Tallescope (4.7m-7.5m platform height), 1 14 rung 3-section Zarges ladder, 1 8 rung 3-section Zarges ladder. 1 8 rung Fibre ladder
LIGHTING: Control; Strand Light Palette VL Lighting Console, 1500 channels, 24 submasters. Dimmers; 170 2.5kW ETC Sensor Dimmers, terminating in 15A sockets and Socapex; 6 5kW ETC Sensor Dimmers, terminating in 32A Ceeform sockets & 4x15A sockets each; 24 2.5KW ETC Sensor Relay Switched, terminating in 15A sockets. Profiles; All Profiles come with 4 shutters, 40 ETC Source 4 15/30deg 750W, 2 ETC Source 4 10deg 750W. Fresnels; 40 Selecon Rama 1.2kW; 8 Selecon Arena 2kW. Beam Lights; 24 PAR64 w/ CP62 1kW, 12 PAR64 w/ CP61 1kW, 1 8way PAR64 ACL set, on 2x 4way bars, black; 1 8way PAR64 ACL set, on 2x 4way bars, silver; 1 8way PAR36 ACL set, on 2x 4way bars, silver. Flood Lights; 15 Iris 1; 1kW, 5 Coda 3, 500W per cell. Follow Spots; 2 Selecon Rua 9/16deg 1.4kW. Mechanical dimmer, mechanical leaf iris, 6 colour changer plus frost (glass) and CT filter (glass). Takes B Size Gobo. Power: 1x 200A/3ph Powerlock; 1x 125A/3ph Ceeform; 3x 63A/3ph (can breakout to single phase and 32A/3ph). 24x 16A power switched from control room (various locations).
SOUND: Control; Yamaha M7CL48K Digital Mixing Console; 48 x Inputs, 16 x outputs. Processing; 1 BSS FCS966 Opel Dual 30 Band Graphic. Left and Right; 3x Acoustica 5212L 500W Mid/High (Each side). Subwoofers; 2x Acoustica S8028 (1 left, 1 right). Centre; 2x Acoustica 5121W 500W Mid/High. Delays; 4x Acoustica 5212L 500W Mid/High. Stage Monitors; 6 Martin Audio LE1200. Aviom Self-Monitoring System; 3 Aviom Personal mixer, 16 inputs from Yamaha mixing console. Playback; 2 Denon DNC635 Compact Disc Player; 2 Tascam MD350 Mini Disc Recorder. Orchestra Pit; 15 RAT Stands with Light, 1Conductor's Stand with 2x Light, Many Chairs. Sound power: 63A single phase / 32A single phase SR; 20A powercon usl, usr, dsl, dsr, auditorium
BACKSTAGE FACILITIES: Dressing rooms; 7, accomm 24+. Telephone line (recharged accordingly). WiFi (recharged) Toilets and Shower facilities located nearby (2 en suite). Washing machine and tumble drier available at request. Ironing Board and Iron, as well as Towels available at Stage Door. Orchestra Pit 40. Green Room: Next to The Stage. Tea and Coffee facilities, as well as microwave and fridge. Band room in basement; accomm. 20. Toilets located nearby.

Tamworth, Staffordshire

TAMWORTH ASSEMBLY ROOMS

Corporation Street, Tamworth, Staffordshire B79 7DN
BO/SD: 01827 709 618 Admin: 01827 709 619 BO Fax: 01827 709582
Email: elanor-hazlehurst@tamworth.gov.uk
Web: www.tamworthassemblyrooms.co.uk
ADMINISTRATION:
Props: Tamworth Borough Council
Entertainment & Events Manager: Elanor Hazlehurst
Box Office Manager: Debra Lewis
Victorian Assembly Hall with raked black box stage, proscenium arch, apron and concealed wings. The Assembly Rooms is the town's most popular building and provides a varied range of entertainment from well known stars such as Bob Geldof and Ken Dodd, to classical concerts, big bands, tribute shows, amateur dramatics, tea dances and antiques fairs. Flat floor auditorium with retractable tiered seating, computerised box office, bar and catering facilities.
Cap: 349
TECHNICAL:
2 scenery bars; front, mid and rear tabs (manual); height to lighting grid - variable; Stage entrances - upstage left, upstage right and treads from auditorium (removable).
Dressing Rooms: 4 cubicles, plus large green room. Ladies and gentlemen's toilets, hot and cold water and show cublcle.
Disable Facilities: Disabled access and wheelchair spaces available. Induction Loop.
Lighting: Console - Jands "event", 96 channel programmable desk with DMX512 output. Dimmer racks - 2 x ETC 36 channel dimmers, DMX controlled. Grid - 3 winched bars above stage; 2 fixed bars above auditorum; 4 wall perches in auditorium. Strand, CCT and Thomas lanterns. 1 x 2Kw CCT follow spot. 4 way talk-back system.
Sound: Consoles - Allen & Heath GL3300. 36 channel, 8 subgroup, 8 aux, 4 mute group, 2 way matrix. Spirit folio notepad. 4 mic/ine channels, 2 stereo line channels, 1 post-fade aux. Martin Audio speakers. C-Audio amplifiers. CD, minidisc and cassette players. AKG, Sennheiser and Shure microphones.

Taunton, Somerset

Pop. 65,000. London 142 miles. STD code 01823

BLACKBROOK PAVILION

Blackbrook Way, Taunton, Somerset TA1 2RW
Tel: 01823 333 435
Email: t.coles@toneleisure.com
Web Site: www.toneleisure.com
ADMINISTRATION:
Props: Taunton Deane Borough Council
Cap: 800
Bookings Manager: Tina Coles
Director Of Leisure: Juliette Dickinson

THE BREWHOUSE

Coal Orchard, Taunton, Somerset TA1 1JL
BO: 01823 283 244
Email: enquiries@tauntontheatre.org.uk
Web Site: www.thebrewhouse.net
ADMINISTRATION:
Props: Taunton Theatre Association Ltd.
Chair & Director: Val Hammond
Directory: Mark Dawson
Policy: Mid scale professional touring drama, dance, opera, one person shows, poetry, conference, amateur drama, operatic & pantomime companies, jazz and folk and classical music.
Perfs: 7.45. Mats. usually Thurs & Sat 2.30.
Seats: 352. Bar and Buffet/Restaurant.
TECHNICAL:
For more information contact the Technical Department on Tel: 01823 274608 or email: technical@thebrewhouse.net.

STAGE DIMENSIONS: Full stage depth (or to U/S black tabs) 9.95m (9.42m) 32ft 8ins (30ft 11ins). Width of pros 10.109m 33ft 2ins. Height of grid 6.63m 21ft 9ins. Height of pros (including header) 5.18m 17ft. Max flying height (LX bars hang at approx 5.8m) 6.32m 20ft 9ins. Hemp bar width 12.50m 41ft. Depth pros to Cyc 6.93m 22ft 9ins. Depth of apron 3.00m 9ft 10ins. SL wing width 2.13m 7ft. SR wing width 7.2m 23ft 8ins. Get-In: Dock door opening width 3.22m 10ft 7ins. Dock door opening height 4.85m 15ft 11ins. Dock/SR shutter door width 4.00m 13ft 2ins. Dock/SR shutter door height 4.88m 16ft.
STAGE: Large scene dock providing

under cover get ins and some workshop facilities, entrance from the dock to SR wing via shutter door. Prompt desk situated in prompt corner (SL wing) on 3.5m (12ft) wonder lead with full headphones system. Limited cue lights available. Red velvet house tabs on hand winch situated by prompt desk (SL wing). 8 x hemp flying lines on aluminium bars, 4 line hemps with a max weight of 100kg each bar. Orchestra pit situated in the apron with lift out traps, max capacity of 15. 15 x illuminated rak stands available. Full soft black masking. 4 sets of black serge legs. 2 x 3ft borders. 2 x 6ft borders. 6 x legs manually tracked on up/down bars, 3 per wing - can be used independently or in conjunction with legs. 2 x sets of permanently rigged black running tabs which are fixed to the grid and unable to move. 1 set D/S of Hemp 7 and 1 set U/S of Hemp 3. Harlequin black dance floor which covers the entire stage floor including the apron, available for use.
LIGHTING: Control: 1 x ETC ion, 1 x universal fader wing 2 x 20, radio remote riggers and 2 x 19" touch screen monitors. 96 x 2.5kw circuits LD90 racks, patch panels are located in SL slot. Profiles: 20 x Source 4 15/30 zoom (permanently rigged on FOH bridge). 10 x Altman Shakespeare 15/35. 2 x Source 4 50 deg. 15 x Source 4 15/30 zoom. 12 x Source 4 25/50 zoom. Fresnels: 20 x 1.2k Selecon Fresnels with Barndoors. 9 x Harmony Fresnels with Barndoors. 10 x Cantata Fresnels with Barndoors. 8 x Prelude 650 Fresnels. 2 x Vision 650 Fresnels with Barndoors (permanently rigged on FOH Bridge as tab warmers). Pars: 38 x Par 64 (CP62). PC: 8 x Vision 2.5k PC with Barndoors. Floods: 12 x Spotlight Domino 1k Floods. Strobes: 2 x Martin Atomic 3000 Strobes. Pin Spots & Birdies: 10 x Pin Spots. 7 x Birdies with transformers. Follow Spots: 2 x Clay Paky Shadow Follow Spots (positioned above LX Box). Misc: 6 x lighting booms (3m high IWB, 6 ways on each boom all on tank trap with castors) & 3 x Shin stands assorted TRS, socapex, gobos & holders. 32 x Grelcos & 3 x Trelcos. 1 x Viper 2.6 smoke machine, 1 x Jem techno fog & 1 x Unique 2 haze machine. 4 x ETC Source 4 Iris.
SOUND: Desks: 1 x Allen & Heath ML4000 40/8/3. 1 x Yamaha MG12/4 Amps: 2 x Crown MAC 1200 (permanently used for FOH speakers and subs), 1 x Crown XLS 602 1200, 1 x Citronic PPX 1200, 1 x Citronic PPX 900, 1 x QSV RMX 1450. Speakers: 2 x Martin audio WT3 (permanently rigged FOH), 6 x XV400B speakers (usually used as monitors), 3 x Tannoy Lynx speakers, 4 x Nexo P58 & Nexo analogue TD controller, 2 x XV1000 Sub bass speakers, Processors: 1 x 4 way mulicom compressor unit, 1 x Klark technic graphic, 1 x Alesis Midiverb, 1 x Ultracurve digital graphic equalizer, Mics and Mic Stands: 4 x Sennheiser lapel radio mics, EW300 G3. 2 x Sennheiser hand held radio mics, EW300 G3, 4 x Beta 58. 8 x Shure SM58, 7 x Shure SM57, 2 x AKG CK91, 2 x AKG SE300B power module, 2 x AKG CK98 Shotgun mic. Module. 7 x Assorted AKG mics, 16 x Boom mic. Stands. 3 x Short mic. Stands. DI Boxes: 5 x DI boxes, 2 x Behringer Ultra DI Pro 4 channel units. Multicores: 33 way hardwired multicore from control room to stage with 8 x speaker returns, 1 x 20 way stage box, Comms: 6 x Techpro BP111 beltpacks, 2 x Altair EM-201 beltpacks, 1 x Altair AM-100/2 headset, 2 x Techpro SMH210 headsets, 2 x Techpro DMH220 double headsets. Playback: CD players: Denon DN-C616, Tascam CD-OIU Pro CD player, MD players: Sony MDS - JB930, Sony MDS-JE780.
BACKSTAGE FACILITIES: 2 large dressing rooms and 2 small dressing rooms all air conditioned; accommodation 50. 5 toilets including 1 disabled shower / toilet. Full disabled access to backstage areas. Green room / crew room with tea coffee making facilities.
Laundry room available with washing machine, tumble dryers, irons and ironing boards. Office space within with telephone and internet access. Wireless internet is also available backstage but needs to be authorised by the resident technicians.

WELLSPRINGS LEISURE CENTRE

Cheddon Road, Taunton,
Somerset TA2 7QP
Tel: 01823 271271
Email: n.townsend@toneleisure.com
Web Site: www.toneleisure.co.uk
Props: Tone Leisure
Events Manager: Nick Townsend
Capacity: Seated - 928; Standing (concert) - 1,100

Telford, Shropshire

Pop. 140,000. London 148 miles.
Newspapers: Shropshire Star (ntly); Telford Journal (fri). STD code 01952

THE INTERNATIONAL CENTRE TELFORD

St. Quentin Gate, Town Centre, Telford,
Shropshire TF3 4JH
Tel: 01952 281 500 Fax: 01952 281 515
Email: sales@southwatereventgroup.com
Web Site: www.southwatereventgroup.co m
Over 11,000m2 pillar less space.
For bookings contact sales@southwatereventgroup.com
Capacity: 6,500

OAKENGATES THEATRE

Limes Walk, Oakengates, Telford,
Shropshire TF2 6EP
Admin: 01952 382370 BO: 01952 382 382 Fax: 01952 382 381
Email: theplace@telford.gov.uk
Web Site: www.theplacetelford.com
ADMINISTRATION:
Props: Telford & Wrekin Council
Manager: Debbie King
Technical Manager: Gary Parton
Policy: One Night Stands, Exhibitions, Pantomime, Comedy, Ballet and Lectures.
Amateur Musicals; Lettings for Banquets, Concerts, Variety, Discos, Dances etc.
Seats: 641, Standing Only 780
Concert. 315 on retractable rake. Bars and Servery.
TECHNICAL:
Stage: Proscenium arch. Performing area 16.5m by 12.5m, pros opening 12.2m by 4.2m. Wing widths 2m SR, 2m SL no rake. Floor sprung wood, suitable for dance (not barefoot). Backstage and understage crossovers, stage not heated. Height of grid 6m - black, beige, burgundy masking - white canvas cyclorama - red house tabs, drawn. 4 by 2 13A sockets, 4 by 15A independent circuits. 100 A3 phase visitors supply. 1 lift in front of stage. Get in via stage lift - dock doors 2m by 2m. Tallescope. Scale stage and lighting plans available.
Lighting: 72 circuits, 15 amp 2kw per channel. Operated rear of auditorium. Visitors supply 3 phase stage left. 33 profile spots, 19 fresnels, 8 floods, 16 pars and 1 cyc batten, 6 Scans.
Sound: Yamaha 24 channel desk EV Delta boxes, Crown amps.
Stage Management: Prompt corner SL. Tecpro cue system with 5 outstations. Show relay to dressing rooms.

Tenby, Pembrokeshire

DE VALENCE PAVILION

Upper Frog Street, Tenby, Pembrokeshire
SA70 7JD
Tel: 01834 842730
Email: tenbytownclerk@btconnect.com
Clerk for the Council: Mr Andrew Davis
Props: Tenby DVP Trust
Capacity: 500-700 depending on seated or standing.

Tewkesbury, Gloucestershire

Pop. 9,104. London 104 miles. STD code 01684

ROSES THEATRE

Sun Street, Tewkesbury, Gloucestershire

GL20 5NX
Admin: 01684 290734 BO: 01684 295074 Fax: 01684 290 941
Email: admin@rosestheatre.org
Web Site: www.rosestheatre.org
ADMINISTRATION:
Director: Debra Rees
Technical Manager: Ian Smith
Finance: Greg Hunt
Marketing and Press Manager: Beckie Smith
Policy: The Roses is a busy and popular arts centre in Tewkesbury with an eclectic programmes of live events, take part activities, exhibitions and festivals. Complete with an exciting film programme of world, independent and UK film. The Roses is a diverse and exciting arts venue.
Perfs: Daily.
Seats: 370. Licensed Bar, Kiosk.
TECHNICAL:
STAGE: Proscenium stage, Flat; Pros. opening 12.19m; Ht. of Pros. 5.79m; Depth of S/Line 8.92m; Ht. of Grid 14.17m; 18 lines, 6 C/W, 9 hemp, 2 Motor Tabs, power O.P. screen; Scenery Flying Ht. 6.71m; Flying Bars 12.19m; W/Widths P.S. 3.05m av., O.P. 3.05m av. Prompt Cnr. P.S.
LIGHTING: Switchboard: Rank Tempus 48 channel. Spots 1 Follow, 2 Perches (8 circ. paired) Gallery (10 circ. paired); Dips 6 P.S., 6 O.P.; 3 Spot Bars, No. 1 15 circuits, No. 2 10 circuits, No. 3 6 circuits.
SOUND: Spirit Folio 12 way, tape deck, 4 AKG 190, Quad 303 amps, all in projection box. Speakers: Tannoy Mansfield 2 stage, 2 auditorium.
DRESSING ROOMS; 3 +; Accom. 40; 1 Shower; Orchestra Pit 14. DISABLED FACILITIES: Disabled Toilet, demountable auditorium seating to accommodate wheelchairs, all disabled facilities on common level with street.
Separate Conference Room.

Thame, Oxfordshire

THAME LEISURE CENTRE

Oxford Road, Thame, Oxfordshire OX9 2BB
Tel: 01844 215607
Email: richard.boulton@gll.org
Web Site: www.better.org.uk
ADMINISTRATION:
Props: GLL
Cap: Large Hall 600; Small Hall 150
Manager: Richard Boulton

Thames Ditton, Surrey

VERA FLETCHER HALL

4 Ember Court Road, Thames Ditton, Surrey KT7 0LQ
Tel: 0845 652 8529 BO: 0844 884 8832
Web Site: www.verafletcherhall.co.uk
ADMINISTRATION:
Contact Helen Mason for bookings. Between hour's of 9am and 5pm weekdays.
Cap: 126

Thetford, Norfolk

BRECKLAND LEISURE CENTRE & WATERWORLD

Croxton Road, Thetford, Norfolk IP24 1JD
Tel: 01842 753 110 Fax: 01842 761 056
Email: richardsavory@parkwood-leisure.co.uk
Web: www.thetford@parkwood-leisure.co.uk
ADMINISTRATION:
Props: Breckland District Council, Run by Parkwood
General Manager: Richard Savory

Thornton Cleveleys, Lancashire

CLEVELEYS COMMUNITY CENTRE

Kensington Road, Thornton Cleveleys, Lancashire FY5 1ER
Tel: 01253 863369
Email: phutton@wyrebc.gov.uk
Web Site: www.wyrebc.gov.uk
ADMINISTRATION:
Props: Wyre Borough Council
Capacity: 100 seats
Contact Peter Hutton Tel: 07802 984600

THORNTON LITTLE THEATRE

Four Lane Ends, Victoria Road, Thornton Cleveleys, Lancashire FY5 3SZ
Tel: 01253 887 693
Email: thorntonlittletheatre@wyre.gov.uk
Web Site: www.thorntonlittletheatre.co.uk
ADMINISTRATION:
Props: Wyre Borough Council
Contact us via Post: Victoria Road, East Thornton Cleveleys, Lancs FY5 3SZ
Head of Culture, Leisure and Tourism: Ian Munro
Email address: ian.munro@wyre.gov.uk
Cap: 197

Thurso, Caithness

CAITHNESS HORIZONS

High Street, Thurso, Caithness KW14 8AJ
Tel: 01847 896508 Fax: 01847 891152
Email: info@caithnesshorizons.co.uk
Web Site: www.caithnesshorizons.co.uk
ADMINISTRATION:
Props: Caithness Horizons
Education Room Cap: 25 Boardroom style, 50 Theatre style.

Tonbridge, Kent

ANGEL LEISURE CENTRE

Angel Lane, Tonbridge, Kent TN9 1SF
Tel: 01732 359 966 Fax: 01732 363 677
Email: angel.leisurecentre@tmbc.gov.uk
Web Site: www.angelcentre.co.uk
Manager: Gary Littlejon
Policy: Multi-purpose Hall used for theatre, cinema, concerts, meetings, sports and social events, conferences, fairs and markets.
Seating/Capacity: 307 seated; 400 standing.

Torbay, Devon

Pop. 112,000. London 193 miles.
Newspapers: Herald Express (ntly); Western Morning News (dly); Torbay Weekender (thurs). STD code 01803

BABBACOMBE THEATRE

Babbacombe Downs Road, Torquay, Devon TQ1 3LU
BO: 01803 328 385 Admin: 01803 322 233 Fax: 01803 322 244
Email: mail@matpro-show.biz
Web: www.babbacombe-theatre.com
ADMINISTRATION:
Props: Matpro Ltd
Cary Point, Babbacombe, Downs Road, Torquay,
Devon TQ1 3LU Tel 01803 322233 Fax 01803 322244
Contact: Colin Matthews
Seats: 600
TECHNICAL:
Stage: Proscenium Stage, Flat; Pros. opening 8.46m; Ht. of Pros. 4.19m; Depth of S/Line 5.03m; Ht. of grid 5.79m; 17 lines, 11 Hemp-to-wire, 6 Hemp; Scenery Flying Ht. 2.89m; Flying Bars 9.75m; W/Widths P.S. 0.91m, O.P. 1.22m; Prompt Cnr. P.S.
Full lighting rig-details on request. Full sound details on request.
Dressing Rooms 5; Accom. 20.

BRIXHAM THEATRE

New Road, Brixham, Devon TQ5 8TA
Tel: 07884166508 BO: 01803 882 717
Email: mpotten@talktalk.net

Web Site: www.batsweb.org.uk
ADMINISTRATION:
Props: Torbay Borough Council
For bookings and further information contact Cecilia Kean
Policy: Summer play season, private hirings remainder of year.
Perfs: Variable.
Seats: 230
TECHNICAL:
Stage: Proscenium, Flat; Pros. opening 7.77m; Ht. of Pros. 3.05m (very high raised stage); Prompt Cnr. 1.83m.
Lighting: Switchboard: Strand 3 preset 18 way; F.O.H. 4 Patt.264; 2 light battens; 1 front spot bar 3 Patt.137, 2 Patt.123, 1 Back Spot for 8 Patt.113, 1 Patt.223, Stage Dips run from Dimmer Pack 4 Patt.223.
Sound Equip: 4 track tape recorder.
Dressing Rooms 4; Accom. 20. When Orchestra rail installed. Accom. 10 musicians.

THE PALACE THEATRE

Palace Avenue, Paignton, Devon TQ3 3HF
BO: 01803 665 800 Mgt: 01803 208 863
Email: alan.davies@torbay.gov.uk
Web: www.palacetheatrepaignton.co.uk
ADMINISTRATION:
Props: Torbay Council
Operations Co-Ordinator: Martin Hoare
Policy: Private hirings throughout the year. Community theatre featuring a range of touring product and local amateur groups.
Perfs: Variable.
Seats: 400
TECHNICAL:
Stage: Pros Arch 3.2m x 7.2m; performance area 7.2m wide, 10m deep; wing width 2m; light grey tempered hardboard floor slightly rakes (please inquire re. floor painting); backstage crossover; stage area centrally heated; ceiling/grid height 6.4m; 21 hemp flying lines - 120kg per set; 3 winch lifted LX bars; black/grey reversible cloth masking, red drawn house tabs, black/grey tab set; 13 amp outlets at PS + OP; small apron and steps to auditorium OP; stage extension over pit available; tumbling safety curtain; orchestra pit avg. 12 piece max; dock door 1.1m x 3.4m with ramp to parking area; stage plans available with full details.
Lighting: Arri Mirage 75 channel DMX desk; Martin 2308 moving light controller @ rear centre of balcony; 48 ways of 10 amp dimming; temporary power 63 amp 3 phase busbar; 16 Quartet PC, 8 Source 4 Profile, 6 Source 4 PAR, 20 PAR 64, 14 Pat743, Roboscan 812 (excess hire charge), 4Pat23, 4 x 3 circuit full width flood battens; Cantata F/S; 2 Solo CIS F/S; 10 Harmony Fresnel; 16 Harmony Profile; 10 lit RAT Music Stands.
Sound: Soundcraft 24-4-2 Mixer @ rear centre of balcony; 2 Crown Macrotech 1220 amps; FOH: 2 x Bass enclosures (2x15"), 2 x Mid/High Speakers; 6 AKG dynamic vocal mics; 2 AKG rifle mics; 2 Crown PCC160 PZM's; 7 Shure SM58 vocals; 6HH monitor speakers + amps; double tape deck; CD deck; 24way multicore from control to stage. Larger PA available on request, please enquire. Backstage tannoy system. Acoustics: music and spoken word.
Stage Management: Prompt corner SL, headset comms. with up to 9 outstations, no cue lights; shows called from prompt corner. CCTV with monitor PS.
Backstage: 4 large, 1 small, 1 spare dressing rooms accommodating 25+; band room available; kitchen with laundry facilities. No disabled access backstage.
Additional: Concert grand piano available on stage; cottage upright in pit/bar, grand in rehearsal space and smaller grand available for pit, minidisc players/recorders, radio mics, gauzes, rostrum and stage decking etc. available to hire. Contact Technical Manager c/o Palace Theatre.

PRINCESS THEATRE

Torbay Road, Torquay, Devon TQ2 5EZ
Admin: 01803 290 288 BO: 0844 871 3023 Tech: 01803 206375 Admin Fax: 01803 290 170
Email: wendybennett@theambassadors.com
Web Site: www.atgtickets.com/torquay
ADMINISTRATION:
Props: The Ambassador Theatre Group (Venues) Ltd
Policy: Summer Shows, Pantomime, Tours (plays, opera, ballet, musicals), conference facilities, Repertory, Concerts.
Perfs: Variable according to function.
Theatre Manager: Wendy Bennett
Technical Manager: Martyn Jenkins
Contact: martynjenkins@theambassadors.com
Press Manager: Leah Miller
Contact: leahmiller@theambassadors.com
Seats: 1,487. 3 Bars within the theatre/restaurant
TECHNICAL:
STAGE: Proscenium, Flat; Pros. opening 13.72m; Ht. of Pros. 6.40m; Depth of S/Line 10.97m; Ht. of Grid 16.00m; 56 lines, 42 C/W, 14 Hemp; Flying Bars 15.24m; W/Widths P.S. 3.96m average (variable), O.P. 9.14m; Prompt Cnr. P.S. False sprung floor available for Ballet presentation. Direct on stage Get-in facilities. Electrically operated orchestra lift. Tallescope. Orchestra Pit acomm. 25 (average).
LIGHTING: 1 x Strand 530I, 350 Channels. 100 x ETC Sensor 2 Dimmers. FOH Rig: 10 x Strand SL Zooms 18/32°, 10 x Source 4 - 26°, 2 x PAR 64 (CP 62), 2 x Robert Juiliet Cyrano Follow Spots. Stage Rig: 30 x Strand Cantata F, 12 x Strand Alto F, 10 x Source 4 - 26°, 50 x PAR 64, 6 x PAR64 Short Nosed Floor cans, 4 x Iris 4 Cyc Floods.
SOUND EQUIP: Allen & Heath ML 4000 Mixing Desk. PPX 1200 w Amp FoH System, PPX 1600 w Amp FoH System, VS 1100 w Amp Monitors, Altec 9849 Speakers FoH System, 4 x Tannoy Cougar Wedges, 1 x Mini Disc Player, 2 x CD Player, 1 x Twin Cassette Player, 2 x DI Boxes, 4 x S M 5 8 M i c r o p h o n e s, 1 x Shure 839 Cond. Lavalier, 2 x AKG CK8 Shotgun Heads, Various Stands 6 x AKG 747.
STAGE MANAGEMENT: 'Clear Com' Talk Back to all out stations & belt packs. Cue lights to all out stations.
DRESSING ROOMS: 11; Accom. 100; 5 Showers. Large wardrobe room with washing machine and tumble dryer.
MEMBERSHIP: TMA

RIVIERA INTERNATIONAL CONFERENCE CENTRE

Chestnut Avenue, Torquay, Devon TQ2 5LZ
Mgt: 01803 299 992 BO: 01803 206 333
Fax: 01803 206 320
Email: enquiries@rivieracentre.co.uk
Web Site: www.rivieracentre.co.uk
General Manager: Simon Jolly
Seating/Capacity: 2,400 (standing); 1,500 (theatre); 1,100 (cabaret).
Major concert, conference and exhibition venue, one night, summer season, rock and pop, boxing, etc.

THE LITTLE THEATRE

St. Marks Road, Torquay TQ1 2EL
Tel: 01803 299330
Web Site: www.toadslittletheatre.co.uk
Props: Toads Little Theatre Company

TORBAY LEISURE CENTRE

Penwill Way, Paignton, Devon TQ4 5JR
Tel/Fax: 01803 522 240
Email: torbay@parkwood-leisurecentre.co.uk
Web Site: www.leisurecentre.com
ADMINISTRATION:
General Manager: Emma Ibbertson
Policy: Multi-purpose leisure & sports centre with facilities for exhibitions, conferences, sports displays and concerts. Also has an outdoor showground and sports pitches.
Seating/Capacity: 2,400 seated; or 3,000 standing & 400 seated.
Bookings Manager: Tina Lee
TECHNICAL:
Full power and stage available, please apply to venue for further details.

Torrance, Dunbartonshire

CALDWELL HALL

16 Campsie Road,, Torrance, Dunbartonshire G64 4BN Scotland
Tel: 07761 812243

Email: caldwellhalls.org@gmail.com
Web Site: www.caldwellhalls-org.co.uk
ADMINISTRATION:
Props: Caldwell Halls Trust Ltd
Cap: Main Hall 83; Committee Room

TORRANCE COMMUNITY CENTRE

7 School Road, Torrance, East Dunbartonshire G64 4BZ
PCB Tel: 0141 574 5730
Email: halls@eastdunbarton.gov.uk
Web Site: www.eastdunbarton.gov.uk
ADMINISTRATION:
Props: East Dunbartonshire Council
Cap: GP Room 46; Committee Room 25; Workshop 35; Lounge 30; Kitchen 25

Totnes, Devon

TOTNES CIVIC HALL

High Street, Totnes Devon TQ9 5SF
Tel: 01803 862147
Email: office@totnestowncouncil.gov.uk
Web Site: www.totnestowncouncil.gov.uk
ADMINISTRATION:
Props: Totnes Town Council
Cap: 324
General purpose hall.

TOTNES PAVILION

Borough Park Road, Totnes TQ9 5JG
Tel: 01803 862992
Email: k.teague@toneleisure.com
Web Site: www.toneleisure.co.uk
ADMINISTRATION:
Props: Tone Leisure
Cap: 200 with disabled access.
Contact for bookings: Kevin Teague
Adaptable function suite.

Tredegar, Gwent

TREDEGAR LEISURE CENTRE

Stable Lane, Tredegar, Gwent NP2 4BH Wales
Tel: 01495 353 395
Email: ashleyowen@blaenau-gwent.gov.uk
Web Site: www.blaenau-gwent.gov.uk
Admin Officer: Joanne Cooper
Seating/Capacity, Hall: 400

Treorchy, Mid Glamorgan

PARK AND DARE THEATRE

Station Road, Treorchy, Mid Glamorgan CF42 6NL Wales
BO: 08000 147111 Mgt: 01443 775654
Mgt Fax: 01443 776 922
Email: simon.h.davey@rctcbc.gov.uk
Web Site: www.rct-arts.co.uk
ADMINISTRATION:
Props: Rhondda Cynon Taff County Borough Council
Cap: 660 Fully equipped theatre, also used as a cinema.
For bookings contact Simon Davey, Manager.

Tring, Hertfordshire

VICTORIA HALL

Akeman Street, Tring, Hertfordshire HP23 6AA
Tel: 01442 228951
Web: www.dacorum.gov.uk/victoriahall
ADMINISTRATION:
Props: Dacorum Borough Council
Cap: 200
Local amateur productions, meetings. Two halls and meeting room. Private hire, banquets, community use.

Troon, Ayrshire

TROON CONCERT HALL

South Beach, Ayr Street, Troon, Ayrshire KA10 6EF Scotland
Tel: 01292 612200
Email: Lifelong.Learning@south-ayrshire.gov.uk
Web Site: www.south-ayrshire.gov.uk
ADMINISTRATION:
Props: South Ayrshire Council
Contacts: Karen Hepburn
Seating/Capacity: 400

Trowbridge, Wiltshire

ARC THEATRE TROWBRIDGE

College Road, Trowbridge, Wiltshire BA14 0ES
Tel: 01225 756 211 Fax: 01225 777 148
BO: 01225 756 376
Email: theatre@arctheatre.org.uk
Web Site: www.arctheatre.co.uk
Theatre Manager: Anthony Bruton
Technical Manager: Frank Bradley
Marketing & Admin Officer: Tracey Sullivan
Policy: Small scale touring, theatre, dance, children's performance. Folk and jazz. Emphasis on young people and participatory activity and contemporary dance/theatre.
Two dressing rooms and access to two further changing facilities for larger casts or choruses.
Seats: 150
Rehearsal Studio: 11.5m x 6.5m with fully sprung floor. Fully mirrored down one length. Piano. Simple lighting rig available for use by negotiation.
Theatre: Full floor space with all seating retracted = 14m x 11.5m. End on performance space (capacity 150) = 10m x 7m.
Entire floor space is fully sprung. Black dance floor is available 10m x 7m. Rostra to create a raised stage is available if required all the seating is raked. Front tabs and back cyclorama for end on performance. Piano.
Technical: 96 circuit rig extending throughout the space for fully flexible use of floor space. Dimmable House Lighting. 80 lanterns inc. follow spot and cyc. Battens. LBX Strand desk with Genius software.
Sound: Soundcraft Spirit live 16-4-2 mixer. Sound system includes cassette, CD, DAT and minidisc. 4 x 200W speakers + 2 x foldback/FX speakers.
S.M: 8 way cuing desk with show relay and 5 beltpacks. Facility panels allow for flexible siting of control desks.

CIVIC CENTRE

St Stephen's Place, Trowbridge, Wiltshire BA14 8AH
Tel: 01225 765072
Email: info@trowbridgecivic.co.uk
Web Site: www.trowbridgecivic.co.uk
ADMINISTRATION:
Props: Trowbridge Town Council
Facilities Manager: Karl Buckingham
The Lansdown Hall: Multi Use Stage Area. Full Sound and light gallery, along with use of two dressing rooms.
Cap: 450 Tables, 600 Concerts and shows.
The Council Chamber:
Cap: 100 Tables, 140 Seated.
The Usher Suite:
Cap: 180 Tables, 200 Other events.

Truro, Cornwall

HALL FOR CORNWALL

Lemon Quay, Truro, Cornwall TR1 2LL
SD: 01872 262 465 BO: 01872 262 466
Fax: 01872 260 246
Email: boxoffice@hallforcornwall.org.uk
Web Site: www.hallforcornwall.co.uk
Hall for Cornwall was opened in 1997. It is a multi-purpose performance venue with five auditorium formats. It is the principal touring venue for Cornwall.
ADMINISTRATION:
Director: Julien Boast
Head of Operations: Simon Crick
Head of Marketing: Lindsey Skinner
Head of Finance: Sara Dauncey
Head of Administration: Dagnija Innus
Head of Education: Michael White
Seating/Capacity:
1,750 comprising of 1,380 standing and 370 seated on balcony.
950 seated with orchestra pit for max.47.
820 seated with extended forestage 560 seated with orchestra pit for max.47. 430 seated with extended forestage.

TECHNICAL:
STAGE: Proscenium Width Variable: 12 - 16 metres. Proscenium Height 6.2 m. Pros to Back Wall 9.4 m. Centre to actor's left wall 16 m. Centre to actor's right wall 13 m. Height to underside of grid 14.8 m. Height to underside of fly galleries 6.5 m. Width between fly galleries 17.5 m. Stage flooring; Ply on 19 mm Timber strip. (painted dark blue) No Rake. Cross over via Basement. Stage Basement; Clear Headroom in trapped area 2.2 m. Orchestra Pit for up to 47, 40 sq. m. Flying; As the Grid is Steel, there is no restriction on the Location of Rigging Points. Flying Height 7.2 m. Double Purchase Counterweights 34 sets fitted. Weight Capacity, per Cradle 350 Kg. Flying Bar lengths adjustable from 17 m. to 20 m. Rigging points. Front of House for Advance Truss. 5 x 500Kg. Complete set of black masking, comprising of 1 x set of full black tabs, 3 x 4mtr deep x 17 m black boarders, 8 x 2m wide x 6 m deep black legs. 1 20 m x 7 m White gauze cyclorama, House tabs, can either be flown or wiped. Assorted weights, braces and sand bags. A Full Merrick Sico Crowd Control Barrier Rostra; 8 x 4 Steel Deck Units, Quantity of. Various Height Legs. Access Equipment: 1 x Tallescope, max. reach 7.5 m. 1 x Large A Frame 4.5 m. 1 x Medium A Frame 3.0 m. 1 x Small A Frame 1.5 m. Get-In: ALL at stage level via Street Level Doors. Maximum width 2.5 metres. Maximum height 2.5 metres.
LIGHTING: ETC Impression 2X. 300 DMX control channels. 999 groups and 999 cues; 48 Sub Masters over 2 pages. ETC Remote Focus Unit. 10 way control Panel for Non Dim Circuits. Dimmers; Situated Stage Left Fly Floor, Zero 88 LTC, 116 x 2.5 KW. Zero 88 LTC 14 x 5.0 KW. House lights have an AMX link to the Lighting Desk. House Lights 8 x 2.5 KW; House Lights 4 x 5.0 KW. Luminaires; All Front of House Luminaires, On Stage Lamp Ladders and Flood Bar are permenantly rigged. Bridge 1; 16 x Thomas Par Cans, (CP 60's); 4 x Teatro 18 / 31 degree; 1.2Kw Profile. Setting Line to Below Bridge 1 5.5 m. Throw from Bridge 1 to Setting Line 9.8 m. Bridge 2; 12 x Teatro 11 / 26 degree; 1.2Kw Profile; 8 x Teatro 18 / 31 degree. 1.2Kw Profile; 6 x Teatro 18 / 31 degree 2.5Kw Profile; Setting Line to Below Bridge 2 10.0 m. Throw from Bridge 2 to Setting Line 13.5 m. Bridge 3; Setting Line to Below Bridge 3 15.3 m. Throw from Bridge 3 to Setting Line 17.6 m. Juliet Perches: Perch 1: 4 x Thomas Par Cans (CP 60's) with Top Hats. Height from Floor to Perch 7.3 m. Throw from Perch to Centre Setting Line 15.0 m. Perch 2: 3 x Thomas Par Can (CP 60's). Height from Floor to Perch 4.5 m. Throw from Perch to Centre Setting Line 14.07 m. Perch 3: 2 x Thomas Par Cans (CP 60's) with Top Hats. Height from Floor to Perch 7.3 m. Throw from Perch to Centre Setting Line 17.87 m. Perch 4: 2 x Thomas Par Cans (CP 60's) with Top Hats. Height from Floor to Perch 4.5 m. Throw from Perch to Centre Setting Line 18.73 m. Pros. Booms; 6 x Thomas, Short Nosed Par Cans (CP 62's). Height from Stage to Top Lamp 6.9 m. Throw to Centre Line 10.3 m. Height from Stage to Bottom Lamp 3.2 m. Throw to Centre Line 8.9 m. Lamp Ladders; 8 Ladders, each consisting of; 4 x Thomas Par Cans, (CP 62's): Height of Top Lamp: 5.9 m. Throw to Centre Line 10.4 m. Height of Bottom Lamp 5.6 m. Throw to Centre Line 10.0 m. Flood Bar; 6 x 4 Compartment 1250 watt, cyclorama floodlights All of the above, lighting equipment is permanently rigged.
SOUND: Acoustics; Being designed as a multi purpose venue, the Hall For Cornwall has a dry acoustic and as such places heavy demand on amplified sound. P.A. System; Taking this into consideration the consultants have designed and installed what is defined as a "sound re-enforcement system." This is aimed at ensuring vocal clarity together with good reproduction of all musical types, and full coverage of the Auditorium. The system comprises of a series of speakers flown off the auditorium lighting bridges, all with the relevant delay times. Together with a pair of speaker mounted on the Pros Booms. PA System ONLY to be used by Venue Sound Technician. Mixing Console; 1 x Crest Century 32 way console frame with; 24 input channels 8 sub groups: Left & Right Mix. also; facility to provide CD and Tape machine remotes. Control Room Monitor System; 2 x Tanoy System 800 speakers mounted on mixer frame. 1 x 2 x 100 w Monitor amplifier. Signal Processing; 1 x Peavy Media Matrix Mini Frame 208, (16 channel) with Monitor, Keyboard & Mouse 3 MM 8840 Digital Interfaces, BOBS: Amplification: 11 x Crest VS 650 Power Amplifiers: 2 x Crest VS 1500 Power Amplifiers: Loudspeaker System; Bridge 1: 10 x Community SLS 920 Loudspeaker & Hanging Frame. Bridge 3: 5 x Community SLS 920 Loudspeaker & Hanging Frame. Bridge 4: 2 x Community SLS 915 Loudspeaker & Hanging Frame: 4 x JBL Control 1's. Pros Right: 2 x Community SLS 920 Loudspeaker & Hanging Frame: Pros Left: 2 x Community SLS 920 Loudspeaker & Hanging Frame. Juliet Perches: 2 x Community CSX 40 ST Sub Base Cabinets. Left & Right Auditorium, Lower Front Perches. OutBoard Equipment; 1 x EMO Rack Light. 2 x Tascam 112 Mk II Tape Machines. 1 x Tascam CD401 Mk II CD Player. 1 x Yamaha SPX 990 FX Processor. 1 x Symetrix 533E Graphic Equaliser. 1 x Dennon DN M1050 R Mini Disk Pro Recorder / Player.
STAGE COMMUNICATIONS: SM desk DSR comprising of: cue lights, colour video monitor, 2 ring comms set. FOH and Back stage paging, all back stage & bridge working lights controlled from SM desk, bells and buzzers for audience and staff calls. Two ring intercom comprising of: 12 metro audio dual circuit belt packs and 12 metro audio single earpiece headsets. Additional communication comprising of 2 channel infra red system, performance telephone system, 6 channel MATV/CATV system, Patching system and 14 way cue lights patch panel.
BACKSTAGE FACILITIES: Dressing room, 1, at stage level with toilet; dressing room, 1, at Mezzanine level with a shower and toilet. Dressing rooms, 2 with a shower and 1 without on the first floor. Orchestra Pit: accommodates 47 musicians. 42 RAT music stands and 1 RAT lit Conductors Stand. 1 Steinway Concert Grand, tuned to A440 and 1 Yamaha Upright.

TRURO COLLEGE

College Road, Truro, Cornwall TR1 3XX
Tel: 01872 267000
Email: Helenward@trurocollege.ac.uk
Web Site: www.truro-penwith.ac.uk
ADMINISTRATION:
Drama Studio: 200 + 2 lecture theatres (200 and 180)
Bookings and lettings: Helen Ward

Tullibody, Clackmannanshire

TULLIBODY CIVIC CENTRE

Abercromby Place, Tullibody, Clackmannanshire FK10 2RS
Tel/Fax: 01259 211791
Email: info@clacksleisure.co.uk
Web Site: www.clacksleisure.co.uk
ADMINISTRATION:
Props: Clackmannanshire Council
Main Hall: 180, Conference Gallery: 30, Function Hall: 120
Kitchen Available.
For bookings Tel: 01259 213131 Fax: 01259 721313

Tunbridge Wells, Kent

Pop. 96,500. London 37 miles.
Newspapers: Kent & Sussex Courier (fri).
STD code 01892

ASSEMBLY HALL THEATRE

Crescent Road, Tunbridge Wells, Kent TN1 2LU
Mgt: 01892 554162 BO: 01892 530613/532072 Tech Man: 01892 554035 Fax: 01892 525203
Email: Brian.McAteer@tunbridgewells.gov.uk
Web Site: www.assemblyhalltheatre.co.uk
ADMINISTRATION:

Tunbridge Wells Borough Council
General Manager: Brian McAteer
Programming: Brian McAteer & Sharon Barnes
Operations Manager: Dawn Gabriel
Technical Manager: Mikey Powell
Box Office Manager: Lauren Stewart
Marketing Manager: Cheri Strudwick
Policy: Multi-purpose hall. Repertory, pantomime, concerts, plays, exhibitions, dances, dinners, meetings, musicals, drama festivals, etc.
Perfs: 300 per annum
Capacity: 980 Seated; 700 standing.
Bar and Buffet.
Olivier Theatre
Stage: Open stage. Thrust format, No rake - revolving stage with integral stage elevators, backstage and understage crossovers. Height of grid 26.4m. 127 computer controlled electric hoists at 0.5m centres, 200kg per hoist - maximum fly height 11m. Get-in via scenery lift 6.7m x 3.8m x 6m. Plans and elevations available.
Lighting:
Strand 500 board with extensive repertoire lighting rig, some moving lights available.
Sound:
Cadac desk, computer assisted J console, operated from rear of auditorium in control box - 48 inputs, 12 subgroups, 12 main groups - Tannoy, D&B and meyer speakers and amps - Sennheiser radio mic system - Siap acoustic enhancement system.
Stage Management:
Extensive comms, Clearcom Matrix system and Clearcom radio communication system.
Backstage:
Dressing rooms, accommodate approx 50 - laundry and wardrobe facilities.
Canteen and staff bar.

Lyttelton Theatre
Proscenium arch. performing area 18m x 15m - pros opening 13.6 - 10.4m x 5-9m. Stage can be raked - floor hardboard on gurjun, suitable for dance, backstage and understage crossovers. Height to grid 23.6m - 73 counterweight sets, single purchase, 0.2m apart - 500kg permitted on bars - maximum flying height 23m. Main elevator 13.6m x 12m - orchestra pit on 3 elevators, 4.5m x 1.6m. Main stage has integrated revolve, 11.5m diameter. Get-in via dick door at street level. Plans and elevation available.
Lighting:
Strand 500 control system with extensive repertoire lighting rig and some moving lights
Sound:
Cadac Concert Series Desk, operated from rear of stalls (window opens) - EV speaker system - cueing at rear of stalls.
Backstage - as Olivier Theatre

Cottesloe Theatre
Flixible courtyard theatre. Performing area up to 9.9m x 19m, wing widths 2.5m SR/SL. Floor can be raked - floor hardboard on gurjun strip, partially suitable for dance. 12 motorised flying bars - 125kg permited on bars - maximum flying height 7.59m - black soft and hard masking - white filled cloth cyclorama. 5 trap apertures in stage end. Get-in via dock door 1.5m above stagewith door aperture 1.3m x 3m. Plans and elevation available
Lighting - as Lyttelton Theatre
Backstage - as Olivier Theatre - band room
Communications: Clearcom - Both wired and wireless
For the disabled: 3 wheelchair spaces in the Olivier, 4 in the Lyttelton, 2 in the Cottesloe - lift to mezzanine restaurant - infra-red audio system - audio - described/captioned and signed performances - assistance available, contact Lyttelton Information Desk.

Tunstall, Staffordshire

TUNSTALL ASSEMBLY HALL
High Street, Tunstall, Staffordshire
Tel: 01782 834 150
Email: julie@juliebennett0.warnedoo.co.uk
ADMINISTRATION:
Props: Stoke on Trent City Council
Capacity: 200

Twickenham, Middlesex

THE LIVE ROOM
Twickenham Stadium Rugby House
Rugby Road Twickenham TW2 7BA
Tel: 020 8831 7986 020 8831 7816
Email: kirstencoleman@rfu.com
Web Site: www.twickenhamexperience.com
The live music and entertainment venue at Twickenham Stadium. Flexible seated and standing capacities to 550.
Contact: Kirsten Coleman

Ulverston, Cumbria

Pop. 13,500. London 270 miles.
Newspapers: Advertiser (thurs); Evening Mail (dly). STD code 01229

CORONATION HALL THEATRE
County Square, Ulverston, Cumbria LA12 7LZ
BO: 01229 587 140 General Enquiries: 01229 588 994
Email: corohall@southlakeland.gov.uk
Web Site: www.corohall.co.uk
ADMINISTRATION:
Props: South Lakeland D.C.
Policy: All types of Stage Performance including Tours, Repertory, Drama, Dance, Opera, Light Entertainment, Comedy, Concerts, etc; also Dances, Conferences etc.
Seats: 636.
We are interested in joint promotions.
TECHNICAL:
Stage: Proscenium, Raked (overall width 16.46m; Pros. opening 8.53m; depth 8.53m)
Lighting: Switchboard: Spots, Limes, etc.
Sound Equip: Microphones and Amplifications systems.
Dressing Rooms 5; Orchestra Front.

Upminster, Essex

NEW WINDMILL HALL
St Mary's Lane, Upminster, Essex RM14 2QH
Tel: 01708 220 242 Fax: 01708 433859
Email: newwindmill@hotmail.co.uk
Web Site: www.nwhall.org.uk
ADMINISTRATION:
Props: London Borough of Havering
S/Cap: 250
For bookings contact Jane Barnford.
Dancing, concerts, variety shows, stage plays, etc. Multi-use stage facilities, FOH spots. Dressing room accommodation.

Uppingham, Rutland

Pop. 3,067. London 89 miles. STD code 01572

UPPINGHAM THEATRE
32 Stockerston Road, Uppingham, Rutland, Leicestershire LE15 9UD
Box Office: 01572 820820
Email: theatre@uppingham.co.uk
Web Site: www.uppinghamtheatre.co.uk
ADMINISTRATION:
Props: The Trustees of Uppingham School
Director of Drama: Clare Rayner
Policy: Tours, local school and amateur prods.
Perfs: 7.30 (no matinees usually), variable.
Seats: 296, Bar and occasional buffets.
TECHNICAL:
Stage: Proscenium arch/performing area 12.2m x 9.75m. Proscenium opening 12.2m x 4.75m. Lift and trap DSC. Forestage 1.22m deep. Orchestra pit 3.05m deep, 9.14m wide, 2.28m height, accommodates 30. Get-in via SR exit - dock doors 3.05m x 6.0m. Tallescope.
Lighting:ETC Express Board 80 Circuits. operated from LX box at back of auditorium.
24 spots, 24 fresnels. Follow spots oper-

ated from LX box or back gantry.
Sound: Teac mixer 8 into 2, CD & Mini Disk, 2 x FOH speakers, 2 x movable ROH speakers. Cassette and CD, operated from LX box . Acoustics suitable for music and spoken word.
Dressing rooms: 3. Rehearsal piano fair.

Wakefield, West Yorkshire

Pop. 300,000. London 200 miles.
Newspapers: Yorkshire Post (dly); Evening Post (dly); Wakefield Express (fri).
STD code 01924

THEATRE ROYAL WAKEFIELD

Drury Lane, Wakefield, West Yorkshire WF1 2TE
Admin: 01924 215 531 BO: 01924 211 311 Minicom: 01924 215 522 Fax: 01924 215 525
Email: mail@theatreroyalwakefield.co.uk
Web: www.theatreroyalwakefield.co.uk
ADMINISTRATION:
Props: Wakefield Theatre Trust
Executive Director: Murray Edwards
Production Manager: Gareth Williams
Seats: 499
Policy: Professional touring, pantomime, amateur work, community and outreach projects. Guarantees, fees and Box Office splits.
TECHNICAL:
Stage: Proscenium arch. Performing area 9.14m x 7.92m - pros opening 7.26m x 4.27m to pelmet. Wing widths, 1.7m S/R, 1.3m S/L. Stage raked, 1 in 30 - floor wood, suitable for some dance, heated stage.
Height of grid 11 .53m U/S, 11.89m D/S. 20 double purchase counterweight flying sets. Black masking, legs and borders - white cyclorama.
TWO traps, 1 C/S with lift, 1 D/S/L no lift. Apron depth 1.22m, extension available, 1.82m to cover orchestra pit 9.14m x 2.44m, accommodates 16.
Get in via rear of theatre through scene dock, roller shutter doors - 3.96m x 2.44m. Tallescope, safety curtain. Scale stage, fly and lighting plans available.
Lighting: Strand 430 board, 96 circuits @ 2.5Kw, 9 circuits @ 5Kw, operated from gallery control room. 200A 3 phase supply available for temporary lighting, 63A single phase supply available for sound. 28 spots, 36 fresnels, 8 floods, 4 Pcs, 36 pars, Strand and Thomas. 2 x CCT 1.2 msr followspots operated from gallery.
Sound: Soundcraft K3 desk, operated from rear of stalls, Spirit folio operated from gallery control room. Renkus Heinz speakers, good stock of AKG and Sure mics and stands. Acoustics suitable for music and spoken word.
Stage management: Prompt corner S/R, intercom 6 outstations, show relay and tannoy to dressing rooms.
Backstage: 5 dressing rooms, access by stage level and stairs. Green room/wardrobe area with washing machine, dryer, iron and board.Tea and coffee making facilities available.
Rehearsal: Upright piano, Yamaha studio grand.

TOWN HALL

Marketplace, Ossett, Wakefield, West Yorkshire WF5 8BE
Tel: 01924 305830
Email: eventsandfunctions@wakefield.gov.uk
Web Site: www.wakefield.gov.uk
ADMINISTRATION:
Props: Wakefield Metropolitan District Council
Cap: 500
Contact for bookings: Events and Functions Team

Wallasey, Wirral

GROSVENOR BALLROOM

Assembly Rooms Grosvenor Street, Wallasey, Wirral CH44 1AQ
Tel: 0151 637 1341
Email: lcfc@liscard.fsbusiness.co.uk
Web Site: www.grosvenorballroom.co.uk
ADMINISTRATION:
Props: Wirral Metropolitan Borough Council
Cap: 300
Theatre, Dancing, Meetings, Bingo, etc.
Reasonable Rates
Well-preserved, original 1950's Ballroom. The Beatles performed here on many occasions. Available for location work. e.g. already used for John Lennon Documentary by BBC and film work by NBC.
For bookings contact Tony Whelligan or Kim Lovell

Wallingford, Oxfordshire

CASTLE LEISURE CENTRE

St George's Road, Wallingford, Oxfordshire OX10 8LP
Tel: 01491 839 755
Email: castle@soll-leisure.co.uk
Web Site: www.soll-leisure.co.uk
ADMINISTRATION:
Props: South Oxfordshire Leisure Ltd
For bookings contact Manager
Tel: 01491 839755 Fax: 01491 835593

CORN EXCHANGE

Market Place, Wallingford, Oxfordshire OX10 0EG
BO: 01491 825 000
Email: warburtons@talk21.com
Web Site: www.cornexchange.org.uk
ADMINISTRATION
Bookings Manager: John Warburton (01491 832 878)
Presents live theatre by the Sinodun Players Ltd and hired in companies. The venue is also available for hire. Also presents commercial cinema.
Steeply tiered seats with very good sight lines.
Capacity: 176
FOH facilities, including Bar. Access (only) for 2 wheelchairs by arrangement.
Backstage dressing rooms and rehearsal rooms.
Box office hours: Fri&Sat 10am to 2.00pm & evenings from 7-8pm
Postal bookings accepted for Theatre.
TECHNICAL
Stage: 25' square total: practical working area: 2o' x 20' x 14' high. Limited flying capability.
Full lighting & sound inventory. Yamaha U3 upright piano. Induction loop for cinema.

Walsall, West Midlands

BOOKMARK BLOXWICH

Elmore Row, Bloxwich, Walsall, West Midlands WS3 2HR
BO/Bkg: 01922 655900 Mob: 07973 492387
Email: bruno.edwards@gmail.com
Web Site: www.walsall.gov.uk/walsalllive
ADMINISTRATION:
Props: Walsall Metropolitan Borough Council
Cap: 150
Theatre Manager: Bruno Edwards
Fully equipped theatre, raised auditorium seating & kitchen facilities.

Walton-on-Thames, Surrey

THE CECIL HEPWORTH PLAYHOUSE

Hurst Grove, Walton-on-Thames, Surrey KT12 1AU
Tel: 01932 254750
Email: elmbridgehalls@pspleisure.org
Web Site: www.placesforpeopleleisure.org
ADMINISTRATION:
Props: PSP Leisure
Cap: Standing 250, Seated 180.

Wantage, Oxfordshire

CIVIC HALL
Portway, Wantage, Oxfordshire OX12 9BX
Tel: 01235 763 456
Email: beacon.wantage@whitehorsedc.gov.uk
Web Site: www.beaconwantage.co.uk
ADMINISTRATION:
Props: Vale of White Horse District Council
Cap: 350
Contact Duty Officer

Warminster, Wiltshire

WARMINSTER CIVIC CENTRE
Sanbourne Road, Warminster, Wiltshire BA12 8LB
Tel: 01985 214847
Email: admin@warminster-tc.gov.uk
Web Site: www.warminster.uk.com
ADMINISTRATION:
Props: Warminster Town Council
Cap: 240 tables, Standing 600 (Different Rooms)
Contact: Ann Hedges

Warrington, Lancashire

PYRAMID AND PARR HALL
Palmyra Square South, Warrington Cheshire WA1 1BL
Admin: 01925 442 368 BO: 01925 442 345 Fax: 01925 443 228
Email: lmackie@culturewarrington.org
Web Site: www.pyramidparrhall.com
ADMINISTRATION:
Venue and Events Managers: Christian Persoglio
Events Officers: Emma Joyce, Laura Mackie and Jennifer Burgess
Administration Manager: Karen Pickazant
Capacity: Parr Hall - Standing:1,100, Seated: 1,000
Pyramid Arts Centre - Studio: 220 seated, Exhibition Hall: 240 max dependent on layout, plus additional smaller spaces

THE ROSE CENTRE (LOWTON CIVIC HALL)
Hesketh Meadow Lane, Lowton, Warrington, Cheshire WA3 2AH
Tel: 01942 610912
Email: lowton@roseleisure.com
Web Site: www.roseleisure.com
ADMINISTRATION:
Props: Rose Leisure
Bookings Officer: Jill 01942 256903
Cap: Main Hall 400, Small Hall 200

Warwick, Warwickshire

PLAYBOX THEATRE COMPANY
The Dream Factory, Tapping Way
Warwick CV34 6LE
Tel: 01926 419 555
Email: info@playboxtheatre.com
Web Site: www.playboxtheatre.com
ADMINISTRATION:
Principal Administrator: Nikki Cross
In April 1999 Playbox Theatre moved into a custom designed creation centre in Warwick. A conception of Playbox with Glenn Howells Architects (UK) and Sceno Plus (Montreal) a national focus for the performing arts and young people, housing productions, workshops, special projects, visiting companies, from UK and overseas. A theatre exclusively for young people.
Cap: Theatre, 250.
TECHNICAL:
STAGE: Dimensions: 16.8m x 12.6m from gantry to gantry, 17.6m x 15m from wall to wall. Floor: Semi-sprung floor which can be painted and used as a fixing point. Rigging: Limited circus rigging points available subject to discussion.
LIGHTING: Fixtures; 6 off Strand Alto F with Barn Doors (2500W), 36 off Strand Cantata F with Barn Doors (1200W), 20 off Strand Quartet F with Barn Doors (650W), 37 off Strand Brio 18/30 Profile (600W), 6 off Coda 500/3, 6 off Coda 1000, 8 off Parcan (CP61), 16 off Parcan (CP62), 3 off Floor Can (CP62), 4 off ETC Source 4 Pars, 6 off Strand SL 23/50 Profile (600W), 1 off Cantata 18/32 Profile (1200W), 12 off Strand Quartet F with Barn Doors (650W) (Not normally available in Kermesse). Control Equipment; 3 off Strand LD 90 dimmers (72 channels). These are hard wired to 58 outlets above trampoline and 14 below the catwalk. 2 off Act6+ 6x10A Dimmer Racks (Not normally available in Kermesse), 1 off ParaDim 6x10A Dimmer Rack, 1 off Strand LBX desk with monitor and riggers remote control (125 channels), 2 off 6way Single Preset manual Desk (Not normally available in Kermesse), 1 off DMX patch field allows operation of desk from control room or FOH, 1 off DMX splitter/buffer provides DMX to dimmers, stage and trampoline, 1 off LxDesigner PC based lighting design CAD system.
SPECIAL EFFECTS: 1 off Jem Stage Smoke Machine (Manual Control), 1 off Jem Stage Hazer (DMX Control), 2 off Antri Low Fog Machines (DMX Control), 2 off High End Data Strobes, 2 off Spotlight UV Cannons, Various Mirror Balls (No rotators).
SOUND: Main Desk; 1 off Soundcraft K1 24 Channel Desk normally operated from control room, 1 off Denon CD Player, 1 off Sony Mini Disk Player, 2 off Denon Cassette Deck, 1 off Rane graphic equaliser (Main Speakers), 1 off Rane graphic equaliser (Monitor Speakers).
STAGE COMMUNICATIONS: 1 off Tecpro Twin Ring System, 1 off Master Station, 10 off Single Channel Belt Packs, 6 off Single Muff Headsets, 4 off Dual Muff Headsets, 4 off Loudspeaker Stations.

Washinton, Tyne and Wear

WASHINGTON LEISURE CENTRE
Town Centre District 1, Washington, Tyne & Wear NE38 7SS
Tel: 0191 219 3400 Fax: 0191 219 3424
Email: craig.jobson@sunderland.gov.uk
Web Site: www.sunderland.gov.uk/leisure
ADMINISTRATION:
Props: Sunderland City Council
General Manager: Craig Jobson
Cap: Main Hall: 1000
Groups Manager: Alison O'Neill
alison.o'neill@sunderland.gov.uk

Waterford, Co Waterford

THEATRE ROYAL
The Mall Waterford Eire
Admin: 00 353 51 853626 BO: 00 353 51 874402
Email: admin@theatreroyal.ie
Web Site: www.theatreroyal.ie
Director: Ben Barnes
Theatre Manager: Mary Boland
Marketing Manager: Oren Little

Watford, Hertfordshire
Pop.77,690. London 17 miles.
Newspapers: Watford Observer (fri). STD code 01923

THE COLOSSEUM
Rickmansworth Road, Watford, Hertfordshire WD17 3JN
Mgt: 01923 474100 BO: 0845 0753 993
Email: info@watfordcolosseum.co.uk
Web Site: www.watfordcolosseum.co.uk
ADMINISTRATION:
Props: HQ Theatres Ltd.
Venue Director: Tim Brinkman
Buildings and Technical Manager: Mike Christofi
Capacity: Seated 1392 (retractable tiered seating on flat floor plus fixed seating in balcony). Standing 2000

Restaurant 106 covers, 200 Unseated. 3 bars, 2 mobile bars, banqueting for up to 600 people using flat floor of main auditorium, 1000 reception. Able to cater for weddings, receptions and conferences.
Foyer passenger lift.
TECHNICAL:
STAGE: Width 49ft, Depth 31.5ft; Height 4.6ft; Disabled platform lift from hall floor to stage. Goods platform lift 8ft x 8ft from stage level/floor level/under stage.
DRESSING ROOMS: Ground Floor: 4 inc Star Dressing Room with ensuite; First Floor: 2 bandrooms.
House tab. No fire curtain. Lighting trusses positioned above stage and throughout hall ceiling.
LIGHTING and SOUND equipment: See Colosseum website for full details of lighting and sound equipment.
Compton Organ - 3 manuals, 16 ranks
Get-in at tailgate to floor level with parking for one trailer and cab.

WATFORD PALACE THEATRE

Clarendon Road, Watford Hertfordshire
WD17 1JZ
BO: 01923 225 671 Mgt: 01923 235 455
Email: enquiries@watfordpalacetheatre.co.uk
Web: www.watfordpalacetheatre.co.uk
ADMINISTRATION:
Lessees: Palace Theatre Watford Ltd
Artistic Director: Brigid Larmour
Policy: 4 weekly Repertory.
Perfs: 7.45pm evenings, Weds & Sat matinees 2.30/3pm
Seats: 607. Bar and café (food available 9.30am-3pm only).
TECHNICAL:
Stage: Proscenium Arch & flat wooden stage floor 0.9m above auditorium floor.
Pros. Opening: 8.3m (w) x 5.4m(h).
Depth of S/Line to back wall: 8.4m plus 0.9 curved forestage.
Crossover corridor behind back wall.
Wingspace: SL 3.1m, SR 2.6m
Orchestra pit: approx 9m x 2m (curved front) 0.3m below auditorium floor
Grid height: 15m. 21 x 10m
Counterweight bars (incl. House Tabs); 19 Hemp sets.
Lighting: 96 ways of dimming, Strand 520i lighting desk
Sound Equip: Allen & Heath ML 5000 48/8/3 & Yamaha 01V sound desks, Pa with d&b FoH speakers
Stage Management desk located SL or SR behind pros.
Dressing Rooms 6; Accom. 20; Orchestra Pit 15.
Membership: TMA

Wellingborough, Northamptonshire

Pop, 68,500 London 70 Miles.
Newpapers: Evening Telegraph (Daily), Citizen (Thur), Northampton Chronicle & Echo (Daily), herald and Post (Thur), TV Advertiser (Wed) STD Code: 01933

SILK VENUE

27 Midland Road, Wellingborough, Northamptonshire NN8 1HF
Tel: 01933 229 417
Email: info@silkwellingborough.co.uk
Web Site: www.silkwellingborough.co.uk
Manager: Billy Druce
Capacity: 350

THE CASTLE

Castle Way, Wellingborough, Northamptonshire NN8 1XA
Mgt: 01933 229 022 BO: 01933 270 007
Fax: 01933 229 888
Email: darren@thecastle.org.uk
Web Site: www.thecastle.org.uk
ADMINISTRATION:
The Castle (Wellingborough) Ltd
Administrator: Phillip Money
Director: Darren Walter
POLICY: The Castle provides a vibrant mixture of 70% professional touring music, dance, drama, film and comedy and an in-house Christmas production. The remaining 30% are hires by local societies and community groups.
Seats: Main Auditorium 501, Studio Theatre 84 (raked seating) - 100 (cabaret seating/standing)
Fully licensed bar & brasserie, exhibition space, art gallery, function rooms including conference facilities, craft workshop.
TECHNICAL:
Main Auditorium: Proscenium stage, flat, country maple flooring (Harlequin dance floor available): Pros. opening 9.72m - 11.88m; Pros. height 5.49m - 6.45m; Depth of S/Line 10.5m - 13.5m with thrust, stage width 20m, Height of Grid 15m; to fly floor 7.5m; 28 C/W Bars & 6 Hemp, 2 tab tracks; Prompt Desk DSL; Backstage or Understage Crossover; Auditorium capable of flat floor format for exhibitions, conferences and dances, full catering and bar facilities on site.
Orchestra Pit (12m x 3m) accommodates 25.
Lighting: Control: Strand 520i in Control Room at Rear of Stalls + Riggers Control; 3 on stage LX Bars + 3 ladders P.S. & O.P.; 3 x FOH Bridges & 2 x FOH Booms each side. Lanterns available: 22 x 2.5kW 14/32 Alto Profiles; 24 x 1.2kW Cantata PC's; 8 x 1.2kW Cantata Fresnels; 36 x 1.2kW Cantata 11/26 Profiles; 5 x 1.5kW Iris 4 cyc battens; 8 x 2kW Cadenza PC PALS lanterns; 2 x 1kW Solo CSI Followspots. Dimmers: 112 x 2.5kW & 8 x 5kW; 18 non-dimming independent channels (16A).
Sound: Soundcraft Spiritlive 16 channel mixer; PA's: 2C-Audio RA1001 & 1 C-Audio SR 707; Speakers flown in central cluster in front of prosc. arch - 2 Community PC264, 1 Community LF212 & 1 JBL2445 & stereo pair (Community) auditorium left & right; 4 full range monitor wedges, 6 stage LS outputs, 24 stage mic inputs, 1 Revox B77 MkII 7.5 & 15 i.p.s. + remote; 2 Denon cassette desks, 1 Marantz CD player, Yamaha SPX 990 multi effects processor, 1 Denon Minidisc player.
Facilities: 2 x 63A single phase and 1 x 32A single phase located in workshop 15m from SL.
Dressing Rooms: Accommodate 64 total, 2 Ground Level with Toilets & Showers; 5 Basement with shared Toilets & Showers; 2 Green Rooms (smoking & non-smoking); Full washing & drying facilities.
Cinema: Flown screen with Integral Dolby Sound System JBL; 16mm & 35mm projectors located in projection room at rear of balcony.
Car Parking: 120 space car park + overspill multi-storey.

STUDIO THEATRE
Multi purpose space available in theatre format 84 seats (chairs on retractable seating unit in raked format); Performance area 8m x 7.5m; cabaret format 112-120 seats or clear space. Beech floor (no rake). No floor coverings available.
Masking: Full set of soft blacks at each end of room, 2 side masking flats.
Lighting: Strand LX 24 Channel 2-way preset desk; 4 x Act 6 dimmers; selection of
Strand quarter - 500W profiles, fresnels etc. Fixed grid covering whole area (approx. 5m from floor).
Sound: Soundcraft Spirit Power Station: 10 mic channels, 2 L&R; QSC Audio USA 850 Amplifier (2 monitor mix) 2 EV SX 200 full range speakers and stands. Mics, playback equipment, monitors available on request.
Facilities: 2 x Dressing Rooms accommodating 12 people; Male & Female toilets.

TITHE BARN

Tithe Barn Road, Wellingborough, Northamptonshire NN8 1HR
Tel: 01933 234 520 Fax: 01933 231 684
Email: jayne.draper@ncsgrp.co.uk
Web Site: www.wellingborough.gov.uk
ADMINISTRATION:
Props: Wellingborough Council
Cap: 200, Stage facilities
For bookings contact: Jayne Draper

Wellington, Somerset

Pop. 14,000. Taunton: 7 miles, Exeter 25 miles. STD Code: 01823

THE WELLESLEY THEATRE

50 Mantle Street, Wellington, Somerset
TA21 8AU
Tel: 01823 666668 Fax: 01823 666880
Email: wellesleycinema@gmail.com
Web Site: www.wellesleycinema.co.uk
ADMINISTRATION
Props: Reel Cinemas
General Manager: Anthony Haywood
Technical Manager: Matthew Redstone

Marketing Manager: Anthony Haywood
Capacity: 400(250 - stalls; 150 - circle)
Policy: Mixed programmes, inc. amateur productions, visiting professional shows, one nighters and regular cinema shows. The Wellesley was built in 1937, it was refurbished in 1991 to original 1930's style and is equipped for cinema, theatre and other uses. Bar in circle, Monthly Comedy Night
TECHNICAL
Stage: pros. arch with apron. Performing width without masking: 7.70m.
Performing depth: front of apron to back wall: 6.00m; house tabs (festoon) to back wall: 3.70m; gold tabs (motorised) to back wall: 2.00m. Opening: Width 7.70m; Height 4.80m. Wing widths SR: 1.30m plus 3.10m into scene dock; SL: 1.20m.
Floor: Boarded painted matt black suitable for dance but not barefoot.
Removable Black carpeting available. No rake. Height to grid: 7.90m. Flying: 8 single hemp sets at 0.15m centres. Max. weight on bars: 150kg. Tab track: Gold tabs (motorised op SR) 1.30m upstage of house tabs. Blue tabs (manual op SL) 3.00m upstage of house tabs. Flying height: 3.00m; masking 2 sets black borders and legs. Cyclorama: Painted wall with black backcloth. Prompt corner: SR adjacent to scene dock. Stage relay: Relay mic and announcement mic outputs relayed to both dressing rooms and general purpose/green room area. Quick change: Space available adjacent to prompt corner. Forestage: 2 sets of steps available. Orchestra Pit: None but musicians usually sited in wide space in front of stage.
Dressing Room 1: Area 122 sq ft, 2 wash basins and Heatrae electric water heater. Make-up lighting and mirrors. Stage relay speaker. Carpeted. Fire Escape. Dressing Room 2: Are 138sq ft. 2 with hand basins and Heatrae water heater. En-suite WC. BT telephone point. Full width hanging rail. Make up lighting and mirrors. Stage relay speaker. Carpeted. Fire Escape.
Green Room/Dressing Room 3: Area 340 sq ft. Hanging rail units and shelving. Carpeted. Stage relay speaker and video monitoring cabling.
Male Cloakroom: High level WC.
Scenery Store: Area 380 sq ft. Double height space with paint frame. Stage management desk and storage. BT telephone point. Fire Escape.
PLEASE NOTE: This information is for guidance only. Visiting companies should satisfy themselves that the theatre meets the physical requirements of their production.

Welwyn Garden City, Hertordshire

Pop. 47,000. London 23 miles.
Newspapers: Welwyn Times (wed); Review (thurs). STD code 01707

THE HAWTHORNE THEATRE

The Campus Welwyn Garden City, Hertfordshire AL8 6BX
Mgt: 01707 357172 BO: 0300 3039 620
Email: m.woolman@welhat.gov.uk
Web Site: www.hawthornetheatre.co.uk
ADMINISTRATION:
Props: Welwyn Hatfield Council
General Manager: Mark Woolman
Technical Manager: Julian Brooks
Marketing & Business Development Manager:Gavin Davies
Policy: Small Scale Drama, Concerts, Ballet, Variety, Film etc.
Capacity 364
TECHNICAL:
The Hawthorne Auditorium
Seats: 326
Stage: Proscenium. Flat; Pros. Opening 10.34m; Ht. of Pros. 4.96m; Depth of S/Line 7.72m; Ht. of Grid 12.19m; 22 lines, 19 C/W, 1 Hemp, 1 pile line, 1 hoist
Lighting: Strand 530i 350/350 channels - 144 circuits - 30 x Parcans - 40 x Fresnels - 40 x Profiles - Follow Spots
Sound : The House System comprises of - 4 x D&B T10 Pont Source Orientation - 2 x D&B E15 Subs - 2 x D&B D6 Amplifiers - 1 x Yamaha LS916 Channel - 2 x Yamaha 2208 monitors
Dressing Rooms: 5, all with show relay monitor and paging systems
Orchestra Pit for up to 20 musicians with RAT music stands
Full Box Office facilities: Patron Edge and Patron Edge Online.
35mm and 16mm projectors and most av aids for conferences. Video projector available on request.

The Hawthorne Studio
Seats: 100
Suitable for small scale theatre, in the round, jazz blues or folk concerts, recitals All sound and lighting imported from Hawthorne Auditorium by negotiation.

VINEYARD BARN

The Vineyard, Welwyn Garden City, Hertfordshire AL8 7PU
Tel: 01707 357 116 Tel: 01707 357 117
Fax: 01707 357162
Email: cwreservations@welhat.gov.uk
Web Site: www.welhat.gov.uk
ADMINISTRATION:
Props: Welwyn Hatfield Council
Cap: Two halls seating 70 & 50
For bookings contact Community Services Tel: 01707 357150

WOODHALL COMMUNITY CENTRE

Mill Green Road, Welwyn Garden City, Hertfordshire AL7 3XD
Tel: 01707 323 305 Fax: 01707 326 990
Email: jakieaugustus@sdogcareservice.co m.uk
Web Site: www.welhat.gov.uk
ADMINISTRATION:
Props: Welwyn Hatfield Council
Cap: 300
For bookings contact Jackie Augustus
Tel: 01707 357192 Fax: 01707 357162

West Kilbride, Ayrshire

WEST KILBRIDE PUBLIC HALL

1 Arthur Street, West Kilbride, Ayrshire KA23 9EN
Tel: 01294 829 590
Email: Tpark71955@aol.com
ADMINISTRATION:
Props: North Ayrshire Council
Cap: Seated 200; Seated with tables 120
Contact Hall Lettings Secretary: Mrs T Park

West Molesey, Surrey

THE MOLE HALL

Bishop Fox Way, West Molesey, Surrey KT8 2JE
Tel: 01932 254750
Email: elmbridgehalls@dcleisure.co.uk
Web Site: www.dcleisurecentres.co.uk
ADMINISTRATION:
Props: D C Leisure
For bookings contact: Bookings Officer: D C Leisure.
Capacity 250 standing, 180 Seated.

Westacre, Norfolk

WESTACRE THEATRE

River Road, Westacre, Norfolk PE32 1UD
Admin: 01760 755 007
BO: 01760 755 800
Email: admin@westacretheatre.com
Web Site: www.westacretheatre.com
River Studios is a 80 seat studio venue committed to developing opportunities for enjoying, appreciating and participating in the performing arts and to presenting a programme of excellence and diversity.
Performing space: Studio 10m x 10m. Can be used in the round (80 seats approx), or end on (75 seats approx). Lighting grid and lanterns and control sound system.

Westbury, Wiltshire

THE LAVERTON HALL

Bratton Road, Westbury, Wiltshire BA13 3EN
Tel: 01373 822126 Council: 01373

866094
Email: l.bale@westburytowncouncil.gov.uk
Web Site: www.thelaverton.co.uk
ADMINISTRATION:
Props: Westbury Town Council
Cap: 200
Contact: Lilly Bale

Weston-Super-Mare, North Somerset

Pop. 80,000. London 136 miles. Newspapers: Weston Mercury (fri); Weston & Worle News (thur). STD code 01934

THE PLAYHOUSE THEATRE

High Street, Weston-super-Mare, North Somerset BS23 1HP
Mgt: 01934 611 758 BO: 01934 645 544
Email: mark.thompson@parkwood-leisure.co.uk
Web Site: www.theplayhouse.co.uk
ADMINISTRATION:
Props: Parkwood Leisure
General Manager: Mark Thompson
Technical Dept:
Contact: 01934 643574
Policy: Touring, Plays, Pantomime, Ballet, Musical Productions, Drama, Opera, One Night Stands, Summer Season, Films
Perfs: 7.30 (once nightly).
Seats: 664. Licensed Bars, Light Refreshments.
TECHNICAL:
STAGE: Traditional Proscenium Arch; W 9.14m, H 5.49m. Stage Floor; W 11.0m, D 6.55m, Forestage; W 9.14m, D 2.29m. Power: 125-amp 3-phase supply with 1 x 125amp Ceeform socket on USR, 32 amp 1 phase, 2 16 amp Ceeform DSL, 63 amp single phase supply with 1 Ceeform 63amp & 1 Ceeform 32amp & 4 Ceeform 16amp all DSR, 4 16 amp Ceeform USL, 12 16 amp Ceeform sockets Stage right fly floor.
STAGE MANAGEMENT: Headsets Intercom to all areas, Call mic to dressing rooms.
FILM EQUIPMENT; 3 x Kodak SAV2000 Slide projectors, 1 x Westar 2000 35mm Sound Projector one with long runner unit, 1 x Electric Rewind Bench, Lenses to give a maximum projection width of : 13'4" (1.33), 13'9" (for silent film 1.34), 16'8" (1.66), 18'6" (1.85), 23'6" (Anamorphic + 2.35).
LIGHTING: Strand Light Palette VX with 3000 channels and DMX control. Lanterns; 54 x 743's complete with barndoors, 52 x Parcans - various types. CP 62 lamps, 16 x CCT Rockettes CP 61, 8 x Par 64 silver with CP 60, 6 x Floor cans CP 62, 10 x Minuette Fresnels 650 Watt, 6 x 808 profiles 2 Kw permanently rigged FOH, 14 x Cantatas 11/26 permanently rigged FOH, 18 x Cantatas 18/32 permanently rigged FOH, 6 x 243 no Barn doors, 25 x 500 watt Minuette floods. 20 rigged on bar 4 (4 circuits), 7 x Ground rows S63, 5 x Coda's 1Kw(One circuit of cyc), 8 x Multipars 575w, 25 x Strand SL 23/50, 6 x Strand SL 15/32, 8 x 19 degree Source fours (rigged in roof) FOH, 2 x Bars of ACL'S. Projector: 1 x Patt 252 Effects projector with fleecy cloud disc; 1 x Fire disc. Follow Spots: 2 x Solo CID 1Kw. Auto Colour: 3 x Martin Robocolor 400, 4 x Colour Mixers CMY, 2 x Par 64 Colour Mixers RGB. U.V. Lighting: 6 x UV 4ft tubes, 2 x UV cannons 400w. Moving lights: 6 x Martin Mac 250 moving heads, 6 x Show-tec Vipers moving mirrors, 1 x Martin 518 moving mirror, 6 x Martin Mac 500 moving heads, 1 x Martin 1220 moving mirror (in roof). LED Lights: 12 x Par 56 lanterns RGB, 2 x Par 64 1 Watt RGB, 7 x Showtec Orbit II moving washes lights, 2 x 8 light blinders. Data Projector: Sanyo PC56 4500 Lumens (subject to hire)
SOUND: Control: Allen & Heath GL4000 - 40 MIC/Line and 4 Stereo Channel - Multi Function Audio Mixing Console-with 2 8way extensions; Behringer DDX 3216 Digital mixer. PA system: 3KW Turbo Sound Speaker System, 6 Foldback sends. Monitors: 6- 500 watt stage monitors. Equipment: 1 x Effects Unit Yamaha SPX 1000, 1 x Effects Unit Yamaha SPX 900, 1 x Behringer Ultra-curve, 1 x Alesis Midiverb 4, 1 x Yamaha 31 band stereo graphic equalizer (FOH), 1 x Yamaha 31 band stereo graphic equalizer (control box), 3 x Alesis Graphic 2 channel, 1 x Denon CD players, 1 x Single cassette recorder, 1 x Tascam CD/Cassette player, 2 x Minidisc E-11's, 2 x Behringer Multicom, 3 x Behringer Autocom, 1 x LA 4 way gate, 2 x Behringer 31 Band graphic Stereo(FOH), 1 x Yamaha MD8 Recorder. An extensive range of Microphones available.
ADDITIONAL: Pyrotechnics: 6 Standard La Maitre units, 2 Angled La Maitre units. Equipment: 1 Yamaha C3S Boudoir grand piano, 2 Upright Piano Challen (1 permanently in Rehearsal Room), 1 Yamaha iS40 Keyboard.
DISABLED ACCESS: Ramped access into the foyer and a lift to the stalls. Spaces for 4 wheelchair users can be accommodated. Wheelchair users should be accompanied. Dedicated disabled toilets available. Infra-red hearing system can be accessed from all seats. Reserve your receiver when booking tickets. Guide dogs permitted. We also offer audio description of some performances.

WINTER GARDENS PAVILION

Royal Parade, Weston-super-Mare, North Somerset BS23 1AJ
Mgt: 01934 417 117 BO: 01934 645 544
Email: wintergardens@parkwood-leisure.co.uk
Web Site: www.thewintergardens.com
ADMINISTRATION:
Props: Parkwood Leisure

General Manager: Mel Procter
Seating/Capacity: 400
For technical details please contact venue.

Wexford, Eire

Pop. 15,000. Newspapers: New Ross Standard (fri for sat); The People (fri for sat). STD code 00 353 53

WEXFORD OPERA HOUSE

High Street, Wexford Ireland
Mgt: 00 353 53 9122400 BO: 00 353 53 9122144 Mgt Fax: 00 353 53 9124289
Email: info@wexfordopera.com
Web Site: www.wexfordopera.com
ADMINISTRATION:
Props: Wexford Festival Trust
Lessee: Wexford Festival Opera
Artistic Director: David Agler(for Festival)
Chief Executive: David Mcloughlin
Policy: Mainly H.Q. for Wexford Festival Opera
Perfs: 8.00
Seats: 771-855. Canteen and Wine Bar.
TECHNICAL:
Stage: Proscenium Stage, Raked; Pros. opening 6.79m; Ht. of Pros. 5.43m; Depth of S/Line 5.33m; Ht. of Grid 13.72m; 20 lines; Scenery Flying Ht. 6.10m; Flying Bars 10.36m; W/Widths P.S. 1.83m; O.P. 1.83m;
Lighting: Switchboard: Location F.O.H. System; Berkey Colortrack, memory system, 96 ways. Lanterns include, Silhouette 30's, Patt.764's, Patt.264's, Patt.223's, 123's, 23's and 23N's.
Sound: Speakers backstage and F.O.H. and all Dressing Rooms.
Dressing Rooms 10; Accom. 100.
Orchestra Pit 45.

Weymouth, Dorset

Pop. 70,000. London 132 miles. Newspapers: Dorset Evening Echo (ntly). STD code 01305

PAVILION THEATRE

The Esplanade, Weymouth, Dorset DT4 8ED
BO: 01305 783225
Admin: 01305 780 909
Email: info@weymouthpavilion.com
Web Site: www.weymouthpavilion.com
ADMINISTRATION:
Props: Weymouth Pavilion CIC
Theatre Manager: Max Grayson (01305 838 535)
Stage Manager: James Perrett. Contact: 01305 838 500 or jamesperrett@weymouth.gov.uk
Policy: Touring house, policy of star name summer show and panto, one night shows, Concerts (Classical & Modern) - facilties for Conferences and Exhibitions.
Open all year.
Performances: By arrangement.

Facilities, Seating: Theatre 996 (raked), Ocean Room: Up to 500 flat floor), 9,000 sq.ft. exhibition.
TECHNICAL:
THEATRE:
STAGE: Pros Height= 5.29m. Pros Width= 10.73m. Pros to Cyc= 7.98m. Pros to Pit Front= 2.57m. Grid Height= 14.6m. Prompt Corner= Stage Left
FLYING: Counterweight flying system; 30 lines (1-5 double purchase, 6-30 single purchase); 1 x advanced bar downstage of pros (lighting) hand winch operated; Fly floor stage right (7.58m high)
LIGHTING: On stage consists of upstage bar of Iris 1 floods (up to 3 colour wash) and 3/4 bars of Fresnel's (harmony/starlettes), par 64's, and source 4's (26 and 36 degree). Advanced/zero bar consists of 4 Fresnel's and 2 source 4 (26 degree). Pros boom consists of 5 par 64's and 2 teatro 1K Fresnel's per side. Circle front consists of 5-6 par 64's per side. FOH bridge consists of 12 source 4 (19 degree). Box position either side consisting of 6 circuits per side. 6 goldenscan 3's and 6 Mac 250's available subject to condition. Strand 550i Lighting Console. ETC Unison Dimmers. 126 Dimmable Circuits (3K).
FOLLOWSPOTS: 2 x Robert Juliat Korrigan (1200W HMI)
SOUND: Allen & Heath GL4800 32 channel mixing desk; Turbosound FOH and Fold back speakers; MC2 Amplifiers; Multicore run= Stage left (45m approx).
DRESSING ROOMS: 12, accomm 90 approx.

OCEAN ROOM (Ballroom):
LIGHTING: Fat Frog Lighting Desk; 44 Circuits on prewired bars overhead spread across dance floor; 30 Par 56's (20 x 300W, 10 x 500W)
SOUND: Turbosound Speakers; Mackie 16 Channel Mixing Desk; Behringer Amplifiers; CD/DVD/Mini Disc Players.
DRESSING ROOMS: By arrangement

Whitby, Yorkshire

Pop. 12,850. London 243 miles.
Newspapers: Whitby Gazette (fri). STD code 01947

WHITBY PAVILION THEATRE

Whitby Pavilion, West Cliff, Whitby, North Yorkshire YO21 3EN
Mgt: 01723 357 874 BO: 01947 458 899
Email: j.gomez-mannion@sivltd.com
Web Site: www.whitbypavilion.co.uk
ADMINISTRATION:
Props: Sheffield International
Policy: Variety (Summer Season). Available Winter Touring. Also used by amateur groups providing plays, musicals, ballet, pantomime, song tournaments, and arts festivals.
Seats: 489. Theatre Bar, Cafe and full Catering facilities.
TECHNICAL:
Stage: Proscenium, Raked; Pros. Opening 7.92m; Ht. of Pros. 4.42m; Depth of S/Line 6.40m; Ht. of Grid 5.79m; 10 line sets, Hemp; W/Widths P.S. 1.83m - 2.44m, O.P. 1.83m - 2.44m; Prompt Cnr. O.P.
Lighting: Switchboard: Strand LBX C/W Genius 75 software situated F.O.H. 6 x 763s, 8x 264s, 2 x Cantata 18/32, 2 x Cantata 11/26 12 parcan, 1 x Harmony 22/40, 12 x 743s, 6 x Harmony F, 5 x 23s, 5 x 123, 2 x Coda 3 Batten, 2 x Coda, 2 x Nocturne, 2 x Colourwheels, 1 x CSI follow spot.
Sound: Studiomaster 12-2 mixer, 4 x JBL speakers FOH, 2 x A.T. Radio mics available. Digital FX processor, foldback system, 2 F.O.H. 1 Cassette Player.
Dressing Rooms 4; Accom. 12.
Cyclorama fitted - Prop. Room & Green Room.

Whitchurch, Shropshire

Pop, 7,768. London 146 miles.
Newspapers: Shropshire Star (dly); Whitchurch Herald (wkly). STD code 01948

CIVIC CENTRE

High Street, Whitchurch, Shropshire SY13 1AX
Tel: 01948 665 761
Email: assistanttownclerk@whitchurch-shropshire-tc.gov.uk
Web: www.2shrop.net/whitchurchtowncouncil
ADMINISTRATION:
Props: Whitchurch Town Council
Policy: One night stands, Touring Theatre, Children's Shows, Live Music, only for hire.
Seats: 400 Show, 200 Seated with tables.
TECHNICAL:
Stage: Proscenium, opening 8.7m, Ht. 3.4m, Depth 13.8m, Bars 10.2 long.
Lighting: Control 20 way. Zero 88 Eclipse with 48 programme matrix and 8 pattern programmable chase. F.O.H. 4 x Patt.23 500w, 6 x Minuette 500w, 4 x Patt.123 500w, 4 x Patt.164 (remote control colour wheel). 2 x 3 Batt., 8 baby floods, 1 x 3 Batt. cyc floods. 1 follow spot.
Sound: P.A. Speakers F.O.H.
Easy get-in on stage level.
Dressing Rooms: 3, 1 Shower.

Whitehaven, Cumbria

Pop. 27,000. London 309 miles.
Newspapers: Evening News & Star (ntly); Cumberland News; Whitehaven News; Times & star (all wkly). STD code 01946

CLEATOR MOOR CIVIC HALL

The Square, Cleator Moor, Cumbria CA25 5AR
Tel/Fax: 01946 810 176
Web Site: www.copelandbc.gov.uk
ADMINISTRATION:
Props: Copeland Borough Council
Cap: 250
Stage and lighting facilities. Dressing rooms. Bar and refreshments.

EGREMONT MARKET HALL

Market Street, Egremont, Cumbria CA22 2DF
Tel: 01946 820 254
Email: markethalloffice@btconnect.com
ADMINISTRATION:
Props: Egremont Town Council
Cap: 200-300
Contact: Margaret Woodburn
Stage and lighting facilities. Dressing rooms. Bar and refreshments.

ROSEHILL THEATRE

Closed for redevelopment for 18 months
Moresby, Whitehaven,
Cumbria CA28 6SE
Mgt: 01946 694039 BO: 01946 692422
Fax: 01946 694039
Email: info@rosehilltheatre.co.uk
Web Site: www.rosehilltheatre.co.uk
ADMINISTRATION:
Props: Rosehill Arts Trust Ltd.
Director: Richard Elder
Policy: Small scale touring venue - drama, classical & popular music, dance & mime, comedy, films, children's shows, youth theatre. Theatre available for private hire.
Perfs: generally 8.00. Season: September to July.
Seats: 208. Bar. Car Park.
TECHNICAL:
Stage: Proscenium, Flat; Pros. opening 5.38m; Ht. of Pros. 3.38m; Depth of S/Line 5.18m; Ht. of Grid 5.33m; 16 lines, Hemp; Scenery Flying Ht. 5.33m; Flying Bars 6.71m; W/Widths P.S. 3.38m, O.P. 3.38m; Prompt Cnr. O.P.
Dressing Rooms 2; Accom. 10.
Other: Steinway Concert Grand Piano.
Rosehill Theatre was founded in 1959 by the late Sir Nicholas Sekers, and designed by Oliver Messel. Set designer for Glyndebourne.

Whitley Bay, Tyne and Wear

PLAYHOUSE WHITLEY BAY

Marine Avenue, Whitley Bay, Tyne and Wear NE26 1LZ
BO: 0844 248 1588 Mgt: 0191 643 2643
Email: phil.smith@smgnewcastle.co.uk
Web: www.playhousewhitleybay.co.uk
ADMINISTRATION:
Props: SMG Europe
Cap: 628 Fully equipped theatre.

Director: Phil Smith
Technical Manager: Simon Phillips
TECHNICAL:
STAGE: 17m x 11.4m to grid Proscenium 9m x 5.7m. Counter weight flying system 30 bars x 300kg. Removable orchestra pit 7.8m wide x 2.8m deep. Music and conductor stands. Stage stair access from auditorium. Stage cloths - legs, boarders, cyc and full blacks. Accessible load in/out. Fully integrated stage managers desk.
LIGHTING: Comprehensive Lighting system.
SOUND: Flexible in house Sound system. Additional power up to 300amps 3phase and a separate 32amps 3phase for sound.
ADDITIONAL: Private parking for production vehicles. Projector and Screen 20' x 11'
BACKSTAGE FACILITIES: 6 backstage rooms with private wc facilities. Backstage laundry equipment.
STAGE COMMUNICATIONS: Intercoms and cue lighting, Show relay and Theatre paging.

WHITLEY BAY ICE RINK

Hillheads Road, Whitley Bay, Tyne and Wear NE25 8HP
Tel: 0191 291 1000 Fax: 0191 291 1001
Email: whitleybayicerink@hotmail.co.uk
Web Site: www.whitleybayicerink.co.uk
Manager: Geraldine Cassidy & Francis Smith
Skating and Venue for Concerts.
Seating/Capacity: 6,000

Wick, Caithness

ASSEMBLY ROOMS

Sinclair Terrace, Wick, Caithness KW1 5AB Scotland
Tel: 01955 602 584
Web Site: www.highland.gov.uk
ADMINISTRATION:
Props: Highlife
Line Manager: William Durrand
Cap: 600

Wigan, Lancashire

HAIGH HALL

Copperas Lane, Haigh, Wigan, Lancashire WN2 1PE
Tel: 01942 832895
Email: hhgen@wlct.org
Web Site: www.haighhall.info
ADMINISTRATION:
Props: Wigan Metropolitan Borough Council
Ballroom: 200 Theatre Style, in the round 250, 220 with tables.

MONACO BALLROOM

Atherton Road, Hindley, Wigan, Lancashire WN2 3EU
Tel: 01942 256903 Bkgs: 0330 5550800
Fax: 01942 610915
Email: info@roseleisure.com
Web Site: www.roseleisure.com
ADMINISTRATION:
Props: Rose Leisure Ltd
Venue Manager: Kim Dixon
Policy: Concerts; Dancing, Functions.
Seating: 400

Wilmslow, Cheshire

WILMSLOW LEISURE CENTRE

Rectory Fields, Wilmslow, Cheshire SK9 1BU
Tel: 01625 533789 Fax: 01625 532481
Email: wlc@cheshireeast.gov.uk
Web Site: www.cheshireeast.gov.uk
ADMINISTRATION:
Props: Cheshire East
Cap: 528. Main Hall Stage Facilities. Multi Purpose venue, with specialist sound and lighting. Other areas also available for hire
Manager: Richard Jones

Wimborne, Dorset

LAYARD THEATRE

Canford School, Canford Magna, Wimborne, Dorset BH21 3AD
BO: 01202 847 525 Mgt: 01202 847 529
BO/Mgt Fax: 01202 847 525
Email: layardtheatre@canford.com
Web Site: www.canford.com
ADMINISTRATION:
Props: Canford School
Capacity: 294; with thrust stage: 266. Circle: 88 seats. Stalls: 178 seats (with thrust stage), 208 seats (without thrust stage), + 2 disabled/wheelchair spaces.
Artistic Director: Christopher Thomas
Technical Manager: Kevin Wilkins
Administration: Christine Haynes
Policy: The Layard provides quality, professional entertainment for the local community as well as the school. This broad audience base is reflected in the variety of events booked - from mid and small-scale provincial touring, to popular music nights.
TECHNICAL:
Contact venue for technical details.

TIVOLI THEATRE

West Borough, Wimborne Minster, Dorset BH21 1LT
Mgt: 01202 849103 BO: 01202 885566
Fax: 01202 849483
Email: charlie@tivoliwimborne.co.uk
Web Site: www.tivoliwimborne.co.uk
ADMINISTRATION:
General Manager: Charlie North Lewis
Technical Manager: Kyle Best
Policy: Concerts, Musicals, Plays, Touring, Opera, Ballet, Comedy, Cinema
Seats: 483, permanently raked stadium design balcony and stalls. Acoustically designed auditorium.
Licensed Bar, coffee lounge
TECHNICAL:
Stage: Proscenium opening with apron. Proscenium opening 9.40. Ht of Pros. 6.40. Depth of apron 2.50. Depth of stage (inc. apron) to back wall 8.40. Width of stage inc. wings 12.94. Wings 1.20.
4 Bars length 9.15m for backcloths. Maximum Ht.7.3m.
Lighting: 3 lighting bars over stage. 1 lighting bar F.O.H. Control - Sirius 24 MK.1 (24 channels).
Sound: Soundcraft Spirit 8. 24 channel mixing desk Behringer Crossovers. In house speaker units powered by B.K.amps or hire in.

Winchester, Hampshire

Pop. 88,800. London 65 miles.
Newspapers: Southern Evening Echo (ntly); Hampshire Chronicle (fri); Winchester Extra (thurs). STD code 01962

CHESIL THEATRE

Chesil St, Winchester SO23 0HU
Tel: 01962 867086 BO: 07527 471539
Email: chesilinfo@chesiltheatre.org.uk
Web Site: www.chesiltheatre.org.uk
For bookings contact Hirings Manager Chris James
Tel: 023 8026 5177
Policy: Home of the Winchester Dramatic Society and available for hire.
Cap: 75

GUILDHALL WINCHESTER

The Broadway, Winchester, Hampshire SO23 9GH
Tel: 01962 840820 Fax: 01962 878458
Email: guildhall@winchester.gov.uk
Web: www.guildhallwinchester.gov.uk
ADMINISTRATION:
Props: Winchester City Council
Bapsy Hall : 615
Manager: Samantha Hiscock
Theatre-style auditorium with limited technical facilities.

STRIPE AUDITORIUM

University of Winchester Winchester, Hampshire SO22 4NR
Tel: 01962 841515 Fax: 01962 842280
Email: conferences@winchester.ac.uk
Web Site: www.winchester.ac.uk
ADMINISTRATION:
Cap: 308
Arts Project Manager: Christian Frances

THEATRE ROYAL WINCHESTER
Jewry Street, Winchester, Hampshire SO23 8SB
Admin Tel: 01962 844600 Box office: 01962 840440 Technical: 01962 844600 Ext 212
Email: mark.courtice@theatreroyalwinchester.co.uk
Web: www.theatreroyalwinchester.co.uk
ADMINISTRATION:
Mid scale presenting theatre
Capacity: 400
Chief Executive: Mark Courtice
General Manager: Anita White
TECHNICAL:
Stage: Proscenium Arch; Level sprung stage with Orchestra pit lift. Width 8,000mm, Depth 9,050mm. 34 bar double purchase counterweight flying system.
Lighting: Strand 530i lighting desk. 108 dimmer channels. 110 lanterns including parcans, profile, fresnels and cyc floods.
Sound: Crest HS 32:4:4 sound desk; full auditorium PA and FX speakers.
Other Facilities: Dressing rooms; 2 for 14. Chorus room. Front and rear digital project facilities and a Haze machine.

Windsor, Berkshire
Pop. 30,360. London 23 miles.
Newspapers: Windsor, SLough & Eton Express (fri). STD code 01753

FARRER THEATRE
Eton College, Windsor, Berkshire SL4 6DW
Tel: 01753 671 164 Fax: 01753 671 059
Email: s.dormondy@eton.org.uk
Web Site: www.etoncollege.com
ADMINISTRATION:
Props: Eton College
Production Manager: Matthew Evered
Stage Manager: Peter Honess
Designer: Pauline Hanson
Policy: Private productions, with occasional amateur and professional performances.
Cap: Seated 400
TECHNICAL:
Stage: Proscenium or Thrust Stage, Flat; opening 11.43m; Ht of Pros. 4.57m or 5.18m; Depth of S/Line 9.14m; Ht of Grid 12.80m; 14 lines C/W 8 hemp; Scenery Flying Ht. 5.03; Flying Bars 11.58m; W/Widths P.S. 3.05m, O.P. 3.05m; Prompt Cnr. P.S. Orchestra Pit: 20.
Lighting: Strand 530 LD90 Dimmers 136 x 2.5KW, 4 x 5KW Lanterns. 10 x Harmony 15/28, 10 x Source 4/26, 30 x SIL 30, 12 x Prelude 16/30, 4 x T84, 20 x Harmony F, 6 x Alto F, 20 x Prelude F, 4 x Prelude PC, 12 x Iris 1 CYC Floods, 3 x Minuette Floods, 5 x Coda 4, 1 x 18 Way IWB, 4 x 12 Way IWB
Sound Equip: Soundcraft 200 Delta 24CH, C Audio Amps, Tannoy TX2 Controllers, JBL Variable Crossovers, JBL Compressor Limiters, Yamaha Graphic EQS, Tascam CD Players, Tascam Tape Decks, Sony Minidisc Players, JBL Mono-cluster, 2 x Tannoy I12, 2 x Tannoy T12, 2 x Tannoy I15, 2 x Tannoy T40, Tecpro System.
Other: Large dressing room complex C/W show relay. Workshop get in via ramp.

THEATRE ROYAL WINDSOR
32 Thames Street, Windsor, Berkshire SL4 1PS
Mgt: 01753 863 444 BO: 01753 853 888
SD: 01753 863 444 Fax: 01753 831 673
Marketing fax: 01753 842 769
Email: info@theatreroyalwindsor.co.uk
Web Site: www.theatreroyalwindsor.co.uk
ADMINISTRATION:
Props: Windsor & Maidenhead Borough Council
Lessee: Bill Kenwright Ltd
Executive Producer: Bill Kenwright
Executive Director: Robert Miles
Sales and Operations Manager: Daniel Herbert
Finance Manager: Anette Nicholls
Policy: Three-weekly (six weeks Pantomime). Own productions without resident company, co-productions and tours.
Perfs: Mon-Sat 8.00; Matinees Thurs 2.30, Sat 4.45, Day-time business conference facilities available.
Seats: 633. Two Bars, Buffet.
TECHNICAL:
Stage: Proscenium, Raked; Pros. opening 8.53m; Ht. of Pros. up to 5.49m; Depth of S/Line 9.14m; Ht. of Grid 16.46m; 40 lines, Hemp; Scenery Flying Ht. 7.62m; Flying Bars 9.75m; W/Widths P.S. 1.83m, O.P. 1.83m; Prompt Cnr. O.P.
Lighting: Strand lighting Gemini 2+ upgrade. 129 circuits (122x2.5kw, 7x5w).
Dressing Rooms 8; Accom. 40; 2 Showers; Orchestra Pit 12.

WINDSOR GUILDHALL
High Street, Windsor, Berkshire SL4 1LR
Tel: 01628 683540 Fax: 01753 865505
Email: guildhall.bookings@rbwm.gov.uk
Web Site: www.rbwm.gov.uk
ADMINISTRATION:
Props: Royal Borough of Windsor & Maidenhead
Cap: 100

Winsford, Cheshire
London 172 miles. Newspapers: Chester Chronicle, Warrington Guardian; Manchester Evening News; Liverpool Echo. STD code 01606

WINSFORD LIFESTYLE CENTRE
The Drumber, Winsford, Cheshire CW7 1AD
Tel: 01606 550700
Email: boxoffice@brioleisure.org
Web Site: www.brioleisure.org
Props: Brio Leisure
Contact Phil Harding: Tel 01606 814640
Capacity: 650 Theatre Style

Wisbech, Cambridgeshire
Pop. 18,000. London 106 miles.
Newspapers: Wisbech Standard (fri); Fenland Citizen (wed); Eastern Daily Press; Evening Telegraph (ntly). STD code 01945

ANGLES THEATRE
Alexandra Road, Wisbech, Cambridgeshire PE13 1HQ
Mgt: 01945 585 587 BO: 01945 474 447
Email: office@anglestheatre.co.uk
Web Site: www.anglestheatre.co.uk
ADMINISTRATION:
Props: Wisbech Angles Theatre Council
Policy: Small scale touring, amateur productions by resident company, other amateur productions, childrens theatre, workshops. The Angles is an original Georgian Theatre built in 1793. It closed during the 1840's and was turned to several different uses before being re-discovered by a group of enthusiasts in 1978. It has now been returned to its original use.
Seats: 105. Bar, Terrace, 2 studios.
TECHNICAL:
Stage: Open, Flat; width wall to wall 7.90m; Ht. to Grid 4.50m; Depth of stage 4.80m; rear of stage extends an extra 1.80m but with only 2.40m height; no wing space - small area at rear of stage.
Lighting: Control is via a Strand 520i way board situated at the rear of the auditorium. Grid consists of I.W.B.'s wired 15 amp patched at racks. 48 way of dimming. Lanterns: 8 x Patt.743, 34 x 650W Fresnel, 8 x 650W Profile, 3 x 650W PC, 6 x 1K Floor Can, 1 x Sil 30.
Sound Equip: 600W Power Amp. Spirit FX8, 16, 2, 2. McGregors speakers. Cassette Deck. Mini Disk and CD player.
Dressing Rooms 1; Accom. 20 (1 extra dressing room occasionally available).

Woking, Surrey
Pop. 90,000. London 28 miles.
Newspapers: Woking News and Mail (wkly); Surrey Advertiser (wkly). STD code 01483

NEW VICTORIA THEATRE
See also the 'Rhoda McGaw Theatre'
The Peacocks Centre, Woking, Surrey GU21 6GQ
Admin: 01483 545938 BO: 0844 871 7645 SD: 01483 545999 SD Fax: 01483 545864 Tech: 01483 545944
Email: calumkemp@theambassadors.com

Web Site: www.atgtickets.com/woking
ADMINISTRATION:
Props: Ambassadors Theatre Group (Venues) Ltd
General Manager: Calum Kemp
Technical Manager: Kevin Shelfer
Marketing Manager: Alys Carter
Policy: Touring, Drama, Opera, Ballet, Musicals, Panto and Concerts.
Seats: New Victoria Theatre: 1,338 without orchestra. 1,308 with orchestra.
Also: 3 fully licensed bars. Lounge wine bar. 2 Coffee Bars. 6 screen multiplex cinemas.
TECHNICAL:
STAGE: Proscenium Arch: Grid Height 19840mm; Prosc Width 7480mm; Width of stage: CL to SL 11460mm: Width of stage CL to SR 11460mm: Distance between fly galleries 18270mm: Back of Prosc wall to rear wall 12000mm: Rear of Dock Door area Width 15000mm: Depth 5000mm. Counterweight bars length 14.00m (with 2m extensions either end); 2 up and down stage motorised bars plus 2 hemp, and 2 counterweight bars.
Trapped area centre stage: Width 6.10m, Depth 4.88m; Rear Stage: Width 15.00m, Depth 5.00m. Get-in direct onto rear stage understage crossover.
LIGHTING: Switchboard: Strand 550 400 channels & moving light software. 202-2.5kw, 36-5kw, 2-10kw, 20 switched non dims. 45-1k Fresnells, 10-2k Fresnells, 60-1k Profiles, 10-2k Profiles, 6-1k cyc Floods, 6-1k Ground rows, 16 x IWBs, 16-Multicore, 2-colour arc follow spots.
SOUND AND COMMUNICATION:
Soundtrack Mega 32-8-2 with matrix. Desk has two positions, either Control Room or Stalls. Electrovoice P.A. Full range music and speech. 180 x 16 Tie lines, 40 video lines 6-F.X. Speakers (Fold back). Stage Managers Desk: Positions Stage Left, Stage Right, Stalls. Twin ring intercom: Infra red hard of hearing, Video and Audio lines to all areas.
ADDITIONAL: Accommodation: 10 Dressing Rooms on 3 levels, all with showers, accommodation for 53, 2 large Band Rooms, Visiting Company Managers Office, Wardrobe with Laundry Rooms.
Lift to all floors.
ORCHESTRA PIT : Max dimensions - width 12.60m, depth 3.40m, max travel from stage level 2.80m. Forestage suspension; 3 motorised flying bars.

RHODA MCGAW THEATRE

The Ambassadors, The Peacocks Centre, Woking, Surrey GU21 1GQ
Admin: 01483 545938 SD: 01483 545999 SD Fax: 01483 545864 BO: 0844 871 7645 Tech: 01483 545944
Email: calumkemp@theambassadors.com
Web Site: www.atgtickets.com/woking
ADMINISTRATION:
Props: Ambassadors Theatre Group (Venues) Ltd
General Manager: Calum Kemp
Technical Manager: Kevin Shelfer
Marketing Manager: Alys Carter
Policy: Touring, Drama, Opera, Ballet, Musicals, Panto and Concerts.
Capacity: 230
TECHNICAL:
Please contact the venue.

Wokingham, Berkshire

WOKINGHAM THEATRE

Cantley Park, Twyford Road, Wokingham, Berkshire RG40 5TU
BO: 0118 978 5363 Mgmt: 0118 989 0395
Email: admin@wokinghamtheatre.org.uk
Web Site: www.wokinghamtheatre.org.uk
ADMINISTRATION:
Cap: 143 (Audio Loop)
Amateur Theatre only. No facilities for Professional Touring Companies. We offer access to wheel chair users.

Wolverhampton, West Midlands

Pop. 252,462. London 123 miles. Newspapers: Express & Star. STD code 01902

ARENA THEATRE

Wulfruna Street, Wolverhampton, West Midlands WV1 1SB
Mgt: 01902 322 380 Mktg: 01902 322 646 Tech: 01902 322 507 BO: 01902 321 321 Fax: 01902 322 599
Email: arena@wlv.ac.uk
Web Site: www.arena.wlv.ac.uk
ADMINISTRATION:
Manager: Neil Reading
Technical Manager: Stephen Payne
Policy: The Arena Theatre is one of the West Midlands longest established and most successful small-scale touring venues.
The Arena offers a multi media venue for the performing arts, that serves a large multi ethnic area. It is an adaptable and professionally equipped space and presents a mixed programme of professional, community and student productions. It is funded by the University of Wolverhampton and
The Arts Council contributes towards the professional programme.
Booking terms: Hire, box office split, guarantee & split, guarantee, co-production, by negotiation
Capacity: 150 (seats) Arena Theatre
Other facilities: 100 (seats) Tilstone Studio, 1 Cafe Bar. Facilities for disabled patrons: 6 wheelchair spaces - assistance available - all house facilities fully accessible.
Non performance activities: conference rooms, rehearsal space, photography exhibition, socials etc
TECHNICAL:
Theatre Space: Stage: Main Theatre End on with side balconies, cross over and wing space. Main Acting Area - Flat surface of 9.53mtr wide x 9.76mtr deep. Height to l/x grid - 4.76mtr. Seating on raked single tier to fire limit of 165. Black curtain surround with optional white cyclorama around a wooden sprung floor of neutral grey with optional black dance floor for dance companies.
Lighting: Strand 520i, soft-patched to 165 x 10amp Avolites digital/analogue dimmer racks. Patched to 165 x 15amp high/mid/dip outlets.
Luminaires: - Substantial, mostly Strand, some ADB floods and Robocolour Pro; 400 Trakspot intelligent lights.
Sound: Comprehensive. Yamaha PM1200 32 channel - 4 Aux - 4 Group. Running 2 x Apogee SA800 amps and 1 x Apogee SA800 bass amp. Through 2 x P500PVD Processor and 1 P10PVS processor. Feeding 4 x Apogee AE5 FOH speakers 1 Apogee AE10 bass-bin and 4 x Mackie floor monitors.
Off-Board: 1 x Dual Cassette Deck player/recorder; 2 x C/D Player; 1 x Mini Disc player/recorder; 1 x Yamaha SPX 1000 effects unit; 1 x Bluthner Leipzig Concert Grand Piano.
Show Production Facilities: CCTV/Audio contact to all backstage, control room and dressing room areas including infra-red to control room, side and back stage. Audio talkback and cue light warnings to all backstage/dressing room areas. 2 x 13 amp isolated ring main at grid and floor level; 5 x Dressing Room all with shower. Green Room and Laundry. Video projector.

BANTOCK HOUSE & PARK

Bantock House Museum Finchfield Road, Wolverhampton, West Midlands WV3 9LQ
Tel: 01902 552 195 Fax: 01902 552 196
Email: bantockhouse@wolverhampton.gov.uk
Web Site: www.wolverhamptonarts.org.uk
Props: Wolverhampton City Council
Contact: Helen Steatham
Capacity: 120

CIVIC HALL

North Street, Wolverhampton, West Midlands WV1 1RQ
Mgt: 01902 552 122 BO: 0870 320 7000 Fax: 01902 552 123 Outdoor Events Dept: 01902 552 099
Email: markblackstock@wolvescivic.co.uk
Web Site: www.wolvescivic.co.uk
ADMINISTRATION:
Manager: Mark Blackstock
Policy: Concert Hall/Theatre used for comedy, pop, classical.
Terms by negotiation.

Capacity: 2,215 seated 3,000 standing.
Contact Marketing Manager: John Penny
TECHNICAL:
Full light and sound facilities suitable for all product, turbosound, mobile lights and theatre lights.

GRAND THEATRE

Lichfield Street, Wolverhampton, West Midlands WV1 1DE
Mgmt: 01902 573 300 BO: 01902 429 212 Mktg: 01902 573 311 SD: 01902 573 320 Fax: 01902 573301
Email: marketing@grandtheatre.co.uk
Web Site: www.grandtheatre.co.uk
ADMINISTRATION:
Props: Wolverhampton City Council
Lessees: Wolverhampton Grand Theatre (1982) Ltd.
Chief Executive: Peter Cutchi
Box Office & Customer Services Manager: Michael Lewis
Financial Controller: Karen Smallwood
Marketing Manager: Iain Watkins
Policy: No 1 Touring: Musicals, Plays, Opera, Ballet, Variety, Concerts & Pantomime.
Seats: 1,200. 3 Bars. Facilities for disabled patrons. Traditional 3 tier theatre, built 1894, Major refurbishment during 1998. Computerised box office (Syn).
Perfs: Variable.
TECHNICAL:
Stage: Proscenium stage, raked 1 in 26; wooden floor; pros. opening 10.41m; Ht. of Pros. 6.50m; Depth of Stage (safety curtain to back wall); P.S. 11.90m, O.P. 12.70m; Depth to last C/W set 10.20m (bridge over rear of stage); Ht. to Grid 16.0m; 45 double purchase c/w sets, length of C/W barrels 12.20m, max load 318kg per barrel; clearance between fly rails 13.00m; clearance under fly galleries and up-stage bridge (min) 6.50m; Wing Widths P.S. 3.60m, O.P. 3.00m; additional storage dock OP side (restricted); Prompt Cnr. PS. (Stage plans available on request).
Lighting: Rank Strand 430 board, 124 circuits, operated from rear of upper circle. 200A 3-phase supply for incoming equipment. 24 spots, 6 parcans, and 2 fresnels permanently rigged FOH. 12 spots, 26 fresnels, 26 parcans, 10 PCs, 14 floods, 1-4 way coda batten, and 8 aeros for use on-stage. 2-CSI follow spots operated from rear of upper circle.
Sound Equip: 1-Soundcraft 32 channel Venue 11 console, & 1-Soundcraft 8 channel Spirit console. Comprehensive JBL system (725s, 728s & 726s). For FOH and EV SX200s and Martin CX1s for monitoring. 2-Revox B77s & cassette deck. 60A single phase supply for incoming equipment.
Stage Management: Prompt corner SL Metro Audio (TP compatible) with outstations as required. CCTV to green room, dress circle bar, and prompt corner. Show relay to dressing rooms. Tannoy to Backstage, FOH and auditorium. Infra Red system for impaired hearing fitted.
Dressing Rooms: 14 (all with showers); accom. 70. Band Room, Green Room, Wardrobe/Laundry Room.
Other: Get-In Doors: Centre back wall, street level, 4.4m high x 2.5m wide.
Orchestra Pit: Approx 22 sq.m. (extends to 50 sq.m. by removing up to 3 rows stalls and rostra). Basic pit accommodation 15-20; fully extended can accommodate up to 55.
Stock Equipment: Full set black serge masking; Izora cyclorama; various rostra, masking flats and drapes.

THE ROBIN 2

The Leisure Factory 20-22 Mount Pleasant Bilston Wolverhampton WV14 7LJ
BO Tel: 01902 401211 Fax: 01902 401418
Email: music@therobin.co.uk
Web Site: www.therobin.co.uk
Director: Mike Hamblett
Capacity: 700

THE SLADE ROOMS

Broad Street, Wolverhampton WV1 1HP
Mgt: 01902 552 122 BO: 0870 320 7000
Fax: 01902 552 123
Email: markblackstock@wolvescivic.co.uk
Web Site: www.wolvescivic.co.uk
ADMINISTRATION:
Manager: Mark Blackstock
Marketing Manager: Jonn Penney
Policy: Concert Hall/Theatre used for comedy, pop, classical.
Terms by negotiation.
Capacity: 150 seated 550 standing.
TECHNICAL:
Full light and sound facilities suitable for all product, turbosound, mobile lights and theatre lights.

WULFRUN HALL

Mitre Fold, North Street, Wolverhampton, West Midlands WV1 1RQ
Mgt: 01902 552 122 BO: 0870 320 7000
Fax: 01902 552 123 Outdoor Events
Dept: 01902 556 706
Email: info@wolvescivic.co.uk
Web Site: www.wolvescivic.co.uk
ADMINISTRATION:
Manager: Mark Blackstock
Policy: Concert Hall/Theatre used for concerts, comedy, pantomime.
Terms by negotiation.
Capacity: 672 seated; 1134 standing.
TECHNICAL:
Full light and sound facilities suitable for all product, turbosound, mobile lights and theatre lights.

Woodbridge, Suffolk

Pop. 7,640. Menton 3,700. London 74 miles. Newspapers: Mercury; Advertiser; East Anglian Daily Times (wkly); Evening Star (ntly). STD code 01394

RIVERSIDE THEATRE

Quay Side, Woodbridge, Suffolk IP12 1BH
Mgt/BO 01394 382174
Email: riversidetheatre@aol.com/ mail@theriverside.co.uk
Web Site: www.theriverside.co.uk
ADMINISTRATION:
Duty Manager: Ms Tina Wiseman
Policy: Amateur and charity productions, conferences, seminars Cinema.
Cap: 260
TECHNICAL:
Cinema and Theatre 264 seats. Dolby Digital Surround EX Sound. Stage acting area 30' wide x 21' deep. 120 circuits lighting. Tannoy P.A.
Dressing Rooms: 60 persons.

Worcester, Worcestershire

Pop. 75,000. London 113 miles.
Newspapers: Evening News (ntly); Berrow's Worcester Journal (thurs). STD code 01905

SWAN THEATRE

The Moors, Worcester WR1 3EF
Tel: 01905 611 714 BO: 01905 611 427
Marketing: 01905 726 969
Email: lizworcesterlive@live.co.uk
Web Site: www.worcesterlive.co.uk
ADMINISTRATION:
Props: Worcester Live
Director: Chris Jaeger
Operations Manager: Mick Symmonds
Technical Manager: Jake Chambers
Marketing Manager: Lorna Philips
Policy: Mixed programme of professional and mid-scale touring. (Weeks split weeks and one nighters of comedy). Also hosts local amateur companies, music and film.
Perfs: 7.30, Mats Saturday 2.30.
Seats: 330. Bar (fully licensed).
TECHNICAL:
Stage: Proscenium with Thrust Apron. Flat; Pros. opening 10.30m; Ht. of Pros. 4.27m; Depth of S/Line 7.32m; Ht. of Grid 5.49m; Prompt Cnr. P.S.
Lighting: ETC Express 48:96 lighting desk, 78 dimmers, operated from rear of auditorium. Lantern Stock 12 CCT Sil. 30, 5 x Patt. 243, 18 x ADB 1k Fresnel, 9 x Patt. 264, 6 x Cantata P.C.,6 x Prelude 16/30, 4 x Prelude 40, 12 x Par 64 (CP62s), 12 x CCT Starlette 1kw Floods, 4 x Strand 'S' Battens, 8 x M16 Birdies, 2 x Patt. 265 follow spots.
Sound Equip: Soundcraft Spirit Live 16/4/2 & Soundcraft Folio SX mixer 20/4. 3 x MD Player, 1 x CD Player, 2 x Tape Decks, Graphic Equaliser, Yamaha SPX90, Various Mics, 2 Electrovoice 200 FOH, 2 JBL Eon 1500 on-stage & other

speakers available. Sound Controlled from rear of auditorum
Stage Management: Prompt corner SL. CCTV monitor of stage. Show relay to all dressing rooms, tannoy to backstage and FOH. Infra Red System for impaired hearing customers.
Dressing Rooms: 6; Accom. 20; 1 Shower, Green Room, Laundry Room.
Orchestra Pit 8.
Membership: TMA

WORCESTER ARTS WORKSHOP

21 Sansome Street, Worcester
Worcestershire WR1 1UH
Tel: 01905 25053
Email: info@worcesterartsworkshop.org.uk
Web: www.worcesterartsworkshop.org.uk
ADMINISTRATION:
Contact: Claire Harker
Cap: 199 max.

Workington, Cumbria

Pop. 28,000. London 310 miles.
Newspapers: West Cumberland Times & Star (wkly); Evening News & Star. STD code 01900

CARNEGIE THEATRE AND ARTS CENTRE

Finkle Street, Workington,
Cumbria CA14 2BD
Tel: 01900 602 122
Email: carnegie@allerdale.gov.uk
Web Site: www.carnegietheatre.co.uk
ADMINISTRATION:
Funding: Venue funded by Allerdale B.C.
Regional Arts Association: North West Arts
Manager: Karen Thompson
Policy: Promote folk, rock, jazz, ballet, M.O.R., variety, country, children's drama. Hire to amateur drama etc. Also promote festivals, rhythm n' blues. Monroe's Bar promotes national and local rock, rhythm and blues, and Indie bands.
Perfs: Available for use 7 days.
Booking Terms: Hire split, guarantee and split, 1/2 calls co-production, negotiation.
Non-performance activities: meeting rooms, rehearsal spaces, socials, craft activities, etc.
Facilities: Seats 354, Monroe's bar 200. Theatre raked. Catering - coffee shop. Bar - special hours certificate to 2.00 a.m. Shop sales area available.
Access: nearest public car park: Vulcans Lane, Railway - Workington Main, Coach terminal - Workington.
Facilities for disabled: 8 wheelchair spaces (level access). Assistance available (contact manager). All house facilities available.
Other facilities: Dance studio 12m x 10m also used for meetings and rehearsal.

TECHNICAL:
STAGE: Proscenium arch. Performing area 9m x 8m - pros opening 7m x 6m - wing widths 2m SR, 2m SL, 6m US. Stage raked, floor sprung wood, suitable for all dance, backstage crossover, stage heated. Height of grid 6m; 2 tab tracks; black Bolton twill legs and borders; gold silk and white canvas cyclorama; gold house tabs, drawn. 4 x 60A and 2 x 30A independent circuits. Forestage 3m x 1m. Orchestra pit 7m x 2m, accommodates 15. Get-in via understage; dock doors 1.5m x 3m. Scale stage and lighting plans available.
LIGHTING: Strand MX48, operated from lighting control room; 22 spots + 48 parcans, 36 fresnels, Rank Strand - 2 followspots, operated from lighting control room.
SOUND: Shure and AKG mics - 1 x cassette - HH PA and Bose theatre speakers. Acoustics suitable for music and the spoken word. Stage Management: 4k Peavey Rig available locally. Intercom to lighting control. Piano: Kawai Baby Grand
BACKSTAGE FACILITIES: 5 dressing rooms, access by stage and theatre balcony; green room; adequate supply of power points. Beverages, liquor and sandwiches available. Rehearsal rooms, piano, good. Advice given on accommodation. Staff - stage and lighting; casuals available; security personel. Backstage facilities not accessible to disabled performers and staff.

Monroe's Bar
STAGE: performing area 5m x 2.5m; height to grid ceiling 3.5m; 8 x 13A sockets. 1 x 30A supply.
LIGHTING: Hired locally.
SOUND: Hired locally. Acoustics suitable for music and spoken word. 4k Peavey Rig available locally.

Worksop, Nottinghamshire

Pop. 37,760. London 160 miles.
Newspapers: Worksop Guardian (fri); Worksop Trader (wed); Worksop Star (ntly). STD code 01909

REGAL CENTRE

Carlton Road, Worksop, Nottinghamshire S80 1PD
Admin: 01909 474458 Fax: 01909 472918
Email: regal.centre@bassetlaw.gov.uk
ADMINISTRATION:
TEMPORARILY CLOSED
Props: Bassetlaw District Council
Manager: Julie Lawrence
Assistant Manager: Richard Kort
Technical Officer: Steve Crisp
Policy: Touring, International & Cultural Shows, Pantomime, Plays, Variety, Amateur, Operatic, Orchestral, Pop, Folk, Jazz, Children's Shows, Concerts, Films, Dance, One Nighters
Perfs: As required
Seats: 326
TECHNICAL:
Stage: Proscenium Stage, Raked 1 in 24, Pros. opening 8.35m; Ht. of Pros. 4.84m; Depth of S/Line 3.7m; 12 lines, Hemp; Scenery Flying Ht. 8.90m; Flying Bars 8m; W/Widths P.S. 2.15m O.P. 2.71m.
Lighting: Control desk - 48 way Sirus memory board which is operated from the control room at the rear of theatre - centre stage.
Stage area - there are three on stage lighting bars. Bar 1 - 12 sockets, 12 CCT 650 watt minuette floods, Bar 2-10 sockets 8 CCT 650 watt minuette floods, 2 par 64s, bar 3 - 3 x 4 bank syke lights. Dip sockets - 8 and they are paired. The first four sockets on bars 1 and 2 are paired going inwards to centre stage. Leaving four individual sockets on bar 1 and two on bar 2.
FOH - FOH Stage bar - 20 sockets with 14 minuette floods and barn doors. 6 CCT 650 watt zoom profiles. Once again the first 8 sockets are paired to centre stage leaving 4 individual sockets. FOH Stage left - side bars - 8 individual circuits with 2 CCT 650 watt profiles. 1 par 64 1kw, 2 sill 30s, 1 sill 15. FOH stage right side bars - as stage left. There are also 2 par 64s 1kw and 2 x 500 watt Powerblazers for use if required. There is no objection to lights being moved around to suit the production being staged.
Follow spot - one 2kw spot and stand.
Film Equip: 1 x 35mm Projector, 4 track Quadrophonic Sound. Dolby Stereo SR.
Dressing Rooms: 4 Accom. 25.
Sound: 12 channel Soundcraft Spirit desk, 12 channels from stage to control room, 2 Bose 802 speakers, 4 fold back monitors, 1 600 watt power amp, 1 250watt power amp for fold back, 3 SM 58 vocal mics, 5 AKG mics, 3 Sure wide range mics, various types of mic stands, 1 twin cassette deck, the Centre does not have a Revox machine.
Communication system - Master station prompt side to LX box, front of house, with head sets or monitors, cue speakers in dressing rooms, two belt packs with sockets on stage, fly floor and numerous places throughout the building. If any further information is required please contact our Technical Officer, Steve Crisp who will be only be too pleased to help.

TOWN HALL

Potter Street, Worksop, Nottinghamshire S81 2AH
Tel: 01909 533 533 Fax: 01909 501 246
Email: customer.services@bassetlaw.gov.uk
Web Site: www.bassetlaw.gov.uk
ADMINISTRATION:
Props: Bassetlaw District Council
Cap: Ceres Suite 150; Assembly Room 150
Buildings Superintendent: Glenn Watson

WORKSOP LEISURE CENTRE
Valley Road, Worksop, Nottinghamshire S81 7EN
Tel: 01909 473937 Fax: 01909 530957
Email: rob.brewin@bpl.org.uk
Web Site: www.bpl.org.uk
ADMINISTRATION:
Props: Barnsley and Premier Leisure
Centre Manager: Glyn Davies
Capacity: 45

Worthing, Sussex

Pop. 98,210. London 58 miles. STD code 01903

ASSEMBLY HALL
Stoke Abbott Road, Worthing West Sussex BN11 1HQ
Tel: 01903 231 799 BO: 01903 211 654
Email: theatres@worthing.gov.uk
Web Site: www.worthingtheatres.co.uk
Mgt offices at: Connaught Theatre, Union Place, Worthing, Sussex BN11 1LG.
ADMINISTRATION:
Props: Worthing Borough Council.
Theatres Manager: Amanda O'Reilly
Technical Manager: Simon Gray
For General Enquiries contact Theatre Administration Officer: Jill Stewart
Policy: Mixed entertainments, programme of shows, concerts, classical concerts, rock concerts, dance, exhibition, conferences etc.
Concert Hall - seating 930 or 1,100 standing.
Buffets, refreshments and bar.
Computerised box office system Flex.
TECHNICAL:
Stage: Concert stage (stepped). Performing area 13.1m x 10.67m. Floor oak strip, suitable for dance, backstage crossover, stage heated. Height to ceiling 9m. Brown tabs at rear. 7 x twin 13A sockets. Forestage 13.1m x 3.66m.
Lighting: Sirius 48 board, 68 circuits, 200A, 3 phase, operated from projection room, 100A 3 phase supply available for temporary board - 48 x 1kw parcans - 2 x Pani 1202 followspots operated from rear of balcony.
Sound: Soundcraft 200B 16:4:2 desk, operated from control room - 6 x TOA 305D full range in stereo through 3 x Harrison x 600 amps - 4 x SM58 and 5 x 545 SD mics, radio mic available on written request - 1 x Denon cassette.
Acoustics suitable for music and spoken word.
Other: Stage management: prompt corner SL. No show relay/Tannoy to dressing rooms.
Backstage: 4 dressing rooms, access by rear of stage. Staff - 1 stage, 1 lighting, 1 sound - casuals available - security personnel upon request. Backstage facilities not accessible to disabled performers and staff.
Additional Information: Steinway concert grand piano available for performers on written request. Organs: Wurlitzer, composite, built 1922 and 1928, installed in present location in 1981.

CONNAUGHT THEATRE
Union Place, Worthing, West Sussex BN11 1LG
Mgt: 01903 231 799 BO: 01903 206 206
Email: theatres@worthing.gov.uk
Web Site: www.worthingtheatres.co.uk
ADMINISTRATION:
Theatres Manager: Amanda O'Reilly
Technical Manager: Simon Gray
Policy: Mixed programme, including films and amateur.
Perfs: Evening Mon-Fri 7.30p.m.; Sat 8p.m.; Mat. Wed 2.00p.m.; Sat. 2.00p.m.
Seats: 525. Two bars and one Restaurant.
TECHNICAL:
Stage: Proscenium with apron raked; (apron flat) DS apron from iron 1.75m; width of apron and pros opening 10.97m; Ht of pros 5.49m; Iron to back wall 7.93m; Ht of grid 12.26m; 32 lines. 7 C/W 27 Hemp; Flying Ht 11.33m; Bars 11.9m. W/Widths PS 1.93m; OP3.90m. Prompt corner movable.
Lighting: Switchboard: Control room in rear audit; Eurolight ovation 96 ways, FOH 21 x 264, 12 CCT 30's, 7 x 764's. Follow Spots 2 x Coemar Pilota 2000. 30 x 1K Fresnels, 3 x 3kw Fresnels. 10 x CCT colour wheels, fully patchable outlet system. 18 Par cans.
Full 35mm projection facilities
Sound Equip: Control Room, Speakers, 2 FOH, 2 rear auditorium, 2 stage, 2 Revox, B77, 1 x Ferrograph, 1 x cassette deck, 1 x CD deck, 1 x soundcraft 16-4-2, various Mics, 1 x MGL09. Dressing rooms 6; Accom. 32; 4 Showers.
Membership TMA

NORTHBROOK THEATRE
Northbrook College Sussex Littlehampton Road, Goring-by-Sea, Worthing, West Sussex BN12 6NU
BO: 01903 273 333 Technical: 01903 273 324
Email: box.office@nbcol.ac.uk
Web Site: www.northbrooktheatre.co.uk
ADMINISTRATION:
Seating: 162 in close fixed seating.
TECHNICAL:
The Northbrook Theatre is a small-scale touring and training venue. It has full counterweight and hemp flying facilities with a 12 metre grid. When used end-on, the proscenium opening is 10m x 5m, and with a 7.3m stage depth. ETC 48/96 Express lighting control, via 78 Permus dimmers. Six of these dimmers are 5kw. 32 hard-wired sound tie lines into soundcraft 12-4-2 peripherals include CD; MD' Revox and Tape. In-depth technical specification and drawings available on website.

PAVILION THEATRE
Marine Parade, Worthing, West Sussex BN11 3PX
Mgt: 01903 231 799 BO: 01903 206 206
Email: theatres@worthing.gov.uk
Web Site: www.worthingtheatres.co.uk
ADMINISTRATION:
Props: Worthing Borough Council;
Theatres Manager: Amanda O'Reilly
Technical Manager: Simon Gray
Contact: simon.gray@worthing.gov.uk
For general enquiries contact Administration Officer: Jill Stewart
Policy: Varied attractions; Summer entertainment June to September. Star concerts, exhibitions, conferences, dinners, dances, wrestling, local society productions.
Perfs: Sound check 5 p.m. Doors open 7 p.m. (Summer) 7.15 p.m. (Winter). Show time 7.45 p.m. (Summer) 8 p.m. (Winter)
Capacity: 850 & 17 Wheelchairs spaces; 1200 Standing; 400 dinner and dances; 600 receptions and dances. Cafe Denton, Buffets, Refreshments & Bar.
Computerised Box Office System Flex.
TECHNICAL:
STAGE: Pros. Arch opening: Width 9.46m. Stage width: 14.10m. Stage depth from front of stage: 7.32m. Stage depth from house tabs: 5.96m. Lift/Orchestra Pit size: Width 10m Depth 2.50m. Height to fly floors down stage: 2.72m. Height to fly floors up stage: 2.58m. Height to stage: 1.05m. Bar length: 9.80m. Raisable forestage; Prompt Cnr. S.M.'s desk with Dressing Room paging & PAC system, 8 station intercom.
LIGHTING: Mixing Desk: Allen & Heath GL3300 32-8-2. Lanterns: F.O.H. 4 Harmony F, 4 Harmony 12, 10 Harmony 22/40 with colour changes, 4 T Spots. Cyc. Bar. 5. 4 section codas. Stage: 40 par cans, 2 Harmony F, 10 Patt.223, plus Patt.60's, 4 Cadenza 12/32, Patt.123's, Patt.243's, 5 Patt.823. 6 Prelude F, 2 Solo CSI Follow Spots.
SOUND: F.O.H. Speakers: 6 x JBL 1750 (3 ASIDE), 2 x JBL 1746 (1 Aside), 2 x JBL 1746 (1 Aside), 2 x JBL TCB Subbass (1 Aside). Amplifiers: Crest Audio 2 x CA12, 3 x CA9 Total Output 12K, 2 x CA4. UREI Platform. Graphics EQS: EMO/Court GE60 + GE15/15. Digital Delay Units: 1 x JBL 7922 (Delays for JB8SR's infill speakers). Effects Units: 1 x Yamaha SPX 900, 2 Yamaha Stereo Comp/Lin, 1 x Stereo Drawmer Noise Gates, 1 Kalesis Midiverb 4. Cassette Desk: 1 x DENON DRW 760. MiniDisc: SONY. C.D. Player: Denon DCD 810A. D.I. Boxes: 4 EMO System Passive Boxes. Inputs/Outputs: 32 Inputs on stage, 4 Monitor returns to stage, currently run as 4 returns to 2 x HH,VX900, 1 x HH,VX600, Powering 4 Marquee. Audio/JBL MA700/+ EV Graphics 2K JBL Control 7. Foldback: 4 Channel 4 Wedges 15 plus Horn. Additional Power: 3 Phase @ 60 Amp per phase Prompt side of stage (U.S.L.) via. Availability: 63

Amp Ceeform 3 Phase 100 Amp via 125 Amp Ceeform U.S.L. Console Positions: Rear of auditorium S.L. of Control Room. Multicore Runs: Along east auditorium floor. Length approx. 24m.
MICROPHONES: 5 Shure SM58, 3 Shure SM57, 3 Shure 565D Unidyne III, 2 Electrovoice PL80, 5AKG C451EB, 4 AKGCKI Capsules, 2 AKG SE300B with CK91 + 2 x CK98 Heads, 4L Sennheiser 509. Radio Mics: 2 Trantec Hand Held Mics, 1 Sennheiser SKM2012/MKE 2.2R Lapel Mics, 1 Sennheiser Hand Held.
DRESSING ROOMS: Total 7: 1 "Star" Dressing Room. Shower Facilities: 2 Unisex, 1 Male, 1 Female.
OTHER: Steinway piano available.
MEMBERSHIP: TMA

Wrexham, Clwyd

THEATR STIWT

Y Stiwt, Broad Street, Rhosllanerchrugog, Wrexham, Clwyd LL14 1RB
Admin: 01978 844 053
BO: 01978 841 300
Email: admin@stiwt.co.uk
Web Site: www.stiwt.co.uk
Props: Stiwt Arts Trust Limited
Theatre Manager: Rebecca Griffiths
Capacity: 490 Seats.

WILLIAM ASTON HALL

Glyndwr University Mold Road, Wrexham, LL11 2AW Wales
Tel: 01978 293 565 Fax: 01978 290 008
Email: conference@glyndwr.ac.uk
Web Site: www.glyndwr.ac.uk
ADMINISTRATION:
Props: Glyndwr University
Licensee: Haydn Hughes
Policy: Music, Dance, Opera, Orchestral and Choral Concerts.
Perfs: 7.30pm
Seats: 880
TECHNICAL:
Stage: Proscenium opening with apron. Flat. Pros opening 8.50; Ht of Pros 4.25. Depth of apron 3m, Depth of stage to cyc 7.50m. Ht of grid 6.50m. 11 hemp lines, no c/w. Width of stage 12m. P/S wings 2.40. O/P wings 2m. Flying bars 10m.
Lighting: Switchboard: Movable, 60 ways.
Sound Equipment according to presentation.
Dressing Rooms: 8 Accom 40 + Orchestra Pit 20.

WREXHAM STUDIO THEATRE

Yale College, Grove Park Road, Wrexham, LL12 7AB Wales
Tel 01978 311794 ext 2078 Fax 01978 291569
Email: lmw@yale-wrexham.ac.uk
ADMINISTRATION:
Props: Yale College
Licensee: Paul Croke
Manager: Paul Hernon
Technical: Lawrence Wood
Policy: Drama, Dance, Music, Touring small scale.
Perfs: 7.30pm
Seats: 132 Theatre style. Max 200
TECHNICAL:
Stage: Studio Theatre 12m square/acting area. End on flexible seating.
Lighting: Switchboard: Strand 520i, 116 dimmers.
Sound as needed.
Dressing Rooms: flexible spaces, showers. Accom. 15-20.

Yeovil, Somerset

Pop. 42,000. London 126 miles.
Newspapers: Express & Star (thurs); Western Gazette (fri); Weekly News (sat); Western Daily Press; Evening Post. STD code 01935

OCTAGON THEATRE

Hendford, Yeovil, Somerset BA20 1UX
Mgt: 01935 845900 BO: 01935 422884
Mktg: 01935 845901
Email: octagontheatre@southsomerset.gov.uk
Web Site: www.octagon-theatre.co.uk
ADMINISTRATION:
Props: South Somerset District Council
Arts and Entertainment Manager: Adam Burgan
Technical Manager - Danny Norris
Admin & Finance Officer - Sharon Athersuch
Policy: Touring, Pantomime, Musicals, Plays, Opera, Ballet, Conferences, Concerts.
Seats: 626, permanently raked.
1 Bar and Cafe Bar.
TECHNICAL:
STAGE: Proscenium arch - Performing area 12.9m x 11m + 1.6m apron - Pros opening 12.9m x 5m - Wing widths 4.6m SR 4.6m SL no rake - Floor sprung wood suitable for all dance - Understage crossover - Height of grid 9.2m (maximum access 6.62m using Genie GR15 Runabout, licence required to operate) - 21 hemp to wire sets & 5 lighting bars on winches - 2 tab tracks - 2 wipe tracks - Black flats, legs, tabs and borders, white cloth cyclorama - Red house tabs - drawn - Orchestra pit accommodates 20 - Get in via own car park.
LIGHTING: Strand 530i control desk running Genius Pro software version 2.4e - 350 channels including Tracker software - 150amp 3 phase supply feeding 8 Strand Lighting LD90 - Dimmer racks - Each rack is supplied via a 63amp 3 phase breaker - 164 x 2.5kw dimmer channels and 13 X 2.5 kw non-dim contactor channels - Lanterns: 18 Cantatas 18/32; 2 Cantatas 26/44; 5 Brios 25/50 profile; 4 sl 25/50; 40 Parcans; 4 Floor Parcans; 32 Fresnels 1 kw; 2 Fresnels 2 kw; 12 Cantata Fresnels; 4 Cantata PC; 5 Thomas cyc battens (4 cell) - 2 Robert Juliat Follow Spots - Additional power 125 amp 3 phase CEEform plug connection TP&N and 60 amp phase CEEform plug connection SL ALL RCD PROTECTED.
SOUND: Desk operated from rear stalls or PS wings; Allen & Heath 16.2 channel Mix Wizard - 1 x EAW 260 - 2 x EAW 290 mounted centrally above stage - 4 x DAS wedge monitors - 4 x monitor feeds - 1 x Teac cassette deck, 1 x Technics CD player, 1 x Dennon DCD 1300 Mini Disc Player - 2 x Sony Mini Disc Players - 2 x SB330 Subs flown - XTA DP61 Processor - MC2 Amps - Acoustics suitable for music and the spoken word - Sound op not supplied by theatre
STAGE MANAGEMENT: Prompt corner SL. Cue lights and ring intercom, outstations as required. Show relay/tannoy to dressing rooms. Small rehearsal studio. Pass Door.
BACKSTAGE FACILITIES: 6 dressing rooms, all with showers, access by stage door. Green Room. Quick-change Room. Props Room. Wardrobe below stage with sink, automatic washing machine, tumble dryer, 5 x 13amp power points. Vending machines. Café Bar.
ADDITIONAL: Staff: 3 Technicians - casuals available. Piano: Yamaha Baby Grand for use on stage only.

York, North Yorkshire

Pop. 200,000. London 196 miles.
Newspaper: York Press. STD code 01904

FRIARGATE THEATRE

Lower Friargate, York YO1 9SL
Admin: 01904 655 317 BO: 01904 613000 Fax: 01904 651 532
Email: info@rltc.org
Web Site: www.ridinglights.org
ADMINISTRATION:
Props: Riding Lights - Artistic Director: Paul Burbridge
Cap: 100
General Manager: Jonathan Brown
Policy: Home to Riding Lights Theatre Company and host to small/mid-scale touring productions. Opened May 2000.
Perfs: 7.30
Bar
TECHNICAL:
Theatre approximately 9m x 9m can be arranged in a number of seating and staging configurations, please call for further details.

GRAND OPERA HOUSE

Cumberland Street, York YO1 9SW
Admin: 01904 678 700 BO: 0844 8713024 Tech: 01904 678 715
Email: lizzierichards@theambassadors.com
Web Site: www.atgtickets.com/york
ADMINISTRATION:
Props: Ambassador Theatre Group (Venues) Ltd.

General Manager: Lizzie Richards
Contact: lizzierichards@theambassadors.com
Box Office Manager: Catherine Richards
Press: Celestine Dubruel
Technical Manager: James Holmes
Contact: jamesholmes@theambassadors.com
Front of House Manager: Gordon Glover
Group Sales Officer: Caroline Usher-Cox
Marketing Manager: Rachel Alexander-Hill
Catering available: Main bar/coffee/food area + 3 bars.
Capacity: 1,000, 5 Wheelchair spaces.
TECHNICAL:
STAGE: Iroko, tongue and groove, semi sprung. Covered with 7mm oil tempered hardboard, painted matt black. Pros. width: 8.093 (29') Depth of stage, From iron 9,064m (29'9") to crossover, From front 9.803m (32'3") to crossover. Pros. height 6.1m (20'). Grid height 13.25m (43'4"), Barrel length 10m (32'10") (between fly floors 40'). Wing space SL 3.6m (11'10"), DS 4.8m (15'8") US, SR 4.8m (15'8"). Get-In; Straight from street to USR. Get- in doors: 2m x 4m. Cyc; Bleached white cotton, 10.2 by 10m drop. Dance Floor; Harlequin STU880 Available on request (Recharged). Orchestra Pit: accomm. approx 40, 9.5m x 4.6m (31'1" x 15'1"), Access from prompt corner; 56 chairs; 4 lit music stands, 2 un-lit music stands, 2 lit conductors stands. Flying; 29 hemp sets, 12 x Variable speed controlled, 450kg motorised bar, 4 x 450kg hand-winched bars.
LIGHTING; 95 ways of Rank Strand Permus 2.5KW dimmers, controlled by a 250channel Strand 520i. 20 x Cantata 11/26 1.2 kw profile. 4 x Cantata 18/32 1.2 kw Profile. 1 x Cantata PC 1.2kw Pebble Convex. 36 x Cantata F 1.2kw Fresnel. 20 x Parcans 1kw (220v) PAR 64. 10 x Coda 4 500w 4-section batten. 1 x Fixed 30' Ladder Bar. 4 x Moveable IWB (20 Circuits) Ladder Bars. Follow Spots; 2 Robert Julian 'Topaze' 1.2kw Followspots with Bullseye laser sights. Lighting Power Supply; 200amp TPNE Powerlock and Cam Locks. 125amp 3 phase CEE Form, 63amp 3 phase CEE Form, 63amp Single Phase CEE Form or 32amp 3 Phase CEE Form.
SOUND: Allen and Heath GL3300 24 channel. Amplifiers; 3 x AUDIO ST400 Mounted in Main rack, 1 x HK VX1200 Monitor amp. Digital Delays; 2 x TOA 310D. Graphic EQ's; 1 x Yamaha Q2031A 31 band stereo. Speakers; UC 2 x HK PR115, DC 2 x TOA 310D Delays, Stalls 2 x HK PR115, On Stage 2 x HK PR211M. 2 x Generic Wedge Monitor. Various Microphones available. Audio playback; Trantec Minidisc With AutoPause, Denon CD, Yamaha rev 100 FX generator.
ADDITIONAL: Comms: Single channel, 6 (+ prompt desk) outstations. Dry Ice (Available by prior consultation). Piano: Hoffman Baby Boudoir Grand.
DRESSING ROOM: 6; Accomm 24; with basin, shower, mirrors & lights. Company "cupboard". Gents, Ladies, and Children's toilets. Maintenance wardrobe, with twin tub, dryer, 2 large sinks and a drip/dry area. Door from stage level dressing room corridor leads directly to prompt corner and steps down to the pit. Free BroadBand Wi-Fi Available in all dressing rooms and backstage.

HELMSLEY ARTS CENTRE

Old Meeting House, Helmsley, York North Yorkshire, YO62 5DW
BO: 01439 771700 (ex. 1)
Admin: 01439 771700
Email: helmsleyarts@yahoo.co.uk
Web Site: www.helmsleyarts.co.uk
ADMINISTRATION:
Director: Em Whitfield Brooks
We are a thriving arts centre offering theatre, music and cinema to a largely rural audience. Also workshops, ballet, exhibitions. meeting room spaces, nt live.
Capacity: Theatre, 140; Studio, 40 Seats.
TECHNICAL:
Please see website.

NATIONAL CENTRE FOR EARLY MUSIC

St Margaret's Church, Walmgate, York YO1 9TL
Tel: 01904 632 220
Email: info@ncem.co.uk
Web Site: www.ncem.co.uk
ADMINISTRATION:
Venue available for hire for concerts, recordings, educational projects, conferences, meetings, workshops and illustrated lectures. State-of-the-art audio-visual equipment.
Conference Manager: Gill Baldwin
Cap: 200

THEATRE ROYAL

Closed from March 2015 -December 2015 for refurbishment
St. Leonards Place, York YO1 7HD
Admin: 01904 658162 BO: 01904 623568
Email: info@yorktheatreroyal.co.uk
Web Site: www.yorktheatreroyal.co.uk
ADMINISTRATION:
Props: York City Council
Lessees: York Citizens' Theatre Trust
Executive Director: Liz Wilson
Artistic Director: Damian Cruden
Production Manager: Jude Cloke
Policy: Resident Repertory Company, occasional Tours, Pantomime
Perfs: times vary
Seats: 863. Restaurant, Coffee Bar, Licensed Bar.
TECHNICAL:
Stage: Proscenium, Raked; Pros. opening 9.14m; Ht. of Pros. 6.40m; Depth of S/Line P.S. 9.75m O.P. 8.53m; Ht. of Grid 14.02m; 30 lines C/W (plus 3 Hemp); Scenery Flying Ht. 6.71m (to mask); W/Widths P.S. 3.66m, O.P. 3.66m. Between Fly Rails 14.02m. Prompt Cnr. P.S. Scene Dock 4.9m x 7.3m extends from P.S. of stage.
Lighting: Switchboard: ADB Vision 10, 160 circuits, 24 X Cantata 18-32, 20 X Sil 30, 2 X Sil 15, 2 X Source 4, 2 X Solo 1k, 30 X 743, 24 X Vision F, 11 X 243, 6 X Starlette 2k Fresnel, 4 X Starlette 2kw PC, 70 X PAR64, 5 X 4 Cell Thomas Batterns, 16 X ADB AC1001 floods.
Sound Equip: Mixer 24-8-2 Soundtracs MX, 16-3 and 8-3 Soundcraft Spirits.2 X Tascam MD801-R MiniDisc, 2 x Revox B77, 2 x Cassette decks, 2 x CD, FOH Wharfedale Force 9 powered by HH amps. Microphones 4 x SM58, 3 X PCC160, 5 X Rifles, 1 X D112.
Dressing Rooms 8; Accom. 62 (all rooms have showers) plus Wardrobe and Laundry.
Orchestra Pit variable by removing stalls seats.
Membership: TMA

YORK BARBICAN

Paragon Street, York YO10 4NT
Mgt: 01904 676332 BO: 0844 8542757
Email: sarah.hodson@smg-europe.com
Web Site: www.yorkbarbican.co.uk
ADMINISTRATION:
Prop: SMG Europe
Programming Manager: Sarah Hodson
Policy: Music of all types, including standing rock shows, variety, and family shows. Also theatre, comedy, ice shows, sporting events and more.
Capacity: 1,400 seated, 1,800 standing.
TECHNICAL:
Contact venue for full technical specifications.

AMATEUR THEATRES

Anglesey

THEATR FACH

Pencraig, Llangefni, Gwynedd LL77 7LA
N Wales
Tel: 01248 722412 Wardrobe Hire: 01248 713931 Chairman: 01248 421601 (Ewan Evans)
Email: moira.welstead@btconnect.com
Web Site: www.theatrfach.co.uk
ADMINISTRATION:
Chairman: John Bond
Vice Chair/Membership Secretary: Moira Welstead
Technician: Dave Collins
Publicity: Richard Paramor
Capacity: 100

Bath, Somerset

THE RONDO THEATRE

St Saviours Road, Bath,
Somerset BA1 6RT
Admin: 01225 444 003
BO: 01225 463 362
Email: director@rondotheatre.co.uk
Web Site: www.rondotheatre.co.uk
ADMINSTRATION:
Theatre Director: Ian McGlynn
Marketing Administration: Alison Farina
Seats: 105
TECHNICAL:
STAGE: 7.9m wide to tab line or 5.5m to the audience. Height is 3.6m to tad line border, approx 4m at side walls and 6m to ceiling for the centre 4m width of the stage. A set of soft black borders and legs are available for masking, and all stage walls are painted black. A dance floor is available in black..
LIGHTING: supply 100 single phase. Dimmers: 5 racks each 6#2kw & 3#1kw for house and control room lighting. Distribution 42 patch circuits. All outlets at ceiling height; boxes marked on plan. Desk: Arri Image. Lanterns: 8 X Patt 743 1kw fresnel, 6 X Berkey 1kw fresnel, 2 X Cantata PC 1kw PC, 2 X Patt 814 1kw PC, 4 X Patt 764 1kw profile, 4 X Sill 40 1.2kw profile, 4 X Patt 123 500 fresnel, 12 X Patt 23 500 fresnel, 2 X Raylight 1kw, 4 X Cycfloods 1kw, 1 X Sil 12 1kw follow spot.
SOUND: 2offNAD 602 cassette, Revox B77, Philips CD player, 12 into 4 mixer, Quad 303 and Quad 606 amps, EV 200 speakers front of Tabs, Yamaha rear stage speakers. Show relay: Stereo mics to control room, with feed to dressing room. Clearcom intercom headsets 3 sets.

Birmingham, West Midlands

HALL GREEN LITTLE THEATRE LIMITED

Pemberley Road, Acocks Green,
Birmingham B27 7RY
Admin: 0121 777 2121 BO: 0121 707 1874
Email: info@hglt.co.uk,
or boxoffice@hglt.co.uk
Web Site: www.hglt.org.uk
ADMINISTRATION:
General Enquiries: Julia Roden. Email: juliaroden@hglt.co.uk
The Youth Theatre: Roy Palmer. Email: youththeatre@hglt.co.uk

Bolton, Lancashire

BOLTON LITTLE THEATRE

Hanover Street, Bolton, Lancashire BL1 4TG
BO: 01204 334400 (Albert Halls) General: 01204524469
Email: boltonlittletheatre@gmail.com
Web Site: www.boltonlittletehatre.co.uk
Contact: Frances Clemmitt
Cap: Main Theatre 163. Forge Theatre 61.

Bradford, West Yorkshire

BRADFORD PLAYHOUSE

Also known as 'The Priestley'
Chapel Street, Little Germany, Bradford, West Yorkshire BD1 5DL
Admin/BO: 01274 820 666 Fax: 01274 822 701
Email: office@bradfordplayhouse.co.uk
Web Site: www.bradfordplayhouse.co.uk
ADMINISTRATION:
We have various areas available for hire. We can accomodate an audience form 70 to 290 people.
General Manager: Charmaine Cooke
Technician: Richard Fisher
TECHNICAL:
Main Stage:
LIGHTING: Strand LBX Lighting desk, 6 x Parcans, 10 x Cantata'a (1k), 9 x Pc (600), 10 x Pc (1200), 14 x Profiles (various), 4 x Cyc Batons, 2 x Working Lights, 4 x Minuets, 2 x 123's,
SOUND: GL2000 sound Desk, Dolby Model CM-35 Six Channel Monitor, AUX PDA 500 Induction Loop, JBL DSC 260 (Digital System Controller), 16 Amps, CD/MD Player (Sony MXD-D40), 3 on stage speakers, 4 JLB Speakers, 10 Cinema speakers, Metro Audio CM2 Master Studio (internal loop) (SM desk), Inter (PA-4000) Public Address Amplification (SM Desk), 6 can's packs + headsets.
FLYING: 1. House tabs, 2. Free, 3. IWB, 4. Legs, 5. Free, 6. Free, 7.Boarder, 8. Tabs, 9. Cinema screen, 10. Boarder, 11. IWB, 12. Legs, 13. Free, 14. Speakers, 15. Free, 16. Boarder, 17. IWB, 18. Free, 19. Back Tabs, 20. Cyc Boarder.
ADDITIONAL: 2 x A Frame Ladders, 1 x Other ladders, 14 x Stage Weights, 1 x Smoke machine.

Studio
LIGHTING: 12 Channel manual desk, 12 Channel Rack, 2 x IWB's
Sound: Nothing

Cheadle Hulme

CHADS THEATRE COMPANY

Mellor Road, Cheadle Hulme, Cheadle, Cheshire SK8 5AU
Tel: 0161 485 2764 Stage Door: 0161 486 1788 BO: 0161 428 8712
Email: btd@chads.co.uk,
or info@chads.co.uk
Web Site: www.chads.co.uk
ADMINISTRATION:
Self financing theatre that stages 7 productions between September and June. Over 200 members and supported by 200 season ticket holders and the general public.
Active youth studio with professional tutors for 13 to 16 year olds.
Own theatre with on going development of the facilities both front of house and back stage.
Seats: 144
For more information on Venue Hire, contact the bookings manager on: theatre-hire@chads.co.uk
TECHNICAL:
For full technical specifications, contact the technical department on: technicalco-ordinator@chads.co.uk.
10m x 6m stage area on common floor level with spacious wing space.
Computerised sound system and rank strand lighting board with FOH and on stage lighting pattens and up to date 500 - 1200 watt lanterns. Full stage flaps, wardrobe (Edwardian to present day), stage props, furniture and support facilities. Induction loop and talk back system.

Coventry, Warwickshire

CRITERION THEATRE
Berkeley Road South, Earlsdon, Coventry, Warwickshire CV5 6EF
Tel: 024 7667 5175
Email: criteriontheatre@hotmail.co.uk
Web Site: www.criteriontheatre.co.uk
Capacity: 120

Gateshead, Tyne and Wear

LITTLE THEATRE
3a Saltwell View, Gateshead, Tyne and Wear NE8 4JS
Tel: 0191 478 2563 BO: 0191 478 1499
Email: susanclark@me.com
Web: www.littletheatregateshead.co.uk
ADMINISTRATION:
Lessees: The Progressive Players
Contact: Lynn Sutton
Cap: 188

Halifax, West Yorkshire

THE PLAYHOUSE
King Cross Street, Halifax, West Yorkshire HX1 2SH
Tel: 01422 365998
Web Site: www.halifaxplayhouse.org.uk
ADMINISTRATION:
Props: The Halifax Thespians
Publicity Manager: Chris Baldock
Director: Jeannie O'Rourke
Cap: 260 Theatre Style (including 2 wheelchair spaces)
TECHNICAL:
SOUND: Control; Yamaha 01V96 Digital Mixing Control. Speakers; Turbo Sound TQ310 situated on Proscenium Arch, Rear Auditorium, 2 mobile placed anywhere on stage. Turbo Sound TQ115 Sub situated on The Rear Wall and Front of Auditorium. Microphones; 12 On Stage Microphone Inputs, 2 Radio Microphones, Sony CD Player, Sony Mini-disc Player, Full Digital Processing & Amplification using Adobe Audition/ShowMagic. For patrons that are hard of hearing there is a Loop System installed, limited hearing devices are available from the duty front of house manager. Canford Headsets for permanent talk-through between the stage manager, sound/lighting control operators.
LIGHTING: Control; Strand LBX desk running Genius 100 channel control with Communiqué and Kaleidoscope. Lamps; Fresnels; 17 Strand Cantata/Starlette 1Kw, 6 Strand Quartet 650W, 17 CCT Minuette 500W. Profiles; 12 Strand SL 650W1 (6 23-50 zoom, 6 15-32 zoom) Size 'B' gobo, 4 CCT Minuette 500W, 2 Strand 22/40, 2 CCT Turbo 1Kw, 1 CCT Silhouette follow-spot. Floods; 5 CCT 4cell cyclorama 500w2, 6 CCT single cell 500W, 4 Strand Coda 500W, 9 Parcan 1KW, One Le-Maitre smoke machine with 2 x 4 metre ducting.

Kenilworth, Warwickshire

THE PRIORY THEATRE
Rosemary Hill, Kenilworth, Warwickshire CV8 1BN
BO: 01926 863 334 Mob: 07774 969996
Email: chairman@priorytheatre.co.uk
Web Site: www.priorytheatre.co.uk
Chairman: Richard Collett
Technical Manager: Stephen Boden
Policy of presenting mixed season of 8 plays, musicals/ pantomime from Sept - July. Outside hiring. Visiting companies. Contact Theatre Manager for further information.
Capacity: 119

TALISMAN THEATRE
Talisman Theatre & Arts Centre Barrow Road, Kenilworth, Warwickshire CV8 1EG
BO: 01926 856 548
Email: talisman.theatre@btinternet.com
Web Site: www.talismantheatre.co.uk
ADMINISTRATION:
Chairman: Ian Roberts
Director of Productions (DoP): Chris Carpenter
Front of House Manager: Wendy McClay
Secretary: Maureen Jones
Cap: 156

Lancaster, Lancashire

GRAND THEATRE
St. Leonard's Gate, Lancaster, Lancashire LA1 1NL
BO: 01524 64 695
Email: ellie@lancastergrand.co.uk
Web Site: www.lancastergrand.co.uk
ADMINISTRATION:
Props: Lancaster Footlights Club
Manager: Ellie Singleton
Policy: Available for hire.
Perfs: Variable according to production. Mixed amateur and professional.
Seats: 460. Licensed Bar.
Toilets and limited access for the disabled installed. Hearing Loop.
TECHNICAL:
STAGE: Proscenium Raked. Pros. opening 6.4m; Ht. of Pros. 5.2m; Stage depth 6.4m; Ht. of grid 12.2m; 30 lines hemp; W/widths PS 2.4m; OP 1.8-4.8m
LIGHTING: Switchboard: Fat Frog 72 channels, rear of auditorium; circuit distribution F.O.H. 16 Stage 56. Spots 24, Freznel 24, Par 64=18, Par 64 Floor=4 Flood 5=9.
SOUND: A+H Sound Desk to circle and PA.
DRESSING ROOMS: 5; accom. 40.
Orchestra Pit 12. Costume hire.
Membership: Little Theatre Guild of Great Britain, NODA.

Leamington Spa, Warwickshire

THE LOFT THEATRE
Victoria Colonnade, Leamington Spa Warwickshire CV31 3AA
BO: 0844 493 4938 Artistic Director: 07885 546442 Chairman: 07763 974264
Email: ad@loft-theatre.co.uk
Web Site: www.loft-theatre.co.uk
ADMINISTRATION:
Chairman: Michael Rayns
Executive Artistic Director: Gus MacDonald
Production Coordinator: Sue Hamilton
Theatre Technician: Tim Elmore
Capacity: 200, Main auditorium
Also: 50 Douglas Ford studio theatre

Leicester, Leicestershire

LEICESTER DRAMA SOCIETY LITTLE THEATRE
Dover Street, Leicester LE1 6PW
Admin: 0116 254 2266 BO: 0116 255 1302 Costume Hire: 0116 254 0472 Fax: 0116 255 0326
Email: admin@lds-mail.net
Web Site: www.thelittletheatre.net
Manager: Philip Royley

London

JACKSONS LANE
Opp Highgate Tube, 269a Archway Road, London N6 5AA
Admin: 020 8340 5226
BO: 020 8341 4421
Email: admin@jacksonslane.org.uk
Web Site: www.jacksonslane.org.uk
ADMINISTRATION:
Props: Haringey Borough Council
Artistic Director: Adrian Berry
General Manager: Ruth Turner
Theatre Technician: Nick Waddel
Email: technical@jacksonslane.org.uk
Policy: To provide a programme of music,

drama, dance, mime and cabaret, representing multi-cultural interests. Training will play a large part in our programme, and many of our staff are trainees and volunteers.
Location: Alongside the Archway Road (A1), opposite Highgate tube. Served by buses 43, 134, X43, 263. Terms: Hire of theatre (negotiable); box office split.
Seats/Capacity: 166
Bars: one in foyer, one in auditorium.
TECHNICAL:
STAGE: End on, flat stage, semi-sprung wood floor, raked. 11m x 8m deep (without wing masking/ black tabs). 8m x 7m deep APPROX. (with wing masking/ black tabs). Grid Height: 6.2m. Get-In: Via 1.5m x 3.5m stage door from Archway Road (A1 facing north). Red route restrictions apply; parking for one hour between 10am and 4pm. Unrestricted parking after 7pm. Underground station car park charges £3 per day.
LIGHTING: Control: Strand 91703 300 Console 125ch 24sub. Lanterns: 10 x 1k Starlette fresnels, 6 x Par 64 (assorted lenses - please check with us), 2 x 650 w Minuette profiles, 6 x 1k Compact 6 fresnels, 12 x 1.2k ETC Source 4, 15/30 zoom profiles, 7 x 1.2k ETC Source 4, 25/50 zoom profiles, 4 x 500w Quartet fresnels, 2 x 3 cell 500w flood units. All lanterns are compete with barn doors, gel frames and shutters as appropriate.
SOUND: Allen and Heath GL 3300. Playback; Numark CDn22 Dual CD Player, 2x RCF Art 315a Powered speakers (Fixed Position). Various Microphones available.
ADDITIONAL: Infrared hearing systems fitted, 1x FXlab Small Hazer, 1x Martin magnum 650 Smoke Machine, 1x 30cm Mirror ball. Video Projector; NEC NP100 2000 lumen Projector. Projection Screen; Matt white front projection screen surface. 9m wide x 5.95m drop.
DRESSING ROOMS; 3, accomm. 20. Iron and ironing board available.
For more information contact Joe Boxshall on joe@jacksonslane.org.uk.

SOUTH LONDON THEATRE

2a Norwood High Street, Wst Norwood, London SE27 9NS
BO: 020 8670 3474
Email: info@southlondontheatre.co.uk
Web Site: www.southlondontheatre.co.uk
ADMINISTRATION:
Chairman: Bob Callender
Capacity: Bell Theatre; 96 Seats. Prompt Corner Studio; 30 - 60 seats.

Newport, Gwent

DOLMAN THEATRE

8 Emlyn Square, Kingsway Centre, Newport, Gwent NP20 1HY Wales
Tel/Fax: 01633 263 670 BO: 01633 251 338
Email: dolmantheatre@btinternet.com
Web Site: www.dolman-theatre.co.uk
ADMINISTRATION:
Props: Newport Playgoers Society
Theatre Manager: Lisa Aston-Griffiths.
Capacity: 400 Seats; full technical capabilities.
Also newly equipped Studio theatre, flexible seating for 40 to 90
Suitable for small plays, talks, meetings.

Nottingham, Nottinghamshire

LACE MARKET THEATRE

Halifax Place, Nottingham NG1 1QN
Tel: 0115 950 7201
Email: info@lacemarkettheatre.co.uk
Web Site: www.lacemarkettheatre.co.uk
ADMINISTRATION:
Proprietor: The Lace Market Theatre Trust Ltd
Youth Theatre Leader: Roger Watson
Costume Hire Manager: Linda Croston
Auditorium Capacity: 118
Studio Capacity: 50
Facilities: Bar.

St Albans, Hertfordshire

ABBEY THEATRE & STUDIO

Westminster Lodge, Holywell Hill, St Albans, Hertfordshire AL1 2DL
Mgt: 01727 847 472 BO: 01727 857 861
Fax: 01727 812 742
Email: manager@abbeytheatre.org.uk
Web Site: www.abbeytheatre.org.uk
ADMINISTRATION:
Props: Abbey Theatre Trust (St. Albans) Ltd
Manager: Tina Swain
Policy: Own amateur use; also occasional touring companies and other local society use.
Perfs: 8.00
Main Theatre: 230, Studio Theatre 78, Bar and Coffee.
TECHNICAL:
Main Theatre:
STAGE: Stage is 3ft above ground level. White cyc wall at rear. Proscenium arch 24 ft wide. 11ft 6in high. Stage depth 22 ft. Full plan and section available on request. Full height fly tower. 6 counterweight lines plus front tabs, 13 hand lines, three winched lighting bars. Well equipped stage managers desk. Black drape traverse, legs and borders. Soundproof control room for sound and lighting at the back of the auditorium.
LIGHTING: 96 Channel desk, 2DMX universes. Variety of Profile, Fresnel, Par Can and Floods available.
SOUND: 16 Channel desk, Minidisc and CD player/recorder, 6 speakers.
BACKSTAGE FACILITIES: Dressing Rooms; 4, accomm. 5 - 6. Green room. The club room is sometimes available, by arrangement, as an extra dressing room for large cast productions.

Studio:
STAGE: Black drapes on three walls. Basic stage managers desk. Techpro communication. Normally separate control rooms for sound and lighting.
LIGHTING: 48 Channel desk, 1DMX universe. Grid of scaffold tubing across the ceiling 14ft above ground level. Variety of Profile, Fresnel, Par Cans and Floods available.
SOUND: 16 channel desk, Minidisc and CD player/recorder,4 speakers.
BACKSTAGE FACILITIES: 3-4 entrances for actors, near each corner. An adjacent room for use as a dressing room or meeting room. Screens can be used to partition this room.

Stockport, Cheshire

STOCKPORT GARRICK THEATRE

Members meet regularly on a Tuesday evening
Exchange Street, Wellington Road South, Stockport, Cheshire SK3 0EJ
BO 0161 480 5866 SD 0161 480 3287
Secretary Tel: 0161 482 4876 (John Wild)
Email: generalsecretary @stockportgarrick.co.uk
Web Site: www.stockportgarrick.co.uk
ADMINISTRATION:
General Secretary: John Wild
Cap: 155
For more information on Venue Hire, contact the theatre on Tel: 0161 480 3827 or email: theatrehire@stockportgarrick.co.uk

Stoke-On-Trent, Staffordshire

STOKE-ON-TRENT REPERTORY THEATRE

Leek Road, Stoke-on-Trent, Staffordshire ST4 2TR
BO: 01782 209 784 Mob: 07721 475890 (Theatre Hire)
Email: m.r@btinternet.com
Web Site: www.stokerep.org.uk
ADMINISTRATION:
Stoke Repertory Players Season (Oct-June)
Planning Director (Theatre Hire): Malcolm Rushton
Technical Manager: Richard Masters
TECHNICAL:
STAGE: 8m x 8m approx plus extended

apron. 24 x digitally motorised flying bars. 13 x hemp bars. Motorised revolving stage - controllable speed and direction. Black legs - borders - red legs; borders - gold legs - borders. Cyclorama, black gauze, white gauze.
LIGHTING: 96 channel lighting rig with Strand 530i lighting desk. Standard 6 Colour Show Rig consisting of 100 plus lanterns of varying types.
SOUND: Soundcraft mixing desk, Nexo FOH speakers (2 x 450w). Twin CD player, twin cassette player, Mini-Disk player, sound editing PC & CD Writer
DRESSING ROOMS; 2.
ADDITIONAL: Large rehearsal room (additional dressing area). Haze & smoke machines, low foggers, UV/Mirror Ball.

Sunderland, Tyne and Wear

ROYALTY THEATRE

The Royalty, Sunderland Tyne & Wear SR2 7PP
Tel: 0191 567 2669 BO: 0191 553 2000
Email: contact@royaltytheatre.co.uk
Web Site: www.royaltytheatresunderland.co.uk
ADMINSTRATION:
Contact: Anna Snell
Cap: 216

Sutton Coldfield, West Midlands

HIGHBURY THEATRE CENTRE

Sheffield Road, Sutton Coldfield, West Midlands B73 5HD
Admin/BO: 0121 373 2761 SD/Mgt: 0121 382 5214
Email: admin1@highburytheatre.co.uk
Web Site: www.highburytheatre.co.uk
ADMINISTRATION:
Props: Highbury Theatre Centre Ltd
Chairman: Steve Bowyer
For Technical Information Contact: Steve Bowyer
Policy: Amateur Little theatre presenting 7 plays per season for 10 performances each and Studio productions 3 a year (6 nights) and touring professional companies (one-night stands).
Box Office open from 7.30pm until 9.30pm
Perfs: 7.30
Seats: 138. Coffee Bar and Licensed Club Bar.
Disabled access, toilets and lifts.
TECHNICAL:
STAGE: Proscenium, Flat; Pros. opening 4.72m; Ht. of Pros. 3.50m; Depth of S/Line 6.55m; Ht. of Grid 7.62m; 42 lines, Hemp; Scenery Flying Ht. 3.66m; Flying Bars 5.49m; W/Widths P.S. 1.83m, O.P. 0.61m; Prompt Cnr. O.P.
LIGHTING: Please contact venue.
SOUND: 2 x tape disks, 1 x mini disk, 1 x CD. Speakers auditorium and stage. Induction loop.
DRESSING ROOMS: 3; Accom. 24.
Private Membership Theatre.
Membership: L.T.G.B.

SUTTON ARTS THEATRE

South Parade, Sutton Coldfield, West Midlands B72 1QU
Admin/BO: 0121 355 5355 Fax: 0121 355 8929
Email: info@suttonartstheatre.co.uk
Web Site: www.suttonartstheatre.co.uk
Chairman: Colin Edge
Capacity: 129

Teignmouth, Devon

CARLTON THEATRE

The Den, Teignmouth, Devon TQ14 8BD
Tel: 01626 778991
Email: info@carltontheatre.com, bookings@carltontheatre.com
Web Site: www.carltontheatre.co.uk
ADMINISTRATION:
Props: Teignbridge District Council
Lessees: Teignmouth Players
Chair: Roger Smith
Theatre Manager: Alex Butler
Capacity: 199
For more information on Venue Hire, contact Sara Austin-Wells on 07866 092376.
TECHNICAL:
SOUND: Mixing Desk; Allen & Heath Z436 and outboard, EQ's, Effects, Twin Denon CD, Tascam Mini disc and Cassette player. 2 x rows of three mics over stage area + three shotguns from No 1 advance FOH. House PA - 4 No. EV Sx300 speakers - all suspended from FOH Lx bars. House PA speakers driven by a Work Power amp. Amps; 2 x Crown XLS 402, 2 x JBL15 speakers (loose), 2 x No. small DB powered speakers, one each side of pross. Jim).
LIGHTING: 4 x Strand 223. 16 x Quartet PC. 6 x Cantata PC. 3 x Celecon P90. 8 x minim PC (not all working). 2 x Minimum 23. 11 Pat 60 flood. 4 x Prelude 16/30. 3 x Furse (fresnel) (not all working). 6 x Parcan 64. 6 x Short nose parcan. 8 X Scroller Parcan 64 + Chroma Q 16frame scrollers. 2 x Pat 23 (not all working). 2 x Pat 123. 14 x Aclaim floods (not all working). 6 x 8 S63 Battens. 10 x Ledj LED Wash lights. 7 x Showtek LED Parcans. 1 x Cantata 11/26 Follow Spot.

Tonbridge, Kent

ANGEL LEISURE CENTRE

Angel Lane, Tonbridge, Kent TN9 1SF
Tel: 01732 359 966 Fax: 01732 363 677
Email: angel.leisurecentre@tmbc.gov.uk
Web Site: www.angelcentre.co.uk
Manager: Gary Littlejon
Policy: Multi-purpose Hall used for theatre, cinema, concerts, meetings, sports and social events, conferences, fairs and markets.
Seating/Capacity: 307 seated; 400 standing.

Wigan, Lancashire

WIGAN LITTLE THEATRE

Crompton Street, Wigan, Lancashire WN1 3SL
BO/ Admin: 01942 242 561 Fax: 01942 242 577
Email: wltuk@yahoo.co.uk
Web Site: www.wiganlittletheatre.co.uk
ADMINISTRATION:
Contact: Martin Green
Cap: 230

Wrexham, Clwyd

GROVE PARK THEATRE

Hill Street, Wrexham LL11 1SN
Mgt: 01978 351981 BO: 01978 351091
Email: info@groveparktheatre.co.uk
Web Site: www.groveparktheatre.co.uk
ADMINISTRATION:
Registered Charity No. 505339
Policy: 6 Whole length plays plus pantomime. Each play runs for nine nights and pantomime for 25 performances.
Cap: 170 (including 1 wheelchair space)

COMEDY & CABARET VENUES

APPLES AND SNAKES
The Albany Douglas Way, London SE8 4AG
Tel: 0845 521 3460 / 0845 521 3460
Email: lucy@applesandsnakes.org
Web Site: www.applesandsnakes.org
MeadCreative Producer: Lisa Mead
Director: Lucy Crompton- Reid
Apples and Snakes stretches the boundaries of poetry in performance and education.
Cap: 90

BANANA CABARET
The Bedford Pub, 77 Bedford Hill, London, SW12 9HD
Tel: 020 8682 8940 (Bedford Pub) Fax: 020 8682 8959
Email: pamela@bananacabaret.co.uk
Web Site: www.thebedford.co.uk / www.bananacabaret.co.uk
Manager: Dave Vickers
Capacity: 220 - 450

BEARCAT CLUB
The Turks Head, 28 Winchester Road, St Margaret's, Twickenham, Middlesex TW1 1LF
Tel: 020 8891 1852 Press: 0207 642 3376
Email: jamespunnett@bearcatcomedy.freeserve.co.uk
Web Site: www.bearcatcomedy.co.uk

THE BEDFORD
77 Bedford Hill, Balham, London SW12 9HD
Tel: 020 8682 8940 Fax: 0208 682 8941
Email: info@thebedford.co.uk
Web Site: www.thebedford.co.uk
ADMINISTRATION:
Operations Manager : Greg Kerr
Email: greg@thebedford.co.uk
Capacity: 270 Theatre Style, 180 The Ballroom, The Tavistock Theatre 70.

THE BELFAST EMPIRE
42 Botanic Avenue, Belfast, County Antrim Northern Ireland
Tel: 028 9024 9276 BO: 0844 2774455
Head Office Tel: 028 9074 6274
Email: kerrie@wineinns.com
Web Site: www.thebelfastempire.com
Props: Wine Inns Ltd
Marketing & Promotions Manager: Kerrie Malone
Bar Manager: Mark Mateer
Empire Basemant: 450
Empire Music Hall: 200
Regular gigs include The Empire Laughs Back. From The Abba Experience to The Asian Dub Foundation, The Belfast Empire and Music Hall has something to meet every musical taste!

THE BLACKFRIARS
36 Bell Street, Glasgow, Strathclyde G1 1LG Scotland
Tel: 0141 552 5924 Fax: 0141 552 2932
Email: info@blackfriarsonline.co.uk
Web Site: www.blackfriarsglasgow.com
Manager: Joan McMillan
Cap: 190

BOUND AND GAGGED COMEDY
Lyndhurst House, 25 Melrose Avenue, London NW2 4LH
All Enquiries: 020 8450 4100 Fax: 020 8450 8985
Email: nigel@boundandgaggedcomedy.com
Web: www.boundandgaggedcomedy.com
Contact: Nigel Klarfeld

BRIXTON COMEDY CLUB
The Dogstar, 389 Coldharbour Lane, London SW9 8LQ
Tel: 020 7633 9539
Email: comedyclubs@aol.com
Web Site: www.brixtoncomedy.co.uk
Occasional Sunday night comedy shows.
Capacity: 100
Manager: Ivor Dembina

CANAL CAFE THEATRE
Canal Café Theatre, The Bridge House, Delamere Terrace, London W2 6ND
Tel: 020 7289 6056 BO: 020 7289 6054
Email: mail@canalcafetheatre.com
Web Site: www.canalcafetheatre.com
ADMINISTRATION:
Theatre Manager: Annie Biddlecombe
Artistic Director: Emma Taylor
Theatre Technician: Stuart Glover
Fringe Pub Theatre specialising in stand-up and farcical acts and productions, in cafe-style layout with bar and food.
Capacity: 60

CHATS PALACE
42-44 Brooksby's Walk, Homerton, Hackney, London E9 6DF
Tel: 020 8533 0227
Email: info@chatspalace.com
Web Site: www.chatspalace.com
ADMINISTRATION:
Capacity; Seated: 100. Standing: 200.
TECHNICAL:
STAGE: Floor area 5.5m x 6m deep, pros opening 5.5m x 3m. Rubberised dance-floor available. Black curtains / white cyclorama / black brick wall. Backstage crossover - just! Stage units form raked seating or can make 5m x 4m stage for music, etc. Traverse, round, other variations possible.
LIGHTS: Zero 88 Fat Frog programmable board. 18 circuit @2kw, operated from back balcony. 50 various fresnels, profiles, PCs and floods, and follow spot.
SOUND: 16.4.2 sound mixing desk operated from back of hall OR 20.2 mixing desk operated from back balcony. 2kW turbosound rig with 1kW monitoring.10 mics, 4 DI boxes, 2xCD, MD, DA, MC. Also available - projector (video/DVD/etc) and screen, 2 x slide projector, turntables and mixer, upright piano (good).
Acoustic suitable for music and spoken word.
BACKSTAGE FACILITIES: One dressing room, stage right. Some wing space both sides.

COLCHESTER COMEDY CLUB
Colchester Arts Centre, St Mary-at-the-Walls, Church Street, Colchester, Essex CO1 1NF
Tel: 01206 500 900 Fax: 01206 500 187
Email: info@colchesterartscentre.com
Web Site: www.colchesterartscentre.com
Contact: Anthony Roberts

COMEDY CAFE
66- 68 Rivington Street, Shoreditch, London EC2A 3AY
Tel: 020 7739 5706 Fax: 020 7256 1242
Email: info@comedycafe.co.uk
Web Site: www.comedycafe.co.uk
Stand-up comedy, doors open from 7.00pm Wed/Thurs but from 6.00pm on Fri. The disco is only on Sat from 7.00pm. Cap: 170. Licenced Bar and restaurant. Available for private and corporate hire, 1500 sq feet, VIP function room upstairs.
Manager: Noel Faulkner
Technical Manager: Borjita Pardo Bestia

THE COMEDY STORE
1A Oxendon Street, London SW1Y 4EE
Club: 020 7839 6642 Mgt: 020 7930 2949 BO: 0844 871 7699 Fax: 020 7024 2069 (Admin Office)
Email: london@thecomedystore.co.uk
Web Site: www.thecomedystore.co.uk
ADMINISTRATION:
General Manager: Loki McKay
For hiring enquiries, contact Loki Mckay: loki@thecomedystore.co.uk
Head of Technical: Simon Mason
Capacity: 400
TECHNICAL:
STAGE: Steel Deck 12 x 8 ft minus 4ft radial curves on front corners.
Expandable to 16 x 10 ft. Black, pleated tabs on back wall (removable).
LIGHTING: Control: Avolites Pearl Expert. Fixtures (moving); Martin MAC250 Kryptons x 4, Martin MiniMAC x 2, Clay Paky HP Minicsans x 4. Fixtures (generic); Source 4 Parcans x 4, Source 4 Parnels x 6, Source 4 Zoom profiles x 4, Source 4

Junior profiles x 4, Strand 650w fresnels x 6, Strand 300w fresnels x 4, Strand 16/30 profiles x 4, Strand 28/40 profiles x 4, Crown shortcan/floorcans Parcans (Silver) x 6 Thomas shortcan Parcans (Silver) x 2, Altmann 20 cell MR16 battens x 2, Jem 24/7 Hazer x 2.
SOUND: 12 channel stage box, 8 channel extension snake. Control: Allen & Heath iLive-112. Main output: 18 x HK Audio CT108, 2 x HK Audio CDR210C Subs, 1 x HK Audio DFC, 7x HK Audio VX2400 Amplifiers. Fold Back; 4 x PS8 Nexo fold back wedges, 1 x LS400 Nexo sub. Proccessing; 3 x Xilica 4in 8out Speaker controllers, 2 x Nexo PS8 Controller (Analogue), 2 x Focusrite twintrack vocal Compressors, 1 x Yamaha SPX990 effects unit. Induction Loop for the hard of hearing covering one large area of seating. Various Microphones available. Playback; Denon DN1800F 2 deck CD player, Sony MDS JE440 minidisc player, G5 Macintosh with iTunes. Audio Recording Suite; Pro Tools HD1 on G5 Macintosh, Pro Tools 192 Digital I/O, Focusrite Octopre C/W Digital Card, Tascam CD-RW750, Genelic 8030A Monitors x 2, Beyer Dynamic DT100 and DT150 Headphones.
AV: Cameras; Fixed focus Sony Super Exware, Pan/tilt remote controlled Sony Super Exware, Fisheye lensed fixed focus Sony Exware. Data Projector; Sony VPL-CX86 3000 lumens. Control; Extron Matrix 8x8, Extron Switcher/scaler, VGA input points from control and stage positions to matrix, 2 x Sony 250Gb Hard Disc/DVD recorder, 4 x Sony LCD TV screens around the venue for show monitoring, 2 x Sony 42" Plasma Screens for overspill viewing.
DRESSING ROOMS; 1 w/ door leading directly to the stage. Accommodates 8. Shower and toilet facilities.

THE COMEDY STORE MANCHESTER

Arches 3 & 4 Deansgate Locks,
Whitworth Street West,
Manchester M1 5LH
Tel: 0161 839 9595 Fax: 0161 839 9696
Email: manchester@comedy-store.net
Web Site: www.thecomedystore.co.uk
Contact: Emilie Jones
Seats: 500

DOWNSTAIRS AT THE KING'S HEAD

2, Crouch End Hill, London N8 8AA
Venue: 020 8340 1028
Admin: 01920 823265
Email: admin
@downstairsatthekingshead.com
Web: www.downstairsatthekingshead.com
Proprietor and Contact: Peter Graham
Cap: Seated 100 & 20 standing
For admin please call (01920) 823 265 between the hours of 9am to 11am

HAMPSTEAD COMEDY CLUB

The Pembroke Castle, 150 Gloucester Avenue, London NW1 8JA
Tel: 020 7633 9539
Email: comedyclubs@aol.com
Web Site: www.hampsteadcomedy.co.uk
Small scale Saturday night comedy venue in North London established for nearly twenty years. Intimate atmosphere with selection of leading UK and international comedy acts. Good shows, good venue, good value.
Basic lighting and good qhality hiuse PA. Small raised stage. Cabaret style seating. Venue capacity 95.

HEADLINERS

George IV, Chiswick High Road, London W4 2DR
Tel: 020 8566 4067
Email: info@headlinerscomedy.com
Web Site: www.headlinerscomedy.com
ADMINISTRATION:
Contact: Simon Randall
Cap: 120 Cabaret Style
Every Friday & Saturday

HELLFIRE COMEDY CLUB

Wycombe Town Hall, Queen Victoria Road, High Wycombe, Buckinghamshire HP11 2XE
BO: 01494 512 000 Admin: 01494 514 444 SD: 01494 552 811
Email: enquiries@wycombeswan.co.uk
Web Site: www.wycombeswan.co.uk
ADMINISTRATION:
Contact: Emma Sullivan
Cap: 250

HEN AND CHICKENS THEATRE

Hen and Chickens Theatre 109 St Pauls Road, London N1 2NA
Tel: 020 7704 2001
Email: henandchickens@aol.com
Web Site: www.henandchickens.com
ADMINISTRATION:
Capacity: 54
For more information on venue hire contact Felicity Wren on henandchickens@aol.com

LEE HURST'S BACKYARD CLUB

The FymFyg Bar, 231 Cambridge Heath Road, London E2 0EL
Tel: 020 7613 1057
Email: backyard@leehurst.com
Web Site: www.leehurst.com
For a great night out of comedy, come to Lee Hurst's comedy club. An MC + 3 comics. A late bar, disco and diner.

JACKSONS LANE

Opp Highgate Tube, 269a Archway Road, London N6 5AA
Admin: 020 8340 5226 BO: 020 8341 4421
Email: admin@jacksonslane.org.uk
Web Site: www.jacksonslane.org.uk
ADMINISTRATION:
Props: Haringey Borough Council
Artistic Director: Adrian Berry
General Manager: Ruth Turner
Theatre Technician: Nick Waddel
Email: technical@jacksonslane.org.uk
Policy: To provide a programme of music, drama, dance, mime and cabaret, representing multi-cultural interests. Training will play a large part in our programme, and many of our staff are trainees and volunteers.
Location: Alongside the Archway Road (A1), opposite Highgate tube. Served by buses 43, 134, X43, 263. Terms: Hire of theatre (negotiable); box office split.
Seats/Capacity: 166
Bars: one in foyer, one in auditorium.
TECHNICAL:
STAGE: End on, flat stage, semi-sprung wood floor, raked. 11m x 8m deep (without wing masking/ black tabs). 8m x 7m deep APPROX. (with wing masking/ black tabs). Grid Height: 6.2m. Get-In: Via 1.5m x 3.5m stage door from Archway Road (A1 facing north). Red route restrictions apply; parking for one hour between 10am and 4pm. Unrestricted parking after 7pm. Underground station car park charges £3 per day.
LIGHTING: Control: Strand 91703 300 Console 125ch 24sub. Lanterns: 10 x 1k Starlette fresnels, 6 x Par 64 (assorted lenses - please check with us), 2 x 650 w Minuette profiles, 6 x 1k Compact 6 fresnels, 12 x 1.2k ETC Source 4, 15/30 zoom profiles, 7 x 1.2k ETC Source 4, 25/50 zoom profiles, 4 x 500w Quartet fresnels, 2 x 3 cell 500w flood units. All lanterns are compete with barn doors, gel frames and shutters as appropriate.
SOUND: Allen and Heath GL 3300. Playback; Numark CDn22 Dual CD Player, 2x RCF Art 315a Powered speakers (Fixed Position). Various Microphones available.
ADDITIONAL: Infrared hearing systems fitted, 1x FXlab Small Hazer, 1x Martin magnum 650 Smoke Machine, 1x 30cm Mirror ball. Video Projector; NEC NP100 2000 lumen Projector. Projection Screen; Matt white front projection screen surface. 9m wide x 5.95m drop.
DRESSING ROOMS; 3, accomm. 20. Iron and ironing board available.
For more information contact Joe Boxshall on joe@jacksonslane.org.uk.

JONGLEURS BLACKPOOL

Winter Gardens, 97 Church Street, Blackpool FY1 1HW
Ticket Hotline: 08700 111 960 Tel: 0845 5192 450
Email: enquiries@jongleurs.com
Web Site: www.jongleurs.com

JONGLEURS COVENT GARDEN

61-65 Great Queen Street, London WC2B 5BZ

Ticket Hotline: 08700 111 960 Tel: 020 7404 6114 (Sway)
Email: info@jongleurs.com
Web Site: www.jongleurs.com

JONGLEURS CROYDON
16 High Street, Croydon CR0 1GT
Ticket Hotline: 08700 111 960 Tel: 0208 6624 949 (Tiger Tiger)
Email: info@jongleurs.com
Web Site: www.jongleurs.com

JONGLEURS GLASGOW
The Glass House, 20 Glassford Street, Glasgow G1 1UL
Ticket Hotline: 08700 111 960 Tel: 0141 5513 4888
Email: enquiries@jongleurs.com
Web Site: www.jongleurs.com

JONGLEURS HAMMERSMITH
Rutland Grove, London W6 9DH
Ticket Hotline: 08700 111 960 Tel: 0208 748 5760
Email: info@jongleurs.com
Web Site: www.jongleurs.com

JONGLEURS NOTTINGHAM
10 Thurland Street, Nottingham NG1 3DR
Admin: 0115 9500120 Tel: 01159 582 305 Ticket Hotline: 08700 111 960
Email: nottingham@jongleurs.com
Web Site: www.jongleurs.com
ADMINISTRATION:
Manager: Adrien Thompson
Jongleurs Comedy Clubs is one of the leading comedy chains in Great Britain with over 16 clubs from Portsmouth to Glasgow. Nottingham is one of Jongleurs flagship venues with a capacity of 450. Jongleurs is the perfect night out with comedy then club until 2am every Thurday, Friday and Saturday night.

JONGLEURS PORTSMOUTH
Gunwharf Quays, Portsmouth PO1 3TP
Ticket Hotline: 08700 111 960 Tel: 0239 288 2244
Email: info@jongleurs.com
Web Site: www.jongleurs.com

THE PIZZAEXPRESS JAZZ CLUB
10 Dean Street, London W1D 3RW
Booking Line: 0845 6027 017 Tel: 0207 437 9595 / 439 4949
Fax: 0207 734 7734
Email: jazz@pizzaexpress.com
Web Site: www.pizzaexpresslive.co.uk/jazzList.aspx
Assistant Music Manager: Charlie David

RADA STUDIOS
16 Chenies Street, London WC1E 7EX
Admin/BO: 020 7307 5060 Fax: 020 7307 5062
Email: studiosboxoffice@rada.ac.uk
Web Site: www.radaenterprises.org
ADMINISTRATION:
General Manager: Stacie Novotny
Seats: 200 max.
Disabled access, licensed bar on ground floor.
The Drill Hall, just off Tottenham Court Road, in London's West End, has a 200 seat theatre,
Studio Theatre, a 50-seat cabaret-style. Club Theatre ,four rehearsal studios, four meeting rooms, a bar, an extensive programme of courses and classes (with changing rooms/ shower facilities) and is open seven days a week.
TECHNICAL:
Recently upgraded lighting system and in-house PA system.
Rehearsal rooms and fully accessible darkroom suite.

SCREAMING BLUE MURDER COMEDY CLUB
The Old Town Hall Theatre, High Street, Hemel Hempstead, Hertfordshire HP1 3AE
Tel: 01442 228 091 Admin: 01442 228095 (Town Hall)
Email: othadmin@dacorum.gov.uk
Web Site: www.oldtownhall.co.uk, www.screamingbluemurdercomedy.com
ADMINISTRATION:
Policy: 9.00pm start.
Seats: The Gallery Bar, 55.

THE STAND COMEDY CLUB
5 York Place, Edinburgh, Mid Lothian EH1 3EB Scotland
Booking Line: 0131 558 7272 Fax: 0131 556 7091
Email: admin@thestand.co.uk, jen@thestand.co.uk
Web Site: www.thestand.co.uk
Contact: Eva Mackay

THE 99 CLUB
28A Leicester Square, London WC2H 7LE
Mob: 07760 488119
Email: info@the99club.co.uk
Web Site: www.99clubcomedy.com
Director: James Woroniecki

THE LINCOLN LOUNGE
52 York Way, Kings Cross, London N1 9AB
Tel: 020 7837 9339
ADMINISTRATION:
Manager: Joyce Whelan
Exhibitions, live music events, cabaret and a laid back bohemian crowd.
Capacity: 130

ARTS CENTRES

Aberdeen, Aberdeenshire

ABERDEEN ARTS CENTRE
33 King Street, Aberdeen AB24 5AA
Scotland
Tel: 01224 635 208 Fax: 01224 626 390
Email: enquiries@aberdeenartscentre.org.uk
Web: www.aberdeenartscentre.org.uk
ADMINISTRATION:
Executive Manager: Paula Gibson
Communications Manager: Cecile Thiry
Administration Manager: Kathleen Innes
Front of House Manager: Cindy Blackmoor
Senior Technician: Barry Sherriffs
TECHNICAL:
For more information on Technical Specifications, visit the theatre website: www.aberdeenartscentre.org.uk
STAGE: Pros. Arch; 13'h x 29'5"w/ 3.96 x 8.97m. Arch to back wall: 19'/ 5.79m. Width wall to wall: 49'4" / 15.04m.
LIGHTING: Control: Etc Express 250 dmx lighting control console. 15 x 6way 2.5kw Paradim digital dimmers. Various lanterns available.
SOUND: Control: 1 x Allan & Heath GL3300. 1 x P.V 231fx Graphic Equaliser with built in F.L.S.
BACKSTAGE: Dressing Rooms; 3, accommodating 12-18. Male and Female toilet facilities. No showers.
STAGE COMMUNICATIONS: Ring Intercom. Show relay to Dressing Rooms with call facilities. Bar Bell situated at Prompt Corner.

Aberystwth, Ceredigion

ABERYSTWYTH ARTS CENTRE
Penglais, Aberystwyth,
Ceredigion SY23 3DE Wales
Tel: 01970 622 882 BO: 01970 623 232
Stage Mgr: 01970 628774
Fax: 01970 622 883
Email: gar21@aber.ac.uk
Web: www.aberystwythartscentre.co.uk
ADMINISTRATION:
Props: University of Wales, Aberystwyth
Director: Gareth Lloyd Roberts
Administrator: Maris Davies
Technical Manager: Nick Bache (Tel: 01970 628774)
Email: nbb@aber.ac.uk
Front of House Manager: Auriel Martin
Policy: Drama, Ballet, Concerts, Recitals, Exhibitions, Courses, conferences and Films plus special events.
Touring professionals/local amateurs. Arts Centre comprises Theatr Y Werin (321 seats) plus Concert Hall (900 seats), Art Galleries, 100 Seat Studio, Cinema, and 3 Dance Studios.
TECHNICAL:
Theatr Y Werin
STAGE: open end or proscenium, flat with thrust or Orchestra Pit. Pros. opening 14.6m/12.7/11.0/9.75m; Ht. of Pros. and fly floors 6m; distance between fly floors 11m; Depth of Stage from Pros 8.93m (with thrust 12.9m); Ht to Grid 15.4m; 22 lines C/W double purchases; Bars 9.5m; Prompt Cnr. S.L. or rear auditorium.
LIGHTING: Switchboard: Rank Strand Gemini 2 rear auditorium.
OTHER: Dressing Rooms 6; Accom. 21; Chorus Room Accom. 30; 2 Shower suites.

Airdrie, Lanarkshire

AIRDRIE ARTS CENTRE
Anderson Street, Airdrie, Lanarkshire ML6 0AA Scotland
Tel: 01236 755 436
Web Site: www.northlanarkshire.gov.uk
Props: North Lanarkshire Council
Contact: Maureen Patterson
Airdrie Arts Centre aims to provide the arts in all its forms to the people of Airdrie

Aldershot, Hampshire

WEST END CENTRE
48 Queens Road, Aldershot,
Hampshire GU11 3JD
Tel: 01252 408 040 BO: 01252 330 040
Fax: 01252 408 041
Email: westendcentre@hants.gov.uk
Web Site: www.westendcentre.co.uk
ADMINISTRATION:
Manager: Barney Jeavons
A multi-disciplinary arts centre with a programme of music, theatre, cabaret, comedy, dance, exhibitions, arts and crafts.
Cap: 200
TECHNICAL:
LIGHTING: 48 15A circuits on internally wired barrel rig, 4 Zero88 Beta Packs (24 x 2KW channels), Zero88 DMX, Jands Event desk - 48 channels. Lanterns: 22 IKW Parcans, 32 650W Minims, 8 650W Profiles, 3 1KW Profiles.
SOUND: Foh: 3 KW Court Acoustic System, 3 QSC RMX 2450 amps, 40 ch Midas Verona Desk, Klark Technic DN360. Monitors: 4 sends controlled from FOH desk, 3 front wedges (Martin LE400) and 1 drum fill , 2 QSC RMX 2425 amps, 2 Klark Technic DN36. Outboard: 1 Drawmer DL441 Quad Compressor, 1 Drawmer DS404 Quad Gate, 1 Lexicon 250, 1 Roland SDE2000 delay. Mics: 6 SM58, 6 SM57, 1 SM91b, 3 D.I. boxes.

Alsager, Cheshire

ALSAGER ARTS CENTRE
MMU Cheshire, Crewe Green Road,
Crewe Cheshire CW1 5DU
Tel: 0161 247 5302
Email: a.a.c@mmu.ac.uk
Web Site: www.axisartscentre.org.uk
ADMINISTRATION:
Artistic Director: Neil Mackenzie
Tel: 0161 247 5353.
Email: n.k.mackenzie@mmu.ac.uk
Administrator: Sue Holt
Tel: 0161 247 5302. Email: s.a.holt@mmu.ac.uk
Senior Technician: Andy Clough
Tel: 0161 247 5316. Email: a.clough@mmu.ac.uk
Capacity: Axis Theatre: 150. Dance Studio: 125. Studio: 90.
TECHNICAL:
Axis Theatre:
LIGHTING: Control; 96 Channels (Zero 88 Chilli Dimmers). ZERO 88 Leap Frog 96 or ETC Express 96 lighting desk.
Lanterns; 22 x CCT Starlette 1000watt Fresnels, 15x Selcon, Acclaim Profiles 18 - 34, 10x Selcon Acclaim Profiles 24 - 44, 6 x Source4 Jr. 25-50, 20+ x Parcans depending on availability, Various stands/scaff etc.
SOUND: Soundcraft E8 8 channel + 2 stereo channel mixing desk, 1 x Crest CA12 power amplifiers, 2 x Ohm speakers with crossover. A larger PA can be installed if needed. Various mics, CD/Minidisc player, LCD Projectors etc. available on request.

Banbury

THE MILL ARTS CENTRE BANBURY
Spiceball Park Spiceball Park Road
Banbury Oxfordshire OX16 5QE
Tel: 01295 279002
Email: tony.snee@oxfordshire.gov.uk
Web Site: www.themillartscentre.co.uk
Head of Centre: Tony Snee
Technical Manager: Carl Lake
Capacity: 200

Barnstaple, Devon

PETROC COLLEGE THEATRE

Old Sticklepath Hill, Sticklepath,
Barnstaple, Devon EX31 2BQ
Tel: 01271 338 091 Fax: 01271 338 121
Email: postbox@petroc.ac.uk
Web Site: www.petroc.ac.uk
ADMINISTRATION:
Contact: Anna Valentine-Marfh
Cap: 120

Basingstoke, Berkshire

CENTRAL STUDIO

Queen Mary's College, Cliddesden Road,
Basingstoke, Hampshire RG21 3HF
Tel: 01256 417 511 BO: 01256 418 318
Fax: 01256 417 501
Email: steph.monger@qmc.ac.uk
Web Site: www.centralstudio.co.uk
ADMINISTRATION:
Theatre Manager: Stephanie Monger
Marketing & Publicity: Jodie Cooper
130 seater auditorium with audience seated on 3 sides (thrust).
Programming small scale touring theatre, live music, dance, film and children's theatre. The venue and its equipment is also available for hire. Central Studio also has access to a 400 seater proscenium arch theatre for larger events.
TECHNICAL:
Please contact Theatre Technician -Ryan Messer

Beaford

BEAFORD CENTRE

Greenwarren House, Beaford, Winkleigh,
Devon EX19 8LU
Tel: 01805 603 201 Fax: 01805 603 202
Email: info@beaford-arts.org.uk
Web Site: www.beaford-arts.org.uk
Director: Mark Wallace

Bellshill, Lanarkshire

BELLSHILL CULTURAL CENTRE

John Street, Bellshill, Lanarkshire ML4
1RJ Scotland
Admin: 01698 346 770
BO: 01698 302 993
Email: motherwellconcerthall@northlan.gov.uk
Web Site: www.northlanarkshire.gov.uk
ADMINISTRATION:
Props: North Lanarkshire Council
Capacity: 220

Billericay, Essex

BILLERICAY ARTS ASSOCIATION

The Fold 72 Laindon Road, Billericay,
Essex CM12 9LD
Tel 01277 659 286
Email: baathefold@yahoo.co.uk
Web Site: www.baathefold.org.uk
ADMINISTRATION:
Registered Charity: Billericay Arts Association
Capacity/Seated: 70
Secretary: Eddie Philpott

Bingley, West Yorkshire

BINGLEY ARTS CENTRE

Main Street, Bingley, West Yorkshire
BD16 2LZ
Tel: 01274 519814
Email: office@bingleyartscentre.co.uk
Web Site: www.bingleyartscentre.co.uk
ADMINISTRATION
Props: Bingley Arts Centre
Main Auditorium Cap: 359

Birkenhead, Merseyside

STARLIGHT YOUTH THEATRE

129 - 131 Telegraph Road, Heswall,
Wirral, Merseyside CH60 0AF
Tel: 0151 342 2706 Mob: 07761 765 782 / 07842 272 808
Email: andy@starlightyouththeatre.co.uk
Web: www.starlightyouththeatre.co.uk
Founders: Andy & Jacqui Miles

Birmingham, West Midlands

MIDLANDS ARTS CENTRE

Cannon Hill Park, Birmingham B12 9QH
Admin: 0121 446 3200 BO: 0121 446 3232 Fax: 0121 446 3201
Email: info@macbirmingham.co.uk
Web Site: www.macbirmingham.co.uk
ADMINISTRATION:
Props: Midlands Arts Centre
Chief Executive: Dorothy Wilson
Head of Administration: Sue Longfils
Head of Communications: Lindsey Cook
Operations Director: Michelle Smith
Policy: Concerts, Films, Visiting Companies, Festivals, Professional Music, Theatre, Literature Events, Education and Comedy Programmes, Exhibitions.

Perfs: Various, 10.30, 13.00, 14.30, 20.00, 19.30.
Seating: the Theatre: 220 (The Theatre can be adapted to suit particular type of play.); the Hexagon: 86; the Open Air Arena Theatre: 470; the Cinema: 150.
Dressing Rooms: the Theatre: 2, the Hexagon: 2; Showers.
Cafe and Bar.
Membership: TMA, ACA

Blackwood, Gwent

BLACKWOOD MINERS INSTITUTE

High Street, Blackwood, Gwent NP12
1BB Wales
BO: 01495 227 206 Fax: 01495 226 457
Email: bmi@caerphilly.gov.uk
Web: www.blackwoodminersinstitute.com
ADMINISTRATION
Props: Caerphilly County Borough Council
General Manager (Programming): Sharon Casey
Email: caseys@caerphilly.gov.uk
Technical Manager: Robin Bainbridge.
Email: bainbr@caerphilly.gov.uk
Cap: Auditorium; Floor level 156 seats, Rake 187 seats, Balcony 56 seats. Total: 399. Abingdon Studio, 20-30.
TECHNICAL:
STAGE: Proscenium arch opening 7.18m x 4.2m. Performance area 8.1m x 6m (including apron). Wing space 1.3m (SR/SL). Height to grid 5.04m at rear of stage, no flying. Tab tracks US, MS, DS. Stage raked 1:24, hardboard, suitable for dance (not barefoot). Dock Doors 2m x 2.5m. 'Flat' - Floor Space Performance Area; Floor space 14m x 9m (with rake & balcony seating only). Floor space 14m x 20m (fully retracted seating). Get-in; via car park at rear of building - double doors into the auditorium. White Cyclorama Cloth. Backstage crossover. Red House Tabs - operated from SR or control room. Orchestra area available by removing 4 rows of seats, accommodates 30. Petrof Baby Grand Piano, 7 Octave (lives on flat). 2 pairs of black legs available (4 in total). 6 of 10 x 6 Hard Black Maskers available. 12 stage weights & braces available. 12 of 6 x 4 steeldeck staging available. 9 of 8 x 4 steeldeck staging available. Various quantities of legs for steeldeck available (sizes 15', 30', 45').
LIGHTING: 3 colour wash & specials, 1 ETC Congo Jnr Lighting desk. Please contact the technical department for more information.
SOUND: Sound system available. Please contact the technical department for more information.
STAGE MANAGEMENT: Prompt positions SL & SR (SR in auditorium)
DRESSING ROOMS; 2, accommodating 34. Access by stairs. (Unfortunately backstage is not accessible for wheelchair users)

Boston, Lincolnshire

BLACKFRIARS ARTS CENTRE

Spain Lane, Boston,
Lincolnshire PE21 6HP
Mgt :01205 363 075 BO: 01205 363 108
Email: director@blackfriars.uk.com
Web www.blackfriarsartscentre.co.uk
ADMINISTRATION:
Props: Blackfriars Arts Centre Ltd
Technical Manager: Megan Rodgers
Policy: Touring, Amateurs, Outreach and Community Arts Development
Auditorium Seats: 229 constant raked. Fully licensed bar.
TECHNICAL:
Stage: Proscenium Stage with 0.91m apron, Flat: Pros. Opening 7.32m; Ht. of Pros. 3.96m; Depth of S/Line 7.32m; Ht. of Grid 9.14m; 17 lines, 20 stage weights. 10 braces; Scenery Flying Ht. 9.14m; Flying Bars 6.40m; W/Widths P.S. 2.05m, O.P. 1.44m; Prompt Cnr. P.S. Vinyl dance floor available with advanced notice.
Lighting: Switchboard: ETC Express 48 Channels; Control Box at rear of Auditorium; 8 1000w Sil 15 with attached Croma-Q Scrollers permanent FOH ;8 Selacon Pacific Profiles FOH; 10 Selacon Cyc. Floods ; 18 650 watt Fresnels ; 36 IWB channels as follow 12 FOH, 2 perch, 10 bar 1, 6 bar 2, 6 bar 3 ; 12 channels as floor dips
Sound Equipment: 1 Spirit Digital 328 Desk, 2 EV sx500 speakers installed in pros., 2 EV sx300 speakers+ 2 EV sx200 speakers for foldback, 2 sm58 mics, 4 AKG C1000s mics, 3 Crown Plate mics, 5 Tie-clip radio mics, 1 Twin Cassette deck, 2 mini disc decks, 2 CD Players with autopause.
Other: Dressing Rooms 3; Accom. 20, Please note no showers. Washing machine & Tumble dryer; Show Relay.

Bracknell, Berkshire

SOUTH HILL PARK ARTS CENTRE

Ringmead, Bracknell,
Berkshire RG12 7PA
Admin: 01344 484 858 BO: 01344 484 123 Fax: 01344 411 427
Email: enquiries@southhillpark.org.uk
Web Site: www.southhillpark.org.uk
ADMINISTRATION:
The Wilde Theatre is part of the Arts Centre complex, which also includes a cinema, recital room, gallery, art and craft studios, workshops, rehearsal rooms, 50 seat studio theatre, and two bars.
Props: Bracknell Forest Borough Council
Chief Executive: Ron McAllister
Technical Manager: Joe Malyan
Tel: 01344 413 531 Email: joe.malyan@southhillpark.org.uk
Policy: In-house theatre and music theatre productions, mid-scale theatre, music theatre and dance tours, concerts, amateur companies.
Seats: 328 (plus 70 standing) or 300 (with orchestra pit).
TECHNICAL:
Wilde Theatre:
STAGE: Stage width; 49', 16m. Prosc. Width; 27'6", 8.4m. Dock Doors - 2390mm x 3920mm. Stage Depth; 30'9", 9.38m. Stage Height, Floor to Grid; 26', 8m. Flying: 14 x Single purchase counterweight sets, 8 x Four line hemp sets, 1 x Separate counterweight set for house tabs. Operated from stage DSL, 1 x Motorised bar for cyclorama, blacks etc.
LIGHTING: Control; ETC Ion, 1000 channels. Dimmers; ETC Sensor dimmers, 130 x 3kW, 6 x 5Kw. Lanterns; 28 x Robert Juliat 310 fresnel 1.2 kW. 8 x Strand Harmony Fresnels 1kW. 4 x Strand Prelude Fresnels 650W. 22 x ETC Source 4 zooms 15/30 750W. 24 x ETC Source 4 zooms 22/50 750W. 4 x Strand Harmony Profiles 1kW. 30 x Parcan CP62 ONLY 1kW. 12 x Strand Iris 1 Floods 1kW. 5 x Strand coda 4 (4 x 500W floods). 2 x UV Canon 300W. 1 x Robert Juliat Marius followspot (1.2kW MSR).
SOUND: Mixer #1, 32 mono/8 VCA / 8 Audio/2 (+4 stereo) Soundcraft MH3. Mixer #2, 12 channel Soundcraft Spirit Folio. Graphics; Clarke Teknik DN360; Also 1 x BSS and 1 x Rane. Effects; 1 x SPX900, 1 x SPX990. Compressor; 8 channel Klark Teknik Square One. CD Player: Denon C630. Minidisc: Denon DNM 2000r. Amps: QSC RMX 5050, Crown Macrotech 2402, Crown 460 CSL. Speakers: 4 x Nexo PS15, 2 x Nexo LS1200, 4 x EV SX300.
STAGE COMMUNICATIONS: Prompt desk is DSR (can be moved into LX box for theatre in-the-round). Cuelight and headset facility. Backstage and foyer tannoy. Show relay to dressing rooms, green room.
Headsets: 5 x single muff. One channel. Flash button. 1 x double muff. One channel. Flash button.
BACKSTAGE FACILITIES: 3, accommodating; 32. 1 x Washing machine, 1 x Tumble dryer, 3 x Toilets, 2 x Showers. Show relay; To all dressing rooms, green room.

Braintree, Essex

TOWN HALL

Market Square, Braintree,
Essex CM7 3YG
Tel: 01376 557 776 Fax: 01376 344 345
Email: geoff.fuller@braintree.gov.uk
Web Site: www.braintree.gov.uk
ADMINISTRATION:
Contact: Geoff Fuller
Cap: 60

Brentford, Middlesex

WATERMANS

40 High Street, Brentford,
Middlesex TW8 0DS
Admin: 020 8232 1019
BO: 020 8232 1010
Email: info@watermans.org.uk
Web Site: www.watermans.org.uk
ADMINISTRATION:
Director: Jan Lennox
General Manager: Rachel Francis
Marketing Director: Erica Weston
Programme Administrator: Jason, Tel: 020 8232 1031 or email jason@watermans.org.uk.
Capacity: Theatre: 239; Foyer Downstairs: 300-400; Studio 1: 80; Studio 2: 20; Cinema: 125; Gallery space: 80. All Available for public hire.
For more information about availability and prices contact the Customer Relationship Managers in charge of hiring:
Day: Mirko Petrovich.
Tel: 020 8232 1019 or mirko@watermans.org.uk
Evening: Edoardo Zollo.
Tel: 020 8232 1019 or edoardo@watermans.org.uk
TECHNICAL:
STAGE: Proscenium arch with small thrust. No rake. Suitable for dance. 1 baby grand piano available for performance, good. Smoke machine.
STAGE MANAGEMENT: PA and tannoy to the dressing rooms
BACKSTAGE FACILITIES: 2 dressing rooms accommodate 10, Green Room, wardrobe with washing machine.
STAFF: Technical staff - 3 technicians, ushers available
Technical specs and lighting plans available. Contact Technical Manager: Ryan Beattie, tel: 020 8232 1042 or ryan@watermans.org.uk.

Brentwood, Essex

BRENTWOOD THEATRE

15 Shenfield Road, Brentwood, Essex CM15 8AG
BO: 01277 200 305 Admin: 01277 230 833 Stage door: 01277 226 658
Email: david@brentwood-theatre.org
Web Site: www.brentwood-theatre.org
ADMINISTRATION:
Props: Brentwood Theatre Trust
Cap: Seated 80-170; Standing 270
Production Manager: David Zelly
Email: david@brentwood-theatre.org

Brentwood Theatre is a professional, community theatre based in the town centre, giving access to professional and non-professional performers. Musicals, plays, recitals, drama, comedy and chil-

dren's shows are all represented at this unique and friendly venue, with a different show nearly every week.
TECHNICAL:
Full lighting and sound rig, jands LX desk soundcraft spirit sound desk 10m x 7m acting area. Flat floor stage. Tiered moveable seating. F.O.H and licensed bar.

Bridgnorth, Shropshire

BRIDGNORTH LEISURE CENTRE

Northgate, Bridgnorth,
Shropshire WV16 4ER
Tel: 01746 761 541
Email: debbie.swales@shropshire.gov.uk
Web Site: www.shropshire.gov.uk
ADMINISTRATION
Props: Bridgnorth District Council
Cap: Main Hall 650; Small Hall 200
Manager: Debbie Swales
Technical Manager: Paul Evans
Lounge bar available.

Bridgwater, Somerset

BRIDGWATER ARTS CENTRE

11-13 Castle Street, Bridgwater,
Somerset TA6 3DD
Tel: 01278 422 700 / 1
Fax: 01278 447 402
Email: info@bridgwaterartscentre.co.uk
Web: www.bridgwaterartscentre.co.uk
ADMINISTRATION:
Centre Manager: Charlie Dearden
Emaill: charlie@bridgwaterartscentre.co.uk
Marketing and Development Officer: Rachel Hill
Email: rachel@bridgwaterartscentre.co.uk
We programme new work, physical theatre, mixed media, new adaptations of classics. It is best to post or email information before making a telephone call.
Capacity: seated 166
TECHNICAL:
For more information contact the Technical Manager, Adrian Baker, on: adrian@bridgwaterartscentre.co.uk.
STAGE: 7.2m w x 3.1m h x 4.08m d. Rake 1.5 degrees. Get in: Through 1.99m by 0.75m door, a couple of steps.
LIGHTING: 2 patt 23 mk II, 650W profile. 8 Strand Quartet 22/40 profile. 1 patt 23 mk I, 650W profile no shutters. 2 Strand Prelude 28/40 profile. 2 Furse SPR, 500W profile no shutters. 2 Strand Prelude F Fresnel. 1 patt 263, 1kW profile. 2 Strand Prelude PC. 4 patt 223, 650W Fresnel. 6 Thomas CP62 1kW parcans. 4 patt 60 floods, 500W. 6 Furse 4.5" lens fresnel, 500W. 24 dimming channels: Jands Event 24 desk, 4 Zero88 betapack six channel dimmers, 2kW/channel, 7kW/pack, 18kW (80A) total power available. All lighting has 15A plugs adn sockets.
SOUND: FOH: 2 RCF Event 3000 speakers 15" + 1"horn; 2 JBL SR 4715 bass speakers 2 x 15"; QSC PLX 3402 amplifier, 1100W/ch.; QSC PLX 3602 amplifier 1100W/ch.; Behringer electronic crossover; DBX 1231 Graphic EQ.
STAGE: 3 x JBL MR902 wedge monitors 12" + 1.75"horn; 2 x RCF Art300 12" + horn; 2 x Yamaha SM15V monitors 15" + horn; QSC USA1310 amplifier 600W/ch; Chevin A500 amplifier 600W/ch; Yamaha Q2031 graphic eq.; Phonic 1/3rd octave graphic eq. Microphones from Shure, Audio Technica, AKG, Beyer etc. 7 di boxes. Control: Allen Heath GL3-16 16 ch. mixer with 4 prefader and 2 postfader auxiliary sends; 16 + 8 multicore; Korg digital reverb; Behringer Multicom, 4 ch. comp/lim; Behringer Composer 2 ch. compressor / gate.
STAGE COMMUNICATIONS: Techpro headset intercom, 5 stations; show relay to dressing rooms
DRESSING ROOMS: 2.

Bridport, Dorset

BRIDPORT ARTS CENTRE

South Street, Bridport, Dorset DT6 3NR
Tel: 01308 427 183 BO: 01308 424 204
Fax: 01308 459 166
Email: info@bridport-arts.com
Web Site: www.bridport-arts.com
ADMINISTRATION:
Director: Lindsay Brooks
Email: lindsay@bridport-arts.com
Programme Manager: Margie Barbour
Marketing Manager: Eleanor Mottram
Capacity: 200 Seated, 300 Standing
Please contact the venue for a tech. spec.

Bristol

ALBANY CENTRE

Shaftesbury Avenue, Montpelier, Bristol, Avon BS6 5LT
Tel: 0117 330 5038
Web Site: www.albanycentre.org

WATERSHED MEDIA CENTRE

1 Canons Road, Bristol, Avon BS1 5TX
Tel: 0117 927 2082 Fax: 0117 921 3958
BO: 0117 927 5100
Email: info@watershed.co.uk, events@watershed.co.uk
Web Site: www.watershed.co.uk
ADMINISTRATION:
Props: Watershed Arts Trust
Managing Director: Dick Penny
Events Manager: Amy Joce
Technical Resources Manager: Ray Luton
Cap: 120, theatre style. Cinema, 200.

Bromley, Kent

RIPLEY ARTS CENTRE

24 Sundridge Avenue, Bromley, Kent BR1 2PX
Tel/ Fax: 020 8464 5816
Email: enquiries@bromleyarts.com
Web Site: www.bromleyarts.com
Administration: Thelma K Richardson
Seating Capacity: 80.

Broxbourne, Hertfordshire

BROXBOURNE ARTS FORUM

67 Riversmead, Hoddesdon,
Hertfordshire EN11 8DP
Tel: 01992 465 383
Chairman: 01992 466627
Email: info@broxbournearts.org.uk
Web Site: www.broxbournearts.org.uk
ADMINISTRATION:
Chairman: J. Malcolm Gordon
Programme Director: Mrs. Lee Rayner

Bury, Lancashire

THE MET ARTS CENTRE

Market Street, Bury, Lancashire BL9 0BW
Mgt: 0161 761 7107 BO: 0161 761 2216
Fax: 08700 520 297
Email: post@themet.biz
Web Site: www.themet.biz
Manager: David Agnew
Technical Manager: Chris McClung

Cardiff, South Glamorgan

CHAPTER ARTS CENTRE

Market Road, Canton, Cardiff, South Glamorgan CF5 1QE Wales
Tel: 029 2031 1050 BO: 029 2030 4400
Email: enquiry@chapter.org
Web Site: www.chapter.org
ADMINISTRATION:
Theatre Manager: Cathy Boyce
Email: cathy.boyce@chapter.org
At our main site in Canton, west of Cardiff City Centre you'll find 3 theatres, 2 cinemas, a gallery, studios, 2 bars, a cafe, over 60 cultural workspaces and more! We're open 7 days a week from 10.00am to 11.00pm (often later) and admission is free, so just drop in and check out what's happening. Chapter Gallery and Shop is open (during exhibitions) from Tues - Sunday, 11am - 8pm.
Cap: 120
For more information on Venue Hire, telephone: 029 2031 1058, or email: nicky.keeping@chapter.org

LLANOVER HALL ARTS CENTRE
Romilly Road, Canton, Cardiff, South Glamorgan CF5 1FH Wales
Tel: 029 2063 1144 Fax: 029 2063 1142
Email: LlanoverHallArts@cardiff.gov.uk
Web Site: www.cardiff.gov.uk
ADMNISTRATION:
Props: Cardiff Council
Contact: Will Barrett Soliz.
Mob: 07961 073830. Email: willbarrettsoliz@talktalk.net
We welcome all middle and small-scale touring companies with at least one months notice. The building has disabled access throughout. Cafe and on-site parking.
TECHNICAL:
STAGE: 18m x 9m x 4.5m(to lighting rig). LIGHTING: Full blackout; 40 circuits, 12 Channel 2 Way Desk, SOUND:Small sound set-up, Mini Disc, 6ft x 6ft stage door, friendly technician! 24 channel Alcora desk; Spirit Folio Sound desk; LCD projection & Graphics PC by arrangement.

Carlisle, Cumbria

THE SANDS CENTRE
The Sands, Carlisle, Cumbria CA1 1JQ
Arts & Events: 01228 625 208 Fax: 01228 625 666 BO: 01228 625 222
Email: sandscentre@carlisle.gov.uk
Web Site: www.thesandscentre.co.uk
ADMINISTRATION:
Props: Carlisle City Council
Manager: Tom Rice
Technical Manager: Richard Lloyd
Policy: Dance, Ballet, Ice shows, Theatre, Musicals, Comedy, Orchestral, Operatic, and Musical Concerts.
Capacity: Main Hall: Theatre style, 1,350, Cabaret style, 650. Secondary Hall: Theatre style, 250, Cabaret: 200. Eden Suite: Theatre style, 75
TECHNICAL:
STAGE: Hall Dimensions; Height from floor to lower grid, 9m (29'6"), Stage to lower grid, 7.7m (25'6"), Hall Dimensions (Floor space without stage), 36m (118') x 26m (85'). Versatile stage size from 1.2m/8ft sq. up to 9.7m (32ft) x 21.9(72ft), average height of 1.2m (4ft). Load-In Access door: w 3.5m (11'4"), h 3.5m (11' 4").
LIGHTING: Control; Strand 520i (250ch). 3 x 4 500w Cell Codas, 16 x 1K Fresnels, 44 x par 64's, 6 x 2K alto Fresnels, 8 x 1K Selecon pacific profiles, 18 x 1.2K 11/26 cantatas'. Followspots; 2 x Robert Juliat 1200w followspots. Dimmers; 108 Dimmers- 60 ways of 2K (Control: Green ginger), 48 ways of 2K (Control: Zero 88 ID1216)
SOUND: Foh rack; CD/MD/FOH EQ/Mon EQ/Delays EQ/Peavey FX unit. Mixer; Allen & Heath GL3300. Delays; 12 x Bose 802 (3 lines separately timed and amplified). Foh speakers; DB Audiotechnic DVA LINE ARRAY comprising, 4x T4 modules per side plus 1x S20 2x18" sub, 2 x Martin Audio F10's - centre fill. Monitors; 2 x Martin Audio F12's. Mics; a selection of mics are available.
STAGE MANAGEMENT: Comms, show relay and backstage paging. No cue lights or any kind of camera/monitor system.
ADDITIONAL: 1 Steinway Concert Grand model D, (please specify tuning pitch), 1 Steinway Baby grand model A, UV lighting, Laser, Strobes, Pyrotechnics, Smoke/Haze/Fog, Naked flame.
BACKSTAGE FACILITIES: Dressing Rooms; 5, with Hot & cold water, Power points, Mirrors, Clothes hooks and Showers. Wardrobe; Automatic washing machine, Tumble dryer, Ironing board + Iron. Production/Company Manager room with internet access. Adequate parking free of charge for most size productions.

Chipping Norton, Oxfordshire

THE THEATRE
2 Spring Street, Chipping Norton, Oxfordshire OX7 5NL
Mgt: 01608 642349 BO: 01608 642350
Fax: 01608 642324
Email: admin@chippingnortontheatre.com
Web: www.chippingnortontheatre.com
ADMINISTRATION:
Props: Council of Company
Stage Manager: Chris Hoad
Email: stage@chippingnortontheatre.com
General Manager: Jo Ludford
Email: operations@chippingnortontheatre.com
Policy: Touring Theatre (including Children's), concerts, films, opera, dance, occasional own productions, including yearly pantomime.
Perfs: Variable
Seats: 213, 4 wheelchairs. Bar, Art Gallery
TECHNICAL:
STAGE: Proscenium Stage, Flat; Width of Pros 5.34m; Ht. of Pros. 3.46m; Depth of Stage 7.9m; W/Widths 1.22m; Ht. of Grid 3.6m. Flying facilities: 15 hemp sets, 4 winched LX bars. Prompt Cnr. P.
LIGHTING: Control: 72 ways. Dressing Rooms 3; Accom. 16.
Membership: TMA

Cirencester, Glocestershire

BREWERY ARTS
Brewery Court, Cirencester, Gloucestershire GL7 1JH
Admin: 01285 657 181 BO: 01285 655 522 Fax: 01285 644 060
Email: admin@breweryarts.org.uk
Web Site: www.breweryarts.org.uk
ADMINISTRATION:
Props: Gloucestershire City Council
Artistic Director: Louise Evans
Email: exhibitions@newbreweryarts.org.uk
Communications Officer: Cora Sild
Email: cora@newbreweryarts.org.uk
Cap: 120 Seated

Clitheroe, Lancashire

PLATFORM GALLERY
Station Road, Clitheroe, Lancashire BB7 2JT
Tel: 01200 443 071 Fax: 01200 414 556
Email: platform.gallery@ribblevalley.gov.uk
Web Site: www.ribblevalley.gov.uk
Contact: Elizabeth Martch-Harry

Colchester, Essex

COLCHESTER ARTS CENTRE
St Mary-at-the-Walls, Church Street, Colchester, Essex CO1 1NF
Tel: 01206 500 900 Fax: 01206 500 187
Email: info@colchesterartscentre.com
Web Site: www.colchesterartscentre.com
ADMINISTRATION:
Director: Anthony Roberts
Technical Manager: Mark Butchers
Small scale venue promoting a wide variety of performing arts including theatre, dance, live art, film, folk, jazz, gigs and clubs.

Cookstown, County Tyrone

THE BURNAVON ARTS & CULTURAL CENTRE
Burn Road, Cookstown, County Tyrone, BT80 8DN Northern Ireland
BO tel: 028 8676 9949 Admin tel: 028 8676 7994 Fax: 028 8676 5853
Email: caroline.sheehy@cookstown.gov.uk
Web Site: www.burnavon.com
ADMINISTRATIN:
Centre Manager: Tony McCance
Email: tony.mccance@cookstown.gov.uk
Venue Administrator: Caroline Sheehy
Technicians: Roy Stewart & Denver McCord
TECHNICAL:
If you require more information on the technical facilities, please contact the Burnavon technical team on 028 8676 9949 or email roy.stewart@cookstown.gov.uk
STAGE: Performing area 8.5m x 6.2m - pros opening 8.5m x 5m. Wing widths- SR 1.4m - SL 1.5m. Floor maple black, no rake , suitable for dance, lino not avail-

able. Crossover 1.2m wide. Grid height 8.5m - max flying height 4m. Get-In via dock door 2.2m x 5m, through scene dock at street level. Orchestra pit - can accommodate 20.
LIGHTING: Strand 520i Lighting Console. 96 circuits at 2.5Kw. DMX Splitter box. 16 Strand 180 SL profiles at 600w. 16 Strand 180 SL profiles at 600w. 16 Strand Cantata fresnels at 1.2Kw with barn doors. 20 parcans at 1 Kw (10 - CP62 medium flood). (10 - CP61 frosted spot). 10 ETC Source Four PARs at 575w. 6 Strand Coda 500 flood battens. 4 Martin Mac 250s. 1 Selecon Chorus 1200 Follow Spot.
SOUND: Control: Allen & Heath GL3300 32:8:2 desk operated from back of auditorium. Allen & Heath GL2200 24:4:2 desk operated from control room (if required). DBX 2231 Equalizer/Limiter with Type III NR (31-Band Stereo Graphic Equalizer). 1 Crown CE 1000. 2 Crown Microtech 2400. Martin Audio WX3A System Controller. 4 Martin Audio EM76 speakers. 2 Martin AudioEM251 subs. 2 Martin Audio EM56 speakers (in-fills). 1 Behringer MDX 4400 (4 channels compression). 1 Denon DN-2000R mini disc player/recorder. 2 Tascam MD-350 mini disc player/recorder. 1 Marantz CC3000 5 disc compact disc player. 1 Tascam 130 cassette player/recorder. 1 Lexicon MPX100 Dual Processor. 24 way patch from desk to SR, 4 returns. 12 way cross patch to SL. 12 way patch to orchestra pit.
STAGE MANAGEMENT: Prompt corner stage right, no cue lights, show relay/tanoy to dressing rooms. Can points - USL & USR, fly floor, sound desk, lighting desk, follow spot.
BACKSTAGE FACILITIES: 2 large dressing rooms & 2 smaller dressing rooms. Green room with access via stage door. Back stage facilities equipped for disabled performers & crew.

Coventry, West Midlands

WARWICK ARTS CENTRE

University of Warwick, Coventry, Warwickshire CV4 7AL
Admin: 024 7652 3734 Tech: 024 7652 3793 Stage Door: 024 7652 2442
Mrkting: 024 7652 4669
Fax: 024 7652 4525
Email: arts.centre@warwick.ac.uk
Web Site: www.warwickartscentre.co.uk
ADMINISTRATION:
Props: University of Warwick
Director: Alan Rivett
Events Manager: Laura Elliot
Tel: 024 7652 4439
Policy: A mixed programme of middle scale touring; opera; concerts; dance and drama with an independent film programme. The Arts Centre has five auditoria: Concert Hall, Theatre, Studio, Conference Room and Film Theatre, also art gallery, a bookshop, restaurant and shop.
Perfs: Nightly (theatre) 7.30p.m. Occasional mid-week/Sat.Mats. 2.30 & 5.00p.m.
Capacity: Theatre 543/573. Studio Theatre, max. 200, (flexible bleachers seating), Cinema 226, Concert Hall 1300.
Cafe Bar, Restaurant open Mon-Sat 9.00a.m. - 8.00p.m.; two licensed bars, large foyer accommodating 2,000. Bookshop open Monday to Saturday.
TECHNICAL:

Main Auditorium:
STAGE: Adjustable pros. arch. Performing area 27.32m x 12.2m - pros. opening 10.98m x 5.35m - 6.4m - wing widths 7.31m SR, 7.31m SL. No rake - floor hardboard over birch ply/demountable, suitable for dance, lino available, backstage crossover, stage heated. Grid height 18.28m - 36 counterweight sets, double purchase, 0.22m apart - no tab track - 250kg permitted on bars - maximum flying height 16.75m. White plaster back wall used as cyclorama - blue house tabs, flown. Forestage 2.74m x 10.98m. Orchestra pit forestage lift/understage area, accommodates 70. Get-in via step 0.91m - dock doors 2.28m x 7.01m. Tallescope. Large paintframe and workshop facilities available.
LIGHTING: Switchboard: Strand 530i; 99 dimmers; 93 at 2kw, 6 at 5kw. Lanterns: 10 SIL 15, 24 SIL 30, 36 1 kw Fresnels, 8 2kw PCs, 5 CCT 4 compartment floods. 4 x SIL 15, 24 x SIL 30, 12 x ADB Europe, 44 x 1kw Fresnel, 8 x 2kw PC, 5 x CCT 4 compartment floods.
SOUND: Turbosound speakers with crest amps: 2 Denon 1050 Minidisk, Soundcraft K3 desk 32/8, Screen.
DRESSING ROOMS: 6, plus large chorus room; 8 showers; Orchestra Pit 30-40.

Studio Theatre:
Lighting switchboard Strand 530; 46 2kw dimmers. Sound: DDA desk 16-8, tannoy CPA 15 + CPA 12 speakers, HH Amps.

Membership: TMA. Association of British Concert Promoters.

Dalkeith, Mid Lothian

DALKEITH ARTS CENTRE

White Hart Street, Dalkeith, Mid Lothian EH22 1AE Scotland
Tel: 0131 663 6986
Email: library.hq@midlothian.gov.uk
Web Site: www.midlothian.gov.uk
Props: Midlothian Council.
Cap: 120

Deal, Kent

ASTOR COMMUNITY THEATRE

Stanhope Road, Deal, Kent CT14 6AB
BO Tel: 01304 381 134 Tel: 01304 370 220
Email: info@theastor.org
Web Site: www.theastor.org
ADMINISTRATION:
Managing Director: James Tillitt
Cap: 150 Theatre Style, 120 Cabaret, 250 Standing.

Dorchester, Dorset

DORCHESTER ARTS CENTRE

School Lane, The Grove, Dorchester, Dorset DT1 1XR
BO: 01305 266 926
Email: enquiries@dorchesterarts.org.uk
Web Site: www.dorchesterarts.org.uk
ADMINISTRATION:
Director: Sharon Hayden
Contact: Irene Archibald
We use the Corn Exchange, owned by the Town Council. Capacity: 150, raked seating. Our outdoor space is Mambury Rings, up to 1000, no electricty.

Downpatrick, County Down

DOWN ARTS CENTRE

2-6 Irish Street, Downpatrick, County Down BT30 6BP Northern Ireland
Tel: 028 4461 0747 Fax: 028 4461 6621
Email: downartscentre@downdc.gov.uk
Web Site: www.downartscentre.com
ADMINISTRATION:
Props: Down District Council
Contact: Donna Rogan (donna.rogan@downdc.gov.uk)
Capacity: 180 Seating, 300 Standing.

Dumfries, Dumfries & Galloway

GRACEFIELD ARTS CENTRE

28 Edinburgh Road, Dumfries DG1 1NW
Tel: 01387 262 084
Email: arts@dumgal.gov.uk
Web Site: www.artandcraftsouthwestscotland.com
Visual Arts Development Officer: Colin Tennant
Email: colin.tennant@dumgal.gov.uk

Durham, County Durham

DURHAM ART GALLERY
Aykley Heads, Durham, County Durham DH1 5TU
Tel: 0191 384 2214 Fax: 0191 386 1770
Email: dli@durham.gov.uk
Web Site: www.durham.gov.uk/dli
Events & Exhibitions Officer: James Lowther

LAMPLIGHT ARTS CENTRE
Lamplight Arts Centre Front Street, Stanley, Co. Durham DH9 0NA
Tel: 01207 218893 BO: 01207 218899
Email: lamplight@leisureworksonline.co.uk
Web Site: www.leisureworksonline.co.uk/lamplightarts.cfm
ADMINISTRATION:
General Manager: Louise Strong
Capacity: 410 Theatre Style
TECHNICAL:
STAGE: Get-in: Street level. A large roller-shutter dock door is located at the left-hand end of the building, with access via a small service road directly in front. Width between pros. Arch, 7.5m, Width behind pros. Arch, 9m, Depth from front edge to cyclorama wall, 7.5m. Stage lift at S/L, connecting the stage to auditorium level and other facilities, to assist disabled performers. Flying facilities; fly tower over the stage, with a hauling gantry positioned S/R. A number of scenery bars, hauled by hemp ropes, which are suitable for flying light-weight scenery.
LIGHTING: Control Desk: Zero 88 "Fat Frog". Power: The venue has an optional 125A, 3-phase cee-form touring socket at S/L. Dimmers: 6 No. 6 x 10A channel Strand Tempus dimmers, analogue-controlled, Via 2 No. demux units. A comprehensive patch-bay is located below the dimmers. An additional 2 No. 63A sockets to facilitate extra dimmers. Lantern Stock: 3 x Cantata Profile 18/32; 3 x Cantata Profile 11/26; 8 x assorted 500W profiles; 12 x 1kw Par cans; 5 x 200W floods; 20 x 1kw fresnels; 4 x 4 x 500w codas, rigged LX4; an assortment of 15A and 13A cables are available.
SOUND: Mixing desk: Midas Venice 32:4:2. Multicore: The multi-core has 12 stage sends, 2 FOH sends, 4 aux. Sends, and 4 talkback sends. Power: an optional 63A single-phase touring socket (cee-form) is located S/L. FOH: 4 x Bose 802 mounted in pairs either side of the proscenium arch. Powered by Yamaha and DVS power amps rack-mounted at S/L. Monitors: 2 x EV 300 cabs powered by a Citronic PPX 450 amp. Maestro induction-loop for hearing-impaired. Ultra-Curve Pro 31 band digital graphic equalizer. Marantz twin cassette deck. Marantz C.D. player. Denon mini-disc player. Yamaha reverb unit Rev500. A small selection of microphones and stands, XLR cables and other connections, is available.
DRESSING ROOMS: 1, with two small integral private rooms, at the rear of the stage, and a green room next door.

Dursley, Gloucestershire

PREMA
South Street, Uley, Dursley, Gloucestershire GL11 5SS
Admin/BO: 01453 860 703
Email: info@prema.demon.co.uk
Web Site: www.prema.demon.co.uk
ADMINISTRATION:
Artistic Director: Gordon Scott (gordon@prema.demon.co.uk)
Technical Officer: Mark Crowe (mark@prema.demon.co.uk)
Cap: 120
Interested in live art/physical theatre.

East Kilbride, South Lanarkshire

EAST KILBRIDE ARTS CENTRE
51-53 Old Coach Road, East Kilbride, South Lanarkshire G74 4DU Scotland
Tel: 01355 261 000 Fax: 01355 261280
Email: lynn.mcdougall@southlanarkshire.gov.uk
Web Site: www.southlanarkshire.gov.uk
Contact: Lynn McDougall

Edinburgh, Mid Lothian

CRAIGMILLAR COMMUNITY ARTS CENTRE
58 Newcraighall Road, Edinburgh, Mid Lothian EH15 3HS Scotland
Tel: 0131 669 8432 Fax: 0131 661 5826
Email: craigmillarcommunityarts@gmail.com
Web: www.craigmillarcommunityarts.org.uk
ADMINISTRATION:
Arts Co-ordinator: Michael Greenlaw
Email: coordinator@craigmillarcommunityarts.org.uk
Events Co-ordinator: Emma Coleman
Email: events@craigmillarcommunityarts.org.uk

NORTH EDINBURGH ARTS CENTRE
15A Pennywell Court Edinburgh EH4 4TZ
Admin/BO: 0131 315 2151
Fax: 0131 332 2521
Email: admin@northedinburgharts.co.uk
Web Site: www.northedinburgharts.co.uk
ADMINISTRATION:
Operations Manager: Sandra Newby
Technician: John McCaffrey
technician@northedinburgharts.co.uk
Open since November 2002, North Edinburgh Arts Centre presents in its 96-150 seat studio theatre, a diverse programme of small-scale UK and international touring theatre, dance, film and live music.

THE SCOTTISH STORYTELLING CENTRE
43-5 High Street, Edinburgh, Mid Lothian EH1 1SR Scotland
Tel: 0131 556 9579 Fax: 0131 557 5224
Email: erica@scottishstorytellingcentre.com
Web: www.scottishstorytellingcentre.co.uk
ADMINISTRATION:
Assistant Manager: Erica Brooks
Policy: We present an exciting programme of live storytelling performances, theatre and literature, plus exciting visual arts, workshops and training events.
Cap: 99 Seated

THEATRE WORKSHOP
Out of the Blue Drill Hall, 36 Dalmeny Street, Edinburgh EH6 8RG Scotland
Tel: 0131 555 3854 Mob: 07725 226 913
Email: keith.tws@hotmail.co.uk, jez.tws@hotmail.co.uk
Web Site: www.theatre-workshop.com
ADMINISTRATION:
Relationship & Development Manager: Keith Bell
Contact: Jez Arrow
Cap: 200

Epping Forest, Essex

EPPING FOREST ARTS
Epping Forest Arts, 25 Hemnall Street, Epping, Essex CM16 4LU
Tel: 01992 564 551 / 9
Email: efa@eppingforestdc.gov.uk
Web Site: www.eppingforestdc.gov.uk
Arts Officer: Felicity Hall

Evesham, Worcestershire

EVESHAM ARTS CENTRE
Victoria Avenue, Evesham, Worcestershire WR11 4QH
Tel 01386 488 83 Mob: 07876 297898
Email: events@eveshamartscentre.co.uk
Web Site: www.eveshamartscentre.co.uk
Capacity: Main Theatre, 312. Studio, 60 seats.
Venue Hire: Chris Bloomfield

Technical Manager: Greg Clarke
TECHNICAL:
If you require more technical information contact the Senior Technician on: tech@eveshamartscentre.co.uk.
STAGE: Proscenium opening 40 feet, Performing Area 40 feetx 20 feet approx, Flat stage with no rake. Height to grid 18 feet. No flying facilities. Orchestra Pit 35 feet x8 feet. Can accommodate 10 musicians + MD. Crossover behind stage. Get in at rear. Scene dock doors approximately 6' wide and 25' high.
LIGHTING: Computer controlled Strand LBX Lighting Console. 36x2 Channels + 24 subs or 48 channels. Assortment of lanterns. DMX Patch.
SOUND: Allen and Heath Mixer GL2200 24+2x2 Martin Speakers. QSC Amps. Denon Dual CD Player. Mini Disc Player.
STAGE MANAGEMENT: Prompt Corner DSL. Flat screen stage video monitor. Tannoy to dressing rooms.
BACKSTAGE FACILITIES: Dressing Rooms; 2, accommodating 20 -24. Shower and toilet facilities. Small Green Room. Audio monitor & flat screen video stage monitor in each DR. Backstage areas accessible to disabled performers and staff.

Exeter, Devon

EXETER PHOENIX
Bradninch Place, Gandy Street, Exeter, Devon EX4 3LS
Admin: 01392 667 065
BO: 01392 667 080
Email: phoenixadmin@exeterphoenix.org.uk
Web Site: www.exeterphoenix.org.uk
ADMINISTRATION:
Director: Patrick Cunningham (01392 667057)
Operations Manager: Rob McCulloch (01392 667060)
Technical Manager: Rick Wolkers
Tel: 07917 133660 Email: rick@exeter-phoenix.org.uk
Capacity: Theatre: Seated 216, Standing 450. Dance Studio, 70.
Black Box Studio, 40.
TECHNICAL:
Technical specification available upon request.

Falmouth, Cornwall

THE POLY
Church Street, Falmouth, Cornwall TR11 3EG
Admin: 01326 319 461 BO: 01326 319 461
Email: info@thepoly.org
Web Site: www.thepoly.org
Programme Director: Dot Peryer
Cap: 180 Seated

Fareham, Hampshire

THE ASHCROFT ARTS CENTRE
Osborn Road, Fareham, Hampshire PO16 7DX
Tel: 01329 235 161 BO: 01329 223 100
Fax: 01329 825 661
Email: ashcroft@hants.gov.uk
Web Site: www.ashcorft.org.uk
ADMINISTRATION:
Centre Director's: Annabel Cook
Technical Manager: James Lucas
Venue for touring professional theatre, music and dance.
Seating capacity of theatre: 117 raked/flexible
Bar/studio can accommodate upto 140 for music/cabaret events.
TECHNICAL:
Theatre performing area at floor level:- 6.1m x 7.6m. Floor, wood on wood rollers, narrow crossover. Height to grid 3.5m. Surrounded by black drapes. Entry via double doors directly onto stage.

Farnham, Surrey

FARNHAM MALTINGS ARTS & COMMUNITY CENTRE
Bridge Square, Farnham, Surrey GU9 7QR
Admin: 01252 718 001 BO: 01252 745 444 Fax: 01252 718177
Email: info@farnhammaltings.com
Web Site: www.farnhammaltings.com
ADMINISTRATION:
Director: Gavin Stride
Marketing Manager: Steve Gibbs
Capacity: Great Hall: 456 seated, 600 standing. Cellar Bar: 200 standing. Barley Room: 150, with own bar. Gallery - 2 flexible interjoined spaces for exhibitions or meetings.

Gainsborough, Lincolnshire

TRINITY ARTS CENTRE
Trinity Street, Gainsborough, Lincolnshire DN21 2AL
Admin: 01427 675 136 BO: 01427 676 655 Fax: 01427 811 198
Email: janet.keens@west-lindsey.gov.uk
Web Site: www.trinityarts.co.uk
ADMINISTRATION:
Props: West Lindsey District Council
General Manager: Janet Keens
Policy: Theatre, film, music, dance, kid's club and stand up comedy.
Cap: 200

Glasgow, Strathclyde

KILMARDINNY HOUSE ARTS CENTRE
50 Kilmardinny Avenue, Bearsden, Glasgow, Strathclyde G61 3NN Scotland
Tel/Fax: 0141 777 3090
Email: culture@eastdunbarton.gov.uk
Web Site: www.eastdunbarton.gov.uk
Props: East Dunbartonshire Council
Manager: David Kenvyn
Cap: 140

Goole, East Riding Of Yorkshire

THE GATE
c/o Goole Town Council, Alfred Taylor House, 17/23 Gladstone Terrace, Goole, East Yorkshire DN14 5AQ
Tel: 01405 763 652 Tel: 01405 720 219 (evening)
Email: charlie.gtc@btconnect.com
Web Site: www.thegategoole.com
ADMINISTRATION:
Policy: Theatre, music, dance, workshops, comedy, art projects.
Programming and Management: Charlie Studdy
Cap:100

Grantham, Lincolnshire

GUILDHALL ARTS CENTRE
St Peters Hill, Grantham, Lincolnshire NG31 6PZ
Tel: 01476 406166 BO: 01476 406158
Fax: 01476 406001
Email: granthamtic@southkesteven.gov.uk
Web Site: www.guildhallartscentre.com
ADMINISTRATION:
Props: South Kesteven District Council
Administration Manager (Room Hire Enquiries): Tracy Purdy
Email; t.purdy@southkesteven.gov.uk
Venue for performing and visual arts events. Full programme of music, drama, dance and workshops.
Cap: 210
TECHNICAL:
If you require more information, please contact the Technician, David Pike via; d.pike@southkesteven.gov.uk.

STAGE: Get-In: Via dock doors at the rear of the stage. Outer door W: 1.36m. H: 2m. Diagonal: 2.43m. Inner door W:

1.35m. H: 2m. Diagonal: 2.43m. Effects: 1 x Goblin Smoke Machine, 1 x Le Maitre Pyro duel detonator and pods (company to supply pyros), 1 x Acer PD116 digital projector (time required for rigging). Stage Power; 1 x 3Ph 63Amp Supply (stage left), 14x 13Amp supply located all around the stage.
LIGHTING: 12 x 1KW CCT Silhouette (15 32) (8 are permanently rigged FOH Bar1), 14 x 1 KW CCT Starlette Fresnel (6 are permanently rigged FOH Bar1), 14 x 650W CCT Minuette Fresnel, 6 x 650W CCT Minuette Profile, 12 x 1KW CCT Floods, 8 x 1KW Thomas Parcan, 2 x 2.5KW CCT Follow-spot, 1 x Bull Frog Zero88 control desk, 9 x zero88 Betapack rack. 6 channels per rack. Max handling 2.4Kw 10 amp per channel (DMX
control), 1 x 6 channel 5-amp switching pack for special effects (analogue control).
LX BARS: FOH Bar 1 at 14 Circuits, FOH Bar 2 at 14 Circuits, FOH Verticals at 6 Circuits, Stage Bar 3 at 14 Circuits, Stage Bar 4 at 14 Circuits.
SOUND: PA System; Fixed 4 x Bose Speakers FOH, Fixed 2 x Hz Speakers SL and SR, 4 x Peavey Wedge Monitors, 1 x Sony MD Player, 1 x Denon CD Player, 2 x Denon Cassette Player, 1 x B77 Revox, 1 x Yamaha SPX900, 1 x 16 channel Soundcraft Delta Mixing Desk.
MICROPHONES: 1 x Sennheiser 365 Radio Mic (handheld), 1 x Sennheiser 100 Radio Mic (handheld), 1 x Sennheiser 100 Radio Mic (lepel), 6 x A.K.G. 321, 2 x A.K.G. C568EB Rifle Mics, 3 x A.K.G. C547BL Condenser Plate Mics
STAGE COMMUNICATIONS: Four belt packs and headsets with 13 stations to provide full talkback communication. There is also incorporated into the system, a show, front of house and dressing room calls and loop system.
BACKSTAGE FACILITIES: Dressing Rooms; 2, with shower and toilet facilities.

Grimsby, NE Lincolnshire

CAXTON THEATRE & ARTS CENTRE

128 Cleethorpe Road, Grimsby, North East Lincolnshire DN31 3HW
BO: 01472 346 251 Tel: 01472 345 167 (after 6.30pm)
Email: Caxton.theatre@ntlworld.com
Web Site: www.caxtontheatre.com
Contact: Ian Hammond
Capacity: 184

Harlech, Gwynedd

THEATR HARLECH

Harlech, Gwynedd LL46 2PU Wales
BO: 01766 780 667
Email: post@theatrharlech.com
Web Site: www.theatrharlech.com
ADMINISTRATION:
Director: Andrew Orton
Status: National Touring House
Purpose-built theatre opened in 1972 - attached to Coleg Harlech (Residential College).
Funding: Venue funded by Arts Council of Wales, Gwynedd Council
Policy: Receiving theatre for professional companies performing in Welsh and English. Willing to premiere show.
Perfs: performances on approx.3-4 days a week - evening shows regularly start at 7.30p.m. - matinees held at 1.00p.m. on weekdays, 2.30p.m. on Saturdays.
Booking terms: Box Office split, guarantee and split.
Non-performance activities: Film, hire to community, snooker, art exhibitions, craft exhibitions, conferences, workshops.
Facilities: seating 260; raked. Catering: Bar and coffee shop/sales area. Access: theatre car park, railway station Harlech.
Facilities for the disabled: assistance available for disabled, ramped entrance, disabled lift. Other facilities: showers in dressing rooms.
TECHNICAL:
Stage: open stage with centre thrust, 'token' proscenium. Performing area 13.10m (apron 3.5m) x 9.90m (inc. apron) - pros. opening 13.10m x 4.72m (min) - 5.63 (max) - wing widths 1.52m. SR, 1.52m. SL No rake - floor sapele timber on joists, suitable for all dance, lino available, crossover, stage heated. 10 hemp sets plus 5 winch sets, tab track. 2 borders, 1 set tabs, surround, 4 tormentors, all black. 4 x 15A independent circuits. Forestage (apron) 3.50m x 13.5m. Get-in via dock door, 3.05m hjigh. Manual scenery hoist. Tallescope. Technical information sheets available.
Lighting: Strand M24 memory board, 60 circuits, 58 @ 2kw, 2 @ 5kw, 160A, 3 phase, operated from Control Room at rear of auditorium - 60A single phase supply stage right - 15 x Sil 30 1k Profiles, 19 x 1k Fresnels (9 x Patt.743, 6 x Harmony F, 4 x ADB0), 6 x Patt.123, 3 x Patt.23, 5 x 6ft battens, 1 x 2kw follow spot.
Sound: Operated from Control Room - Soundcraft Delta 200B 8-4-2 mixer, 2 x Carver 1.5 amps, 4 x Tannoy Puma speakers, 1 x Revox A77, 1 x Phillips CD, 2 x Casette Decks, 3 x Shure SM 58, mics, 3 x Shure 545F.

Harrow, Middlesex

HARROW ARTS CENTRE/TRAVELLERS STUDIO THEATRE

Uxbridge Road, Hatch End Pinner, Middlesex HA5 4EA
BO: 020 8416 8989 Fax: 020 8428 0121
Email: harrowartscentre@harrow.gov.uk
Web Site: www.harrowarts.com
Props: Arts Culture Harrow
Arts Centre Management: Jo Saunders
Technical Manager: Patrick Biles (patrick.biles@harrow.gov.uk)
Capacity: Elliot Hall, 350; Studio, 120.

Hastings, East Sussex

STABLES THEATRE & ART GALLERY

The Bourne, Hastings, East Sussex TN34 3BD
Tel/ BO: 01424 423221 Second line (VoIP): 05603 149539
Email: info@stables-theatre.co.uk
Web Site: www.stables-theatre.co.uk
ADMINISTRATION:
Chairman: Tim Pearce (tim.pearce@stables-theatre.co.uk)
We do 10 in house productions a year plus host local groups and professional items.
Cap: 120 Seated.
For more information on venue hire contact: Veronica Sceal. Email: veronica.sceal@stables-theatre.co.uk

Havant, Hampshire

THE SPRING ARTS AND HERITAGE CENTRE

56 East Street, Havant, Hampshire PO9 1BS
Admin/ BO: 023 9247 2700 Hirings: 023 9224 9060 Tech: 023 9224 9066
Email: info@thespring.co.uk
Web Site: www.thespring.co.uk
ADMINISTRATION:
Technical & Maintenance Manager: Simon Gray
Email: simong@thespring.co.uk
Marketing Manager: Darren Corps
Email: darrenc@thespring.co.uk
Cap: 130

Hebden Bridge, West Yorkshire

ARVON FOUNDATION

The Ted Hughes Arvon Centre, Lumb Bank, Heptonstall, Hebden Bridge, West Yorkshire HX7 6DF UK
Tel/Fax: 01422 843 714
Email: lumbbank@arvonfoundation.org
Web Site: www.arvonfoundation.org
Centre Director: Rebecca Evans and Liz Flanagan
Runs week long residential writing cours-

es, in all genres, throughout the year. A chance to live and work alongside professional writers and participate in writing workshops, as well as have one -to-one tutorial times Lumb Bank is set in a beautiful valley in West Yorkshire the former home of Ted Hughes.
Capacity: 18

Hemel Hempstead, Hertfordshire

LIFE AND SOUL ACADEMY

Boxmoor Hall, St Johns Road, Hemel Hempstead, Hertfordshire HP1 1JR
Tel: 01442 233050 Fax: 01442 233051
Email: info@lifeandsoulacademy.co.uk
Web Site: www.lifeandsoulacademy.co.uk
Managing Director: Miss Sally Jane Ilsley
Life and Soul Academy exists to provide creative opportunities and to offer the highest level of performing arts tuition accessible to the entire community with complete inclusion. The Academy provides a wide range of classes and workshops covering all aspects of dance and the arts.

Hereford, Herefordshire

THE COURTYARD

Herefordshire's Centre for the Arts.
Edgar Street, Hereford, Herefordshire HR4 9JR
Admin: 01432 346 500 BO: 01432 340 555 Front of House: 01432 346 530
Email: foh@courtyard.org.uk
Web Site: www.courtyard.org.uk
ADMINISTRATION:
Head of Sales & Marketing: Curtis Fulcher (curtis.fulcher@courtyard.org.uk)
Operations Manager: Alex Green (alex.green@courtyard.org.uk)
Front of House Manager: Phil Pearcy (phil.pearcy@courtyard.org.uk)
Production Manager: Carl Hulme (carl.hulme@courtyard.org.uk)
Policy: Multi-arts, including touring theatre, comedy, dance, music, film and visual arts; plus own productions inc. pantomimes.
Capacity: Seats 418 (main house) + 130 (studio theatre). Café-bar and restaurant in building plus rehearsal/meeting spaces.
TECHNICAL:
STAGE: W: 10M x H: 7.6M x D: 11M. Pit Capacity: 10+ (please call to discuss configurations). Prompt desk in Prompt Corner (Stage Left): Show Relay, Video Monitor and Cueing System. Prompt Side Wing Width: 7.6M. O.P. Wing Width: 5.2M. Access via dock doors: Height 5M, Width 3M. Dock and stage are flat to outside car park; Transit vans can be backed directly into dock. Backstage crossover via dock. Soft Black Marking: 4 x Legs, 4 x Borders, 2 x Sets of Full Blacks. Hard Masking: 8 x Black Masking Flats, White Cyclorama, White Gauze. Stage Weights: Approx. 20. Ballet Booms: 8 c/w 4 x Boom Arms.
LIGHTING: Strand 520i Lighting Desk - 250 channels and up to 2000 attributes c/w 2 TFT Monitors and Keyboard. Strand 301 Backup Lighting Desk. Stage Electrics R120 Wired Strand Focus Remote. 164 ADB Dimmers - Consisting of 160 x 2.5K and 4 x 5K. 8 x ADB 1K 11/23 Profiles. 8 x ADB 1K 15/31 Profiles. 10 x 15/30 Source 4 Zoom Profiles. 4 x 25/50 Source 4 Zoom Profiles. 2 x Fixed 50 Source 4 Profiles. 2 x Cantata 18/32 Profiles. 4 x Cantata 26/44 Profiles. 20 x ADB 1k Fresnels (10 without barn doors). 10 x ADB 1k PC c/w barn doors. 5 x Strand 2k Fresnel (4 c/w barn doors). 42 x Thomas Par 64 Par Can. 4 x Thomas Floor Can. 4 x 4 unit ADB Circuit Cyc top light floods. 6 x Iris single unit floods. 2 x Robert Juliat Buxies Followspot c/w Colour changer. 2 x Source 4 Iris'. 8 x ADB Gobo Holders. 8 x Source 4 Gobo Holders. 6 x Cantata Gobo Holders.
SOUND: Allen and Heath GL4000 40 channel Mixing Desk. 2 x Sony MDSJE510 Mini Disk Players. 1 x Sony CDP - XE330 CD Player. 1 x Yamaha SPX900 Professional Digital Multi-Effects Unit. 1 x Yamaha REV500 Digital Reverberator. 2 x Yamaha Q2031B 1/3 Octave 2 Channel Graphic Equaliser. 1 x Yamaha GQ1031C 1/3 Octave 1 Channel Graphic Equaliser. 1 x Behringer Composer Pro MDX2200 2-Channel Compressor/Limiter/Expander/Gate and Peak Limiter. 1 x Behringer Multicom Pro MDX4400 4-Channel Compressor/Limiter and Peak Limiter. 4 x XTA DP200 DSP Multiprocessor. 5 x Crest VS1100 Power Amplifiers. 1 x Crest VS1500 Power Amplifier. 2 x Crest VS650 Power Amplifiers. 2 x Mackie Fussion 3000 Active Full Range Loudspeakers. 2 x Mackie Fussion 1800 Active Sub Bass Loudspeakers. 2 x Mackie Fussion 1800S Passive Sub Bass Loudspeakers. 19 x JBL Control 1AT Small Fill Speakers. 2 x Community CSX28 - S2 Fold Back Monitor Speakers. 2 x EAW (replica) 15" Wedges. Hearing Impaired System / Audio Show Relay / Video Show Relay. Canford/Tecpro Ring Intercom Communications System
DRESSING ROOMS: 4 over 3 levels. Accommodating 33. Toilet and shower facilities and show relay and calls via the SM desk in all dressing rooms. Green Room - Fridge, Microwave, Kettle, Washing Machine and Dryer. Iron and Ironing Board available on request. Strictly non-smoking.

Hexham, Northumberland

QUEEN'S HALL ARTS CENTRE

Beaumont Street, Hexham Northumberland NE46 3LS
BO: 01434 652 477 Fax: 01434 652 476
Email: annette.dickson@queenshall.co.uk
Web Site: www.queenshall.co.uk
ADMINISTRATION:
General Manager: Annette Dickson
Senior Technician: Alex Perry
Cap: 350
TECHNICAL:
STAGE: Dimensions: Proscenium width 9040mm, 29'8", Proscenium line to rear wall 7560mm, 24'9", Forestage to rear wall 8660mm, 28'5", Grid height c 12000mm, Proscenium height c 7000mm. Flying: 11 sets of double purchase counterweighted bars, 15 sets of 3 line hemp bars, Bar length c 9050mm, Bar operated from fly floor stage right, 5 of the c/w bars (no 2, 4, 6, 8 & 9) are permanently assigned as LX bars and are non negotiable.
LIGHTING: Cable remote, ETC Congo Jnr with v5.1 software, 82 at 2kw, 8 at 5kw dimmers, 28 at Lito 1kw Fresnels, 9 at Selecon HP 1200 Fresnels, 6 at ETC S4 Zoom 25/50 Profiles, 3 at Strand SL 23/50 Profiles, 3 at Strand SL 15/30 Profiles, 2 at Selecon Pacific 23/50 Cool Beam Profiles, 14 at 1kw par cans, 6 at ETC S4 Zoom 15/30 Profiles, 4 at Strand SL 15/32 Profiles, 2 at Strand SL 23/50 Profiles, 4 at Lito Quad Eye Floods (c/frames 53cm x 39cm), 1 at CSI Follow Spot, Colour stock (limited) - Lee, Colortran.
SOUND: Tascam MD 350 Minidisk Player/Recorder, Sony Minidisk player/Recorder, DN-C635 pro CD, Numark twin CD Player, Soundcraft LX7 Mixer 24/4/2, 2 X Dbx stereo 15 band EQ (inserted on monitor sends), 4 at Tannoy V12 FOH speakers, 4 at 15" Dual concentric Stage Monitors, 2 at AKG D310 mics, 3 at Shure SM57 mics, 5 at Shure SM58 mics, 2 at Sennheiser Evolution 664 Condenser mics, 2 at Sennheiser 602 mics, 2 at Behringer B5 Condenser mics, 2 at Behringer C2 Stereo pair Condenser mics, 2 at Evolution 300 series radio mic packs, 2 at Lavalier tie clip mics, 1 at Evolution 300 series Handheld mic, 10 at boom stands.
STAGE MANAGEMENT: Sound Logic Intercom, cue lights, belt pack ring, show relay/tannoy system. Sound and light operated from box (rear of circle).
DRESSING ROOMS: 2, accommodating a total of 14. 3 x Shower and toilets. Overspill dressing room can be arranged with advance notice.

Hull, East Yorkshire

HULL TRUCK THEATRE

Hull Truck Theatre Company
Hull Truck Theatre, 50 Ferensway,
Hull HU2 8LB
Admin: 01482 224 800 BO: 01482 323 638 Publicity: 01482 325 012
Email: kate.denby@hulltruck.co.uk
Web Site: www.hulltruck.co.uk
ADMINISTRATION:
Artistic Director: Mark Babych
Executive Director: Janthi Mills-Ward
General Manager: Ian Archer
Head of Production: Fran Maskell
Membership: TMA (Touring)
Policy: Resident productions; comedy and jazz nights; incoming productions; jazz and literature festivals; education and outreach activity; youth theatre activity.
Capacity: 437 Maximum, Studio Capacity 134
For more information on hiring, email: events@hulltruck.co.uk.
TECHNICAL:
STAGE: Thrust Stage: Area 8.1m x 7.5m, no rake, floor ply on concrete, lino not available. Height of grid: 3.5m, black box masking. Get-in at rear, stage level. Back Doors 1.4m x 2.6m. Scale stage, fly + LX plans available 1:50 and 1:25 metric.
Electrics: operated from control room overlooking stage on S.R. side of auditorium
LIGHTING: Lee Colortran Prestige 1000 board, 55 circuits @ 10A, 30 x 1kw fresnels; 20 x 650w PC's; 6 x Sil 30's. Full list on demand. 3 phase operated SR of auditorium (20 spots Berkley/Strand 30 fresnals).
SOUND: Soundcraft 16:4: 2 desk, Revox, cassette, quadreverb and assorted mics. (contact theatre for more information).
DRESSING ROOMS: 2. Accom: 20

Ilminster, Somerset

DILLINGTON HOUSE

Ilminster, Somerset TA19 9DT
Tel: 01460 258 648 Fax: 01460 258 615
Email: dillington@somerset.gov.uk
Web Site: www.dillington.co.uk
ADMINISTRATION:
Props: Somerset County Council
Director: Wayne Bennett
For more information about what we can offer and various tariffs available e-mail or telephone the conference team at jelliott@somerset.gov.uk or 01460 258 611.

Inverness, Scotland

EDEN COURT THEATRE

Eden Court, Bishops Road,
Inverness IV3 5SA Scotland
Admin: 01463 239 841
BO: 01463 234 234
Email: admin@eden-court.co.uk
Web Site: www.eden-court.co.uk
ADMINISTRATION:
Director: Colin Marr
Policy: Open all year housing all forms of touring entertainment from opera to popular music, concerts, ballet, modern dance, drama and films. Full Conference facilities.
Seats: 840 on three levels. Three Foyer Bars, Restaurant and Cocktail Bar, Exhibitions in the stalls foyer and in additional adjacent rooms. 2 cinemas
TECHNICAL:
For further details of Eden Court's technical specifications email: bshanks@eden-court.co.uk

Irvine, Ayrshire

HARBOUR ARTS CENTRE

114-116 Harbour Street, Irvine, Ayrshire KA12 8PZ Scotland
Admin: 01294 274 059 BO: 01294 274 059 Fax/Answerphone: 01294 271 419
Email: mblackwood@north-ayrshire.gov.uk
Web Site: www.harbourarts.org.uk

Jersey, Channel Islands

JERSEY ARTS CENTRE

Phillips Street, St Helier, Jersey JE2 4SW Channel Islands
Admin: 01534 700 400 BO: 01534 700 444 Director: 01534 700 420 Technical: 01534 700415 Fax: 01534 700 401
Email: enquiries@artscentre.je
Web Site: www.artscentre.je
ADMINISTRATION;
Director: Daniel Austin
Marketing Manager: Michelle Parker
Box Office Manager: Denise Renouf
Cap: Phililps Street Theatre, 250. St James' Church: 300 seated, 450 standing.
Policy: To present a world of exciting, innovative, wide-ranging, challenging, professional and community arts in a welcoming, high-quality and accessible environment.
TECHNICAL:
Phillips Street Theatre:
STAGE: End-on with soft pros. arch; steeply raked seating. Flat acting area; 11m x 8m.
LIGHTING: Dimming & Control: 1 Zero-88 Bullfrog, A/B manual preset (48 channel narrow mode - 96 in Wide), 20 pages of 24 Sub-Masters, 400 programmable memories (inc point cues), 24 moving light fixture controls, 2 x DMX universe, 3 Zero-88 Chill DMX dimmer racks, 2.4Kw / channel. Dimming or non-dimming option, 1 63A three-phase power supply is available in the theatre's dimming room on a standard 5-pin Cee-form socket.
Luminaries: Profiles; 4 Arena 2000w CP43, 2 Cadenza 19/32 2000w CP43, 6 Cantata 26/44 1200w T29, 1 adapted to fit b-size, gobo rotator, 6 Cantata 18/32 1200w T29, 6 ZS1200M 18/34 1200w T29, Fixed on FOH bar, with scroller, 3 CCT Silhouette 3 1000w T19, 6 Source 4 25/50 750w HPL750, 6 Prelude 28/40 650w T26, 5 Prelude 16/30 650w T26. Floods; 10 Cantata F (blue) 1200w T29 Barndoors, 5 Cantata F (green) 1000w T19 Barndoors, 20 Par 64 1000w CP62 or CP60 or CP61, 5 Prelude F 650w T26, 2 CCT Minuette 500w K1 (linear) on floor plates, Cyclorama Floods, 5 Coda 4 (fixed Cyc floods) 5 x 300w K9 (linear). FX; 12 Smart 7.25 Scroller DMX Control 11 colour 6 rigged on FOH bar, 8 Par 16, Birdie 50w EXN On floor plates, 1 Strobe Unit With controller, 1 Smoke Machine With local remote, 1 B-size Gobo rotator For use in 26/44, 1 Mirror Ball 18" With rotator, All units come with Gel frames as appropriate. All lanterns are fitted with 15A plugs.
SOUND: 1 Soundcraft Live-8, 24-8-2 mixing desk, 2 QSC Audio RMX 1450 (450w per channel.), 4 Tannoy Puma loudspeakers, 150w RMS; 8 ohms, 1 Yamaha SPX 990 Stereo multi-effects processor, 2 Yamaha Q2031A dual band graphic equalizer, 2 Sony MD520 minidisc player recorder, 1 Tascam MD-350 minidisc player recoder, 1 Marantz CD-80 Compact disc player, 1 Demon DRM-595 Single Tape Player, 2 Revox B77 1/4" tape machine. 7 1/2 & 15 IPS with variable speed, 1 JVC AL-F3 Record deck 33rpm, 2 AKG D80 microphones, 2 AKG D321 microphones, 7 Shure SM58 microphones, 2 Senheisser e300 radio mic receiver, 1 Senheisser e300 lapel mic, 1 Senheisser e300 hand held radio mic, 2 Behringer 2 channel Ultra-DI DI120, DI boxes, 8 High boom microphone stands, SM58 clips. Various lengths of microphone cable are available.
AV: 1 2400 Lumin Proxima Digital Projector, 1 DVD player - Phillips DVD634, Region 2, 1 DVD player - GVG DV995, multi region, 1 Video Player - Sanyo VHR H200, 1 5.1 Surround Sound Amp - Sony STR-DB940, 4 TOA surround Sound fills at rear of auditorium split L & R, 1 Kodak SA-V 2050 Slide projector, 1 75 - 120mm lens (for above), 1 Infra red remote and receiver, 2 80 slide carousels, 1 OverHead Projector, 1 6m x 4.5m Matt white front projection screen, on Elstree electric top roller, -Suspended

from the grid 3.9m up stage of the setting line. Height is variable.
STAGE COMMUNICATIONS: 1 Techpro. MS 721 master station, 2 Techpro. fixed headset stations (control room), 5 Belt packs, 2 Dual circuit belt packs, 6 Single muff headsets, 3 Double muff headsets, 7 Loudspeaker (relay/calls) stations, 1 6-2 3rd generation loop mixer, 1 200w deaf-aid loop amplifier.
DRESSING ROOMS; 3, accommodating 14. 4 Toilets, 2 Showers, mirrors, mirror lights, wash basins. Green Room; accommodating 10.

St. James' Church:
St James' Flexible church area with fixed stage in apse; additional staging available. Disabled access. Acting area variable; 32 x 2.4kw dimmers; Jands Events plus lighting board. Soundcraft 24:8 board.

Kendal, Cumbria

BREWERY ARTS CENTRE

122a Highgate, Kendal,
Cumbria LA9 4HE
Admin: 01539 722 833 Fax: 01539 730 257 BO: 01539 725 133
Email: boxoffice@breweryarts.co.uk
Web Site: www.breweryarts.co.uk
ADMINISTRATION:
Director: Richard Foster
Technical Manager: Steve Parnaby
Marketing Officer: Debbie Bond
Cap: Theatre: 260 seated. Malt Room: 200 without catering (seating up to 120) or 175 with catering.
This multi-purpose arts centre also has a second music and theatre venue (known as the Malt Room), exhibition spaces, studio space, as well as two cinema auditoria.
TECHNICAL:
For more information contact the Technical Team on: technical@breweryarts.co.uk
STAGE: 9m wide, 8.5m deep, no rake, hardboard, black finish, semi-sprung understage and backstage crossover. Stage heated. Wings: SR width 1.5m, SL width 3m and some dock area not full height. No House Tabs, no other curtain list. Black Box Masking, Tallescope.
LIGHTING BOARD: ARRI "Focus" Desk.

Leicester

LEICESTERSHIRE ARTS IN EDUCATION

Knighton Fields Centre, Herrick Road, Leicester LE2 6DH
Tel: 0116 270 0850 Fax: 0116 270 4928
Email: artsined@leics.gov.uk
Web Site: www.leicestershire.gov.uk
ADMINISTRATION:
Props: Leicester and Leicestershire County Council
Services Manager: Sandy Hay, Catherine Hutchen
Cap: Theatre: 128 Seated

PHOENIX SQUARE: FILM AND DIGITAL MEDIA

4 Midland Street, Leicester LE1 1TG
Mgt: 0116 242 2835 BO: 0116 242 2800
Email: ros.hill@phoenix.org.uk
Web Site: www.phoenix.org.uk
ADMINISTRATION:
Partnership Initiative: De Montfort University & Leicester City Council
Lessees: Leicester Arts Centre Ltd
CEO: John Rande
Operations Manager: Ros Hill
Policy: Broad based arts centre promoting the best film and multi-cultural arts exhibitions.
Perfs: Eves 7 days a week, Saturday Family Film Matinees.
Seats: Screens; (1) 220, (2) 120, (3) 30. Courtyard Suite; Standing 100, Theatre Style 70. Recording Studio. Screen Lounge Cafe Bar Licensed open 9am - 11p.m. Building open 7 days a week.

Letchworth Garden City

PLINSTON HALL

Broadway, Letchworth Garden City, Hertfordshire SG6 3NX
Hall Bookings 01462 672 003
Fax: 01462 480 279
Email: denis.hill@lgchf.com
Web Site: www.plinston.com
ADMINISTRATION:
Props: Letchworth Heritage Foundation
General Manager: Denis Hill
Cap: Standing 400, Seating 296, Cabaret seating (round tables) 200.
TECHNICAL:
STAGE: Room area: 16.6m x 14.9m with adjacent integrated bar area and lounge. Full proscenium stage with area: 14m x 6.1m and 4m clearance. Ground floor with side access. Air conditioning. Parquet dance floor.
LIGHTING: Cabaret lighting with AMC lighting control
SOUND: 4-microphone stage sound. Induction loop.
ADDITIONAL: Broadwood upright piano. Retractable projection screen with data or carousel projection.

Lisburn, County Antrim

ISLAND ARTS CENTRE

Island Arts Centre, Lagan Valley Island, Lisburn, County Antrim BT27 4RL
Northern Ireland
Tel: 028 92 509 509 BO: 028 92 509 254
Textphone: 028 92 509 508
Email: arts.info@island.lisburn.gov.uk
Web Site: www.islandartscentre.com
ADMINSTRATION:
Island Arts Centre provides a balanced and accessible programme of Arts-related activities. It encourages active participation from the community by producing and promoting the Arts, and increasing the level of opportunities for the local community to participate in the arts.
Props: Lisburn City Council
Community Arts Officer: Lesley Wilson
Email: lesley.wilson@island.lisburn.gov.uk
Technical Contacts: Cathal (028 92 509 515) Email: cathal@island.lisburn.gov.uk
Capacity: Main Auditorium, Seats 430. Studio Theatre: 110 Theatre Style, 70 Cabaret Style, 150 Standing.
TECHNICAL:
Studio Theatre;
STAGE: 10m W x 6m 40cm D. Height to the upstage bar of grid of 3.5m and 3.9m to rest of grid. Curtain Tracks: 1 x 30m perimeter curtain track covering three sides of the theatre. Stage drapes : 8 x 3m x 3.5m drop drapes in black wool surge creating a perimeter curtain of 30m in total. Drapes have Velcro to edges and tab hooks to top with chain at base.
LIGHTING: Desk: 1 x Strand 300 with 520 software, 1 x Avolites Tiger. Lighting grid is 10m by 10m made from alloy. 40 x Socket outlets are positioned within the grid. 8 x Floor Sockets. 4 USL & 4 USR. Dimmers: 3 x Act 6 dimmer racks 10amp per channel with twin socket outlets, 2 x ETC Smartpack (12 ways per pack), 1 x 48 way patch panel. (42 ways of dimming). Luminaries: 12 x ETC Source 4 25-50 zoom profiles, 20 x Strand Quartet Fresnels 650w (12 with barn doors), 6 x Strand Coda 500w, 8 x Robe 240 AT colour wash.
SOUND: 1 x Camco Q6 Power amplifier, 1 x AP 30 induction loop amplifier, 1 x Talk back power supply, 1 x Yamaha LS9 16 channel mixing desk, 4 x Martin Audio F15+ suspended from ceiling. (Floor to bottom of speakers is 3.3m), 1 x CD player, 1 x Mini Disc player.

Liverpool, Merseyside

BLUECOAT ARTS CENTRE

Bluecoat Chambers, School Lane, Liverpool, Merseyside L1 3BX
Tel: 0151 702 5324 Fax: 0151 707 0048
Email: info@thebluecoat.org.uk
Web Site: www.bluecoatartscentre.com
ADMINISTRATION:
Chief Executive: Alastair Upton
Artistic Director: Bryan Biggs
General Manager: Zoe Chapman
Technical Manager: Tom Smith
Seats: 200

GREAT GEORGES COMMUNITY CULTURAL PROJECT (THE BLACK-E)

1 Great George Street, Liverpool, Merseyside L1 5EW
Tel: 0151 709 5109 Fax: 0151 709 4822
Email: hires@theblack-e.co.uk
Web Site: www.theblack-e.co.uk
ADMINISTRATION:
Co-Directors: Bill Harpe and Sally Morris
Cap: 300 Seated, 550 Standing.
TECHNICAL:
Fixed pipe internally wired grid consisting of 10 internally wired bars, each carrying 12 * 3KW dimmed circuits on 15A outlets (120 Dimmed circuits at grid level). Grid level bars have 2 hard power outlets on 16A , and a DMX point. Upper balcony (~6.5M above the floor) has a similar bar providing another 48 dimmed circuits, with a total of 8 further hard power points. 6 way sockapex points in each corner below the lower balcony providing for any required stage level dimmed power.

Livingston, West Lothian

HOWDEN PARK CENTRE

Howden, Livingston, West Lothian EH54 6AE Scotland
BO: 01506 777666 Tel: 01506 773858
Email: arts@westlothian.gov.uk
Web Site: www.howdenparkcentre.co.uk
ADMINISTRATION:
Events Co-ordinator: Fiona Haldane
Tel: 01506 773853, Email: venuehire@westlothian.gov.uk
Policy: Year round programme of adult and children's theatre performances, children's and adults' art, music and drama classes, regular music performances with a strong scottish/ folk theme, monthly folk club and jazz club, art gallery.
Local authority run arts and conference centre comprising 292 seat theatre with full sound and lighting spec, dressing room and workshop area, 200 capacity multi purpose hall with sprung wooden floor, art gallery, 200 capacity lounge area with kitchen and bar. Box office facilities. Full disabled access throughout, disabled toilets and parking, induction loop in theatre.
TECHNICAL:
STAGE: Pros. opening: 9.2m wide max x 8.9m high max. Depth from back of pros. wall: 6.9m. Depth of forestage: 2.6m max. Stage centre line to stage right wall: 9m. Stage centre line to stage left wall: 9m. Width between fly galleries: 15.8m. Height to underside of stage suspension steels: 9.9m. Clear height beneath galleries: 6.5m. Get-In: Scene dock/stage level access from road level. 1 x roller shutter door - external to scene dock - 3m wide x 2.5m high. 1 x double door - scene dock to space 1 - 2.4m wide x 2m high. 1 x acoustic sliding door - scene dock to stage - 3m wide x 5.3m high.
LIGHTING: Control: Zero 88 Leap Frog 96 operated from control room at rear of auditorium. Fixed Dimmers: Zero 88 Chilli Pro hard-wired dimmers in theatre dimmer room. House Lights: 6 x circuits controlling mixture of TH downlights and LED step lights via Zero 88 control system. These can also be controlled via the lighting desk. Internally Wired Bars: 9 No 3.2m long 6-circuit internally wired bars with multicore cables and connectors. 1 No 11m long 4-circuit internally wired bar for cyc lighting, with cable tripe and connectors (permanently rigged on LX winch 4.). Fresnels/PCs: 10 x Selecon Acclaim 650W Fresnel. 10 x Selecon Rama 1kW Fresnel. 4 x Strand Harmony 1kW Fresnel. 4 x Selecon SF1000 1kW Fresnel. 4 x Selecon Rama 1kW PC. Profiles: 8 x Selecon Acclaim 650W 24-44° profile. 4 x Selecon Acclaim 650W 18-34° profile. 12 x Selecon Pacific 1kW 12-28° profile. 6 x Selecon Pacific 1kW 23-50° profile. 3 x Altman Leko 1kW 26° axial profile (dedicated to rear auditorium position). PARs: 6 x Vision PAR64 standard black with CP62 MFL lamp. 16 x Thomas PAR64 standard black with EXG WFL lamp. 4 x Thomas PAR64 short nose black with CP95 WFL lamp. 6 x Thomas Birdies fitted with GU10 36° dichroic lamps. Cyc floods: 5 x Selecon Hui 800W asymmetric 4-compartment cyc floods. 5 x Selecon Hui 500W asymmetric 4-compartment cyc groundrow floods. 9 x Strand Coda 500/1 asymmetric single cyc floods (6 used as stage working light). Followspot: 1 x Rank Strand P774 1.2Kw with sight, 6-way colour magazine and iris. All luminaires complete with lamp, wire mesh guard or safety glass, metal colour frames, 48mm hook clamp with fixing bolt/washer/wing nut assembly, and safety bond.
SOUND: Mixer: Yamaha LS916 with ADAT expansion card and Focusrite interface (= analogue 24 in/16out plus digital in/outs). Alternative operating position for house or brought-in mixers at rear of auditorium. Outboard gear: 2 x Professional CD player (MP3 compatible), 1 x Professional minidisc player/recorder, 1 x Sony minidisc player/recorder, 1 x BSS dual channel graphic EQ, 1 x tc electronics M1XL multi-effects unit, Main speaker system: Centre cluster: 2 x Martin Audio F15, Prosc L+R: 1 x Martin Audio F15, Rear bridge delay: 3 x Martin Audio AQ8, Monitors: 4 Turbosound TXD12m, 2 x TOA SL122M, Loudspeaker lines: 20 No, including main loudspeaker lines. Various microphones available.
STAGE COMMUNICATIONS: Portable stage manager's desk with connectors DSL and DSR. Includes clock, cue light controls and paging controls. Cue lights: 10 outlets for plug-in units. Intercom: Twin ring, with 19 outlets plus link to rack in communications room. Video: 17 x BNC outlets to patch in control room, plus 6 x tie line links to rack in communications room. Colour camera at rear of auditorium. Paging: Paging points DSL, on stage manager's desk, and in control room.
BACKSTAGE FACILITIES: Dressing rooms; 3-4, accommodating 15. Basin and shower facilities, and paging/show relay loudspeaker. 1 x disabled WC with WHB. Laundry facilities: 1 x Hotpoint automatic washing machine, 1 x Hoover 9Kg condensing tumble dryer.

Llantwit Major, Vale Of Glamorgan

ST DONATS ARTS CENTRE

St Donats Castle, Llantwit Major, Vale Of Glamorgan CF61 1WF South Wales
Tel: 01446 799104 BO: 01446 799 100
Fax: 01446 799 101
Email: admin@stdonats.com
Web Site: www.stdonats.com
ADMINISTRATION:
Artistic Director: David Ambrose
Cap: 230 Seated
TECHNICAL:
If you require Technical specifications, contact the technical department on email; technical@stdonats.com or tel; 01446 799098.

Lochgelly, Fife

LOCHGELLY CENTRE THEATRE

Bank Street, Lochgelly, Fife KY5 9RD Scotland
Tel: 01592 583 367
Email: william.gibson@onfife.com
Web Site: www.onfife.com
Facility Manager: William Gibson
Capacity: 379 + 15 Wheelchairs

London

THE ALBANY

Theatre and community centre.
Douglas Way, Deptford, London SE8 4AG
Admin: 020 8692 0231 BO: 020 8692 4446 Fax: 020 8469 2253
Email: senay.gaul@thealbany.org.uk
Web Site: www.thealbany.org.uk
ADMINISTRATION:
The Albany is a lively, intimate and friendly venue with an exciting programme of the very best in theatre, live music, cabaret, family shows, club nights and multimedia events in informal cabaret-style seating.
CEO/Artistic Director: Gavin Barlow
Operations & Administration: Senay Gaul
Room Bookings & Venue Hires: Lily Hannell

Production & Events: Ben Stephens
Head of Communications: Amber Massie-Bloomfield
Box Office: Vicky Harrison
Front of House: Kate Miners (reception@thealbany.org.uk)
Policy: Variety of events, including music, theatre, dance, spoken word, clubs and family events.
Capacity: Main Auditorium: 300 seated/ 500 standing. Studio/ Conference Rooms: 12 - 100.

ALL SAINTS ARTS CENTRE

122 Oakleigh Road North,
London N20 9EZ
Tel: 020 8445 8388
Email: arts@allsaints.uk.com
Web Site: www.allsaints.uk.com
Senior Personnel: Gregory Platten
Theatrespace/Main Hall with Café Chartres serving breakfasts
Licensed bar until 11pm & 1pm Fridays & Saturdays
Proscenium arch stage with a 7.23m x 7m performing area.
For dance, the Theatrespace has an interior sprung floor & there is a reversible Harlequin floor that can be used here or in the Studio. The Theatrespace seats a maximum of 365, raked.
Height to ceiling 6.1m - tab track, and black / brown reversible cyclorama.

Studio/Small Hall/Wheatley Bar
The Studio space is suitable for use as dressing rooms for the Theatrespace or for small events in its own right. The performing area is variable, up to 6.71m x 3.66m, with the height to the apex of the ceiling 7.62m. Wooden floor with no rake. Seats 50. Gantry for 2 projectors.
Table tennis/pool/air hockey/football table/intendo Wii. Boudoir & upright pianos.

Church
Performing area 6.71m x 9.76m. Stone tiled floor with rostra available. Height to apex 15.25m. Seats 350 in fixed pews. Lighting and sound available. Yamaha grand piano. Synthesizer. OHP.
Organ 1984 built by Nigel Church, situated at rear, very good condition. Small electric organ.

Spire
Facilities for recording and editing.
Available for hire for band practice ~ £5 per hour
Full Peavy / H.H PA, FX, /Mapex 5PC Drums/keyboard and microphones available on request

ARTS DEPOT

5 Nether Street, Tally Ho Corner, North Finchley, London, N12 0GA
Admin: 020 8369 5455 BO Tel: 020 8369 5454 Fax: 020 8369 5476
Email: info@artsdepot.co.uk
Web Site: www.artsdepot.co.uk
ADMINISTRATION:
Director: Tracy Cooper
Artsdepot was conceived by the local community and built to provide new and improved services, in fact a larger version of The Bull Arts Centre in High Barnet.
Policy: Theatre, Music, Dance, Comedy, Spoekn Word, Children.
Pentland Theatre: Seats: 395, 500 standing.
Studio Theatre: Seats: 148
Gallery and Cafe / Bar
For more information on venue hire contact; Events Department on 020 8369 5471 or events@artsdepot.co.uk.

BANGLADESH ARTS CENTRE

24 Pembridge Gardens, London W2 4DX
Tel: 020 7229 9404 Fax: 020 7229 5197
Email: bangladeshcentre@hotmail.co.uk
Web Site: www.bangladeshcentre.info
Contact: Mr S Mustafizur Rahan

BARBICAN CENTRE

Silk Street, Barbican, London EC2Y 8DS
Mgt: 020 7638 4141 BO: 020 7638 8891
SD: 020 7382 7676 Fax: 020 7382 7270
Email: info@barbican.org.uk
Web Site: www.barbican.org.uk
ADMINISTRATION:
Managing Director: Sir Nicholas Kenyon
Head of Programming: Louise Jeffries
Head of Theatre: Tony Racklin
BITE - Theatre Production Manager: Simon Bourne
Head of Music: Huw Humphreys
Head of Cinema: Robert Rider
Facilities for the disabled: Barbican Hall, 16 wheelchair spaces plus escorts; Barbican Theatre, 11 wheelchair spaces plus escorts; The Pit, 2 wheelchair space plus escort. Lifts, chairlifts and assistance available, ring box office on 020 7638 8891. Level access and free parking on presentation of disabled car registration certificate.
For more information on hiring, contact the venue on: artistichire@barbican.org.uk
Theatre Capacity: 1,160

BATTERSEA ARTS CENTRE

Venue undergoing restoration, capacity unknown until 2016
Lavender Hill, London SW11 5TN
Mgt: 020 7223 6557 BO: 020 7223 2223
Fax: 020 7978 5207 Admin: 020 7326 8239
Email: boxoffice@bac.org.uk, or mailbox@bac.org.uk
Web Site: www.bac.org.uk
ADMINISTRATION:
Artistic Director: David Jubb
Executive Manager: Rebecca Holt
Technical Manager: Kevin Miles
Theatre: Multi-purpose performance space. Capacity: 200 +
Lower Hall Capacity: 100 - 200
Recreation Room Capacity: 50 - 100
Policy: To work with artists and audiences towards the development of innovative forms of theatre.
For venue hire contact the theatre on: venues@bac.org.uk.
TECHNICAL:
STAGE (Theatre): The playing area (on floor) is normally 27 feet x 21 feet.
LIGHTING: 6 X Harmony 1k Fresnels all with Barndoors, 10 X Cantata 1.2k Fresnels all with Barndoors, 10 X Cantata 1.2k Profiles 18/32 with Rotary Gobo Gate, 15 X 650w Prelude Fresnels all with Barndoors, 8 X Thomas Pars all CP 62.
LX Desk: ETC Express:- 120 Channels 2k per way Digital.
SOUND: Soundcraft K1 Sound Desk 16-4, 1 X Denon DCD -425 single C.D. Programmable, 1 X Denon DRM 550 single cassette unit, 2X EV P1250 PWR Amps, 1 X EV XP200 Cross Over, 4 X EV S x 200 Midd and Top Speakers, 2 X EV Sb 120 Bass Speakers, 1 X Alesis Quadravert, Relevant Cables, Patch Bay.
Please contact the Technical Manager for full technical specifications.

BHAVAN INSTITUTE OF INDIAN ART & CULTURE

4a Castletown Road, West Kensington, London W14 9HE
Tel: 020 7381 3086 / 4608 Fax: 020 7381 8758
Email: info@bhavan.net
Web Site: www.bhavan.net
ADMINISTRATION:
Executive Director: Dr M.N. Nandakumara
Administrative Manager: John Muir
Accounts Manager: Bihari Khamar
Capacity: Theatre, 295. Hall, 100.

CHATS PALACE

42-44 Brooksby's Walk, Homerton, Hackney, London E9 6DF
Tel: 020 8533 0227
Email: info@chatspalace.com
Web Site: www.chatspalace.com
ADMINISTRATION:
Capacity; Seated: 100. Standing: 200.
TECHNICAL:
STAGE: Floor area 5.5m x 6m deep, pros opening 5.5m x 3m. Rubberised dance-floor available. Black curtains / white cyclorama / black brick wall. Backstage crossover - just! Stage units form raked seating or can make 5m x 4m stage for music, etc. Traverse, round, other variations possible.
LIGHTS: Zero 88 Fat Frog programmable board. 18 circuit @2kw, operated from back balcony. 50 various fresnels, profiles, PCs and floods, and follow spot.
SOUND: 16.4.2 sound mixing desk operated from back of hall OR 20.2 mixing desk operated from back balcony. 2kW turbosound rig with 1kW monitoring.10 mics, 4 DI boxes, 2xCD, MD, DA, MC.
Also available - projector (video/DVD/etc) and screen, 2 x slide projector, turntables and mixer, upright piano (good).
Acoustic suitable for music and spoken

word.
BACKSTAGE FACILITIES: One dressing room, stage right. Some wing space both sides.

COLLAGE ARTS

The Chocolate Factory, Wood Green, London, N22 6XJ
Tel: 020 8365 7500 Fax: 020 8365 8686
Email: info@collage-arts.org
Web Site: www.collage-arts.org
ADMINISTRATION:
Executive Director: Manoj Ambasna
Administrator: Sam Clarke
Collage Arts runs events and projects. It organises exhibitions, literature events and community festivals. Currently the Arts Development Programme concentrates on building relationships with community, organisations and education to deliver a range of comprehensive arts projects with an educational element. Our work challenges issues around social exclusion, both within and outside the education sector. Collage Arts develops, and manages a wide range of projects, including artists' residencies, creative mentoring scheme, and work with HMP Holloway. Collage Arts offers advice and support through regular surgery sessions. Various studios available for hire. For more information contact Administrator, Sam Clarke, on 020 8365 7500 or via email sam@collage-arts.org.

FAIRFIELD HALLS

Park Lane, Croydon, Surrey CR9 1DG
Mgt/SD: 020 8681 0821 BO: 020 8688 9291 Marketing Fax: 020 8603 3862
Admin Fax: 020 8603 3838
Email: info@fairfield.co.uk
Web Site: www.fairfield.co.uk
ADMINISTRATION:
Props: Fairfield (Croydon) Ltd
Chief Executive: Simon Thomsett
Technical Manager: Chris Whybrow
Head of Operations: John Bartliff
Policy: Concert Hall, Music, Films, Pop, Jazz, Opera, Comedy, Conferences, Ballet.
Capacity: Seats: 1998 max.
Foyer, Coffee shop, Restaurant, Bars, Banqueting & Conference Rooms.
TECHNICAL:
STAGE: Concert Platform, mechanical variable sections.
LIGHTING: Switchboard: Strand Lightboard 'M' commanding 120 channels 200amp 3 phase and 60 amp single phase power supplies available for temporary supply; F.O.H. spots 42 CCT profiles. 2 spot bars available on electric hoist. Selection of lamps; P.A.R. cans and fresnels.
Get-in via platform lift, Direct Access & Parking. No flying facilities, but good grid provision and soft blacks for upstage masking.
SOUND EQUIPMENT: 7kw fully integrated Meyer sound system with permanent mixing position.
OTHER: Dressing Rooms: 7, accom. 200; 3 showers; Orchestra Pit 28.90 orch. music stands, 2 Steinway concert D type Grand Pianos; seats 120 orch. max 250 choir seats.
Staff: 5 Technicians - Casual Crew.
A registered charity.

FAIRKYTES ARTS CENTRE

51 Billet Lane, Hornchurch, Essex RM11 1AX
Tel: 01708 456 308 Fax: 01708 475 286
Email: fairkytes@havering.gov.uk
Web Site: www.havering.gov.uk
ADMINISTRATION:
Arts Co-ordinator: Mark Etherington
Supervisor: John Shadwell
Converted Georgian house seating 40, used for many kinds of arts and crafts activities. Also small studio theatre seating 100. Spacious garden is suitable for drama performances if a company tours all its own equipment.

JACKSONS LANE

Opp Highgate Tube, 269a Archway Road, London N6 5AA
Admin: 020 8340 5226
BO: 020 8341 4421
Email: admin@jacksonslane.org.uk
Web Site: www.jacksonslane.org.uk
ADMINISTRATION:
Props: Haringey Borough Council
Artistic Director: Adrian Berry
General Manager: Ruth Turner
Theatre Technician: Nick Waddel
Email: technical@jacksonslane.org.uk
Policy: To provide a programme of music, drama, dance, mime and cabaret, representing multi-cultural interests. Training will play a large part in our programme, and many of our staff are trainees and volunteers.
Location: Alongside the Archway Road (A1), opposite Highgate tube. Served by buses 43, 134, X43, 263. Terms: Hire of theatre (negotiable); box office split.
Seats/Capacity: 166
Bars: one in foyer, one in auditorium.
TECHNICAL:
STAGE: End on, flat stage, semi-sprung wood floor, raked. 11m x 8m deep (without wing masking/ black tabs). 8m x 7m deep APPROX. (with wing masking/ black tabs). Grid Height: 6.2m. Get-In: Via 1.5m x 3.5m stage door from Archway Road (A1 facing north). Red route restrictions apply; parking for one hour between 10am and 4pm. Unrestricted parking after 7pm. Underground station car park charges £3 per day.
LIGHTING: Control: Strand 91703 300 Console 125ch 24sub. Lanterns: 10 x 1k Starlette fresnels, 6 x Par 64 (assorted lenses - please check with us), 2 x 650 w Minuette profiles, 6 x 1k Compact 6 fresnels, 12 x 1.2k ETC Source 4, 15/30 zoom profiles, 7 x 1.2k ETC Source 4, 25/50 zoom profiles, 4 x 500w Quartet fresnels, 2 x 3 cell 500w flood units. All lanterns are compete with barn doors, gel frames and shutters as appropriate.
SOUND: Allen and Heath GL 3300. Playback; Numark CDn22 Dual CD Player, 2x RCF Art 315a Powered speakers (Fixed Position). Various Microphones available.
ADDITIONAL: Infrared hearing systems fitted, 1x FXlab Small Hazer, 1x Martin magnum 650 Smoke Machine, 1x 30cm Mirror ball. Video Projector; NEC NP100 2000 lumen Projector. Projection Screen; Matt white front projection screen surface. 9m wide x 5.95m drop.
DRESSING ROOMS; 3, accomm. 20. Iron and ironing board available.
For more information contact Joe Boxshall on joe@jacksonslane.org.uk.

MILLFIELD ARTS CENTRE

Silver Street, Edmonton, London N18 1PJ
Tel: 020 8803 5283 Fax: 020 8807 3892
BO: 020 8807 6680
Email: m.day@millfieldtheatre.co.uk
Web Site: www.millfieldtheatre.co.uk
Millfield Arts Centre is North London's premier venue of Theatre, Comedy, Music, Dance and hosts an array of different classes and work shops.
Cap: 362
For more information about technical specifications at Millfield Theatre, please contact Marc Day on Tel: 020 8887 7319, Mob: 07983 987218, or Email: m.day@millfieldtheatre.co.uk.

OVAL HOUSE THEATRE

52-54 Kennington Oval, London SE11 5SW
Admin: 020 7582 0080 BO: 020 7582 7680 Fax: 020 7820 0990
Email: info@ovalhouse.com
Web Site: www.ovalhouse.com
ADMINISTRATION:
Props: Christ Church (Oxford) University Clubs
Lessees: C.C.O.U.C.
General Manager: Wendy Dempsey
Email: wendy.dempseyt@ovalhouse.com
Head of Press and Marketing: Debbie Vannozzi
Email: debbie.vannozzi@ovalhouse.com
Policy: New work, emerging companies, women's, lesbian & gay, black and Asian, work relevant to local audiences.
Performance and Rehearsal space.
Two performance spaces, upstairs and downstairs 50 and 100 capacity respectively.New cafe & cabaret space; extra dance studio and rehearsal space.

RADA STUDIOS

16 Chenies Street, London WC1E 7EX
Admin/BO: 020 7307 5060 Fax: 020 7307 5062
Email: studiosboxoffice@rada.ac.uk
Web Site: www.radaenterprises.org
ADMINISTRATION:
General Manager: Stacie Novotny

Seats: 200 max.
Disabled access, licensed bar on ground floor.
The Drill Hall, just off Tottenham Court Road, in London's West End, has a 200 seat theatre,
Studio Theatre, a 50-seat cabaret-style. Club Theatre ,four rehearsal studios, four meeting rooms, a bar, an extensive programme of courses and classes (with changing rooms/ shower facilities) and is open seven days a week.
TECHNICAL:
Recently upgraded lighting system and in-house PA system.
Rehearsal rooms and fully accessible darkroom suite.

THE RED HEDGEHOG

255 - 7 Archway Road, Highgate London N6 5BS
Tel: 020 8348 8485 BO: 0208 348 5050
Fax: 020 7900 3350
Email: clare.f@theredhedgehog.co.uk
Web Site: www.theredhedgehog.co.uk
ADMINISTRATION:
Fringe theatre, music and visual arts.
Artistic Director: Clare Fisher
Specialist Events Organiser: Natasha Graham.
Contact: eventhire [AT] theredhedgehog.co.uk
For more information on hiring the venue email: theatrehire@theredhedgehog.co.uk

RIVERSIDE STUDIOS

Closed for redevelopment until 2018
Crisp Road, Hammersmith, London W6 9RL
Mgt: 020 8237 1000 BO: 020 8237 1111
Fax: 020 8237 1001
Email: online@riversidestudios.co.uk
Web Site: www.riversidestudios.co.uk
ADMINISTRATION:
Artistic Director: William Burdett-Coutts
Programme Manager: Michael Harris
Technical Director: Ruari Cormack
Technical Manager: James Donovan
Opening Times: 7 days a week.
Capacity: Studio 2 - 400 (seated); Studio 3 - 156. Cinema - 200 (seated).
TECHNICAL:
Studio 2:
STAGE: Dimensions: 18m x 21m. Normal Stage Area: Open: 6-9m x 15m (depending on seating layout), With wings: 6-9m x 12m (depending on seating layout), Height to Grid: 6.9m, Bars normally dead around 5.5m, Average lantern lens height: 5.2m, Main Access Door: 4m(w) x 2.5m(h). Stage Flooring: Concrete. Harlequin Liberty sprung wooden floor is available, maximum area 15m x 9m. No screw fixing or similar to either the concrete or Harlequin floor is possible. Black Harlequin Cascade Dance floor is available on request. Rigging: 48 point hoists SWL 150kg on tracking system position to suit. Usual configuration: 8 bars (15m width). Electric power: Production lighting is via 3 phases, 800 amps per phase. Production Sound is via 63A 1 phase. Other Available: 125A 3 phase Cee-form, 63A 1 phase Cee-form.
SOUND: ALLEN & HEATH GL3300 824C Mixing Console, 4 x LOGIC SYSTEM LS15 500W 8ohm Passive Loudspeaker, 2 x LOGIC SYSTEM Ethos B1 15 500W 4ohm Bass, 3 x LAB GRUPPEN IP 2100 2 x 700W Power Amplifier, BSS Minidrive FDS336 2 Input 6 Output Speaker Management Sys, 2 x Fender 115-ELC onstage monitors w/amp.
LIGHTING: Desk: Strand 530i, Dimmers: ADB EUROTRACK 96 x 3Kw, 48 x 5Kw. Lighting stock: Variable & shared between both Studio's 2 & 3: We maintain a stock of generic lanterns: ETC Source Four zoom & fixed degree profiles. ETC Source Four Parnel. Strand Patt 743 Fresnel. Cantata PC1.2kW. Coda 1kW Flood. Parcan CP62/61/60. Arri 2kW Fresnel (pole op). All lanterns on 16A Cee-form. Limited colour stock.
BACKSTAGE FACILITIES: Dressing Rooms: Up to 5 available. No Green Room. Wardrobe: Washing machine and dryer available.

Studio 3: 11m x 11m. (Normal Stage Area 11m x 5.5m)
Cinema: 16/35mm projection facilities.
A multi-resource arts centre also including bar, restaurant, gallery, rehearsal space and TV studio
Ex BBC film studios available for performance or commercial hire. Easy get-in access from street.

SOUTHWARK ARTS FORUM

Unit K106 The Biscuit Factory, Tower Bridge Business Complex, 100 Clements Road, London SE16 4DG
Tel: 020 7231 3222
Email: admin@southwarkartsforum.org
Web Site: www.southwarkartsforum.org
Marketing & Communications Manager: Katy Fattuhi

THE TABERNACLE

35 Powis Square, Talbot Road London W11 2AY
Tel: 0207 221 9700
Email: niki@tabernaclew11.com
Web Site: www.tabernaclew11.com
ADMINISTRATION:
General Manager: Matthew Phillip
Operations Manager: Niki Kudar
Email: niki@tabernaclew11.com
Policy: Concerts, Corporate Events, Film Screenings, Cabaret, Private Functions, Dinner & Dance, Stand-Up, Conferences, Meetings & Lectures, Ballroom Dancing, Awards Ceremonies, Fashion Shows & Galas, Film and TV location shoots, Theatre Performances.
The newly renovated building is fully accessible and houses a theatre, a contempory art gallery and well equiped dance, digital arts and sound studios.

Capacity: 499 Standing, 260 Theatre Style

THE AFRICA CENTRE

Richmix Culture Foundation 35-47 Bethnal Green Road London E1 6LA
Tel: 020 7836 1973
Email: info@africacentre.org.uk
Web Site: www.africacentre.org.uk
ADMINISTRATION:
Administrator: Kojo Akuffo

WACARTS

Hampstead Town Hall Centre 213 Haverstock Hill, London NW3 4QP
Tel: 020 7692 5800 Events: 020 7692 5809
Email: events@wacarts.co.uk
Web Site: www.wacarts.co.uk
ADMINISTRATION:
Events Manager: Craig Huxley
Email: craig.huxley@wacarts.co.uk
Cap: Council Chamber Room 120, Main Hall 250, Smaller Hall 120 Standing. Dance Studios and smaller rooms available to hire.

YAA ASANTEWAA ARTS AND COMMUNITY CENTRE

1 Chippenham Mews, London W9 2AN
Tel: 020 7286 1656
Email: admin@yaaasantewaa.com
Web Site: www.yaaasantewaa.com
ADMINISTRATION:
Community arts and social centre, providing cultural, artistic, educational and recreational activities relevant to the needs of the local population.
TECHNICAL:
Small studio theatre (60 seats) with adequate light and sound. Large hall for music show, cabarets. Seats 200 with adequate lighting and sound, also disabled access.

Loughborough, Leicestershire

CHARNWOOD ARTS COUNCIL

Loughborough Library, 31 Granby Street, Loughborough, Leicestershire LE11 3DU
Tel: 01509 822 558 Fax: 01509 822 559
Email: info@charnwoodarts.com
Web Site: www.charnwoodarts.com
ADMINISTRATION:
Director: Kevin Ryan. Email: kevr@charnwoodarts.com
Administrator: Terry Allen.
We are a community arts organisation, programming activities, workshops, performances in a number of venues, but are not an arts centre and do not have a venue of our own.

Maidenhead, Berkshire

NORDEN FARM CENTRE FOR THE ARTS

Altwood Road, Maidenhead, Berkshire SL6 4PF
Mgt: 01628 682 555 BO: 01628 788 997
Hire: 01628 682 555 Fax: 01628 682 525
Email: admin@nordenfarm.org
Web Site: www.nordenfarm.org
ADMINISTRATION:
Director: Jane Corry, Email: jane.corry@nordenfarm.org
A hi-tech, performing and visual arts centre. Offering innovative, multi-artform work and wide community participation.
Capacity: Max, 265. Studio Theatre, 100.
TECHNICAL:
If you require more information contact the technical department, tel: 01628 682 561, email: technicians@nordenfarm.org.
STAGE: 8 4-line single purchase counterweight set (Complete with rope lock and guides), 8 4-line handline flying sets, 1 T60 tab track 10m o/all. Curtains and Drapes; 1 Cross Stage Border, 2.5m Drop, 4 Cross Stage Border, 2m Drop, 6 Pairs of legs (6m drop), 1 Pair of Mid-stage traveler tabs, 1 Cyclorama Cloth, 1 Gauze.
LIGHTING: Desk; Strand 520i. Dimmers; Strand LD-90 96 @ 2.5 Kw, 18 @ 5.0 kW. Luminaries; 10 Strand SL 15/32 (Profile), 30 Strand SL 23/50 (Profile), 14 1.2kW Cantata PC, 20 Par-64 lantern, 24 Quartet PC, 8 500W Coda-4, 4 500w Nocturne single floods. Floor Stands; 4 Floor Stands, 4 Folding single-extension floor stands. Accessories; 20 Slot-in iris for profiles, 10 Gobo holders for 600w profiles Size B, 24 Internally wired bars (6way aprox 2.5m long), 2 6-way drop box.
SOUND: Mixing Desk; Soundcraft K2. Dual Power Amplifiers; 4 Crown MT-600. Loudspeakers; 4 EAW JF200e, 4 EAW SM122e (Foldback wedges), 2 Floor stands (K&M 21300), 1 Sub Bass unit (this is intended for the Cinema sound). Signal Processing; 1 SPX 990 Reverb/Fx, 1 Dual compressor/limiter, 2 One third octave equalizer. Digital Signal Processing; BSS Audio Soundweb 9088 (With 8 line level inputs and 8 line level outputs). IR Hard of Hearing System; Sennheiser Infra Red Hard of Hearing System with 20 Stethoscope receivers. Playback/Recording; 1 Cassette recorder/player Denon DN720R, 1 Sampler Akai S3000XL (32 MB RAM memory and 16MB Flash memory option), 1 Mini disk recorder/player Denon DN M2000R, 2 Compact disc player Denon DN-650F. Powered Monitors; 2 JBL EON10p. Microphones/DI; 3 SM58 Beta, 3 SM58, 2 SM57 Beta, 2 SM57, 2 AKG C747, 2 AKG C1000, 4 DI Boxes, 2 Beyer MCE 86n(C). FX; 1 Jem ZR22-DMX Smoke Machine, 1 LeMatre Pyro system inc 2x 2way pods & 2x 1way pods. LX Board; 1 Zero88 24 channel 2 preset manual board.
STAGE COMMUNICATIONS: 8 Technical intercom user belt packs and Headsets.

Manchester

ROYAL NORTHERN COLLEGE OF MUSIC

124 Oxford Road, Manchester M13 9RD
Hiring: 0161 907 5289 BO: 0161 907 5555
Email: info@rncm.ac.uk
Web Site: www.rncm.ac.uk
ADMINISTRATION:
Props: Royal Northern College of Music
Events Manager: Tom Besford, Email: tom.besford@rncm.ac.uk
Policy: Productions of Opera and Drama. Available for hire by Opera and Ballet and Theatre Companies.
Perfs: 7.15 or 7.45
Capacity: Theatre; 607 (+ 50 in orchestra pit if not used).Concert Hall; Level 1- 445 Fully open with balcony 610, Small ensemble layout 730. Carol Nash Recital Room - 100. Studio Theatre - 120. Coffee Bar and Licensed Bar.
TECHNICAL:
Theatre:
STAGE: Pros. Opening 13.72 m, Pros. Height 6.10 m, Depth of Stage 8.53 m, Depth of Rear stage 9.84 m
LIGHTING: 530i Strand control console, 350 Channels.
SOUND: For recording: 20XLR lines which run back to the Recording Department. A permanent PA system which is suitable for speech and some music. There is also a 4.5 KW Martin PA rig.

Studio Theatre:
STAGE: Dimensions; 7.5m x 7.5m.
LIGHTING: Strand Lighting 300 Series. 60 circuits
SOUND: Same as above.

Melrose, Scotland

MELROSE THE WYND THEATRE

7 The Wynd, Melrose, Roxburghshire TD6 9PA
Tel: 01896 820 028 Fax: 01896 823 854
Tech Mobile: 07871549818
Email: bookings@thewynd.com
Web Site: www.thewynd.com
ADMINISTRATION:
Manager: Joe and Marc Clough
Scottish Borders central venue annual 60 + performance programme of drama and music. Always looking for new professional touring performers.
Capacity: Permanent seating, 90. Max: 100.
TECHNICAL:
STAGE: Wooden stage floor, at ground level. Wing Depth = 1 metre Working area of 6.00m x 6.00m, extending to 8.00m x 8.00m with no rear tabs or wings. Front edge of stage to back wall: 6.00m. Aproned Proscenium Arch. No Rake Access for performers via stage doors (rear stage left), or through auditorium rear and front. No crossover. 4 x double 13A mains points for general use. 4 x single XLR points for stage mounted mics (mixed/regenerated in Tech Room). Heated Stage Area House Tabs - grey wool serge, on automated track Legs. Black wool serge, 2 pairs, on Hall Swivel arms. Widths: 1.00m and 1.50m Rear Tabs - black or grey wool serge on full wipe tracks.
LIGHTING: Control; Alcora Zero-88. Digital programmable board, 100 scene/sequence memories, sequential and manual playback, 12/24 control channels. 2 x ACT 6 Strand Lighting Dimmer Racks (additional racks rq'd for 24 channel mode). 4 independent switched. 15A circuits for on-stage props etc. Lighting Rig: 4 bars, 6 circuits per bar. 3 bars over stage area, 1 bar to rear of FOH. 2 additional circuits, side wall-mounted, above audience seating. 4 additional circuits, wall-mounted at low level in stage area. Dedicated circuit for follow spot in Tech Room. Operates independently of board/dimmers. Follow Spot: Bar in Tech Room. Lighting Tripod. Luminaires: 1 x 500W TechnoArt Nova Follow Spot, 6 x 500W TechnoArt Nova Fresnels, barn doors fitted. 4 x 500W Lampo Fresnels, barn doors fitted 4 x 500W TechnoArt Nova Floods, barn doors fitted. 2 x 500W Lampo profiles. 2 x 500W Wide Angle Focus Spots.
SOUND: Sony CDP-XE310 CD Player Sony MDS-JE520 Mini Disk Deck Sony, TCKE200 Tape Deck, Mixing, Amplification & Regen. Operated from Tech Room, Phonic MM122 mixing desk. Philips SQ8 Mixing Amp. Microphones; 2 x Boundary Mics (fixed), 4 additional XLR mic points on stage, 1 x Beyer Dynamic, M03 2 x Beyer Dynamic M05, 1 x Bandridge Vocal Mic, 2 x Shure SM57. Mixing/Amplification; StudioMaster Powerhouse Vision 708 Powered Mixing Desk. 350 Watts per channel, 6 mic/line channels each with 3-band mid-sweep EQ, an insert and 4 sends, 2 post, and 2 pre-fade. Additional 2 stereo line/mono channels. Onboard delay and reverb facilities. Loudspeakers; 2 x 150 watt FOH speakers 1 x 150 watt powered wedge foldback 1 x 150 watt wedge foldback. Microphones; 1 x Beyer Dynamic M03 2 x Beyer Dynamic M05 1 x Bandridge Vocal Mic 2 x Shure SM57. Patching; 1 x 30m MultiCore - 8 inputs, 4 outputs, all XLR. 4 x passive DI Boxes. 1 x 4 way Phantom Power Unit. All essential cabling.
BACKSTAGE FACILITIES: Dressing Room;1, with 2 wash basins and toilet. Access to backstage, Tech Room and rear theatre door.

Newcastle-upon-Tyne, Tyne and Wear

PEOPLE'S THEATRE

Stephenson Road, Newcastle-upon-Tyne, Tyne and Wear NE6 5QF
Tel: 0191 265 5020 op 2 (BO)
Email: peoplesvenuemanager@hotmail.com
Web Site: www.peoplestheatre.co.uk
ADMINISTRATION:
Props. & Lessees: Peoples Theatre Arts Group Ltd
Policy: Repertory, Arts Centre, Amateur.
Venue Manager: Steven Robertson
Technical Manager: Peter Harrison
Perfs: Evenings 7.30
Seats: Variable up to 514, Studio 90. Two Bars.
TECHNICAL:
STAGE: Proscenium, Flat; Pros. Opening 10.36m; Ht. of Pros. 4.27m - 6.10m; Depth of S/Line 10.36m + 4.60m thrust forestage; Ht. of Grid 10.67m; 10 lines, Hemp; Scenery Flying Ht. 4.87m; Flying Bars 9.14m; W/Widths P.S. 5.49m, P.O. 1.83m; Prompt Cnr. P.S.
LIGHTING: Switchboard: Strand GSX, 96 ways; 22 F.O.H. Spots, all 1k various Flats 3 circuits; Cyc. 4 circuits; Dips 8 each side; 2 Perches; 3 Spot Bars, 30 Spots Patts.243,223,123; Bridge 12 circuits T-spots (12) + Patt.93's.
SOUND: Uher 5 channel stereo mixer; Stereo amplifier 200w (Pioneer 8500); Mono R.A. Amplifier; 2 Akai 4000 DS Stereo tape decks; Pioneer PC112D turntable; Shure cartridge M75D; 4 Moving coil mics (AKG - 2 hand, 2 shotgun); 4 mic stands; 2 stage speakers; 2 F.O.H. speakers (tannoy); 2 Overhead speakers; 4 channel microphone mixer Shure M68FCE; 4 point low impedance microphone system.
DRESSING ROOMS: 3; Accom. 40; 2 Showers; 1 Bathroom; 3 lavatories; 5 hand basins; Orchestra Pit 20.

Newport, Gwent

THE RIVERFRONT

Bristol Packet Wharf, Kingsway, Newport, Gwent NP20 1HG
Admin: 01633 656 677 BO: 01633 656 757 Marketing: 01633 656 674
Email: the.riverfront@newport.gov.uk
Web Site: www.newport.gov.uk/riverfront
ADMINISTRATION:
Theatre & Arts Director: Nicolas Young
Technical Manager: Chris Davies
Capacity: Theatre, 489. Studio; 128.
TECHNICAL:
Theatre:
STAGE: proscenium opening: 11.4m. wide x 6.5m. Depth from back of proscenium wall: 11m Depth of Apron:3m.Grid Height: 17.4 Wing space: 4m Single Purchase Counterweights 31 sets Bar length 16m Get in door 3m wide x 4.5m high 0.6m. above road level in loading bay.
LIGHTING: Control; ETC Expression-ECS 2 F.O.H. bridges 3 F.O.H. motorised bar hoists Two perch positions PS and OP.
SOUND: Soundcraft 24 channel MH4. 16 Martin Audio EM76 including L&R centre cluster and delays 2 Martin Audio EM201 minidisk and CD Communications Full Sm facilities F .O.H. calls ring intercom cue lights show relay CCTV.
DRESSING ROOMS: 6 on two floors holding 2, 6,2, 4,20,20

Studio:
STAGE: End on with all round balcony. Flat floor space:Approx. 11.2m wide x 12.3m deep (seats stored) Approx. ll.2m wide x 6.1m deep (seats out).Get-in to scene dock - 3m wide x 3.9m high. Scene dock to stage- 2.5m wide x 2.9m high 0.6m. above road level in loading bay.
LIGHTING: Control ETC Express 24/48 80 ways dimming
SOUND: Soundcraft 16 channel Kl. Comunications F.O.H. calls ring intercom, cue lights, show relay.
DRESSING ROOMS; 2 holding 20 and 10 Orchestra Pit: 20 Musicians Recording Studio Fully equipped studio with Adat, CD burner and minidisk and hold up to 10 musicians. Wardrobe Facilities are situated on the first floor behind the Theatre Dance studio on first floor F.O.H.

Newport, Isle of Wight

THE QUAY ARTS CENTRE

Sea Street, Newport, Isle of Wight PO30 5BD
Admin/ BO: 01983 822 490 Fax: 01983 526 606
Email: info@quayarts.org
Web Site: www.quayarts.org
ADMINISTRATION:
Operations Manager: Peter Farwell or Jo Cowan
Email: p.farwell@quayarts.org / j.cowan@quayarts.org
Policy: Theatre, comedy, music, dance, kids and literature. Cinema showing modern and classic films.
Cap: Studio Theatre 115 - 134, depending on layout of the stage.
TECHNICAL:
STAGE: Wooden sprung floor; a Harlequin dance floor (grey or black) is available, approx. 6 x 10m. White cyclorama and black full width tabs at the rear, and adjustable side masking. Limited wing space. Width (between side masking tracks) 8.4m (27'6"), Depth (to back tabs) 6.5m (21'3") - 76 seats / 5.0m (16'4") - 115/134 seats, Height (to grid) 4.2m (13'9")
LIGHTING: 72 Strand LD90 dimmers controlled by a Strand GSX console (125 ch DMX, 24 subs, 200cues). 10 x Strand Cantata fresnel with barndoors (1200w). 12 x Strand Quartet fresnel with barndoors (650w). 6 x CCT Minuet fresnel with barndoors (650w). 1 x Minuet profile (650w). 6 x Strand Prelude 16/30 profile (650w). 2 x Strand Prelude 28/40 profile (650w). 1 x iris for Prelude. 4 x Strand Coda 500/3 cyc flood (3 x 500w). 4 x Source4 PAR with lenses (575w). Gobo holders for Prelude (size B), gel frames, basic gel stock. 6 x 4m boom bar + 12 x boom arm.
SOUND: control via an Allen & Heath GL2200 console (24/4/2, 6 aux). Front of house PA - Yamaha P3500 amplifier + Community CSX35-S2 speakers. Stage monitors - Crest Audio VS 650/450 amplifiers + Behringer F1220 wedges (4). Ashly MQX 2150 graphic equaliser (2 x 15 band). Lexicon Alex digital reverb/delay. 2 x Technics CD player with auto cue. Sony MiniDisk recorder. Pioneer multi-region DVD player. Samsung multi-standard VHS recorder. Sanyo XGA LCD projector. 4m x 3m cinema screen (can be masked according to projection format). 3 x Shure SM58 vocal mic. 3 x Shure SM57 instrument mic. 2 x AKG D880 vocal mic. 2 x AKG D770 instrument mic. 1 x AKG D550 bass instrument/kick drum mic. 1 x AKG C1000S condenser mic. 4 x DI box. 10 x boom stand. 3 x short boom stand. 2 x table stand. Tie-clip radio mic (UHF diversity). Canford wired comms system with 4 belt packs + headsets. 2 channel infra-red audio system is installed.

Newry, County Down

SEAN HOLLYWOOD ARTS CENTRE

1a Bank Parade, Newry, County Down BT35 6HP Northern Ireland
Tel: 028 3031 3180 Fax: 028 30266839
Email: jacqueline.turley@newryandmourne.gov.uk
Web Site: www.newryandmourne.gov.uk
ADMINISTRATION:
Props: Newry & Mourne District Council
Facilities manager: Jacqueline Turley
Policy: To promote good Theatre and Arts in the Newry and Mourne area.
Seating: Auditorium; 150 seats.
TECHNICAL:
STAGE: Area: Flat stage with Proscenium Arch. Width 6.28m, Depth 6.28m, Height 6.5m. Passenger lift to all floors. House intercom system.
LIGHTING: Rank Strand AMC System with 60 No. circuits.
ADDITIONAL: Rooms: Auditorum. 2 Dressing Rooms. Green Room. Exhibition Areas. Coffee Bar. Photographic Studio etc. Rehearsal room.

Northampton

NORTHAMPTON COLLEGE ARTS CENTRE

Northampton College, Booth Lane,
Northampton NN3 3RF
College Reception: 01604 734 218 Tel (Julie Tetnam): 01604 734 201 Fax 01604 734 296
Programme Leader of Performing Arts: Julie Tetnam
Cap: 72 Seated

Northern Ireland, Ulster

UNIVERSITY OF ULSTER

School of Creative Arts, Northland Road, Londonderry BT48 7JL Northern Ireland
Tel: 028 716 75396 Fax: 028 716 75473
Email: g.monaghan@ulster.ac.uk; r.ohagan@ulster.ac.uk
Web Site: www.ulster.ac.uk
Administration/Courses:
Drama Course Director: Dr Lisa Fitzpatrick.

Norwich, Norfolk

NORWICH ARTS CENTRE

Reeves Yard, St. Benedicts Street,
Norwich, Norfolk NR2 4PG
Admin: 01603 697 662 BO: 01603 660 352
Email: stuart@norwichartscentre.co.uk
Web Site: www.norwichartscentre.co.uk
Director: Stuart Hobday
Operations Manager: Bradley Glasspoole
Seating Capacity: 120

THE KING OF HEARTS

7-15 Fye Bridge Street Norwich NR3 1LJ
Admin: 01603 766 129 BO: 01603 611412 Fax: 01603 617 816
Email: enquiries@kingofhearts.org.uk
Web Site: www.kingofhearts.org.uk
ADMINISTRATION:
Artistic Director: Aude Gotto
Manager: Jane Neville
Policy: The Music Room is available for hire. Ideal for chamber music, recitals, storytelling and poetry readings. We are not licensed for plays.
Capacity: 80.
Green room with kitchen and shower. No stage, theatrical lighting or curtain. Additional rooms available for catering functions, rehearsals, etc. Steinway piano and harpsichord.

Paisley, Renfrewshire

PAISLEY ARTS CENTRE

New Street, Paisley, Renfrewshire PA1 1EZ Scotland
Tel: 0300 300 1210
Email: ram.els@renfrewshire.gov.uk
Web Site: www.renfrewshire.gov.uk
ADMINISTRATION:
Arts and Museum Manager: Mhairi Cross
Paisley Arts Centre and Paisley Town Hall are managed by Renfrewshire Arts, part of Renfrewshire Council's department of Education and Leisure Services. Paisley Arts Centre houses a 151 seat theatre and programmes all year round with drama, dance, comedy and music events. Paisley Arts Centre also has a workshop space available for hire. Paisley Town Hall is a magnificent Victorian building which programmes large scale music events and is available to hire for weddings, conferences, meetings and social events. Renfrewshire Council also has numerous other community halls available for hire. For more information on hiring the venue, email: eventhires@renfrewshire.gov.uk
TECHNICAL:
Paisley Arts Centre and Paisley Town Hall are fully technically equiped and serviced buildings.

Penzance, Cornwall

ACORN THEATRE

Parade Street, Penzance, Cornwall TR18 4BU
Tel: 01736 363545
Email: admin@theacornpenzance.co.uk
Web Site: www.theacornpenzance.com
ADMINISTRATION:
Contact: Vanessa Jackson
Technician: Steve Warhurst
Tel: 01736 363545
Capacity:
Main Auditorium; Standing, 170, Balcony, 53, Closely seated, 170. Cabaret, 100.
Small downstairs auditorium: Capacity 80 max.
Basement Bar; Standing, 80. Cabaret, 60. Seated, 80., dressing room.
TECHNICAL:
STAGE: Performing area; 8m x 6m (total 42m2). Black box masking - back wall used as cyclorama. Access to a grey harlequin dance floor. Baby Grand piano (there is a charge to have this tuned). Get In; Access via ramp in Union Street carpark. One parking permit is available for carpark behind venue.
LIGHTING: Desk; ZERO 88 FROG with screen. Dimmers; STRAND ACT 6, ZERO 88 BETA PACKS. 4 permanently set up giving 24 channels. 2 more can be added giving 36 channels running the FROG in wide mode. Lanterns; 10 x Quartete profiles, 12 x Quartete frenels, 6 x Par64, 10 x Par 36 pin spots, 4 x ADB profiles, 8 x ADB frenels, 5 x Patt 23, 2 x Strand 833.
SOUND: Main Auditorium; Soundcraft K2 24 channelAlesis HD24, Alesis Masterlink ml9000, Tascam MD305, Denon DN-T620 cd/cassette, Bheringer DEQ9624, Bheringer GEQ3102 x 3, Bheringer Composer x 2, Bheringer Multiygate x 2, Lexicon MPX1, Alesis Midiverb 4. F.O.H speakers and amps. Martin EM75, EV SB180, Bheringer CX3400 crossover, Yamaha PC2602 amp, EV P3000 amp.
Lower Auditorium; Soundcraft Powerstation 600, Denon DN-T620 cd/cassette, Martin EM75. Monitors; Viscount Base 12 self powered x 2, DAS 15A selfpowered x 2, Bose 802 pair.
Microphones; AKG C1000 x 4, AKG C416 x 2, AKG C411 x 2, AKG D770 x 2, AKG D3700 x 3, AKG Full drumset, Shure SM58 x 6, Shure SM57 x 6, Shure SM58 radio mics x 2, AudioTechnica AT804 x 2, Sennhiser 602E
DRESSING ROOMS; 2, limited washing facilities.

Peterhead, Aberdeenshire

PETERHEAD COMMUNITY EDUCATION CENTRE

Balmoor Terrace, Peterhead,
Aberdeenshire AB42 1EP Scotland
Tel: 01779 477 277 Fax: 01779 471 041
Email: keith.byers@aberdeenshire.gov.uk
Web Site: www.aberdeenshire.gov.uk
Manager: Keith Byers
Seating Capacity: 300

Poole, Dorset

LIGHTHOUSE, POOLE'S CENTRE FOR THE ARTS

21 Kingland Road, Poole,
Dorset BH15 1UG
BO: 0844 406 8666
Email: info@lighthousepoole.co.uk
Web Site: www.lighthousepoole.co.uk
ADMINISTRATION:
Props: Poole Arts Trust Ltd
Lessees: Poole Arts Trust Ltd
Policy: Mixed programme with Concert Hall used for classical and popular music and in its flat floor mode for rock, cabaret, dances and exhibitions. Theatre used for touring repertory company, opera and ballet. Full-time cinema, studio, art gallery and function rooms.
Capacity: Concert Hall, 1473, Rock, 2459. Theatre, 669. Cinema, 103. Function Rooms, 240. Studio, 135. Foyer Bars and Cafe Bar.
TECHNICAL:

Concert Hall:
STAGE: Orchestra seating for 120 and choir seating for 140. Details available on request. Steinway 'D' concert piano available.
DRESSING ROOMS: 4 Guest Artiste Rooms each with shower.
3 chorus changing rooms (approx. 25 each).
Theatre:
STAGE: Proscenium: Width 9900mm, Ht. 5400mm; Max. Width 19880mm; between Flyrails 13899mm; Depth 9900mm. Orchestra Pit: Approx 25 persons, on lift. Converts to forestage.
Other technical information available on request.

Portsmouth, Hampshire

THE THIRD FLOOR ARTS CENTRE

Central Library, Guildhall Square, Portsmouth, Hampshire PO1 2DX
Tel: 01293 834 184 Fax: 023 9283 4904
Email: arts@portsmouthcc.gov.uk
Web Site: www.portsmouth.gov.uk
Arts Officer: Jane Leech
Capacity: 120
Our brand new 120 seat theatre plays host to visiting and local theatre companies, plus our ever popular children's shows, live music and dance productions. There are classes and workshops across various artforms and for varying age ranges and abilities, and we also have a new gallery space with ongoing exhibitions throughout the year. The Arts Centre is also available for hire. We have numerous function rooms available for rehearsals, meetings, classes and workshops.

Potters Bar, Hertfordshire

THE WYLLYOTTS THEATRE

Darkes Lane, Potters Bar, Hertfordshire EN6 2HN
BO: 01707 645 005 Admin: 01707 660067 Fax: 01707 649 849
Email: ginny.williams@hertsmereleisure.co.uk
Web Site: www.wyllyottstheatre.co.uk
ADMINISTRATION:
Props: Hertsmere Leisure
Theatre Manager: Ginny Williams
Cap: 421 for stage shows, 120 for dinners, exhibitions, art gallery, museum, 3 conference rooms, cafe and bar. Also used as part time Cinema

Preston, Lancashire

CHARTER THEATRE

Guild Hall Ltd Lancaster Road, Preston, Lancashire PR1 1HT
Tel: 01772 804 440 BO: 01772 804 444
Email: info@prestonguildhall.co.uk
Web Site: www.prestonguildhall.com
ADMINISTRATION:
Props: The Villa Group
General Manager: Melanie Hutchings
Contact: 01772 440 266 or melanie.hutchings@prestonguildhall.co.uk
Marketing Manager: Hannah Slater
Contact: 01772 440 263 or hannah.slater@prestonguildhall.co.uk
Senior Technician: James Hubbard
Contact: 01772 440 269 or james.hubbard@prestonguildhall.co.uk
Policy: Various
Seats: 780. (Stalls: 578, Circle: 202)Bars, Restaurant, Lounge Bar
TECHNICAL:
STAGE: Proscenium Arch - Orchestra pit used as thrust. Performing area 12.2m x 10.5m - pros opening 9.4m x 4.88m - wing widths 2.44m SL, 9.75m SR. No rake - floor lino on wood, semi sprung, suitable for all dance, backstage crossover, stage heated. Height of grid 15.07m - 3 hemp, 33 counterweight sets, single purchase - 2 tab tracks - 500kg permitted on bars - maximum flying height 7.3m - black and white legs and borderes - white filcloth gauze cyclorama - purplehouse tabs, flown. 2 x 13 amp ring mains. Orchestra pit (electrical) 3 levels front stage 10.25m x 2.35m entrance from under stage in lowest position. Auditorium level can be used to accommodate 40 musicians, entrance from side stage pass door. Get-in via lift and scenery hoist 3.05m x 2.44m. Tallescope. Scale stage, fly and lighting plans available.
LIGHTING: Ovation board with macro wing and moving light wing, Arri smart rack dimmers 150 circuits, 144 @ 2.5kw, operated from rear of auditorium - 100A 3 phase and 200A 3 phase supplies available on stage for temporary board - 52 profiles, 46 fresnels, 40 pars, 2 x Strand CSI followspots, operated from FOH.
SOUND: DDA 24:8:2 desk, operated from FOH - FOH and FX turbo speakers, 1 Kw PA system - 10 various mics _ Revox B77 reel -to-reel, Tascam DAT, Tascam Minidisc, Cassette tape systems - facilities for recording and editing. Acoustics suitable for music and spoken word.
STAGE MANAGEMENT: Prompt corner SL, cue lights and headsets, 8 outstations - show relay to dressing rooms.
BACKSTAGE: 7 dressing rooms, accommodating 34, 16 showers, facilities for disabled performers, access to stage by stairs and lift - green room - band room - quick change rooms - wardrobe in dressing room area with washing machine and dryers, 4 x 13amp sockets. Refreshments from front of house. Piano, Bechstein grand, excellent - stage doorkeeper and security personnel. Advice given on accommodation. Staff - 2 stage, 1 lighting, 1 sound casuals available.
ADDITIONAL: 35mm film projection, wide screen and cinemascope. Dolby stereo sound with surround.

WORDEN ARTS AND CRAFTS CENTRE

Worden Park, Leyland, Preston, Lancashire PR25 1DJ
Tel: 01772 625 505 Fax: 01772 6222287
Email: wordenarts@southribble.gov.uk
Web Site: www.worden-arts.co.uk
ADMINISTRATION:
Available for private functions, weddings, theatre and concerts. For more info contact Maree Robinson or Ian Thomas.
Cap: Marsden Theatre; 140
TECHNICAL:
Technical support available on request.

Radlett, Herts

THE RADLETT CENTRE

1 Aldenham Avenue, Radlett, Hertfordshire WD7 8HL
Admin/Tech: 01923 857 546 Fax: 01923 857 592 BO: 01923 859291
Email: admin@radlettcentre.com
Web Site: www.radlettcentre.co.uk
ADMINISTRATION:
General Manager: Greg Dexter
Technical Manager: Paul Foskett
Capacity: 300

Reading, Berkshire

SOUTH STREET

21 South Street, Reading, Berkshire RG1 4QU
Tel: 0118 9375 234 BO: 0118 960 6060
Email: 21southstreet@reading.gov.uk
Web Site: www.readingarts.com
Manager: John Luther
Technical Manager: Rick Bull
Contact: Sally-Ann Gilmour

Rhyl, Denbighshire

RHYL MUSEUM & ARTS LIBRARY

Church Street, Rhyl, Denbighshire LL18 3AA Wales
Tel: 01745 353 814 Fax: 01745 331 438

Email: alastair.barber@denbighshire.gov.uk
Web Site: www.denbighshire.gov.uk
ADMINISTRATION:
Props: Denbighshire County Council
Principal Community Librarian: Mr Alastair Barber

Salisbury, Wiltshire

SALISBURY ARTS CENTRE

Bedwin Street, Salisbury, Wiltshire SP1 3UT
BO: 01722 321 744 Fax: 01722 331 742
Tel: 01722 430700
Email: info@salisburyarts.co.uk
Web Site: www.salisburyartscentre.co.uk
ADMINISTRATION:
Props: St. Edmunds Arts Trust
Cap: 400 standing. 160 Seated

Scarborough, North Yorkshire

UNIVERSITY OF HULL (SCARBOROUGH CAMPUS)

Scarborough Campus, Filey Road, Scarborough, North Yorkshire YO11 3AZ
Tel: 01723 362 392 Tel: 01723 357289 (Andrew Head) Fax: 01723 370 815
Email: a.head@hull.ac.uk
Web Site: www.hull.ac.uk
Administration/Courses:
Admissions Tutor: Andrew Head
BA (Hons): Theatre & Performance Studies, MA Theatre & Contemporary Practice. In combination with Dance, Digital Media and Design Technologies, Creative music Technology and English.

Scotland, Cumbernauld

CUMBERNAULD THEATRE

Cumbernauld Theatre, Kildrum, Cumbernauld, Glasgow, North Lanarkshire G67 2BN Scotland
Admin: 01236 737 235 BO: 01236 732 887
Email: info@cumbernauldtheatre.co.uk
Web: www.cumbernauldtheatre.co.uk
ADMINISTRATION:
Artistic Director: Ed Robson
Venue Technician: Sean Smith
Administration and Resources Manager: Jean Cairns
Policy: Home productions. Touring Theatre Companies, Music, Mime, Theatre in Education, Dance, Exhibitions, Films, Workshops
Seats: 258 (main auditorium): 60 (studio)
TECHNICAL:
For more information contact the Technical Department on:
technical@cumbernauldtheatre.co.uk
STAGE: Permanent Thrust Stage, adaptable to be 'in the round'. 6.9m wide x 13.5m deep x 5.53m to grid; Control Room at back of auditorium.
LLIGHTING: Arri Imagine II memory desk, Arri smartracks 96 x 2.5kw; 14 x T64, 6 x T84, 26 x Patt.73, 18 x Patt.23, 19 x Patt.123 12HD; 6 ind. circuits all 2k; All connections 15 amp 3 pin round.
SOUND: Revox B77 .DAT. CD., Dennon cass; Garrard SO25; Mixer:Soundtracks 24:4:2.
DRESSING ROOMS; 2.
STUDIO: Performing space 7.1m x 4.19m x 2.7m to grid. Pulsar MS4 72 way board, Racks 2k dimmers. All connections 15 amp round pin.
Membership: TMA, FST

Scotland, Dundee

BONAR HALL

University of Dundee, Park Place, Dundee, Tayside DD1 4HN Scotland
Tel: 01382 227 684
Email: emoore@dundeereptheatre.co.uk
Web Site: www.dundeerep.co.uk
Seating/Capacity: Main Hall 458, Ustinov Room Capacity: 160
Events Manager: Eve Moore

Shrewsbury, Shropshire

THE GATEWAY EDUCATION AND ARTS CENTRE

Chester Street, Shrewsbury, Shropshire SY1 1NB
Tel: 01743 361 120 / 355159 Fax: 01743 358 951
Email: gateway.centre@shropshire.gov.uk
Web Site: www.shropshire.gov.uk/gateway.nsf
ADMINISTRATION:
Adult & Community Learning Manager: Sarah Bromley
Performance Space: Cap: 100, flat floor, tiered seating available.

THE HIVE

5 Belmont, Shrewsbury SY1 1TE
Tel: 01743 234 970 Fax: 01743 234 971
Email: admin@hiveonline.org.uk
Web Site: www.hiveonline.org.uk
Director: Allyson Lanning

Spalding, Lincolnshire

SOUTH HOLLAND CENTRE

Market Place, Spalding, Lincolnshire PE11 1SS
Tel/ BO: 01775 764 777
Email: shcentre@sholland.gov.uk
Web Site: www.southhollandcentre.co.uk
ADMINISTRATION:
Props: South Holland District Council
General Manager: Sally Harrison
Cap: 342 Seated

Stamford, Lincolnshire

STAMFORD ARTS CENTRE

27 St. Marys Street, Stamford, Lincolnshire PE9 2DL
Mgt/ Admin: 01780 480846 BO: 01780 763203
Email: emma@stamfordartscentre.com
Web Site: www.stamfordartscentre.com
ADMINISTRATION:
Props: South Kesteven District Council
Programming: Graham Burley
Technical Manager: Adrian Hill
Policy: Integral part of Stamford Arts Centre. Theatre is used by touring professional companies/artistes and is available for hire by amateur groups. Drama, dance, mime and music presented. Induction loop and lift for disabled.
Seats: 166. Bar and catering facilities available.
TECHNICAL:
STAGE: Proscenium flat; Pros. opening 8.27m. Ht. of Pros. 3.35m; W/Widths P.S. 0.91m, O.P. 0.91m
LIGHTING: Switchboard: Sirius 24. Control room rear of auditorium; F.O.H. spots. Lanterns: 10 CCT Minuette Profile 650w, 6 Strand Patt 813 Profile 500w, 2 Patt 23 Profile 500w, 17 Patt 803 Fresnels 650w, 8 CCT Minuette Fresnels 650w.
SOUND: Speakers either side of pros. arch. Hill LC 400 Amplifier, Technics Cassette Player, Denon CD player, 8 channel mixer desk.
DRESSING ROOMS: 2; Accom. 24; Basins and toilets. No Orchestra Pit

Stirling, Stirlingshire

MACROBERT

University of Stirling, Stirling FK9 4LA Scotland
Mgt: 01786 467 155 Box Office: 01786 466 666 Fax: 01786 466 600

Email: info@macrobert.org
Web Site: www.macrobert.org
ADMINISTRATION:
Head of Technical and Production: Mark Ritchie
Tel: 01786 466602, Email: mark.ritchie@macrobert.org
Operations Manager: Elizabeth Fuller
Email: elizabeth.fuller@macrobert.org
Policy: Mixed touring - Opera, Ballet, Drama, Concerts, Recitals, etc. Stirling Film Theatre.
Perfs: Usually 7.30 or 8.00p.m.
Seats: 466 raked tier. The Playhouse Children's Theatre, 100. Bar/cafe, Coffee Bars.
TECHNICAL:
Mainhouse (Theatre & Film):
STAGE: Flat, varnished hardwood. Stage width, 18.70 m/ 64', Pros. Width, 9.75 m/ 32', Height 5.50 m/ 18', Stage depth: 9900 m/ 32'5", Forestage depth, 2690m/ 8' 9". Height to grid, 14.30 m/ 47'. Stage to fly floor, 6.30 m/ 20'7", Stage to Flyfloor handrail, 8.20 m, Stage to underside of Catwalk cross over, 7.40 m, Counterweight bar length, 12.20 m/ 40'. 25 Stage weights. Full "black box" masking available. Rear wall white(ish) for use as cyc. Tallescope and variety of ladders available. Full show relay/ backstage call system. Forestage/Orchestra pit on lift with accommodation for up to 22 musicians.
LIGHTING: ETC Expression 3 (174 circuits). Lanterns: 45 x Robert Juliat 310THF 1.2K with Barn Doors, 25 x Source4 Zoom 15-30 Profile, 10 x source4 zoom 25-50 Profile, 8 x source4 Junior 25-50 Profile, 10 x Strand Brio 18/30, 18 x Coda 1K, 18 x Source4 par Mixture of CP60/61/63, 20 x Parcan ALL CP62, 2 x Selecon Performer MSR 1200w Followspot with 6 colour magazine. Stands; 8 Tank Base with 3 meter scaff poles and 4 boom arms each
SOUND: 4 x D+B 602M Monitor Speakers, 2 x D+B 18-1 Bass. Allen and Heath ML4000 Mixing desk. 2 x Sony MDS_E10 mini disc Player. 1 x Sony CDR-W33 CD player. 2 x Denon CD Players DN-C615. 1 x Tascam 112MK2 cassette Player. 1 x Yamaha SPX990. 4 channels BSS FCS 966 Graphic EQ. 4 channels BSS DPR 422 Compressor. Soundweb 9088ii 1 x Tascam 112MK2 cassette Player. 1 x TC Electronics M2000 Effects/reverb unit. 1 x TC Electronics D-Two Delay Unit. 2 x Flown Foh D+B C6's pairs. 2 x Flown E3's for Centre Fill (powerd by 1 Epac amp).
BACKSTAGE FACILLITIES: Dressing Rooms; 4 principles, 2 chorus. Accommodation for up to 30. Green room, Quick-change room. Laundry room with facilities.

Playhouse Children's Theatre:
STAGE: Stage depth; 6.375m from front of seating bank to rear wall. Stage width: 5.987m at rear wall. 8.541m at front of seating. Height 6.7m. Floor is of varnished hardwood. Loading bay 1.2 m above roadway. Ramp provided. Accessible by 40' trailer. Outer get-in door; width 1.8m, height, 2.1m. Inner get-in door, width 1.6m, height 2.4m.
LIGHTING: ETC Express 24/48 desk (35 dimmers) & 12 extra dimmers on 2 x 13amp power supply. 30 x Source4 Parnel, 6 x Source4 Zoom Profile 15/30's, 2 x Source4 Zoom Profile 25/50, 10 x Source4 Par.
SOUND: Soundcraft 8 ch. Mixer. 2 x MD Players. 2 x CD Players.

Stornoway, Isle of Lewis, Scotland

AN LANNTAIR ARTS CENTRE

Kenneth Street, Stornoway, Isle of Lewis HS1 2DS
Tel: 01851 703 307 BO: 01851 708 480
Fax: 01851 708 499
Email: info@lanntair.com
Web Site: www.lanntair.com
ADMINISTRATION:
Chief Technician: Mike Adkins (mike@lanntair.com)
Programme: Performing Arts, Cinema, Auditorium Management and Hire: Alex Macdonald (alex@lanntair.com)
Capacity: 200.
Full bar and catering facilities.
For full details of hiring the auditorium please contact Alex Macdonald on 01851 703307 or email alex@lanntair.com
TECHNICAL:
STAGE: Proscenium opening: 8m. wide x 4.8m. high. Depth from back of proscenium wall (max/min): 10m/5.6m. Depth of demountable forestage: 2m. Stage centre line to stage right wall (max): 8.5m. Stage centre line to stage left wall (max); 7.5m. Width between fly galleries: 9.6m. Height to underside of stage suspension steels: 11m. Clear height beneath galleries: 6.5m. Stage Floor: Stage surface 6mm oil tempered hardboard on 25mm ply. Get-In: Scene dock/stage level access from road level. Door: external to scene dock - 3m wide x 3m high. Door: scene dock to art gallery - 3m wide x 4.5m high. Door: scene dock to stage - 2.2m wide x 3.1m high.
SOUND: House mixer: Allen & Heath 24 channel GL2200. Control room: Rear auditorium with opening window. Microphone lines: 46 No, including links to bar/restaurant. Audio lines: 40 No, including links to bar/restaurant. Radio mic antenna lines: 2 No. Microphone/audio patching: Control room. Outboard gear: CD player, minidisc player/recorder, cassette deck, digital effects unit, graphic EQ, all contained in mobile effects rack. Main speaker system: Centre cluster: Martin Audio EM76. Prosc L+R: Martin Audio EM186. Rear balcony delay: Martin Audio EM26. Link to bar/restaurant music/calls loudspeakers for "open space" events. Effects loudspeaker lines: 16 No, including links to bar/restaurant.
LIGHTING: Two fixed lighting bridges in auditorium. Auditorium side proscenium vertical lighting booms. Follow spot location at centre of third bridge. Lighting control desk: ETC Express 24/28. Operated from control room at rear of auditorium.
Hand held rigger's control. Dimmers: Zero 88 Chilli Pro hard-wired 10A dimmers. Load circuits as follows: FOH: 6 No, Flys: 6 No, Stage: 6 No, House Lights: 6 No. Zero 88 Install 6 10A patchable dimmers. 18 No circuits available. Patch panel with load circuits as follows: FOH : 24 No, Flys: 24 No, Stage: 24 No. 6 No 15A non-dim (switched) circuits controlled from panel in control room. Load circuits appear on patch panel. 12 No DMX sockets at all principal lighting positions. 1-in 3-out DMX splitter available at DMX patch panel in control room. 23 No Ethernet sockets, including links to bar/restaurant. Ethernet patch in control room. Space for future distribution hub. Separate Ethernet patch in scene dock store for art gallery. 4 No Ethernet sockets in art gallery, plus link to building-wide IT network
BACKSTAGE FACILITIES: Dressing Rooms, 2: accommodating 7 to 10, with Washbasin and shower. Separate adjacent disabled WC with accessible shower. Green room area with kitchen. Store off scene dock.

Sunbury-on-Thames, Middlesex

RIVERSIDE ARTS CENTRE

Run by voluntary community association
59 Thames Street, Sunbury, Middlesex TW16 5QF
Tel: 01932 789249 Tel: 01932 782850 (Eric Champion)
Web Site: www.riversidearts.co.uk
ADMINISTRATION:
Cap: 150
Manager: Eric Champion
For bookings contact Peter Anderson, bookings secretary
Tel: 020 8890 6586
Props: Spelthorne Borough Council

Swindon, WIltshire

THE ARTS CENTRE

Devizes Road, Swindon, Wiltshire SN1 4BJ
Tel: 01793 466 565 Fax: 01793 422 827
BO: 01793 614 837
Email: artscentre@swindon.gov.uk
Web Site: www.swindon.gov.uk/artscen-

tre
ADMINISTRATION:
Manager: Clarry Bean
Tel: 01793 466565 or email: chbean@swindon.gov.uk
Marketing & Communications Manager: Nicki Western
Mob: 07786 020958. Email: nwestern@swindon.gov.uk
Technical Manager: Matt Davis
Mob: 07500 226836. Email: midavis@swindon.gov.uk
Capacity: 224 (4 wheelchair spaces replace 12 seats)
TECHNICAL:
STAGE: Width of proscenium: 6.72 m, Height of proscenium: 3.23 m. Width of stage (max): 8.62 m. Height to grid (no access): 4.75 m. Depth of stage: 4.96M (min) - 6.10 m (max).
DRESSING ROOMS: 3. Toilet, basin, and shower facilities.
STAGE COMMUNICATIONS: Sound & LX (Control Room), to Stage Manager (Prompt Corner). Tannoy to bar and dressings room operated from PC and Control Room.

Taunton, Somerset

THE BREWHOUSE

Coal Orchard, Taunton, Somerset TA1 1JL
BO: 01823 283 244
Email: enquiries@tauntontheatre.org.uk
Web Site: www.thebrewhouse.net
ADMINISTRATION:
Props: Taunton Theatre Association Ltd.
Chair & Director: Val Hammond
Directory: Mark Dawson
Policy: Mid scale professional touring drama, dance, opera, one person shows, poetry, conference, amateur drama, operatic & pantomime companies, jazz and folk and classical music.
Perfs: 7.45. Mats. usually Thurs & Sat 2.30.
Seats: 352. Bar and Buffet/Restaurant.
TECHNICAL:
For more information contact the Technical Department on Tel: 01823 274608 or email: technical@thebrewhouse.net.
STAGE DIMENSIONS: Full stage depth (or to U/S black tabs) 9.95m (9.42m) 32ft 8ins (30ft 11ins). Width of pros 10.109m 33ft 2ins. Height of grid 6.63m 21ft 9ins. Height of pros (including header) 5.18m 17ft. Max flying height (LX bars hang at approx 5.8m) 6.32m 20ft 9ins. Hemp bar width 12.50m 41ft. Depth pros to Cyc 6.93m 22ft 9ins. Depth of apron 3.00m 9ft 10ins. SL wing width 2.13m 7ft. SR wing width 7.2m 23ft 8ins. Get-In: Dock door opening width 3.22m 10ft 7ins. Dock door opening height 4.85m 15ft 11ins. Dock/SR shutter door width 4.00m 13ft 2ins. Dock/SR shutter door height 4.88m 16ft.
STAGE: Large scene dock providing under cover get ins and some workshop facilities, entrance from the dock to SR wing via shutter door. Prompt desk situated in prompt corner (SL wing) on 3.5m (12ft) wonder lead with full headphones system. Limited cue lights available. Red velvet house tabs on hand winch situated by prompt desk (SL wing). 8 x hemp flying lines on aluminium bars, 4 line hemps with a max weight of 100kg each bar. Orchestra pit situated in the apron with lift out traps, max capacity of 15. 15 x illuminated rak stands available. Full soft black masking. 4 sets of black serge legs. 2 x 3ft borders. 2 x 6ft borders. 6 x legs manually tracked on up/down bars, 3 per wing - can be used independently or in conjunction with legs. 2 x sets of permanently rigged black running tabs which are fixed to the grid and unable to move. 1 set D/S of Hemp 7 and 1 set U/S of Hemp 3. Harlequin black dance floor which covers the entire stage floor including the apron, available for use.
LIGHTING: Control: 1 x ETC ion, 1 x universal fader wing 2 x 20, radio remote riggers and 2 x 19" touch screen monitors. 96 x 2.5kw circuits LD90 racks, patch panels are located in SL slot. Profiles: 20 x Source 4 15/30 zoom (permanently rigged on FOH bridge). 10 x Altman Shakespeare 15/35. 2 x Source 4 50 deg. 15 x Source 4 15/30 zoom. 12 x Source 4 25/50 zoom. Fresnels: 20 x 1.2k Selecon Fresnels with Barndoors. 9 x Harmony Fresnels with Barndoors. 10 x Cantata Fresnels with Barndoors. 8 x Prelude 650 Fresnels. 2 x Vision 650 Fresnels with Barndoors (permanently rigged on FOH Bridge as tab warmers). Pars: 38 x Par 64 (CP62). PC: 8 x Vision 2.5k PC with Barndoors. Floods: 12 x Spotlight Domino 1k Floods. Strobes: 2 x Martin Atomic 3000 Strobes. Pin Spots & Birdies: 10 x Pin Spots. 7 x Birdies with transformers. Follow Spots: 2 x Clay Paky Shadow Follow Spots (positioned above LX Box). Misc: 6 x lighting booms (3m high IWB, 6 ways on each boom all on tank trap with castors) & 3 x Shin stands assorted TRS, socapex, gobos & holders. 32 x Grelcos & 3 x Trelcos. 1 x Viper 2.6 smoke machine, 1 x Jem techno fog & 1 x Unique 2 haze machine. 4 x ETC Source 4 Iris.
SOUND: Desks: 1 x Allen & Heath ML4000 40/8/3. 1 x Yamaha MG12/4 Amps: 2 x Crown MAC 1200 (permanently used for FOH speakers and subs), 1 x Crown XLS 602 1200, 1 x Citronic PPX 1200, 1 x Citronic PPX 900, 1 x QSV RMX 1450. Speakers: 2 x Martin audio WT3 (permanently rigged FOH), 6 x XV400B speakers (usually used as monitors), 3 x Tannoy Lynx speakers, 4 x Nexo P58 & Nexo analogue TD controller, 2 x XV1000 Sub bass speakers, Processors: 1 x 4 way mulicom compressor unit, 1 x Klark technic graphic, 1 x Alesis Midiverb, 1 x Ultracurve digital graphic equalizer, Mics and Mic Stands: 4 x Sennheiser lapel radio mics, EW300 G3. 2 x Sennheiser hand held radio mics, EW300 G3, 4 x Beta 58. 8 x Shure SM58, 7 x Shure SM57, 2 x AKG CK91, 2 x AKG SE300B power module, 2 x AKG CK98 Shotgun mic. Module. 7 x Assorted AKG mics, 16 x Boom mic. Stands. 3 x Short mic. Stands. DI Boxes: 5 x DI boxes, 2 x Behringer Ultra DI Pro 4 channel units. Multicores: 33 way hardwired multicore from control room to stage with 8 x speaker returns, 1 x 20 way stage box, Comms: 6 x Techpro BP111 beltpacks, 2 x Altair EM-201 beltpacks, 1 x Altair AM-100/2 headset, 2 x Techpro SMH210 headsets, 2 x Techpro DMH220 double headsets. Playback: CD players: Denon DN-C616, Tascam CD-OIU Pro CD player, MD players: Sony MDS - JB930, Sony MDS-JE780.
BACKSTAGE FACILITIES: 2 large dressing rooms and 2 small dressing rooms all air conditioned; accommodation 50. 5 toilets including 1 disabled shower / toilet. Full disabled access to backstage areas. Green room / crew room with tea coffee making facilities.
Laundry room available with washing machine, tumble dryers, irons and ironing boards. Office space within with telephone and internet access. Wireless internet is also available backstage but needs to be authorised by the resident technicians.

TACCHI-MORRIS ARTS CENTRE

School Road, Monkton Heathfield, Taunton, Somerset TA2 8PD
Admin: 01823 414 144 BO: 01823 414 141 Fax: 01823 414 127
Email: info@tacchi-morris.com
Web Site: www.tacchi-morris.com
ADMINISTRATION
Policy: We are committed to promoting work in the area of International understanding in Drama, Dance and Music. We are interested in high quality performances and workshops suitable for the community and young people. Our mission is to become a Centre of Excellence in Education in the Performing Arts.
Centre Administrator: Nicky Morgan
Technical Manager: Martin Worrall
Capacity: 250 seats (Main House Studio Theatre) or seats can be rearranged for promenade or "in-the-round" work.
Full disabled access to both stalls and balcony, foyer bar and terrace cafe.
TECHNICAL
STAGE: Pros opening 15m; performing area 14m x 10m; height of pros 6m; no rake sprung floor, full set of black wook drapes to form "black box". Get in via dock doors at stage/ground level 5.50 (w) and 4.75 (ht). Moveable stage management desk, show relay to dressing rooms and FOH bells/buzzers and tannoy.
LIGHTING (Main House): Strand 91370 LBX 125ch genius. Large FOH and overstage grid, control box at rear of balcony, large stock of new lanterns, T-bars, etc.
SOUND (Main House): Soundcraft live

4mk II 16:4:4:2 mixer; 4 Martin audio speakers; 2 Yamaha MS205 monitor speakers (powered); Demon CD Player; Tasca 301 minidisk player. Plus a selection of cardioid and vari-motion dynamic microphones.
DRESSING ROOMS: 2, and green room.

DANCE/ DRAMA STUDIO:
Smaller drama studio (10m x 10.50m) with full set black wool drapes, lighting rig and control room and dance studio (10m x 10.50m) with dance floor, wall mirrors, full drapes and lighting rig. Both studios have their own changing facilities.

Teddington, Middlesex

LANDMARK ARTS CENTRE

Ferry Road, Teddington, Middlesex TW11 9NN
Tel: 020 8977 7558 Fax: 020 8977 4830
Email: info@landmarkartscentre.org
Web Site: www.landmarkartscentre.org
ADMINISTRATIVE:
Arts Centre Manager: Lesley Bossine
Email: lesley@landmarkartscentre.org
Operational & Technical Manager: Tim Cannings
Email: tim@landmarkartscentre.org
Main Hall Capacity: 220 - 320. Additional spaces available for rehearsals or workshops.
TECHNICAL:
Limited lighting is available.
Stage Area: - 2 Spots, 8 fixed 500 Watt floods
Extra lighting available. All lighting is side mounted onto ladder beams, no tressing over stage area. Limited sound equipment available; smoke machines used must be water based.

Torrington, Devon

PLOUGH ARTS CENTRE

9-11 Fore Street, Torrington, Devon EX38 8HQ
Tel: 01805 622 552 BO: 01805 624 624
Fax: 01805 622 113
Email: mail@theploughartscentre.org.uk
Web Site: www.plough-arts.org
ADMINISTRATION:
Director: Richard Wolfenden Brown
Email:
richard@theploughartscentre.org.uk
Technical Manager: David Thynne
Email: david@theploughartscentre.org.uk
Home to high quality and diverse arts events and films, plus a range of Plough Projects for the local community.
Cap: 240
TECHNICAL:
STAGING: 8'X4' wooden staging with three different size steel legs: 17cm, 37cm, 57cm.
POWER: Single 32a socket into: 6 x 13amp double sockets on stage, 3 phase in control room for lighting.
LIGHTING: 1 x jester lighting desk zero 88. 24 submasters (soft patching is available - but if you need to soft patch I recommend you tour your own desk.). 3 x zero 88 dimmer pack. 1 x strand dimmer pack act 6 (total channels 24) 48 individual lights. No more then 2k per channel. Lighting leads etc. Fresnel lamps x13. Profiles x 12. Parcans x7. Moving lights X 2 (imove 75). Mirror lights X 2 (skytec dmx dj scan 250). Firecraker x 1. Ic4 x 2 colour floor lights.
SOUND: RCF PA. 1x Yamaha o1v digital mixing desk (12 channels). 4 x subs 8001 as. 2 x tops 6001 a. 2 x rcf monitors Art series (these often get used for front of house on poles from the subs). 3 x opera monitors. 2 x 31 band DBX graphics (FOH). 4 x 31 Graphics (Foldback). 50 x XLR leads. 5 x sm 58 microphones. 4 x sm 57 microphones. 2 x Rode condenser microphones. 2 x Behringer Condenser microphones. 1 x AKG D112 microphone. DI boxes X 5 ultra DI Behringer. 12 x tall microphone stands. 6 x short microphone stands. 1 x multicore 16/6. 1 x CD Player. 1 x mini disk player.
DRESSING ROOMS; 2, accommodating up to 12 people. Full length and smaller wall mirrors. Two toilets. One single hand basin. Iron and ironing board.
ADDITIONAL: Handheld radios. Broadwood baby grand Piano. White 6.5m wide rigged on back wall

Tunbridge Wells, Kent

TRINITY THEATRE

Church Road, Tunbridge Wells, Kent TN1 1JP
Admin: 01892 678 670 BO: 01892 678 678
Email: info@trinitytheatre.net
Web Site: www.trinitytheatre.net
ADMINISTRATION:
Artistic Manager: John Martin (john@trinitytheatre.net)
Technical Manager: Simon Diaper (technical@trinitytheatre.net)
TECHNICAL:
STAGE: Performing Area: Depth - Setting line to cyclorama - 6.5m (21ft); Width - Standard Wings - 8m (26ft); Width - Transverse masking - 11m (36ft); Height - Floor to underside of Grid - 10.7m (20ft), Bars normally hung at - 6m (20ft). NB: Loading Bay Door: 5'5" wide x 6'7" high. Masking: 4 Pair Black Wool Serge Legs - 6m (20ft) deep; 1 Set Black Wool Serge Tabs - on track up stage crossover; 2 of Black Canvas flats 8ft x 4ft; 2 of Black Canvas flats 8ft x 2ft. Orchestra Pit: Could accommodate up to 7 musicians (normally only available for min week long bookings). Rostrum: 3 of 8ft x 4ft x 24ins; 3 of 8ft x 4ft x 15ins; 2 of 8ft 6ins x 3ft x 6.5ins; 1 of 7ft x 3ft x 6.5ins; 1 Pair 2 step treads; 1 Pair single step treads. Stage Power: 6 Double 13amp Sockets (3 each side). Other: White Cyclorama, Dance Floor, 60 of Chairs (various condition), Props Tables (various), Braces & Weights, Ladders (various), Tallescope. Piano: 1 of 8ft yamaha Grand; 1 of Technics Electronic piano.
LIGHTING: Mixer: Allen & Heath SC + 41 bxa 16-4-2 + aux 2 pre/2 post. FX Unit: Yamaha SPX 990. Mixer can be sited a) Control Room, b) Rear of Auditorium, c) Front of Balcony, d) Centre Stage Left, e) Centre Stage Right, f) Upstage Left.
SOUND: Main Amp: 2 x Crest Vs1100 (550 watt/chan). Main Speakers (FOH): 2 x EAW MS103 with active crossover. Foldback Amp: Peavey M-2600 Stereo Power Amp 100w RMS per channel. Foldback Speakers: 4 x Wedge Monitor Cabinets (2 mixes only). Mini Discs: 2 x Sony Mini Disc Recorders/Players. Tape Decks: 2 x Technics Stereo Twin Cassette Deck. Technics Model 1500 2 Track reel to reel (NO Auto Stop) hub adaptors and remotes available. Speeds 9.5cm, 19cm, 38cm (3.75ips, 7.5ips, 15ips). Microphones: 7 x Shure SM58; 7 x Shure SM57; 2 x Realistic PZM; 3 x DOD Stage Direct Boxes (DI). Mic Stands: 12 x Boom; 2 x Vertical. Tie Lines: 16 Mic Lines and 4 Speaker lines between UL corner of stage and control positions. Talk Back Tec Pro: Control room to various stage and auditorium positions 6 Headsets). Show relay and paging to dressing rooms.

Wakefield

WAKEFIELD ARTS CENTRE

Wakefield College, Thornes Park, Wakefield, West Yorkshire WF2 8QZ
Admin: 01924 215 531 BO: 01924 211 311 Fax: 01924 215 525
Email: mail@theatreroyalwakefield.co.uk
Web Site: www.wakefieldtheatres.co.uk
ADMINISTRATION:
Presents a mixed programme of professional and student productions. The innovative programme includes dance, drama, music, physical theatre and comedy.
Executive Director: Murray Edwards
Technical Manager: Gareth Williams
Email: gareth.williams@theatreroyalwakefield.co.uk
Main Auditorium: 220 seats. 176 on a powered telescopic seating rig. 44 permanently fixed on balcony.
TECHNICAL:
STAGE: Performing area 11.4m x 5.8m - to wings. Wing widths (removable), 1.8m SR/SL, 2.1m across back. Floor - level varnished wood, suitable for some dance with dance floor available on request. Height of grid 5.1m Centre bars can be hand winched to assist rigging. Full set of

black drapes - Retractable white projection screen. Get in via foyer double doors, 2.0m x 1.7m - steps or ramp access.
LIGHTING: Zero 88 Sirius 48 desk, power supply 3 phase, 5-amp socket to 10 amp dimmers. Lanterns: 12 x 1Kw profiles, 6 x 650W profiles, 12 x 1Kw fresnels, 8 x 650W fresnels, 8 x furse floods, 2 x pars.
SOUND: Soundcraft Delta 16-4-2 desk, operated from rear of auditorium(control room). EV S-200 speakers, Quad 520f amp, QSC audio amp. Denon CD, Cassettex2, Minidisc. Sure mics x 6 and stands, Sennheiser Radio mics lapel and handheld. Stage management - Tecpro master base station & 2 x beltpacks, show relay to dressing rooms.
BACKSTAGE FACILITIES: 2 large dressing rooms beneath stage - access via stairs at rear of stage.

Wales, Newtown

THEATR HAFREN

Llanidloes Road, Newtown, Powys SY16 4HU Wales
Admin: 01686 614565 Mktg: 01686 614556 BO: 01686 614555
Email: admin@theatrhafren.co.uk
Web Site: www.thehafren.co.uk
ADMINISTRATION:
Props: Powys County Council
Administrator: Sara Clutton
Marketing Manager: Del Thomas
A venue/arts centre in Mid Wales, approximately 35 minutes drive from Shrewsbury.
Cap: 568 Seated
Receiving theatre - broad-based programme ranging from community use to national tours of dramas, comedian and pop stars/bands.
TECHNICAL:
See website for detailed technical specifications, or email: tech@theatrhafren.co.uk.

Wales, Pontypridd

THE MUNI ARTS CENTRE

Gelliwastad Road, Pontypridd, Rhondda Cynon Taff CF37 2DP Wales
Admin: 01443 485 934 BO: 08000 147 111 Fax: 01433 401 832
Email: leon.kruger@rhondda-cynon-taff.gov.uk
Web Site: muni.rct-arts.org
ADMINISTRATION:
Props: Rhondda Cynon Taff Borough Council
Manager: Leon Kruger
Cap: 346 Seated, 200 Cabaret, 400 Standing.

Wales, Swansea

TALIESIN ARTS CENTRE

Swansea University Singleton Park Swansea SA2 8PZ Wales
Admin: 01792 29 52 38 Tech: 01792 295 492 BO: 01792 602 060
Email: office@taliesinartscentre.co.uk
Web Site: www.taliesinartscentre.co.uk
ADMINISTRATION:
Props: University College of Swansea
Manager: Sybil Crouch. Email: s.e.crouch@swansea.ac.uk
Technical Management Team: Dave Palmer
Email: d.palmer@swansea.ac.uk
Policy: Drama, dance, opera, concerts, films. Mixed programme touring and in-house productions.
Perfs: 7.30 nightly
Seats: 330 Theatre Style, Space for 2 wheelchairs. Bar, Foyer, Ceri Richards Art Gallery, Bookshop.

TECHNICAL:
STAGE: Flat floored stage with adjustable proscenium walls; forestage lift to pit; wood floor covered hardboard. Proscenium opening 9.6m to 15.9m. Max stage width 20m. Depth 9.3m, with thrust 11.6m. Floor to roof beams 10.5m. Floor to fly galleries 6.0m. 16 4 line hemp sets rated at 250Kg s.w.l. 6 I.W.B. winch sets. 4 pairs black legs. 3 black borders. Motorised F.o.h. Tabs - Gold, 1 cyclorama, 1 set of Black Travellers, walls brown painted brick.
LIGHTING: 4 FOH lighting bridges plus booms on adjustable side walls, 6 on stage internally wired lighting bars on power winches, 4 Side lighting stands, Desk: Strand 530, 150 channels - 138 x 2.5kw and 12x 5kw dimmers. Control to rear of auditorium. Lanterns: 10 x SL Zoom 15/32, 20 x SL Zoom 23/50. 10 x Cantata PC's, 20 x Cantata Fresnels, 6 Alto 2kw Fresnels (all with barn doors). 10 Prelude 16/30. 10 Prelude fresnels. 10 x 500w Coda Floods. 16 x 1kw Coda floods permanently hung on cyc bar, 24 Par Cans. Film: 2 x Century 35mm film projectors, 1 x fumeo 16mm film projector, 2 x Kodak 2010 slide projectors, 2 x Simda 3040 slide projectors with dissolve.
SOUND: 24/8/1 Soundcraft Series 2 mixer. F.O.H. speakers: 4 x Sherman. Portable monitors 4 x JBL (M330) MK2. 4 x JBL Monitor wedges. 2 x Sherman stacks for main PA. Microphones 4 x shure beta 58 radio mics, 6 x shure beta 58, 2 x SM58, 4 x shure beta 57, 2 x AKG D3600 Cardiod Instrument mics, 3 x crown p.c.c. 1 x denon twin cassette deck, 1 x denon cd player, 2 denon DN-1100 minidisc machine, 1 tascam DA20 DAT machine, 2 Yamaha SPX 990, 3 x Yamaha 2301 equalisers. Drawmer 4 ch Compressor.
STAGE COMMUNICATIONS: Stage managers desk (prompt), rehearsal desk auditorium/control room, intercom and cue lights to all areas, 4 x dressing rooms for 28 artists at stage level. Green room, laundry, showers, access to workshop and scene dock at stage level from roadway.

THEATR FELINFACH

Dyffryn Aeron, Ceredigion SA48 8AF Wales
Tel: 01570 470 697 Fax: 01570 471 030
Email: theatrfelinfach@ceredigion.gov.uk
Web Site: www.theatrfelinfach.com
ADMINISTRATION:
Policy: Theatre in education/community theatre, drama in education for children, resource centre, youth theatre centre, 90% of which Welsh language.
Head of Theatr Felin-fach: Dwynwen Lloyd Evans
Booking Terms: Hire, Box Office split, guarantee & split, guarantee by negotiation.
Other: Functions, Conferences, Educational Projects, Youth Theatre Groups.
Cap: 260, raked.
TECHNICAL:
STAGE: Pros. arch with apron. Performing area 12.2m x 7.92. Working height of grid 4.27m - self-rigged hemp flying system. 1 Tab track & wipe tracs, max flying height 4.84 black tabs, legs & borders, black vinyl covered floor.
LIGHTING: strand 520, 47 Circuits - 18 spots, 23 fresnels, 4 4-circuit battens, Strand - 2 followspots.
SOUND: Allen & Heath 16:4:2 desk - 4 speakers, Tascam 32 0.25" tape system, Denon CD player, Tascam Mini Disc.

Washington, Tyne and Wear

THE ARTS CENTRE WASHINGTON

Biddick Lane, Fatfield, District 7, Washington, Tyne and Wear NE38 8AB
Mgt/BO: 0191 219 3455 Fax: 0191 219 3458
Email: pauline.haughey@sunderland.gov.uk
Web Site: www.artscentrewashington.com
ADMINISTRATION:
Creative Director: Helen Green
Email: helen.green@sunderland.gov.uk
Manager: Pauline Haughey,
Email: pauline.haughey@sunderland.gov.uk
Capacity: 110 Seated
TECHNICAL:
110 seated Theatre, 2 Function Rooms, Gallery, Public Bars, Recording Studio and Artists' Studios.

Watford, Hertfordshire

PUMP HOUSE THEATRE AND ARTS CENTRE

Run by volunteers, hosts varied programme of theatre, dance, music & children's theatre group
Local Board Road, Lower High Street, Watford Herts WD17 2JP
Tel 01923 241362 Fax 01923 222792
Email: info@pumphouse.info
Web Site: www.pumphouse.info
This thriving Theatre and Arts Centre offers a wide variety of entertainment and interests for all ages. Our bars serve traditional cask ales and the selection of guest beers from around the country changes each week in the Colne River Room, which plays host to many music events and can also be hired for private functions.

Whitstable, Kent

HORSEBRIDGE ARTS & COMMUNITY CENTRE

11 Horsebridge Road, Whitstable, Kent CT5 1AF
Tel/Fax: 01227 281174
Email: info@horsebridge-centre.org.uk
Web Site: www.horsebridge-centre.org.uk
ADMINISTRATION:
Capacity: 150 Seated, 200 Standing.
General Manager: Liz Daone
Policy: We aim to encourage good and innovative productions in as wide a range as possible to enrich the life of the local community, in the fields of music, theatre, dance, film, comedy, cabaret and childrens shows.
TECHNICAL:
Please contact for technical details.

Wick, Caithness

LYTH ARTS CENTRE

Lyth, Wick, Caithness KW1 4UD Scotland
Tel: 01955 641 270 Fax: 01955 641360
Email: william246@btinternet.com
Web Site: www.lytharts.org.uk
Lively combined arts programme.
TECHNICAL:
LAC1 Studio Theatre:
Play area: 20'6" (6.3m) square, 15' (4.57m) high to ceiling, and 12' high to clear lanterns. Seats for 60 end-on or 72 with seats side of stage. Thick black Bolton curtains around walls, 11' high at sides and 13' high at stage rear wall. Worn, varnished redwood floor. Ceiling and all visible surfaces painted black.
LIGHTING: Grid; 48mm allow tubing suspended 150mm from ceiling at 1.925m centres in a rectangular pattern. Quartet Lights: 8 x 500watt Fresnels, 2 x 500watt PCs, 2 x 500watt 22/40 spots. Selecon Acclaim Lights: 6 x 500watt Fresnels, 2 x 500watt PCs, 2 x 500watt 22/50 spots, this lighting lives permanently on the overhead grid but can be moved around as required. All fresnels and PCs have barn doors. All lamps have gel frames. Selection of gels. 4 x Zero88 Betapack dimmer racks (each with 6 channels and 12 sockets) sited backstage. Zero88 Alcora 24 channel desk which lives at the LX desk but is portable. 24 moveable lighting cables clipped to grid and routed back to racks plus 4 extra cables. House lights on separate dimmer on a trailing cable to LX desk or portable. 15' A-frame ladder, 11' straight ladder, 6' step-ladder.
SOUND: Allen and Heath Wizard desk - 12 channel (8 mono and 2 stereo), Nexo PS 10 amp, Denon DCD-685 CD player, Tascam MD-350 mini disc player, 2 x Nexo PS 10 speakers, 25m x 24 channel multi-core cable link from desk to stage on stage: 6 x Shure SM58 microphones, 2 x AKG C 1000 condenser microphones, 8 x boom stands, 6 x Behringer DI boxes, 4 x EV Sx100a stage monitors 8 music stands. Instruments available either in LAC1 or LAC2: Steinway B grand piano 6'10" (black high gloss) 2004, Yamaha Model U3 upright piano 4'3" (black high gloss) 1985, Roland RS100 keyboard with Peavey KB/A60 amplifier, Roland HP800 keyboard with build in amp, Second System for use in LAC2 Foyer and other venues, Mackie DFx 12 mixer, Gothard S/F case for mixer, 2 x Mackie srm 450 speakers, 2 x speaker stands.
LAC2 Foyer when used as performance space:
Dimensions: 43'8" (13.3m) x 17'5" (5.3m) x 12'4" (3.76m) high. French windows opening onto veranda and sheltered garden. Counter forming bar and serving hatch to kitchen. Large chimney piece with open log fire. Lounge seating for 24, stacking chairs for 36, and veranda seats for 16.
ACCOMMODATION: The centre has its own on-site accommodation annex specially designed for visiting Performers.

Wolverhampton, West Midlands

BILSTON CRAFT GALLERY

Mount Pleasant, Bilston, Wolverhampton, West Midlands WV14 7LU
Tel: 01902 552 507 Fax: 01902 552 504
Email: BilstonCraftGallery@wolverhampton.gov.uk
Web Site: www.wolverhamptonart.org.uk
ADMINISTRATION:
Hire Space co-ordinator: Laura Marsh
Tel: 01902 552051. Email: laura.marsh@wolverhampton.gov.uk
ArtforumContact: Jen Dooner
Tel: 01902 552055 Email: Jen.Dooner@wolverhampton.gov.uk

WOLVERHAMPTON ARTS GALLERY

Lichfield Street, Wolverhampton, West Midlands WV1 1DU
Tel: 01902 552 055 Fax: 01902 552 053
Email: ArtGallery@wolverhampton.gov.uk
Web Site: /www.wolverhamptonart.org.uk

Workington, Cumbria

CARNEGIE THEATRE AND ARTS CENTRE

Finkle Street, Workington, Cumbria CA14 2BD
Tel: 01900 602 122
Email: carnegie@allerdale.gov.uk
Web Site: www.carnegietheatre.co.uk
ADMINISTRATION:
Funding: Venue funded by Allerdale B.C.
Regional Arts Association: North West Arts
Manager: Karen Thompson
Policy: Promote folk, rock, jazz, ballet, M.O.R., variety, country, children's drama. Hire to amateur drama etc. Also promote festivals, rhythm n' blues. Monroe's Bar promotes national and local rock, rhythm and blues, and Indie bands.
Perfs: Available for use 7 days.
Booking Terms: Hire split, guarantee and split, 1/2 calls co-production, negotiation.
Non-performance activities: meeting rooms, rehearsal spaces, socials, craft activities, etc.
Facilities: Seats 354, Monroe's bar 200. Theatre raked. Catering - coffee shop. Bar - special hours certificate to 2.00 a.m. Shop sales area available.
Access: nearest public car park: Vulcans Lane, Railway - Workington Main, Coach terminal - Workington.
Facilities for disabled: 8 wheelchair spaces (level access). Assistance available (contact manager). All house facilities available.
Other facilities: Dance studio 12m x 10m also used for meetings and rehearsal.
TECHNICAL:
STAGE: Proscenium arch. Performing area 9m x 8m - pros opening 7m x 6m - wing widths 2m SR, 2m SL, 6m US. Stage raked, floor sprung wood, suitable for all dance, backstage crossover, stage heated. Height of grid 6m; 2 tab tracks; black Bolton twill legs and borders; gold silk and white canvas cyclorama; gold house tabs, drawn. 4 x 60A and 2 x 30A independent circuits. Forestage 3m x 1m. Orchestra pit 7m x 2m, accommodates 15. Get-in via understage; dock doors 1.5m x 3m. Scale stage and lighting plans available.

LIGHTING: Strand MX48, operated from lighting control room; 22 spots + 48 parcans, 36 fresnels, Rank Strand - 2 followspots, operated from lighting control room.
SOUND: Shure and AKG mics - 1 x cassette - HH PA and Bose theatre speakers. Acoustics suitable for music and the spoken word. Stage Management: 4k Peavey Rig available locally. Intercom to lighting control. Piano: Kawai Baby Grand
BACKSTAGE FACILITIES: 5 dressing rooms, access by stage and theatre balcony; green room; adequate supply of power points. Beverages, liquor and sandwiches available. Rehearsal rooms, piano, good. Advice given on accommodation. Staff - stage and lighting; casuals available; security personel. Backstage facilities not accessible to disabled performers and staff.

Monroe's Bar
STAGE: performing area 5m x 2.5m; height to grid ceiling 3.5m; 8 x 13A sockets. 1 x 30A supply.
LIGHTING: Hired locally.
SOUND: Hired locally. Acoustics suitable for music and spoken word. 4k Peavey Rig available locally.

York, Yorkshire

HELMSLEY ARTS CENTRE

Old Meeting House, Helmsley, York North Yorkshire, YO62 5DW
BO: 01439 771700 (ex. 1) Admin: 01439 771700
Email: helmsleyarts@yahoo.co.uk
Web Site: www.helmsleyarts.co.uk
ADMINISTRATION:
Director: Em Whitfield Brooks
We are a thriving arts centre offering theatre, music and cinema to a largely rural audience. Also workshops, ballet, exhibitions. meeting room spaces, nt live.
Capacity: Theatre, 140; Studio, 40 Seats.
TECHNICAL:
Please see website.

POCKLINGTON CIVIC ARTS CENTRE

Oak House, Market Place, Pocklington, York YO42 2AR
Tel: 01759 301 547
Email: janet@pocklingtonartscentre.co.uk
Web Site: www.pocklingtonartscentre.co.uk
ADMINISTRATION
Venue Manager: Janet Farmer
Technical Manager: Tom Morris
Policy: Performances of theatre, music, comedy, children's shows, poetry and cinema, as well as a Tourist Information facility and visual arts exhibition space.
Capacity: 200 (fixed raked seating) Plus Studio Seating 70
TECHNICAL:
STAGE: Width 9.5m (Between Downstage Black Legs), Depth 5.5m, Height To Grid 4.25m, White Cyc @ Stage Rear, Wing Space 1.5m Stage Left & Right, Crossover Via Dressing Rooms, Stage Managers Console Stage Left with all essential functions, Plentiful Supply of 13A Sockets stage Left & Right. Get-In: Via Doors or rear of building and stairs to stage area. Please contact us in advance if your set is large or heavy. Parking Space for Loading/Unloading.
LIGHTING: Sirius 48 Lighting Desk in projection box at rear of auditorium. On stage control also available. 136 Way Patching to fixed lighting positions. 9 Independently switched motor control outlets. Lantern Stock: 2 Strand SL 15/32 Profile Spots (650w), 4 Strand Quartet 15/25 Profile Spots (650w), 2 Strand Quartet 22.40 Profile Spots (650w), 8 Thomas Par Cans (1kw), 4 Strand Cantata Fresnell Spotlights (1kw), 30 Strand Quartet F Fresnell Spotlights, 6 Strand Quartet PC Pebble Convex Spots (650w), 4 Strand S Type Battens (4 colours).
SOUND: Soundcraft 4 16 Channel Mixer desk in projection box at rear of auditorium. 24 Signal, 9 return feed and 12 londspeaker sockets in stage area linked to patch pannel. 4 Shure SM58 Microphones on boom stands. 2 EMO direct injection boxes. Dennon DCD715 CD Player. Dennon DN 770R Cassette Recorder. Yamaha GQ2015A graphic equaliser to main auditorium speakers. Yamaha REV 100 Digital Reverb unit. 2 Tannoy T300 Main Stage Loudspeakers. 1 Tannoy T300 Used as Stage Monitor. 1 Tannoy T300 Spare. Signal and Loudspeaker lines are patchable via patchfield in projection box.
STAGE COMMUNICATIONS: Tech Pro system (Operable from SM desk or LX control positions). Backstage relay & calls to dressing rooms. Headset communications between stage left and right and LX / sound operators. If required, sound and lighting desks can be resited at rear of auditorium by special arrangement.
DRESSING ROOMS: 2 Dressing Rooms with make up benches, 2 Shower / Toilet Cubicles, Tea and Coffee making Facilities.

LOCAL AUTHORITIES

County Leisure Departments

BEDFORDSHIRE COUNTY COUNCIL
County Hall, Cauldwell Street, Bedford MK42 9AP
Tel: 01234 408 485 Fax: 01234 316 070
Email: lynne.taylor@bedscc.gov.uk
Web Site: www.bedfordshire.gov.uk
Arts County Officer: Lynne Taylor
Strategic Director For Learning: David Doran
Strategic Director For Enviornment: Mike Kenworthy

CHESHIRE COUNTY COUNCIL
Cheshire County Council Arts, Service, Goldsmith House, Hamilton Place, Chester, Cheshire CH1 1SE
Tel 01244 602 839 Fax 01244 602 805
Email: audrey.siddall@cheshire.gov.uk
Web Site: www.cheshire.gov.uk/arts
Arts and Culture Officer: Jane Dawson
Administrator: Audrey Siddall

HAMPSHIRE COUNTY COUNCIL
County Arts Office, Mottisfont Court, High Street, Winchester, Hampshire SO23 8ZF
Tel 01962 841841 Fax 01962 841644
Email: arts@hants.gov.uk
Web Site: www.hants.gov.uk/arts
Head of Arts, Tourism & Marketing: Nicola Horsey
Arts Development Officer: Tim Kelly
Director of Arts Marketing Hampshire: Adrienne Pye

LINCOLNSHIRE COUNTY COUNCIL
County Offices, Newland, Lincoln LN1 1YQ
Tel: 01522 552 831 Fax: 01522 552 811
Email: david.lambert@lincolnshire.gov.uk
Education and Cultural Services
County Arts Development Officer: David Lambert

NORFOLK COUNTY COUNCIL
Norfolk Museums Service, Shirehall, Market Avenue, Norwich, Norfolk NR1 3JQ
Tel: 01603 493 625 Fax: 01603 493 623
Email: museums@norfolk.gov.uk
Web www.norfolk.gov.uk/leisure/museums
Head of Norfolk Museums Service: Vanessa Trevelyan

NORTHAMPTONSHIRE COUNTY COUNCIL
Arts Development Team, 125-129 Kettering Road, Northampton NN1 4AZ
Tel: 01604 233 122 Fax: 01604 603 070
Email: lgates@northamptonshire.gov.uk
Contact: Arts Development Officer: Louise Gates

OXFORDSHIRE COUNTY COUNCIL
Cultural Services, Central Library, Westgate, Oxford OX1 1DJ
Tel: 01865 810 191 Fax: 01865 810 187
Email: richard.munro@oxfordshire.gov.uk
Web Site: www.oxfordshire.gov.uk
Head of Cultural Services Learning & Culture: Richard Munro

SOMERSET COUNTY COUNCIL
c/o Library Admin Centre, Mount Street, Bridgewater, Somerset TA6 3ES
Tel: 01278 454 604 Fax: 01278 452 787
Email: sisherwood@somerset.gov.uk
Web Site: www.somersetarts.com
Arts Officer: Sue Isherwood
Public Art Officer: John Brady

STATE OF GUERNSEY
Beau Sejour Leisure Centre, Amherst, St Peter Port, Guernsey GY1 2DL Channel Islands
Tel: 01481 747 210 Fax: 01481 747 298
Email: penny.weaver@recreation.gov.gg
Web Site: www.freedomzone.gg
Director of Recreation: David Chilton
Events Manager: Penny Weaver

WILTSHIRE COUNTY COUNCIL
Department of Libraries & Heritage, Bythesea Road, Trowbridge, Wiltshire BA14 8BS
Tel: 01225 713 709 Fax: 01225 713 993
Email: paulinedyer@wiltshire.gov.uk
Web Site: www.wiltshire.gov.uk
Head of Service: Pauline Dyer, ALA DMS MIMgt
Assistant to Head of Heritage Services: Caroline Kempthorn

England & Wales

ALLERDALE BOROUGH COUNCIL
Allerdale House, Workington, Cumbria CA14 3YJ
Tel: 01900 702 702 Fax: 01900 326 346
Email: heritage.arts@allerdale.gov.uk
Web Site: www.allerdale.gov.uk
Arts Development Officer, Rachael Jones
Tel 01900 702 613

ARNOLD NOTTINGHAMSHIRE
Gedling Borough Council, Civic Centre, Arnot Hill Park, Arnold
Nottingham NG5 6LU
Tel: 0115 901 3957 / 3901 Tel Leisure Services: 0115 967 5359
Fax: 0115 967 0114
Email: contactgedling.cc@nottscc.gov.uk

ARUN DISTRICT COUNCIL
Arun Civic Centre, Maltravers Road, Littlehampton, West Sussex BN17 5LF
Tel: 01903 737 500 Fax: 01903 725 254
Email: info@arun.gov.uk
Web Site: www.arun.gov.uk
Marketing & Information Officer: Mary Aslett

ASHFIELD DISTRICT COUNCIL
Cultural Services Urban Road, Kirkby-in-Ashfield, Nottingham NG17 8DA
Tel: 01623 450 000 Fax: 01623 457 530
Email: j.elmer@ashfield-dc.gov.uk
Web Site: www.ashfield-dc.gov.uk
Leisure Centres Liason Officer: Joy Elmer

AYLESBURY VALE DISTRICT COUNCIL
Civic Centre, Market Square, Aylesbury, Buckinghamshire HP20 1UF
Tel: 01296 585 527
Email: sfulchini@aylesburyvaledc.gov.uk
Web Site: www.aylesburycivic.co.uk

BARNSLEY METROPOLITAN BOROUGH COUNCIL
Central Offices: Kendray Street, Barnsley, South Yorkshire S70 2TN
Tel: 01226 770 770 Fax: 01226 773 594
Email: grahamnoble@barnsley.gov.uk
Assistant Director for Culture, Sport & Tourism: Graham Noble

BARROW-IN-FURNESS BOROUGH COUNCIL
28 Duke Street, Barrow-in-Furness, Cumbria LA14 2LD
Tel: 01229 884 784 Fax: 01229 894 703
Email: jmarwood@barrowbc.gov.uk
Web Site: www.barrowbc.gov.uk
Business Manager: Dave Ramage

BARRY TOWN COUNCIL
7 Gladstone Road, Barry, South Glamorgan CF62 8NA Wales
Tel: 01446 738 663 Tel: 01446 704 714

(Arts and Culture Department)
Email: tcharding@valeofglamorgan.gov.uk
Contact Arts & Culture Manager: Tracy Harding

BASINGSTOKE & DEANE BOROUGH COUNCIL
Civic Offices, London Road, Basingstoke, Hampshire RG21 4AH
Tel: 01256 845 597 Fax: 01256 845 642
Email: s.easton@basingstoke.gov.uk
Web Site: www.basingstoke.gov.uk
Arts & Heritage Manager: Symon Easton

BASSETLAW DISTRICT COUNCIL
Sports & Arts Development, 17B The Square, Retford, Nottinghamshire DN22 6DB
Tel: 01909 533 485 Fax: 01909 534 569
Email: peter.clark@bassetlaw.gov.uk
Web Site: www.bassetlaw.gov.uk
Principal Officer (Community Leisure): Peter Clark
Admin Assistant: Karen Sim

BATH & NORTH EAST SOMERSET COUNCIL
Bath Tourism Bureau, Abbey Chambers, Abbey Churchyard, Bath, Somerset BA1 1LY
Tel: 01225 477 708 Fax: 01225 477 221
Email: tourism@bathnes.gov.uk
Web Site: www.bathnes.gov.uk / www.visitbath.co.uk
Marketing Assistant: Kate Blagrove

BEDFORD BOROUGH COUNCIL
Town Hall, St Pauls Square, Bedford MK40 1SJ
Tel: 01234 267 422 Fax: 01234 221 606
Email: centralp@bedford.gov.uk
Web Site: www.bedford.gov.uk
Borough Arts & Leisure Officer: Mr John Moore

SOUTH BEDFORDSHIRE DISTRICT COUNCIL
The District Offices, High Street North, Dunstable, Bedfordshire LU6 1LF
Tel: 01582 472 222 Fax: 01582 474 009
Email: Jane.Moakes@southbeds.gov.uk
Web Site: www.southbeds.gov.uk

BERWICK-UPON-TWEED BOROROUGH COUNCIL
Council Offices, Wallace Green, Berwick-upon-Tweed, Northumberland TD15 1ED
Tel: 01289 330 044 Fax: 01289 330 540
Web Site: www.berwickonline.org.uk
Director of Regeneration & Development: James Milne
Head of Accountancy: Richard Dell
Environmental and Community Services Officer: Rob Marriner

BIRMINGHAM CITY COUNCIL
The Council House, Victoria Square, Birmingham B1 1BB
Tel: 0121 303 1111 Tel: 0121 303 9944
Web Site: www.birmingham.gov.uk
Director of Leisure and Community Services
Art Facilities Manager; Neil Johnston

BLABY DISTRICT COUNCIL
Council Offices, Desford Road, Narborough, Leicester LE19 5EP
Tel: 0116 275 0555 Fax: 0116 275 0368
Email: culturalservices@blaby.gov.uk
Web Site: www.blaby.gov.uk
Arts Development Officer: Ruth Lloyd

BLACKPOOL BOROUGH COUNCIL
PO Box 50 Town Hall Blackpool, Lancashire FY1 1AD
Tel: 01253 477 477 Fax: 01253 478 210
Email: firstname.lastname@blackpool.gov.uk
Web Site: www.blackpool.gov.uk
Head of Tourism: Mrs J Seddon
Conference and Promotions Manager: M Roffey

BLAENAU GWENT COUNTY BOROUGH COUNCIL
Central Depot, Barleyfield Industrial Estate, Brynmawr, Blaenau Gwent NP23 4YF Wales
Tel: 01495 355 601 Fax: 01495 312 357
Email: dione.morris@blaenau-gwent.gov.uk
Web Site: www.blaenau-gwent.gov.uk
Director of Community Services: Robin Morrison

BLYTH VALLEY DISTRICT COUNCIL
BV Arts Network, Blyth CEC, Ridley Street, Blyth, Northumberland NE24 3AG
Tel: 01670 542 868
Email: DGarrett@BlythValley.gov.uk
Web Site: www.blythvalley.gov.uk
Arts Development Officer: David Garrett
Also email:
blythvalleyartsnet@hotmail.com

BOROUGH OF TELFORD & WREKIN
Education & Culture Civic Offices Telford, Shropshire TF3 4WF
Tel: 01952 202 532 Fax: 01952 203 061
Email: jean.escott@telford.gov.uk
Web Site: www.telford.gov.uk
Oakengates Theatre Manager: Psyche Hudson
Arts & Entertainments Manager: Mrs J Escott
Tel: 01952 202 532 Fax: 01952 290 628

BOURNEMOUTH BOROUGH COUNCIL
Bournemouth Int Centre, Exeter Road, Bournemouth, Dorset BH2 5BH
Tel: 01202 456 400 Fax: 01202 456 500
Tech Fax: 01202 454 786 Tech Co-Ord: 01202 451 891
Email: conference.bic@bournemouth.gov.uk
Web Site: www.bic.co.uk
Director: Kevin Sheehan
Technical Co-ordinator: Christian Knighton

BRACKNELL FOREST BOROUGH COUNCIL
Time Square, Market Street, Bracknell, Berkshire RG12 1JD
Tel: 01344 424 642 Fax: 01344 352 187
Email: customer.services@bracknell-forest.gov.uk
Web Site: www.bracknell-forest.gov.uk
Director of Leisure Services: Vincent Paliczke

BRADFORD METROPOLITAN DISTRICT COUNCIL
Arts, Heritage & Leisure Dept, Second Floor, Jacobs Well, Bradford, West Yorkshire BD1 5RW
Tel: 01274 432 646 Fax: 01274 434 676
Web Site: www.bradford.gov.uk
Director: Jane Glaister
Head Of Theatre, Arts & Festivals: Sheena Wrigley
Tel: 01274 431 573 Fax: 01274 434 676

BRADFORD-ON-AVON TOWN COUNCIL
St. Margaret's Hall, St. Margaret's Street, Bradford-on-Avon, BA15 1DE
Tel: 01225 864240
Email: town-clerk@bradforduponavon-town.freeserve.co.uk
Web Site: www.bradfordonavontown.com
Town Clerk: Mrs D Holmes

BRAINTREE COUNCIL
Causeway House, Bocking End, Braintree, Essex CM7 9HB
Tel: 01376 552 525 Fax: 01376 552 626
Email: denis.housden@braintree.gov.uk
Web Site: www.braintree.gov.uk
Head of Leisure Services: Denis Housden

BRENTWOOD CENTRE
Doddinghurst Road, Brentwood, Essex CM15 9NN United Kingdom
Tel 01277 215 151 Fax: 01277 229 694
Email: info@brentwood-centre.co.uk
Web Site: www.brentwood-centre.co.uk
All recreation facilities are under the control of Brentwood Borough Council.
Contacts: Mr Bob McLinkock, Tom Clerk, Kim Anderson.

BRIDGEND COUNTY BOROUGH COUNCIL
Education, Leisure & Community Services Dept, Sunnyside, Bridgend, Mid Glamorgan CF31 4AR Wales
Tel: 01656 642 610 Fax: 01656 642 675
Email: jonesge@bridgend.gov.uk
Web Site: www.bridgend.gov.uk
Director of Education, Leisure and Community Services: Graham Avery

BRIDGNORTH DISTRICT COUNCIL
Westgate, Bridgnorth, Shropshire WV16 5AA
Tel: 01746 713 100 Fax: 01746 764 414
Email: contactus@bridgnorth-dc.gov.uk
Web Site: www.bridgnorth-dc.gov.uk
Chief Executive & Clerk: John Harmeston, BSc(Econ)

BRIGHTON & HOVE CITY COUNCIL
Culture & Regeneration, Kings House, Grand Avenue, Hove, East Sussex BN3 2LS
Tel: 01273 292 530 Fax: 01273 292 532
Email: sarah.tanburn@brighton-hove.gov.uk
Web Site: www.brighton-hove.gov.uk
Director of Culture and Regeneration: Sarah Tanburn

BRISTOL CITY COUNCIL
Colston Street, Bristol, BS1 5AR
Admin: 0117 922 3673 Bkg: 0117 922 3693 BO: 0117 922 3686 / 3682 Bkg
Fax: 0117 922 3681
Email: colstonhall@bristol-city.gov.uk
Web Site: www.bristol-city.gov.uk
Operations Manager: Nick Craney
Concert Planning: Paul Preager
Concert hall presenting symphony orchestras, touring rock & pop concerts, opera, comedy and large scale meetings and conferences. Also available in a part standing format.
Capacity: 2075/1840

BROADLAND DISTRICT COUNCIL
Cultural Services Department, Thorpe Lodge, Yarmouth Road, Norwich, Norfolk NR7 0DU
Tel: 01603 430 563 Fax: 01603 700 339
Email: kirstin.hughes@broadland.gov.uk
Web Site: www.broadland.gov.uk
Arts Development Officer: Kirstin Hughes

BROMSGROVE DISTRICT COUNCIL
Recreation & Tourism Section, The Council House, Burcot Lane, Bromsgrove, Worcestershire B60 1AA
Tel: 01527 873 232 Fax: 01527 881 414
Email: daleh@bromsgrove.gov.uk
Web Site: www.bromsgrove.gov.uk

BROXBOURNE BOROUGH COUNCIL
Bishops College, Churchgate, Cheshunt, Waltham Cross, Hertfordshire EN8 9XQ
Tel: 01992 785 555 Fax: 01992 451 132
Email: leisure@broxbourne.gov.uk
Web Site: www.broxbourne.gov.uk
Halls Manager: David Cooper
Tel 01992 441931 Fax 01992 451132

BROXTOWE BOROUGH COUNCIL
Directorate of Housing, Health and Leisure Services, Foster Avenue, Beeston, Nottingham NG9 1AB
Tel: 0115 917 7777 Fax: 0115 917 3508
Email: hhl@broxbch.demon.co.uk
Web Site: www.broxtowe.gov.uk
Director: Mr Ted Czerniak
Assistant Director (Leisure): Adam Hall
Other Contacts: Clare Janes, Kaye Needham

SOUTH BUCKINGHAMSHIRE DISTRICT COUNCIL
Capswood, Oxford Road, Denham, Bucks, UB9 4LH
Tel: 01895 837 306
Email: leisure@southbucks.gov.uk
Web Site: www.southbucks.gov.uk
Chief Executive: Chris Furness
Head of Leisure: Lynn Trigwell (ext 215)
Arts Officer: Michelle Cope (ext 303)

BURNLEY BOROUGH COUNCIL
William Thomson, Recreation Centre, Red Lion Street, Burnley, Lancashire BB11 2AE
Tel: 01282 425 011 Fax: 01282 664 464
Email: enquiries@burnley.gov.uk
Web Site: www.burnley.gov.uk
Arts & Entertainments Tourism Manager: Karen Bradford

BURY METROPOLITAN BOROUGH COUNCIL
Craig House Dept of Competitive Services, Central Bookings, 3rd Floor, 5 Bank Street, Bury, Lancashire BL9 0DN
Tel: 0161 253 5903 Fax: 0161 253 5902
Email: buryvenues@bury.gov.uk
Web Site: www.bury.gov.uk
Contact: Anne or Christine for central bookings Bury venues.

CAERPHILLY COUNTY BOROUGH COUNCIL
Leisure Services Department, Caerphilly Road, Ystrad Mynach, Hengoed, CF82 7EP Wales
Tel: 01443 815 588 Fax: 01443 816 832
Email: info@caerphilly.gov.uk
Web Site: www.caerphilly.gov.uk
Head of Lifelong Learning and Leisure: Peter Gomer

CAMBRIDGE CITY COUNCIL
The Guildhall, Cambridge CB2 3QJ
Tel 01223 457 000
Email: jondh@cambridge.gov.uk
Web Site: www.cambridge.gov.uk
Marketing & Promotions Manager: Pauline Haughey (Fax: 01223 457 529)

EAST CAMBRIDGESHIRE COUNTY COUNCIL
Community Services Dept, Babylon Bridge, Waterside, Ely, Cambridgeshire CB7 4AU
Tel: 01353 665 555 Fax: 01353 668 819
Email: darren.dixon@eastcambs.gov.uk
Web Site: www.eastcambs.gov.uk
Economic & Community Development Officer: Darren Dixon

SOUTH CAMBRIDGESHIRE DISTRICT COUNCIL
South Cambridgeshire Hall, Cambourne Business Park Cambourne Cambridge CB3 6EA
Tel: 08450 450 5000
Fax: 01954 713 149
Email: scdc@scambs.gov.uk
Web Site: www.scambs.gov.uk
Chief Executive: JS Ballantyne
Arts Development Officer: Andy O'Hanlon
South Cambridgeshire District Council works with professional and voluntary arts organisations to help create the conditions in which artists, audiences and participants will thrive.

CANNOCK CHASE DISTRICT COUNCIL
Civic Centre, Beecroft Road, Cannock, Staffordshire WS11 1BG
Tel: 01543 462 621 Fax: 01543 462 317
Email: karenbradford@cannockchasedc.gov.uk
Web Site: www.cannockchasedc.gov.uk
Manager: Tom Walsh
Bookings contact: Sue Logan
Head of Leisure Services: Karen Bradford

CANTERBURY CITY COUNCIL
Council Offices, Military Road, Canterbury, Kent CT1 1YW
Tel: 01227 862 201 Fax: 01227 470 599
Email: janine.marsh@canterbury.gov.uk
Web Site: www.canterbury.gov.uk
Leisure and recreation: Janine Marsh Tel: 01227 862 527

CARADON DISTRICT COUNCIL
Luxstowe House, Liskeard, Cornwall PL14 3DZ
Tel: 01579 341 000 Fax: 01579 341 001
Email: postmaster@caradon.gov.uk
Web Site: www.caradon.gov.uk
Chief Executive: Jack Neal

CARDIFF COUNTY COUNCIL
St David's Hall, The Hayes, Cardiff, South Glamorgan CF10 1SH Wales
Tel: 029 2087 8500 Fax: 029 2087 8517
Email: judi.richards@cardiff.gov.uk
Web Site: www.stdavidshallcardiff.co.uk
Arts and Events Manager: Judi Richards
Manager: Tony Williams
Contact Programme Manager: Sue King

CARLISLE CITY COUNCIL
Civic Centre, Rickergate, Carlisle, Cumbria CA3 8QG
Tel: 01228 817 000 Fax: 01228 817 048
Email: markbev@carlisle.gov.uk
Web Site: www.carlisle-city.gov.uk

CARMARTHEN TOWN COUNCIL
Leisure and Recreation Ty'Nant, Trostre Business Park, Llanelli, Carmarthenshire SA14 9UT
Tel: 01267 228 202
Email: leisure@carmarthenshire.gov.uk
Web Site: www.carmarthenshire.gov.uk
Town Clerk, Carmarthen Town Council: S J Anderson

CARRICK DISTRICT COUNCIL
Carrick Leisure Ltd, Gyllyngdune Cottage, 41 Melvill Road, Falmouth, Cornwall TR11 4AR
Tel 01872 224400 Fax 01872 260077
Leisure & Tourism Dept: Tel: 01326 310980 Fax: 01326 310981
Email: info@carrickleisure.org.uk
Web Site: www.carrick.gov.uk
Head of Tourism and Leisure: Alan Horn

CASTLE MORPETH BOROUGH COUNCIL
Longhirst Hall, Longhirst, Morpeth, Northumberland NE61 3LR
Tel: 01670 794 795 Fax: 01670 794 781
Email: sarah.hudson@castlemorpeth.gov.uk
Web Site: www.castlemorpeth.gov.uk
Chief Executive: K. Dunbar

CASTLE POINT BOROUGH COUNCIL
Council Offices, Kiln Road, Thundersley, Benfleet, Essex SS7 1TF
Tel: 01268 882 200 Fax: 01268 882 464
Email: NThomas@castlepoint.gov.uk
Web Site: www.castlepoint.gov.uk
Director of Leisure & Technical Services: Nigel Thomas
Head Of Leisure & Technical Services: Tony Galloway

CEREDIGION COUNTY COUNCIL
Cultural, Education & Community Services Dept, County Offices, Aberystwyth, Ceredigion SY23 2DE
Tel: 01970 633 700 / 617 911 Fax: 01970 615 348
Email: geraintl@ceredigion.gov.uk
Web Site: www.ceredigion.gov.uk
Assistant Director: Mr D Geraint Lewis

CHELMSFORD ESSEX BOROUGH COUNCIL
Civic Centre, Duke Street, Chelmsford, Essex CM1 1JE
Tel: 01245 606606
Email: mailbox@chelmsfordbc.gov.uk
Web Site: www.chelmsfordbc.gov.uk
Leisure & Cultural Services: Debbie Skeet
Tel: 01245 606563
Email: debbie.skeet@chelmsfordbc.gov.uk

CHELTENHAM BOROUGH COUNCIL
Town Hall, Imperial Square, Cheltenham, Gloucestershire GL50 1QA
Tel: 01242 521 621 BO: 01242 227 979
Fax: 01242 573 902
Email: townhall@cheltenham.gov.uk
Web Site: www.cheltenham.gov.uk
Head of Festivals and Entertainments: J P Tyndall

CHERWELL DISTRICT COUNCIL
Bodicote House, White Post Road, Bodicote, Banbury, Oxfordshire OX15 4AA
Tel: 01295 252 535 Fax: 01295 263 155
Email: nicola.riley@cherwell-dc.gov.uk
Web Site: www.cherwell-dc.gov.uk
Contact:
Arts & Tourism Manager: Nicola Riley Tel: 01295 221724

CHESTER LE STREET DISTRICT COUNCIL
Civic Centre, Newcastle Road, Chester le Street, County Durham DH3 3UT
Tel: 0191 387 1919 Fax: 0191 387 1583
Email: billlightburn@chester-le-street.gov.uk
Web Site: www.chester-le-street.gov.uk
Leisure Development Manager: Bill Lightburn

CHESTERFIELD BOROUGH COUNCIL
Leisure Services, Stevensons Chambers, 6-8 Corporation Street, Chesterfield, Derbyshire S41 7TP
Tel: 01246 345 345 Fax: 01246 345 252
Email: carole.copeland@chesterfield.gov.uk
Web Site: www.chesterfield.gov.uk
Arts Development Officer: Carole Copeland

CHICHESTER DISTRICT COUNCIL
East Pallant House, East Pallant, Chichester, West Sussex PO19 1TY
Tel: 01243 785 166 Fax: 01243 776 766
Email: helpline@chichester.gov.uk
Web Site: www.chichester.gov.uk
Head Of Cultural Services: Greg Mayhew
Arts & Heritage Development Manager: Anne Bone

CHILTERN DISTRICT COUNCIL
Council Offices, King George V Road, Amersham, Buckinghamshire HP6 5AW
Tel: 01494 732 759 Fax: 01494 586 503
Email: davidgar@chiltern.gov.uk
Web Site: www.chiltern.gov.uk
Community Arts Officer: David Gardner
see also: www.chilternartsforum.co.uk

CHORLEY BOROUGH COUNCIL
Council Offices, Gillibrand Street, Chorley, Lancashire PR7 1AL
Tel: 01257 515 808
Email: chris.mellor@chorley.gov.uk
Web Site: www.chorley.gov.uk
Cultural Services Manager: Chris Mellor.

CHRISTCHURCH BOROUGH COUNCIL
Civic Offices, Bridge Street, Christchurch, Dorset BH23 1AZ
Tel: 01202 495 000 Fax: 01202 482 200
Email: s.stewart-haddow@christchurch.gov.uk
Web Site: www.christchurch.gov.uk
Duty Manager: Sarah Stewart-Haddow

COLCHESTER BOROUGH COUNCIL
Charter Hall Colchester Leisure World
Charter Hall, Leisure World, Cowdray Avenue, Colchester, Essex CO1 1YH
Tel: 01206 282946 Box Office: 01206 282020 Event Manager: 01206 282956
Fax: 01206 282 024
Email: claire.jackson@colchester.gov.uk
Web Site: www.charter-hall.co.uk
Event Manager: Claire Jackson

CONFERENCE LEEDS
Leonardo Building 2 Rossington Street, Leeds, West Yorkshire LS2 8HD
Tel: 0113 247 6501 / 6502 Fax: 0113 247 7047
Email: conferenceleeds@leeds.gov.uk
Web Site: www.leeds.gov.uk
Free venue finding service.

CONGLETON BOROUGH COUNCIL
Community Development, Council Offices, Westfields, Middlewich Road, Sandbach, Cheshire CW11 1HZ
Tel: 01270 769 332 Fax: 01270 768 460
Email: craig.nicholson@congleton.gov.uk
Web Site: www.congleton.gov.uk
Contact: Craig Nicholson

CONWY BOROUGH COUNCIL
Tourism and Leisure, Town Hall, LLANDUDNO, Conwy, LL30 2UP Wales

Tel: 01492 574 000 Fax: 01492 592 114
Email: gwen.roberts@conwy.gov.uk
Web Site: www.conwy.gov.uk
Senior Marketing Officer Tourism: Gwen Roberts

COPELAND BOROUGH COUNCIL

Commercial & Cultural Services Catherine Street, Whitehaven, Cumbria CA28 7NY
Tel: 01946 852 585 Fax: 01946 852 791
Email: tchilcott@copelandbc.gov.uk
Web Site: www.copelandbc.gov.uk
Head Of Commercial & Cultural Services: Terry Chilcott

CORBY BOROUGH COUNCIL

Grosvenor House, George Street, Corby, Northamptonshire NN17 1QB
Tel: 01536 464042 Fax 01536 464 044
Email: dot.mann@corby.gov.uk
Web Site: www.corby.gov.uk

NORTH CORNWALL DISTRICT COUNCIL

Council Offices, 3/5 Barn Lane, Bodmin, Cornwall PL31 1LZ
Tel 01208 893 333 Fax: 01208 893 455
Email: steve.kessell@ncdc.gov.uk
Web Site: www.ncdc.gov.uk
Tourism Officer: Steve Kessell

COTSWOLD DISTRICT COUNCIL

Leisure Services Trinity Road, Cirencester, Gloucestershire GL7 1PX
Tel: 01285 623451 Fax: 01285 653 713
Email: claire.newport@cotswold.gov.uk
Web Site: www.cotswold.gov.uk
Senior Events Officer: Claire Newport

COVENTRY CITY COUNCIL

Culture and Leisure, Floor 2, West Orchard House, 28-34 Corporation Street, Coventry, Warwickshire CV1 1GF
Tel: 024 7683 2368 Fax: 024 7683 2470
Email: carole.littlewood@coventry.gov.uk
Web Site: www.coventry.gov.uk
Contact: Carol Littlewood

CRAVEN DISTRICT COUNCIL

Granville Street, Skipton, North Yorkshire BD23 1PS
Tel: 01756 706 408 Fax: 01756 706 410
Email: cjohnson@cravendc.gov.uk
Web Site: www.cravendc.gov.uk
Arts & Exhibitions Officer: Catherine Johnson

CRAWLEY COUNCIL

Community Arts, Hawth Theatre, Hawth Avenue, Crawley, West Sussex RH10 6YZ
Tel: 01293 552 941 Fax: 01293 533 362
Email: community.arts@crawley.gov.uk
Web Site: www.crawley.gov.uk
Arts Development Officer: Carolyn Murphy

We're here to offer projects and help to individuals and community groups of all ages, abilities and interests.

CREWE & NANTWICH BOROUGH COUNCIL

Municipal Buildings, Earle Street, Crewe, Cheshire CW1 2BJ
Tel: 01270 537777 Fax: 01270 537605
Email: leisure@crewe-nantwich.gov.uk
Web Site: www.crewe-nantwich.gov.uk
Arts and Culture Manager: Jane Ashcroft on 01270 537 321.
mail: jane.ashcroft@crewe-nantwich.gov.uk

DACORUM BOROUGH COUNCIL

Old Town Hall High Street, Hemel, Hemel Hempstead, Hertfordshire HP1 3AE
Tel 01442 228 097 Fax: 01442 234 072
Email: sara.railson@dacorum.gov.uk
Web Site: www.oldtownhall.co.uk
Arts & Entertainment Manager: Sara Railson

DARLINGTON BOROUGH COUNCIL

Feethams, Darlington, County Durham DL1 5QT
Tel: 01325 380651 Fax: 01325 486 987
Email: enquiries@darlington.gov.uk
Web Site: www.darlington.gov.uk
Director of Contract Services: CJ Brown
Head of Theatre & Arts: Peter Cutchie

DAVENTRY DISTRICT COUNCIL

Leisure and Community Services Lodge Road, Daventry, Northamptonshire NN11 5AF
Tel :01327 302 534 Fax: 01327 701 654
Email: shawes@daventrydc.gov.uk
Arts Officer: Sonia Hawes

DENBIGHSHIRE COUNTY COUNCIL

Council Offices, Wynnstay Road, Ruthin, Clwyd LL15 1YN Wales
Tel: 01824 706 000 Fax: 01824 705 026
Email: tony.hughes@denbighshire.gov.uk
Web Site: www.denbighshire.gov.uk
Chief Executive: HV Thomas
Chairman: Cllr EW WIlliams
(Acting) Head of Tourism & Leisure: Tony Hughes
Russell House, Churton Road, Rhyl, Denbighshire LL18 3dp
Tel 01824 706410 Fax 01824 344516

DERBY CITY COUNCIL

Assembly Rooms Market Place, Derby DE13A
Tel: 01332 255 441 Fax: 01332 255 788
Email: peter.ireson@derby.gov.uk
Web Site: www.derby.gov.uk
Head of Entertainmnets: Peter Ireson

DERBYSHIRE DALES DISTRICT COUNCIL

Town Hall, Bank Road, Matlock, Derbyshire DE4 3NN
Tel: 01629 580 580 Tel: 01629 761 231 (Lousie Cresswell) Fax: 01629 761 167
Email: tourism@derbyshiredales.gov.uk
Web Site: www.derbyshiredales.gov.uk
Chief Executive: Mr D Wheatcroft
Personnel Assistant: Juliette Normington
Contact Tourism Manager: Lousie Cresswell

NORTH EAST DERBYSHIRE DISTRICT COUNCIL

Council Offices, Saltergate, Chesterfield, Derbyshire S40 1LF
Tel: 01246 231 111 Fax: 01246 221 260
Email: carol.copeland@chesterfield.gov.uk
Web Site: www.ne-derbyshire.gov.uk
Arts Project Officer: Carol Copeland

SOUTH DERBYSHIRE DISTRICT COUNCIL

Civic Offices, Civic Way, Swadlincote, Derbyshire DE11 0AH
Tel: 01283 221000
Email: malcolm.roseburgh@south-derbys.gov.uk
Web Site: www.south-derbys.gov.uk
Cultural Regeneration Officer: Rachel Walker
Tel: 01283 595 772
Fax: 01283 228 158

EAST DEVON DISTRICT COUNCIL

Exmouth Pavilion (capacity 900) Manor Pavilion, Sidmouth (capacity 280)
Council Offices, Station Road, Knowle, Sidmouth, Devon EX10 8HL
Tel: 01395 516 551 Fax: 01395 517572
Email: iramsey@eastdevon.gov.uk / jthomas@eastdevon.gov.uk
Web Site: www.eastdevon.gov.uk
Arts Officer: Ishbel Ramey
Bookings Contact: Jenny Thomas

DONCASTER METROPOLITAN BOROUGH COUNCIL

Arts Service Directorate of Education and Culture
PO Box 266 The Council House, College Road, South Yorkshire DN1 3AD
Tel: 01302 737 327 Fax: 01302 737 223
Email: sarah.richards@doncaster.gov.uk
Web Site: www.doncaster.gov.uk

EAST DORSET DISTRICT COUNCIL

Council Offices, Furzehill, Wimborne, Dorset BH21 4HN
Tel: 01202 886 201 Fax: 01202 841 390
Email: leisure.development@eastdorset.gov.uk
Web Site: www.eastdorsetdc.gov.uk
Chief Executive: Mr A Breakwell
Head of Leisure: Neil Farmer

NORTH DORSET DISTRICT COUNCIL
Nordon, Salisbury Road, Blandford Forum, Dorset DT11 7LL
Tel: 01258 484 008 Fax: 01258 484 007
Email: wsmith@north-dorset.gov.uk
Web Site: www.north-dorset.gov.uk
Community Development Manager: W Smith

DOVER DISTRICT COUNCIL
White Cliffs Business Park, Dover, Kent CT16 3PJ
Tel: 01304 821 199 Fax: 01304 872 345
Email: artsandevents@dover.gov.uk
Web Site: www.dover.gov.uk
Arts Contact: Cheryl Gilling Email: cheryl-gilling@dover.gov.uk

DUDLEY COUNCIL
Council House, Priory Road, Dudley, West Midlands DY1 1HF
Tel: 01384 815 513
Email: policy.cexec@dudley.gov.uk
Web Site: www.dudley.gov.uk
Leisure & cukture: Ken Dunbar
Tel. 01384 815500

DURHAM CITY ARTS
Byland Lodge, Hawthorn Terrace, Durham, County Durham DH1 4TD
Tel: 0191 384 2214
Email: jan@durhamcityarts.demon.co.uk
Web Site: www.durham.gov.uk
Arts Development Manager: Neil Hillier
Local Arts Development Agency for City of Durham District.

EASINGTON DISTRICT COUNCIL
Council Offices, Seaside Lane, Easington Village, Peterlee, County Durham SR8 3TN
Tel: 0191 527 0501 Fax: 0191 527 3868
Email: dave.clarke@easington.gov.uk
Arts Development Officer: David Clarke
tel: 0191 5270501 Ext 2238
Interested in small to mid-scale theatre, dance etc; small to large scale music; and open air attractions. Also in performing arts groups offering workshops etc.

EAST RIDING COUNTY COUNCIL
County Hall, Cross Street, Beverley, East Riding Of Yorkshire HU17 9BA
Tel: 01482 887 700 Fax: 01482 884 940
Email: alan.moir@eastriding.gov.uk
Web Site: www.eastriding.gov.uk
Head Of Libraries & Community Services: Alan Moir

EASTBOURNE BOROUGH COUNCIL
Dept Of Tourism & Leisure, College Road, Eastbourne, East Sussex BN21 4JJ
Tel: 01323 415 401 Fax: 01323 638 686
Email: chris.jordan@eastbourne.gov.uk
Web Site: www.eastbourne.org
Director of Tourism & Leisure: Ronald G Cussons
Theatres General Manager: Chris Jordan

EASTLEIGH BOROUGH COUNCIL
The Point, Leigh Road, Eastleigh, Hampshire SO50 9DE
Tel: 023 8062 7800
Email: gregory.nash@eastleigh.gov.uk
Web Site: www.thepoint-online.co.uk
Head of Arts & Tourism: Cheryl Butler
Director of The Point: Gregory Nash

EDEN DISTRICT COUNCIL
Town Hall, Corney Square, Penrith, Cumbria CA11 7QF
Tel: 01768 212 323 Fax: 01768 890 470
Email: doug.huggon@eden.gov.uk
Head of Leisure Services: Doug Huggon

ELLESMERE PORT BOROUGH COUNCIL
Community Leisure Dept, 4 Civic Way, Ellesmere Port, Cheshire CH65 0BE
Tel: 0151 356 6789 Fax: 0151 355 0508
Email: community.leisure@ellesmereport-neston.gov.uk
Web: www.ellesmereport-neston.gov.uk
Chief Executive & Town Clerk: S Ewbank, LLB FBIM
Community Leisure Officer: PA Hearfield, BSc (Econ) DMA MILAM

ELMBRIDGE BOROUGH COUNCIL
Leisure & Cultural Services, Civic Centre, High Street, Esher, Surrey KT10 9SD
Tel Dirct: 01372 4745 68 Swchbrd: 01372 474 474 Fax: 01372 474 939
Email: leisure@elmbridge.gov.uk
Web Site: www.elmbridge.gov.uk/leisure
Head of Leisure & Cultural Services: Lynn Carpenter
Arts Development Officer: Maggs Latter

EPSOM & EWELL BOROUGH COUNCIL
Town Hall, The Parade, Epsom, Surrey KT18 5BY
Tel: 01372 742 226 Fax: 01372 726 228
Email: TMitchell@epsom-ewell.goc.uk
Web Site: www.epsom-ewell.gov.uk
Borough Recreation Department, Venues Manager: Trevor Mitchell

EREWASH BOROUGH COUNCIL
Town Hall, Long Eaton, Nottingham NG10 1HU
Tel: 0115 907 2244 Fax: 0115 946 8236
Email: paul.hogan@erewash.gov.uk
Web Site: www.erewash.gov.uk
Service Head Of Leisure & Cultural Services: Paul Hogan

EXETER CITY COUNCIL
Civic Centre, Exeter, Devon EX1 1JN
Tel 01392 277 888 Fax 01392 265 265
Email: hazel.ball@exeter.gov.uk
Web Site: www.exeter.gov.uk
Head of Community & Environment: Hazel Ball (Tel: 01392 265 105)
Halls Promotions Manager: David Lewis (Tel: 01392 265 937)

FAREHAM BOROUGH COUNCIL
Civic Offices, Civic Way, Fareham, Hampshire PO16 7PR
Tel: 01329 236 100 Fax: 01329 822 732
Email: leisuredev@fareham.gov.uk
Web Site: www.fareham.gov.uk
Director of Leisure & The Environment: Peter Grimwood (Tel: 01329 824541)

FENLAND DISTRICT COUNCIL
Fenland Hall, County Road, March, Cambridgeshire PE15 8NQ
Tel: 01354 622 399 Hall Tel: 01354 654 321 Fax: 01354 622 358
Email: rcassidy@fenland.gov.uk
Web Site: www.fenland.gov.uk
Head of Leisure: Richard Cassidy

FLINTSHIRE COUNTY COUNCIL
County Hall, Mold, Flintshire CH7 6NB Scotland
Hall Bkgs Tel: 01352 752 121 Leisure Services Mgr: 01352 702452 Fax: 01352 702 458
Email: sheila.kirby@flintshire.gov.uk
Web Site: www.flintshire.gov.uk
Leisure Services Manager: Mike Hornby
Arts Officer: Sheila Kirby

FOREST OF DEAN DISTRICT COUNCIL
Council Offices, High Street, Coleford, Gloucestershire GL16 8HG
Tel: 01594 812 381 Fax: 01594 812 314
Email: rosalind.cookson@fdean.gov.uk
Web Site: www.fdean.gov.uk
Arts Development Officer: Rosalind Cookson

FYLDE BOROUGH COUNCIL
Town Hall Lytham St Anne's, Lancashire FY8 1LW
Tel: 01253 658 470 Fax: 01253 713 754
Email: helenk@fylde.gov.uk
Web Site: www.fylde.gov.uk
Art Development Officer: Helen Knowles
450-capacity venue available for hire. Also a receiving venue.

GATESHEAD METROPOLITAN BOROUGH COUNCIL
Caedmon Hall, Central Library, Prince Consort Road, Gateshead, Tyne and Wear NE8 4LN
Tel: 0191 433 8400 Fax: 0191 477 7454
Email: suehurrell@gateshead.gov.uk
Web Site: www.gatesheadmbc.gov.uk/ca

edmon
Head of Cultural Development: William J Macnaught, MA ALA
Creativity Development Manager: Ednie Wilson
Full sound and light rig.

GLOUCESTER CITY COUNCIL
Culture, Learning & Leisure, Gloucester City Council, Herbert Warehouse, The Docks, Gloucester GL1 2EQ
Tel: 01452 396 620 Fax: 01452 396 622
Email: leisure@gloucester.gov.uk
Web Site: www.gloucester.gov.uk
Head of Leisure Services: Steve Elway
Arts and Festival Manager: Caroline Leverton Tel: 01452 396 369 Fax: 01452 384 734

GOSPORT BOROUGH COUNCIL,
Town Hall High Street Gosport, Hampshire PO12 1EB
Arts Dep Tel: 023 9260 3598 Council Tel: 023 9258 4242
Email: ndrayco@stvincent.ac.uk
Arts Development Officer: Nigel Draycott

GRAVESHAM BOROUGH COUNCIL
Woodville Halls, Woodville Place, Gravesend, Kent DA12 1DD
Tel: 01474 337457 Fax: 01474 337 455
Email: brian.tourle@gravesham.gov.uk
Web Site: www.gravesham.gov.uk
Arts and Heritage Manager: Brian N Tourle
Seats: 800

GREAT YARMOUTH BOROUGH COUNCIL
Tourism Division Town Hall, Great Yarmouth, Norfolk NR30 2PX
Tel: 01493 846 342 Fax: 01493 846 221
Email: tourism@great-yarmouth.gov.uk
Web Site: www.great-yarmouth.co.uk
Head ofTourism: Alan Carr

GUILDFORD BOROUGH COUNCIL
Millmead House, Millmead, Guildford, Surrey GU2 4BB
Tel: 01483 444 700 Fax: 01483 444 717
Email: milesj@guildford.gov.uk
Web Site: www.guildfordborough.co.uk
Director of Leisure Services: Jim Miles BA DipAA MILAM

GWYNEDD COUNCIL
Caernarfon, Gwynedd LL55 1SH Wales
Tel 01286 679089 Fax 01286 677347
Email: celf@gwynedd.gov.uk
Web Site: www.gwynedd.gov.uk
Assistant Director: Culture: Gareth Haulfryn Williams

HAMBLETON DISTRICT COUNCIL
Civic Centre, Stonecross, Northallerton, North Yorkshire DL6 2UU
Tel: 01609 779 977 Fax: 01609 767 228
Email: kate.staines@hambleton.gov.uk
Web Site: www.hambleton.gov.uk
Head of Leisure and Tourism Services: Mr David Goodwin

EAST HAMPSHIRE DISTRICT COUNCIL
Community & Leisure Services Division, Penns Place, Petersfield, Hampshire GU31 4EX
Tel: 01730 266 551 Fax: 01730 234 385
Email: daphne_gardner@easthants.gov.uk
Web Site: www.easthants.gov.uk
Corporate Director Of Community: Daphne Gardner

HARBOROUGH DISTRICT COUNCIL
Council Offices, Adam and Eve Street, Market Harborough, Leicestershire LE16 7AG
Tel: 01858 821 291 Fax: 01858 821 002
Email: s.wright@harborough.gov.uk
Web Site: www.harborough.gov.uk / www.contourandcream.co.uk
Head of Policy - Peter Butcher

HARTLEPOOL BOROUGH COUNCIL
Arts & Museums Dept, Sir William Grey House, Clarence Road, Hartlepool, Cleveland TS24 8BT
Tel: 01429 523 438 Fax: 01429 523 477
Email: maureenburgon@hartlepool.gov.uk
Acting Arts Development Officer: Maureen Burgon

HASTINGS BOROUGH COUNCIL
Leisure & Cultural Development 4 Robertson Terrace, Hastings, East Sussex TN34 1JE
Tel: 01424 781 122 Fax: 01424 781 133
Email: mmarsh@hastings.gov.uk
Web Site: www.hastings.gov.uk
Executive Director, Leisure and Cultural Development: Mike Marsh
Leisure Manager: Martin Etchells

HAVANT BOROUGH COUNCIL
Community Services, Civic Offices, Civic Centre Road, Havant, Hampshire PO9 2AX
Tel: 023 9247 4174 ext 276 Fax: 023 9244 6459
Email: tim.slater@havant.gov.uk
Web Site: www.havant.gov.uk
Head of Cultural Services: Tim Slater

HEREFORDSHIRE COUNCIL
Grange House, PO Box 44, Leominster, Herefordshire HR6 8NP
Tel: 01432 261 818 Fax: 01568 611 046
Email: mbateman@herefordshire.gov.uk
Web Site: www.herefordshire.gov.uk
Principal Arts Officer: Melanie Bateman

EAST HERTFORDSHIRE DISTRICT COUNCIL
Wallfields, Pegs Lane, Hertford, Hertfordshire SG13 8EQ
Tel: 01279 655 261 Fax: 01992 554 877
Email: stephen.wilson@eastherts.gov.uk
Head of Community Development: Will O'Neil
Arts and Development Officer: Stephen Wilson

NORTH HERTFORDSHIRE DISTRICT COUNCIL
Gernon Road, Letchworth, Hertfordshire SG6 3JF
Tel: 01462 474 237 Fax: 01462 474 500
Email: maria.iredale@north-herts.gov.uk
Web Site: www.north-herts.gov.uk
Arts Development Officer: Maria Iredale

HORSHAM DISTRICT COUNCIL
North Street, Horsham, West Sussex RH12 1RG
Tel: 01403 215 100 Fax: 01403 215 250
Email: chris.dier@horsham.gov.uk
Web Site: www.horsham.gov.uk
General Manager: Michael Gattrell
Director of Community Development & Leisure Services: Chris Dier
Cap: 423

HUNTINGDONSHIRE DISTRICT COUNCIL
Pathfinder House, St Marys Street, Huntingdon, Cambridgeshire PE29 3TN
Tel 01480 388 057 Fax 01480 388 273
Email: arts@huntsdc.gov.uk
Web Site: www.huntsleisure.org/arts
Head of Community Services: Peter Jones

HYNDBURN BOROUGH COUNCIL
Hyndburn Leisure, Town Hall, Blackburn Road, Accrington, Lancashire BB5 1LA
Tel: 01254 380 289 Fax: 01254 380 291
Email: hyndburnsc@lihtrust.freeserve.co.uk
Web Site: www.leisureinhyndburn.co.uk
Chief Executive: David Welsey
The following halls are under the Management of P Baron. All have a Sunday Licence and Stage facilities.
Accrington Town Hall (400 Cap).
Oswaldtwistle Civic Theatre (472 Cap).

IPSWICH BOROUGH COUNCIL
Town Hall & Corn Exchange, King Street, Ipswich, Suffolk IP1 1DH
Tel 01473 433 465 Fax 01473 433 450
Email: karen.athroll@ipswich.gov.uk
Web Site: www.ipswich.gov.uk
Lettings Officer: Karen Athroll

ISLE OF ANGLESEY COUNTY COUNCIL
Education & Leisure, Llangefni, Isle Of Anglesey LL77 7TW Wales
Tel: 01248 750 057 Fax: 01248 752 999
Email: rpjed@anglesey.gov.uk
Web Site: www.anglesey.gov.uk
Head Of Education & Leisure: Richard Parry Jones

ISLE OF WIGHT COUNCIL
c/o Wight Leisure, 17 Quay Street, Newport, Isle of Wight PO30 5BA
Tel: 01983 823 828 Fax: 01983 823 369
Email: info@wightleisure.com
Web Site: www.wightleisure.com
Managing Director: Annie Horne
Marketing Manager: Andy Newman
Events Manager: Charlotte Pratt

KENNET DISTRICT COUNCIL
Devizes Visitor Centre, Cromwell House, Market Place Devizes, Wiltshire SN10 1JG
Tel: 01380 729 408 Fax: 01380 730 319
Email: colin.brown@kennet.gov.uk
Web Site: www.visitkennet.co.uk
Leisure, Arts & Entertainment Manager: Colin Brown

KETTERING BOROUGH COUNCIL
Tourist Information Centre, The Coach House, Sheep Street, Kettering, Northamptonshire NN16 0AN
Tel: 01536 410266 Fax: 01536 534 370
Email: tic@kettering.gov.uk
Web Site: www.kettering.gov.uk

KING'S LYNN & WEST NORFOLK BOROUGH COUNCIL
Kings Lynn Corn Exchange, Tuesday Market Place, King's Lynn Norfolk PE30 1JW
Tel: 01553 765 565 Fax: 01553 762 141
Email: entertainment_admin@west-norfolk.gov.uk
Web Site: www.kingslynncornexchange.co.uk
Manager: Ellen McPhillips
Technical Manager: Dave Savage
Cap: 736

KIRKLEES METROPOLITAN COUNCIL
Cultural and Leisure Services, Red Doles Lane, Huddersfield West Yorkshire HD2 1YF
Tel: 01484 226 300 Fax: 01484 226 342
Email: glenis.burgess@kirklees.gov.uk
Web Site: www.kirklees.gov.uk
Arts Officer: Glenis Burgess

KNOWSLEY BOROUGH COUNCIL
Leisure Services Dept, PO Box 22, Municipal Buildings, Archway Road, Huyton, Liverpool, Merseyside L36 9YX
Tel: 0151 443 3459 Fax: 0151 443 3492
Email: john.bell@knowsley.gov.uk
Web Site: www.knowsley.gov.uk
Director of Leisure Services: John Bell
Assistant Director: Paul Bewick (Tel: 0151 443 3461)

SOUTH LAKELAND DISTRICT COUNCIL
South Lakeland House, Lowther St, Kendal, Cumbria LA9 4DL
Tel: 01539 733 333 Fax: 01539 740 300
Email: i.winterslewis@southlakeland.gov.uk
Web Site: www.southlakeland.gov.uk
Culture and Economic Prosperity Services Manager: David Sykes
Events and Promotions Officer: Imelda Winters-Lewis

LANCASTER CITY COUNCIL
Arts & Events Dept, The Platform, Station Buildings, Central Promenade, Morecambe, Lancashire, LA4 4DB
Tel: 01524 582 815 Fax: 01524 832 745
Email: mlucas@lancaster.gov.uk
Web Site: www.lancaster.gov.uk
Contact: Mary Lucas

LEICESTER CITY COUNCIL
New Walk Centre, Welford Place, Leicester LE1 6ZG
Tel: 0116 254 9922 Fax: 0116 252 6499
Email: dmh.office@leicester.co.uk
Web Site: www.leicester.gov.uk
Director of Arts & Leisure: Michael Gallagher
Hall Manager: Richard Haswell
Granville Road, Leicester LE1 7RU Tel 0116 223 3113

LEWES DISTRICT COUNCIL
Community Services, PO Box 2708, Southover House, Southover Street, Lewes, East Sussex BN7 1DY
Tel: 01273 471 600 Fax: 01273 479 011
Email: lewesdc@lewes.gov.uk
Web Site: www.lewes.gov.uk

LICHFIELD DISTRICT COUNCIL
Lichfield Garrick, Castle Dyke, Lichfield, Staffordshire WS13 6HR
Tel: 01543 412 110 Fax: 01543 412 120
BO: 01543 412 121
Web Site: www.lichfieldgarrick.com
Artistic Director: Paul Everitt

CITY OF LINCOLN COUNCIL
City Hall, Beaumont Fee, Lincoln Lincolnshire LN1 1DD
Tel 01522 881 188 Fax 01522 560 049
Tel: 01522 526 450 (Lincolnshire Tourism)
Email: rob.bradley@lincoln.gov.uk
Web Site: www.lincoln-info.org.uk
Contact Tourism Services Manager: Rob Bradley

NORTH LINCOLNSHIRE BOROUGH COUNCIL
The Baths Hall, 59 Doncaster Road, Scunthorpe, South Humberside DN15 7RG
Tel: 01724 280 444 Fax: 01724 861 341
Email: terry.wincott@northlincs.gov.uk
Web Site: www.northlincs.gov.uk
Entertainments & Theatre Manager: Mr Terry Wincott

EAST LINDSEY DISTRICT COUNCIL
Tourism, Arts and Public, Relations Section, Manby Park, Louth, Lincolnshire LN11 8UP
Tel: 01507 329 411 Fax: 01507 327 149
Email: bob.suich@e-lindsey.gov.uk
Web Site: www.e-lindsey.gov.uk
Head of Tourism, Arts & Public Relations, ELDC: Bob Suich

LIVERPOOL CULTURE COMPANY
3rd Floor, Millennium House, Victoria Street, Liverpool, Merseyside L1 6JH
Tel: 0151 233 2008 Fax: 0151 233 6333
Email: jason.harborow@liverpool.gov.uk
Web Site: www.liverpool08.com
Head of Tourism, Arts and Heritage: Keith Davies
Chief Operating Officer: Jason Harborow

LLANELLI TOWN COUNCIL
The Old Vicarage, Town Hall Square, Llanelli, Carmarthenshire SA15 3DD Wales
Tel: 01554 774 352 Fax: 01554 770 376
Email: enquiries@llanellitowncouncil.gov.uk
Web Site: www.llanellitowncouncil.gov.uk

LUTON BOROUGH COUNCIL
Luton Borough Council Leisure & Cultural Services Dept., Wardown Park Offices, Old Bedford Road, Luton, Bedfordshire LU2 7HA
Tel: 01582 746 700 Bkgs: 01562 400 272 Fax: 01582 546 762
Email: fahimq@watford.gov.uk
Web Site: www.luton.gov.uk
Director of Leisure and Cultural Services: David Sutton
Bookings Contact: Lisa Roe
Contact: Fahim Qureshi

MACCLESFIELD BOROUGH COUNCIL
Town Hall, Macclesfield, Cheshire SK10 1DX
Tel: 01625 504 215 Main Tel: 01625 500 500 Fax: 01625 504 203
Email: l.parton@macclesfield.gov.uk
Web Site: www.macclesfield.gov.uk
Head of Admin: Lindsey Parton

MALDON DISTRICT COUNCIL
Council Offices, Princes Road, Maldon, Essex CM9 5DL
Tel: 01621 854 477 Fax: 01621 852 575
Email: customer.services@maldon.gov.uk
Web Site: www.maldon.gov.uk
Chief Executive: Steve Packham

MALVERN HILLS DISTRICT COUNCIL
The Council House, Avenue Road, Malvern, Worcestershire WR14 3AF
Tel: 01684 862 271 Tel: 01684 862410
Fax: 01684 862 473
Email: dot.hill@malvernhills.gov.uk
Web Site: www.malvernhills.gov.uk
Contact Room Bookings Officer: Dot Hill

MANCHESTER CITY COUNCIL
Leisure Division, Bellvue Leisure Centre, Pink Bank Lane, Longsight, Manchester M12 5GL
Tel: 0161 953 2451 Fax: 0161 953 2492
Email: leisure@manchester.gov.uk
Web Site: www.manchester.gov.uk
For enquiries about Leisure Centres and Halls in Parks contact the Leisure Services Department on the above number and for enquiries about theatres contact the Library Theatre on 0161 234 1913.

MANSFIELD DISTRICT COUNCIL
Civic Centre, Chesterfield Road South, Mansfield, Nottinghamshire NG19 7BH
Tel: 01623 463 463 Fax: 01623 463 900
Email: mdc@mansfield-dc.gov.uk
Web Site: www.mansfield-dc.gov.uk
Operations Manager: Bill Brown (Leisure Centres contact)
Acting Head of Leisure: Craig Bonar (Theatres contact)

MELKSHAM TOWN COUNCIL
The Town Hall, The Market Place, Melksham, Wiltshire SN12 6ES
Tel: 01225 704 187 Fax: 01225 707 858
Email: townhall@melkshamtown.co.uk
Web Site: www.melkshamtown.co.uk
Town Clerk: Mr J Crook

MENDIP DISTRICT COUNCIL
Cannards Grave Road, Shepton Mallet, Somerset BA4 5BT
Tel: 01749 343 399 Fax: 01749 344 050
Email: eppsn@mendip.gov.uk
Web Site: www.mendip.gov.uk
Arts Development Officer: Nicola Epps (ext 335)

MERTHYR TYDFIL COUNTY BOROUGH COUNCIL
Leisure Services Department, Civic Centre, Castle Street, Merthyr Tydfil, Mid Glamorgan CF47 8AN Wales
Tel: 01685 725 000 Fax: 01685 722 146
Email: tourism.heritage@merthyr.gov.uk
Web Site: www.merthyr.gov.uk
Tourism & Events Operations Officer: Wayne Edwards (Add: See Civic Centre above)
Acting Manager of Rhydyacar Leisure Centre & Recreation Facilities(North): TBA (Add: Rhydayacar, Merthyr Tydfil, Mid Glamorgan CF48 1UT Wales; Tel: 01865 37 149)
Manager of Recreation Facilities South at Abervan Community Centre: Richard Marsh (Add: Pant Glas Road, Abervan, Merthyr Tydfil, Mid Glamorgan CF48 4CH Wales; Tel: 01443 690 606)

MID BEDFORDSHIRE DISTRICT COUNCIL
The Limes, 12 Dunstable Street, Ampthill, Bedfordshire, MK45 2JU
Tel: 01525 842 244 Fax: 01525 842 209
Email: hilary.western1@midbeds.gov.uk
Web Site: www.midbeds.gov.uk
Youth & Community Arts Worker: Hilary Western
Head of Community Services, Leisure & Tourism: Roy Waterfield
Tourism Development Officer: Sandra Einon

MID DEVON DISTRICT COUNCIL
Phoenix House, Tiverton, Devon EX16 6PP
Tel: 01884 234 333 Fax: 01884 234 908
Email: rkelley@middevon.gov.uk
Web Site: www.middevon.gov.uk
Community Development Manager: Robert Kelley
Economic Development Manager: Michelle Bailey

MID SUSSEX DISTRICT COUNCIL
Leisure Services Dept, 'Oaklands' Oaklands Road, Haywards Heath, West Sussex RH16 1SS
Tel: 01444 458 166 Fax: 01444 477 464
Email: bent@midsussex.gov.uk
Web Site: www.midsussex.gov.uk

MIDDLESBROUGH BOROUGH COUNCIL
Cultural Services P.O. Box 134 First Floor Civic Centre Middlesbrough, Cleveland TS1 2YB
Tel: 01642 729137 Fax: 01642 729964
Email: judith_croft@middlesbrough.gov.uk
Web Site: www.middlesbrough.gov.uk
Entertainment and Events Manager: Judith Croft

MILTON KEYNES COUNCIL
Saxon Court, 502 Avebury Boulevard, Milton Keynes, Buckinghamshire MK9 3HS
Tel: 01908 691 691 Fax: 01908 253 304
Email: shane.downer@milton-keynes.gov.uk
Web Site: www.milton-keynes.gov.uk
Assistant to the Principal Community Economy and Culture Officer: Val Emsley (Tel: 01908 253 186)
Public Art Development Officer: Bridget Crump (Tel: 01908 253 163)
Heritage Development Officer: Shane Downer (Tel: 01908 253 690)

MOLE VALLEY DISTRICT COUNCIL
Dorking Halls, Reigate Road, Dorking, Surrey RH4 1SG
Tel: 01306 879 200 Fax: 01306 877 277
Email: dorking.halls@molevalley.gov.uk
Web Site: www.dorkinghalls.co.uk
Administration Manager: Debra White
Technical Manager: James Knight

MONMOUTHSHIRE COUNTY COUNCIL
County Hall, Croesyceiliog, Cwmbran, Gwent NP44 2XH Wales
Tel: 01633 644 550 Fax: 01633 644 488
Email: kevinsmith@monmouthshire.gov.uk
Web Site: www.monmouthshire.gov.uk
Cultural Services Manager: Kevin Smith
Arts Development Officer: Esko Reinikainen
The Council owns and operates the Borough Theatre in Abergavenny

NEATH & PORT TALBOT COUNTY BOROUGH COUNCIL
Arts & Entertainments Dept, Civic Centre, Port Talbot, West Glamorgan SA13 1PJ Wales
Tel: 01639 763 333 Fax: 01639 899 801
Email: l.laurence@npt.gov.uk
Web Site: www.npt.gov.uk
Head Of Lifelong Learning, Culture & Leisure: Russell Ward (Tel: 01639 763 144)
Arts and Entertainment Officer: Mrs L Laurence (Tel: 01639 763 149)

NEWARK & SHERWOOD DISTRICT COUNCIL
District Council Offices, Kelham, Newark, Nottinghamshire NG23 5QX
Tel: 01636 650 000 Fax: 01636 655 725
Email: mark.stephens@newark-sherwood-dc.gov.uk
Web: www.newark-sherwooddc.gov.uk
Cultural Services Manager: Mark Stephens

NEWCASTLE BOROUGH COUNCIL
Civic Offices, Merrial Street, Newcastle-under-Lyme, Staffordshire ST5 2AG
Tel: 01782 717 717 Fax: 01782 711 032
Email: janet.baddeley@newcastle-staffs.gov.uk
All Correspondence to;
Head of Community Services: Mr A Hudson
Administrative Assistant: Mrs Justine Tait

(Tel: 01782 742 504)
For more general Arts enquiries contact; Senior Events & Promotions Officer in Media & Communications: Janet Baddeley

NEWPORT CITY COUNCIL
Lifelong Learning & Leisure Dept, Continuing Learning & Leisure Division, Civic Centre, Newport, Gwent NP20 4UR Wales
Tel: 01633 232 824
Email: chrissmith@newport.gov.uk
Web Site: www.newport.gov.uk
Contact: Nick Cadman - 01633 656 637

NORTH NORFOLK DISTRICT COUNCIL
Council Offices, Holt Road, Cromer, Norfolk NR27 9EN
Tel: 01263 513 811 Fax: 01263 517 013
Email: arts@north-norfolk.gov.uk
Web Site: www.north-norfolk.gov.uk
Arts Officer: Brenda Seymour

SOUTH NORTHAMPTONSHIRE COUNCIL
Council Offices, Springfields, Towcester, Northamptonshire NN12 6AE
Tel: 01327 322 334 Fax: 01327 322 074
Email: anna.hayward@southnorthants.gov.uk
Web Site: www.southnorthants.gov.uk
Leisure Policy Officer: Ashley Davey
Arts Development Officer: Anna Hayward

NORWICH CITY COUNCIL
City Hall, Norwich, Norfolk NR2 1WG
Tel: 01603 212 137 Fax: 01603 213 003
Email: helenselleck@norwich.gov.uk
Web Site: www.norwich.gov.uk
Head of Communications: Nicki Rotsof
Cultural Officer: Vaughan Aston (Tel: 01603 213017)
Events Manager: Helen Selleck

NOTTINGHAM CITY COUNCIL
Leisure & Community Dept, Arts, Tourism and Heritage Div Castle Gate House, 24-30 Castle Gate, Nottingham NG1 7AT
Tel: 0115 915 5555
Email: sharon.svaniglia@nottinghamcity.gov.uk
Web Site: www.nottinghamcity.gov.uk
Principal Arts Officer: Sharon Svaniglia

NUNEATON & BEDWORTH BOROUGH COUNCIL
The Town Hall, Coton Road, Nuneaton, Warwickshire CV11 5AA
Tel: 024 7637 6376 Ents Mgr: 024 7637 6705
Email: catherine.nisbet@nuneatonandbedworthbc.gov.uk
Web www.nuneatonandbedworthbc.gov.uk
Entertainments Manager: Peter J Ireson
Arts Development Officer: Erica Stotto

OLDHAM METROPOLITAN BOROUGH COUNCIL
Civic Centre, West Street, Oldham, Lancashire OL1 1XJ
Tel 0161 911 4076 Fax 0161 911 3222
Email: ecs.artsandevents@oldham.gov.uk
Exec Director of Education and Cultural Services: Chris Berry
Assistant Director Lifelong Learning & Culture: Nick Ford

OXFORD CITY COUNCIL
Leisure Services Dept, Ramsey House, 10 St Ebbes Street, Oxford OX1 1PT
Tel 01865 249 811 Fax: 01865 252 254
Email: parks@oxford.gov.uk
Web Site: www.oxford.gov.uk
Head of Leisure: John Bolton (Tel: 01865 252 228)
Arts & Heritage Manager: Neil Smith (Tel: 01865 252 829)

PEMBROKESHIRE COUNTY COUNCIL
County Library, Dew Street, Haverfordwest, Pembrokeshire SA61 1SU Wales
Tel: 01437 775 246 Fax: 01437 767 092
Email: christine.willison@pembrokeshire.gov.uk
Web Site: www.pembrokeshire.gov.uk
Head Of Cultural Services: Neil Bennett
Theatre Manager: Melanie Lucking (Theatr Gwaun)
Arts Officer: Christine Willison

PENDLE LEISURE LTD
Pendle Borough Council Bank House, 61 Albert Road, Colne, Lancashire BB8 0BP
Tel: 01282 661 234 Fax: 01282 661 221
Email: info@pendleleisuretrust.co.uk
Web Site: www.pendleleisuretrust.co.uk
Leisure Services Manager: Phil Storey

PENWITH DISTRICT COUNCIL
Council Offices, St Clare, Penzance, Cornwall TR18 3QW
Tel: 01736 362 341
Email: barbara.mathews@penwith.gov.uk
Web Site: www.penwith.gov.uk
Bookings Contact: Clare James/Tina Beeley

PETERBOROUGH CITY COUNCIL
Bayard Place, Broadway, Peterborough, Cambridgeshire PE1 1HZ
Tel: 01733 237 073 Fax: 01733 235 462
Email: trevor.gibson@peterborough.gov.uk
Web Site: www.peterborough.gov.uk
Director of Leisure Services: Trevor Gibson

CITY OF PLYMOUTH COUNCIL
Dept for Lifelong Learning, Plymouth, Devon PL1 2AA
Tel: 01752 307 000 Fax: 01752 307 139
Email: paul.kelly@plymouth.gov.uk
Web Site: www.plymouth.gov.uk
Principal Arts Development Officer: Paul Kelly

POOLE BOROUGH COUNCIL
Poole Arts Development Mngr, 4 High Street, Poole, Dorset BH15 1BW
Tel: 01202 633972 Fax: 01202 660896
Email: n.moore@poole.gov.uk
Web Site: www.boroughofpoole.com
Arts Development: Nickola Moore

PORTSMOUTH CITY COUNCIL
City Arts Dept, Civic Offices, Portsmouth, Hampshire PO1 2AD
Tel: 023 9283 4185 Fax: 023 9283 4159
Email: claire.looney@portsmouthcc.gov.uk
Web Site: www.portsmouthcc.gov.uk
Acting City Arts Officer: Claire Looney

POWYS COUNTY COUNCIL
County Hall, Llandrindod Wells, Powys LD1 5LG Wales
Tel: 01597 826 469 Fax: 01874 826 243
Email: theart.powys@powys.gov.uk
Web Site: www.powys.gov.uk
Manager: Vicki Thomas

PRESTON CITY COUNCIL
Regeneration, Community & Leisure Services Dept, Guild Hall, Lancaster Road, Preston, Lancashire PR1 1HT
Admin: 01772 203 456 BO: 01772 258 858 Fax: 01772 881 716
Email: s.jones@preston.gov.uk
Web Site: www.prestonguildhall.com
Head of Leisure Services: Steven Jones

READING BOROUGH COUNCIL
Arts & Leisure Dept, Civic Centre, Reading, Berkshire RG1 7TD
Tel: 0118 939 0900 Fax: 0118 958 9770
Email: chris.smith@reading.gov.uk
Web Site: www.reading.gov.uk
Head of Arts and Theatres: Andrew Ormston (Tel: 0118 939 0123)
Arts Development Officer: Tammy Bedford (Tel: 0118 939 0394)

REDCAR & CLEVELAND BOROUGH COUNCIL
Development Department, Tourism Section
Arts & Cultural Development, Kirkleatham Museum, Redcar, Yorkshire TS10 5NW
Tel: 01642 471 069 Fax: 01642 472 395
Email: julia_marsden@.redcar-cleveland.gov.uk
Web Site: www.redcar_cleveland.gov.uk
Tourism Officer: Julia Marsden

REDDITCH COUNCIL
Town Hall, Alcester Street, Redditch, Worcestershire B98 8AH

Tel: 01527 64252 Fax: 01527 65216
Email: hilary.ward@redditchbc.gov.uk
Web Site: www.redditchbc.gov.uk

REIGATE & BANSTEAD BOROUGH COUNCIL
Leisure Services, Castlefield Road, Reigate, Surrey RH2 0SH
Tel: 01737 276 000 Fax: 01737 276 404
Email: sarah.groom@reigate-banstead.gov.uk
Web Site: www.reigate-banstead.gov.uk
Contact/ Admin:
Head of Leisure Services: Sarah Groom
Manager: Tom Kealey
Technical Manager: John Hewitt
Sales & Marketing Manager: Penny Shoubridge
Admin Manager: Tracey Wainwright
Marketing & Publicity Manager: Sarah Wenban
House Manager: Janet Franklin
Asst. Technical Manager: Marc Watkins

RESTORMEL BOROUGH COUNCIL
Borough Offices, 39 Penwinnick Road, St Austell, Cornwall PL25 5DR
Tel: 01726 223 300 Fax: 01726 223 301
Email: jaberdeen@restormel.gov.uk
Web Site: www.restormel.gov.uk
Arts Enquiries: Jonathan Aberdeen (Tel: 01726 223 439)
Trading Officer: Mr Paul Warby (Tel: 01726 223 447)

RHONDDA CYNON TAFF COUNTY BOROUGH COUNCIL
Leisure & Tourism Department
Community Leisure Dept, Corporation Building, Depot Road, Aberdere, Rhondda Cynon Taff CF44 8DL
Tel: 01685 885 630 Marketing Dep: 01443 424 000 Fax: 01685 885 631
Email: events@rhondda=cynon-taff.gov.uk
Head Of Community Leisure: Cyril Chivers

SOUTH RIBBLE BOROUGH COUNCIL
Leisure & Commercial Services, Civic Centre, West Paddock, Leyland, Preston, Lancashire PR25 1DH
Tel: 01772 421 491 Ext 5510 Fax: 01772 625 363
Email: info@southribble.gov.uk
Web Site: www.southribble.gov.uk
Chief Executive: Mrs J Hunter
Leisure Commercial Services Manager: David Seager DMS, MILAM(Dip)
Capacity: 150

RIBBLE VALLEY BOROUGH COUNCIL
Council Offices, Church Walk, Clitheroe, Lancashire BB7 2RA
Tel: 01200 414 479
Email: katherine.rodgers@ribblevalley.gov.uk
Web Site: www.ribblevalley.gov.uk
Leisure & Tourism Manager: Chris Hughes
Arts Development Officer: Katherine Rodgers

RICHMONDSHIRE DISTRICT COUNCIL
Fryers Wynd, Richmond, North Yorkshire DL10 4RT
Tel: 01748 829 100 Fax: 01748 850 897
Email: enquiries@richmondshire.gov.uk
Web Site: www.richmondshire.gov.uk
Economic, Cultural and Leisure Unit Manager: Geoff Thompson

ROCHDALE METROPOLITAN BOROUGH COUNCIL
Municipal Offices, Smith Street, Rochdale, Lancashire OL16 1XG
Tel: 01706 647 474 Fax: 01706 659 475
Email: beate.mielemeier@rochdale.gov.uk
Web Site: www.rochdale.gov.uk
Arts Development Officer: Beate Mielemeier

ROCHFORD DISTRICT COUNCIL
Leisure Department, South Street, Rochford, Essex SS4 1BW
Tel: 01702 318 171 Fax: 01702 545 737
Email: caroline.coats@rochford.gov.uk
Web Site: www.rochford.gov.uk
Arts Development Officer: Caroline Coats

ROSSENDALE BOROUGH COUNCIL
Bacup Leisure Hall, Burnley Road, Bacup, Lancashire L13 8AE
Bacup Trust: 01702 242 311 Bacup Leisure Hall Tel: 01706 875 550
Email: daleconnearn@rltrust.co.uk
Web Site: www.rossendale.gov.uk
Bacup Leisure Hall Manager: Dale Connearn
Cap: 400
Leisure Hall with 2x bars, kitchen, 2x squash courts, lounge area, large main hall with stage, single storey, disabled access.

ROTHER DISTRICT COUNCIL
Town Hall, London Road, Bexhill-on-Sea, East Sussex TN39 3JX
Tel: 01424 787 878 Fax: 01424 787 520
Email: communityservices@rother.gov.uk
Web Site: www.rother.gov.uk
Arts Development Officer: Michael Rycroft

ROTHERHAM BOROUGH COUNCIL
Community Arts c/o Rotherham Arts Centre, Walker Place, Rotherham, South Yorkshire S65 1JH
Tel: 01709 823636 Fax: 01709 823 653
Email: guy.kilminster@rotherham.gov.uk
Web Site: www.rotherham.gov.uk
Libraries, Museums and Arts Manager: Guy Kilminster
Principal Officer, Community Arts: Lizzie Alageswaran

ROYAL BOROUGH OF WINDSOR & MAIDENHEAD
Community Partnerships
Town Hall, St Ives Road, Maidenhead, Berkshire SL6 1RF
Tel: 01628 796 460 Fax: 01628 796 121
Email: mark.taylor@rbwm.gov.uk
Web Site: www.rbwm.gov.uk
Head of Library Services: Mark Taylor

RUGBY BOROUGH COUNCIL
Technical Services Dept., Town Hall, Evreux Way, Rugby, Warwickshire CV21 2LB
Tel: 01788 533 533 Fax: 01788 533 778
Email: ian.fraser@rugby.gov.uk
Web Site: www.rugby.gov.uk
Chief Recreation & Amenities Officer: R Honeybunn

RUNNYMEDE BOROUGH COUNCIL
Civic Offices, Station Road, Addlestone, Surrey KT15 2AH
Tel: 01932 838 383 Ext 5684 Fax: 01932 855 135
Email: JennyS@runnymede.gov.uk
Web Site: www.runnymede.gov.uk
Venue Booking Co-Ordinator: Jenny Soffe

RUSHCLIFFE BOROUGH COUNCIL
Leisure Services Dept, Civic Centre, Pavilion Road, West Bridgford, Nottingham NG2 5FE
Tel: 0115 981 9911 Fax: 0115 945 5882
Email: info@rushcliffe.gov.uk
Web Site: www.rushcliffe.gov.uk
Leisure Facilities Manager: Brian Knowles

RUSHMOOR BOROUGH COUNCIL
Council Offices, Farnborough Road, Farnborough, Hampshire GU14 7JU
Tel: 01252 398 398 Fax: 01252 398 765
Email: rmann@rushmoor.gov.uk
Web Site: www.rushmoor.gov.uk
Arts and Cultural Officer: Richard Mann

RYEDALE DISTRICT COUNCIL
Ryedale House, Old Malton Road, Malton, North Yorkshire YO17 0HH
Tel: 01653 600 666 Fax: 01653 696 801
Email: yvette.turnball@ryedale.gov.uk
Web Site: www.ryedale.gov.uk
Arts, Grants and Lottery Officer: Yvette Turnbulll

SALFORD CITY COUNCIL
Minerva House, Pendlebury Road, Swinton Greater Manchester M27 4EQ

Tel: 0161 778 0123 Fax: 0131 728 6234
Email: faith.mann@salford.gov.uk
Web Site: www.salford.gov.uk
Assistant Director Lifelong Learning and Leisure: Faith Mann

SALISBURY DISTRICT COUNCIL
The Council House, Bourne Hill, Salisbury, Wiltshire SP1 3UZ
Tel: 01722 434 307 Fax: 01722 434 500
Email: rachel.efemey@salisbury.gov.uk
Web Site: www.salisbury.gov.uk
Chief Executive: RK Sheard
Principal Arts Officer: Rachel Efemey

SANDWELL METROPOLITAN BOROUGH COUNCIL
Arts in Sandwell, Education & Lifelong Learning The Old Courts, Market Street, Oldbury, West Midlands B69 4DH
Tel: 0121 569 4927 Fax: 0121 544 3854
Email: garry_morris@sandwell.gov.uk
Web Site: www.sandwellartsfocus.co.uk
Arts Manager: Garry Morris

SEDGEFIELD BOROUGH COUNCIL
Council Offices, Spennymoor, County Durham DL16 6JQ
Tel: 01388 816 166 Fax: 01388 815 374
Email: kbanner@sedgefield.gov.uk
Web Site: www.sedgefield.gov.uk
Head of Leisure Services: Phil Ball
Arts Development Officer: Katy Ball

SEDGEMOOR DISTRICT COUNCIL
Bridgwater House, King Square, Bridgwater, Somerset TA6 3AR
Tel: 01278 435 435 Fax: 01278 444 076
Email: arts@sedgemoor.gov.uk
Web Site: www.sedgemoor.gov.uk
Chief Executive: Mr Kerry Rickards
Head of Tourism, Culture & Marketing: Mrs Elaine Ford
Arts Officer: Chris Sidaway

SEFTON METROPITAN BOROUGH COUNCIL
Leisure Services Dept, Pavillion Buildings, 99/105 Lord Street, Sefton, Merseyside PR8 1RH
Admin: 0151 934 2383 Fax: 0151 934 2370
Email: leisure.services@sefton.gov.uk
Web Site: www.sefton.gov.uk
Chief Tourism & Attractions Officer: Ken Waymin

SELBY DISTRICT COUNCIL
Civic Centre, Portholme Road, Selby, North Yorkshire YO8 4SB
Tel: 01757 705 101 Fax: 01757 292 020
Email: chris.jones@selbytowncouncil.co.uk
Selby Arts Centre, The Town Hall, York Street, Selby YO8 4AJ
Tel: 01757 708 449
Contact: Chris Jones

SHEPWAY DISTRICT COUNCIL
Civic Centre, Castle Hill Avenue, Folkestone, Kent CT20 2QY
Tel: 01303 852 442 Fax: 01303 852 303
Email: len.mayatt@shepway.gov.uk
Web Site: www.shepway.gov.uk
Strategic Director: Stephen Hagues
Cultural Services Manager: Len Mayatt

SHREWSBURY & ATCHAM BOROUGH COUNCIL
The Guildhall, Frankwell Quay, Shrewsbury Shropshire SY3 8HQ
Tel: 01743 281 000 Fax: 01743 281 016
Email: geraint.morgan@shrewsbury.gov.uk
Director of Community Services:Geraint Morgan

NORTH SHROPSHIRE DISTRICT COUNCIL
Edinburgh House, New Street, Wem, Shrewsbury, Shropshire SY4 5DB
Tel: 01939 232 771 Fax: 01939 238 422
Email: rbentley@northshropshiredc.gov.uk
Web Site: www.northshropshiredc.gov.uk
Arts Development Officer: Richard Hepenstall

SOLIHULL METROPOLITAN BOROUGH COUNCIL
Council House, Education, Libraries & Arts, PO Box 20, Bushell Drive, Solihull, West Midlands B91 3QU
Tel: 0121 704 6000 Fax: 0121 704 6669
Email: kfishwick@solihull.gov.uk
Web Site: www.solihull.gov.uk
Arts Development Officer: Kat Fishwick

NORTH SOMERSET COUNCIL
Town Hall, Walliscote Grove Road, Weston-super-Mare, North Somerset BS23 1UJ
Tel 01934 888 888 Fax: 01934 418 194
Arts Development Fax: 01934 852 762
Email: fiona.matthews@n-somerset.gov.u k
Arts Development Officer: Fiona Matthews

SOUTH HAMS DISTRICT COUNCIL
Follaton House, Plymouth Road, Totnes, Devon TQ9 5NE
Tel: 01803 861 406 Fax: 01803 861 181
Email: robert.green@southhams.gov.uk
Web Site: www.southhams.gov.uk
Marketing & Tourism Officer: Robert Green

SOUTH HOLLAND DISTRICT COUNCIL
Priory Road, Spalding, Lincolnshire PE11 2XE
Tel: 01775 761 161 Fax: 01775 711 054
Email: ecole@sholland.gov.uk
Web Site: www.sholland.gov.uk
Arts Development Officer: Emily Cole

SOUTHAMPTON CITY COUNCIL
Southampton Guildhall, Civic Centre, West Marland Road, Southampton, Hampshire SO14 7LP
Tel: 023 8083 2453 Fax: 023 8023 3359
Email: christine.rawnsley@southampton.gov.uk
Web Site: www.southampton.gov.uk
Arts Development Officer: Christine Rawnsley

SPELTHORNE BOROUGH COUNCIL
Leisure Services
Council Offices, Knowle Green, Staines, Middlesex TW18 1XB
Tel: 01784 446 338 / 01784 446 433
Fax: 01784 446 463
Email: k.roe@spelthorne.gov.uk
Web Site: www.spelthorne.gov.uk
Head of Community Services: Liz Borthwick
Arts & Heritage Development Officer: Kirsteen Roe
Spelthorne Borough Council supports, develops and promotes arts and heritage opportunities in the borough. Please note the council no longer runs an arts venue, but does have links with non council-run local venues.

ST ALBANS CITY & DISTRICT COUNCIL
Civic Centre, St Peter's Street, St Albans, Hertfordshire AL1 3JE
Tel: 01727 819 470 Fax: 01727 861 561
Email: a.varley@stalbans.gov.uk
Web Site: www.stalbans.gov.uk
Arts Officer: Nicola Paddick

ST EDMUNDSBURY BOROUGH COUNCIL
Borough Offices, Angel Hill, Bury St Edmunds, Suffolk IP33 1XB
Tel: 01284 757 630 Fax: 01284 757 631
Email: nick.wells@stedsbc.gov.uk
Web Site: www.buryfestival.co.uk
Festival Manager: Nick Wells

ST HELENS METROPOLITAN BOROUGH COUNCIL
Recreation Dept, Wesley House, Corporation Street, St Helens, Merseyside WA10 1HF
Tel: 01744 455 453 Fax: 01744 455 330
Email: pmeredith@sthelens.gov.uk
Web Site: www.sthelens.gov.uk
Acting Principal Youth Officer: Willy Holland (Tel: 01744 455 466; Fax: 01744 455 350)
Family Learning, Arts & Community

Services: Pam Meredith (Tel: 01744 455 466
Rivington Centre, Rivington Road, St Helens, Merseyside WA10 4ND

STAFFORD BOROUGH COUNCIL
Civic Offices, Riverside, Stafford, Staffordshire ST16 3AQ
Tel: 01785 619 000 Fax: 01785 619 419
Email: lhulse@staffordbc.gov.uk
Web Site: www.staffordbc.gov.uk
Director of Development: D J Pinnock
Leisure Services Officer: Jim Arnold
Community Events Manager: L Hulse

STAFFORDSHIRE MOORLANDS DISTRICT COUNCIL
Moorlands House, Stockwell Street, Leek, Staffordshire ST13 6HQ
Tel: 01538 483 483 Fax: 01538 483 474
Email: customer.services@staffsmoorlands.gov.uk
Web Site: www.staffsmoorlands.gov.uk
Head of Leisure: Mr Duncan Cowie
Leisure Officer: Mr Phil Jepson

SOUTH STAFFORDSHIRE DISTRICT COUNCIL
Council Offices, Wolverhampton Road, Codsall, West Midlands WV8 1PX
Tel: 01902 696 000 Fax: 01902 696 546 (Leisure)
Email: r.henley@sstaffs.gov.uk
Web Site: www.sstaffs.gov.uk
Head of Leisure Services: David Heywood
Arts Development Officer: Sheena Lucas

STEVENAGE BOROUGH COUNCIL
Corinthian Conference & Entert c/o Stevenage Leisure Ltd, Stevenage Leisure & Arts Centr Lytton Way, Stevenage, Hertfordshire SG1 1LZ
Tel: 01438 242 242 Conference Tel: 01438 242 638 (Wendy Covell)
Conference Fax: 01438 231 101
Email: wendy.covell@stevenage-leisure.co.uk
Props: Stevenage Borough Council
Head of Culture & Leisure Services: Aiden Sanderson
Contact Conference, Events & Hire Manager: Wendy Covell

STOCKPORT METROPOLITAN BOROUGH COUNCIL
Stockport Arts Team
Arts Officer, Romiley Forum, Compstall Road, Romiley, Stockport, Cheshire SK6 4EA
Tel: 0161 430 6570 Fax: 0161 406 6782
Email: stockportartsteam@yahoo.co.uk
Web Site: www.smbc.gov.uk
Principal Arts Officer: Victoria Munich
Arts Development Officers: Jez Dolan, Shirley Lundstram

STOCKTON-ON-TEES BOROUGH COUNCIL
Wynyard House, Town Centre, Billingham, Cleveland TS23 2LN
Tel: 01642 526 466 Tel: 01642 526 465 (Jan Doherty) Fax: 01642 358 501
Email: jan.doherty@stockton.gov.uk
Web Site: www.stockton.gov.uk
Arts Service Manager: Jan Doherty
Arts Development Officer: Rachel Willis

STOKE-ON-TRENT CITY COUNCIL
Venues & Catering Dept, Civic Centre, Glebe Street, Stoke-on-Trent Staffordshire ST4 1RT
Tel: 01782 232 732 Fax 01782 236 584
Email: tony.meigh@stoke.gov.uk
Web Site: www.stoke.gov.uk
Venues & Catering Manager: Tony Meigh

STOWMARKET TOWN COUNCIL
Milton House, Milton Road South, Stowmarket, Suffolk IP14 1EZ
Tel: 01449 612 060 Fax: 01449 775 103
Email: emilym@stowmarket.org
Web Site: www.stowmarket.org
Deputy Town Clerk: Emily Metcalfe

STROUD DISTRICT COUNCIL
Ebley Mill, Westward Road, Stroud, Gloucestershire GL5 4UB
Tel: 01453 766 321 Fax: 01453 754 955
Email: amar.dave@stroud.gov.uk
Web Site: www.stroud.gov.uk
Recreation Officer: Ashley Tucker

SUFFOLK COASTAL DISTRICT COUNCIL
Council Offices, Melton Hill, Woodbridge, Suffolk IP12 1AU
Tel: 01394 383 789 Fax: 01394 385 100
Email: scdc@suffolkcoastal.gov.uk
Web Site: www.suffolkcoastal.gov.uk
Leisure Management & Marketing Officer: Mrs Chris Robinson
Seats: 917

SUNDERLAND CITY COUNCIL
Burden Road, Sunderland Tyne and Wear SR2 7DN
Tel: 0191 553 1000 Fax: 0191 553 1460
Email: terry.walsh@sunderland.gov.uk
Web Site: www.sunderland.gov.uk
Director of Education and Community Services: Terry Walsh

SURREY HEATH BOROUGH COUNCIL
Surrey Heath House, Knoll Road, Camberley, Surrey GU15 3HD
Tel: 01276 707 603 Box Office: 01276 707 600
Email: nick.mowat@surreyheath.gov.uk
General Manager of The Camberley Theatre: Nick Mowat

SWANLEY TOWN COUNCIL
Council Offices, St. Marys Road, Swanley, Kent BR8 7BU
Tel: 01322 665 855 Fax: 01322 613 000
Email: towncouncil@swanley.org.uk
Town Clerk: Mr Brian Daley
Marketing Manager - Banqueting Section: Angela Warren, Paula Smith

SWANSEA CITY & COUNTY COUNCIL
Culture & Recreation, The County Hall Oystermouth Road Swansea, South Glamorgan SA1 3SN Wales
Tel: 01792 636 000 Fax: 01792 635 408 / 187
Email: tracy.ellioc@swansea.gov.uk
Web Site: www.swansea.gov.uk
Director of Regeneration: David Evans
Head of Service, Culture & Support Services: Iwan Davies
Principal Officer Culture & Regeneration: Andrew Davies

SWINDON BOROUGH COUNCIL
Education & Community
Premier House, Station Road, Swindon, Wiltshire SN1 1TZ
Tel: 01793 463 000 Ext: 6544 Fax: 01793 466 568
Email: hmiah@swindon.gov.uk
Web Site: www.swindon.gov.uk
Strategic Arts & Community Officer: Helen Miah

TAMWORTH BOROUGH COUNCIL
Tamworth Assembly Rooms
Culture & Community Services, Marmion House, Lichfield Street, Tamworth, Staffordshire B79 7BZ
Tamworth Information Centre: 01827 709 618 Admin: 01827 709 619
Email: joanne-marshall@tamworth.gov.uk
Manager of the Assembly Rooms: David Tomlinson
Email address: david_tomlinson@tamworth.gov.uk

TANDRIDGE DISTRICT COUNCIL
Tandridge Leisure Ltd, The Naafi, Weston Drive, Caterham-on-the-Hill, Surrey CR3 5XY
Tel: 01883 331 547 Fax: 01883 341 945
Email: kpotter@theatre-exchange.org.uk
Web Site: www.theatre-exchange.org.uk
Artistic Director: Katy Potter

TAUNTON DEANE BOROUGH COUNCIL
The Deane House, Belvedere Road, Taunton, Somerset TA1 1HE
Tel: 01823 356 356 Fax: 01823 356 329
Email: omb@tauntondeane.gov.uk
Web Site: www.tauntondeane.gov.uk
Customer Support Manager: Angela Eldridge

TEESDALE DISTRICT COUNCIL
43 Galgate, Barnard Castle, County Durham DL12 8EL
Tel: 01833 696 280 Fax: 01833 637 269
Email: tourism@teesdale.co.uk
Arts Development Officer: Rosie Cross

TEIGNBRIDGE DISTRICT COUNCIL
Forde House, Brunel Road, Newton Abbot, Devon TQ12 4XX
Tel: 01626 215607 Fax: 01626 215 613
Email: dpollard@teignbridge.gov.uk
Web Site: www.teignbridge.gov.uk
Head of Leisure & Tourism: Karen Christie
Arts Development Officer: Doff Pollard

TENDRING DISTRICT COUNCIL
Leisure Section, Town Hall, Station Road, Clacton-on-Sea, Essex CO15 1SE
Tel: 01255 253 208 Fax: 01255 253 200
Email: rfoster@tendringdc.gov.uk
Entertainments Officer: Bob Foster

TEST VALLEY BOROUGH COUNCIL
Leisure Services Dept, Beech Hurst, Weyhill Road, Andover, Hampshire SP10 3AJ
Tel: 01264 368 844 Fax: 01264 368 899
Email: mjohnson@testvalley.gov.uk
Web Site: www.testvalley.gov.uk
Senior Arts Officer: Michael Johnson

THANET DISTRICT COUNCIL
Cecil Street, Margate, Kent CT9 1XZ
Tel: 01843 577 000 Fax: 01843 290 906
Email: chris.tull@thanet.gov.uk
Web Site: www.thanet.gov.uk
Public Affairs Manager: Gillian Shepherd
Senior Leisure Officer: Chris Tull

THE BRINDLEY
High Street Runcorn, Cheshire WA7 1BG
Tel: 0151 907 8360 Fax: 0151 907 8361
Email: sue.davies@halton.gov.uk
Web Site: www.thebrindley.org.uk
Howard Cockcroft BA (Hons) Dip Lib ALA
Cultural and Tourism Manager: Sue Davis

THE HARLINGTON
Fleet Road, Fleet, Hampshire GU51 4BY
Tel: 01252 811009
Email: culturalservices@hart.gov.uk
Web Site: www.hart.gov.uk

THREE RIVERS DISTRICT COUNCIL
Three Rivers House, Northway, Rickmansworth, Hertfordshire WD3 1RL
Tel: 01923 776 611 Fax: 01923 896 119
Email: andrea.plaistow@threerivers.gov.uk
Web Site: www.threerivers.gov.uk
Community Arts Development Officer: Andrea Plaistow

TONBRIDGE & MALLING BOROUGH COUNCIL
Tonbridge Castle, Tonbridge, Kent TN9 1BG
Tel 01732 770 929 Fax: 01732 770 449
Email: lyndsey.bennett@tmbc.gov.uk
Arts & Leisure Contact: Lyndsey Bennett

TORFAEN COUNTY BOROUGH COUNCIL
Civic Centre, Pontypool, Torfaen NP4 6YB Wales
Tel: 01633 628950 Fax: 01633 628935
Email: victoria.walden@torfaen.gov.uk
Web Site: www.torfaen.gov.uk
Assistant Arts Development Officer: Victoria Walden

TORRIDGE DISTRICT COUNCIL
Riverbank House, Bideford, Devon EX39 2QG
Tel: 01237 428 700 Fax: 01237 478 849
Email: vanessa.saunders@torridge.gov.uk
Web Site: www.torridge.gov.uk
Contact Head of Regeneration: Vanessa Saunders
Tourism Development Officer: Jo Boyd

TRAFFORD METROPOLITAN BOROUGH COUNCIL
Trafford Town Hall, Talbot Road, Stretford, Manchester M32 0YT
Tel: 0161 911 8673 Fax: 0161 911 8693
Email: chris.pratt@trafford.gov.uk
Web Site: www.trafford.gov.uk
Director of Education, Arts & Leisure: Christopher Pratt

TROWBRIDGE TOWN COUNCIL
10-12 Fore Street, Trowbridge, Wiltshire BA14 7HA
Council Tel: 01225 765 072 Hall Tel: 01225 762 439 Hall Fax: 01225 762 644
Email: lancea@trowbridge.gov.uk
Town Clerk: Mr Lance Allen

TUNBRIDGE WELLS BOROUGH COUNCIL
Town Hall, Mount Pleasant Road, Tunbridge Wells, Kent TN1 1RS
Tel: 01892 554 230 Fax: 01892 534 227
Email: arts@tunbridgewells.gov.uk
Web Site: www.tunbridgewells.gov.uk
Leisure Development & Projects Manager: Sally Staples

TYNEDALE COUNCIL
Prospect House, Hexham, Northumberland NE46 3NH
Tel: 01434 652 200 Fax: 01434 652 425
Email: sarah.wilson@tynedale.gov.uk
Web Site: www.tynedale.gov.uk
Director of Leisure & Tourism: Lynn Turner

NORTH TYNESIDE COUNCIL
c/o Buddle Arts Centre, 258b Station Road, Wallsend, Tyne and Wear NE28 8RG
Tel: 0191 200 7133 Fax: 0191 200 7142
Email: mike.campbell@northtyneside.gov.uk
Web Site: www.northtyneside.gov.uk
Arts Manager: Mike Campbell

SOUTH TYNESIDE COUNCIL
Lifelong Learning & Leisure Directorate
Facilities & Events Section
Central Library, Prince Georg Square, South Shields, Tyne and Wear NE33 2PE
Tel: 0191 427 1717 Fax: 0191 427 0469
Email: andy.buyers@s-tyneside-mbc.gov.uk
Web Site: www.s-tyneside-mbc.gov.uk
Recreation Manager: Bryan Atkinson
Events Officer: Andy Buyers
Tel: 0191 424 7985

UTTLESFORD DISTRICT COUNCIL
Council Offices, London Road, Saffron Walden, Essex CB11 4ER
Tel: 01799 510 348 Fax: 01799 510 550
Email: gbradley@uttlesford.gov.uk
Web Site: www.uttlesford.gov.uk
Leisure Manager: Gaynor Bradley

VALE ROYAL BOROUGH COUNCIL
Community Services Directorate Wyvern House, The Drumber, Winsford, Cheshire CW7 1AH
Tel: 01606 862 862 Fax: 01606 862 100
Email: singram@valeroyal.gov.uk
Web Site: www.valeroyal.gov.uk
Leisure Services Officer: C Bottomly
Entertainments & Events Officer:

WAKEFIELD METROPOLITAN DISTRICT COUNCIL
Cultural Services, PO Box 262, Wakefield, West Yorkshire WF1 1ZA
Tel: 01924 305 799 Fax: 01924 305 793
Email: apoppleton@wakefield.gov.uk
Web Site: www.wakefield.gov.uk
Senior Development Officer: Adele Poppleton
We do not operate our own theatre venues but we can give advice about venues in our area.

WALSALL METROPOLITAN BOROUGH COUNCIL
Civic Centre, Darwall Street, Walsall, West Midlands WS1 1TZ
Tel: 01922 653 170 Fax: 01922 721 682
Email: pompaa@walsall.gov.uk
Web Site: www.walsall.gov.uk
Promotions & Events Manager: Antonia Pompa

WANSBECK DISTRICT COUNCIL
Leisure Dept, Front Street, Bedlington, Northumberland NE22 5TU
Tel: 01670 532 200 Fax: 01670 843484
Email: k.hudson@wansbeck.gov.uk
Web Site: www.wansbeck.gov.uk
Arts and Entertainments Officer: Kate Hudson
Cultural Services Manager: Nicholas Baumfield

WARMINSTER TOWN COUNCIL
Dewey House, North Row, Warminster, Wiltshire BA12 9AD
Tel: 01985 214 847 Fax: 01985 847 326
Email: admin@warminstergov.co.uk
Town Clerk: Heather Abernethie

WARRINGTON BOROUGH COUNCIL
Parr Hall, Palmyra Square, Warrington, Cheshire WA1 1BL
Tel: 01925 442 345
Email: parrhall@warrington.gov.uk
Web Site: www.parrhall.gov.uk
Director of Community Services: Alan Stephenson
Entertainments Manager: John Perry
Arts Officer: Gail Thorne

WARWICK DISTRICT COUNCIL
Riverside House, Milverton Hill, Leamington Spa, Warwickshire CV32 5QG
Tel: 01926 450 000 Leisure & Amenities Dept, PO Box 2177, Leamington Spa, Warwickshire CV32 5QG Tel: 01926 737 153 (Peter Nicholson) Fax: 01926 456 210
Email: peter.nicholson@warwickdc.gov.uk
Web Site: www.warwickdc.gov.uk
Amenities Officer: Dale G Best, B Ed, DMS (Rec. Man) M Inst BRM MRMA
Entertainments Manager: Peter Nicholson
Heritage & Arts Manager: Jeffrey Watkin

NORTH WARWICKSHIRE BOROUGH COUNCIL
Community Services Dept, PO Box 6, The Council House, South Street, Atherstone, Warwickshire CV9 1BG
Tel: 01827 719 207 Fax: 01827 717 383
Email: simonpowell@northwarks.gov.uk
Web Site: www.northwarks.gov.uk
Assistant Director Of Community Development: Simon Powell

WATFORD BOROUGH COUNCIL
Town Hall, Watford, Hertfordshire WD17 3EX
Tel: 01923 226 400 Fax: 01923 278 100
Email: marion.duffin@watford.gov.uk
Web Site: www.watford.gov.uk/leisure
Arts Team: Victoria Kayte, Lynda Allen, Belinda Gregory

WAVENEY DISTRICT COUNCIL
Community Services, Mariner's Street, Lowestoft, Suffolk NR32 1JT
Tel: 01502 523 302 Fax: 01502 538 179
Email: info@marinetheatre.co.uk
Web Site: www.marinetheatre.co.uk
Head of Tourism and Leisure: Peter Waring
Venues Manager: Martin T D Halliday
Events Administrator: Ken Jarmin
Waveney District Council owns and operates The Marina Theatre, Lowestoft; Beccles Public Hall, Beccles and Halesworth Rifle Hall, Halesworth.

WEAR VALLEY DISTRICT COUNCIL
Civic Centre, Crook, County Durham DL15 9ES
Tel: 01388 761 544 Fax: 01388 766 660
Email: d.plews@wearvalley.gov.uk
Web Site: www.wearvalley.gov.uk
Cultural Services Manager: David Plews

WELLINGBOROUGH BOROUGH COUNCIL
Council Offices, Swanspool, Wellingborough, Northamptonshire NN8 1BP
Tel: 01933 229 777 Fax: 01933 231 762
Email: sbull@wellingborough.gov.uk
Web Site: www.wellingboough.gov.uk
Head Of Cultural Services: Adrian Lowther

WELWYN-HATFIELD COUNCIL
The Campus West Arts & Conf Centre, Campus West, Welwyn Garden City, Hertfordshire AL8 6BX
Tel: 01707 357 000 Fax: 01707 357 162
Email: contact-WHC@welhat.gov.uk
Web www.welhat.gov.uk/leisureculture
Director of Leisure and Community Services: Mark Poppy
Community Arts Officer: Joanne Wilson
Facilities Manager: Mark Woolman

WEST BERKS DISTRICT COUNCIL
Council Offices Market Street Newbury Berkshire RG14 5LD
Tel: 01635 42400 Fax: 01635 519479
Email: info@westberks.gov.uk
Web Site: www.westberks.gov.uk
Head of Culture and Youth Services: David Appleton

WEST DEVON BOROUGH COUNCIL
Kilworthy Park, Drake Road, Tavistock, Devon PL19 0BZ
Tel: 01822 813 600 Fax: 01822 813 634
Email: postcentre@westdevon.gov.uk
Web Site: www.westdevon.gov.uk
Chief Executive: David Incoll
Economic & Leisure Dev Mgr: Tim Beavon

WEST DORSET DISTRICT COUNCIL
Leisure & Tourism Division, Stratton House High West Street, Dorchester, Dorset DT1 1UZ
Tel: 01305 252 261 / 252 250 Fax: 01305 257 039
Email: jude.hunter@westdorset-dc.gov.uk
Web Site: www.westdorset-dc.gov.uk
Cultural Development Officer: Jude Hunter

WEST LANCASHIRE DISTRICT COUNCIL
52 Derby Street, Ormskirk, Lancashire L39 2DF
Tel: 01695 577 177 Fax: 01685 585 113
Email: customer.services@westlancsdc.gov.uk
Web Site: www.westlancsdc.gov.uk
Recreation Manager: Peter Tooley

WEST SOMERSET DISTRICT COUNCIL
ART Life, West Somerset Community College, Bircham Road, Alcombe, Minehead, Somerset TA24 6AY
Tel: 01643 704 661
Email: info@artlife-somerset.co.uk
Web Site: www.artlife-somerset.co.uk
Co-ordinator: Tracey Roberts

WEST WILTSHIRE DISTRICT COUNCIL
Bradley Road, Trowbridge, Wiltshire BA14 0RD
Tel: 01225 776 655 Fax: 01225 774 085
Email: mmorgan@westwiltshire.gov.uk
Web Site: www.westwiltshire.gov.uk

WEYMOUTH & PORTLAND BOROUGH COUNCIL
The Pavillion Theatre The Esplanade Weymouth, Dorset DT4 8ED
Tel: 01305 783225 Fax: 01305 789 922
Email: colinworth@weymouth.gov.uk
The Weymouth Pavillion and Arts Manager: Colin Worth

WIGAN METROPOLITAN BOROUGH COUNCIL
Robin Park Indoor Sports Ctre 1st Floor, Loire Drive, Robin Park, Wigan, Lancashire WN5 0UL
Tel: 01942 244 991 (switchboard) Fax: 01942 828 540
Email: c.wyatt@wiganmbc.gov.uk
Web Site: www.wiganmbc.gov.uk
Director of Leisure: RF Hill
Contact Community Regenerations Officer: Chris Wyatt

NORTH WILTSHIRE DISTRICT COUNCIL
Monkton Park Offie, Monkton Hill, Chippenham, Wiltshire SN15 1ER

Tel: 01249 706 111 Arts Dep Tel: 01249 706 496 Fax: 01249 444 650
Email: elee@northwilts.gov.uk
Web Site: www.northwilts.gov.uk
Director of Arts Development: E Lee

WINCHESTER CITY COUNCIL
Cultural Services Division, Development Directorate, Winchester City Council, Avalon House, Chesil Street, Winchester, Hampshire SO23 0HU
Tel: 01962 848 303 Fax: 01962 841 427
Email: mmichalowicz@winchester.gov.uk
Web Site: www.winchester.gov.uk
Arts & Development Officer: Marilyn Michalowicz

WIRRAL METROPOLITAN BOROUGH COUNCIL
Pacific Road Arts and Exhibition Centre, Pacific Road, Birkenhead, Wirral CH41 1LJ
Tel: 0151 650 0343 Fax: 0151 666 0009
Email: robsmith@wirral.gov.uk
Web Site: www.wirral.gov.uk
Principal Arts Offier: Rob Smith

WOKINGHAM DISTRICT COUNCIL
Council Offices, Shute End, Wokingham, Berkshire RG40 1WQ
Tel: 0118 974 6000 Fax: 0118 978 9078
Email: karen.jordan@wokingham.gov.uk
Web Site: www.wokingham.gov.uk
Chief Executive: Ms Jane Earl

WOLVERHAMPTON CITY COUNCIL
Civic Centre St. Peters Square, Wolverhampton WV1 1SH
Council Tel: 01902 556 556 Civic Hall Tel: 01902 552 122 Fax: 01902 555 138
Web Site: www.wolverhampton.gov.uk
Contact Civic Hall Marketing Manager: Chrissie Rushton

WORCESTER CITY COUNCIL
Cultural & Leisure Services, Orchard House, Farrier Street, Worcester WR1 3BW
Tel: 01905 723 471 Fax: 01905 722 350
Email: irutherford@cityofworcester.gov.uk
Web Site: www.cityofworcester.gov.uk
Museum & Arts & Heritage Manager: Iain Rutherford

WORTHING BOROUGH COUNCIL
Pavillion Theatre, Marine Parade, Worthing, West Sussex BN11 3PX
Tel: 01903 239 999, ext. 1142 Fax: 01903 821 124
Email: theatres@worthing.gov.uk
Web Site: www.worthing.gov.uk
General Manager is Worthing Theatres: Peter Bailey

WREXHAM COUNTY BOROUGH COUNCIL
Memorial Hall, Bodhyfryd, Wrexham LL12 7AG Wales
Tel: 01978 292 683 Fax: 01978 292 611
Email: george.lacy@wrexham.gov.uk
Web Site: www.wrexham.gov.uk
Arts and Entertainment Officer: George A Lacy (Tel: 01978 292 683)

WYCHAVON DISTRICT COUNCIL
Civic Centre, Queen Elizabeth Drive, Pershore, Worcestershire WR10 1PT
Tel: 01386 565 000 Fax: 01386 553 657
Email: tracy.grubb@wychavon.gov.uk
Web Site: www.wychavon.gov.uk
Community Development Officer: Tracy Grubb
Leisure Development Officer: Sue Healey

WYCOMBE DISTRICT COUNCIL
Arts Development Officer
Community & Housing Queen Victoria Road, High Wycombe, Buckinghamshire HP11 1BB
Tel: 01494 421 887 Fax: 01494 421 808
Email: katie.tyssen@wycombe.gov.uk
Web Site: www.wycombe.gov.uk
Arts Development Officer: Katie Tyssen

WYRE BOROUGH COUNCIL
Wyre Civic Centre, Breck Road, Poulton le Fylde, Lancashire FY6 7PU
Tel: 01253 887 482 Fax: 01253 887 210
Email: ilamond@wyrebc.gov.uk
Web Site: www.wyrebc.gov.uk
Arts Officer: Ian Lamond

WYRE FOREST DISTRICT COUNCIL
Cultural & Leisure Services, Arts Development, Green Street, Kidderminster, Worcestershire DY10 1HA
Tel: 01562 732 977 Fax: 01562 732 905
Email: loz.samuels@wyreforestdc.gov.uk
Web Site: www.wyreforestdc.gov.uk
Arts Development Officer: Loz Samuels
Assistant Arts Development Officer: Susannah Ronan
Contact: susannah.ronan@wyreforestdc.gov.uk

London

BEXLEY COUNCIL
Directorate Of Educ & Leis Ser Hill View Drive, Welling, Kent DA16 3RY
Tel: 020 8303 7777 Fax: 020 8308 4926
LeisureLink: Welling High Street, Welling, Kent DA16 1TQ Tel: 020 8301 9200; Fax: 020 8301 9222
Email: tina.bates@bexley.gov.uk
Web Site: www.bexley.gov.uk
Leisure Development Manager: Janet Stone (Extension 4239)

CORPORATION OF LONDON
PO Box 270, Guildhall, London EC2P 2EJ
Tel: 020 7606 3030 Fax: 020 7332 1119
Email: CHB-Secriat@corpoflondon.gov.uk
Web Site: www.cityoflondon.gov.uk

CROYDON CLOCKTOWER
Katharine Street, Croydon CR9 1ET
Tel: 020 8253 1037 Fax: 020 8253 1032
BO: 020 8253 1030
Email: jonathan.kennedy@croydon.gov.uk
Web: www.croydon.gov.uk/clocktower
Head of Cultural Services. Stephen Halsey
Croydon Clocktower boasts the David Lean Cinema (capacity 68) Braithwaite Hall (for music, theatre and dance, capacity 165) and museum and gallery spaces in South London's premiere arts complex.

LONDON BOROUGH OF BARKING
Civic Centre, Dagenham, Essex RM10 7BN
Tel: 020 8592 4500 Fax: 020 8227 2098
Email: enquiries@barking-dagenham.gov.uk
Web: www.barking-dagenham.gov.uk

LONDON BOROUGH OF BARNET
Cultural Services, Building 4, North London Business Park, Oakleigh Road South London N11 3DL
Tel: 020 8359 7760 Fax: 020 8359 3246
Email: emily.chaplin@barnet.gov.uk
Web Site: www.barnet.gov.uk
Cultural Services: Pam Usher

LONDON BOROUGH OF BRENT
The New Bridge Park Sports Complex, Brenf Field, Harrow Road, London NW10 0RG
Bkg: 020 8937 3737 Fax: 020 8937 3708
Email: david.saunders@brent.gov.uk
Web Site: www.brent.gov.uk
Bookings Manager: David Saunders

LONDON BOROUGH OF CAMDEN
Arts & Tourism Services, The Crowndale Centre, 218 Eversholt Street, London NW1 1BD
Tel: 020 7974 1647 Fax: 020 7974 1615
Email: arts.tourism@camden.gov.uk
Web Site: www.camden.gov.uk
London Borough of Camden, Director of Leisure and Community Services: Ian McNicol
Assistant Director: Fiona Dean

LONDON BOROUGH OF EALING
The Halls Booking Team Perceval House 14-16 Uxbridge Road, London W5 2HL
Tel: 0208 825 6064 Bkgs: 0208 825 6060 Fax: 0208 825 6069
Web Site: www.ealing.gov.uk

LONDON BOROUGH OF ENFIELD

Alternative Website: www.fortyhallbanqueting.co.uk
Civic Centre Silver Street Enfield, Middlesex EN1 3XQ
Council Tel: 020 8379 1000 Forty Hall Tel: 020 8363 4774 Leisure Tel: 0208 379 3201 Fax: 020 8379 4453
Email: jill.bukin@enfield.gov.uk
Web Site: www.enfield.gov.uk
Director of Cultural & Leisure Services: Peter Lewis

LONDON BOROUGH OF GREENWICH

Communication The Basement Town Hall, Wellington Street, Woolwich SE18 6PW
Tel: 020 8921 6408 Fax: 020 8921 5252
Email: andy.bragg@greenwich.gov.uk
Web Site: www.greenwich.gov.uk
Contact: Andy Bragg

LONDON BOROUGH OF HACKNEY

Town Hall not available for hiring after August 2006
Hackney Town Hall, Mare Street, London E8 1EA
Tel: 020 8356 3299 Fax: 020 8356 2569
Hall Lettings: 2 Hillman Street, London E8 1DY Tel: 020 8356 3409
Email: townhallreception@hackney.gov.uk
Web Site: www.hackney.gov.uk

LONDON BOROUGH OF HAMMERSMITH & FULHAM

Town Hall, King Street, London W6 9JU
Reception Tel: 0208 753 4040 Hall Lettings: 020 8753 2136 (Helen Pinnington)
Email: helen.pinnington@lbhf.gov.uk
Web Site: www.lbhf.gov.uk
Contact Helen Pinnington

LONDON BOROUGH OF HARROW

People First Directorate Community & Culture Service
Milton house Civic Centre, Station Road, Harrow, Middlesex HA1 2UW
Tel: 020 8863 5611 Arts Dep Tel: 020 8424 1904 Fax: 020 8424 1817
Email: stephen.porter@harrow.gov.uk
Web Site: www.harrow.gov.uk
Senior Arts Manager: Stephen Porter
Arts Manager Assistant: Wendy Lockwood

LONDON BOROUGH OF HAVERING

The Queen's Theatre Billet Lane, Hornchurch, Essex RM11 1QT
Web Site: www.havering.gov.uk
Contact Production Manager: Dave Godin

LONDON BOROUGH OF HILLINGDON

Central Library, High Street, Uxbridge, Middlesex UB8 1UW
Tel: 01895 250 111 Fax: 01895 273 636
Web Site: www.hillingdon.gov.uk
Contact Head of Cultural Services: P Mccaffery

LONDON BOROUGH OF HOUNSLOW

Chiswick Town Hall Heathfield Terrace, London W4 4JN
Tel: 0845 456 2975 Fax: 0845 456 2977
Email: melina.costelloe@cip.org.uk
Web Site: www.hounslow.gov.uk
Manager of Arts & Events: Steve Pascal
Contact Corporate & PR Communications Executive: Melina Costelloe

LONDON BOROUGH OF LAMBETH

Lambeth Arts
Arts Department, International House, Canterbury Crescent, Brixton, London SW9 7QE
Tel: 020 7926 0760 Fax: 020 7926 0751
Email: artsweb@lambeth.gov.uk
Web Site: www.lambeth.gov.uk/arts
Head Of Arts: Helen Ridge
The Lambeth Arts Web provides advice and up-to-date news on what's on in Lambeth, including information on resources, workshops, jobs, commissions, events and the latest exhibitions.

LONDON BOROUGH OF MERTON

Merton Hall 78 Kingston Road, London SW19 1LA
Tel: 020 8545 3651 Hall Bkgs: 020 8545 3664 Fax: 020 8545 3653
Email: josephine.jasper@merton.gov.uk
Web Site: www.merton.gov.uk
Head Of Community & Cultural Services: Richard Rawes
Contact Arts Development Officer: Maureen Pepper
Contact Bookings Officer: Josephine Jasper

LONDON BOROUGH OF NEWHAM

Leisure Services Dept, 29 Broadway, London E15 4BQ
Bkgs Tel: 020 8534 7835
Email: juliette.patterson@newham.gov.uk
Web Site: www.newham.gov.uk

LONDON BOROUGH OF REDBRIDGE

Leisure Services, Lynton House 255-259 High Rd Ilford, Essex IG1 1NY
Tel 020 8708 3533 Fax: 020 8708 3178
Email: jacqueline.eggleston@redbridge.gov.uk
Web Site: www.redbridge.gov.uk
Arts Development Manager: Jacqueline Eggleston
Arts Development Officer: Samantha Goodey

LONDON BOROUGH OF RICHMOND-UPON-THAMES

Education Arts & Leisure Dept, Regal House, London Road, Twickenham, Middlesex TW1 3QB
Tel: 020 8831 6138 Fax: 020 8891 7714
Email: leisure@richmond.gov.uk
Web Site: www.richmond.gov.uk

LONDON BOROUGH OF SOUTHWARK

Arts & Cultural Dept John Smith House, 144-152 Walworth Road, London SE17 1JL
Tel: 020 7525 5078 Fax: 020 7525 5070
Email: anya.whitehead@southwark.gov.uk
Web Site: www.southwark.gov.uk
Arts Development Officer: Anya Whitehead

LONDON BOROUGH OF SUTTON

Secombe Theatre 42 Cheam Road, Sutton, Surrey SM1 2SS
Bkgs Tel: 020 8770 6990
Email: catherine.pearce@sutton.gov.uk
go to www.suttontheatres.co.uk for more info.

LONDON BOROUGH OF TOWER HAMLETS

Brady Centre, 192/196 Hanbury Street, London E1 5HU
Tel: 020 7364 7900 Fax: 020 7364 7901
Email: bradycentre.lbth@dial.pipex.com
Web Site: www.towerhamlets.gov.uk
Manager: Jerry Deeks
Technical Manager: Suna Miah
Arts and Events Section: Caterina Loriggio Tel: 020 7364 7907
Cap: 200
Technical Support available for Sound/Light: £25 per hour. List of Equiptment available for hire can be obtained by emailing above.

LONDON BOROUGH OF WANDSWORTH

Wandsworth Town Hall, Arts Office, Room 224a, Wandsworth High Street, London SW18 2PU
Tel: 020 8871 7037 / 7380 Fax: 020 8871 7630
Email: arts@wandsworth.gov.uk
Web Site: www.wandsworth.gov.uk
Principal Arts Officer: Charlie Catling

LONDON BOROUGH WALTHAM FOREST

Lifelong Learning, PO Box 414, Sycamore House, Forest Road, Walthamstow, London E17 4SY

Te: 020 8496 4651 Events Manager: 020 8496 4623 BO/Sales: 020 8521 7111 020 8496 3000
Email: linda.corringan@walthamforest.gov.uk
Web Site: www.walthamforest.gov.uk
Borough Arts Officer: Eamon O'Mackail
Halls Manager: Andy Lamarque (Tel: 020 8509 6902)
Senior Events Officer: Steve Pascal (Tel: 020 8496 4661)
Events Officer: Glenn Watson

ROYAL BOROUGH OF KENSINGTON & CHELSEA
Marketing and Arts Service, 2nd Floor, Central Library, Phillimore Walk, London W8 7RX
Tel: 020 7361 3003 Tel: 020 7361 3202 (Amanda Smethurst)
Email: amanda.smethurst@rbkc.gov.uk
Web Site: www.rbkc.gov.uk
Arts Service Manager: Amanda Smethurst
Arts Development Manager: Abby Viner

ROYAL BOROUGH OF KINGSTON
Kingston Library, Fairfield Road, Kingston-upon-Thames, Surrey KT1 2PS
Tel: 020 8547 6418 Fax: 020 8547 6426
Email: libraries.admin@rbk.kingston.gov.uk
Web Site: www.kingston.gov.uk/libs
Contact Valerie Smith for bookings for Tudor Hall, Surbiton Library Hall and New Malden Library Hall.

WESTMINSTER CITY COUNCIL
Arts Unit, Westminster City Council, Westminster City Hall, 64 Victoria Street, London SW1E 6QP
Tel 020 7641 2814 / 2498 Fax 020 7641 8083
Email: artsunit@westminster.gov.uk
Web Site: www.westminster.gov.uk
Arts Manager: Cheryl Harris

Northern Ireland

ANTRIM BOROUGH COUNCIL
Steeple Road, Antrim, County Antrim BT41 1BJ Northern Ireland
Tel: 028 9446 3113
Email: philip.magennis@antrim.gov.uk
Web Site: www.antrim.gov.uk
Assistant Director - Arts & Community: Maureen Armstrong (Email: maureen.armstrong@antrim.gov.uk)
Arts & Heritage Development Officer: Kate Wimpress (Email: clotworthyartscentre@hotmail.com)
Clotworthy Arts Centre, Antrim Castle Gardens, Randalstown Road, Antrim BT41 4LH. Tel: 028 9442 8000.

BALLYMONEY BOROUGH COUNCIL
Riada House, 14 Charles Street, Ballymoney, County Antrim BT53 6DZ Northern Ireland
Tel: 028 2766 0200 Fax: 028 2766 7659
Email: info@ballymoney.gov.uk
Web Site: www.ballymoney.gov.uk
Director of Leisure and Amenities: WJ Paul
Cultural Services Officer: Margaret Edgar
VENUES

TOWN HALL
24 High Street, Ballymoney, County Antrim BT53 6DZ
Tel: 028 2766 0227
S/Cap: Main Hall, 360 (Aud. 250; Balcony 160); Minor Hall 90 max.

JOEY DUNLOP LEISURE CENTRE
33 Garryduff Road, Ballymoney, County Antrim BT53 7AU
Tel: 028 2766 5792
S/Cap: Main Hall 550

BANBRIDGE DISTRICT COUNCIL
Council Offices, Downshire Road, Banbridge, County Down BT32 3JY Northern Ireland
Tel: 028 4066 0600 Fax: 028 4066 0601
Email: info@banbridgedc.gov.uk
Web Site: www.banbridgedc.gov.uk
Director of Leisure Services: Mike Reith

BELFAST CITY COUNCIL
Client Services Dept, Leisure Services Section, The Cecil Ward Building, 4-10 Linenhall Street, Belfast, County Antrim BT2 8BP Northern Ireland
Tel: 028 9032 0202 Fax: 028 9024 4301
Email: holmesl@belfastcity.gov.uk
Web Site: www.belfastcity.gov.uk
Head of Community and Leisure Services: Brian Morrison

BURNAVON ARTS & CULTURAL CENTRE
Burn Road, Cookstown, County Tyrone BT80 8DN Northern Ireland
Box office: 028 8676 9949
Administration: 028 8676 7994 Fax: 028 86765853
Email: burnavon@cookstown.gov.uk
Web Site: www.burnavon.com
Manager - Tony McCance

CARRICKFERGUS TOWN COUNCIL
Tourist Information Centre, Antrim Street, Carrickfergus, County Antrim BT38 7DG Northern Ireland
Tel: 028 9335 8049 Tel: 028 9336 6666 (Lynda Murphy)
Email: lyndam@carrickfergus.org
Web Site: www.carrickfergus.org
Contact the Director of Leisure Services: Mr Norman Houston
Arts & Events Officer: Lynda Murphy

CASTLEREAGH BOROUGH COUNCIL
Community & Leisure Dept, Bradford Court, Upper Galwally, Belfast, County Antrim BT8 6RB Northern Ireland
Tel: 028 9049 4500 Fax: 028 9049 4555
Email: edwardpatterson@castlereagh.gov.uk
Web Site: www.castlereagh.gov.uk
Director Of Community & Leisure: Edward Patterson

COLERAINE BOROUGH COUNCIL
Cloonavin, 66 Portstewart Road, Coleraine, County Londonderry BT52 1EY Northern Ireland
Tel 028 7034 7234 Fax 028 7034 7239
Email: leisure@colerainebc.gov.uk
Web Site: www.colerainebc.gov.uk
Events Officer:Christine McKee

CRAIGAVON BOROUGH COUNCIL
Arts Development
Pinebank House CARC Tullygally Road, Craigavon, County Armagh BT65 5BY Northern Ireland
Tel: 028 3831 2400 Fax: 028 3834 2402
Email: emma.wilson@craigavon.gov.uk
Web Site: www.craigavon.gov.uk
Arts Development Officer: Emma Wilson
Our programme is aimed to compliment and support the Arts initiatives and projects going on in the Craigavon area. Performing arts programme, arts workshops (visual arts, music and dance + drama, residencies and bursaries).

DERRY CITY COUNCIL
Recreation & Leisure Dept, 98 Strand Road, Derry, Londonderry BT48 7NN Northern Ireland
Tel: 028 7136 5151 Fax: 028 7126 4858
Email: john.meehan@derrycity.gov.uk
Web Site: www.derrycity.gov.uk
Director of Recreation and Leisure: John Meehan

DOWN DISTRICT COUNCIL
24 Strangford Road, Downpatrick, County Down BT30 6SR Northern Ireland
Tel: 028 4461 0852 Fax: 028 4461 0851
Email: sharon.o'connor@downdc.gov.uk
Web Site: www.downdc.gov.uk
Director of Cultural & Economic Dev: Sharon O'Connor
Arts Officer: Cathie McKimm

DUNGANNON & SOUTH TYRONE BOROUGH COUNCIL
Community Arts Studio, Unit T11, Dungannon Enterprise Centre, 2 Coalisland Road, Dungannon, County

Tyrone BT71 6JT Northern Ireland
Tel: 028 8775 3626 Fax: 028 8775 3789
Email: ddas@talk21.com
Web Site: www.dungannon.gov.uk
Community Arts Officer: Aine Dolan

FERMANAGH DISTRICT COUNCIL

Town Hall, Townhall Street, Enniskillen, County Fermanagh BT74 7BA Northern Ireland
Tel: 028 6632 5050 Fax: 028 6632 2024
Email: eamonn.bradley@fermanagh.gov.uk
Director of Enviromental Services(Venues): Mr Robert Gibson

VENUES

ARDHOWEN THEATRE & ARTS CENTRE
Dublin Road, Enniskillen, Co. Fermanagh.
Manager & Artistic Director: Eamonn Bradley
Admin 028 6632 3233 BO 028 6632 5440
Fax 028 6632 7102
S/Cap: in Main Theatre 295.
S/Cap: in Studio 60.

LAKELAND FORUM
Broadmeadow, Enniskillen BT74 7EF
Tel 028 6632 4121
Fax 028 6632 8622
Manager: Iain Kennedy
S/Cap: Main Hall 1,000

CASTLE PARK LEISURE CENTRE
11 Water Street, Lissnaskea, Enniskillen BT92 OLZ
Tel 028 6672 1299
Manager: Elizabeth Wilson
Tel: 028 677 21299
Email: liz.wilson@fermanagh.gov.uk
S/Cap: Main Hall, 1000

BAWNACRE CENTRE
Irvinestown, Co. Fermanagh, BT94 1EE
Tel 028 6662 1177
Fax 028 6662 8082
Manager: George Beacom
S/Cap: Main Hall 800
Purpose built stage facilities with full lights and curtains.
Minor Hall - Suitable for workshops and exhibitions and concerts. S/Cap: 320

COMMUNITY CENTRES
Belcoo Community Centre, Garrison Road, Belcoo
For Bookings and Enquiries Contact: Mrs N Cavanagh on
028 663 86424
S/Cap: 360 Stage Facilities.
Ederney Community Centre, High Street, Ederney.
For Bookings and Enquiries Contact: Mr Ken Goreham on
028 686 31774.
S/Cap: 360 Stage Facilities.
Kesh Community Centre, Mantlin Road, Kesh, Co. Fermanagh BT93 1TT
For Booking and Enquiries Contact: Mr Glenn Moore on 028 686 32158
S/Cap: 360 Stage Facilities.
Newtownbutler Community Centre, Bridge Street, Newtownbutler
For Bookings and Enquiries Contact: Mr Tom Crudden on 028 677 38638
S/Cap: 150.
Roslea Community Centre, Monaghan Road, Roslea
For Bookings and Enquiries Contact: Mr Patsy McPhillips on 028 677 51413.
S/Cap: 360.

LARNE BOROUGH COUNCIL

Smiley Buildings, Victoria Road, Larne, County Antrim BT40 1RU Northern Ireland
Tel: 028 2827 2313 Fax: 028 2826 0660
Email: kingl@larne.gov.uk
Web Site: www.larne.gov.uk
Community & Leisure Services: Lorraine King

LIMAVADY BOROUGH COUNCIL

7 Connell Street, Limavady, County Londonderry BT49 0HA Northern Ireland
Tel: 028 7772 2226 Fax: 028 7772 2010
Email: geraldine.smyth@limavady.gov.uk
Events & Cultural Officer: Geraldine Smyth

TOWN HALL
Main Street, Limavady
S/Cap: 360.
Stage Facilities.

ROE VALLEY RECREATION CENTRE
Greystone Road, Limavady.
S/Cap: 800
Stage Facilities.

MAGHERAFELT DISTRICT COUNCIL

Council Offices, 50 Ballyronan Road, Magherafelt, County Londonderry BT45 6EN Northern Ireland
Tel: 028 7939 7979 Fax: 028 7939 7980
Email: info@magherafelt.gov.uk
Web Site: www.magherafelt.gov.uk

MOYLE DISTRICT COUNCIL

Moyle District Council, Sheskburn House, 7 Mary Street, Ballycastle, County Antrim BT54 6QH Northern Ireland
Tel: 028 2076 2225 / 3300 (3pm-10pm)
Fax: 028 2076 2515
Email: kmcgarry@moyle-council.org
Web Site: www.moyle-council.org
Leisure Services Manager: Kevin McGarry

NEWRY AND MOURNE DISTRICT COUNCIL

Newry Arts Centre 1A Bank Parade, Newry, County Down BT35 6HP Northern Ireland
Tel: 028 3031 3180 Fax: 028 3031 3077
Email: jacqueline.turley@newryand-mourne.gov.uk
Web Site: www.newryandmourne.gov.uk
For Events Enquiries contact Public Relations Officer: Hilary Halliday (Tel: (028 3031 3233)
For Hall Bookings contact Clerks Secretary Irene Kane on main number listed.

NEWTOWNABBEY DISTRICT COUNCIL

Mossley Mills, Newtownabbey, County Antrim BT36 5QA Northern Ireland
Tel: 028 9034 0000 Fax: 028 9034 0200
Email: info@newtownabbey.gov.uk
Web Site: www.newtownabbey.gov.uk

NORTH DOWN BOROUGH COUNCIL

Community Services Department Town Hall The Castle Bangor, County Down BT20 4BT Northern Ireland
Tourist Info Centre: 028 9127 8032
Tourist Info Centre Fax: 028 9146 7744
Arts Office: 028 9127 8032 Arts Office Fax: 028 9127 4466
Email: hilary.mcmullan@northdown.gov.uk
Arts Officers: Paula Clamp, Gail Prentice
Contact Community Halls Manager: Hilary Mcmullan

OMAGH DISTRICT COUNCIL

Council Offices, The Grange, Mountjoy Road, Omagh, County Tyrone BT79 7BL Northern Ireland
Tel: 028 8224 5321 Fax: 028 8224 3888
Email: frank.sweeney@omagh.gov.uk / jean.brennan@omagh.gov.uk
Web Site: www.omagh.gov.uk
Head of Arts and Tourism: F Sweeney
Arts Development Officer: Jean Brennon
VENUES
OMAGH LEISURE CENTRE
Old Mountfield Road, Omagh
S/Cap: 550
Portable stage facilities.

Scotland

ABERDEEN CITY COUNCIL

Arts and Recreation Department
St Nicholas House, Broad Street, Aberdeen AB10 1XJ Scotland
Tel: 01224 522 000 Fax: 01224 648 256
Email: dhendry@arts-rec.aberdeen.net.uk
Web Site: www.aberdeencity.gov.uk
Chief Executive: Douglas Paterson
Director of Arts & Recreation: Brian Woodcock
Assistant Director: Alan Fulton
General Manager (Performing Arts Venues): Duncan Hendry

ABERDEENSHIRE COUNCIL

Woodhill House Annex, Westburn Road, Aberdeen AB16 5GJ Scotland
Tel: 01224 664 873
Web Site: www.aberdeenshirearts.org.uk

Chief Executive: Alan Campbell
Director of Education and Recreation: Hamish Vernal
Arts Development Officer (North): Saskia Gibbon
Arts Development Officer (Central): Sheila Waterhouse
Arts Development Officer (South): Mindy Grewar
Aberdeen Arts Centre (374)
Aberdeen International Youth Festival and Aberdeen Alternative Festival is funded by the City Council but is managed independently.
VENUES
Banchory Town Hall (290)
Banff Town Hall (200)
Dalrymple Hall, Fraserburgh (400)
Deeside Community Education Centre, Aboyne (270)
Fordyce Street, Rosehearty (200)
Inverurie Town Hall (534)
Learney Hall, Torphins (300).
Lumphanan Village Hall (100)
Macduff Town Hall (350)
Macduff Arts Centre (200)
Peterhead Community Education Centre (321 but 306 if orchestra used).
Portsoy Town Hall (350)
Rescue Hall, Peterhead (250)
St. Laurence Hall, Laurencekirk (300)
Stewarts Hall, Huntly (400)
Stonehaven Town Hall (474)

ANGUS COUNCIL

County Buildings, Market Street, Forfar, Angus DD8 3WF Scotland
Tel: 01307 461 460 Fax: 01307 462 590
Email: cultural@angus.gov.uk
Web Site: www.angus.gov.uk
Chief Executive: A B Watson
Cultural Services Manager: Norman Atkinson
Arts Officer: Patricia McGowan
VENUES
Webster Theatre, Arbroath (606)
City Hall, Brechin (360)
Inglis Memorial Hall, Edzell (180)
Reid Hall, Forfar (829)
Town Hall, Kirriemuir (368)
Town Hall, Montrose (669)

ARGYLL & BUTE COUNCIL

Kilmory, Lochgilphead, Argyll PA31 8RT Scotland
Tel: 01546 604 121 Fax: 01546 603 934
Email: willie.young@argyll-bute.gov.uk
Web Site: www.argyll-bute.gov.uk
Head of Community Regeneration: Donald McVicar
Principal Leisure Officer: Willie Young

EAST AYRSHIRE COUNCIL

London Road, Kilmarnock, Ayrshire KA3 7DU Scotland
Tel: 01563 576 000 Fax: 01563 574 062
Email: michelle.laats@east-ayrshire.gov.uk
Web Site: www.east-ayrshire.gov.uk
Chief Executive: Fiona Lees
Director of Community Services: William Stafford
Halls Officer: Derek Spence (Tel: 01563 576 703)
VENUES
The Palace Theatre, Kilmarnock (503)
Cumnock Town Hall (500)
Cumnock Academy Assembly Hall (250)
The Grand Hall, Kilmarnock (900)
Town Hall Darvel (400)
Morton Hall Newmilns (400)
Institute Stewarton (300)
Public Hall Dunlop
John Fulton Memorial Hall Fenwick
Contact Performing Arts Development Officer: Michelle Laats

NORTH AYRSHIRE COUNCIL

Cunniham House, Aivine, Ayrshire, KA12 8EE Scotland
Tel: 01294 32 44 94 Fax: 01294 32 42 10
Email: arts@north-ayrshire.gov.uk
Web Site: www.north-ayrshire.gov.uk
VENUES
Magnum Main Hall: Capacity 1278 seated and 2000 standing.
Magnum Theatre, Irvine: 323 capacity.
Theatres are: The Magnum Leisure Centres Main Hall and Theatre Complex in Irvine (as above); Barrfields Pavilion, Largs (470); Civic Theatre, Ardrossan (250); The Council also gives financial assistance to the Harbour Arts Centre at Irvine Main Halls are: Blacklands Hall, Kilwinning (300); Saltcoats Town Hall (200); Dunlop Memorial Hall, Dreghorn (350); Walker Memorial Hall, Kilbirnie (500 main hall, 150 lesser hall); Hayocks Hall (150); Dalry Public Hall (200 main hall, 50 lesser hall); Beith Townhouse (200); William Knox Institute, Kilbirnie (120); West Kilbride Public Hall (200); Millport Town Hall (300 main hall, 200 lesser hall); Garrison Ballroom, Millport (800); Development Association Hall, Millport (220); Volunteer Rooms, Irvine (400).

SOUTH AYRSHIRE COUNCIL

PO Box 1966, Wellington Square, Ayr KA7 1DR Scotland
Tel: 01292 612 000
Email: mike.mccabe@south-ayrshire.gov.uk
Web Site: www.south-ayrshire.gov.uk
Chief Executive: George Thorley (Fax: 01292 612 158)
Director of Education Services: Michael McCabe (Fax: 01292 612 258)
Theatres Manager: Gordon Taylor (Fax: 01292 880 044)
VENUES
The Gaiety Theatre Ayr seats 570 and is open all the year round: Revue, Panto, Drama, Opera, Dance, etc. The Civic Theatre, Ayr seats 345 and offers a professional season of small scale touring productions throughout the year apart from Town Hall which seats 700 persons, the area also has the following medium and municipal halls. Beach Pavilion Girvan, total seating 610-summer shows, dances, sporting and general purpose use as well as private hire. The Citadel, Ayr, total audience capacity 1,200, dependent on layout for rock concerts, conferences, etc. Available for private hire. Troon Concert Hall - 886 for theatrical shows. Available for dances, conferences, private hire. Walker Hall, Troon - 294 for concerts, film shows, small functions. (Part of the concert hall complex and is adjacent to Troon Concert Hall). Maybole Town Hall - for concerts, films, private hire. Seating 260

CLACKMANNANSHIRE COUNCIL

Room 28, Limetree House, Alloa, Clackmannanshire FK10 1EX Scotland
Tel: 01259 452 487 Fax: 01259 452 240
Email: arts@clacks.gov.uk
Web Site: www.clacksweb.org.uk
Contact: Arts Development Officer

DUMFRIES AND GALLOWAY COUNCIL

Council Offices, English Street, Dumfries, Dumfries & Galloway DG1 2DD Scotland
Tel: 01387 260 000 Fax: 01387 260 029
Email: lesliej@dumgal.gov.uk
Web Site: www.dumgal.gov.uk
Chief Executive: Phil Jones
Arts Manager: Rebecca Coggins
Director for Education and Community Services: Fraser Sanderson
Museums Manager: David Lockwood Tel 01387 253374
VENUES
Loreburn Hall - Dumfries; Sanquhar Town Hall, Hillview Leisure Centre - Kirkconnel; Robert Burns Centre Film Theatre; Dumfries Museum; Dumfries Ice Bowl; Burns House; Sanquhar Tolbooth Museum; Old Bridge House Museum; Dumfries Archive Centre, Robert Burns Centre, Ryan Centre Theatre (Stranraer) Town Halls in Kirkcudbright, Castle Douglas, Dalbeattie and New Galloway. Langholm Buccleuch Hall (400); Annan, Lockerbie, Lochmaben and Moffat. Independent theatres in Lockerbie, Moffat, Dalbeahie, Castle Douglas and Whithorn. Contact DGAA on 01387 253 383.

EAST DUNBARTONSHIRE COUNCIL

Broomhill Industrial Estate, Kilsyth Road, Kirkintilloch, Glasgow, Strathclyde G64 2TR Scotland
Tel: 0141 578 8000 Fax: 0141 762 0934
Email: culture@eastdunbarton.gov.uk
Web Site: www.eastdunbarton.gov.uk
Head of Performance & Development: Gordon Smith
Tel: 0141 761 4810 Email: gordon.smith@eastdunbarton.gov.uk
VENUES
Kirkintilloch Town Hall, Lenzie Hall, War Memorial Hall Bishopbriggs, Brackenbrae

House, Milton of Campsie Hall, Memorial Hall Lennoxtown, Caldwell Hall, Torrance Community Centre , Westerton Hall, Kessington Hall, Bearsden Hall, Milngavie Town Hall, Kilmardinny House, Maxholme.

DUNDEE CITY COUNCIL

Leisure & Arts Department, Floor 13, Tayside House, Dundee, Tayside DD1 3RA Scotland
Tel: 01382 434 030 Fax: 01382 434 451
Email: susan.pasfield@dundeecity.gov.uk
Web Site: www.cairdhall.gov.uk
Director of Leisure & Arts: Steve Grimmond
Caird Hall: Susan Pasfield
VENUES
The Caird Hall (capacity 2,167) was recently refurbished thanks to funding from the Scottish Arts Council Lottery Grant and Dundee City Council. The Hall is hired for concerts, conferences, exhibitions, graduation ceremonies etc. Within the Caird Hall complex is: The Marryat Hall - capacity varies from 225 to 344 depending on use.
The Steps Theatre, seating capacity 250 is available for hire for Conferences, Lectures, Seminars etc. The Steps Theatre is located in the Wellgate Library.
The Repertory Theatre opened in May 1982 and has its own resident company.
Current entertainments under Council aegis include concerts, variety, opera and amateur productions.
Dundee, the industrial heart of holiday country has a population of 187,371.

FALKIRK COUNCIL ARTS SECTION

Community Services, FTH, West Bridge Street, Falkirk, Stirlingshire FK1 5RS Scotland
Tel: 01324 506 177 Fax: 01324 501 272
Email: venue@falkirk.gov.uk
Web Site: www.fthentertainments.org
Director of Community Services: Maureen Campbell
Principal Officer Arts: Paul Eames
Arts Development Officer (Drama & Dance): Hazel Beattie
Arts Development Officer (Music): Jennifer Hunter
VENUES
Falkirk Town Hall Theatre 250 -650, Concert Hall 900; Grangemouth Town Hall (600); Bo'ness Town Hall (500).

FIFE COUNCIL

Arts Development Dept, The Tower Block, Auchterderran Centre, Woodend Road, Cardenden, Lochgelly, Fife KY5 0NE Scotland
Tel: 01592 414 714 Fax: 01592 414 727
Email: andrew.neil@fife.gov.uk
Arts Policy Co-Ordinator: Andrew Neil
VENUES
Theatres: Adam Smith Theatre, Kirkaldy, including Auditorium (475), Beveridge Studio (200), funciton Suite (200), Rothese Halls, Glenrothes (700/300).
Halls: St Andrews Town Hall (350), Corn Exchange Cupar (450), Blyth Hall Newport (400), Easter Town Hall Anstruther (250), Gregory Hall Tayport (250), Carnegie Hall, Dunfermline (590), Lochgelly Centre (463), Iverkeithing Civic Centre (400), Lochgelly Town Hall (300), Baldridgeburn (390), Dell Farquaarson (390).

GLASGOW CITY COUNCIL

Culture & Services Dept, 20 Trongate, Glasgow, G1 5ES Scotland
Tel: 0141 287 8943 Fax: 0141 287 8909
Email: charles.bell@cls.glasgow.gov.uk
Web Site: www.glasgow.gov.uk
Arts Development Mngr: Charles Bell
Operations Manager: Kevin Meek
Technical Manager: Graham Shand
Event Manager: Colin Martley
Media & PR: Lynne McPhee

HIGHLAND COUNCIL

Headquarters, Glenurquhart Road, Inverness IV3 5NX Scotland
Tel: 01463 702 000 Fax: 01463 711 177
Email: judi.menabney@highland.gov.uk
Web Site: www.highland.gov.uk
Contact Director of Cultural Services: Judi Menabney
Contact: Adnes Swanson (Tel: 01463 702 049)

BADENOCH & STRATHSPEY
Council Offices, Ruthven Road, Kingussie PH21 1EJ Scotland
Tel: 01540 664 500 Fax: 01540 661 004
Area Cultural & Leisure Services Manager: Graham Watson

CAITHNESS
Offices: District Council Offices, Wick, Caithness KW1 4AB Scotland
Tel: 01955 603 761 Fax: 01955 604 524
Area Cultural & Leisure Services Manager: Ian Robertson
Assembly Rooms Wick (636)
Town Hall Thurso (250)

INVERNESS
The Town House, Inverness IV1 1JG Scotland
Tel: 01463 724 224 Fax: 01463 712 850
Arts Officer: Adrian Clarke
Area Cultural & Leisure Services Manager: Gunars Libeks
Eden Court Theatre (800)

LOCHABER
Highland Council, Mamore House, Fort William PH33 6EL Scotland
Tel: 01397 702 102 Fax: 01397 702 107
Area Cultural & Leisure Services Manager: Hugh Allison

NAIRN
The Court House, High Street, Nairn IV12 4AU Scotland
Tel: 01667 458 521 Fax: 01667 452 056
Area Cultural & Leisure Services Manager: Graham Watson
Recreation & Entertainment Assistant: Miss Anne Sudder
The Council will provide a programme of municipal entertainment summer seasons in addition to allowing the usual Fair and visiting Circus.

ROSS & CROMARTY
County Buildings, Dingwall IV15 9QN Scotland
Tel: 01349 868 477 Fax: 01349 863 107
Arts Development Officer: Nick Fearne
Area Cultural & Leisure Services Officer: Peter Hoffman
There is a great deal of local voluntary effort in promotion of entertainment in this area which has increased over the years. Professional shows are making use of the large halls. The Duthac Centre (formerly the Tain Town Hall) has been leased by the Highland Council to a Management Committee and there is a part-time Management on the premises. (Telephone Tain 894422). Local drama groups continue to develop and there are three Art Societies and one Film Society and a very active Camera Club in the area. Other main halls are Dingwall (400); Fearn (100); Evanton (120); Portmahomack (120); Averon Centre, Alness (200); Invergordon Arts Centre (100); Fortrose (80-100); Muir of Ord (150); Cromarty (150); Milnafua (60); Population is now 44,000 in 1,236,000 acres, mostly settled on eastern coastal plain where industry has arrived; sparsely populated in central and Wester Ross. Tourism is strong on western seaboard. Industry in the east includes farming, distilling, oil rig platform construction, oil support, related industries. Two Arts Development Officers have been appointed for the Area and a Burgeoning Community Arts Movement involving a number of artists in residence and general arts residencies is under way. Artists in residence include Dance, Community Drama, Writer, Traditional Music, Visual Arts and Music.

SKYE & LOCHALSH
Tigh na Sgire Park Lane, Portree, Isle of Skye IV51 9GP Scotland
Tel: 01478 612 341 Fax: 01478 613 828
Area Cultural & Leisure Services Manager: Roger Miket

SUTHERLAND
Main Street, Golspie, Sutherland KW10 6RB Scotland
Tel: 01408 633 033 Fax: 01408 633 120
Area Cultural & Leisure Services Officer: Graham Nichols

INVERCLYDE COUNCIL

Highholm Centre, Highholm Avenue, Port Glasgow, Renfrewshire PA14 5JN

Scotland
Tel: 01475 714 852 Fax: 01475 714 871
Email: willie.wilson@inverclyde.gov.uk
Web Site: www.inverclyde.gov.uk
Head of Leisure & Community Support Services: Willie Wilson

NORTH LANARKSHIRE COUNCIL

PO Box 14, Civic Centre, Motherwell, Lanarkshire ML1 1TW Scotland
Tel: 01698 302 999 Fax: 01698 268 806
Email: motherwellconcerthall@northlan.gov.uk
Web Site: www.northlanarkshire.gov.uk
Marketing: Claire French
VENUES
Motherwell Theatre (395); Concert Hall (S/Cap: 1,008, Standing/Cap: 1,800 and Bellshill Cultural Centre are main venues. Airdrie Arts Centre Theatre (170). Sir John Wilson Town Hall, Airdrie has a Large Hall (900) and a Lesser Hall (110)

SOUTH LANARKSHIRE COUNCIL

116 Cadzow Street, Hamilton, Lanarkshire ML3 6HP Scotland
Tel: 01698 454 444 Fax: 01698 452 619
Email: jim.jardine@southlanarkshire.gsx.gov.uk
Assistant Halls Manager: Jim Jardine
VENUES
East Kilbride Arts Centre, Carluke Recreation Centre (350), Municipal Hall, Biggar (520), Memorial Hall, Lanark (550), New District Hall, Carluke (500).

EAST LOTHIAN COUNCIL

John Muir House, Brewery Park Haddington, East Lothian EH41 3HA Scotland
Tel: 01620 827 827 Fax: 01620 827 888
Email: lsmith@eastlothian.gov.uk
Web Site: www.eastlothian.gov.uk
Chief Executive: John Lindsay
Director of Community Services: Bruce Walker
Principal Arts Officer: Lesley Smith
Tel: 0131 665 3711
VENUES
The Brunton Theatre at Musselburgh seats up to 305. Props: East Lothian Council; Principal Arts Officer: Lesley Smith

MID LOTHIAN COUNCIL

Fairfield House, 8 Lothian Road, Dalkeith, Mid Lothian EH22 3ZP Scotland
Tel: 0131 270 7500 Fax: 0131 271 3375
Email: yvonne_anderson@midlothian.gov.uk
Web Site: www.midlothian.gov.uk
Enquiries and bookings for leisure centres and community halls - but also can supply further information about contacts for other venues.
VENUES
Cowan Institute, Penicuik (300); Danderhall Leisure Centre (400); Mayfield Leisure Centre (400); Gorebridge Leisure Centre (400); Newtongrange Leisure Centre (350); Ladywood Leisure Centre, Penicuik (450); Dalkeith Arts Centre (150); Bonnyrigg Leisure Centre.

MORAY COUNCIL

Council Office, High Street, Elgin, Morayshire IV30 1BX Scotland
Tel: 01343 563 206 Fax: 01343 563 402
Email: marian.ogg@moray.gov.uk
Web Site: www.moray.org.uk
Educational Services Administrator: Marion Ogg
VENUES
Seven halls of which Elgin is best equipped for theatre (accommodates 743)
See provincial venues section.

ORKNEY ISLANDS COUNCIL

Council Offices, School Place, Kirkwall, Orkney KW15 1NY Scotland
Tel: 01856 873 535 Fax: 01856 876 327
Email: kieren.henderson@orkney.gov.uk
Web Site: www.orkney.gov.uk
Staff Tutor for Expressive Arts: Penny Aberdein
VENUES
The main theatre provision is based on Orkney Arts Theatre, which has a capacity of 324.
Bookings Manager: Mr Robert Presland
Tel: 01856 872410
The Council also owns and runs the Phoenix Cinema which is also used for concerts. The seating capacity is 520.
Bookings Manager: Mr Kieren Henderson
Physical Address: 27-29 Victoria Street, Kirkwall, KW15 1NY

PERTH & KINROSS COUNCIL

c/o Perth & Kinross Leisure, Company Head Office, 2 High Street, Perth, Perth & Kinross PH1 5PH Scotland
Tel: 01738 477 900 Fax: 01738 477 910
Email: leisure@pkc.gov.uk
Web: www.perthandkinrossleisure.co.uk
City Hall Bookings: Danya Gray (Tel: 01738 477 912)
VENUES
Private company managing Local Authority venues, on behalf of the Local Authority.
Perth City Hall (1,500) is available for conferences, concerts, etc. Other public halls for hire at Pitlochry, Aberfeldy, Crieff, Auchterarder, Kinross, Coupar Angus and Blairgowrie Perth Lesser City Hall (350) for smaller productions. Perth Theatre (600) stage repertory drama with a resident company. Pitlochry Festival Theatre (500) has summer rep.

RENFREWSHIRE COUNCIL

Renfrewshire Arts
Education & Leisure, Town Hall, Abbey Close, Paisley, Renfrewshire PA1 1JF Scotland
Tel: 0141 887 1007 Fax: 0141 840 1779
Email: moira.orr@renfrewshire.gov.uk
Web Site: www.renfrewshire.gov.uk
Paisley Arts Centre and Paisley Town Hall are managed by Renfrewshire Arts, part of Renfrewshire Council's department of Education and Leisure Services. Paisley Arts Centre houses a 158 seat theatre and programmes all year round with drama, dance, comedy and music events. Paisley Arts Centre also has a workshop space available for hire. Paisley Town Hall is a magnificent Victorian building which programmes large scale music events and is available to hire for weddings, conferences, meetings and social events. Renfrewshire Council also has numerous other community halls available for hire.
Seated: 800
Dancing: 200
Contact Functions Manager: Moira Hall
Pailey Arts Centre and Paisley Town Hall are fully technically equiped and serviced buildings. Full technical specifications are available by telephoning 0141 887 1010 for Paisley Arts Centre or 0141 887 1007 for Paisley Town Hall.

EAST RENFREWSHIRE COUNCIL

Council Offices, Eastwood Park, Rouken Glen Road, Giffnock, Glasgow, Strathclyde G46 6UG Scotland
Tel: 0141 577 3000 Fax: 0141 620 0884
Email: ken.mckinlay@eastrenfrewshire.gov.uk
Web Site: www.eastrenfrewshire.gov.uk
Chief Executive: Peter Daniels (Tel: 0141 577 3009 Fax: 0141 638 8969)
Director of Community & Leisure: Ann Saunders (Tel: 0141 577 3096 Fax: 0141 577 3100)
Head of Cultural Services: Ken McKinlay (Tel: 0141 577 3103 Fax: 0141 577 3100)
Principal Leisure Officer: Mrs Chris Wyse (Tel: 0141 577 3912 Fax: 0141 577 3919)

VENUES
The Eastwood Theatre has S/Cap of 300. Main halls are Fairweather Hall, Crookfur Pavilion, Capelrig House, at Newton Mearns; Thorntree Hall at Thornliebank; Rhuallan House, Carmichael Hall, Eastwood House, Woodfarm Mini-Sports Centre and Woodfarm Pavilion all at Giffnock; Duff Memorial Hall at Busby; Montgomery Hall at Eaglesham; Muirend Pavilion at Muirend; Netherlee Pavilion at Netherlee and Clarkston Hall and Overlee Pavilion both at Clarkston.

SCOTTISH BORDERS COUNCIL

Scottish Borders Council HQ, Newtown St. Boswells, Nr Melrose, Roxburghshire TD6 0SA Scotland
Tel: 01835 824 000 ext 503 Fax: 01835 825 031
Email: a.scott2@scotborders.gov.uk
Web Site: www.scotborders.org.uk
Leisure Manager: Douglas Folen

Head of Cultural Services: Alan Hassan
VENUES
Venues: Volunteer Hall, Galashiels (capacity 553 seats); Victoria Hall, Selkirk (capacity 664 seats); Corn Exchange, Melrose (capacity 304 seats). Hawick Town Hall (634), Kelso Talt Hall (700), Jedburgh Town Hall (450).
Contact Halls Manager: A Scott
Contact Administrative assistant in Community Education: Carolyn Smith
Email: csmith@scotborders.gov.uk

SHETLAND ISLANDS COUNCIL

Comunity Services Dept, Hayfield House, Hayfield Lane Lerwick, Shetland Islands ZE1 0QD Scotland
Tel: 01595 744 006 Fax: 01595 744 056
Email: community.development@shetland.gov.uk
Web Site: www.shetland.gov.uk
Head of the Community Services Dept: George Smith
VENUES
The Garrison Theatre in Market Street, Lerwick re-opened in 1990 following major refurbishment. It is Britain's most northerly theatre with a capacity of 287, and is managed as part of Islesburgh Community Centre, King Harald Street, Lerwick. The Islesburgh Community Centre is used regularly for a variety of events including the Shetland Folk Festival, Accordion and Fiddle Festival, exhibitions, drama, dance and music productions and workshops. In addition there are 56 community halls, many of which have been renovated and refurbished over the past 10 years. These community halls are managed by local committees and most include stage/performance facilities.

STIRLING COUNCIL COMMUNITY SERVICES

Viewforth, Pitt Terrace, Stirling FK8 2ET Scotland
Tel: 01786 443 240 Fax: 01786 442 538
Email: hewittj@stirling.gov.uk
Web Site: www.stirling.gov.uk
Chief Executive: Keith Yates
Director of Community Services: Janice Hewitt
Head of Libraries, Heritage & Culture: Allan Gillies
VENUES
Albert Hall (850) Tolbooth (up to 400 standing).

THE CITY OF EDINBURGH COUNCIL

Culture & Leisure Department, 23-25 Waterloo Place, Edinburgh, Mid Lothian EH1 3BH Scotland
Tel: 0131 529 7844 Fax: 0131 529 7846
Email: lynne.halfpenny@edinburgh.gov.uk
Web Site: www.edinburgh.gov.uk
Head of Museums & Arts: Lynne Halfpenny on 0131 529 3657

WEST DUNBARTONSHIRE COUNCIL

Dept of Culture & Education, Ledenford House, Helenslee Road, Dunbarton G82 4AH Scotland
Switchboard: 01389 737 000
Fax: 01389 608 044
Email: jill.graham@west-dunbarton.gov.uk
Web Site: www.west-dunbarton.gov.uk
Senior Arts Development Officer: Jill Graham (Tel: 01389 608 042)
VENUES
Denny Civic Theatre, Dumbarton: (345) used by both professional and amateur companies for hire will promote.
Burgh Hall, Dumbarton: varied use, concert dance etc.
Clydebank Town Hall, Clydebank: (550) musicals, pantomime, concerts etc. Both amateur and professional bookings, terms negotiable.

WEST LOTHIAN COUNCIL

Arts & Cultural Services, Craigs Farm Campus, Maree Walk, Craigshill, Livingston, West Lothian EH54 5BP Scotland
Tel: 01506 777 585 Fax: 01506 777 590
Email: ColinHutcheon@westlothian.org.uk
Arts Manager: Colin Hutcheon
Lindsay House, South Bridge Street, Bath Gate, eh48 1ts.
Arts Development Officer: Susan Thores
Arts Development Programme
Howden Park Centre, Howden, Livingston EH54 6AE, Tel 01506 433634
VENUES
Howden Park Centre is an Arts Centre comprising 270 seat theatre with conference hall and workshop space. Many community halls throughout the district.

WESTERN ISLES COUNCIL

Comhairlie Nan Eilean Siar (CNES)
Council Buildings, Sandwick Road, Stornoway, Isle of Lewis HS1 2BW Scotland
Tel: 01851 709 548 Fax: 01851 705 796
Email: bill-houston@cne-siar.gov.uk
Web Site: www.cne-siar.gov.uk
Deputy Director of Leisure: Bill Houston

PRODUCTION

1ST FRAMEWORK
32-36 Loman Street London SE1 0EH
Tel: 020 7922 7873
Email: info@1stframework.org
Web Site: www.1stframework.org
Manager: Peter Avery. Contact: peter.avery@1stframework.org
Senior Personnel: Maxine Webster

ABSTRACT IMAGES
117 Willoughby House, Barbican, London EC2Y 8BL
Tel: 020 7638 5123
Email: productions@abstract-images.co.uk
Contact: Howard Ross
London, fringe and middle-scale tours of UK and Europe. Recent critically acclaimed productions include Martin Sherman's ground-breaking play "Bent", Jim Cartwright's "Road", and the London premiere of Lanford Wilson's "Balm in Gilead".

ACT THEATRE PRODUCTIONS LTD
20-22 Stukeley Street,
London WC2B 5LR
Tel: 020 3077 8900 Fax: 020 7242 3548
Email: info@actproductions.co.uk
Web Site: www.actproductions.co.uk
Managing Director: J. Alan Davis
Acting General Manager: Janet Powell

A.I.R. LIMITED
AIR House, Spennymoor, County Durham DL16 7SE
Tel: 01388 814 632 Fax: 01388 812 445
Email: info@airagency.com
Web Site: www.airagency.com
Directors: Colin Pearson, John Wray

AKA
115 Shaftesbury Avenue, Cambridge Circus, London WC2H 8AF
Tel: 020 7836 4747
Email: reception@akauk.com
Web Site: www.akauk.com
Managing Director: Kate Turnball

ALL ELECTRIC PRODUCTIONS & DAVID FOSTER MANAGEMENT
40 Lidgate Street Poundbury Dorchester Dorset DT1 3SJ
Tel: 01305 259605
Email: info@allelectricproductions.co.uk
Web: www.allelectricproductions.co.uk
Contact: David Foster
Agent / Personal Manager / Producer specialising in Theatre shows, Musical shows, Concert & Jazz, Speakers & Presenters.

AMBASSADOR THEATRE GROUP LTD
Charing Cross Branch
39 - 41 Charing Cross Road, London WC2H 0AR
Admin: 020 7534 6100 Admin Fax: 020 7534 6109
Email: info@theambassadors.com
Web Site: www.theambassadors.com
ADMINISTRATION:
Joint CEO and Creative Director: Howard Panter
Head of Production: Meryl Faiers (020 7534 6120)

AMBASSADOR THEATRE GROUP LTD (HEAD OFFICE)
The Peacocks Centre, Woking, Surrey GU21 6GQ
Tel: 01483 545 800 Fax: 01483 770 477
Email: info@theambassadors.com
Web Site: www.theambassadors.com
Joint Chief Executive: Rosemary Squire
Marketing Director: Pat Westwell
Finance & Commercial Director: Helen Enright
Head Office Administrator: Kathy Longdon

ACTORS OF DIONYSUS
25 St Luke's Road Brighton East Sussex BN2 9ZD
Tel/Fax: 01273 680 375
Mob: 07957 471 949
Email: info@actorsofdionysus.com
Web Site: www.actorsofdionysus.com / www.aodsummerschool.com
Artistic Director: Tamsin Shasha
Contact: tamsin@actorsofdionysus.com
Education Officer: Mark Katz
Contact: mark@actorsofdionysus.com
Development Officer: Helen Blesky
Contact: helen@actorsofdionysus.com
General Manager: Lianna Valenti

ARTS MANAGEMENT (REDROOFS ASSOCIATES)
Agency Office, Littlewick Green Maidenhead, Berkshire SL6 3QY
Tel: 01628 822982 Fax: 01628 882461
Email: junemrose@me.com
Web Site: www.redroofs.co.uk
Contact: June Rose
Specialising in: Children and younger actors

ATC
(Actors Touring Company)
The Tab Centre 3 Godfrey Place London E2 7NT
Tel: 0207 033 7360 Fax: 0207 739 8298
Email: atc@atctheatre.com
Web Site: www.atc-online.com

Artistic Director: Bijan Sheibani
Executive Director: Hannah Bentley
Administrator & Events Manager: Kendall O'Neill
Artistic Associate: Ellen McDougall

BARKING DOG THEATRE COMPANY
14 Leaside Mansions Fortis Green, London N10 3EB
Tel: 020 7117 6321
Email: mike@barkingdog.co.uk/ info@barkingdog.co.uk
Web Site: www.barkingdog.co.uk
Director: Mike Brooks
Administrator: Siaran Brooks
Children's Theatre in Education

B.E. EVENT HIRE
Ashtrees, Kirby Bellars, Melton Mowbray, Leicestershire LE14 2DU
Tel: 01664 812 627 Fax: 01664 813 727
Email: info@beeventhire.co.uk
Web Site: www.beeventhire.co.uk
Partners: Caroline Evans and Simon Evans
Furniture Hire for events.

BEHIND YOU PRODUCTIONS
35 Elvaston Way Tilehurst Reading Berkshire RG30 4LX
Tel: 0118 901 2624
BO Tel: 0118 942 9391
Email: info@byptheatregroup.co.uk
Web Site: /www.byptheatregroup.co.uk
Chairman/Company Stage Manager: Steve Gill
Secretary: Mike Goom
Directors: Pam & Richard Johnson

BEVERLEY ARTISTES LTD
Beverley House, 14 Beatrice Terrace Shiney Row Houghton-Le-Spring Tyne & Wear DH4 4QW
Tel: 0191 3854163
Email: info@beverleyartistes.com
Web Site: www.beverleyartistes.com
Contact: Paul Taylor

BIG BEAR MUSIC
PO BOX 944, Edgbaston, Birmingham B16 8UT
Tel: 0121 454 7020
Email: admin@bigbearmusic.com/ tim@bigbearmusic.com
Web Site: www.bigbearmusic.com
Senior Personnel: Tim Jennings, Jim Simpson
Big Bear Music promote jazz, blues and swing through concert and club tours, UK and European festivals, the Starbucks Birmingham International Jazz Festival and Marbella Jazz Festival (Spain).

THE BIRMINGHAM STAGE COMPANY
Suite 228, The Linen Hall, 162 Regent Street, London W1B 5TB
Tel: 020 7437 3391 Fax: 020 7437 3395
Email: info@birminghamstage.com
Web Site: www.birminghamstage.com
Manager/ Actor: Neal Foster
Executive Producer: Philip Compton

BOB SONS PRODUCTIONS LTD
PO Box 34, Sandy,
Bedfordshire SG19 2XL
Tel: 020 7222 1154 Fax: 020 7222 1147
Email: robertjohnwillis@btinternet.com
Contact: Robert Willis

THE JAMES BRANDON COMPANY
Cherry Tree House, 1 Cherry Tree Street,, Elsecar, South Yorkshire S74 8DG
Tel: 01226 742 886
Email: info@jamesbrandon.co.uk
Web Site: www.jamesbrandon.co.uk
Managing Director: James Brandon
Production and agency specialising in pantomime, tribute and variety shows, illusion, design and special effects. Radio, Media and road shows. Specialist in corporate events and one-off bespoke entertainments.

SHANE BROGAN MUSIC PRODUCTIONS
PO BOX 26253 Ayr South Ayrshire KA7 1YF Scotland, UK
Mob: 07762 472 187
Email: shane@shanebrogan.com
Web Site: www.shanebrogan.com
Musician: Shane D Brogan
Accordionist specialising in Jazz, Classical, Popular, Ethnic, Music, etc.; Pianist/Keyboardist; Composer/Arranger; Private Music Teacher.

GARRY BROWN ASSOCIATES (INT) LTD
27 Downs Side, Cheam, Sutton, Surrey SM2 7EH
Tel: 020 8643 3991 Fax: 020 8770 7241
Email: gbaltd@btconnect.com
Senior Personnel: Garry Brown, Helen Machell, Brenda Capper, Denise Webb
Specialising in: Entertainment for Major Shipping Lines and Hotels Worldwide providing a range of artistes, particularly dance teams.

NICA BURNS PRODUCTIONS
Nimax Theatres Limited, 1 Lumley Court, Off 402 Strand, London WC2R 0NB
Tel: 020 7395 0783 Fax: 020 7240 4540
Email: stephanie.creed@nimaxtheatres.com
Web Site: www.nimaxtheatres.com
Contact: Stephanie Creed

CALIBRE PRODUCTIONS LTD
Chasewood Lodge Walford Road, Ross-on-Wye, Herefordshire HR9 5PQ
Tel: 01989 566 644 Fax: 01989 566 627
Email: admin@calibreproductions.co.uk
Web Site: www.calibreproductions.co.uk
Contact: Ed or Lynn O'Driscoll
Producers of "Beyond Broadway", "Kings Of Swing", " Masters of the Musical", "Absolute Swing", "A Night at the Opera", "Sounds of the 60s" and "Classic Response"

CCB EVENTS LTD
54-56 Station Approach, South Ruislip, Middlesex HA4 6SA
Tel: 01923 842 569
Email: Robbiewilson@aol.com
Managing Director: Robbie Wilson

CHALKFOOT THEATRE ARTS
5 Gold Street Stalbridge Dorset DT10 2LX
Tel: 01963 362937
Email: info@chalkfoot.org.uk
Web Site: www.chalkfoot.org.uk
Artistic Director: Philip Dart
Chalkfoot Thearte Arts (the touring and outreach arm of Channel Theatre Compnay) serves the people of south east England and beyond by touring productions of a high standard which entertain, inform and inspire. The company is committed to touring non-theatre venues and it takes its work into a wide range of communities. The company also works with many different groups on projects which promote personal and social development and develop creativity. Also see CHANNEL THEATRE COMPANY.

CHANCE PROMOTIONS
The Nook, Bee Lane, Penwortham, Preston PR1 9TU
Tel: 01772 321 160
Email: info@legendschance.com
Web Site: www.legendschance.com
Managing Directors: Trevor Chance, Brenda Chance
Creative Musical director: Richard Chance
Choreographer: Wendy Holland
Company Production Manager: Tony Harvey
Specialising in Look/Sound Alike Shows & Tributes.

CHANNEL THEATRE PRODUCTIONS LTD
5 Gold Street Stalbridge Dorset DT10 2LX
Tel: 01963 362937
Email: info@channel-theatre.co.uk
Web Site: www.channel-theatre.co.uk
Artistic Director: Philip Dart
Associate Director: Claudia Leaf
Channel Theatre company works regionally and nationally on special commissions, training programmes (school and business), theatre production projects, theatre in education programmes and writing commissions. .The company delivers high quality projects to a wide range of venues/client groups. For touring and outreach, see CHALKFOOT THEATRE ARTS.

CHAPLINS TV LTD
Chaplins House, Unit A & B, The Acorn Centre, Roebuck Road, Hainault, Essex IG6 3TU
Tel: 020 8501 2121 Fax: 020 8501 3336
Email: enquiries@chaplinspantos.co.uk
Web Site: www.chaplinspantos.co.uk
Managing Directors: J Holmes
Touring Shows. Full Package provided. Television Production.

DUGGIE CHAPMAN ASSOCIATES
Clifton House 106 Clifton Drive Blackpool, Lancashire FY4 1RR
Tel: 01253 403177
Mobile: 07976 925 504
Email: info@duggiechapmanassociates.co.uk
Web: www.duggiechapmanassociates.co.uk
Director: Duggie Chapman
Artiste Booking: Beryl Johnson
Duggie Chapman Associates is Britain's longest running promoter of touring music hall presenting Star Variety Summer Shows and Pantomimes. Specialists in late bookings for managements. Name Package shows always available at short notice.

CHARING CROSS THEATRE
The Arches, Villiers Street, London WC2N 6NL
Tel: 0207 930 5868
Email: jon@charingcrosstheatre.co.uk
Web Site: www.charingcrosstheatre.co.uk
Senior Personnel: Jon Chai
Commercial theatre producers.
A 265 seat proscenium arch theatre in the heart of the West End. Promoting theatre, comedy and music. Also available to hire for rehearsal space, auditions, conferences and screenings. There is a separate restaurant and three bars. Intelligent Lighting are responsible for all technical aspects of the theatre, they can be contacted through the mainline number.

CHESTER BENSON PRODUCTIONS
PO Box 4227, Worthing, West Sussex BN11 5ST
Tel: 01903 248 258 Fax: 01903 700 389
Email: dave@davebensonphillips.co.uk
Web Site: www.davebensonphillips.co.uk
Proprietor: Dave Benson Phillips
A small company that's big on creating live shows and interactive experiences for children and adults. Over 20 years in the business, video & television! Producing "The all new Dave Benson Phillips Show", "Benson's Jumparound Activity Centres" and "Get Your Own Back". All shows are perfect for indoor/outdoor events.

CHICHESTER FESTIVAL THEATRE AND MINERVA THEATRE
Festival Theatre Oaklands Park, Chichester, West Sussex PO19 6AP
Tel: 01243 784437 BO: 01243 781312
Fax: 01243 787288
Email: admin@cft.org.uk
Web Site: www.cft.org.uk
Artistic Director: Jonathan Church
Executive Director: Alan Finch
Theatre Manager: Janet Bakose
Technical Co-ordinator: Sam Garner-Gibbons
Chichester Festival Capacity: 1206
Minerva Theatre Capacity: 283

CHICKENSHED THEATRE
Chase Side, Southgate, London N14 4PE
Tel: 020 8351 6161 Fax: 020 8292 0202
BO: 020 8292 9222
Email: info@chickenshed.org.uk
Web Site: www.chickenshed.org.uk
ADMINISTRATION:
Chief Executive: Jane Paterson-Todd (janep@chickenshed.org.uk)
Theatre Manager: Francis Thomas
Press & Publicity: Susan Jamson (susanj@chickenshed.org.uk)
Registered Charity.
Provision of works of performance art, which are original, creative and inclusive.
Excellence without exclusion.
52 staff with 100+ volunteers.
1,000 young people participate weekly.

MICHAEL CODRON PLAYS LTD
Aldwych Theatre Offices, Aldwych, London WC2B 4DF
Tel: 020 7240 8291 Fax: 020 7240 8467
Director: Michael Codron CBE
General Manager/Productions: Paul O'Leary

COLE KITCHENN PERSONAL MANAGEMENT
ROAR House 46 Charlotte Street London W1T 2GS
Tel: 0207 427 5680 / 427 5681
Fax: 0207 353 9639
Email: info@colekitchenn.com
Web Site: www.colekitchenn.com
Personal Management:
Managing Director/Agent: Stuart Piper
Contact:stuart@colekitchenn.com
Senior Agent: Oliver Thomson
Contact: oliver@colekitchenn.com
Agent: Alex Segal
Contact: alex@colekitchenn.com
Associate Agents: Jo Fell and Ashley Vallance
Contact: jo@colekitchenn.com, ashley@colekitchenn.com
Talent Manager: Lucy Marriott
Contact: lucy@colekitchenn.com
Chairman: Jonathan Shalit
Contact: jonathan@roarglobal.com
Director: Guy Kitchenn
Contact: guy@colekitchenn.com
Agents for Actors and Creatives.

MAX COLLIE RHYTHM ACES
26 Wendover Road, Bromley, Kent BR2 9JX
Tel: 020 8460 1139 Fax: 020 8466 7005
Email: max@maxcollie.fsnet.co.uk
Web Site: www.maxcollie.co.uk
Senior Personnel: Max Collie
Specialising in Traditional and New Orleans Jazz

CLIVE CONWAY PRODUCTIONS
32 Grove Street, Oxford OX2 7JT
Tel: 01865 514 830 Fax: 01865 514 409
Email: info@celebrityproductions.org
Web: www.cliveconwayproductions.com
Managing Director: Clive Conway
Producing celebrity entertainments featuring Britain's leading actors, writers, musicians and politicians.

CRAGRATS LTD
Lawster House, 140 South Street, Dorking, Surrey RH4 2EU
Tel: 08444 774 100
Email: enquiries@cragrats.com
Web Site: www.cragrats.com
Managing Director: William Akerman
Business Support Manager: Nicky Miles
Leeds Office: Roudfoundry Media Centre, Foundry Street, Leeds, LS11 5QP
CragRats Ltd is the market innovator and leader in bespoke theatre productions for young people, businesses and training organisations. CragRats Ltd is committed to communicating messages and motivating audiences throughout the UK, producing projects that range from issue-based theatre, initiative awareness shows, communication skills, corporate training as well as full-length theatre productions. See our web site for further company details.

CURLYWILLY PROD LTD.
Unit 3b Bailey Gate Industrial Estate, Sturminster Marshall, Wimborne, Dorset BH21 4DB
Tel: 01258 857 070 Mob: 07970 956 621
Email: carol@curlywilly.co.uk
Web Site: www.curlywilly.co.uk
Proprietor: Carol Kerley

DAVID IAN PRODUCTIONS LTD
5th Floor 53 Parker Street London WC2B 5PT
Tel: 020 7427 8380 Fax: 020 7427 8381
Email: hello@davidianproductions.com
Web Site: www.davidianproductions.com
Chairman: David Ian
Managing Director: Max Finbow

DELPHINE Y DOMINGO
4 Cormorant Rise, Worcester, Worcestershire WR2 4BA
Tel: 01905 424 083
Email: delphineflamenco@tiscali.co.uk
Contact: D Auchterlonie
Also known as "Flamenco Productions", specialising in quality Flamenco Music and Dance for Television, Theatre, Promotion and Education.

DEP ARTS LTD
Yorkshire Dance Centre 3 St. Peters Buildings, Leeds West Yorkshire LS9 8AH
Tel: 0113 234 6911 Mob: 07970 718 785
Email: admin@departsltd.com
Web Site: www.departsltd.com
Independent Producer: David Edmunds
The company not ony specialises in producing Dance & Physical Theatre, but also provides consultancy services for arts based organisations or companies, including: Touring, Artist Development and Marketing.

DISNEY THEATRICAL PRODUCTIONS (UK)
Alternative website: www.thelionking.co.uk
The Lyceum Theatre, 21 Wellington Street, London WC2E 7DA
Tel: 020 7845 0900 Fax: 020 7845 0999
Email: DTPUKpress@disney.co.uk
Web: www.disney.co.uk/musicaltheatre

THE DRAMA HOUSE
The Clockhouse, St Mary Street, Nether Stowey Somerset TA5 1LJ
Email: jack@dramahouse.co.uk
Web Site: www.dramahouse.co.uk
Chairman/Chief Executive: Jack Emery

DRAMATIS PERSONAE LTD
19 Regency Street, London, SW1P 4BY
Tel: 020 7834 9300
Email: ns@nathansilver.com
Directors: Nathan Silver & Nicolas Kent

E3 ARTISTS LTD
56 Shorts Gardens, London WC2H 9AN
Tel: 020 7836 4759
Email: enquiry@e3grouponline.com
Web Site: www.e3grouponline.com
Senior Personnel: Phil Riley

ENGLISH NATIONAL OPERA
London Coliseum, St Martin's Lane, London WC2N 4ES
Admin: 020 7836 0111 Mgt: 020 7845 9215 BO: 0871 911 0200 Tech: 020 7845 9459 Fax: 020 7845 9296
Email: personnel@eno.org
Web Site: www.eno.org
Directors of the English National Opera:
Chief Executive: Loretta Tomasi
Artistic Director: John Berry
Technical Director: Geoff Summerton

ENGLISH STAGE COMPANY LTD
Royal Court Theatre, Sloane Square, London SW1W 8AS
Admin: 020 7565 5050 Press: 0207 565 5063 Fax: 020 7565 5001

Email: info@royalcourttheatre.com
Web Site: www.royalcourttheatre.com
Artistic Director: Dominic Cooke

ENGLISH TOURING THEATRE

25 Short Street, London SE1 8LJ
Tel: 020 7450 1990 Fax: 020 7633 0188
Email: jclaire@ett.org.uk
Web Site: www.ett.org.uk
Touring high quality theatre to the widest possible audience.
Director: Rachel Tackley
Executive Producer: Jane Claire
Production Manager: Felix Davies

ENTERTAINERS COMPANY LTD.

The UK's No.1 Entertainment Agency
200 London Road, Hadleigh, Benfleet, Essex SS7 2PD
Tel: 01702 427 100 / 0870 233 0836
Fax: 01702 427 109 Mob: 07850 111616
Email: enquiries@entertainers.co.uk
Web Site: www.entertainers.co.uk / www.easytheatres.co.uk
Director: Michael Taylor (michael@entertainers.co.uk)
Senior Personnel: Ben Hatton
The one stop shop for entertainment.

ENTERTAINERS MANAGEMENT LTD

200 London Road, Hadleigh, Benfleet, Essex SS7 2PD
Tel: 01702 427 100 Fax: 01702 427 109
Mob: 07850 111616
Email: enquiries@entertainers.co.uk
Web Site: www.easytheatres.com
Senior Personnel: Ben Hatton
Director: Michael Taylor
Contact: michael@entertainers.co.uk
The UK's no 1 entertainment agency.

ESIP LTD

PO Box 4702, Henley-on-Thames, Oxfordshire RG9 9AA
Tel: 0118 940 6812 Fax: 0870 122 4634
Email: ruben@esip.co.uk, info@esip.co.uk
Web Site: www.esip.co.uk
Director: John Ellson
Press and Marketing: Emma Perry
Promoter, Production and Tour Manager: Ruben Cordero
Events Producer: Dominic Nieper

FACE FRONT INCLUSIVE THEATRE LTD

52 The Market Square, Edmonton Green Shopping Centre Edmonton, London N9 0TZ
Tel: 020 8350 3461
Email: info@facefront.org
Web Site: www.facefront.org
Artistic Director: Annie Smol
Administrator and Tour Booker: Tracey Viechweg
Face Front is a company of disabled and non-disabled artists who create multi-layered theatre which is accessible to all.
The company works extensively in schools and other educational settings producing high quality Theatre In Education and participatory workshop programmes suitable for all ages over 5 years. Drama techniques include role-play, improvisation, storytelling, poetry and image work to raise issues relating to educational and home environments, including bullying, racism, disability and domestic violence.
Contact the company directly for more information on hiring the on-site studio; the high ceiling and sprung dance floor make it suitable for rehearsals, auditions, meetings and community events.

FALSE IMPRESSIONS

207 Mersham Road, Thornton Heath, Surrey CR7 8NU
Tel: 01803 615 600/ 615 700 (Anne George) Mob: 07968 828 530
Email: richardleigh@falseimpressions.co.uk
Web Site: www.falseimpressions.co.uk
Theatrical Magical Advisor: Richard Leigh
Contact: Anne George (anne@trevorgeorge.co.uk)
False Impressions is a production company which specialises in the unusual field of stage illusion and magic shows of all genres.
Productions:
- The Magic Cavern
- Late Night Magic in the West End
- The Side Show of Wonders
- The Ice Cave Magic Show
- The Magic Toy Theatre
- The Haunted Magic Show

FAME FACTORY PRESENTATIONS

Wits End, 300 Bishops Drive, Oakwood, Derby DE21 2DR
Tel: 01332 833933
Email: fame.factory@ntlworld.com
Company Director: Maxine D Harrison
Managing Director: Gerry Graham Harrison
Pantomime, touring shows, show production, workshops and hire of scenery/costumes/props.

FIERY ANGEL LTD

22-24 Torrington Place, London WC1E 7HJ
Tel: 020 7907 7040 Fax: 020 7436 6287
Email: mail@fiery-angel.com
Web Site: www.fiery-angel.com
Producer: Edward Snape
Head of Finance: Richard Brundle
Marketing and Sales Manager: Bonnie Royal

VANESSA FORD PRODUCTIONS

Upper House Farm, Upper House Lane, Shamley Green, Near Guildford, Surrey GU5 0SX
Tel: 01483 278 203 Fax: 01483 271 509
Email: info@vanessafordproductions.co.uk
Web: www.vanessafordproductions.co.uk
Directors: Vanessa Ford & Glyn Robbins

FULL HOUSE PRODUCTIONS

High Tree Cottage, Prince Hold Road, Lower Way, Thatcham, Berkshire RG19 3TH
Tel: 01635 862 822 Mobile: 07860 238946
Email: foreverin.bluejeans@sky.com
Web Site: www.foreverinbluejeans.uk.com
Senior Personnel: Carol & Bob Newman
Agents and Producing Managements for "Forever In Blue Jeans", and Voice of the Heart "Karen Carpenter"

TREVOR GEORGE ENTERTAINMENTS LTD

PO Box 135, Torquay, Devon TQ1 3ZW
Tel: 01803 615 600 / 700 Fax: 01803 615 888 Mobile: 07502 042 995
Email: anne@trevorgeorge.co.uk
Web Site: www.trevorgeorge.co.uk
Senior Personnel: Anne George, Beverley Korman

GO ENTERTAINMENTS

The Arts Exchange, Dane Mill Congleton, Cheshire CW12 1LA
Tel: 01260 276 627 Fax: 01260 270 777
Email: info@arts-exchange.com
Web Site: www.arts-exchange.com
Contact: Phillip or Carol Gandey
Big tops up to 5000 people worldwide supply.

HARVEY GOLDSMITH PRODUCTIONS LTD

5th Floor,Langham House 308 Regent Street London W1B3AT
Tel: 020 7224 1992 Fax: 020 7224 0111
Email: mail@harveygoldsmith.com
Web Site: www.harveygoldsmith.com
Managing Director: Harvey Goldsmith

DAVID GRAHAM ENTERTAINMENT LTD

72 New Bond Street, London W1S 1RR
Tel: 0870 321 1600 Fax: 0870 321 1700
Prod: 0870 321 1900
Email: info@davidgraham.co.uk
Web Site: www.davidgrahamentertainment.com
Producer: David Graham

GROOVY MOVIES.TV

First Floor 23 York Road, Hove, East Sussex BN3 1DJ
Tel: 01273 7300 00 Mob: 07718 914 068

Web Site: www.groovymovies.tv
Contacts: Mark 'Yeti' Cribb
TV & Video for music, comedy, commercial and live productions, aswell as comedy scripting and direction. Credits include: Right Size, Kiki Dee, Future Dance & Steven Berkoff.

GUY CHAPMAN ASSOCIATES LTD
See Target Live

HANDSHAKE LTD
2 Holly House, Mill Street, Uppermill, Saddleworth, Lancashire OL3 6LZ
Tel: 01457 819 350 Fax: 01457 810 052
Email: info@handshakegroup.com
Web Site: www.handshakegroup.com
Managing Director: Stuart Littlewood
Promoters / Producers / Managers of Live Entertainment. Handshake Ltd is a member of the Concert Promoters Association (CPA).

HAYMARKET THEATRE COMPANY
Haymarket Theatre, Wote Street, Basingstoke, RG21 7NW
BO: 01256 844244 Admin: 01256 819797
Email: info@haymarket.org.uk
Web Site: www.anvilarts.org.uk
Chief Executive: Christine Bradwell
Producing theatre - up to 8 in house shows 6-8 visiting shows. Season: September to June. Shows run between 1 and 4 weeks. Developing community and education programme.

GLYNIS HENDERSON PRODUCTIONS
69 Charlotte Street, London W1T 4PJ
Tel: 020 7580 9644 Fax: 020 7436 1489
Email: info@ghmp.co.uk
Web Site: www.ghmp.co.uk
Director and Executive Producer: Glynis Henderson
General Manager: Claudia Courtis
Specialising in: Visual Musical, Comedy, Dance, Including STOMP and Ennio Marchetto
Produces Shows:
Cool Heat, Urban Beat, Rich Fulcher, Harlem Gospel Choir, Ennio Marchetto, Modern Problems in Science, Paul Morocco & Olé, Stomp and the Wadaiko Ichiro Drummers.

THE HISS & BOO COMPANY LTD
1 Nyes Hill, Wineham Lane, Bolney, West Sussex RH17 5SD
Tel: 01444 881 707 Fax: 01444 882 057
Email: ian@hissboo.co.uk
Web Site: www.hissboo.co.uk
Managing Director: Ian Liston
Membership: TMA

HOIPOLLOI
Office F, Dale's Brewery, Gwydir Street, Cambridge CB1 2LJ
Tel: 01223 322 748
Email: info@hoipolloi.org.uk
Web Site: www.hoipolloi.org.uk
Artistic Director: Shon Dale-Jones
Executive Producer: Simon Bedford

PAUL HOLMAN ASSOCIATES LTD
Morritt House 58 Station Approach, South Ruislip, Ruislip, Middlesex HA4 6SA
Tel: 020 8845 9408 Fax: 020 8839 3124
Email: enquiries@paulholmanassociates.co.uk
Web: www.paulholmanassociates.co.uk
Managing Director: Paul Holman
Pantomimes, summer shows, concerts,educational workshops and plays.

HQ THEATRES LTD
2nd Floor 161 Drury Lane Covent Garden London WC2B 5PN
Tel: 020 7430 5370 Fax: 020 7430 5388
Email: info@hqtheatres.com
Web Site: www.hqtheatres.com
ADMINISTRATION:
Props: Qdos Entertainment
Chief Executive Officer: Derek Nicholls
General Manager: Stuart Shanks
Managing Director, HQ Hospitality: James Giles
HQ Theatres operates the following venues:
Cliffs Pavilion (Southend), Palace Theatre (Southend), Beck Theatre (Hayes), G Live (Guildford), Orchard Theatre (Dartford), Wycombe Swan Theatre & Town Hall (High Wycombe), Wyvern Theatre (Wiltshire), White Rock Theatre (Hastings), Watford Colosseum (Watford). G Live (Guildford)

IAN FRICKER (THEATRE) LTD
3rd Floor, 146 Strand, London WC2R 1JD
Tel: 020 7836 3090 Fax: 020 7836 3078
Email: mail@ianfricker.com
Web Site: www.ianfricker.com
Producer: Ian Fricker
Associate Producer: Louise Toeman
West End and National Touring producer of quality Drama, Plays and Musicals.

ICE PRODUCTIONS
Warwick Corner 42 Warwick Road, Kenilworth, Warwickshire CV8 1HE
Tel: 01926 864 800 Fax: 01926 740 559
Email: admin@ice-productions.com
Web Site: www.ice-productions.com
Contact: Sean Griffiths

IMAGE MUSICAL THEATRE COMPANY
23 Sedgeford Road, Shepherds Bush, London W12 0NA
Tel: 020 87439380 Fax: 020 87499294
Email: brian@imagemusicaltheatre.co.uk
Web: www.imagemusicaltheatre.co.uk
Producer/ Director: Brian Thresh
Specialising in new musicals for the touring circuit, theatres and schools, the company produces two family/ children's participation musicals and one full length adult musical each year.

IMAGINATION ENTERTAINMENTS LTD
25 Store Street, London WC1E 7BL
Tel: 020 7323 3300 Fax: 020 7462 2885
Email: entertainments@imagination.com
Web Site: www.imagination.com
Contact: Guy Stevenson

IMAGINE THEATRE LTD
2 Brandon House Woodhams Road Middlemarsh Business Park Coventry, CV3 4FX
Tel: 024 7630 7001 Fax: 024 7630 7559
Mob: 07721 426 398 (Steve)
Email: info@imaginetheatre.co.uk
Web Site: www.imaginetheatre.co.uk
Managing Director: Steven Boden
Production Assistant: Louise Redmond
Imagine Theatre are a pantomime and theatre production company. The company produces traditional family pantomimes in over 30 venues across the country, and operates an extensive scenery, prop & costume department.

JACARANDA THEATRE COMPANY
Top Floor 97 Fortess Road London NW5 1AG
Email: jacarandatheatre@yahoo.co.uk
Web Site: www.jacarandatheatre.com
Artistic Director: Debra Low
Jacaranda Theatre Company produces and promotes innovative, cutting-edge Australian theatre to theatre audiences in the UK and abroad. In addition to presenting new work, Jacaranda strives to showcase plays of an internationally transferable nature, as well as sharing the rich variety of Australian culture.

BRIAN JACKSON FILMS LTD
39/41 Hanover Steps, St Georges Fields, Albion Street, London W2 2YG
Tel: 020 7402 7543 Fax: 020 7262 5736
Email: brianjfilm@aol.com
Web Site: www.brianjacksonfilms.com
Managing Director: Brian Jackson

JAYS UK LTD
The Manor House, Burgh Castle, Great Yarmouth, Norfolk NR31 9QL
Admin: 01493 780 223 Tel: 01493 844 172 Mob: 07852 939444
Email: chrisjay@jays-uk.com
Web Site: www.hippodromecircus.co.uk
Managing Directors: Peter & Christine Jay

JESTER PRODUCTIONS
Flat 6, Shaftesbury House, Grange Road, Ealing, London W5 5UA
Tel/Fax: 020 8840 5316
Manager: Jack Seaton

GARETH JOHNSON LTD
Plas Hafren, Eglwyswrw, Crymych, Pembrokeshire SA41 3UL Wales
Tel: 01239 891368 Fax: 01239 800 089
Email: gjltd@mac.com
Web Site: www.garethjohnsonltd.com
Director: Gareth Johnson
General Management and Producers for Musicals and Drama in London and the UK. It also undertakes production and administrative consultancies.

KAOS THEATRE
3rd Floor, 43 Chandos Place, London WC2N 4HS
Tel/ Fax: 020 7379 6204
Email: admin@kaostheatre.com
Web Site: www.kaostheatre.com
Artistic Director: Xavier Leret
Executive Director: Sharon Schaffer
Producer: Rebekah Cross
An ensemble company producing new work, adaptations and classics for touring nationally and internationally.
Policy: We aim to make non-elitist experimental theatre and present it to as wide an audience as possible. We create highly original work combining physical theatre, text, story-telling, devising, song, music and video. KAOS is about ideas, imagination and collaboration.

ROBERT C KELLY LTD
PO Box 5597 Glasgow, Strathclyde G77 9DH Scotland
Tel: 0141 533 5856
Email: robert@robertckelly.co.uk
Web Site: www.robertckelly.co.uk
Senior Personnel: Robert C Kelly

KENNEDY STREET ENTERPRISES LTD
Kennedy House, 31 Stamford Street, Altrincham, Cheshire WA14 1ES
Tel: 0161 941 5151 Fax: 0161 928 9491
Email: kse@kennedystreet.com
Managing Director: Danny Betesh

BILL KENWRIGHT LTD
BKL House, 1 Venice Walk, London W2 1RR
Tel: 020 7446 6200 Fax: 020 7446 6246
Email: info@kenwright.com
Web Site: www.kenwright.com
Managing Director: Bill Kenwright
Financial Director: Alan Sharp
Commercial Director: Steve Potts
Producer: Julius Green

MIG KIMPTON PRODUCTIONS
19 Wingfield Street, London SE15 4LN
Tel: 020 7732 8669 Fax: 020 7732 8672
Mob: 07831 838851
Email: mig@migkimpton.com
Web Site: www.migkimpton.com
ContactL Mig Kimpton

THE KRUGER ORGANISATION - TKO
PO Box 130, Hove, East Sussex BN3 6QU
Tel: 01273 550 088 Fax: 01273 540 969
Email: h.kruger@tkogroup.com
Web Site: www.tkogroup.com
Senior Personnel: Drn Jeffrey Kruger MBE, Howard Kruger
Specialising in Concert & Event Promotions and Management.

LEE MENZIES LIMITED
20-22 Stukeley Street, London WC2B 5LR
Email: leemenzies@leemenzies.co.uk
Web Site: www.leemenzies.co.uk
Manager: Lee Menzies

LEISURE AT SEA LTD
27 Downs Side, Cheam, Surrey SM2 7EH
Tel: 020 8643 3991 Fax: 020 8770 7241
Email: GBALTD@compuserve.com
Contact: Garry Brown

JOHNNY & BARBARA LEY TRAMPOLINE & CLOWN PROMOTIONS
14 Stanshaw Close, Frenchay, Bristol, BS16 1JY
Tel: 0117 956 5599 Mobile: 07791 871 848
Contact: John & Barbara Ley

LINE-UP PMC
10 Matthew Close, Newcastle upon Tyne NE6 1XD
Tel / Fax: 0191 275 9745 Mob: 07808 300 906
Email: chrismurtagh@line-up.co.uk
Web Site: www.line-up.co.uk
Senior Personnel: Chris Murtagh

LIVE NATION MUSIC UK
Regent Arcade House, 1st Floor, 19-25 Argyll Street, London W1F 7TS
Tel: 020 7009 3333 Fax: 0870 0949100
Email: barry.clayman@livenation.co.uk
Web Site: www.livenation.co.uk
Contact: Barry Clayman OBE

LONDON BUBBLE (BUBBLE THEATRE CO LTD)
5 Elephant Lane, London SE16 4JD
Tel 020 7237 4434 Fax 020 7231 2366
Email: admin@londonbubble.org.uk
Web Site: www.londonbubble.org.uk
ADMINISTRATION:
Props: Bubble Theatre Company Ltd.
Creative Director: Jonathan Petherbridge
Administrator: Lucy Bradshaw
Policy: to tour a variety of productions to adults and children throughout the Greater London area in community and traditional venues, and, during the summer, to London's parks and open spaces. The aim is to develop a popular theatre style which is bold and bright, fast and physical, open and accessible.

CAMERON MACKINTOSH LTD
1 Bedford Square, London WC1B 3RB
Tel: 020 7637 8866 Fax: 020 7436 2683
Email: info@camack.co.uk
Web Site: www.cameronmackintosh.com
Managing Director: Nick Allot

MAESTRO MUSIC INTERNATIONAL
Crown Villa, 14 Crown Lane, Theale, Reading, Berkshire RG7 5BQ
Tel/Fax: 0118 930 3239 Mob: 07836 369678
Email: mail@maestromusicinternational.co.uk
Web: www.maestromusicinternational.com
Managing Director: Norman Rogerson; or Ian Collins Tel: 01798 874651
Mob:07860 702772
Other websites: www.londontattoo.co.uk or www.birminghamtattoo.co.uk
Specialising in military groups from the UK and internationally.

MANCHESTER YOUNG PEOPLE'S THEATRE LTD
See "Contact Theatre", Manchester Listing (Provincial Venues)

MANTAPLAN LTD
Douglas Drive, Godalming, Surrey GU7 1HJ
Tel: 01483 420 088 Fax: 01483 424 566
Email: production@mantaplan.com
Web Site: www.mantaplan.com
Managing Director: Andy Ayres
Administration: Jenny Hall

MATTHEWS PRODUCTIONS
Matpro Ltd, Cary Point, Babbacombe Downs, Torquay, Devon TQ1 3LU
Tel: 01803 322233 Fax: 01803 322244
Email: info@babbacombe-theatre.com
Web: www.babbacombe-theatre.com
Director: Colin Matthews
General Manager: Sharon Waring

MAVERICK THEATRE COMPANY
12 Lydney Grove, Birmingham B31 1RB
Tel: 0121 444 0933
Email: info@mavericktheatre.co.uk
Web Site: www.mavericktheatre.co.uk
Artistic Director: Nick Hennegan
Administrator: Deborah Scattergood.

MCLEOD AGENCY LTD
Established 1970
First Floor 6 The Square Hessle East Yorkshire HU13 0AA
Tel: 01482 565 444 Fax: 01482 353 635
Email: info@themcleodagency.co.uk
Web Site: www.mcleodagency.co.uk
Senior Personnel: Liz Hugill
Entertainment Agency & Artiste Management.

THE MEDIEVAL HALL
Sarum St Michael, Cathedral Close, Salisbury, Wiltshire SP1 2EY
Tel: 01722 324 731 Mob: 07814 970945
Email: info@medieval-hall.co.uk
Web Site: www.medieval-hall.co.uk
ADMINISTRATION:
Props: John and Jane Waddington
Policy: Music, theatre, exhibitions etc.
Capacity: 140

MIDLANDS ARTS CENTRE
Cannon Hill Park, Birmingham B12 9QH
Admin: 0121 446 3200 BO: 0121 446 3232 Fax: 0121 446 3201
Email: info@macbirmingham.co.uk
Web Site: www.macbirmingham.co.uk
ADMINISTRATION:
Props: Midlands Arts Centre
Chief Executive: Dorothy Wilson
Head of Administration: Sue Longfils
Head of Communications: Lindsey Cook
Operations Director: Michelle Smith
Policy: Concerts, Films, Visiting Companies, Festivals, Professional Music, Theatre, Literature Events, Education and Comedy Programmes, Exhibitions.
Perfs: Various, 10.30, 13.00, 14.30, 20.00, 19.30.
Seating: the Theatre: 220 (The Theatre can be adapted to suit particular type of play.); the Hexagon: 86; the Open Air Arena Theatre: 470; the Cinema: 150.
Dressing Rooms: the Theatre: 2, the Hexagon: 2; Showers.
Cafe and Bar.
Membership: TMA, ACA

MOUTHPIECE PRODUCTIONS LTD
PO Box 145, Inkberrow, Worcester WR7 4EL
Tel: 01527 850149
Email: info@mouthpieceuk.co.uk, Keith@mouthpieceuk.co.uk
Web: www.mouthpieceproductions.net
Contact: Keith Potts, Karin Heslop, Chris Jaeger
Theatre production company providing both national and regional touring theatre.

MUCH LOVED PRODUCTIONS LTD
The British Philharmonic Concert Orchestra
8 Oaks Farm Drive, Darton, Barnsley, South Yorkshire S75 5BZ
Tel: 01226 380 175 Fax: 01226 380 566
Mob: 07802 959 594
Email: jeremy@mlpltd.com
Web Site: www.mlpltd.com
Senior Personnel: Mr JM Peaker, Mr M Peaker, Mrs JA Peaker
Specialising in all types of entertainment and corporate hospitality concerts.
Shows and productions incorporating the British Philharmonic Concert Orchestra.

THE NATIONAL SYMPHONY ORCHESTRA
177 John Ruskin Street, London SE5 0PQ
Tel: 020 7703 3148 Fax: 020 7703 5334
Email: enquiries@nso.co.uk
Web Site: www.nso.co.uk
Manager/Artistic Director: Anne Collis
Co-Artistic Director: Justin Pearson
Music Director: Anthony Inglis

NATIONAL THEATRE
South Bank, London SE1 9PX
Admin: 020 7452 3333 BO: 020 7452 3000 Fax: 020 7452 3344
Email: tours@nationaltheatre.org.uk
Web Site: www.nationaltheatre.org.uk
Director: Nicholas Hytner
Executive Director: Tessa Ross
Head of Production: Mark Dakin
Head of Technical Resources: Rob Barnard
Director of Marketing: Alex Bayley
Olivier Capacity: 110 - 1160
Lyttelton Capacity: 890
Dorfman Capacity: 250 - 400
Open in 1976, designed by Sir Denys Lasdun.
Policy: To present an ecletic mix of new plays and classics.
No performance on Sunday - evening shows starts at 7.30pm, matinees on Saturday and one other day at 2 - 2.30pm.
Other activities: Art and photography exhibitions, live foyer music daily, platform perfomances and other events throughout the year, conducted tours of the building, educational workshops, bookshop, outdoor performance events during summer.

NETT UK
45 Elizabeth Avenue, Hove, East Sussex BN3 6WA
Tel: 01273 565 627
Email: info@nettuk.com
Web Site: www.nettuk.com
Contact: Nick Taggart
Highly professional theatre production and management company for UK and overseas theatre, touring shows, events and concerts.
Full sales, marketing, public relations and I.T. departments.
Enquiries by email welcome.

NEW PANTOMIME PRODUCTIONS LTD
27 Shooters Road, Enfield, Middlesex EN2 8RJ
Tel: 0208 363 9920
Email: simonbarry@nppltd.freeserve.co.uk
Main contact: Simon Barry
Company Secretary: Brian Pridmore (pridmorebri@aol.com)

NEW SHAKESPEARE COMPANY - OPEN AIR THEATRE
The Ironworks, Inner Circle, Regents Park, London NW1 4NR
Tel: 08443 753 460 BO: 0844 826 4242
Email: boxoffice@openairtheatre.com
Web Site: www.openairtheatre.org
Artistic Director: Timothy Sheader
Executive Director: William Village
Administrator/ Education Assistant: Hannah Falvey

NEWPALM PRODUCTIONS
26 Cavendish Avenue, Finchley, London N3 3QN
Tel: 020 8349 0802 Mrkting: 01702 475 237 Fax: 020 8346 8257
Email: office@newpalm.co.uk , lionel@newpalm.co.uk
Web Site: www.newpalm.co.uk
Managing and Artistic Director: John Newman
Executive Director: Daphne Palmer
General Manager: Lionel Chilcott
Established 32 years. Producing repertory seasons, major tours, West End and abroad.

PAUL NICHOLAS AND DAVID IAN ASSOCIATES LTD
5th Floor 53 Parker Street London WC2B 5TT
Tel: 020 7427 8380 Fax: 020 7427 8381
Email: info@davidianproductions.com
Web Site: www.davidianproductions.com
General Manager: Max Finbow

NICHOLAS HENNEGAN LIMITED
33a Prebend Mansions, Chiswick High Road, London W4 2LU
Tel: 0789 49 50 176 Fax: 020 8582 7506
Email: nick@nicholashennegan.com
Web Site: www.nicholashennegan.com
Creative Producer: Nick Hennegan M.A.

NICK LEIGH ASSOCIATES LTD
The Lilac House, 32 Deneside, East Dean, Eastbourne, East Sussex BN20 0JG
Tel/Fax: 01323 423 439 Mobile: 07710 824 304
Email: nlauk@btinternet.com
Senior Personnel: Nick Leigh

NIMAX THEATRES LTD
1 Lumley Court, Off 402 Strand, London WC2R 0NB
Tel:020 7395 0780 Fax: 020 7240 4540
Email: general@nimaxtheatres.com
Web Site: www.nimaxtheatres.com
Chief Executive: Nica Burns
Executive Director: Joan Moynihan
General Manager: Emma Brünjes

NOEL GAY ORGANISATION
19 Denmark Street, London WC2H 8NA
Tel: 020 7836 3941 Fax: 020 7287 1816
Email: info@noelgay.com
Web Site: www.noelgay.com
Chief Executive Officer: Alex Armitage
Managing Director: Nick Ranceford-Hadley

NORMAN MEADMORE LTD
23 Westfield Road, Bishop's Stortford, Hertfordshire CM23 2RE
Tel: 01279 652371 Fax: 01279 757903
Managing Director: Andrew Meadmore

NORTHERN STAGE
Barras Bridge, Newcastle-upon-Tyne, Tyne and Wear NE1 7RH
Admin: 0191 232 3366 BO: 0191 230 5151 Fax: 0191 242 7257
Email: info@northernstage.co.uk
Web Site: www.northernstage.co.uk
ADMINISTRATION:
Chief Executive:
Artistic Director: Lorne Campbell
Director of Theatre Operations: Edmund Nickols
Administrative Director: Susan Coffer
Professional middle-scale venue with up to 15 weeks per year devoted to festivals, touring theatre and middle-scale dance. The theatre is now the home for core work for Northern Stage. Other activities include daytime conferences/seminars, foyer installations, exhibitions and participatory workshops.

THE OKAI COLLIER COMPANY
The Bell Tower, St. Barnabas Church, Grove Road, London E3 5TG
Tel: 020 8980 5716/ 020 8981 6511
Mob: 07947 338 704
Email: info@okaicollier.co.uk
Web Site: www.okaicollier.co.uk
Artistic Director: Omar F. Okai
CEO/Producer: Simon James Collier

OPERA NORTH
Opera North, Grand Theatre, 46 New Briggate, Leeds LS1 6NU
Tel: 0113 243 9999
Marketing: 0113 223 3500
Email: info@operanorth.co.uk
Web Site: www.operanorth.co.uk
ADMINISTRATION:
General Manager: Richard Ashton
Marketing Manager: Hazel Arthur
Technical & Operations Director: Ric Green

OPERETTA FOR ALL
185 Syon Lane, Isleworth, Middlesex TW7 5PU UK
Tel/Fax: 020 8560 5988
Performing Management: Angela Jenkins
Package deals; musicals, operetta, music hall etc.

OVATION
Upstairs at the Gatehouse, Highgate Village, London N6 4BD
Tel: 020 8340 4256 Fax: 020 8340 3466
Email: events@ovationproductions.com
Web Site: www.ovationproductions.com / www.ovationtheatres.com
Partners: Katie & John Plews

PAINES PLOUGH
4th Floor, 43 Aldwych, London WC2B 4DN
Tel: 020 7240 4533 Fax: 020 7240 4534
Email: office@painesplough.com
Web Site: www.painesplough.com
Artistic Directors: George Perrin and James Grieve
Producer: Tara Wilkinson
General Manager: Claire Simpson
Administrative Assistant: Hanna Streeter
A national touring company specialising in accessible new plays.

PANTONI PANTOMIMES
205 Bexhill Road, St Leonard's-on-Sea, East Sussex TN38 8BG
Tel: 01424 443 400 Fax: 01424 714 847
Mob: 07770 600262
Email: david@pantoni.com
Web Site: www.pantoni.com
Managing Director: David Lee
Director/ Choreographer: Rita Proctor
Theatrical producers specialising in first class pantomimes, floorshows for cruise lines, holiday centres and corporate events. Also producing children's shows and theatre tours.

PLAYBOARD PUPPET THEATRE
The Black Barn The Street, Tibenham, Norwich NR16 1QA
Tel/Fax: 020 7226 5911
Email: buttonmoon@btconnect.com
Web Site: www.buttonmoon.tv
Director: Ian Allen
Administrator: Vicky Clinch
Puppets In Vision. Playboard Puppets presents its creations of imagination workshops in all forms of puppetry at the Norfolk Barn. Courses run from Spring to Autumn. Playboard Puppets is famous for the cult TV series "Button Moon", and many more. The Company has been going for 35 years touring shows, doing theatre workshop and television with puppetry; where participants get the feel of working on a spoof puppet murder mystery.

PLAYERS' THEATRE
12 Bentinck Street, London W1U 2ER
Tel: 020 7839 1134 Mob: 07770 281746
Email: enquiries@playerstheatre.co.uk
Web Site: www.playerstheatre.co.uk
ADMINISTRATION:
Props: Players Theatre Club
Chairman of Players' Restoration Committee: Bill Halson
Promotion: Laura Davies
Policy: Victorian Music Hall, Melodrama & Pantomime.
Outside hire available

PMA PRODUCTIONS LIMITED
The Old Stables 38 Church Street, Barrowford, Nelson, Lancashire BB9 6EB
Tel / Fax: 01282 612503 Prod Mob: 07768 013469
Email: info@pmaproductions.co.uk, Georgepma1@mac.com
Web Site: www.pmaproductions.co.uk
ADMINISTRATION:
Artistic Director / Producer: George Critchley
Specialising in: Pantomimes, Children's Theatre, Corporate Presentations and Theatre in Education.

P&O CRUISES
Carnival House 100 Harbour Parade, Southampton SO15 1ST
Tel: 0845 358 5585 Mrkting Tel: 023 8065 6701 Fax: 023 8065 7030
Email: reservations@pocruises.com
Web Site: www.pocruises.com
Managing Director: David Dingle
Marketing Manager: Philip Price

PRELUDE
Suite 3,Ground Floor Nimax House 20 Ullswater Crescent Coulsdon Surrey CR5 2HR
Tel: 020 8660 6647 Fax: 010 8660 6657
Email: sales@preludeentertainment.co.uk
Web Site: www.preludeentertainment.co.uk
Managing Director: Rodney Prout
Administrator: Julianne Basten
Specialising in a variety of entertainment for corporate and private events.

PREMIER STAGE PRODUCTIONS LTD
Unit 16, Randalls Road Mole Business Park Leatherhead Surrey KT22 7BA
Tel: 01372 362722
Email: info@premier-productions.co.uk
Web: www.premier-productions.co.uk
Directors: Jason Francis and Nick George
Booking & Production Manager: Stephen Smart
Specialising in Children's Theatre Shows.

PSYCHODROME PRODUCTIONS
85 Charing Cross Road, London WC2H 0AA
Email: robertfarrar@hotmail.com

Web Site: www.psychodrome.co.uk
Contact: Robert Farrar

QDOS ENTERTAINMENT
Qdos House, Queen Margarets Road, Scarborough, North Yorkshire YO11 2YH
Tel: 01723 500 038 Fax: 01723 361 958
Email: info@qdosentertainment.co.uk
Web Site: www.qdosentertainment.co.uk
Chairman: Nick Thomas
Producers, theatre operators, talent management, as well as suppliers of sets, scenery and costumes for hire.

QDOS PANTOMIMES
2nd Floor, 161 Drury Lane, London WC2B 5PN
Tel: 0207 430 7900 Fax: 0207 831 6329
Email: www.pantomime.com
ADMINISTRATION:
Props: Qdos Entertainment
Chairman: Nick Thomas
Managing Director: Michael Harrison

THE REALLY USEFUL GROUP
22 Tower Street, London WC2H 9TW
Tel: 020 7240 0880 Fax: 020 7240 1204
Email: reception@reallyuseful.co.uk
Web Site: www.reallyuseful.com
Proprieter: Andrew Lloyd Webber
Head of Theatres: Barney Wragg
Chief Financial Officer: Bishu Chakraborty
Legal and Business Affairs: Jonathan Hull
Chairman: Mark Wordsworth

THE REP COLLEGE
17 St. Mary's Avenue, Purley-on-Thames, Berkshire RG8 8BJ
Tel: 0118 942 1144
Email: contact@repcollege.co.uk , tudor@repcollege.co.uk
Web Site: www.repcollege.co.uk
Directors: David Tudor and Elizabeth Lane

REPLAY PRODUCTIONS
Old Museum Arts Centre, 7 College Square North, Belfast BT1 6AR
Tel: 028 9032 2773 Fax: 028 9032 2724
Email: info@replaytheatreco.org, admin@replaytheatreco.org
Web Site: www.replaytheatreco.org
Artistic Director: Anna Newell
Operations Manager: Fiona Bell
Administrative Officer: Irene Swift
Executive Director: Einear Henry
Award-winning Replay Productions is a professional educational theatre company based in Belfast. Est. in 1988, Replay is dedicated to providing high quality theatre that entertains, educates and stimulates children and young people of all abilities whilst supporting and inspiring the adults that work with, and care for them. The company tours schools and venues throughout Northern Ireland. All projects provide unique curriculum support, encourage increased understanding, development and learning (both at school level and in life skills) and promote concepts of cultural identity and diversity.

RIDING LIGHTS
Friargate Theatre, Lower Friargate, York YO1 9SL
Tel: 01904 655 317 BO: 01904 613 000
Fax: 01904 651 532
Email: rltc@rltc.org
Web Site: www.ridinglights.org
Executive Director: Jonathan Brown
Artistic Director: Paul Burbridge
Touring company ranging from small scale and community work to major touring productions. 100 seat studio theatre in York.

THE RIPLEY-DUGGAN PARTNERSHIP
Theatre Production Brokerage
21 Goodge Street, London W1T 2QG
Tel: 020 7436 1392 Fax: 020 7436 1395
Email: info@ripleyduggan.com
Contact: Gregg Ripley-Duggan
Administrator: Pascal Ciudicelli

RIVERBANK PRODUCTIONS
Ickworth 9 Firbank Drive Woking Surrey GU21 7QT
Tel: 020 7117 6321
Email: tom/mike@riverbankproductions.co.uk
Web: www.riverbankproductions.co.uk
Directors: Mike Brooks, Tom O'Shea, Emma Frederick
Touring Children's Shows through UK and Ireland

MICHAEL ROSE LTD
The Old Dairy, Throop Road, Holdenhurst, Bournemouth, Dorset BH8 0DL
Tel: 01202 522 711 Fax: 01202 522 311
Email: michael@michaelroseltd.com
Directors: Michael Rose, David Morgan

ROYAL EXCHANGE THEATRE
St. Ann's Square Manchester M2 7DH
SD: 0161 833 9333 BO: 0161 833 9833
Fax: 0161 832 0881
Email: marketing@royalexchange.co.uk
Web Site: www.royalexchange.co.uk
ADMINISTRATION:
Funded by NWAB; Association of Greater Manchester
Local Authority: Manchester City Council
Artistic Director: Sarah Frankcom
Executive Director: Fiona Gasper
Producer (Studio): Richard Morgan
Marketing Director: Clare Will
Senior Press Officer: John Goodfellow
History: Largest theatre-in-the-round in the country, opened in 1976. Auditorium is futuristic steel and glass structure built within the Great Hall (now a vast foyer) of Manchester's former Cotton Exchange (present building dates from 1921). Theatre architects were Levitt Bernstein Associates (in collaboration with Richard Negri). Royal Exchange is situated in city centre, entrances in Cross Street and St. Ann's Square. The Theatre was completely refurbished in 1998 following extensive bomb damage, with Studio theatre added.
For the Disabled: Up to 8 wheelchair spaces - sound reinforcement system - Braille performances, audio description. Studio fully accessible with 6 wheelchair spaces.
Seats: 750 raked on three levels. Studio 120 on flat floor, flexible.
Catering: Self-service, fully licensed Café Exchange 12.00pm. Evening restaurant 5.30pm - curtain up. Bar Exchange 9.30am - 11.00pm. 4 interval bars. Group catering for pre-show refreshments on request. Function rooms for hire.

ROYAL SHAKESPEARE COMPANY
Chapel Lane Stratford-upon-Avon, Warwickshire CV37 6BB
Tel: 01789 296655 BO: 0844 800 1110
Fax: 01789 294810
Email: dean.asker@rsc.org.uk
Web Site: www.rsc.org.uk
Theatre Manager: James Kitto
Communications Officer: Dean Asker

SANDOW CLOWNS
59 Thoresby Close, Bridlington, East Yorkshire YO16 7EN
Tel: 01262 671 492 Fax: 01262 675 543
Mob 1: 07969 933 236 Mob 2 :07964 274 186
Email: fossett@supanet.com
Web Site: www.sandowclowns.co.uk
Contact: Tom Bratby or Sheila Bratby
Clown show "circus party" on stage, in the round, schools, civic venues, galas.

SCHTANHAUS
Please see 'Paines Plough' listing
14 Thanet Lodge, Mapesbury Road, London NW2 4JA
Tel: 07973 343 429 (Emma Stenning)
Fax: 0870 285 1677
Email: emmas@schtanhaus.co.uk, mail@schtanhaus.co.uk
Web Site: www.schtanhaus.co.uk
Executive Producers: Emma Stenning or Tom Morris
Financial Director: Daniel Morgenstern
Producer: Sally Gibson and Catherine Morgenstern

SCOTTISH CHAMBER ORCHESTRA
4 Royal Terrace, Edinburgh, Mid Lothian EH7 5AB Scotland
Tel: 0131 557 6800 Fax: 0131 557 6933
Email: info@sco.org.uk, roy@sco.org.uk
Web Site: www.sco.org.uk
Managing Director: Roy McEwan
Concerts Director: Judith Colman
Marketing Director: Ann Monfries
Finance Director: Graham Reid

SERIO ENSEMBLE
24 Garton House, 119 Hornsey Lane, Islington, London N6 5XB
Tel: 020 7281 7683 Fax: 0121 501 6729
Email: serio_ensemble@hotmail.com
Artistic Director: Charles Serio

SHETLAND ARTS DEVELOPMENT AGENCY
Mareel Lerwick, Shetland ZE1 0WQ Scotland
Tel: +44 (0)1595 743843
Email: info@shetlandarts.org
Web Site: www.shetlandarts.org
Director: Gwilym Gibbons
Head of Development: Kathy Hubbard
Marketing Officer: Lisa Ward
Office Administrator: Lynda Anderson
Administrative Assistant: Helen Smith
Shetland Arts seeks to promote all art forms in Shetland, running an Arts Office and the Garrison Theatre in Lerwick, and Bonhoga Gallery in Weisdale Mill, and promotes a year round programme of music, craft, theatre, literature, visual arts, dance and film events.

MARC SINDEN PRODUCTIONS
1 Hogarth Hill, London NW11 6AY
Tel: 020 8455 3278 Fax: 020 8455 3278
Email: producer@sindenproductions.com
Web Site: www.sindenproductions.com
Contact by post only.
Director: Marc Sinden

SOHO THEATRE COMPANY
21 Dean Street, London W1D 3NE
Tel: 020 7287 5060 Fax: 020 7287 5061
Email: amandaj@sohotheatre.com
Web Site: www.sohotheatre.com
Artistic Director: Steve Marmion
Admin Producer: Mark Godfrey
Writers Centre Director: Nina Stiger
Soho Theatre Company is dedicated to the discovery and development of new writers. The company reads and reports on over 1500 scripts a year and runs an extensive development programme, which gives writers advice, support, workshops, rehearsed readings and commissions. The venue includes a 150 seat theatre, 80 seat studio and a Writers' Centre as well as a bar, restaurant, offices, rehearsal rooms and, uniquely, space for writers - everything the company needs to house its bold, artistic policy under one roof. The eclectic and diverse programme presents bold new plays alongside new and established comedians. For further information on the venue or the company's work contact Soho Theatre Company.

SONIA FRIEDMAN PRODUCTIONS LTD
A subsidiary of the Ambassador Theatre Group
Duke of York's Theatre 104 St. Martin's Lane, London WC2N 4BG
Tel: 020 7845 8750 Fax: 020 7845 8759
Email: office@soniafriedman.com
Web Site: www.soniafriedman.com
ADMINISTRATION:
Producer: Sonia Friedman
General Manager: Diane Benjamin
Head of Production: Pam Skinner

SPARE TYRE THEATRE COMPANY
Unit 3.22, Canterbury Court, 1-3 Brixton Road, London SW9 6DE
Tel: 0207 061 6454
Email: lucy@sparetyre.org, berni@sparetyre.org
Web www.sparetyretheatrecompany.co.uk
Artistic Director / CEO: Richard Oyarzabal
General Manager: Berni Bishop
Administrator: Lucy Dalzell
Theatre training company running projects with disadvantaged groups such as young people with learning disabilities, gay men and lesbians and third age elders. Productions are toured locally.

SPILLERS PANTOMIMES LTD
Park House, 1 Millstream Green, Willesborough, Ashford, Kent TN24 0SU
Tel: 01233 666 839 Mob: 07773 330 015
Email: jkspillers@talktalk.net / bev.berridge@btinternet.com
Managing Director: John Spillers
Production Director: Bev Berridge
Production Co-ordinator: Elizabeth Kay
Producers of pantomimes and musical shows for over 20 years.
Our style of production is 'Traditional Pantomime' with a 'Modern Twist'

SPLATS ENTERTAINMENT
5 Denmark Street, Covent Garden, London WC2H 8LP
Mob: 07944 283659 Tel: 0800 028 8101
Email: mike@splatsentertainment.co.uk
Web Site: www.splatsentertainment.co.uk
Contact: Steve Richards
Theatre Director: Mike Redwood

BARRIE STACEY U.K. PRODUCTIONS LTD
7-8 Shaldon Mansions, 132 Charing Cross Road, London WC2H 0LA
Tel: 020 7836 6220 / 4128 Fax: 020 7836 2949
Email: hopkinstacey@aol.com
Directors: Keith and Barrie Stacey
Tours 1st class Childrens' Musicals and Songbooks: 'West End To Broadway', 'Cole Porters Story', 'Jerome Kern Songbook'.

STAGESAFE
13 Portland Road, Street, Somerset BA16 9PX
Tel: 01458 445 186 Mob: 07831 437 062
Email: info@stagesafe.co.uk
Web Site: www.stagesafe.co.uk
Senior Personnel: Chris Hannam
Stagesafe provide health and safety services to the live music, event and entertainment industries.

STAGESTRUCK LTD
Flint Hall, Anstey, Buntingford, Hertfordshire SG9 0DN
Tel: 1763 848 011 Fax: 1763 848 969
Email: liz@stagestruck.com
Web Site: www.stagestruck.com
Managing Director: Liz Bagnall
Creative Director: Karl Elliott
HR Advisor: Meera Godhania

THE STENNETT COMPANY
Craig-y-Nos, Rhiwbina Hill, Cardiff, South Glamorgan CF14 6UP Wales
Tel: 029 2062 5276 Mob: 07974 677559
Email: ceristennett@gmail.com
Partners: Stan Stennett, Ceri Stennett & Roger Stennett

ROBERT STIGWOOD ORGANISATION LTD
Barton Manor, Barton Estate, East Cowes, Isle of Wight PO32 6LB
Tel: 01983 280 676 Fax: 01983 293 923
Senior Personnel: Robert Stigwood, Patrick Bywalski, David Herring.
Theatrical and Film Producers.

SUFFOLK SUMMER THEATRES
4 Foster Close Southwold Suffolk IP18 4LE
Tel: 01502 724462
Email: enquiries@southwoldtheatre.org
Web Site: www.southwoldtheatre.org
Producers: Peter Adshead (General Manager)
Anthony Falkingham (Artistic Director & Administrator) and Mark Sterling.
Producing summer rep season at St. Edmund's Hall, Southwold & the Jubilee Hall, Aldeburgh.
Twitter: @suffolktheathre
Fackbook: Southwold & Aldeburgh Summer Theathre

SWANSEA LITTLE THEATRE COMPANY LTD
Dylan Thomas Theatre, Maritime Quarter, 7 Gloucester Place, Swansea SA1 1TY
Tel: 01792 473238
Email: info@dylanthomastheatre.org.uk
Web: www.swansealittletheatre.org.uk
Artistic Chairman and Contact: Dreena Morgan-Harvey

SWEENEY ENTERTAINMENTS
Methven House 26 Stoke Road Methwold Norfolk IP26 4PE
Tel: 01366 380333 Fax: 05601 158592
Email: info@sweeneyentertainments.co.uk
Web: www.sweeneyentertainments.co.uk
Contact: Julie Sweeney
Theatrical tour booking and production company.

T.B.A. MUSIC
1 St. Gabriels Road, London NW2 4DS
Tel: 0845 120 3722 Fax: 0700 607 0808
Email: peter@tbagroup.co.uk
Director: Peter Benda
TMA Members

TALKING HEADS PRODUCTION LTD
2-4 Noel Street, London W1F 8GB
Tel: 020 7292 7575 Fax: 020 7292 7576
Email: johnsachs@talkingheadproductions.com
Web Site: www.talkingheadsproductions.com
Senior Personnel: John Sachs
Specialising in film production, music supervision, casting and supervision of animation and production.

TARGET LIVE
45-51 Whitfield Street, London W1T 4HB
Tel: 020 3372 0950 / 0900 Fax: 020 3372 0951 / 0901
Email: info@target-live.co.uk, david.bloom@target-live.co.uk
Web: www.target-media.co.uk/index.html
Manager: Guy Chapman

TASTE PRODUCTIONS
Beaminster School, Newtown, Beaminster, Dorset DT8 3EP
Tel: 01308 862633
Email: tasteproductions@gmail.com
Web Site: www.tasteproductions.co.uk
Producer/Director: Valerie Goodwin

TEG PRODUCTIONS LTD
Third Floor, 26 Goodge Street London W1T 2QG
Tel: 020 7379 1066 Fax: 020 7836 9454
Email: enquiries@tegproductions.com
Web Site: www.tegproductions.com
Theatre producers presenting both plays and musicals in London's West End and on UK national tour.

THAT'S ENTERTAINMENT ASSOCIATES
Upham Hall, Green Lane, Kessingland, Lowestoft, Suffolk NR33 7RP
Tel: 01502 742 011 Mob: 07970 421403
Email: kenny.cantor@virgin.net
Web www.cantorstheatreschool.co.uk
Senior Personnel: Kenny Cantor
Supply, produce and direct various types of entertainment for holiday centres, cruise ships, etc.

THE LONDON THEATRE COMPANY
46 Wormholt Road, London W12 0LS
Tel: 020 8749 2619 Fax: 020 8749 0358
Email: mt@TheLondonTheatreCompany.co.uk
The London Theatre Company is primarily an international touring company for productions originating in London.

THE ONE NIGHT BOOKING COMPANY
1 Hogarth Hill, London NW11 6AY
Tel: 020 8455 3278
Email: info@onenightbooking.com
Web Site: www.onenightbooking.com
Contact: Marc Sinden
Contact by post only.
Also see listings for sister companies, MARC SINDEN PRODUCTIONS and UK THEATRE AVAILABILITY.

THE TOURING CONSORTIUM
41 Beresford Road London N8 0AL
Tel: 08445 880 848
Email: info@touringcorsortium.com
Web Site: www.touringconsortium.com
Producer: Jenny King
Associate Producer: Neale Birch
Production Assisstant: Anne McArthur
Financial Administration: Bob Thomas
Marketing: Jane Morgan Associates

THEATRE IS
The Hat Factory 65-67 Bute Street Luton LU1 2EY
Tel: 01582 481 221
Email: info@theatreis.org, stuart@theatreis.org
Web Site: www.theatreis.org
Contacts: Stuart Mullins, Creative Director; Michael Corley, Communications Co-ordinator.
Our mission is to research, develop and produce the best possible performing arts for the young people of the East of England aged 25 and under.
In placing young people at the heart of our organization we respect them as consumers and makers of theatre. We will therefore, pioneer new ways of making theatre for young people empowering them to become the cultural leaders of the future.

THEATRE OF COMEDY COMPANY LTD
Shaftesbury Theatre, 210 Shaftesbury Avenue, London WC2H 8DP
Tel: 020 7379 3345 Fax: 020 7836 8181
Email: lrugg@toc.dltentertainment.co.uk
Executive Producer: James Williams
Company founded in 1983 by Ray Cooney and leading comedy actors and writers.

THEATRE PRODUCTIONS LTD
Linton House, 1 High Street, Linton, Derbyshire DE12 6QL
Tel: 0845 8802427 Fax: 01283 763106
Email: sales@theatre-productions.com
Web Site: www.theatre-productions.com
Producer/ Director: Stephen Leatherland
Sales and Marketing Director: Karie Musson
Production and Stage Manager: Russell Gould
One of Britain's leading and innovative production companies. Its' repertoire of new plays, musicals, variety and concert based Shows have proven both popular and commercially successful throughout the World.

THEATRE ROUNDABOUT LTD
859 Finchley Road, London NW11 8LX
Tel: 020 8455 4752 Mob: 07774 638800
Email: info@theatreroundabout.co.uk
Web Site: www.theatreroundabout.co.uk
Senior Personnel: William Fry

THEATRE ROYAL, STRATFORD EAST
Gerry Raffles Square, Stratford, London E15 1BN
Mgt: 020 8534 7374 BO: 020 8534 0310
Press Office: 020 8279 1110 Fax: 020 8534 8381
Email: theatreroyal@stratfordeast.com
Web Site: www.stratfordeast.com
Executive Director: Mary Caws
Artistic Director: Kerry Michael
General Manager: Lee Henderson
Press Department contact: fmussell@stratfordeast.com
The bulk of the year is taken up with own productions of new plays. No permanent company and a minimum technical and administrative staff. Play choice ranges from family shows like pantomimes, musicals, melodramas and farces through to controversial modern work, particularly with appeal to young audiences.
Occasional Sunday events, including variety and comedy nights.

ANDREW TREAGUS ASSOCIATES LTD
35 Soho Square, London W1D 3QX
Tel: 020 7851 0150 Fax: 020 7851 0151
Email: admin@at-assoc.co.uk
Contact: Andrew Treagus
Administrator: Philip Effemey
Theatrical General Management.

TRENDS ENTERTAINMENT
Unit 4, 9 Chorley Road, Blackpool, FY3 7XQ
Tel: 01253 396 534
Email: info@trendsentertainment.com
Web Site: www.trendsentertainment.com
Contact: Antony Johns

TRIUMPH PROSCENIUM PRODUCTIONS LTD
(See also Duncan C Weldon Productions Ltd)
33-39 Parsons Green Lane Fulham London SW6 4HH
Tel: 0905 657 0113
Email: dweldon@paulelliott.ltd.uk

TURTLE KEY ARTS
Ladbroke Hall, 79 Barlby Road, London W10 6AZ
Tel: 020 8964 5060 Fax: 020 8964 4080
Email: info@turtlekeyarts.org.uk
Web Site: www.turtlekeyarts.org.uk
Contact: Charlotte Cunningham, Alison King, Sean Dawson, Alan Bowyer, Ruth Naylor-Smith
Turtle Key Arts is a dynamic & versatile arts performance company that combines production, education, training & technical skills to serve theatre, dance companies, venues and disability organisations. Succesful productions range from children's work to physical theatre, dance and drama. Turtle Key act as producers and managers to a number of companies as well as producing their own shows and running a busy education and disability arts department.

UK ARTS INTERNATIONAL
1st Floor, 6 Shaw Street, Worcester WR1 3QQ
Tel: 01905 264 24 Fax: 01905 228 68
Email: janryan@ukarts.com
Web Site: www.ukarts.com
Director: Jan Ryan
Associate Director: Michelle Knight
Marketing Officer and Project Administration: Hayley Priddin
Presents & produces provocative and culturally diverse work in the UK & overseas.

UK PRODUCTIONS LTD
Churchmill House, Ockford Road, Godalming, Surrey GU7 1QY
Tel: 01483 423 600 Fax: 01483 418 486
Email: mail@ukproductions.co.uk
Web Site: www.ukproductions.co.uk
Director: Martin Dodd
Production Manager: Andy Batty
Administrator: Jo Day

UK THEATRE AVAILABILITY
1 Hogarth Hill, London NW11 6AY
Tel: 020 8455 3278
Email: mail@uktheatreavailability.co.uk
Directors: Marc Sinden, Carol Macdonald
Contact by post only.

VAMPIRES ROCK LTD
PO Box 8729, Newark, NG24 9BD
Tel: 01949 851 530 Fax: 01949 850 605
Email: nicky@vampiresrock.com
Web Site: www.vampiresrock.com
Director: Steven Murray
PR & Publicity: Jane Hirst
Merchandise & Website Information: Becky Cooney

ANTHONY VANDER ELST PRODUCTIONS
The Studio, 14 College Road, Bromley, Kent BR1 3NS
Tel: 020 8466 5580
Contact: Helen Melville

DENIS VAUGHAN MANAGEMENT
PO Box 2826, London N21 3WT
Tel: 020 7486 5353 Fax: 020 8224 0466
Email: dvaughanmusic@dial.pipex.com
Senior Personnel: Denis Vaughan

KEVIN WALLACE LTD
Amadeus House 27B Floral Street London WC2E 9DP
Tel: 020 7812 7238
Email: kevin@kevinwallace.co.uk
ADMINISTRATION:
Producer: Kevin Wallace

WELLIE BOOT PRODUCTIONS
P.O. Box 332, Rochdale, Lancashire OL12 7WD
Tel: 01706 353545 Fax: 01706 353545
Email: dale.mulgrew@zen.co.uk, jimmy@jimmycricket.co.uk
Web Site: www.jimmycricket.co.uk
Manager: Jimmy Cricket
Contact: Dale Mulgrew
Wellie Boot Productions is the ever popular Irish comedian Jimmy Cricket's entertainment Company. And There's More: We have many exciting shows and products featuring Jimmy on offer across all event platforms and we can provide creative solutions for your entertainment requirements.

WHIRLIGIG THEATRE
14 Belvedere Drive, Wimbledon, London SW19 7BY
Tel: 020 8947 1732 Fax: 020 8879 7648
Email: david.woodplays@virgin.net
Web Site: www.davidwood.org.uk
Directors: David Wood & John Gould
Administrator: Barry Sheppard
Whirligig no longer tours annually, but is open to offers for Christmas seasons and one-off productions, particularly of The Gingerbread Man.

WISE BUDDAH MUSIC RADIO
74 Great Titchfield Street, London W1W 7QP
Tel: 020 7307 1600 / 7447 Fax: 020 7307 1601
Email: info@wisebuddah.com
Web Site: www.wisebuddah.com
Senior Personnel: Maria Williams (maria.williams@wisebuddah.com)
Programming and audio production services.

WIZARD PRESENTS
The Coach House, Love Lane, Kings Langley, Hertfordshire WD4 9HL
Tel: 01923 260015 Mob 1: 07548 620 965 Mob 2: 07858 465 448
Email: danya@wizardpresents.co.uk
Web Site: www.wizardpresents.co.uk
Directors: Jon Miller & Danya Miller
Formed in 1995, this partnership of Bubble Lodge and Jon Miller was created to create, develop and produce new works.

WSG PRODUCTIONS LTD
14 Belvedere Drive, Wimbledon, London SW19 7BY
Tel: 020 8947 1732 Fax: 020 8879 7648
Email: david.woodplays@virgin.net
Web Site: www.davidwood.org.uk
Directors: David Wood & John Gould

SCOTT-PAUL YOUNG ENTERTAINMENTS LTD
(Spy Productions)
Northern Lights House, 110 Blandford Road North, Langley, Near Windsor, Berkshire SL3 7TA
Tel/Fax: 01753 693 250
Email: castingdirect@spy-ents.com
Web Site: www.spy-lightentsworld.com
Managing Director: Scott-Paul Young
Artists management and exclusive representation for films, television, commercials, theatre, sports and modelling events and all areas of the light entertainment industry.

YOUNG VIC THEATRE
66 The Cut, London SE1 8LZ
Mgt: 020 7922 2800 / 2805 BO: 020 7922 2922 Fax: 020 7820 2805
Email: info@youngvic.org
Web Site: www.youngvic.org
ADMINISTRATION:
Artistic Director: David Lan
Executive Director: Lucy Woollatt
General Manager: David Fletcher

Policy: Theatre.
Perfs: Phone or write or see Press for details.
Seats: 500- 600; Studio Space number 1: up to 160; Studio Space number 2: 80
Bar and restaurant.

ZAP ART
18 Beaconsfield Villas, Brighton BN1 6HD
Tel: 01273 500842 Fax: 01273 206 960
Email: dave.reeves@zapuk.com
Web Site: www.zapart.co.uk
Directors: Dave Reeves
Creative producers of the festivals, street theatre events & large scale spectaculars.

Theatre Owners/ Management

AMBASSADOR THEATRE GROUP LTD
39 - 41 CHARING CROSS ROAD, LONDON WC2H 0AR
Admin: 020 7534 6100
Admin Fax: 020 7534 6109
info@theambassadors.com
www.theambassadors.com

Charing Cross Branch
ADMINISTRATION:
Joint CEO and Creative Director: Howard Panter
Head of Production: Meryl Faiers (020 7534 6120)

AMBASSADOR THEATRE GROUP LTD (HEAD OFFICE) THE PEACOCKS CENTRE, WOKING, SURREY GU21 6GQ

Tel: 01483 545 800 Fax: 01483 770 477
info@theambassadors.com
www.theambassadors.com
Joint Chief Executive: Rosemary Squire
Marketing Director: Pat Westwell
Finance & Commercial Director: Helen Enright
Head Office Administrator: Kathy Longdon

HQ THEATRES LTD 2ND FLOOR 161 DRURY LANE COVENT GARDEN LONDON WC2B 5PN

Tel: 020 7430 5370 Fax: 020 7430 5388
info@hqtheatres.com
www.hqtheatres.com
ADMINISTRATION:
Props: Qdos Entertainment
Chief Executive Officer: Derek Nicholls
General Manager: Stuart Shanks
Managing Director, HQ Hospitality: James Giles
HQ Theatres operates the following venues:
Cliffs Pavilion (Southend), Palace Theatre (Southend), Beck Theatre (Hayes), G Live (Guildford), Orchard Theatre (Dartford), Wycombe Swan Theatre & Town Hall (High Wycombe), Wyvern Theatre (Wiltshire), White Rock Theatre (Hastings), Watford Colosseum (Watford). G Live (Guildford)

LIVE NATION MUSIC UK REGENT ARCADE HOUSE, 1ST FLOOR, 19-25 ARGYLL STREET, LONDON W1F 7TS

Tel: 020 7009 3333 Fax: 0870 0949100
barry.clayman@livenation.co.uk
www.livenation.co.uk
Contact: Barry Clayman OBE

NIMAX THEATRES LTD 1 LUMLEY COURT, OFF 402 STRAND, LONDON WC2R 0NB

Tel:020 7395 0780 Fax: 020 7240 4540
general@nimaxtheatres.com
www.nimaxtheatres.com
Chief Executive: Nica Burns
Executive Director: Joan Moynihan
General Manager: Emma Brünjes

Ballet, Opera & Dance Companies

ADZIDO DANCE ENSEMBLE

Canonbury Business Centre, 202 New North Road, London N1 7BL
Tel: 0171 359 7453 Fax: 0171 704 0300
Email: pat@adzido.co.uk, info@adzido.co.uk
Web: www.adzido-pan-african-dance.co.uk
ADMINISTRATION:
Artistic Director: George Dzikunu
Touring & Marketing Director: Amanda Davis
Email: amanda@adzido.co.uk

RICHARD ALSTON DANCE COMPANY

The Place, 16 Flaxman Terrace, London WC1H 9PY
Tel: 020 7387 0324 Fax: 020 7383 5700
Email: radc@theplace.org.uk
Web Site: www.theplace.org.uk
Director: Richard Alston
Rehearsal Director: Martin Lawrance

BALLET CENTRAL

10 Herbal Hill, Clerkenwell Road, London EC1R 5EG
Tel: 020 7837 6332 Fax: 020 7833 5571
Email: companymanager@csbschool.co.uk
Web: www.centralschoolofballet.co.uk
ADMINISTRATION:
Director: Sarah Matthews
Ballet Central Company Manager: Emma Larid
A company of 16 young dancers undertaking British regional tours from March to July each year. Mixed programme of classical, jazz and contemporary works.

BALLET IRELAND

Agher, Summerhill, Co Meath Eire
Tel: +353 (0) 46 955 7585 Fax: +353 (0) 46 955 7585 Mob: +353 (0) 86 8261196
Email: balletireland@eircom.net
Web Site: www.balletireland.com
Managing Director: Anne Maher
Ballet Ireland is a classically based company touring two major seasons a year in Ireland and the UK.

BIRMINGHAM OPERA COMPANY

205 The Argent Centre, 60 Frederick Street, Birmingham B1 3HS
Tel: 0121 246 6644 Fax: 0121 246 6633
Email: info@birminghamopera.org.uk
Web Site: www.birminghamopera.org.uk
ADMINISTRATION:
Artistic Director: Graham Vick
General Manager: Jean Nicholson

BIRMINGHAM ROYAL BALLET

Thorp Street, Birmingham B5 4AU
Tel: 0121 245 3500 Fax: 0121 245 3570
Email: info@brb.org.uk
Web Site: www.brb.org.uk
Director: David Bintley
Chief Executive: Christopher Barron
Based in Birmingham and touring to London, other cities throughout Great Britain and overseas.

BUXTON FESTIVAL

10-26 July 2015
3 The Square, Buxton, Derbyshire SK17 6AZ
Admin: 01298 70395 BO: 0845 127 2190
Accommodation: 01298 25106 Fax: 01298 72289
Email: info@buxtonfestival.co.uk
Web Site: www.buxtonfestival.co.uk
Chairman:Lord Hattersley
General Manager: Glyn Foley
Artistic Director: Andrew Greenwood
Buxton Opera House S/Cap: 950

CARL CAMPBELL DANCE COMPANY 7

Caribbean Dance Theatre, Kingswood House, Kingswood Estate Seeley Drive, London SE21 8QR
Tel/Fax/Minicom: 020 8670 4792 Mobile: 07740201586
Email: ccdc7@easynet.co.uk
Web Site: www.ccdc7.co.uk
Artistic Director: Carl Campbell
Carl Campbell Dance Company 7 has been in existance for over 30 years and is Britain's only contemporary Caribbean Dance Theatre. The Company has a deep commitment to the educational development of Caribbean Dance Culture as a performing art.

CANDOCO DANCE COMPANY

2T Leroy House, 436 Essex Road, London N1 3QP
Tel: 020 7704 6845 Fax: 020 7704 1645
Email: info@candoco.co.uk
Web Site: www.candoco.co.uk
ADMINISTRATION:
A contemporary dance company of disabled and non-disabled dancers, performing both national and international productions.
Co-Artistic Director: Pedro Machado and Stine Nilsen
General Manager: Joanne Lyons
Studio rehearsal address: ANTC, Wood Lane, Stanmore, HA7 4AP, Middlesex, UK.

CARL ROSA OPERA

359 Hackney Road, Shoreditch London E2 8PR
Tel: 020 7613 0777 Fax: 020 7613 0859
Email: info@carlrosaopera.co.uk
Web Site: www.carlrosaopera.co.uk
ADMINISTRATION:

Musical Director: Wyn Davies
Artistic Director: Peter Mulloy
Honorary Head of Artistic Development: Valerie Masterson CBE
The Carl Rosa Opera is Britain's oldest opera company, founded in 1873. We tour between twenty and forty weeks a year, with a touring company and orchestra of sixty-five. Our repertory is presently Opera, Operetta, Gilbert & Sullivan and Musical Theatre. We present our stage productions in number one Theatres and Concert Halls only, but have plans to also produce mid-scale tours with a full education programme. We have a music Library and make/produce our own sets, costumes and props from our own studios. Yearly tour to America also Australia, New Zealand & Canada every second year. Visits festivals in Russia, France, Italy and Greece.

CEDAR DANCE ANIMATIONS

42 Gunton Road, London E5 9JS
Email: info@cedardanceanimations.com
Web: www.cedardanceanimations.com
Contact: Janet Randell
Cedar Dance Animations is involved in the introduction and promotion of innovative performance and education material in the field of 3D animation and digital dance.

THE CHOLMONDELEYS

(See also The Featherstonehaughs)
Unit 1.1, Lafone House, The Leather Market, 11-13 Leather Market Street, London SE1 3HN
Tel: 020 7378 8800 Fax: 020 7378 8810
Email: admin@thecholmondeleys.org
Web Site: www.thecholmondeleys.org
Artistic Director/ Choreographer: Lea Anderson
General Manager: Jo Stendall

CHOU CHOU BALLET COMPANY

27 Iona Close, Ravensbourne Park, Catford, London SE6 4YN
Tel: 020 8690 6329 Fax: 020 8690 6329
Contact: Mrs R Gordon
A company of young performers (age 8-17) who perform both classical repertoire and authentic character dance from many cultures. Available for concerts, open-air and indoor. Videos, workshops, demonstrations undertaken.

CLONTER OPERA THEATRE

Swettenham Heath, Congleton, Cheshire CW12 2LR
Admin: 01260 224 638 BO: 01260 224 514 Marketing: 01260 224 638 Fax: 01260 224 742
Email: clonter@clonteropera.com
Web Site: www.clonteropera.com
Artistic Director: Jeffery Lockett

CO -OPERA CO.

5 Orchard Business Centre, Kangley Bridge Road, London SE26 5AQ
Tel: 020 8699 8650
Email: info@co-opera-co.org
Web Site: www.co-opera-co.org
Artistic Director: Kate Flowers
General Manager: Paul Need

DANCE UMBRELLA

15-31 October 2015
1 Brewery Square London SE1 2LF
Tel: 020 7407 1200
Email: mail@danceumbrella.co.uk
Web Site: www.danceumbrella.co.uk
Artistic Director: Emma Gladstone
Executive Director : Anu Giri
Dance Umbrella is London's international contemporary dance Festival and supports and encourages the best of the new in dance work both in Britain and overseas.

DANCE UNITED

Interchange Studios, Hampstead Town Hall, 213 Haverstock Hill, London NW3 4QP
Tel: 0207 431 6647 Fax: 0207 794 9989
Email: info@dance-united.com
Web Site: www.dance-united.com
ADMINISTRATION:
Artistic Director: Tara-Jane Herbert
Projects Manager: Camilla Joysury
Marketing Coordinator: Rowena Evans
Dance United brings individuals and communities together to seek creative solutions to artistic challenges, triggering a process that develops social interaction and personal growth in participants. The company believes that dance has a unique quality that can, when delivered through a tried-and-tested methodology, create profound and life-changing experiences for those it works with.

DELPHINE Y DOMINGO

4 Cormorant Rise, Worcester, Worcestershire WR2 4BA
Tel: 01905 424 083
Email: delphineflamenco@tiscali.co.uk
Contact: D Auchterlonie
Also known as "Flamenco Productions", specialising in quality Flamenco Music and Dance for Television, Theatre, Promotion and Education.

DIVERSIONS DANCE COMPANY

Dance House, Wales Millennium Centre, Pierhead Street, Cardiff Bay, CF10 4PH Wales
Tel: 029 20 635600 Fax: 029 20 635601
Email: info@ndcwales.co.uk
Web Site: www.diversionsdance.co.uk
ADMINISTRATION:
Artistic Director: Ann Sholem
Technical Director: Joe Fletcher
Marketing & Publicity Officer: Clare Nedin
A company of 11 dancers touring a mixed programme of contemporary dance by international choreographers throughout the UK and overseas.

D'OYLY CARTE OPERA COMPANY

295 Kennington Road, London SE11 4QE
Tel : 0844 606 0007 Fax: 020 7820 0240
Email: mail@doylycarte.org.uk
Web Site: www.doylycarte.org.uk
Chairman: David Walton
General Manager: Ian Martin
Music Director: John Owen Edwards
Founded by Richard D'Oyly Carte in the 1870's, the Company has been performing the opera's of Gilbert and Sullivan for almost 130 years.

DV8 PHYSICAL THEATRE

Artsadmin, Toynbee Studios, 28 Commercial Street, London E1 6AB
Tel: 020 7655 0977 Fax: 020 7247 5103
Email: dv8@artsadmin.co.uk
Web Site: www.dv8.co.uk
Artistic Director: Lloyd Newson
Operations manager: Louise Eltringham
Production Manager: Jamie Maisey

EARTHFALL

Chapter, Market Road, Cardiff, South Glamorgan CF5 1QE Wales
Tel: 029 2022 1314 Mobile: 07900 496428 (Marketing) Fax: 029 2034 2259
Email: earthfall@earthfall.org.uk
Web Site: www.earthfall.org.uk
ADMINISTRATION:
Artistic Directors: Jessica Cohen & Jim Ennis
Email: artistic@earthfall.org.uk
General Manager: Stephan Stockton
Marketing Officer: Lewis Gwyther
Radical dance theatre touring throughout the UK and overseas, using live music, text, film and extreme dance.

ENGLISH COUNTRY GARDEN OPERA COMPANY

Upper House Farm, Upper House Lane, Shamley Green, Near Guildford, Surrey GU5 0SX
Tel: 01483 278 203
Email: vanessa@vanessafordproductions.co.uk
Web: www.vanessafordproductions.co.uk
Director: Vannessa Ford

ENGLISH NATIONAL BALLET LTD

Markova House, 39 Jay Mews, London SW7 2ES
Tel: 020 7581 1245 Fax: 020 7225 0827
Email: info@ballet.org.uk, comments@ballet.org.uk
Web Site: www.ballet.org.uk
ADMINISTRATION:
Artistic Director: Wayne Eagling
Technical Director: Alan Riches
Director of Operations: Andrew Morgan

ENGLISH NATIONAL OPERA
London Coliseum, St Martin's Lane, London WC2N 4ES
Admin: 020 7836 0111 Mgt: 020 7845 9215 BO: 0871 911 0200 Tech: 020 7845 9459 Fax: 020 7845 9296
Email: personnel@eno.org
Web Site: www.eno.org
Directors of the English National Opera:
Chief Executive: Loretta Tomasi
Artistic Director: John Berry
Technical Director: Geoff Summerton

ENGLISH TOURING OPERA
52 - 54 Rosebery Avenue, London EC1R 4RP
Tel: 0207 833 2555 Fax: 0207 713 8686
Email: shawn.mccrory@englishtouring-opera.org.uk
Web: www.englishtouringopera.org.uk
ADMINISTRATION:
General Director: James Conway
Email: james.conway@englishtouringopera.org.uk
Marketing Manager: Esyllt Wyn Owen
Email: esyllt.wynowen@englishtouringopera.org.uk
Production Manager: Steve Hawkins
Email: steve.hawkins@englishtouringopera.org.uk

ENGLISH YOUTH BALLET
(Janet Lewis Enterprises)
Appledowne The Hillside Orpington Kent BR6 7SD
Tel/Fax: 01689 856747
Email: misslewis@englishyouthballet.co.uk
Web Site: www.englishyouthballet.co.uk
Director: Janet Lewis
General Manager: Bridget Hearne
Administration: Susie James
Choreographers: Julianne Rice-Oxley, Dominic Marshall, Roddie Patrizio
English Youth Ballet - An overwhelming success. Always presenting internationally known artists in the leading roles, English Youth Ballet's policy is to give young dancers outside London an opportunity to perform in full length classical ballets with-in a professional setting. The cast of up to a 100 young dancers for each production is chosen from within a fifty mile radius of each regional theatre.

THE FEATHERSTONEHAUGHS
(See also The Cholmondeleys)
Unit LF 1.1, Lafone House, The Leathermarket, 11-13 Leathermarket Street, London SE1 3HN
Tel: 020 7378 8800 Fax: 020 7378 8810
Email: admin@thecholmondeleys.org
Web Site: www.thecholmondeleys.org
Artistic Director: Lea Anderson
General Manager: Jo Stendall

FIRST ACT OPERA INTERNATIONAL
Mulberry House & Studio, School Road, Tunstall, Woodbridge, Suffolk IP12 2JQ
Tel: 01728 688 456 / 0845 6441461 Fax: 0870 134 1834
Email: figaro@firstactopera.co.uk
Web Site: www.firstactopera.co.uk
Managing Director: Elaine Holden
Artistic Director: Fraser Grant
Producer: John von Nuding

FLAMENCO PASION
Tel: 01992 812 488 Mob: 07903 524 630
Email: flamencolondon@gmail.com
ADMINISTRATION:
Contact: Sandra La Espuelita
The rhythms, excitement and passion of authentic Spanish Flamenco dance across the UK and abroad.

GLYNDEBOURNE FESTIVAL OPERA
Glyndebourne, New Road, Ringmer, Lewes, East Sussex BN8 5UU
Mgt/SD: 01273 812 321
BO: 01273 813 813
Email: info@glyndebourne.com
Web Site: www.glyndebourne.com
ADMINISTRATION:
Box Office and Customer Service Manager: Donna Marsh, email: donna.marsh@glyndebourne.com
Head of Communications: Laura Jukes, email: laura.jukes@glyndebourne.com
Production Managers: Tom Harrison email: tom.harrison@glyndebourne.com
Policy: Festival Opera Season
New Opera House opened in May 1994. Please contact venue for further details.
Cap: 1200

HADDO HOUSE CHORAL AND OPERATIC SOCIETY / HADDO PLAYERS
Haddo House Hall, Methlick, Ellon, Aberdeenshire AB41 7EQ Scotland
BO/ Tel: 01651 851 111
Email: secretary@haddochoral.org.uk
Web Site: www.haddochoral.org.uk

HEARTSTONE
Mayfield, High Street, Dingwall, Ross & Cromarty IV15 9SS Scotland
Tel: 01349 865 400 Fax: 01349 866 066
Email: info@heartstone.co.uk
Web Site: www.heartstone.co.uk
Director: Sita Kumari

INDEPENDENT BALLET WALES
30 Glasllwch Crescent, Newport, South Wales NP20 3SE
Tel: 01633 253 985 Mob Tel: 07778 411338 Fax: 01633 221 690
Email: dariusjames@welshballet.co.uk
Web Site: www.welshballet.co.uk
ADMINISTRATION:
Artistic Director: Darius James
Administrative Director: Yvonne Williams
Email: yvonnewilliams@welshballet.co.uk
Wales' own independent ballet company specialising in National and International touring.

IRIE! DANCE THEATRE
Moonshot Centre Fordham Park, Angus Street, London SE14 6LU
Tel: 020 8691 6099 Fax: 020 8694 8464
Web Site: www.iriedancetheatre.com
Artistic Director: Beverley Glean
IRIE!'s dance style is a unique fusion of African, Caribbean and Western Contemporary Dance.

JIVING LINDY HOPPERS
c/o JLA (Jeremy Lee Associates)
80 Great Portland Street, London W1W 7NW
Tel: 020 7907 2800
Email: talk@jla.co.uk, suzypayne@jla.co.uk
Web Site: www.jla.co.uk
ADMINISTRATION:
Authentic Jazz Dance group managed by Jeremy Lee Associates.
Admin: Suzy Payne

KALAMANDALAM VIJAYAKUMAR (KATHAKALI ACTOR)
1 Holland Road, Woolston, Southampton SO19 9FW
Tel: 023 8042 0114 Fax: 023 8044 4468
Mobile: 07740 123070
Email: info@kathakali.net
Web Site: www.kathakali.net
Offers solo Kathakali performances, work-shops, courses, full company perform-ances to include top international artists from India. We tour nationally and interna-tionally to make quality Kathakali available to all. UK tour include Kathakali classical dance drama from Kerala, South India.

THE KOSH
59 Stapleton Hall Road, London N4 3QF
Tel: 020 8374 0407 Fax: 020 8374 5661
Email: info@thekosh.com
Web Site: www.thekosh.com
Artistic Director: Michael Merwitzer
Choreographer: Sian Williams

LATIN MOTION
PO Box 8311, Birmingham B16 0LQ
Tel: 0121 454 5009 Fax: 0121 246 3555
Mob: 07973 402 911
Email: info@latinmotion.co.uk, mauricio@latinmotion.co.uk
Web Site: www.latinmotion.co.uk
Contact: Mauricio Reyes

LUDUS DANCE
Ludus Dance Centre, Assembly Rooms, King Street, Lancaster, Lancashire LA1 1RE
Tel: 01524 35 936 Fax: 01524 847 744
Email: info@ludusdance.org
Web Site: www.ludusdance.org
ADMINISTRATION:
Project Co-ordinator: Hannah

Robertshaw
Technical Stage Manager: David Forrest
Email: david.forrest@ludusdance.org
Britain's leading dance company for young people. Award winning shows, workshops, teaching packs, inset, videos, the works! High impact in Theatres, Festivals, Schools and the Community. Still unique after 35 years.

MOVING VISIONS DANCE THEATRE
Clifton Lodge, St. Margarets Drive, Twickenham TW1 1QN
Tel: 0208 892 9960 Fax: 0208 892 8090
Email: ross.mckim@rambertschool.org.uk
Web Site: www.rambertschool.org.uk
Contact: Ross McKim

NORTHERN BALLET THEATRE
St. Cecilia Street, Quarry Hill, Leeds LS2 7PA
Tel: 0113 220 8000 Fax: 0113 220 8001
Email: info@northernballet.com
Web: www.northernballettheatre.co.uk
ADMINISTRATION:
Artistic Director: David Nixon OBE
General Manager: Steve Hughes
Technical Director: Andy Waddington
Britain's leading classical dance drama company produces new full length versions of the classics as well as new classical and modern works. Touring the UK for up to 26 weeks a year with availability for overseas tours. Current repertoire includes: Romeo & Juliet, A Streetcar Named Desire, A Christmas Carol, Madame Butterfly, Gershwin Programme.

OPERA DELLA LUNA
7 Cotmore House, Fringford, Bicester, Oxfordshire OX27 8RQ
Tel: 01869 325 131 Fax: 01869 323 533
Email: enquiries@operadellaluna.org
Web Site: www.operadellaluna.org
Artistic Director: Jeff Clarke

OPERA NORTH
Opera North, Grand Theatre, 46 New Briggate, Leeds LS1 6NU
Tel: 0113 243 9999 Marketing: 0113 223 3500
Email: info@operanorth.co.uk
Web Site: www.operanorth.co.uk
ADMINISTRATION:
General Manager: Richard Ashton
Marketing Manager: Hazel Arthur
Technical & Operations Director: Ric Green

OPERA RARA
134-146 Curtain Road, London EC2A 3AR
Tel: 020 7613 2858 Fax: 020 7613 2261
Email: info@opera-rara.com
Web Site: www.opera-rara.com
ADMINISTRATION:
Managing Director: Stephen Revell
Production Co-ordinator: Kim Panter

PAVILION OPERA
Eastwood Farm, Chilsham Lane, Herstmonceux, Hailsham, East Sussex BN27 4QH
Tel: 01526 378 231 / 01323 833 853
Fax: 01526 378315
Email: freddie@pavilionopera.com
Web Site: www.pavilionopera.com
Manager: Freddie Stockdale

PEGASUS OPERA COMPANY
The Brix St Matthews Brixton Hill, London SW2 1JF
Tel: 020 8123 1178 Fax: 020 7501 9501
Email: admin@pegopera.org
Web Site: www.pegopera.org
Artistic Director & Founder / Trustee: Lloyd Newton
Projects Manager: Talita Moffatt

PHOENIX DANCE THEATRE
St. Cecilia Street, Leeds LS2 7PA
Tel: 0113 236 8130 Fax: 0113 244 4736
Email: info@phoenixdancetheatre.co.uk
Web: www.phoenixdancetheatre.co.uk
ADMINISTRATION:
Rehearsal Director: Tracy Tinker
Email: tracy.tinker@phoenixdancetheatre.co.uk
Technical Manager: John Slater
Email: john.slater@phoenixdancetheatre.co.uk
A repertory dance company of 10 dancers, presenting a diverse range of contemporary work on the middle to large scale.

PLAN B
25 Beinn View, Conon Bridge, Dingwall, Ross-Shire IV7 8DG
Tel: 07977 211138
Email: projects@planbcreative.org
Web Site: www.planbcreative.org
Contact: Frank McConnell
Collaborative Dance Theatre.

POWYS DANCE
Powys Dance Centre, Arlais Road, Llandrindod Wells, Powys LD1 5HE Wales
Tel: 01597 824 370
Email: powys.dance@powys.gov.uk
Web Site: www.dawnspowysdance.org
Contact: Amanda Griffkin
Capacity: 120

RAMBERT DANCE COMPANY
94 Chiswick High Road, London W4 1SH
Tel: 020 8630 0600 Fax: 020 8747 8323
Email: rdc@rambert.org.uk
Web Site: www.rambert.org.uk
ADMINISTRATION:
Artistic Director: Mark Baldwin
Music Director: Paul Hoskins
Rehearsal Directors: Mikaela Polley and Simon Cooper

ROYAL OPERA HOUSE
Floral Street, Covent Garden, London WC2E 9DD
Tel: 020 7240 1200 BO: 020 7304 4000
Email: mark.duffy@roh.org.uk
Web Site: www.roh.org.uk
ADMINISTRATION:
Chief Executive: Alex Beard
Creative Director, ROH 2: Deborah Bull
Head of Development: Amanda Saunders
Head of Development Events: Caroline Dalziel
Director of Finance: Sally O'Neill
Head of Marketing: Layla Amirshahi
Head of Production: David Pritchard
Director of Press and Communications: Christopher Millard
Capacity Main House: 2,256; Linbury Studio Theatre: approx 420; Clore Studio Upstairs: approx 170. The Royal Opera House can be hire for commercial events. For more information on Venue Hire contact Hire Manager, Mark Duffy: Tel: +44 (0)20 7212 9482 or Email: mark.duffy@roh.org.uk

SALSA AMBIENTE
Oankays, Springfarm Road, Camelsdale Haslemere, Surrey GU27 3RH
Tel: 01428 643 127 Mob: 07855 504 470
Email: enquiries@salsaambiente.com
Web Site: www.salsaambiente.com
Proprietor: David Bresslaw, Lyndsey Holloway
Salsa dance performances/tuition and Salsa club.

SALSATECA DANCE SCHOOL
Tel: 07891 446256 Mob: 07817 481 243
Email: admin@salsateca.co.uk
Web Site: www.salsateca.co.uk
Contact: Nicolas Angitano, Alex Velez
Based in and around London, Ljubljana and Zagreb, Salsateca offers One to One Salsa lessons, Group lessons, Dance Shows, and Djs.

SCOTTISH BALLET
Tramway, 25 Albert Drive, Glasgow G41 2PE Scotland
Tel: 0141 331 2931 Fax: 0141 424 0757
Email: sb@scottishballet.co.uk
Web Site: www.scottishballet.co.uk
ADMINISTRATION:
Artistic Director: Ashley Page
Company Manager: John Aitken
Head of Marketing & Communications: Kirsten Cockburn
Email: kirsten.cockburn@scottishballet.co.uk
Production Manager: Tim Palmer
Email: tim.palmer@scottishballet.co.uk

SCOTTISH OPERA
39 Elmbank Crescent, Glasgow, Strathclyde G2 4PT Scotland
Tel: 0141 248 4567 / 242 0595 Fax: 0141 221 8812
Email: information@scottishopera.org.uk

Web Site: www.scottishopera.org.uk
ADMINISTRATION:
Head of Music: Derek Clark (0141 242 0585)
Director of Marketing & Communications: Helen Ireland
Technical & Operations Director: Steve Green (0141 352 4011)

SHOBANA JEYASINGH DANCE COMPANY
Moving Arts Base, Syracusae, 134 Liverpool Road, London N1 1LA
Tel: 020 7697 4444 Fax: 020 7697 4455
Email: admin@shobanajeyasingh.co.uk
Web Site: www.shobanajeyasingh.co.uk
ADMINISTRATION:
Artistic Director: Shobana Jeyasingh
Executive Producer: Sanjivan Kohli

THE CLASSICAL OPERA COMPANY
Britannia House, 11 Glenthorne Road, London W6 0LH
Tel: 020 8846 9744
Email: info@classicalopera.co.uk
Web Site: www.classicalopera.co.uk
Founded in 1997 by conductor Ian Page, the company specialises in the music of Mozart and his contemporaries, performing with its own period-instrument orchestra.

THE GARDEN OPERA COMPANY
82 Kynaston Road, London N16 0ED
Tel: 020 7241 3563 Mob: 07968 158 948
Email: info@gardenopera.co.uk
Web Site: www.gardenopera.co.uk
ADMINISTRATION:
Executive and Artistic Director: Peter Bridges
Associate Production Director: Martin Lloyd-Evans

TRIPSICHORE PERFORMING COMPANY
41 Roundwood Road, London NW10 9TP
Tel: 020 8459 2416
Email: Tripsichore@msn.com
Web Site: www.tripsichore.com
Artistic Director: Edward Clark
Performers:Edward Clark, Nikki Durrant, Valentina Candiani, Bertie Russell, Toby Gillingham, Martin McDougall and Desiree Kongerod
Perform as Tripsichore Yoga Theatre.

UNION DANCE COMPANY
Culturally Diverse Contemporary Dance
Top Floor 6 Charing Cross Road, London WC2H 0HG
Tel: 020 7836 7837 Fax: 020 7836 7847
Email: info@uniondance.co.uk
Web Site: www.uniondance.co.uk
ADMINISTRATION:
Artistic Director: Corrine Bougaard
Email:
corrine.bougaard@uniondance.co.uk
Administration: Ruby Jobey
Email: ruth.jobey@uniondance.co.uk

WAYNE MCGREGOR, RANDOM HOUSE
Sadler's Wells, Rosebery Avenue, London EC1R 4TN
Tel: 020 7278 6015 Fax: 020 7278 5469
Email: random@randomdance.org
Web Site: www.randomdance.org
ADMINISTRATION:
Artistic Director: Wayne McGregor
Technical Director: Christopher Charles
Communications Manager: Nicola Christie

WEXFORD FESTIVAL OPERA
Wexford Opera House, High Street, Wexford Ireland
Tel: 00 3535 3912 2400 BO: 00 353 53 91 22 144
Email: info@wexfordopera.com
Web Site: www.wexfordopera.com
ADMINISTRATION:
Artistic Director: David Agler. Email, david@wexfordopera.com
Operations Manager: Aisling White. Email, aisling@wexfordopera.com
Technical Director: David Stuttard. Email, techdirector@wexfordopera.com

YORKSHIRE DANCE CENTRE
3 St Peters Building, St Peters Square, Leeds, West Yorkshire LS9 8AH
Tel: 0113 243 9867 Fax: 0113 259 5700
BO: 0113 243 8765
Email: admin@yorkshiredance.com
Web Site: www.yorkshiredance.com
ADMINISTRATION:
General Manager: Edwina Simpson
Facilities Manager: Dawn Wilkinson
Head of Communications: Antony Dunn
Email: antonydunn@yorkshiredance.com

Classes and workshops from beginners to professionals. Also studio hire for auditions, rehearsals, etc. Phone for details and free programme.
Also hot desks for short or long term letting. Flexible way of hiring individual office spaces. Fully accessible. Meeting room hire and reception & administration services.

Orchestras

THE ACADEMY OF ANCIENT MUSIC
32 Newnham Road, Cambridge CB3 9EY
Tel: 01223 301 509 Fax: 01223 323202
Email: info@aam.co.uk
Web Site: www.aam.co.uk
ADMINISTRATION:
Chief Executive: Michael Garvey
Orchestra Manager: Andrew Moore
Administration Manager: Samantha Fryer

ACADEMY OF ST MARTIN IN THE FIELDS
4th Floor, 8 Baltic Street East, London EC1Y 0UP
Tel: 020 7702 1377 Fax: 020 7481 0228
Email: info@asmf.org
Web Site: www.asmf.org
ADMINISTRATION:
Artistic Director: Kenneth Sillito
Marketing Manager: Holly Cumming
Email: hollycumming@asmf.org

AEOLIAN SINFONIA (23-70)
25 Roy Road, Northwood, Middlesex HA6 1EQ
Tel: 01923 828 055
Email: philip-gibson@supanet.com
Music Director: Philip Gibson

ALL SOULS ORCHESTRA
Langham Arts, St Pauls Church, Robert Adam Street, London W1U 3HW
Tel: 020 7935 7246 Fax: 020 7935 7486
Email: office@langhamarts.org
Web Site: www.allsoulsorchestra.org
Music Director/Principal Conductor: Noel H Tredinnick

THE AMADEUS CHORUS & ORCHESTRA
14 Jubilee Close, Pamber Heath, Tadley, Hampshire RG26 3HP
Tel: 0118 970 0816
Email: enquiries@amadeusorchestra.co.uk
Web Site: www.amadeusorchestra.co.uk
Principal Conductor: Philip Mackenzie
Orchestra Administrator: Biff Norton

AMBACHE
9 Beversbrook Road, London N19 4QG
Tel/Fax: 020 7263 4027
Email: diana@ambache.co.uk
Web Site: www.ambache.co.uk
Musical Director: Diana Ambache

AMICI CHAMBER ORCHESTRA
20 Oakhill Drive, Welwyn, Hertfordshire AL6 9NW
Tel: 01438 715 740
Email: nrspringthorpe@aol.com
Music Director/Principal Conductor: Dr. Nigel Springthorpe

APOLLO CHAMBER ORCHESTRA
43 Clifden Road, London E5 0LL
Tel: 020 8986 4101
Email: info@apollochamberorchestra.com
Web Site: www.apollochamberorchestra.com
Music Director: David Chernaik

BATH PHILHARMONIA
7A Bridge Street, Bath BA2 4AS
Tel: 01225 444153 BO: 01225 463 362
Email: info@bathphil.co.uk
Web Site: www.bathphil.co.uk
ADMINISTRATION:
General Manager: Ali Groves, ali@bath-phil.co.uk
Music Director: Jason Thornton, jason@bathphil.co.uk
Orchestral Manager: James Waterhouse, james@bathphil.co.uk

BBC CONCERT ORCHESTRA
220A Drama Building, Television Centre, Wood Lane, London W12 7RJ
Tel: 020 8576 0333 Fax: 020 8576 0356
Email: bbcco@bbc.co.uk
Web Site: www.bbc.co.uk/concertorchestra
General Manager: Andrew Connolly
Orchestra Manager: Alex Walden
Promotions and Marketing Manager: Lisa Owen-Jones

BBC NATIONAL ORCHESTRA OF WALES
BBC Hoddinott Hall, Cardiff Bay Cardiff CF10 5AL South Wales
Tel: 0800 052 1812 Fax: 0292 055 9721
Email: now@bbc.co.uk
Web Site: www.bbc.co.uk/wales/now
Director: David Murray
Orchestra Manager: Byron Jenkins

BBC PHILHARMONIC
New Broadcasting House, Oxford Road, Manchester M60 1SJ
Tel: 0161 244 4001 Fax: 0161 244 4211
Email: philharmonic@bbc.co.uk
Web Site: www.bbc.co.uk/philharmonic
Marketing Assistant: Caroline Smith

BBC SCOTTISH SYMPHONY ORCHESTRA
City Halls, Candleriggs, Glasgow, Strathclyde G1 1NQ Scotland
Tel: 0141 552 0909 Fax: 0141 552 6078
Email: bbcsso@bbc.co.uk
Web Site: www.bbc.co.uk/bbcsso
ADMINISTRATION:
Chief Conductor: Donald Runnicles
Principal Guest Conductor: Ilan Volkov
Associate Guest Conductor: Andrew Manze
Artist-in-Association: Matthias Pintscher
Conductor Laureate: Jerzy Maksymiuk
Director: Gavin Reid
Manager, Orchestra and Concerts: Joan Morrison
The BBC Scottish Symphony Orchestra is one of Britain's most versatile orchestras, with a huge repertoire ranging from the most complex modern scores to the great classics, from music by Scottish composers to film scores and music for television. Founded in 1935 (and since 2006 based at City Halls in Glasgow), the orchestra appears in the UK's most prestigious events like the BBC Proms and Edinburgh International Festival, and plays in venues all over Scotland. Abroad, it has appeared in many of the great musical centres of Europe and has toured the USA, South America and been twice to China. The majority of its performances are broadcast on BBC Radio 3, and its innovative concert programmes and acclaimed recordings have made it the recipient of numerous awards, including four Gramophone Awards.

BBC SYMPHONY ORCHESTRA
Room 14, Maida Vale Studios, Delaware Road, London W9 2LG
Tel: 020 776 52140
Email: bbcso@bbc.co.uk, mauro.silva@bbc.co.uk
Web: www.bbc.co.uk/symphonyorchestra
General Manager: Paul Hughes
Orchestra Manager: Sussana Simmons
Marketing Manager: Sarah Hirons
Marketing and Publicity Assistant: Mauro Silva
Chief Producer: Ann McKay
Planning & Chorus Administrator: Alison Dancer

BELMONT ENSEMBLE OF LONDON
24 Hassendean Road, London SE3 8TS
Tel: 020 8293 3298 Mobile: 07976 278476
Email: belmontensemble@gmail.com
Web Site: www.belmontensemble.com
Contact: Peter G Dyson

BERNARDI CHAMBER ENSEMBLE & ORCHESTRA
Part of the Bernardi Music Group
The Plat, Thakeham Road, Coolham, Horsham, West Sussex RH13 8QD
Tel: 01403 741685
Email: andrew@BernardiMusicGroup.com
Web Site: www.bernardimusicgroup.com
Contact: Andrew Bernardi

BIRMINGHAM CONTEMPORARY MUSIC GROUP
CBSO Centre, Berkley Street, Birmingham B1 2LF
Tel: 0121 616 2616 Fax: 0121 616 2622
Email: info@bcmg.org.uk
Web Site: www.bcmg.org.uk
Artistic Director: Stephen Newbould
General Manager: Jackie Newbould

BOURNEMOUTH SYMPHONY ORCHESTRA
2 Seldown Lane, Poole, Dorset BH15 1UF
Markting: 01202 644714 BO: 01202 669925
Email: jbueker@bsorchestra.co.uk
Web Site: www.bsolive.com
Orchestra Manager: Rebecca Goode
Marketing Manager: Johanna Büker

BRANDENBURG SINFONIA
9 Queen Anne's Terrace , Leatherhead, Surrey, KT22 7HR
Gen Tel/ Fax: 01372 209 817 Office: 01306 508 055 Mobile: 07770 937 328
Email: info@brandenburg.org.uk
Web Site: www.brandenburg.org.uk
Artistic Director: Robert Porter

BRIGHTON PHILHARMONIC ORCHESTRA
41 George Street, Brighton BN2 1RJ
Tel: 01273 622900 Fax: 01273 697887
Email: mail@brightonphil.org.uk
Web Site: www.brightonphil.org.uk
General Manager: Judith Clark

THE BRITISH CONCERT ORCHESTRA
The British Concert Orchestra (Founded 1945) Ltd
1 Alston Close, Long Ditton, Surbiton, Surrey KT6 5QS
Tel: 0208 398 2559 Mob: 07802 254924
Email: frankrenton@tiscali.co.uk
Web: www.britishconcertorchestra.co.uk
Orchestra Manager: Frank Renton

BRITISH PHILHARMONIC CONCERT ORCHESTRA
8 Oaks Farm Drive, Darton, Barnsley, South Yorkshire S75 5BZ
Tel: 01226 380 175 Fax: 01226 380 566
Email: info09@britishphilharmonicorchestra.com
Web Site: www.britishphilharmonicorchestra.com
Musical Director: Lee Longden
Orchestra Manager: Russell Swift
Orchestra for all occasions.

BRITTEN SINFONIA
13 Sturton Street Cambridge CB1 2SN
Tel: 01223 300 795 Fax: 01223 302 092
Email: info@brittensinfonia.co.uk
Web Site: www.brittensinfonia.co.uk
ADMINISTRATION:
Chief Executive: David Butcher
Concerts Director: Hannah Donat
Artistic Planning Director: Nikola White
Orchestra Manager: Hannah Tucker
Marketing Director: Claire Bowdler

CHAMBER ORCHESTRA OF EUROPE
27 Great Peter Street, London SW1P 3LN
Tel: 020 7070 3333 Fax: 020 7070 3330
Email: redbird@coeurope.org
Web Site: www.coeurope.org
ADMINISTRATION:
Peter Readman (Executive Chairman), Readman@coeurope.org

General Manager: Simon Fletcher, Simon.Fletcher@coeurope.org
Coralia Galtier (Marketing and PR Manager), coralia@coeurope.org

CITY OF LONDON SINFONIA
28 Great Tower Street, London EC3R 5AT
Tel: 020 7621 2800 Fax: 020 7626 5593
Email: info@cls.co.uk
Web Site: www.cityoflondonsinfonia.co.uk
Artistic leaders: Stephen Layton and Michael Collins

CITY OF PETERBOROUGH SYMPHONY ORCHESTRA
55 Sapperton, Werrington, Peterborough, Cambridgeshire PE4 5BS
Tel: 01733 576 797 Fax: 01733 755 939
Email: helmutcartwright@yahoo.co.uk
Web Site: www.cpso.org.uk
Chairman: Steve Osborn
Administration Contact: Wes Gibbon
Conductor: Mr Russell Keable

CORELLI CHAMBER ORCHESTRA
155 Hewlett Road, Cheltenham, Gloucestershire GL52 6UD
Tel: 01242 570 383
Email: warwick@corelliconcerts.co.uk
Web Site: www.corelliconcerts.co.uk
Director: Warwick Cole
General Manager: Rachel Abbess
Corelli Concerts began when Warwick Cole founded the Corelli Chamber Orchestra. Initially a modern-instrument string orchestra specialising in music the 18th century, it soon developed its programming presenting 19th and 20th music in conjunction with its core repertoire. Although based in Cheltenham (England), it has performed throughout the UK for music festivals, societies and clubs.

DANTE ALIGHIERI ORCHESTRA
East West Arts Ltd, 93b Cambridge Gardens, London W10 6JE
Tel: 020 8960 5889 Fax: 020 8968 5541
Email: anupbiswscellist@yahoo.com
Music Director: Anup Kumar Biswas

ENGLISH BACH FESTIVAL ORCHESTRA
15 South Eaton Place, London SW1W 9ER
Tel: 020 7730 5925 Fax: 020 7730 1456
Email: info@ebf.org.uk
Web Site: www.ebf.org.uk
Artistic Director: Lina Lalandi-Emery (OBE)

ENGLISH BAROQUE SOLOISTS
See also, Monteverdi Choir and Orchestra.
Level 9, 25 Cabot Square, London E14 4QA
Tel: 020 7719 0120 Fax: 020 7719 0099
Email: info@monteverdi.org.uk
Web Site: www.monteverdi.co.uk
Chair: Tom Graham
Artistic Director: Sir John Eliot Gardiner CBE
General Manager: Riitta Hirvonen

ENGLISH CHAMBER ORCHESTRA
2 Coningsby Road London W5 4HR
Tel: 020 8840 6565 Fax: 020 8567 7198
Email: mail@englishchamberorchestra.co.uk
Web: www.englishchamberorchestra.co.uk
Administrative Director: Pauline Gilbertson
Orchestra Manager: Charlotte Templeman

ENGLISH CLASSICAL PLAYERS
25b Epsom Lane South, Tadworth, Surrey KT20 5TA
Tel: 01737 888 083 Fax: 01737 888 203
Email: info@ecp.uk.com
Web Site: www.ecp.uk.com
Artistic Director: Jonathan Brett
General Manager: Alison Kelly
Playing strength 18-65. Classical early romantic repertoire. ABO category one member. Concerts and Orchestral workshops. EOB approved.

ENGLISH CONCERT
8 St.George's Terrace, London NW1 8XJ
Tel: 020 7911 0905 Fax: 020 7911 0904
Email: ec@englishconcert.co.uk
Web Site: www.englishconcert.co.uk
ADMINISTRATION:
Artistic Director: Harry Bicket
General Manager: Felix Warnock, felix@englishconcert.co.uk
Orchestral Manager: Sarah Fenn, sarah@englishconcert.co.uk

ENGLISH FESTIVAL ORCHESTRA
151 Mount View Road, London N4 4JT
Tel: 020 8341 7809 Fax: 020 8340 3352
Email: info@englishfestivalorchestra.co.uk
General Manager: Trevor Ford
Concert Manager: Marianne Barton

ENGLISH HAYDN ORCHESTRA
20 West Castle Street, Bridgnorth, Shropshire WV16 4AB
Tel: 01746 763 591
Email: forms@englishhaydn.com, mike@englishhaydn.com
Web Site: www.haydn.org.uk
ADMINISTRATION:
Festival Director: Sandra Reid
Festival Treasurer: Mike Proudman
Classical Orchestra performing on instruments of the period.
Concerts based around Joseph Haydn and late 18th/ early 19th century composers.

ENGLISH NATIONAL OPERA ORCHESTRA
London Coliseum, St Martin's Lane, London WC2N 4ES
Tel: 020 7836 0111 / 7845 9215 Fax: 020 7845 9296
Email: personnel@eno.org
Web Site: www.eno.org.uk
Orchestra Leader: Janice Graham
Orchestra Manager: Jonathan Manners

ENGLISH SINFONIA
PO Box 202 Wantage, Oxfordshire OX12 2BG
Tel: 0845 643 1379
Email: englishsinfonia@tesco.net
Web Site: www.englishsinfonia.co.uk
General Manager: Sally Ann Ewins
Artistic Director: Janice Graham

ENGLISH SYMPHONY ORCHESTRA
Stockwood Business Park, Redditch, Worcestershire B96 6SX
Tel: 01386 791021 BO: 01386 791 044
Email: info@eso.co.uk
Web Site: www.eso.co.uk / www.elgar-festival.com
ADMINISTRATION:
City Office address: 16-20 Deansway, Worcester, WR1 2ES.
Head of Finance & Administration (Head Office): Alison King, Email: alison@eso.co.uk
Contact (City Office): Peter Sheeran, email: peter.sheeran@btinternet.com

EUROPEAN UNION BAROQUE ORCHESTRA
Hordley, Wootton, Woodstock, Oxfordshire OX20 1EP
Tel: 01993 812 111 Fax: 01993 812 911
Email: info@eubo.org.uk
Web Site: www.eubo.org.uk
ADMINISTRATION:
General Director: Paul James
Orchestra Manager: Emma Wilkinson
Pre-professional training orchestra selected from the best young musicians from throughout the European Union. An initiative of the European Parliament supported by the European Commission and Microsoft.

EUROPEAN UNION CHAMBER ORCHESTRA
Hollick, Yarnscombe, Devon EX31 3LQ
Tel: 01271 858 249 Fax: 01297 858 375
Email: eucorch1@aol.com
Web Site: www.etd.gb.com
Director General: Ambrose Miller
Music Directors: Hans-Peter Hofmann, Eva Stegeman, Gernot Süssmuth, Matthias Wollong

EUROPEAN WOMEN'S ORCHESTRA
Toynbee Studios, 28 Commercial Street, London E1 6LS
Tel: 020 8800 4131 Fax: 020 8802 6614
Conductor/Music Director: Odaline de la Martinez
Administrator: Jayne Rollason

EX CATHEDRA CHOIR AND BAROQUE ORCHESTRA
611b The Big Peg 120 Vyse Street, Hockley, Hockley, Birmingham B18 6NF
Tel: 0121 200 1511 Fax: 0121 200 1522
Email: info@ex-cathedra.org
Web Site: www.ex-cathedra.org
Artistic Director: Jeffrey Skidmore
General Manager: Peter Trethewey, peter@excathedra.co.uk

GABRIELI CONSORT & PLAYERS
372 Old Street, London EC1V 9LT
Tel: 020 7613 4404 Fax: 020 7613 4414
Email: info@gabrieli.com
Web Site: www.gabrieli.com
Artistic Director: Paul McCreesh
General Manager: Nicola Loughrey
Administrator and Marketing Officer: Nicola Difrancesco

GUILDFORD PHILHARMONIC ORCHESTRA
Millmead House, Millmead, Guildford, Surrey GU2 4BB
Tel: 01483 444666 BO: 01483 444777
Email: guildfordphil@guildford.gov.uk
Web: www.guildfordphilharmonic.co.uk
General Manager: Nicola Goold

HALLE CONCERTS SOCIETY
The Bridgewater Hall, Manchester M1 5HA
Tel: 0161 237 7000 Fax: 0161 237 7029
BO: 0161 907 9000
Email: info@halle.co.uk
Web Site: www.halle.co.uk
Marketing and Press Officer: Liz Robinson

HALLE ORCHESTRA
See Halle Concerts Society Listing

THE HANOVER BAND
The Old Market, Upper Market Street, Hove, East Sussex BN3 1AS
Tel: 01273 740292
Email: enquiries@thehanoverband.com
Web Site: www.hanoverband.co.uk
Orchestral Manager: Marylin Thomas
Tel: 01273 740295 Email : marylin.thomas@theoldmarket.co.uk

HAVANT CHAMBER ORCHESTRA
23 Grove Road, Havant, Hampshire PO9 1AR
Chairman: 023 9247 4681 Admin: 023 9248 3228 BO: 01329 231942 (Ferneham Hall)
Email: sandra.craddock@ntlworld.com
Web: www.havantorchestras.hampshire.org.uk
ADMINISTRATION:
Conductor and Music Director: Peter Craddock
Administrator: Sandra Craddock
Venue Address: Ferneham Hall, Osborn Road, Fareham, Hampshire, PO16 7DB.

HAVANT SYMPHONY ORCHESTRA
152 West Street, Havant, Hampshire PO9 1LP
Chairman: 023 9247 4681 Admin: 023 9248 3228 BO: 01329 231942 (Ferneham Hall)
Email: sandra.craddock@ntlworld.com
Web Site: www.havantorchestras.hampshire.org.uk
ADMINISTRATION:
Conductor and Music Director: Peter Craddock
Administrator: Sandra Craddock
Venue Address: Ferneham Hall, Osborn Road, Fareham, Hampshire, PO16 7DB

ISLE OF WIGHT SYMPHONY ORCHESTRA
94 Carisbrooke High Street, Newport, Isle of Wight PO30 1NU
Tel: 01983 525364
Email: chairman@iwso.info, administrator@iwso.info
Web Site: www.iwso.info
Chairman : Mrs Emma Dixey
Administration : Mr Tim Isard
Orchestra Manager : Mr Mark Gregory

JUPITER ORCHESTRA
57 White Horse Road, London E1 0ND
Tel: 020 7790 5883
Email: gr@gregoryrose.org
Web Site: www.gregoryrose.org
Conductor: Gregory Rose

THE BERT KAEMPFERT ORCHESTRA
PO Box 389, Banstead, Surrey SM7 1RT
Tel: 01737 370 138 Fax: 01737 354 822
Email: orchestra@bertkaempfert.co.uk
Web Site: www.bertkaempfert.co.uk
Director: Tony Fisher

THE KING'S CONSORT
The Old Rectory, Old Bury Road, Alpheton, Sudbury, Suffolk CO10 9BT
Tel: 01284 826044 Fax: 01284 826 041
Email: info@tkcworld.org
Web Site: www.tkcworld.org
ADMINISTRATION:
General Manager: Viola Scheffel
Artistic Director: Robert King
One of the world's leading period instrument orchestras and choruses with a busy British, mainland European and international touring schedule for over 25 years; 95 award-winning CD recordings in the catalogue plus major Hollywood film sound tracks.

LITTLE SYMPHONY ORCHESTRA
14 Beaumont Road, Purley, Surrey CR8 2EG
Tel: 020 8668 5883
Email: darrelldavison@hotmail.com
Music Director: Darrell Davison

LONDON CHAMBER ORCHESTRA
1 London Bridge, London SE1 9BG
Tel: 020 3318 2982 Fax: 0870 706 4931
Email: info@lco.co.uk
Web Site: www.lco.co.uk
General Manager: Step Parikian

LONDON CHAMBER PLAYERS
10 Wycombe Gardens, London NW11 8AL
Tel: 020 8455 6799 Fax: 020 8455 6799
Email: london-players@excite.com
Music Director: Sheila Sunshine

LONDON CITY CHAMBER ORCHESTRA
The Old School, 3-5 Bridge Street, Hadleigh, Suffolk IP7 6BY
Tel: 01473 822 596 Fax: 01473 824 175
Email: thomas.mcintosh@minstrelmusic.co.uk
Web Site: www.minstrelmusic.co.uk
Administrator: M H V Reckitt
Music Director: Thomas McIntosh

LONDON CONCERT ORCHESTRA
Raymond Gubbay Limited. Dickens House, 15 Tooks Court, Cursitor Street London EC4A 1QH
Tel: 020 7025 3750 Fax: 020 7025 3751
Email: info@raymondgubbay.co.uk
Web Site: www.raymondgubbay.co.uk
Chairman: Raymond Gubbay
Managing Director: Anthony Findlay
Senior Events Manager: Terry Eldridge

LONDON FESTIVAL ORCHESTRA
The Warehouse, 13 Theed Street, South Bank, London SE1 8ST
Tel: 020 7928 9250 / 1
Fax: 020 7928 9252
Email: orchestra@lfo.co.uk
Web Site: www.lfo.co.uk
Artistic Director: Ross Pople

LONDON GALA ORCHESTRA
14 Lytton Road, London E11 1JH
Tel: 020 8556 8294 Fax: 020 8556 8658
Email: wilf.goddard@tiscali.co.uk
Web Site: www.londongalaorchestra.com
Managing Director: Wilf Goddard
Contact: Lynne Dore
The LGO promotes 5 concerts a year and is engaged by National Trust, Halls, Music Societies, etc. for about another 20 concerts & theatre work. In addition plays at conferences/functions both as a concert or background.

LONDON HANDEL SOCIETY
Horton House 8 Ditton Street, Ilminster, Somerset TA19 0BQ
Tel: 01460 53500 Box Office: 01460 54660
Email: c-hodgson@btconnect.com
Web Site: www.handel.cswebsites.org
Musical Director: Laurence Cummings
Festival Director: Catherine Hodgson
Associate Director & Leader: Adrian Butterfield

LONDON MOZART PLAYERS
Suite 26 Suffolk House, College Road, Croydon CR0 1PE
Tel: 020 8686 1996 Fax: 020 8686 2187
Email: info@lmp.org
Web Site: www.lmp.org
Managing Director: Simon Funnell
General Manager: David Wilson
Marketing Manager: Femke de Vos Burchart

LONDON PHILANOVA ORCHESTRA
43 Briton Hill Road, Sanderstead, Surrey CR2 0JJ
Tel: 020 8657 1662
Music Director: Philip Winter

LONDON PHILHARMONIC ORCHESTRA
89 Albert Embankment, London SE1 7TP
Tel: 020 7840 4200 Fax: 020 7840 4201
BO: 020 7840 4242
Email: david.burke@lpo.org.uk
Web Site: www.lpo.org.uk
Chief Executive & Artistic Director: Timothy Walker
General Manager & Finance Director: David Burke

LONDON SCHUBERT PLAYERS
72 Warwick Gardens, London W14 8PP
Tel/Fax: 020 7603 1396
Email: lsp@londonschubertplayers.co.uk
Web Site: www.constantinsilvestri.com
Director: John Gritten
Artistic Director: Anda Anastasescu

LONDON VIENNESE CONCERT ORCHESTRA
52 Helen Avenue, Feltham, Middlesex TW14 9LB
Tel/Fax: 020 8751 0417
Email: nrgft@hotmail.com
Contact: Keith Harmon

MANCHESTER CAMERATA
RNCM, 124 Oxford Road, Manchester M13 9RD
Tel: 0161 226 8696 Fax: 0161 226 8600
Email: info@manchestercamerata.com
Web: www.manchestercamerata.com
Music Director: Douglas Boyd
Orchestra Manager: Jo Barclay
Chamber orchestra serving the North of England, in residence at Bridgewater Hall.

MANCHESTER CONCERT ORCHESTRA
Raymond Gubbay Ltd Dickens House, 15 Took's Court, London EC4A 1LB
Tel: 020 7025 3750 Fax: 020 7025 3751
Email: info@raymondgubbay.co.uk
Web Site: www.raymondgubbay.co.uk
Chairman: Raymond Gubbay
Managing Director: Anthony Findlay

MILTON KEYNES CITY ORCHESTRA
3 Theatre Walk, Central Milton Keynes, Buckinghamshire MK9 3PX
Tel: 01908 558 311 Fax: 01908 558 312
Email: anna.denny@mkco.org, nick.cutts@mkco.org
Web Site: www.mkco.org
General Manager: Anna Denny
Operations Manager: Nick Cutts

MONTEVERDI CHOIR & ORCHESTRA LTD
Level 9, 25 Cabot Square, London E14 4QA
Tel: 020 8871 4750 Fax: 020 8871 4751
Email: info@monteverdi.org.uk
Web Site: www.monteverdi.co.uk
General Manager: Riitta Hirvonen
Music Director: Sir John Eliot Gardiner
(See also, English Baroque Soloists)

MORAY STRING QUARTET
Kildonan, Young Street, Elgin, Moray IV30 1TH Scotland
Tel: 01343 543 531
Email: elaine.stables@btinternet.com
Web Site: www.moraystringquartet.com
ADMINISTRATION:
Director: Elaine Stables
Secretary: Peter Zanre
Formed 15 years ago from principal players of the Moray Chamber Orchestra, the String Quartet have been playing together for 12 years and have a rich repertoire of classical, folk, jazz, film and popular music to suit many occasions.

MUSIC PROJECTS/LONDON
11 Elmwood Road, Chiswick, London W4 3DY
Tel: 020 8994 9528
Email: richard.bernas@btopenworld.com
Contact: Richard Bernas

MUSICIANS TOURING COMPANY
Ty-Wrth-Y-Coed, Cwmystwyth, Aberystwyth, Ceredigion SY23 4AF
Tel: 01974 282631/01432 341988 Fax: 01432 341988
Contact: Robert Spearing

NEW CHAMBER ORCHESTRA
130 High Street, Oxford OX1 4DH
Tel: 01865 378514 Fax: 01865 722953
Email: ncd@rightonit.co.uk
Music Director: Andrew Zreczycki
Chair: Philip Vincent

NEW ENGLISH CONCERT ORCHESTRA
24 Royston Street, Potton, Sandy, Bedfordshire SG19 2LP
Tel: 01767 260815 Fax: 01767 261729
Email: neco@lindsaymusic.co.uk
Manager: Carole Lindsay-Douglas

NEW ENGLISH ORCHESTRA
PO Box 11740, Birmingham B13 0WN
Tel/Fax: 01905 613 771
Email: enquiry@newenglishorchestra.org
Web Site: www.newenglishorchestra.org
Artistic Director and Principal Conductor: Nigel Swinford

NEW LONDON ORCHESTRA
34 Grosvenor Gardens, London SW1W 0DH
Tel: 020 7823 5523 Fax: 020 7823 6373
Email: admin@nlo.co.uk
Web Site: www.nlo.co.uk
Artistic Director: Ronald Corp
Orchestra Fixer & Concert Manager: Antonia Kent

THE NEW WIND ORCHESTRA
119 Woolstone Road, Forest Hill, London SE23 2TQ
Tel: 020 8699 1101 Fax: 020 8699 2219
Email: catherinepluygers@hotmail.com
Contact: Catherine Pluygers

NORTHERN CHAMBER ORCHESTRA
799 Wilmslow Road, Manchester M20 2RR
Tel: 0161 247 2220 Fax: 0161 247 6899
Email: info@ncorch.co.uk
Web Site: www.ncorch.co.uk
General Manager: Jonathan Thackeray
Marketing: Sally Smith

O2 PRODUCTIONS LTD
Chestnut Barn, North Stoke,
Bath BA1 9AT
Tel: 0117 932 9530 Fax: 0117 932 9531
Mob: 07836 784 999
Email: bill@o2productionsltd.co.uk
Musician Contractors: Bill Occleshaw, Leah Occleshaw
Musicians contracted for theatrical productions, recording sessions, TV & radio work. West End theatre and tours covered.

ORCHESTRA DA CAMERA
3 Barnstaple Close, Coventry CV5 7PJ
Tel: 02476 405283
Email: enquiries@orchestradacamera.co.uk
Web Site: www.orchestradacamera.co.uk
Orchestra Manager: Tony Ayres

ORCHESTRA OF OPERA NORTH
Grand Theatre, 46 New Briggate, Leeds, West Yorkshire LS1 6NU
Tel: 0113 243 9999
Marketing: 0113 223 3500
Email: info@operanorth.co.uk
Web Site: www.operanorth.co.uk
Head of Music: Martin Pickard

ORCHESTRA OF THE AGE OF ENLIGHTENMENT
Kings Place, 90 York Way, London N1 9AG
Tel: 020 7239 9370 Fax: 020 7239 9399
Email: info@oae.co.uk
Web Site: www.oae.co.uk
Orchestra Manager: Philippa Brownsword
Email: philippa.brownsword@oae.co.uk

ORCHESTRA OF WELSH NATIONAL OPERA
Wales Millennium Centre, Bute Place, Cardiff CF10 5AL South Wales
Switchboard: 029 2063 5000 Fax: 029 2048 3050
Email: ian.douglas@wno.org.uk
Web Site: www.wno.org.uk
Company Manager: Ian Douglas
Head of Music Staff: Russell Moreton

PALM COURT THEATRE ORCHESTRA & COMPANY
Winkton Lodge Cottage, Salisbury Road, Winkton, Christchurch, Dorset BH23 7AR
Tel: 01202 484 185 Fax: 01202 471 920
Email: godwin@palm-court.demon.co.uk
Web Site: www.palmcourttheatre.co.uk
Management: Palm Court Theatre Productions
Senior Personnel: Patricia Godwin

PHILHARMONIA ORCHESTRA
11 York Road, London SE1 7NX
Tel: 020 7921 3903 Fax: 020 7921 3950
Email: alice.walton@philharmonia.co.uk
Web Site: www.philharmonia.co.uk
Managing Director: David Whelton
Media & Marketing Director: Alice Walton

THE PICCADILLY DANCE ORCHESTRA
Directed by Michael Law
27 Caesar Avenue, Kingsnorth, Ashford, Kent TN23 3PZ
Tel: 01233 612 183
Email: mail@pdo.org.uk
Web Site: www.pdo.org.uk
Contacts: Michael Law, Alan S Bennett-Law
Stylish and swinging stage and dance orchestra, specialising in the 20's, 30's and 40's, and ballroom.
Resident at the Savoy Hotel since 1997.
Currently touring, "Chasing the Blues Away", "Midnight in Mayfair".

JOHN REID STRING QUARTET
14 Upper Bar, Newport,
Shropshire TF10 7EJ
Tel: 01952 825 235 Fax: 01952 814 734
Mobile: 07966 434761
Email: jpreid2408@aol.com
Director: John Reid

ROYAL LIVERPOOL PHILHARMONIC ORCHESTRA
Philharmonic Hall, Hope Street,
Liverpool L1 9BP
BO: 0151 709 3789 Admin: 0151 210 2895 Fax: 0151 210 2902
Email: info@liverpoolphil.com
Web Site: www.liverpoolphil.com
Head of Programming: Sandra Parr
Orchestra Manager: Julian Munro

ROYAL PHILHARMONIC ORCHESTRA
16 Clerkenwell Green, London EC1R 0QT
Tel: 020 7608 8800 Fax: 020 7608 8801
Email: info@rpo.co.uk
Web Site: www.rpo.co.uk
Artistic Director and Principal Conductor: Charles Dutoit

ROYAL SCOTTISH NATIONAL ORCHESTRA
Henry Wood Hall, 73 Claremont Street, Glasgow, Strathclyde G3 7JB
Tel: 0141 226 3868 Fax: 0141 221 4317
Email: info@rsno.org.uk
Web Site: www.rsno.org.uk
Marketing Manager: Carol Fleming
Orchestra Manager: Ewen McKay

SINFONIA OF LONDON
Pigeon House Meadow, 27 Grove Road, Beaconsfield, Buckinghamshire HP9 1UR
Tel: 01494 677934
Email: Sinfoniaoflondon@aol.com
Executive Director: Peter Willison
Secretary: Sally Birkett

SINFONIA VERDI
11 Stewart Road, Harpenden
Hertfordshire AL5 4QE
Tel/Fax: 01582 469 166
Email: sv@firstmaestro.com
Contact: David Murphy
Concerts, Education Workshops, Music for Coprorate Functions.

SOUTH YORKSHIRE SYMPHONY ORCHESTRA
1 Springfield Close, Eckington, Sheffield, South Yorkshire S21 4GS
Mob: 07846 199224
Email: paul@syso.co.uk
Web Site: www.syso.co.uk
Contact: Paul Scott

ST JAMES'S BAROQUE PLAYERS
120 Chewton Road, London E17 7DN
Tel: 020 8223 0772 Fax: 020 8926 2979
Email: petermccarthy@waitrose.com
Contact: Peter McCarthy
Music Director: James O'Donnell

STEINITZ BACH PLAYERS
London Bach Society
73 High Street, Old Oxted, Surrey RH8 9LN
Tel: 01883 717372 Fax: 01883 715851
Email: lbs@lonbachsoc.demon.co.uk
Web Site: www.bachlive.co.uk
Administrator: Mrs Margaret Steinitz
Orchestral Manager: Philippa Brownsword

SURREY CHAMBER ORCHESTRA
25b Epsom Lane South, Tadworth, Surrey KT20 5TA
Tel: 01737 813273 Fax: 01737 215676
Email: lyn@classicconcerts.org.uk
Music Director: Jonathan Brett
Administration: Lyn Mumford

THAMES CHAMBER ORCHESTRA
41 Shirley Drive, Hounslow, Middlesex TW3 2HD
Tel: 020 8894 2068
Email: info@thameschamberorchestra.co.uk
Web: www.thameschamberorchestra.co.uk

THE CHAMBER ORCHESTRA OF WALES
4, Chandler's Reach, Georgebank, Mumbles, Swansea SA3 4EP
Tel: 01792 366495 Mobile: 07860 725934
Email: griff.harries@virgin.net
Web Site: www.toporchestra.com / www.topfixer.com
Director: Gruffydd John Harries

ULSTER ORCHESTRA
Ulster Hall, Bedford Street, Belfast BT2 7FF Northern Ireland
Tel: 028 9023 9900 Fax: 028 9026 0483
Email: info@ulsterorchestra.com
Web Site: www.ulsterorchestra.com
Orchestra Manager: Andrew Smith
Email: andrew@ulsterorchestra.com
Head of Marketing and Development: Lydia Gamble

VIRTUOSI OF ENGLAND
14 Beaumont Road, Purley, Surrey CR8 2EG
Tel/Fax: 020 8668 5883
Email: darrelldavison@hotmail.com
Musical Director: Darrell Davison

VIVA THE ORCHESTRA OF THE EAST MIDLANDS
Beaufort Business Centre, Beaufort Street, Derby, Derbyshire DE21 6AX
Tel: 01332 207 570
Email: info@vivaorch.co.uk
Web Site: www.vivaorch.co.uk
Concert Manager: Matthew Lax
Principal Conductor: André de Ridder

VIVALDI CONCERTANTE
35 Laurel Avenue, Potters Bar, Hertfordshire EN6 2AB
Tel: 01707 650 735 Mob: 07771 681 687
Founder: Joseph Pilbery
Leader: Alison Kelly

WORTHING SYMPHONY
Assembly Hall, Stoke Abbott Road, Worthing, West Sussex BN11 1HQ
BO: 01903 206 206 Admin: 01903 231 799 Fax: 01903 215 337
Email: theatres@worthing.gov.uk
Orchestra Administrator: David Smith
Principal Conductor: John Gibbons

YORKSHIRE CONCERT ORCHESTRA
Torridon House, 104 Bradford Road, Wrenthorpe, Wakefield, West Yorkshire WF1 2AH
Tel: 01924 371 496
General Manager: Brian Greensmith

Principal Festivals

England

CHELTENHAM JAZZ FESTIVAL
29 April-04 May 2015
Cheltenham Festivals, 109-111 Bath Road Cheltenham, Gloucestershire GL53 7LS
Music Admin: 01242 511211 BO: 01242 227 979 Music Admin Fax: 01242 256457
Email: jazzfestival@cheltenhamfestival.com
Web Site: www.cheltenhamfestivals.com
Jazz Festival Executive Director: Ian George
Advisor: Tony Dudley-Evans
Jazz Festival Producer: Steve Symons
Temporary Venues: The Big Top (cap: 1,300)
Jazz Arena (cap: 600)
One of the biggest jazz events in the country, bringing some of the biggest names in jazz to the town, as well as providing a platform for the stars of the future.

ACOUSTIC FESTIVAL OF BRITAIN
19-21 June 2015 Uttoxeter Racecourse
Festival Office PO Box 64
Carmarthenshire SA18 9AB
Tickets Tel: 0333 9000 919
Email: info@acousticfestival.co.uk
Web Site: www.acousticfestival.co.uk

AGEAS SALISBURY INTERNATIONAL ARTS FESTIVAL
22 May-06 June 2015
87 Crane Street Salisbury, Wiltshire SP1 2PU
Tel: 01722 332 241
Email: info@salisburyfestival.co.uk
Web Site: www.salisburyfestival.co.uk
Contacts: Caroline Peacock, Maria Bota
A multi arts festival with an em[phasis on music of all kinds (theatre, dance,circus) and outdoor events.

ALDEBURGH FESTIVAL OF MUSIC & THE ARTS
12-28 June 2015
Snape Maltings Concert Hall, Snape, Saxmundham, Suffolk IP17 1SP
Tel: 01728 687100 Fax: 01728 687120
Email: enquiries@aldeburgh.co.uk
Web Site: www.aldeburgh.co.uk
Chief Executive: Roger Wright

BATH FRINGE FESTIVAL
22 May-07 June 2015
103 Walcot Street Bath, Somerset BA1 5BW
Tel:: 01225 480 079
Email: admin@bathfringe.co.uk
Web Site: www.bathfringe.co.uk
Chairperson: Briony Waite
Administrator: Wendy Matthews

BATH INTERNATIONAL MUSIC FESTIVAL
15 -25 May 2015
Third Floor, Abbey Chambers Kingston Buildings Bath, Somerset BA1 1NT
Admin: 01225 462231 BO: 01225 463 362 Fax: 01225 310 377 Box Office Address: 2 Church Street, Bath, Somerset BA1 1NL
Email: info@bathfestivals.org.uk
Web Site: www.bathfestivals.org.uk
Bath International Music Festival was founded in 1948. It presents a diverse programme of music featuring some of the finest performers in the world. Classical, Early, Opera, Jazz, Flamenco, World, Contemporary, Folk, etc.
The festival takes place over 17days in the beautiful Georgian City of Bath.
Please contact the festival for full details.

BATH LITERATURE FESTIVAL
27 February-08 March 2015
Third Floor, Abbey Chambers Kingston Buildings Bath, Somerset BA1 1NT
Admin: 01225 462231 BO: 01225 463 362 Fax: 01225 310 377 Box Office Address: 2 Church Street, Bath, Somerset BA1 1NL
Email: info@bathfestivals.org.uk
Web Site: www.bathfestivals.org.uk
Bath Literature Festival includes talks, debates, workshops and film shows as well as many well-known faces within the world of literature.

BBC PROMS
17July - 12 September 2015
(Admin Address) Broadcasting House Portland Place, London W1A 1AA
BO: 0845 401 5040
Email: proms@bbc.co.uk
Web Site: www.bbc.co.uk/proms
Tickets for concerts are sold at the Box Office, at the Royal Albert Hall.

BRIDLINGTON ARTS FESTIVAL
Festival takes place annually in May.
6 Belgrave Road Bridlington, East Ridings Of Yorkshire YO15 3JR
01262 674244
Email: geo.mitchell@uwclub.net
Web Site: www.bridlingtonartsfestival.com
Contact: Mrs Georgie Mitchell

BRIGHTON FESTIVAL
02-25 May 2015
12A Pavilion Buildings, Castle Square, Brighton, East Sussex BN1 1EE
Tel: 01273 709709 Fax: 01273 707505
Email: info@brightonfestival.org
Web Site: www.brightonfestival.org
Largest Arts Festival in England. Covers theatre, music, opera, dance, literature, street theatre, film & media, exhibitions.

BUXTON FESTIVAL
10-26 July 2015
3 The Square, Buxton, Derbyshire SK17 6AZ
Admin: 01298 70395 BO: 0845 127 2190
Accommodation: 01298 25106 Fax: 01298 72289
Email: info@buxtonfestival.co.uk
Web Site: www.buxtonfestival.co.uk

Chairman:Lord Hattersley
General Manager: Glyn Foley
Artistic Director: Andrew Greenwood
Buxton Opera House S/Cap: 950

CAMBRIDGE FOLK FESTIVAL
30 July-02 August 2015
Arts & Entertainments Cambridge City Council, The Guildhall, Cambridge CB2 3QJ
Tel: 01223 457 555 Fax: 01223 457 229
Email: eddie.barcan@cambridge.gov.uk
Web: www.cambridgefolkfestival.co.uk
Contact: Eddie Barcan
Venue: Cherryhinton Hall Grounds, Cambridge

CHELTENHAM LITERATURE FESTIVAL
02-11 October 2015
Cheltenham Festivals, 109 Bath Road Cheltenham, Gloucestershire GL53 7LS
Literature Admin: 01242 511211
Literature BO: 0844 880 8094 Literature Admin Fax: 01242 256 457
Email: clair.greenaway @cheltenhamfestivals.com
Web Site: www.cheltenhamfestivals.co.uk
Literature Festival Artistic Director: Sarah Smyth
Literature Festival Executive Director: Clair Greenaway
Literature Festival Manager: Christin Stein
Principal Venues: Town Hall (cap: 1,000), Everyman Theatre (cap: 650), The Centaur (cap: 2,500) The Bacon Theatre (cap: 550) .

CHELTENHAM MUSIC FESTIVAL
30 June-11 July 2015
Cheltenham Festivals, 109-111 Bath Road Cheltenham, Gloucestershire GL53 7LS
Music Admin: 01242 511211 Music BO: 0844 880 8094 Music Fax: 01242 256457
Email: music@cheltenhamfestival.com
Web Site: www.cheltenhamfestivals.com
Artistic Director: Meurig Bowen
Music Festival Manager: Holly Traynor
Principal Venues: Town Hall (cap: 1,000), Pittville Pump Room (cap: 400)
Beginning in 1945 as a showcase for British contemporary music, this event has become one of the UK's finest classical music festivals with a repertoire which now includes contemporary music from across Europe.

CHICHESTER FESTIVAL THEATRE AND MINERVA THEATRE
Summer Festival Season of Plays
Festival Theatre, Oaklands Park, Chichester, West Sussex PO19 6AP
Tel: 01243 784437 BO: 01243 781312
Fax: 01243 787288
Email: admin@cft.org.uk
Web Site: www.cft.org.uk
Artistic Director: Jonathan Church
Executive Director: Alan Finch
Theatre Manager: Janet Bakose
Technical Co-ordinator: Sam Garner-Gibbons
Chichester Festival Capacity: 1306
Minerva Theatre Capacity: 283

CHICHESTER FESTIVITIES
24 June - 14 July 2013
Canon Gate House, South Street, Chichester, Sussex PO19 1PU
Tel: 01243 785 718 Fax: 01243 528 356
Email: info@chifest.org.uk
Web Site: www.festivalofchichester.co.uk
Director: Amanda Sharp

CHIPPENHAM FOLK FESTIVAL
22-25 May 2015
Festival Office, The Cause Music and Arts Centre, The Causeway, Chippenham, Wiltshire SN15 3DD
Tel: 01249 657 190
Email: info@chippfolk.co.uk
Web Site: www.chippfolk.co.uk
A traditional based folk festival set in the heart of Chippenham beside the River Avon. Up to sixteen venues used daily plus fringe events. 2-3,000 people attend the festival which is in its 35th year. Concerts, ceilidhs, dances, morris and ritual displays. Workshops and sessions abound in a family based festival to suit all ages.

CITY OF LONDON FESTIVAL
22 June-10 July 2015
Fitz Eylwin House 25 Holborn Viaduct London EC1A 2BP
Tel: 020 7583 3585 Fax: 020 7353 0455
BO: 0845 120 7502
Email: admin@colf.org
Web Site: www.colf.org
Festival Director: Paul Gudgin

DANCE UMBRELLA
15-31 October 2015
1 Brewery Square London SE1 2LF
Tel: 020 7407 1200
Email: mail@danceumbrella.co.uk
Web Site: www.danceumbrella.co.uk
Artistic Director: Emma Gladstone
Executive Director : Anu Giri
Dance Umbrella is London's international contemporary dance Festival and supports and encourages the best of the new in dance work both in Britain and overseas.

END OF THE ROAD FESTIVAL
04-06 September 2015
25 St. Johns Road, East Grinstead, West Sussex RH19 3LG
Email: simon@endoftheroadfestival.com
Web Site: www.endoftheroadfestival.com
Press Contact: Seb Emina

EXETER FESTIVAL
25 June - 10 July 2010
Civic Centre, Paris Street, Exeter, Devon EX1 1JJ
Tel: 01392 265 200 Fax: 01392 265 366
Email: festival@exeter.gov.uk
Web Site: www.exeter.gov.uk
Festival Manager: Lesley Maynard

GREENWICH + DOCKLANDS FESTIVALS
26 June-04 July 2015
The Borough Hall Royal Hill London SE10 8RE
Tel: 020 8305 1818 Fax: 020 8305 1188
Email: admin@festival.org
Web Site: www.festival.org
Artistic Director: Bradley Hemmings
Senior Projects Manager: Sophie Akbar

GUILFEST MUSIC
10-12 July 2015
54 Haydon Place, Guildford, Surrey GU1 4NE
Tel: 01483 454 159 Fax: 01483 306 551
Email: www.guilfest.co.uk
Web Site: www.guilfest.co.uk

HARROGATE INTERNATIONAL FESTIVAL
July 2015
32 Cheltenham Parade Harrogate, North Yorkshire, HG1 1DB
Tel: 01423 562 303
Email: info@harrogate-festival.org.uk
Web Site: www.harrogate-festival.org.uk
Festival Director: Sharon Canavar

HENLEY LITERARY FESTIVAL
September 2015
Henley
Tel: 01491 572436
Email: info@henleyliteraryfestival.co.uk
Web Site: www.henleyliteraryfestival.co.uk

KING'S LYNN FESTIVAL
12-25 July 2015
Suite 2, Third Floor Bishop's Lynn House 18 Tuesday Market Place King's Lynn, Norfolk PE30 1JW
Tel: 01553 767 557 Fax: 01553 767 688
Email: info@kingslynnfestival.org.uk
Web Site: www.kingslynnfestival.org.uk
Contact: Joanne Mawson

L.I.F.T (LONDON INTERNATIONAL FESTIVAL OF THEATRE)
June 2016 (Bi-annual)
The Institute of Contempory Arts, 12 Carlton House Terrace London SW1Y 5AH
Tel: 020 7093 6340 Fax: 020 7093 1304
Email: info@liftfest.org.uk
Web Site: www.liftfest.org.uk
Offering London audiences a year round

opportunity to see the best of UK and international theatre work.

LEEDS INTERNATIONAL PIANOFORTE COMPETITION THE
26 August-13 September 2015 (Every 3 years)
Pianoforte Competition Office, The University of Leeds, Leeds, West Yorkshire LS2 9JT
Tel: 0113 2446586
Email: pianocompetition@leeds.ac.uk
Web Site: www.leedspiano.com

LONDON INTERNATIONAL MIME FESTIVAL
08-31 January 2015
Somerset House South Wing Strand London WC2R 1LA
Tel: 020 7637 5661
Email: direction@mimelondon.com
Web Site: www.mimelondon.com
Directors: Joseph Seelig & Helen Lannaghan
Largest, longest running festival of its kind in the world, established in 1977. Showcase for innovative international visual theatre, mime, clown and circus-based arts, taking place annually in the last three weeks in January. Participation is by invitation only.

LONDON JAZZ FESTIVAL
13-22 November 2015
51 Kingsway Place, Sans Walk, Clerkenwell London EC1R 0LU
Tel: 020 7324 1880 Fax: 020 7324 1881
Email: david@serious.org.uk
Web Site: www.londonjazzfestival.org.uk
Contact: John Cumming

MANCHESTER IRISH FESTIVAL
c/o 36 Wilbraham Road Fallowfield Manchester M14 7DW
Tel: 0770 237 1966
Email: info@the manchesteririshfestival.co.uk
Web: www.manchesteririshfestival.co.uk
Co-Chair: Kevin Fitzpatrick
Festival takes place annually in March (around St Patrick's Day) and we celebrate all aspects of Irish culture - music, comedy, theatre, special events, etc.

NATIONAL ARTS DAY
Check national press for details. The nation's day for the arts. This special day is set aside once each year on Mid-Summer day, June 24th, with the aim of praising the level of participation in the awareness of the arts generally.

NATIONAL STUDENT DRAMA FESTIVAL
28 March-03 April 2015
Woolyard 54 Bermondsey Street London SE1 3UD
Tel: 020 7036 9027
Email: info@nsdf.org.uk
Web Site: www.nsdf.org.uk
Festival Director: Michael Brazier

OPEN AIR THEATRE - SEASON
15 May-12 September 2015
Regent's Park Open Theatre Inner Circle Regents Park London NW1 4NR
Tel/Mgt: 08443 753460 BO: 0844 8264242
Email: info@openairtheatre.com
Web Site: www.openairtheatre.com
Artistic Director: Timothy Sheader

POLESDEN LACEY FESTIVAL
July 2015
Polesden Lacey Open Air Th., National Trust, Polesden Lacey, Dorking, Surrey RH5 6BD
Admin: 01372 452048
Email: polesdenlacey@nationaltrust.org.uk
Web Site: www.nationaltrust.org.uk/southeastevents
Festival Coordinator: Andrea Selley

ST ALBANS INTERNATIONAL ORGAN FESTIVAL
08-18 July 2015
PO Box 80, St Albans, Hertfordshire AL3 4HR
Tel: 01727 844 765 Fax: 01727 868941
Email: info@organfestival.com
Web Site: www.organfestival.com
Administrator: Linda Hamling

THE CANTERBURY FESTIVAL
17-31 October 2015
Festival House 8 Orange Street, Canterbury, Kent CT1 2JA
Admin Tel: 01227 452 853
Email: info@canterburyfestival.co.uk
Web Site: www.canterburyfestival.co.uk
Festival Director: Rosie Turner
Marketing Manager: Rachel Pilard
Festival Administrator: Tia Austen
An annual multi-arts Festival showcasing the very best in local, national & international talent across the arts forms. Two weeks each October. Full programme available from August.

THE WANSBECK MUSIC FESTIVAL
18-22 March 2015
2 Russell Terrace Bedlington Northumberland NE22 5SZ
Tel: 01670 823 384
Email: e.gilliancdstewart2013@gmail.com
Web: www.wansbeckmusicfestival.co.uk
Contact: Mrs Gillian Stewart

THE TRI-TOWN FESTIVAL
Formerly known as the Wansbeck Festival. Takes place in August annually c/o Wansbeck District Council, Front Street West, Bedlington, Northumberland LE22 5TU
Tel: 01670 843 200 Fax: 01670 843 484
Email: k.hudson@wansbeck.gov.uk
Contact Arts & Entertainment Manager: Kate Hudson

YORK EARLY MUSIC FESTIVAL
Summer Festival: 3-11 July 2015
Christmas Festival: 4-13 December 2015
The National Centre for Early Music, St Margaret's Church Walmgate, York YO1 9TL
Tel: 01904 632 220 Fax: 01904 612 631
Email: info@ncem.co.uk
Web Site: www.ncem.co.uk
Britain's largest festival of early music. Concerts in historic houses, churches throughout York. Plus illustrated lectures, walks & talks.

Northern Ireland

BELFAST FESTIVAL AT QUEEN'S
16 October-01 November 2015
Lanyon North Queen's University Belfast University Road Belfast, County Antrim BT7 1NN Northern Ireland
Tel: 028 9097 1034
Email: r.wakely@.qub.ac.uk
Web Site: www.belfastfestival.com
Festival Director: Richard Wakely
Marketing Manager: Susan McCleary

Scotland

BLAS FESTIVAL
06 - 14 September 2013
Aros, UpperKnockbain Road Dingwall Ross-shire IV15 9NR Scotland
Tel: 01349 865349 (General)
Fax: 08720 221864
Email: donnamacrae@gmail.com
Web Site: www.blas-festival.com
Contact:
Festival Director: Donna Macrae
Email: management@blas-festival.com
Artistic Director: Brian O hEadhra
Email: arts@blas-festival.com
Press & Media Manager: Cailean Maclean
Email: pr@blas-festival.com
Only Major Scottish Festival of Gaelic and Highland Music and Culture. 50 plus events across the Scottish Highlands and Islands.

BLAS FESTIVAL
September 2015 Run by Feisean nan Gaidheal
111 Academy Street, Inverness IV1 1LX
Tel: 01463 225559
Email: arthur@feisean.org
Web Site: www.feisean.org
Chief Executive of Organisers: Arthur

Cormack
Only Major Scottish Festival of Gaelic and Highland Music and Culture, 50 plus events across the Scottish Highlands and Islands.

EDINBURGH FESTIVAL FRINGE
07-31 August 2015
Festival Fringe Society Ltd, 180 High Street, Edinburgh, Mid Lothian EH1 1QS Scotland
Tel: 0131 226 0026 Fax: 0131 226 0016
Email: admin@edfringe.com
Web Site: www.edfringe.com
The Edinburgh Fringe is an open arts festival with noartistic selection. The Fringe Society is an advisory office offering expert and unbiased advice on how to bring a show to the Fringe. The office also promotes the Festival year-round, produces a central programme for all Fringe events and runs a box office selling tickets on behalf of all Fringe participants.

EDINBURGH INTERNATIONAL FESTIVAL
07-31 August 2015
The Hub, Castlehill, Royal Mile, Edinburgh, Mid Lothian EH1 2NE Scotland
Tel: 0131 473 2099 Fax: 0131 473 2002
Email: carrie.bell@eif.co.uk
Web Site: www.eif.co.uk

PERTH FESTIVAL OF THE ARTS
21-31 May 2015
3-5 High Street, Perth, Perth & Kinross PH1 5PH Scotland
Tel: 07774 181 768
Email: info@perthfestival.co.uk
Web Site: www.perthfestival.co.uk
Festival Administrator: Mrs Sandra Ralston
11 day annual festival at the end of May concerning classical music, opera, jazz, blues, dance, folk, comedy and rock music.

Wales

FISHGUARD INTERNATIONAL MUSIC FESTIVAL
71 High Street Fishguard, Pembrokeshire, SA65 9AW Wales
Tel: 01348 873237
Email: bpjones.fimf@outlook.com/info@fishguardmusicfestival.co.uk
Web Site: www.fishguardmusicfestival.co.uk
Contact: Bronwen Jones

LLANGOLLEN INTERNATIONAL MUSICAL EISTEDDFOD
07-12 July 2015
Eisteddfod Office, Royal International Pavilion, Abbey Road, Llangollen, Denbighshire, LL20 8SW Wales
Tel: 01978 862 000 Fax: 01978 862 002
Email: info@international-eisteddfod.co.uk
Web: www.international-eisteddfod.co.uk
Income Generation Manager: Christine Dukes
International festival of music and dance, held each July.

Small Scale Touring Companies

ACTION SPACE MOBILE
Mapplewell & Staincross Village Hall, Darton Lane, Mapplewell, Barnsley, South Yorkshire S75 6AL
Tel: 01226 391 112
Email: contact@actionspacemobile.org
Web Site: www.actionspacemobile.org
Manager: Karen Shore
Artistic Director: Mary Turner
Action Space Mobile is a Community Arts Organisation, with a collection of workers with specialist skills in various media such as drama, arts and crafts, dance and movement, music and information technology. We have 'In The Boat Theatre' company, 'All Of Us' theatre company, 'Step by Step' dance group and 'Cross the Sky' arts group. Amongst other groups/projects.

ACTORS INCORPORATED
19 Rectory Gardens, London SW4 0EE
Tel: 020 7978 1142
Contact: Richard Leighton

APOLLO THEATRE (LITTLE THEATRE GUILD MEMBER)
Pyle Street, Calbourne, Newport, Isle of Wight PO30 1JT
Tel: 01983 527 267
Contact Artistic Manager: Michael Arnell
Contact Public Relations Officer: Peter Boffin

APPLAUSE PRODUCTIONS
31 Wimborne Road West, Wimborne, Dorset BH21 2DG
Tel: 01202 887 439 Fax: 01202 849 943
Email: admin@derekgrant.co.uk
Web Site: www.derekgrant..co.uk
Small and medium touring production available - children's shows and pantomimes. Part of the Derek Grant Organisation.

ARC THEATRE COMPANY
The Malt House, Newbold Road, Desford, Leicester LE9 9GS
Tel/Fax: 01455 828400

ATC
(Actors Touring Company)
The Tab Centre 3 Godfrey Place London E2 7NT
Tel: 0207 033 7360 Fax: 0207 739 8298
Email: atc@atctheatre.com
Web Site: www.atc-online.com
Artistic Director: Bijan Sheibani
Executive Director: Hannah Bentley
Administrator & Events Manager: Kendall O'Neill
Artistic Associate: Ellen McDougall

ATTIK DANCE COMPANY
The Barbican Theatre Castle Street Plymouth PL1 2NJ
Tel: 01752 252510 Fax: 01752 222209
Email: info@attik.org.uk
Web Site: www.attik.org.uk

B ARTS
16 Barracks Square, Barracks Road, Newcastle-under-Lyme, Staffordshire ST5 1LG
Tel: 01782 717 326 Fax: 01782 717 190
Email: info@pandaemonium.biz
Web Site: www.pandaemonium.biz
Working creativley for change: touring theatre, international projects, work with displaced people and settled communities in UK and Europe.

BABBLING VAGABONDS STORY TELLING THEATRE
Top Floor Flat, Bakewell Town Hall, Bath Street, Bakewell, Derbyshire DE45 1BX
Tel/Fax: 01629 815 110 Post to be directed to: PO Box 6116, Bakewell, Derbyshire, DE45 1YE
Email: info@babblingvagabonds.co.uk
Web Site: www.babblingvagabonds.co.uk
Joint Artistic Directors: Phil Coggins, Mark Hornsey, Tara Saunders
We create original Children's Theatre shows that tour to professional venues, community spaces and schools throughout the year. We also create site-specific performances and bespoke theatre arts projects for people of all ages.

BARBER/LUNT PRODUCTIONS
Dean Clough, Halifax, West Yorkshire HX3 5AX
Tel/Fax: 01422 330 101
Email: barberlunt@aol.com
Administrator: Angela Saville
Artistic Directors: Maureen Lunt, John Barber

BELVOIR PLAYERS
258 Belvoir Drive, Belfast, County Antrim BT8 7DU Northern Ireland
Tel: 028 90 649 835 Fax: 028 90 491 213
Email: belvoir@belvoirplayers.org
Web Site: www.belvoirplayers.org
Artistic Director: Richard Mills

BENCHTOURS PRODUCTIONS LIMITED
Bonnington Mill, 72 Newhaven Road, Edinburgh, Mid Lothian EH6 5QG Scotland
Tel: 0131 555 3585
Email: info@benchtours.com
Web Site: www.benchtours.com
Catherine Gillard: Director
Peter Clerke: Director
Scottish-based international touring theatre ensemble, also specialising in educational/outreach programmes, including special needs work.

BORDERLINE THEATRE
North Harbour Street, Ayr KA8 8AA Scotland
Tel: 01292 281010 Fax: 01292 263825
Email: enquiries@borderlinetheatre.co.uk
Web Site: www.borderlinetheatre.co.uk
Marketing Manager: Paul Brunton
Producer: Eddie Jackson

BILL BROOKMAN PRODUCTIONS LTD
101 Ashby Road, Loughborough, Leicestershire LE11 3AB
Tel: 01509 236 175 Fax: 01509 219 873
Email: office@billbrookman.co.uk
Web Site: www.billbrookman.co.uk
Manager: Bill Brookman
Specialising in Street Performance.
A large developed experienced street theatre company combining street music, street gypsy dancing, fire, stiltwalking, puppetry. Large sets. Celebratory theatre.

THE CENTRE FOR PERFORMANCE RESEARCH
6 Science Park, Aberystwyth, Ceredigion SY23 3AH Wales
Tel: 01970 622 133 Fax: 01970 622 132
Email: cprwww@aber.ac.uk
Web Site: www.thecpr.org.uk
Producer: Judie Christie
Artistic Director: Richard Gough
Marketing Director: Antony Pickthall
The Centre for Performance Research (CPR) is a multi-faceted theatre organisation based in Wales and working internationally. The CPR produces innovative performance work; arranges workshops, conferences, lectures and master classes; collaborates and exchanges with theatre companies of international significance; publishes and distributes theatre books and runs a multicultural performance resource centre.
The CPR's main aims are:
To develop and improve the knowledge, understanding and practice of theatre in its broadest sense, to affect change through investigation, sharing and discovery. To integrate theory and practice. To dig to discover origins and roots, to push and pioneer, to extend boundaries, perception and possibilities.

CENTRE OCEAN STREAM
1 Holland Road, Southampton, Hampshire SO19 9FW
Tel: 023 8042 0114 Fax: 02380 444 468
Mobile: 07740 123070
Email: kathakali@interalpha.co.uk
Contact: Barbara Vijayakumar
To explore the Language of Living Colour and the creative connections between the visual and performing arts through the abstract work of Centre Ocean Stream and the classical work of Kathakali.

CERTAIN CURTAIN THEATRE COMPANY
Unit 128, Oyston Mill, Strand Road, Preston, Lancashire PR1 8UR
Tel: 01772 731 024
Email: cctheatre@yahoo.com
Web Site: www.cctheatre.co.uk
Directors: Claire Moore, John Woudberg
Original work tailored to all ages includes T.I.E., issue-based, public performances, musicals and workshops. We are an award winning company.

CHALKFOOT THEATRE ARTS
5 Gold Street Stalbridge Dorset DT10 2LX
Tel: 01963 362937
Email: info@chalkfoot.org.uk
Web Site: www.chalkfoot.org.uk
Artistic Director: Philip Dart
Chalkfoot Thearte Arts (the touring and outreach arm of Channel Theatre Compnay) serves the people of south east England and beyond by touring productions of a high standard which entertain, inform and inspire. The company is committed to touring non-theatre venues and it takes its work into a wide range of communities. The company also works with many different groups on projects which promote personal and social development and develop creativity. Also see CHANNEL THEATRE COMPANY.

CHANNEL THEATRE PRODUCTIONS LTD
5 Gold Street Stalbridge Dorset DT10 2LX
Tel: 01963 362937
Email: info@channel-theatre.co.uk
Web Site: www.channel-theatre.co.uk
Artistic Director: Philip Dart
Associate Director: Claudia Leaf
Channel Theatre company works regionally and nationally on special commissions, training programmes (school and business), theatre production projects, theatre in education programmes and writing commissions. .The company delivers high quality projects to a wide range of venues/client groups. For touring and outreach, see CHALKFOOT THEATRE ARTS.

CHRISTALA ROSINA POETRY CONCERTS
38 Merrymeet, Woodmansterne, Near Banstead, Surrey SM7 3HT
Tel: 01737 371 761 No fax number
Email: christalarosina@hotmail.com
Web Site: www.christalarosina.co.uk
Poetry Concerts: Modern Romantic poet, Christala Rosina, performs her beautiful, passionate and inspiring poetry to classical and celtic accompaniment by harpist, Luisa-Maria Cordell. Christala also works with other instrumentalists.

CLEAN BREAK THEATRE COMPANY
2 Patshull Road, London NW5 2LB
Tel: 020 7482 8600 Fax: 020 7482 8611
Email: general@cleanbreak.org.uk
Web Site: www.cleanbreak.org.uk
Clean Break is the only theatre organisation in the UK for women whose lives have been directly affected by the criminal justice system. Based in purpose-built studios in London's Kentish Town, Clean Break runs an innovative programme of theatre performances and new writing projects, drama-based education, professional development and training, and advocacy.

CLOSE FOR COMFORT THEATRE CO
34 Boleyn Walk, Leatherhead, Surrey KT22 7HU
Tel: 01372 378 613 / 01483 837 830
Email: close4comf@aol.com
Web: www.hometown.aol.com/close4comf
Producers: Janet Gill, Glenn Johnson
We bring LIVE THEATRE to your house! Sit back and let yourself be entertained in the comfort of your living room. No travelling. No traffic. No queueing for tickets. No crowds. All we ask is that a minimum of 10 people are gathered together in your home.
We are based in Surrey, but, as strolling players, we perform all over England!

COMPASS THEATRE COMPANY
Carver Street Institute, 24 Rockingham Lane, Sheffield S1 4FW
Tel: 0114 275 5328 Fax: 0114 278 6931
Email: info@compasstheatrecompany.com
Web www.compasstheatrecompany.com
General Manager: Craig Dronfield
Artistic Director: Neil Sissons
Administrative Assistant: Damian Sackett

CORNELIUS & JONES PRODUCTIONS
49 Carters Close, Sherington, Newport Pagnell, Buckinghamshire MK16 9NW
Tel: 01908 612 593 Fax: 01908 616779
Email: admin@corneliusjones.com
Web Site: www.corneliusjones.com
Co-Directors: Sue Leech & Neil Canham
Cornelius & Jones is a small touring theatre company founded in 1986, performing for both children and adults in schools and theatres.

CRAGRATS LTD

Lawster House, 140 South Street,
Dorking, Surrey RH4 2EU
Tel: 08444 774 100
Email: enquiries@cragrats.com
Web Site: www.cragrats.com
Managing Director: William Akerman
Business Support Manager: Nicky Miles
Leeds Office: Roudfoundry Media Centre, Foundry Street, Leeds, LS11 5QP
CragRats Ltd is the market innovator and leader in bespoke theatre productions for young people, businesses and training organisations. CragRats Ltd is committed to communicating messages and motivating audiences throughout the UK, producing projects that range from issue-based theatre, initiative awareness shows, communication skills, corporate training as well as full-length theatre productions. See our web site for further company details.

CUT-CLOTH THEATRE

41 Beresford Road, London N5 2HR
Tel: 020 7503 4393

DANCE UNITED

Interchange Studios, Hampstead Town Hall, 213 Haverstock Hill,
London NW3 4QP
Tel: 0207 431 6647 Fax: 0207 794 9989
Email: info@dance-united.com
Web Site: www.dance-united.com
ADMINISTRATION:
Artistic Director: Tara-Jane Herbert
Projects Manager: Camilla Joysury
Marketing Coordinator: Rowena Evans
Dance United brings individuals and communities together to seek creative solutions to artistic challenges, triggering a process that develops social interaction and personal growth in participants. The company believes that dance has a unique quality that can, when delivered through a tried-and-tested methodology, create profound and life-changing experiences for those it works with.

DEAD EARNEST THEATRE

57 Burton Street, Sheffield S6 2HH
Tel/Fax: 0114 233 4579
Email: info@deadearnest.co.uk
Web Site: www.deadearnest.co.uk
Artistic Director: Ashley Barnes
Associate Producer: Neil Adleman
Projects Co-ordinator: Louise Ingham
Drama Project Leader: Rachel Scott
Dead Earnest theatre creates work that seeks to recognise, challenge and change the ways that we behave towards each other. Our work is characterised by new writing and a desire to test the present on the lessons of the past. We compliment our touring work with interactive training pieces, based on 'Forum theatre' and community empowerment workshops.

EASTERN ANGLES THEATRE COMPANY

Sir John Mills Theatre, Gatacre Road, Ipswich, Suffolk IP1 2LQ
Tel: 01473 218 202 Fax: 01473 384 999
Box Office: 01473 211 498
Email: admin@easternangles.co.uk
Web Site: www.easternangles.co.uk
Artistic Director: Ivan Cutting
General Manager: Jill Streatfeild
Marketing Officer: Anna Travers
Stage Manager: Penny Griffin

EMPTY SPACE THEATRE COMPANY

32 Kenbrook House, Leighton Road,
London NW5 2QN
Tel: 0870 909 0102 Fax: 0870 909 0103
Email: estc@dircon.co.uk
Artistic Director: Andrew Holmes

ESCAPE ARTISTS

42 Woodlark Road, Cambridge CB3 0HS
Tel: 01223 301 439 Fax: 01223 522 301
Email: houdini@escapeartists.co.uk
Web Site: www.escapeartists.co.uk
Director: Matthew Taylor
Administrator: Christine Cellier

THE EUROPEAN THEATRE COMPANY

39 Oxford Avenue, London SW20 8LS
Tel: 020 8544 1994 Fax: 020 8544 1999
Email: admin@europeantheatre.co.uk
Web Site: www.europeantheatre.co.uk
Contact: Jennie Graham
The European Theatre Company is a unique and innovative, professional touring company wihich performs high-quality, foreign language theatre in schools, colleges, theatres and art centres throughout the United Kingdom. The company regularly tours French, German and billingual productions specifically aimed at language learners and enthusiasts, motivating audiences by bringing European theatre alive in a fun, imaginative, lively and colourful way that is easy to understand.

FALSE IMPRESSIONS

207 Mersham Road, Thornton Heath, Surrey CR7 8NU
Tel: 01803 615 600/ 615 700 (Anne George) Mob: 07968 828 530
Email: richardleigh@falseimpressions.co.uk
Web Site: www.falseimpressions.co.uk
Theatrical Magical Advisor: Richard Leigh
Contact: Anne George (anne@trevorgeorge.co.uk)
False Impressions is a production company which specialises in the unusual field of stage illusion and magic shows of all genres.

Productions:
- The Magic Cavern
- Late Night Magic in the West End
- The Side Show of Wonders
- The Ice Cave Magic Show
- The Magic Toy Theatre
- The Haunted Magic Show

FECUND THEATRE

9 Albany Close, Barton on Sea, New Milton, Hampshire BH25 7HE
Tel: 01425 623 674
Email: helenh@fecund.co.uk
Web Site: www.fecund.co.uk
Contact: Beverley Reid - Creative Producer
Fecund theatre annually research and create an exciting, original and provocative theatrical experience; fusing current social issues with the physical potential of the actor. We are pioneering and pushing the bounds of the dramatic construct and the expectations of our audience.
Fecund tours nationally and provides educational and commercial residences and workshops; encouraging creative and experiential understanding of theatre and video technology.

FORCED ENTERTAINMENT

Workstation, 15 Paternoster Row, Sheffield S1 2BX
Tel: 0114 279 8977 Fax: 0114 221 2170
Email: fe@forcedentertainment.com
Web Site: www.forcedentertainment.com
Artistic Director: Tim Etchells
General Manager: Matt Burman
Marketing Manager: Rachel Thorne
Administrator: Eileen Evans

FOREST FORGE THEATRE COMPANY

The Theatre Centre, Crow Arch Lane, Ringwood, Hampshire BH24 1SF
Tel: 01425 470 188 Fax: 01425 471 158
Email: karen.jeffries@forestforge.co.uk
Web Site: www.forestforge.co.uk
Artistic Director: Sean Aita
Administrative Director: Karen Jeffries

FOURSIGHT THEATRE LTD

Newhampton Arts Centre, Dunkley Street, Wolverhampton, West Midlands WV1 4AN
Tel: 01902 714 257 Fax: 01902 428 413
Email: admin@foursighttheatre.co.uk
Web Site: www.foursighttheatre.co.uk
Artistic Director: Naomi Cooke
Foursight Theatre creates unusual, uncompromising and multi-disciplinary works which review history through the eyes of women: unknown, famous and infamous. Foursight is committed to creating total theatre - an holistic style of performance rooted in physical theatre. Work is experimental in both process & form.
Foursight tours nationally & internationally and provides educational workshops and residencies.
Funding: Arts Council England, West Midlands, Wolverhampton Council.

FUSE THEATRE FOR YOUNG PEOPLE
13 Hope Street, Liverpool,
Merseyside L1 9BH
Tel: 0151 708 0877 Fax: 0151 707 9950
Email: info@fusetheatre.com
Web Site: www.fusetheatre.co.uk
General Manager: Michael Quirke

GOG THEATRE COMPANY
Ostia, Overleigh Street
Somerset BA16 0TJ
Tel: 01458 445494 Fax: 01458 840063
Directors: Tom Clark, Caryne Clark

GRAEAE THEATRE COMPANY
LVS Resource Centre, 356 Holloway Road, London N7 6PA
Tel: 020 7700 2455 Fax: 020 7609 7324
Minicom: 020 7700 8184
Email: info@graeae.org
Web Site: www.graeae.org
Led by Artistic Director Jenny Sealey, the leading theatre company of diabled artists. In new and classic plays, TIE and accredited training, particular emphasis given to the creative, integrated use of sign language and audio description.

GRAND THEATRE OF LEMMINGS
38 High Street, Manningtree,
Essex CO11 1AJ
Tel: 01206 391 632 Fax: 01206 392 402
Email: lemmings@dircon.co.uk
Web Site: www.lemmings.dircon.co.uk
Contact: David Danzig
The Lemmings specialise in visual comedy producing a range of street theatre acts and a touring theatre show.

GREEN GINGER
Tobacco Factory Theatre, Raleigh Road, Bristol BS3 1TF Wales
Tel/Fax: 0117 922 5599
Email: mail@greenginger.net
Web Site: www.greenginger.net
Artistic Directors: Terry Lee and Chris Pirie
Versatile street and stage theatre shows available for all occasions and events indoors or out. "Green Ginger push puppetry to the limits and then, disturbingly, a bit further" Terry Gilliams (Patron).

HOBGOBLIN THEATRE COMPANY
Head Office: 2 Heston Road,
Redhill RH1 5HY
Tel: 0800 5300384 Mob: 07775 861165
Email: info@hobgoblintheatrecompany.co.uk
Web: www.hobgoblintheatrecompany.co.uk
Contact: Hannah Bowen, Dan Ellis, James Anthony.
Hobgoblin Theatre Company are a touring theatre in education company committed to delivering high quality, entertaining educational plays and drama workshops to schools across the UK.

HOIPOLLOI
Office F, Dale's Brewery, Gwydir Street, Cambridge CB1 2LJ
Tel: 01223 322 748
Email: info@hoipolloi.org.uk
Web Site: www.hoipolloi.org.uk
Artistic Director: Shon Dale-Jones
Executive Producer: Simon Bedford

HORSE AND BAMBOO THEATRE
Horse and Bamboo Centre, Waterfoot, Rossendale, Lancashire BB4 7HB
Tel: 01706 220 241 Fax: 01706 831 166
Email: info@horseandbamboo.org
Web Site: www.horseandbamboo.org
CEO: Helen Jackson
Producer: Esther Ferry-Kennington
Operations Manager: Christopher Hodgson.
Capacity: 200

IAN SAVILLE: SAVILLE MAGIC
8 Aylesbury Street, London NW10 0AS
Tel: 020 8621 0157 Mob: 07949 164793
Email: ian@redmagic.org.uk
Web Site: www.redmagic.co.uk
Contact: Ian Saville

IDOLRICH (THEATRE ROTTO PRODUCTIONS)
21 Lower Park Road, Hastings, East Sussex TN34 2LB
Tel: 01736 365158 / 01424 203944
Mobile: 07973 521274
Email: julia@theatre-rotto.fsnet.co.uk / model@theatrerotto.co.uk
Web Site: www.theatrerotto.co.uk / www.idolrich.co.uk
Idolrich specialises in animated visual theatre.
Current productions:
The Model. 55 minutes Theatre production.
Dolling Up. Street / Shop Window Production.
Sleeping / Waking. Installation Gallery and Foyer.
Also workshops Schools educational pack work with an inclusive audience
The Model. A multimedia performance using Puppetry.

THE I.E. THEATRE
Units 1 & 2 St George's, Victoria Place, Axminster, Devon EX13 5NQ
Tel: 01297 631 607
Email: ietheatre@fsmail.net
Artistic Director: Steve Black

IN TOTO THEATRE
Reg. Charity No: 1081192
186 Peckham High Street,
London SE15 5EG
Tel: 020 7639 8009 Fax: 020 7639 4279
Email: in-toto@dircon.co.uk
Web Site: www.in-tototheatre.co.uk
Artistic Director: Ms Sarah Carter
We are a small visual theatre company producing accessible 'total theatre' to a broad-based audience. We combine the use of puppetry, mask, movement, live music and acting and since 1988 have been touring shows and workshops to schools, community groups and art venues.

IN YER FACE CHRISTIAN THEATRE COMPANY
Provision of theatre and drama related services.
Mill House, Mill Lane, Cheadle,
Cheshire SK8 2NT
Tel: 0161 491 3090
Email: inyerface@domini.org
Web Site: www.inyerface.org.uk
Our main aim is to present the Christian message to 11-25 year olds through our own hard-hitting, humorous and in-yer-face material. About half our time is devoted to providing schools' packages. We've worked in over 100 high schools across the country, providing assemblies, a range of RE, drama and PSHE lessons, ending week-long residencies with our current show. We also provide sketch and story based shows, drama and life skills workshops, and seminars for faith based organisations such as churches and the Salvation Army, and non-faith based organisations such as the Police, the Prison Service and local councils.

INNER STATE THEATRE COMPANY
15 Denmark Street, Lancaster,
Lancashire LA1 5LY
Tel/Fax: 01524 37838
Email: christine@innerstate.co.uk
Web Site: www.innerstate.co.uk
Contact: Andy Andrews/Christine Bissell
Highly adaptable theatre with music, suitable for non-theatre venues as well as arts centres. The two actors are experienced in both street theatre and conventional theatre and consequently have developed a very direct style of performance which draws from both.

IOU
Dean Clough Mills, Halifax, West Yorkshire HX3 5AX
Tel: 01422 369 217 Fax: 01422 330 203
Email: info@ioutheatre.org
Web Site: www.ioutheatre.org
IOU creates work across a variety of media, including indoor and outdoor touring theatre productions, site-specific events, interactive digital works, video, installations and exhibitions. Features of work - new visual/non-scripted, company devised, specially composed music, various scales - cast of one to thirty.

ISLAND THEATRE COMPANY LTD
Church Street, King's Island, Limerick Eire
Tel: 00 353 61 410 433
Fax: 00 353 61 400 997
Email: info@islandtheatrecompany.ie
Web Site: www.islandtheatrecompany.ie
Manager: Alice Kennelly
Administrator: Gillian Fenton
Technical Manager: Mike Burke
Founded in 1988, Island Theatre Company has been producing high quality theatre for audiences in Limerick city, the Mid-West and all over Ireland, with a mixture of established classics and new writing. It has gained a national reputation for innovation and excellence.

KALA CHETHENA KATHAKALI TROUPE LTD
1 Holland Road, Woolston, Southampton, Hampshire SO19 9FW
Tel: 023 8042 0114 Fax: 023 8044 4468
Mobile: 07740 123070
Email: info@kathakali.net
Web Site: www.kathakali.net
Policy: To present International Kathakali (Classical dance drama from Kerala S. India) throughout G.B. with full troupe performances, solo performances, workshops, residences and courses. Plus an exhibition of costumes with related performances and workshops.
We tour Kathakali, highly visual and performed by top international artists and from Kerala, South India.

KAOS THEATRE
3rd Floor, 43 Chandos Place, London WC2N 4HS
Tel/ Fax: 020 7379 6204
Email: admin@kaostheatre.com
Web Site: www.kaostheatre.com
Artistic Director: Xavier Leret
Executive Director: Sharon Schaffer
Producer: Rebekah Cross
An ensemble company producing new work, adaptations and classics for touring nationally and internationally.
Policy: We aim to make non-elitist experimental theatre and present it to as wide an audience as possible. We create highly original work combining physical theatre, text, story-telling, devising, song, music and video. KAOS is about ideas, imagination and collaboration.

KNEEHIGH THEATRE
14 Walsingham Place, Truro, Cornwall TR1 2RP
Tel: 01872 267 910 Fax: 01872 267 919
Email: office@kneehigh.co.uk
Web Site: www.kneehigh.co.uk
General Manager: Victoria Hutchinson
Artistic Director: Emma Rice
Production Manager: Alex Wardle
Creative Director: Mike Shepherd

THE LAKESIDE THEATRE
Department of Literature, University of Essex, Wivenhoe Park, Colchester, Essex CO4 3SQ
Tel: 01206 873 718
Email: timh@essex.ac.uk
Web Site: www.essex.ac.uk
Technical Manager: Tim Hatcher

LIP SERVICE
116 Longford Road, Chorlton, Manchester M21 9NP
Tel/Fax: 0161 881 0061
Email: info@lip-service.net
Web Site: www.lip-service.net
Artistic Directors: Maggie Fox, Sue Ryding
Tour Organisation: Lip Service
Tel: 0161 881 0061
Marketing and Administration: Jenny Harris

LIVE THEATRE
27 Broad Chare, Newcastle upon Tyne NE1 3DQ
Tel: 0191 261 2694 (4 Lines) BO: 0191 232 1232 Fax: 0191 232 2224
Email: clairet@live.org.uk
Web Site: www.live.org.uk
Artistic Director: Max Roberts
Executive Director: Jim Beirne
Marketing Manager: Claire Trueman

THE LONG OVERDUE THEATRE COMPANY
22 Ridges View, Little London, Andover, Hampshire SP11 6JF
Tel: 01264 391 900 Mobile: 07776 148 230 Fax: 01264 324 993
Email: admin@longoverdue.co.uk
Web Site: www.longoverdue.co.uk
Director: Allen J Watts
Producer: Eddie Nias
Policy: Producing and performing small to mid-scale touring productions with a particular emphasis on quality and innovation. The company tours across the UK with its own lighting rig and sound system, meaning the shows are extremely technical. The company tours up to three shows simultaneously throughout the year, with one always being for children. Each production has a complete original music store that helps give Long Overdue its well known cinematic feel.

LUDUS DANCE
Ludus Dance Centre, Assembly Rooms, King Street, Lancaster, Lancashire LA1 1RE
Tel: 01524 35 936 Fax: 01524 847 744
Email: info@ludusdance.org
Web Site: www.ludusdance.org
ADMINISTRATION:
Project Co-ordinator: Hannah Robertshaw
Technical Stage Manager: David Forrest
Email: david.forrest@ludusdance.org
Britain's leading dance company for young people. Award winning shows, workshops, teaching packs, inset, videos, the works! High impact in Theatres, Festivals, Schools and the Community. Still unique after 35 years.

LYNX THEATRE AND POETRY
The Old Post Office, High Street, Stoke Ferry, Norfolk PE33 9SF
Tel: 01366 500 799
Email: Jackie@lodore.demon.co.uk
Contact: William Alderson
william.alderson@mac.com
Contact: Jacqueline Mulhallen

MEETING GROUND THEATRE COMPANY
4 Shirley Road, Nottingham NG3 5DA
Tel: 0115 962 3009 / 020 7263 9807
Email: my.tanya@ntlworld.com
Web Site: www.meetingground.co.uk
Artistic Directors: Tanya Myers, Stephen Lowe, Tom Wright
International and experimental collaborations. One production per annum.
Average audience 300.

MIDLAND ACTORS THEATRE
25 Merrishaw Road, Northfield, Birmingham B31 3SL
Tel: 0121 608 7144 / 07946 006511
Fax: 0121 608 7144
Email: news@midlandactorstheatre.co.uk
Web www.midlandactorstheatre.co.uk
Artistic Director: David Allen
MAT is dedicated to telling stories. We stage classics and new work based on stories, myths and legends from different cultures. We tour to theatres and also offer productions and workshops to schools. Recent works include 'Macbeth', 'Lady Chatterley's Lover' and 'Prospero's Island'.

MIKRON THEATRE CO LTD
Marsden Mechanics, Peel Street, Marsden, Huddersfield HD7 6BW
Tel/Fax: 01484 843 701
Tel: 01484 840 633
Email: admin@mikron.org.uk
Web Site: www.mikron.org.uk
Artistic Director: Mike Lucas
Associate Director: Richard Povall
Associate Administrators: Jessica Tuck, Lynne Newlove

MIND THE GAP
Queens House, Queens Road, Bradford, West Yorkshire BD8 7BS
Tel: 01274 544683 Fax: 01274 544501
Email: arts@mind-the-gap.org.uk
Web Site: www.mind-the-gap.org.uk
Artistic Director: Tim Wheeler
Mind the Gap is a theatre company. We believe in quality, equality and inclusion. Our mission is to dismantle barriers to artistic excellence so that learning-dis-

abled artistes and non-disabled artistes can appear alongside one another as equals.

MOONSHINE PRODUCTIONS
Alpine House, 4 Northfields, Kilburn, Belper, Derbyshire DE56 0LW
Tel: 01332 780462
Contact: Sue Reaney
Moonshine formed in 1993 and is based in the Amber Valley area of Derbyshire. The Company presents original work of local writers focusing on the heritage of the community. We also provide a mobile audio-description service for all visual, artistic and musical events.

NATIONAL STUDENT THEATRE COMPANY
20 Lansdowne Road, Muswell Hill, London N10 2AU
Tel: 020 8883 4586 Fax: 020 8883 7142
Email: holly@nsdf.org.uk
Web Site: www.nsdf.org.uk
Contact: Clive Wolfe
Reconstituted for each summer vacation since 1977. Over 125 productions (new and old work). 19 Edinburgh Fringe awards. Auditions advertised in The Stage, at the annual National Student Drama Festival and on Website.

NATURAL THEATRE COMPANY
Widcombe Institute, Widcombe Hill, Bath, North Somerset BA2 6AA
Tel: 01225 469 131 Fax: 01225 442 555
Email: info@naturaltheatre.co.uk
Web Site: www.naturaltheatre.co.uk
Contact: Helen Chamberlain
Combining our unique style of visual comedy with an impeccable eye for detail, we produce a delightfully absurd kind of street theatre and walkabout entertainment. With over 100 different scenarios we can bring a humorous touch or memorable intervention to any event, in every conceivable situation. Go ahead, challenge us!

NETI-NETI THEATRE COMPANY
Quinton Kynaston School Marlborough Hill St John's Wood London NW8 0NL
Tel/Fax: 020 8458 3251
Contact: Rita Mishra

NEW CENTURY THEATRE COMPANY
9 St. Agnes Close Studley Warwickshire B80 7JQ
Tel: 01527 852 070
Email: enquiries@newcenturytheatre.co.uk
Web Site: www.newcenturytheatre.co.uk
Associate Producer: Jennifer Rigby
Midlands based company providing employment for recently graduated actors; touring classic comedies to rural venues throughout the Midlands and North Wales.

NO LIMITS
No Limits Theatre Company, Dundas Street, Monkwearmouth, Sunderland, Tyne & Wear SR6 0AY
Tel: 0191 565 3013
Email: info@nolimitstheatre.org.uk
Web Site: www.nolimitstheatre.org.uk
Artistic Director: Janet Nettleton
Theatre Director: Alan Parker
Administrator: Karen Suleiman
A leading company for people with and without a learning disability that produces dynamic and innovative performances and promotes inclusive arts practise. Suitable for a wide range of venues. Also available for workshops, residencies, consultancy and training.

NOFIT STATE CIRCUS
PO Box 238 Cardiff CF24 0XS Wales
Tel: 029 2022 1330 / 40
Email: info@nofitstate.com
Web Site: www.nofitstate.org
General Manager: Alison Woods
Production Assistant: Zoe Munn
Nofit State has a long track record of creating extraordinary mixed scale multi-media circus productions: from small community performances to large scale professional productions involving a company of 45 on the road; from tented tours to site specific events and theatre shows.

NTC TOURING THEATRE COMPANY LTD
The Playhouse, Bondgate Without, Alnwick NE66 1PQ
Tel: 01665 602586 Fax: 01665 605837
Email: admin@ntc-touringtheatre.co.uk
Web Site: www.ntc-touringtheatre.co.uk
General Manager: Anna Flood

ONATTI THEATRE COMPANY
9 Field Close, Warwick CV34 4QD
Tel: 01926 495 220
Email: info@onatti.co.uk
Web Site: www.onatti.co.uk
Tours primary schools with a national curriculum-based plays. Tours secondary schools with plays in Spanish. Tours outdoor summer theatre to stately homes. Tours English plays to South America. Tours plays in French and Spanish for secondary schools.

OXFORDSHIRE TOURING THEATRE COMPANY
The Annexe, SS Mary & John School Meadow Lane Oxford OX4 1TJ
Tel: 01865 249 444 Fax: 01865 247 266
Email: info@ottc.oxfordshire.co.uk
Web Site: www.ottc.org.uk
Artistic Director: Brendan Murray

PADDY THE CLOWN
39 Elm Street, Roath, Cardiff, South Glamorgan CF24 3QS Wales
Tel: 029 2048 6550
Email: paddy@paddytheclown.com
Web Site: www.paddytheclown.com
Contact: Paddy Faulkner
Touring theatres nationwide. Also available for private functions, outdoor events and promotions. International Award Winning Show.

PASCAL THEATRE COMPANY
35 Flaxman Court, Flaxman Terrace, Bloomsbury, London WC1H 9AR
Tel: 020 7383 0920 Fax: 020 7419 9798
Email: pascaltheatreco@aol.com
Web Site: www.pascal-theatre.com
Artistic Director: Julia Pascal
Administrator: Graeme Braidwood
Education Officer: Liselle Terret

PENTABUS THEATRE CO.
Bromfield, Ludlow, Shropshire SY8 2JU
Tel: 01584 856 564 Fax: 01584 856 254
Email: john@pentabus.prestel.co.uk
Web Site: www.pentabus.co.uk
Artistic Director: Orla O'Loughlin
Contact: John Moreton, Development Director

THE PHANTOM CAPTAIN
618b Finchley Road, London NW11 7RR
Tel/Fax: 020 8455 4564
Email: ziph@macunlimited.net
Web Site: http://phantomcaptain.net-firms.com
Artistic Director: Neil Hornick
Stage and Environmental shows, festival and conference events, workshop residences, creative event consultation.

PILOT THEATRE
Production Office, York Theatre Royal, St Leonard's Place West Yorkshire YO1 7HD
Tel: 01904 635 755 Fax: 01904 656 378
Email: info@pilot-theatre.com
Web Site: www.pilot-theatre.com
General Manager: Liz Richards
Artistic Director: Marcus Romer
Administrative Producer: Amanda J Smith
Produce new touring work for young people and new audiences. National Brief funded by Arts Council of England and Arts Council, Yorkshire.

POINT BLANK THEATRE COMPANY
Alternative website: www.pointblank.org.uk
Open Performance Centre Unit 2 67 Earl Street Sheffield S1 4PY
Tel: 0114 249 3650 Fax: 0114 249 3655
Email: pete@the-opc.co.uk
Web Site: www.the-opc.co.uk
Artistic Director: Steven Jackson
Company Manager: Pete Burchill

PROTEUS THEATRE COMPANY
Queen Mary's College, Cliddesden Road, Basingstoke, Hampshire RG21 3HF
Tel: 01256 354 541 Fax: 01256 356 186
Email: info@proteustheatre.com
Web Site: www.proteustheatre.com
Artistic Director: Mark Helyar
General Manager: Julie Bladon
Associate Director: Deborah Wilding
Proteus produces performance and participatory theatre for urban and rural communities.

QUANTUM THEATRE FOR SCIENCE
The Old Button Factory, 1- 11 Bannockburn Road, Plumstead London SE18 1ET
Tel / Fax: 020 8317 9000
Email: office@quantumtheatre.co.uk
Web Site: www.quantumtheatre.co.uk
General Manager: Mr Michael Whitmore

RED LADDER THEATRE COMPANY
3 St Peters Buildings, York Street, Leeds, West Yorkshire LS9 8AJ
Tel: 0113 245 5311 Fax: 0113 245 5351
Email: wendy@redladder.co.uk
Web Site: www.redladder.co.uk
Red Ladder is a national touring theatre company producing high quality theatre for young people, 13-25. Commissions new writing and performs in small scale theatre venues and youth and community venues.
Other activities include the Asian theatre school, workshops, projects and training events for young people and youth workers.
Touring times: April - July, September - December.
Equipment carried - touring lighting rig and full sound/ theatre set.

RED SHIFT THEATRE COMPANY
TRG2 Trowbray House, 108 Weston Street, London SE1 3QB
Tel: 020 7978 9787 Fax: 020 7378 9789
Email: emma@redshifttheatreco.co.uk
Web: http://www.redshifttheatreco.co.uk
General Manager: Emma Rees
Artistic Director: Jonathan Holloway
Administrator: Kate Ward

RED SKY PRODUCTIONS
PO Box 27, Stroud, Gloucestershire GL6 0YQ
Tel/ Fax: 01453 885088
Email: johnny@redskyrecords.co.uk
Contact: Johnny Coppin
We specialise in British musical productions. Shows available are an annual Christmas show - "All on a Winter's Night" - a feast of Christmas songs and stories touring December 2010", plus "Edge of Day" - A tribute to Laurie Lee, and "Songs on Lonely Roads" - The story of composer/poet Ivor Gurney.

REMOULD THEATRE COMPANY
Humberside Cultural Enterprise Centre Middleton Street, Hull, East Yorkshire HU3 1NB
Tel: 01482 226 157 Fax: 01482 326 190
Artistic Director: Rupert Creed
Administrative Director: Averil Coult
Administrator: Sara Hawkins
Educator and Outreach Office: Carolyn Mendelsohn

SCARLET THEATRE COMPANY
Studio 4, The Bull, 68 High Street, Barnet, Hertfordshire EN5 5SJ
Tel: 020 8441 9779 Fax: 020 8447 0075
Email: admin@scarlettheatre.co.uk
Web Site: www.scarlettheatre.co.uk
Artistic Director: Grainne Byrne
Creates highly artistic theatre using a variety of starting points. The work is either: devised, made through radical adaptations of classics or little known European plays & new writing.

SGRIPT CYMRU
New Writing Company
Chapter, Heol Y Farchnad, Treganna, Caerdydd, Cardiff CF5 1QE Wales
Tel: 029 2023 6650 Fax: 029 2023 6651
Email: sgriptcymru@sgriptcymru.com
Web Site: www.sgriptcymru.com
Artistic Director: Simon Harris
Administrative Director: Mai Jones
Associate Director: Elen Bowman
The national new writing theatre company for Wales, seeking out, developing and presenting work of contemporary Welsh and Wales-based writers working in both Welsh and English.
In addition, the company offers rehearsed readings and regular development workshops.

SNAPSHOT
453 Silk House, Park Green, Macclesfield, Cheshire SK11 7QJ
Mobile: 07889 745594
Email: mikhobson2000@yahoo.com
Web: www.snapshotproductions.co.uk
Artistic Director: Chris Bright
Administration: Michael Hobson

SNARLING BEASTIES
27 Grosvenor Road, Harborne, Birmingham B17 9AL
Tel: 02476 365650

SPIKE THEATRE
13a Hope Street Liverpool L1 9BQ
Tel: 0151 709 8552
Email: mail@spiketheatre.com
Web Site: www.spiketheatre.com
Theatre company.

SPOTLITES THEATRE COMPANY LTD
Kings Theatre, 338 High Street, Chatham, Kent ME4 4NR
Tel: 01634 403 737 Fax: 01634 829 468
Email: office@spotlites.co.uk
Web Site: www.spotlites.co.uk
Managing Director: Rachel King
Provide innovative performing arts and theatre for, with and by young people aged 5-30 years.
Full Lx + SD (fat frog and mini disc).
Large studio performing space, free tech for show and free mailing list.

STRATHCONA THEATRE COMPANY
Unit Ko3 Tower Bridge Bus Com, 100 Clements Road, London SE16 4DG
Tel: 020 7740 2440 Fax: 020 7394 1232
Email: stc@strathco.demon.co.uk
Web Site: www.strathco.demon.co.uk
Artistic Directors: Ann Cleary, Ian McCurrach
Administrator: Sian Astrop

TAMASHA THEATRE COMPANY
Unit E, 11 Ronalds Road, London N5 1XJ
Tel: 020 7609 2411 Fax: 020 7609 2722
Email: info@tamasha.org.uk
Web Site: www.tamasha.org.uk
Joint Artistic Directors: Kristine Landon Smith and Sudha Bhuchar

TELLING TALES THEATRE COMPANY
19 Bradford Road, St Johns, Wakefield, West Yorkshire WF1 2RF
Tel: 01924 379 654
Email: tellingtales@bromtell.freeserve.co.uk
The company presents original plays concerned with significant social and political issues of our time, with projected imagery and live music often complementing the drama. "Blue Murder: The Killing of Derek Bentley" received widespread acclaim (The Stage, The Times, The Late Night Show on BBC2) as did "Jacknife", set at the time of the Yorkshire Ripper Murders. Latest productions include "Blistered", a one man show concerned with a convicted arsonist, "Prisoners", a show devised from Amnesty International source material concerning political prisoners throughout the world, and "Blizzard", a show concerned with the last hours in the life of Scott of the Antarctic.

THE DEREK GRANT ORGANISATION
13 Beechwood Rd, West Moors, Dorset BH22 0BN
Tel: 01202 855 777 Fax: 01202 855 777
Email: admin@derekgrant.co.uk
Web Site: www.derekgrant.co.uk
Small and medium scale touring productions available - top quality children's shows, comedy, variety (star names) and music hall.

THEATRE ALIBI
Northcott Studio Theatre, Emmanuel Road, Exeter, Devon EX4 1EJ
Tel/Fax: 01392 217 315
Email: alibi@eclipse.co.uk
Web Site: www.theatrealibi.co.uk
Artistic Director: Nikki Sved
General Manager: Jenny Lawrence, Annemarie MacDonald
ALIBI creates contemporary new work for adults and for young people, touring it to a wide range of venues.

THEATRE IS
The Hat Factory 65-67 Bute Street
Luton LU1 2EY
Tel: 01582 481 221
Email: info@theatreis.org, stuart@theatreis.org
Web Site: www.theatreis.org
Contacts: Stuart Mullins, Creative Director; Michael Corley, Communications Co-ordinator.
Our mission is to research, develop and produce the best possible performing arts for the young people of the East of England aged 25 and under.
In placing young people at the heart of our organization we respect them as consumers and makers of theatre. We will therefore, pioneer new ways of making theatre for young people empowering them to become the cultural leaders of the future.

THE THEATRE OF LITERATURE
51 The Cut, London SE1 8LF
Tel: 020 7638 0599/ 020 7620 2900 Fax: 020 7928 5930
Email: info@calderpublications.com
Web Site: www.calderpublications.com
Senior Personnel: John Calder
Professional reading of modern literature by professional actors/actresses. Also associated with the Godot Company performing Beckett plays in the UK and abroad.

THEATRE ROUNDABOUT LTD
859 Finchley Road, London NW11 8LX
Tel: 020 8455 4752 Mob: 07774 638800
Email: info@theatreroundabout.co.uk
Web Site: www.theatreroundabout.co.uk
Senior Personnel: William Fry

THEATRE SET UP
12 Fairlawn Close, Southgate, London N14 4JX
Tel/Fax: 020 8886 9572
Email: enquiries@ts-u.fsnet.co.uk
Web Site: www.ts-u.co.uk
Touring productions of Shakespeare's plays, mostly outdoors in UK and internationally in historic and beautiful sites with 8 cast.

THEATRE WORKSHOP
Out of the Blue Drill Hall, 36 Dalmeny Street, Edinburgh EH6 8RG Scotland
Tel: 0131 555 3854 Mob: 07725 226 913
Email: keith.tws@hotmail.co.uk, jez.tws@hotmail.co.uk
Web Site: www.theatre-workshop.com
ADMINISTRATION:
Relationship & Development Manager: Keith Bell
Contact: Jez Arrow
Cap: 200

THW PRODUCTIONS
22 Maclise Road, London W14 0PR
Email: mileseady@yahoo.co.uk
Contact: Miles Eady

TICKLISH ALLSORTS
57 Victoria Road, Wilton, Salisbury SP2 0DZ
Tel/Fax: 01722 744 949
Mob: 07721 992994
Email: garynunn@ntlworld.com
Web Site: www.ticklishallsorts.co.uk
Senior Personnel: Gary A Nunn
Childrens Entertainments, shows, puppets, musical comedy, workshops. Established 1981. Performances and workshops. RSPB National Touring Roadshows.

TRESTLE THEATRE COMPANY
Trestle Arts Base, Russet Drive, St Albans, Hertfordshire AL4 0JQ
Tel: 01727 850 950
Email: admin@trestle.org.uk
Web Site: www.trestle.org.uk
ADMINISTRATION:
Artistic Director: Emily Gray
Buildings and Finance Manager: Clare Winter
Trestle Theatre Company was founded in 1981 and has enjoyed 30 successful years of touring mask and Physical led theatre. Trestle creates and tours theatrical productions and operates Trestle Arts Base as a performance venue. Trestle also produces international residencies and tours and delivers education programmes across the UK and abroad. The Company aims to engage audiences and participants in an interactive, inclusive and inventive experience of theatre.
Trestle Arts Base - Fully equipped studio theatre,rehearsal room and meeting room, all available for hire to professional and amateur companies for previews and runs
Capacity: 80 - 125

TRIANGLE
5 Parrotts Grove, Coventry, Warwickshire CV2 1NQ
Tel: 024 7636 2210 Mktg: 07770 601533
Email: info@triangletheatre.co.uk
Web Site: www.triangletheatre.co.uk
Artistic Director: Carran Waterfield
Touring nationally and internationally.
Current repertoire: 'Godiva, the Naked Politician', 'Undercover - a Work Demonstration', 'The Life and Work of Bette Davis'.
Policy: To work with biographical and autobiographical material to create exciting theatre productions.
Features: Well-respected company, particularly for its educational work.
Non-performance activities: Workshop and residencies in practical theatre-making, specialised work with young people and children.
Touring: 2-week residencies, available all year for festivals, museums, art galleries and theatres. Preferred audience size - 100.

VOLCANO THEATRE COMPANY
Swansea Institute, Townhill Road, Swansea, West Glamorgan SA2 0UT Wales
Tel: 01792 281 280
Email: volcano.tc@virgin.net
Web Site: www.volcanotheatre.co.uk
Administrator: Claudine Conway
Artistic Directors: Fern Smith & Paul Davies
General Manager: Katie Keeler
Volcano is an international touring theatre company with a reputation for energetic, unpredictable and arresting theatre that combines strong visual impact, physical presence and intelligent text. The company's work ranges from experimental new writing and devised work to iconoclastic reworkings or deconstructions of classics.

WOMEN AND THEATRE
The Friend's Institute, 220 Moseley Road, Highgate, Birmingham B12 0DG
Tel: 0121 440 4203 Fax: 0121 446 4280
Email: womenandtheatre@btinternet.com
Web Site: www.womenandtheatre.co.uk
Women and Theatre is a small scale touring company producing all new work. The company is also a specialist provider of theatre in health education.

ZIP THEATRE
Newhampton Centre Dunkley Street, Wolverhampton, West Midlands WV1 4AN
Tel: 01902 572 250 Fax: 01902 572 251
Email: cathy@ziptheatre.co.uk
Web Site: www.ziptheatre.co.uk
Company Secretary: Cathy Pemberton
Zip Theatre is a multi-cultural theatre and music company touring both original and classic productions. The company also works extensively in education.

Middle Scale Touring Companies

ABINGDON TOURING THEATRE COMPANY
Abingdon Touring Theatre "Sycamores", Station Yard, Steventon, Abingdon, Oxfordshire OX13 6RX
Tel: 07747 038410 Fax: 01235 820906
Email: simon@attc.org.uk
Web Site: www.attc.org.uk
Artistic Director: Simon Coates

APPLAUSE PRODUCTIONS
31 Wimborne Road West, Wimborne, Dorset BH21 2DG
Tel: 01202 887 439 Fax: 01202 849 943
Email: admin@derekgrant.co.uk
Web Site: www.derekgrant..co.uk
Small and medium touring production available - children's shows and pantomimes. Part of the Derek Grant Organisation.

BABBLING VAGABONDS STORY TELLING THEATRE
Top Floor Flat, Bakewell Town Hall, Bath Street, Bakewell, Derbyshire DE45 1BX
Tel/Fax: 01629 815 110 Post to be directed to: PO Box 6116, Bakewell, Derbyshire, DE45 1YE
Email: info@babblingvagabonds.co.uk
Web Site: www.babblingvagabonds.co.uk
Joint Artistic Directors: Phil Coggins, Mark Hornsey, Tara Saunders
We create original Children's Theatre shows that tour to professional venues, community spaces and schools throughout the year. We also create site-specific performances and bespoke theatre arts projects for people of all ages.

BIG WHEEL THEATRE COMPANY (TIE)
Exmouth Market Centre, PO Box 18221, London EC1R 4WJ
Tel: 020 7689 8670
Email: info@bigwheel.org.uk
Web Site: www.bigwheel.org.uk
Contact: Roland Allen
Capacity: 80

BLACK CAT THEATRE COMPANY
Shakespeare House, 7 Jersey Crescent, LIghtwood, Stoke-on-Trent, Staffordshire ST3 4TJ
Tel/Fax: 01782 341 200 Mobile: 07778 864415
Email: office@blackcattheatre.co.uk
Web Site: www.blackcattheatre.co.uk

BOX CLEVER
52 - 54 Kennington Oval, London SE11 5SW
Tel: 020 7793 0040 Fax: 020 7357 8188
Email: admin@boxclevertheatre.com
Web Site: www.boxclevertheatre.com
Artistic Director and Writer-in-Residence: Michael Wicherek
General Manager: Jemima Lee
Box Clever is a writer-led, multi-disciplinary touring company, creating challenging and inspiring contemporary theatre with and for young people.

BILL BROOKMAN PRODUCTIONS LTD
101 Ashby Road, Loughborough, Leicestershire LE11 3AB
Tel: 01509 236 175 Fax: 01509 219 873
Email: office@billbrookman.co.uk
Web Site: www.billbrookman.co.uk
Manager: Bill Brookman
Specialising in Street Performance.
A large developed experienced street theatre company combining street music, street gypsy dancing, fire, stiltwalking, puppetry. Large sets. Celebratory theatre.

CARL ROSA OPERA
359 Hackney Road, Shoreditch London E2 8PR
Tel: 020 7613 0777 Fax: 020 7613 0859
Email: info@carlrosaopera.co.uk
Web Site: www.carlrosaopera.co.uk
ADMINISTRATION:
Musical Director: Wyn Davies
Artistic Director: Peter Mulloy
Honorary Head of Artistic Development: Valerie Masterson CBE
The Carl Rosa Opera is Britain's oldest opera company, founded in 1873. We tour between twenty and forty weeks a year, with a touring company and orchestra of sixty-five. Our repertory is presently Opera, Operetta, Gilbert & Sullivan and Musical Theatre. We present our stage productions in number one Theatres and Concert Halls only, but have plans to also produce mid-scale tours with a full education programme. We have a music Library and make/produce our own sets, costumes and props from our own studios. Yearly tour to America also Australia, New Zealand & Canada every second year. Visits festivals in Russia, France, Italy and Greece.

THE CHERUB COMPANY LONDON
9 Park Hill, London W5 2JS
Tel: 020 8723 4358
Email: mgieleta@cherub.org.uk
Web Site: www.cherub.org.uk
Director: Michael Gieleta
Producer: Rebecca Miller
Casting Associate: Jim Arnold
Email: jimarnold79@yahoo.com

COMPASS THEATRE COMPANY
Carver Street Institute, 24 Rockingham Lane, Sheffield S1 4FW
Tel: 0114 275 5328 Fax: 0114 278 6931
Email: info@compasstheatrecompany.com
Web: www.compasstheatrecompany.com
General Manager: Craig Dronfield
Artistic Director: Neil Sissons
Administrative Assistant: Damian Sackett

COMPLICITE
14 Anglers Lane, London NW5 3DG
Tel: 020 7485 7700 Fax: 020 7485 7701
Email: email@complicite.org
Web Site: www.complicite.org
Artistic Director: Simon McBurney
Administrative Producer: Judith Dimant
Administrator: Polly Stokes
Education & Marketing: Natasha Freedman
Finance: Sharon Kwan

EMERGENCY EXIT ARTS
Rothbury Hall, Azof Street, London SE10 0EF
Tel: 020 8853 4809 Fax: 020 8858 2025
Email: info@eea.org.uk
Web Site: www.eea.org.uk
ADMINISTRATION:
Artistic Director: Deb Mullins
Admin and Communications Officer: Jules Hodgson
Address for Postal Correspondence: PO Box 570, Greenwich London, SE10 OEE
Emergency Exit Arts is an outdoor performing arts company, touring work throughout the UK and Europe.

FALSE IMPRESSIONS
207 Mersham Road, Thornton Heath, Surrey CR7 8NU
Tel: 01803 615 600/ 615 700 (Anne George) Mob: 07968 828 530
Email: richardleigh@falseimpressions.co.uk
Web Site: www.falseimpressions.co.uk
Theatrical Magical Advisor: Richard Leigh
Contact: Anne George (anne@trevorgeorge.co.uk)
False Impressions is a production company which specialises in the unusual field of stage illusion and magic shows of all genres.
Productions:
- The Magic Cavern
- Late Night Magic in the West End
- The Side Show of Wonders
- The Ice Cave Magic Show
- The Magic Toy Theatre
- The Haunted Magic Show

FORKBEARD FANTASY
PO Box 1241, Bristol BS99 2TG
Tel: 0117 930 9933 Fax: 0117 930 9922
Email: ff@forkbeardfantasy.co.uk
Web Site: www.forkbeardfantasy.co.uk
Co-directors: Tim Britton, Chris Britton, Penny Saunders.
Company Manager: Janice May

FOURSIGHT THEATRE LTD
Newhampton Arts Centre, Dunkley Street, Wolverhampton, West Midlands WV1 4AN
Tel: 01902 714 257 Fax: 01902 428 413
Email: admin@foursighttheatre.co.uk
Web Site: www.foursighttheatre.co.uk
Artistic Director: Naomi Cooke
Foursight Theatre creates unusual,

uncompromising and multi-disciplinary works which review history through the eyes of women: unknown, famous and infamous. Foursight is committed to creating total theatre - an holistic style of performance rooted in physical theatre. Work is experimental in both process & form.
Foursight tours nationally & internationally and provides educational workshops and residencies.
Funding: Arts Council England, West Midlands, Wolverhampton Council.

FRANTIC ASSEMBLY
31 Eyre Street Hill, London EC1R 5EW
Tel: 020 7841 3115
Email: admin@franticassembly.co.uk
Web Site: www.franticassembly.co.uk
Artistic Director: Scott Graham
Executive Producer: Despina Tsatsas
Learn and Train Manager: Inga Hirst
Administrator: Donna Marie Howard
Frantic Assembly creates vivid and dynamic theatre renowned for its unique physical style combining movement, design, music and text. A touring company producing new and innovative work nationally and internationally, Frantic also delivers its educational Learn & Train programme to institutions worldwide. See website for further details.

FRANTIC THEATRE COMPANY
Bay Trees, 32 Woodlane, Falmouth, Cornwall TR11 4RF
Tel: 0870 165 7350
Email: patrick@frantictheatre.com
Web Site: www.frantictheatre.com
Artistic Director: Patrick Walsh

DAVID GLASS ENSEMBLE
4 The Leathermarket, Weston Street, London SE1 3ER
Tel: 020 7357 9200 Fax: 020 7357 9199
Email: dg.ensemble@virgin.net

THE GRAND UNION
Shoreditch Town Hall, 380 Old Street, London EC1V 9LT
Tel: 020 7729 8729 Fax: 020 7729 8789
Email: mail@grandunion.org.uk
Web Site: www.grandunion.org.uk
Artistic Director: Tony Haynes

HEADLONG THEATRE
Chertsey Chambers, 12 Mercer Street, London WC2H 9QD
Tel: 020 7438 9940
Email: info@headlongtheatre.co.uk
Web Site: www.headlongtheatre.co.uk
Artistic Director: Rupert Goold
Executive Producer: Henny Finch

HEBE THEATRE COMPANY
Paradise Now Mow Hill Witnesham Ipswich Suffolk IP6 9EH
Tel: 01473 785672 Mob: 07818 459561
Email: c.mugleston672@btinternet.com
Web: www.thehebetheatre company.onesuffolk.net
Contact: Charles Mugleston
The Hebe Theatre Company was formed in 2009 to promote greater awareness of The Spiritual Classic's - The Universal Wisdom of Mankind.
It currently tours beautiful multi-media staged readings of the universally popular mystical Love Poem @The Ruba'iyat of Omar Khayyam' "A Masterpiece" Professor Daniel Karlin

HORSE AND BAMBOO THEATRE
Horse and Bamboo Centre, Waterfoot, Rossendale, Lancashire BB4 7HB
Tel: 01706 220 241 Fax: 01706 831 166
Email: info@horseandbamboo.org
Web Site: www.horseandbamboo.org
CEO: Helen Jackson
Producer: Esther Ferry-Kennington
Operations Manager: Christopher Hodgson.
Capacity: 200

HULL TRUCK THEATRE
Hull Truck Theatre Company
Hull Truck Theatre, 50 Ferensway, Hull HU2 8LB
Admin: 01482 224 800 BO: 01482 323 638 Publicity: 01482 325 012
Email: kate.denby@hulltruck.co.uk
Web Site: www.hulltruck.co.uk
ADMINISTRATION:
Artistic Director: Mark Babych
Executive Director: Janthi Mills-Ward
General Manager: Ian Archer
Head of Production: Fran Maskell
Membership: TMA (Touring)
Policy: Resident productions; comedy and jazz nights; incoming productions; jazz and literature festivals; education and outreach activity; youth theatre activity.
Capacity: 437 Maximum, Studio Capacity 134
For more information on hiring, email: events@hulltruck.co.uk.

IMAGE MUSICAL THEATRE COMPANY
23 Sedgeford Road, Shepherds Bush, London W12 0NA
Tel: 020 87439380 Fax: 020 87499294
Email: brian@imagemusicaltheatre.co.uk
Web: www.imagemusicaltheatre.co.uk
Producer/ Director: Brian Thresh
Specialising in new musicals for the touring circuit, theatres and schools, the company produces two family/ children's participation musicals and one full length adult musical each year.

IOU
Dean Clough Mills, Halifax, West Yorkshire HX3 5AX
Tel: 01422 369 217 Fax: 01422 330 203
Email: info@ioutheatre.org
Web Site: www.ioutheatre.org
IOU creates work across a variety of media, including indoor and outdoor touring theatre productions, site-specific events, interactive digital works, video, installations and exhibitions. Features of work - new visual/non-scripted, company devised, specially composed music, various scales - cast of one to thirty.

KAOS THEATRE
3rd Floor, 43 Chandos Place, London WC2N 4HS
Tel/ Fax: 020 7379 6204
Email: admin@kaostheatre.com
Web Site: www.kaostheatre.com
Artistic Director: Xavier Leret
Executive Director: Sharon Schaffer
Producer: Rebekah Cross
An ensemble company producing new work, adaptations and classics for touring nationally and internationally.
Policy: We aim to make non-elitist experimental theatre and present it to as wide an audience as possible. We create highly original work combining physical theatre, text, story-telling, devising, song, music and video. KAOS is about ideas, imagination and collaboration.

KNEEHIGH THEATRE
14 Walsingham Place, Truro, Cornwall TR1 2RP
Tel: 01872 267 910 Fax: 01872 267 919
Email: office@kneehigh.co.uk
Web Site: www.kneehigh.co.uk
General Manager: Victoria Hutchinson
Artistic Director: Emma Rice
Production Manager: Alex Wardle
Creative Director: Mike Shepherd

LIP SERVICE
116 Longford Road, Chorlton, Manchester M21 9NP
Tel/Fax: 0161 881 0061
Email: info@lip-service.net
Web Site: www.lip-service.net
Artistic Directors: Maggie Fox, Sue Ryding
Tour Organisation: Lip Service
Tel: 0161 881 0061
Marketing and Administration: Jenny Harris

LONDON BUBBLE (BUBBLE THEATRE CO LTD)
5 Elephant Lane, London SE16 4JD
Tel 020 7237 4434 Fax 020 7231 2366
Email: admin@londonbubble.org.uk
Web Site: www.londonbubble.org.uk
ADMINISTRATION:
Props: Bubble Theatre Company Ltd.
Creative Director: Jonathan Petherbridge
Administrator: Lucy Bradshaw
Policy: to tour a variety of productions to adults and children throughout the Greater London area in community and

traditional venues, and, during the summer, to London's parks and open spaces. The aim is to develop a popular theatre style which is bold and bright, fast and physical, open and accessible.

THE LONG OVERDUE THEATRE COMPANY
22 Ridges View, Little London, Andover, Hampshire SP11 6JF
Tel: 01264 391 900 Mobile: 07776 148 230 Fax: 01264 324 993
Email: admin@longoverdue.co.uk
Web Site: www.longoverdue.co.uk
Director: Allen J Watts
Producer: Eddie Nias
Policy: Producing and performing small to mid-scale touring productions with a particular emphasis on quality and innovation. The company tours across the UK with its own lighting rig and sound system, meaning the shows are extremely technical. The company tours up to three shows simultaneously throughout the year, with one always being for children. Each production has a complete original music store that helps give Long Overdue its well known cinematic feel.

MIGHTY ZULU NATION THEATRE COMPANY (MZN)
Tel/Fax: 01484 358 068
Email: mzntheatre2@yahoo.co.uk
Web Site: www.emci.co.uk
Acclaimed Educational Multicultural Zulu Experience presented by professional multi-talented Zulu performers from the city of Durban, Kingdom of Kwazulu-Natal in South Africa.

MOPA THEATRE COMPANY
1 Hill Farm Road, Whittlesford, Cambridgeshire CB2 4NB
Tel: 01223 839414 Fax: 01223 839414
Email: NicMOPA@aol.com
Artistic Director: Nic Brownlie
Touring masterclasses in Stanislavski and Brecht with a play production as well.

MRD PRODUCTIONS
Wigmore Lane, Eythorne, Kent CT15 4AW
Tel: 01304 830 321 Fax: 01304 831 181
Email: mrdproductions@btconnect.com
Web Site: www.thedancer.co.uk
Production Manager: Mike Carrington
Theatre production company, doing regional and touring theatre.

NATURAL THEATRE COMPANY
Widcombe Institute, Widcombe Hill, Bath, North Somerset BA2 6AA
Tel: 01225 469 131 Fax: 01225 442 555
Email: info@naturaltheatre.co.uk
Web Site: www.naturaltheatre.co.uk
Contact: Helen Chamberlain
Combining our unique style of visual comedy with an impeccable eye for detail, we produce a delightfully absurd kind of street theatre and walkabout entertainment. With over 100 different scenarios we can bring a humorous touch or memorable intervention to any event, in every conceivable situation. Go ahead, challenge us!

NEW PERSPECTIVES THEATRE COMPANY
Park Lane, Nottingham NG6 0DW
Tel: 0115 927 2334 Fax: 0115 927 1612
Email: info@newperspectives.co.uk
Web Site: www.newperspectives.co.uk
General Manager: Chris Kirkwood (0115 973 9121)

NITRO
(Formerly Black Theatre Co-operative)
6 Brewery Road, London N7 9NH
Tel: 020 7609 1331 Fax: 020 7609 1221
Email: info@nitro.co.uk
Web Site: www.nitro.co.uk
Artistic Director: Felix Cross
Project Manager: Sophia Tarr
SLAMDUNK: New hip hop dance musical, set in the world of basketball and streetball. Slamdunk is created by Felix Cross (Artistic Director of Nitro) and Benji Reid, the music has been written by Soweto Kinch, one of this year's Mercury Music and Mobo prize nominees.
Further production - Oga's Ark by Gabriel Gabadamosl loosely based on Animal Farm by George Orwell.

NOFIT STATE CIRCUS
PO Box 238 Cardiff CF24 0XS Wales
Tel: 029 2022 1330 / 40
Email: info@nofitstate.com
Web Site: www.nofitstate.org
General Manager: Alison Woods
Production Assistant: Zoe Munn
Nofit State has a long track record of creating extraordinary mixed scale multi-media circus productions: from small community performances to large scale professional productions involving a company of 45 on the road; from tented tours to site specific events and theatre shows.

NOLA RAE/LONDON MIME THEATRE
49 Springcroft Avenue, London N2 9JH
Tel: 020 8444 6248 Fax: 020 8883 9751
Email: vwest@dircon.co.uk
Web Site: www.nolarae@btinternet.com
Contact: Valerie West

NORTHERN BROADSIDES THEATRE COMPANY
Dean Clough, Halifax, West Yorkshire HX3 5AX
Tel: 01422 369 704 Fax: 01422 383 175
Email: sue@northern-broadsides.co.uk
Web: www.northern-broadsides.co.uk
General Manager: Sue Andrews

OPERA CIRCUS
Three Chimneys Pymore Lane, Dottery, Bridport, Dorset DT6 5PS
Tel: 01308 420 751 Mob Tel: 07785 774 909 Fax: 01308 421 325
Email: info@operacircus.co.uk
Web Site: www.operacircus.co.uk
Artistic Director & Performer: Tina Ellen Lea
Associate Director: David Pearl
Chairperson: Fiona Whytehead
Company Secretary: Chris Grady
Opera Circus is an experimental opera and music theatre company. It is singer led, devises and commissions new work and tours extensively both in the UK and internationally with the aim of reaching new audiences for opera/music theatre and broadening existing ones.

PAINES PLOUGH
4th Floor, 43 Aldwych, London WC2B 4DN
Tel: 020 7240 4533 Fax: 020 7240 4534
Email: office@painesplough.com
Web Site: www.painesplough.com
Artistic Directors: George Perrin and James Grieve
Producer: Tara Wilkinson
General Manager: Claire Simpson
Administrative Assistant: Hanna Streeter
A national touring company specialising in accessible new plays.

PASCAL THEATRE COMPANY
35 Flaxman Court, Flaxman Terrace, Bloomsbury, London WC1H 9AR
Tel: 020 7383 0920 Fax: 020 7419 9798
Email: pascaltheatreco@aol.com
Web Site: www.pascal-theatre.com
Artistic Director: Julia Pascal
Administrator: Graeme Braidwood
Education Officer: Liselle Terret

PEEPOLYKUS
26 Eldon Terrace, Bristol BS3 4NZ
Tel: 0117 9539 882
Email: people@fish.co.uk
Web Site: www.peepolykus.com
Contact: John, Javier, David.
Company Manager: Kim Lawrence
Artistic Directors: John Nicholson, Javier Marzan, David Sant
Peepolykus create devised Comic Theatre with universal appeal. Since 1996, we have produced eight shows for small to mid-scale touring and have won several awards. We have toured extensively all over the world often under the auspicies of the British Council.

PEOPLE SHOW
Brady Arts Centre 192-196 Hanbury Street London E1 5HU
Tel: 020 7729 1841
Email: people@peopleshow.co.uk
Web Site: www.peopleshow.co.uk
ADMINISTRATION:
Cap: Seating: 80

PILOT THEATRE
Production Office, York Theatre Royal, St Leonard's Place
West Yorkshire YO1 7HD
Tel: 01904 635 755 Fax: 01904 656 378
Email: info@pilot-theatre.com
Web Site: www.pilot-theatre.com
General Manager: Liz Richards
Artistic Director: Marcus Romer
Administrative Producer: Amanda J Smith
Produce new touring work for young people and new audiences. National Brief funded by Arts Council of England and Arts Council, Yorkshire.

QUANTUM THEATRE FOR SCIENCE
The Old Button Factory, 1- 11 Bannockburn Road, Plumstead London SE18 1ET
Tel / Fax: 020 8317 9000
Email: office@quantumtheatre.co.uk
Web Site: www.quantumtheatre.co.uk
General Manager: Mr Michael Whitmore

QUEST THEATRE COMPANY
3c Mecklenburgh Street, Bloomsbury, London WC1N 2AH
Tel/Fax: 020 7713 0342
Email: davidcraik@freelancersintheuk.com
Artistic Director: David Craik
Policy: To provide opportunities of seeing unusual and thought provoking plays from around the world, preferably in non-naturalistic and visually stimulating formats. Emphasis is on cross-cultural structure and interest.

THE ROCK 'N' ROLL TRAVELLIN' THEATRE COMPANY
Unit C7, Aven Business Centre, Aven Industrial Park, Tickhill Road, Maltby, Rotherham, South Yorkshire S66 7QR
Tel: 07768 220887 / 07880 887572 Fax: 01709 816298
Email: pwp3@tutor.open.ac.uk
Web Site: www.rrttc.co.uk
Contact: Peter Piper, Christine Smith
Entertainment organisation with specialism in producing tribute shows and live music based on 50's/60's culture. Themed events for theatre, corporate and private events. Up to 15 piece band featuring rhythm, brass & strings.

SCENE PRODUCTIONS
277 Barkham Road, Wokingham, Berkshire RG41 4BY
Tel/Fax: 01483 821 005
Email: info@sceneproductions.co.uk
Web Site: www.sceneproductions.co.uk
Contact: Katharine Hurst, Kelly Taylor
Specialists in touring Brechtian theatre. We tour schools, theatres and art centres with productions tailor made to suit Advanced Level Examination requirements. The work is fun, engaging, energetic and accessible.

SCHTANHAUS
Please see 'Paines Plough' listing
14 Thanet Lodge, Mapesbury Road, London NW2 4JA
Tel: 07973 343 429 (Emma Stenning)
Fax: 0870 285 1677
Email: emmas@schtanhaus.co.uk, mail@schtanhaus.co.uk
Web Site: www.schtanhaus.co.uk
Executive Producers: Emma Stenning or Tom Morris
Financial Director: Daniel Morgenstern
Producer: Sally Gibson and Catherine Morgenstern

SHARED EXPERIENCE THEATRE COMPANY
27 - 29 Vauxhall Grove, London SW8 1SY
Tel: 020 7587 1596 Fax: 020 7735 0374
Email: admin@sharedexperience.org.uk
Web Site: www.sharedexperience.org.uk
Artistic Directors: Nancy Meckler, Polly Teale
Policy: To explore a physical way of working through a diverse range of theatrical forms.
Two centrally heated studios in the heart of London.
Studio 1: 62' x 28' - rest room
Studio 2: 30' x 21' - competitive rates.

SPHINX THEATRE COMPANY
25 Short Street, London SE1 8LJ
Tel: 020 7401 9993 / 4 Fax: 020 7401 9995
Email: admin@sphinxtheatre.co.uk
Web Site: www.sphinxtheatre.co.uk
Artistic Director: Sue Parrish
General Manager: Susannah Kraft Levene
Policy: New writing by women
Membership: ITC & TMA
For all bookings and production enquiries contact: Susannah Kraft Levene.

TALAWA THEATRE COMPANY
3rd Floor, 23/25 Great Sutton Street, London EC1V 0DN
Tel: 020 7251 6644 Fax: 020 7251 5969
Email: hq@talawa.com
Web Site: www.talawa.com
Executive Director: Deborah Sawyerr
Artistic Director: Patricia Cumper

TAMASHA THEATRE COMPANY
Unit E, 11 Ronalds Road, London N5 1XJ
Tel: 020 7609 2411 Fax: 020 7609 2722
Email: info@tamasha.org.uk
Web Site: www.tamasha.org.uk
Joint Artistic Directors: Kristine Landon Smith and Sudha Bhuchar

THE DEREK GRANT ORGANISATION
13 Beechwood Rd, West Moors, Dorset BH22 0BN
Tel: 01202 855 777 Fax: 01202 855 777
Email: admin@derekgrant.co.uk
Web Site: www.derekgrant.co.uk
Small and medium scale touring productions available - top quality children's shows, comedy, variety (star names) and music hall.

THE GODOT COMPANY
51 The Cut, London SE1 8LF
Tel: 020 7633 0599 / 020 7620 2900
Fax: 020 7928 5930
Email: godot@calderpublications.com
Web Site: www.calderpublications.com

THEATR NA N'OG
Unit 3, Millands Road Industrial Estate, Neath, Neath Port Talbot SA11 1NJ
Tel: 01639 641771 Fax: 01639 647941
Email: drama@theatr-nanog.co.uk
Web Site: www.theatr-nanog.co.uk
Artistic Director: Geinor Styles
Administrator: Janet Huxtable
Education Officer: Rachel Lloyd

THEATR POWYS
The Drama Centre, Tremont Road, Llandrindod Wells, Powys LD1 5EB Wales
Tel: 01597 824 444 Fax: 01597 824 381
Email: theatr.powys@powys.gov.uk
Web Site: www.theatrpowys.co.uk
Artistic Director: Ian Yeoman
General Manager: Nikki Leopold
Administrator: Sue Early

THEATRE ABSOLUTE
57 - 61 Corporation Street, Coventry, West Midlands CV1 1GQ
Tel: 0247 625 7380
Email: info@theatreabsolute.co.uk
Web Site: www.theatreabsolute.co.uk
Producer: Ms Julia Negus

THEATRE CRYPTIC
CCA 350 Sauchiehall Street, Glasgow, G2 3JD
Tel: 0141 354 0544 Fax: 0141 354 0545
Email: admin@cryptic.org.uk
Web Site: www.cryptic.org.uk
Artistic Director: Cathie Boyd
General Managher: Claire Moran
Administrator: Stephenie Wright
Theatre Cryptic is an award winning Scottish performing arts company established in 1994. It is committed to creating multi-disciplinary projects to 'ravish the senses' through international artistic collaborations. The focus of the Company's work is the theatrical presentation of a commissioned score or text, using visuals or mixed media. Since 1995 the company has toured to Canada, Columbia, Croatia, France, Czech Republic, Germany, Hungary, Ireland, Italy, Latvia, Mexico and Venezuela, including the Iberoamericano Festival in Bogota and BITE at the Barbican Centre, London.

TOWER THEATRE COMPANY
54a Canonbury Road London N1 2DQ
Admin Tel/Fax: 020 7226 5111 BO: 020 7226 3633
Email: info@towertheatre.freeserve.co.uk
Web Site: www.towertheatre.org.uk
Administrators: Ruth Sanderson and Jonathan Norris
London-based company mainly performing at the Bridewell Theatre, Fleet Street and in various North London venues. Awaiting new permanent premises.

TRESTLE THEATRE COMPANY
Trestle Arts Base, Russet Drive, St Albans, Hertfordshire AL4 0JQ
Tel: 01727 850 950
Email: admin@trestle.org.uk
Web Site: www.trestle.org.uk
ADMINISTRATION:
Artistic Director: Emily Gray
Buildings and Finance Manager: Clare Winter
Trestle Theatre Company was founded in 1981 and has enjoyed 30 successful years of touring mask and Physical led theatre. Trestle creates and tours theatrical productions and operates Trestle Arts Base as a performance venue. Trestle also produces international residencies and tours and delivers education programmes across the UK and abroad. The Company aims to engage audiences and participants in an interactive, inclusive and inventive experience of theatre.
Trestle Arts Base - Fully equipped studio theatre,rehearsal room and meeting room, all available for hire to professional and amateur companies for previews and runs
Capacity: 80 - 125

TWO HATS THEATRE COMPANY
21 Maynard Avenue, Warwick CV34 4PU
Tel: 07738 352 995
Email: info@two-hats.org
Web Site: www.two-hats.org
Artistic Director: James Claridge
Company Director: Andy Cresswell
Company Administrator: Roger Harding

WORD AND ACTION (DORSET)
15 King Street, Wimborne, Dorset BH21 1DZ
Tel: 01202 883 197
Email: info@wordandaction.com
Web Site: www.wordandaction.com
Community theatre with thirty two years experience. Annual national and international tours. Offers performances, workshops and courses across the community including schools, day centres, residential homes, hospitals and prisons.

ZIP THEATRE
Newhampton Centre Dunkley Street, Wolverhampton, West Midlands WV1 4AN
Tel: 01902 572 250 Fax: 01902 572 251
Email: cathy@ziptheatre.co.uk
Web Site: www.ziptheatre.co.uk
Company Secretary: Cathy Pemberton
Zip Theatre is a multi-cultural theatre and music company touring both original and classic productions. The company also works extensively in education.

ZIPPO'S CIRCUS
Circus Headquarters, Enborne, Newbury, Berkshire RG20 0LD
Admin: 07836 641 277 BO: 0774 811811 / 07900 141516 Fax: 07050 244 867
Email: zipposcircus@yahoo.com
Web Site: www.zipposcircus.co.uk
Contact: Martin Burton

Community Theatre

AGE EXCHANGE THEATRE TRUST
The Reminiscence Centre, 11 Blackheath Village, London SE3 9LA
Tel: 020 8318 9105 Fax: 020 8318 0060
Email: administrator@age-exchange.org.uk
Web Site: www.age-exchange.org.uk
Contact: Suzanne Lockett

BABBLING VAGABONDS STORY TELLING THEATRE
Top Floor Flat, Bakewell Town Hall, Bath Street, Bakewell, Derbyshire DE45 1BX
Tel/Fax: 01629 815 110 Post to be directed to: PO Box 6116, Bakewell, Derbyshire, DE45 1YE
Email: info@babblingvagabonds.co.uk
Web Site: www.babblingvagabonds.co.uk
Joint Artistic Directors: Phil Coggins, Mark Hornsey, Tara Saunders
We create original Children's Theatre shows that tour to professional venues, community spaces and schools throughout the year. We also create site-specific performances and bespoke theatre arts projects for people of all ages.

BANNER THEATRE COMPANY
Oaklands Centre, Winleigh Road, Birmingham B20 2HN
Tel: 0845 458 1909
Email: info@bannertheatre.co.uk
Web Site: www.bannertheatre.co.uk
Artistic Director: Dave Rogers
Stage Manager: Deborah Aston
Community theatre company producing musical/multimedia documentary productions on current social issues. Bases its work on 'actuality' (people's experiences captured by audio/video), and performs mainly to community/non-theatre audiences.

BRUVVERS THEATRE COMPANY
36 Lime Street, Ouseburn, Newcastle-upon-Tyne, Tyne and Wear NE1 2PQ
Tel: 0191 261 9230 Fax: 0191 209 2482
Email: mikeofbruvvers@hotmail.com
Web Site: www.bruvvers.co.uk
Artistic Director: Michael Mould
One of the surviving sixties groups. Providing year round theatre for all age ranges. 35 years touring experience at home and abroad, self contained show for any venue. Award winning company, ensemble musical theatre of the highest order.
Focus of operation: Greater Newcastle

C & T THEATRE COMPANY
University of Worcester, Henwick Grove, Worcester WR2 6AJ
Tel: 01905 855436 Fax: 01905 855132
Email: info@candt.org
Web Site: www.candt.org
Artistic Director: Paul Sutton
Producer: Rob Lines
Company & Finance Administrator: Sylvia Cahill
C & T is a Theatre Company mixing performance & digital media, enabling creative learning & democratic opportunities for all, particularly children, young people & those at risk of social exclusion.

CHALKFOOT THEATRE ARTS
5 Gold Street Stalbridge Dorset DT10 2LX
Tel: 01963 362937
Email: info@chalkfoot.org.uk
Web Site: www.chalkfoot.org.uk
Artistic Director: Philip Dart
Chalkfoot Thearte Arts (the touring and outreach arm of Channel Theatre Compnay) serves the people of south east England and beyond by touring productions of a high standard which entertain, inform and inspire. The company is committed to touring non-theatre venues and it takes its work into a wide range of communities. The company also works with many different groups on projects which promote personal and social development and develop creativity. Also see CHANNEL THEATRE COMPANY.

THE CHELSEA THEATRE
7 World's End Place, King's Road, London SW10 0DR
Admin Tel: 020 7352 1967
Email: admin@chelseatheatre.org.uk
Web Site: www.chelseatheatre.org.uk
ADMINISTRATION:
Artistic Director: Francis Alexander
Marketing and Advertisment Management: Kathryn Stephens-Berry
Policy: In-house producing and Small scale touring.
Committed to the presentation of new work. Also workshops & full youth arts programme..
Seats: 110 Adults, 140 Children

COMMON PULSE THEATRE
c/o Cardiff Casting, Chapter Arts Centre, Market Road, Canton, Cardiff, South Glamorgan CF5 1QE Wales
Tel: 029 2023 3321 Fax: 029 2023 3380
Email: admin@cardiffcasting.co.uk
Web Site: www.cardiffcasting.co.uk
Company Managers: Chris Durnall, Caroline Bunce
Community theatre company presenting modern contemporary plays, touring Wales.

EMERGENCY EXIT ARTS
Rothbury Hall, Azof Street, London SE10 0EF
Tel: 020 8853 4809 Fax: 020 8858 2025
Email: info@eea.org.uk
Web Site: www.eea.org.uk
ADMINISTRATION:
Artistic Director: Deb Mullins
Admin and Communications Officer: Jules Hodgson
Address for Postal Correspondence: PO Box 570, Greenwich
London, SE10 OEE
Emergency Exit Arts is an outdoor performing arts company, touring work throughout the UK and Europe.

GLOUCESTERSHIRE COMMUNITY THEATRE SOCIETY
Painswick Inn Project, Gloucester Street, Stroud, Gloucestershire GL5 1QG
Tel: 01453 759 400 Fax: 01453 759211
Email: gctsadmin@ukonline.co.uk

HIJINX THEATRE
Wales Millenium Centre, Bute Place, Cardiff Bay, South Glamorgan CF10 5AL Wales
Tel: 029 2030 0331 / 2063 5620 Fax: 029 2030 0332 / 2063 5621
Email: info@hijinx.org.uk
Web Site: www.hijinx.org.uk
Artistic Director: Gaynor Lougher
Administrative Director: Val Hill
Administrative Assistant: Simone Ali
Publicity and Marketing Officer: Ceri Legg

NEW PERSPECTIVES THEATRE COMPANY
Park Lane Business Centre, Park Lane, Nottingham NG6 0DW
Tel: 0115 927 2334
Email: info@newperspectives.co.uk
Web Site: www.newperspectives.co.uk
Artistic Director: Daniel Buckroyd
Marketing and Administrative Officer: Felix Mussell

SOUTHWICK COMMUNITY CENTRE
24 Southwick Street Southwick West Sussex BN42 4TE
BO Tel: 01273 597 094 Admin Tel: 01273 592 819 Fax: 01273 596475
Email: enquiries@southwickcommunitycentre.org.uk
Web: www.southwickcommunitycentre.org.uk
ADMINSTRATION:
Southwick community centre offers a wide range of rooms of varying sizes, a fully fitted kitchen, well stocked bar and central dining/catering area. These facilities and capacities are situated alongside a modern and fully equipped theatre.
The Barn Theatre can cater for 100 guests for sit down meals, 161 seats (either flat floor or raked theatre style) for a theatrical performance and up to 250 for a stand up concert. The theatre is fully equipped with lighting, sound systems, large stage, changing rooms, many seating options, spacious sprung dance floor and access to excellent bar and catering facilities. A grand piano and organ are also available.

SPARE TYRE THEATRE COMPANY
Unit 3.22, Canterbury Court, 1-3 Brixton Road, London SW9 6DE
Tel: 0207 061 6454
Email: lucy@sparetyre.org, berni@sparetyre.org
Web Site: www.sparetyretheatrecompany.co.uk
Artistic Director / CEO: Richard Oyarzabal
General Manager: Berni Bishop
Administrator: Lucy Dalzell
Theatre training company running projects with disadvantaged groups such as young people with learning disabilities, gay men and lesbians and third age elders. Productions are toured locally.

SPECTACLE THEATRE LIMITED
Coleg Morgannwg Rhondda, Llwynpia, Tonypandy, Mid Glamorgan, CF40 2TQ South Wales
Tel: 01443 430 700 Fax: 01443 439640
Email: info@spectacletheatre.co.uk
Web Site: www.spectacletheatre.co.uk
Artistic Director: Steve Davis
Administrator Director: Sandra Jones
Marketing Manager: Elaine Lord

TE POOKA
The Big Red Door, 10 Lady Lawson Street, Edinburgh EH3 9DS
Tel: 0131 228 4567 Tel/ Fax: 0131 221 0734
Email: info@tepooka.org
Web Site: www.tepooka.org
Te Pooka provides high quality street theatre, performing arts and community participatory events to communities across Scotland, the UK and abroad. A network of artists with diverse backgrounds including fine arts, drama and music, te pooka is available for street shows, walkabout performance, stage shows and processions. Te Pooka productions feature dramatic fire performance routines, vibrant costumes, drumming, outrageous stilt-walking, giant puppets, lanterns and fire installations.

THE ARC
39 Weston Drive, Caterham, Surrey CR3 5XY
Tel: 01883 330 380
Email: info@the-arc-caterham.co.uk
Web Site: www.the-arc-caterham.co.uk
Centre Director: Beth Wood
Administrator (Membership, Techincal Enquiries): Hayley Rose
Corporate Events: David Rowan

THE PLAY HOUSE, CATALYST AND LANGUAGE ALIVE! THEATRE COMPANY
Home of Catalyst, Language Alive! and Play House Projects
Longmore Street, Birmingham B12 9ED
Tel: 0121 464 5712 Fax: 0121 464 5713
Email: info@theplayhouse.org.uk
Web Site: www.theplayhouse.org.uk
Artistic and Educational Director: Deborah Hull
Chief Executive: Gary Roskell
Administrator: Gavin Medza
The Play House also runs a range of projects that extend education beyond the classroom and into the community.
'Catalyst' specialises in devising and performing theatre in health education programmes that explore issues relating to personal, social and health education.
Language Alive! is a theatre in education company that has been bringing the curriculum to life for 3- 11 year olds across Birmingham since 1986.

THEATR NA N'OG
Unit 3, Millands Road Industrial Estate, Neath, Neath Port Talbot SA11 1NJ
Tel: 01639 641771 Fax: 01639 647941
Email: drama@theatr-nanog.co.uk
Web Site: www.theatr-nanog.co.uk
Artistic Director: Geinor Styles
Administrator: Janet Huxtable
Education Officer: Rachel Lloyd

THEATR POWYS
The Drama Centre, Tremont Road, Llandrindod Wells, Powys LD1 5EB Wales
Tel: 01597 824 444 Fax: 01597 824 381
Email: theatr.powys@powys.gov.uk
Web Site: www.theatrpowys.co.uk
Artistic Director: Ian Yeoman
General Manager: Nikki Leopold
Administrator: Sue Early

THEATRE VENTURE
Stratford Circus, Theatre Square, Stratford, London E15 1BX
Tel: 020 8519 6678
Email: info@theatre-venture.org
Web Site: www.theatre-venture.org
Executive Director: Gary Horsman
Associate Producer: Jane D'Aulby

THEATRO TECHNIS
26 Crowndale Road, London NW1 1TT
Tel: 020 7387 6617
Email: info@theatrotechnis.com
Web Site: www.theatrotechnis.com
ADMINISTRATION:
Director: George Eugeniou
Policy: The studio is available to theatre, film and TV companies, offering a bar and foyer, an amphitheatre performing space, dressing rooms.
Seating Capacity: 105 Fixed, Max 120.
Disabled access for the audience and for the companies.

TURTLE KEY ARTS
Ladbroke Hall, 79 Barlby Road, London W10 6AZ
Tel: 020 8964 5060 Fax: 020 8964 4080
Email: info@turtlekeyarts.org.uk
Web Site: www.turtlekeyarts.org.uk
Contact: Charlotte Cunningham, Alison King, Sean Dawson, Alan Bowyer, Ruth Naylor-Smith
Turtle Key Arts is a dynamic and versatile arts performance company that combines production, education, training and technical skills to serve theatre, dance companies, venues and disability organisations.
Succesful productions range from children's work to physical theatre, dance and drama. Turtle Key act as producers and managers to a number of companies as well as producing their own shows and running a busy education and disability arts department.

WORD AND ACTION (DORSET)
15 King Street, Wimborne, Dorset BH21 1DZ
Tel: 01202 883 197
Email: info@wordandaction.com
Web Site: www.wordandaction.com
Community theatre with thirty two years experience. Annual national and international tours. Offers performances, workshops and courses across the community including schools, day centres, residential homes, hospitals and prisons.

YOUNG ACTORS THEATRE & AGENCY
70-72 Barnsbury Road, London N1 0ES
Tel: 020 7278 2101 Fax: 020 7833 9467
Email: info@yati.org.uk
Web Site: www.yati.org.uk
Director: Andrew Harries
Agents: Dyana Daulby and Lucy O'Meara
Community Theatre and Management Agency.
The Community Theatre runs evening drama classes for all ages, from 6 upwards.
The Management Agency specialises in representation of children from the age of 6-17, as well as representing adults of all ages.

Mime & Physical Theatre

FRANTIC ASSEMBLY
31 Eyre Street Hill, London EC1R 5EW
Tel: 020 7841 3115
Email: admin@franticassembly.co.uk
Web Site: www.franticassembly.co.uk
Artistic Director: Scott Graham
Executive Producer: Despina Tsatsas
Learn and Train Manager: Inga Hirst
Administrator: Donna Marie Howard
Frantic Assembly creates vivid and dynamic theatre renowned for its unique physical style combining movement, design, music and text. A touring company producing new and innovative work nationally and internationally, Frantic also delivers its educational Learn & Train programme to institutions worldwide. See website for further details.

DESMOND JONES - MIME AND PHYSICAL THEATRE
20 Thornton Avenue, London W4 1QG
Tel: 020 8747 3537
Email: enquiries@desmondjones.co.uk
Web Site: www.desmondjones.co.uk
Director: Desmond Jones
To encourage people to see theatre as a much more exciting physical medium than it is, and to teach mime and physical theatre to the highest standards.

MIMIKA
26 Highbury Terrace, Leeds, West Yorkshire LS6 4ET
Tel/Fax: 0113 274 0053
Email: mimika@btinternet.com

NO LIMITS
No Limits Theatre Company, Dundas Street, Monkwearmouth, Sunderland, Tyne & Wear SR6 0AY
Tel: 0191 565 3013
Email: info@nolimitstheatre.org.uk
Web Site: www.nolimitstheatre.org.uk
Artistic Director: Janet Nettleton
Theatre Director: Alan Parker
Administrator: Karen Suleiman
A leading company for people with and without a learning disability that produces dynamic and innovative performances and promotes inclusive arts practise. Suitable for a wide range of venues. Also available for workshops, residencies, consultancy and training.

THEATRE DE L'ANGE FOU
Unit 2, Belgravia Workshops, 157 - 163 Marlborough Road, London N19 4NF
Tel: 020 7263 9339
Email: info@angefou.co.uk
Web Site: www.angefou.co.uk
Directors: Corinne Soum, Steven Wasson

TRESTLE THEATRE COMPANY
Trestle Arts Base, Russet Drive, St Albans, Hertfordshire AL4 0JQ
Tel: 01727 850 950
Email: admin@trestle.org.uk
Web Site: www.trestle.org.uk
ADMINISTRATION:
Artistic Director: Emily Gray
Buildings and Finance Manager: Clare Winter
Trestle Theatre Company was founded in 1981 and has enjoyed 30 successful years of touring mask and Physical led theatre. Trestle creates and tours theatrical productions and operates Trestle Arts Base as a performance venue. Trestle also produces international residencies and tours and delivers education programmes across the UK and abroad. The Company aims to engage audiences and participants in an interactive, inclusive and inventive experience of theatre.
Trestle Arts Base - Fully equipped studio theatre,rehearsal room and meeting room, all available for hire to professional and amateur companies for previews and runs
Capacity: 80 - 125

Street Theatre

DESPERATE MEN THEATRE COMPANY
Epstein Buildings,
Mivart Street, Easton, Bristol, BS5 6JL
Tel: 0117 939 3902 Mob: 0777 5911 620
Email: office@desperatemen.com
Web Site: www.desperatemen.com
Creative Producer: Richard Headon

MAHOGANY CARNIVAL DESIGN LTD
28 High Street,
Harlesden, London NW10 4LX
Tel: 020 8961 4446
Email: costumes@mahoganycarnival.com
Web Site: www.mahoganycarnival.com
Artistic Director: Clary Salandy
Structural Engineer: Michael Ramdeen
A unique design and production company offering exciting and innovative costumes and shows for a variety of events, including Theatre and Circus.

SCIENCE IN A SUITCASE
Tel: 01508 473 016 Mob: 07850 222 028
Email: info@dodifferent.co.uk
Web Site: www.dodifferent.co.uk
Ken Farquhar produces accessible comedy science shows for family audience suitable for a multitude of venues.

Children's Theatre, TIE Companies and Young Peoples Theatre

ACTION THEATRE
5 Grove Road Chelmsford CM2 0EY
Tel: 01621 868 133
Mobile: 07771 571 260
Email: mail@actiontheatre.co.uk
Web Site: www.actiontheatre.co.uk
Artistic Director: Tom Foster
We specialise in short courses and workshops, suitable for years 6 - 13. Courses take place throughout the UK, particularly London, Cambridge, Essex and the South-West.

ACTION TRANSPORT THEATRE
Whitbey Hall Stanney Lane Ellesmere Port CH65 9AE
Tel: 0151 357 2120 Fax: 0151 356 4057
Email: karen@actiontransporttheatre.org
Web Site: www.actiontransporttheatre.org
Executive Director: Sarah Clover
General Manager: Karen Parry
Production Manager: Mike Francis
A new writing company creating plays for, by & with young people.

BABBLING VAGABONDS STORY TELLING THEATRE
Top Floor Flat, Bakewell Town Hall, Bath Street, Bakewell, Derbyshire DE45 1BX
Tel/Fax: 01629 815 110 Post to be directed to: PO Box 6116, Bakewell, Derbyshire, DE45 1YE
Email: info@babblingvagabonds.co.uk
Web Site: www.babblingvagabonds.co.uk
Joint Artistic Directors: Phil Coggins, Mark Hornsey, Tara Saunders
We create original Children's Theatre shows that tour to professional venues, community spaces and schools throughout the year. We also create site-specific performances and bespoke theatre arts projects for people of all ages.

BARBER/LUNT PRODUCTIONS
Dean Clough, Halifax, West Yorkshire HX3 5AX
Tel/Fax: 01422 330 101
Email: barberlunt@aol.com
Administrator: Angela Saville
Artistic Directors: Maureen Lunt, John Barber

THE BARBICAN THEATRE
Castle Street, Plymouth, Devon PL1 2NJ
Tel: 01752 267 131
Email: info@barbicantheatre.co.uk
Web Site: www.barbicantheatre.co.uk
ADMINISTRATION:
Director: Sheila Snellgrove
Artistic Director: Mark Laville
Theatre Administration and Box Office: Dan Baker
Technician: Jamie Smith (01752) 242015
Policy: Young People's Theatre Centre, small scale touring venue for Dance and experimental/new work. Producer of TIE touring issue-based work.
Cap: 140

BIG WHEEL THEATRE COMPANY (TIE)
Exmouth Market Centre, PO Box 18221, London EC1R 4WJ
Tel: 020 7689 8670
Email: info@bigwheel.org.uk
Web Site: www.bigwheel.org.uk
Contact: Roland Allen
Capacity: 80

BIGFOOT THEATRE COMPANY
The Devas Club, 2a Stormont Road, London SW11 5EN
Tel: 0800 644 6034 Fax: 0870 8681067
Email: info@bigfoot-theatre.co.uk
Web Site: www.bigfoot-theatre.co.uk
Executive Director: Karl Wozny

BLAH BLAH BLAH! (TIE)
The Westpark Centre, Spen Lane, Leeds LS16 5BE
Tel: 0113 274 0030
Email: admin@blahs.co.uk
Web Site: www.blahs.co.uk
Artistic Director: Anthony Haddon
Touring Co-ordinator & Administrator: Cas Bulmer
The Blahs create theatre for young audiences. We work with professional writers, designers and actors to create high quality theatre experiences in schools, youth centres and small scale venues.

BOX CLEVER
52 - 54 Kennington Oval, London SE11 5SW
Tel: 020 7793 0040 Fax: 020 7357 8188
Email: admin@boxclevertheatre.com
Web Site: www.boxclevertheatre.com
Artistic Director and Writer-in-Residence: Michael Wicherek
General Manager: Jemima Lee
Box Clever is a writer-led, multi-disciplinary touring company, creating challenging and inspiring contemporary theatre with and for young people.

BRUVVERS THEATRE COMPANY
36 Lime Street, Ouseburn, Newcastle-upon-Tyne, Tyne and Wear NE1 2PQ
Tel: 0191 261 9230 Fax: 0191 209 2482
Email: mikeofbruvvers@hotmail.com
Web Site: www.bruvvers.co.uk
Artistic Director: Michael Mould
One of the surviving sixties groups. Providing year round theatre for all age ranges. 35 years touring experience at home and abroad, self contained show for any venue. Award winning company, ensemble musical theatre of the highest order.
Focus of operation: Greater Newcastle

CATHERINE WHEELS THEATRE COMPANY
Brunton Theatre, Ladywell Way, Musselburgh, Midlothian EH21 6AF
Tel: 0131 653 5255
Email: admin@catherinewheels.co.uk
Web Site: www.catherinewheels.co.uk
Artistic Director: Gill Robertson
Producer: Paul Fitzpatrick
Award-winning Theatre Company producing work for children and young people. Tours to small and medium scale venues throughout the UK and internationally.

CERTAIN CURTAIN THEATRE COMPANY
Unit 128, Oyston Mill, Strand Road, Preston, Lancashire PR1 8UR
Tel: 01772 731 024
Email: cctheatre@yahoo.com
Web Site: www.cctheatre.co.uk
Directors: Claire Moore, John Woudberg
Original work tailored to all ages includes T.I.E., issue-based, public performances, musicals and workshops. We are an award winning company.

CHICKENSHED THEATRE
Chase Side, Southgate, London N14 4PE
Tel: 020 8351 6161 Fax: 020 8292 0202
BO: 020 8292 9222
Email: info@chickenshed.org.uk
Web Site: www.chickenshed.org.uk
ADMINISTRATION:
Chief Executive: Jane Paterson-Todd (janep@chickenshed.org.uk)
Theatre Manager: Francis Thomas
Press & Publicity: Susan Jamson (susanj@chickenshed.org.uk)
Registered Charity.
Provision of works of performance art, which are original, creative and inclusive. Excellence without exclusion.
52 staff with 100+ volunteers.
1,000 young people participate weekly.

COMPANY OF ANGELS
126 Cornwall Road, London SE1 8TQ
Tel: 020 7928 2811
Email: info@companyofangels.co.uk
Web Site: www.companyofangels.co.uk
Director: John Retallack
General Managers: Vanessa Fagan and Virginia Leaver

CRAGRATS LTD
Lawster House, 140 South Street, Dorking, Surrey RH4 2EU
Tel: 08444 774 100
Email: enquiries@cragrats.com
Web Site: www.cragrats.com

Managing Director: William Akerman
Business Support Manager: Nicky Miles
Leeds Office: Roudfoundry Media Centre, Foundry Street, Leeds, LS11 5QP

CragRats Ltd is the market innovator and leader in bespoke theatre productions for young people, businesses and training organisations. CragRats Ltd is committed to communicating messages and motivating audiences throughout the UK, producing projects that range from issue-based theatre, initiative awareness shows, communication skills, corporate training as well as full-length theatre productions. See our web site for further company details.

CROYDON YOUTH THEATRE ORGANISATION (YPT)

Shoestring Theatre, Oakley Road, South Norwood, London SE25 4XG
BO: 020 8655 1098
Web Site: www.cyto.org.uk
Artistic Director: Viv Berry
Workshops and performances in Theatre, Dance and Music for young people aged 13-25.

DAYLIGHT THEATRE (TIE)

66 Middle Street, Stroud, Gloucestershire GL5 1EA
Tel: 01453 763 808
Email: info@daylighttheatre.co.uk
Web Site: www.daylighttheatre.co.uk
Contact: Hugh Young

FACE FRONT INCLUSIVE THEATRE LTD

52 The Market Square, Edmonton Green Shopping Centre Edmonton, London N9 0TZ
Tel: 020 8350 3461
Email: info@facefront.org
Web Site: www.facefront.org
Artistic Director: Annie Smol
Administrator and Tour Booker: Tracey Viechweg
Face Front is a company of disabled and non-disabled artists who create multi-layered theatre which is accessible to all. The company works extensively in schools and other educational settings producing high quality Theatre In Education and participatory workshop programmes suitable for all ages over 5 years. Drama techniques include role-play, improvisation, storytelling, poetry and image work to raise issues relating to educational and home environments, including bullying, racism, disability and domestic violence.
Contact the company directly for more information on hiring the on-site studio; the high ceiling and sprung dance floor make it suitable for rehearsals, auditions, meetings and community events.

FACE PAINTING BY JENNIE

Hop Cottage, Rectory Lane, Herongate Essex CM13 3PR
Tel: 01277 811 813
Email: jennie.penkul@bigfoot.com
Contact: Mrs J Penkul

FREEHAND THEATRE (CT)

1 Reynard Villas, Mayfield Grove, Baildon, Shipley, West Yorkshire BD17 6DY
Tel: 01274 585 277
Email: admin@freehandtheatre.co.uk
Web Site: www.freehandtheatre.co.uk
Co-Directors: Lizzie Allen and Simon Hatfield.
Freehand theatre was formed in 1982. Since then, it has been delighting audiences with its inventive style of puppetry. Productions are aimed primarily at children (3 to 7 year olds) and family audiences. The company regularly performs in schools, arts centres, small theatres, etc. Technically sufficient. Maximum audience: 140.

FUSE THEATRE FOR YOUNG PEOPLE

13 Hope Street, Liverpool, Merseyside L1 9BH
Tel: 0151 708 0877 Fax: 0151 707 9950
Email: info@fusetheatre.com
Web Site: www.fusetheatre.co.uk
General Manager: Michael Quirke

GAZEBO THEATRE COMPANY

The Town Hall Church Street Bilston, West Midlands WV14 0AT
Tel: 01902 497222 Fax: 01902 497244
Email: admin@gazebotie.org
Web Site: www.gazebotie.org
Artistic Director: Michael O'Hara
Strategic Director: Pamela Cole Hudson

GIANT PRODUCTIONS

Giant 121 - 127 Saltmarket, Glasgow G1 5LF
Tel: 0141 552 8231
Email: info@giantproductions.org
Web Site: www.giantproductions.org
Artistic Director: Maria McCavene

GREEN CANDLE DANCE COMPANY

Oxford House Derbyshire Street, London E2 6HG
Tel: 020 7739 7722 Fax: 020 7729 8272
Email: info@greencandledance.com
Web Site: www.greencandledance.com
Artistic Director: Fergus Early
Development Manager: Annie Pooley
Administator: Suzanne Firth
Green Candle makes shows for children, young adults and older people, performing in theatres, arts centres, schools, community centres, day centres, residential homes, and hospitals across London and beyond as well as running workshops and education projects for people of all ages and abilities.

GREENWICH & LEWISHAM YOUNG PEOPLES THEATRE

The Tramshed, 51 - 53 Woolwich New Road, London SE18 6ES
Tel: 020 8854 1316
Email: info@glypt.co.uk, zoe.bateman@glypt.co.uk
Web Site: www.glypt.co.uk
ADMINISTRATION:
Artistic Director: Jeremy James. Email: jeremy@glypt.co.uk
General Manager: Zoë Lally. Email: zoe@glypt.co.uk
Administrator: Zoe Bateman
Capacity: 110 Theatre Style. Studio Capacity 40

HALF MOON YOUNG PEOPLE'S THEATRE (YPT)

43 Whitehorse Road, London E1 0ND
Tel: 020 7265 8138 Box Office: 020 7709 8900 Fax: 020 7709 8914
Email: admin@halfmoon.org.uk
Web Site: www.halfmoon.org.uk
ADMINISTRATION
Director: Chris Elwell
Production and Technical Manager: Fred Beaufort
Leading provider of professional theatre training, youth theatre and arts projects for young people across London. Regular programme of shows for young people.
Capacity: 66- 90

HOBGOBLIN THEATRE COMPANY

Head Office: 2 Heston Road, Redhill RH1 5HY
Tel: 0800 5300384 Mob: 07775 861165
Email: info@hobgoblintheatrecompany.co.uk
Web: www.hobgoblintheatrecompany.co.uk
Contact: Hannah Bowen, Dan Ellis, James Anthony.
Hobgoblin Theatre Company are a touring theatre in education company committed to delivering high quality, entertaining educational plays and drama workshops to schools across the UK.

IAN SAVILLE: SAVILLE MAGIC

8 Aylesbury Street, London NW10 0AS
Tel: 020 8621 0157 Mob: 07949 164793
Email: ian@redmagic.org.uk
Web Site: www.redmagic.co.uk
Contact: Ian Saville

IMAGE MUSICAL THEATRE COMPANY

23 Sedgeford Road, Shepherds Bush, London W12 0NA
Tel: 020 87439380 Fax: 020 87499294
Email: brian@imagemusicaltheatre.co.uk
Web: www.imagemusicaltheatre.co.uk
Producer/ Director: Brian Thresh

Specialising in new musicals for the touring circuit, theatres and schools, the company produces two family/ children's participation musicals and one full length adult musical each year.

THE INSPIRATIONAL SCIENCE THEATRE COMPANY
Tel: 01508 473 016 Mob: 07850 222 028
Email: info@dodifferent.co.uk
Web Site: www.dodifferent.co.uk
Dr Ken Farquhar has produced and performed many science and maths based theatre shows and workshops for primary and high school pupils.

INTERPLAY THEATRE TRUST
Armley Ridge Road, Leeds, West Yorkshire LS12 3LE
Tel: 0113 263 8556 Fax: 0113 231 9285
Email: info@interplayleeds.co.uk
Web Site: www.interplayleeds.co.uk
Executive Director: Jude Wright
Artistic Director: Steve Byrne

LAMBETH CHILDREN'S THEATRE CO LTD (CT)
27 Wingmore Road, London SE24 0AS
Tel: 020 7733 5270 Fax: 020 7326 0146
Email: lambch@globalnet.co.uk
Contact: Raymond Cook

LEARNING THROUGH ACTION (TIE)
Founded 1983
Learning Through Action Centre High Close School, Wiltshire Road, Wokingham, Berkshire RG40 1TT
Tel: 0870 770 7985 Fax: 0870 770 7986
Email: ltacentreoffice@aol.com
Web: www.learning-through-action.org.uk
Contact: Annette Cotterill

THE LITTLE ANGEL THEATRE
14 Dagmar Passage, Cross Street, London N1 2DN
BO Tel: 020 7226 1787
Email: info@littleangeltheatre.com
Web Site: www.littleangeltheatre.com
Artistic Director/Chief Executive: Peter Glanville
General Manager: Lynette Shanbury
Technical Manager: David Duffy

M6 THEATRE COMPANY
M6 Studio Theatre, Hamer C.P. School, Albert Royds Street, Rochdale, Lancashire OL16 2SU
Tel: 01706 355 898
PR/ Media: 01706 355898
Email: info@m6theatre.co.uk
Web Site: www.m6theatre.co.uk
Artistic Producer: Dorothy Wood
Production Manager: Joss Matzen
General Manager: Deborah Palmer

MAGIC CARPET THEATRE COMPANY
18 Church Street, Sutton-on-Hull, East Yorkshire HU7 4TS
Tel: 01482 709 939 Fax: 01482 787 362
Mobile: 07785 260 038
Email: jon@magiccarpettheatre.com
Web Site: www.magiccarpettheatre.com
Magic Carpet tour exciting new works to venues, schools and festivals in the UK and abroad.
Formed in 1982 Magic Carpet are a professional touring children's theatre company. Touring Mr Shell's Seaside Spells by Anthony Peters and workshops in 2005.

NEWFOUND THEATRE
Tel/Fax: 07753237209
Tel: 0845 539 0173
Email: newfoundtheatre@gmail.com
Web Site: www.newfoundtheatre.com
Theatre in education company producing origional performances and workshops that tour into schools and other youth venues. Also provide corporate and role play pieces.

OILY CART COMPANY
Smallwood School Annexe Smallwood Road, London SW17 0TW
Tel: 020 8672 6329 Fax: 020 8672 0792
Email: oilies@oilycart.org.uk
Web Site: www.oilycart.org.uk
Artistic Director: Tim Webb
Head of Design: Claire De Loon
Composer & Musical Director: Max Reinhardt
General Manager: Kathy Everett
Production Manager: Jesus Gamon

OLDHAM THEATRE WORKSHOP
Old Museum, Greaves Street, Oldham, Lancashire OL1 1DN
Mgt/BO: 0161 911 3240
Email: otw@oldham.gov.uk
Web Site: www.oldhamtheatreworkshop.co.uk
ADMINISTRATION:
Props: Oldham Metropolitan Borough Council
Artistic Director: James Atherton
Policy: Own Productions; Touring productions; Summer Schools; Workshops.
Cap: 80

PADDY THE CLOWN
39 Elm Street, Roath, Cardiff, South Glamorgan CF24 3QS Wales
Tel: 029 2048 6550
Email: paddy@paddytheclown.com
Web Site: www.paddytheclown.com
Contact: Paddy Faulkner
Touring theatres nationwide. Also available for private functions, outdoor events and promotions. International Award Winning Show.

PEGASUS THEATRE
Magdalen Road, Oxford OX4 1RE
Admin: 01865 812160 BO: 01865 812150 Fax: 01865 812170
Email: info@pegasustheatre.org.uk
Web Site: www.pegasustheatre.org.uk
ADMINISTRATION:
Policy: Small scale touring venue. Home of the Oxford Youth Theatre
Perfs: Approx. evenings 8.00pm
CEO/ Artistic Director: Jonathan Lloyd
Office Manager: Jessica McHugh
Head of Technical and Production: Dave Thwaites

PIED PIPER THEATRE COMPANY
1 Lilian Place, Coxcombe Lane, Chiddingfold, Surrey GU8 4QA
Tel: 01428 684 022
Email: twpiedpiper@aol.com
Web Site: www.piedpipertheatre.co.uk
Contact: Tina Williams

PLAYBOX THEATRE COMPANY
The Dream Factory, Tapping Way Warwick CV34 6LE
Tel: 01926 419 555
Email: info@playboxtheatre.com
Web Site: www.playboxtheatre.com
ADMINISTRATION:
Principal Administrator: Nikki Cross
In April 1999 Playbox Theatre moved into a custom designed creation centre in Warwick. A conception of Playbox with Glenn Howells Architects (UK) and Sceno Plus (Montreal) a national focus for the performing arts and young people, housing productions, workshops, special projects, visiting companies, from UK and overseas. A theatre exclusively for young people.
Cap: Theatre, 250.

POLKA THEATRE FOR CHILDREN
240 The Broadway, Wimbledon, London SW19 1SB
Admin: 020 8545 8325 BO: 020 8543 4888
Email: info@polkatheatre.com
Web Site: www.polkatheatre.com
ADMINISTRATION:
Prop: Polka Children's Theatre Ltd.
Artistic Director: Peter Glanville
Email: peter@polkatheatre.com
Head of Finance and Administration: Bernadette Cava
Email: bernadette@polkatheatre.com
Technical Manager: Chris Randall
Email: chris@polkatheatre.com
Policy: Children's Theatre Repertoire and visiting Children's Theatre Companies.
Seats: Main Theatre; 300. Adventure Theatre; 60-70
Children's Restaurant, Exhibitions, Playground.

PROFESSOR CRUMP
8 St Marks Road, London W7 2PW
Tel/Fax: 020 8566 1575
Mob: 07966 233 220
Email: paul@professorcrump.co.uk
Web Site: www.professorcrump.co.uk
Contact: Paul Goddard
Clown, Stilt, Character Entertainer plus Children's Entertainment.

QUANTUM THEATRE FOR SCIENCE
The Old Button Factory, 1- 11 Bannockburn Road, Plumstead
London SE18 1ET
Tel / Fax: 020 8317 9000
Email: office@quantumtheatre.co.uk
Web Site: www.quantumtheatre.co.uk
General Manager: Mr Michael Whitmore

QUICKSILVER THEATRE (CT)
The New Diorama, 15- 16 Triton Street, London NW1 3BF
Email: talktous@quicksilvertheatre.org
Web Site: www.quicksilvertheatre.org.uk, www.newdiorama.com
Joint Artistic Director & Chief Executive: Guy Holland
Joint Artistic Director: Carey English
General Manager: Jemima Lee
Theatre & Programming Manager: David Byrne

REPLAY PRODUCTIONS
Old Museum Arts Centre, 7 College Square North, Belfast BT1 6AR
Tel: 028 9032 2773 Fax: 028 9032 2724
Email: info@replaytheatreco.org, admin@replaytheatreco.org
Web Site: www.replaytheatreco.org
Artistic Director: Anna Newell
Operations Manager: Fiona Bell
Administrative Officer: Irene Swift
Executive Director: Einear Henry
Award-winning Replay Productions is a professional educational theatre company based in Belfast. Est. in 1988, Replay is dedicated to providing high quality theatre that entertains, educates and stimulates children and young people of all abilities whilst supporting and inspiring the adults that work with, and care for them. The company tours schools and venues throughout Northern Ireland. All projects provide unique curriculum support, encourage increased understanding, development and learning (both at school level and in life skills) and promote concepts of cultural identity and diversity.

ROYAL COURT YOUNG WRITERS' PROGRAMME
Sloane Square, London SW1W 8AS
Tel: 020 7565 5050 Fax: 020 7565 5001
Email: studio@royalcourttheatre.com
Web Site: www.royalcourttheatre.com
Literary Manager: Christopher Campbell
Senior Reader: Nic Wass

SANDOW CLOWNS
59 Thoresby Close, Bridlington, East Yorkshire YO16 7EN
Tel: 01262 671 492 Fax: 01262 675 543
Mob 1: 07969 933 236 Mob 2 :07964 274 186
Email: fossett@supanet.com
Web Site: www.sandowclowns.co.uk
Contact: Tom Bratby or Sheila Bratby
Clown show "circus party" on stage, in the round, schools, civic venues, galas.

SCHOOLPLAY PRODUCTIONS LTD
15 Inglis Road, Colchester, Essex CO3 3HU
Tel: 01206 540 111 Fax: 01206 766 944
Email: schoolplay@inglis-house.demon.co.uk
Web: www.schoolplayproductions.co.uk

SCIENCE IN A SUITCASE
Tel: 01508 473 016 Mob: 07850 222 028
Email: info@dodifferent.co.uk
Web Site: www.dodifferent.co.uk
Ken Farquhar produces accessible comedy science shows for family audience suitable for a multitude of venues.

SHAKESPEARE 4 KIDZ
Drewshearne Barn, Crowhurst Lane End, Oxted, Surrey RH8 9NT
Tel: 01342 894548 Fax: 01342 893754
Email: office@shakespeare4kidz.com
Web Site: www.shakespeare4kidz.com
Chief Executive Director: Julian Chenery

SHEFFIELD THEATRES EDUCATION DEPARTMENT (TIE, YPT & YT)
55 Norfolk Street, Sheffield S1 1DA
BO: 0114 249 6000 Admin: 0114 249 5999 Fax: 0114 249 6003
Email: creativedevelopment@sheffieldtheatres.co.uk
Web: www.sheffieldtheatres.co.uk/education
Creative Producer: Andrew Loretto
Education Officer: Sarah Clough

SNAPSHOT
453 Silk House, Park Green, Macclesfield, Cheshire SK11 7QJ
Mobile: 07889 745594
Email: mikhobson2000@yahoo.com
Web: www.snapshotproductions.co.uk
Artistic Director: Chris Bright
Administration: Michael Hobson

SPECTACLE THEATRE LIMITED
Coleg Morgannwg Rhondda, Llwynpia, Tonypandy, Mid Glamorgan, CF40 2TQ South Wales
Tel: 01443 430 700 Fax: 01443 439640
Email: info@spectacletheatre.co.uk
Web Site: www.spectacletheatre.co.uk

Artistic Director: Steve Davis
Administrator Director: Sandra Jones
Marketing Manager: Elaine Lord

STARLIGHT YOUTH THEATRE
129 - 131 Telegraph Road, Heswall, Wirral, Merseyside CH60 0AF
Tel: 0151 342 2706 Mob: 07761 765 782 / 07842 272 808
Email: andy@starlightyouththeatre.co.uk
Web: www.starlightyouththeatre.co.uk
Founders: Andy & Jacqui Miles

TAG THEATRE COMPANY
Citizens Theatre, 119 Gorbals Street, Glasgow G5 9DS Scotland
Switchboard: 0141 429 5561 Tel: 0141 429 0022 Fax: 0141 429 7374
Email: anna@citz.co.uk
Web Site: www.citz.co.uk
ADMINISTRATION:
Director: Guy Hollands
Administrative Director: Anna Stapleton
Head of Production: Chris McDougall
Head of Citizens Learning & TAG: Martin Travers
TAG is Scotland's National theatre company for young people.

TARA ARTS
356 Garratt Lane, London SW18 4ES
Tel: 020 8333 4457 Fax: 020 8870 9540
Email: tara@tara-arts.com
Web Site: www.tara-arts.com
ADMINISTRATION:
Artistic Director: Jatinder Verma
Marketing Officer: Katie Elston
Studio Programmer: Mukul Ahmed, mukul@tara-arts.com

TASTE PRODUCTIONS
Beaminster School, Newtown, Beaminster, Dorset DT8 3EP
Tel: 01308 862633
Email: tasteproductions@gmail.com
Web Site: www.tasteproductions.co.uk
Producer/Director: Valerie Goodwin

TE POOKA
The Big Red Door, 10 Lady Lawson Street, Edinburgh EH3 9DS
Tel: 0131 228 4567
Tel/ Fax: 0131 221 0734
Email: info@tepooka.org
Web Site: www.tepooka.org
Te Pooka provides high quality street theatre, performing arts and community participatory events to communities across Scotland, the UK and abroad. A network of artists with diverse backgrounds including fine arts, drama and music, te pooka is available for street shows, walk-about performance, stage shows and processions. Te Pooka productions feature dramatic fire performance routines, vibrant costumes, drumming, outrageous stilt-walking, giant puppets, lanterns and fire installations.

THE ARC
39 Weston Drive, Caterham,
Surrey CR3 5XY
Tel: 01883 330 380
Email: info@the-arc-caterham.co.uk
Web Site: www.the-arc-caterham.co.uk
Centre Director: Beth Wood
Administrator (Membership, Techincal Enquiries): Hayley Rose
Corporate Events: David Rowan

THE GLOBE PLAYERS
36 St James' Avenue, Hampton Hill,
Middlesex TW12 1HH
Tel: 020 8979 5497 Fax: 020 8941 6776
Email: theglobeplayers@gmail.com
Contact: Jennifer McEvoy

THEATR IOLO
The Old School Building Cefn Road,
Mynachdy Cardiff CF14 3HS
Tel: 029 2061 3782 Fax: 029 2052 2225
Email: info@theatriolo.com
Web Site: www.theatriolo.com
ADMINISTRATION:
Artistic Director: Kevin Lewis
Administrative Director: Wendy York
Education Officer: Glenys Evans
Formed in 1987 Theatr Iolo is a professional company which creates theatre especially for young people. We take the very best of live theatre to schools and small-scale venues across South Wales and beyond.

THEATR NA N'OG
Unit 3, Millands Road Industrial Estate,
Neath, Neath Port Talbot SA11 1NJ
Tel: 01639 641771 Fax: 01639 647941
Email: drama@theatr-nanog.co.uk
Web Site: www.theatr-nanog.co.uk
Artistic Director: Geinor Styles
Administrator: Janet Huxtable
Education Officer: Rachel Lloyd

THEATRE CENTRE YOUNG PEOPLE'S THEATRE CO.
Shoreditch Town Hall, 380 Old Street,
London EC1V 9LT
Tel: 020 7729 3066 Fax: 020 7739 9741
Email: admin@theatre-centre.co.uk
Web Site: www.theatre-centre.co.uk
Artistic Director: Natalie Wilson
General Manager: Charles Bishop
Registered Office: Hanover House, 14 Hanover Square,
London W1S 1HP

THEATRE EXCHANGE LTD
9a Station Road West, Oxted, Surrey
RH8 9EE
Tel: 01883 724599
Email: arts@tandridgeleisure.co.uk
Web Site: www.theatre-exchange.org.uk
ADMINISTRATION:
Creative Directors: Katy Potter & Andrew Mulquin
Administrators: Lisa Phillips & Andrea Oxlade
Through a creative exchange between practitioners and young people we seek to promote access to training and production work to high numbers of young people. We seek to explore and expand creative techniques and to produce high standard theatre and educational work with an emphasis on new writing.

THEATRE IS
The Hat Factory 65-67 Bute Street
Luton LU1 2EY
Tel: 01582 481 221
Email: info@theatreis.org, stuart@theatreis.org
Web Site: www.theatreis.org
Contacts: Stuart Mullins, Creative Director; Michael Corley, Communications Co-ordinator.
Our mission is to research, develop and produce the best possible performing arts for the young people of the East of England aged 25 and under.
In placing young people at the heart of our organization we respect them as consumers and makers of theatre. We will therefore, pioneer new ways of making theatre for young people empowering them to become the cultural leaders of the future.

THEATRE WORKSHOP
Out of the Blue Drill Hall, 36 Dalmeny Street, Edinburgh EH6 8RG Scotland
Tel: 0131 555 3854 Mob: 07725 226 913
Email: keith.tws@hotmail.co.uk, jez.tws@hotmail.co.uk
Web Site: www.theatre-workshop.com
ADMINISTRATION:
Relationship & Development Manager: Keith Bell
Contact: Jez Arrow
Cap: 200

TICKLISH ALLSORTS
57 Victoria Road, Wilton,
Salisbury SP2 0DZ
Tel/Fax: 01722 744 949
Mob: 07721 992994
Email: garynunn@ntlworld.com
Web Site: www.ticklishallsorts.co.uk
Senior Personnel: Gary A Nunn
Childrens Entertainments, shows, puppets, musical comedy, workshops.
Established 1981. Performances and workshops. RSPB National Touring Roadshows.

UNICORN
147 Tooley Street, Southwark,
London SE1 2HZ
BO: 020 7645 0560 Admin/ SD: 020 7645 0500 Fax: 020 7700 3870
Email: admin@unicorntheatre.com
Web Site: www.unicorntheatre.com
General Manager: Anneliese Davidsen
Artistic Director: Tony Graham

WHIRLIGIG THEATRE
14 Belvedere Drive, Wimbledon,
London SW19 7BY
Tel: 020 8947 1732 Fax: 020 8879 7648
Email: david.woodplays@virgin.net
Web Site: www.davidwood.org.uk
Directors: David Wood & John Gould
Administrator: Barry Sheppard
Whirligig no longer tours annually, but is open to offers for Christmas seasons and one-off productions, particularly of The Gingerbread Man.

YOUNG ACTORS THEATRE & AGENCY
70-72 Barnsbury Road, London N1 0ES
Tel: 020 7278 2101 Fax: 020 7833 9467
Email: info@yati.org.uk
Web Site: www.yati.org.uk
Director: Andrew Harries
Agents: Dyana Daulby and Lucy O'Meara
Community Theatre and Management Agency.
The Community Theatre runs evening drama classes for all ages, from 6 upwards.
The Management Agency specialises in representation of children from the age of 6-17, as well as representing adults of all ages.

YOUNG PLEASANCE (YPT)
The Pleasance Theatre's own "very remarkable company" (BBC Scotland).
Pleasance Theatre Trust Ltd, Carpenter's Mews, North Road, Islington,
London N7 9EF
Tel: 020 7619 6868 Fax: 020 7700 7366
BO: 020 7609 1800
Email: yp@pleasance.co.uk
Web Site: www.pleasance.co.uk
Artistic Directors: Kathryn Norton & Tim Norton
Director of the Pleasance: Anthony Alderson

YVONNE ARNAUD THEATRE
Millbrook, Guildford, Surrey GU1 3UX
Mgt/SD: 01483 44 00 77 BO: 01483 44 00 00 Fax: 01483 564 071
Email: yat@yvonne-arnaud.co.uk
Web Site: www.yvonne-arnaud.co.uk
ADMINISTRATION:
Props: Yvonne Arnaud Theatre Trust;
Lessees: Yvonne Arnaud Theatre Management Ltd;
Director: James Barber
General Manager: Brian Kirk
Commercial Operations: Dave Palmer
Box Office Manager: Tim Slater
Head of Marketing: Dan McWilliam
Press Officer: Laura Butler
Technical Stage Manager: Liza Cheal

Circus

BLACKPOOL TOWER CIRCUS
Blackpool Tower, Promenade, Blackpool, Lancashire FY1 4BJ
Tel: 01253 622 242 (Switchboard) Tel: 01253 627 776 Fax: 01253 297 937
Email: laciendresz@btconnect.com, towerinfo@leisure-parcs.co.uk
Web Site: www.theblackpooltower.com
Contact Managing Director: Laci Endresz
Props: Tip Top Entertainments
Capacity: 1,400

THE CHINESE STATE CIRCUS
(Exchange Events Ltd)
Arts Exchange, Dane Mill, Broadhurst Lane, Congleton, Cheshire CW12 1LA
Tel: 01260 276627
Email: info@arts-exchange.com
Web Site: www.arts-exchange.com
Contact: Peter Massera
Promoters of Gandey's Circus, Cirque Surreal, Circus USA, Circus Starr, The Chinese State Circus and Ice Fantasia. Lady Boys of Bangkok and Fist of the Dragon.

CIRCUS BERZERCUS
41 Danes Road, Exeter, Devon EX4 4LS
Tel: 01392 669 873
Email: admin@circusberzercus.co.uk
Web Site: www.circusberzercus.co.uk
Contact: Judith Sturman (Adminstrator)
Fun-filled family entertainment for theatres, fundraising and events as well as corporate work. Top notch comedy show. Workshops available covering many circus skills including juggling, plate spinning, tightrope, unicycling, diabolo, stilt walking, clowning and presentation, Send for free brochure.

MAHOGANY CARNIVAL DESIGN LTD
28 High Street, Harlesden, London NW10 4LX
Tel: 020 8961 4446
Email: costumes@mahoganycarnival.com
Web Site: www.mahoganycarnival.com
Artistic Director: Clary Salandy
Structural Engineer: Michael Ramdeen
A unique design and production company offering exciting and innovative costumes and shows for a variety of events, including Theatre and Circus.

NOFIT STATE CIRCUS
PO Box 238 Cardiff CF24 0XS Wales
Tel: 029 2022 1330 / 40
Email: info@nofitstate.com
Web Site: www.nofitstate.org
General Manager: Alison Woods
Production Assistant: Zoe Munn
Nofit State has a long track record of creating extraordinary mixed scale multimedia circus productions: from small community performances to large scale professional productions involving a company of 45 on the road; from tented tours to site specific events and theatre shows.

OCKHAM'S RAZOR
Turtle Key Arts, Ladbroke Hall, 79 Barlby Road, London W10 6AZ
Tel: 00 44 7792 486 890
Email: ali@turtlekeyarts.org.uk
Web Site: www.ockhamsrazor.co.uk
Contact: Alison King
An aerial theatre company combining circus, visual, and physical theatre to make work that is arresting and entertaining. Their first piece, Memento Mori won Jeunes Talents Cirque in 2004.

THE ENTERTAINMENT CORPORATION
The Park, Oaksey, Malmesbury, Wiltshire SN16 9SD
Tel: 01666 575 200 Fax: 01666 575 243
Email: admin@theentertainmentcorp.co.uk
Web Site: www.euroentcorp.co.uk
Presenting: The Moscow State Circus, The Chinese State Circus and Continental Circus Berlin.

ZIPPO'S CIRCUS
Circus Headquarters, Enborne, Newbury, Berkshire RG20 0LD
Admin: 07836 641 277 BO: 0774 811811 / 07900 141516 Fax: 07050 244 867
Email: zipposcircus@yahoo.com
Web Site: www.zipposcircus.co.uk
Contact: Martin Burton

ZIPPOS CIRCUS PRODUCTIONS LTD
Circus HQ, Enborne, Nr Newbury, Berkshire RG20 0LD
Tel: 07836 641 277 Fax: 07050 244 867
BO: 0774 811811 / 07900 141516
Email: zipposcircus@yahoo.com
Web Site: www.zipposcircus.co.uk
Director: Martin Burton
Zippos Circus is a traditional style circus, featuring jugglers, acrobats, aerialists, clowns and horses. The show itself, and big top, are available for private and corporate functions.

Puppet Companies

ACTION SPACE MOBILE
Mapplewell & Staincross Village Hall, Darton Lane, Mapplewell, Barnsley, S75 6AL
Tel: 01226 391 112
Email: contact@actionspacemobile.org
Web Site: www.actionspacemobile.org

BLUE SKY THEATRE
2 Pembury Road, Worthing, West Sussex BN14 7DN
Tel: 01299 266634 Fax: 01299 266561
Email: office@blueskytheatre.com
Web Site: www.blueskytheatre.com
Artistic Directors: Mary and Glyn Edwards
Small to mid scale touring specialising in new work for the under 5's. A Puppetlink Company supported by Arts Council of England West Midlands.

CORNELIUS & JONES PRODUCTIONS
49 Carters Close, Sherington, Newport Pagnell, Buckinghamshire MK16 9NW
Tel: 01908 612 593 Fax: 01908 616779
Email: admin@corneliusjones.com
Web Site: www.corneliusjones.com
Co-Directors: Sue Leech & Neil Canham
Cornelius & Jones is a small touring theatre company founded in 1986, performing for both children and adults in schools and theatres.

PIP CRITTEN'S STRING CIRCUS
12 Trelawney Avenue, St Budeaux, Plymouth, Devon PL5 1RH
Tel: 01752 361 210 Mobile: 07771 967804
Email: pip@pipcritten.com, sue@pipandsue.co.uk
Web Site: www.pipcritten.com

EMERGENCY EXIT ARTS
Rothbury Hall, Azof Street, London SE10 0EF
Tel: 020 8853 4809 Fax: 020 8858 2025
Email: info@eea.org.uk
Web Site: www.eea.org.uk
ADMINISTRATION:
Artistic Director: Deb Mullins
Admin and Communications Officer: Jules Hodgson
Address for Postal Correspondence: PO Box 570, Greenwich
London, SE10 0EE
Emergency Exit Arts is an outdoor performing arts company, touring work throughout the UK and Europe.

FAR AND WIDE PUPPETS
Baltic Wharf Business Park, St. Peters Quay, Totnes, Devon TQ9 5EW
Mob: 07950 998911
Email: tony.gee@themoveablefeast.co.uk
Web Site: www.farandwidepuppets.co.uk
Contact: Tony Gee
Storytelling, puppetry and theatre for a wide range of venues. Specialised in workshops. Whole school productions.

FAULTY OPTIC - LIZ WALKER COMPANY
5 Underbank Old Road, Holmfirth, Huddersfield, West Yorkshire HD9 1EA
Tel: 01484 682 442

Mobile: 07856 860 679
Email: faultyoptic@faultyoptic.co.uk
Web Site: www.faultyoptic.co.uk
Administrator: Sue Tongue
Surreal puppetry for an adult rather than a children's audience - Tours UK and Europe.

FREEHAND THEATRE (CT)
1 Reynard Villas, Mayfield Grove, Baildon, Shipley, West Yorkshire BD17 6DY
Tel: 01274 585 277
Email: admin@freehandtheatre.co.uk
Web Site: www.freehandtheatre.co.uk
Co-Directors: Lizzie Allen and Simon Hatfield.
Freehand theatre was formed in 1982. Since then, it has been delighting audiences with its inventive style of puppetry. Productions are aimed primarily at children (3 to 7 year olds) and family audiences. The company regularly performs in schools, arts centres, small theatres, etc. Technically sufficient. Maximum audience: 140.

GREEN GINGER
Tobacco Factory Theatre, Raleigh Road, Bristol BS3 1TF Wales
Tel/Fax: 0117 922 5599
Email: mail@greenginger.net
Web Site: www.greenginger.net
Artistic Directors: Terry Lee and Chris Pirie
Versatile street and stage theatre shows available for all occasions and events indoors or out. "Green Ginger push puppetry to the limits and then, disturbingly, a bit further" Terry Gilliams (Patron).

HARLEQUIN PUPPET THEATRE
Cayley Promenade, Rhos-on-Sea, Colwyn Bay, North Wales LL28 4EP
Tel: 01492 548 166
Email: chris@punchandjudy.com
Web Site: www.puppets.uk.com
Contact: Chris Somerville
Capacity for theatre 118
Performances 3.00pm during school holidays.

HORSE AND BAMBOO THEATRE
Horse and Bamboo Centre, Waterfoot, Rossendale, Lancashire BB4 7HB
Tel: 01706 220 241 Fax: 01706 831 166
Email: info@horseandbamboo.org
Web Site: www.horseandbamboo.org
CEO: Helen Jackson
Producer: Esther Ferry-Kennington
Operations Manager: Christopher Hodgson.
Capacity: 200

IAN AND FRIENDS
35 Hibernia Point, Wolvercote Road, London SE2 9TL
Tel/Fax: 020 8310 4376 Mobile: 07860 183471
Email: info@ianandfriends.co.uk
Web Site: www.gingernutt.com
Contact: Ian Thom

IN THE BOAT THEATRE COMPANY
c/o Action Space Mobile, Mapplewell & Staincross Village Hall, Darton Lane, Barnsley, South Yorkshire S75 6AL
Tel: 01226 391 112
Email: contact@actionspacemobile.org
Web Site: www.actionspacemobile.org
Artistic Director: Mary Turner
Company Manager: Ruth Jones

THE INTERNATIONAL PURVES PUPPETS
Puppet Tree House, Broughton Road, Biggar, Lanarkshire ML12 6HA Scotland
Tel: 01899 220631
Email: admin@purvespuppets.com
Web Site: www.purvespuppets.com
Contact: Jill and Ian Purves
Touring shows also workshops, in-service courses, guided tours in our own theatre. Puppet museum.

JACOLLY PUPPET THEATRE
Kirkella Road, Yelverton, Devon PL20 6BB
Tel/Fax: 01822 852 346
Email: theatre@jacolly-puppets.co.uk
Web Site: www.jacolly-puppets.co.uk
Directors: Jacqueline Ilett and Holly Griffin
Jacolly Puppet Theatre has been touring theatres, schools and festivals around Britain and abroad since it was formed in 1977. Whilst all shows aim to entertain and most play to family audiences, many are also educational, aimed at primary school aged children, on themes that include: insects; energy-saving; caring for the seashore; road safety and bullying.

JOHN PEEL PUPPET THEATRE
Flat 2, 169 New Kings Road, London SW6 4SN
Tel: 01592 744934 Fax: 01592 749404
Mobile: 07782315510
Email: nclaire2@hotmail.com
Contact: Michael Wilding
Traditional Fairy Stories performed by hand-made glove puppets in mobile theatre. No gimics, old fashioned values. Theatre for under sixes our speciality. 8 foot height clearance. Suitable for rooms, halls and studio theatres.

THE LITTLE ANGEL THEATRE
14 Dagmar Passage, Cross Street, London N1 2DN
BO Tel: 020 7226 1787
Email: info@littleangeltheatre.com
Web Site: www.littleangeltheatre.com
Artistic Director/Chief Executive: Peter Glanville
General Manager: Lynette Shanbury
Technical Manager: David Duffy

LITTLE ANGEL THEATRE "HOME OF BRITISH PUPPETRY"
14 Dagmar Passage, London N1 2DN
Admin: 020 7359 8581 BO: 020 7226 1787
Email: info@littleangeltheatre.com
Web Site: www.littleangeltheatre.com
ADMINISTRATION:
Technical Manager: David Duffy
Front of House Supervisor: Alex Carter
Policy: Resident & Touring Puppet Theatre.
Perfs: Wednesday to Sunday. Varied.
Disabled Access.
Seats: 100

MAJOR MUSTARD'S TRAVELLING SHOW
1 Carless Avenue, Harborne, Birmingham B17 9EG
Tel: 0121 426 4329 Fax: 0121 427 2358
Email: mm@majormustard.com
Web Site: www.majormustard.com
Director: Mike Frost
Major Mustard presents the very best in puppetry entertainment. Puppetry for all the family.

MOVINGSTAGE MARIONETTE COMPANY
Producers of Marionette drama
35 Blomfield Road, London W9 2PF
Tel: 020 7249 6876 Mob: 07 836 202 745
Email: puppet@movingstage.co.uk
Web Site: www.puppetbarge.com, www.movingstage.co.uk
Directors: Juliet Rogers and Gren Middleton
Operators of the Puppet Theatre Barge. A fully equipped puppet theatre with seating for 60 persons. Able to tour most venues. Maximum audience 200. Carry fully equipped puppet booth with lighting and sound.
Office Address: 78 Middleton Road, London, E8 4BP, UK

NO STRINGS PUPPET THEATRE
Archway House, Mansfield Road, Edwinstowe, Nottinghamshire NG21 9HF
Tel: 01623 824 210
Email: sue_kpuk@hotmail.com
Directors: Alan Kirkpatrick; Sue Murray
Indoor and outdoor performances for all ages, workshops for schools and community projects. Street specialist - queues, crowds, parks, town centres - will venture anywhere. Can tailor to 'era' - medieval, Victorian etc.

NORWICH PUPPET THEATRE
St James, Whitefriars, Norwich, Norfolk NR3 1TN
Mgt: 01603 615 564 BO: 01603 629 921
Fax: 01603 617 578
Email: info@puppettheatre.co.uk

Web Site: www.puppettheatre.co.uk
ADMINISTRATION:
General Manager: Ian Woods
Marketing Coordinator: Kerry Leathley
Workshop Coordinator: Denise Hargrave
Director: Joy Haynes
Education and Outreach: Rosie Walker
Status: Puppet Theatre
Policy: Norwich Puppet Theatre is a touring company with almost unique benefit of own home theatre base with raked auditorium, studio performance space and workshops. Produces work for all ages from 3 years upwards which tours throughout the UK and Europe. Where possible live music is included in productions. Willing to premiere show.
Facilities: Seating in main house 185 raked. 4 wheelchair spaces, level access - all house facilities fully accessible. Induction loop system.
Studio theatre 50 informal, level access. The Octagon exhibition gallery. Licensed bar. Food brought in for specific functions.

PLAYBOARD PUPPET THEATRE
The Black Barn The Street, Tibenham, Norwich NR16 1QA
Tel/Fax: 020 7226 5911
Email: buttonmoon@btconnect.com
Web Site: www.buttonmoon.tv
Director: Ian Allen
Administrator: Vicky Clinch
Puppets In Vision. Playboard Puppets presents its creations of imagination workshops in all forms of puppetry at the Norfolk Barn. Courses run from Spring to Autumn. Playboard Puppets is famous for the cult TV series "Button Moon", and many more.

PRESTO PUPPET THEATRE
Church Cottage, Madeley,
Crewe CW3 9PL
Tel: 01782 752 495
Email: nigel@prestopuppets.co.uk
Web Site: www.prestopuppets.co.uk
Directors: Nigel Lawton and Robin Lawrence

PUPPETCRAFT
1 Venton Oak Cottages, Dartington,
Totnes, Devon TQ9 6DW
Tel/Fax: 01803 867 778
Email: enquiry@PuppetCraft.co.uk
Web Site: www.puppetcraft.co.uk
Artistic Director: John Roberts
One of Britain's most successful touring puppet troupes.

THE PUPPETEERS' COMPANY
PO Box 350, Brighton,
East Sussex BN2 1TZ
Tel: 01273 687 183 Fax: 01273 601 004
Email: admin@.thepuppeteers.co.uk
Web Site: www.thepuppeteers.co.uk

SHADOWSTRING THEATRE
'Tropiquaria', Washford Cross, Watchet,
West Somerset TA23 0QB
Tel: 01984 640 688 Home No: 01984 634 253
Email: shadowstring@freenet.co.uk
Web Site: www.tropiquaria.co.uk
Director: Paul Doran
Shadowstring is Theatre based. February to October, and tours schools, theatres and community venues in November and December only. Capacity: 100

SMALL WORLD THEATRE
Canolfan Byd Bychan, Bath House Road,
Cardigan, Dyfed SA43 1JY Wales
Tel/ Fax: 01239 615 952
Email: info@smallworld.org.uk
Web Site: www.smallworld.org.uk,
www.whatevertheweatherwales.co.uk
ADMINISTRATION:
Administrator: Tracy Knight
Director: Ann Shrosbree
Artistic Director: Bill Hamblett
Small World Theatre is a small to medium scale touring company. They also work with development education culture for development overseas and participatory theatre. SWT is a company limited by guarantee with charitable aims.
Policy: To use the universal language of theatre to communicate important ideas and feelings to young people and adults in a non-exploitative way. To experiment with techniques which increase the effectiveness and excitement of live performance. To promote international cultural links through theatre. To exchange and learn from other cultures. To write, produce and perform shows that reflect local and global concerns that are common to all people. To teach and exchange skills with interested groups including extensionists, teachers, artists and other performers. To help groups and communities through participatory methods make sense of information, transforming it into commonly held knowledge.
Non-Performance Activities: Workshops in puppetry, drama, masks, mime, educational programme.

CHRIS SOMERVILLE PUPPETS
Harlequin Puppet Theatre Cayley
Promenade, Rhos on Sea, Colwyn Bay,
Clwyd LL28 4EP
Tel: 01492 548166
Email: chris@punchandjudy.com
Web Site: www.puppetmagic.co.uk
Director: Chris Somerville

STAR PUPPETS
83 Cromwell Road, Rushden,
Northamptonshire NN10 0EG
Tel: 01933 316 188
Email: starpuppets@yahoo.co.uk
Director: Christopher Covington

STOATERIETY
255A Bacup Road, Rawtenstall
Lancashire BB4 7PA
Tel/ Fax: 01706 603 448
Mob: 07866 826460
Email: john@stoaterietypuppets.co.uk
Web Site: www.stoaterietypuppets.co.uk
Contact: John Jaques
Providing Puppet Shows for entertainment and Education purposes for over twenty years

TE POOKA
The Big Red Door, 10 Lady Lawson
Street, Edinburgh EH3 9DS
Tel: 0131 228 4567
Tel/ Fax: 0131 221 0734
Email: info@tepooka.org
Web Site: www.tepooka.org
Te Pooka provides high quality street theatre, performing arts and community participatory events to communities across Scotland, the UK and abroad. A network of artists with diverse backgrounds including fine arts, drama and music, te pooka is available for street shows, walkabout performance, stage shows and processions. Te Pooka productions feature dramatic fire performance routines, vibrant costumes, drumming, outrageous stilt-walking, giant puppets, lanterns and fire installations.

TICKLISH ALLSORTS
57 Victoria Road, Wilton,
Salisbury SP2 0DZ
Tel/Fax: 01722 744 949
Mob: 07721 992994
Email: garynunn@ntlworld.com
Web Site: www.ticklishallsorts.co.uk
Senior Personnel: Gary A Nunn
Childrens Entertainments, shows, puppets, musical comedy, workshops.
Performances and workshops. RSPB National Touring Roadshows.

TREASURE TROVE PUPPET COMPANY
54 High Street, Caergwrle,
Flintshire LL12 9LL Wales
Tel: 01978 761 053 Mob: 07802 800 817
Email: treasure.trove@virgin.net
Web: www.treasuretrovepuppets.co.uk
Directors: Stephen Sharples.
Operation includes: Puppets for all occasions, small/middle scale touring, workshops and demonstrations.
Makers of puppets. Extensive touring nationally and internationally.

WHISPER AND SHOUT COMPANY
2 Bridge Street, Cainscross, Stroud,
Gloucestershire GL5 3EP
Tel: 01453 750009
Email: whisperandshout@tiscali.co.uk
Web Site: www.whisperandshout.co.uk
Directors: Diane Humphrey and Fred Ward

MEDIA & PUBLIC RELATIONS

Media: Publicity

Fan Club Administration

T PETERS ASSOCIATES (TPA)
84 Chalkwell Avenue, Westcliff-on-Sea, Essex SS0 8NN
Tel: 01702 474 411
Email: info@t-peters.co.uk
Web Site: www.t-peters.co.uk
Proprietor: Tai'ang Peters
Proprietor email: tai'ang@t-peters-associates.freeserve.co.uk
"Fan Clubs of the Stars". We specialise in running fan clubs for stars. A complete service including membership and all merchandise business worldwide.

Press Cutting Agencies

GORKANA GROUP
140 Old Street, London EC1V 9BJ
Tel: 020 7674 0200
Email: enquiries@gorkana.com
Web Site: www.gorkana.com

INTERNATIONAL PRESS CUTTING BUREAU
224/236 Walworth Road, London SE17 1JE
Tel: 020 7708 2113 Fax: 020 7701 4489
Email: ipcb2000@aol.com

MCCALLUM MEDIA MONITER
Tower House, 10 Possil Road, Glasgow, Strathclyde G4 9SY Scotland
Tel: 0141 333 1822 Fax: 0141 333 1811
Email: contact@press-cuttings.com
Web Site: www.press-cuttings.com
For all your Scottish & UK press monitoring needs.

ROMEIKE & CURTICE LTD
Hale House, 290/296 Green Lane, London N13 5TP
Tel: 020 8882 0155 / 0800 289543 Fax: 020 8882 6716
Email: info@romeike.com
Web Site: www.romeike.com

Press and Publicity Agents

ABLAZE PR
94 Omega Works, 4 Roach Road, London E3 2PF
Tel: 0208 533 9899 Mobile: 07990 680 303Mobile: 07990 680 303
Email: jo@ablazepr.com
Web Site: www.ablazepr.com
Agents: Jo Rogue; Nadia Khan
Ablaze PR are a fresh, young public relations consultancy offering national, regional and online press campaigns, club promotions, image and music consultancy. The aim of the company is to work closely with artists and clients to develop them to their full potential, exploring all areas of growth. As a youthful, dynamic company we offer all the benefits of a more organic service which stretches to cater to your requirements.

ABSTRAKT PR
21d Gloucester Street, Pimlico, London SW1V 2DB
Tel/Fax: 020 7834 0440
Mobile: 07976 247 026
Email: abstrakt@abstraktpublicity.co.uk
Web Site: www.abstraktpublicity.co.uk
Contact: Anna Goodman
Abstrakt was formed in 1999 and since then has provided dance, theatre, live art and performance sectors with a meticulous and imaginative promotional service, maximizing artist profiles via press, radio and online publicity, regular progress reports and full press kits. Their client roster includes diverse companies and projects such as SACRED, Chelsea Theatre's annual live art programme, State of Emergency - A pioneering dance organisation, Italian physical theatre company Teatro Kismet, and Jonzi D's annual collaboration with Sadlers Wells - Breakin' Convention - The international festival of Hip Hop dance.
ARTISTES REPRESENTED:
Dance:
Breakin Convention
Robert Hylton Urban Classicism
Theatre:
Vayu Naidu Theatre Company
Radio:
Bespoken Word (Radio 4)
Benji Reid

ALAN JAMES PR AGENCY
Email: promo@ajpr.co.uk
Web Site: www.ajpr.co.uk
Contact: Richard Jones
National Radio and TV Music promotional agency.
ARTISTES REPRESENTED:
Ash
Badly Drawn Boy
Cord
Elbow
The Flaming Lips
Funeral For A Friend
Klaxons
Mystery Jets
The Futureheads
The Pipettes
The Subways

ASSASSINATION MUSIC PROMOTIONS
Tudor House, Pinstone Way, Gerrards Cross, Buckinghamshire SL9 7BJ
Tel: 01753 893 665 Fax: 01753 889 888
Mobile: 07932 105140 (Rupert)
Email: amp@assassination.co.uk
Web Site: www.assassination.co.uk
Contacts: Rupert Withers, Richard Daniels
Press Agency, plugging agency, marketing and promotions consultants, internet site management, artiste and label management.
A2 Records: Details as above except website - www.a2records.com
ARTISTES REPRESENTED:
Oliver Dawson Saxon

AVALON PUBLIC RELATIONS
4a Exmoor Street, London W10 6BD
Tel: 020 7598 7222 Fax: 020 7598 7223
Email: publicrelations@avalonuk.com
Web Site: www.avalonuk.com
Contact: Ed Thomson, Daniel Bee

BAD MOON PUBLICITY
19b All Saints Road, London W11 1HE
Tel: 020 7221 0499 Fax: 020 7792 0257
Email: jenny@badmoon.co.uk
Contact: Jenny Myles
ARTISTES REPRESENTED:
Arctic Monkeys
Kaiser Chiefs
The Cribs
Hell is for Heroes
Jetplane Landing
My Morning Jacket
Sinead O'Connor
Seal Club Clubbing Club
Viking Skull

BEST PR
29-31 Cowper Street, London EC2A 4AT
Tel: 020 7608 7403
Email: fiona@bestest.co.uk
Agent: Fiona Crosbie
ARTISTES REPRESENTED:
Belle & Sebastian
Jarvis Cocker

Morrissey
Sigur Ros
Super Furry Animals
The Futureheads
Tilly and the Wall

BIG CAT GROUP LTD
Vincent House, 92-93 Edward Street,
Birmingham B1 2RA
Tel: 0121 248 4697 Fax: 0121 248 4699
Email: info@bcguk.com
Web Site: www.bigcatgroup.com
Director: Mr Morgan

BORKOWSKI PR
71 Kingsway, London WC2B 6ST
Tel: 020 7404 3000
Email: markb@borkowski.co.uk
Web Site: www.borkowski.co.uk
Contact: Mark Borkowski, Ali Redford, Vicki Watson

BOS PERFORMANCE MARKETING
Vine Cottage, Isington Lane, Isington,
Alton, Hampshire GU34 4PW
Tel: 07967 724453
Email: chris@bospm.com
Web Site: www.wsom.co.uk
The Company offers; Marketing & Promotion for Venues, Festivals, Tours and Events; Poster & Leaflet Distribution; Direct Mail; Telemarketing; Media Competitions; Press Launches.
Contacts: Chris or Julie Maddocks

BRIAN MACLAURIN AGENCY
Brian Maclaurin Associates Ltd 2 Queen Caroline Street, London W6 9DX
Tel: 0208 323 8154 Mob: 077 630 72841
Email: mix@brianmaclaurin.com
Web Site: www.maclaurin.com
Agent: Brian Maclaurin
Pa to Brian Maclaurin: Mikele Miren Ugarte
Media and public relations agency.

ARTISTES REPRESENTED:
Colin Montgomerie
Shelley Rudman
Chris Tarrant
Ian Woosnam

BUSINESS OF CULTURE LTD
6 Paddington Street, London W1U 5QG
Tel: 020 7224 5680
Email: info@businessofculture.com
Web Site: www.businessofculture.com
Founder Directors: William Tayleur, Graeme Jennings
Business of Culture Ltd is a dedicated arts and cultural consultancy offering a range of services to venues, local authorities, arts councils and other organisations. Services include strategic analysis and planning, market research, internal and external auditing, development strategies, consultation on staffing and practical freelance marketing.

JAMES BYRNE ASSOCIATES
3 Mansell Close, Widnes,
Cheshire WA8 9WL
Tel: 0151 420 6200
Email: jamesbyrne@easy.com
Press and Media Relations, Celebrity PR, Corporate PR, Media Promotions and Protection 24-hour Service. Many famous clients national and international.

CAUSE AND EFFECT MARKETING, PUBLICITY AND DISTRIBUTION
Shawfield Farm Scrapers Hill, Muddles Green, Near Lewes,
East Sussex BN8 6HJ
Tel/Fax: 01825 873188
Mobile: 07785 776759
Email: publicity@causeeffect.prestel.co.uk
Flexible distribution company specialising in high profile poster and leaflet/brochure campaigns dealing with a large number of prominent theatre and marketing offices. Operates nationwide.

CHAPMAN GUY ASSOCIATES
33 Southampton Street, Covent Garden,
London WC2E 7HE
Tel: 020 7379 7474 Fax: 020 7379 8484
Email: guy@g-c-a.co.uk
Director: Guy Chapman
GCA's Press team build imaginative PR campaigns around the individual needs of each client. We are also experienced working alongside corporate PR companies on large-scale projects. We manage clients drawn from across the arts and entertainment business.

MAX CLIFFORD ASSOCIATES LTD
49-50 New Bond Street,
London W1Y 9HA
Tel: 020 7408 2350 Fax: 020 7409 2294
Email: max@mcapr.co.uk
Contact: Ann-Marie Thomson

CONGRATULATIONS CO LTD
South Lodge Court, Ironsbottom, Sidlow,
Reigate, Surrey RH2 8QG
Tel: 01293 863500
Email: congratulations@aol.com
Promotional Director: Philip A Peck

COOKING VINYL
10 Allied Way, Warple Way,
London W3 0RQ
Tel: 020 8600 9200
Email: joolz@cookingvinyl.com
Web Site: www.cookingvinyl.com
Head of Press and Promotions: Joolz Bosson

ARTISTES REPRESENTED:
Billy Bragg
Buzzcocks
Bruce Cockburn
Cowboy Junkies
Hanson
Janis Ian
Ziggy Marley
North Mississippi All Stars
Gary Numan
Seafood
South
The Bluetones
Richard Thompson

CORPORATE PUBLIC RELATIONS LTD
PO Box 12, Haslemere,
Surrey GU27 3AH
Tel: 01428 654 011 Fax: 01428 651 401
Email: corporatepr@aol.com

DAVE WOOLF PR
2nd Floor, 53 Goodge Street, London W1T 1TG
Tel: 020 7436 5529 Fax: 020 7637 8776
Email: dave@dwl.uk.net
Web Site: www.dwl.uk.net
Agent: Dave Woolf

ARTISTES REPRESENTED:
Musicians:
Martina Topley Bird
Jamiroquai
Jay Kay
Beverley Knight
Seth Lakeman
Courtney Pine
Jay Sean
Louise Setara
Joss Stone
KT Tunstall

THE CLIVE DAVIS PARTNERSHIP
Unit 9 Clyde Works, Clyde Road,
Wallington, Surrey SM6 8PZ
Tel: 020 8669 8268 Fax: 020 8773 4945
Email: clive.davis@virgin.net

DDA
192-198 Vauxhall Bridge Road,
London SW1V 1DX
Tel: 020 7932 9800 Fax: 020 7932 4950
Email: info@ddapr.com
Web Site: www.ddapr.com
Public relations: now the pre-eminent consultancy in the sector
Event management: which was formed in 2001, manages the presence of many major film companies and producers at film festivals and markets around the world, including Cannes, Venice, Toronto and Berlin.The division also organises conferences, seminars and events for a wider,
non-film client base.
Productions: was formed in 1997, to produce the European Film Awards under auspices of the European Film Academy at every stage from the event itself to broadcast. The company is involved at every stage from the event itself through to the TV broadcast. We are also involved

in other internationally recognised festivals.
Consulting: The establishment of this new division is intended to formalize our wide experience of corporate and crisis public relations in the film industry.

DOG DAY PRESS
59-61 Farringdon Road,
London EC1M 3JB
Tel: 020 7691 8687
Mobile: 07730 682 312
Email: lauren@dogdaypress.com
Web Site: www.dogdaypress.com
Contact: Lauren Zoric

ARTISTES REPRESENTED:
Antony & The Johnsons
Bat For Lashes
Calexico
Clap Your Hands Say Yeah
Jamie Lidell
Lambchop
Joanna Newsom
Richard Swift

DOROTHY HOWE PUBLICITY & PRESS
Tel: 020 8995 3920 Fax: 020 8994 9963
Email: press@dorothyhowe.co.uk
Contact: Dorothy Howe

ARTISTES REPRESENTED:
The Stranglers
The Fall
Laura Zakian

DVORA LEWIS PR
12 Pilgrims Lane, London NW3 1SN
Tel: 020 7435 9257
Fax: 020 7435 1417
Email: dl@dvoralewis.com
Agent: Dvora Lewis

ARTISTES REPRESENTED:
London Symphony Orchestra

KAREN EARL SPONSORSHIP
Gunpowder House, 66 Great Suffolk Street, London SE1 0BL
Tel: 020 7202 2800 Fax: 020 7702 2802
Email: info@karen-earl.co.uk
Web Site: www.karen-earl.co.uk
Office Manager: Rowena Kenyon
KES sponsorship consultancy offers the keys to answering the following questions:- What should you sponsor? How should you sponsor? And how do you make it work?
KES event management gives clients original, innovative, and overall clever event solutions.

EMMETT & SMITH
1 Nine Elms Lane, London SW8 5NQ
Tel: 020 7819 4800 Fax: 020 7627 0134
Email: info@emmettandsmith.com
Web Site: www.emmettandsmith.com

ENGLISH NATIONAL OPERA
London Coliseum, St Martin's Lane,
London WC2N 4ES
Admin: 020 7836 0111 Mgt: 020 7845 9215 BO: 0871 911 0200 Tech: 020 7845 9459 Fax: 020 7845 9296
Email: personnel@eno.org
Web Site: www.eno.org
Directors of the English National Opera:
Chief Executive: Loretta Tomasi
Artistic Director: John Berry
Technical Director: Geoff Summerton

EVENTS CONNECT
15 Faversham House, 15 Jewbury, York YO31 7PL
Mobile Tel: 07904 376629.
Email: viviennelee01@aol.com
Web Site: www.eventsconnect.co.uk
Contact: Vivienne Lee
A Model Management company: representing fashion and photographic models in the York area.
Event Management: Events big and small, fashion show production a speciality, organisers of Miss York, an area final for Miss England
Public Relations: personal press and media promotion offered to models, actors, sports people.

ARTISTES REPRESENTED:
Actors/Voice Overs:
Mike Burns
Models/Personal Appearances:
Miss York

FERRARA PR
Tel: 0207 7290147
Mob Tel: 07946 523 007
Email: rosalia@ferrarapr.com
Web Site: www.ferrarapr.com
Contact: Rosalia Ferrara

ARTISTES REPRESENTED:
Avenue D
Bez
Clint Boon
Domino Bones
Siobhan Fahey
Grant 'Daddy G' Marshall
Terry Hall (The Specials)
Mani
Finley Quaye
Kevin Rowland (Dexy's Midnight Runners)
Shaun Ryder

FIFTH ELEMENT
258 Belsize Road, London NW6 4BT
Tel: 020 7372 2128 Fax: 020 7624 3629
Email: cat@fifthelement.biz
Web Site: www.fifthelement.biz
Agent: Cat Hockley

ARTISTES REPRESENTED:
Musicians:
Hey Negrita
Abigail Hopkins
Jo O'Meara
Jamie Pearce
Silver Sun
Status Quo

FRANK PR
20-23 Mandela Street, London NW1 0DU
Tel: 020 7693 6999 Fax: 020 7693 6998
Email: amstad@frankpr.it
Web Site: www.frankpr.it
Contact: David Fraser

ARTISTES REPRESENTED:
Tim Campbell
Lord Alan Sugar
Ronnie O'Sullivan

FULL PORTION MEDIA
Unit 7, The Coda Centre, 189 Munster Road, London SW6 6AW
Tel: 0845 225 1500 Fax: 0845 225 1501
Email: info@fullportion.com
Web Site: www.fullportion.com
Agent: Aroon Maharajh

ARTISTES REPRESENTED:
TV Presenters:
Alison Bell
Andy Collins
Candice Fagan
Ryan O'Meara
Polly Parsons
James Whale
Sarah Whitefoot
Performers:
Kym Mazelle
Reality Stars:
Faria Alam
Pete Burns
James Hewitt
Maggot
Makosi Musambasi
Shilpa Shetty
Chefs:
Roberto Conte
Jean Christophe Novelli
Authors:
Richard Dunwoody MBE
Miscellaneous:
Darryn Lyons

GERRY LUNDBERG PUBLIC RELATIONS
24 South Frederick Street, Dublin 2
Tel: 00 353 1 679 8476 Fax: 00 353 1 675 1875
Email: glundpr@aol.com
Agent: Gerry Lundberg

ARTISTES REPRESENTED:
Riverdance - The Show

IAN GRANT CUMMING PUBLIC RELATIONS
8 St.Bernards Crescent, Edinburgh, Mid Lothian EH4 1NP Scotland
Tel: 0131 315 2424 Fax: 0131 332 9957
Email: hn@iangrantcumming.com
Contact: Helen Narracott

GREY SWAN
12b Carholme Road, London SE23 2HS
Tel: 07931 791 807
Email: tim@greyswan.org.uk
Web Site: www.greyswan.org.uk
Artistic Directors: Timothy Stubbs Hughes

Grey Swan is a visionary arts consultancy company that aims to support new and experimental work by providing personal attention to the next generation of theatre makers.

GUY CHAPMAN ASSOCIATES LTD
See Target Live

HACKFORD JONES PR
32 Berwick Street, London W1F 8RL
Tel: 020 7287 9788 Fax: 020 7287 9731
Email: kris@hackfordjonespr.com
Assistant Publicist: Kris Angus

ARTISTES REPRESENTED:
Donna Air
Ant & Dec
Edith Bowman
Fearne Cotton
Hilary Duff
Jenni Falconer
Sadie Frost
Duncan James
Vernon Kay
Myleene Klass
Jesse McCartney
Molly McQueen
Jayne Middlemiss
Lisa Snowdon
Melanie Sykes
Margherita Taylor
Simon Webbe (Blue)

HALL OR NOTHING
11 Poplar Mews, Uxbridge Road, London W12 7JS
Tel: 020 8740 6288 Fax: 020 8749 5982
Email: gillian@hallornothing.com
Web Site: www.hallornothing.com
Agent: Gillian Porter

ARTISTES REPRESENTED:
Performers:
The Beautiful South
Black Rebel Motor Cycle Club
Emma Bunton
Editors
Feeder
Kasabian
Manic Street Preachers
Muse
Oasis
Towers Of London

HARRISON COWLEY
154 Great Charles Street, Birmingham B3 3HU
Tel: 0121 236 7532 Fax: 0121 236 7220
Email: ritchies@harrisoncowley.com
Web Site: www.harrisoncowley.com
Contact: Ritchie Sibthorpe

HERMANA PR
Unit 244, Bonmarche Centre, 241-251 Ferndale Road, London SW9 8BJ
Tel: 020 77338009 Mobile: 020 77338009 Fax: 020 7733 0037
Email: alison@hermana.co.uk
Contact: Alison Millar

ARTISTES REPRESENTED:
Bobby Conn and the Glass Gypsies
Chicago Underground
Giant Sand
Trans Am

HOWARD OLSON PROMOTIONS
16 Penn Avenue, Chesham, Buckinghamshire HP5 2HS
Tel: 01494 785 873 Fax: 01494 784 760
Email: helson1029@aol.com
Senior Personnel: Howard Elson, Antony Bishop.

ARTISTES REPRESENTED:
Don Fardon
Roger Whittaker

YVONNE I'ANSON PUBLICITY
33 Arne House, Tyers Street, London SE11 5EY
Tel: 020 7582 3172 Fax: 020 7793 1941
Email: dame@yvielove.glowinternet.com

IVANHOE PROMOTIONS
Flat 10,Portadene 6 Portarlington Road West Cliff Bournemouth Dorset BH4 8BT
Tel: 01202 768954 Mob: 07773 171741
Email: anthony.hardman587@ntlworld.com
Web Site: www.ivanhoeleisure.com
Consultation,Publicity,Marketing,Agent
Contact: Anthony James Hardman

JEAN LEVY PR AGENCY
47 Lancaster Gate, Hyde Park, London W2 3NA
Tel: 020 7262 1993 Fax: 020 7262 1993
Email: jeanlevy@onetel.com
Agent: Jean Levy

ARTISTES REPRESENTED:
Brian Poole & the Tremoles
Phil Cool
Buddy Greco
Neil Innes
Gerry Marsden
Al Martino
The Searchers
Ken Wharfe

JOANNA BURNS PR
LDA House, 44B The Broadway, London NW7 3LH
Tel: 020 8906 3444 Fax: 020 8906 9242
Email: joanna@joannaburnspr.com
Web Site: www.joannaburnspr.com
Agent: Joanna Burns

ARTISTES REPRESENTED:
Cosmic Rough Riders
Celine Dion
Gloria Estefan
Jeff Finlan
Delta Goodrem
Lemar
Jennifer Lopez
Sigur Ros

KAS MERCER/MERCENARY PR
Studio 210, Saga Centre, 326 Kensal Road, London W10 5BZ
Tel: 0208 354 4111 Fax: 0208 354 4112
Mobile: 07904 157720
Email: kas.mercer@mercenarypublicity.co m
Web Site: www.mercenarypublicity.com
Agent: Kas Mercer

ARTISTES REPRESENTED:
Jamie Cullum
Dashboard Confessional
Fightstar
Goo Goo Dolls
Juliette and the Licks
Metallica
Motley Crue
Nightmare Of You
Rooster
Stereophonics

KIRWIN MEDIA
10 Tower Court, London WC2H 9NU
Tel: 020 7240 9224 Fax: 020 7240 0979
Email: Lynne@kirwinmedia.co.uk

LAKE-SMITH GRIFFIN ASSOCIATES
418 Strand, London WC2R 0PT
Tel: 020 7836 1020 Fax: 020 7836 1040
Email: lakesmithgriffin@aol.com

LEEP MARKETING & PR
5 Nassau House, 122 Shaftesbury Avenue, London W1D 5ER
Tel: 020 7439 9777 Fax: 020 7439 8833
Email: info@leep.biz
Web Site: www.leep.biz
Marketing, press and publicity for the Arts, with an emphasis on fresh ideas and innovative thinking, coupled with detailed and thorough execution of every campaign we work on.

MACBETH MEDIA RELATIONS
Suite 3, Mountfort House 15-16 Barnsbury Square, London N1 1JL
Tel: 020 7700 5959 Fax: 020 7700 1329
Email: ginny@macbethmediarelations.co.uk
Web: www.macbethmediarelations.co.uk
Executive Director: Ginny Macbeth
Macbeth Media Relations is a public relations agency which specialises in classical music. Since its formation in 1990, the company has built its reputation and client base by helping international artists, orchestras and festivals to develop a clear and distinctive profile in a highly competitive field of activity.

MARTIN SHIPPEN ARTS MARKETING AND MEDIA
91 Dyne Road, London NW6 7DR
Tel / Fax: 020 7372 3788
Mob: 07956 879165
Email: m.shippen@virgin.net

MEDIA JUNCTION ADVERTISING SERVICES LTD
40a Old Compton Street, Soho,
London W1D 4TU
Tel: 020 7434 9919 Fax: 020 7434 9929
ISDN: 020 7851 0353
Email: mailbox@mediajunction.co.uk
Web Site: www.mediajunction.co.uk
Media Junction is a full-service advertising agency specialising in media planning, buying and design for the UK arts and entertainment industry.

MOLLISON CONSULTING
14 Iliffe Yard, London SE17 3QA
Tel: 020 7708 4630 Fax: 020 7740 6424
Email: sbryce@lineone.net
Web Site: www.mollison.com.au
Managing Director: Simon Bryce
Specialist arts and entertainment marketing consultancy.

MP PROMOTIONS
Hollywood House, Portway, Nr
Birmingham B48 7HG
Tel: 01564 829 214 Fax: 01564 826 513
Email: mppromotions@btinternet.com
Contact Agent: Mike Perry
ARTISTES REPRESENTED:
David Essex
Daniel O'Donnell

NATIONAL THEATRE
South Bank, London SE1 9PX
Tel: 020 7452 3232 Fax: 020 7452 3230
Email: press@nationaltheatre.org.uk
Web Site: www.nationaltheatre.org.uk
Head of Press: Lucinda Morrison
Lyttelton Theatre - Cap: 900
Olivier Theatre - Cap: 1200
Cottesloe Theatre - Cap: 350

NONSTOP PROMOTIONS
Studio 39, Aaron House Business Centre,
6 Bardolph Road, Richmond,
Surrey TW9 2LS
Tel: 020 8334 9994 Fax: 020 8334 9995
Email: admin@nonstop1.co.uk
Agent: Niki Sanderson

JAMES PARKER ASSOCIATES
(Jim Parker - Publicity and Marketing)
67 Richmond Park Road,
London SW14 8JY
Tel/Fax: 020 8876 1918
Email: jimparkerjpa@hotmail.com

PIVOTAL PR
4 Heathgate Place, 75-83 Agincourt Road, London NW3 2NU
Tel: 020 7424 8688 Fax: 020 7424 8699
Email: info@pivotalpr.co.uk
Web Site: www.pivotalpr.co.uk
Agent: Bjorn Hall
ARTISTES REPRESENTED:
Blackalicious
Paul Oakenfold
The Chemical Brothers
KT Tunstall

POSITIVE PUBLIC RELATIONS, MARKETING & MEDIA
Upper Floor, 6 James Terrace,
Fencehouses, Houghton le Spring, Tyne and Wear DH4 6LQ
Tel/Fax: 0191 385 9470
Proprietor: Dave Brown
Specialist arts & entertainment company providing full media, marketing and PR service.

PREMIER PR
91 Berwick Street, London W1F 0NE
Tel: 020 7292 7361 / 62
Email: amelia.hallett@premierpr.com
Web Site: www.premierpr.com
Agent: Amelia Hallett, Pippa Beng, Sara Keene
ARTISTES REPRESENTED:
Kenneth Branagh
Kelly Brook
Pierce Brosnan
Daniel Craig
Alice Evans
Adam Garcia
Eva Green
Kate Winslet
Jude Law
David Morrissey
Sophie Okonedo
Michelle Ryan

PUBLIC EYE COMMUNICATIONS LTD
Suite 318, Plaza, 535 Kings Road,
Chelsea, London SW10 0SZ
Tel: 020 7351 1555 Fax: 020 7351 1010
Email: lisa@publiceye.co.uk
Managing Director:

Contact: Clara Parkes, Lisa Minoprio

PUBLICITY CONNECTION
3 Haversham Lodge, Melrose Avenue,
London NW2 4JS
Tel: 020 8450 8882 Fax: 020 8208 4219
Email: sharon@thepublicityconnection.com
Web: www.thepublicityconnection.com
Contact: Sharon Chevin

PURPLE PR
28 Savile Row, London W1S 2EU
Tel: 020 7439 9888 Fax: 020 7439 9887
Email: info@purplepr.com / firstname@purplepr.com
Web Site: www.purplepr.com
Agents: Harriet Matthews, Kelly Rush, Mark Kean, Emily Peters
ARTISTES REPRESENTED:
Adele
Kirsty Almeida
Beyonce
Bjork
Nadine Coyle
Beth Ditto
Example
Florrie
Fugative
Giant Steps
Glee
Goldfrapp
Gypsy & the Cat
Erik Hassle
Heights
Hurts
Imogen Heap
Jessie J
Kelly Rowland
Mika
Lisa Mitchell
Pearl & The Puppet
Talay Riley
Ruby Goe
Sia
Solange
Sam Sparro
Sharleen Spiteri
Sugababes
The Heartbreakers
The Ting Tings

PUSH PR
41 Exmouth Market, London EC1R 4QL
Tel: 0207 278 2121
Email: ian@pushpr.co.uk
Web Site: www.pushpr.co.uk
Specialist Entertainment Public Relations Company.

REPUBLIC MEDIA
Studio 202, Westbourne Studios, 242
Acklam Road, London W10 5JJ
Tel: 020 8960 7449 Fax: 020 8960 7524
Email: tom@republicmedia.net
Web Site: www.republicmedia.net
PR Agent: Tom Green
ARTISTES REPRESENTED:
Tasmin Archer
Crazy Frog
Katie Melua
Nizlopi
Shelly Poole
The Puppini Sisters
Tony Christie

RILEY ADVERTISING LTD
6 Briset Street London EC1M 5NR
Tel: 020 7022 4000 Fax: 020 7022 4005
Email: ken.kane@eurorscg-riley.co.uk
Web Site: www.eurorscg-riley.co.uk
Managing Director: Ken Kane

RKM PUBLIC RELATIONS LTD
London - Los Angeles
19b Grosvenor Gardens,
London SW1W 0BB
Tel: 020 7856 2233 Fax: 020 7821 1369
Email: info@rkmpr.com
Web Site: www.rkmpr.com
Contact: Robert Montague
Specialists in entertainment public relations and media management.

ROYAL OPERA HOUSE
Covent Garden
London WC2E 9DD
Tel: 020 7240 1200 Tel: 020 7212 9458Tel: 020 7212 9458 Fax: 020 7212 9502
Email: christopher.millard@roh.org.uk
Web Site: www.royaloperahouse.org.uk
Opera: Ann Richards 020 7212 9132
Ballet: Janine Limberg 020 7212 9165
Director of Press & Communications: Christopher Millard 020 7212 9458

SAINTED PR
Suite 35, Pall Mall Deposit, 124-128 Barlby Road, London W10 6BL
Tel: 0208 962 5700 Fax: 020 8962 5701
Email: elin@saintedpr.com
Web Site: www.saintedpr.com
Agent: Elin Carlsson

ARTISTES REPRESENTED:

Air
Angus & Julia Stone
Camden Crawl
Coldcut
Daft Punk
Embrace
The Kills
Massive Attack
Sons & Daughters
Travis

SCREAM PROMOTIONS
4th Floor, 57 Poland Street,
London W1F 7NW
Tel: 020 7434 3446 Fax: 020 7434 3449
Email: tcooke@instantemail.t-mobile.co.uk
Web Site: www.screampromotions.co.uk
SCREAM is a London based TV and radio promotions company who represent artists including Morrissey, Iron Maiden, De La Soul and Kelly Osbourne. We also look after the TV and radio for big events including The Brit Awards, The Carling Weekend: Reading and Leeds Festivals, and Download. We represent the following events for national promotion:
BRITs 2007
O2 Wireless Festival
Carling Weekend: Reading and Leeds
Download festivals

ARTISTES REPRESENTED:

Black Sabbath
Brakes
Buckcherry
Clutch
Danko Jones
Dropkick Murphys
Europe
From First To Last
GWAR
Iron Maiden
Juliette and the Licks
Les Encompetants
Linchpin
LORDI
Metric
Motley Crue
Nizlopi
Ox Eagle Lion
Saosin
Snowfight In The City Centre
Soil
The Stranglers
The Answer
The Mescalites
The Morning After Girls
White Rose Movement

IVOR SPENCER
President of the Guild of Intl Professional Toastmasters
12 Little Bornes, Dulwich,
London SE21 8SE
Tel: 020 8670 5585 Fax: 020 8670 0055
Mobile: 07860 313835
Web Site: www.ivorspencer.com
Ivor Spencer is the only Toastmaster to have officiated at over 1,000 Royal Events. Toastmaster of the Year 2000 and Lifetime achievement award.

TARGET LIVE
45-51 Whitfield Street, London W1T 4HB
Tel: 020 3372 0950 / 0900 Fax: 020 3372 0951 / 0901
Email: info@target-live.co.uk, david.bloom @target-live.co.uk
Web: www.target-media.co.uk/index.html
Manager: Guy Chapman

TAYLOR HERRING PUBLIC RELATIONS
11 Westway Centre, 69 St. Marks Road, London WS10 6JG
Tel: 0208 206 5151 Fax: 0208 206 5155
Email: Nicola.James@taylorherring.com
Web Site: www.taylorherring.com
Agent: James Herring
Contact: Nicola James

ARTISTES REPRESENTED:

Abigail Clancy
Judy Finnigan
Daisy Goodwin
Carrie Grant
David Ian
Richard Madeley
Margaret Mountford
Lord Alan Sugar
Catherine Tate
Abi Titmuss
Robbie Williams

THE OUTSIDE ORGANISATION
Butler House, 177 -178 Tottenham Court Road, London W1T 7NY
Tel: 020 7436 3633 Fax: 020 7436 3632
Email: fiona.finlow@outside-org.co.uk
Web Site: www.outside-org.co.uk
Agents: Fiona Finlow, Annabel Fox, Natasha Mensah, Stuart Bell, Sophie Green, Celena Aponte, Henry Jacob, Vicky Brooks, Nadine Bibi

ARTISTES REPRESENTED:

Bon Jovi
David Bowie
Naomi Campbell
Craig David
Il Divo
Ronan Keating
Sir Paul McCartney
Liz McClarnon
Gary Rhodes
Westlife
Keisha White
The Who
Ronnie Wood

PETER THOMPSON ASSOCIATES
Flat 1, 12 Bourchier Street, London W1V 5HN
Tel: 020 7439 1210 Fax: 020 7439 1202
Email: info@ptassociates.co.uk

TOAST PRESS
Room 210, Bon Marche Building, 241-251 Ferndale Road, London SW9 8BJ
Tel: 0207 326 1200
Email: christopher@toastpress.com
Web Site: www.toastpress.com
Agent: Ruth Drake
Contact: Christopher Moore

ARTISTES REPRESENTED:

Amp Fiddler
Bugz in the Attic
Shy Child
Soulwax
The Streets
The Maccabees

UNLEASHED PR
Tel: 07904 403913
Email: craig@unleashedpr.com
Web Site: www.unleashedpr.com
Agents: Craig Pass, Emma Hadley

ARTISTES REPRESENTED:

911
Donnaleigh Bailey
Sam Brodie
Simon Cole
Jimmy Constable
James Fox
Kavana
Lee Latchford-Evans
Makosi Musambasi
Lee Otway
Kieron Richardson (Hollyoaks actor)
Samantha Rowley
Becki Seddiki
Spiral (aka Glen Coroner)
Cassie Sumner

SIMON WHITTAM PUBLICITY
Hillside House, Lower Row, Kingsand, Cornwall PL10 1NW
Tel: 01752 823 414 Fax: 01752 416 420
Email: info@simonwhittam.co.uk
Web Site: www.simonwhittam.co.uk

ARTISTES REPRESENTED:

Jan Leeming
Stuart Miles
Maggie Moone
Isla St Clair

Corporate Clients:

Cornish Traditional Cottages

Educate Ltd
Fairhaven Holiday Cottages
Scotts Castle Holidays

Z'EST PUBLIC RELATIONS
207 Eardley Road London SW16 5TQ
Tel: 020 8679 3232 Fax: 020 8679 7171
Email: ian@zestpr.co.uk
Web Site: www.zestpr.co.uk
Joint M.D: Ian Roberts
Strategic celebrity and creative arts PR (Specialists in singers and international classical musicians)

Theatre Critics

BIRMINGHAM MAIL
Diane Parkes Tel: 0121 234 5477
Email: diane.parkes@birminghammail.net
Roz Laws Tel: 0121 234 5421

BIRMINGHAM POST
Diane Parkes Tel: 0121 234 5477
Email: diane.parkes@birminghammail.net
Roz Laws Tel: 0121 234 5421
Email: roz.laws@sundaymercury.net

DAILY EXPRESS
Paul Callan, Simon Edge
Julie Carpenter Tel: 020 8612 7377
Email: simon.edge@express.co.uk
Email: julie.carpenter@express.co.uk

DAILY MAIL
Quentin Letts Tel: 020 7938 6000
Email: quentin.letts@dailymail.co.uk

DAILY STAR
Nigel Pauley Tel: 020 8612 7373
Email: nigel.pauley@dailystar.co.uk

DAILY TELEGRAPH
Dominic Cavendish Tel: 020 7931 2000

EDINBURGH EVENING NEWS
Liam Rudden Tel: 0131 620 8675
Email: liam.rudden@scotsman.com

FINANCIAL TIMES
Martin Hoyle Tel: 020 7873 3662
Email: martinhoyle@btinternet.com

THE GUARDIAN
Michael Billington Tel: 020 3353 4602
Email: michael.billington@guardian.co.uk

JEWISH CHRONICLE
John Nathan Tel: 020 7415 1500
Email: jsnathan@mac.com

INDEPENDENT
David Lister Tel: 020 7005 2000
Email: d.lister@independent.co.uk

MANCHESTER EVENING NEWS
Tel: 0161 832 7200

MORNING STAR
Robert Tanitch Tel: 020 8510 0815

NEWCASTLE EVENING CHRONICLE
Gordon Barr Tel: 0191 201 6294
Email: gordon.barr@mcjmedia.co.uk

OBSERVER
Susannah Clapp Tel: 020 3353 4221
Email: revue@observer.co.uk

OXFORD MAIL & TIMES
Jeremy Smith Tel: 01865 425 435
Chris Gray Tel: 01865 425471

SCOTSMAN
Joyce McMillan Tel: 0131 620 8620
Email: joyce.mcmillan@scotsman.com

SCOTTISH DAILY RECORD
Rick Fulton Tel: 0141 309 3118
Email: r.fulton@dailyrecord.co.uk

THE STAGE
Emma Harlen Tel: 020 7939 8482
Email: emma@thestage.co.uk

THE STANDARD
Henry Hitchings Tel: 020 7938 7592

SUNDAY EXPRESS
Mark Shenton Tel: 07984 471098
Email: shentonmark@btinternet.com

SUNDAY TELEGRAPH
Tim Walker Tel: 020 7931 3653

SUNDAY TIMES
John Peter Tel: 020 7782 5000

TIME OUT
Caroline McGinn Tel: 020 7813 6064
Email: carolinemcginn@timeout.com

THE TIMES
Libby Purves Tel: 020 7782 5000

VARIETY
Jill Lawless Tel: 020 7427 4214
Email: jlawless@ap.org

YORKSHIRE POST
Nick Ahad Tel: 0113 243 2701

Media: Print

Local Daily Press

THE ARGUS
(BRIGHTON)
Crowhurst Road, Brighton, East Sussex BN1 8AR
Tel: 01273 544 544 Fax: 01273 566 114
Email: lottie.elson@theargus.co.uk
Web Site: www.theargus.co.uk
Editor: Michael Beard
Marketing and promotions: Lottie Elson

AUDIENCE MEDIA & LIVE UK LTD
26 Dorset Street London W1U 8AP
Tel: 0207 486 7007 Fax: 0207 486 2002
Email: info@audience.uk.com
Web Site: www.audience.uk.com
Managing Editor: Steve Parker
Email: steve@audience.uk.com
Office & Administration Manager: Emma Harvey Lawrence
Email: emma@audience.uk.com

NORTH WEST EVENING MAIL
(BARROW-IN-FURNESS)
Furness Newspaper, Newpaper House, Abbey Road, Barrow-in-Furness, Cumbria LA14 5QS
Switchboard: 01229 840 100 Newsdesk: 01229 840 151 Fax: 01229 840164
Email: ann.mcvea@nwemail.co.uk
Web Site: www.nwemail.co.uk
Publishing director: Jonathan Lee
Email: jonathan.lee@nwemail.co.uk, Tel: 01229 840101
Head of Production and Commercial Development: Ann McVea

THE BATH CHRONICLE
(BATH)
Westpoint James Street West Bath, Somerset BA1 2DA
Tel: 01225 322 306 Fax: 01225 322 291
Email: features@bathchron.co.uk
Web Site: www.thisisbath.co.uk
Features Editor: Georgette McCready
Theatre Writer: Christopher Hansford

BELFAST TELEGRAPH
(BELFAST)
PO Box 25, 124-144 Royal Avenue, Belfast, County Antrim BT1 1EB
Tel: 028 9026 4000 Fax: 028 9055 4504
Email: gwalker@belfasttelegraph.co.uk
Web Site: www.belfasttelegraph.co.uk

BIRMINGHAM EVENING MAIL - BIRMINGHAM POST
(BIRMINGHAM)
PO Box 18 Floor 6, Fort Parkway, Birmingham B24 9FF
Tel: 0121 234 5536 Fax: 0121 234 5564
Email: newsdesk@birminghammail.net
Web Site: www.birminghammail.co.uk
Birmingham Mail Editor: David Brookes
Email: david_brookes@mrn.co.uk
Birmingham Post Editor: Alun Thorne
Email: alun.thorne@birminghampost.net

LANCASHIRE EVENING TELEGRAPH
(BLACKBURN)
Newspaper House, 1 High Street, Blackburn, Lancashire BB1 1HT

Tel: 01254 678 678 Fax: 01254 680 429
Email: janson@nqnw.co.uk
Web Site: www.lancashiretelegraph.co.uk
Editor: Francesca Winrow
Features Editor: John Anson

THE GAZETTE
(BLACKPOOL)
Blackpool Gazette & Herald Ltd Avroe House, Avroe Crescent, Blackpool Business Park, Blackpool, Lancashire FY4 2DP
Tel: 01253 400 888 Fax: 01253 361870
Email: Jacqui.Morley@blackpoolgazette.co.uk
Web Site: www.blackpoolgazette.co.uk
Editor: John Rhodes
Chief Feature Writer: Jacqui Morley

THE DAILY ECHO
(BOURNEMOUTH)
Southern Newspapers Plc, Richmond Hill, Bournemouth, Dorset BH2 6HH
Tel: 01202 554 601 Fax: 01202 292 115
Email: newsdesk@bournemouthecho.co.uk
Web Site: www.bournemouthecho.co.uk
Editor: Neal Butterworth

TELEGRAPH & ARGUS
(BRADFORD)
Hall Ings, Bradford, West Yorkshire BD1 1JR
Tel: 01274 729 511 Fax: 01274 393 685
Email: newsdesk@telegraphandargus.co.uk
Web: www.thetelegraphandargus.co.uk
Editor: Perry Austin-Clarke

BRISTOL EVENING POST
(BRISTOL)
Temple Way, Bristol, Avon BS99 7HD
Tel: 0117 9343 330 Fax: 0117 934 3575
Email: epnews@bepp.co.uk
Web Site: www.thisisbristol.com

BURTON MAIL
(BURTON ON TRENT)
65-68 High Street, Burton-on-Trent, Staffordshire DE14 1LE
Tel: 01283 512 345 Fax: 01283 515 351
Email: editorial@burtonmail.co.uk
Web Site: www.burtonmail.co.uk

CAMBRIDGE EVENING NEWS
(CAMBRIDGE)
Cambridge Newspapers Ltd, Winship Road, Milton, Cambridge CB24 6PP
Tel: 01223 434 434 Fax: 01223 434 415
Email: newsdesk@cambridge-news.co.uk
Web Site: www.cambridge-news.co.uk
Managing Director: Graham Ayres

SOUTH WALES ECHO
(CARDIFF)
Western Mail & Echo, 6 Park Street, Cardiff CF10 1XR
Tel: 029 2022 3333 Fax: 029 2058 3624
Email: enquiries@mediawales.co.uk
Web Site: www.walesonline.co.uk
Editor: Tim Gordon
Marketing Manager: Grant Bignell

GLOUCESTERSHIRE ECHO
(CHELTENHAM)
Cheltenham Newspaper Co., 1 Clarence Parade, Cheltenham, Gloucestershire GL50 3NY
Tel: 01242 278 000 / 081
Fax: 01242 271848
Email: echo.news@glosmedia.co.uk
Web: www.thisisgloucestershire.co.uk

EVENING GAZETTE
(COLCHESTER)
Essex County Newspapers Ltd, Oriel House, 43-44 North Hill, Colchester, Essex CO1 1TZ
Tel: 01206 506000 Fax: 01206 508274
Email: gazette.newsdesk@nqe.com
Web Site: www.thisisessex.co.uk
Editor: Martin McNeil

COVENTRY EVENING TELEGRAPH
(COVENTRY)
Corporation Street, Coventry, Warwickshire CV1 1FP
Tel: 024 7663 3633 Fax: 024 7655 0869
Email: darren.parkin@coventrytelegraph.net
Web Site: www.coventrytelegraph.net
Managing Director: Debbie Davies
Editor: Darren Parkin

DAILY POST
(LIVERPOOL)
Liverpool Daily Post & Echo, PO Box 48, Old Hall Street, Liverpool, Merseyside L69 3EB
Tel: 0151 227 2000 Fax: 0151 472 2506
Email: maria.breslin@liverpool.com
Web Site: www.liverpooldailypost.co.uk
Head of Content: Maria Breslin
Features: Jane Haase

DERBY EVENING TELEGRAPH
(DERBY)
Derby Evening Telegraph Ltd, Northcliffe House, Meadow Road, Derby DE1 2DW
Tel: 01332 291 111 Fax: 01332 253 027
Email: npowlson@derbytelegraph.co.uk
Web Site: www.thisisderbyshire.co.uk
Managing Director: Tim Tichen
Theatre: Nigel Powlson

EVENING NEWS
(EDINBURGH)
The Scotsman Publications, 108 Holyrood Road, Edinburgh, Midlothian EH8 8AS
Tel: 0131 620 8620 Fax: 0131 620 8616 (Editorial)
Email: bmiles@scotsman.com
Web Site: www.scotsman.com
Contact Sales Manager: Brendan Miles

THE SCOTSMAN
(EDINBURGH)
The Scotsman Publications, Barclay House, 108 Holyrood Road, Edinburgh, Midlothian EH8 8AS
Tel: 0131 620 8620 Fax: 0131 620 8616 (Editorial)
Email: enquiries@scotsman.com
Web Site: www.scotsman.com

EVENING PRESS
(YORK)
PO Box 29, 76-86 Walmgate, York North Yorkshire YO1 9YN
Tel: 01904 653 051 Fax: 01904 612 853
Email: newsdesk@thepress.co.uk
Web Site: www.thisisyork.co.uk
Arts Reporter: Charles Hutchinson

GUERNSEY EVENING PRESS & STAR
(GUERNSEY)
Braye Road, Vale, Guernsey GY1 3BW Channel Island
Tel: 01481 240 240 Fax: 01481 240 290
ISDN: 01481 243657
Email: rdigard@guernsey-press.com

EVENING COURIER
(HALIFAX)
Halifax Courier Ltd, PO Box 19, Kings Cross Street, Halifax,
West Yorkshire HX1 2SF
Tel: 01422 260200 Fax: 01422 330021
Email: john.furbisher@halifaxcourier.co.uk
Web Site: www.halifaxtoday.co.uk
Editor: John Furbisher

HARTLEPOOL MAIL
(HARTLEPOOL)
Northeast Press Ltd, New Clarence House, Wesley Square, Hartlepool, Teesside TS24 8BX
Tel: 01429 239 333 Fax: 01429 869 024
Email: mail.news@northeast-press.co.uk
Web Site: www.hartlepooltoday.co.uk

HULL DAILY MAIL
(HULL)
PO Box 34, Blundells Corner, Beverley Road, Hull, East Yorkshire HU3 1XS
Tel: 01482 327 111 Fax: 01482 584 353
Email: g.deacon@hdmp.co.uk

THE EAST ANGLIAN DAILY TIMES
(IPSWICH)
30 Lower Brook Street, Ipswich, Suffolk IP4 1AN
Tel: 01473 230023 Fax: 01473 211391
Email: julian.ford@eadt.co.uk
Web Site: www.eadt.co.uk
Features Editor: Julian Ford

IRISH NEWS
(BELFAST)

113-117 Donegall Street, Belfast, County Antrim BT1 2GE
Tel: 028 9032 2226 Fax: 028 9033 7505
Email: newsdesk@irishnews.com

JERSEY EVENING POST
(JERSEY)
PO Box 582, Five Oaks, St.Saviour, Jersey JE4 8XQ
Tel: 01534 611 611 Fax: 01534 611 622
Email: editorial@jerseyeveningpost.com
Web Site: www.thisisjersey.com

LANCASHIRE EVENING POST
(LANCASHIRE)
Olivers Place, Fulwood, Preston, Lancashire PR2 9ZA
Tel: 01772 254 841
Editorial Fax: 01772 880 173
Email: marc.jackson@lep.co.uk
Web Site: www.prestontoday.net

BOLTON EVENING NEWS
(LANCASHIRE)
Newspaper House, Churchgate, Bolton, Lancashire BL1 1DE
Tel: 01204 522 345 Fax: 01204 365 068
Email: ben_editorial @lancashire_newsquest.co.uk
Web Site: www.thisisbolton.co.uk
Chief Theatre Critic: Nigel McFarlane

YORKSHIRE EVENING POST
(LEEDS)
Yorkshire Post Newspapers, Wellington Street, Leeds, West Yorkshire LS1 1RF
Tel: 0113 243 2701 Editorial Fax: 0113 244 3430
Email: eped@ypn.co.uk
Web Site: www.leedstoday.net

LINCOLNSHIRE ECHO
(LINCOLN)
Brayford Wharf East, Lincoln LN5 7AT
Tel: 01522 820 000 Fax: 01522 804 493
Email: editor@lincolnshireecho.co.uk
Web Site: www.thisislincolnshire.co.uk

MANCHESTER EVENING NEWS
(MANCHESTER)
164 Deansgate, Manchester M3 3RN
Tel: 0161 832 7200 Fax: 0161 834 3814
Email: newsdesk@men-news.co.uk
Web Site: www.manchesteronline.co.uk

CHRONICLE & ECHO
(NORTHAMPTON)
Northamptonshire Newspapers, Upper Mounts, Northampton NN1 3HR
Tel: 01604 467000 Fax: 01604 467190
Email: melissa.taylor@northantsnews.co.uk
Web Site: www.northantsnews.co.uk

NOTTINGHAM EVENING POST
(NOTTINGHAM)
Nottingham Post Group Ltd., Castle Wharf House, Nottingham NG1 7EU
Tel: 0115 948 2000 Fax: 0115 964 4000
Email: newsdesk @nottinghameveningpost.co.uk
Web Site: www.thisisnottingham.co.uk

OLDHAM EVENING CHRONICLE
(OLDHAM)
Hirst Kidd & Rennie Ltd., PO Box 47, 172 Union Street, Oldham, Lancashire OL1 1EQ
Tel: 0161 633 2121 Fax: 0161 627 0905
Editorial Fax: 0161 652 2111
Email: features@oldham-chronicle.co.uk
Web Site: www.oldham-chronicle.co.uk
Arts and Entertainment Editor: Paul Genty
The paper publishes nightly, Mon-Fri, with an arts preview supplement each Wednesday, a lifestyle supplement each Tuesday, and a free weekly edition each Thursday sharing some content with the evening editions. We prefer email rather than fax or mail.

READING EVENING POST
(READING)
8 Tessa Road, Reading, Berkshire RG1 8NS
Tel: 0118 918 3000 Fax: 0118 959 9363
Email: features@reading-epost.co.uk

SHEFFIELD TELEGRAPH
(SHEFFIELD)
York Street, Sheffield S1 1PU
Tel: 0114 273 8818 Fax: 0114 272 5978
Email: starnewsdesk@rim.co.uk
Web Site: www.sheffweb.co.uk

THE SOUTHERN DAILY ECHO
(SOUTHAMPTON)
Newsquest Southern, Newspaper House, Test Lane, Redbridge, Southampton, Hampshire SO16 9JX
Tel: 023 8042 4777 Fax: 023 8042 4545
Email: kelly.bendall@soton-echo.co.uk
Web Site: www.dailyecho.co.uk
Contact Marketing Manager: Kelly Bendall

SENTINEL
(STOKE ON TRENT)
Staffordshire Sentinel, Newspapers Ltd., Sentinel House, Etruria, Stoke-on-Trent ST1 5SS
Tel: 01782 602 525 Fax: 01782 201 167
Email: charlotte.littlejones@thesentinel.co.uk
Web Site: www.thisisstaffordshire.co.uk
Contact: Charlotte Littlejones

SUNDERLAND ECHO
(SUNDERLAND)
Northeast Press Ltd., Echo House, Pennywell Industrial Estate, Sunderland SR4 9ER
Tel: 0191 534 3011 Fax: 0191 534 5975
Email: alistair.robinson @northeast-press.co.uk

SOUTH WALES EVENING POST
(SWANSEA)
South Wales Publications Ltd, PO Box 14, Adelaide Street, Swansea SA1 1QT
Tel: 01792 510000 Fax: 01792 469665 (editorial) Fax: 01792 514599 (advertising)
Email: cathy.duncan@swwp.co.uk
Web Site: catherine.ings@swwp.co.uk

SWINDON ADVERTISER
(SWINDON)
Newsquest, 100 Victoria Road, Old Town, Swindon Wiltshire SN1 3BE
Tel: 01793 528144 Fax: 01793 542434
Email: scrouch@newswilts.co.uk

THE PORTSMOUTH NEWS
The News Centre, Hilsea, Portsmouth, Hampshire PO2 9SX
Tel: 023 9266 4488 Fax: 023 9267 3363
Email: barry.rutter@thenews.co.uk
Web Site: www.thenews.co.uk
Entertainments Editor: Barry Rutter
Theatre Critic: Mike Allen

HERALD EXPRESS
(TORQUAY)
West Country Publications, Harmsworth House, Barton Hill Road, Torquay, Devon TQ2 8JN
Tel: 01803 676 000 Fax: 01803 676 799 (Advertising) 01803 676 299 (Aditorial)
Email: newsdesk@heraldexpress.co.uk
Web Site: www.thisissouthdevon.co.uk

NORTHEAST PRESS LTD
(TYNE AND WEAR)
Shields Gazette, Chapter Row, South Shields, Tyne and Wear NE33 1BL
Tel: 0191 427 4800 Fax: 0191 456 8270
Email: Marilyn.Welsh@northeast-press.co.uk
Web Site: www.shieldsgazette.com
Contact Sales Field Manager: Marilyn Welsh

Local Weekly Press

BARKING & DAGENHAM POST NEWSPAPERS
(ESSEX)
539 High Road, Ilford, Essex IG1 1UD
Tel: 020 8478 4444 Fax: 020 8592 7407
Email: kevin.poulter@archant.co.uk
Editor: Laura Adams
Email: laura.adams@archant.co.uk
Contact Advertising Manager: Graham Willis
Email: Graham.willis@archant.co.uk
Sales Manager: Kevin Poulter

BEDFORDSHIRE TODAY
(BEDFORDSHIRE)

Bedford Times & Citizen, 11-13 Mill Street, Bedford Bedfordshire MK40 3EU
Newsdesk: 01234 409 100 Advertising: 01234 405 060 Fax: 01234 409 140
Email: editorial@timesandcitizen.co.uk
Web Site: www.bedfordtoday.co.uk

READING & BERKSHIRE NEWSPAPER
(BERKSHIRE)
50-56 Portman Road, Reading, Berkshire RG30 1BA
Tel: 0118 955 3333 Fax: 0118 939 1619
Email: news@ readingchronicle.co.uk
Web Site: www.readingchronicle.co.uk
Editor: Sally Stevens
Commercial Manager: Dene Tonna

BRADFORD TARGET
(BRADFORD)
Hall Ings, Bradford, West Yorkshire BD1 1JR
Tel: 01274 730 000 Fax: 01274 393 685
Email: editorial.features@telegraphandargus.co.uk
Web: www.thetelegraphandargus.co.uk
Free weekly paper that comes out on Friday.

WESTERN DAILY PRESS
(BRISTOL)
Temple Way, Bristol, Avon BS99 7HD
Tel: 0117 934 3209 Fax: 0117 934 3574
Email: s.weldon@bepp.co.uk
Web Site: www.thisisbristol.com

BURNLEY EXPRESS & NEWS
(LANCASHIRE)
East Lancashire Newspapers Ltd Bull Street, Burnley, Lancashire BB11 1DP
Tel: 01282 426 161 Fax: 01282 435 332
Email: margaret.parsons@eastlanc-snews.co.uk
Web Site: www.burnleyexpress.net
Newsdesk: Margaret Parsons

CAMBRIDGE EVENING NEWS
(CAMBRIDGE)
Cambridge Newspapers Ltd, Winship Road, Milton, Cambridge CB24 6PP
Tel: 01223 434 434 Fax: 01223 434 415
Email: newsdesk@cambridge-news.co.uk
Web Site: www.cambridge-news.co.uk
Managing Director: Graham Ayres

EVENING GAZETTE
(COLCHESTER)
Essex County Newspapers Ltd, Oriel House, 43-44 North Hill, Colchester, Essex CO1 1TZ
Tel: 01206 506000 Fax: 01206 508274
Email: gazette.newsdesk@nqe.com
Web Site: www.thisisessex.co.uk
Editor: Martin McNeil

PACKET NEWSPAPERS
(CORNWALL)
Falmouth Business Park, Bickland Water Road, Falmouth, Cornwall TR11 4SZ
Tel: 01326 213 333 Fax: 01326 212 108
Email: packet@packetseries.co.uk
Web Site: www.packetseries.co.uk

CUMBRIAN NEWSPAPERS GROUP
(CUMBRIA)
Newspaper House, Dalston Road, Carlisle, Cumbria CA2 5UA
Tel: 01228 612 600 fax: 01228 600 601
Email: guy.forester@cngroup.co.uk
Web Site: www.cngroup.co.uk
General Manager: Guy Forester
The Publishing Division is responsible for the Group's newspaper publishing and associated activities in Cumbria, Northumbria, Northern Lancashire and Scotland. The main publishing centres are based in Carlisle, Barrow-in-Furness and Hexham, with other offices in the principal towns of the region. The Divison publishes two daily evening papers, five paid-for weeklies, and a range of free newspapers, directories, magazines and niche publications. It also has a thriving new media business and each of the papers have their own website.

FIFE FREE PRESS GROUP
(FIFE)
PO Box 3, 23-25 Kirk Wynd, Kirkcaldy, Fife KY1 1EP Scotland
Tel: 01592 598 811 Fax: 01592 204 180
Email: ffpnews@fifetoday.co.uk
Web Site: www.fifeonline.co.uk

GLOUCESTERSHIRE COUNTY GAZETTE SERIES
(GLOUCESTERSHIRE)
Reliance House, Long Street, Dursley, Gloucestershire GL11 4LS
Tel: 01453 544 000 Fax: 01453 540 208
Email: gazette.news@dursleygazette.co.uk
Web Site: www.gazetteseries.co.uk
Editor: Skip Walker
Arts Editor: Jayne Bennett
Email: jayne.bennett@gwent-wales.co.uk

HIGHLAND NEWS GROUP
(INVERNESS)
13 Henderson Road, Inverness IV1 1SP Scotland
Tel: 01463 713 700 Fax: 01463 221 251

KENT MESSENGER GROUP NEWSPAPERS
(KENT)
75 Shoe Lane, London EC4A 3BQ
Tel: 020 7353 3311 Fax: 020 7353 7396
Web Site: www.kentonline.com

KENT REGIONAL NEWSPAPERS
(KENT)
12 New Road Avenue, Chatham, Kent ME4 6AT
Tel: 01634 841 741 Fax: 01634 400 477
Email: newsdesk.medway@kentregional-newspapers.co.uk

YORKSHIRE POST NEWSPAPERS
(LEEDS)
PO Box 168, Wellington Street, Leeds, West Yorkshire LS1 1RF
Tel: 0113 243 2701
Editorial Fax: 0113 244 3430
Email: eped@ypn.co.uk
Web Site: www.leedstoday.net

LINCOLNSHIRE NEWSPAPER
(LINCOLNSHIRE)
5 & 6 Church Lane, Boston, Lincolnshire PE21 6ND
Tel: 01205 311433 Fax: 01205 352913
Email: julia.ogden@jpress.co.uk
Web Site: www.bostonnow.co.uk

NORTH LONDON NEWSPAPERS
(LONDON)
161 Tottenham Lane, London N8 9BU
Tel: 020 8340 6868 Fax: 020 8342 5730
Email: ollie.lane@archant.co.uk
Web Site: www.islingtongazette.com

NEWSQUEST OXFORDSHIRE
(OXFORD)
Osney Mead, Oxford OX2 0EJ
Tel: 01865 425 262 / 471
Email: cgray@nqo.com
Web Site: www.thisisoxfordshire.co.uk

SCOTTISH & UNIVERSAL NEWSPAPERS LTD
(STIRLING)
40 Upper Craigs, Stirling FK8 2DW
Tel: 01786 448 855 Marketing Dep: 01698 283 200 Fax: 01786 459 470
Email: hamiltonadvertisers@s-un.co.uk
Web Site: www.s-un.co.uk

SURREY AND SUSSEX NEWSPAPERS
Trinity House, 51 London Road, Reigate, Surrey RH2 9PR
Tel: 01737 732000 Fax: 01737 732267 (editorial) Fax: 01737 732001 (advertising)
Email: news@ssn.co.uk
Web: www.surreyandsussexonline.co.uk

SURREY ADVERTISER GROUP
(SURREY)
The Stoke Mill, Woking Road, Guildford, Surrey GU1 1QA
Tel: 01483 508700 Fax: 01483 508751
Email: newsdesk@surreyad.co.uk
News Editor: Mr Tony Green

SURREY COMET & GUARDIAN
Unecol House 819 London Road,
Cheam, Surrey SM3 9BN
Tel: 020 8329 9424 Fax: 020 8744 1748
Email: tchurch@london.newsquest.co.uk
Human Resources Manager: Trudy Church

TARGET SERIES
(BRADFORD)
Hall Ings, Bradford, West Yorkshire BD1 1JR
Tel: 01274 730 000 Fax: 01274 393 685
Email: donna.ough@newsquest.co.uk
Web Site: www.thisisbradford.co.uk
Entertainment Advertising Contact: Donna Ough
Free weekly paper that comes out on a Thursday.

THE COMET
(HERTFORDSHIRE)
Bank House Primett Road, Stevenage, Hertfordshire SG1 3EE
Tel: 01438 866075 Fax: 01462 436384
Email: esther.roscoe@archant.co.uk

BERROWS WORCESTER JOURNAL
(WORCESTERSHIRE)
Hylton Road, Worcester WR2 5JX
Tel: 01905 748200 Fax: 01905 748213 (advertising) Fax: 01905 748009 (editorial)
Email: stewart.gilbert@midlands.newsquest.co.uk

Major Newspapers

DAILY EXPRESS
The Northern & Shell Building, 10 Lower Thames Street, London EC3R 6EN
Tel: 0208 612 7000
Email: expressletters@express.co.uk
Web Site: www.express.co.uk

DAILY MAIL
Evening Standard Co Ltd, Northcliffe House, 2 Derry Street, London W8 5TT
Tel 020 7938 6000 Fax 020 7937 4463
Email: letters@dailymail.co.uk, news@dailymail.co.uk
Web Site: www.dailymail.co.uk
Editor: Paul Dacre
Managing Director: Guy Zitter

DAILY MIRROR
Mirror Group Newspapers, 1 Canada Square, Canary Wharf, London E14 5AP
Tel: 020 7293 3000 Fax: 020 7293 3409
Email: mirrornews@mirror.co.uk
Web Site: www.mirror.co.uk

DAILY STAR
The Northern & Shell Building, 10 Lower Thames Street, London EC3R 6EN
Tel: 0208 612 7000 Fax: 020 7922 7960
Email: news@dailystar.co.uk
Web Site: www.dailystar.co.uk

DAILY TELEGRAPH
Telegraph Group Ltd, 1 Canada Square, London E14 5AP
Tel: 020 7538 5000 Fax: 020 7538 7650
Email: dtnews@telegraph.co.uk
Web Site: www.telegraph.co.uk

EVENING STANDARD
2 Derry Street, London W8 5TT
Tel: 020 7938 6000 Fax: 020 7937 3745
Email: editor@standard.co.uk
Web Site: www.thisislondon.co.uk
Editor: Geordie Greig
Deputy Editor: Sarah Sands

FINANCIAL TIMES
1 Southwark Bridge, London SE1 9HL
Tel: 020 7873 3000 Fax: 020 7873 3929
Email: peter.aspden@ft.com
Web Site: www.ft.com
Arts Editor: Peter Aspden
Public Relations Officer: Joanna Manning-Cooper
joanna.manning-cooper@ft.com

THE GUARDIAN
Kings Place 90 York Way, London N1 9GU
Tel: 020 3353 2000 Fax: 020 7713 4366
Email: home@guardian.co.uk
Web Site: www.guardian.co.uk

JEWISH CHRONICLE
25 Furnival Street London EC4A 1JT
Tel: 020 7415 1616 Fax: 020 7405 9040
Email: editorial@thejc.com
Web Site: www.thejc.com
Theatre Critic: John Nathan

MAIL ON SUNDAY
Evening Standard Co Ltd, Northcliffe House, 2 Derry Street, London W8 5TS
Tel: 020 7938 6000 Fax: 020 7937 3745
Email: jon.odonnell@mailonsunday.co.uk
Web Site: www.mailonsunday.co.uk
Editor: Jon O'Donnell

THE MORNING STAR
52 Beachy Road, London E3 2NS
Tel: 020 8510 0815 Fax: 020 8986 5694
Email: adhead@peoples-press.com
Web Site: www.morningstaronline.co.uk

THE OBSERVER
119 Farringdon Road, London EC1R 3ER
Tel: 020 7713 4221 Fax: 020 7713 4225
Email: home@guardian.co.uk

THE PEOPLE
Mirror Group Newspapers, 1 Canada Square, Canary Wharf, London E14 5AP
Tel: 020 7293 3000 Fax: 020 7293 3405
Email: shakira.wood@mgn.co.uk
Display Advertising Assistant: Shakira Wood

THE SUN
1 Virgina Street, London E98 1SN
Tel: 020 7782 4000 Fax: 020 7782 5605
Email: features@the-sun.co.uk
Web Site: www.the-sun.co.uk

THE SUNDAY EXPRESS
Express Newspapers plc, Ludgate House, 245 Blackfriars Road, London SE1 9UX
Tel: 020 7928 8000
Email: chris.cassidy@express.co.uk
Web Site: www.express.co.uk
Contact Advertising Department: Chris Cassidy

SUNDAY SPORT
Sports Newpapers, 19 Great Ancoats Street, Manchester M60 4BT
Tel: 0161 236 4466 Advertising Tel: 01162 690 012 Fax: 020 7267 2166
Email: jane.field@sportnewspapers.co.uk
Web Site: www.sundaysport.com
Contact Newsdesk Editor: Jane Field

THE SUNDAY TELEGRAPH
Telegraph Group Ltd, 1 Canada Square, Canary Wharf, London E14 5DT
Tel: 020 7538 5000 Fax: 020 7538 6242
Email: paul.gobbins@telegraph.co.uk
Contact Advertising Department:: Paul Gobbins

THE TIMES
Times House, 1 Pennington Street, London E98 1TT
Tel: 020 7782 5000 Fax: 020 7782 5988
Email: cara.battigan@thetimes.co.uk
Web Site: www.timesonline.co.uk
Contact Promotions Manager: Cara Battigan

Magazines & Trade Papers

AMATEUR STAGE (1946)
Next Phase Media Ltd, Suite 404 Albany House, 324-326 Regents Street, London, W1B 3HH
Tel: 020 7622 6670 Fax: 0871 714 6996
Email: editor@asmagazine.co.uk
Web Site: www.amateurstagemagazine.co.uk
Editor: Douglas Mayo
Monthly features include new play & book reviews. West End reviews, production reports, technical information, production diary, interviews, education, training,

news & other relevant articles.
Monthly: £2.40 per copy.
Subscriptions: 1 Year UK £24 2 Year UK £40 Europe £32
£46 Rest of World.

AUDIENCE MEDIA & LIVE UK LTD

26 Dorset Street London W1U 8AP
Tel: 0207 486 7007 Fax: 0207 486 2002
Email: info@audience.uk.com
Web Site: www.audience.uk.com
Managing Editor: Steve Parker
Email: steve@audience.uk.com
Office & Administration Manager: Emma Harvey Lawrence
Email: emma@audience.uk.com

THE BIG ISSUE

1-5 Wandsworth Road, London SW8 2LN
Tel: 020 7526 3200 Fax: 020 7526 3201
Email: charles.howgego@bigissue.com
Web Site: www.bigissue.com
Editor: Charles Howgego
Marketing Manager: Lisa Woodman

BILLBOARD

5th Floor, Endeavour House, 189 Shaftesbury Avenue, London WC2H 8TJ
Tel: 020 7420 6003 Fax: 020 7420 6014
Email: lbrandle@eu.billboard.com
Web Site: www.billboard.com / www.billboard.biz
Contact Global Editor & billboard London Bureau Chief:
Mark Sutherland
Email: msuther@eu.billboard.com
Group Editorial Director (based in new york): Scott McKenzie

BLUES & SOUL

153 Praed Street, London W2 1RL
Tel: 020 7402 6869 (editorial) Tel: 020 7402 6897 (advertising) Fax: 020 7224 8227
Email: editorial@bluesandsoul.com
Web Site: www.bluesandsoul.com
Editor: Bob Kilburn
Advertising Manager: Del Strong

BROADCAST

33-39 Bowling Green Lane, London EC1R 0DA
Tel: 020 7505 8452 Fax: 020 7505 8020
Email: admin@broadcastnow.co.uk
Web Site: www.broadcastnow.co.uk
Editor: Lisa Campbell

THE CELEBRITY BULLETIN

10 Wiseton Road, London SW17 7EE
Tel: 020 8672 3191 Fax: 020 8672 2282
Email: enquiries@celebrity-bulletin.co.uk
ADMINISTRATION:
Editor: Neil Goddard
Subscription: published twice weekly - Mondays and Thursday, £80.00 per month; £75.00 per month if paid by bankers order or per annum.
Information about everyone in the news world-wide, including London arrivals, International arrivals, International activities, events and Biographies.

CLASSICAL MUSIC MAGAZINE

241 Shaftesbury Avenue, London WC2H 8TF
Tel: 020 7333 1733 Fax: 020 7333 1769 / 1736
Email: classical.music@rhinegold.co.uk
Web Site: www.rhinegold.co.uk
Editor: Keith Clarke

CUESHEET MUSIC REPORT

23 Belsize Crescent, London NW3 5QY
Tel: 020 7794 2540 Fax: 020 7794 7393
Email: cuesheet@songlink.com
Web Site: www.cuesheet.net
Editor: David Stark
Confidential newsletter published twice a month (22 issues per year), listing UK/US Film, TV companies seeking music, scores and/or songs for their projects. The leads are sent by e-mail only.
Subscription: £495.55 per year
1 month trial £49.50 (2 issues).

DANCE TODAY !

Formerly "Ballroom Dancing Times"
45-47 Clerkenwell Green, London EC1R 0EB
Tel: 020 7250 3006 Fax: 020 7253 6679
Email: dt@dancing-times.co.uk / danceto-day!@dancing-times.co.uk
Web Site: www.dancing-times.co.uk
Editor: Mary Clarke
Monthly: 2nd week of month.
£1.76 per issue; £19.25 p.a. inland, £22.50 overseas surface, £25.00 by air-mail.
All forms of social dance. Interviews with top dance personalities. Expert advice on style and techniques. Variations in Modern, Latin & Sequence by some of the greatest names in ballroom dancing. Mail order book service. Comprehensive list of diary dates. Competition reports & excellent photographs.

DANCING TIMES

45-47 Clerkenwell Green, London EC1R 0EB
Tel: 020 7250 3006 Fax: 020 7253 6679
Email: dt@dancing-times.co.uk
Web Site: www.dancing-times.co.uk
ADMINISTRATION:
Editorial Team: Jonathan Gray, Zoë Anderson, Simon Oliver
Monthly: 1st of month
£2.96 per issue; £32.45 p.a. inland; £39.45 overseas surface and £42.00 by airmail.
Established since 1910 with international circulation. Ballet, Contemporary dance, Stage dancing, from general critical, historical and technical angles. Preliminary arrangements must be made for freelance articles. Photographs. Book reviews. Calendar of forthcoming performances, touring dates. News and reports from festivals, schools, etc.

EMPIRE

Mappin House, 4 Winsley Street, London W1W 9HF
Tel: 020 7436 1515
Email: marie.maurice@emap.com
Web Site: www.emap.com
Editor: Emma Cochran

ENCORE

See also, 'Johnny Mans Productions'
P.O.Box 196, Broxbourne, Hertfordshire EN10 7WG
Tel: 0845 467 0792
Email: encoremags@aol.com, johnny-mansagent@aol.com
Web Site: www.johnnymansproductions.co.uk
Props: Johnny Mans Productions
Independent Trade Monthly for Show Products and Venues.
British theatre and concert hall monthly listings, plus news on venues, theatre managers, producers, promoters, societies, agencies, artistes and shows.
Yearly subscription priced at £25.00.

EQUITY JOURNAL

Guild House, Upper St Martin's Lane, London WC2H 9EG
Tel: 020 7379 6000 (switchboard) Fax: 020 7379 7001
Email: info@equity.org.uk
Web Site: www.equity.org.uk
Editor: Martin Brown
Four times a year. Free to members.
£12.00 per annum to non-members.
Journal of British Actors' Equity Association (Incorporating the Variety Artists' Federation).

FREIZE MAGAZINE

3-4 Hardwick Street, London EC1R 4RB
Tel: 020 7833 7270 Fax: 020 7833 7271
Email: dan@freize.com
Contact: Dan Fox

GQ

Conde Nast Publications Ltd, Vogue House, 1 Hanover Square, London W1S 1JU
Tel: 020 1752 3731 Fax: 020 7493 1345
Email: dylan.jones@condenast.co.uk
Web Site: www.gq-magazine.co.uk
Editor: Dylan Jones
PA to Editor: Antonia McKay

HARPERS & QUEEN

National Magazine House, 72 Broadwick Street, London W1F 9EP
Tel: 020 7439 5000 Fax: 020 7439 5506

Email: francesca.martin@natmags.co.uk
Web Site: www.harpersandqueen.co.uk
Editor: Lucy Yeomans
Arts and Entertainment Editor: Francesa Martin

I-D MAGAZINE
124 Tabernacle Street, London EC2A 4SA
Tel: 020 7490 9710 Fax: 020 7490 9737
Email: art/editor/fashion/advertising@i-dmagazine.co.uk
Web Site: www.i-dmagazine.com
Editor: Ben Reardon

I.E.A.M.
(The Official Journal fo the Institute of Entertainment and Arts Management)
17 Drake Close, Horsham, West Sussex RH12 5UB
Tel/Fax: 0870 241 7248
Email: admin@ieam.co.uk
Web Site: www.ieam.co.uk
Administrator/Editor: Shirley Carpenter
We are a member organisation mostly comprising of theatre managers and associated services. Publish free of charge yearbook listing all members.

LOADED
IPC Magazine, Kings Reach Tower, Stamford Street, London SE1 9LS
Tel: 020 7261 5562 Fax: 020 7261 5557
Email: andrew_woods@ipcmedia.com
Web Site: www.loaded.co.uk
Editor: Martin Daubney
Deputy Editor: Andrew Wood

MOJO
Mappin House, 4 Winsley Street, London W1W 8HF
Tel: 020 7312 8716 Fax: 020 7182 8596
Email: mojo@emap.com / phil.alexander@emap.com
Web Site: www.mojo4music.com
Managing Editor: Phil Alexander
Deputy Editor: Andrew Male

MUSIC WEEK
CMP Information, 7th Floor, Ludgate House, 245 Blackfriars Road, London SE1 9UR
Editorial Tel: 020 7921 8348 / 8358
Email: martin@musicweek.com
Web Site: www.musicweek.com
Publisher: Ajax Scott
Editor: Martin Talbot
News Editor: Paul Williams
Email: paulw@musicweek.com

NEW MUSICAL EXPRESS
The Blue Fin Building, 110 Southwark Street, London SE1 0SU
Tel: 020 7261 5000
Email: conor_mcnicholas@ipcmedia.com
Web Site: www.nme.com / www.ipcmedia.com
Editor: Conor McNicholas
Deputy Editor: Krissi Mursion

OPERA
36 Black Lion Lane, London W6 9BE
Tel: 020 8563 8893 Fax: 020 8563 8635
Email: editor@opera.co.uk
Web Site: www.opera.co.uk
Editor: John Allison

POLLSTAR UK LTD
Suite 5, 24 Highbury Grove, London N5 2EA
Tel: 020 7359 1110 Fax: 020 7359 1131
Email: sarah / charlie / gammon@pollstar.com
Web Site: www.pollstar.com
Managing Director: Charlie Presburg
Marketing Director: Sarah Hayward
News & Features Writer: John Gammon

PRESSGANG
The Official Magazine of the Liverpool Education & Lifelong Learning Service "Excellence In Liverpool" Project
Tel/Fax: 0151 708 8864
Email: heneghandeclan@yahoo.co.uk
Proprietor: Declan Heneghan
Pressgang is an A4 full-colour, glossy, bi-monthly youth magazine written by gifted and talented pupils aged between 14-18 from schools across the Liverpool area on their work experience placement, under the supervision of a qualified journalist. Published by Wordplay Media Limited, it operates on a fully commercial basis, accepting advertising from all appropriate sources and is circulated free to schools, libraries and youth centres across Liverpool and beyond. It covers a wide variety of topics and has featured senior government ministers and leading figures from the world of music, sport and entertainment.

Q
Mappin House, 4 Winsley Street, London W1W 8HF
Tel: 020 7182 8000 Fax: 020 7182 8547
Email: q@emap.com
Web Site: www.q4music.com
Editor: Paul Rees
Editorial Assistant: Nasarene Asghar

SCREEN INTERNATIONAL
33-39 Bowling Green Lane, London EC1R 0DA
Tel: 020 7505 8080 Fax: 020 7505 8117
Email: colinbrown1@earthlink.net
Web Site: www.screendaily.com
Editor-in-Chief: Colin Brown
Editor: Michael Gubbins

SONGLINK INTERNATIONAL
23 Belsize Crescent, London NW3 5QY
Tel: 020 7794 2540 Fax: 020 7794 7393
Email: david@songlink.com
Web Site: www.songlink.com
Editor: David Stark
Monthly publication listing artist and companies looking for songs, co-writers, music industry contacts, etc.

SONGWRITING AND COMPOSING MAGAZINE
The Guild Of International Songwriters & Composers
Sovereign House, 12 Trewartha Road, Praa Sands, Penzance, Cornwall TR20 9ST
Tel: 01736 762 826 Fax: 01736 763 328
Email: songmag@aol.com
Web Site: www.songwriters-guild.co.uk
Senior Personnel: Roderick G Jones
The Guild Of International Songwriters & Composers has been publishing Songwriting And Composing Magazine quarterly since 1986. Throughout each year, it contains reviews, articles, profiles, and information relating to music publishers, record companies, management companies, production companies, artistes and songwriters. It also provides contact information on publishers seeking songs and instrumental themes, record companies seeking artistes, management companies seeking acts for development and much more.

THE STAGE
Stage House, 47 Bermondsey Street, London Bridge London SE1 3XT
General Tel: 020 7403 1818 Editorial Fax: 020 7939 8478 Advertising Fax: 020 7939 8479
Email: gen_enquiries@thestage.co.uk
Web Site: www.thestage.co.uk / www.showcall.co.uk
Editor: Brian Attwood
For Features and Reviews, contact: Emma Harlen
Weekly tabloid newspaper: Thursday. £1.50 per copy.
Subscription Rate: £58.50 per annum or £53.00 by direct debit.
Covers professional stage (including variety, clubs, opera, dance, technical etc., professional and student showcases), television and radio; show business news, reviews and shows, programmes and books; forthcoming shows and relevant developments; illus; line and half-tone.

TATLER
Conde Nast Publications Ltd, Vogue House, Hanover Square, London W1S 1JU
Tel: 020 7499 9080 Fax: 020 7409 0891
Email: georgie.greig@condenast.co.uk
Web Site: www.tatler.co.uk
Editor: Georgie Greig
Managing Editor: Ahlya Fateh

THE TIP SHEET
Email: KingOfHits@aol.com
Web Site: www.tipsheet.co.uk

Commercial Director: Callaghan O'Rourke
Editor: Joe Taylor
Weekly magazine and CD, published by Revvolution Publishing, for individuals in the Music Business who love music more than Business.

TIME OUT
Time Out Magazine Ltd, Universal House, 251 Tottenham Court Road, London W1T 7AB
Tel: 020 7813 3000 Fax: 020 7323 3438
Email: editorial@timeout.com
Web Site: www.timeout.com
ADMINISTRATION:
Publisher and Managing Director: Mark Elliott
Editor: Mark Frith
Theatre Editor: Caroline McGinn
Price: £2.99 per weekly copy.
Commentary and listings of theatre, arts and entertainment events in London, including fringe theatre.

VANITY FAIR
Conde Nast Publications Ltd, Vogue House, Hanover Square, London W1S 1JU
Tel: 020 7499 9080 Fax: 020 7493 1962
Email: firstname.surname@condenast.co.uk
Web Site: www.vanityfair.co.uk
Editor-in-Chief (based in New York): Graydon Carter
London Editor: Henry Porter
Associate Publisher: Tia Graham
Publishing Director: Annie Holcroft
Advertisement Director: Holly Beynon

VARIETY
3rd Floor, Procter House, 1 Procter Street, London WC1V 6EU
Tel: 0207 911 1924 Fax: 0207 911 1922
Email: dana.harris@variety.com
Web Site: www.variety.com
Editor: Dana Harris
Weekly - £5.00
The paper of record for global entertainment business.

VOGUE
Vogue House, Hanover Square, London W1S 1JU
Tel: 020 7499 9080 Fax: 020 7408 0559
Email: voguemagazine@condenast.co.uk
Web Site: www.vogue.co.uk
Editor: Alexandra Shulman

Media: Radio

BBC Local Radio

BBC COVENTRY & WARWICKSHIRE
Hole Court, 1 Grayfriars Road, Coventry, Warwickshire CV1 2WR
Tel: 024 7686 0086 Fax: 024 7657 0100
Email: coventry.warwickshire@bbc.co.uk
Senior Producer: Sue Curtis

BBC ESSEX
PO Box 765, Chelmsford, Essex CM2 9XB
Tel: 01245 616000 Fax News Room: 01245 492983
Email: essex@bbc.co.uk
Managing Director: Margaret Hyde

BBC GMR
PO Box 951, Oxford Road, Manchester M60 1SJ
Tel: 0161 200 2020 Fax: 0161 244 3122
Email: michelle.daniel@bbc.co.uk
Editor: Karen Hannah
Marketing Manager: Michelle Daniel

BBC HEREFORD & WORCESTER
Hylton Road, Worcester WR2 5WW
Tel: 01905 748485 Fax: 01905 748006
Email: worcester@bbc.co.uk
Senior Broadcast Journalist: Mark Hellings

BBC LONDON 94.9 FM
35 Marylebone High Street, London W1U 4QA
Tel: 020 7224 2424 Fax: 020 7487 2908 / 020 7208 9661
Email: yourlondon@bbc.co.uk
Web Site: www.bbc.co.uk/london
Manager: David Robey

BBC NORTH YORKSHIRE - RADIO YORK
For North Yorkshire
20 Bootham Row, York YO3 7BR
Tel: 01904 641351 Fax: 01904 540339
Email: radio.york@bbc.co.uk
Web Site: www.bbc.co.uk/york
Editor: Matt Youdale

BBC ORKNEY
Castle Street, Kirkwall, Orkney KW15 1DF
Tel: 01856 873939 Fax: 01856 872908
Email: radio.orkney@bbc.co.uk
Senior Producer: John Ferguson

BBC OXFORD
(incorporating BBC Radio Oxford)
269 Banbury Road, Oxford OX2 7DW
Tel: 0845 9311 444 Fax: 08459 311 555
Email: radio.oxford.news@bbc.co.uk
Managing Editor: Steve Taschini

BBC RADIO BRISTOL
Whiteladies Road, Bristol, Avon BS8 2LR
Tel: 0117 974 1111 Fax: 0117 923 8323
Phone - In: 0845 900 5 955 Travel: 0845 900 6 955 Actionline: 0845 900 7 955
Email: radio.bristol@bbc.co.uk
Web Site: www.bbc.co.uk/radiobristol
Managing Editor: Jenny Lacey

BBC RADIO CAMBRIDGESHIRE
104 Hills Road, PO Box 96, Cambridge CB2 1LD
Tel: 01223 259 696 Fax: 01223 589 850
Email: cambs@bbc.co.uk
Editor: Andrew Wilson

BBC RADIO CLEVELAND
Broadcasting House, PO Box 95 FM, Newport Road, Middlesborough, Cleveland TS1 5DG
Tel: 01642 225 211 Fax: 01642 211 356 / 219 837
Email: cleveland.news@bbc.co.uk
Web Site: www.bbc.co.uk/england/radio-cleveland
Editor: Andrew Glover

BBC RADIO CORNWALL
Phoenix Wharf, Truro, Cornwall TR1 1UA
Tel: 01872 275421 Fax: 01872 275045
Email: radio.cornwall@bbc.co.uk
Manager: Ed Goodridge

BBC RADIO CUMBRIA
Annetwell Street, Carlisle, Cumbria CA3 8BB
Tel: 01228 592444 Fax: 01228 511195
Email: radio.cumbria@bbc.co.uk
Web Site: www.bbc.co.uk/cumbria
Managing Editor: Nigel Dyson

BBC RADIO DERBY
56 St.Helens Street, PO Box 269, Derby DE1 3HL
Tel: 01332 361111 Fax: 01332 290794
Email: radio.derby@bbc.co.uk
Web Site: www.bbc.co.uk/england/radioderby

BBC RADIO DEVON
PO Box 1034, Plymouth, Devon PL3 5BD
Tel: 01752 260323 Fax: 01752 234595
Email: radio.devon@bbc.co.uk
Web Site: www.bbc.co.uk/radiodevon
Manager: John Lilly

BBC RADIO GLOUCESTERSHIRE
Portland Court, London Road, Gloucester GL1 1SW
Tel: 01452 308 585 Fax: 01452 309 491
Email: radio.gloucestershire@bbc.co.uk
Web Site: www.bbc.co.uk/england/radiogloucestershire
Manager: Mark Hurrell

BBC RADIO GUERNSEY
Broadcasting House, Bulwer Avenue, St. Thompsons Guernsey GY2 4LA Channel Islands

Tel: 01481 200 600
Email: radio.guernsey@bbc.co.uk
Web Site:
www.bbc.co.uk/england/radioguernsey
Editor: David Martin

BBC RADIO HUMBERSIDE
Queens Court, Queens Gardens, Hull,
East Yorkshire HU1 3RH
Tel: 01482 323 232 Fax: 01482 226 409
Email: radio.humberside@bbc.co.uk
Web Site: www.bbc.co.uk
Managing Editor: Helen Thomas
Assistant Editor: Derek McGill

BBC RADIO JERSEY
18 Parade Road, St Hellier,
Jersey JE2 3PL
Tel: 01534 870000 Fax: 01534 732569
Email: radiojersey@bbc.co.uk
Web Site: www.bbc.co.uk/jersey
Managing Editor: Denzil Dudley
Assistant Editor: Matthew Price

BBC RADIO KENT
The Great Hall, Mount Pleasant Road,
Tunbridge Wells, Kent TN1 1QQ
Tel: 01892 670 000 Fax: 01892 549 118
Email: radio.kent@bbc.co.uk
Web Site: www.bbc.co.uk/england
Manager: Paul Leaper

BBC RADIO LANCASHIRE
Darwen Street, Blackburn,
Lancashire BB2 2EA
Tel: 01254 841 025 / 262 411
Fax: 01254 680 821
Email: jacquie.williams@bbc.co.uk
Arts Editor: Jacquie Williams, PO Box
339, Liverpool, L69 3TR
Pager: 01523 437315

BBC RADIO LEEDS
2 St Peters Square, Leeds,
West Yorkshire LS9 8AH
Tel: 0113 244 2131 Fax: 0113 242 0652
Email: radio.leeds@bbc.co.uk
Web Site: www.bbc.co.uk/radioleeds

BBC RADIO LEICESTER
Epic House, Charles Street,
Leicester LE1 3SH
Tel: 0116 251 6688 Fax: 0116 251 1463
Email: radioleicester@bbc.co.uk
Web Site: www.bbc.co.uk/radioleicester
Manager: Kate Squire

BBC RADIO LINCOLNSHIRE
PO Box 219, Radion Buildings, Newport,
Lincoln LN1 3XY
Tel: 01522 511411 Fax: 01522 511058
Email: radio.lincolnshire@bbc.co.uk
Web: www.bbc.co.uk/radiolincolnshire
Managing Editor: Charlie Partridge

BBC RADIO MERSEYSIDE
55 Paradise Street, Liverpool,
Merseyside L1 3BP
Tel: 0151 708 5500 Fax: 0151 794 0988
Email: radio.merseyside@bbc.co.uk
Web: www.bbc.co.uk/radiomerseyside
Managing Editor: Liam Fogarty

BBC RADIO NEWCASTLE
Broadcasting Centre, Newcastle-upon-
Tyne, Tyne and Wear NE99 1RN
Tel: 0191 232 4141 Fax: 0191 232 5082
Email: radionewcastle.news@bbc.co.uk
Web Site: www.bbc.co.uk/radionewcastle
Managing Editor: Graham Moss

BBC RADIO NORFOLK
The Forum, Millenium Plane, Norwich,
Norfolk NR2 1BH
Tel: 01603 617411 Fax: 01603 633692
Email: radionorfolk@bbc.co.uk
Web Site: www.bbc.co.uk/radionorfolk
Manager: David Clayton

BBC RADIO NORTHAMPTON
Broadcasting House, Abington Street,
Northampton NN1 2BH
Tel: 01604 239 100 Fax: 01604 230 709
Email: northamptonshire@bbc.co.uk
Manager: Laura Moss

BBC RADIO NOTTINGHAM
London Road, Nottingham NG2 4UU
Tel: 0115 955 0500 Fax: 0115 902 1983
Manager: Kate Squire

BBC RADIO SCOTLAND
Broadcasting House, Queen Margaret
Drive, Glasgow, Strathclyde G12 8DG
Scotland
Tel: 0141 338 2000 Fax: 0141 334 0614
Email: scottish.planning@bbc.co.uk

BBC RADIO SCOTLAND (BORDERS)
Ettrick Riverside, Selkirk, Selkirkshire TD7
Tel: 01750 21884 Fax: 01750 22400
Email: selkirk.news@bbc.co.uk
Richard Gordon

BBC RADIO SHEFFIELD
54 Shoreham Street, Sheffield, South
Yorkshire S1 4RS
Tel: 0114 273 1177 Fax: 0114 247 5454
Email: radio.sheffield@bbc.co.uk
Web Site: www.bbc.co.uk/radiosheffield
Managing Editor: Gary Keown

BBC RADIO SHROPSHIRE
PO Box 96, Shropshire SY1 3WW
Tel: 01743 248 484 Fax: 01743 271 702
Email: radio.shropshire@bbc.co.uk
Web: www.bbc.co.uk/shropshireradio
Managing Editor: Tim Pemberton

BBC RADIO SOLENT
Broadcasting House, 10 Havelock Road,
Southampton, Hampshire SO14 7PW
Tel: 023 8063 1311 Fax: 023 8033 9648
Email: radio.solent@bbc.co.uk
Managing Editor: Mia Costello

BBC RADIO STOKE
Cheapside, Stoke-on-Trent,
Staffordshire ST1 1JJ
Tel: 01782 208 080 Fax: 01782 289 115
Email: radio.stoke@bbc.co.uk
Managing Editor: Sue Owen

BBC RADIO SUFFOLK
St.Matthews Street, Ipswich,
Suffolk IP1 3EP
Tel: 01473 250 000 Fax: 01473 210 887
Email: suffolk@bbc.co.uk
Web: www.bbc.co.uk/england/radiosuffolk
Managing Editor: Gerald Main

BBC RADIO ULSTER
BBC Broadcasting House, Belfast,
County Antrim B2 8HQ Northern Ireland
Tel: 02890 338 000
Email: ni_news@bbc.co.uk

BBC RADIO WALES & RADIO CYMRU
Broadcasting House, Llantrisant Road,
Llandaff, Cardiff,
South Glamorgan CF5 2YQ
Tel: 029 2032 2000 Fax: 029 2032 2290
Email: newsgathering.wales@bbc.co.uk
Senior Producer: Nick Evans

BBC RADIO WILTSHIRE
Broadcasting House, Prospect Place,
Swindon, Wiltshire SN1 3RW
Tel: 01793 513 626 Fax: 01793 513 650
Email: amelia.claydon-smith@bbc.co.uk
Web Site: www.bbc.co.uk/wiltshire
Managing Editor: Tony Worgan
Contact: Amelia Claydon-Smith

BBC SCOTLAND (DUMFRIES)
Elmbank, Lovers Walk, Dumfries,
Dumfriesshire DG1 1NZ
Tel: 01387 268008 Fax: 01387 252568
ISDN: 01387 250432
Email: dumfries@bbc.co.uk
Editor: Willy Johnson

BBC SHETLAND
Pitt Lane, Lerwick, Shetland Isles ZE1
0DW
Tel: 01595 694747 Fax: 01595 694307
Email: radio.shetland@bbc.co.uk

BBC SOUTHERN COUNTIES RADIO
Broadcasting Centre, Guildford,
Surrey GU2 5AP
Tel: 01483 306306 Fax: 01483 304952

Email: southern.counties.radio@bbc.co.uk
Managing Editor: Neil Pringle
Contact for Press Releases: News Editor

BBC THREE COUNTIES RADIO
PO Box 3cr, Hastings Street, Luton,
Bedfordshire LU1 5XL
Tel: 01582 637400 Fax: 01582 401467
Email: 3cr@bbc.co.uk
Managing Editor: Mark Norman

BBC W M
The Mailbox Birmingham B1 1RF
Tel: 0121 567 6000 Fax: 0121 567 6025
Email: bbcwm@bbc.co.uk
Web Site: www.bbc.co.uk/radiowm
Manager: Keith Beech

COMMUNITY AND AREA STATIONS BBC HIGHLAND
7 Culduthel Road, Inverness IV2 4AD
Scotland
Tel: 01463 720720 Fax: 01463 236125
Email: inverness.news@bbc.co.uk
Managing Editor: Ishbel McLennan

RADIO NAN GAIDHEAL
Rosebank, Church Street, Stornoway
HS1 2LF
Tel: 01851 705000 Fax: 01851 704633
Email: naidheachd@bbc.co.uk

RADIO NAN GAIDHEAL BBC SCT
Clydsdale Bank Buildings, Somerled
Square, Portree, Isle of Skye IV51 9EH
Tel: 01478 612005 HQ admin: 01463
720720 Fax: 01478 612792
Web Site: www.bbc.co.uk/scotland

BBC National Radio

BBC RADIO 1,2,3,4,5
Broadcasting House, Portland Place,
London W1A 1AA
Tel: 020 7580 4468 Info Office: 0870
0100 222 Fax: 020 7637 1360
Email: newsbeat@bbc.co.uk
Web Site: www.bbc.co.uk

BBC WORLD SERVICE DRAMA
New Broadcasting House Portland Place,
Bush House, The Strand,
London W1A 1AA
Tel: 020 3614 0421
Email: david.hitchinson@bbc.co.uk
Web Site: www.bbc.co.uk/worldservice
Head of Radio Drama: Gordon House

Independent Local Radio

2 TEN FM
PO Box 2020, Reading,
Berkshire RG31 7FG
Tel: 0118 945 4400 Fax: 0118 928 8539
Email: karen.crowther@creation.com
Web Site: www.2tenfm.co.uk
Community & Events Officer: Karen
Crowther
Programme Controller: Tim Parker

2CR FM + CLASSIC GOLD 828
5-7 Southcote Road, Bournemouth,
Dorset BH1 3LR
Tel: 01202 234 900 Fax: 01202 234 909
Email: nicci.ryan@gcapmedia.com
Web Site: www.musicradio.com

96.6 TFM/MAGIC 1170MW
Radio House, Yale Crescent, Teesdale,
Thornaby Stockton-on-Tees, Cleveland
TS17 6AA
Tel: 01642 888 222 Fax: 01642 868 288
Email: tfmreception@tfmradio.com
Web Site: www.tfmradio.co.uk
Managing Director: Cath Ellington
Engineer: Antony Hill
Other Contacts: Colin Paterson, Dawn
Gibson

96.9 VIKING FM
Commercial Road, Hull, East Yorkshire
HU1 2SG
Tel: 01482 325 141 Fax: 01482 587 067
Web Site: www.vikingfm.co.uk

ABSOLUTE RADIO
1 Golden Square, London W1F 9DJ
Tel: 020 7434 1215 Fax: 020 7434 1197
Email: info@absoluteradio.co.uk
Web Site: www.absoluteradio.co.uk

BEACON RADIO & RADIO WABC
267 Tettenhall Road, Wolverhampton,
West Midlands WV6 0DE
Tel: 01902 461 300
Email: newswolverhampton@creation.com
Web Site: www.musicradio.com

BELFAST CITY BEAT
Lamont Building, 46 Stranmillis
Embankment, Belfast, County Antrim
BT9 5FN Northern Ireland
Tel: 028 9020 5967 Fax: 028 9020 0023
Email: studio@citybeat.co.uk
Web Site: www.citybeat.co.uk

BRMB FM (96.4)
9 Brindleyplace, 4 Oozells Square,
Birmingham B1 2DJ
Tel: 0121 245 5000 Fax: 0121 245 5245
Email: info@brmb.co.uk
Web Site: www.brmb.co.uk

BROADLAND 102
47-49 Colegate, Norwich,
Norfolk NR3 1DB
Tel: 01603 630 621 Fax: 01603 671 167
Email: sales@broadland102.co.uk
Web Site: http://broadland102.musicradio.com/homepage.jsp

CAPITAL FM
30 Leicester Square, London WC2H 7LA
Tel: 020 7766 6000 Fax: 020 7766 6100
Email: newsdesk@capitalradio.com
Web Site: www.capitalradio.com
95.8 fm

CAPITAL GOLD
30 Leicester Square, London WC2H 7LA
Tel: 020 7766 6000 Fax: 020 7766 6100
Email: emma.liddiard@capitalradiogroup.com
Web Site: www.capitalgold.com
1548 AM

CAPITAL GOLD
PO Box 2000, Brighton, East Sussex
BN41 2SS
Tel: 01273 430111 Fax: 01273 424783
Email: jasonkluver@capitalradiogroup.com
Web Site: www.capitalgold.com
102.4 to 103.5 fm

CENTRAL FM
Forth Valley's Finest
201 High Street, Falkirk, Stirlingshire FK1
1DU Scotland
Tel: 01324 611 164 Fax: 01324 611 168
Email: mail@centralfm.co.uk
Web Site: www.centralfm.co.uk

CLASSIC AMBER GOLD
47-49 Colegate, Norwich, Norfolk NR3
1DB
Tel: 01603 666 000 Fax: 01603 671 167
Email: laurette.holmes@classicgolddigital.com
Web Site: www.classicgolddigital.com

CLASSIC FM
7 Swallow Place, London W1B 2AG
Tel: 020 7343 9000 Fax: 020 7344 2700
Email: charlotte.rosier@classicfm.com
Web Site: www.classicfm.com

CLYDE 1
Clydebank Business Park, Clydebank,
Dumbartonshire G81 2RX Scotland
Tel: 0141 565 2200 Fax: 0141 565 2301
Email: victoria.paterson@radioclyde.com
Web Site: www.radioclyde.com
Chart and contemporary hits stations for
Glasgow. Local news and sports informa-

tion, presenter profiles, scheduling and music section including Scottish music.
Contact Sales Marketing Manager: Victoria Paterson

CLYDE 2
Clydebank Business Park, Clydbank, Dumbartonshire G81 2RX
Tel: 0141 565 2200 Fax: 0141 565 2302
Email: victoria.paterson@radioclyde.com
Web Site: www.radioclyde.com
Easy listening station for Glasgow. Local news and sports information, music, station and presenter profiles. Available on AM, DAB and live web stream.
Contact Marketing Sales Manager: Victoria Paterson

CONNECT FM
Centre 2000, Robinson Close, Telford Way Industrial Estate, Kettering, Northamptonshire NN16 8PU
Tel: 01536 412413 Fax: 01536 517390
Email: info@connectfm.com
Web Site: www.connectfm.com
Programme Controller: Danny Gibson

COOL FM
PO Box 974, Belfast, County Antrim BT1 1RT Northern Ireland
Tel: 028 9181 7181 Fax: 028 9181 4974
Email: music@coolfm.co.uk
Web Site: www.coolfm.co.uk
Managing Director: Mr John-Paul Valentine

DOWNTOWN RADIO
Newtownards, Co.Down BT23 4ES
Tel: 028 9181 5555 Fax: 028 9181 5252
Email: programmes@downtown.co.uk
Web Site: www.downtown.co.uk

ESSEX FM/BREEZE
19-20 Cliftown Road, Southend-on-Sea, Essex SS1 1SX
Tel: 01702 333711 Fax: 01702 345224 (Sales & Marketing)
Email: studios@essexfm.co.uk
Web Site: www.essexfm.co.uk

FORTH
13-17 Forth Street, Edinburgh, Midlothian EH1 3LF Scotland
Tel: 0131 556 9255 Advertising Tel: 0131 475 1302 Fax: 0131 558 3277
Email: justine.murphy@radioforth.com
Web Site: www.forthonline.com
Contact Sales Executive: Justine Murphy

FOX FM
Brush House, Pony Road, Oxford OX4 2XR
Tel: 01865 871 000 Fax: 01865 871 043
Email: reception@foxfm.co.uk
Web Site: www.foxfm.co.uk

GALAXY 101
Millennium House, 26 Baldwin Street, Bristol, Avon BS1 1SE
Tel: 0117 901 0101 Fax: 0117 901 4666
Email: p.redmore@galaxy101.co.uk
Web Site: www.galaxy101.co.uk
Sales Controller: Paul Redmore

GEM AM
29-31 Castle Gate, Nottingham NG1 7AP
Tel: 0115 952 7000 Fax: 0115 912 9333
Email: gemam@musicradio.com

GWR FM
Wessex House 1 Passage Street Bristol, Avon BS99 7SN
Tel: 0117 984 3200 Fax: 0117 984 3205
Email: reception@gwrfmmusicradio.com
Web Site: www.musicradio.com

HEART
5 Abbey Court Fraser Road Priory Business Park Bedford MK44 3WH
Tel: 01234 272 400 Fax: 01234 235009
Email: news@heart.co.uk
Web Site: www.heart.co.uk
Programme Controller: Tony Dibbin

HEART 106.2
The Chrysalis Group, Chrysalis Building, 13 Bramley Road, London W10 6SP
Tel: 020 7468 1062 Fax: 020 7470 1052
Email: danielle.ford@heart1062.co.uk
Web Site: www.heart1062.co.uk
Contact Head of Marketing: Danielle Ford
Contact Head of Sales: Dan Durling
Email: dan.durling@heart1062.co.uk

IMAGINE FM
Regent House, Heaton Lane, Stockport, Cheshire SK4 1BX
Tel: 0161 609 1425/6
Fax: 0161 609 1441
Email: danielvincent@imaginefm.net

INVICTA FM
Radio House, John Wilson Business Park, Whitstable, Kent CT5 3QX
Tel: 01227 772004 Fax: 01227 771558
Email: info@invictaradio.co.uk
Web Site: www.invictafm.com

INVICTA SUPERGOLD
Radio House, John Wilson Business Park, Whitstable, Kent CT5 3QX
Tel: 01227 772004 Fax: 01227 774474
Email: info@Invictaradio.co.uk
Web Site: www.invictafm.com

107.6 KESTREL FM
2nd Floor, Paddington House, The Walks Shopping Centre, Basingstoke, Hampshire RG21 7LJ
Tel: 01256 694 000 Fax: 01256 694 111
Chairman: Andy Craig

Managing Director: Kim Chapman
Programme Manager: Stuart McGinley
Sales Director: Amanda Dandridge
Best music from the past 30 years, local news and information.

KISS 100
Mappin House, 4 Winsley Street, London W1W 8HF
Tel: 020 7975 8100
Email: liz.fands@emap.com
Web Site: www.kiss100.com
Contact Sales Executive: Liz Fands

MAGIC 105.4
Mappin House 4 Winsley Street, London W1W 8HF
Tel: 0207 182 8233 Fax: 0207 182 8165
Email: studio@magic.fm
Web Site: www.magicfm.com
Managing Director: Sheila Porritt

MAGIC 1152
(owned by EMAP Radio plc)
? Pilgrim Street, Newcastle upon Tyne NE1 6BF
Tel: Advertising Tel: Fax: Advertising Fax:
Email: pauline.peniche@metroandmagic.com
Web Site: www.magic1152.co.uk
Contact Advertising Manager: Pauline Peniche

MAGIC 999
PO Box 301, St.Pauls Square, Preston, Lancashire PR1 1YE
Tel: 01772 47 77 00 Fax: 01772 477 701
Email: nikki.murray@rockfm.co.uk
Web Site: www.magicradio.com / www.rockfm.co.uk

MANX RADIO
Broadcasting House, PO Box 1368, Isle of Man IM99 1SW
Tel: 01624 682 600 Fax: 01624 682 604
Email: postbox@manxradio.com
Web Site: www.manxradio.com
Managing Director: Anthony Pugh
Programme Manager: Chris Williams
Sales and Marketing Manager: John Marsom

MERCURY FM & CLASSIC GOLD
The Stanley Centre, Kelvin Way, Manor Royal Industrial Estate, Crawley, West Sussex RH10 9SE
Tel: 01293 519161 Fax: 01293 636 039
Email: sam.eatwell@musicradio.com
Web Site: www.mercuryfm.co.uk
Contact Sales Co-ordinator: Sam Eatwell

THE NEW 96.3 AIRE FM
PO Box 2000, 51 Burley Road, Leeds, West Yorkshire LS3 1LR
Tel: 0113 283 5500 Fax: 0113 283 5501

Email: aire.news@radioaire.com
Web Site: www.radioaire.co.uk

PICCADILLY 1152
Castlequay, Manchester M15 4PR
Tel: 0161 288 5000 Fax: 0161 288 5001
Email: news@k103.co.uk
Web Site: www.k103.co.uk
Programme Director: Andy Robson

PLYMOUTH SOUND
Earls Acre, Plymouth, Devon PL3 4HX
Tel: 01752 275600 Fax: 01752 275605
Email: alison.wyse@musicradio.com

THE PULSE
Penine House, Forster Square, Bradford, West Yorkshire BD1 5NE
Tel: 01274 203040 Fax: 01274 203130
Email: news@pulse.co.uk
Web Site: www.pulse.co.uk

Q103
The Vision Park, Histon, Cambridge CB4 9WW
Tel: 01223 235255 Fax: 01223 235161
Email: reception@Q103.musicradio.com
Programme Controller: Craig Morris

RADIO BORDERS
Tweedside Park, Tweedbank, Galashiels, Selkirkshire TD1 3TD
Tel: 01896 759444 Fax: 01896 759494
Email: keith@radioborders.com
Web Site: www.radioborders.com

RADIO CITY
St John's Beacon, Houghton Street, Liverpool, Merseyside L1 1RL
Tel: 0151 472 6800 Fax: 0151 472 6821
Email: mike.sarath@radiocity.co.uk
Web Site: www.radiocity.co.uk
Contact Sales Manager: Mike Sarath

RADIO TYNESIDE
The Studios, General Hospital, Westgate Road, Newcastle-upon-Tyne, NE4 6BE
Tel: 0191 273 6970 Fax: 0191 273 3558
Email: info@radiotyneside.co.uk
Web Site: www.radiotyneside.co.uk
Station Director: DL Nicholson MBE
Station Director: M Bland
Recruitment: C Eggett
Radio Tyneside is a large hospital broadcasting service for Newcastle and Gateshead. It broadcasts twenty-four hours a day to the hospital community on 1575AM and on Patientline Channel 6 in 4 hospitals. Its main output is music-based, covering fifty years of easy listening, plus specialised music programmes.

RAM FM
35-36 Irongate, Derby DE1 3GA
Tel: 01332 205 577 Fax: 01332 851 111
Email: ramfm@musicradio.com

ROYAL 1 RADIO
Glasgow Royal Infirmary, 84-106 Castle Street, Glasgow, Strathclyde G4 0SF
Tel: 0141 211 4835
Email: mayrutherford@yahoo.com
Company Secretary: May Rutherford

SCOT FM
No 1 Shed, Albert Quay, Edinburgh, Mid Lothian EH6 7DN Scotland
Tel: 0131 625 8400 Fax: 0131 625 8401
Email: mick.hall@scot-fm.com

SEVERN SOUND
Bridge Studios, Eastgate Centre, Gloucester GL1 1SS
Tel: 01452 313 200 Fax: 01452 313 213
Email: reception@severnsound.musicradio.com
Web Site: www.koko.com

SIBC
Market Street, Lerwick, Shetland ZE1 0JN Scotland
Tel: 01595 695 299 Fax: 01595 695 696
Email: info@sibc.co.uk
Web Site: www.sibc.co.uk

SIGNAL 2
Stoke Road, Stoke-on-Trent, Staffordshire ST4 2SR
Tel: 01782 7441 300
Fax: 01782 7441 351
Email: signal2@signalradio.com
Web Site: www.signalradio.com

SIGNAL ONE
Stoke Road, Stoke-on-Trent, Staffordshire ST4 2SR
Tel: 01782 7441 300
Fax: 01782 741 341
Email: khoward@signalradio.com
Web Site: www.signalradio.com

SOUTH WEST SOUND
Unit 40, The Loreburn Centre, High Street, Dumfries, Dumfriesshire DG1 2BD
Tel: 01387 250999 Fax: 01387 265629
Email: fiona.blackwood@southwestsound.co.uk
Web Site: www.west-sound.co.uk

SOUTHERN FM
PO Box 2000, Brighton, East Sussex RG9 4DP
Tel: 01273 430 111 Fax: 01273 430 098
Email: melanie.wood@capitalradiogroup.co.uk
Web Site: www.southernfm.com
Contact News Editor: Claire Martin
Email: claire.martin@capitalradiogroup.co.uk
Contact Sales Support Co-ordinator: Melanie Wood

SPECTRUM RADIO LTD
4 Ingate Place, London SW8 3NS
Tel: 020 7627 4433 Fax: 020 7627 3409
Email: enquiries@spectrumradio.net
Web Site: www.spectrumradio.net
Manager: Paul Hogan

SUN FM
PO BOX 1034, Sunderland, Tyne and Wear SR5 2YL
Tel: 0191 548 1034 Fax: 0191 548 7171
Email: julie.bartle@sun-fm.com
Web Site: www.sun-fm.com
Marketing Officer: Julie Bartle
Music, local news and information for the city of Sunderland and surrounding areas.

SUNRISE RADIO (YORKSHIRE)
Sunrise House, 30 Chapel Street, Bradford, West Yorkshire BD1 5DN
Tel: 01274 735043 Fax: 01274 728534
Email: sales@sunriseradio.fm
Web Site: www.sunriseradio.fm

SWANSEA SOUND 1170/96.4FM THE WAVE
Victoria Road, Gowerton, Swansea, West Glamorgan SA4 3AB
Tel: 01792 511170 Fax: 01792 511965
Email: info@swanseasound.co.uk
Web Site: www.swanseasound.co.uk

TALK SPORT
18 Hatfields, London SE1 8DJ
Tel: 020 7959 7800 Fax: 020 7959 7804
Email: jon.don-carolis@talksport.co.uk
Web Site: www.talksport.net
Contact Senior Commercial Director: Jon Don-Carolis

TAY
P.O. Box 1028 Dundee DD3 7YH
Tel: 01382 200800 Sales Tel: 01382 423 207 Fax: 01382 423252
Email: lesley.mckenzie@radiotay.co.uk
Web Site: www.radiotay.co.uk
Contact Sales Director: Lesley Mckenzie

TEN 17 FM
Latton Bush Business Centre, Southern Way, Harlow, Essex CM18 7BB
Tel: 01279 432415 Fax: 01279 445289

TRENT FM
29-31 Castle Gate, Nottingham NG1 7AP
Tel: 0115 952 7000 Fax: 0115 912 9333
Email: nicci.ryan@gcapmedia.com
Web Site: www.trentfm.co.uk
Marketing Manager: Nicci Ryan

UJIMA RADIO
The Ceed (Charity) Ltd,
Ujima House, 97-107 Wilder Street, Bristol, Avon BS2 8QU
Tel: 0117 942 9555 Fax: 0117 942 6999

Email: kevin@ceed.co.uk
Web Site: www.ceed.co.uk

WEST SOUND MW AND WEST FM
Radio House, 54 Holmston Road, Ayr Ayrshire KA7 3BE
Tel: 01292 283 662 Fax: 01292 283 665
Email: westsound@srh.co.uk
Web Site: www.west-sound.co.uk

WYVERN FM
5-6 Barbourne Terrace, Worcester WR1 3JZ
Tel: 01905 612 212 Fax: 01905 746 637
Email: jo.clark@gcapmedia.com
Web Site: www.wyvernfm.co.uk

Media: Television

BBC TV Stations

BBC ABERDEEN
Broadcasting House, Beechgrove Terrace, Aberdeen AB15 5ZT
Tel: 01224 625233 Fax: 01224 384899
Email: news.aberdeen@bbc.co.uk

BBC BRISTOL & BBC WEST
Broadcasting House, Whiteladies Road, Bristol, Avon BS8 2LR
Tel: 0117 973 2211 Fax News Room: 0117 974 1537
Email: pointswest@bbc.co.uk
Web Site: www.bbc.co.uk/bristol

BBC EAST
The Forum, Millenium Plain, Norwich, Norfolk NR2 1BH
Tel: 01603 619 331 Fax News Room: 01603 667865
Email: look.east@bbc.co.uk

BBC EAST MIDLANDS
BBC London Road, Nottingham NG2 4UU
Tel: 0115 955 0500 Fax News Room: 0115 902 1983
Email: emt@bbc.co.uk

BBC EDINBURGH
The Tun, 111 Hollywood Road, Edinburgh, Midlothian EH8 8PG
Tel: 0131 225 3131 Fax: 0131 248 4220
Email: scottish.planning@bbc.co.uk

BBC MIDLANDS
BBC The Mail Box Commercial Street, Birmingham B1 1RF
Tel: 0121 432 8888 Fax: 0121 432 8634
Email: midlandstoday@bbc.co.uk

BBC NORTH
New Broadcasting House, PO Box 27, Oxford Road, Manchester M60 1SJ
Tel: 0161 200 2020 Fax: 0161 244 3122
Email: lawrence.mann@bbc.co.uk
Web Site: www.bbc.co.uk/manchester
Head of Programming: Lawrence Mann

BBC NORTHERN IRELAND
Broadcasting House, Ormeau Avenue, Belfast, County Antrim BT2 8HQ Northern Ireland
Tel: 028 9033 8000 Fax: 028 9033 8800
Email: ni_news@bbc.co.uk

BBC SCOTLAND
Broadcasting House, Queen Margaret Drive, Glasgow, Strathclyde G12 8DG Scotland
Tel: 0141 339 8844 Fax: 0141 334 0614
Email: scottish.planning@bbc.co.uk

BBC LONDON & SOUTH EAST
Newsroom South East, 35 Marylebone High Street London W1M 4AA
Tel: 020 8743 8000
Email: yourlondon@bbc.co.uk
Web Site: www.bbc.co.uk/london

BBC SOUTH WEST
Broadcasting House, Seymour Road, Plymouth, Devon PL3 5BD
Tel: 01752 229201 Fax: 01752 234595
Email: radio.devon@bbc.co.uk

BBC TELEVISION (LEEDS)
Television Centre, 2 St Peters Square, Leeds, West Yorkshire LS9 8AH
Tel: 0113 244 1188 Fax: 0113 243 9387
Email: look.north@bbc.co.uk
Web Site: www.bbc.co.uk/england/looknorthyorkslincs

BBC TELEVISION (NEWCASTLE)
Broadcasting Centre, Barrack Road, Newcastle-upon-Tyne, Tyne and Wear NE99 2NE
Tel: 0191 232 1313 Fax: 0191 221 0112
Email: newcastlenews@bbc.co.uk

BBC TV
Television Centre, Wood Lane London W12 7RJ
Tel: 020 8743 8000
Email: jana.bennett@bbc.co.uk
Web Site: www.bbc.co.uk
Contact Programme Director: Jana Bennett

BBC TV SOUTH
Broadcasting House, Havelock Road, Southampton SO14 7PU
Tel: 023 8022 6201 Fax: 023 8033 9931
Email: newsg.south@bbc.co.uk

BBC WALES
Broadcasting House, Llantrisant Road, Llandaff, Cardiff, South Glamorgan CF5 2YQ
Tel: 029 2032 2000 Fax: 029 2055 2973
Email: newsgathering.wales@bbc.co.uk

Independent Television

CHANNEL FOUR TV CO LTD
124 Horseferry Road, London SW1P 2TX
Tel: 020 7396 4444
Email: klygo@channel4.com
Web Site: www.channel4.co.uk
Director of Programmes: Kevin Lygo
Press Office contact: Loretta de Souza

CHANNEL TV
Television Centre, La Pouquelaye, St Hellier, Jersey JE1 3ZD
Tel: 01534 816 816 Fax: 01534 816 817
Email: michael.lucas@channeltv.co.uk
Web Site: www.channeltv.co.uk
Managing Director: Michael Lucas

FIVE
22 Long Acre, London WC2E 9LY
0845 7 050505Tel: 084 570 50 505
Email: news@five.tv
Web Site: www.five.tv
Director of Programmes: Dan Chambers
Senior Programme Controller (News, Current Affairs and Docs): Chris Shaw
Controller of Special Events and Pop Features: Sham Sandhu
Controller of Daytime, Arts and Religion: Kim Peat
Controller of Features and Entertainment: Ben Frow
Comedy Controller: Graham Smith

GMTV
The London Television Centre, Upper Ground, London SE1 9TT
Tel: 020 7827 7000 Fax: 020 7827 7001
Email: info@gm.tv
Web Site: www.gm.tv

GRAMPIAN TV
Grampian TV, The Television Centre Craigshaw Business Park, West Tullos Aberdeen AB12 3QH Scotland
Tel: 01224 848 848 Fax: 01224 848 800
Email: lyndsay.scatterty@stv.tv
Web Site: www.stv.tv
Head of Public Relations:Lindsay Scatterty

ITV1 ANGLIA
Anglia House, Norwich, Norfolk NR1 3JG
Tel: 01603 615 151 Fax: 01603 761 245
Email: kaz.coulson@itv.com
Web Site: www.angliatv.co.uk

ITV1 CENTRAL ENGLAND
Gas Street, Birmingham West Midlands
B1 2JT
Tel: 0121 643 9898 Fax: 0121 634 4898
Email: dutyoffice@itv.com
Web Site: www.carlton.com

ITV1 GRANADA
Quay Street, Manchester M60 9EA
Tel: 0161 832 7211 Fax: 0161 827 2180
Email: info@itv.com
Web Site: www.itvregions.com/Granada/

ITV1 LONDON WEEKDAYS
101 St Martin's Lame,
London WC2N 4RF
Tel: 020 7240 4000 Fax: 020 7240 1775
Email: planning@itvlondon.com
Web: http://www.itvregions.com/london/

ITV1 LONDON WEEKENDS
London Television Centre, Upper Ground,
London SE1 9LT
Tel: 020 7620 1620 Fax: 020 7261 3115
Email: planning@itvlondon.com

ITV1 TYNE TEES
The Television Centre, City Road,
Newcastle-upon-Tyne, Tyne and Wear
NE1 2AL
Tel: 0191 261 0181 Fax: 0191 261 2302
Email: tyne-tees@itv.com
Web Site: www.tynetees.tv

ITV1 WALES
The Media Centre, Culverhouse Cross,
Cardiff, CF5 6XJ Wales
Tel: 029 2059 0590 Fax: 029 2059 7183
Email: matthew.barroccu@itv.com
Contact Advertising Officer: Matthew
Barroccu

ITV1 WEST COUNTRY
Langage Science Park, Plymouth, Devon
PL7 5BQ
Tel: 01752 333 333 Advertising Tel:
01752 333 311 Fax: 01752 333 444

ITV1 WEST OF ENGLAND
The Television Centre, Bath Road, Arnos
Vale, Bristol, Avon BS4 3HG
Tel: 0117 972 2722 Fax: 0117 971 7685
Email: itvwest@itv.com
Web Site: www.itvregions.com/west

ITV1 YORKSHIRE
104 Kirkstall Road Leeds, West Yorkshire
LS3 1JS
Tel: 0113 222 8529 Fax: 0113 222 8526
Email: info@yorkshiretv.com
Web Site: www.itvregions.com/Yorkshire
Rights Manager for Entertainment,
Daytime & International Productions:
Janet Pitts
Email address: janet.pitts@itv.com

S4C
Parc Ty Glas, Llanishen, Cardiff, CF14
5DU Wales
Tel: 029 2074 7444 Fax: 029 2075 4444
Email: s4c@s4c.co.uk
Web Site: www.s4c.co.uk

SCOTTISH TV
200 Renfield Street, Glasgow, Strathclyde
G2 3PR Scotland
Tel: 0141 300 3000 Fax: 0141 300 3030
Email: graeme.pattullo@stv.tv
Web Site: www.scottishtv.co.uk
Head of Sales: Graeme Pattullo

SCREAM FILMS
Lamb House Church Street, London W4
2PD
Tel: 0208 995 8255 Fax: 0208 995 8456
Web Site: www.screamfilms.co.uk
Creative Director: Southan Morris
Head of Production: Susie Dark
Producer: Rob Farquhar
Head of Development: Lisa Plasco

STREETWISE TV
11-15 Betterton Street, Covent Garden,
London WC2H 9PB
Tel: 020 7470 8825 Fax: 020 7470 8826
Email: Streetwise_tv@hotmail.com
Contact: Ian Whittingham, Vincent James,
Zach O'Ryan.
Streetwise TV is a young and dynamic company run by an exciting and enthusiastic team, with a breadth of skills and experience sourced from television, music and recording and the press. We specialise in dramas, documentaries and youth TV. Currently we are in the process of applying for a european cable TV license. Zach O'Ryan, is the artiste we represent and are developing our programmes around.

UTV
Havelock House, Ormeau Road, Belfast,
BT7 1EB Northern Ireland
Tel: 028 9032 8122 Fax: 028 9024 6695
Email: info@utvplc.com
Web Site: www.utvlive.com/television/

Satellite & Cable TV

CNBC EUROPE
Unit 1/1, Harbour Yard, Chelsea Harbour,
London SW10 0XD
Tel: 020 7352 9205 Fax: 020 7352 9628
Email: CBlenkinsop@cnbceurope.com
Director of Marketing and
Communications: Charlotte Blenkinsop

THE DISCOVERY CHANNEL
160 Great Portland Street, London W1W
5QA
Tel: 0207 462 3619
Email: lynn.li@bskyb.com
Web Site: www.discoverychannel.co.uk
Contact PR Manager: Lynn Li

ITV1, ITV2, ITV3 & ITV4
200 Gray's Inn Road, London WC1X 8HF
Tel: 020 7843 8000 Fax: 020 7843 8158
Email: thomas.green@itv.com
Web Site: www.itv.com
Contact Business Development Manager:
Thomas Green

MTV MUSIC TELEVISION EUROPE
180 Oxford Street, London W1D 1DS
Tel: 020 7284 7777 Fax: 020 7284 7788
Web Site: www.mtv.co.uk
Senior Personnel: Dylan Jones

NICKELODEON UK
15-18 Rathbone Place, London W1T 1HU
Tel: 020 7462 1000 Fax: 020 7462 1030
Email: louise.condon@nickelodeon.co.uk
Web Site: www.nickelodeon.co.uk

SCI-FI CHANNEL
5-7 Mandeville Place, London W1U 3AR
Tel: 020 7535 3500 Fax: 020 7535 3537
Email: austin.o'dowd@nbcuni.com
Web Site: www.uk.scifi.co.uk
Contact Sales Operations Manager:
Austin O'Dowd

SKY TELEVISION
Grant Way, Isleworth, Middlesex TW7
5QD
Tel: 020 7705 3000 Fax: 020 7705 3030
Web Site: www.sky.co.uk

VIRGIN MEDIA
Export House, Cawsey Way, Woking,
Surrey GU21 6QX
Tel: 020 7299 5888
Email: info@virginmedia.com
Web Site: www.virginmedia.com

WARNER BROS INTERNATIONAL TELEVISION
98 Theobalds Road, London WC1X 8WB
Tel: 020 7984 5400 Fax: 020 7984 5001

PUBLISHING

Theatre Publishers

AMBER LANE PRESS
Cheorl House, Church Street, Charlbury
Oxfordshire OX7 3PR
Tel/Fax: 01608 810 024
Email: info@amberlanepress.co.uk
Web Site: www.amberlanepress.co.uk
Plays and books on drama & theatre. No longer actively publishing.

ANCHORAGE PRESS LTD
Cressrelles Publishing
10 Station Road Ind. Estate, Colwall,
Malvern, Herefordshire WR13 6RN
Tel/Fax: 01684 540 154
Email: simon@cressrelles.co.uk
Web Site: www.cressrelles.co.uk
Contact: Simon Smith
Leading American publisher of plays for children, including Little Women and the Wizard of Oz.

A & C BLACK PUBLISHERS LTD
A division of Bloomsbury Publishing Plc
36 Soho Square, London W1D 3QY
Tel: 020 7758 0200 Fax: 020 7758 0222
Email: salesoffice@acblack.com,
hflood@acblack.com
Web Site: www.acblack.com
Contact: Naomi Robinson
A&C Black publish a wide range of backstage handbooks, actors' guides, audition books, dance books, costume and make-up manuals, and New Mermaid's classic plays. We also publish the Writers' & Artists' Yearbook and books on writing for television, theatre and radio.
Please write for detailed catalogues.

BROWN, SON & FERGUSON LTD
Incorporating James Gowans (Trade Bookbinders) James Munro & Co.
4-10 Darnley Street, Glasgow, Strathclyde G41 2SD Scotland
Tel: 0141 429 1234 (24 hours) Fax: 0141 420 1694
Email: info@skipper.co.uk
Web Site: www.skipper.co.uk
"Scottish Plays" series of play texts see www.scottishplays.co.uk

CABBELL PUBLISHING LTD
Woodman Works, 204 Durnsford Road,
London SW19 8DR
Tel: 020 8971 8450 Fax: 020 8971 8480
Email: andrew.todd@cabbell.co.uk
Web Site: www.cabbell.co.uk
Contact: Andrew Todd

CAMBRIDGE UNIVERSITY PRESS
The Edinburgh Building, Shaftesbury Road, Cambridge CB2 8RU
Tel: 01223 312393 Fax: 01223 315 052
Email: information@cambridge.org
Web Site: www.cambridge.org/uk
Publicity Executive: Gretchen Carroll
Classic play-texts, books on Theatre studies,
Theatre history and Drama criticism.
Major Shakespeare publisher. Theatre Reference books, and publications of leading journals, including Theatre Research International, Theatre Survey and New Theatre Quarterly. It is the oldest press in the world and is a charitable enterprise.

CELEBRITY BULLETIN LTD
8 - 10 Wiseton Road, London SW17 7EE
Tel: 020 8672 3191 Fax: 020 8672 2282
Email: equiries@celebrity-bulletin.co.uk
Contact: Neal Goddard
Publisher of the twice weekly "The Celebrity Bulletin" which lists arrivals in London and activities of celebrities world-wide.

CHATTO & WINDUS
Random House, 20 Vauxhall Bridge Road, London SW1V 2SA
Tel: 020 7840 8400 Fax: 020 7840 8778
Email: wsmith@randomhouse.co.uk
Web Site: www.randomhouse.co.uk
Contact: Willis Smith

CONTINUUM
The Tower Building, 11 York Road,
London SE1 7NX
Tel: 020 7922 0880 Fax: 020 7928 7894
Email: info@continuumbooks.com
Web Site: www.continuumbooks.com
Head of Marketing: Petra Green,
pgreen@continuumbooks.com

FABER & FABER LTD
Bloomsbury House, 74 - 77 Great Russell Street, London WC1B 3DA
Tel: 020 7927 3800 Fax: 020 7927 3801
Web Site: www.faber.co.uk
Whether you are an avid drama buff or an occasional theatre-goer, Faber's books on theatre studies, plays and screenplays are sure to be of interest. Faber do not accept unsolicited scripts.

SAMUEL FRENCH LTD
52 Fitzroy Street, Fitzrovia, London W1T 5JR
Tel: 020 7387 9373 Fax: 020 7387 2161
Email: theatre@samuelfrench-london.co.uk
Web: www.samuelfrench-london.co.uk

J. GARNET MILLER
Cressrelles Publishing
10 Station Road Ind. Estate, Colwall,
Malvern, Herefordshire WR13 6RN
Tel/Fax: 01684 540 154
Email: simon@cressrelles.co.uk
Web Site: www.cressrelles.co.uk
Contact: Simon Smith
Publishers of plays & Theatre Textbooks, offering adaptations of classics such as Pride and Prejudice, Jane Eyre and Wuthering Heights

ROBERT HALE LTD
Clerkenwell House, 45-47 Clerkenwell Green, London EC1R 0HT
Tel: 020 7251 2661 Fax: 020 7490 4958
Email: enquire@halebooks.com
Web Site: www.halebooks.com
Fiction and non-fiction, Biographies, Production handbooks.

HARPER COLLINS
77 - 85 Fulham Palace Road,
Hammersmith, London W6 8JB
Tel: 020 8741 7070 Fax: 020 8307 4440
Email: enquiries@harpercollins.co.uk
Web Site: www.harpercollins.co.uk
Chief Executive and Publisher: Victoria Barnsley OBE

KENYON-DEANE
Cressrelles Publishing
Unit 10, Station Road Ind. Est., Colwall,
Malvern, Herefordshire WR13 6RN
Tel/Fax: 01684 540 154
Email: simon@cressrelles.co.uk
Web Site: www.cressrelles.co.uk
Contact: Simon Smith
Plays & Theatre Textbooks, specialising in all-women cast and short plays. European Agents for Anchorage Press, leading American Publishers of Plays for Young People.

LOKI BOOKS LTD
38 Chalcot Crescent, London NW1 8YD
Tel/Fax: 020 7722 6718
Email: all@lokibooks.vianw.co.uk
Web Site: www.lokibooks.com
Contact: Marion Baraitser
Plays by women. Plays for theatre in education. Plays from international series.

METHUEN PUBLISHING LTD
8 Artillery Row, London SW1P 1RZ
Tel: 020 7802 0018 Fax: 020 7828 1244
Email: ntummons@methuen.co.uk
Web Site: www.methuen.co.uk
Publishing Director: Naomi Tummons
UK's, major publisher of Theatre books and Playtexts.
Complete catalogue available.

MOORLEY'S PRINT & PUBLISHING LTD
23 Park Road, Ilkeston,
Derbyshire DE7 5DA
Phone Day Tel/Fax: 0115 932 0643 (24 hours)
Email: webenquiries@moorleys.co.uk
Web Site: www.moorleys.co.uk
Religious Playtexts.

NELSON THORNES
Delta Place 27 Bath Road, Cheltenham,
Gloucestershire GL53 7TH
Tel: 01242 267287 Fax: 01242 253695
Email: cservices@nelsonthornes.com
Web Site: www.nelsonthornes.com
Publishers of textbooks and playscripts for secondary education

NEW PLAYWRIGHTS' NETWORK
Cressrelles Publishing
10 Station Road Industrial Estate, Colwall,
Malvern, Herefordshire WR13 6RN
Tel/Fax: 01684 540 154
Email: simon@cressrelles.co.uk
Web Site: www.cressrelles.co.uk
Contact: Simon Smith
Set up in the 1970s to promote the best work from new writers, the publisher offers plays, from short pieces, to one-acts, full length plays and pantomimes, for all-women, mixed and youth casts.

NODA PANTOMIMES
NODA House, 58-60 Lincoln Road,
Peterborough PE1 2RZ
Tel: 01733 865790 Fax: 01733 319506
Email: info@noda.org.uk
Web Site: www.noda.org.uk
Publishing Officer: Virginia McDermid
Agents and Publishers for top panto scriptwriters. Over 90 versions of the popular titles.

OBERON BOOKS LTD
521 Caledonian Road, London N7 9RH
Tel: 020 7607 3637 Fax: 020 7607 3629
Email: info@oberonbooks.com
Web Site: www.oberonbooks.com
Publisher: James Hogan
Publishers of Playtexts and theatre books.

ONEWORLD CLASSICS
243 - 253 Lower Mortlake Road,
Richmond, Surrey TW9 2LL
Tel: 020 8948 9550 Fax: 020 8948 5599
Email: info@oneworldclassics.com
Web Site: www.oneworldclassics.com
ADMINISTRATION:
Launched in Spring 2007 as a joint venture between Alma Books and Oneworld Publications, the company aims to expand the literary canon in the English-speaking world through a series of mainstream and lesser-known classics. In September 2007, the company expanded on its classics collection by acquiring the legendary Calder Publications list (founded 1949), and now boasts the new Calder Collection series and the Overture Opera Guides.
Sales and Marketing Director: Elisabetta Minervini
Calder Bookshop: 51 TheCut, London SE1 8LF, Tel. +44 (0)20 7620 2900.

THE ORION PUBLISHING GROUP
Orion House, 5 Upper St Martin's Lane,
London WC2H 9EA
Tel: 020 7240 3444 Fax: 020 7240 4822
Email:
publicity.enquiries@orionbooks.co.uk
Web Site: www.orionbooks.co.uk
Fiction, Screenplays, Media, Biographies, Childrens Books

OXFORD UNIVERSITY PRESS
Great Clarendon Street, Oxford OX2 6DP
Tel: 01865 556767 Fax: 01865 556646
Email: webenquiry.UK@oup.com
Web Site: www.oup.co.uk

PEARSON EDUCATION
Edinburgh Gate, Harlow,
Essex CM20 2JE
Tel: 01279 623 623 Fax: 01279 431 059
Email: sean.burke@pearson.com
Web Site: www.pearsoned-ema.com
President, Pearson UK: Rod Bristow
Marketing Manager: Sean Burke
Education/Drama.

PHAIDON PRESS LIMITED
18 Regents Wharf, All Saints Street,
London N1 9PA
Tel: 020 7843 1000 Fax: 020 7843 1010
Email: enquiries@phaidon.com
Web Site: www.phaidon.com
Publishers of books on the Arts.
Head of Publicity: Jennifer Lea, jlea@phaidon.com
Sales & Marketing Director: James Booth-Clibborn

RHINEGOLD PUBLISHING LTD
239 - 241 Shaftesbury Avenue, London
WC2H 8TF
Tel: 020 7333 1720 Marketing: 020 7333 1762 Fax: 020 7333 1765
Email: enquiries@rhinegold.co.uk, marketing@rhinegold.co.uk
Web Site: www.rhinegold.co.uk
Publishers of British Performing Arts Yearbook, British Music Yearbook, Music Education Yearbook, Opera Now, Classical Music, Music Teacher, The Singer, Early Music Today, Piano, Arts Marketing.

RICHMOND HOUSE PUBLISHING COMPANY LTD
Suite D, 4-6 Canfield Place,
London NW6 3BT
Tel: 020 7224 9666
Email: sales@rhpco.co.uk
Web Site: www.rhpco.co.uk
General Managers: Spencer Block, Gloria Gordon
Leading publishers of theatrical and entertainment directories and website databases, including 'The British Theatre Directory', 'Artistes & Agents', and 'The Official London Seating Plan Guide' (an A4 computer plans of major theatre and concert venues in London).

ROBSON BOOKS
Part of Anova Books Group Limited
Anova Books Group Limited, The Old Magistrates Court, 10 Southcombe Street, London W14 0RA
Tel: 020 7605 1400 Fax: 020 7605 1401
Email: customerservices@anovabooks.com
Web Site: www.anovabooks.com

ROUTLEDGE ITP
2 Milton Park, Milton, Abingdon,
Oxfordshire OX14 4RN
Tel/ Fax: 020 7017 6252
Email: talia.rodgers@routledge.co.uk
Web Site: www.routledge.com
Editorial (Theatre and Performance Studies): Talia Rodgers
Leading British Publisher of books on theatre, dance and performance studies.

SCHOOLPLAY PRODUCTIONS
15 Inglis Road, Colchester, Essex CO3 3HU
Tel: 01206 540 111 Fax: 01206 766 944
Email: schoolplay@inglis-house.demon.co.uk
Web: www.schoolplayproductions.co.uk
SchoolPlay Productions is the specialist UK company publishing plays and musicals (scripts, scores and cassettes) for performance by youth groups and schools. A summary catalogue is available on request. The full catalogue can be found on our web-site.

SIMON & SCHUSTER
1st Floor, 222 Gray's Inn Road, London
WC1X 8HB
Tel: 020 7316 1900 Fax: 020 7316 0332
Email: enquiries@simonandschuster.co.uk
Web Site: www.simonandschuster.com
Founded in 1924, Simon & Schuster, Inc. caters for general interest publishing, and provides consumers worldwide with a diverse range of quality books across a wide variety of genres and formats.

THAMES AND HUDSON LTD
181a High Holborn, London WC1V 7QX
Tel: 020 7845 5000 Fax: 020 7845 5050
Email: sales@thameshudson.co.uk
Web Site: www.thamesandhudson.com
Managing Director: Jamie Camplin
Theatre History and Biography

VIRGIN BOOKS
20 Vauxhall Bridge Road,
London SW1V 2SA
Tel: 020 7386 3300 Fax: 020 7386 3360
Email: marketing@virgin-books.co.uk
Web Site: www.virginbooks.com
List includes stage and screen series of biographies and books on voice from Cicely Berry.

WARNER/CHAPPELL MUSIC LTD
(formerly English Theatre Guild)
The Warner Building, 28 Kensington Church Street, London W8 4EP
Tel: 0207 938 0000 Fax: 0207 368 2777
Email: webmaster@warnerchappell.com
Web Site: www.warnerchappell.co.uk
Musicals Administrator: Claire Osborn
Award-winning music publishing company and rights holder, holding an extensive catalogue including "Happy Birthday To You", "Rhapsody in Blue", "Winter Wonderland".

JOSEF WEINBERGER LTD
12-14 Mortimer Street, London W1T 3JJ
Tel: 020 7580 2827 (4 lines)
Fax: 020 7436 9616
Email: general.info@jwmail.co.uk
Web Site: www.josef-weinberger.com
Editor: Chistopher Moss
Publisher and rightsholder of musicals and agents for Music Theatre International and the Rodgers & Hammerstein Theatre Library.

Newspapers & Theatrical Magazines

AMATEUR STAGE (1946)
Next Phase Media Ltd, Suite 404 Albany House, 324-326 Regents Street, London, W1B 3HH
Tel: 020 7622 6670 Fax: 0871 714 6996
Email: editor@asmagazine.co.uk
Web: www.amateurstagemagazine.co.uk
Editor: Douglas Mayo
Monthly features include new play & book reviews. West End reviews, production reports, technical information, production diary, interviews, education, training, news & other relevant articles.
Monthly: £2.40 per copy.
Subscriptions: 1 Year UK £24 2 Year UK £40 Europe £32
£46 Rest of World.

ARTS PROFESSIONAL
Unit 5 Pioneer Court, Chivers Way, Histon, Cambridge CB24 9PT
Tel: 01223 200200 Fax: 01223 200201
Email: editors@artsprofessional.co.uk
Web Site: www.artsprofessional.co.uk
Sales and Operations Manager: Paul Minett
Editor: Nosheen Iqbal
Publisher: Brian Whitehead
Co-Editors and Publishers.

THE CELEBRITY BULLETIN
10 Wiseton Road, London SW17 7EE
Tel: 020 8672 3191 Fax: 020 8672 2282
Email: enquiries@celebrity-bulletin.co.uk
ADMINISTRATION:
Editor: Neil Goddard
Subscription: published twice weekly - Mondays and Thursday, £80.00 per month; £75.00 per month if paid by bankers order or per annum.
Information about everyone in the news world-wide, including London arrivals, International arrivals, International activities, events and Biographies.

DANCE RESEARCH
Edinburgh University Press, 22 George Square, Edinburgh, Mid Lothian EH8 9LF
Tel: 0131 650 4218 Fax: 0131 650 3286
Email: wea@nildram.co.uk
Web Site: www.eupjournals.com
Editor: Richard Ralph (wea@nildram.co.uk)
Subscription rates Volume 29, 2011 (2 issues).
Institutions: UK £107; USA $215; elsewhere £118
Individuals: UK £51.50; USA $106; elsewhere £57
The Journal of the Society for Dance Research covers a broad spectrum of dance topics, ranging from the history of European theatrical dance to dance anthropology and Renaissance spectacle.
Society of Dance Research: The Society for Dance Research c/o Helen Thomas, London College of Fashion, 20 John Princes Street, London W1G OBJ, UK.
www.dancebooks.co.uk/sdr-uk

DANCING TIMES
45-47 Clerkenwell Green,
London EC1R 0EB
Tel: 020 7250 3006 Fax: 020 7253 6679
Email: dt@dancing-times.co.uk
Web Site: www.dancing-times.co.uk
ADMINISTRATION:
Editorial Team: Jonathan Gray, Zoë Anderson, Simon Oliver
Monthly: 1st of month
£2.96 per issue; £32.45 p.a. inland; £39.45 overseas surface and £42.00 by airmail.
Established since 1910 with international circulation. Ballet, Contemporary dance, Stage dancing, from general critical, historical and technical angles. Preliminary arrangements must be made for freelance articles. Photographs. Book reviews. Calendar of forthcoming performances, touring dates. News and reports from festivals, schools, etc.

ENCORE
See also, 'Johnny Mans Productions'
P.O.Box 196, Broxbourne,
Hertfordshire EN10 7WG
Tel: 0845 467 0792
Email: encoremags@aol.com, johnny-mansagent@aol.com
Web: www.johnnymansproductions.co.uk
Props: Johnny Mans Productions
Independent Trade Monthly for Show Products and Venues.
British theatre and concert hall monthly listings, plus news on venues, theatre managers, producers, promoters, societies, agencies, artistes and shows.
Yearly subscription priced at £25.00.

EQUITY JOURNAL
Guild House, Upper St Martin's Lane,
London WC2H 9EG
Tel: 020 7379 6000 (switchboard)
Fax: 020 7379 7001
Email: info@equity.org.uk
Web Site: www.equity.org.uk
Editor: Martin Brown
Four times a year. Free to members.
£12.00 per annum to non-members.
Journal of British Actors' Equity Association (Incorporating the Variety Artists' Federation).

MUSICAL STAGES MAGAZINE
PO Box 8365, London W14 0GL
Tel: 020 7603 2227 Fax: 020 7603 2221
Email: editor@musicalstages.co.uk
Web Site: www.musicalstages.co.uk
Editor/ Proprietor: Lynda Trapnell
Production Editor: Howard Sherwood
Musical Stages magazine - the only UK glossy just for musical theatre and cabaret

NEW THEATRE QUARTERLY
Cambridge University Press, Edinburgh Building, Shaftesbury Road, Cambridge CB2 2RU
Tel: 01223 312 393 Fax: 01223 315 052
Email: information@cambridge.org
Web Site: www.cambridge.org
Quarterly: £15 per copy, £22 p.a. for Equity Members, £32 p.a. for individuals, £65 p.a. for UK institutions.

OPERA (1950)
Opera Magazine, 36 Black Lion Lane,
London W6 9BE
Tel: 0208 748 0911
Email: info@opera.co.uk
Web Site: www.opera.co.uk
ADMINISTRATION:
Editor: John Allison, Tel: 0208 748 0911
Email: john@opera.co.uk, editor@opera.co.uk
Publishing manager: Andrew Miles
Tel: 020 8563 8893, Email: andrew@opera.co.uk
Circulation & distribution: David Blackett, Imagine Magazine Sales & Marketing, david.blackett@imaginemag.net 0845 6120094

PRODUCTION AND CASTING REPORT

6 - 14 Underwood Street,
London N1 7JQ
Tel: 020 7549 2578 Fax: 020 7566 8238
Email: info@pcrnewsletter.com
Web Site: www.pcrnewsletter.com
Subscription Rates: £22.46 a month
Production and Casting Report offers the latest auditions and job openings for actors, agents, and technicians.
Published weekly.

SPEECH AND DRAMA JOURNAL

53 Oxford Road, Temple Cowley, Oxford OX4 2ER
Web Site: www.stsd.org.uk
Subscription rates: £7.50 per annum; £5.50 per annum for trade; £3.50 per single copy, publication dates: 14th May, 14th November.
Speech and Drama is published twice yearly by the Society of Teachers of Speech and Drama. It covers drama, theatre, speech, musical theatre and areas of allied interest, directed towards students, professionals and educationalists at all levels. Illustrated.

THE STAGE

Stage House, 47 Bermondsey Street, London Bridge London SE1 3XT
General Tel: 020 7403 1818 Editorial Fax: 020 7939 8478 Advertising Fax: 020 7939 8479
Email: gen_enquiries@thestage.co.uk
Web Site: www.thestage.co.uk / www.showcall.co.uk
Editor: Brian Attwood
For Features and Reviews, contact: Emma Harlen
Weekly tabloid newspaper: Thursday.
£1.50 per copy.
Subscription Rate: £58.50 per annum or £53.00 by direct debit.
Covers professional stage (including variety, clubs, opera, dance, technical etc., professional and student showcases), television and radio; show business news, reviews and shows, programmes and books; forthcoming shows and relevant developments; illus; line and half-tone.

THEATRE NOTEBOOK (1945)

Society for Theatre Research, c/o The National Theatre Archive, 83 - 101 The Cut, London SE1 8LL
Email: theatrenotebook@str.org.uk
Web Site: www.str.org.uk
Editors: Trevor Griffiths, Robin Cave
Three times a year: February, June, October. Free to STR members, £20 for non-members. Articles on all aspects of theatre research; queries and answers; book reviews.

THEATRE RECORD

131 Sherringham Avenue,
London N17 9RU
Tel: 020 8737 8489 Fax: 020 8893 9677
Email: admin@theatrerecord.com
Web Site: www.theatrerecord.com
Editor: Ian Shuttleworth
Fortnightly.
Price £165 p.a. / US$360 p.a.0/ 330eurosp.a.
Full details of actors and production staff for all new plays and shows opening in London, with reprints of full reviews from critics of the major newspapers and journals (including Guardian, Observer, Time Out, etc.). Also A-Z of current productions and news of coming openings in London and outside. Includes Regional premieres, book reviews and production photographs. Simply, the most informative theatre journal in Britain

THEATRE RESEARCH INTERNATIONAL

Cambridge University Press, Edinburgh Building, Shaftesbury Road, Cambridge CB2 8RU
Tel: 01223 326 186 Professor Elaine Aston, Editor Department of Theatre Studies, Lancaster University, Lancaster, LA1 4YW, UK Email: e.aston@lancaster.ac.uk
Email: shoffmann@cambridge.org
Web Site: www.journals.cambridge.org
The journal of the International Federation for Theatre Research, Theatre Research International publishes articles on theatre practices in their social, cultural, and historical contexts, their relationship to other media of representation, and to other fields of inquiry. The journal seeks to reflect the evolving diversity of critical idioms prevalent in the scholarship of differing world contexts.
Contact: Sally Hoffmann

TIME OUT

Time Out Magazine Ltd, Universal House, 251 Tottenham Court Road,
London W1T 7AB
Tel: 020 7813 3000 Fax: 020 7323 3438
Email: editorial@timeout.com
Web Site: www.timeout.com
ADMINISTRATION:
Publisher and Managing Director: Mark Elliott
Editor: Mark Frith
Theatre Editor: Caroline McGinn
Price: £2.99 per weekly copy.
Commentary and listings of theatre, arts and entertainment events in London, including fringe theatre.

TOTAL THEATRE MAGAZINE

University of Winchester, Faculty of Arts, Sparkford Road, Winchester,
Hampshire SO22 4NR
Tel: 01962 827107
Editorial: 07752 142526
Email: max@totaltheatre.org.uk
Web Site: www.totaltheatre.org.uk
Editor: Dorothy Max Prior

VARIETY

3rd Floor, Procter House, 1 Procter Street, London WC1V 6EU
Tel: 0207 911 1924 Fax: 0207 911 1922
Email: dana.harris@variety.com
Web Site: www.variety.com
Editor: Dana Harris
Weekly - £5.00
The paper of record for global entertainment business.

WHAT'S ON STAGE MAGAZINE

Bandwidth Communications Ltd, 5th Floor, Palace Theatre, 109 - 113 Shaftesbury Avenue, London W1D 5AY
Switchboard: 0207 287 7106 Fax: 0207 494 3041
Web Site: www.whatsonstage.com
News, features, interviews, previews and reader offers.
Published 6 times a year.
Available to members only.
Editorial Director: Terri Paddock

Annuals and Directories

ARTISTES & AGENTS DIRECTORY

(incorporating the Corporate Event Organiser)
Richmond House Publishing Co., Suite D, 4-6 Canfield Place, London NW6 3BT
Tel: 020 7224 9666
Email: sales@artistesandagents.co.uk
Web Site: www.artistesandagents.co.uk
The "comprehensive entertainment directory" listing UK Agents and who they represent. Artistes & Agents contains over 20,000 working artistes from all aspects of the industry including the corporate sector - after dinner speakers, sports personalities, actors and actresses as well as the entire music and entertainment Industry. Other sections include TV & Radio, Production, Event Management & suppliers, venues, media & Public Relations and professional services.

BRITISH AND INTERNATIONAL MUSIC YEARBOOK

Rhinegold Publishing Ltd., 241 Shaftesbury Avenue, London WC2H 8TF
Tel: 01832 270 333 (sales) Tel: 020 7333 1733 (advertising) Fax: 020 7333 1769 (advertising) Tel: 020 7333 1760 (listings)
Fax: 020 7333 1766
Email: bmyb@rhinegold.co.uk
Web Site: www.rhinegold.co.uk
Annually.

The "bible" of the classical music industry; listings for orchestras, opera, choirs, performers, composers, agents, promoters, venues, associations, competitions, festivals, recording and broadcasting, education, marketing, publishers, suppliers and services, and many more.

BRITISH THEATRE DIRECTORY
Richmond House Publishing Co, Suite D, 4-6 Canfield Place, London NW6 3BT
Tel: 020 7224 9666
Email: sales@britishtheatredirectory.co.uk
Web: www.britishtheatredirectory.co.uk
Published annually.
The "bible" of the showbusiness and entertainment industry. Published annually since 1971. It's invaluable to all who work in the theatre world. Contains over 2,000 venues and over 10,000 contacts.

CONTACTS
The Spotlight, 7 Leicester Place, London WC2H 7RJ
Tel: 020 7437 7631 Fax: 020 7437 5881
Email: info@spotlight.com
Web Site: www.spotlight.com
Pub: The Spotlight (as Spotlight Casting Directory). Annually
Price: £11.50 + £3.50 post & packing (UK).
Content: Brief factual contact information (names, addresses, phone nos, emails) on theatres, management, agents, casting directors, commercial concerns, publications, organisations, critics. TV and radio companies and stations, film companies and studios, costume, make-up, coaches, free listings and paid advertising.

INSTITUTE OF ENTERTAINMENT & ARTS MANAGEMENT YEARBOOK
Mole End, 13 Chilberton Drive, Merstham, Surrey RH1 3HL
Tel: 01737 644 665
Email: admin@ieam.co.uk
Web Site: www.ieam.co.uk
Press & Promotions Officer: Louise Fowkes
The internal publication for the membership of IEAM. Encompassing the aims and objectives of the Institute, listing members' contact details and giving information on forthcoming events.

THE OFFICIAL LONDON SEATING PLAN GUIDE
Suite D, 4-6 Canfield Place, London NW6 3BT
Tel: 020 7224 9666
Email: sales@rhpco.co.uk
Web Site: www.rhpco.co.uk
Price £14.95 + £1.50 per copy p&p.
In A4 Format with updates of the state of the art collection of seating plans for all London's major theatres and concert venues.

PR PLANNER - UK AND EUROPE
Chess House, 34 Germain Street, Chesham, Buckinghamshire HP5 1SJ
Tel: 01494 797260 Fax: 01494 797224
Email: jason.middleton@romeike.com
Web Site: www.romeike.co.uk
Contact Sales: Jason Middleton

THE PRESENTERS CONTACT FILE
Presenter Promotions, 123 Corporation Road, Gillingham, Kent ME7 1RG
Tel/Fax: 01634 851 077
Email: info@presenterpromotions.com
Web Site: www.presenterpromotions.com
Contact: Colin Cobb
Directory for presenters and voice artistes looking for work in the UK. Very useful for new entrants into the TV & Radio Industry.

RHINEGOLD GUIDE TO MUSIC EDUCATION
Rhinegold Publishing Ltd., 241 Shaftesbury Avenue, London WC2H 8TF
Tel: 01832 270 333 (sales) Tel: 020 7333 1733 (advertising) Tel: 020 7333 1760 (listings) Fax: 020 7333 1766 / 69
Email: meyb@rhinegold.co.uk
Web Site: www.rhinegold.co.uk
Annually.
The definitive guide to music education for parents, teachers, students and musicians.

SHOWCALL
The Stage Newspaper Ltd., Stage House, 47 Bermondsey Street, London Bridge, London SE1 3XT
Tel: 020 7403 1818 Fax: 020 7403 1418
Adveritising Fax: 020 7378 0480
Email: marcus@thestage.co.uk
Web Site: www.showcall.co.uk
Annual. Illustrated Directory of artistes etc. for light entertainment bookers.

SPOTLIGHT CASTING SERVICES
Casting directories for Stage and Screen
Casting rooms and studios
The Spotlight 7 Leicester Place London WC2H 7RJ
Tel: 020 7437 7631 Fax: 020 7437 5881
Email: info@spotlight.com
Web Site: www.spotlight.com
Directory of over 30,000 performers including actors, actresses, dancers, presenters, child performers and stunt artists for use when casting for TV, Film, Stage, Commercials, etc. Available in book format and as a searchable online directory at www.spotlight.com.
Spotlight also offers audition rooms and studios with the very latest in video-casting technology.

THE WHITE BOOK
First Floor, Bank House, 23 Warwick Road, Coventry, Warwickshire CV1 2EW
Tel: 02476 551171 Fax: 02476 551172
Email: admin@whitebook.com
Web Site: www.whitebook.co.uk
Annual: January.
Price: £90 inclusive of p&p (to UK destinations).

Performing Arts Booksellers

Alton

DANCE BOOKS LTD
The Old Bakery, 4 Lenten Street, Alton, Hampshire GU34 1HG
Tel: 01420 86138 Fax: 01420 86142
Email: dl@dancebooks.co.uk
Web Site: www.dancebooks.co.uk
Specialist booksellers and publishers of books on dance and all forms of human movement.

Bicester

RAY DASILVA
58 Shreen Way Gillingham Dorset OX26 2BE
Tel : 01747 835 558
Email: dasilva@puppetbooks.co.uk
Web Site: www.puppetbooks.co.uk
Directors: Ray and Joan DaSilva
New and second-hand books relating to all aspects of puppet theatre

Cambridge

PETER WOOD
20 Stonehill Road, Great Shelford, Cambridge CB2 5JL
Tel/Fax: 01223 842419
Email: peterwoodbooks@waitrose.com
Web Site: www.booksatpbfa.com
Holds stock of books and ephemera on theatre. Also cinema, music, opera, television. Comprehensive catalogues issued. Sondheim memorabilia always available. Private premises, browsers very welcome by appointment.

Carlisle

ANNE FITZSIMONS
3 Croft Park, Wetheral Carlisle, Cumbria CA4 8JH
Tel/Fax: 01228 562 184
Specialist dealer in rare and out of print

books, ephemera and memorabilia on all aspects of the performing arts. Regular catalogues issued. Private premises. Postal only, three first class stamps for current catalogue.

Glastonbury

EDDIE BAXTER-BOOKS (BTD)
booksearch service
The Old Mill House, West Pennard, Somerset BA6 8ND
Tel/Fax: 01749 890 369
Mail order out of print and new books, with emphasis on dance bands, jazz, cinema and theatre. Free search facility. No find - No fee.

Harrogate

THEATRESHIRE BOOKS
Dacre Hall, Dacre, Harrogate, North Yorkshire HG3 4ET
Tel: 01423 780 497 Fax: 01423 781 957
Email: theatreshire@theatresearch.co.uk
Web Site: www.abebooks.com/home/theatreshire
Specialises in theatre books, especially architecture, technical and theatre history, printed and e-mail catalogues available on request. Book searches undertaken.

London

BOOK BAZAAR
42 Sydney Street, London SW3 6PS
Tel: 020 7352 6810 Fax: 020 7351 5728
Email: caralancaster@aol.com
Cara Lancaster.
New and secondhand Technical Theatre Books, Lighting, Costume, Scenery, Props, Catalogues issued. Postal business only.

DAVID DRUMMOND AT PLEASURES OF PAST TIMES
11 Cecil Court, Charing Cross Road London WC2N 4EZ
Tel/Fax: 020 7836 1142
Email: drummond@popt.fsnet.co.uk
Web Site: www.t
Out of print theatre books and ephemera of performing arts. Hire facilities and research undertaken for principals of accredited bodies (notice required).
Hours: Weekdays 11.00am - 2.30 pm; 3.30 - 5.45pm. Saturday: First in month 11.00am - 2.30pm. Extended hours by prior arrangement.

SAMUEL FRENCH LTD
52 Fitzroy Street, Fitzrovia, London W1T 5JR
Tel: 020 7387 9373 Fax: 020 7387 2161
Email: theatre@samuelfrench-london.co.uk
Web: www.samuelfrench-london.co.uk

LOUISE GRANT
65 Parkside Drive, Edgware, Middlesex HA8 8JU
Tel: 020 8958 5862
Email: louisegrant@edgware65.fsnet.co.uk
Theatre programmes, posters, autographs and other theatrical ephemera (postal only or by appointment).

GREENROOM BOOKS
9 St James Road, Ilkley, West Yorkshire LS29 9PY
Tel: 01943 607 662 Mobile: 17773 243926
Email: greenroombooks@blueyonder.co.uk
Web: www.ukbookworld.com/members/greenroom
Contact: Geoff Oldham
Dealers in secondhand and antiquarian books on the performing arts. We deal by post only and enquiries are welcome by telephone and email.

ICA ARTS BOOKSHOP
Nash House, 12 Carlton House Terrace, The Mall, London SW1Y 5AH
Tel: 020 7766 1452 Fax: 020 7873 0051
Email: bookshop@ica.org.uk
Web Site: www.ica.org.uk
Stocks books and hard-to-obtain periodicals with emphasis on contemporary cultural studies, art and philosophy. Also has a wide range of artists postcards and ICA exhibition catalogues.

KIRKDALE BOOKSHOP
272 Kirkdale, Sydenham, London SE26 4RS
Tel: 020 8778 4701 Fax: 020 8776 6293
Email: kirkdalebookshop@hotmail.com
Booksellers: Small stock of both new and secondhand books on music, the theatre and the cinema.

NATIONAL THEATRE BOOKSHOP
National Theatre, South Bank, London SE1 9PX
Tel: 020 7452 3456 / 8 Fax: 020 7452 3457 Ansaphone: 020 7452 3460
Email: bookshop@nationaltheatre.org.uk
Web Site: www.nationaltheatre.org.uk/bookshop
Bookshop open 10.00am - 10.45pm Monday - Saturday (check times on Bank Holidays). Olivier + Cottesloe bookstalls open at performance times. Shops carry a wide range of playtexts, books on all aspects of the stage, theatrical biographies/auto biographies, posters, cards, videos, audio cassettes, CDs, DVDs clothing and merchandise. For current stock lists please send s.a.e. Worldwide mail order service available.

JOSEF WEINBERGER LTD
12-14 Mortimer Street, London W1T 3JJ
Tel: 020 7580 2827 (4 lines) Fax: 020 7436 9616
Email: general.info@jwmail.co.uk
Web Site: www.josef-weinberger.com
Editor: Chistopher Moss
Publisher and rightsholder of musicals and agents for Music Theatre International and the Rodgers & Hammerstein Theatre Library.

Newmarket

C.D. PARAMOR
25 St Mary's Square, Newmarket, Suffolk CB8 0HZ
Tel: 01638 664416
Email: cdparamor@btopenworld.com
Bookseller specialising in books and ephemera in the performing arts. Both new and out-of-print and antiquarian. Free search service for elusive material undertaken. Visitors welcome by appointment. Private premises.

Stratford

THE RSC COLLECTION
Royal Shakespeare Theatre, Stratford-upon-Avon, Warwickshire CV37 6BB
Tel: 01789 262 870
Email: collection@.rsc.org.uk
Web Site: www.rsc.org.uk
Contact: David Howells
Open Mon - Fri 1.30 - 6.30. Saturdays 10.30 - 6.30 Sunday 11.30 - 4.30 pm. Exhibition of theatre material; theatre tours; Sales - wide variety of material including RSC publications and books covering all aspects of theatre.

RSC SHOPS
Royal Shakespeare Theatre, Stratford-upon-Avon, Warwickshire CV37 6BB
Tel: 01789 412601 Fax: 01789 412639
Email: retail@rsc.org.uk
Web Site: www.rsc.org.uk
Hours of opening: 9.15am - 9.00pm
Play texts and theatre books relating to Shakespeare and RSC productions and general theatre interest books. Souvenirs, posters, programmes and gifts.
Mail Order available.

ROBERT VAUGHAN ANTIQUARIAN BOOKSELLERS
20 Chapel Street, Stratford-upon-Avon, Warwickshire CV37 6EP
Tel: 01789 205 312
Antiquarian booksellers, specialising in rare and out of print books on Shakespeare and the performing arts. Members of the Antiquarian Booksellers Association (International).

TRAINING & EDUCATION

Examination Boards

TRINITY GUILDHALL
89 Albert Embankment, London SE1 7TP
Tel: 020 7820 6100 Fax 020 7820 6161
Email: drama@trinityguildhall.co.uk
Web: www.trinityguildhall.co.uk/drama
Contact: Briana Sweeney
Trinity Guildhall offers the widest possible range of accredited assessments in Drama and Speech subjects from Grade and Certificate exams in Acting and Speaking, Communication Skills and Musical Theatre & Performance Arts to Diplomas in Performing, Public Speaking, Teaching, Education Studies and Directing.

Members of the Conference of Drama Schools

ACADEMY OF LIVE AND RECORDED ARTS (ALRA)
Studio One
Royal Victoria Patriotic Bldg, Fitzhugh Grove, Trinity Road,
London SW18 3SX
Tel: 020 8870 6475 Fax: 020 8875 0789
Email: acting@alra.demon.co.uk
Web Site: www.alra.demon.co.uk
Administration/Courses:
Principal: Pat Trueman
3 year full-time Actors Course (accredited by N.C.D.T.)
1 year Course in Acting (accredited by N.C.D.T.)
1 year stage management course & Technical Arts Course
Total training in the performing arts - Film, TV, Theatre
Short courses/continuing professional development in theatre, film, TV and radio.

ARTSED LONDON SCHOOLS OF ACTING & MUSICAL THEATRE
Cone Ripman House, 14 Bath Road, Chiswick,
London W4 1LY
Tel: 020 8987 6666 Fax: 020 8987 6699
Email: dean@artsed.co.uk
Web Site: www.artsed.co.uk
Dean: Iain Read
Director School of Acting: Jane Harrison
3yr full time BA (Hons) Acting 18+, 1 yr full time MA Acting 21+
1 yr p/time post-diploma BA (Hons) Acting 21+
The school offers the highest possible vocational training. Its aim is to train effective, reflective, contemporary practitioners for work in theatre, television, film, broadcasting and other performance media.
Course accredited by NCDT. Member of the Conference of Drama Schools.
Director School of Musical Theatre: Ian Watt-Smith
3 yr full time BA (Hons) Musical Theatre.
Training the Complete Performer through unrivalled tuition in dance, acting, singing by leading professionals. Course accredited by CDET.
60 Dance and Drama Awards available.
All courses validated by City University.
Main and Studio theatres, 40 studios available for hire evenings, weekends, vacations. Contact Facilities Manager: 020 8987 6688

BIRMINGHAM SCHOOL OF ACTING
Millenium Point, Curzon Street,
Birmingham B4 7XG
Tel: 0121 331 7200
Email: info@bsa.uce.ac.uk
Web Site: www.bsa.uce.ac.uk
Birmingham School of Acting (BSA), the Midlands' only accredited drama school, has moved to a new £4 million purpose built premises in Millennium Point.
BSA offfers two full-time courses in acting, the BA (Hons) Acting (3 years) and Graduate Diploma in Acting (1 year).

BRISTOL OLD VIC THEATRE SCHOOL
2 Downside Road, Clifton,
Bristol, Avon BS8 2XF
Tel: 0117 973 3535 Fax: 0117 980 9258
Email: enquiries@oldvic.ac.uk
Web Site: www.oldvic.ac.uk
Administration/Courses:
Principal: Paul Rummer
Full-time courses:
Undergraduate-
Professional Acting 3yr/2yr/1yr
Professional Acting for Overseas students 1yr
Professional Stage Management 3yr/2yr
Costume 2yr
Postgraduate-
Design 4 term
Directing 4 term
Scenic Art 1yr
Theatre Arts Management 1yr
Theatre Production Management 1yr
See our website for full details of our training courses, theatre productions, summer courses, and youth theatre. An Affiliate of the Conservatoire for Dance and Drama.

ROSE BRUFORD COLLEGE
Lamorbey Park Burnt Oak Lane,
Sidcup, Kent DA15 9DF
Tel: 020 8308 2600 Fax: 020 8308 0542
Email: enquiries@bruford.ac.uk
Web Site: www.bruford.ac.uk
Administration/Courses:
Principal: Alistair Pearce
Courses: BA (Hons) Degrees in Acting, Actor Musician.
Directing, Lighting Design, Stage Management, Costume Production, Theatre Design, Music Technology, Sound and Image Design, Scenic Arts, European Theatre Arts BA (Hons), American Theatre Arts BA (Hons), MA Theatre Practices.
By Distance Learning: Opera Studies, Theatre Studies, MA Theatre & Performance Studies. MA Dramatic Writing.
All courses validated by the University of Manchester.
2 Theatres on site: The Rose, 330 seats; The Barn Theatre, 96 seats

CENTRAL SCHOOL OF SPEECH AND DRAMA
Embassy Theatre, 64 Eton Avenue, Swiss Cottage,
London NW3 3HY
Tel: 020 7722 8183 Fax: 020 7722 4132
Email: enquiries@cssd.ac.uk
Web Site: www.cssd.ac.uk
Administration:
FULL TIME COURSES
Undergraduate
Acting; BA (Hons); 3 years - NCDT
Music Theatre; BA (Hons) Acting; 3 years - NCDT
BA (Hons) Acting (Collaborative & Devised Theatre); 3 years - NCDT
BA (Hons) Acting (Theatre Practice)
BA (Hons)Drama, Applied Theatre and Education; 3 years
BA (Hons) Theatre Practice: Costume Construction; 3 years
BA (Hons) Theatre Practice: Design for the Stage
BA (Hons) Theatre Practice: Performance Arts
BA (Hons) Theatre Practice: Production Lighting
BA (Hons) Theatre Practice: Puppetry
BA (Hons) Theatre Practice: Prop Making
BA(Hons) Theatre Practice: Scenic Art
BA (Hons) Theatre Practice: Scenic Construction
BA (Hons) Theatre Practice: Stage Management
BA (Hons) Theatre Practice: Technical

and Production
BA (Hons) Theatre Practice: Theatre Lighting Design
BA (Hons) Theatre Practice: Theatre Sound
Graduate
MA Acting
Acting for Screen; MA; 1 year (subject to validation)
Actor Training and Coaching; MA; 1 year (subject to validation)
MA Advanced Theatre Practice, 1 year
MA Applied Theatre
MA/MFA Creative Producing
MA Drama and Movement Therapy (Sesame); 1 year Movement Studies
MA Movement Studies
MA Music Theatre
MA Performance Practices and Research
MA Scenography
MA Theatre Studies
MA/MFA Voice Studies; 1 year
MA/MFA Writing for Stage and Broadcast Media; 1 year (subject to validation)
PGCE Drama
PGCE Media Studies; 1 year
PG Certificate in Applied Theatre with Young People
Research Degrees (MPhil/PhD)

CYGNET TRAINING THEATRE

New Theatre, Friars Gate,
Exeter, Devon EX2 4AZ
Tel: 01392 277 189
Email: cygnetarts@btinternet.com
Administration/Courses:
Principal: Monica Shallis
Three year full-time professional acting course.
Options: Acting with Directing
Acting with Music
Acting with Stage Management
Training in the context of a working theatre company with widespread touring.

DRAMA CENTRE LONDON

Central Saint Martins 10 Black Hill
London EC1R 5LQ
Tel: 020 7514 8778 Fax: 020 7514 8777
Email: drama@linst.ac.uk
Web Site: www.csm.linst.ac.uk/drama
3 year full-time BA (Hons) Acting Course. Accredited by the National Council for Drama Training.
BA (Hons) Acting Course validated by University of the Arts London).
BA (Hons) Directing Course (validated by University of the Arts London).
MA Performance:- Screen Acting; Screen Directing; Script Writing; Movement Direction (validated by University of the Arts London).
MA in European Classical Acting (subject to validation)
Foundation in Performance (validated by University of the Arts London).
Foundation in Performance (from 2006, subject to validation).
Drama Centre London is a centre within Central Saint Martins College of Art & Design.

EAST 15 ACTING SCHOOL

Hatfields, Rectory Lane,
Loughton, Essex IG10 3RY
Tel: 020 8508 5983 Fax: 020 8508 7521
Email: east15@essex.ac.uk
Web Site: www.east15.ac.uk
Administration/Courses:
Director: John Baraldi
Full Time:
Three year BA Degree in Acting
Three year BA Degree in Contemporary Theatre
Two/Three Year Foundation Degree/BA Hons in Technical Theatre Studies
Two/Three Year Foundation Degree/BA Hons in Specialist Performance Skills (Stage Combat)
Two/Three Year Foundation Degree/BA Hons in Community Theatre
One Year MA/Diploma in Acting
One Year MA/Diploma in Acting for TV, film and Radio
Two Year MA in Professional Theatre
One Year Cert HE in Theatre Arts
Summer drama courses, workshops, Sunday workshops and Easter workshops

GSA CONSERVATOIRE

Millmead Terrace,
Guildford, Surrey GU2 4YT
Tel: 01483 560 701 Fax: 01483 535 431
Email: enquiries@conservatoire.org
Web Site: www.conservatoire.org
Administration/Courses:
Director of School: Peter Barlow
BA (Hons) Theatre, Acting (3 years) [Validated by University of Surrey]
BA (Hons) Theatre, Musical Theatre (3 years) [Validated by University of Surrey]
Diploma in acting (1 year postgraduate)
MA in Musical Theatre [subject to validation] (1 year postgraduate]
Professional Production Skills Diploma 2 Year
Professional Production Skills Diploma 1 Year
BA (Hons) Professional Production Skills Extension to 1 and 2 year courses.

GUILDHALL SCHOOL OF MUSIC & DRAMA

The Barbican Centre, Silk Street,
London EC2Y 8DT
Tel: 020 7628 2571 Fax: 020 7256 9438
Email: info@gsmd.ac.uk
Web Site: www.gsmd.ac.uk
Administration/Courses:
Principal: Genista McIntosh
Director of Drama: Peter Clough
Director of Technical Theatre Studies: Sue Thornton
9 term professional acting course leading either to BA(Hons)
Degree in acting. 9 term Stage Management course leading to a BA(Hons) Degree in Stage Management & Technical Theatre.
Part-time tuition available in speech and drama.
Junior drama class for 13-18 year olds on Saturdays.

ITALIA CONTI ACADEMY OF THEATRE ARTS

Italia Conti House, 23 Goswell Road,
London EC1M 7AJ
Tel: 020 7608 0044 Fax: 020 7253 1430
Acting School: 72 Landor Road, London SW9 9PH Tel: 020 7733 3210 Fax: 020 7737 2728
Email: baacting.italiaconti@btinternet.com, admin@italiaconti.co.uk
Web Site: www.italiaconti-acting.co.uk
Administration/Courses:
Principal: Ms Anne Sheward
GOSWELL ROAD SCHOOL:
Junior and student courses in performing arts, dance, drama and singing including GCSE.
Age 9+ full-time education. Weekend associate classes: Age 3 to adult in all. Student courses 16+ (1 and 3 year full-time). Diploma & B.A Hons Degree.
LANDOR ROAD SCHOOL:
Provides actor training for adult students. 3-year full-tim BA(Hons) Acting course for adult students. Accredited by the National Council for Drama Training, validated by South Bank University. Performing Arts and Singing courses also available for students 16+.

LAMDA (LONDON ACADEMY OF MUSIC AND DRAMATIC ART)

155 Talgarth Road,
London W14 9DA
Tel: 020 8834 0500 Fax: 020 8834 0501
Email: enquiries@lamda.org.uk
Web Site: www.lamda.org.uk
Principal: Peter James
Vice Principal: Colin Cook
Finance Director: Philip Newton
Director Stage Management & Technical Courses: Rob Young
Admissions: Jo Butterworth
Courses: 3 year Acting Course (9 Terms) NCDT Accredited
1 year Classical Acting Course (2 Terms)
2 year Stage Management Technical Theatre Course (6 Terms) NCDT Accredited
Postgraduate one year Diploma Course.
2 Year Postgraduate Acting Course.
Musical Director & Repetiteur (1 place)
Designers (2 Places)
Director (2 places)
Carpentry (1 place)
Movement Instruction (1 Place)
4 week and 8 week Shakespeare and Stage Management Summer Workshops.

MANCHESTER METROPOLITAN UNIVERSITY

Faculty Of Art & Design, Ormond Building,
Lower Ormond Street,
Manchester M15 5BX
Tel: 0161 247 1705 Fax: 0161 247 6393
Email: n.dowling@mmu.ac.uk
Administration/Courses:
3 year Acting Course leading to Ba (Hons) Theatre Arts (Acting).

MOUNTVIEW ACADEMY OF THEATRE ARTS
Ralph Richardson Memorial Studios,
Kingfisher Place, Clarendon Road,
London N22 6XF
Tel: 020 8881 2201 Fax: 020 8829 0034
Email: enquiries@mountview.ac.uk
Web Site: www.mountview.ac.uk
Principal: Paul Clements
General Manager: Jacqui Leigh
Director of Acting Courses: Amir Korangy
Director of Musical Theatre Courses: Paul Sabey
Director of Technical Theatre Courses: Francesca Faulkner - Greatorex
Registrar: Angela Wharton
PR & Marketing Director: Yvonne I'Anson
Courses:
Full-time Courses:
3 year BA (Hons) Acting and Musical Theatre*
1 year (4 term) Postgraduate Acting and Musical Theatre*
2 year BA (Hons) Technical Theatre*
1 year Postgraduate Technical Theatre*
1 year Directors course
1 year Postgraduate Course in Screen and Radio Performance.
1-year MA in Performance - Acting*, Musical Theatre* and Classical Acting options
*Courses accredited by the NCDT.
Part-time courses:
Adult evening foundation courses in Acting, Acting for the screen and Musical Theatre.
Courses and holiday workshops for children and teeenagers.

THE OXFORD SCHOOL OF DRAMA
Sansomes Farm Studios,
Woodstock, Oxfordshire OX20 1ER
Tel: 01993 812 883 Fax: 01993 811 220
Email: info@oxford.drama.ac.uk
Web Site: www.oxford.drama.ac.uk
Contact: The Administrator
Courses:
Three-year diploma in acting and one-year acting course. Both are accredited by the National Council for Drama Training and are part of the government's Dance and Drama Awards scheme.
Six-month foundation course for students aged 17+.
Member of the Conference of Drama Schools.

QUEEN MARGARET UNIVERSITY COLLEGE
School of Drama & Creative Industries
Gateway Theatre, Elm Row,
Edinburgh, Mid Lothian EH7 4AH
Scotland
Tel: 0131 3173900 BO: 0131 317 3939
Fax: 0131 317 3902
Email: ahunt@qmuc.ac.uk
Web Site: www.qmuc.ac.uk
Courses:
BA/BA (Hons) Drama and Theatre Arts, Theatre Production. Postgrad: Cultural Management and Policy, Festivals Producing, Dramatic Writing. Doctoral school.
MA/MFA Advanced Stage and Screen Practice
BA/BA(Hons) Acting and Performance
BA/BA(Hons) Performance Production and Management

ROYAL ACADEMY OF DRAMATIC ART (RADA)
62 - 64 Gower Street,
London WC1E 6ED
BO: 020 7908 4800 Mgt: 020 7636 7676
Fax:: 020 7908 4739
Email: enquiries@rada.ac.uk
Web Site: www.rada.org
Administration/Courses:
Principal: Nicholas Barter M.A.
9 term (3 year) full time Acting course.
6 term (2 year) full-time Theatre Technical Arts course.
4 term full-time Stage Electrics course.
4 term full-time Scenic Construction course.
4 term full-time Property Making course.
4 term full-time Scenic Painting course.
4 term full-time Wardrobe Skills course.

ROYAL SCOTTISH ACADEMY OF MUSIC AND DRAMA
100 Renfrew Street,
Glasgow, Strathclyde G2 3DB Scotland
Tel: 0141 332 4101 Fax: 0141 332 8901
Email: development@rsamd.ac.uk
Web Site: www.rsamd.ac.uk
Administration/Courses:
Principal: John Wallace
Director of School of Drama: Donna Soto-Morettini
4 year full-time course leading to BA (Contemporary Theatre Practice) Honours.
3 year full-time stage course leading to BA (Technical & Production Arts) (Accredited by the NCDT).
3 Year full-time acting course leading to BA (Acting). (Accredited by the NCDT).
2 Year (HND extension) full-time course leading to BA (Digital Film and Television).
1 Year full-time or up to 5 year part-time Master of Drama(MDra) (Acting/Directing).
1 Year full-time course leading to Master of Performance (Musical Theatre).
New Athenaem Theatre: Proseneum Arch Theatre Seats 350
Chandler Studio Theatre: Black Box Seats150 Flexibly
Alexander Gibson opera Studio: Seats 150
Guinness Roon: Recital Room Seats 150
Academy Concert Hall: Seats 350

ROYAL WELSH COLLEGE OF MUSIC AND DRAMA
Castle Grounds, Cathays Park,
Cardiff, CF10 3ER Wales
Tel: 029 2034 2854 Fax: 029 2039 1304
Email: info@rwcmd.ac.uk
Web Site: www.rwcmd.ac.uk
Administration/Courses:
Principal: Hilary Bowlding
Vice Principal Academic: Melinda Drowley
Vice Principal Resources: Peter Curran
Vice Principal Enterprise: David Jackson
Drama trains students for the professional theatre as Actors, Designers or Stage Managers.
The College's principle concern is to provide each individual student with a thorough professional training which will enable him/her to achieve his/her full potential as an artist and craftsman.
Courses aim to equip students with the appropriate knowledge, skills and techniques for a career in Theatre and Drama while at the same time stimulating personal enthusiasm, creativity and flair. The College offers the following courses:
Three year:
BA Acting (Hons)
BA Theatre Design (Hons)
BA Stage Management (Hons)
One year:
Postgraduate Diploma: Stage Management
Postgraduate Diploma: Arts Management
Postgraduate Diploma: Theatre Design
Graduate Diploma: Acting
Graduate Diploma: Theatre Design
RWCMD has purpose-built teaching spaces and workshops, studio and rehearsal facilities. The principal performance areas are the Bute Theatre and Caird Studio.

Other Full Time Colleges and Stage Schools

THE ACADEMY DRAMA SCHOOL
189 Whitechapel Road, London E1 1DN
Tel: 020 7377 8735 Tel: 020 7624 5400
Email: ask@the-academy.info
Web Site: www.the-academy.info
Full-time drama training held entirely in the evening and at weekends. Also full and part-time day and evening courses.

THE ARDEN SCHOOL OF THEATRE
City Campus, Whitworth Street,
Manchester M1 3HB
Tel/Fax: 0161 279 7257
Email: ast@ccm.ac.uk
Contact: David O'Shea

THE ARTS INSTITUTE AT BOURNEMOUTH
Wallisdown, Poole, Dorset BH12 5HH

Tel: 01202 363 279 Fax: 01202 363 335
Email: rwright@aib.ac.uk
Administration/Courses:
Course Director: Richard Wright
BA (Hons) Arts and Event Production - a 3 year full-time course preparing students for careers in the management and administration of the arts, with an emphasis on live project work.

ARTTS INTERNATIONAL
Highfield Grange, Bubwith, North Yorkshire YO8 6DP
Tel: 01757 288 088 Fax: 01757 288 253
Email: admin@artts.co.uk
Web Site: www.artts.co.uk
Director: Geoffrey Bicker
Residential skill centre, offering intensive multi-media, multi-skilling courses in theatre, video/film, television and radio. One year diploma course in Acting, Directing or Production Operations.

BIRD COLLEGE CONSERVATOIRE FOR THEATRE ARTS
Birkbeck Centre, Birkbeck Road, Sidcup, Kent DA14 4DE
Tel: 020 8300 6004 / 3031
Fax: 020 8308 1370
Email: admin@birdcollege.co.uk
Web Site: www.birdcollege.co.uk
Principal: Sue Passmore
Contact: Erica Lawrence
3 year National Diploma in Dance (Musical Theatre) and BA (Hons) Degree course.

BIRMINGHAM THEATRE SCHOOL
Old Repertory Theatre, Station Street, Birmingham B5 4DY
All enquiries Tel/Fax: 0121 643 3300
Email: info@birminghamts.demon.co.uk
Web Site: www.the-birmingham-theatre-school.com
Courses:
1 year acting diploma course - 17+
1 year open access theatre training course
2 year Higher National Diploma in Performing Arts - Theatre Acting (*accredition September 2000) - 18+
Part time evening and weekend courses ages 5 and upwards.
Sarah Watts - Head of Arts and Administration

THE BRIDGE THEATRE TRAINING COMPANY
Cecil Sharp House, 2 Regents Park Road, London NW1 7AY
Tel: 020 7424 0860 Fax: 020 7424 9118
Email: admin@thebridge-ttc.org
Web Site: www.thebridge-ttc.org
Patron: Carmen Munroe
Artistic Directors: Mark Akrill and Judith Pollard
Courses:
Two Year Professional Acting Course - An intensive training for a career in professional acting.
One Year Postgraduate/Post-Experience Acting Course - Training for a career in professional acting for those who already have a degree (not necessarily in Drama) or for those who have Drama or related experience.
Courses are based in held at Cecil Sharp House in Camden Town, Central London.

BRISTOL SCHOOL & COLLEGE OF DANCING
Lansdown Road, Clifton, Bristol, BS8 3AB
Tel: 01278 434 081 Fax: 01278 434 080
Email: admin@thebristolschoolofdancing.co.uk
Principal: Mrs A Redgrave
Full-time college for ages 16+, and part-time for all ages from 5+.

ROSE BRUFORD COLLEGE
Lamorbey Park Burnt Oak Lane, Sidcup, Kent DA15 9DF
Tel: 020 8308 2600 Fax: 020 8308 0542
Email: enquiries@bruford.ac.uk
Web Site: www.bruford.ac.uk
Administration/Courses:
Principal: Alistair Pearce
Courses: BA (Hons) Degrees in Acting, Actor Musician.
Directing, Lighting Design, Stage Management, Costume Production, Theatre Design, Music Technology, Sound and Image Design, Scenic Arts, European Theatre Arts BA (Hons), American Theatre Arts BA (Hons), MA Theatre Practices.
By Distance Learning: Opera Studies, Theatre Studies, MA Theatre & Performance Studies. MA Dramatic Writing.
All courses validated by the University of Manchester.
2 Theatres on site: The Rose, 330 seats; The Barn Theatre, 96 seats

CENTRAL SAINT MARTINS COLLEGE OF ART & DESIGN
Southampton Row, London WC1B 4AP
Tel: 020 7514 7000 Fax: 020 7514 7254
Email: info@csm.arts.ac.uk
Web Site: www.csm.arts.ac.uk
Administration/Courses:
BA (Hons) Theatre Design, 3 year full-time course.
Course Director: MIchael Spencer
MA in European Scenography, 1 year full time course.
Director: Peter Brooks

CENTRAL SCHOOL OF BALLET
10 Herbal Hill, Clerkenwell Road, London EC1R 5EG
Tel: 020 7837 6332 Fax: 020 7833 5571
Email: info@csbschool.co.uk
Web www.centralschoolofballet.co.uk
Administration/Courses:
Director: Jane Hackett
Founding Directors: Christopher Gable CBE, Ann Stannard
Course: Three year course leading to a BA (Hons) in Professional Dance and Performance.
Students accepted from 16.
CSB is an affiliate of the Conservatoire for Dance and Drama. Students achieve a high standard through a varied curriculum with Ballet and Contempory Dance as major subjects and additional studies in Jazz Dance, choreography, drama, music, singing and academic work. The course is accredited by the Council for Dance Education and Training.
Ballet Central, the school's touring company is a unique opportunity for final year students to experience the professional theatre.
Funded places are available for all eligible EU students and there are some scholarships for non EU students.

CENTRE STAGE ACADEMY OF PERFORMING ARTS
Dance, Drama School
24 Northlea Avenue, Thackley, Bradford, West Yorkshire BD10 8LX
Tel/Fax: 0113 202 9020
Email: centrestage@blueyonder.co.uk
Web: www.centre-stage-academy.co.uk
Academy Principle: C.D. Bicker

CHICHESTER COLLEGE OF ARTS
Westgate Fields, Chichester, West Sussex PO19 1SB
Tel: 01243 786 321 Fax: 01243 527 884
Email: info@chichester.ac.uk
Web Site: www.chichester.ac.uk
Head of Performing Arts: Mrs Jacqui Penrose
All Enquiries to Admissions Assistant: Glenda Ford
Courses: BTEC First Diploma in Performing Arts
BTEC National Diploma in Performing Arts
BTEC Professional Development Certificate and Diploma
BTEC Professional Certificate in Musical Theatre
BTEC Certificate in Stage Management
HND Performing Arts / Devised Theatre
Age: 16+

CIRCOMEDIA
Britannia Road, Kingswood, Bristol, Avon BS15 8DB
Tel: 0117 947 7288
Email: info@circomedia.com
Web Site: www.circomedia.com
ADMINISTRATION:
Full time professional training in contemporary circus with physical theatre. Two year professional training programme.
One year course leading to an OCR diplo-

ma. Three month introductory course.
BTEC National Diploma in performing arts. Part Time teacher training course leading to Certificate of Adult Education Evening Classes. Schools and Community Outreach Programme.
Agency for workshops, team building and performance.

CITY OF WESTMINSTER COLLEGE
25 Paddington Green, London W2 1NB
Tel: 020 7723 8826 Arts Administration: 020 7258 2789
Email: mary.prince@cwc.ac.uk
Web Site: www.cwc.ac.uk
Head of School, Media Lighting & Performing Arts: Steve J Dowrick
We offer a quality range of Performing Arts and Theatre skills courses which are mainly delivered at the Colleges Cockpit Theatre, providing students with valuable direct theatre experience.
Contact Media and Student Recruitment Officer: Mary Prince

COURT THEATRE TRAINING COMPANY
The Courtyard, Bowling Green 40 Pitfield Street London N1 6EU
Tel/Fax: 020 7739 6868
Email: info@courttheatretraining.org.uk
Web Site: www.thecourtyard.org.uk
Principal: June Abbott
General Manager: Tim Gill
Courses:
2 year actors in training: Full time
1 year theatre design: Full time
1 or 2 year director's course: Full time,
1 year stage management
1 year (4 terms) postgraduate acting - full time
All courses are full time Monday to Friday 09.30 to 18.30.

CROYDON COLLEGE
Art & Design Dept, Barclay Road, Croydon, Surrey CR9 1DX
Tel: 020 8686 5700 ext 3623 Fax: 020 8760 5944
Email: info@croydon.ac.uk
Web Site: www.croydon.ac.uk
Senior Personnel: Jackie Fletcher, Helen Morlewska, Linda Eke, Robert Muller
BA (Hons) in Theatre Design/Foundation degree in Theatre Practice.

DANCE ACADEMY SOUTHWEST
Dance Station, Alexandra Park, Fishponds, Bristol, Avon BS16 2BG
Tel: 0117 965 5660
Email: admin@344dance.freeserve.co.uk
Web Site: www.dancestation.org.uk
Administration/Courses:
Principal: Kathy Plaster L.I.S.T.D Dip
Full time and part time professional dance, musical theatre and teacher training course.

Ballet: ISTD Imperial and RAD, Jazz, Modern, Tap, National, Contemporary RAD & ISTD vocational and Teaching exams., Drama (LAMDA exams), Singing, A Level Dance & Theatre Studies, BTEC National Diploma: Dance

KATHLEEN DAVIS STAGE SCHOOL & COLLEGE FOR PERFORMING ARTS
202-205 High Street West, Sunderland, Tyne and Wear SR1 1UA
Tel: 0191 522 0365/0191 5657374
Mobile: 07768 357450
Email: k.davisdance@aol.com
Please contact Kathleen Davis for training and choreography. Juveniles for professional shows, choreography and own dance group.

DRAMA STUDIO LONDON LTD
Grange Court, 1 Grange Road, London W5 5QN
Tel: 020 8579 3897 Fax: 020 8566 2035
Email: admin@dramastudiolondon.co.uk
Web Site: www.dramastudiolondon.co.uk
Administration/Courses:
Principal: Peter Craze
1 year full time Postgraduate Acting course. (Accredited by National Council for Drama Training).
1 year full time Directing Course.
Age 21+.

ECOLE DE MIME CORPOREL DRAMATIQUE
Belgravia Workshop, Unit 207, 157 Marlborough Road, London N19 4NF
Tel: 020 7263 9339 Fax: 020 7263 9339
Email: infoschool@angefou.co.uk
Web Site: www.angefou.co.uk
Principal: Steven Wasson
Administrator: Corinne Soum
20 hour weekly training programme in Movement theatre and corporal mime, based on the technique of Etienne Decroux, including: Technique, Repertoire, Improvisation and Composition.

EXPRESSIONS
3 Newgate Lane, Mansfield, Nottinghamshire NG18 2LB
Tel: 01623 424334 Fax: 01623 647337
Email: expressions-uk@btconnect.com
Web Site: www.expressions-uk.com
Principal: Maxine Glasby
Director of Theatre: Daniel Head
Head of Vocal/Musical Theatre: Barry Farnsworth
3 year musical theatre course full time.
East Midlands based casting agency representing children and musical theatre graduates.

GAIETY SCHOOL OF ACTING
Meeting House Square, Temple Bar, Dublin 2 Eire
Tel: 00 353 1 679 9277
Fax: 00 353 1 679 9568
Email: gaietyschool@indigo.ie
Web Site: www.gaietyschool.com
Chairman of the Board: Joe Dowling
Director: Patrick Sutton
2 year Full time Intensive Acting Programme*
1 year Part Time Performance Course*
1 year Part Time Foundation Course (Evenings)
10 week introduction to Drama Course (Evenings)
Practical Playwriting Course (Evenings)
Drama weekends
Young Gaiety 6-16 years (Saturdays)
Youth Theatre Workshop 16-19 years
Youth Theatre Company 16-19 years
Summer Schools for Adults and Children
Irish International Theatre Summer School
International January Term Programme on Irish Theatre
*Entry by audition - Dublin, London & New York.
For further details contact Administration.

GREASEPAINT MAKE-UP PLACEMENT AGENCY
143 Northfield Avenue, Ealing, London W13 9QT
Tel: 020 8840 6000 Fax: 020 8840 3983
Email: agency@greasepaint.co.uk
Web Site: www.greasepaint.co.uk
Senior Personnel: Julia & Hannah Cruttenden
Greasepaint offers two interlinked services as a school and Agency. The Agency specialises in allocating highly skilled make-up and hair designers to TV, film, theatre and fashion productions at competitive rates. The School offers 14-week TV, Film and Theatre (make-up, prosthetics & hair) courses three times a year, and 4-week Fashion (make-up & hair) courses four times a year.

THE HERTFORDSHIRE THEATRE SCHOOL
Queen Street House, 40 Queen Street, Hitchin, Hertfordshire SG4 9TS
Tel: 01462 421 416
Email: info@htstheatreschool.co.uk
Web Site: www.htstheatreschool.co.uk
Administration/Courses:
Co-Principals: John Gardiner and Kirk Foster
Contact: Annie Wilkinson
Full-time 3 year course in Acting and Musical Theatre.
Full-time 1 year post-graduate course in Acting and Musical Theatre.
Age 18+

HOPWOOD HALL COLLEGE
Rochdale Road, Middleton, Manchester M24 6XH
Tel: 0161 643 7560 Fax: 0161 643 2114
Email: john.binns@hopwood.ac.uk
Web Site: www.hopwoodhall
Head Of Arts: John C Binns

HOXTON HALL

130 Hoxton Street, London N1 6SH
Tel: 020 7684 0060 Fax: 020 7729 3815
Email: office@hoxtonhall.dabsol.co.uk
Web Site: www.hoxtonhall.dabsol.co.uk
Contact: Franck Bordese
Courses:
Full and part time one year courses in Community Theatre accredited by Middlesex University. Modules in devising, acting, theatre in education, music and songwriting, working with text etc.
Full and part time one year courses in Theatre
Technicals and Stagecraft. Modules in costume, theatre management, lighting, sound, stagecraft and music technology etc.
These are access to Higher Education Courses, attendance of which guarantees the student an interview for relevant courses at Middlesex University.
Our full time courses have been specially designed not to affect the benefit entitlement of Students.

KENT INSTITUTE OF ART & DESIGN AT MAIDSTONE

Oakwood Park, Oakwood Road, Maidstone, Kent ME16 8AG
Tel: 01622 757 286 Fax: 01622 621 100
Email: swheeler@ucreative.ac.uk
Web Site: www.ucreative.ac.uk
Administration/Courses:
Director: Vaughan Grylls, Higher DFA (Lond) FRSA
MA Media Arts & Communication Design.
B.A.(Hons) 3 year courses in Graphic Design, Illustration, Animation, Video with Film or Photography & Media Arts. BTEC HND in Graphic Design and Illustration.
Contact Admissions Officer: Sharon Wheeler

LABAN

Creekside, London SE8 3DZ
Tel: 020 8691 8600 Fax: 020 86918400
Email: info@laban.org
Web Site: www.laban.org
Administration/Courses:
Director: Mr Anthony Bowne
Enquiries: Admissions Officer
BA (Hons) Dance Theatre - 3 years f/t
Professional Diploma in Dance Studies - 10months f/t or 20months p/t
Postgraduate Certificate: Dance in Community -1 yr f/t or 2 yr p/t
Specialist Diploma: Dance Notating - 40 weeks, 2 half days per week
MA Choreography - 13 months f/t
MA Dance Performance
MA European Dance Theatre Practice
MA Scenography (Dance)- Light, Body and Space course options - 1 yr f/t or 2 yr p/t
MSc Dance Science
Graduate Diploma in Performance - 1 year f/t only for people who have already completed three years in recognised dance company (Transitions Dance Company)
MPhil or PhD Research Degrees - f/t or p/t

LAINE THEATRE ARTS

The Studios, East Street, Epsom, Surrey KT17 1HH
Tel: 01372 724 648 Fax: 01372 723 775
Email: info@laine-theatre-arts.co.uk
Web Site: www.laine-theatre-arts.co.uk
Principal: Betty Laine

LEEDS COLLEGE OF MUSIC

3 Quarry Hill, St Peter's Square, Leeds, West Yorkshire LS2 7PD
Tel: 0113 222 3400 Fax: 0113 243 8798
Email: enquiries@lcm.ac.uk
Web Site: www.lcm.ac.uk
Administration/Courses:
Principal: D. Hoult Mus.B, MPhil, GRSM, ARMCM
Vocal studies and performance experience for full-time students (2 and 3 year courses) and part-time course students.

THE LONDON ACADEMY OF PERFORMING ARTS

St Matthew's Church, St Petersburg Place, London W2 4LA
Tel: 020 7727 0220 Fax: 020 7727 0330
Email: admin@lapadrama.com
Web Site: www.lapadrama.com
Administrative Director: Mr Brian Parsonage Kelly
Administration/Courses:
The Academy offers the following courses:
1 Year Post Graduate Diploma with 3 options - Classical Acting, Musical Theatre, Directing
Twelve week full-time Classical Acting Semesters.
Four week full-time Summer Shakespearean Acting Course (beginners and advanced)

LONDON CENTRE FOR THEATRE STUDIES

12-18 Hoxton Street, London N1 6NG
Tel/Fax: 020 7739 5866 Tel: 020 7739 1577
Email: ldncts@aol.com
Web Site: www.lcts.co.uk
Director: David Harris
The full time and part time acting courses realistically prepare actors for employment in the profession. Excellence is achieved by helping students develop their self confidence and realise their talent potential.
Course: The Actors Company - 1 year full-time course culminating in 6 weeek repertory season at the Jermyn St Theatre in the West End.

LONDON CONTEMPORARY DANCE SCHOOL

The Place, 17 Dukes Road, London WC1H 9PY
Tel: 020 7387 0152 Fax: 020 7387 3976
Email: lcds@theplace.org.uk
Web Site: www.theplace.org.uk
Administration/Courses:
Director: Veronica Lewis MBE
Full-time certificate and degree courses in Contemporary Dance & Choreography.
Evening classes. Vacation courses.

LONDON SCHOOL OF FILM, MEDIA AND PERFORMANCE

Regent's College Inner Circle, Regents Park, London NW1 4NS
Tel: 020 7487 7505 Fax: 020 7487 7425
Email: LSFMP@regents.ac.uk
Web Site: www.regents.ac.uk/LSFMP
Courses offered: Acting Foundation Course, BA (Hons) Acting and Global Theatre, BA (Hons) Creative Industries, BA (Hons) Screenwriting and Producing, MA Writing for Screen and Stage.
Beautiful Central London location.
Scholarships available.

LONDON STUDIO CENTRE

42-50 York Way, London N1 9AB
Tel: 020 7837 7741 Fax: 020 7837 3248
Email: enquire@london-studio-centre.co.uk
Web: www.london-studio-centre.co.uk
Director: Nicholas Espinosa
Head of Studies: Robert Penman
Courses:
3-year Theatre Dance course (classical ballet, contemporary dance, jazz theatre dance, music theatre, dance education) leading to either a BA (Hons) degree (currently validated by Middlesex University), a Diploma in Higher Education (currently validated by Middlesex University), or a London Studio Centre Diploma; 1-year Professional Diploma specialising in classical ballet, contemporary dance, jazz theatre dance or music theatre; 1-year dance education programme (currently validated by Middlesex University) ;
Specialist classical ballet route thorugh all Year 3 programmes; 3-week Summer course; Evening classes (access course).
The theatre dance course is accredited by the CDET. Entry to all programmes by audition.

MASTERS PERFORMING ARTS COLLEGE

Arterial Road, Rayleigh, Essex SS6 7UQ
Tel/Fax: 01268 777 351
Email: info@mastersperformingarts.co.uk
Web Site: www.mastperformingarts.co.uk
Senior Personnel: Wendy Headford
Full time college for Performing Arts.

MIDLANDS ACADEMY OF DANCE AND DRAMA

Building B, Century House, 428 Carlton Hill, Nottingham NG4 1QA
Tel: 0115 911 0401
Email: admin@maddcollege.supanet.com
Web Site: www.maddcollege.co.uk
Patron: David Essex OBE
Courses offered: 3 Year professional musical theatre course, 1 Year foundation

course. Scholarships available for boys and girls. Summer school 26th - 30th July.

NATIONAL FILM AND TELEVISION SCHOOL
Beaconsfield Studios, Station Road, Beaconsfield, Buckinghamshire HP9 1LG
Tel: 01494 671 234 Fax: 01494 674 042
Email: info@nftsfilm-tv.ac.uk
Web Site: www.nftsfilm-tv.ac.uk
Contact: The Registry
Postgraduate and professional training in film and television. 2-year MA courses in: Animation Direction, Cinematography, Composing for Film and Television, Documentary Direction, Editing, Fiction Direction, Producing, Production Design, Sound Post-Production, or Screenwriting. Diploma courses in Digital Post-Production, Script Development (part-time), Sound Recording, TV Producing - Factual Entertainment, and Visual & Special Effects Producing. Also the UK's leading provider of short courses for professionals.

OLDHAM COLLEGE
School of Performing Arts Rochdale Road, Oldham, Lancashire OL9 6AA
Tel: 0161 624 5214 Fax: 0161 785 4231
Email: keith.washington@oldham.ac.uk
Web Site: www.oldham.ac.uk
Courses:
National diploma courses in acting, dance, popular music, stage management, media, theatre lighting and sound audio engineering, television and video. Higher national diploma courses in acting, dance, arts administration, theatre lighting and sound design, stage management.

PERFORMERS COLLEGE
Southend Road, Corringham, Essex SS17 8JT
Tel: 01375 672 053 Fax: 01375 672 353
Email: pdc@dircon.co.uk
Web Site: www.performerscollege.co.uk
Full time Theatre dance training.

THE POOR SCHOOL
Reg.Charity No. 1084706
242 Pentonville Road, London N1 9JY
Tel: 020 7837 6030 Fax: 020 7837 5330
Email: acting@thepoorschool.com
Web Site: www.thepoorschool.com
Contact: Paul Caister
Full-time drama training scheduled in the evenings and at weekends and charged for at cost.

RAVENSCOURT THEATRE SCHOOL
Head Office: Tandy House, 30-40 Dalling Road, Hammersmith, London W6 0JB
Tel: 020 8741 0707 (4 lines) Fax: 020 8741 1786
Email: ravenscourt@hotmail.com

REDROOFS THEATRE SCHOOL & COLLEGE
Littlewick Green, Maidenhead, Berkshire SL6 3QY
Tel: 01628 822 982 Fax: 01628 822 461
Email: sam@redroofs.co.uk
Web Site: www.redroofs.co.uk
Courses:
Full-time professional training for students over 16.
Full-time professional training for children 7-16 with
general education.
Full-time Screen Acting Course for Post-Graduates.

RETFORD INTERNATIONAL COLLEGE
(Stage and Character/Special Effects)
11 Grove Street, Retford, Nottinghamshire DN22 6JP
Tel: 01777 707371 Fax: 01777 860374
Email: retcol@msn.com
Courses in basic make-up, photographic, television, competitive make-up, film and stage make-up, special effects, hair design and wig making. City and guilds wig making certificate. ITEC diploma in Stage & Character make-up. Beauty therapy and hairdressing also available. Grant maintained. No academic fees payable.

RICHMOND DRAMA SCHOOL
Parkshot Centre, Parkshot, Richmond, Surrey TW9 2RE
Tel: 020 8940 0170 ext.325 Fax: 020 8332 6560
Email: david.whitworth@racc.ac.uk
Web Site: www.racc.ac.uk
Courses:
Full time drama school (one year course).
Diploma validated by TRAC
Nationally recognised Access course.

ROYAL ACADEMY OF DANCE FACULTY OF EDUCATION
36 Battersea Square, London SW11 3RA
Tel: 020 7326 8000 Fax: 020 7924 3129
Email: info@rad.org.uk / faculty@rad.org.uk
Web Site: www.rad.org.uk
Director Of Education: Prof Joan White
Chief Executive: Luke Rittner
Artistic Director: Lynn Wallis
Finance and Administrative Director: Richard Thom
Membership Manager: Ray Bolton
3 year BA (Hons) Degree course in Ballet Education.
Certificate in Benesh Movement Notation (distance learning).
Diploma in Dance Education (distance learning).
BA(Hons) in Dance Education (distance learning).
Certificate of Higher Education: Dance Teaching (distance learning).
Professional Dancers Teaching Diploma (3 months intensive)
Post Graduate Certificate in Education: Dance Teaching (PGCE:DT) Certificate in Ballet Teaching Studies (CBTS) (Distance Learning).

ROYAL ACADEMY OF MUSIC
Marylebone Road, London NW1 5HT
Tel: 020 7873 7483 Fax: 020 7873 7484
Email: mth@ram.ac.uk
Web Site: www.ram.ac.uk
Administration/Courses:
Principal: Curtis Price
Director of Opera: Michael Rosewell
Head of Musical Theatre: Mary Hammond
Head of Vocal Studies: Mark Wildman
One Year Intensive Musical Theatre Course for Graduate, mature students and for professionals wishing to refocus their career.

SOUTH WEST ACADEMY OF DRAMATIC ARTS (SWADA)
Filton College, Filton Avenue, Filton, Bristol BS34 7AT
Email: bakerm@filton.ac.uk
Artistic Director: Marie Baker

BARBARA SPEAKE STAGE SCHOOL
East Acton Lane, East Acton, London W3 7EG
Tel: 020 8743 1306 Fax: 020 8743 1306
Email: cpuk@aol.com
Web Site: www.barbaraspeake.com
Ages 4-16
Full-time education to GCSE and professional artistic training.

STELLA MANN COLLEGE OF PERFORMING ARTS
10 Linden Road, Bedford MK40 2DA
Tel: 01234 213 331 Fax: 01234 217 284
Email: administrator@stellamanncollege.co.uk
Web Site: www.stellamanncollege.co.uk
Three year full time performance course including; Jazz, Classical Ballet, Contemporary, Tap, Musical Theatre, Singing, Acting, Partner work. Teacher training opportunities available. Lower school caters for pupils aged + 3yrs.

THE ACTORS PROFESSIONAL CENTRE LTD
1a Tower Street, London WC2H 9NP
General Tel: 020 7240 3940 Admin: 020 7632 8013 Room Hire Tel: 020 7632 8012 Membership Enquiries: 020 7632 8003 Fax: 020 7240 3896
Email: admin@actorscentre.co.uk
Web Site: www.actorscentre.co.uk
Artistic Director: Matthew Lloyd
General Manager: Toma Dim
Theatre Producer: Laura Kriefman
Operations Manager: Richard Williams

THE CIRCUS SPACE

Coronet Street, London N1 6HD
Tel: 020 7729 9522 Fax: 020 7729 9422
Email: jane@thecircusspace.co.uk
Web Site: www.thecircusspace.co.uk
ADMINISTRATION:
Joint Chief Executives: Jane Rice-Bowen and Kate White
Operations Director: Jonathan Dix
Higher Education Courses Director: Tim Roberts
Participation and Outreach Director: Eira Gibson
Director of Circus Development: Daisy Drury
Finance and Administration Director: Edward Halshaw
Head of Marketing and Communication: Philip Nichols
Venue Hire: Alex Horder (alex@thecircusspace.co.uk)

THE INTERNATIONAL SCHOOL OF SCREEN ACTING

3 Mills Studios, Unit 3, Sugar House Business Centre 24 Sugar House Lane, London E15 2QS
Tel: 020 8555 575
Email: office@screenacting.co.uk
Web Site: www.screenacting.co.uk
Acting & Voice Director: David Craik
Film Acting: Mark Normandy
Acting & Script Analysis: Michael Eriera

THE ROYAL BALLET SCHOOL

46 Floral Street, Covent Garden, London WC2E 9DA
Tel: 020 7836 8899 Fax: 020 7845 7080
Email: enquiries@royalballetschool.co.uk
Web Site: www.royalballetschool.co.uk
Administration/Courses:
Director: Gailene Stock
Assistant Director: Jay Jolley
Classical ballet training, juniors 11-16; seniors, 16 plus; Junior associate scheme (age 9+).
The Royal Ballet School is a split site school, its lower school based at White Lodge in Richmond, its upper school at Covent Garden, opposite the Royal Opera House. The Royal Ballet School is a world-class centre of excellence, training and educating British and foreign students towards a career as a ballet dancer. It aims to supply the Royal Ballet and other international companies with dancers from the school.

THE URDANG ACADEMY

The Old Finsbury Town Hall, Rosebery Avenue, London EC1R 4RP
Tel: 020 7713 7710 Fax: 020 7278 6727
Email: info@theurdangacademy.com
Web Site: www.theurdangacademy.com
Managing Director: Solange Urdang
Principal: Stephanie Pope ARAD (dip PDTC)
Full-Time Courses: BA(Hons) in Professional Dance and Musical Theatre, The National Diploma in Professional Musical Theatre, The National Diploma in Professional Dance, Foundation Course. Evening and Part-Time courses also available.

TRINGPARK ARTS EDUCATIONAL SCHOOL

Tring Park, Tring, Hertfordshire HP23 5LX
Tel: 01442 824 255 Fax: 01442 891 069
Email: info@tringpark.com
Web Site: www.tringpark.com
Principal: Mr Stefan Anderson
Full time education in drama, dance and musical theatre
Age 8-18

UNITED KINGDOM DANCE & DRAMA FEDERATION

18 Ashbourne Grove, Stoke-on-Trent ST1 5QW
Tel/Fax: 01782 257820 Mob: 0772 013 5076
Email: info@ukddf.co.uk
Web Site: www.ukddf.co.uk
Dance education to teacher standards. Training for professional dance careers. Teacher membership welcome. Qualified staff and regular guest teachers. Full syllabus and music.

WESTMINSTER KINGSWAY COLLEGE

Regents Park Centre, Longford Street, London NW1 3HB
Tel: 020 7556 8000 Fax: 020 7391 6400
Email: courseinfo@westking.ac.uk
Web Site: www.westking.ac.uk
Administration/Courses:
Artistic Director: Jean Hitchinson
Westminster Kingsway College Performing Arts Centre offers a range of courses in Dance, Drama, Media, Music and Musical Theatre, BTEC, A-Levels and Evening Classes.

WIMBLEDON SCHOOL OF ART

Merton Hall Road, Wimbledon, London SW19 3QA
Tel: 020 8408 5000 Fax: 020 8408 5050
Email: info@wimbledon.arts.ac.uk
Web Site: www.wimbledon.ac.uk
Administration/Courses:
Principal: George Blacklark
Courses: All Higher Education courses are validated by University of Surrey.
BA (Hons) Theatre with areas of specialisation including Design for Performance, Technical Arts and Special Effects, Set Design for Stage and Screen, Costume Interpretation and Costume Design. Plus, new foundation degree in Theatre Lighting Design and Practise, two years full time.
3 Years Full time MA Theatre:
Visual Language of Performance, 1 year Full Time.

SYLVIA YOUNG THEATRE SCHOOL

1 Nutford Place, London W1H 5YZ
Tel: 020 7258 2330 Fax: 020 7723 8543
Email: info@sylviayoungtheatreschool.co.uk
Web Site: www.sylviayoungtheatreschool.co.uk
Full time stage training/Saturday classes/Summerschool.

Part Time Colleges and Stage Schools

ACT AT SCHOOL DRAMA WORKSHOP

PO Box 834, Hemel Hempstead, Hertfordshire HP3 9ZP
Tel: 01442 252 907 Fax: 01442 241 099
Email: lindafrench@apmtraining.co.uk
Web Site: www.apmtraining.co.uk
Contact: Linda French
Drama Training for children aged 4-19. Annual live theatre and film productions, and pre-drama school coaching.

ALISON AXFORD THEATRE SCHOOL

5 Elmsleigh Park Paignton Devon TQ1 2EL
Tel: 07407 713516
Email: alisonaxford@uwclub.net
Web Site: www.alisonaxford-theatreschool.co.uk

ALLSORTS

34 Pember Road, London NW10 5LS
Tel/Fax: 020 8969 3249
Email: info@allsortsdrama.com
Web Site: www.allsortsdrama.com
Senior Personnel: Sasha Leslie, Melissa Healy
Allsorts provide part time drama tuition, weekdays, weekends and holidays for ages 3 and above, in over 20 venues across London. Also management for professional work in TV and film.

ANGLIA SUMMER SCHOOLS

15 Inglis Road, Colchester, Essex CO3 3HU
Tel: 01206 540 111 Fax: 01206 766 944
Email: anglia@inglis-house.demon.co.uk
Web Site: www.inglis-house.demon.co.uk/anglia
Residential Theatre Performance Courses for 13 to 19 year olds during Summer Holidays. Also non-residential courses for 8 to 13 year olds in London and Colchester. Immersed in every aspect of stagework - acting, singing, dancing,

lighting, stage management, make up, auditions - each course ends with a performance of a show created during the holiday

THE ARTS FACTORY
Tel: 020 8445 2744
Email: theartsfactory@uk2.net
Drama, Music, Dance and Craft.
Summer Day Camps for boys and girls aged 8-15 years.

JOAN BARNES THEATRE SCHOOL
20 Green Street, Hazlemere, High Wycombe, Buckinghamshire HP15 7RB
Tel: 01494 523 193
Courses:
Part time tuition in Speech and Drama.
All ages: 3 years to adult

B.L.A. ACADEMY OF THEATRE ARTS
Performance House, 20 Passey Place, London SE9 5DQ
Tel: 020 8850 9888 Fax: 020 8850 9944
Email: bla@dircon.co.uk
Web Site: www.theatretraining.com
Principals: Miss Susan Pendergast & Mrs Maureen P. Hussey
Headmaster: Mr Ian Thomson
Full time & part time Theatre School of Performing Arts. Academic, full time up to GCSE age 7 to 16 years. Sunday schools, evening classes and summer schools. Call for details.

BLOWOUT SAX
South Lodge, North Parade, Bath, B.A.N.E.S. BA2 4EU
Tel: 01225 339 007 Mobile: 07773 737 880
Email: markarcher@blowoutsax.com
Web Site: www.blowoutsax.com
School Director: Mark Archer
School, shop and musicians.

BODEN STUDIOS
99 East Barnet Road, New Barnet, Hertfordshire EN4 8RF
Studio Tel: 020 8447 0909 Fax: 020 8449 5212
Email: Bodens2692@aol.com
Web Site: www.bodenstudios.com
Contact: Mo Boden

BOLTON PHOENIX
Bark Street, Bolton BL1 2AZ
Tel: 01204 535 861
Email: info@boltonpheonix.co.uk
Web Site: www.boltonphoenix.co.uk
Artistic Director: Wendy Ellis
Arts Development Officer: Lee Brennan
Education Officer: Caroline Coates
The Phoenix aims to offer the highest quality performing arts workshops and facilities, at the lowest possible cost. The Phoenix encourages open access to the arts for all young people.
Inc: Theatre, Rehearsal Rooms, Dance Studio, Dark Room,
Recording Studio, Video editing Suite, Costume & Theatrical Equipment Hire.

BURTON COLLEGE
Lichfield Street, Burton-on-Trent, Staffordshire DE14 3RL
Tel: 01283 494 400 Fax: 01283 494 800
Email: neil.willis@burton-college.ac.uk
Web Site: www.burton.college.ac.uk
Administration/Courses:
Senior Course Tutor: Neil Willis
Junior Youth Theatre: Age 7+.
Senior Youth Theatre: Age 16+.
First Diploma in Performing Arts (1 year).
National Diploma in Performing Arts (2 years f-t).
A-Levels in Theatre Studies, Film, Dance and Music.

CANTORS THEATRE SCHOOL & CENTRE
Office ~ Uppham Hall, Green Lane, Kessingland. NR33 7RP IN LOWESTOFT ~ OULTON BROAD ~ BECCLES & HALESWORTH
UNIT 7, Lowestoft Enterprise Park, School Road, Lowestoft, SUFFOLK NR33 9NA
Tel: 01502 742011 (office) Mobile: 07970 421403
Email: kenny.cantor@virgin.net
Web: www.cantorstheatreschool.co.uk
Proprietors:Caron and Kenny Cantor
WHAT WE TEACH: Singing, Movement, Drama, Elocution, Confidence, Team building, Tap Dancing, Ballet, Voice, Production, Audition Technique, Jazz, Microphone Technique, Theatrical Make-up, Stage Management

CENTRE STAGE SCHOOL OF PERFORMING ARTS
Holy Trinity, Trinity Walk, Hampstead, London NW3
Tel: 020 7328 0788 Other Centres: St Clement & St James', Holland Park, London W11
Email: vickiw@dircon.co.uk
Web Site: www.centrestageschool.co.uk
Contact: Vicki Woolf
Drama, Dance and Singing. Three hour classes every morning and afternoon. Also private coaching in Acting, Public Speaking and Interview Techniques.

CHADSWORTH STAGE SCHOOL (CLAYGATE)
21 Hinchley Drive, Hinchley Wood, Esher, Surrey KT10 0BZ
Tel: 020 8398 8104
Email: chadsworth@dial.pipex.com
Web: www.chadsworthstageschool.co.uk
Principal: Michelle Mackrell
Age: 2-18

DANCE WORKS
16 Balderton Street, London W1K 6TN
Tel: 020 7629 6183 Studio Hire Hotline: 020 7318 4100
Email: info@danceworks.net
Web Site: www.danceworks.net
We offer Europe's largest selection of dance classes, 7 large multi-purpose studios for hire, men's and women's changing facilities with showers, a lounge/ networking area which includes internet access and our first floor therapy centre, Natureworks.

DEBBIE FYFFE THEATRE SCHOOL
5 Narrow Way, Bromley, Kent BR2 8JB
Tel/Fax: 020 8462 9939
Email: enquiries@dfts.co.uk
Administration/Courses:
Courses in tap, modern ballet, jazz, drama and singing for ages 2 to 19 years.
Please contact for a brochure.

GAIETY SCHOOL OF ACTING
Meeting House Square, Temple Bar, Dublin 2 Eire
Tel: 00 353 1 679 9277 Fax: 00 353 1 679 9568
Email: gaietyschool@indigo.ie
Web Site: www.gaietyschool.com
Chairman of the Board: Joe Dowling
Director: Patrick Sutton
2 year Full time Intensive Acting Programme*
1 year Part Time Performance Course*
1 year Part Time Foundation Course (Evenings)
10 week introduction to Drama Course (Evenings)
Practical Playwriting Course (Evenings)
Drama weekends
Young Gaiety 6-16 years (Saturdays)
Youth Theatre Workshop 16-19 years
Youth Theatre Company 16-19 years
Summer Schools for Adults and Children
Irish International Theatre Summer School
International January Term Programme on Irish Theatre
*Entry by audition - Dublin, London & New York.
For further details contact Administration.

GREASEPAINT: SCHOOL OF TV, FILM, THEATRE & FASHION MAKE-UP
Studio: 143 Northfield Avenue, Ealing, London W13 9QT
Tel: 020 8840 6000 Fax: 020 8840 3983
Email: info@greasepaint.co.uk
Web Site: www.greasepaint.co.uk
Courses:
Intensive 14 week courses (January, May, September), comprising 7 weeks Make-up, 4 weeks Prosthetics and 3 weeks Hair. 4 weeks fashion make-up and hair courses also available also workshops and private lessons.

JENNIFER HALEY STAGE SCHOOL

Toad Hall, 67 Poppleton Road, Whips, London E11 1LP
Tel: 020 8504 1946 Mob: 077 99778 565
Training in dance, drama and singing for both children and adults (part-time). RAD, ISTD, LAMDA.

HEAVEN ACADEMY OF PERFORMING ARTS

The Prospect, 15 Lords Hill, Coleford, Gloucestershire GL16 8BG
Tel: 01594 837 919
Music/Arts Director: Yasmine Hazell

JIGSAW ARTS

64-66 High Street, Barnet, Herts EN5 5SJ
Tel: 020 8447 4530
Email: admin@jigsaw-arts.co.uk
Web Site: www.jigsaw-arts.co.uk
Weekend performing arts schools. New Term starts 20th January - 24th March. Schools in Finchley, London, Essex and Hertfordshire. Please visit our website or call for prospectus.

LIVERPOOL CENTRE FOR ARTS DEVELOPMENT TRAINING LTD (CADT)

2a Franceys Street, Off Brownlow Hill Liverpool Merseyside L3 5YQ
Tel: 0151 707 1404 Fax: 0151 709 7102
Email: liz@lcad.org.uk
Web Site: www.lcad.org.uk
Director: Liz Lacey
Business Consultant: All Gunning
Information Co-ordinator: Susan Loftus

MORLEY COLLEGE THEATRE SCHOOL

61 Westminster Bridge Road, London SW1 7HT
Tel: 020 7450 1885 Fax: 020 7928 4074
Email: enquiries@morleycollege.ac.uk
Web Site: www.morleycollege.ac.uk
Part-time classes for adults
Director: C/O Keith Brazil

JACKIE PALMER STAGE SCHOOL

30 Daws Hill Lane, High Wycombe, Buckinghamshire HP11 1PW
Tel: 01494 520 978 / 525 938 Fax: 01494 510 479
Email: jackie.palmer@btinternet.com
Age 3-18 years
Evenings and Weekends

PLAYBOARD PUPPET THEATRE

The Black Barn The Street, Tibenham, Norwich NR16 1QA
Tel/Fax: 020 7226 5911
Email: buttonmoon@btconnect.com
Web Site: www.buttonmoon.tv
Director: Ian Allen
Administrator: Vicky Clinch
Puppets In Vision. Playboard Puppets presents its creations of imagination workshops in all forms of puppetry at the Norfolk Barn. Courses run from Spring to Autumn. Playboard Puppets is famous for the cult TV series "Button Moon", and many more. The Company has been going for 35 years touring shows, doing theatre workshop and television with puppetry; where participants get the feel of working on a spoof puppet murder mystery.

THE QUESTORS THEATRE

Mattock Lane, Ealing, London W5 5BQ
Tel: 020 8567 0011
Email: andrea@questors.org.uk
Web Site: www.questors.org.uk
Administration/Courses:
Director of Studies: David Emmet.
Intensive 2 year part-time training course in acting: weekends and evenings - age 18 plus.
1 year introductory course: Saturdays - age 17-20.
Young People's groups: weekday evenings and Saturdays - age 5-17.

REDROOFS THEATRE SCHOOL & COLLEGE

Littlewick Green, Maidenhead, Berkshire SL6 3QY
Tel: 01628 822 982 Fax: 01628 822 461
Email: sam@redroofs.co.uk
Web Site: www.redroofs.co.uk
Courses:
Full-time professional training for students over 16.
Full-time professional training for children 7-16 with
general education.
Full-time Screen Acting Course for Post-Graduates.

SUSAN ROBERTS ACADEMY OF PERFORMING ARTS LTD

57 High Point, Heath Road, Weybridge, Surrey KT13 8TP
Tel: 01932 840 434 Fax: 020 7247 8810
Email: susan@sra-performingarts.co.uk
Web Site: www.sra-performingarts.co.uk
Principal: Susan Roberts
RAD Ballet. ISTD. Tap, Ballet and Modern. Freestyle Jazz. Singing. Drama. Lamda. GCSE Drama & GCSE Dance. Musical Production.

STAGECOACH HACKNEY AND ISLINGTON

269 Wick Road Hackney London E9 5DG
Tel: 020 3222 5544
Email: hackney@stagecoach.co.uk
Web: www.stagecoach.co.uk/hackney
Gary Hughes

STAGECOACH HIGH WYCOMBE

28 College Avenue, Maidenhead, Berkshire SL6 6AX
Principal: Eirian Davies

STAGECOACH THEATRE ARTS

The Courthouse, Elm Grove, Walton-on-Thames, Surrey KT12 1LZ
Tel: 01932 254 333 Fax: 01932 222 894
Email: enquiries@stagecoach.co.uk
Web Site: www.stagecoach.co.uk
Co-Founding Directors: Stephanie Manuel, David Sprigg
The UK's original and largest part-time performing arts schools network for children aged 4-18years. Over 600 schools across the UK and Ireland teaching young people to sing, dance and act, at weekends, after-school and holiday workshops.

STAGEWORKS THEATRE SCHOOL

48 Hathaway Gardens, Romford, Essex RM6 5TL
Tel: 020 8599 6253 / 020 8598 8241
Fax: 020 8599 6253
Email: stageworktheatreschool@hotmail.com
Senior Personnel: Ted Heath, Peter Dayson
A theatre school for children of all ages to train in all aspects of theatre life to the highest possible standard.

THE ACTORS THEATRE SCHOOL

32 Exeter Road, London NW2 4SB
Tel: 020 8450 0371
Email: info@theactorstheatreschool.co.uk
Web: www.theactorstheatreschool.co.uk
Contact: Eamonn Jones
A fast track foundation course.
Visit our website for more information re: Courses & Publications.

THEATRE TRIBE ACADEMY

38 Beatty Road, Stoke Newington London N16 8EB
Tel: 020 3239 3149
Email: contactus@theatretribe.co.uk
Web Site: www.theatretribe.co.uk
Director: Emma Brooke
Theatre Tribe is London's premiere workshop academy for the performing arts, offering Musical Theatre experiences to young people wishing to learn from industry pros with experience of both the West End and National Tours.

THEATRETRAIN HIGHGATE

Acland Burghley School
London NW5 1UJ
Tel: 07724 433914
Email: highgate@theatretrain.co.uk
Web Site: www.theatretrain.co.uk
Centre Director: Geraldine Aves
Our classes run 10am-1pm on Saturdays

during school term
Our classes are for 6-18 yrs. We have 3 age groups, 6-9, 9-12 and 13-18.
Each group gets an hour of singing, dance and drama. Every year we produce a show. This can be a local show involving just our centre held in a local Theatre, or a London show involving 6-8 Theatretrain centres. These shows take place in the West End or our Gala shows which take place at the Royal Albert Hall involving 24 Theatretrain Centres (around 1,000 Children)
This year Theatretrain is celebrating 20 years of our large scale shows by taking 3,000 Theatretrain students and performing at the 02 Arena in a show on the same scale as the Opening ceremony of the Olympic games.

YOUNG ACTORS THEATRE & AGENCY
70-72 Barnsbury Road, London N1 0ES
Tel: 020 7278 2101 Fax: 020 7833 9467
Email: info@yati.org.uk
Web Site: www.yati.org.uk
Director: Andrew Harries
Agents: Dyana Daulby and Lucy O'Meara
Community Theatre and Management Agency.
The Community Theatre runs evening drama classes for all ages, from 6 upwards.
The Management Agency specialises in representation of children from the age of 6-17, as well as representing adults of all ages.

YOUNG PERFORMERS THEATRE SCHOOL
Ground Floor, 3 Clements Court, Clements Lane, Ilford, Essex IG1 2QY
Tel: 020 8518 0200 Fax: 020 8518 0212
Emergency Number: 077 0203 1519
Principal: Sandra Filek
Administrator: Sara Filek
Stage school for agest 2 to 20.

SYLVIA YOUNG THEATRE SCHOOL
1 Nutford Place, London W1H 5YZ
Tel: 020 7258 2330 Fax: 020 7723 8543
Email: info@sylviayoungtheatreschool.co.uk
Web Site: www.sylviayoungtheatreschool.co.uk
Full time stage training/Saturday classes/Summerschool.

Universities

ANGLIA RUSKIN UNIVERSITY
East Road, Cambridge CB1 1PT
Tel: 01223 363 271 Ext 2223
Fax: 01223 417 700
Email: a.beaumont@anglia.ac.uk
www.anglia.ac.uk
Programme Leader: Pam Pfrommer
Course Administrator: Allison Beaumont
MA Arts Management
A one year full time, or two year part time, programme leading to good networking and employment opportunities.

UNIVERSITY OF BIRMINGHAM
Drama & Theatre Arts Dept. Edgbaston, Birmingham B15 2TT
Tel: 0121 414 5998
Fax: 0121 414 2244
Email: jabatham@bham.ac.uk
www.drama.bham.ac.uk
Contact: Julie Batham
Courses:
3 year full-time course in drama and theatre Arts leading to B.A. (Hons) degree.
3 year full-time course Dance and Theatre Arts leading to B.A. (Hons) degree.
1 year full time course leading to M.Phil in Playwriting Studies.
Postgraduate research degrees leading to M.A. M.Phil or Ph.D. in Drama or Dance.

UNIVERSITY OF CENTRAL ENGLAND IN BIRMINGHAM
School of Theatre Design, Corporation Street, Birmingham B4 7DX
Tel: 0121 331 5800
Fax: 0121 333 6020
Email: mick.durman@uce.ac.uk
www.uce.ac.uk
Administration/Courses:
Head of Theatre Design: Paul Barrett
Education Course Directors: Steve Lewis, Simon Spencer
Courses:
3 year full-time Theatre Design course leading to BA (Hons.).
Specialist Drama in Education course leading to the Post Graduate Certificate in Education, 1 year full-time.
MA course in Drama in Education, full-time or part-time.
Birmingham Institute of Art & Design
MA Scenography 1Yr Full Time, 2 Yr Part Time at theatre design.

UNIVERSITY OF BRIGHTON
Hillbrow, Denton Road, Eastbourne, East Sussex BN20 7SR
Tel: 01273 600 900
Fax: 01273 643 704
Email: r.royce@brighton.ac.uk
www.brighton.ac.uk
Administration/Courses:
Contact: Dr Richard Royce
4-year B.A. QTS in P.E. with Dance.
1 -year Post-graduate course in Dance.
1-year Post-graduate course in P.E. (including Dance).

UNIVERSITY OF BRISTOL
Drama Department: Theatre, Film, Television, Cantocks Close, Woodland Road, Bristol, Avon BS8 1UP
Tel: 0117 954 5481
Email: mark.sinfield@bris.ac.uk
www.bris.ac.uk/drama
Administration/Courses:
Head of Drama Department: Simon Jones
3 year full-time course in Drama leading to B.A. (Hons) degree.
3 year joint courses in Drama and English or a Modern language. The Modern Language Course involves a fourth year of study abroad.
1 or 2 year postgraduate studies leading to M.Phil, M.Litt or PhD by dissertation.
1 year full time or two year part time post-graduate course leading to MA in Television Studies.
1 year postgraduate course leading to MA in Film and Television, Production.
1 year full time or 2 year part time MA in Cultural Performance.
1 year full time or 2 year part time MA in Cinema Studies.

UNIVERSITY OF WALES INSTITUTE CARDIFF (UWIC)
School of Education, Cyncoed Road, Cyncoed, Cardiff, South Glamorgan CF2 6XD Wales
Tel: 029 2050 6555
Fax: 029 2050 6589
Email: education@uwic.ac.uk
www.uwic.ac.uk
Administration/Courses:
B.A. Education (Hons): Secondary Drama

CITY UNIVERSITY
Dept. of Cltrl Policy & Mgt School of Arts, Northampton Square, London EC1V 0HB
Tel: 020 7040 8753
Fax: 020 7477 8887
Email: m.dines@city.ac.uk
www.city.ac.uk/artspolicy
Courses:
Email: artspol@city.ac.uk
Certificate in Museum & Gallery Management In Practice
Diploma in Cultural Management (previously Diploma in Arts Administration): 1 year full-time or 2 year part-time.
MA Courses: Arts Management, Museum & Gallery Management, and Arts Criticism (1 year full-time or 2 year part-time).
Research: facilities exist for students to undertake research degrees of MPhil and PhD. Further details: send 12" x 9" sae to above address.

DE MONTFORT UNIVERSITY
Dept. of Performing Arts, Crown Building, Newarke Street, Leicester LE1 9BH
Tel: 0116 250 6185
Fax: 0116 250 6188
Email: mrhuxley@dmu.ac.uk / mwp@dmu.ac.uk
www.dmu.ac.uk
Head: Michael Huxley
Admissions: Professor Michael Patterson
3 year full-time Theatre, Dance, Performing Arts.
MA in Theatre.

UNIVERSITY OF ESSEX
Centre for Theatre Studies University of Essex Wivenhoe Park Colchester, Essex CO4 3SQ
Tel: 01206 873333
Fax: 01206 873598
Email: pennyw@essex.ac.uk
www.essex.ac.uk
Administration/Courses:
Further Information: Secretary of Theatre Studies Dept - Sheila Forster 01206 872806
Contact Executive Officer at Centre for Theatre Studies:
Penny Woollard

UNIVERSITY OF EXETER
School of Performance Arts (Drama) Thornlea, New North Road, Exeter, Devon EX4 4LA
Tel: 01392 264 580
Fax: 01392 264 594
Email: drama@exeter.ac.uk
www.ex.ac.uk/drama
Administration/Courses:
Head of School of Performance Arts: Christopher McCullough
Courses:
3 year full-time drama course leading to single Honours Degree.
NB: Courses include practical training in performance and technical theatre.
MA courses in Applied Drama, Drama Research, Playwriting, Script-development and MA/MFA courses in Staging Shakespeare and Theatre Practice. Two and three year registration for MPhil and PhD welcomed. We also offer a new PhD in Performance Practice (A practice based doctoral programme)

UNIVERSITY OF GLASGOW
Dept. of Theatre, Film and Television Studies, Gilmorehill Centre for Theatre, Film and Television, University Avenue, Glasgow, Strathclyde G12 8QQ Scotland
Tel: 0141 339 8855 Ext 3809
Email: d.goldie@admin.gla.ac.uk
www.arts.gla.ac.uk/tfts
Administration/Courses:
Professor of Drama: Jan McDonald.
3 year full-time course in theatre studies with other options including film and television studies leading to M.A. general degree.
4 year full-time course in theatre studies leading to MA (Hons) degree.
4 year full-time course in theatre studies with a joint subject and other options including film and television studies leading to M.A. (Hons) degree.
Postgraduate courses leading to M.Litt., M.Phil or Ph.D.
N.B. Courses include some practical work

UNIVERSITY OF HERTFORDSHIRE
School of Humanities and Education, Wall Hall, Aldenham, Watford, Hertfordshire WD2 8AT
Tel: 01707 284800
Fax: 01707 284870 (General Office)
Email: s.1.riley@herts.ac.uk
www.herts.ac.uk/humanities/hum-c-drama.html

UNIVERSITY OF HUDDERSFIELD
Division of Drama, Theatre & Performance, School of Music & Humanities St. Peters Building, St. Peters Street, Huddersfield, West Yorkshire HD1 1RA
Tel: 01484 422288
Fax: 01484 478428
Email: m.jessup@hud.ac.uk
Administration/Courses:
Head of Drama: Dr. Steve Nicholson
BA (Hons) 3 years full-time Drama
BA (Hons) 3 years full-time Drama and Media
B.A.(Hons) 3 years full-time Drama with Music
BA (Hons) 3 years full-time Drama and English
All the above may also be available on a part-time basis.
Also opportunities for postgraduate study for the degrees of M.Phil and Phd.

HULL UNIVERSITY
Drama Department, Gulbenkian Centre, Hull, East Yorkshire HU6 7RX
Tel: 01482 466 210
Email: p.j.lambert@hulll.ac.uk
www.hull.ac.uk/drama/
Administration./Courses:
Administrator: Mrs Paula Lambert
Head of Department: A.J. Meech
3 year full-time drama course leading to B.A. Single Honours Degree.
3 year full-time course in drama with American Studies or English or modern languages, or Music, or Theology leading to B.A. Joint Honours Degree.
1 year full-time course in Theatre Production leading to M.A. by assessment, examination and dissertation.
Postgraduate research leading to M.Phil. or Ph.D. in dramatic literature or theatre history by dissertation.
N.B. Single Honours and MA courses include some practical training.

UNIVERSITY OF KENT AT CANTERBURY
Eliot College, The University, Canterbury, Kent CT2 7NS
Tel: 01227 764000 extn. 7567 (Drama dept.)
Fax: 01227 827464
Email: f.a.barbe@kent.ac.uk
www.kent.ac.uk
Administration/Courses:
4 year Single Honours Course with final year devoted to directing, devising or theatre administration.
3 year Combined Honours Course and 3 year Visual and Performed Arts Course.
Postgraduate research leading to M.A. and Ph.D. by dissertation.
N.B. Single Honours and Combined Honours Courses include practical training. Board of Drama and Theatre Studies has new Drama Studio building, Studio Theatre and access to Audio-visual Studio and the Gulbenkian Theatre.
Contact Drama Teacher: Frances Barbe

KINGSTON UNIVERSITY
Faculty of Education, Kingston Hill Theatre, Kingston Hill, Kingston, Surrey KT2 7LB
Tel: 020 8547 2000
Fax: 020 8546 7116
Email: k.grieves@kingston.ac.uk
www.kingston.ac.uk
Administration/Courses:
Tutor: Pam Bowell.
English and Drama as part of 4 year full-time Education course leading to B.Ed.(Hons), includes educational drama and T.I.E. work.
Also education drama in professional studies component in above course.
Contact Director of Research:

UNIVERSITY OF LANCASTER
Theatre Studies, Music and Art Lancaster Institute for the Contemporary Arts, Bailrigg, Lancaster, Lancashire LA1 4YW
Tel: 01524 594 156
Fax: 01524 39021
Email: e.aston@lancaster.ac.uk
www.theatre-studies.lancs.ac.uk
Administration/Courses:
Head of Theatre Studies: Professor Elaine Aston
BA Hons in Theatre Studies
Combined B.A. (Hons) Degree in Theatre Studies and English/French/German Educational Studies.
1 year full time or 2 year part time MA in Theatre Studies
Also M Phil.

UNIVERSITY OF LEEDS
Leeds, West Yorkshire LS2 9JT
Tel: 0113 233 4720
Fax: 0113 233 4774
Email: m.j.batty@leeds.ac.uk
www.leeds.ac.uk/theatre
Administration/Courses:
Professor of Drama and Theatre Studies and Director of the Workshop Theatre: Philip Roberts
Full-time postgraduate course in Theatre Studies leading to M.A. Degree (Degree by instruction); also postgraduate research in Drama and/or Theatre Studies leading to Degrees of M.Phil or Ph.D.
Undergraduate course in B.A. English Lit. and Theatre Studies (Hons).

LONDON METROPOLITAN UNIVERSITY
Department of Humanities, Arts and Languages
166-120 Holloway Road, London N7 8DB
Tel: 020 7423 0000
Email: admissions@londonmet.ac.uk
www.londonmet.ac.uk
Administration/Courses:
3 year full-time honours degree in Theatre Studies and another subject.
3 year full-time honours degree in Performing Arts
3 year full-time honours degree in Theatre Studies
Part-time honours degree in Theatre Studies and another subject.
Part-time honours degree in Theatre Studies.
Part-time honours degree in Performing Arts.

LOUGHBOROUGH UNIVERSITY OF TECHNOLOGY
Department of English and Drama,
Loughborough University, Loughborough, Leicestershire LE11 3TU
Tel: 01509 263171
Fax: 01509 269994
Email: c.j.mcknight@lboro.ac.uk
Courses:
3 year full-time single or combined honours (with English as a minor) course leading to B.A. (Hons) degree. The course is weighted equally between Textual studies and practical investigation and performance including the use of sound and TV apparatus in well equipped theatre workshops.
Postgraduate work (full and part-time) leading to M.A. Theatre and higher degrees by research, M.Phil or Ph.D.

MANCHESTER METROPOLITAN UNIVERSITY
The Institute of Education, (Didsbury), 799 Wimslow Road, Didsbury, Manchester M20 2RR
Tel: 0161 247 2336
Fax: 0161 247 6368
Email: j.rainer@mmu.ac.uk
Administration/Courses:
Subject Leader for Drama in School of Education: John Rainer
Drama as main course in secondary level studies leading to the postgraduate certificate in education.
Drama can be studied in a 4 year full time course leading to 4 year BA (QTS) (Hons)
School of Theatre Course Leader: Niamh Dowling Tel: 0161 247 2000 ext 1308
Communication Media Dept. 3 year full time Acting course for intended professionals leading to BA(Hons) in Theatre Arts (Acting). All enquiries to main university at All Saints Building, Manchester M15 6BH.

UNIVERSITY OF MANCHESTER
Drama Department, Oxford Road, Manchester M13 9PL
Tel: 0161 275 4982
Fax: 0161 275 4994
Email: drama@man.ac.uk
www.manchester.ac.uk
Administration/Courses:
Subject Leader: Professor Viv Gardner
Secretary: Ben Nation
3 year full-time course in drama leading to B.A. (Hons) degree.
3 year full-time Joint Honours course in Drama with English B.A. (Hons) degree.
4 year full-time course in English and Drama B.A. (Double Hons) degree.
3 Year full-time Joint Honours Music and Drama
1 year full-time postgraduate diploma course in drama.
1 year full-time and 2 year part-time MA in Theatre Studies
1 year full-time and 2 year part-time MA in Screen Studies
1 year full-time and 2 year part-time MA in Applied Theatre
M.Phil. and Ph.D. research by thesis.

MIDDLESEX UNIVERSITY
School of Arts Trent Park, Bramley Road, Oakwood, London N14 4YZ
Tel: 020 8411 5000
Email: j.dare@mdx.ac.uk
Adminstration/Courses:
Contact: Mr I. Watts, Mrs J. Dare
BA (Hons) Drama and Theatre Studies: Programme Leader Arthur Husk. 3 year full-time course situated at Trent Park.
BA (Hons) Theatre Technical Arts: Programme Leader Nick Herrett. Degree focusing on all technical theatre aspects: sound, lighting, stage management etc
PGCE Drama: 1 year full-time course. Programme Leader: Kenneth Taylor. Situated at Trent Park.
MA Performing Arts: Programme Leader Sidney Henderson. 2 year part-time course. Drama available as a major study in an interdisciplinary programme involving post graduate students in Music and Dance as well.
MA/MFA Theatre Directing: Programme LEader: Prof Leon Rubin 1 or 2 year programme redesigned to prepare the professional theatre director. This degree is very practical in content.
Enquiries for all courses should be addressed to: Admissions, Middlesex University, Cat Hill, Cockfosters, Herts Tel 020 8362 5000

UNIVERSITY OF NORTHUMBRIA AT NEWCASTLE
Faculty of Arts, School of Art, Lipman Building, University of Northumbria, Newcastle-upon-Tyne, Tyne and Wear NE1 8ST
Tel: 0191 227 4975
Fax: 0191 227 3632
Email: s.paterson@unn.ac.uk
Administration/Courses:
Contact: Sharon Patterson Tel 0191 227 3742
BA (Hons) Drama Three-year full-time course, with emphasis on theatre/drama in the community.
Contact: Dr.Warwick Dobson Tel 0191 227 3168
BA (Hons) Performance Three year full time course aims to produce multi-skilled performers who meet the demands of current professional practice.

NOTTINGHAM TRENT UNIVERSITY
Nottingham Trent School of Art & Design Theatre Design, Burton Street, Nottingham NG1 4BU
Tel: 0115 848 2833
Fax: 0115 848 4086
Email: rachael.hvall@hvall@ntu.ac.uk
www.ntu.ac.uk
Administration/Courses:
Programme Leader: Matt Hawthorn
Programme Co-ordinator: Rachael Hvall
BA(Hons) 3 year full-time course in Theatre Design

QUEEN MARGARET UNIVERSITY COLLEGE
School of Drama & Creative Industries
Gateway Theatre, Elm Row, Edinburgh, Mid Lothian EH7 4AH Scotland
Tel: 0131 3173900
BO: 0131 317 3939
Fax: 0131 317 3902
Email: ahunt@qmuc.ac.uk
www.qmuc.ac.uk
Courses:
BA/BA (Hons) Drama and Theatre Arts, Theatre Production. Postgrad: Cultural Management and Policy, Festivals Producing, Dramatic Writing. Doctoral school.
MA/MFA Advanced Stage and Screen Practice
BA/BA(Hons) Acting and Performance
BA/BA(Hons) Performance Production and Management

QUEEN MARY COLLEGE
University of London
327 Mile End Road, London E1 4NS
Tel: 020 7975 5555
Fax: 020 7975 5500
Email: s.g.eddleston@qmul.ac.uk
www.qmul.ac.uk
Director of Drama: Paul Heritage
Contact: Drama Secretary: Susan Cook for more information
3 or 4 year course in drama with either: English, French, German, Hispanic Studies or Russian, leading to a BA. Degree. The practical Drama is taught by The Central School of Speech and Drama.

READING UNIVERSITY
Dept of Film and Drama, Bulmershe Court, Woodlands Avenue, Earley, Reading, Berkshire RG6 1HY
Tel: 0118 931 8878
Fax: 0118 931 8873
Email: e.a.silvester@reading.ac.uk
Courses:
BA. Single Hons Subject Film + Drama.
BA. Combined Hons Subject Film + Drama with one of: English, German, Italian.
PGCE Drama with Contextual Studies.
MA Film and Drama
BA. Hons in Theatre Arts, Education and Deaf Studies.

ROYAL HOLLOWAY UNIVERSITY OF LONDON
Department of Drama & Theatre Egham Hill, Egham, Surrey TW20 0EX
Drama Tel: 01784 443 922
Email: Drama@rhbnc.ac.uk
www.rhul.ac.uk/drama
Administration/Courses:
Head of Department: Professor David Wiles
3 year course in Drama and Theatre Studies leading to BA(Hons).
4 year course in International Theatre (France) leading to BA(Hons)
4 year course in International Theatre (Australia) leading to BA(Hons)
3 year combined Hons course in Drama and Theatre Studies, plus one other subject (English; French; Classics; Music; German; Italian; Creative Writing).
MA in Theatre, one year full time, two years part time. Taught course.
Pathways: Applied Drama; Directing; Performance Studies; Playwriting.
MA in Greek Theatre Performance, one year full time. Taught course.
MA in Physical Theatre, one year full time, Two years part-time.
MA in Research, one year full time, two years part time.
M.Phil. by research. Thesis may be submitted after 2 years.

SLADE SCHOOL OF FINE ART
University College London, Gower Street, London WC1E 6BT
Tel: 020 7679 2313
Email: slade.enquiries@ucl.ac.uk
www.ucl.ac.uk/slade
Administration/Course:
Slade Professor: John Aiken
Head of Theatre Design course: Philip Prowse
MA, MFA and Graduate Diploma in Fine Art

UNIVERSITY OF SUNDERLAND
School of Arts, Design & Communications, Backhouse Park Ryhope Road, Sunderland SR2 7EF
Tel: 0191 515 3294
Fax: 0191 515 2132
Email: ingrid.fairfax@sunderland.ac.uk
Administration/Courses:
Head of School Arts, Design & Communications:
Professor Flavia Swann
3 year full-time BA (Hons) Creative Arts Studies including a Drama/Theatre option.
Contact Admissions Officer: Ingrid Fairfax

UNIVERSITY OF SURREY ROEHAMPTON
School of Arts, Jubilee Building, Digby Stewart College, Roehampton Lane, London SW15 5PH
Tel: 020 8392 3230
Email: m.bancroft@roehampton.ac.uk
www.roehampton.ac.uk
Administration/Courses:
BA, BSc, BA with QTS, MA, PGCE, Dips, Certs. Subjects include drama, dance, music. Dips and Certs in arts admin, drama therapy, music therapy, dance movement therapy, music, etc. Many programmes available full and part-time. M.A. Shakespeare and Performance, MA Ballet Studies.

UNIVERSITY OF ULSTER
School of Creative Arts, Northland Road, Londonderry BT48 7JL Northern Ireland
Tel: 028 716 75396
Email: g.monaghan@ulster.ac.uk; r.ohagan@ulster.ac.uk
www.ulster.ac.uk
Administration/Courses:
Drama Course Director: Dr Lisa Fitzpatrick
3 Year FT BA Hons Drama
3 Year FT BA Hons Humanities
Combined with Drama as Major/Minor optionThis is an industry-relevant degree with a focus on contemporary performance practice. It is part of the School of Creative Arts and seeks to work across disciplines with Music, Dance, Design and Creative Technologies.
Specialism offered within the course includes:
Performance theory and practice, arts management, and community drama.
Currently the programme has a strong contemporary performance emphasis with modules in Site Specific Performance, Music Theatre, Avant Garde Performance, Storytelling and Performance and Irish Theatre, in addition to Acting and Directing. Students are encouraged to develop and apply their own interests and specialisms culminating in an Independent Project in Year 3.
Applicants should email/phone/fax for further information.

UNIVERSITY OF GLAMORGAN
School of Electronics University of Glamorgan Pontypridd, Mid Glamorgan CF37 1DL
Tel: 01443 482509
Fax: 01443 482943
Email: cmgriffi@glam.ac.uk
www.glam.ac.uk
Office Manager: Mr Chris Griffiths
The University of Glamorgan offers as BSc (Hons) in Lighting Technology and a BSc (Hons) in Live Event Technology.
Students on these courses study a wide range of subjects from Electrical Theory IIE16th, Flying and Rigging, Lighting and Sound Design, Video, TV and Business and Safety.

UNIVERSITY OF LEEDS
School Of Performance & Cultural Studies, Bretton Hall Campus, West Bretton, Wakefield, West Yorkshire WF4 4LG
Tel: 01924 832 095
Email: j.e.richardson@leeds.ac.uk
www.leeds.ac.uk
Contact: Jane Richardson
Bretton Hall is the country's leading college for the arts and education.
Powerhouse 1 is our touring venue.
Courses: BA (Hons) in: Dance, Theatre (Design and Technology), Theatre: Acting, Theatre Studies, Performance Management.

UNIVERSITY OF LONDON - GOLDSMITHS COLLEGE
Drama Department, New Cross, London SE14 6NW
Tel: 020 7919 7414
Fax: 020 7919 7413
Email: drama@gold.ac.uk
www.goldsmiths.ac.uk
Administration/Courses:
Contact: Departmental Office: David Smith
Head of Department: Brian Roberts
3 year f/t course in Drama and Theatre Arts leading to a BA (Single Hons) Degree.
MA Theatre Arts Scheme - 1 yr f/t or 2 yr p/t
MA in Arts Admin and Cultural Policy
MA in Directing
MA in Performance
MA in Theatre Education
MA in Stenography
MA in Writing for Performance
(ALL courses include shared course Theatre Making and Culture)
MA in Performance and Culture 1 yr f/t or 2 yr p/t
Postgraduate research leading to M.Phil. or Ph.D. by thesis. The Drama Department's work takes place in three independently equipped Studios and in the George Wood Theatre (an adaptable 250-seat theatre). The Drama Department also has its own Design, Wardrobe and Workshop facilities.
See Website for more information.

UNIVERSITY OF WARWICK
School of Theatre Studies, Coventry, Warwickshire CV4 7AL

Tel: 024 7652 3020
Email: c.brennan@warwick.ac.uk
www.warwick.ac.uk/fac/arts/Theatre_S/
Administration/Courses:
Chairman: Prof. Jim Davis
Contact: Kate Brennan: 3 year BA Single Honours in Theatre and Performance Studies and Postgraduate research into Theatre Studies leading to M.A., M.Phil., Ph.D.
Contact: Oliver Bennet: Taught M.A. course (full and part-time) in European Cultural Policy and Management.
Contact: Dr Chris Bilton : MA in Creative and Media Enterprises

UNIVERSITY OF WOLVERHAMPTON

Drama and Performance, University of Wolverhampton, Wulfruna Street, Wolverhampton, West Midlands WV1 1SB
Tel: 01902 322 795
Email: Kirstie.Bailey@wlv.ac.uk
www.wlv.ac.uk
Administration/Courses:
Head of Drama & Performance, Principal Lecturer: Dr Ruth Shade
A new B.A. in Drama and Performance started in 2005 - a vocationally-focused degree.
B.A. Hons Drama combined with one other subject - Full time 3 year.
B.A. Performing Arts - Full time 3 year.

Colleges and Institutes of Higher Education

BISHOP GROSSETESTE COLLEGE LINCOLN

Department of Drama, Newport, Lincoln LN1 3DY
Tel: 01522 527 347 Fax: 01522 530 243
Email: registry@bgc.ac.uk
Web Site: www.bgc.ac.uk
BA (Hons) Drama in the Community
BA (Hons) Teaching Studies & Drama with QTS

UNIVERSITY COLLEGE CHESTER

Dept Of Performing Arts, Parkgate Road, Chester, Cheshire CH1 4BJ
Tel: 01244 375 444 Fax: 01244 392 890
Email: kmsmith@chester.ac.uk / performingarts@chester.ac.uk
Offering the following degree courses:
BA Dance
BA Drama & & Theatre Studies
BA Perfomance and New Media
BA Popular Music Performance

MA Performance Practice

DARTINGTON COLLEGE OF ARTS

Dartington Hall Estate, Totnes, Devon TQ9 6EJ
Tel: 01803 862 224 Fax: 01803 863 569
Email: registry@dartington.ac.uk
Web Site: www.dartington.ac.uk
Creative Enterprise Manager: James Toler
Registry: Academic Registrar
Courses:
B.A.(Hons) Arts & Cultural Management
B.A.(Hons) Choreography
B.A. (Hons) Music
B.A.(Hons) Theatre
B.A. (Hons) Fine Art (Contempory Practices)
B.A. (Hons) Arts & Performance
B.A. (Hons) Writing
MA Contempory Arts and other specialisations.
All honours degrees and taught masters have interdisciplinary elements and opportunities for combined studies across disiplines.

DRAMA & THEATRE STUDIES

Liverpool Hope at Everton
Haigh Street, Liverpool, Merseyside L3 8QB
Tel: 0151 291 3451 Fax: 0151 291 3191
Email: enquiry@hope.ac.uk
Web Site: www.hope.ac.uk
BA (Hons) Combined Studies
BA (Hons) Creative and Performing Arts
Postgraduate Diploma in Community Theatre Enterprise

EDGE HILL COLLEGE OF HIGHER EDUCATION

Drama Dept., St.Helen's Road, Ormskirk L39 4QP
Tel: 01695 584760 Fax: 01695 584313
Email: enquiries@edgehill.ac.uk
Web Site: www.edgehill.ac.uk
Head of Department: Dr Elizabeth Hare
Courses:
BA(Hons) Drama
BA(Hons) Drama combined with English, Media, Writing or Education Studies

HOMERTON COLLEGE

Hills Road, Cambridge CB2 2PH
Tel: 01223 507111 Fax: 01223 507120
Email: admissions@homerton.cam.ac.uk
Web Site: www.homerton.cam.ac.uk
BA (Hons) Education with English and Drama. Homerton College is a college of the University of Cambridge. We accept students on the Faculty of Education's degree course - Education Studies with English and Drama.

UNIVERSITY OF HULL (SCARBOROUGH CAMPUS)

Scarborough Campus, Filey Road, Scarborough, North Yorkshire YO11 3AZ
Tel: 01723 362 392 Tel: 01723 357289 (Andrew Head) Fax: 01723 370 815
Email: a.head@hull.ac.uk
Web Site: www.hull.ac.uk
Administration/Courses:
Admissions Tutor: Andrew Head
BA (Hons): Theatre & Performance Studies, MA Theatre & Contemporary Practice. In combination with Dance, Digital Media and Design Technologies, Creative music Technology and English.

KING ALFRED'S UNIVERSITY COLLEGE

Performance Gym, Sparkford Road, Winchester, Hampshire SO22 4NR
Tel: 01962 827 492 Fax: 01962 827 512
Email: sharon.armstrong@wkac.ac.uk
Web Site: www.wkac.ac.uk
Admin/Courses:
Head of School, Community and Performing Arts: Professor Anthony Dean
BA (Hons): Drama, Theatre and TV Studies; Drama Studies; Performing Arts; Dance Studies; Screen Production; Music Theatre
BA/BSc Combined Hons: Drama Studies; Dance Studies; Performing Arts
MA Theatre for Development.; MA Performing Arts

THE LIVERPOOL INSTITUTE FOR PERFORMING ARTS

Mount Street, Liverpool, Merseyside L1 9HF
Tel: 0151 330 3000 Fax: 0151 330 3131
Email: reception@lipa.ac.uk
Web Site: www.lipa.ac.uk
Administration/Courses:
3 year full-time degrees:
BA (Hons) Arts, Music and Entertainment Management
BA (Hons) Performing Arts (Acting)
BA (Hons) Performing Arts (Dance)
BA (Hons) Performing Arts (Music)
BA (Hons) Music
BA (Hons) Theatre and Performance Design
BA (Hons) Theatre and Performance Technology
BA (Hons) Sound Technology
One-year full-time diplomas:
LIPA Diploma in Performing Arts (Acting)
LIPA Diploma in Performing Arts (Dance)
LIPA Diploma in Performing Arts (Song)
LIPA Diploma in Popular Music and Sound Technology
One-year full-time Postgraduate Diplomas:
Postgraduate Diploma in Acting
Postgraduate Diploma in Musical Dance Theatre

LIVERPOOL JOHN MOORES UNIVERSITY

Drama Section, Dean Walters, St.James Road, Liverpool, Merseyside L1 7BR
Email: j.quine@lgmu.ac.uk
Administration/Courses:

Head of Drama: David Llewellyn,
Tel 0151 231 5068
Fax 0151 231 5049
Programme Administrator: Emma Watson
Tel 0151 231 5068
B.A.(Hons) Drama; M.A.Drama

MANCHESTER METROPOLITAN UNIVERSITY: MMU CHESHIRE
Dept. of Contemporary Arts, Alsager Campus, Hassall Road, Alsager ST7 2HL
Tel: 0161 247 5302/3 Fax: 0161 247 6377
Email: admissions.ca@mmu.ac.uk
Web Site: www.mmu.ac.uk
Administration/Courses:
Dept. Administrator: Betty Buckley
B.A. Contemporary Arts, B.A. Joint Honours (++) (++ = Dance, Drama, Music, Visual Arts, Writing, Community Arts, Arts and Cultural Enterprise). B.A. Contemporary Theatre and Performance.
B.A. Dance.
For information and admissions contact: Admissions Office, MMU Cheshire, Crewe Green Road, Crewe.

MOUNTVIEW ACADEMY OF THEATRE ARTS
Ralph Richardson Memorial Studios, Kingfisher Place, Clarendon Road, London N22 6XF
Tel: 020 8881 2201 Fax: 020 8829 0034
Email: enquiries@mountview.ac.uk
Web Site: www.mountview.ac.uk
Principal: Paul Clements
General Manager: Jacqui Leigh
Director of Acting Courses: Amir Korangy
Director of Musical Theatre Courses: Paul Sabey
Director of Technical Theatre Courses: Francesca Faulkner - Greatorex
Registrar: Angela Wharton
PR & Marketing Director: Yvonne I'Anson
Courses:
Full-time Courses:
3 year BA (Hons) Acting and Musical Theatre*
1 year (4 term) Postgraduate Acting and Musical Theatre*
2 year BA (Hons) Technical Theatre*
1 year Postgraduate Technical Theatre*
1 year Directors course
1 year Postgraduate Course in Screen and Radio Performance.
1-year MA in Performance - Acting*, Musical Theatre* and Classical Acting options
*Courses accredited by the NCDT.
Part-time courses:
Adult evening foundation courses in Acting, Acting for the screen and Musical Theatre.
Courses and holiday workshops for children and teenagers.

UNIVERSITY COLLEGE OF NORTHAMPTON
Park Campus, Broughton Green Road, Northampton NN2 7AL
Tel: 01604 735500
Email: admission@northampton.ac.uk
Web Site: www.northampton.ac.uk
Administration/Courses:
BA (Hons) Performance Studies, Performing Arts, Drama, Language, Music, Arts
MA, Theatre Studies.

ST MARY'S UNIVERSITY COLLEGE
School of Communication, Cultural and Creative Arts
Drama Dept, Strawberry Hill, Twickenham, Middlesex TW1 4SX
Tel: 020 8240 4103
Email: youngs@smuc.ac.uk
Administration/Courses:
Drama Programme, Director: Mr Trevor Walker
Secretary: Mrs Susan Young
Physical Theatre Programme, Director: Dr Josephine Machon
3 year Single Hons, and Joint Hons Modular Degree programmes Educational Studies. Degrees validated by the University of Surrey.

SUSSEX DOWNS COLLEGE
Mountfield Road, Lewes, East Sussex BN7 2XH
Tel: 01273 483 188 Fax: 01273 478 561
Email: info@sussexdowns.ac.uk
Administration/Courses:
Principal: John Blake
Full time GNVQ in Performing Arts. Full time Music preparatory course. A-Level theatre studies and dance. Large hall with sprung dance floor plus three performance areas and gymnasium. TV studio. Full technical support.

TRINITY COLLEGE, CARMARTHEN
Department of Theatre Studies, College Road, Carmarthen SA31 3EP Wales
Tel: 01267 676 767 Fax: 01267 676 766
Email: r.maidment@trinity-cm.ac.uk
Courses:
BA(Hons) Acting
B.A.(Hons) Theatre Studies.
BA (Hons) Theatre Design and Production
MA Educational Drama

YORK ST JOHN COLLEGE
School of Arts, Lord Mayor's Walk, York YO31 7EX
Tel: 01904 624 624
Email: d.richmond@yorksj.ac.uk
Web Site: www.yorksj.ac.uk
BA (Hons) Performance: Dance: music: Theatre
BA (Hons) Film & Television Production
MA Contemporary Arts Practise
Foundation Degree: Creative Industries and Technologies.
Contact head of performance programme: David Richmond

Coaches

ACTING & AUDITION SUCCESS
53 West Heath Court, North End Road, London NW11 7RG
Tel: 020 8731 6686
Email: philiprosch@homechoice.co.uk
Contact: Philip Rosch, BA (Hons); LAMDA Gold Medal (Hons)
Private one-to-one acting and audition tuition, concentrating on powerful technique and dynamic sight-reading.
Exceptional results for drama school.
Tutor is professional Equity actor with numerous TV, Film and Theatre credits
Philip Rosch, LALAM (Distinction); LAMDA Communication Award; William Poe Verse nomination; member of Association of Guildhall teachers.

KENNETH CAMPBELL
Parkhills, 6 Clevelands Park, Northam, Bideford, Devon EX39 3QH
Tel: 01237 425 217
Email: kencam@tinyworld.co.uk
Teaches singing and elocution.

NINA FINBURGH
1 Buckingham Mansions, West End Lane, London NW6 1LR
Tel/Fax: 020 7435 9484
Email: ninafinburgh@aol.com
Web Site: www.ninafinburgh.com

DESMOND JONES - MIME AND PHYSICAL THEATRE
20 Thornton Avenue, London W4 1QG
Tel: 020 8747 3537
Email: enquiries@desmondjones.co.uk
Web Site: www.desmondjones.co.uk
Director: Desmond Jones
To encourage people to see theatre as a much more exciting physical medium than it is, and to teach mime and physical theatre to the highest standards.

LESLIE ORTON L.R.A.M., L.L.A.M., A.N.E.A.
141 Ladybrook Lane, Mansfield, Nottinghamshire NG18 5JH
Tel: 01623 626082

TERRY POWELL A.C.P., L.N.E.A., CERT ED. LONDON UNIVERSITY
35 Schofield Avenue, Witney, Oxfordshire OX28 1JR
Tel: 01993 704 820
Email: dramascope@btinternet.com
Web Site: www.dramascope.co.uk
Member of the Society of Teachers of Speech and Drama.
Teaching all aspects of acting, speech and drama, audition preparation including workshops and lectures

SANDRA SINGER ASSOCIATES
21 Cotswold Road, Westcliff-on-Sea, Essex SS0 8AA
Tel: 01702 331 616
Email: sandrasingeruk@aol.com
Web Site: www.sandrasinger.com
Senior Personnel: Sandra Singer
Film, TV, Musical Theatre Specialists, for adults and children. Specialist entertainment for Film & TV, Magic etc. Also represents composers and choreographers

SOLID ENTERTAINMENTS
46 Wellowgate, Grimsby, North East Lincolnshire DN32 0RA
Tel: 01472 349 222
Email: solidentertainments@live.co.uk
Web Site: www.solidentertainments.com
Contact Bookings Manager: Stephen Stanley
Concert promoter and ticket agency, plus supplier of coaches to concerts and crowd control barrier hire.

Drama Advisers

Avon

MARY HARLOW
Bristol Education Centre, Sheridan Road, Horfield, Bristol, Avon BS7 0PU
Tel: 0117 931 1111 Fax: 0117 931 1619
Email: musicservices@bristol-city.gov.uk

Cheshire

JOHN DOONA
Drama Adviser, Woodford Lodge Professional Centre, Woodford Lane West, Winsford, Cheshire CW7 4EH
Tel: 01606 814300
Email: john.doona@cheshire.gov.uk

County Durham

ACTION IN MANAGEMENT
1st Floor, Reform Place, North Road, Durham, County Durham DH1 4RZ
Tel: 0191 384 9900 Fax: 0191 384 9922
Email: aim@actioninmanagement.co.uk
Web: www.actioninmanagement.co.uk
Managing Director: Christine Pearce
Drama and Management Consultants: Action in Management (for Businesses)

Devon

MARTIN PHILLIPS
Great Moor House, Bittern Road, Sowton, Exeter, Devon EX2 7NL
Tel: 01392 384 833 Fax: 01392 384 880
Email: mhphilli@devon.gov.uk

Kent

DAVID TOWNSEND
Kent Advisory Service, Oxford Road, Maidstone, Kent ME15 8AW
Tel: 01622 203800 Fax: 01622 670509

Leicestershire

CATHERIN HUTCHON
The County Drama & Dance Adviser, Leicestershire Arts in Education, Head of Performing Arts, The Knighton Field Centre, Herrick Road, Leicester LE2 6DH
Tel: 0116 270 0850 Fax: 0116 270 4928
Email: chutcheon@leics.gov.uk

London

KEITH HOMER
Redbridge Drama Centre Churchfields, South Woodford, London E18 2RB
Tel: 020 8504 5451 Fax: 020 8505 6669
Email: rdc@redbridgedramacentre.co.uk
Web: www.redbridgedramacentre.co.uk

Mid Lothian

JOHN A TURNER
Adviser for Aesthetic Subjects City of Edinburgh Council, Wellington Court, 10 Waterloo Place, Edinburgh, Mid Lothian EH1 3EG Scotland
Tel: 0131 469 3043 Fax: 0131 469 3311
Email: john.turner@educ.edin.gov.uk

Middlesex

HELEN SAVVA
General Education Adviser, PO Box 22, Civic Centre, Harrow, Middlesex HA1 2UW
Tel: 020 8427 1291

Northumberland & North Tyneside

CATHERINE REEVES
Hepscott Educational Development Centre, Hepscott Park, Stannington, Morpeth, Northumberland NE61 6NF
Tel: 01670 533000 Direct Tel: 01670 533519 Fax: 01670 533591
Web Site: www.northumberland.gov.uk
General Adviser with Special responsibility for English, Drama and Media Education.

Strathclyde

RONNIE A.F. MACKLE
Glasgow City Council, 25 Cochrane Street, Glasgow, Strathclyde G1 1HL Scotland
Tel: 0141 287 3793 Fax: 0141 287 5038
Email: ronnie.mackie@education.glasgow.gov.uk

Suffolk

JOSS LEADER
Advisory Teacher to Drama, Northgate Arts Centre, Sidegate Lane West, Ipswich, Suffolk IP4 3DF
Tel: 01473 281 866 Fax: 01473 286 068
Email: joss.leader@educ.suffolkcc.gov.uk

Sussex, West

ANNE FENTON
West Sussex County Youth Theatre General Adviser (Drama), North-Eastern Area, Professional Centre, Furnace Drive, Furnace Green, Crawley, West Sussex RH10 6JB
Tel: 01293 435 629 Fax: 01293 435 601
Email: WSCYT@hotmail.com

Trafford

GARTH JONES
Drama Adviser, Trafford Metropolitan Borough Arndale House, Chester Road, Stretford M32 9BH
Tel: 0161 912 3143 Fax: 0161 912 1182

West Yorkshire

PAUL KAISERMAN
Education Leeds ArtForms, The West Park Centre, Spen Lane, Leeds, LS16 5BE
Tel: 0113 230 4074 Fax: 0113 230 4073
Email: educ.artforms@educationleeds.co.uk
Web Site: www.educationleeds.co.uk
Director of ArtForms: Paul Kaiserman

Wiltshire

ROGER DAY M.A., ADV.DIP.ED,FRSA
Independent Drama Adviser, The Barn, Wedhampton, Devizes, Wiltshire SN10 3QE
Tel: 01380 840 128 Fax: 01380 840 128
Email: day.barn@talk21.com

ORGANISATIONS

Societies & Organisations

ABINGDON OPERATIC SOCIETY
Correspondence Address: 21 St James Road, Radley, Abingdon, Oxfordshire OX14 3AH
Tel: 01235 529 658
Email: john@eddy98.freeserve.co.uk
Production Co-ordinator: W John Eddy

ACTORS' BENEVOLENT FUND
6 Adam Street, London WC2N 6AD
Tel: 020 7836 6378 Fax: 020 7836 8978
Email: office@abf.org.uk
Web Site: www.actorsbenevolentfund.co.uk
Patron: H.R.H. The Prince of Wales
President: Penelope Keith, O.B.E.
Registered Charity No. 206524
Founded in 1882 by Sir Henry Irving and a group of his friends, the A.B.F. provides assistance to members of the theatrical profession who because of old age, ill health or accident are suffering hardship. Financial help is provided by grants and allowances. Assistance can also be given with nursing home fees.

ACTORS' CHURCH UNION
St Paul's Church, Bedford Street, Covent Garden, London WC2E 9ED
Tel: 020 7240 0344
Email: actors_church_union@yahoo.co.uk
Web Site: www.actorschurchunion.org
Senior Chaplain: Canon Richard Truss
Hon. Treasurers: David Chivers, John de Lannoy
Founded in 1899, members and associates serve the profession through their interest, their action - often in association with other related bodies - and their prayers. Additionally, more than 200 honorary chaplains serve all members of the profession in theatres, studios, and schools at home and overseas. As well as spiritual counsel and practical advice, material help is given when possible. Through the Children's Charity, for example, funds are available for theatrical parents facing difficulties with the costs of their children's education.

ACTORS' CHARITABLE TRUST
Reg Charity No. 206809
Africa House, 64/78 Kingsway, London WC2B 6BD
Tel: 020 7242 0111 Fax: 020 7242 0234
Email: robert@tactactors.org.uk
Web Site: www.tactactors.org.uk
President: Lord Attenborough, C.B.E.
Hon. Treasurer: Tim Denham
Chairpeople: Angela Thorne and Simon Williams.
General Secretary: Robert Ashby
Founded in 1896, the Trust gives financial aid to the children of actors and actresses during family crisis, and administers Denville Hall - the residential and nursing home for elderly members of the theatrical profession.

THE AGENTS' ASSOCIATION (GREAT BRITAIN)
54 Keyes House, Dolphin Square, London SW1V 3NA
Tel: 020 7834 0515 Fax: 020 7821 0261
Email: association@agents-uk.com
Web Site: www.agents-uk.com
President: Simon Quarmby
Administrator: Carol Richards
The Agents' Association Ltd, founded in 1927, has in its membership not only the principal agencies of Great Britain but a wide cross-section of entertainment agents thoughout the country.
Its functions are primarily for the benefit of members, but activities cover the entertainment agency business in particular and the whole of the entertainment industry in general. In major matters connected with the latter it acts in co-ordination with leading organisations both inside and outside the industry.
A full time office with staff operates from London and an executive council of management meets regularly to run the affairs of the association. Elected representatives and branches cover the entire United Kingdom and all members are governed by strict rules and regulations.
Applications for membership are welcomed from all entertainment agents and should be addressed to the Administrator.

ARTS AND BUSINESS
Nutmeg House, 60 Gainsford Street, Butler's Wharf, London SE1 2NY
Tel: 020 7378 8143 Fax: 020 7407 7527
Email: head.office@AandB.org.uk
Web Site: www.AandB.org.uk
Chief Executive: Colin Tweedy
Arts and Business vision is to hekp build communities by developing creative partnerships between business and the arts. The UK authority on arts sponsorship and new types of arts/business relationships, it provides a wide range of services to over 350 business members and 1000 arts organisations, including professional development programmes and New Partners, an incentive programme for sponsors of the arts.

ARTS MARKETING ASSOCIATION
7a Clifton Court, Cambridge CB1 7BN
Tel: 01223 578 078 Fax: 01223 245 862
Email: info@a-m-a.co.uk
Web Site: www.a-m-a.co.uk
Director: Pam Henderson
Events & Services Manager: Kate Whitlock
Marketing Manager: Julie Aldridge
Events Officer: Annabel Busher
Benefits of membership include: Up to date information on current issues affecting arts marketing and audience develepment, professional development opportunities, networking and practical support. Over 1900 members.

ARTSADMIN
Toynbee Studios, 28 Commercial Street, London E1 6AB
Tel: 020 7247 5102
Email: admin@artsadmin.co.uk
Web Site: www.artsadmin.co.uk
Managing Directors: Judith Knight and Gill Lloyd
Admin & Studios Manager: Jessica Denning
Marketing & development manager: Jennifer Tomkins
Studio Hire, Management Company.

ARTSLINE
54 Chalton Street, London NW1 1HS
Tel: 020 7388 2227 Fax: 020 7383 2653
Email: access@artsline.org.uk
Web Site: www.artsline.org.uk / www.artslineonline.com
Administrator: Maureen Robinson
Information service for disabled people about access to the arts and entertainments in London. Phone line open Mon-Fri 9.30am-5.30pm.
Artsline's database is London's premier database for access information. We have a user database and encourage people to log in giving us their details. Artsline designs and delivers disabliity equality and disability awareness training for front of house staff. we also conduct access audits and surveys for venues and work with architects from inception to completion of projects. Full reports are provided.

ASSOCIATION OF BRITISH THEATRE TECHNICIANS
55 Faringdon Road, London EC1M 3JB
Tel: 020 7242 9200 Fax: 020 7242 9303
Email: office@abtt.org.uk
Web Site: www.abtt.org.uk
Executive Director: Howard Bird
Treasurer: Richard York
Administrator: Jenny Straker.

An Association formed in 1961 to provide a forum for discussion among technicians in the presentation industry, to collect and disseminate information of a technical nature to arrange in-service training, to influence draft standards and regulations affecting the industry and to advise and assist all those involved in the planning and construction or reconstruction of new and existing theatres. The Association is a member of the Theatres Advisory Council and acts as technical advisor to the Council. Associate Membership is open to all who are interested in technical aspects of the Presentation Industry; Corporate Membership is awarded to experienced professional technicians.

ASSOCIATION OF LIGHTING DESIGNERS

PO Box 89, Welwyn Garden City, Hertfordshire AL7 1ZW
Tel/Fax: 01707 891 848
Email: office@ald.org.uk
Web Site: www.ald.org.uk
The Association was formed to provide a forum devoted to the development of the art and craft of stage lighting.
Membership open to all those professionally engaged in stage lighting. Associate membership open to amateurs and students.

BECTU

Broadcasting Entertainment Cinematograph & Theatre Union
373-377 Clapham Road, London SW9 9BT
Tel: 020 7346 0900 Fax: 020 7346 0901
Email: info@bectu.org.uk
Web Site: www.bectu.org.uk
General Secretary: Gerry Morrisey
Assistant General Secretary: Luke Crawley
Supervisory Official: Willy Donaghy
Journal Editor: Janice Turner
Trade union for backstage, technical, front-of-house, administrative and support workers in theatre and arts centres.
Publishes the Stage Screen & Radio journal (10 issues annually).

BRITISH ACADEMY OF SONGWRITERS, COMPOSERS AND AUTHORS

British Music House, 26 Berners Street, London W1T 3LR
Tel: 020 7636 2929 Fax 020 7636 2212
Email: info@britishacademy.com
Web Site: www.britishacademy.com
Head of Membership: Kizzy Donaldson
Professional membership organisation representing the interests of music writers of all genres. Provides legal, business and artistic advice. Publishes magazines "The Works" and "FourFour". Administers Ivor Novello Awards, British Composer Awards and Song Search UK.

BRITISH ARTS FESTIVALS ASSOCIATION

3rd Floor, Whitechapel Library, 77 Whitechapel High Street, London E1 7QX
Tel: 020 7247 4667 Tel: 020 7240 4532
Fax: 020 7247 5010
Email: info@artsfestivals.co.uk
Web Site: www.artsfestivals.co.uk
Administrator: Kim Hart
Meeting point of arts festivals in the UK. BAFA aims to strengthen the arts festivals network and is also a point of information point for the 100 + festivals who have membership.

BRITISH ASSOCIATION OF CHOREOGRAPHERS

16 Durham Road, London N2 9DN
Tel/Fax: 020 8444 9437
Email: ddermant@dermant.com
Administrator: Fionna McPhee
Aims and objects of BAC: BAC is an independant, non unionised and non profit making body established to raise the professional profile of choreographers. BAC also seeks to lobby for improved conditions for choreographers and to liaise with the Choreographers' Committee of Equity on the introduction of standard agreements in all sectors of the media; to advise and assist members in all matters relating to professional practise; to offer training workshops, master classes and observer schemes; and to provide platforms where choreographers can meet and liaise with each other and with artists in other performance related disciplines.

THE BRITISH BALLET ORGANIZATION

Woolborough House, 39 Lonsdale Road, Barnes, London SW13 9JP
Tel: 020 8748 1241 Fax: 020 8748 1301
Email: info@bbo.org.uk
Web Site: www.bbo.org.uk
Examining and Teaching Society.
Exams in Ballet, Tap, Jazz, Modern and Freestyle. Induction to Dance Teaching Certificate (QCA recognised qualification). Diploma in Dance Teaching (QCA recognised qualification).

THE BRITISH FEDERATION OF FESTIVALS

Festivals House, 198 Park Lane, Macclesfield, Cheshire SK11 6UD
Tel: 0870 7744 290 Fax: 0870 7744 292
Email: info@festivals.demon.co.uk
Web Site: www.festivals.demon.co.uk
HQ of the amateur festival movement with 330 festival members and 400 professional adjudicator members.

BRITISH FILM INSTITUTE

21 Stephen Street, London W1P 2LN
Tel: 020 7255 1444 Fax: 020 7436 7950
Email: amanda.nevill@bfi.org.uk
Web Site: www.bfi.org.uk
Director: Amanda Nevill

BRITISH LIBRARY SOUND ARCHIVE

96 Euston Road, London NW1 2DB
Tel: 020 7412 7676 Fax: 020 7412 7441
Email: sound-archive@bl.uk
Web Site: www.bl.uk/soundarchive
The British Library Sound Archive holds more than 1 million discs, 200,000 tapes and a growing number of videos. In addition to commercially published recordings there is a wide range of BBC and other broadcast material, and many unique unpublished recordings. Subjects covered include all kinds of music, wildlife sounds. The spoken word collections are extensive, embracing documentary recordings, oral history, language and dialect recordings, and poetry and drama. Productions at the Royal National Theatre and RSC have been recorded since 1964, and coverage has extended more recently to the Royal Court (since 1971) and many fringe and provincial venues.
The Recorded Sound Information Service answers enquiries about the sound and video collections. There are extensive holdings of books, periodicals, record company catalogues and discographies.
The Listening & Viewing Service provides access to the Sound Archive's collections of sound and video. Users need to hold a valid British Library reader's pass.
Opening times are as for the British Library's reading rooms:
10.00 to 20.00 Monday
09.30 to 20.00 Tuesday to Thursday
09.30 to 17.00 Friday and Saturday
(correct as of January 2005)

BRITISH MUSIC HALL SOCIETY

c/o The Honorary Secretary, 'Meander' 361 Watford Road, Chiswell Green, St Albans Herts AL2 3DB
Tel: 01727 768 878
Email: patricknewley@yahoo.com
Web Site: www.music-hall-society.com
President: Roy Hudd OBE
Vice-Presidents: Mary Sparks, Jack Seaton, Wyn Calvin MBE, J.M Marshall OBE
Chairman: Johnny Dennis
Vice-Chairman: Daphne Bailey
Hon. Secretary: Daphne Masterton
Treasurer: Lawrence Cheadle
Membership Secretary: Howard Lee
Minutes Secretary: Mary-Jane Burcher
Life Patron: Sir Cliff Richard OBE
The aims of the Society are to preserve theatre and miscellania, including properties, photos, etc., to keep alive the tradition of this particularly British institution and to actively support this entertainment wherever and whenever produced. They have members all over the world, and many public figures are in membership.

BRITISH MUSIC INFORMATION CENTRE

Lincoln House, 75 Westminster Bridge Road, London SE1 7HS
Tel: 020 7928 1902 Fax: 020 7928 2957
Email: info@bmic.co.uk
Web Site: www.bmic.co.uk
ADMINISTRATION:
Director: Matthew Greenal
A resource centre for new music. Services include scores and recording collection, live events programme and enquiry service. Open to the public Monday to Friday 12 noon - 5 pm.

BRITISH RESORTS ASSOCIATION

Crown Buildings, Eastbank Street, Southport, Merseyside PR8 1DL
Tel: 0151 934 2286 Fax: 0151 934 2287
Email: bresorts@sefton.u-net.com
Web Site: www.britishresorts.co.uk
Honorary Secretary: Mr G Haywood, LL.B., A.C.I.S and Barrister
Hon. Treasurer: Mr A Yates
Director: Peter Hampson.
The only Association currently open to all Local Authorities (regardless of type), Tourist Boards and simlar organisations with common aims within the United Kingdom, Isle of Man and Channel Islands, who have strong commitment to the promotion and development of inland and coastal resort tourism.

THE CELEBRITIES GUILD OF GREAT BRITAIN

Knight House, 29-31 East Barnet Road, New Barnet, Hertfordshire EN4 8RN
Tel: 020 8449 1234 / 1515 Fax: 020 8449 4994
Email: ella.glazer@tiscali.co.uk
Web Site: www.celebritiesguild.org.uk
Founder: Ella Glazer MBE (1977)
Patrons: Victor Hochhauser, David Jacobs CBE DL, Lord Janner of Braunstone QC MP, Janet Suzman, Maria Friedman, Henry Goodman.
Trustees: Michael Freedland, Ella Glazer MBE, Robert Rietti.
The Celebrities Guild is a registered charity organising events to raise funds to buy equipment for people who are disabled, with the help of many famous people.

CENTRAL COUNCIL FOR AMATEUR THEATRE

39 Harestock Road, Winchester SO22 6NT
Tel: 01962 889 356
Email: ccatchair@aol.com
Contact: Tom Williams
CCAT was formed in 1975 when the main national organisations representing strand of amateur theatre agreed to cooperate to pursue common objectives and concerns. The role of CCAT is essential to seek to influence national policies relating to resourcing and regulation of amateur theatre. This role is realised through representation on bodies such as the Voluntary Arts Network and through specific projects.
CCATs present policies are concerned with expanding the collaboration between writers and companies to increase the level of new writing for amateur theatre and to this end has, with Arts Council England facilitated the publication of a good practice guide for amateur theatre companies and playwrights.
CCAT promotes good practice and safe working throughout amateur theatre in the UK and seeks to ensure that its member bodies offer consistent advice on management and safety issues. It is working with other bodies to heighten the profile of amateur theatre an ensure the celebration of excellence.

CENTRE FOR CREATIVE COMMUNITIES

118 Commercial Street, London E1 6NF
Tel: 020 7247 5385 Fax: 020 7247 5256
Email: info@creativecommunities.org.uk
Web: www.creativecommunities.org.uk
Executive Director: Jennifer Williams.
Promotes utilisation of the arts and education in Community Development. Maintains a reference library, and publishes an e-newsletter, "Interchanges". Does not run programmes or give funds.

THE CLUB FOR ACTS AND ACTORS

Incorporating the Concert Artistes Association
20 Bedford Street, Strand, London WC2E 9HP
Tel/Fax: 020 7836 3172 (office) Tel: 020 7836 2884 (club)
Email: office@thecaa.org
Web Site: www.thecaa.org
President: Bill Pertwee
Secretary: Barbara Daniels.
The Club for Acts and Actors.
This is an association of artistes in all branches of entertainment, and was founded in 1897. The objects of the Association are the safeguarding of artistes' interests; the promotion of good fellowship and cooperation amongst its members, the fostering of public interest in entertainment; the provision of opportunities for artistes to perform and to meet those who are likely to be helpful to them in their profession. Amongst the privileges and benefits of membership are the facilities of a central West End Club as headquarters, 20 Bedford Street, Strand, London WC2; benevolent grants, sickness grants; a classified list of members for the use and guidance of members, agents and entertainment providers; dressing room accommodation; introduction by the Committee to special medical consultants.

COMBINED THEATRICAL CHARITIES APPEAL

2nd Floor West, 11 Garrick Street, London WC2E 9AR
Tel: 020 7379 8274 Fax: 020 7379 8273
Email: ctc@trtf.com
The Council exists to co-ordinate the work of the member Charities and attract donations and legacies for their benefit.
In addition, to centralising appeals for funds which can in turn be applied where most needed The member charities are The Actors' Benevolent Fund, The Actors' Charitable Trust, The Actors' Church Union, Denville Hall, The Royal Theatrical Fund, The Equity Trust Fund, The Evelyn Norris Trust, King George's Fund for Actors and Actresses, The Theatrical Ladies' Guild.
within the Charities.
Each Charity remains individual and autonomous but co-operates with others in providing the best possible service to those members of the theatrical profession - from stage doorkeeper to director from actress to wardrobe mistress - who are in need of aid.

COMMUNITY MATTERS

(National Federation of Community Organisations)
12-20 Baron Street, London N1 9LL
Tel: 020 7837 7887 Fax: 020 7278 9253
Email: communitymatters@community-matters.org.uk
Web Site: www.communitymatters.org.uk
Chief Executive: David Tyler
Our vision is for active and sustainable communities in which everyone is valued and can play their full part.
Community Matters pursues this vision by supporting and developing the capacity of community organisations and representing their interests at a national level.

CONCERT PROMOTERS ASSOCIATION

6 St Marks Road, Henley-on-Thames, Oxfordshire RG9 1LJ
Tel: 01491 575 060
Email: carolesmith.cpa@virgin.net
Please address all correspondence to the Company Secretary, C.P.A. at the above address.

CONFERENCE OF DRAMA SCHOOLS

Conference of Drama Schools P.O. Box 34252 London NW5 1XJ
Email: info@cds.drama.ac.uk
Web Site: www.drama.ac.uk
The Conference of Drama Schools was formed to strengthen the voice of UK member schools. It encourages the highest standards of vocational training in acting and technical theatre. The CDS publishes the full colour 72 page Guide to Professional Training in Drama and Technical Theatre.

The 2006 edition will be published in April 2005. Single copies of the Guide are available free-of-charge to UK addresses from French's Theatre Bookshop. Please contact them by writing to
52 Fitzroy Street, London, W1T 5JR, by telephoning 020 7255 4300, by emailing theatre@samuelfrench-london.co.uk or by visiting them - they are 2 minutes walk from Warren Street underground station. The Guide can also be downloaded from the CDS website.

COUNCIL FOR DANCE EDUCATION AND TRAINING (UK)

Old Brewer's Yard, 17-19 Neal Street, Covent Garden, London WC2H 9UY
Tel: 020 7240 5703 Fax: 020 7240 2547
Email: info@cdet.org.uk
Web Site: www.cdet.org.uk
The Council for Dance Education and Training is the national standards body of the professional dance industry. It accredits programmes of training in vocational dance schools and holds the Register of Dance Awarding Bodies and the directory of teaching societies whose syllabuses have been inspected and approved by the Council. It is the body of advocacy of the dance education and training communities and offers a free and comprehensive information service, Answers for Dancers, on all aspects of vocational dance provision to students, parents, teachers dance artists and employers.

THE CRITICS' CIRCLE

c/o 69 Marylebone Lane, London W1U 2PH
Tel: 020 7224 1410 (office hours only)
Email: info@catherinecooperevents.co.uk
Web Site: www.criticscircle.org.uk
President: Mike Dixon
Administrator: Catherine Cooper
Founded in 1913 the Critics' Circle aims to promote the aims of criticism, to uphold its integrity in practice, to foster and safeguard the professional interests of its members, to provide opportunities for social intercourse among them, and to support the advancement of the arts. Membership is by invitation only.

DANCERS' CAREER DEVELOPMENT

Rooms 222-227 Africa House, Kingsway, London WC2B 6BG
Tel: 020 7404 6141 Fax: 020 7242 3331
Email: linda@thedcd.org.uk
Web Site: www.thedcd.org.uk
Executive Director: Linda Yates
Dancers' Career Development (DCD) offers educational advice, career coaching, emotional counselling, CV and interview guidance, grants for retraining, business start-up grants,
and on-going support for professional dancers whose performing career is drawing to a close.

DEPARTMENT OF CULTURE, MEDIA & SPORT

2-4 Cockspur Street, London SW1Y 5DH
Tel: 020 7211 6200 Fax: 020 7211 6210
Email: david.lammy@culture.gov.uk
Web Site: www.culture.gov.uk
Culture Minisiter: David Lammy
We aim to improve the quality of life for all through cultural and sporting activities, to support the pursuit of excellence and to champion the tourism, creative and leisure industries.

THE DIRECTORS' GUILD OF GREAT BRITAIN

8 Flitcroft Street, London WC2H 8DL
Tel: 020 7836 3602 Fax: 020 7836 3603
Email: guild@dggb.co.uk
Web Site: www.dggb.co.uk
Chief Executive: Jim Whiteford
Administrative Director: Debs Paterson
Training Co-ordinator: Saskia van Roomen
The Guild represents directors in all media: film, television, theatre, radio, opera, commercials, corporate, multimedia and new technology. It is a trade union, offering help with contracts, a campaigning voice, policy to influence the future of the industry, and advice for members to meet and share their skills. Publishes "Direct Magazine" and "Directory of Numbers".

DRAMA ASSOCIATION OF WALES/CYMDEITHAS DDRAMA CYMRU

The Old Library, Singleton Road, Splott, Cardiff, South Glamorgan CF24 2ET Wales
Tel: 029 2045 2200 Fax: 029 2045 2277
Email: aled.daw@virgin.net
Director: Aled Rhys-Jones
Administrator: Gary Thomas
At the heart of the Drama Association of Wales member services is the largest specialist Drama Lending Library in the World! There are over 250,000 volumes of plays, biographies, critical works and technical theatre books in the DAW Library which includes the entire Playsets and Lending Collections of the former British Theatre Association. Both National and International members are served by post from Cardiff.
DAW offers a tremendous range of services to Community Drama. Script Hire, an extensive training programme, New Writing and Youth Theatre. Its members include amateur and professional practitioners, educationalists and playwrights.

DUMFRIES & GALLOWAY ARTS ASSOCIATION

28 Edinburgh Road, Dumfries, Dumfries & Galloway DG1 1JQ Scotland
Tel: 01387 253 383 Fax: 01387 253 303
Email: helen@dgaa.net
Web Site: www.dgaa.net

EDINBURGH FESTIVAL SOCIETY

Edinburgh International Festival, The Hub, Edinburgh's Festival Centre, Castlehill, Royal Mile, Edinburgh, Mid Lothian EH1 2NE
Tel: 0131 473 2001 Fax: 0131 473 2002
Email: marketing@eif.co.uk
Web Site: www.eif.co.uk

ENGLISH FOLK DANCE AND SONG SOCIETY

Cecil Sharp House, 2 Regents Park Road, London NW1 7AY
Tel: 020 7485 2206 Fax: 020 7284 0534
Fax Library: 020 7284 0523
Email: info@efdss.org
Web Site: efdss.org.
Education &Teacher Training Officer: Diana Campbell Jewitt
Librarian: Malcolm Taylor
The EFDSS promotes a wide range of music, dance and performance events plus a regular education programme.

ENGLISH REGIONAL ARTS BOARDS

5 City Road, Winchester, Hampshire SO23 8SD
Tel: 01962 851 063 Fax: 01962 842 033
Email: enquiries@artscouncil.org.uk
Web Site: www.arts.org.uk
Administrator: Carolyn Nixson

EQUITY

Incorporating the Variety Artistes' Federation
Guild House, Upper St Martin's Lane, London WC2H 9EG
Tel: 020 7379 6000 Fax: 020 7379 7001
Email: info@equity.org.uk
Web Site: www.equity.org.uk
Scottish Office:
Equity, 114 Union Street, Glasgow G1 3QQ Scotland Tel: 0141 248 2472
North West Office:
Equity, Express Networks, 1 George Leigh Street, Manchester M4 5DL Tel: 0161 244 5995
North East Office:
Equity, The Workstation, 15 Paternoster Road Sheffield S1 2BX
01142 759 746
Wales and South West Office:
Equity, Transport House, 1 Cathedral Road, Cardiff, South Glamorgan CF1 9SD Wales Tel: 01222 397 971
Midlands Office:
Equity, PO Box 1221, Warwick CV34 5EF
Tel: 01926 408 638
Equity was formed in 1930 and its early members soon established the basic proposition which has held the Union together ever since - that only with complete organisation can Equity achieve solutions to the problems of casual

employment and short-term engagements.
Although the membership was originally from the acting profession, this has progressively broadened to include stage management, theatre designers and directors, dancers, opera singers and many others in the entertainment industry. This process was assisted by the inclusion of the Variety Artistes' Federation in 1967.
Standard Contracts laying down minimum terms and conditions have been negotiated with individual employers, or employer's associations in virtually every section of entertainment.
Equity is affiliated to the International Federation of Actors, the TUC and Scottish TUC, the Federation of Entertainment Unions, the Theatres' Advisory Council, the Radio and Television Safeguards Committee, the National Council for Drama Training and the Council for Dance Education and Training, ITI, WCA, British Copyright Council, NCCL, AMNESTY, Save London's Theatres Campaign, Performers Alliance.

THE FEDERATION OF SCOTTISH THEATRE

Suite 8, Waterside House, 46 Shore, Leith, Edinburgh EH6 6QU Scotland
Tel: 0131 467 2525 Fax: 0131 467 2838
Email: Lizzi@scottishtheatre.org
Web Site: www.scottishtheatre.org
Director: Lizzi Nicoll
Admin Assistant: Margie Jones

FILM ARTISTES' ASSOCIATION

373-377 Clapham Road, London SW9 9BT
Tel: 020 7346 0900 Fax: 020 7346 0901
Email: smacdonald@bectu.org.uk
Web Site: www.bectu.org.uk

FRIENDS OF SHAKESPEARE'S GLOBE

21New Globe Walk, London SE1 9DT
Tel: 020 7928 5665 Fax: 020 7928 5661
Email: friends@fosg.org
Web Site: www.shakespeare-globe.org/friends

THE GILBERT AND SULLIVAN SOCIETY

c/o Valerie Colin-Russ, 7/20 Hampden Gurney Street, London W1H 5AX
Tel:
Email: peter.mountsteven@harlow.gov.uk
Contact Peter Mountsteven

GRAND ORDER OF WATER RATS

328 Gray's Inn Road, London WC1X 8BZ
Tel: 020 7278 3248 Fax: 020 7278 1765
Email: info@gowr.net, charities@gowr.net
Web Site: www.gowr.net
Administrator: Fran Simmons
King Rat: Joe Pasquale
GOWR Charities Fund, 328 Gray's Inn Road, London WC1X 8BZ.
The Grand Order of Water Rats was formed in 1889. The Membership, which is limited to 200, is only open to members of the Light Entertainment profession, and their activities are social and benevolent.
The Companions H.R.H. The Duke of Edinburgh, H.R.H. The Prince of Wales and H.R.H. Prince Michael of Kent.

GUILD OF DRAMA ADJUDICATIONS

25 The Drive, Bengeo Hertford SG14 3DE
Tel: 01992 581 993 (Hon Secretary)
Email: crossley@bengeo25.freeserve.co.uk
Web Site: www.amdram.co.uk/goda
Contact Secretary: Joan Crossley

GUILD OF INTERNATIONAL PROFESSIONAL TOASTMASTERS

12 Little Bornes, Dulwich, London SE21 8SE
Tel: 020 8670 5585 Fax: 020 8670 0055
Web Site: www.ivorspencer.com
Life President: Ivor Spencer
The Guild Members officiate at functions all over the United Kingdom and undertake engagements abroad. They are expert organisers who arrange authentic British Banquets with the traditional ceremonies (Loving Cup, Baron of Beef, etc.) anywhere in the world. The Guild Toastmasters are experts at officiating on Royal occasions.
Conferences and Banquets from 12 to 10,000 guests organised.

THE GUILD OF INTERNATIONAL SONGWRITERS & COMPOSERS

Sovereign House, 12 Trewartha Road, Praa Sands, Penzance, Cornwall TR20 9ST
Tel: 01736 762 826 Fax: 01736 763 328
Email: songmag@aol.com
Web Site: www.songwriters-guild.co.uk
Chairman: Roderick Jones

IMPERIAL SOCIETY OF TEACHERS OF DANCING

Imperial House, 22/26 Paul Street, London EC2A 4QE
Tel: 020 7377 1577 Fax: 020 7247 8979
Email: chiefexecutive@istd.org.uk
Web Site: www.istd.org.uk
Chief Executive: John Singleton
Chairman: Robert Grover

INCORPORATED SOCIETY OF MUSICIANS

10 Stratford Place, London W1C 1AA
Tel: 020 7629 4413 Fax: 020 7408 1538
Email: membership@ism.org
Web Site: www.ism.org
Chief Executive: Neil Hoyle
Head of Committee & Professional Services: Alison Pickard
Head of Legal & General Services: Susanna Thompson
Head of Finance & Systems: Ralph Seed
Marketing & Development Manager: Danny Whatmough
The ISM is the UK's professional body for all musicians -performers, composers and teachers-supplying its members with a comprehensive range of advisory, support and information services.

INDEPENDENT THEATRE COUNCIL (ITC)

12 The Leathermarket, Weston Street, London SE1 3ER
Tel: 020 7403 1727 Fax: 020 7403 1745
Email: admin@itc-arts.org
Web Site: www.itc-arts.org
Director: Charlotte Jones
Membership Co-Ordinator: Fiona Cameron
Training Co-ordinator: Hazel Tsoi
The Independent Theatre Council (ITC) is the UK management association for the performing arts. Since 1974 ITC has been empowering and supporting its diverse membership by: providing high quality management, legal and financial advice; developing tailored arts management training; creating excellent networking opportunities and representing the sector with a powerful, articulate voice. ITC is committed to working with a range of partners to promote, develop and support its members.

INSIGHT ARTS TRUST

7-15 Greatorex Street, London E1 5NF
Tel: 020 7247 0778 Fax: 020 7247 8077
Email: iat@insightartstrust.demon.co.uk
Contact: Sharon Kennet
Offers opportunities to ex-prisoners and those on probation, to find new directions for themselves through the medium of the arts. Organises arts-based crime-awareness programmes in a variety of community settings. Leads offending behaviour programmes in prisons and probation centres.

INSTITUTE OF ENTERTAINMENT & ARTS MANAGEMENT

17 Drake Close, Horsham, West Sussex RH12 5UB
Tel: 0870 241 7248
Email: admin@ieam.co.uk
Web Site: www.ieam.co.uk
Administrator: Shirley Carpenter
Formed in 1982, the Institute provides its members with a means of meeting colleagues within the entertainments and arts industry for training, discussions and information, together with the opportunity to attend professional and social events.

Members receivethe IEAM Monthly Newsletter, detailing forthcoming events, services and, on occasion, highlighting items of current concern in the business. IEAM attend a number of high profile trade shows throughout the year, and present an annual award to an individual who has shown an "outstanding contribution to the entertainment and arts industry". Membership is open to Venue Managers and their staff, Production Companies, Agents and any other such bodies within the entertainment and arts field.

INSTITUTE OF LEISURE & AMENITY MANAGEMENT
ILAM House, Lower Basildon, Reading, Berkshire RG8 9NE
Tel: 01491 874800 Fax: 01491 874801
Email: info@ilam.co.uk
Web Site: www.ilam.co.uk
President: 96/97 Peter Morrall, 97/98 Alan Barber, 98/99 Gordon Bates, 99/00 Mike Fulford, 00/01 Dave Evans, 01/02 Len Croney, 02/03 Fiona Grossart, 03/04 Andrew Kerr.
Chief Executive: Lloyd Conway
The Institute of Leisure and Amenity Management came into being on January 1st 1983 as a result of the merger of four professional organisations engaged in Leisure and Amenity Management, one of which was the Institute of Municipal Entertainments (IME).
ILAM has continued IME's role in offering qualifications to arts and entertainments professionals which have developed alongside the evolving vocational qualifications and which take account of prior academic or vocational achievements.
ILAM actively represents arts and entertainments professionals in consultation and negotiation with Government and national agencies. The Panel's aims are to promote good practice within the specialisms; improve and facilitate communications with other bodies; promote and support ILAM Members' awareness and involvement with issues affecting management of cultural activities, including education and training; to produce and distribute information in appropriate format to achieve the aims and objectives outlined above.
All enquiries should be addressed to the Cheif Executive, ILAM, ILAM House, Lower Basildon, Reading, Berkshire, RG8 9NE.

INTER-ACTION
c/o HMS President (1918), Victoria Embankment, Near Blackfriars Bridge, London EC4Y 0HJ
Tel: 020 7583 2652 Fax: 020 7583 2840
Email: edbiaction@aol.com
Contact: Ed Berman MBE
Community Resource, Education and Social Enterprise centre. Performance space available.

INTERNATIONAL SHAKESPEARE ASSOCIATION
c/o Dr Vick Walton, Shakespeare Centre, Henley Street, Stratford-upon-Avon, Warwickshire CV37 6QW
Tel: 01789 204 016 Fax: 01789 294 911
Email: isa@shakespeare.org.uk
Executive Secretary and Treasurer: Dr Vick Walton

INTERNATIONAL THEATRE EXCHANGE
(UK Centre IATA)
c/o Drama Association of Wales The Old Library, Singleton Road, Splott Cardiff CF24 2ET
Tel: 02920 452 200
Email: mlovegrove3@aol.com
Commitee Board Member: Majorie Lovegrove

INTERNATIONAL THEATRE INSTITUTE
ITI @ Goldsmiths College, University of London, Lewisham Way, New Cross, London SE14 6NW
Tel: 020 7919 7276 Fax: 020 7919 7277
Email: iti@gold.ac.uk
Web Site: http://iti.gold.ac.uk
Chairman: Neville Shulman, O.B.E.
Administrator: Mischa Twitchin
The ITI is an International Organisation for Theatre created under the auspices of Unesco. The ITI plays an active role in promoting cultural exchange, including facilitating international contacts, events, seminars and conferences. The ITI also celebrates international dance day and world theatre day with the presentation of the annual ITI award for excellence in international dance and award for excellence in international theatre.

IRISH ACTORS' EQUITY GROUP
of the Services Industrial Professional Technical Union
9th Floor, Liberty Hall, Dublin 1 Eire
Tel: 00 353 1 858 6403 Fax: 00 353 1 874 3691
Email: equity@siptu.ie
Web Site: www.irishactorsequity.ie
President: Vincent McCabe
Vice-President: Padraig Murray
Group Secretary: Jane Boushell
Irish Actors' Equity Group is modelled on British and American Equity lines. Actors' Equity is a member of the Culture division of the Services Industrial Professional Technical Union. The Group which is a registered Trade Union with a negotiation licence, has been established to protect the rights of Irish Actors, to organise and improve the conditions of those engaged in the acting profession, to propose legislation favourable to the interest of the group. The Group's rules and regulations for film Companies on location in Ireland have been agreed to by the British Film Producers Association Ltd. A reciprocal arrangement with British Actors' Equity allows a free exchange of artistes between the two countries.

THE IRVING SOCIETY
10 Kings Avenue, London W5 2SH
Tel: 020 8566 8301
Email: secretary@theirvingsociety.org.uk
Web Site: www.theirvingsociety.org.uk
Hon Secretary: Michael Kilgarriff
The Irving Society seeks to celebrate the Theatre in the Age of Sir Henry Irving, the Victorian actor/manager. The society meets 5 times a year, in; February, April, June, September, November and issues a newsletter, "The Irvingite" four times a year and a journal, "First Knight" twice a year.

THE LIGHTING ASSOCIATION
Stafford Park 7, Telford, Shropshire TF3 3BQ
Tel: 01952 290 905 Fax: 01952 290 906
Email: enquiries@lightingassociation.com
Web Site: www.lightingassociation.com

THE LITTLE THEATRE GUILD OF GREAT BRITAIN
181 Brampton Road, Carlisle, Cumbria CA3 9AX
Tel: 01228 522 649
Email: chrysbar@tiscali.co.uk
Web Site: www.uktw.co.uk/clubs/itg.htm
Secretary: Mrs Barbara C Watson
P.r.o: Michael Shipley (Tel: 01204 304 103)
Objects: The Little Theatre Guild of Great Britain was inaugurated in May 1946, with the following objects: "To promote close co-operation between the Little Theatres constituting its membership, to act as co-ordinating and representative body on behalf of the Little Theatres and generally to maintain and further the highest standards in the art of theatres as practised by existing Little Theatres and to assist in and encourage the establishment of other Little Theatres. The Guild is strictly non-political and non-sectarian."
Membership: Membership is confined to independant organisations which control (usually by actual ownership) their own established theatres and which have satisfied the Guild as to their non-commercial character, general aims and artistic standards. Applications must be sponsored by two long-standing members of the Guild, who have seen their work and are willing to recommend admission

LONDON THEATRE COUNCIL
32 Rose Street, London WC2E 9ET
Tel: 020 7557 6700 Fax: 020 7557 6799
Guild House, Upper St Martin's Lane, London WC2H 9 Tel: 020 7379 6000
Fax: 020 7379 7001
Email: enquiries@solttma.co.uk
Communications re Managers should be addressed to Richard Pulford and com-

munications re Artistes should be addressed to Ian McGarry.
Chairman: Harvey McGregor, QC.
The Council represents SOLT (The Society of London Theatre) and Equity (British Actors` Equity Association). Its purpose is to mediate between managers and the artists employed by them in the West End of London. It does so primarily through the use of standard contracts of employment but the Council also facilitates the settlement of any disputes arising from these contracts.

THE RAYMOND MANDER & JOE MITCHENSON THEATRE COLLECTION

University of Bristol, Theatre Collection, Vandyck Building, Cantocks Close, Bristol, BS8 1UP
Tel: 0117 331 5086
Email: theatre-collection@bristol.ac.uk
Web Site: www.bristol.ac.uk/theatrecollection
Collection Manager: Jo Elsworth
The Theatre Collection is one of the world's largest and most significant collectionsrelating to the history of the British theatre. It is an accredited museum and research facility that is open to the public.Founded in 1951, its collections cover all aspects of theatre from seventeenth century up to the present day and include original documents, photographs, artwork, objects, costumes and an extensive library. Significant archive collections include London Old Vic, Bristol Old Vic and the world renowned Raymond Mander and Joe Mitchenson Collection. It is now used extensivley by authors, designers, publishers, BBC and television producers as well as local students and international academic scholars.
Commercial picture requests are handled through Arena Pal.

THE MASSENET SOCIETY

Flat 2, 79 Linden Gardens,
London W2 4EU
Tel: 020 7229 7060
Founder/Director: Miss Stella J Wright

MECHANICAL COPYRIGHT PROTECTION SOCIETY LTD

Elgar House, 41 Streatham High Road, London SW16 1ER
Tel: 020 8769 4400 Fax: 020 8378 7300
Email: mediaquery@mcps-prs-alliance.co.uk
Web Site: www.mcps.co.uk
The Society was formed in 1910 for the purpose of licensing on behalf of music copyright owners, the recording of their works for all purposes and the collection and distribution of the resulting fees and royalties.
Through reciprocal agreements with the majority of other mechanical collection organisations the interests of the Society's own Members are represented in most countries of the world where copyright is respected. Likewise MCPS represents the mechanical right interests, in its own territory, of virtually all composer, author and publisher members of foreign Societies and Agencies. Copyright clearance and licence may be obtained from the Society to cover the recording on disc, tape, sound, film track, video, etc. of works in its repertoire on application to the above address.

METIER

Glyde House, Glydegate, Bradford, West Yorkshire BD5 0BQ
Tel: 01422 381 618 Fax: 01274 391 566
Email: claire@metier.org.uk
Web Site: www.metier.org.uk
Chief Executive: Duncan Sones
Head of Research and Information: Jane Fear
Marketing Manager: Mags Roche
Research Co-ordinator: Martin Wilson

MID WALES CIRCUIT

Red House, Bettws, Newtown, Powys SY16 3LE Wales
Tel: 01686 610 554
Email: julie@turners4.freeserve.co.uk
Contact: Julie Turner
Member venues: Theatr Hafren, Newtown; Aberystwyth Arts Centre; Wyeside Arts Centre, Builth Wells; Theatr Ardudwy, Harlech; Theatr Felinfach, Nr. Lampeter; Theatr Brycheiniog, Brecon; Theatr Mwldan, Cardigan; The Welfare, Ystradgynlais.
Policy:As the consortium of all the major professionally managed venues in Mid Wales, the Circuit works together in the areas of promoting, networking, training, fundraising and lobbying.

THE MUSIC CLUB OF LONDON

24 Burywick, Harpenden, Hertfordshire, AL5 2AH
Tel: 01582 763 457 Mobile: 07808 044397 Fax: 01582 763 452
Email: suitters@btinternet.com
Web Site: www.musicclublondon.com
Contact: Bryan Suitters

MUSICIANS BENEVOLENT FUND

7 - 11 Britannia Street, London WC1X 9JS
Tel: 020 7239 9100 Fax: 020 7713 8942
Email: info@helpmusicians.org.uk
Web Site: www.helpmusicians.org.uk
The Musicians Benevolent Fund is the music business' own charity - the largest of its kind in the UK. Each year it spends about £1.7 million helping around 1,400 people of any age, and who in any area of the music business who are in need as a result of illness, accident or other misfortune.

MUSICIANS SOCIAL AND BENEVOLENT COUNCIL

100a Weston Park, Crouch End, London N8 9PP
Tel/Fax: 020 8348 9358
Honourary Secretary: Geraldine Chalmers
The council assists musicians in sickness and distress. Income is derived from contributions by orchestras, donations and legacies.
Funds urgently needed. The music profession is open to anyone who plays well enough to get into it. Once in, the rewards, not necessarily financial, are immense in terms of job satisfaction.
Musicians are always trying to play better, and better again, not just for money, not just for a living, but because they love music and the making of it so much.
Freelance players are always at risk. Cash goes immediately to, for instance, a bass guitarist with a broken arm. To a cellist, mother of two, whose hand was too badly hurt in a car crash that she can't (yet) hold her bow.
You would normally have seen her on the Barbican concert platform. Now she's stuck at home in fear for the future.
If you love the symphony you last heard her play in, or the Jazz concert you went to, please help us get people back to work.

MUSICIANS' UNION

National Office: 60/62 Clapham Road, London SW9 0JJ
Tel: 020 7582 5566 Fax: 020 7582 9805
Email: info@musicianunion.org.uk
Web Site: www.musiciansunion.org.uk
General Secretary: John Smith
Assistant General Secretaries: Horace Trubridge, Howard Evans
London Official: Bob Bennett
Secretary to the Theatre Section: Dave Webster
The Musicians' Union is the principal organisation of musicians in Britain. It is a trade union affiliated to the TUC and the Labour Party, the Theatres' Advisory Council, the Federation of Entertainment Unions, and the National Music Council.
As a trade union its principal object is the regulation and improvement of salaries, fees and working conditions of its members. Agreements have been made with the TMA, SOLT and theatre proprietors.
The MU campaigns to "Keep music Live".
Music is the beating heart of theatre productions. Take the musicians away and you lose one of the vital elements of the live theatre experience.
The Union has over 30,000 members, and branches have been established in over 70 towns. It occupies a leading position in the International Federation of Musicians.
The National Office, and most branches, maintain benevolent funds for the relief of distress.

NATIONAL ASSOCIATION OF TEACHERS IN FURTHER & HIGHER ED.

27 Britannia Street, London WC1X 9JP
Tel: 020 7837 3636 Fax: 020 7837 4403
Email: hq@natfhe.org.uk
Web Site: www.natfhe.org.uk

NATIONAL ASSOCIATION OF YOUTH THEATRES

Arts Centre, Vane Terrace Darlington, County Durham DL3 7AX
Tel: 01325 363 330 Fax: 01325 363 313
Email: nayt@aol.com
Web Site: www.nayt.org.uk
Director: Ben Ayrton
Administrator: Judith Clapham

NATIONAL CAMPAIGN FOR THE ARTS

Pegasus House, 37-43 Sackville Street, London W1S 3EH
Tel: 020 7333 0375 Fax: 020 7333 0660
Email: nca@artscampaign.org.uk
Web Site: www.artscampaign.org.uk
President: Melvyn Bragg
Chair: Joan Bakewell CBE
Campaign Officer: Alice Judd
Campaign Officer: Oliver Rickman
Director Victoria Todd

The UK's only independent lobbying organisation representing all the arts. Founded in 1985 it seeks to safeguard, promote and develop the arts and win public and political recognition for the importance of the arts as a key element in our national culture. It is funded through membership subscriptions to ensure its independence and does not receive any public subsidy. Members gain access to the NCA's information and advice, networks, seminars, conferences and publications. Membership is open to organisations and individuals working in, or with an interest in, the arts.

NATIONAL COUNCIL FOR DRAMA TRAINING (NCDT)

1-7 Woburn Walk, Bloomsbury, London WC1H 0JJ
Tel/Fax: 020 7387 3650 Fax: 020 7387 3860
Email: info@ncdt.co.uk
Web Site: www.ncdt.co.uk
Chair: Sir Brian Fender
Director: Adele Bailey
The NCDT was established in 1976 with the object of encouraging the highest possible standards of vocational education and training for drama in the United Kingdom and to provide a forum within which the different sides of the profession can discuss matters of common interest in relation to such training. The Council is an independent body, registered as a charity, and is financed by its member organisations - Equity, TMA, SOLT, BBC,the Conference of Drama Schools, Channel Four Television, Granada and donations from a number of the independent television companies.

NATIONAL ENTERTAINMENT AGENTS COUNCIL

PO Box 112, Seaford, East Sussex BN25 2DQ
Tel: 0870 755 7612 Fax: 0870 755 7613
Email: chrisbray@neac.org.uk
Web Site: www.neac.org.uk
Chairman: Alan Pope
Vice Chairmen: Keith Stitchman, Alan Bennet
General Secretary: Chris Bray
Treasurer: Derek Dalibney
Hon. President: Derek Wells.
An active Trade Organisation for Entertainment Agents.
Broadly speaking, the N.E.A.C. is to Entertainment Agents what ABTA is to Travel Agents. The Council is open to all Agents who are prepared to adhere to the Code Of Conduct, which is nationally recognised, and adhere to the highest standards of ethical behaviour.
Members receive or have access to Legal and Technical Advice and Support, regular Newsletters, Branch and National Meetings, Showcases, Inter Trading and many other benefits, all regulated under the Rules of the Council and the Code Of Conduct.
The Council has a Disciplinary Procedure to hear and resolve any complaints against its members.

NATIONAL OPERATIC AND DRAMATIC ASSOCIATION

NODA House, 58-60 Lincoln Road, Peterborough, PE1 2RZ
Tel: 0870 770 2480 Fax: 0870 770 2490
Email: everyone@noda.org.uk
Web Site: www.noda.org.uk
Chief Executive: Mark Pemberton
A registered charity established in 1899, NODA is the largest umbrella body for AMATEUR THEATRE in the UK. Elected Councillors and Regional Representatives support its members at local level. Benefits include a quarterly national magazine, area magazines and directories, summer school, advisory and emergency services and a computerised mailing list. Insurance, Pantomime scripts, make-up and music, theatre books at discounts to members are also available via its trading company, NODA Ltd.

THE NATIONAL OUTDOOR EVENTS ASSOCIATION

7 Hamilton Way, Wallington, Surrey SM6 9NJ
Tel: 020 8669 8121 Fax: 020 8647 1128
Email: secretary@noea.org.uk
Web Site: www.noea.org.uk
President: Richard Limb
General Secretary: John Barton.
Founded in 1979, the Association exists to promote standards, status and interests of the world of Outdoor Events and is the forum for local authorities, show organisers and suppliers of equipment and services in general.
The Association provides a comprehensive range of relevant services aimed at creating business opportunities, developing skills and improving the quality of events. NOEA runs a national convention. A series of Regional Conferences is held during the closed season.
NOEA works closely with 'Event & Venues specialist' the journal for the Events Industry. NOEA publishes an annual directory of Members and copies may be obtained upon application.

NATIONAL YOUTH MUSIC THEATRE

5th Floor, The Palace Theatre, Shaftesbury Avenue, London W1V 8AY
Tel: 020 7734 7478 Fax: 020 7734 7515
Email: enquiries@nymt.org.uk
Web Site: www.nymt.org.uk
Manager: Jon Bromwich
Music theatre productions and workshops for 11-19 year old actor, singer, dancers and instrumentalists. UK tours including the Edinburgh Festival. International tours have included Canada, USA and Japan. Talent-spotting, our open national auditions, held every January.

NATIONAL YOUTH THEATRE OF GREAT BRITAIN

443-445 Holloway Road, London N7 6LW
Tel: 020 7281 3863 Fax: 020 7281 8246
Email: info@nyt.org.uk
Web Site: www.nyt.org.uk
Artistic Directors: John Hoggarth and Paul Roseby
Executive Director: Sid Higgins

THE PERFORMANCE POETRY SOCIETY

Bourne Place, 158b Brunswick Road, Birmingham B12 8PF
Tel: 0121 442 4488
Email: performancepoetry@amserve.net

PERFORMING ARTS

Performing arts
British Council 10 Spring Gardens, London SW1A 2BN
Tel: 020 7389 3080 Fax: 020 7389 3088/3057
Email: firstname.lastname@britishcouncil.org / theatredance@british
Web Site: http://theatredance.britishcouncil.org / www.britishcouncil.org/arts
Director of Performing Arts/Head of Music: John Kieffer
Deputy Director of Performing Arts/Head of Drama and Dance: Sally Cowling
The British Council works to enhance the

reputation of the UK both as a source of excellence and vitality in the arts, and as a valued partner in international artistic and educational exchange. It is not an arts funder in the same sense as the Arts Councils and regional arts boards. Rather, its aims are to update international perceptions of Britain, create international partnerships and mount collaborative educational activity through the arts and to enhance the exports of the UK's creative industries. The British Council is represented in 230 towns and cities in 109 countries and work in the arts in any particular country is bound up with the aims, objectives and target audiences in that country. For more information see our website.

PERFORMING RIGHT SOCIETY (PRS)

29/33 Berners Street, London W1T 3AB
Tel: 020 7580 5544 Fax: 020 7306 4455
Email: adam.singer@mcps-prs-alliance.co.uk
Web Site: www.prs.co.uk
Chairman: Elis Rich
Chief Executive: Adam Singer
PRS is an association of composers, authors and publishers of music which exists to collect royalties for the non-dramatic public performance and broadcasting of their copyright works. PRS is affiliated to similar societies throughout the world. A PRS licence is required for the use of its international repertoire in concert and variety, as overture, entr'acte or exit music, or for any other form of live or mechanical performance (excluding operas, operettas, music plays, specially written music for plays, revues or pantomimes (apart from interpolations therein of independent items), and ballets). Further information from Alan Scott-Neve, Local Authorities and Theatres.

PHONOGRAPHIC PERFORMANCE LTD

1 Upper James Street, London W1F 9DE
Tel: 020 7534 1000 Fax: 020 7534 1111
Email: ppo.info@ppluk.com
Web Site: www.ppluk.com
PPL is a non profit making company set up by the record industry in 1934 to grant licences to anyone who wants to play records, tapes or CD's in public. PPL looks after the rights of over 12,000 different record labels. This means that 95% of commercially available recordings in the UK need a PPL licence when they are broadcast or played in public. The revenue generated from PPL's licence fees is distributed to record companies and their performers.

PUPPET CENTRE TRUST

The Puppet Centre, Battersea Arts Centre, Lavender Hill, London SW11 5TN
Tel: 020 7228 5335 Fax: 020 7228 8863
Email: pct@puppetcentre.demon.co.uk
Web Site: www.puppetcentre.com
Contact: Penny Francis/Peter Charlton
Resource centre devoted to promoting the arts of animation and puppetry. Small museum display. Open to general public 2pm-6pm Wednesday & Saturday, admission free.

PUPPETEERS UK

63 Kennedy Road, Bicester,
Oxon, OX26 2BE
Tel / Fax: 01869 245 793
Email: admin@pupeteersuk.com
Web Site: www.puppeteersuk.com
Chair: Clive Chandler
Secretary: Ray DaSilva
PUK is the network organisation for puppetry in the United Kingdom representing the combined membership of the national and regional puppetry organisations. It provides an overall co-operative and inclusive framework within which they can all flourish and has brought a renewed spirit of co-operation and co-ordination across the whole sector leading to an increased mutual exchange of information and a sharing of good practice between all stakeholders and the wider public. PUKs aim is to provide a united voice and an effective lobby for increased recognition of puppetry, to increase opportunities for artists, to develop audiences, and help establish a better understanding of the value and cultural significance of puppetry as an artform. The first key project? Supported by Arts Council England? Has been the creation of the website which contains a
comprehensive online directory of puppeteers and puppetry services in the UK.

RADIUS

(The Religious Drama Society of Great Britain) - an interdenominational body
RADIUS, PO Box 34493 London W6 9WK
Tel: 020 7401 2422
Email: office@radius.org.uk
Web Site: www.radius.org.uk
Patrons: Most Rev Rt Hon Rowan Williams Archbishop of Canterbury, Dame Judi Dench.
President: The Rt. Revd. Peter Firth.
Radius exists to encourage drama which illuminates the human condition. Its work is directed towards improving the standard of writing, production acting of plays and for Christian education and outreach. It offers advice, the use of a unique library, a Summer School, Training Days, and a quarterly magazine.

ROY CASTLE LUNG CANCER FOUNDATION

200 London Road, Liverpool, Merseyside L3 9TA
Tel: 0151 794 8800 Fax: 0151 794 8888
Email: williamsc@roycastle.liv.ac.uk
Web Site: www.roycastle.org.uk
Celebrity and Special Events Manager: Cheryl Williams

THE ROYAL BALLET BENEVOLENT FUND

c/o Royal Opera House, London WC2E 9DD
Tel: 01273 747 268 Fax: 01273 776 138
Email: info@rbbf.org.uk
Web Site: www.rbbf.org.uk
Contact: Clementine Cowl

THE ROYAL SOCIETY OF MUSICIANS

10 Stratford Place, London W1C 1BA
Tel: 020 7629 6137 Fax: 020 7629 6137
Email: enquiries@royalsocietyofmusicians.co.uk
Web Site: www.theroyalsocietyofmusiciansofgreatbritain.co.uk
Administrator: Maggie Gibb
The Society, a charity for musicians run by musicians, provides grants and support to professional musicians and their families in need because of accident, illness or old age whether or not they are members. Founded in 1738 as the Fund for Decay'd Musicians, early members included Handel, Arne, Boyce and Sammartini. Today this historic and vibrant Society maintains its tradition of responding swiftly to needs of colleagues.

ROYAL THEATRICAL FUND (EST. 1839)

(incorporated by Royal Charters 1853 & 1974)
11 Garrick Street, London WC2E 9AR
Tel: 020 7836 3322 Fax: 020 7379 8273
Email: admin@trtf.com
Web Site: www.trtf.com
Patron: Her Majesty The Queen
President: Sir Donald Sinden, CBE
Secretary: Mrs R. M. Foster
Registered Charity No. 222080

THE ROYAL VARIETY CHARITY

Formerly the Entertainment Artistes' Benevolent Fund
Brinsworth House, 72 Staines Road, Twickenham TW2 5AL
Admin Enquiries Tel: 020 8898 8164
Brinsworth Enquiries
Only: 020 8894 1351
Email: enquiries@royalvarietycharity.org
Web Site: www.royalvarietycharity.org
Patrons: H. M. The Queen
Hon. Life President: Laurie Mansfield
Chairman: Giles Cooper

RSA

The Royal Society for the Encouragement of Arts Manufacturers & Commerce
8 John Adam Street, London WC2N 6EZ
Tel: 020 7839 5049 Fax: 020 7321 0271
Email: conference@rsa.org.uk
Web Site: www.theplacetomeet.org.uk

Contact: Karen Palmer

SCOTTISH YOUTH THEATRE
Scotland's national theatre for and by young people.
3rd Floor, Forsyth House, 11 Union Street, Glasgow, G1 3TA Scotland
Tel: 0141 221 5127 Fax: 0141 221 9123
Email: info@scottishyouththeatre.org
Web Site: www.scottishyouththeatre.freeserve.org
Organisation offering young people (3-25 years) the chance to take part in most aspects of performance art, working with theatre professionals as a means to encourage social, artistic and self-development.

THE SCREENWRITERS WORKSHOP
Euroscript Ltd 64 Hemingford Road, London N1 1DB
Tel: 07958 244 656
Email: paul.bassettdavies@euroscript.co.uk
Web: www.screenwritersworkshop.co.uk
Forum for writers and novice aspiring writers for contact, information and tuition. Script reading service.

THE SESAME INSTITUTE (UK)
Christchurch, 27 Blackfriars Road, London SE1 8NY
Tel/Messages: 020 7633 9690
Email: sesameinstituteuk@btinternet.com
Web Site: http://www.btinternet.com/~sesameuk
Drama and Movement in Therapy.
Full time training - Central/Sesame. Short courses. Sesame Practitioners provided.
General Enquiries - The Sesame Institute.
Full time training - The Central School of Speech & Drama, London (Tel: 020 7722 8183).

THE SHAKESPEARE CENTRE
Henley Street, Stratford-upon-Avon, Warwickshire CV37 6QW
Tel: 01789 204 016 Fax: 01789 296 083
Email: info@shakespeare.org.uk
Web Site: www.shakespeare.org.uk
Headquarters of the Shakespeare Birthplace Trust. Facilities include research library on Shakespeare's life, work and times, incorporating the collections of the Royal Shakespeare Theatre; Educational courses; Poetry Festival, etc.
Enquiries to Director: Roger Pringle, MA.

THE SHAW SOCIETY
51 Farmfield Road, Bromley, Kent BR1 4NF
Tel: 020 8697 3619
Email: anthnyellis@aol.com
Secretary: Barbara Smoker
Sub: £15 or $30 p.a.

SHREWSBURY & DISTRICT ARTS ASSOCIATION
The Gateway Educ & Arts Centr, Chester Street, Shrewsbury, Shropshire SY1 1NB
Tel: 01743 361120 Fax: 01743 358 951
Email: gate-ed@hotmail.com / joyce.allaway@shrewsbury.gov.uk
Contact: Mrs Janet Tudor

THE SOCIETY FOR THEATRE RESEARCH
c/o The Theatre Museum, 1e Tavistock Street, London WC2E 7PR
Email: e.cottis@btinternet.com
Web Site: www.str.org.uk
President: Timothy West CBE
Vice-Presidents: Jack Reading, George Speaight, Margaret Collins, Neville Hunnings, Mike Ostler.
Chairman: Pieter van der Merwe
Hon. Secretaries: Eileen Cottis, Frances Dann; Treasurer: Barry Sheppard.
The Society aims to link those interested in the history and technique of the theatre in the United Kingdom and encourage further research into these subjects. It publishes the journal "Theatre Notebook' and one or more annual volumes as well as holding lectures and other events and disburses up to £4,000 annually in grants towards research. It also presents an annual Theatre Book Prize, currently of £400.

THE SOCIETY OF AUTHORS LTD
84 Drayton Gardens, London SW10 9SB
Tel: 020 7373 6642 Fax: 020 7373 5768
Email: info@societyofauthors.org.uk
Web Site: www.societyofauthors.org.uk

SOCIETY OF BRITISH THEATRE DESIGNERS
Also at this address: Association of British Technicians and Society of Theatre Consultants
4th Floor 55 Farringdon Road London EC1M 3JB
Tel: 020 7242 9200 Fax: 020 7242 9370
Email: office@ abtt.org.uk
Web Site: www.theatredesign.org.uk
Secretary: Peter Ruthven Hall
Administrator (ABTT): Jenny Straker
The Society exists to enhance the interests and status of the theatre design profession, covering sets, costumes and lighting.
Organises exhibitions and debates on current issues affecting Theatre Design.

SOCIETY OF LEISURE CONSULTANTS AND PUBLISHERS
1 Sandringham Close, Sandringham Park, Tarleton, Lancashire PR4 6UZ
Tel: 01772 816 046 Mobile: 07752 722462
Director: J. B. A. Sharples
Represents consultants and publishers in the field of entertainment and the arts management, recreation, catering, tourism, marketing, public relations, recruiting, advertising, and the leisure industry and related interests.

THE SOCIETY OF LONDON THEATRE
32 Rose Street, London WC2E 9ET
Tel: 020 7557 6700 Fax: 020 7557 6799
Email: enquiries@solttma.co.uk
Web Site: www.officiallondontheatre.co.uk
President: Sir Stephen Waley-Cohen
Chief Executive: Richard Pulford
Employers` organisation for West End theatres and producers. Providing industrial relations, legal services, and collective marketing and advocacy for the members. Organisers of the annual Laurence Olivier Awards. Publishers of the official London Theatre Guide. Promoters of Theatre Tokens.

THE SOCIETY OF THEATRE CONSULTANTS
4th Floor 27 Old Gloucester Street, London WC1N 3AX
Tel: 020 7419 8767
Email: mailto:info@theatreconsultants.org.uk
Web Site: www.theatreconsultants.org.uk
Chairman: Anne Minors
Hon. Secretary: Michael Holden
Hon. Treasurer: Chris Baldwin
Permanent Secretary: Jenny Straker
A Professional Society whose members advise on the feasibility, management planning and detail design of Theatres, Concert Halls, Conference Centres, Arts Centres, etc.

STAGE MANAGEMENT ASSOCIATION
55 Faringdon Road, London EC1M 3JB
Tel: 020 7242 9250 Fax: 020 7242 9303
Email: admin@stagemanagementassociation.co.uk
Web Site: www.stagemanagementassociation.co.uk
Chairman: Alan Wallace
Hon. Secretary: Kevin Mullery
Membership: Open to anyone working in or interested in stage management.
Objects of the Association: To support and represent stage management in the UK. Members' Meetings: Held regularly.
Training: Run one day courses to acquire new skills, update stage management skills and develop careers in production, company or general management. Open to members and non-members.
Employment: A list of members available for work is circulated to managements each month on request.
Publications: FREE Career Guide available from website, other publications for sale.

STAGE ONE (FORMERLY THEATRE INVESTMENT FUND LTD)
Reg.Charity No.271349
32 Rose Street, London WC2E 9ET
Tel: 020 7557 6737 Fax: 020 7557 6799
Email: enquiries@stageone.uk.com
Web Site: www.stageone.uk.com
Chief Executive: Nick Salmon
Chairman: David Dein
Vice-Chairman: Paul Elliott

STANDING CONFERENCE OF UNIVERSITY DRAMA DEPARTMENTS
School of English, University of Leeds, Woodhouse Lane, Leeds, West Yorkshire LS2 9JT
Tel: 0113 343 4739 Fax: 0113 343 4774
Email: mark@scudd.org.uk
Web Site: www.scudd.org.uk
Secretary: Richard Boon

TAKE ART! LTD
The Mill Flaxdrayton Farm South Petherton, Somerset TA13 5LR
Tel: 01460 249450 Fax: 01460 249455
Email: chris@takeart.org
Web Site: www.takeart.org
Executive Director: Ralph Lister
Director of Dance & Theatre: Chris Fogg
Marketing & Administrative Co-ordinator: Becci Davis
Dance Administrator: Anna Golding
We deliver Theatre Somerset - the theatre locality plan for the county - and operate Flax303, a new theatre company for Somerset.

THE LONDON THEATRE COUNCIL
Same address for: The Society of London Theatre; Stage 1 and The Theatrical Managers Association
32 Rose Street, London WC2E 9ET
Tel: 020 7557 6700 Fax: 020 7557 6799
Guild House, Upper St Martin's Lane, London WC2H Tel: 020 7379 6000 Fax: 020 7379 7001
Email: enquiries@solttma.co.uk
Communications re Managers should be addressed to Richard Pulford. Joint Secretary) and communications re Artistes should be addressed to Ian McGarry (Joint Secretary).
Chairman: Harvey McGregor, QC.
The Council represents TMA (Theatrical Management Association) and Equity (British Actors' Equity Association). Its purpose is to mediate between managers and the artists employed by them in the UK theatre, outside the West End of London. It does so primarily through the use of standard contracts of employment but the Council also facilitates the settlement of any disputes arising from these contracts.

THE MAGIC CIRCLE
Centre for the Magic Arts, 12 Stephenson Way, London NW1 2HD
Tel: 020 7387 2222 Fax: 020 7387 5114
Email: enquiries@TheMagicCircle.co.uk
Web Site: www.themagiccircle.co.uk
President: Alan Shaxon
Secretary: Chris Pratt
The Magic Circle is an association aimed at the promotion of magic as an art and the establishment of a centre where magicians can meet.

THE SOCIETY OF TEACHERS OF SPEECH AND DRAMA (STSD)
73 Berry Hill Road, Mansfield, Nottinghamshire NG18 4RU
Tel: 01623 627 636 Fax: 0141 577 1942
Email: chairman@stsd.org.uk
Web Site: www.stsd.org.uk
Hon. Chairman: Mrs J Speculand
Hon. Press Officer: Mrs J Guy
STSD exists to promote the effective use of the English language in speaking, business, speech and all forms of communication. STSD was formed to protect the interests of professionally qualified specialist teachers of Speech, Drama, Communication and Presentation Skills. We encourage good standards of teaching and promote the study and knowledge of Speech & Drama Art in every form.

THEATRE MUSEUM
The National Museum of the Performing Arts
Russel Street, London WC2E 7PR
Tel: 020 7943 4700 Fax: 020 7943 4777
Email: m.jones@vam.ac.uk
Web Site: www.theatremuseum.org
The Theatre Museum exists to provide the national record of stage performance in Britain and to increase the public understanding and enjoyment of the performing arts through the expert interpretation of its collections. In its main premises in Covent Garden, the Museum houses permanent displays and special exhibitions drawn from its unrivalled collections, together with a shop. It runs a popular events and education programme. A study room is also available for research by appointment. Both the Paintings Gallery and Studio Theatre are available for corporate hire. The public entrance is in Russell Street and admission is free.
Director: Geoffrey Marsh
Events Manager: Malcolm Jones
Studio Capacity: 80 seats, Paintings Gallery: 100 seats
Policy: Studio Theatre used for group workshops. Paintings gallery occasionally used to showcase musicals or playreadings. Both are used for talks, lectures and demonstrations.
Regular events and some performance work. Talks and seminars.
Occasional 'trade' events and conferences. Available for corporate hire, parties, press launches etc.

THE THEATREGOERS' CLUB OF GREAT BRITAIN
Harling House, 47-51 Great Suffolk Street, London SE1 0BS
Tel: 020 7450 4040 Fax: 020 7450 4041
Email: info@theatregoers.co.uk
Web Site: www.theatregoers.co.uk
President: Susan Hampshire
Vice President: Gary Wilmot, Michael Ball, Dulcie Gray CBE
Chairman: Sir Eddie Kulukundis OBE,
The largest theatre Club in the UK, established in 1978. Members enjoy a wide selection of West End and regional theatre, with luxury coach travel.

THE THEATRES TRUST
22 Charing Cross Road, London WC2H 0QL
Tel: 020 7836 8591 Fax: 020 7836 3302
Email: info@theatrestrust.org.uk
Web Site: www.theatrestrust.org.uk
Chairman: Rupert Rhymes, OBE
Director: Peter Longman
Consultants: John Earl and Jonathan Lane
Administrator: Paul Connolly
The Trust was set up by Parliament to promote the better protection of theatres. Its 15 Trustees are appointed by the Secretary of State for Culture, Media and Sport. Local Authorities are required by Government order to consult the Trust when considering planning applications affecting land on which there is a theatre. However, the Trust's work extends far more widely and covers other planning issues, advice on theatre buildings to grant-making bodies, including the Lottery distribtors, and in relevant matters helping theatre managements and preservation bodies. The Trust works closely with an associated Charitable Fund sharing the same Trustees, staff and offices.

THE THEATRICAL GUILD
Reg Charity no. 206669
11 Garrick Street London WC2E 9AR
Tel: 020 7240 6062
Email: admin@ttg.org.uk
Web Site: www.ttg.org.uk
The Theatrical Guild is a national charity supporting those that work in theatres. Established in 1891 we are dedicated to looking after theatre staff in times of need. We help in a variety of ways including offering educational sponsorship, one-off grants as well as access to councelling and welfare advice.
Patrons: Keira Knightley and Simon Russell Beale
Contact: Laura Hannon

THEATRICAL MANAGEMENT ASSOCIATION

32 Rose Street, London WC2E 9ET
Tel: 020 7557 6700 Fax: 020 7557 6799
Email: enquiries@solttma.co.uk
Web Site: www.tmauk.org
President: Derek Nicholls
Chief Executive: Richard Pulford
TMA is the UK's national trade association for theatre managers, producers, venues and arts professionals. Services for its members include industrial relations and legal advice, information services, a quarterly magazine Prompt, and the annual Theatre Awards. Information about membership is available from the address above.

TTA (THEATRICAL TRADERS ASSOCIATION)

c/o Cricket Street, Denton, Manchester M34 3DR
Tel: 0161 335 0220 Tel: 0845 126 0631 (Jim Birney from Just Tickets) Fax: 0161 320 3928
Chairman: Bob Howorth
Membership of firms serving the entertainment industry who mainly specialise in supplying amateur organisations.
Contact Committee Member Mr Jim Birney, who is also Managing Director of Just Tickets.

UNIMA - BRITISH CENTRE

(Union Internationale de la Marionnette)
Tel: 020 7848 3165 Fax: 020 7848 3182
Email: chris.abbott@kcl.ac.uk
Secretary: Chris Abbott
British arm of international association affiliated to UNESCO serving to unite people around the world who contribute to the development of Puppet Theatre.
BrUNIMA is a membership organisation of professional and amateur puppeteers with a team of Professional Consultants in most aspects of puppetry. Organises events for puppeteers, usually with an international focus. Publishes BrUNIMA Bulletin 3 times a year, " a members' newsletter" and occasional publications.

THE UNIVERSITY OF BRISTOL THEATRE COLLECTION

Department of Drama, Cantocks Close, Bristol BS8 1UP
Tel: 0117 331 5086 Fax: 0117 331 5082
Email: theatre-collection@bris.ac.uk
Web Site: www.bristol.ac.uk/theatrecollection
Keeper: Jo Elsworth
Assistant Keeper: Rachel Hassall
The Theatre Collection covers most areas of theatre research and history. It is rich in primary source material, including playbills, photographs, prints, and original scenery and costume designs. Its holdings include the London and Bristol Old Vic archives, The Herbert Beerbohm Tree collection, the Women's Theatre Collection and a large design collection.
There is also an extensive reference library and collection of journals, plus an enquiry service.
Visiting hours are from Mondays to Fridays, 9.15am to 4.45pm. Appointment reccommended.

THE VARIETY & LIGHT ENTERTAINMENT COUNCIL

54 Keyes House, Dolphin Square, London SW1V 3NA
Tel: 020 7834 0515 Fax: 020 7821 0261
Guild House: Upper St Martin's Lane, London, WC2H 9EG Tel: 020 7379 6000 Fax: 020 7379 7001
Email: association@agents-uk.com
Joint Secretaries: Kenneth Earle (Dolphin Square) Christine Payne (Guild House)
The V.L.E.C. exists to promote and regulate good relations between Managers, Agents and Artistes engaged in the Variety and light entertainment business.
In particular the Council maintains machinery for the adoption and operation of Standard Contract for all Live Entertainment and the settlement of disputes arising therefrom.
The constitution of the Council includes The Agents' Association (Great Britain), the Association of Circus Proprietors, British Actors' Equity Asociation, the Institute of Leisure & Amenity Management, the National Association of Licensed House Managers, Society of London Theatres and the Theatrical Management Association and Musicians Union.

VARIETY CLUB CHILDREN'S CHARITY LTD

93 Bayham Street, London NW1 0AG
Tel: 020 7428 8100 Fax: 020 7428 8123
Email: info@varietyclub.org.uk
Web Site: www.varietyclub.org.uk
Head of Events: Babs Tandy

WRITERNET

Cabin V, Clarendon Buildings, 25 Horsell Road, London N5 1XL
Tel: 020 7609 7474 Fax: 020 7609 7557
Email: info@writernet.org.uk
Web Site: www.writernet.org.uk
Executive Director: Jonathan Meth
Writernet is a national research and development organisation for new writing for all forms of live and recorded performance.
The Trust aims to encourage new writing and promote the work of writers currently under-represented, believing the continuing emergence of vital and challenging writing to be essential to the future of the industry.
Writernet publishes a range of information pertinent to writers on all aspects of development and production in the form of guides and a six-weekly journal which includes articles and reviews on aesthetic and practical issues.
Writernet also runs a script-reading service and a link service between writers and producers, organises debates and seminars and undertakes research projects.

WRITERS' GUILD OF GREAT BRITAIN

15 Britannia Street, London WC1X 9JN
Tel: 020 7833 0777 Fax: 020 7833 4777
Email: admin@writersguild.org.uk
Web Site: www.writersguild.org.uk
Chair: Graham Lester George
General Secretary: Bernie Corbett
Trade Union for professional writers in TV, film, theatre, radio, books and new media.

Funding Organisations

ARTS COUNCIL ENGLAND

14 Great Peter Street, London SW1P 3NQ
Tel: 020 7333 0100 Fax: 020 7973 6590
Email: enquiries@artscouncil.org.uk
Web Site: www.artscouncil.org.uk
Chief Executive: Peter Hewitt
Chairman: Gerry Robinson

ARTS COUNCIL OF WALES

9 Museum Place, Cardiff CF10 3NX Wales
Tel: 029 2037 6500 Fax: 029 2022 1447
Email: info@artswales.org.uk
Web Site: www.artswales.org.uk
Chief Executive: Peter Tyndall
The Arts Council of Wales is the national organisation with specific responsibility for the funding and strategic development of the arts in Wales. Most of its funds come from the National Assembly for Wales but it also receives funds from other sources. Distributes National Lottery funds to the arts in Wales.
For a guide to schemes and grants available please visit the website.

DIRECTORY OF SOCIAL CHANGE

24 Stephenson Way, London NW1 2DP
Tel: 020 7209 5151 Fax: 020 7391 4808
Email: info@dsc.org.uk
Web Site: www.dsc.org.uk
DSC is the largest provider of information and training for the UK voluntary and community sectors. Activities include training courses, conferences, Charityfare, publishing books and hosting fund raising websites.

NESTA

The National Endowment for Science Technology and the Arts
Fishmonger' Chambers 110 Upper Thames Street, London EC4R 3TW

Tel: 020 7645 9500
Email: nesta@nesta.org.uk
Web Site: www.nesta.org.uk
Chairman: Chris Powell
Chief Executive: Janet Morrison
Invests in UK creativity and innovation. Set up by Act of Parliament in 1998, it uses the interest on a National Lottery endowment to pioneer ways of supporting and promoting innovation and creativity across science.

THE PRINCES TRUST
18 Park Square East, London NW1 4LH
Tel: 020 7543 1234 / 0800 842 842 Fax: 020 7543 1200
Email: info@princes-trust.org.uk
Web Site: www.princes-trust.org.uk
UK's largest charity for young people, helping 14-30 year olds to develop confidence, learn new skills, get into work and start their own businesses.

THE PRS FOUNDATION
29-33 Berners Street, London W1T 3AB
Tel: 020 7306 4044 Fax: 020 7306 4814
Email: info@prsfoundation.co.uk
Web Site: www.prsfoundation.co.uk
Foundation Manager: Charlotte Ray
Applications Manager: Ben Lane
Foundation Administrator: Clarissa Carlyon
The UK's largest independent funder specifically for new music of any genre. Aims are to encourage, promote and stimulate the creation and performance of all genres of music and to help people have a positive experience of new music. Supports a diverse range of new music activities, including many unique and ground-breaking projects, collaborations and initiatives. Achieves its aims via a wide range of funding schemes which have their own application form (available on the website) and deadline. Please note that PRSF cannot support recordings, equipment or individuals.

Society of Theatre Consultants

ANDY HAYLES
Charcoalblue Ltd 33 Rushworth Street, London SE1 0RB
020 7928 0000
Email: andy@charcoalblue.com

PETER ANGIER
Carr & Angier, The Old Malthouse, Clarence Street, Bath, Somerset BA1 5NS
Tel: 01225 446 664 Fax: 01225 446 654
Email: peter@carrandangier.co.uk
Web Site: www.carrandangier.co.uk

CHRIS BALDWIN
ACT Consultant Services, 2 The Old Wood Mill, Church Lane, Madingley, Cambridge CB23 8AF
Tel: 01954 210 766
Email: cbaldwin@actconsultantservices.co.uk
Web: www.actconsultantservices.co.uk
Contact: Chris Baldwin
ACT Consultant Services is a multi-disciplinary practice covering arts strategies, business plans and market analysis through to feasibility studies and detailed design development of arts and entertainment buildings to include the visual and performing arts.

MARTIN CARR
Madron, Ostlings Lane, Bathford, Bath, Somerset BA1 7RW
Tel: 01225 859 792 Fax: 01225 852 174
Email: mjcarr@mjcarr.plus.net

RAY CARTER
Next Stage, Judds Farm, Winsor Lane, Winsor, Southampton, Hampshire SO40 2HG
Tel: 023 8081 2011 Fax: 023 8081 2213
Email: ray@nextstage.org.uk

DAVID TAYLOR
Arup 155 Avenue of the Americas New York New York 10013 USA
001 212 897 1411
Email: david.taylor@arup.com

GERBRAND BORGDORFF
HWP Theateradvies bv Herengracht 162
1016 BP Amsterdam Netherlands
0031 20 627 2248
Email: gerbrand@theateradvies.nl

JEREMY GODDEN
Theatre Projects Consultants, 4 Apollo Studios, Charlton Kings Road, London NW5 2SW
Tel: 020 7482 4224 Fax: 020 7284 0636
Email: jg@tpcworld.net
Web Site: www.tpcworld.com

LEONARD GREENWOOD
Theatre Projects Consultants, 4 Apollo Studios, Charlton Kings Road, London NW5 2SW
Tel: 020 7482 4224 Fax: 020 7284 0636
Email: lg@tpcworld.net
Web Site: www.tpcworld.com

MICHAEL HOLDEN
Octagon Business Park, Hospital RoadHospital Road, Little Plumstead, Norwich NR13 5FH
Tel: 01603 721 511 Fax: 01603 721 650
Email: michael@adrianjamesacoustics.co.uk
Web www.adrienjamesacoustics.co.uk
Theatre Consultants, designers of new buildings or the adaption and refurbishment of existing buildings. Management Consultants experienced in the formation of Trusts and other management structures.

IAN ALBERY
Quartiere des Chavrieres 26450 Roynac France
Email: ian@albery.com

JEFF PHILLIPS
8 Essex Close, Morden, Surrey SM4 4NP
020 8337 3004
Email: jeffphillips@blueyonder.co.uk

LOUIS JANSSEN
HWP Theateradvies bv Herengracht 162
1016 BP Amsterdam Netherlands
0031 20 627 2248
Email: louis@theateradvies.nl

LOUIS K. FLEMING
Theatre Projects Consultants L 4 Apollo Studios Charlton Kings Road London NW5 2SW
020 7482 4224
Email: valou@flemex.freeserve.co.uk

IAIN MACKINTOSH
Theatre Projects Consultants L 4 Apollo Studios, Charlton Kings Road, London, NW5 2SW
Tel: 020 7482 4224 Fax: 020 7284 0636
Email: iainmackintosh@talktalk.net
Web Site: www.tpcworld.com

KEITH MCLAREN
Carr & Angier, The Old Malthouse, Clarence Street, Bath, Somerset BA1 5NS
Tel: 01225 446 664 Fax: 01225 446 654
Email: keith@carrandangier.co.uk
Web Site: www.carrandangier.co.uk

ANNE MINORS PERFORMANCE CONSULTANTS LTD
ABTT Chairman Society of Theatre Consultants
Unit 2 St Gerorges Court, 131 Putney Bridge Road, London SW15 2PA
Tel: 020 8877 5860 Fax: 020 8875 9385
Email: anne.minors@ampcstudio.com
Web Site: www.ampcstudio.com
Principal: Anne Minors
Performance consultants to the entertainment industry, whether the performance is a concert, drama, opera or other form of gathering. We specialise in producing facilities that work artistically and operationally as well as being a delight for the audience.

PAUL COVELL
Settlands, Sackmore Lane, Marnhull, Dorset DT10 1PN

Tel/Fax: 01258 820 248 Mobile: 07795 186 329
Email: office@paulcovell.co.uk
Web Site: www.paulcovell.co.uk
Theatre & Lighting Consultant.

PETER RUTHVEN HALL
166a Old South Lambeth Road, London SW8 1XX
020 7735 9966
Email: ruthvenH@aol.com

RICHARD BRETT
Theatreplan Llp 27 Colonnade, London WC1N 1JA
020 7841 0440
Email: richard@theatreplan.net

CHRISTOPHER RICHARDSON
Theatre Futures, Carpenters Mews, North Road, Islington, London N7 9EF
Tel: 020 7700 6877 Fax: 020 7700 7366
Email: nick@cngr.co.uk

ALAN G RUSSELL
Theatre Projects Consultants, 4 Apollo Studios, Charlton Kings Road, London NW5 2SW
Tel: 020 7482 4224 Fax: 020 7284 0636
Email: agr@tpcworld.net
Web Site: www.tpcworld.com

EMMA SAVAGE
Carr and Angier, The Old Malthouse, Clarence Street, Bath, Somerset BA1 5NS
Tel: 01225 446 664 Fax: 01225 446 654
Email: emma@carrandangier.co.uk
Web Site: www.carrandangier.co.uk

DAVID STAPLES
Theatre Projects Consultants, 4 Apollo Studios, Charlton Kings Road, London NW5 2SW
Tel: 020 7482 4224 Fax: 020 7284 0636
Email: dts@tpcworld.net
Web Site: www.tpcworld.com

STEVE ROBERTS
Anne Minors Performance Consu 2 St. George Court Putney Bridge Road London SW15 2PA
01225 446 664
Email: steve.p.roberts@talktalk.net

ANDRE TAMMES
Lighting Design Partnership, The Coach House 16 Jamaica Street Lane North Edinburgh EH3 6HQ
0131 226 2002
Email: andre@ldpi.net

TOM DAVIS
Theatre Projects Consultants L 4 Apollo Studios Charlton Kings Road London NW5 2SW
020 7482 4224
Email: td@tpcworld.net

DAVID WILMORE
Theatresearch, Dacre Hall, Dacre, Harrogate, North Yorkshire HG3 4ET
Tel: 01423 780 497 Fax: 01423781 957
Email: david@theatresearch.co.uk
Web Site: www.theatresearch.co.uk
Practice specialises in the restoration, planning and conservation of historic theatres, especially those design by Frank Matcham. National Lottery applications, Conservation Plans and Feasibility Studies all undertaken.

Arts Councils and Regional Arts Boards

ARTS COUNCIL ENGLAND
14 Great Peter Street, London SW1P 3NQ
Tel: 020 7333 0100 Fax: 020 7973 6590
Email: enquiries@artscouncil.org.uk
Web Site: www.artscouncil.org.uk
Chief Executive: Peter Hewitt
Chairman: Gerry Robinson

ARTS COUNCIL ENGLAND, EAST
Eden House, 48-49 Bateman Street, Cambridge CB2 1LR
Tel: 01223 454 400 Fax: 0870 242 1272
Email: enquiries@artscouncil.org.uk
Web Site: www.artscouncil.org.uk
Chief Executive: Andrea Stark
Chair: Prof Stuart Timperley
Theatre: Alan Orme
Dance: Salette Gresset
We aim to encourage access to the arts and artistic expression for the widest possible range of people. To promote lifelong learning in, through and about the arts. To stimulate excellence and innovation in all aspects of arts activity. To act as an advocate on behalf of the arts. To sustain and stimulate growth in the regions cultural economy. To provide a portfolio of funding services and expertise, placing the Board at the centre of cultural development for the region.

ARTS COUNCIL ENGLAND, EAST MIDLANDS
St Nicholas Court, 25-27 Castle Gate, Nottingham, NG1 7AR
Tel: 0845 300 6200 Fax: 0115 950 2467
Email: fiona.mitchell-innes@artscouncil.org.uk
Web Site: www.arts.org.uk
Chair: Stephen Lowe
East Midlands Arts is one of ten regional Arts Boards that cover the whole of England. The area of benefit includes Derbyshire, Rutland, Leicestershire, Nottinghamshire, Northamptonshire and Lincolnshire serving a population of nearly four million people. The Board represents a wide range of expertise in the arts, management, finance, marketing and local government. Its members work to enhance arts education, develop the cultural industries and promote excellence in artistic endeavour.

ARTS COUNCIL ENGLAND, LONDON
2 Pear Tree Court, London EC1R 0DS
Tel: 020 7608 6100 Fax: 020 7608 4100
Textphone: 020 7608 4101
Email: london@artscouncil.org.uk
Web Site: www.artscouncil.org.uk
Regional Executive Director: Sarah Weir
Director of External & Strategic Relations: Jennifer Edwards
Director of Arts: Greg Hilty
Head of Theatre: Sian Alexander
Arts Council England, London is the London regional office of Arts Council England, the national development agency for the arts in England.
Restrictions:Arts Council England does not give grants to individual students.
Beneficial Area: 32 boroughs of London and the Corporation of London.
Finances: 2002/03
Budget/Expenditure(grants) £60.6m
Type of Beneficiary: Arts organisations, artists, local authoriites, local education authorities.
Submission of applications made to single funding programme - grants for the arts - with no set deadlines. There are general criteria which relate to all applications and include: artistic, strategic and managerial effectiveness, and financial requirements.
Reports: approximately 4 newsletters per annum.

ARTS COUNCIL ENGLAND, NORTH EAST
Central Square, Forth Street, Newcastle-upon-Tyne, NE1 3PJ
Tel: 0191 255 8500 / 8585 Fax: 0191 230 1020
Email: kate.roebuck@artscouncil.org.uk
Web Site: www.artscouncil.org.uk
Regional Executive Director: Mark Robinson
Chair: Tom Shakespeare
Head of Performing Arts: Mark Mulqueen
Performing Arts Officer: Mark Monument
Administrator: Kate Roebuck
Covers Tees Valley, County Durham, Tyne and Wear and Northumberland.
Arts council for England, Northeast principal objective is to promote the arts in the north.
Major Drama includes the RSC's Newcastle residency, the International Season at the Newcastle Playhouse and many specialist festivals. Details of the region's venues and promoters can be

obtained from the Performing Arts Unit. Arts Council for England, Northeast is strongly supportive of indigenous work, supporting a major producing company, Northern Stage, and many small and medium scale touring companies.
In addition, new playwriting is actively supported through New Writing North.

ARTS COUNCIL ENGLAND, SOUTH WEST

Bradninch Place, Gandy Street, Exeter, Devon EX4 3LS
Tel: 01392 218 188 Fax: 01392 413 554
Email: southwest@artscouncil.org.uk
Web Site: www.artscouncil.org.uk
Executive Director: Nick Capaldi
Regional Chair: Prof Alan Livingston
Director of Arts Development: Hilary Garnham
Team Leader Performing Arts: Paul Goddard
Theatre Officer: Kate Dean
The Performing Arts Team is responsible for developing and implementing Arts Council England's theatre policy in the South West. We work in partnership with artists, arts organisations, local authorities, trusts and business sponsors. Key to our aims to develop theatre in the region are 9 locality plans which create an infrastructure for artists to develop their work and provide opportunities to increase capacity for theatre activity across the South West region.
Arts Council invest in theatre activity through two main routes. Regular funding for regionally important arts organisations accounts for a large proportion of our available funds. Grants for the Arts, our scheme for individuals, organisations and national touring provides funding for activities which meet the priorities of the fund, listed in the guidance notes. Information about the scheme can be accessed via our website, www.artscouncil.org.uk or by requesting a pack by calling 0845 300 6100.

ARTS COUNCIL ENGLAND, WEST MIDLANDS

82 Granville Street, Birmingham B1 2LH
Tel: 0845 300 6200 Fax: 0121 643 7239
Email: enquiries@artscouncil.org.uk
Web Site: www.artscouncil.org.uk
Regional Executive Director: Sally Luton

ARTS COUNCIL ENGLAND, YORKSHIRE

21 Bond Street, Dewsbury, West Yorkshire WF13 1AX
Tel: 0845 300 6200 Fax: 01924 466 522
Email: enquiries@artscouncil.org.uk
Web Site: www.artscouncil.org.uk
Regional Executive Director: Andy Carver
Chair: Sir Norman Adsetts, OBE
Team Leader - Finance and Operations: Sally Dowell
Director Of Performing Arts: Ivor Davies
Music Officer: Andrew Herbert
Dance Officer: Jane Marescaux
Visual Arts Officer: Jennifer Hallam
Literature Officer: Jane Stubbs
Visual Arts Officer (media): Emma Cheshire

ARTS COUNCIL OF NORTHERN IRELAND

MacNeice House, 77 Malone Road, Belfast, County Antrim BT9 6AQ Northern Ireland
Tel: 028 9038 5200
Email: reception@artscouncil-ni.org
Web Site: www.artscouncil-ni.org/
Chairperson: Rosemary Kelly
Chief Executive: Roisin McDonough
Arts Development Director: Philip Hammond

ARTS COUNCIL OF WALES

9 Museum Place, Cardiff CF10 3NX Wales
Tel: 029 2037 6500 Fax: 029 2022 1447
Email: info@artswales.org.uk
Web Site: www.artswales.org.uk
Chief Executive: Peter Tyndall
The Arts Council of Wales is the national organisation with specific responsibility for the funding and strategic development of the arts in Wales. Most of its funds come from the National Assembly for Wales but it also receives funds from other sources. Distributes National Lottery funds to the arts in Wales.
For a guide to schemes and grants available please visit the website.

HARINGEY ARTS COUNCIL

The Chocolate Factory, Unit 104 Building B, Clarendon Road, London N22 6XJ
Tel: 020 8365 7500 Fax: 020 8365 8686
Email: info@haringeyartscouncil.org
Development Officer Artforms: Dana Captainino

NORTH CORNWALL ARTS

College Road Camelford Camelford Cornwall PL32 9TL
Tel: 01840 214 220 Fax: 01840 214 221
Email: info@ncarts.org.uk
Web Site: www.ncarts.org.uk
Arts Development Director: Sue Richardson

RENFREWSHIRE ARTS

Paisley Town Hall, Abbey Close, Paisley, Renfrewshire PA1 1JF Scotland
Tel: 0141 887 1007 Fax: 0141 840 1779
Email: arts.els@renfrewshire.gov.uk
Web Site: www.renfrewshire.gov.uk
Paisley Arts Centre and Paisley Town Hall are managed by Renfrewshire Arts, part of Renfrewshire Council's department of Education and Leisure Services. Paisley Arts Centre houses a 158 seat theatre and programmes all year round with drama, dance, comedy and music events. Paisley Arts Centre also has a workshop space available for hire. Paisley Town Hall is a magnificent Victorian building which programmes large scale music events and is available to hire for weddings, conferences, meetings and social events. Renfrewshire Council also has numerous other community halls available for hire.

THE SCOTTISH ARTS COUNCIL

12 Manor Place, Edinburgh, EH3 7DD Scotland
Tel: 0131 226 6051 Fax: 0131 225 9833
Email: help.desk@scottisharts.org.uk
Web Site: www.scottisharts.org.uk
The Scottish Arts Council is the main arts development agency in Scotland and distributes funds from the Scottish Executive and National Lottery to develop the arts in Scotland.

SOUTH EAST ARTS

Union House, Eridge Road, Tunbridge Wells, Kent TN4 8HF
Tel: 01892 515 210 Fax: 01892 549 383
Email: info@seab.co.uk
Web Site: www.arts.org.uk
Chief Executive: Felicity Harvest
Acting Chairs: Joan White, Neil Chapman
Director of Visual and Media Arts: Michael Craven
Director of Performing Arts: Dermot O'Brien
Director of Strategy & External Affairs: Debra Reay
Director of Resources: Clive Russell
Research and Information Officer: Jill Hogan
Drama Officer: Judith Hibberd
South East Arts (SEA) is the regional arts development agency for Kent, Surrey, East Sussex, West Sussex and the unitary authorities of Brighton & Hove and Medway.
We are one of ten regional arts boards in England and part of the national arts funding system working closely with the Arts Council of England.
SEA is a company limited by guarantee and a registered charity; managed by a board of 18 members drawn from the arts community, business sector and local authorities. SEA has 42 staff members consisting of senior management, specialist artform and non artform officers and administrators.
SEA,s mission is to develop, support, lobby for and promote the arts of the highest quality and widest range for the benefit of people living, working, being educated in or visiting the south east of England. We offer funding, advice, information and other services and collaborate with a range of strategic partners throughout the region.

SOUTHERN ARTS

13 St Clement Street, Winchester, Hampshire SO23 9DQ
Tel: 01962 855 099 Fax: 01962 861 186

Email: info@southernarts.co.uk
Web Site: www.arts.org.uk
Chief Executive: Robert Hutchinson
Chair: David Astor CBE
Theatre Officer: Nicolas Young
Southern Arts is the arts development agency for Berkshire, Buckinghamshire, Hampshire, Isle of Wight, Oxfordshire, Wiltshire and South East Dorset. It works in partnership with local authorities and other regional agencies and aims to place the arts at the heart of the region's cultural, social, economic and educational life.

National Tourist Boards

CUMBRIA TOURIST BOARD
Ashleigh, Holly Road, Windermere,
Cumbria LA23 2AQ
Tel: 015394 44444 Fax: 015394 44041
Email: info@golakes.co.uk
Web Site: www.golakes.co.uk
Also www.cumbriatourism.info

EAST OF ENGLAND TOURIST BOARD
Toppesfield Hall, Hadleigh,
Suffolk IP7 5DN
Tel: 0870 225 4800 Fax: 0870 225 4890
Email: information@eetb.org.uk
Web Site: www.eastofenglandtourist-board.com

GREATER GLASGOW & CLYDE VALLEY TOURIST BOARD
11 George Square, Glasgow,
Strathclyde G2 1DY
Tel: 0141 566 4030 Fax: 0141 248 9541
Email: conventions@seeglasgow.com
Web Site: www.seeglasgow.com
Contact: Molly Doheny

HEART OF ENGLAND TOURISM
Larkhill Road, Worcester,
Worcestershire WR5 2EZ
Tel: 01905 761 100 Fax: 01905 763 450
Email: jenny.redfern@visitheartofengland.com
Web Site: www.visitheartofengland.com

ISLE OF MAN DEPARTMENT OF TOURISM & LEISURE
Sea Terminal Buildings, Douglas,
Isle of Man IM1 2RG
Tel: 01624 686 801 (General Enquiries)
Tel: 01624 686 868 (Brochure Line)
Tourist Information: 01624 686 766
Email: tourism@gov.im
Web Site: www.gov.im/tourism

JERSEY TOURISM VISITOR SERVICES CENTRE
Liberation Square, St Helier, Jersey JE1 1BB Channel Islands
Tel: 01534 500 700 / 777 / 888
Fax: 01534 500 808
Email: info@jersey.com
Web Site: www.jersey.com
Experienced Information & Reservations Officers available throughout the year to assist you in any enquiry you have.

VISIT LONDON
6th Floor 2 More London Riverside,
London SE1 2RR
Admin tel: 020 7234 5800 General Info: 0207 428 3689
Email: zadams@visitlondon.com
Web Site: www.visitlondon.com
Contact UK sales manager: Zanine Adams

NORTHERN IRELAND TOURIST BOARD
St.Anne's Court, 59 North Street, Belfast, County Antrim BT1 1NB Northern Ireland
Tel: 028 9023 1221 Fax: 028 9024 0960
London Contact: Tourism Ireland, 150 New Bond Street, London, W1S 2AQ Tel: 020 7581 0800, fax: 020 7493 9065
Email: info@nitb.com
Web: wwwdiscovernorthernireland.com

NORTHUMBRIA TOURIST BOARD
1 Northeast, The Tourism Team, Stella House, Goldcrest Way, Newburn Riverside Newcastle-Upon-Tyne NE15 8NY
Tel: 0191 229 6200 Fax: 0191 229 6201
Email: enquiries@ntb.org.uk
Web Site: www.visitnorthumbria.com

SOUTH EAST ENGLAND TOURIST BOARD
The Old Brew House, Warwick Park,
Tunbridge Wells, Kent TN2 5TU
Tel: 01892 540 766 Fax: 01892 511 008
Email: enquiries@seetb.org.uk
Web Site: www.southeastengland.uk.com

SOUTH WEST TOURISM
Woodwater Park, Pynes Hill, Rydon Lane,
Exeter, Devon EX2 5WT
Tel: 0870 442 0830 Fax: 0870 442 0840
Email: ldale@swtourism.co.uk
Public Relations Manager: Liz Dale
Marketing Manager: Kirsty Cumming
Contact details:
kcumming@swtourism.co.uk

TOURISM SOUTH EAST
40 Chamberlayne Road, Eastleigh,
Hampshire SO50 5JH
Tel: 023 8062 5400 Fax: 023 8062 0010
Email: enquiries@tourismse.com
Web Site: www.tourismsouthest.com

VISIT BRITAIN
Thames Tower, Black's Road, London
W6 9EL
Tel: 020 8846 9000 Fax: 020 8563 0302
Email: seren.welch@visitbritain.org
Web Site: www.visitbritain.com
Chief Exec: Tom Wright
Marketing Manager: Seren Welch

VISIT WALES
Brunel House, 2 Fitzalan Road, Cardiff,
South Glamorgan CF24 0UY Wales
Tel: 029 2049 9909 Fax: 029 2048 5031
Email: info@visitwales.com
Web Site: www.visitwales.com
London Office: WIB Visitor Centre C/o MWB Business Exchange, 78 Cannon Street, London EC4N 6NQ. Tel: 020 7222 8097

VISITSCOTLAND
23 Ravelston Terrace, Edinburgh,
Scotland EH4 3TP Scotland
Tel: 0131 332 2433 Fax: 0131 343 1513
London Office: 19 Cockspur Street,
London SW1Y 5BL Fax: 020 7930 1817
Email: info@visitscotland.com
Web Site: www.visitscotland.com

YORKSHIRE TOURIST BOARD
312 Tadcaster Road, York, North
Yorkshire YO24 1GS
Tel: 01904 707 961 Fax: 01904 701 414
Email: info@ytb.org.uk
Web Site: www.yorkshiretouristboard.net

SUPPLIERS & SERVICES

Access Equipment

ALUMINIUM ACCESS PRODUCTS LTD
Unit 8, Acorn Business Centre, Acorn Court, Butts Street, Leigh, Lancashire WN7 3DD
Tel: 01942 514 318 Mob: 07811 450417
Fax: 01942 518 979
Email: info@tallescope.co.uk
Web Site: www.tallescope.co.uk
Contact: Frank Partington, Robert Deakin

FLINT HIRE & SUPPLY LTD
Theatrical Chandlers
Queen's Row, London SE17 2PX
Tel: 020 7703 9786 Sales Fax: 020 7708 4189
Email: sales@flints.co.uk
Web Site: www.flints.co.uk
Contacts: Josefin Söderlund, Alasdair Flint, Richard Black
Flints are the major retailer of theatrical goods in the UK, established 25 years ago to provide a single source for specialist theatre hardware and materials.
Sales and Hire of Zarges ladders, Megadek Staging and Access Towers.
Scenery building hardware and scenic paints also supplied.

RMD KWIKFORM
Brickyard Road, Walsall, West Midlands WS9 8BW
Tel: 01922 743 743 Fax: 01922 743 693
Email: info@rmdkwikform.com
Web Site: www.rmdkwikform.com

UPRIGHT UK LTD
Unit F1 Halesfield 4, Telford, Shropshire TF7 4AP
Tel: 01952 872721 Fax: 01952 685255
Email: rmunn@upighteuro.com
Web Site: www.upright.co.uk
Instant Zip-Up are one of the leading access specialists in the UK, with over 40 years of experience. The Instant Tallescope aluminium work platform is one of a range of access products extensively used in theatres throughout the country.
Contact UK Customer Services Administrator: Rachel Munn

ZARGES UK
Formerly 'Light Alloy Ltd'
8 Holdom Avenue, Bletchley, Milton Keynes MK1 1QU
Tel: 01908 641 118 Fax: 01908 648 176
Email: sales@zarges.co.uk
Web Site: www.zarges.co.uk
Sales Administrator: Olive Baldry
Aluminium alloy containers and trolleys for storage and transport, widest range of access equipment in the UK.

Accountancy & Financial Services

BOWKER ORFORD
15-19 Cavendish Place, London W1G 0DD
Tel: 020 7636 6391 Fax: 020 7580 3909
Email: mail@bowkerorford.com
Web Site: www.bowkerorford.com
Contact: Rashpal Parmar

BREBNERS
130 Shaftesbury Avenue London W1D 5AR
Tel: 020 7734 2244 Fax: 020 7287 5315
Email: jose.goumal@brebners.com, partners@brebners.com
Web Site: www.brebners.co.uk
Simon Cryer, Jose Goumal and Michael Burton are the contacts for our Media related services. These cover all aspects of financial and taxation advice and support both at production and individual level.

BRECKMAN & COMPANY
49 South Molton Street, London W1K 5LH
Tel: 020 7499 2292 Fax: 020 7408 1151
Email: info@breckmanandcompany.co.uk
Web Site: www.breckmanandcompany.co.uk
Chartered Certified Accountants: Graham Berry, Richard Nelson, Kevin Beale, Robert Breckman
Specialists in the Arts & Entertainment industry with over 40 years experience.
We act for Freelancers, Limited Companies and charities.

DALES EVANS & CO LTD
(Chartered Accountants)
88-90 Baker Street, London W1U 6TQ
Tel: 020 7298 1899 Fax: 020 7298 1871
Email: reception@dalesevans.co.uk
Directors: Lester Dales, Paul Makin

DELOITTE & TOUCHE LLP
Hill House, 1 Little New Street, London EC4A 3TR
Tel: 020 7936 3000 Fax: 020 75831198
Web Site: www.deloitte.co.uk
Taxation and accounting services. We have wide experience of West End and overseas theatrical productions, international licencing, VAT and witholding tax planning.

GOODMAN JONES
29-30 Fitzroy Square, London W1T 6LQ
Tel: 020 7388 2444 Fax: 020 7388 6736
Email: info@goodmanjones.com
Web Site: www.goodmanjones.co.uk
Contact: Julian Flitter

KINGSTON SMITH W1
141 Wardour Street, London W1F 0UT
Switchboard: 020 7304 4646 Fax: 020 7304 4647
Email: ci@kingstonsmith.co.uk
Web Site: www.kingstonsmith.co.uk
Contact: Cliff Ireton

MARTIN GREENE RAVDEN
55 Loudoun Road, St John's Wood, London NW8 0DL
Tel: 020 7625 4545 Fax: 020 7625 5265
Email: mgr@mgr.co.uk
Web Site: www.mgr.co.uk
ATF Group Managing Director: Alan Marks
Business Planning and Tax Services Director: Paul Simnock
Chartered Accountants and Business Managers - Audit, Accountancy and Tax Compliance, Business Management, Tour Accounting, Withholding Tax Clearances, Royalty Examinations, Litigation Support.

NYMAN LIBSON PAUL
Regina House, 124 Finchley Road, London NW3 5JS
Tel: 020 7433 2400 Fax: 020 7433 2401
Buckinghamshire Office: Room 107 Pinewood Studios, Pinewood Road, Iver Heath, Buckinghamshire, SL0 0NH Tel: 01753 656428
Email: mail@nlpca.co.uk
Web Site: www.nlpca.co.uk
Contact: Paul Taiano
Established for over 78 years with specialist knowledge of the Theatre and Entertainment industries, providing accountancy, audit, and taxation services for companies and individuals. Specialist tax services for UK and overseas clients.

PRO ACTIVE RESOLUTIONS
Forester Building 29-35 Saint Nicholas Place Leicester LE1 4LD
Tel: 0116 224 7122
Email: arts@proactiveresolutions.com
Web Site: www.proactiveresolutions.com
Contact: Mahmood Reza
Accounting, tax and financial services specifically for the arts sector.

Advisory Services

ANIMAL FREE ADVISORY SERVICE
Member of Animal Welfare Filming Federation
28 Greeves Road, High Wycombe, Buckinghamshire HP13 7JU
Mob: 07956 564715
Email: animalswork1@yahoo.co.uk
Web Site: www.animalswork.co.uk
Manager: Trevor Smith
Senior Personnel: Graham Johnson
Provides advisory service to production companies on the usage of animals, covering safety and legal requirements, whilst ensuring their safety and protection from harm.

Animal Hire

AMAZING ANIMALS
(Heythrop Zoological Gardens Ltd)
Church Hill, Wilmington, Dartford, Kent DA2 7DZ
Tel: 01322 626 309 (HO) Fax: 01322 289 932 Training Quarters: 01608 683 389
Training Quarters Address: Heythrop, Chipping Norton, Oxon OX7 5TU
Email: jclubb@amazinganimals.co.uk
Web Site: www.amazinganimals.co.uk
Contact: Kath Brown

ANIMAL AMBASSADORS
Old Forest, Hampstead Norreys Road, Hermitage, Berkshire RG18 9SA
Tel/Fax: 01635 200 900 Mob: 07831 558 594
Email: info@animalambassadors.co.uk
Web: www.animalambassadors.co.uk
Senior Personnel: Kay Weston
Specialises in the Supply and Training of Animals for Film and Television.

ANIMAL WORLD
Member of Animal Welfare Filming Federation
28 Greaves Road, High Wycombe, Buckinghamshire HP13 7JU
Mobile: 07956 564715
Email: animalswork1@yahoo.co.uk
Web Site: www.animalswork.co.uk
Senior Personnel: Trevor Smith (07956 564715)
Established in1973. Specialising in providing animals to the entertainment industry, while ensuring their safety and protection from harm. Famous Animals who star on TV and in Films.

ANIMALS GALORE
208 Smallfield Road, Horley, Surrey RH6 9LS
Tel: 01342 842 400 Fax: 01342 841 546
Email: info@animals-galore.co.uk
Web Site: www.animals-galore.co.uk
Contact: Mrs Cindy Newman
Suppliers of animals for Theatre, Films, Television, Still Photgraphy, etc.

Architects

ALL CLEAR DESIGNS LTD
3 Devonshire Mews, London W4 2HA
Tel: 020 8400 5093 Fax: 020 8400 5094
Email: mail@allclear.co.uk
Web Site: www.allclear.co.uk
Director: James Holmes-Siedle
Specialists in making buildings accessible for disabled people. Architectural services include access audits, feasibility studies and construction. Experience with theatres and listed buildings. Assistance with advice with funding included.

TIM BENTON ARCHITECTS
33 Northgate, Sleaford, Lincolnshire NG34 7BX
Tel/Fax: 01529 304 524
Email: tim_benton@btopenworld.com
Unravel the mysteries of Building for the Arts by contacting Tim Benton Architects of Sleaford, Lincolnshire, who normally make no charge for an initial visit. They offer a nationwide, prompt, proficient, pertinent and personal service.

BURRELL FOLEY FISCHER
Isis House 67-69 Southwark Street London SE1 0HX
Tel: 020 7620 6114
Email: mail@bff-architects.co.uk
Web Site: www.bff-architects.co.uk
Contact: Mark Foley
Burrell Foley Fischer have some 24 years experience of designing specialist facilities for a wide range of arts organisations ranging from small fringe venues through to major theatres, concert halls and opera houses in the U.K. and abroad.
Our experience also includes cinema and educational and training facilities, media centres and gallery design. Through the other work of the practice we are also able to offer advice on the design of ancillary facilities and Urban Design expertise where the project is of a greater size, scope and complexity.
As well as advising small scale venues, our past and current clients include many of the major national and international performing companies and organisations including the Almeida Theatre, The Riverside Studios, The Royal Ballet, South Bank Arts Centre. The Sports Council, and The Arts Council of England. We can offer specialist advice on the design of dance facilities.

CREFFIELDS (TIMBER & BOARDS) LTD
Flameproof boards.
Unit 6, Marcus Close, Tilehurst, Reading, Berkshire RG30 4EA
Tel: 0118 945 3533 Fax: 0118 945 3633
Email: info@creffields.co.uk
Web Site: www.creffields.co.uk
Creffields is one of the UK's leading suppliers of
flame-proofed sheet materials and soft woods for the
exhibition and theatrical trades.
Large stocks are held allowing for urgent orders to be delivered promptly; together with Premierbond portable contact spray glue system.

JOHN ROWE-PARR, ARCHITECTS
The Studio, Partingdale Lodge, Partingdale Lane, London NW7 1NS
Tel: 07710 477 899
Email: john@johnroweparr.co.uk
Web Site: www.johnroweparr.co.uk
Our professional expertise has been well established over 15 years and we are now the leading consultancy practice specialising in the restoration of historic and new theatres throughout the UK, including important London venues.
Working exclusively on demanding and tight program management projects we provide skills beyond the normal role of architectural design including site feasability studies and lottery funding applications.

Aroma Effects

DALE AIR LTD
Anglo Brands Ltd, Bridge End Mills, Tong Lane, Whitworth, Rochdale OL12 8BG
Tel: 0845 305 8468 Fax: 01706 853 625
Email: info@daleair.com
Web Site: www.daleair.com
Dale Air Ltd has provided themed aromas for over 20 years.

Bill Posters & Hoarding Sites

ADSHEL LTD
33 Golden Square, London W1R 3PA
Tel: 020 7478 2200
Email: jennifer.claytonsmith@clearchannel.co.uk
Web Site: www.adshel.com

EYE AIRPORTS
Ivy Mill, Crown Street, Failsworth M35 9BG
Tel: 0161 219 7708
Email: mikecleary@eyeairports.com
Web Site: www.eyeairports.com
Contact: Mike Cleary

TITAN OUTDOOR
Formerly known as Maiden Outdoor
128 Buckingham Palace Road, London SW1W 9SA
Tel: 020 7838 4000 Fax: 020 7838 4002
Liverpool Office: Churchill House, Tithebarn Street, Liverpool L2 2PJ Tel: 0151 236 5353 Fax: 0151 236 0123
Email: fergus.calder@titanoutdoor.co.uk

Box Office Services & Ticket Agents

ABBEY BOX OFFICE LTD
Suite 8.21, 64 Victoria Street, London SW1E 6QP
Tel: 020 7798 9200 Covent Garden Office: 30 Jubilee Market, Covent Garden, WC2E 8BE Tel: 020 7240 3400
Email: info@abbey-leisure.co.uk
Web Site: www.abbeyboxoffice.co.uk

ALUSET SECURITY TICKETS
2-6 Brookvale Road, Langley Mill, Nottingham NG16 4AX
Tel: 01773 769 317 Fax: 01773 716 206
Email: steve@aluset.com
Web Site: www.aluset.com
Contact: Steve Thomas
As the leading ticket printer, Aluset supply a complete range of tickets from simple continuous stationery to highly secure stadium tickets. Our thermal tickets are used successfully in all types of printers including BOCA, Gazelle, TOR, Star. We believe our quality will improve your image.

ARTIFAX
17A West Street, Epsom, Surrey KT18 7RL
Tel: 01372 587 587
Email: admin@artifax.net
Web Site: www.artifax.net
Directors: Sarah Verge
With a commitment to the cultural community for over 20 years, Artifax is a leading provider of management solutions designed to meet the unique requirements of cultural venues, organisations and the people who run them. Our flagship software, Artifax Event, is a schedule and event management system that handles all aspects of space-related bookings and tour scheduling. Visit www.artifax.net for more details.

BEMROSEBOOTH
Stockholm Road, Hull HU7 0XY
Tel: 01482 826 343
Email: info@bemrosebooth.com
Web Site: www.bemrosebooth.com
For all your ticketing solutions contact BemroseBooth, manufacturers of all thermal tickets variants (Boca, Databox, Zebra etc), roll tickets, and swipe cards.

ENTA TICKETING SOLUTIONS LTD
9 Bonhill Street, London EC2A 4PE
Tel: 020 7448 5900
Email: sales@enta.com
Web Site: www.enta.com
Managing Director: John Gibson
ENTA is a ticketing and marketing software that runs in all Windows environments including XP. The product is developed to satisfy the needs of arts and leisure organisations requiring a sophisticated solution delivered to the highest possible standards.

GROUP LINE
37 Firrst Floor, Long Acre, Covent Garden, London WC2E 9JT
Tel: 020 7420 9700
Email: enquiries@groupline.com
Web Site: www.groupline.com
Come to us first for all your West End Theatre trips, we are the official group sales organisation for London's biggest hits. A completely free service providing group reductions, advice and sale or return payment scheme. No booking fees.

JUST TICKETS
Jim Birney is also Secretary of the Theatrical Traders Association (TTA)
23 Wood Lane Sonning Common Near Reading Berkshire RG4 9SJ
Tel: 0845 126 0631 (Jim Birney) Fax: 0845 833 0646
Email: sales@just-tkts.com
Web Site: www.just-tkts.com
Managing Partner: Jim Birney
Computer text & laser printed tickets. General admission and reserved tickets for all professional and leisure events & venues. Vertical & Horizontal tickets available up to 1/3rd A4 size. Quick, easy and inexpensive. Roll and Draw/Lottery tickets also available.
Box Office Systems stationary supplier. Price list, sample tickets and order forms available.

KALAMAZOO SECURITY PRINT
Unit 1, Arrow Valley, Claybrook Drive, Redditch, Worcestershire B98 0FY
Tel: 08445 766 770 Fax: 08445 766 886
Email: kalamazoo@ksp.co.uk
Web Site: www.kalamazoosecure.co.uk
Contact: Julian Coghlan
Pre-printed tickets, souvenir tickets, thermal tickets and gift vouchers are just some of the products available from Kalamazoo. All of our products can be personalised to meet customer needs and our thermal tickets are compatible with all types of printers.

KEITH PROWSE TICKETING
Formerly known as First Call Ticketing
Seatem House, 39 Moreland Street, London EC1V 8BB
Tel: 0870 840 1111
Email: queries@keithprowse.com
Web Site: www.keithprowse.com
Keith Prowse Ticketing leading supplier of Theatre, Sport, Concerts, Events and Attraction tickets. With a 24 hour credit card telephone booking service Keith Prowse Ticketing offers the widest variety of entertainment and a service second to none.

LASHMARS THEATRE TICKETS
First Floor, 37 Long Acre, Covent Garden, London WC2E 9JT
Tel: 0800 912 6966 Fax: 020 7240 5248
Email: enquiries@lashmars.com
Web Site: www.lashmars.com
All major credit cards accepted.
Mon/Sat 9.30 a.m - 7 p.m

LONDONTHEATREBOOKINGS.COM
1 Cranbourn Alley London WC2H 7AW
Tel: 020 7851 0300 Fax: 020 7494 0267
Email: groups@londontheatrebookings.com
Web www.londontheatrebookings.com
Contact: Ryan Woods
Open Mon/Sat 9 a.m. - 7 p.m.

THE METRIC GROUP LTD
Metric House, Westmead Industrial Estate, Westlea, Swindon SN5 7AD
Tel: 01793 647800 Fax: 01793 647802
Email: sales@metricgroup.co.uk
Web Site: www.metricgroup.co.uk
Sales Manager: Richard Boultbee
Design, Manufacture, Supply, Installation, Commissioning and Maintenance of mechanical and electronically controlled Ticket Issuing Machines for fixed applications (such as car parks) and mobile applications (such as public service vehicles)

PAC3000 LTD
Lawrence House, Magdalen Street, Eye, Suffolk IP23 7AJ
Tel: 01379 872 710 Fax: 01379 872 717
Email: mail@pac3000.com
Web Site: www.pac3000.com
Contact: Steven Johnstone
PAC provides courier products, wristbands and promotional products.

PCF PRINT MANAGEMENT LTD
Oak House, Langstone Business Village, Langstone Park, Langstone, Newport, Gwent NP18 2LH Wales
Tel: 01633 415 570 Fax: 01633 415 599
Email: info@pcf.co.uk
Web Site: www.pcf.co.uk
Sales Manager and Director: Ian Hoare
PCF!tickets are ticket suppliers for all software box office ticketing systems, includ-

ing; tickets.com dataculture, BOCA, CATS, etc, etc,...
PCF will help you with all your needs - tickets, ticket holders, envelopes & labels, membership and reward cards, as well as letterheads, complimentary slips and business cards.

PERFORMANCE TICKET PRINTERS LTD
The Smithy, Brownlow Heath, Congleton, Cheshire CW12 4TJ
Tel: 01260 276 164 Fax: 01260 270 984
Email: mailbox@ticketprinters.co.uk
Web Site: www.ticketprinters.co.uk
Directors: John Arnold, Joan Arnold
Contacts: Austin Pickles, Ruth Heasman
Computer printed Theatre Tickets. Quick, easy and inexpensive.

PIRAN PRINT LTD
Unit 1, Southgate Technology Park, Pennygillam Way, Launceston, Cornwall PL15 7ED
Tel: 08450 617 181
Email: enquiries@piranprint.com
Web Site: www.piranprint.com
Contact: Nigel Schofield
Security ticket printers, stock sizes, colours, logos, reserved, numbered; Try Us! Hologram and foil also available for added security.

PREMIER ROLLS (SOUTH) LTD
Stewart Close, Eccleshill, Bradford, West Yorkshire BD2 2EE
Tel: 0845 222 9000 Fax: 01274 633 203
Email: south@premrolls.co.uk
Web Site: www.premierrollssouth.com
Contact: John Melville Gibbs, Alex Day

SEE TICKETS
The Hollows, St. James's Street, Nottingham NG1 6FJ
Sales Tel: 0870 264 3333 Tel: 0115 912 9000 (Martin Brown) Fax: 0115 948 4345
London Tel: 0207 4945 019 London Sales Tel: 0207 850 8537 London Marketing Tel: 0207 850 8114 0115 912 9105
Email: rebecca.macleary@seetickets.com
Web Site: www.seetickets.com
Contact Marketing Sales Co-ordinator: Rebecca Macleary

STARGREEN BOX OFFICE
20/21A Argyll Street, London W1F 7TT
Tel: 020 7734 8932 Fax: 020 7734 8006
Email: debbiestargreen@btlick.com
Web Site: www.stargreen.com
Contact Sales Manager: Debbie

THE TICKET BANK
The Old SchoolHouse, Hinguar Street, Shoeburyness, Southend-on-Sea SS3 9AN
Tel: 01702 306 293 Fax: 07802 271 757
Email: info@ticketbankonline.com
Web Site: www.ticketbank.co.uk
Senior Personnel: Steve Davis
We specialising in on-line booking.

TICKET ZONE
3 Barum Gate, Barnstaple, Devon EX32 8QD
Tel: 01271 323 355 Fax: 01271 375 902
Email: customerservices@ticketzone.co.uk
Web Site: www.ticketzone.co.uk
With more than 25 years ticketing history, we offer a wide range of "back office" ticket sales support services for all styles of events and venues. Uniquely Ticket Zone can also seamlessly interface with your core box office software to sell straight from your inventory, supporting you brand values and securing your customer data. Clients include leading Football Clubs, Pop and Comedy Promoters, plus major Arts Venues.

TICKETLINE (UK) LTD
47 Westgate Street, Cardiff, South Glamorgan CF10 1TL Wales
Tel: 029 2023 0130 Fax: 029 2023 0196
Email: admin@ticketlineuk.com
Web Site: www.ticketlineuk.com
Pop Concert and Theatre Ticket Agency and Concert Promoter.

TICKETMASTER UK LIMITED
4 Pentonville Road, London N1 9HF
Tel: 020 7344 4000 (Reception)
Bookings: 0844 844 0444
Fax: 020 7915 0411
Email: sales@ticketmaster.co.uk
Web Site: www.ticketmaster.co.uk
General Manager: Chris Edmonds
As the world's leading live entertainment ticketing and marketing company, Ticketmaster currently serves more than 10,000 clients worldwide across multiple event categories, providing exclusive ticketing services for leading arenas, stadiums, professional sports teams and leagues, performing arts venues, museums, and theatres. Ticketmaster provides ticketing solutions, marketing and distribution through a number of channels including www.ticketmaster.co.uk in the UK and LiveNationEntertainment.com, one of the largest e-commerce sites on the web.

TICKETS.COM LTD
252 Upper Third Street, Milton Keynes MK9 1NP
Tel: 01908 232 404 Fax: 01908 232 414
Email: uksales@tickets.com
Web Site: www.tickets.com/provenue
Managing Director: Derek Palmer
Tickets.com solutions are now used by over 500 organisations across the UK and Ireland. We provide venues with a variety of ticketing options including: Internet, call centre and collection kiosks. All solutions offer ticketing, marketing, venue management and CRM functionality.

TICKETSOLVE
GEC, Taylor's Lane, Dublin 8
Tel: +353 (0)1 524 0954/ 01865 987 667
London Office: 600 Commercial Road, London, E14 7LB.
Email: pfadden@ticketsolve.com
Web Site: www.ticketsolve.com
Managing Director: Paul Fadden
TicketSolve is the best value complete CRM ticketing solution managing Box office, Online, agent and phone sales.

WEST END THEATRE BOOKINGS LTD
c/o E-Commerce, Encore Tickets, Barnard's Inn, 86 Fetter Lane, London EC4A 1EN
Tel: 020 7492 9969
Email: customerservices@encoretickets.co.uk
Web: www.westendtheatrebookings.com
Director of Operations: Linda Svensson
West End Theatre Bookings is one of London's leading ticket agencies and a member of Star. We specialise in all West End theatre tickets plus theatre breaks & group bookings.

WORLD TICKETING SYSTEMS LTD
York House, Empire Way, Wembley, Middlesex HA9 0QL
Tel: 07031 15 99 62
Fax: 07031 15 99 69
Email: info@worldticketingsystems.com
Web: www.worldticketingsystems.com
A stable and robust product used around the world, it was originally developed 21 years ago for use at the Wembley complex. The system was produced by an independent software company with extensive experience in both agency and venue ticketing.
Although World Ticketing Systems is the system of choice for large and multi-site venues, smaller, independent venues can also benefit from this cost-effective, managed service. The clear and effective interface allows accurate and fast sales with little training.

Car & Coach Hire

AMERICAN STRETCH LIMOUSINES
Holmlea, Town Street, South Killingholme, Immingham North Lincolnshire DN40 3DA
Tel: 01472 345 233 Mob: 07932 633227
Email: enquiry@americanstretchlimo.co.uk
Web: www.americanstretchlimo.co.uk
American stretched limousine hire and chauffeur drive.
4 Limos.

BM COACHES
BM House, Silverdale Road, Hayes,

Middlesex UB3 3BH
Tel: 0208 848 7711 Fax: 0208 848 7722
Email: info@bmcoaches.co.uk
Web Site: www.bmcoaches.co.uk

CAREY WORLDWIDE CHAUFFERED SERVICES
Commerce Road, Brentford, Middlesex
TW8 8LH
Tel: 020 8326 7600
Email: reservations.uk@carey.com/
sales@careyuk.com
Web Site: www.careyuk.com
Carey Worldwide Chauffered Services provide high quality late model vehicles and professional chauffeurs in 480 cities and 75 countries.

LANCASTER CARS
Cardiff House, Tilling Road,
London NW2 1LJ
Tel: 020 8452 1122 Fax: 020 7183 3335
Email: info@lancastercars.co.uk
Web Site: www.lancastercars.co.uk
24/7 service for the supply of saloon and estate cars, MPVs, small and large vans, same-day courier service.

LIMCO EXECUTIVE LIMOUSINE SERVICE
Birch Farm, White Stubbs Lane,
Broxbourne, Hertfordshire EN10 7QA
Tel: 01992 479 555
Email: limco@btconnect.com
The UK's finest American Stretched Limousine Company. Luxurious Limousines for any occasion/event. Fully experienced in film and television work; corporate hospitality etc. Highly professional service.

STARDES LTD
Ashes Buildings, Old Lane, Holbrook
Industrial Estate, Halfway,
Sheffield S20 3GZ
Tel: 0114 251 0051 Fax: 0114 251 0555
Email: dhs@stardes.co.uk
Web Site: www.stardes.co.uk
Contact: Sue or David Steinberg
Executive Car and Minibus, Truck and Van Rental, Concert Tour Transportation, Walk ramps. Transportation Consultants.

TRISTAR CARS LIMITED
Units 1 & 2, Hortam Road, West Drayton
Middlesex UB7 8BQ
Tel: 01895 432 001 Fax: 01895 432 095
Events: 01895 432 121
Events Fax: 01895 432 090
Email: events@tristarworldwide.com
Web Site: www.tristarworldwide.com
CEO: Dean De Beer

WHEALS FAR-GO
Unit 5, 13-15 Sunbeam Road, London
NW10 6JP
Tel: 020 8965 4600 / 8200 Fax: 020 8965 0699
Email: wfg@whealsfargo.com
Web Site: www.whealsfargo.com

WRIGHT BROS (COACHES) LTD
Central Garage, Nenthead, Alston,
Cumbria CA9 3NP
Tel: 01434 381 200 Fax: 01434 382 089
Email: info@wrightbros.co.uk
Web Site: www.wrightbros.co.uk
Contact: Gary Wright

Y-NOT TOURING SERVICES CO
37 Friars Street, Sudbury, Suffolk CO10 2AG
Tel: 01787 312 405 Mob: 07831 173 351
Email: ynottsc@aol.com
Web Site: www.y-nottouring.com
Contact: Antony Moule

Casting

BOSS CASTING
Fourways House, 57 Hilton Street,
Manchester M1 2EJ
Tel: 0161 237 0101 Fax: 0161 236 1237
Email: info@bosscasting.co.uk
Web Site: www.bosscasting.co.uk
Contacts: Debra Burns, Cath Ashworth, Michelle Davenport
Casting Agency for TV, Films and theatre.

FACADE
43a Garthorne Road, London SE23 1EP
Tel: 020 8291 7079
Email: facade@cobomedia.com
Managing Partner: Richard Andrews
Creation, promotion and production of new musicals. Casting, Budgeting and General Management services.

HUBBARD CASTING
14 Rathbone Place, London W1T 1HT
Tel: 0207 631 4944 Fax: 0207 636 7117
Email: info@hubbardcasting.com
Web Site: www.hubbardcasting.com
London Contact: Ros & John Hubbard

THE NARROW ROAD COMPANY LTD
2nd Floor, Grampian House 144
Deansgate, Manchester M3 3EE
Tel/Fax: 0161 833 1605
Email: manchester@narrowroad.co.uk
Web Site: www.narrowroad.co.uk
Director: Elizabeth Stocking

SANDRA SINGER ASSOCIATES
21 Cotswold Road, Westcliff-on-Sea,
Essex SS0 8AA
Tel: 01702 331 616 Fax: 01702 339 393
Email: sandrasingeruk@aol.com
Web Site: www.sandrasinger.com
Senior Personnel: Sandra Singer
Film, TV, Musical Theatre Specialists, for adults and children. Specialist entertainment for Film & TV, Magic etc. Also represents composers and choreographers

ANNE VOSSER CASTING
156 Lower Farnham Road, Aldershot,
Hampshire GU12 4EL
Tel: 01252 404 716 Mob: 07968 868 712
Email: anne@vosser-casting.co.uk
Web Site: www.vosser-casting.co.uk

Catering & Confectionery

3663
Buckingham Court, Kingsmead Business Park, London Road, High Wycombe
HP11 1JU
Tel: 0370 3663 100 Fax: 0370 3663 199
Web Site: www.3663.co.uk
Event Organiser: Michael Johns

CENTERPLATE
Mitchell House, Town Road, Hanley,
Stoke-on-Trent, Staffordshire ST1 2QA
Tel: 01782 222 000 Fax: 01782 222 099
Email: enquiries@centerplate.co.uk
Web Site: www.thelindleygroup.com
PR and Press: Shirley Braithwaite
Provision of catering and licensed bars within theatres, leisure and sporting venues for public, executive and corporate hospitality.
A complete catering service offered to include operational and design facilities provided with over 40 years worth of experience.

DALEBROOK SUPPLIES LTD
Eastways Industrial Estate, Witham,
Essex CM8 3UA
Tel: 01376 510 101 Fax: 01376 510 153
Email: sales@dalebrook.com
Web Site: www.dalebrook.com
Display Solutions for a variety of Catered occassions.

EAT TO THE BEAT LTD
Global Infusion Court, Nashleigh Hill
Chesham, Buckinghamshire HP5 3HE
Tel: 01494 790 700 Fax: 01494 790 701
Email: hello@globalinfusiongroup.com
Web Site: www.eattothebeat.com
Leading international crew and production caterer for the music, theatre, film and television industries. Offering trained Chefs, temporary kitchens and vast logistical experience to create memorable events. Often working closely with sister company Upbeat Event Design to offer a complete range of services.

FYI
Formerly known as 'Upbeat Event Catering'
Global Infusion Court, Nashleigh Hill, Chesham, Buckinghamshire HP5 3HE
Tel: 01494 790 700 Fax: 01494 790 701
Email: hellogigfyi@gigfyi.com
Web Site: www.gigfyi.com
ADMINISTRATION:
Global Operations Director: Bonnie May
UK Sales and Marketing Manager: Laura Horobin
Upbeat Event Catering & Design is all the things you never thought you would find in one place.
Practical imagineers, orderly, flexibility, experienced innovators, and approachable professionals, who cover every aspect of an event including food design, venue finding, technical support, entertainment, event theme application and management.

THE HOUSE OF DORCHESTER
19 Newman Lane, Alton, Hampshire GU34 2QW UK
Tel: 01420 84181 Fax: 01420 543047
Email: sales@hodchoc.com
Web Site: www.hodchoc.com
Manufacturers of handmade fine quality chocolates. Wide range of very attractive boxes of varying shapes and designs.
We are able to personalise the majority of boxes with Theatre names and logos of a particular production.

LONDON'S FLYING CHEF
38 Great Suffolk Street, London SE1 0UE
Tel/ Fax: 020 7633 0099
Email: orders@flyingchef.co.uk
Web Site: www.flyingchef.co.uk
Managing Director: Lee Skinner
Operation Manager: Sarah Hughes
Catering and Events company.

ORCHIDS
(Exclusive Hospitality Service for Theatres)
197-199 Main Street, Wilsden, Bradford, West Yorkshire BD15 0HR
Tel: 01535 273292 Fax: 01535 273818
Email: info@caterleisure.co.uk
Web Site: www.caterleisure.ltd.uk
Chairman: Stuart Peacock
Specialist catering and licensed bars exclusively for theatres. Part of Caterleisure Limited.
Thirty Four years experience of high quality service anywhere in the UK.

R & R ICE CREAM LTD
Richmond House, Leaming Bar Industrial Estate, Northallerton, North Yorkshire D17 9UL
Tel: 01677 423 397 Fax: 01677 428 102
Email: info@uk.rr-icecream.eu
Web Site: www.rr-icecream.eu
UK Sales Director: Mike Fraine

SAUCERY CATERING
Watchcott, Nordan, Leominster, Herefordshire HR6 0AJ
Tel: 01568 614 221 Mob: 07836389160
Email: saucery@aol.com
Web Site: www.saucery.net
Contact: Alison Taylor
Completely mobile catering, any occasion for all requirements.
Video, concert, locations etc.
Crew meals, hospitality, special diets, cooked on site to order, fully trained chefs.

THE EVENT HIRE COMPANY
Subsidiary organisation of 'The Crown Group'
Crown House 855 London Road, Grays, RM20 3LG
Tel : 01708 335 184
Fax : 01708 341 909
Email: sales@eventhireonline.co.uk
Web Site: www.eventhireonline.co.uk
Full catering and event hire services, including a comprehensive range of high quality equipment and event furniture.

UNILEVER
Walton Court, Station Avenue, Walton-on-Thames, Surrey KT12 1NT
Tel: 020 7822 5252
Email: gavin.mitchell@unilever.com
Web Site: www.unilever.com
Business Development Manager: David Birrell

Circus Equipment & Juggling Suppliers

FIRETOYS LTD
Unit 8 and 9, Westergate Business Centre, Brighton BN2 4QN
Tel: 01273 607 088 Fax: 01273 687 500
Email: mail@firetoys.com
Web Site: www.firetoys.co.uk

HWL (UK) LTD
Cricket Street, Denton, Manchester M34 3DR
Tel: 0161 335 0220 Fax: 0161 320 3928
Email: guns@hwltd.co.uk
Web Site: www.hwltd.co.uk
Contact: Bob Howorth
Hirers of all types of furniture, set dressing, decorative lighting, pictures, hand props etc. Also specialist hirers of weapons and blank firing guns.

NATIONAL FESTIVAL CIRCUS
Tober House, PO Box 2, Brierley Hill, West Midlands DY5 3LR
Tel: 01384 423 496
Email: clownsgalore123@AOL.com
Web: www.nationalfestivalcircus.co.uk

SWAMP CIRCUS
10 Lower Market Street, Penryn, Cornwall TR10 8BG
Tel: 01326 377008
Email: swampoffice@btopenworld.com
Web Site: www.swampcircus.co.uk
Contact: Brett or Eve
Supplies professional juggling and circus equipment, stilts and dance gear.

Cleaning & Hygiene

ANDY LOOS
Unit 22, Hartlebury Trading Estate, Hartlebury, Kidderminster, Worcestershire DY10 4JB
Tel: 01299 254420 Fax: 01299 251947
Email: info@andyloos.co.uk
Web Site: www.andyloos.com
Co-Founders: Tony Ray and Richard Philpot
Portable toilet and shower facilities, and mobile WC units.

BRITISH NOVA WORKS LTD
Neville House, Beaumont Road, Bambury, Oxfordshire OX16 1RB
Tel: 01295 251 721 Fax: 01295 254 061
Mob: 07971 150 203
Email: sales@britishnova.co.uk
Web Site: www.britishnova.co.uk
Sales Director: Pat Cooper
Manufacturers of all floor care products, including seals, polishes, cleaners and maintainers, as well as the famous 'NOVAFROST' which freezes chewing gum and makes it easier to remove.

DIRECTA (UK) LTD
Cold Norton, Chelmsford, Essex CM3 6UA
Tel: 01621 828 882 Fax: 01621 828 072
Email: head.office@directa.co.uk
Web Site: www.directa.co.uk
Five good reasons to buy from Directa:
1. Competitive Prices
2. Speedy Nationwide Delivery
3. Free Technical Advice
4. Strict Quality Control
5. BS EN ISO 9001:2000
For free catalogue phone: 01621 828882

RENTOKIL HYGIENE LTD
Rentokil House, Garland Road, East Grinstead, West Sussex RH19 1DY
Tel: 01342 327 171 / 0845 60 20 900
Fax: 01342 324 852
Email: specialisthygiene-enquiry@rentokil-initial.com
Web Site: www.rentokil-hygiene.co.uk
Washroom Hygiene and Preventive Maintenance. Drains Maintenance. Catering Hygiene.
Kitchen deep cleaning. Air hygiene. Emergency disinfection service water hygiene.

Coin Counting & Cash Registers

DE LA RUE CASH SYSTEMS (UK)
Unit 7/8 Wolfe Close, Parkgate Industrial Estate, Knutsford, Cheshire WA16 8XJ
Tel: 01565 654 662 Fax: 01565 658 657
Email: tom.martin@uk.delarue.com
Web Site: www.delarue.com
Sales and Marketing Manager: Tom Martin
Sales and Servicing of Cash Handling Equipment. Coin Counting/Sorting Machines, Note Counters, Systems. Service support network.

ECR RETAIL SYSTEMS
297-303 Edgware Road Collindale
London NW9 6NB
Tel: 08451 70 00 77
Email: sales@ecr-systems.co.uk
Web Site: www.ecr-systems.co.uk
Sales & Rentals of Cash Registers

Computer Systems & Electronic Publicity

ARTIFAX
17A West Street, Epsom, Surrey KT18 7RL
Tel: 01372 587 587
Email: admin@artifax.net
Web Site: www.artifax.net
Directors: Sarah Verge
With a commitment to the cultural community for over 20 years, Artifax is a leading provider of management solutions designed to meet the unique requirements of cultural venues, organisations and the people who run them. Our flagship software, Artifax Event, is a schedule and event management system that handles all aspects of space-related bookings and tour scheduling. Visit www.artifax.net for more details.

BEMROSEBOOTH
Stockholm Road, Hull HU7 0XY
Tel: 01482 826 343
Email: info@bemrosebooth.com
Web Site: www.bemrosebooth.com
For all your ticketing solutions contact BemroseBooth, manufacturers of all thermal tickets variants (Boca, Databox, Zebra etc), roll tickets, and swipe cards.

CANFORD AUDIO PLC
Crowther Road, Washington, Tyne and Wear NE38 0BW
Admin: 0191 418 1000 UK Sales: 0191 418 1122 International Sales: 0191 418 1133 Technical Support: 0191 418 1144
Hires: 0191 418 1166 Fax: 0191 418 1001
Email: info@canford.co.uk
Web Site: www.canford.co.uk
Sales & Operations Manager: Ian Elliott
Canford Audio was founded in 1976, and is unchallenged as the UK's largest pro-audio manufacturer and distributor.

CLEAR-COM COMMUNICATION SYSTEMS
Clear-Com is part of the HME Company
2000 Beach Drive, Cambridge Research Park, Cambridge, CB5 9TP
Tel: 01223 815 000 Fax: 01223 815 099
Email: customerservicesEMEA@clearcom.com
Web Site: www.clearcom.com
Regional Sales Manager: Nicki Fisher

MACULA/EBS
12 St Giles Tower, Gables Close, Camberwell, London SE5 7QE
Tel: 020 7701 2799 Mobile: 07968 201 848
Email: enquiries@ebsnet.co.uk
Web Site: www.ebsnet.co.uk
Contact: Mark Wheeler
Agency administration system for windows.

MOTOROLA LTD
Viables Industrial Estate, Jays Close, Basingstoke, Hampshire RG22 4PD
Tel: 01256 358 211
Email: garymarshall@motorolasolutions.com
Web Site: www.mot.com
Motorola Hire, offered through Customer Access, provides an efficient and reliable service including:-
Competitive rates, full equipment range, accessories (at no extra cost), delivery/collection service, licensing, free telephone service.

Chief Marketing Officer: Eduardo Conrado

PCF PRINT MANAGEMENT LTD
Oak House, Langstone Business Village, Langstone Park, Langstone, Newport, Gwent NP18 2LH Wales
Tel: 01633 415 570 Fax: 01633 415 599
Email: info@pcf.co.uk
Web Site: www.pcf.co.uk
Sales Manager and Director: Ian Hoare
PCF!tickets are ticket suppliers for all software box office ticketing systems, including; tickets.com dataculture, BOCA, CATS, etc, etc,...
PCF will help you with all your needs - tickets, ticket holders, envelopes & labels, membership and reward cards, as well as letterheads, complimentary slips and business cards.

RESOURCES CENTRE LTD
Cambridge House, 128 Park Road, Camberley, Surrey GU15 2LW
Tel: 01276 670 000 Fax: 01276 670 010
Hire and Supply of P.A. Systems. Supply of Operating Technicians.

SCANLITE VISUAL COMMUNICATIONS LTD
Data House, Mowbray Drive, Blackpool FY3 7UZ
Tel: 01253 302 723 Fax: 01253 300 484
Email: David.Carter@scanlite.co.uk
Web Site: www.scanlite.co.uk
Managing Director: David Carter
Electronic displays, internal, external graphic screens, Game show score boards, custom built matrix displays. Sales, rentals service, design.

TICKETS.COM LTD
252 Upper Third Street, Milton Keynes MK9 1NP
Tel: 01908 232 404 Fax: 01908 232 414
Email: uksales@tickets.com
Web Site: www.tickets.com/provenue
Managing Director: Derek Palmer
Tickets.com solutions are now used by over 500 organisations across the UK and Ireland. We provide venues with a variety of ticketing options including: Internet, call centre and collection kiosks. All solutions offer ticketing, marketing, venue management and CRM functionality.

UK THEATRE WEB
37 Severn Avenue, Weston-super-Mare, Avon BS23 4DG
Tel: 01934 626 344
Email: info@uktw.co.uk
Web Site: www.uktw.co.uk
Contact: Robe Iles
The UK Theatre Web provides information about the UK theatre, opera and ballet scene to users all over the world via the Internet. UK Theatre Web is the premier index and information site for UK performing arts. In addition to promotional activities in UK Theatre Web provides free listings, tours and performances via "What`s On Stage".

Cooling & Heating System Hire

AGGREKO UK
Aggreko House, Orbital 2, Voyager Drive, Orbital Retail Centre, Cannock, Staffordshire WS11 8XP
Tel: 01543 476000 Fax: 01543 476001
Email: info@aggreko.co.uk
Web Site: www.aggreko.co.uk
Manager: Stuart Parsons
Aggreko provides rental energy solutions including power, temperature control and

100% oil-free compressed air systems to companies worldwide. Service Centres operate on a 27/7/365 basis.

ARCOTHERM(UK) LTD
Unit 11, Ecclesbourne Park, Clover Nook Road, Cotes Park Industrial Estate, Somercotes, Alfreton, Derbyshire DE55 4RF
Tel: 0845 600 44 99
Email: enquiry@arcotherm.co.uk
Web Site: www.arcotherm.co.uk

Costume (Cleaning & Cleaning Equipment)

CELEBRITY CLEANERS
9 Greens Court, London W1F 0HJ
Tel: 020 7437 5324 (24 Hours)
Westminster Branch: Neville House, 27 Page Street, London, SW1P 4JS
Tel: 020 7821 1777
Email: enquiries@celebritydrycleaners.co.uk
Web Site: www.celebritydrycleaners.co.uk
Contact: Robert Shooman or Sylvia Willingham
Specialist Dry Cleaners to the Theatre Profession and Theatrical Costumiers. Situated in the heart of Theatreland.

NORRIS STEAM SERVICES (LONDON) LTD
6c Sheep Lane, Hackney, London E8 4QS
Tel: 020 7923 4345
Email: robert@norrissteam.co.uk
Web Site: www.norrissteam.com
Managing Director: Norris Shepherdson
Marketing Manager: Robert Shepherdson
Sales Manger: Josh Taylor
Complete range of portable steamers & light weight boiler & iron systems to suit all requirements & budgets. Sales & hire available.

PROPRESS STEAMERS & IRONS
Unit 3, The Pavillions 2 East Road, Wimbledon SW19 1UW
Tel: 020 8417 0660 Fax: 020 8544 9468
Email: info@propress.co.uk
Web Site: www.propress.co.uk
Portable Steamers.

UPSTAGE THEATRICAL DRYCLEANERS
Unit 7- 8, Acorn Production Centre, 105 Blundell Street, London N7 9BN
Tel: 020 7609 9119
Email: upstage@lineone.net
Web Site: www.emily-may.co.uk

Managing Director: Peter Salmon
Storage available in secure, dry premises; 10 minutes from London's West End; Collection/delivery nationwide; East Access; Parking; Stage lit fitting room. Competitive long and short term rates. Storage available in secure premises, 10 mins Londons W.E.
Collection/delivery nationwide easy access, parking, competitive long and short term rates.

Costume (Hire & Sale)

ABBEY THEATRE
Abbey Theatre, Westminster Lodge, Holywell Hill, St Albans, Hertfordshire AL1 2DL
Admin Tel: 01727 847472
Email: manager or hire@abbeytheatre.org.uk
Web Site: www.abbeytheatre.org.uk
Theatre Manager: Tina Swain

ANGELS THE COSTUMIERS
1 Garrick Road, London NW9 6AA
Tel: 020 8202 2244 Fax: 020 8202 1820
Email: info@angels.uk.com
Web Site: www.angels.uk.com
ADMINISTRATION:
Chairman: Tim Angel
Production Director: Richard Green
Revue And Pantomime Costumes:
Angels Fancy Dress, 119 Shaftesbury Avenue, London, WC2H8AE
Tel: 020 7836 5678, Fax: 020 7240 9527
Email: party@fancydress.com, Web: www.fancydress.com
Contact: Emma Angel

ARTISTES' THEATRE SHOP
23 City Road, Chester, Cheshire CH1 3AE
Tel: 01244 320 271 / 330 Fax: 01244 319 688
Email: carolsmith31@hotmail.com
Web Site: www.theatreshop.co.uk / www.dancewearuk.co.uk
Retail sale ballet shoes and requisites - Full range of theatrical make-up and costume hire. costumes also made to order both period and fancy dress for retail sales.

AURORA DANCEWEAR AND COSTUME
Unit 6, Rufus Business Centre, 22 Ravensbury Terrace, Earlsfield, London SW18 4RL
Tel: 020 8287 5092 Fax: 020 8287 1114
Email: auroracostume@aol.co.uk
Web Site: www.auroradancewear.co.uk

BABOUCHA SHOES
PO Box 405, Potters Bar, Hertfordshire EN6 9AB
Tel: 01707 859 502
Email: sales@baboucha.com
Web Site: www.baboucha.com
Theatrical and fashion shoe makers. Footwear for all occasions. Period, panto, Victorian etc. Also matching belts and bags, made in almost any leather or fabric.

BATH THEATRICAL COSTUME HIRE
Unit 8, Wallbridge Industrial Estate, Frome, Somerset BA11 5JZ
Tel/Fax: 01373 472 786
Email: baththeatrical@talktalk.net
Web Site: www.baththeatrical.com
Over 5,000 square feet of wardrode space crammed with costume, hats, wigs, accessories and make-up. For productions set from Ancient Rome to 20th Century New York. Open Tuesday - Friday 10am-5pm, Saturday 10am-4pm or by appointment.

BIRMINGHAM COSTUME HIRE
Suites 209-210, Jubilee Trade Centre, 130 Pershore Street, Birmingham B5 6ND
Tel: 0121 622 3158 Fax: 0121 622 2758
Email: info@birminghamcostumehire.co.uk
Contact: Lynn Smith, Paul Spilsbury
Over 20,000 professional costumes, original period clothing and uniforms plus accessories.

BOB MASSEY ASSOCIATES
9 Worrall Avenue, Arnold, Nottingham NG5 7GN
Tel: 0115 967 3969
Email: bm.associates@virgin.net
Manager: Bob Massey

BOLTON PHOENIX
Bark Street, Bolton BL1 2AZ
Tel: 01204 535 861
Email: info@boltonpheonix.co.uk
Web Site: www.boltonphoenix.co.uk
Artistic Director: Wendy Ellis
Arts Development Officer: Lee Brennan
Education Officer: Caroline Coates
The Phoenix aims to offer the highest quality performing arts workshops and facilities, at the lowest possible cost. The Phoenix encourages open access to the arts for all young people.
Inc: Theatre, Rehearsal Rooms, Dance Studio, Dark Room,
Recording Studio, Video editing Suite, Costume & Theatrical Equipment Hire.

BRISTOL COSTUME SERVICES LTD
Filwood House, Filwood Road, Fishponds, Bristol BS16 3RY
Tel: 0117 965 9555 Fax: 0117 965 9550

Email: bcsbristol@aol.com
Web: www.bristolcostumeservices.com
Contact: Jennie Falconer
A large selection of costumes from Roman to the Present Day. Costume & Design Staff for television and film.

CARNIVAL STORE
95 Hammersmith Road,
London W14 0QH
Tel: 020 7603 7824 / 2918
Email: info@carnivalstore.co.uk
Web Site: www.carnivalstore.co.uk
Contact: U Stephanides
Fancy dress and animal costumes on hire or made to order. Novelties - ie, Venetian masks, make-up, hats, wigs, Halloween decorations, Christmas decorations, Star Wars, Star Trek, Harry Potter, Lord of the Rings, Spiderman children's costumes to buy or hire.

CHRISKA STAGE SUPPLIES
Arkledge House 41 Howey Lane
Frodsham Cheshire WA6 6DD
Tel: 01928 739 166
Email: info@backcloths.com
Web Site: www.backcloths.com

COSPROP LTD
469 - 475 Holloway Road,
London N7 6LE
Tel: 020 7561 7300 Fax: 020 7561 7310
Email: enquiries@cosprop.com
Web Site: www.cosprop.com
Contact: Bernie Chapman
Costumes and Props for hire, 1700-1960's. Hire and making-new-to-hire of period men's and women's costumes. Professional hire only.

CURLYWILLY PRODUCTIONS LTD
Unit C4, Admiralty Park, Off Station Road,
Holton Heath, Poole Dorset BH16 6HX
Mobile: 07970 956 621
Email: carol@curlywilly.co.uk
Web Site: www.curlywilly.co.uk
Proprietor: Carol Kerley
Creative Designers, Consultants, Bespoke Makers of Costumes, Character Heads, Animal Mascots, Props,Scenery, Large Board Games. For use in Theatre, TV, Promotional Events, Public Relations etc Whatever the size of your budget we will cater to your every requirement. All items sold are made by us in our own studios, therefore we have total control during every stage

DAUPHINE'S OF BRISTOL
7 Cleeve Road, Downend,
Bristol BS16 6AD
Tel/ Fax: 01179 560 805
Email: support@dauphines.co.uk
Web Site: www.dauphines.co.uk
Proprietor: Mrs M. Bills
Costumes, wigs for purchase or hire. Make-up supplies and make-up artists available for film, T.V and stage work.

EMPORIUM
330-332 Creek Road, Greenwich,
London SE10 9SW
Tel: 020 8305 1670
Email: emporiumoriginals@mac.com
Contact: Jonathan Hale
Suppliers of mens and ladies costume, textiles and accessories, 1930's - 1970's. Large stocks of leather jackets, hats, dresses, tops, coats and suits etc. Tailoring Specialist. New stock constantly arriving.

FUN'N'FROLIC
16a Richfield Avenue, Reading RG1 8EQ
Tel: 0118 950 8597 Fax: 0118 959 9481
Email: jan@funnfrolic.co.uk
Web Site: www.funnfrolic.co.uk
Contacts: Jan Marketis, Dan Parsons
Suppliers of theatrical make-up, wigs and party goods, with a stock of over 7,500 costumes to hire.

DAPHNE HILSDON
13 Oaken Ground, Rockwell Green,
Wellington, Somerset TA21 9DP
Tel: 01823 661772
Email: daphnehilsdon@btinternet.com
Web Site: www.daphne-hilsdon.co.uk
Supplier of Historical Costumes
Contact: Miss D. Hilsdon

HIREARCHY CLASSIC & CONTEMPORARY COSTUME
45 Palmerston Road, Boscombe,
Bournemouth, Dorset BH1 4HW
Tel: 01202 394 465
Email: hirearchy1@gmail.com
Web Site: www.hirearchy.co.uk
Specialising in the hire of ladies and gents costumes from medieval to present day. Also accessories, make-up, wigs, militaria, jewellery, textiles and luggage.

JAZZ HOT DANCEWEAR
12 The Broadway, Broadstairs, Kent
CT10 2AD
Tel: 01843 600022
Email: sales@ukdancewear.co.uk
Web Site: www.thedancer.co.uk
Contact: Mitch Carrington
Suppliers of dancewear to the trade and general public. All major brands stocked.

JANET LEWIS ENTERPRISES
Appledowne House, The Hillside,
Orpington, Kent BR6 7SD
Tel: 01689 856 747
Email: misslewis@englishyouthballet.co.uk
Web Site: www.englishyouthballet.co.uk
Professional ballet costumes and sets for hire. Ballet floor also available.

MADWORLD
Where Quality and Service Come First
69-85 Tabernacle Street,
London EC2A 4BD
Tel: 020 7253 1003 Gatwick Branch: 1 Barns Court, Turners HIll Road, Crawley Down, West Sussex, RH10 4HQ Tel: 01342 714 056 Fax: 01342 718 558
Email: gatwickshop@madworld.co.uk, city shop@madworld.co.uk
Web Site: www.madworld.co.uk
Contact: Shane Fosten
Costume Hire, Fancy Dress, Make Up, Masks, Bargain wigs. London and Gatwick.

MAHOGANY CARNIVAL DESIGN
28 High Street, Harlesden,
London NW10 4LX
Tel: 020 8961 4446
Email: costumes@mahoganycarnival.com
Web Site: www.mahoganycarnival.com
Artistic Director: Clary Salandy
Structural Engineer: Michael Ramdeen
A unique design and production company offering exciting and innovative costumes and shows for a variety of events, including Theatre and Circus.

MODERN AGE VINTAGE CLOTHING
65 Chalk Farm Road, London NW1 8AN
Tel: 020 7482 3787 Mobile: 07702 958 995
Email: vintage-clothing@modern-age.co.uk
Web Site: www.modern-age.co.uk
Manager: Julia Dollimore
Contact: Basil Anastasi
Mens & Womens Clothing from 1940s to 1970s. To buy or hire. Open 7 days a week 10.30 to 6.00pm.
Contact: Basil Anastasi.

MOVIETONE FROCKS
65 Chalk Farm Road, London NW1 8AN
Tel: 0207 482 3787 Mob: 07702 958 995
Email: movietonefrocks@btinternet.com
Web Site: www.movietonefrocks.com
Mens and Womens Clothing and accessories from 1920's to 1970's. By appointment only - contact Julia Dollimore

PROPS 'N' FROCKS
Unit 1 Rectory Lane, Battlesbridge,
Wickford, Essex SS11 7QR
Tel: 01245 327 156
Email: info@props-n-frocks.co.uk
Web Site: www.propsandfrocks.co.uk
Managing Director: Adele Wiseman

PROPS GALORE
Subsidiary of the Farley Group
1-17 Brunel Road, London W3 7XR
Tel: 020 8746 1222 Fax: 020 8354 1866
Email: propsgalore@farley.co.uk
Web Site: www.farley.co.uk
Specialists in the hire of period textiles, jewellery and accessories.

RON BRIGGS DESIGN
1 Bedford Mews, Off Bedford Road, East

Finchley, London N2 9DF
Tel: 020 8444 8801
Email: costumes@ronbriggs.com
Web Site: www.ronbriggs.com
Contact: Ron Briggs, Mike Littlewood
Bespoke costume makers for stage & screen. Over 25 years producing quality ladies & men's costumes internationally for musicals, dance, plays and variety. Suppliers to the West End (Chitty, Far Pavilions, Movin' Out, Saturday Night Fever). No costume hire.

ROYAL SHAKESPEARE COMPANY
(Costume Hire Dept), Timothys Bridge Road, Stratford-upon-Avon, Warwickshire CV37 9UY
Tel: 01789 205920
Email: costume.hire@rsc.org.uk
Web Site: www.rsc.org.uk
Thousands of period costumes from past RSC productions are available for hire to schools, dramatic societies, theatres, films and television.

SCREEN PRODUCTS LTD
Tel: 07926 196 471
Email: info@dirtydown.co.uk
Web Site: www.dirtydown.co.uk
Contact: Alan Taylor
Dirty Down sprays are "dirty" translucent dyes used extensively in film, theatre, and television on costumes, scenery and props. Make things look dirty/old. Rust, Mould, Frost/Snow and ice are Special Effects Sprays.

STAGE COSTUME
Unit 2, Victoria Industrial Park, Victoria Road, Dartford DA1 5AJ
Tel: 01322 311 787
Email: enquiries@stagecostume.co.uk
Web Site: www.stagecostume.co.uk
Contact: Roger Criey

THE COSTUME STUDIO
Montgomery House, 159-161 Balls Pond Road, London N1 4BG
Tel: 020 7275 9614 Fax: 0207 923 9065
Email: costume.studio@btconnect.com
Web Site: www.costumestudio.co.uk
Manager: Peter Evans
A huge selection of historical period and repro clothing, accessories, footwear and wigs for hire. Design and manufacturing also available. Quotes given.

THEATRE ROYAL (PLYMOUTH)
Production Wardrobe Departmen, Theatre Royal Production Centre Cattedown Plymouth PL4 0SJ
Tel: 01752 230331 Fax: 01752 225985
Email: dina.hall@theatreroyal.com
Web Site: www.theatreroyal.com
Contact: Dina Hall
Costume makers for theatre and film. Makers of period and modern costumes, men's and ladie's tailoring, costume alterations, costume fitting and refurbishment, dyeing and breaking down.

THEATRICAL COSTUME HOUSE
Opening Times: 9.30 am - 3 pm (Mon-Fri)
83 Brunswick Road, Southend-on-Sea, Essex SS1 2UL
Tel: 01702 461 573 Fax: 01702 603 163
Email: info@theatricalcostumehouse.co.uk
Web Site: www.theatricalcostumehouse.co.uk
Manager: Miss P.C. Sendell
Theatrical Costumiers of the highest quality. Pantomime, Summer Season, Musicals, Repertory.

TRENDS ENTERTAINMENT
Unit 4, 9 Chorley Road, Blackpool, FY3 7XQ
Tel: 01253 396 534
Email: info@trendsentertainment.com
Web Site: www.trendsentertainment.com
Contact: Antony Johns

WHALEYS (BRADFORD) LTD
Harris Court, Great Horton, Bradford, West Yorkshire BD7 4EQ
Tel: 01274 576 718 Fax: 01274 521 309
Email: kevin.woodhead@whaleysltd.co.uk
Web Site: www.whaleys.co.uk/stage
General Manager: Mr Kevin Woodhead
Sales Manager: Barry Hardisty
Sales Office: David Carroll
Drapes/Backdrops/Borders/Legs etc. Full range of standard flameproof stage fabrics. Orders made up to customer specification. Also huge range of fabrics for costume (many ready for printing/dyeing).

Costume Fabrics

WEST YORKSHIRE FABRICS
Warehouse Address: Unit 5, Milestone Court, Stanningley, Leeds, West Yorkshire LS28 6HE
Tel: 0113 225 6550 Fax: 0870 443 9842
Email: njs@stroud-brothers.demon.co.uk
Contact: Neil Stroud
Administration Address: West Yorkshire House,
20 High Ash Drive, Alwoodley, Leeds, West Yorkshire LS17 8RA
Suppliers of wool suiting, Venetians, baratheas, melton, Linen and stretch fabrics to the theatre and opera industry for over 30 years. No minimum order. Credit cards accepted.

Creatives

THE LUXFACTOR GROUP (UK)
Fleet Place, Nelson Drive, Petersfield, Hampshire GU31 4SJ
Tel: 0845 370 0589 Fax: 0845 370 0588
Email: info@luxfactor.co.uk
Web Site: www.luxfactor.co.uk
Managing Director & Agent: Michael D. Finch
Primarily representing Lighting, Sound, Video, Set, Costume and Scenic Designers, LUXFactor picks up where others are left bewildered. With clients on four continents we truly are an international agency. LUXFactor Client Management operates on a flexible international timeline status and during "theatre' hours too!

CLARE VIDAL-HALL
57 Carthew Road, London W6 0DU
Tel: 020 8741 7647 Fax: 020 8741 9459
Email: cvh@clarevidalhall.com
Web Site: www.clarevidalhall.com
Managing Director: Clare Vidal-Hall

Creche Facilities

CHILDSPLAY EVENT SERVICES
Briar House, Caldbec Hill, Battle, East Sussex TN33 0JR
Tel/Fax: 01424 775 450
Email: info@kidsco.co.uk
Web Site: www.kidsco.co.uk
Senior Personnel: Nick Bryant
Specialising in Childrens Event Organisation & Management. Agents for children's entertainers.

LEAPFROG DAY NURSERY
Thornton Lodge, 6 West Lane, Thornton, Bradford, West Yorkshire BD13 3HX
Tel: 01274 834 358 Fax: 01274 834 525
Email: sales@leapfrogdaynurseries.co.uk

Design, Printing & Publicity

3D-4D.COM
46 Calthorpe Street, London WC1X 0JZ
Tel: 0500 555 245
Email: enquiries@3d4d.com
Web Site: www.3D4D.com
Flexible holographic designs for posters, invitations and much more. Large-format Lenticulars for set design.

4 PRINT & DESIGN LTD
Unit 2 St. Josephs Business Park, St. Josephs Close, Hove,
East Sussex BN3 7ES
Tel: 01273 712 520
Email: sales@4printanddesign.co.uk
Web Site: www.4printanddesign.co.uk
Contact: Jo Gibson

ACTION T-SHIRTS
Unit 6, Dover House Industrial Estate, Witley, Surrey GU8 5QZ
Tel: 01483 860 270
Email: sales@action-t-shirts.co.uk
Web Site: www.action-t-shirts.co.uk
Managing Director: Oliver Smith
Highly competitive prices, fast delivery shipping anywhere in the UK, and same day print service on orders up to 500 T-shirts. Plain garments also available ex-stock!

AKA
115 Shaftesbury Avenue, Cambridge Circus, London WC2H 8AF
Tel: 020 7836 4747
Email: reception@akauk.com
Web Site: www.akauk.com
Managing Director: Kate Turnball

ALUSET SECURITY TICKETS
2-6 Brookvale Road, Langley Mill, Nottingham NG16 4AX
Tel: 01773 769 317 Fax: 01773 716 206
Email: steve@aluset.com
Web Site: www.aluset.com
Contact: Steve Thomas
As the leading ticket printer, Aluset supply a complete range of tickets from simple continuous stationery to highly secure stadium tickets. Our thermal tickets are used successfully in all types of printers including BOCA, Gazelle, TOR, Star. We believe our quality will improve your image.

ARTS CONTACT
Kenyon House, 104 Redbourne Road, Hibaldstow, Brigg, Lincolnshire DN20 9NP
Tel: 01652 656 775 Mob: 07831 166692 / 07860 374723
Email: sheila@artscontact.co.uk
Web Site: www.artscontact.co.uk
Directors: Sheila Thorpe, Tony Hyslop
A unique creative bulk distribution service for Arts publicity print, for any Arts event, anywhere in the U.K.

BERFORTS LTD
17 Burgess Road, Ivyhouse Lane Industrial Estat Hastings, East Sussex TN35 4NR
Tel: 01424 722 733 Fax: 01424 721 777
Email: sales@berfort.co.uk
Web Site: www.berfort.co.uk
Contact: Mr D Edwards
For all photo publicity cards and show business printing.

BLUE ANT DESIGN LTD
Unit 9-12, The Foundry Business Park, Seager Road, Faversham Kent ME13 7FD
Tel: 01795 534 433 Fax: 01795 530 808
Email: info@blueantdesign.com
Web Site: www.blueantdesign.com
Managing Director: Duncan Fielder
Creative Director: Jill Fielder
We create innovative material for theatres, leisure industries, galleries and museums. In house production facilities and installation crew make our service quality driven and cost effective.

CANTATE COMMUNICATIONS
1st Floor, 30 Cowcross Street, London EC1M 6DQ
Tel: 0203 651 1690
Email: info@cantatecommunications.com
Web: www.cantatecommunications.com
Business Development Manager: Simon Henry/ Till Siegers
Specialist theatre printers, e.g. programmes, souvenir brochures and publicity for the RNT, ENO, RSC, BBC, RPO etc.
Comprehensive quality service. Our design subsidiary arc associates has worked for Bolshoi, ENO, BBC etc.

COLOR PRODUCTS LTD
Unit 5, Tile House Farm, Birds Green Lane, Willingale, Ongar, Essex CM5 0PN
Tel: 08456 585212
Email: colorproducts@aol.com
Contact: Peter Randall
Manufacturers of flight case labels, equipment labels, touring labels, cable and cable coding labels, printed vinyl tapes and floor graphics.

DESIGN IT
Mill House 3 Saddleworth Road, Elland, Halifax, West Yorkshire HX5 0RY
Tel: 01422 377761 Fax: 01422 371141
Email: studio@designit-uk.com
Web Site: www.designit-uk.com
Partner: Martin Pinder
Specialists in the design & production of promotional material for the arts & theatres. Design for print, branding, advertising, web site design, construction and print management.

DEWYNTERS PLC
Wellington House, 125 Strand, London WC2R 0AP
Tel: 020 7321 0488 Fax: 020 7321 0104
Email: info@dewynters.com
Web Site: www.dewynters.com
Client Management: Kirsty Doubleday
Dewynters is the UK entertainment industry's leading
full-service agency. We provide marketing, design, advertising, promotions, new media and merchandise skills across a broad spectrum. The agency's fields of expertise comprise theatre, opera, dance, music, galleries, museums, events, television and film. Our ground-breaking campaigns are synonymous with the energy and impact of modern entertainment - powerful, innovative and effective.

GREY SWAN
12b Carholme Road, London SE23 2HS
Tel: 07931 791 807
Email: tim@greyswan.org.uk
Web Site: www.greyswan.org.uk
Artistic Directors: Timothy Stubbs Hughes
Grey Swan is a visionary arts consultancy company that aims to support new and experimental work by providing personal attention to the next generation of theatre makers.

HASTINGS PRINTING CO LTD
Drury Lane, St Leonard's-on-Sea, East Sussex TN38 9BJ
Tel: 01424 720 477 Fax: 01424 434 086
Email: admin@hastings-print.co.uk, studio@hastingsprint.com
Web Site: www.hastings-print.co.uk
Managing Director: Alison Knoll
Design and printing specialising in the Entertainment Industry.
Service include:
- Pre-press: scanning, Apple Mac and PC, computer to plate, ISDN and broadband link
- Press: press sizes from B1 to B3, printing single to five colour
- Binding: fold, stitch and trim
- Mailing: address to Royal Mail sortation, inserting, polywrapping, mailing, Royal Mail daily collection.
- Service: direct contact with staff (no voice mails), named contacts, staff available to visit if required, our own van delivery service, ISO quality standard.

IMAGES CONCEPTS
Evans Business Centre, Hartwith Way, Harrogate, North Yorkshire HG3 2XA
Tel: 01423 813 581
Email: hello@imageconcepts.co.uk
Web Site: www.imageconcepts.co.uk

JOHN GOOD LTD
Progress Way, Binley Industrial Estate, Coventry, Warwickshire CV3 2NT
Tel: 024 7665 2800
Email: info@johngood.com
Web Site: www.johngood.com
Advertising, sales and print sales address:
Court Farm Barns,
Medcroft Road, Tackley,
Oxford. OX5 3AL
Tel: 01993 777 700 Fax: 01993 777 701
Contact: Adrian Collett
Specialist suppliers of quality design and printing services to the theatre and music industry, providing in-house advertising sales, editorial, design and print for programmes and promotional material to a wide range of theatres, concert halls, touring companies and promoters.

KALL KWIK PRINTING
16 Gravel Lane, London E1 7AW
Tel: 020 7247 3556 Fax: 020 7377 1676
Email: john@centrepoint.kallkwik.co.uk

Web Site: www.kallkwik.co.uk/centrepoint
Contacts: John Mooney
All types of printing and copying. Scripts copied and bound. Programmes and inserts. Presentation documents, CV's, booklet making service.

KAYMAR PRINT LTD
Kaymar Industrial Estate, Trout Street, Preston, Lancashire PR1 4DL
Tel: 01772 562 211 Fax: 01772 257 813
Email: sales@kaymarprint.com
Web Site: www.kaymarprint.com
Manager: Mark Brindle
Silkscreen Printer.

MARLER HALEY LTD
45 Booth Drive, Park Farm Industrial Estate, Wellingborough, Northamptonshire NN8 6GR
Tel: 01933 676 952 Fax: 01933 674 549
Email: info@marlerhaley.co.uk
Web Site: www.marlerhaley.co.uk
Sales and Marketing Director: Andrew Pocock
Comprehensive range of display and exhibition equipment; Roller banner stands, Pop Up displays and Panel displays.

MODELBOX
41c Market Street, Hatherleigh, Devon EX20 3JP
Tel: 01837 810 923 Mob: 07802 370 000
Email: info@modelbox.co.uk
Web Site: www.modelboxplans.com
Contact: Stephen Wentworth
Modelbox maintains a database of over 350 theatre drawings in CAD format. Plans are available in paper and electronic format. Theatre survey, plan conversion, pre-production and tour preparation services available. design services for lighting and set designers.

NEWMAN DISPLAYS LTD
23 Pakenham Street, London WC1X 0LB
Tel: 020 7278 1400 Fax: 020 7278 0996
Email: info@newman-displays.com
Web Site: www.newman-displays.com
Contact: Mark Hollington

NEWSIGNS
13 The Arches, Maygrove Road, London NW6 2EB
Tel: 020 7328 9251 Fax: 020 7328 9251
Email: newsigns@hotmail.co.uk
Proprietor: Mr L Gibbons

PCF PRINT MANAGEMENT LTD
Oak House, Langstone Business Village, Langstone Park, Langstone, Newport, Gwent NP18 2LH Wales
Tel: 01633 415 570 Fax: 01633 415 599
Email: info@pcf.co.uk
Web Site: www.pcf.co.uk
Sales Manager and Director: Ian Hoare
PCF!tickets are ticket suppliers for all software box office ticketing systems, including; tickets.com dataculture, BOCA, CATS, etc, etc,...
PCF will help you with all your needs - tickets, ticket holders, envelopes & labels, membership and reward cards, as well as letterheads, complimentary slips and business cards.

PERFORMANCE TICKET PRINTERS LTD
The Smithy, Brownlow Heath, Congleton, Cheshire CW12 4TJ
Tel: 01260 276 164 Fax: 01260 270 984
Email: mailbox@ticketprinters.co.uk
Web Site: www.ticketprinters.co.uk
Directors: John Arnold, Joan Arnold
Contacts: Austin Pickles, Ruth Heasman
Computer printed Theatre Tickets. Quick, easy and inexpensive.

PIRAN PRINT LTD
Unit 1, Southgate Technology Park, Pennygillam Way, Launceston, Cornwall PL15 7ED
Tel: 08450 617 181
Email: enquiries@piranprint.com
Web Site: www.piranprint.com
Contact: Nigel Schofield
Security ticket printers, stock sizes, colours, logos, reserved, numbered; Try Us! Hologram and foil also available for added security.

THE POSTCARD COMPANY
Graham & Sons (Printers) Ltd 51 Gortin Road, County Tyrone, Omagh BT79 7HZ Northern Ireland
Tel: 028 8224 9222 Fax: 028 8224 9886
Email: sales@thepostcardcompany.com
Web Site: www.thepostcardcompany.co m
Managing Director: Rodney Billiers
Specialist printers of high quality full-colour postcards, promotional cards, greetings cards and business cards to the entertainment world. Offering an unrivalled service with a quick order turnaround of 10 working days and at the lowest prices in UK & Ireland. Phone now for our free sample pack!

PRINTERS INC & DESIGN LTD
Vetch House, 58 Penshurst Gardens, Edgware, Middlesex HA8 9TU
Tel: 020 8905 4743
Email: printers.inc@btinternet.com
Contact Michael Plosker
Specialists in the design and printing of brochures, programmes and leaflets.

PUBLICITY & DISPLAY LTD
1 Corium House, Douglas Drive, Godalming, Surrey GU7 1HJ
Tel: 01483 428 326 Fax: 01483 424 566
Email: print@pubdis.com
Web Site: www.pubdis.com
Contact: Tim Cox
Design/print of posters, passes, leaflets, tickets and stickers for the entertainment industry. Mon-Thur: 9-5:30; Fri 9-5

R.N.R. CHARLESWORTH
39 Clay Close, Dilton Marsh, Westbury, Wiltshire BA13 4DU
Tel/Fax: 01373 865 582
Email: nc@vaudeville-postcards.com
Web Site: www.vaudeville-postcards.com
Proprietor: Nicholas Charlesworth
Publishers of Theatre postcards, and distribution of Theatre books. Over 320 stock postcard subjects. Wholesale terms available.

REAL PUBLICITY (ENCORE MAGAZINE -JMP)
See also, 'Johnny Mans Productions' and 'Encore Magazine'
P.O.Box 196, Broxbourne, Hertfordshire EN10 7WG
Tel: 0845 467 0792/ 01992 470 907
Mob: 07974 755 997
Email: johnnymansagent@aol.com
Web Site: www.johnnymansproductions.c o.uk
Contacts: Johnny Mans, Philip Crowe

SCHWARTZ
Unit 2 Hutton Ind. Estate Wash Road, Hutton, Brentwood, Essex CM13 1TA
Tel: 01277 205 090
Email: enquiries@schwartz-printing.co.uk
Web Site: www.schwartz-printing.co.uk
Leaflets, brochures, BD cards, posters, escalator panels - you name it, we print it for the theatre world nationwide. In-house repro and finishing and daily nationwide delivery ensure keen prices and a super-efficient service.

TECHNOPRINT
Rods Mills, Rods Mill Lane, Morley, Leeds, West Yorkshire LS27 9BD
Tel: 0113 253 3920 Fax: 03300 883 991
Email: sales@technoprint.co.uk
Managing Director: J.M.Snee
Long-standing suppliers of quality leaflets, posters, programmes, 'what's-on' guides etc. Typesetting, design, scanning, repro, printing and finishing in-house. PC and MAC disks accepted. Competitive prices. Friendly knowledgeable staff.

TECHNOPRINT
The Old School, Meadowbank, Winsford, Cheshire CW7 2PG
Tel: 01606 861298 Fax: 01606 550 866
Email: all@technoprint.net
Web Site: www.technoprint.net
Managing Director: Alan Ryan

UK FLYERS
Suite 210 Victory House, Somers Road North Portsmouth Hants PO1 1PJ
Tel: 023 9229 3050 Fax: 023 9229 5258

Email: sales@ukflyers.com
Web Site: www.ukflyers.com
Contact: Jim Cochrane

Disability Services & Support

ACCESS AUDIO LTD
Wintonfield House, New Winton, East Lothian, EH33 2NN
Tel: 0131 663 0777 Fax: 0131 660 9777
Email: info@accessaudio.co.uk
Web Site: www.accessaudio.co.uk
Managing Director: Douglas Telford
Radio and infrared communication system suppliers & installers. Audio description equipment specialists.

LOUISE DYSAN AT VISABLE PEOPLE - DISABLED ARTISTS
P.O. Box 80 Droitwich, WR9 0ZE
Tel: 01386 555 170
Email: louise@visablepeople.com
Web Site: www.visablepeople.com
Contact: Louise Dyson
VisABLE is the UK's first professional agency representing only actors and models with disabilities.

M & R COMMUNICATIONS
7 Bell Industrial Estate, 50 Cunnington Street, Chiswick, London W4 5HB
Tel: 020 8995 4714 Fax: 020 8995 5136
Email: office@m-rcom.com
Web Site: www.m-rcom.com
Technical Director: Jean Henriot
Office Manager: Ben Denness
Infra-red and radio systems for audio description and foreign language productions.

SOUND ASSOCIATES LTD
81 Island Farm Road, West Molesey, Surrey KT8 2SA
Tel: 020 8939 5900 Fax: 020 8939 5901
Email: glodge@soundassociates.co.uk
Web Site: www.soundassociates.co.uk
Managing Director: Graham Lodge

STAGETEXT
First Floor, 54 Commercial Street, London E1 6LT
Tel: 020 7377 0540 Fax: 020 7247 5622
Email: enquiries@stagetext.org
Web Site: www.stagetext.org
Executive Director: Nigel McCune
Communications Director: Laura Arenes
Live Events Programme Officer: Deepa Shastri
Stagetext provides and promotes the use of captioning in Arts and Entertainment venues so that events are accessible to deaf, deafened and hard of hearing people.

SWALLOW LIFTS
Unit 5, Swallow House, Central Place, Portland Road, South Norwood London SE25 4PR
Tel: 020 8654 6938 Fax: 020 8654 5935
Email: info@swallowlifts.co.uk, darren.pons@swallowlifts.co.uk
Web Site: www.swallowlifts.co.uk
Contact: Darren Pons

VOCALEYES
First Floor, 54 Commercial Street, London E1 6LT
Tel: 020 7375 1043
Email: enquiries@vocaleyes.co.uk
Web Site: www.vocaleyes.co.uk
Theatre Programme Organiser: Michael Kenyon
VocalEyes provides audio descriptions for blind or partially sighted people in order to enhance engagement with the arts, such as theatre, opera and dance.

Drapes, Furnishings & Fabrics

ABAKHAN FABRICS
Coast Road, Mostyn, Flintshire CH8 9DX North Wales
Tel: 01745 562 100 Fax: 01745 562 101
Email: customerservices@abakhan.co.uk
Web Site: www.abakhan.co.uk
Online and Retail Suppliers of Fabrics and Haberdashery for Costume and Theatrical use including Calico, Satin, Chiffon, Tulle, Spandex, Cotton, Velvet and Furnishing Fabrics, Trimmings, Ribbon, Lace, Buttons and more.

ACRE JEAN LTD
Unit 7, Kimber Centre, 54 Kimber Road, London SW18 4PP
Tel: 020 8877 3211 Fax: 020 8877 3213
Email: enquiries@acrejean.com
Web Site: www.acrejean.com
ADMINISTRATION:
Managing Director: Ross Maxwell
General Manager: Gary Holder
Installations Director: Colin Hannah
Hire Desk: Colin Fairley

Acre Jean Ltd has been in business since 1984 serving the entertainment, conference, television and film industries. Being specialists in the hire, manufacture and installation of drapes for acoustic, masking and presentation purposes, we have installed drapes for pop shows on a regular basis at Wembley Arena, Wembley Stadium and Earls Court.

We have also provided drapes for conference centres, exhibition halls, leisure centres and studios across the length and breadth of Great Britain and abroad. Our constantly expanding stock now includes Wool Serge
in black, Chromakey blue, Chromakey green and grey; Sharkstooth Gauze in black, white and grey; Velvet in black, royal blue, plum red, admiral red, midas gold, leaf green, pewter grey and rose pink. Also white filled cloth and star cloths.

MAISON HENRY BERTRAND LTD
52 Holmes Road, London NW5 3AB
Tel: 020 7424 7000 Fax: 020 7424 7001
Email: sales@henrybertrand.co.uk
Web Site: www.henrybertrand.co.uk
Joint Managing Director: Katy Bercovitch and Andrew Gilbert
UK Sales Director: Jamie Morgan
Suppliers of fine silk fabrics to theatrical costumiers and TV.

BLACKOUT LTD
280 Western Road, London SW19 2QA
Tel: 020 8687 8400 Fax: 020 8687 8500
Email: sales@blackout-ltd.com
Web Site: www.blackout-ltd.com
Managing Director: Martin Wood
Hire & Sales Co-Ordinator: Will Bryant
Blackout specialises in the manufacture for hire and sale of high quality flame retardant drapes and star cloths. We offer full consultancy, installation rigging and 24 hr backup service and can be relied upon to make any project happen. We also provide painted cloths to any size and artistic specification.

BRODIE & MIDDLETON LTD
30-31 Store Street, London WC1E 7QE
Tel: 020 7836 3289 Fax: 020 7497 0554
Email: info@brodies.net
Web Site: www.brodies.net
Manager: Yanko Tihov
Established 1840. Located in the heart of theatreland. Supplier of Rosco and Bristol scenic colour, UV colour, dyes, glitters, metal leaf, gilding materials, brushes, pigments, fire proofing, scenic canvas, drapes, backcloths, gauzes and varnishes and artists materials.

CAMEO CURTAINS
6 Greenwood Court, Taylor Business Park, Risley, Warrington, Cheshire WA3 6DD
Tel/Fax: 01925 765 308 Head Office: 01354 677 796
Email: sales@cameocurtains.co.uk
Contact: Mr Springthorpe
Manufacturers of Quality stage and auditorium drapes, rostra, blinds, blackout curtains, gauzes and canvas. Also repairs, cleaning and reflameproofing service.

CAMIRA FABRICS
The Watermill, Wheatley Park, Mirfield West Yorkshire WF14 8HE

Tel: 01924 490 591 Fax: 01924 495 605
Email: info@camirafabrics.com
Web Site: www.camirafabrics.com
Technical Manager: Mick Coll
Supplier of 100% wool seating fabric for Auditoria at home and abroad.
Unbeatable quality at affordable prices.

CCT LIGHTING LTD
Unit 3, Ellesmere Business Park, Haydn Road, Nottingham NG5 1DX UK
Tel: 0115 985 8919
Fax: 0115 985 7091
Email: office@cctlighting.co.uk
Web Site: www.cctlighting.com
Directors: John Shore, Richard Stokes, Gary Redfern
CCT Lighting manufacture flameproofed velour and Bolton Twill curtains in a wide range of colours, quoted to specification. Also distributed are the entire Rosco range of products including scenic and projection materials.
(Main function: Manufacture of Lighting and accessories)

CHRISKA STAGE SUPPLIES
Arkledge House 41 Howey Lane
Frodsham Cheshire WA6 6DD
Tel: 01928 739 166
Email: info@backcloths.com
Web Site: www.backcloths.com

CLYDE CANVAS
4B East Mains, Ingliston Road, Edinburgh, Mid Lothain EH28 8NB Scotland
Tel: 0131 335 3685 Mob: 07810 123 360
Email: sales@purvis-marquees.co.uk
Web Site: www.purvis-marquees.co.uk
Contact: John Brown
Purvis Marquees is one of Britains leading companies for manufacture, hire and sale of quality marquees and fabric structures.

CREATIVE DRAPING
Unit 3, 29 Mount Avenue, Mount Farm, Milton Keynes MK1 1LS
Tel: 01908 368 141
Email: info@creativedraping.com
Web Site: www.creativedraping.com
Senior Personnel: Susie Carlino
Specialist in draping venues and stages for the nightclub and party events. We hire and make props and banners.

DALSTON MILL FABRICS
69-73 Ridley Road, Dalston, London, E8 3NP
Tel: 0207 249 4129
Email: info@dalstonmillfabrics.co.uk
Web Site: www.dalstonmillfabrics.co.uk
General Manager: Edward Kogun
Specialising in dress and dance fabrics.

EMPEE SILK FABRICS LTD
31 Commercial Road, Edmonton, London N18 1TP
Tel: 020 8887 6000 Fax: 020 8887 6000
Email: empee@wholesalefabrics.co.uk
Web Site: www.wholesalefabrics.co.uk
Wholesalers of a huge range of dress and theatrical fabrics including satins, nets, velvets, cottons, wools, corduroys and many more. We sell stocks and clearance lines off at very low prices.

GERRIETS OF GREAT BRITAIN LTD
18 Verney Road, London SE16 3DH
Tel: 020 7639 7704 Fax: 020 7732 5760
Email: info@gerriets.co.uk
Web Site: www.gerriets.com
Director Sales and Marketing: Stewart Crosbie
Suppliers and manufacturers of theatrical and display plastics, textiles and finished soft goods.

HANDS ON PRODUCTION SERVICES
79 Loanbank Quadrant, Glasgow G51 3HZ Scotland
Tel: 0141 440 2005
Email: info@hands-on-uk.com
Web Site: www.hands-on-uk.com
Hire of Weapons, Heraldic Shields, Armour and Allied Properties for Theatre, Film and Publicity Work.
We are the only BBC approved contractors in Scotland and have the authority of the Scottish executive to supply prohibited weapons under section 5 of the firearms act.

HARBER IMAGE LINE
1-3 Hillstone Barns, Brook Street, Hargrave, Wellingborough, Northamptonshire NN9 6BP
Tel: 01933 624 079 Fax: 01933 460 253
Email: harbersales@btconnect.com
Web Site: www.harberimageline.com

HAWTHORN THEATRICAL LTD
Crown Business Park, Old Dalby, Leicestershire LE14 3NQ
Tel: 01664 821111 Fax: 01664 821119
Email: info@hawthorns.uk.com
Web Site: www.hawthorns.uk.com
Managing Director: Martin Hawthorn
Hire, Installation, design and sales of lighting, sound, staging, rigging, drapes, impact sales, starcloth and special effects.
Hire and sales open 7 days a week, main dealers for all leading brands.
London Office: Unit F, Western Trading Estate, London, NW10 7LU, Tel: 020 8955 6900

HOUSE COUTURIER
285 New Kings Road, London SW6 4RD
Tel: 020 7371 9255
Email: info@housecouturier.eu
Web Site: www.housecouturier.eu
Contact: Anne Thompson

REX HOWARD (DRAPES) LTD
Unit F, Western Trading Estate, Trading Estate Road, London NW10 7LU
Tel: 020 8955 6940 Fax: 020 8955 6901
Email: rex.howard@hawthorns.uk.com
Web Site: www.hawthorns.uk.com / www.rex-howard.co.uk
Stage Drapes of every description, gauzes, flame-proof textile materials for sale and hire.

J & C JOEL LTD
Corporation Mill, Corporation Street, Sowerby Bridge, West Yorkshire HX6 2QQ
Tel: 01422 833835 Fax: 01422 835157
Email: sales@jcjoel.com
Web Site: www.jcjoel.com
Specialists in Flame Retardant Fabrics, manufacturers and installers of theatrical

drapes and stage equipment. Probably the largest stock of flame retardant fabrics, tracks and all stage hardware, starcloths, dance flooring and portable staging.
Sales Manager: Oliver Marns

KEN CREASEY LTD
34 Queens Row, London SE17 2PX
Tel: 020 7277 1645 Fax: 020 7277 1701
Email: info@kencreasey.com
Web Site: www.kencreasey.com
Specialist curtain maker for Stage, Cinema, Contract, Exhibition, Draperies and Fabric supplier.

LANCELYN LIGHTING (NORTHWEST)
Poulton Road, Bebington, Wirral CH63 9LN
Tel: 0151 334 8991 (24Hours) Fax: 0151 334 4047 Oxford Office: Ferry Hinksey Road, Oxford, England, OX2 0BY Tel: 01865 722 468 Fax: 01865 728 791
Email: northwest@lancelyn.co.uk
Web Site: www.lancelyn.co.uk
Sales and Branch Manager: Paul Cook (paul@lancelyn.co.uk)
Optical & special effects, Pyrotechnics supplied and delivered.

LANCELYN THEATRE SUPPLIES
Ferry Hinksey Road, Oxford OX2 0BY
Tel: 01865 722 468 Fax: 01865 728 791
Email: oxford@lancelynoxford.co.uk
Web Site: www.lancelyn.co.uk
Sales and Branch Manager: Reg Berry
Email: reg@lancelynoxford.co.uk
Marketing, Admin & Office Manager: Sara Ingham
Made to measure curtains, supply and fix, repair and cleaning.

JD MCDOUGALL LIMITED
4 McGrath Road, London E15 4JP
Tel: 020 8534 2921 Fax: 020 8519 8423
Email: mail@mcdougall.co.uk
Web Site: www.mcdougall.co.uk
Director: Mr I McDougall
Stage Drapes, Vision Gauzes, Backcloths, Cyclorama cloths, Flameproof textile materials for Scenery Construction and Stage Effects.

NEVTEX INTERLOOP LTD
PO Box 87, 29 Stoney Street, Nottingham NG1 1LR
Tel: 0115 959 8781 Fax: 0115 950 2687
Email: sales@nevtex.co.uk
Web: www.nevtex.co.uk
Contact: Robert Grummitt
Wolesale & mail order of nevtex: fabrics, feathers & dresses. Trimmings to the theatrical & dance costumier.

NORTHERN STAGE SERVICES LTD
Trent Industrial Estate, Duchess Street, Shaw, Oldham, Lancashire OL2 7UT
Tel: 01706 849 469 Fax: 01706 840 138
Email: Info@nstage.co.uk, david.baxter@nstage.co.uk
Web Site: www.nstage.co.uk
Specialists in stage lighting, sound and curtain equipment.
Managing Director: Patrick Colin
Sales Manager: David Baxter
Business Administrator: Kelly Tracey

ONLINE FABRICS
388-394 Foleshill Road, Coventry CV6 5AN
Tel: 024 7668 7776 Fax: 024 7668 1656
Email: info@online-fabrics.co.uk
Web Site: www.online-fabrics.co.uk
Contact: Dee Tahim
The largest fabric retailers in the Midlands, with thousand of Fabric Products to choose from.

PERRY SCENIC LTD
Unit D & E, 100 Dudley Road East, Oldbury, West Midlands B69 3EB
Tel: 0121 552 9696 Fax: 0121 552 9697
Email: enquiries@perryscenic.com
Web Site: www.perryscenic.com
Contact: Michael Perry , Tony Guest, Jonathan Perry
Comprehensive service at competitive prices. Set Builders, Engineering, Scenic Artists, Sculptors, Prop Makers, Design, Drapes, Effects for Theatre, Film, TV, Exhibition and Pop Tours.

PG STAGE ELECTRICAL
Studio House, Tameside Work Centre, Ryecroft Street, Ashton-under-Lyme, Lancashire OL7 0BY
Tel: 0161 830 0303
Email: sales@pgstage.co.uk or info@pgstage.co.uk
Web Site: www.pgstage.co.uk
Supply of Tabs, Legs, Cycloramas, Festoons, Borders, Nets, Gauzes and Astrocloths. Design and installation of writing audio and mechnical systems. Also lighting and audio suppliers.

PROMPT SIDE LTD
14 Mulberry Court, Bourne Road, Crayford DA1 4BF
Tel: 01322 554 455 Fax: 01322 529 282
Email: info@promptside.co.uk
Web Site: www.promptside.co.uk
Managing Director: Peter Baker

RUSSELL & CHAPPLE
30-31 Store Street, London WC1E 7QE
Tel: 020 7836 7521 Fax: 020 7497 0554
Email: info@randc.net
Web Site: www.randc.net
Contacts: Yanko Tihov
Supplying theatres for over 200 years. Made to order drapes & backcloths and supplier of all basic materials: scenic canvas, calico, duck, hessian. Also supplying scenic & artists colours.

SEASONS TEXTILES LIMITED
9 Gorst Road, London NW10 6LA
Tel: 020 8965 6161 Fax: 020 8961 6433
Email: enquiries@seasonstextiles.net
Web Site: www.seasonstextiles.co.uk
Manager: Sue Toone
Hire and purchase of textiles for film, television, photography and interior design. To hire - large selection of tapestries, drapes and soft furnishings. To order - extensive range of fabrics, wallpapers and trimmings at competitive prices.

SHOWTEX
Oude Gentweg 100, 2070 Burcht, Belgium
Tel: 01706 819746 Mob: 07765 341 878
Email: suzanne.wynne@showtex.com
Web Site: www.showtex.com
Sales Representative UK: Suzanne Wynne

STAGE ELECTRICS
Third Way, Avonmouth, Bristol, Avon BS11 9YL
Hire & Sales: 0117 938 4000 Accounts: 0117 937 9550 Admin: 0117 982 7282 Admin Fax: 0117 916 2825 Fax: 0117 916 2828
Email: bristol@stage-electrics.co.uk
Web Site: www.stage-electrics.co.uk
One of the UK's largest suppliers of technical equipment to the entertainment, leisure, conference and presentation industries.
Offering sales and hire of lighting, sound, rigging, staging and all related equipment.
Head of Marketing: Adam Blaxill
Managing Director: Dan Aldridge
London Branch:
175 Long Lane, London SE1 4PN
Tel: 020 7939 3000 Fax: 020 7939 3001
E-Mail: london@stage-electrics.co.uk

Exeter Branch:
1 Swan Units, Heron Road, Sowton Industrial Estate, Exeter EX2 7LL
Tel: 01392 824 100 Fax: 01392 891 116
E-Mail: exeter@stage-electrics.co.uk

THE EVENT HIRE COMPANY
Subsidiary organisation of 'The Crown Group'
Crown House 855 London Road, Grays, RM20 3LG
Tel : 01708 335 184
Fax : 01708 341 909
Email: sales@eventhireonline.co.uk
Web Site: www.eventhireonline.co.uk
Full catering and event hire services, including a comprehensive range of high quality equipment and event furniture.

VARIA TEXTILES LTD
197 Kings Road, Kingston-upon-Thames, Surrey KT2 5HJ
Tel: 020 8549 8590 Fax: 020 8549 8290
Email: varia@variatextile.co.uk
Web Site: www.varia-uk.com
Contact: Karl Leuthenmayr
We have in stock a complete range of fire resistant products. We also arrange for fabric to be made up. Front Projection Screens can be custom-made. Please ask for a quotation.

VISUAL BLISS
5 Memory Cross, Landscove, Ashburton, Newton Abbot, Devon TQ13 7NB
Tel: 01803 762 326
Email: office@visualbliss.co.uk
Web Site: www.visualbliss.co.uk
Proprietor: Colin Quinsey
Specialists in UV Backdrops. A huge range of backdrops, effects and modern designs. Available to rent or purchase, all made to respond to UV lighting. Also 3D props.

WHALEYS (BRADFORD) LTD
Harris Court, Great Horton, Bradford, West Yorkshire BD7 4EQ
Tel: 01274 576 718 Fax: 01274 521 309
Email: kevin.woodhead@whaleysltd.co.uk
Web Site: www.whaleys.co.uk/stage
General Manager: Mr Kevin Woodhead
Sales Manager: Barry Hardisty
Sales Office: David Carroll
Drapes/Backdrops/Borders/Legs etc. Full range of standard flameproof stage fabrics. Orders made up to customer specification. Also huge range of fabrics for costume (many ready for printing/dyeing).

Effects & Fireworks

AIRLIQUIDE UK LTD
Station Road, Coleshill, Birmingham B46 1JY
Tel: 0800 637 737 Fax: 01675 467 022
Email: genenq.aluk@airliquide.com
Web Site: www.uk.airliquide.com
Suppliers of 'Cardice' solid carbon dioxide as pellets, blocks and slices for for effects amongst others. Available from Regional Depots. Contact above address for details.

ANY EFFECTS
Ton Farm, Clifford, Hereford HR3 5HL
Tel: 0800 298 3484
Email: tom@anyeffects.com
Web Site: www.anyeffects.com
Managing Director: Tom Harris
Provision of special effects to the film, television and commercial industry as well as live theatre, events and exhibitions. Specialising in fire and explosion, rain, atmospherics, mechanical effects and stunt preparation. Comprehensive breakaway (shatterglass) department.

AQUAGRAPHICS
Velt House, Velthouse Lane, Elmore, Gloucester GL2 3NY
Tel: 01452 729903
Email: info@mtfx.com
Web Site: www.mtfx.com
Aquagraphics is an exciting and inspiring new water display screen! It is a dynamic flexible water display screen made up of droplets of controlled falling water to form words and logos with infinite design and animation possibilities. Each module is 2.4m in length and can be supplied with or without a display booth. Aquagraphics has a myriad of different exciting applica-

tions such as Conferences, Party Venues, Product Launches, Exhibition Stands, Shopping Malls.

AURORA LIGHTING HIRE LTD
Unit 21, Greenford Park, Ockham Drive, Greenford, London, UB6 0FD
Tel: 0208 813 2777
Email: info@auroratv.co.uk
Web Site: www.auroratv.co.uk
Contact: Sam Crook / Nick Edwards
Providing professional, cost-effective lighting services including design, crewing, hire and sales for all aspects of the entertainment industry from theatre and commercial events to schools and education.

CCT LIGHTING LTD
Unit 3, Ellesmere Business Park, Haydn Road, Nottingham NG5 1DX UK
Tel: 0115 985 8919
Fax: 0115 985 7091
Email: office@cctlighting.co.uk
Web Site: www.cctlighting.com
Directors: John Shore, Richard Stokes, Gary Redfern
CCT Lighting manufacture flameproofed velour and Bolton Twill curtains in a wide range of colours, quoted to specification. Also distributed are the entire Rosco range of products including scenic and projection materials.

CINEBUILD LTD
Broadcast Engineering Centre, Eastbourne Road, Blindley Heath, R7 6JP
Tel: 020 7582 8750
Email: cinebuild@btclick.com
Web Site: www.cinebuild.co.uk
Directors: Tony Neale, Patrick Neale
We supply all types of breakaway glass for television and film, plus sales and hire of special effects and props - snow, mist, rain, cobwebs and dust.

CONCEPT ENGINEERING LTD
Unit 5/7, Woodlands Business Park, Woodlands Park Avenue, Maidenhead, Berkshire SL6 3UA
Tel: 01628 825 555 Fax: 01628 826 261
Email: info@conceptsmoke.com
Web Site: www.concept-smoke.co.uk
Manager: Trevor Dunnington
Smoke generators and Snow effects.

CONFETTI CREATIONS
Velt House, Velthouse Lane, Elmore, Gloucester GL2 3NY
Tel: 01452 729903
Email: info@mtfx.com
Web Site: www.mtfx.com
Confetti Creations bring you a fantastic range of confetti, glitter and streamer effects to bring the extra WOW factor to your event.
Through Confetti Creations you will be able to find almost any shape and size of confetti or glitter in almost any colour. Put this together with a rainbow of streamers and you have everything you need to enhance your event. We can custom cut confetti to your own shape or have confetti printed with an image. Confetti Creations also have one of the largest ranges of cannons available, from the large Master Blaster to the Single Shot Cannons.

CONTINENTAL LASERS (UK)
B105 Portview Trade Centre, 310 Newtownards Road, Belfast, County Antrim BT4 1HE Northern Ireland
Tel: 028 9045 8658 Fax: 028 9046 1550
Mobile: 07860 800283
Email: info@continental-lasers.com
Web Site: www.continental-lasers.com
Proprietor: Brian Bennington
Since 1982 Continental Lasers have proved to be among the top laser display companies in the world for performance and innovation. The hire of systems for corporate events and spectactulars is handled by Continental Show Laser.

DALE AIR LTD
Anglo Brands Ltd, Bridge End Mills, Tong Lane, Whitworth, Rochdale OL12 8BG
Tel: 0845 305 8468 Fax: 01706 853 625
Email: info@daleair.com
Web Site: www.daleair.com
Dale Air Ltd has provided themed aromas for over 20 years.

DEFINITIVE SPECIAL PROJECTS LTD
High Tree Farm, Wood End, Stevenage, Hertfordshire SG2 7BB
Tel: 01438 869 005 Fax: 01438 869 006
Email: info@laserlightshows.co.uk
Web: www.definitivespecialprojects.co.uk
Contact: Steve Hitchins
Definitive provides specialist entertainment laser lighting to enhance your event whatever the size of your venue, in the UK or overseas.

DIRECTA (UK) LTD
Cold Norton, Chelmsford, Essex CM3 6UA
Tel: 01621 828 882 Fax: 01621 828 072
Email: head.office@directa.co.uk
Web Site: www.directa.co.uk
Five good reasons to buy from Directa:
1. Competitive Prices
2. Speedy Nationwide Delivery
3. Free Technical Advice
4. Strict Quality Control
5. BS EN ISO 9001:2000
For free catalogue phone: 01621 828882

DRAGONFIRE LTD
Tuthill Rise, Stoke Lacy, Bromyard, Herefordshire HR7 4QZ
Tel: 01885 490 538
Email: info@dragonfire.co.uk
Web Site: www.dragonfire.co.uk
Managing Director: Mr Andrew Goodwin
Dragonfire is a leading supplier of firework displays, indoor pyrotechnics, special effects, fire sculptures and even giant puppets. We specialise in shows timed to music and in spectacular shows integrating pyrotechnics with lasers, lighting, dancing flames and fountains.

DRAX LIGHTING LTD
Unit 21B Icknield Way Farm, Tring Road, Dunstable, Bedfordshire LU6 2JX
Tel: 01582 475 614 Fax: 01582 475 669
Email: richard@draxlighting.com, info@draxlighting.com
Web Site: www.draxlighting.com
Contact: Richard Foster
Drax specialises in event lighting design and equipment supply for stage shows, outdoor productions and corporate events. Drax hire and sell quality lighting, sound and effects equipment for static, touring or short term use. Dry hire or hire with crew is available for both professional and amateur events, UK and worldwide. Hire equipment includes profiles, fresnels, PARs, floods, followspots, moving lights, rigging, special effects systems and dimmers. Control systems available include Avolites, Artistic Licence and Zero 88.

EMERGENCY HOUSE
Manchester Road, Marsden, Huddersfield, West Yorkshire HD7 6EY
Tel: 0161 339 1362 Fax: 01484 845 061
Email: info@emergencyhouse.co.uk
Web Site: www.emergencyhouse.co.uk
Full range of visual effects.
Contact: Evan Green-Hughes or Jonathan Carter

EMF TECHNOLOGY LTD
Unit 1A, Thurley Business Units, Pump Lane, Grazeley, Reading RG7 1LL
Tel: 0118 988 7647 Fax: 0118 988 7651
Email: info@emftechnology.co.uk
Web Site: www.emftechnology.co.uk
Contact: Stuart Roberts
EMF are specialist suppliers of stage flame effects & bespoke flame effects, high power projection and 8KW searchlights for theatre productions and events.

EUROSOUND (UK) LTD
44 High Street, Clayton West, Huddersfield HD8 9NS
Tel: 01484 866 066 Fax: 01484 866 299
Email: eurosounduk@yahoo.co.uk
Web Site: www.eurosound.co.uk
Contact: Paul Martin

EXPLOSIVE DEVELOPMENT LTD
Gateside Factory, Sanquhar, Dumfriesshire DG4 6JP Scotland
Tel: 01659 50531 Fax: 01659 50526
Email: simon@explosive-developments.co.uk
Manager: Simon Walker
Suppliers of all types of special effects.

FBX LTD
Unit 3b Chestnut Ind Estate, Bassingham, Lincoln LN5 9LL
Tel: 01522 788 818 Fax: 01522 788 890
Web Site: www.fbxltd.co.uk
Senior Personnel: Philip Oliver
Manufacturers of theatrical special effects and specialised chemicals; aerosol special effects; Kobweb artificial cobwebs in cans or special gun. Snocene quality decorative snow; Kolsnow falling snow; frost effect; New Poliac clear flame-resistant decorative lacquer; gold/silver lacquer; fluorescent effects; black/green paint/stencil aerosols; brush on crystal effects for glass; portable gas-filled fire extinguishers.

FIREWORKS LONDON
102 East Barnet Road, Barnet, Hertfordshire EN4 8RE
Tel: 020 8441 9427 Mob: 07930 863 282
Email: info@fireworks-london.co.uk
Web Site: www.fireworks-london.co.uk

FLASHLIGHT LTD
Unit A3, Axis Point, Hilltop Road, Heywood, Lancashire OL10 2RQ
Tel: 01706 625 866 Fax: 01706 620 756
Email: sales@flash-light.co.uk
Web Site: www.flash-light.co.uk
Contact: Rob Williamson
Flashlight are the ' one-stop shop' for entertainment lighting, accessories and consumables. We are main stockists for ETC, Lee Filters, Arri, Martin Professional, Zero 88, Pulsar, Doughty, Rosco, Philips, Le Maitre.

GLOWSHOP
The Light House 582-584 Hagley Road West, Birmingham B68 0BS
Tel: 0121 423 2000 Fax: 0121 423 2050
Email: sales@uv-light.co.uk
Web Site: www.glowshop.com
Managing Director: Paul Jackson
Specialist company dedicated to sales of UV lighting, UV reactive invisible / UV revealing and glow in the dark products.

GRADAV HIRE & SALES LTD
Elstree Light and Power, The Power House, Elstree Film Studios, Shenley Road, Borehamwood, Herts WD6 1JG
Tel: 020 8324 2100 Fax: 020 8324 2933
Email: office@gradav.co.uk
Web Site: www.gradav.co.uk
Sale & Dry Hire of technical equipment for theatre - including animation effects, moving head lanterns, radio mics & systems and Prolyte trussing. We also supply consummables.

HANDS ON PRODUCTION SERVICES
79 Loanbank Quadrant, Glasgow G51 3HZ Scotland
Tel: 0141 440 2005
Email: info@hands-on-uk.com
Web Site: www.hands-on-uk.com
Hire of Weapons, Heraldic Shields, Armour and Allied Properties for Theatre, Film and Publicity Work.

HSL (HIRE) LTD
Unit E & F, Glenfield Park, Philips Road, Blackburn Lancashire BB1 5PF
Tel: 01254 698 808 Fax: 01254 698 835
Email: simon@hslgroup.com, contact@hslgroup.com
Web Site: www.hslgroup.com
Contact: Simon Stuart

HWL (UK) LTD
Cricket Street, Denton, Manchester M34 3DR
Tel: 0161 335 0220 Fax: 0161 320 3928
Email: guns@hwltd.co.uk
Web Site: www.hwltd.co.uk
Contact: Bob Howorth
Hirers of all types of furniture, set dressing, decorative lighting, pictures, hand props etc. Also specialist hirers of weapons and blank firing guns.

ICE COOLING LTD
Unit 12, Central Park Estate, Staines Road, Hounslow TW4 5DJ
Tel: 01276 22 929 Mob: 07778 486227
Email: dryicesales@googlemail.com
Web Site: www.ice-cooling.co.uk
Senior Personnel: Richard Walker
Supplier of dry ice, produced in blocks, pellets or slices. Together with full range of insulated containers. Deliveries nationwide.

KIMBOLTON FIREWORKS LIMITED
7 High Street, Kimbolton, Huntingdon, Cambridgeshire PE28 0HB
Tel: 01480 860 988 Fax: 01480 861 277
Email: info@kimboltonfireworks.co.uk
Web Site: www.kimboltonfireworks.co.uk
Display fireworks for outside use.

LANCELYN THEATRE SUPPLIES
Ferry Hinksey Road, Oxford OX2 0BY
Tel: 01865 722 468 Fax: 01865 728 791
Email: oxford@lancelynoxford.co.uk
Web Site: www.lancelyn.co.uk
Sales and Branch Manager: Reg Berry
Email: reg@lancelynoxford.co.uk
Marketing, Admin & Office Manager: Sara Ingham
Made to measure curtains, supply and fix, repair and cleaning.

LASER CREATIONS INTERNATIONAL LTD (LCI)
55 Merthyr Terrace, Barnes, London SW13 8DL
Tel: 020 8741 5747 Fax: 020 8748 9879
Email: contact@lci-uk.com
Web Site: www.lci-uk.com
Managing Director: Marlyn Weeks
Originally famous for its laser spectaculars, LCI has extended its portfolio to include waterscreens, dancing waters, digital video projection, pyrotechnics and other special effects.

LE MAITRE LTD
6 Forval Close, Wandle Way, Mitcham, Surrey CR4 4NE
Tel: 020 8646 2222 Fax: 020 8646 1955
Email: info@lemaitreltd.com, elaine.peake@lemaitreltd.com
Web Site: www.lemaitreltd.com
Managing Director: Karen Haddon, Richard Wilson
UK Sales Manager: Elaine Peake
Events Director: Karen Haddon
Manufacturers of dry ice machines, smoke machines, coloured smoke cartridges, flash puffs, coloured fire, cartridges, maroons, firing systems and related products. Pyrotechnic manufacturers, stockists and operators.

LIGHT WORKS LIMITED
2a Greenwood Road, London E8 1AB
Tel: 020 7249 3627 Fax: 020 7254 0306
Email: charlie@light-works.co.uk
Web Site: www.light-works.co.uk
Contact: Charlie Paton

LM PRODUCTIONS LLP
Unit 6H, Southbourne Business Park, Courtlands Road, Eastbourne, East Sussex BN22 8UY
Tel: 01323 432 170 Fax: 01323 432 171
Email: info@lm-productions.com
Web Site: www.lm-productions.com
Contact: Stephen Harvey
Laser display and special effects.

MARTIN PROFESSIONAL PLC
Cranborne House, Cranborune Industrial Estate, Cranbourne Road, Potters Bar, Hertfordshire, EN6 3JN
Tel: 0203 0021 170
Email: uksales@martin.dk
Web Site: www.martinpro.co.uk

MERCIA THEATRE SERVICES
2A Hotel Street, Coalville, Leicestershire LE67 3EP
Tel: 01530 263 454 Fax: 01530 260 206
Email: merciaarts@yahoo.co.uk
Contact: Simon Nickerson
Lighting: Sales of accessories and consumables including colour filter, cables, connectors, fixing hardware, adhesive tapes, lamps. Sales of lanterns and control systems. Installation service.
Sound: Sales of accessories and consumables including cables, connectors, batteries, sound effects CD's.. Extensive range of hardware including microphones, mixing desks, amplifiers, speakers, CD, cassette and mini disc players, induction loop and Infra-red systems. Installation service. PA hire for indoor / outdoor meetings, conferences and events.
Effects: Sales of hardware and consumables for pyrotechnic and special effects.
Make-up: Sales of make-up by Ben Nye and Mehron. Also an extensive range of wigs, masks and costume accessories.
Mail order catalog available.

MIKE & ROSI COMPTON
11 Woodstock Road, Croydon, Surrey CR0 1JS
Tel: 020 8680 4364 Mobile: 07900 258646 (Mike)
Email: mikeandrosicompton@btopenworld.com
We make props, mechanical visual effects, costumes and models, we specialise in the unusual, but can do almost anything! No hiring.

MTFX LTD SPECIAL EFFECTS
Velt House, Velt House Lane, Elmore, Gloucester, GL2 3NY
Tel: 01452 729 903
Email: info@mtfx.com
Web Site: www.mtfx.com
Managing Director: Mark Turner
MTFX make events, concerts and tours worldwide go with a bang!
From fireworks, pyrotechnics, water screens and confetti, we create the effects that make events and productions unforgettable. MTFX is internationally renowned for its high quality special effects. Our expertise and experience in physical, pyrotechnic, mechanical and atmospheric effects means you can trust us to create the effects you need on time and on budget. For the ultimate impact, Firedance provides a dancing flame spectacular to give an occasion that extra special WOW factor with up to 48 jets of fire 8m high synchronised to music with millisecond accuracy.

MTFX LTD SPECIAL EFFECTS (CARDIFF)
The Television Centre, Culverhouse Cross, Cardiff CF5 6XJ
Tel: 01452 729 903
Email: info@mtfx.com
Web Site: www.mtfx.com

OPTIKINETICS (UK) LIMITED
38 Cromwell Road, Luton, Bedfordshire LU3 1DN
Tel: 01582 411 413 Fax: 01582 400 613
Email: ukadmin@optikinetics.com
Web Site: www.optikinetics.co.uk

PAINS FIREWORKS
Romsey Road, Whiteparish, Salisbury, Wiltshire SP5 2SD
Tel: 01794 884 040 Fax: 01794 884 015
Email: sales@painsfireworks.co.uk
Web Site: www.painsfireworks.co.uk
Theatrical & Conference Effects.
Pyrotechnics.

PHOENIX FIREWORKS
Founder Member of the British Pyrotechnist's Association
Hill Park Farm, Wrotham Hill Road, Wrotham, Sevenoaks, Kent TN15 7PX
Tel: 01732 822 788/ 01732 822 659
Email: info@PhoenixFireworks.co.uk
Web Site: www.phoenixfireworks.co.uk
Suppliers of fireworks displays in the UK.

POLLEX PROPS
Leac Na Ban, Tayvallich, Lochgilphead, Argyll PA31 8PF
Tel: 01546 870 310
Email: pollexprops.firebrand@btinternet.com
Web:
www.pollexpropsfirebrand.moonfruit.com
Contact: Alexander Hamilton
Props, special effects for theatre, television and advertising. No hiring.

PRG UK
The Cofton Centre, Groveley Lane, Longbridge, B31 4PT
Tel: 0845 470 6400
Email: ukinfo@prg.com
Web Site: www.prg.com
Contact: Rich Rowley
With the largest inventory of rental lighting stock in Europe, PRG is the consummate supplier of lighting to the business of entertainment and in particular the theatre.

QUICKSILVER UK LTD
17 Hyde Road, Denton, Manchester M34 3AF
Tel: 0161 320 7232 Fax: 0161 335 9871
Email: contact@quicksilverfireworks.co.uk
Web Site: www.quicksilverfireworks.co.uk

ROSCOLAB LTD
Blanchard Works, Kangley Bridge Road, Sydenham, London SE26 5AQ
Tel: 020 8659 2300 Fax: 020 8659 3153
Email: contact@rosco.com
Web Site: www.rosco.com
Shrink mirrors, breakaways. Rear & front projection screens, scenic materials, scenic paint systems. Lighting colour media including diffusion. Comprehensive range of gobos.
Director of Sales: Cristian Arroyo

SANDLING FIREWORKS
First Floor Offices SE45 Gloucester Airport, Staverton, Gloucestershire GL51 6SP
Tel: 01452 855 915 Fax: 01452 855 917
Email: sales@sandlingfireworks.co.uk
Web Site: www.sandlingfireworks.com
Importers and manufacturers of fireworks professionally fired displays and suppliers of D.I.Y. kits (retail and trade).

SDD SOUND & LIGHT LTD
Temple Gardens, Staines, Middlesex TW18 3NQ
Tel: 01784 455 666 Fax: 01784 455 642
Email: info@sddsoundandlight.com
Web Site: www.sddsoundandlight.com
Rental, sales, repair and installation of all types and brands of equipment from multi channel radio microphone systems to intelligent lighting. Visit our website for our catalogue.

THE SEARCHLIGHT CO
Unit 9, Cromer Hyde Farm, Lemsford, Welwyn Garden City, Herts AL8 7XD
Tel: 01707 331621 Fax: 0870 838 1073
Email: enquiries@searchlight.co.uk
Web Site: www.searchlight.co.uk

SGB WORLD SERVICE
Empire Buildings, 49 Church Street, Stoke, Stoke-on-Trent Staffordshire, ST4 1DQ
Tel: 01782 749 749
Email: sales@fireworkempire.co.uk
Web Site: www.fireworkempire.co.uk

SHELL SHOCK FIREWORK COMPANY
Furze Hill Farm, Knossington, Oakham, Leicestshire LE15 8LX
Tel: 01664 454 994 Mob: 07768 684910
Web Site: www.shellshockfireworks.co.uk
Specialist firework display team in UK and Internationally. Also provide pyro and effects. Importers of high quality material from Spain, Malta, etc.

SMART LIVE
30 Maiden Lane, London WC2E 7JS
Tel: 0207 836 0562 Fax: 0207 836 1044
Email: smartlive@smartgroupltd.co.uk
Web Site: www.smartlive.co.uk
Creating events with edge.
Special event production company comprising set designers, choreographers, and artistic directors. Technically, we boast sound engineers, lighting technicians and stage managers. We combine our creative and technical talents to stage the most amazing themed events ever.

SNOW BUSINESS
The Snow Mill, Bridge Road, Ebley, Stroud, Gloucestershire GL5 4TR
Tel/Fax: 01453 840 077
Email: snow@snowbusiness.com
Web Site: www.snowbusiness.com
Commercial Director: Luke Buxton
Snow Business design snow and winter effects for film, television and live events. We supply over one hundred types of artificial snow as well as the real thing. We also have a wide range of application equipment to suit the type of snow required and the area to be covered. We are able to dress the largest of sets quickly with minimal fuss and manpower, even out of doors in the most adverse weather conditions.

SNOWBOY SYSTEMS LTD
Unit 10, Glen Industrial Estate, Essendine, Stamford, Lincolnshire PE9 4LE
Tel: 01780 752166
Email: website@snowboy.co.uk
Web Site: www.snowboy.co.uk
Managing Director: Harry Stokes
All special effects equipment hire and services. Manufacturers of the 'Snowboy' (falling snow machine) for realistic, quick clearing snow effects.

STAGE TWO LIMITED
Unit J, Penfold Estate, Imperial Way, Watford, Hertfordshire WD24 4YY
Tel: 01923 230 789 Fax: 01923 255 048
Email: info@stage-two.co.uk
Web Site: www.stage-two.co.uk
Hire or Sale of sound, lighting and special effects for all applications. Special effects Flash Pots, Maroons, Bullet Hits.

THEATRICAL PYROTECHNICS LTD
The Loop, Manston Airport, Manston, Ramsgate, Kent CT12 5DE
Tel: 01843 823 545 Fax: 01843 822 655
Email: tpl@opalbroadband.net
Web Site: www.tplpyro.co.uk
Contacts: Sue Sturges, Malcolm Armstrong
Special effects manufacturers. Flash Pots, Maroons, Bullet Hits, Battle items. Manufacturer and supplier of special effects for stage, films and television. The best SFX anywhere!

TRAFALGAR LIGHTING LTD
Also see sister company, 'Make Up Effects'
9 Northway, London N9 0AD
Tel: 020 8887 0082 Fax: 020 8887 0072
Email: hire@trafalgarlighting.co.uk
Web Site: www.trafalgarlighting.co.uk
Sales and hire of lighting, sound and power distribution equipment for all forms of entertainments. Free advice.

WATER SCULPTURES LIMITED
Unit 4, Stevant Way, White Lund, Morecambe, Lancashire LA3 3PU
Tel: 01524 377 07 (2 lines)
Email: info@watersculptures.co.uk
Web Site: www.watersculptures.co.uk
Managing Director: Byll Elliot
Specialists in the Design and Installation of all types of Water features, from rain and fog effects to pools, fountains and waterfalls. Many years of experience in Theatre.

Emergency Services

AMBULANCE SERVICES FILM UNIT
19 Cleve Avenue, Brentwood Essex SM14 4WD
Mobile: 07887 765 153
Fax: 01277 22 55 55
Email: alex787@tiscali.co.uk

MIDLAND FIRE PROTECTION SERVICES
Unit 6, Bayton Way, Exhall, Coventry, West Midlands CV7 9ER
Tel: 02476 367 766
Email: info@midlandfire.co.uk
Web Site: www.midlandfire.co.uk
Contact: Robin Crane

S.O.S DOCTORS DIRECT
Buckingham House East, Buckingham Parade, The Broadway, Stanmore, Middlesex HA7 4EB
Tel: 0800 9889 999 / 020 8416 1510
Email: mail@doctorsdirect.co.uk
Web Site: www.doctorsdirect.co.uk
24 Hour visiting doctor service. Clinic services and medical assessments for insurance companies are also available.

ST JOHN AMBULANCE
27 St John's Lane, London EC1M 4BU
Tel: 08700 104 950
Email: customer_services@stjohnsupplies.co.uk
Web Site: www.sja.org.uk

Event & Conference Organisers

CIRCA GROUP
16 Church Road, Tunbridge Wells, Kent TN1 1JP
Tel: 01892 517 500 Fax: 01892 527 702
Email: info@circagroup.co.uk
Web Site: www.circagroup.co.uk
Film and video production, projection and technical consultancy and corporate event organisers.

CATHERINE COOPER EVENTS
Tel: 020 7483 1181
Email: info13@catherinecooperevents.co.uk
Web: www.catherinecooperevents.co.uk
Contact: Catherine Cooper
Extensive contact in theatre, the media and beyond. Complete event management and public relations or work to your specification, to create memorable and unique occasions.

CREATIVE LEISURE GLOBAL LTD
16Q Top Barn Business Centre, Top Barn Farm Worcester Road, Holt Heath, Worcester WR6 6NH
Tel: 01905 622 275 Mob: 07889 201 670
Email: info@creativeleisure.co.uk
Web Site: www.creativeleisure.co.uk
Contacts: Bruce Bennet
Active features for Events, Shows and Promotions where Public Participation is important. Can Design, Build and Manage. Range includes Climbing, Skiing and Snowboarding ramps, Treeless Ropes Course Real and Synthetic Ice rinks etc. Can also provide REAL Snow and Ice.

DOUB7E SEVEN EVENTS LTD
Authorised House 4 Endowood Road Sheffield, S7 2LZ
Tel: 0114 2362 874 Mob: 07966 060777
Email: roop@77events.co.uk
Web Site: www.77events.co.uk
Contact: Roop Mullins
We supply entertainment for private and corporate events, ranging from celebrities, bands, speakers to magicians and walkabout entertainment.

GALAXY EVENTS
Galaxy House, Mian Yard, 86 Wallis Road, London E9 5LN
Tel: 0208 1330 558
Email: info@galaxy-events.co.uk
Web Site: www.galaxy-events.co.uk
Senior Personnel: Mel Harvey
Artist Management and Event Coordination.

I.C.E. PRODUCTIONS
Warwick Corner, 42 Warwick Road, Kenilworth, Warwickshire CV8 1HE
Tel: 01926 864 800
Email: web@ice-productions.com/ birmingham@ice-productions.com
Web Site: www.ice-productions.com
Entertainment and Video Production services. Festival and Event production. Short films and pop promos.

IN 2 EVENTS
1 Silverthorne Way, Waterlooville, Hampshire PO7 7XB
Tel: 08453 102 222 Fax: 08453 100 282
Email: info@in2events.co.uk
Web Site: www.in2events.co.uk
Complete event management and planning.

IOGIG LTD
39 Equinox House Wakering Road, Barking, Essex IG11 8RN
Tel: 020 7112 8907
Email: ian@iogig.com
Web Site: www.iogig.com
Contact: Ian Taylor
We provide theatre and event production services for business and the entertainment industry, including planning, costing, set design and construction, sound and lighting design, equipment hire, management and all the disciplines required to stage high quality concerts, productions or events.

MC PRODUCTION GROUP
Unit SU4A, Lansbury Estate, 102 Lower Guildford Road, Woking, Surrey GU21 2EP
Tel: 01483 884488.
Web Site: www.mcpg.co.uk

MUSICTALKS
33 Palmeira Road, Bexleyheath, Kent DA7 4UU
Tel/ Fax: 020 8301 6366 Mob: 07798641400
Email: info@musictalks.biz
Web Site: www.musictalks.biz
Contact: Pauline Slane
MusicTalks realises that no two functions are the same, so each of our bespoke events are tailored to your individual needs, ensuring guests speak of the occasion long after they have gone home. With our professional, yet fun approach, you can be sure of commitment, adaptability and professionalism at all times. There isn't a problem that cannot be solved - just a solution waiting to be found! We welcome all enquiries both corporate and private.

POINT SOURCE PRODUCTIONS LTD
Unit 5 Kimpton trade & Business Centre, Minden Road, Sutton, Surrey SM3 9PF
Tel: 020 8254 2620 Fax: 08701 696 736
Email: info@pslx.co.uk
Web Site: www.pslx.co.uk
Point Source Productions can organise, plan and supply technical services, including lighting, sound, AV and staging, for Corporate, Theatre and Live Events.

SOUND & LIGHT PRODUCTIONS
PO Box 32295 London W5 1WD UK
Tel: 0870 0660272 Fax: 0870 0660273
Email: slp@soundandlightproductions.co.uk
Web Site: www.soundandlightproductions.co.uk
Executive Directors: John and Jan Denby
We are an Event Management Company Established in 1986. No event is too small or too large for us to handle.

Film, Video & Audio Visual

AVCOM HIRE
Stanlake Mews, London W12 7HS
Tel (Sales): 020 8735 3424 Tel (Hire): 020 8735 3410 Accounts: 020 8735 3444
Email: hire@avcom.co.uk, sales@avcom.co.uk
Web Site: www.avcom.co.uk
Rental of Audio Visual Equipment.

BCS MULTIMEDIA
Video Productions - Graphics
Grantham House, Macclesfield, Cheshire SK10 3NP
Tel: 01625 615 379
Email: pppconsultants@aol.com
Web Site: www.purplesat.com
Computer graphic specialists for the music industry. Video light shows for live performance or video production. Main agents for Video DJ effects equipment. Sales, hire or leasing.

BLACK LIGHT
West Shore Trading Estate, West Shore Road, Edinburgh EH5 1QF Scotland
Tel: 0131 551 2337 Fax: 0131 551 6827
Email: feedback@black-light.com
Web Site: www.black-light.com
Managing Director: Gavin Stewart
Hire and Events Manager: Calder Sibbard
Sales: Karen Fairlie

CIRCA GROUP
16 Church Road, Tunbridge Wells, Kent TN1 1JP
Tel: 01892 517 500 Fax: 01892 527 702
Email: info@circagroup.co.uk
Web Site: www.circagroup.co.uk
Film and video production, projection and technical consultancy and corporate event organisers.

CTL AUDIO VISUAL SERVICES LTD
Unit 2, Britannia Business Park, Quarry Wood, Aylesford, Kent ME20 7NT
Tel: 01622 719 151 Fax: 01622 716 425
Email: info@ctlav.co.uk
Web Site: www.ctlav.co.uk
Managing Director: Robert J. Owen
CTLAV has been designing, installing and maintaining fully integrated audiovisual systems for well over 20 years.

DTL BROADCAST LIMITED
5 Johnsons Industrial Estate, Silverdale Road, Hayes, Middlesex UB3 3BA
Tel: 020 8813 5200 Fax: 020 8813 5022
Email: info@dtl-broadcast.com
Web Site: www.dtl-broadcast.com
Managing Director: Anwar Sultan

ELECTROSONIC LTD
Hawley Mill, Hawley Road, Dartford, Kent DA2 7SY
Tel: 01322 222 211 Fax: 01322 282 282
Email: info@electrosonic.co.uk
Web Site: www.electrosonic.co.uk
Manufacture and supply of audio visual and video control equipment from single screen up to multi-media spectaculars.

ETC UK LTD T/A THE PROJECTION STUDIO
Unit 4a, 13 Tarves Way, London SE10 9JP
Tel: 0208 2934 270 Fax: 020 8594 1243
Email: info@theprojectionstudio.com
Web Site: www.theprojectionstudio.com
Contacts: Ross Ashton , Steve Larkins
If you need to fill any space with exciting images, then we can offer you the solution. The PIGI system is the world's most versatile and powerful image projection system.

FLASHLIGHT LTD
Unit A3, Axis Point, Hilltop Road, Heywood, Lancashire OL10 2RQ
Tel: 01706 625 866 Fax: 01706 620 756
Email: sales@flash-light.co.uk
Web Site: www.flash-light.co.uk
Contact: Rob Williamson
Flashlight are the ' one-stop shop' for entertainment lighting, accessories and consumables. We are main stockists for ETC, Lee Filters, Arri, Martin Professional, Zero 88, Pulsar, Doughty, Rosco, Philips, Le Maitre.

FUTURIST PROJECTS LTD
Unit 1, White Swan Yard, Otley, LS21 1AE
Tel: 0113 279 0033 Fax: 0113 301 0255
Email: info@futurist.co.uk
Web Site: www.futurist.co.uk
Managing Director: Jamie Hudson
Financial Director: Jamie Hudson
AV, Theatrical Productions, Lighting and Sound Specialists.

GROOVY MOVIES.TV
First Floor 23 York Road, Hove, East Sussex BN3 1DJ
Tel: 01273 7300 00 Mob: 07718 914 068
Web Site: www.groovymovies.tv
Contacts: Mark 'Yeti' Cribb
TV & Video for music, comedy, commercial and live productions, aswell as comedy scripting and direction. Credits include: Right Size, Kiki Dee, Future Dance & Steven Berkoff.

HALL STAGE LIMITED
Unit 4, Cosgrove Way, Luton, Bedfordshire LU1 1XL
Tel: 0845 345 4255 Fax: 0845 345 4256
Email: sales@hallstage.com
Web Site: www.hallstage.com
Managing Director: Charles Haines
Technical Director: Phil Wells
Stage Sales Services Manager: Scott Oake
Sales Co-ordinator: Alison Price
Designs and manufactures standard and special products for the stage, screen, AV and industrial market.
Hall Stage and Theatre Supplies formed in 1895. Equipment ranges include T60 and T70 curtain track systems for all applications. Specialist products include rolloer or flying safety curtains, counterweight sets, hemp rope sets, the DynaGlide powered and manual hoists for powered fling and lighting bar operations, DynaLine pulleys, motor control systems, and a selection of theatrical and scenic hardware fittings.

HD PRO AUDIO
6 Eversley Way, Thorpe Industrial Estate, Egham, Surrey TW20 8RG
Tel: 01784 433 687 Fax: 01784 479 910
Email: info@hdproaudio.co.uk
Web Site: www.hdproaudio.co.uk
Managing Director: Andy Huffer
HD Pro Audio are the UK's leading independent supplier and installer of professional audio visual systems.

I.C.E. PRODUCTIONS
Warwick Corner, 42 Warwick Road, Kenilworth, Warwickshire CV8 1HE
Tel: 01926 864 800
Email: web@ice-productions.com/ birmingham@ice-productions.com
Web Site: www.ice-productions.com
Entertainment and Video Production services. Festival and Event production. Short films and pop promos.

IMAGINE THEATRE LTD
2 Brandon House Woodhams Road Middlemarsh Business Park Coventry, CV3 4FX
Tel: 024 7630 7001 Fax: 024 7630 7559
Mob: 07721 426 398 (Steve)
Email: info@imaginetheatre.co.uk
Web Site: www.imaginetheatre.co.uk
Managing Director: Steven Boden
Production Assistant: Louise Redmond
Imagine Theatre are a pantomime and theatre production company. The company produces traditional family pantomimes in over 30 venues across the country, and operates an extensive scenery, prop & costume department.

JVC PROFESSIONAL EUROPE
JVC House, JVC Business Park, 12 Priestley Way, London NW2 7BA
Tel: 020 8208 6200 Fax: 020 8208 6260
Email: info@jvcpro.co.uk
Web Site: www.jvcpro.co.uk
General Manager: John Kelly
Service Manager: Mike Turner
Marketing Manager: Liz Cox
Professional Video Manufacturer

KEY AUDIO VISUAL
Black Tower Studios, 15 Bracondale, Norwich, Norfolk NR1 2AL
Tel: 01603 616 661 Fax: 01603 616 668
Email: daniel.forster@keyav.com
Web Site: www.keyav.com
Contact: Katrina Colgan

KIRKPATRICK SOUND ENGINEERING
1 Clover Drive, The Paddocks, Pickmere, Knutsford, Cheshire WA16 0WF
Tel/Fax: 01565 733 200 Mobile: 07831 504 404
Email: roy@kirkpatrick4sound.co.uk
Web Site: www.kirkpatrick4sound.co.uk
Contact: Roy Kirkpatrick
Professional sound and communication systems and equipment. Sales, installation, hire and system design. Also Magnetic Induction Loop Systems.

LASER CREATIONS INTERNATIONAL LTD (LCI)
55 Merthyr Terrace, Barnes, London SW13 8DL
Tel: 020 8741 5747 Fax: 020 8748 9879
Email: contact@lci-uk.com
Web Site: www.lci-uk.com
Managing Director: Marlyn Weeks
Originally famous for its laser spectaculars, LCI has extended its portfolio to include waterscreens, dancing waters, digital video projection, pyrotechnics and other special effects.

LE MARK GROUP
Houghton, Huntingdon, Cambridgeshire PE28 2DH
Tel: 01480 494 540
Email: linda@lemark.co.uk / info@lemark.co.uk
Web Site: www.lemark.co.uk
Sales Director: Linda Gibbons
Le Mark have serviced the theatre industry over the last 25 years with their range of self-adhesive products. We are well known for introducing new innovative products and winning awards for Blacktak & Slipway.

LINE-UP PMC
10 Matthew Close, Newcastle upon Tyne NE6 1XD
Tel / Fax: 0191 275 9745 Mob: 07808 300 906
Email: chrismurtagh@line-up.co.uk
Web Site: www.line-up.co.uk
Senior Personnel: Chris Murtagh

MCL
Catesby Park, Eckersall Road, Kings Norton, Birmingham B38 8SE
Tel: 0121 433 8899 Fax: 0121 433 8891
London Office: 14 Ockham Drive, Greenford Park, Greenford, London, UB6 0FD Tel: 0208 839 7010
Fax: 0208 839 7011
Email: info@mclcreate.com
Web Site: www.mclcreate.com
General Manager (Birmingham): Mark Simkin
Operations Manager (Birmingham): Paul Mandeville
Hire Manager (Birmingham): Chris Cheatle
Conference, exhibition and presentation equipment hire. Audio visual sound and lighting.

PAUL BARKER LTD
Crosslands Barn, Main Street, Stanbury, Haworth, West Yorkshire BD22 0HB
Tel: 01535 643 686 Fax: 01535 648 586
Mobile: 07830 207123
Email: paul@paulbarker.com
Web Site: www.paulbarker.com
Concert promoter: Paul Barker
Promotes live bands and theatre concerts.

PLANET HIRE LTD
Unit 5,10 Centre 59-71 River Road Barking Essex IG11 0DR
Tel: 0845 230 1234 Fax: 0845 230 1235
Email: info@planethire.co.uk
Web Site: www.planethire.org.uk
Whether you're holding a conference,attending an exhibition or holding a meeting we have the AV/IT equipment that you will need.

PRG UK
The Cofton Centre, Groveley Lane, Longbridge, B31 4PT
Tel: 0845 470 6400
Email: ukinfo@prg.com
Web Site: www.prg.com
Contact: Rich Rowley
With the largest inventory of rental lighting stock in Europe, PRG is the consummate supplier of lighting to the business of entertainment and in particular the theatre. Whether it's the lighting rig for a touring musical production, a West End show or opera at the Royal Albert Hall, we have the knowledge, the equipment and the expertise to ensure your success, every time.

RESOURCES CENTRE LTD
Cambridge House, 128 Park Road, Camberley, Surrey GU15 2LW
Tel: 01276 670 000 Fax: 01276 670 010
Hire and Supply of P.A. Systems. Supply of Operating Technicians.

THE SCREEN COMPANY
Unit 9, St. Martin's Business Centre, St. Martin's Way, Bedford MK42 0LF
Tel: 01234 220 502
Email: sales@thescreencompany.co.uk
Web Site: www.thescreencompany.co.uk
Contacts: Lynn Jackson
Producer and retailer of Projection screens.

SECOND HOME STUDIOS
Second Home Studios, 26a Oxford Street, Birmingham B5 5NR
Tel: 07876 406 336/ 0121 208 9916
Email: chris@secondhomestudios.com
Web Site: www.secondhomestudios.com
Contact: Chris Randall
Specialist in projection design for integration into stage productions with experience in film, animation, design and visual effects. Complete service from inception of ideas to provision of playback equipment.

SOUND ALIBI PRODUCTIONS
92 Hartley Avenue, Woodhouse, Leeds, West Yorkshire LS6 2HZ
Tel/Fax: 0113 243 0177 Mobile: 07810 268192
Email: andy@soundalibi.co.uk
Web Site: www.soundalibi.co.uk
Contact: Andy Wood (partner)
Digital media production company specialising in video (documentation/creative/projections) for theatre and dance projects. Friendly efficient service, from concept development to finished product.

SOUND ASSOCIATES LTD
81 Island Farm Road, West Molesey, Surrey KT8 2SA
Tel: 020 8939 5900 Fax: 020 8939 5901
Email: glodge@soundassociates.co.uk
Web Site: www.soundassociates.co.uk
Managing Director: Graham Lodge

TMB
21 Armstrong Way, Southall, Middlesex UB2 4SD
Tel: 020 8574 9700 Fax: 020 8574 9701
Email: tmb-info@tmb.com
Web Site: www.tmb.com
Contact: Paul Hartley
Value added distributor of production lighting equipment, sound and lighting cabling and power distribution. TMB's product range includes all major US and European production lighting and hardware including all touring expendable supplies.

TERRALEC LTD
Osprey House, Featherby Way, Purdeys Industrial Estate, Rochford, Essex SS4 1LD
Tel: 01702 547 571 Fax: 01702 541 075
Email: sales@terralec.com
Web Site: www.terralec.co.uk
Suppliers of professional stage lighting, audio equipment, lighting control, microphones, staging, trussing, hardware, accessories & much more! For: Theatre, stage, commercial events and the entertainment industry.

TMC
Hillam Road, Bradford, West Yorkshire BD2 1QN
Tel: 01274 370 966 Fax: 01274 308 706

Email: sales@tmc.ltd.uk
Web Site: www.tmc.ltd.uk
Contact: Chris Smith
Highly specialised from the outset. TMC (The Music Company) is regarded as one of Britain's foremost centres of expertise in sound and vision technology, a position acknowledged by many industry awards and citations.
Product lines include radio mics, loudspeakers, amplifiers, mixing consoles, DVD players, video projectors, Plasma Screens and tour guide systems.
TMC are agents for d&b audiotechnik, Funktion 1, Turbosound, Allen & Heath, Crest Audio, Sennheiser, Trantec, Sony, Pioneer and Sanyo. To name but a few ...
Emergency call out service also available.

TORPEDO FACTORY LTD
The Old Torpedo Factory, St. Leonards Road, London NW10 6ST
Tel: 020 8537 1000 Fax: 020 8537 1001
Email: s.maskell@tfg.com
Web Site: www.tfg.com
Project Manager: Steve Maskell
Gordon Audio Visual provides leading edge technical services for events, meetings and related activities. Lighting, set design and construction, projection, audio systems, webcasting, streaming, pre- and post-production facilities and more.

TRANTEC
TOA Corporation (UK) Ltd, HQ3 Unit 2, Hook Rise South, Surbiton, Surrey KT6 7LD
Tel: 0870 774 0987 Fax: 0870 777 0839
Email: info/sales@toa.co.uk
Web Site: www.trantec.co.uk
Head of Sales & Marketing: Brett Downing
Trantec offer a full range of both VHF and UHF radio microphones for all theatrical performances. All Trantec products are designed and manufactured in the UK and are fully DTI approved.

XL VIDEO
2 Eastman Way, Hemel Hempstead, Hertfordshire HP2 7DU
Tel: 01442 849 400 Fax: 01442 849 401
Email: theatre@xlvideo.tv
Web Site: www.xlvideo.tv
Contact: Malcolm Mellows
XL Video's specialist Theatre Department offers a wide range of video-visual equipment and services to Theatre and the Arts, including all types of Video Projections, Plasma, LCD and LED Displays.

Fire Safety & Security Systems

ADT FIRE AND SECURITY PLC
Security House, The Summit, Hanworth Road, Sunbury-on-Thames, Middlesex TW16 5DB
Tel: 01932 743 333 Fax: 01932 743 155
Web Site: www.adt.co.uk
Fire protection, intruder detection and alarm CCTV, access control and building management systems.

ARNOLD LAVER TIMBERWORLD
478 Basingstoke Road, Reading, Berkshire RG2 0QN
Tel: 0118 975 1100 Fax: 0118 975 1900
Email: sales@reading.timberworld.co.uk
Web Site: www.timberworld.co.uk
Director: Barry Stimpson
Specialist suppliers of Flame Retardent Plywood Chipboard, MDF, Hardboard & Softwood to Class '1' and Class '0'.

BRISTOL (UK) LTD
1 Sutherland Court, Moor Park Industrial Centre, Tolpits Lane, Watford WD18 9SP
Tel: 01923 779 333 Fax: 01923 779 666
Email: tech.sales@bristolpaint.com
Web Site: www.bristolpaint.com
Managing Director: Mark Chapman
Manufactures of water-based paints and coatings for the Film, Television and Theatre sectors, and Exhibition & Visual Merchandising Industries. Also available: Reversible, instant lay, flat PVC studio / dance flooring which can be decorated with exclusive water based PVC painting system; Special range of paints and matching fabric for visual effects backings; Anti-Graffiti coating; Range of Fire protection products. Newly available: Stardust range of Glitter paints.

CHUBB FIRE & SECURITY LIMITED
A UTC Fire & Security Company
Oak House, Littleton Road, Ashford, TW15 1TZ
Tel: 01784 424 100
Email: info@chubb.co.uk
Web Site: www.chubb.co.uk
Portable and fixed fire protection systems and equipment.

GFA PREMIER
Premier House, 2 Jubilee Way, Elland, West Yorkshire HX5 9DY
Tel: 01422 377 521 Fax: 01422 314 311
Email: customer.service@gfapremier.co.uk
Web Site: www.gfa.co.uk
Fire Fighting Equipment.

J & C JOEL LTD
Corporation Mill, Corporation Street, Sowerby Bridge, West Yorkshire HX6 2QQ
Tel: 01422 833835 Fax: 01422 835157
Email: sales@jcjoel.com
Web Site: www.jcjoel.com
Specialists in Flame Retardant Fabrics, manufacturers and installers of theatrical drapes and stage equipment. Probably the largest stock of flame retardant fabrics, tracks and all stage hardware, starcloths, dance flooring and portable staging.
Sales Manager: Oliver Marns

KINGDOM INDUSTRIAL SUPPLIES LIMITED
6/10 Bancrofts Road, Eastern Industrial Estate, South Woodham Ferrers, Chelmsford, Essex CM3 5UQ
Tel: 01245 322177 Fax: 01245 325878
Email: customer.services@kingdom-group.co.uk
Web Site: www.kingdomgroup.com
Operations Manager: Martin Everitt
Email: martin.everitt@kingdomgroup.com
Suppliers of safety signage, adhesive tapes, protective clothing and allied Industrial Consumables.

MMM GROUP
Globe Works, Lower Bridgeman Street, Bolton, Lancashire BL2 1DG
Tel: 01204 363688 Tel: 01204 387410
Fax: 01204 526260
Email: info@mmm.co.uk
Web Site: www.mmm.co.uk
Safety Equipment Suppliers.

SANTIA FIRE SERVICES
The Safety Centre, Mountergate, Norwich NR1 1PY
Tel: 08702 402 545 Mgt: 0844 335 0135 (Head Office)
Email: lynn.boxall@santia.co.uk
Web Site: www.santia-fireservices.co.uk
Fire risk assessment, Fire Fighting Equipment, Fire Detection and Fire Alarm Systems, Emergency Lighting, Fire Safety Training.

SOLENT SOUNDS SYSTEMS LTD
7 Mitchell Point, Ensign Park, Hamble, Southampton, Hampshire SO31 4RF
Tel: 023 8045 6700 Fax: 023 8045 6789
Email: sales@solentsound.com
Web Site: www.solentsound.com
Manager: Ray Gatehouse
Technical Manager: Adam Gatehouse

STOCKSIGNS LTD
43 Ormside Way, Redhill RH1 2LG
Tel: 01737 764 764 Fax: 01737 763 763
Email: sales@stocksigns.co.uk
Web Site: www.stocksigns.co.uk
Contact: Ms Joanna Godden
All types of signs from stock or specially made to order. Safety signs are the main business. Please ask for free quotation.

TEXTILES FR
Unit 4B Wharfedale Road, Euroway Industrial Estate, Bradford, West Yorkshire BD4 6SG

Tel: 01274 651 230 Fax: 01274 651 305
Email: sales@textilesfr.co.uk
Web Site: www.textilesfr.co.uk
General Manager: Jason Magee
Office Manager: Kim Button
Flame retard fabrics for use as curtains or upholstery.

TOR COATINGS
Portobello Industrial Estate, Birtley, Chester le Street, County Durham DH3 2RE
Tel: 0191 410 6611 Fax: 0191 492 0125
Email: enquiries@tor-coatings.com
Web Site: www.tor-coatings.com
Managing Director: Colin Carter
Flame retardent solutions for drapes, fabrics and theatre props.
Stockists in London and around UK.

UTC FIRE & SECURITY UK LTD
UTC is owned by GE Security
8 Newmarket Court, Chippenham Drive, Milton Keynes MK10 0AQ
Tel: 01908 281 981
Email: peter.crussell@fs.utc.com, leslie.nortje@fs.utc.com
Web Site: www.gesecurity.co.uk
Regional Director UK & Ireland: John Davies
UK Sales Manager: Peter Crussell
Technical Services Manager: Leslie Nortje
Intrusion and Fire Protection.

WALKER FIRE UK LTD
Unit 81, Roman Way, Longridge Road, Ribbleton, Preston PR2 5BB
Tel: 01772 693 777 Fax: 01772 693 760
Email: uk@walkerfire.com
Web Site: www.walkerfire.com
Contact: David Cosgrove

Flight Case Labels

COLOR PRODUCTS LTD
Unit 5, Tile House Farm, Birds Green Lane, Willingale, Ongar, Essex CM5 0PN
Tel: 08456 585212
Email: colorproducts@aol.com
Contact: Peter Randall
Manufacturers of flight case labels, equipment labels, touring labels, cable and cable coding labels, printed vinyl tapes and floor graphics.

LE MARK GROUP
Houghton, Huntingdon, Cambridgeshire PE28 2DH
Tel: 01480 494 540
Email: linda@lemark.co.uk / info@lemark.co.uk
Web Site: www.lemark.co.uk
Sales Director: Linda Gibbons
Le Mark have serviced the theatre industry over the last 25 years with their range of self-adhesive products. We are well known for introducing new innovative products and winning awards for Blacktak & Slipway.

Flight Cases & Packing Chests

1ST OAKLEIGH CASES LTD
10 The Summit Centre, Summit Road, Potters Bar, Hertfordshire EN6 3QW
Tel: 01707 655 011 Fax: 01707 646 447
Email: sales@1st-oc.com
Web Site: www.1st-oakleighcases.com
Designers and manufacturers of a full range of flight cases for Lighting and Audio Visual Equipment, props, wigs and all things theatrical.

ADDA SUPER CASES LIMITED
PO Box 366, Oakington, Cambridge CB4 5AX
Tel: 01223 233 101 Fax: 01223 233 080
Email: sales@adda-super-cases.co.uk
Web Site: www.addasupercases.com
ADMINISTRATION:
Directors: Monica Saunders, Cheryl Bereznyckyj, Derrick Saunders
ADDA have been supplying cases to the entertainment industry since 1978.
Cases can be made to order in either polyethelene or aluminium. Alternatively, you can choose from their extensive range held in stock.

ANGLO PACIFIC INTERNATIONAL PLC
5-9 Willen Field Road, London NW10 7BQ
Tel: 020 8965 1234 Fax: 020 8965 3988
Email: info@anglopacific.co.uk
Web Site: www.anglopacific.co.uk
Managing Director: Steve Perry
Ocean freight, air freight, trucking, full carnet services, forwarders to the performing arts.

CP CASES LTD
Unit 11, Worton Hall Industrial Estate, Worton Road, Isleworth, Middx TW7 6ER
Tel: 0208 568 1881 Fax: 0208 568 1141
Email: info@cpcases.com
Web Site: www.cpcases.com
Sales Contact: Chris Gers
Designers and manufacturers of re-usable cases and containers for commercial, industry and military applications. Amazon Cases is a division of CP specialising in rotomoulded cases and racks.
Also flight cases, 19" rack cases and 19" accessories, protective bags and covers.

ADAM HALL LTD
10 The Seedbed Business Centre, Vanguard Way, Shoeburyness, Essex SS3 9QY
Tel: 01702 613 922 Fax: 01702 617 168
Email: mail@adamhall.co.uk
Web Site: www.adamhall.com
Contact: Mark Stimpson
Distributor and supplier of fittings and hardware for flight cases and loudspeaker cabinets. Own brand stands for lighting, sound and musical instruments. Newly launched Adam Hall Cables. Sole distributor of Amphenol Audio Connectors, Palmer Professional Audio Tools and Power Amplifiers.

JOHN HENRY'S LTD
16-24 Brewery Road, London N7 9NH
Tel: 020 7609 9181 Fax: 020 7700 7040
Email: info@johnhenrys.com
Web Site: www.johnhenrys.com
Event Production: Pepin Clout
Rehearsal Studios: Andrea Westwood
Backline Production: Tark Bates

LE MARK GROUP
Houghton, Huntingdon, Cambridgeshire PE28 2DH
Tel: 01480 494 540
Email: linda@lemark.co.uk / info@lemark.co.uk
Web Site: www.lemark.co.uk
Sales Director: Linda Gibbons
Le Mark have serviced the theatre industry over the last 25 years with their range of self-adhesive products. We are well known for introducing new innovative products and winning awards for Blacktak & Slipway.

SSE HIRE LTD
Burnt Meadow House, Burnt Meadow Road, North Moons Moat, Redditch B98 9PA
Tel: 01527 528 822 Fax: 01527 528 840
Email: hire@sseaudio.com, spencer.beard@sseaudio.com
Web Site: www.sseaudiogroup.com
Managing Director: John Penn
Operations Director: Spencer Beard
Flightcase manufacture. Risers and set supply. PA systems sales and rental

TERRALEC LTD
Osprey House, Featherby Way, Purdeys Industrial Estate, Rochford, Essex SS4 1LD
Tel: 01702 547 571 Fax: 01702 541 075
Email: sales@terralec.com
Web Site: www.terralec.co.uk
Suppliers of professional stage lighting, audio equipment, lighting control, microphones, staging, trussing, hardware, accessories & much more! For: Theatre, stage, commercial events and the entertainment industry.

Floors & Floor Covering

BRISTOL (UK) LTD
1 Sutherland Court, Moor Park Industrial Centre, Tolpits Lane, Watford WD18 9SP
Tel: 01923 779 333 Fax: 01923 779 666
Email: tech.sales@bristolpaint.com
Web Site: www.bristolpaint.com
Managing Director: Mark Chapman
Manufactures of water-based paints and coatings for the Film, Television and Theatre sectors, and Exhibition & Visual Merchandising Industries. Also available: Reversible, instant lay, flat PVC studio / dance flooring which can be decorated with exclusive water based PVC painting system; Special range of paints and matching fabric for visual effects backings; Anti-Graffiti coating; Range of Fire protection products. Newly available: Stardust range of Glitter paints.

COLOR PRODUCTS LTD
Unit 5, Tile House Farm, Birds Green Lane, Willingale, Ongar, Essex CM5 0PN
Tel: 08456 585212
Email: colorproducts@aol.com
Contact: Peter Randall
Manufacturers of flight case labels, equipment labels, touring labels, cable and cable coding labels, printed vinyl tapes and floor graphics.

CREFFIELDS (TIMBER & BOARDS) LTD
Flameproof boards.
Unit 6, Marcus Close, Tilehurst, Reading, Berkshire RG30 4EA
Tel: 0118 945 3533 Fax: 0118 945 3633
Email: info@creffields.co.uk
Web Site: www.creffields.co.uk
Creffields is one of the UK's leading suppliers of
flame-proofed sheet materials and soft woods for the
exhibition and theatrical trades.
Large stocks are held allowing for urgent orders to be delivered promptly; together with Premierbond portable contact spray glue system.

DIRECTA (UK) LTD
Cold Norton, Chelmsford, Essex CM3 6UA
Tel: 01621 828 882 Fax: 01621 828 072
Email: head.office@directa.co.uk
Web Site: www.directa.co.uk
Five good reasons to buy from Directa:
1. Competitive Prices
2. Speedy Nationwide Delivery
3. Free Technical Advice
4. Strict Quality Control
5. BS EN ISO 9001:2000
For free catalogue phone: 01621 828882

FORBO-NAIRN LTD
PO Box 1, Kirkcaldy, Fife KY1 2SB Scotland
Sales: 01592 643 777 Fax: 01592 643 999
Email: info.uk@forbo.com
Web Site: www.forbo-flooring.co.uk
Manufacturer of linoleum, contract vinyl and cushioned vinyl floor coverings.

GILT EDGE CARPETS LTD
255 New Kings Road, London SW6 4RB
Tel: 020 7731 2588 Fax: 020 7736 3042
Email: sales@giltedgecarpets.co.uk
Web Site: www.giltedgecarpets.co.uk
Contact: Paul Nangle
Carpet suppliers and layers. Also Hardwood flooring.

GLOBAL EXPERIENCE SPECIALISTS
Silverstone Drive, Gallagher Business Park, Coventry CV6 6PA
Tel: 02476 380 000 Fax: 02476 380 001
Email: enquiry@ges.com
Web Site: www.ges.com
Office Manager: Jo Mummery-Smith
Hire of furniture, floorcoverings and floral.

HARLEQUIN (BRITISH HARLEQUIN PLC)
Festival House, Chapman Way, Tunbridge Wells, Kent TN2 3EF
Tel: 01892 514888 Fax: 01892 514222
Email: enquiries@harlequinfloors.com
Web Site: www.harlequinfloors.com
Sales Manager: Rebecca Conway
Established in 1979, Harlequin produces a world renowed range of portable and permanent floors, together with three sprung floor systems. Our floors are used by stages and studios worldwide for a variety of applications including dance, drama, opera, exhibitions, tours and concerts. We also provide tape, storage bags and carts, roll straps, cleaning and maintenance products, as well as ballet barres. Harlequin's offices are located in the UK, USA, Luxembourg, Australia and Hong Kong.

J & C JOEL LTD
Corporation Mill, Corporation Street, Sowerby Bridge, West Yorkshire HX6 2QQ
Tel: 01422 833835 Fax: 01422 835157
Email: sales@jcjoel.com
Web Site: www.jcjoel.com
Specialists in Flame Retardant Fabrics, manufacturers and installers of theatrical drapes and stage equipment. Probably the largest stock of flame retardant fabrics, tracks and all stage hardware, starcloths, dance flooring and portable staging.
Sales Manager: Oliver Marns

LE MARK GROUP
Houghton, Huntingdon, Cambridgeshire PE28 2DH
Tel: 01480 494 540
Email: linda@lemark.co.uk / info@lemark.co.uk
Web Site: www.lemark.co.uk
Sales Director: Linda Gibbons
Le Mark have serviced the theatre industry over the last 25 years with their range of self-adhesive products. We are well known for introducing new innovative products and winning awards for Blacktak & Slipway.

ENA SHAW LTD
22-26 Duke Street, St Helens, Merseyside WA10 2JR
Tel: 01744 731 333 Fax: 01744 451 613
Email: keith.barlow@enashaw.co.uk
Web Site: www.enashawhome.co.uk
All types of carpets and floorcoverings, curtains and stage curtains supplied and fitted.

STAGE SOLUTIONS
45 Chruch Road, Hove, East Sussex, BN3 2BE
Tel: 01273 783 710
Email: info@stagesolutions.uk.com
Web Site: www.stagesoltutions.uk.com
Warehouse: 10 Second Avenue, Chatham, Kent ME4 5AU
Maltbury designs, manufactures, delivers and installs staging for every kind of venue, both professional and amateur.
We have over 20 years' experience of the entertainment industry.
We also supply seating, truss and crowd control barriers.

VARIA TEXTILES LTD
197 Kings Road, Kingston-upon-Thames, Surrey KT2 5HJ
Tel: 020 8549 8590 Fax: 020 8549 8290
Email: varia@variatextile.co.uk
Web Site: www.varia-uk.com
Contact: Karl Leuthenmayr
We have in stock a complete range of fire resistant products. We also arrange for fabric to be made up. Front Projection Screens can be custom-made. Please ask for a quotation.

Floral Decorations & Plant Hire

DZD
Lower Ground Floor, 145 Tottenham Court Road, London W1T 7NE
Tel: 020 7388 7488 Fax: 020 7388 7499
Email: sales@dzd.co.uk
Web Site: www.dzd.co.uk
Sales Office Manager: Matthew Winn
Design Director: Sonya Storm
Visual Merchandising and Display Props and Fabrics.

FLOWERS BY SUZANNE
141 Moor Lane, North Hykeham, Lincoln LN6 9AA
Tel: 01522 690105 Mob: 07881 943441
Email: mark@flowersbysuzanne.co.uk
Web Site: www.flowersbysuzanne.com
Director: Mark Hollingworth

FLOWERWORKS
15 Windsor Street, Uxbridge, Middlesex UB8 1AB
Tel: 01895 810 008
Email: sales@flowersuxbridge.co.uk
Web Site: www.flowersuxbridge.co.uk

FREDERICKS DESIGNER FLOWERS
2 Warish Hall Farm, Warish Hall Road, Takeley, Essex CM22 6NZ
Tel: 07791 102 997
Email: info@fdflowers.co.uk
Web Site: www.fredericksdesignerflowers.co.uk
Managing Director: Frederick William

HANGING GARDEN LTD
Wildmoor Lane, Sherfield-on-Loddon, Hook, Hampshire RG27 0HL
Tel: 01256 880 647 Fax: 01256 880 651
Email: nick@hanginggarden.co.uk
Web Site: www.hanginggarden.co.uk
Contact: Nick Kirby
We hire tropical and exterior plants, statues, balustrade columns and all types of props.

IMPRESSIVE DISPLAYS
Sister company Tippetts Florist
17-19 The Parade, Oadby, Leicester LE2 5BB
Tel: 0116 271 2443 Fax: 0116 271 0914
Email: tippettsflorist@gmail.co.uk
Web Site: www.tippettsflorist.com
Contact: Margaret Tippetts

JAMIE ASTON FLOWERS
226 Great Portland Street, London W1W 5AA
Tel: 020 7387 0999
Email: admin@jamieaston.com
Web Site: www.jamieaston.com
Contact: Jamie Aston
Floral arrangements, corporate events and London-based flower school.

LEAFLIKE
Olympic House, Southmead Park, Collett, Sidcot OX11 7WB
Sales Tel: 08000 282 888 Admin Tel: 01235 515 050
Email: info@leaflike.co.uk
Web Site: ww.leaflike.co.uk
Contact: Mr Stephen Abernethie
Very lifelike, artificial trees, plants and floral displays. "So Lifelike - They're Unreal". Sales and rentals.

PALM BROKERS LTD
Cenacle Nursery, Taplow Common Road, Burnham, Slough, Berkshire SL1 8NW
Tel: 01628 663 734 Fax: 01628 661 047
Email: ask@palmbrokers.com
Web Site: www.palmbrokers.com
Suppliers of plants and theatrical props for hire, and provides set dressing services throughout Europe.

PEEBLES EXHIBITION FLORIST LTD
Fillongley Mill Farm, Tamworth Road, Fillongley, Coventry, Warwickshire CV7 8DZ
Tel: 01676 542 234 Fax: 01676 542 456
Email: martinpeebles@btinternet.com
Web Site: www.peeblesflorists.co.uk
Floral Displays for Banquets, Conferences, Corporate Events, County Shows, Hospitality, Launches, Open Days, Outdoor Events, Press Day, Weddings.

PREWETT MILLER - FLOREAT (LONDON)
53 Connaught Street, London W2 2BB
Tel: 020 7723 4683 Fax: 020 7723 6998
Email: prewettmiller@hotmail.com
Director: J.W.M. Miller
Hire of plants, etc. and floral displays of every description.

REPLICA PLANTS
Unit 3,Tenth Ave Trade Park Team Valley Trading Estate Gateshead Tyne & Wear NE11 0HL
Tel: 0191 4877594 Fax: 0191 4877679
Email: sales@replicaplants.co.uk
Web Site: www.replicaplants.co.uk

Flying Ballet

FLYING BY FOY LTD
Unit 4, Borehamwood Enterprise Centre, Theobald Street, Borehamwood, Hertfordshire WD6 4RQ
Tel: 020 8236 0234
Email: enquiries@flyingbyfoy.co.uk
Web Site: www.flyingbyfoy.co.uk
Senior Flying Director: Adam Bailey
General Mangager: Nick Porter
We can create the effect of people flying, weightlessness, flying carpets, underwater scenes and much, much more. So give us a call to discuss your production needs.

FREEDOM FLYING
Unit 14, Nonsuch Industrial Estate, Kiln Lane, Epsom, Surrey KT17 1DH
Admin Tel: 01372 744 233 Fax: 01372 744 234 Mobile: 07768 436 976 (Ben Haynes)
Email: info@freedom-flying.co.uk
Web Site: www.freedom-flying.co.uk

Contact: Ben Haynes
Many years experience in creating specialist flying effects for all types of productions and venues, including:- Theatre, Television, Corporate Events, Pop Videos, Still Photo Shoots, Hangings etc.

HI-FLI LTD
2 Boland Drive, Manchester M14 6DS
Tel/Fax: 0161 224 6082
Email: mikefrost@hi-fli.co.uk
Web Site: www.hi-fli.co.uk
Contact: Mike Frost
Personnel and prop flying effects. Rigs available for most venues and budgets.

KIRBY'S/AFX
Peter Pan since 1904
8 Greenford Avenue, Hanwell, London W7 3QP
Tel/Fax: 020 8723 8552 Mobile: 07958 285 608
Email: mail@afxuk.com, mail@kirbysflying.co.uk
Web Site: www.kirbysflying.co.uk

Health & Safety

BRITISH SAFETY COUNCIL
70 Chancellors Road, London W6 9RS
Tel: 020 8741 1231 Fax: 020 8741 4555
Email: customer.service@britsafe.org
Web Site: www.britsafe.org
The British Safety Council works hand-in-hand with the world's leading companies, developing safe systems of work. We research and develop new health and safety products and services, and lobby on key health & safety and environmental issues.

HEALTH & SAFETY ADVICE
PO Box 32295, London W5 1WD
Tel: 0870 066 0272 Fax: 0870 066 0273
Email: info@health-safetyadvice.co.uk
Web Site: www.health-safetyadvice.co.uk
Health and Safety Consultants, risk assessments, management etc. Planning, dealing with local authorities and obtaining lisences for events etc.

IGTC LTD
Unit 32, Jubilee Drive, Loughborough, Leicestershire LE11 5XS
Tel: 0845 2020 235 Fax: 0870 7202 265
Email: sales@safetystoredirect.co.uk
Web Site: www.safetystoredirect.co.uk
Safety equipment and wear.

MATT-LX LTD
Unit 3,Vinehall Business Ctr Vinehall Road, Robertsbridge, East Sussex TN32 5JW
Tel: 0845 6808692
Email: matt.lx@mattlx.com
Web Site: www.mattlx.com
Project Manager: Rob Clutterham
MattLX is a specialist technical event production company, providing lighting and design, Audio Visual, equipment supply, programmers, operators, installation, training and Health & Safety services, for Theatre, Arts, Entertainment, Leisure, Marine, TV and Corporate Events.

SMART ADVICE HEALTH AND SAFETY LTD
6 Drakes Way, Portishead, BS20 6LB
Tel: 01275 848 641 Mob: 07768 345 446
Email: info@smart-advice.co.uk
Web Site: www.smart-advice.co.uk
We do all areas of health and safety; inspections, training. Risk assessments, event safety, licensing and provide medics for events. We are fire consultants and also food hygiene consultants. We are fully qualified with many years experiance.

THE EVENT SAFETY SHOP LTD
59 Prince Street, Bristol BS1 4QH
Tel: 0117 904 6204 Fax: 0117 922 1497
Email: info@the-eventsafetyshop.co.uk
Web: www.the-eventsafetyshop.co.uk
A Health and Safety Company dedicated to meeting the specific health and safety needs of the entertainment and conference industry.

TOWERGATE RISK SOLUTIONS
New Zealand House, 160 - 162 Abbey Foregate, Shrewsbury SY2 6AL
Tel: 0870 4115 516
Email: shrewsbury@towergate.co.uk
Web: www.towergaterisksolutions.co.uk
Managing Director: Nigel Mills

WALKER FIRE UK LTD
Unit 81, Roman Way, Longridge Road, Ribbleton, Preston PR2 5BB
Tel: 01772 693 777 Fax: 01772 693 760
Email: uk@walkerfire.com
Web Site: www.walkerfire.com
Contact: David Cosgrove

Hospitality Agents

ACF HOSPITALITY LTD
Aldwick Court Farm, Redhill, Bristol BS40 5RF
Tel: 01934 862 305 Fax: 01934 863 308
Email: info@acfteambuilding.co.uk
Web Site: www.acfhospitality.co.uk
Sales/Marketing Director: Mr Mark Fanning

CAVENDISH HOSPITALITY
161-169 Uxbridge Road, London W13 9AU
Tel: 020 8567 3530
Email: sales@cavendishg.com
Web Site: www.cavendishg.com
Sales Director: Philip Driver

HUDSON HAYS HOSPITALITY
Unit 21, Hays Galleria, Tooley Street, London SE1 2HD
Tel: 020 7378 9090 Fax: 020 7929 5483
Email: info@galleriaevents.com
Web Site: www.galleriaevents.com
Director: Michael Quinn

KEITH PROWSE
Park View, 82 Oxford Road, Uxbridge, Middlesex UB8 1UX
Tel: 0845 602 8989
Email: enquiries@keithprowse.co.uk
Web Site: www.keithprowse.co.uk
Contact: Maria Barrett

PALL MALL CORPORATE HOSPITALITY
34 New Cavendish Street, London W1G 8UB
Tel: 020 7467 2500 Fax: 020 7467 2505
Email: enquiries@pall-mall.net
Web Site: www.pall-mall.net
Hospitality Manager: Lisa Ulldemolins
Pall Mall offers hospitality for major sporting and social events worldwide.

Hotel Booking Services

THE APARTMENT SERVICE
Tuition House, 5-6 Francis Grove, London SW19 4DT
Tel: 020 8944 1444 Fax: 020 8944 6744
Email: res@apartment.co.uk
Web Site: www.apartmentservice.com
Director of Sales: Melanie Degand
Seviced apartment booking company.

BRITANNIA HOTELS LTD
35 Portland Street, Manchester M1 3LA
Tel: 0161 228 2288 Fax: 0161 236 9154
Email: patrick.fitzgerald@britanniahotels.com
Web Site: www.britanniahotels.com
Contact: Simon Bowen
363 Bedrooms.

CLASSIC BRITAIN
3 Dunlop Street, Strathaven, Lanarkshire ML10 6LA
Tel: 0845 1306 241
Email: enquiries@classicbritain.com
Web Site: www.classicbritain.com
General Manager: Andrew Simpson
Reservation Contacts: Individual Bookings - Pamela Low, Group Reservations - Fiona Beaton, Nathalie Brohan or Mark Simpson

Insurance

ADAM BROTHERS CONTINGENCY LTD
A division of Griffiths & Armour Global Risks Ltd
145 Leadenhall Street, London EC3V 4QT
Tel: 020 7090 1109
Email: dclose@griffithsandarmour.com
Web Site: www.adambrothers.co.uk
ADMINISTRATION:
Contact: David Close
Non-appearance insurance for Theatrical and Concert Managements, Producers, Artistes and Agents.
Cancellation/Abandonment Insurance for all types of events. "It is better to have insurance for 100 years and not need it - than to need it for one day and not have it."

DOODSON ENTERTAINMENT
Century House, Pepper Road, Hazel Grove, Stockport, Cheshire SK7 5BW
Tel: 0161 419 3000 Fax: 0161 419 3030
Email: info@doodsonbg.com
Web Site: http://www.doodsonbg.com
We have provided specialist insurance advice and support to the Theatre Industry for over 35 years. We have unrivalled experience and provide unsurpassed service in all aspects of the business. We have well established relationships with specialist insurers who share our commitment to this market.

EVENT INSURANCE SERVICES
Event House 20A Headlands Business Park Ringwood, Hampshire BH24 3PB
Tel: 01425 470360 Fax: 01425 474905
Email: info@events-insurance.co.uk
Web Site: www.events-insurance.co.uk
There is a high demand in the events industry for insurance policies which fully protect against misfortune.
In response, Event Insurance Services has developed a wide range of packages with an uncomplicated approach to suit all organisers' needs from the smallest to largest shows or exhibitions, to corporate days and weddings.

GORDON & CO
Brokers for Dance UK
2 Sekforde Court, 217 St. John Street, London EC1V 4LY
Tel: 020 7251 2255 Fax: 020 7251 1477
Email: robert.israel@gordonandco.co.uk
Web Site: www.firststepinsurance.co.uk / www.gordonandco.co.uk
Director: Robert Israel
General Insurance for West End theatres, producers, ballet and dance companies. Non appearance and all types of Personal Insurance.

HANOVER PARK COMMERCIAL LIMITED
3rd Floor, Sunley House, 4 Bedford Park, Croydon CR0 2AP
Tel: 0845 345 0815 Fax: 0845 345 0816
Email: performance@hanover-park.co.uk
Web Site: www.performance-hpc.co.uk
Contact: Andrew Leen
All types of insurance for the media industry. Buy online!

HISCOX
Hiscox House, Sheepen Road, Colchester CO3 3XL
Tel: 01206 788 812 London Office: 1 Great St Helens, London, EC3A 6HX Tel: 020 7448 6000
Email: chris.parker@hiscox.com, enquiry@hiscox.com
Web Site: www.hiscox.co.uk
Regional Manager: Chris Parker
Regional Manager - London PSCD: Derrick Potton

G.M. IMBER & SONS LTD
77a High Street, East Grinstead, West Sussex RH19 3DD
Tel: 0870 606 6668 Fax: 020 7252 3656
Email: info@gmisl.co.uk
Web Site: www.gmisl.co.uk
Contact: Bill, Sven and Matt Imber.

LAYTON BLACKHAM INSURANCE BROKERS
Western House, 246 High Holburn, London WC1V 7EX
Tel: 0870 160 0201 Fax: 020 7415 3910
Email: lb@layton-blackham.co.uk, sales@layton-blackham.co.uk
Web Site: www.layton-blackham.co.uk

W & P LONGREACH
America House 2 America Square London EC3N 2LU
Tel: 020 7929 4747 Fax: 020 7929 4884
Email: enquiries@wandp-longreach.com
Web Site: www.wandp-longreach.com
Contacts: Mike Russell and Andy Rudge
Specialist insurance brokers to theatre owners, producers and suppliers with competitive schemes for all aspects of theatre, including non-appearance, cancellation, hazardous work, the productions and the bricks and mortar.

NYMAN LIBSON PAUL
Regina House, 124 Finchley Road, London NW3 5JS
Tel: 020 7433 2400 Fax: 020 7433 2401
Buckinghamshire Office: Room 107 Pinewood Studios, Pinewood Road, Iver Heath, Buckinghamshire, SL0 0NH Tel: 01753 656428
Email: mail@nlpca.co.uk
Web Site: www.nlpca.co.uk
Contact: Paul Taiano
Established for over 78 years with specialist knowledge of the Theatre and Entertainment industries, providing accountancy, audit, and taxation services for companies and individuals. Specialist tax services for UK and overseas clients.

ROBERTSON TAYLOR INSURANCE BROKERS LTD
Lloyds Brokers, Authorised and regulated by the Financial Services Authority
33 Harbour Exchange Square, London, E14 9GG
Tel: 020 7510 1234 Fax: 020 7510 1134
Alternative Office: 5 Plato Place, 72-74 St Dionis Road, Fulham, London SW6 4TU
Tel: 020 7510 1234 Fax: 020 7736 4803
Email: enquiries@rtib.co.uk
Web Site: www.robertson-taylor.com
Managing Director: John Silcock
Specialist Insurance Brokers to the Entertainment Industry, including first class insurance and risk management advice to all aspects of Music, Theatre, TV, Film, Video, Conference, Exhibitions and Sports.

THEATRES MUTUAL
Zurich Insurance PLC, Zurich Real Estate Insurance, 1st Floor, London Underwriting Centre, 3 Minster Court, London EC3R 7DD
Tel: 020 8212 4246 Mob: 07875 885 638
Fax : 020 7648 3352
Email: martin.litwin-roberts@uk.zurich.com
Web Site: www.zurich.com
Contact: Martin Litwin-Roberts, Anne Marie Chedzoy, Rosalyn Curwen
Specialists in insurance for theatres and theatrical productions both amateur and professional.

TICKETPLAN LTD
Leigh House, Broadway West, Leigh-on-Sea, Essex SS9 2DD
Tel:01702 482 284 Fax: 01702 471 714
Email: graham@ticketplangroup.com
Web Site: www.ticketplangroup.com
Managing Director: Graham Berg
Operations Director: Mark Felman
TicketPlan cancellation protection has now become a standard customer requirement. The Scheme provides patrons with the peace of mind of knowing that, in the event of cancellation, the purchase price of their tickets can be refunded. TicketPlan is underwritten by Allianz Cornhill and provides an opportunity for venues to earn substantial commission revenue, whilst justifying a "no refund" cancellation policy.

TOWERGATE RISK SOLUTIONS
New Zealand House, 160 - 162 Abbey Foregate, Shrewsbury SY2 6AL
Tel: 0870 4115 516
Email: shrewsbury@towergate.co.uk
Web: www.towergaterisksolutions.co.uk
Managing Director: Nigel Mills

Internet Consultants & Design

LONDON THEATRE GUIDE ON-LINE
33 Friar Lane Warsop Mansfield Notts
NG20 0HX
Tel: 020 7193 3608
Email: admin@londontheatre.co.uk
Web Site: www.londontheatre.co.uk
Contact: Darren Dalglish
News, listings, reviews, seating plans, tickets, maps, venues, tours and walks, and more.

PICTURE PRODUCTION COMPANY
6-8 Kingley Court, London W1B 5PW
Tel: 020 7439 4944 Fax: 020 7434 9140
Email: sales@theppc.com
Web Site: www.theppc.com

SARDI'S
6 Redbridge Lane East, Redbridge IG4 5ES
Tel: 020 8551 6720 Fax: 020 8551 1200
Email: sardis@axident.clara.net

SIGNALS
Broadgates, Market Place, Henley-on-Thames, Oxfordshire RG9 2AA
Tel: 01491 571 812 Fax: 01491 575 193
Email: digital@signals.co.uk
Web Site: www.signals.co.uk

WRG
Merchant's Warehouse, 21 Castle Street, Manchester M3 4LZ
Tel: 0845 313 0000 Fax: 0845 313 0011
Email: info@wrg.uk.com
Web Site: www.wrg.uk.com

XTREME
5a Church Square, Market Harborough, Leicestershire LE16 7NB
Tel/ Fax: 01858 434700
Email: david@xtremeid.co.uk
Web Site: www.xtremeid.co.uk
Contact: David Stevenson

Leaflet Distributors

ARTS CONTACT
Kenyon House, 104 Redbourne Road, Hibaldstow, Brigg, Lincolnshire DN20 9NP
Tel: 01652 656 775 Mob: 07831 166692 / 07860 374723
Email: sheila@artscontact.co.uk
Web Site: www.artscontact.co.uk
Directors: Sheila Thorpe, Tony Hyslop
A unique creative bulk distribution service for Arts publicity print, for any Arts event, anywhere in the U.K.

IMPACT DISTRIBUTION LTD
Tuscany Wharf, 4b Orsman Road, London N1 5QJ
Tel: 020 7729 5978 Fax: 020 7729 5994
Email: hello@impactideas.co.uk
Web Site: www.impactideas.co.uk
Managing Director: Simon Drysdale
Leaflet and poster distribution for the arts. A fast effective and flexible service at competitive rates. Call today for a free quote and information pack.

PCF PRINT MANAGEMENT LTD
Oak House, Langstone Business Village, Langstone Park, Langstone, Newport, Gwent NP18 2LH Wales
Tel: 01633 415 570 Fax: 01633 415 599
Email: info@pcf.co.uk
Web Site: www.pcf.co.uk
Sales Manager and Director: Ian Hoare
PCF!tickets are ticket suppliers for all software box office ticketing systems, including; tickets.com dataculture, BOCA, CATS, etc, etc,...
PCF will help you with all your needs - tickets, ticket holders, envelopes & labels, membership and reward cards, as well as letterheads, complimentary slips and business cards.

TAKEONE MEDIA
The Boulevard, Orbital Park, Ashford, Kent TN24 0GA
Tel: 01233 211 211
Email: sales@takeonemedia.co.uk
Web Site: www.takeonemedia.co.uk
Managing Director: Philippa Harris
Sales Director: David Johnston
Display and distribution of brochures for the entertainment and leisure industry. Targeted audiences and weekly merchandising to ensure cost effective control of advertising print.

Legal & Professional Services

ALL CLEAR DESIGNS LTD
3 Devonshire Mews, London W4 2HA
Tel: 020 8400 5093 Fax: 020 8400 5094
Email: mail@allclear.co.uk
Web Site: www.allclear.co.uk
Director: James Holmes-Siedle
Specialists in making buildings accessible for disabled people. Architectural services include access audits, feasibility studies and construction. Experience with theatres and listed buildings. Assistance with advice with funding included.

BLAKE MORGAN SOLICITORS
Watchmaker Court, 33 St John's Lane, London EC1M 4DB
Tel: 020 7405 2000 Fax: 0844 620 3402
Email: info@blakemorgan.co.uk
Web Site: www.blakemorgan.co.uk

CARR & ANGIER
The Old Malthouse, Clarence Street, Bath, Somerset BA1 5NS
Tel: 01225 446 664 Fax: 01225 446 654
Email: info@carrandangier.co.uk
Web Site: www.carrandangier.co.uk
Principal & Theatre Consultant: Peter Angier
Consultancy services for the arts, entertainment and conference industries. Feasibility studies, planning and technical systems design for new and refurbishment projects.

CLINTONS SOLICITORS
55 Drury Lane, London WC2B 5RZ
Tel: 020 7379 6080 Fax: 020 7240 9310
Email: info@clintons.co.uk
Web Site: www.clintons.co.uk
Legal Executive: Gary Lux
Practice Manager: Dianne Middleton
We are solicitors specialising in the Entertainment Industry and we have wide experience of all matters relating to theatre, acting for producers, writers, composers, designers, directors and performers.

HARBOTTLE & LEWIS LLP
Hanover House, 14 Hanover Square, London W1S 1HP
Switchboard: 020 7667 5000 Fax: 020 7667 5100
Email: info@harbottle.com
Web Site: www.harbottle.com
Contact: Neil Adleman
Harbottle & Lewis LLP advise organisations, individuals and agents through out the theatre, film and television industries on a range of issues, both professional and personal. Our clients include producers, touring companies, theatre owners, funded companies, trade associations, writers, directors, designers, composers, arrangers, performers and literary and talent agents.

MICHAEL HOLDEN
Octagon Business Park, Hospital RoadHospital Road, Little Plumstead, Norwich NR13 5FH
Tel: 01603 721 511 Fax: 01603 721 650
Email: michael@adrianjamesacoustics.co.uk
Web: www.adrienjamesacoustics.co.uk
Theatre Consultants, designers of new buildings or the adaption and refurbishment of existing buildings. Management Consultants experienced in the formation of Trusts and other management structures.

MICHAEL SIMKINS LLP
Lynton House, 7 -12 Tavistock Square, London WC1H 9LT
Tel: 020 7874 5600 Fax: 020 7874 5601
Email: info@simkins.com
Web Site: www.simkins.com
Contact: David Franks, Catherine Fehler (Theatre). Nigel Bennett (Film and TV). Robert Allan (Music).
Theatrical Division: As one of the leading theatre practices in London we advise producers, investors, theatre owners and creative team members in all aspects of theatrical production and investment. Our experience includes worldwide licensing as well as a wide range of West End, Broadway and out of town productions and tours.

MUSICIANS BENEVOLENT FUND
7 - 11 Britannia Street, London WC1X 9JS
Tel: 020 7239 9100 Fax: 020 7713 8942
Email: info@helpmusicians.org.uk
Web Site: www.helpmusicians.org.uk
The Musicians Benevolent Fund is the music business' own charity - the largest of its kind in the UK. Each year it spends about £1.7 million helping around 1,400 people of any age, and who in any area of the music business who are in need as a result of illness, accident or other misfortune.

RUSSELL-COOKE SOLICITORS
8 Bedford Row, London WC1R 4BX
Tel: 020 7405 6566 Fax: 020 7831 2565
Alternative Address: 2 Putney Hill, London, SW15 6AB Tel: 020 8789 9111
Fax: 020 8780 1194
Email: Matt.Bosworth@russell-cooke.co.uk
Web Site: www.russell-cooke.co.uk
Partners: Matt Bosworth, Peter Cadman, James Carroll.

SCHILLINGS
41 Bedford Square, London WC1B 3HX
Tel: 020 7034 9000 Fax: 020 7034 9200
Email: legal@schillings.co.uk
Web Site: www.schillings.co.uk
Contact: Mr Schilling

SHEPHERD AND WEDDERBURN
1 Exchange Crescent, Conference Square, Edinburgh, Mid Lothian EH3 8UL Scotland
Tel: 0131 473 5366 Glasgow Office: 33 Bothwell Street, Glasgow, G2 6NL Tel: 01412 754 771 Fax: 01412 754 781
Email: lynneangela.jeffrey@shepwedd.co.uk
Web Site: www.shepwedd.co.uk
Contact: Lynne Angela Jeffrey

THEATREPLAN LLP
27 Colonnade, London WC1N 1JA
Tel: 020 7841 0440 Fax: 020 7841 0450
Email: info@theatreplan.co.uk
Web Site: www.theatreplan.co.uk
Practice Manager: Paul Connolly
Planning, space and equipment design services for theatres, conference venues and concert halls. Design of rigging, lighting, audio-visual and video systems and equipment.

THEATRES MUTUAL
Zurich Insurance PLC, Zurich Real Estate Insurance, 1st Floor, London Underwriting Centre, 3 Minster Court, London EC3R 7DD
Tel: 020 8212 4246 Mob: 07875 885 638
Fax : 020 7648 3352
Email: martin.litwin-roberts@uk.zurich.com
Web Site: www.zurich.com
Contact: Martin Litwin-Roberts, Anne Marie Chedzoy, Rosalyn Curwen
Specialists in insurance for theatres and theatrical productions both amateur and professional.

Lighting & Lighting Equipment Suppliers

A.C. LIGHTING LTD
Centauri House, Hillbottom Road, High Wycombe, Buckinghamshire HP12 4HQ
Tel: 01494 446 000 Fax: 01494 461 024
Leeds Office: Hawksworth Commercial Centre, Elder Road, Leeds LS13 4AT Tel: 0113 255 7666 Fax: 0113 255 7676
Email: ken.coker@ac-et.com
Web Site: www.ac-et.com
ADMINISTRATION:
Company Manager: Ken Coker
Marketing Manager: Laurie Giraudeau
In-house Production Manager: Andrew Smith
One of the largest distributors of professional lighting equipment, accessories and consumables. Multi-million pound stock holding, representing most of the world's leading manufacturers. Specialist Scroll Express and Cable Express manufacturing services.

ANDOLITE LTD
Unit A, Rennie Gate, West Port Industrial Estate, Andover, Hampshire SP10 3TU
Tel: 01264 356445 Fax: 01264 334 401
Email: sales@andolite.co.uk
Web Site: www.andolite.co.uk
Managing Director: Alan Good

ANYTRONICS LIMITED
Units 5 & 6, Hillside Industrial Estate, London Road, Horndean, Waterlooville, Hampshire PO8 0BL
Tel: 023 9259 9410 Fax: 023 9259 8723
Email: sales@anytronics.com
Web Site: www.anytronics.com
Manager: Mr. Robert Hall
Technical Manager: Mr. Simon Fickling
Manufacturers of a range of high powered strobes, modular lighting control systems plus a universal range of switching/dimming power packs.

ARRI (GB) LTD
4 Highbridge, Oxford Road, Uxbridge, Middlesex UB8 1LX
Tel: 01895 457 000 Fax: 01895 457 001
Email: sales@arri-gb.com, smoran@arrirental.com
Web Site: www.arri.com
Senior Client Contact ARRI Lighting Rental: Sinead Moran
UK Business Development Manager: Martin Carnell
Email: mcarnell@arri-ct.com
As well as sales and support for Arri lighting equipment, we also offer a wide range of stands, suspension lamps, filter and electrical accessories.

ARTISTIC LICENCE (UK) LTD
Studio 1 Spectrum House, 32-34 Gordon House Road, London NW5 1LP
Tel: 020 8863 4515 Fax: 020 8426 0551
Email: company@artisticlicence.com
Web Site: www.artisticlicence.com
Admin Assistant: Alison House
Artistic Licence design and manufacture stage lighting control equipment.
Products include: Ethernet & DMX512 distribution, Protocol conversion, Ethernet & DMX Test Equipment, PC Based Virtual Lighting control and LED lighting.

A.S.G. STAGE PRODUCTS LTD
Redgate Road, South Lancashire Ind. Estate, Ashton-in-Makerfield, Wigan, Lancashire WN4 8DT
Tel: 01942 718 347 Fax: 01942 718 219
Email: post@asgstage.co.uk
Web Site: www.asgstage.co.uk
Projects Manager: Paul McFerran
Since 1973 we have specialised in the supply and installation of performance facilities to professional, amateur and educational theatres - including tracks, curtains, rigging, lighting, sound, projection, seating and staging.

AURORA LIGHTING HIRE LTD
Unit 21, Greenford Park, Ockham Drive, Greenford, London, UB6 0FD
Tel: 0208 813 2777
Email: info@auroratv.co.uk
Web Site: www.auroratv.co.uk
Contact: Sam Crook / Nick Edwards
Providing professional, cost-effective lighting services including design, crewing, hire and sales for all aspects of the entertainment industry from theatre and commercial events to schools and education.

AVOLITES LTD
184 Park Avenue, London NW10 7XL
Tel: 020 8965 8522 Fax: 020 8965 0290
Email: steve@avolites.com
Web Site: www.avolites.com
Sales Director: Steve Warren
Manufacture and sale of highest quality dimming systems memory and manual lighting control consoles. Dry hire department for all AVO products, including moving light's consoles.

BANDIT LITES
235 Ampthill Road, Bedford MK42 9QH
Tel: 01234 363820 Fax: 01234 365382
Email: bandituk@banditlites.com
Web Site: www.banditlites.com
Chief Executive: Lester Cobrin

BLACK LIGHT
West Shore Trading Estate, West Shore Road, Edinburgh EH5 1QF Scotland
Tel: 0131 551 2337 Fax: 0131 551 6827
Email: feedback@black-light.com
Web Site: www.black-light.com
Managing Director: Gavin Stewart
Hire and Events Manager: Calder Sibbard
Sales: Karen Fairlie

BLACKWING LTD
Barnes Farm, Battlesea Green, Stradbroke, Eye, Suffolk IP21 5NE
Tel: 01379 388519
Email: enquiries@blackwingltd.com
Web Site: www.blackwingltd.com
Managing Director: Torben Merriott
Company Secretary: Pamie Merriott
Lighting, Audio, and Special Effects, Steel Deck Staging - hire and sales.

BUBBLES LIGHTING LTD
Units 20 - 21, Black Moor Business Park, New Road, Maulden, Bedford MK45 2BG
Tel: 01525 402 400 Fax: 01525 404 399
Email: info@bubbleslighting.com
Web Site: www.bubbleslighting.com
Managing Director: P J Bottoms

CAPITAL CABLES
Unit C1/C2, Frogmore Industrial Estate, Motherwell Way, Grays, Essex RM20 3XD
Tel: 01708 864 464 Fax: 01708 865 385
Email: london.016@ukcables.co.uk
Web Site: www.ukcables.co.uk
Manager: David O'Neill
Capital Cables is one of the countries leading suppliers of cables and accessories for the lighting and sound industries.
UK Cables Ltd. can offer much more than just cable distribution and has a vast array of Cable and Cable Management Products at your disposal.

C.A.V. (CONTRACT AUDIO VISUAL)
Unit 3, Venture Business Centre, Madleaze Road, Gloucester GL1 5SJ
Tel: 01452 505 500 Fax: 01452 502 600
Email: sales@cav.co.uk
Web Site: www.cav.co.uk
Proprietor: Hans Beier
LCAV (Contract Audio Visual) is a large production services company based in Gloucestershire. We provide solutions from basic unmanned hire of sound and lighting equipment through to total production services for large scale events, concerts, tour and conferences.

CCT LIGHTING LTD
Unit 3, Ellesmere Business Park, Haydn Road, Nottingham NG5 1DX UK
Tel: 0115 985 8919 Fax: 0115 985 7091
Email: office@cctlighting.co.uk
Web Site: www.cctlighting.com
Directors: John Shore, Richard Stokes, Gary Redfern
CCT Lighting manufacture flameproofed velour and Bolton Twill curtains in a wide range of colours, quoted to specification. Also distributed are the entire Rosco range of products including scenic and projection materials.
(Main function: Manufacture of Lighting and accessories)

CENTRAL EVENTS UK LTD
The Barn Fifield Farm Marlston Road Marlston Nr Hermitage Berkshire RG18 9UN
Tel: 01235 760 342 Fax: 01635 202 088
Email: heidi.smith@s-l-v.co.uk
Web Site: www.central-production.co.uk
Senior Personnel: Jim Williams
Specialise in production of rigging, staging, lighting, PA, theming, power distribution, marquees and catering for corporate and private parties.
At Central Events UK, we pride ourselves in being a full service events management company whcih gives us the freedom to offer the very best in service, product and price to our customers.

CENTRAL THEATRE SUPPLIES
1186 Stratford Road, Hall Green, Birmingham West Midlands B28 8AB
Tel: 0121 778 6400
Email: enquiries@centraltheatresupplies.co.uk
Web: www.centraltheatresupplies.co.uk
Manager: David Harwood
Technical Manager: Ian Knight
Birmingham based Central Theatre Supplies have a large hire department supplying professional stage lighting, control systems and effects. We sell products from many leading manufacturers. Consumables are always in stock.

CLD DISTRIBUTION LTD
Philips House, Drury Lane, Ponswood Industrial Estate, St Leonards on Sea, East Sussex TN38 9BA
Tel: 01424 722 944 Fax: 01424 722 945
Email: sales@cld-dist.co.uk
Web Site: www.cld-dist.com
Contact: Sandra Connolly
sandra@cld-dist.co.uk

THE CLOUD ONE GROUP LTD
24 Proctor Street, Birmingham B7 4EE
Tel: 0845 269 7711 Fax: 0121 333 7799
Email: info@cloudone.net
Web Site: www.cloudone.net
Contact: Paul Stratford
Sound, lighting, staging, sales, hire, installation, consultancy.

COMMERCIAL ELECTRONICS (JERSEY) LTD
4 Springside, La Rue de la Monnaie, Trinity, Jersey JE3 5DG Channel Islands
Tel: 01534 865 858 Fax: 01534 863 759
Mobile: 07797 720640
Email: crickb@delta-av.com
Web Site: www.delta-av.com
Service Manager: Cristin Bouchet
Strand Lighting main dealers and service agents for the Channel Islands. Full lighting, Audio-Visual and Sound Hire facilities. Lamps, colour/diffusion medium, gaffa tape and other accessories always in stock. Dealers for Strand Lighting.

CONTINENTAL LASERS (UK) LTD
B105 Portview Trade Centre, 310 Newtownards Road, Belfast, County Antrim BT4 1HE Northern Ireland
Tel: 028 9045 8658 Fax: 028 9046 1550
Mobile: 07860 800283
Email: info@continental-lasers.com
Web Site: www.continental-lasers.com
Proprietor: Brian Bennington
Since 1982 Continental Lasers have proved to be among the top laser display companies in the world for performance and innovation. The hire of systems for corporate events and spectactulars is handled by Continental Show Laser. Attention to detail results in a service that can be relied upon time after time. Continental Lasers can offer breathtakingly intricate Aquabatic water displays.

CP SOUND LTD
Units 14 & 15, Penton Hook Marina, Staines Road, Chertsey, Surrey KT16 8PY
Tel: 01932 571 849 Fax: 01932 850 725
Email: info@cpsound.co.uk
Web Site: www.cpsound.co.uk
Manager: Colin Pattenden
CP Sound is a pro-active, creative and progressive thinking company that specifies, supplies and installs sound, lighting and audio visual systems for a diverse selection of venues and situations.

D.W.TUCKNOTT LIGHTING & FX
23 Connaught Road, Seaford, East Sussex BN25 2PT
Tel: 01323 895 850
Email: arpadmodels@hotmail.com

Contact: Mr Tucknott
Theatrical Equipment suppliers, lighting and effects hire service.

DC LIGHTING LTD
2nd Floor, Unit 11 Harrier Park, Hawksworth, Didcot, Oxfordshire OX11 7PL
Tel: 01235 511 003 Fax: 01235 511 004
Email: sales@dclighting.co.uk
Web Site: www.dclighting.co.uk
Contact: Don Campbell
D C Lighting Ltd carries a full range of branded Studio, Theatre, Video and Photographic lamps. We can also supply lanterns, cable, plugs, gel etc and offer a friendly and efficient service. Account or credit card facilities available.

DESISTI
15 Old Market Street, Thetford, Norfolk IP24 2EQ
Tel: 01842 752 909 Fax: 01842 753 746
Email: info@desisti.co.uk
Web Site: www.desisti.co.uk
Director: William Smillie
Manufacturers and Distributors of Lights and suspension equipment.

DOUGHTY ENGINEERING LIMITED
Crow Arch Lane, Ringwood, Hampshire BH24 1NZ
Tel: 01425 478961 Fax: 01425 474481
Email: sales@doughty-engineering.co.uk
Web: www.doughty-engineering.co.uk
Production Director: Stephen Wright
Marketing Director: Julian Chiverton
Doughty Engineering are often described as "Mind Over Metal" specialists. Among the areas we manufacture for are products for the Stage Lighting, Grip and Theatre markets.

DRAX LIGHTING LTD
Unit 21B Icknield Way Farm, Tring Road, Dunstable, Bedfordshire LU6 2JX
Tel: 01582 475 614 Fax: 01582 475 669
Email: richard@draxlighting.com, info@draxlighting.com
Web Site: www.draxlighting.com
Contact: Richard Foster
Drax specialises in event lighting design and equipment supply for stage shows, outdoor productions and corporate events. Drax hire and sell quality lighting, sound and effects equipment for static, touring or short term use. Dry hire or hire with crew is available for both professional and amateur events, UK and worldwide. Hire equipment includes profiles, fresnels, PARs, floods, followspots, moving lights, rigging, special effects systems and dimmers. Control systems available include Avolites, Artistic Licence and Zero 88.

HOWARD EATON LIGHTING LTD
Winterlands, Resting Oak Hill, Cooksbridge, Lewes, East Sussex BN8 4PR
Tel: 01273 400 670 Fax: 01273 408 900
Email: info@helluk.com
Web Site: www.helluk.com
Managing Director: Howard Eaton
Manufacture, supply, installation and service of Special Effects, Custom Lighting, DMX Networks, Digital Dimming, Cue Lights & S.M. Desks, Chain Hoist Controls, Radio Controlled Lighting, Plugboxes & Facility Panels. Hire of Genie Personnel Lifts.

EDMUNDSON ELECTRICAL
Alpha House, 59-61 Park Royal Road Park Royal, London, NW10 7JJ
Tel: 020 8963 6800 Fax: 020 8963 9810
Email: park-royal.501@eel.co.uk
Web Site: www.edmundson-electrical.co.uk
Suppliers of lighting equipment.
Commercial and domestic.

PHILIP L EDWARDS (THEATRE LIGHTING)
5 Highwood Close, Glossop, Derbyshire SK13 6PH
Tel/Fax: 01457 862 811 (24 Hours)
Email: enquiries@plethltg.demon.co.uk
Contacts: Christine E Edwards, Philip L Edwards
Comprehensive Lighting Hire, Sales and Design Service. Stockists of Filters, Spares and Pyrotechnics. Brochure on request.

ELSTREE LIGHT & POWER
15 North Gate, Alconbury Airfield, Huntingdon, Cambridgeshire PE28 4WX
Tel: 01480 443 800 Fax: 01480 443 888
Email: info@elp.tv
Web Site: www.elp.tv
Concert, stage and television lighting.

ENLIGHTENED LIGHTING LTD
26-28 Emery Road, Brislington, Bristol, BS4 5PF
Tel: 01179 727 123 Fax: 01173 292 325
Email: info@enlightenedlighting.co.uk
Web Site: www.enlightenedlighting.co.uk
Contact: Andrew Bartlett
Enlightened Lighting offer stage lighting, sound, AV, staging, rigging. Hire, production, installation, sales, Web shop.

ENLIGHTENMENT
The Rubicon Centre, Broad Ground Road, Lakeside, Redditch, Worcestershire B98 8YP
Tel: 0845 257 1992
Email: info@enlightenment.co.uk
Web Site: www.enlightenment.co.uk
Contact: Paul Swansborough
Established since 1997 and trading online since 2006. Enlightenment is the UK on-line source for stage lighting, sound, audio visual and rigging equipment to the entertainment industry. Enlightenment is a main dealer for Showtec, DAP Audio and Dutch Media Tools.

ENTEC SOUND & LIGHT
517 Yeading Lane, Northolt, Middlesex UB5 6LN
Tel: 020 8842 4004 Fax: 020 8842 3310
Email: sales@entec-soundandlight.com
Web Site: www.entec-soundandlight.com
Entec is the UK's longest established lighting and sound company. Entec delivers quality audio and lighting, professional technicians, staging, sets and project management for any event. You name it - we can do it!

ENTERTAINMENT LIGHTING CO LTD
49 The Broadway, Cheam, Sutton, Surrey SM3 8BL
Tel: 020 8643 9084 / 020 8643 1562
Fax: 020 8770 1911 Mobile: 0771 4413088
Email: sales@elclampsonline.com
Web Site: www.elclampsonline.com
Contact: Michael Hawkes
Major stockists of all theatre and front of house lamps (GE, Philips, Osram and Sylvania). Trade counter now open daily 9am - 5pm Monday to Friday for sales and order collection.

ETC LTD
Unit 26-28 Victoria Industrial Estate, Victoria Road, London W3 6UU
Tel: 020 8896 1000 Fax: 020 8896 2000
Email: uk@etcconnect.com
Web Site: www.etcconnect.com
Sales Manager for UK & Ireland: Mark White
ETC is one of the World's leading manufacturers of professional stage lighting, control and dimming equipment. Product range includes Source Four range of luminaires; Congo, SmartFade, Express and Emphasis control consoles; IES Sine Wave, Sensor and SmartPack dimming.

ETC UK LTD T/A THE PROJECTION STUDIO
Unit 4a, 13 Tarves Way, London SE10 9JP
Tel: 0208 2934 270 Fax: 020 8594 1243
Email: info@theprojectionstudio.com
Web Site: www.theprojectionstudio.com
Contacts: Ross Ashton , Steve Larkins
If you need to fill any space with exciting images, then we can offer you the solution. The PIGI system is the world's most versatile and powerful image projection system.

EUROSOUND (UK) LTD
44 High Street, Clayton West, Huddersfield HD8 9NS
Tel: 01484 866 066 Fax: 01484 866 299
Email: eurosounduk@yahoo.co.uk

Web Site: www.eurosound.co.uk
Contact: Paul Martin

FINELINE
The Old Quarry, Clevedon Road, Failand, Bristol, North Somerset BS8 3TU
Tel: 01275 395 000 Fax: 01275 395 001
Email: contact@fineline.uk.com
Web Site: www.fineline.uk.com
Contact: Darren Wring

FLASHLIGHT LTD
Unit A3, Axis Point, Hilltop Road, Heywood, Lancashire OL10 2RQ
Tel: 01706 625 866 Fax: 01706 620 756
Email: sales@flash-light.co.uk
Web Site: www.flash-light.co.uk
Contact: Rob Williamson
Flashlight are the ' one-stop shop' for entertainment lighting, accessories and consumables. We are main stockists for ETC, Lee Filters, Arri, Martin Professional, Zero 88, Pulsar, Doughty, Rosco, Philips, Le Maitre.

FRANCIS SEARCHLIGHTS (1990) LTD
Union Road, Bolton, Lancashire BL2 2HJ
Tel: 01204 558 960 Fax: 01204 558 979
Email: cashton@francis.co.uk
Web Site: www.francis.co.uk
General Manager: Paul Saddler

FUTURE MEDIA
Unit 2, Grange Road Industrial Estate, Christchurch, Dorset BH23 4JD
Tel: 01425 270 511 Tel: 020 7100 0511 (London) Tel: 0121 314 0511 (Midlands)
Fax: 01425 278 615
Email: info@futuremediasystems.co.uk
Web: www.futuremediasystems.co.uk
Managing Director: Luke Siemaszko
Future Media specialise in Sound, Lighting and Video equipment. We are just as happy to provide a complete multimedia rig, or to sell just a single piece of equipment. We can supply only, hire, or install as required. Our emphasis is on providing a quality service, value for money, and excellent support. We can provide a full range of equipment from all manufacturers at competitive prices. Theatre sound and communication systems, radio microphones, stage and effects lighting, video cameras and projection, show control, trussing, staging, infra - red and induction loop systems and consumables are all items we are keen to talk to you about!

FUTURIST PROJECTS LTD
Unit 1, White Swan Yard, Otley, LS21 1AE
Tel: 0113 279 0033 Fax: 0113 301 0255
Email: info@futurist.co.uk
Web Site: www.futurist.co.uk
Managing Director: Jamie Hudson
Financial Director: Jamie Hudson

AV, Theatrical Productions, Lighting and Sound Specialists.

GE LIGHTING LTD
Old Tiffield Road, Tove Valley Business Park, Towcester, NN12 6PF
Tel: 0808 156 0221 Fax: 0800 169 8284
Email: englishcustomercontactteam @ge.com
Web Site: www.gelighting.com/eu
The enormous variety of lamps now manufactured by GE Lighting Ltd has been developed to the current high level of sophistication as the result of extensive and continuing research in many branches of Physics. GE has never been content to merely match the performance of its competitors - always the research has continued which has made GE the leading light source manufacturers in the world.
Products: High voltage stage and studio quartz and discharge lamps.

GLOWSHOP
The Light House 582-584 Hagley Road West, Birmingham B68 0BS
Tel: 0121 423 2000 Fax: 0121 423 2050
Email: sales@uv-light.co.uk
Web Site: www.glowshop.com
Managing Director: Paul Jackson
Specialist company dedicated to sales of UV lighting, UV reactive invisible / UV revealing and glow in the dark products.

GLS LIGHT & SOUND PRODUCTION LTD
Alpha Building, Willments Industrial Estate, Hazel Road, Southampton SO19 7HS
Tel: 023 8043 6622 Fax: 023 8043 6633
Email: info@glslighting.com
Web Site: www.glslighting.com
Contact: Claire Lewis, Ms J Turner

GOBOLAND UK
The Atrium, Curtis Road, Dorking, RH4 1XA
Tel: 020 7060 4626 Fax: 020 7060 4625
Email: info@goboland.co.uk
Web Site: www.goboland.com
Goboland is manufacturer of high quality Black Steel and Glass Gobos for all luminaires. We offer a friendly and professional Custom Gobo service and our Collection Gobos can be viewed online at www.goboland.co.uk

GRADAV HIRE & SALES LTD
Elstree Light and Power, The Power House, Elstree Film Studios, Shenley Road, Borehamwood, Herts WD6 1JG
Tel: 020 8324 2100 Fax: 020 8324 2933
Email: office@gradav.co.uk
Web Site: www.gradav.co.uk
Sale & Dry Hire of technical equipment for theatre - including animation effects, moving head lanterns, radio mics & systems

and Prolyte trussing. We also supply consummables.

HAWTHORN THEATRICAL LTD
Crown Business Park, Old Dalby, Leicestershire LE14 3NQ
Tel: 01664 821111 Fax: 01664 821119
Email: info@hawthorns.uk.com
Web Site: www.hawthorns.uk.com
Managing Director: Martin Hawthorn
Hire, Installation, design and sales of lighting, sound, staging, rigging, drapes, impact sales, starcloth and special effects.
Hire and sales open 7 days a week, main dealers for all leading brands.
London Office: Unit F, Western Trading Estate, London, NW10 7LU, Tel: 020 8955 6900

HENLEY THEATRE SERVICES LTD
Unit 2, Centenary Business Park, Station Road, Henley-on-Thames, Oxfordshire RG9 1DS
Tel: 01491 412347 Fax: 01491 412349
Email: office@henleytheatre.com
Web Site: www.henleytheatre.com
Contact: Derek Gilbert
Hire and Sales of Lighting, Rigging, Staging, Sound, & Communications; Crewing; Design; Consultancy; Installations; Training; Annual Inspections; PAT Testing; & Repairs.

HSL (HIRE) LTD
Unit E & F, Glenfield Park, Philips Road, Blackburn Lancashire BB1 5PF
Tel: 01254 698 808 Fax: 01254 698 835
Email: simon@hslgroup.com, contact@hslgroup.com
Web Site: www.hslgroup.com
Contact: Simon Stuart
Every client is special, each commission totally unique, our in house event management process ensuring that your project is carefully monitored, from the taking of your detailed instructions, through design and planning, and ultimately the installation and staging of the event itself.

IMAX LIGHTING LTD
Unit 12-13, Bonville Road, Brislington Bristol BS4 5QG
Tel: 0117 971 9625
Email: info@imaxlighting.co.uk
Web Site: www.imaxlighting.co.uk
Supplier of Lighting, Rigging and Power Distribution equipment to the Arts, Event's and Entertainment Industry

CHRIS JAMES & CO LTD
Chris James Lighting Filters, 43 Colville Road, London W3 8BL
Tel: 020 8896 1773 Fax: 020 8896 1774
Email: cj@chrisjamesfilters.com
Web Site: www.chrisjamesfilters.com
A comprehensive range of over 150

effects, colour correction and diffusion filters and a 'live' performance range of 50 high temperature filters and sundries including reflectors, scrim, blackwrap and blackout film, etc.

JPL SERVICES
15 High Street, Rampton, Cambridge CB24 8QE
Tel: 01954 250 851 Fax: 01954 250 543
Email: info@jplgenerators.co.uk
Manager: Chris Kelk
Silent generators. Lighting equipment for hire. Contract work with fit up crews for indoor/outdoor presentations, festivals, marquees etc.

KAVE THEATRE SERVICES
Unit 1 and 2, 55 Victoria Road, Burgess Hill, West Sussex RH15 9LH
Tel: 01444 245 500 Fax: 01444 243 355
Email: sales@kave.co.uk
Web Site: www.kave.co.uk
Sales Manager: Michael Mackie Clarke

LANCELYN LIGHTING (NORTHWEST)
Poulton Road, Bebington, Wirral CH63 9LN
Tel: 0151 334 8991 (24Hours) Fax: 0151 334 4047 Oxford Office: Ferry Hinksey Road, Oxford, England, OX2 0BY Tel: 01865 722 468 Fax: 01865 728 791
Email: northwest@lancelyn.co.uk
Web Site: www.lancelyn.co.uk
Sales and Branch Manager: Paul Cook (paul@lancelyn.co.uk)
Optical & special effects, Pyrotechnics supplied and delivered.

LANCELYN THEATRE SUPPLIES
Ferry Hinksey Road, Oxford OX2 0BY
Tel: 01865 722 468 Fax: 01865 728 791
Email: oxford@lancelynoxford.co.uk
Web Site: www.lancelyn.co.uk
Sales and Branch Manager: Reg Berry
Email: reg@lancelynoxford.co.uk
Marketing, Admin & Office Manager: Sara Ingham
Made to measure curtains, supply and fix, repair and cleaning.

LASER CREATIONS INTERNATIONAL LTD (LCI)
55 Merthyr Terrace, Barnes, London SW13 8DL
Tel: 020 8741 5747 Fax: 020 8748 9879
Email: contact@lci-uk.com
Web Site: www.lci-uk.com
Managing Director: Marlyn Weeks
Originally famous for its laser spectaculars, LCI has extended its portfolio to include waterscreens, dancing waters, digital video projection, pyrotechnics and other special effects.

JIM LAWS LIGHTING
Westend Lodge, West End Corner, Wrentham, Beccles, Suffolk NR34 7NH
Tel: 01502 675 264 Mob: 07776 238 249
Email: jimlawslighting@btconnect.com
Period Entertainment Lighting. Hire and Sales, lighting Design service.

LEE FILTERS
Central Way, Walworth Ind. Estate, Andover, Hampshire SP10 5AN
Tel: 01264 366 245 Fax: 01264 355 058
Email: ecruffell@leefilters.com
Web Site: www.leefilters.com
Contact: Ralph Young, Paul Topliss
Manufacturers of light filter in both polyester and polycarbonate. Flame Retardant to BS5750 when stated. Also, manufacturers of Photographic Colour Correction and colour Printing Filters and optical Resin Camera Filters.

LIGHT WORKS LIMITED
2a Greenwood Road, London E8 1AB
Tel: 020 7249 3627 Fax: 020 7254 0306
Email: charlie@light-works.co.uk
Web Site: www.light-works.co.uk
Contact: Charlie Paton

LIGHTFACTOR SALES LTD
Unit 20, Greenhill Crescent, Watford Business Park, Watford, Hertfordshire WD18 8JA
Tel: 01923 698 080 Fax: 01923 698 081
Email: info@lightfactor.co.uk
Web Site: www.lightfactor.co.uk
Lightfactor sales offer a wide range of leading-edge lighting equipment for theatre applications including the versatile LDR range of lanterns from Italy, and the High End Systems family of intelligent fixtures from the US.

LIGHTING PARTNERS LTD
Unit 22 The IO Centre, Croydon Road, Beddington, Croydon CR0 4WQ
Tel: 0844 800 3412 Fax: 0844 800 3413
Email: sales@usedlighting.co.uk
Web Site: www.usedlighting.co.uk / www.stagelighting.co.uk
Co-Managing Directors: Iain Dennis, David Morgan
Used Professional Equipment: Tested, Cleaned, Complete.

LIGHTSTORM TRADING LTD
5 Orchard Business Centre, Kangley Bridge Road, London SE26 5AQ
Tel: 0208 676 7902 Fax: 0208 778 2310
Email: sales@lightstormtrading.co.uk
Web Site: www.lightstormtrading.co.uk
Contact: Rod Bartholomeusz.

LM PRODUCTIONS LLP
Unit 6H, Southbourne Business Park, Courtlands Road, Eastbourne, East Sussex BN22 8UY
Tel: 01323 432 170 Fax: 01323 432 171
Email: info@lm-productions.com
Web Site: www.lm-productions.com
Contact: Stephen Harvey
Laser display and special effects.

MAINLY LIGHTING & TECHNOLOGY LTD
15 Low Farm Place, Moulton Park Industrial Estate Northampton NN3 6HY
Tel: 01604 790 900 Fax: 07053 635 613
Email: paul@mushroomlighting.com
Web Site: www.mushroomlighting.com
Contact: Mr Paul R Butler
Lighting Design & Supply, for hire and permanent installation.

MAINSTAGE PRESENTATION TECHNOLOGY LTD
Butler Works, Wyresdale Road, Lancaster LA1 3JJ
Tel: 01524 844 099 Fax: 01524 841 808
Email: info@mainstageltd.com
Web Site: www.mainstageltd.com
Managing Director: Mike Sweetland

MALDWYN BOWDEN INTERNATIONAL LTD
168 Edward Street, Brighton, East Sussex BN2 0JB
Tel: 01273 607 384 Fax: 01273 694 408
Email: mbi@mistral.co.uk
Web Site: www.mistral.co.uk/mbi
Maldwyn Bowden International design, supply and install sound and lighting systems for theatres and clubs and can also provide equipment on hire.

THE MANCHESTER LIGHT AND STAGE LTD
76 - 78 North Western Street, Manchester M12 6DY
Tel: 0161 273 2662 Fax: 0161 273 2664
Office Address: 6 St Johns Road, Heaton Mersey, Stockport SK4
Email: info@manchesterlightandstage.com
Web Site: www.manchesterlightandstage.com
Contact: Bruce Mitchell, Jim Gee
Lighting Hire and Sales "Steeldeck" Hire and Sales - Marquee Hire, Event Management - Site Electrics. Catwalks, outdoor roofs & stages.

MARTIN PROFESSIONAL PLC
Cranborne House, Cranborune Industrial Estate, Cranbourne Road, Potters Bar, Hertfordshire, EN6 3JN
Tel: 0203 0021 170
Email: uksales@martin.dk
Web Site: www.martinpro.co.uk

MATT-LX LTD
Unit 3,Vinehall Business Ctr Vinehall Road, Robertsbridge, East Sussex TN32 5JW

Tel: 0845 6808692
Email: matt.lx@mattlx.com
Web Site: www.mattlx.com
Project Manager: Rob Clutterham
MattLX is a specialist technical event production company, providing lighting and design, Audio Visual, equipment supply, programmers, operators, installation, training and Health & Safety services, for Theatre, Arts, Entertainment, Leisure, Marine, TV and Corporate Events.

MC PRODUCTION GROUP
Unit SU4A, Lansbury Estate, 102 Lower Guildford Road, Woking, Surrey GU21 2EP
Tel: 01483 884488.
Web Site: www.mcpg.co.uk

MCL
Catesby Park, Eckersall Road, Kings Norton, Birmingham B38 8SE
Tel: 0121 433 8899 Fax: 0121 433 8891
London Office: 14 Ockham Drive, Greenford Park, Greenford, London, UB6 0FD Tel: 0208 839 7010 Fax: 0208 839 7011
Email: info@mclcreate.com
Web Site: www.mclcreate.com
General Manager (Birmingham): Mark Simkin
Operations Manager (Birmingham): Paul Mandeville
Hire Manager (Birmingham): Chris Cheatle
Conference, exhibition and presentation equipment hire. Audio visual sound and lighting.

GRAHAM J MCLUSKY
55 High Street, Metheringham, Lincoln LN4 3DZ
Tel: 0800 026 0766 Mobile: 07831 569993
Email: mail@graham-mclusky.co.uk
Web Site: www.treeble.demon.co.uk

MERCIA THEATRE SERVICES
2A Hotel Street, Coalville, Leicestershire LE67 3EP
Tel: 01530 263 454 Fax: 01530 260 206
Email: merciaarts@yahoo.co.uk
Contact: Simon Nickerson
Lighting:
Sales of accessories and consumables including colour filter, cables, connectors, fixing hardware, adhesive tapes, lamps. Sales of lanterns and control systems. Installation service.
Sound: Sales of accessories and consumables including cables, connectors, batteries, sound effects CD's. Extensive range of hardware including microphones, mixing desks, amplifiers, speakers, CD, cassette and mini disc players, induction loop and Infra-red systems. Installation service. PA hire for indoor / outdoor meetings, conferences and events.
Effects: Sales of hardware and consumables for pyrotechnic and special effects.

Make-up: Sales of make-up by Ben Nye and Mehron. Also an extensive range of wigs, masks and costume accessories. Mail order catalog available.

MGC LAMPS LTD
1 Sovereign Centre, Farthing Road, Ipswich Suffolk IP1 5AP
Tel: 01473 466 300 Fax: 01473 240 081
Email: david@mgc-lamps.com / uksales@mgc-lamps.com
Web Site: www.mgc-lighting.com
Established for over 30 years as one of Europe's largest stage & studio lamp distributors, stocking over a million pounds worth of lighting consumables and LED products.

MICO LIGHTING
Troydale Lane, Pudsey, West Yorkshire LS28 9LD
Tel: 0113 256 7113 Fax: 0113 257 2358
Email: sales@mico.co.uk
Web Site: www.mico.co.uk
Contact: Sales Office
Specialist in all types of lighting.

MIDLAND SOUND HIRE
PA Systems, Lighting and Sound Reinforcement
53 Gorse Farm Road, Great Barr, Birmingham B43 5LS
Tel: 0778 792 2437 Tel: 07050 636 367 - Andrew Andley
Email: mshpasound@googlemail.com
2 kw to 10 kw PA sound systems for live bands, DJs, college and university events, festivals, tours and corporate events.
200 watt to 2 kw sound systems for vocalists, DJs and live bands.
2 kw/10 kw rigs: 12/16/24 channel mixers, 2/4 way aux foldback & full onstage mix, graphics, echo and reverb, fully experienced engineers.
Equipment Inc., AKG Altec, Allen & Heath, Audio Technica, Behringer, Beyer, Carlsboro, HH, JBL, Peavey, RCF, Shure & Studiomaster, EV, Crown, PSL.
Lighting rig: Par 56/64 spots (4/6 each side), 2 stands, strobe, rwisters, ultra violets, control desk and engineer.

MM PRODUCTIONS
Unit 10 Smeaton Close, Severalls Industrial Park, Colchester CO4 9QY
Tel: 01206 845 947 Tech (Out of Hours): 07850 792 263
Web Site: www.mmproductions.co.uk
Email:
Sound Hire & Sales: inquiries@mmproductions.co.uk
Lighting Hire & Sales: lx@mmproductions.co.uk
Managing Director: Martyn Hunt

NORTHERN LIGHT
Assembly Street, Edinburgh EH6 7RG Scotland
Tel: 0131 622 9100 Fax: 0131 622 9101
Email: enquiries@northernlight.co.uk
Web Site: www.northernlight.co.uk
Management: John Allen, Dave Webster
Stockists for Strand Lighting. Hall Stage Products, Roscolab UK and Le Maitre Pyrotechnics. Stage Lighting Hire and Sales, Production Lighting Design, manufacturers of stage drapes, socket outlet boxes, facilities panels, working light control systems and sound and communication systems to consultants' specifications, specialist Electrical Contracting.

NORTHERN STAGE SERVICES LTD
Trent Industrial Estate, Duchess Street, Shaw, Oldham, Lancashire OL2 7UT
Tel: 01706 849 469 Fax: 01706 840 138
Email: Info@nstage.co.uk, david.baxter@nstage.co.uk
Web Site: www.nstage.co.uk
Specialists in stage lighting, sound and curtain equipment.
Managing Director: Patrick Colin
Sales Manager: David Baxter
Business Administrator: Kelly Tracey

ON EVENT PRODUCTION COMPANY
Formerly Panda Hire Ltd.
Acton House, Acton Grove, Acton Road Industrial Estate, Long Eaton, Nottingham NG10 1FY
Tel: 01159 222 959 Fax: 01159 735 918
Email: sales@lovingitlive.co.uk
Web Site: www.lovingitlive.co.uk
MD: Guy Eaton
Operations Director: Paul White
Production Director: Chris Vernon-Smith
Hire Manger: James Pemblington
We hire PA / Staging / Lighting / Truss & Power distribution for either dry hire or as a complete package with engineers and/or event management.

ONE STAGE PRODUCTIONS LTD
11 Bramley Close, Cogenhoe, Northampton NN7 1LY
Tel: 0870 774 3522
Mobile: 07956 234192
Email: john@one-stage.com
Web Site: www.one-stage.com
Contacts: John Ryan, Jody Ryan
With a strong team of IT and Audio design staff we offer a friendly and professional service as suppliers of market leading equipment suitable for theatre, conferencing, exhibitions, broadcasting and touring. We also have an experienced team working in project and tour management.

OPTIKINETICS (UK) LIMITED
38 Cromwell Road, Luton, Bedfordshire LU3 1DN
Tel: 01582 411 413 Fax: 01582 400 613
Email: ukadmin@optikinetics.com
Web Site: www.optikinetics.co.uk

PANALUX LIMITED
Manchester Road, Kearsley, Bolton, Lancashire BL4 8RL
Tel: 01204 794 000 Fax: 01204 571 877
Email: ian.swindells@panalux.biz
Web Site: www.panalux.biz
Contact: Ian Swindells

PERFORMANCE LIGHT AND SOUND LTD
Unit 10, Cowley Road, London W3 7XA
Tel: 020 8743 4680
Email: sales@lmccaudio.co.uk
Web Site: www.lmcaudio.co.uk
Importers and distributers of chassis loudspeakers and lighting and cable.

PG STAGE ELECTRICAL
Studio House, Tameside Work Centre, Ryecroft Street, Ashton-under-Lyme, Lancashire OL7 0BY
Tel: 0161 830 0303
Email: sales@pgstage.co.uk or info@pgstage.co.uk
Web Site: www.pgstage.co.uk
Supply of Tabs, Legs, Cycloramas, Festoons, Borders, Nets, Gauzes and Astrocloths. Design and installation of writing audio and mechnical systems. Also lighting and audio suppliers.

PHOSPHENE
Milton Road South, Stowmarket, Suffolk IP14 1EZ
Tel: 01449 770 011
Email: phosphene@btconnect.com
Web Site: www.phosphene.co.uk
Proprietor: Cliff Dix
Hire and sales of lamps, lanterns, radio mics and control equipment by all major manufacturers. Production design, rigging and operation for all styles. Specialise in "One nighters" in unusual venues; product launches, fashion shows, etc.

PKE LIGHTING
Unit E7, Walter Leigh Way, Moss Industrial Estate, Leigh, Lancashire WN7 3PT
Tel: 01942 678 424 Fax: 01942 678 423
Email: sales@pkelighting.com
Web Site: www.pkelighting.com
General Manager: Chris Hughes

POINT SOURCE PRODUCTIONS LTD
Unit 5 Kimpton trade & Business Centre, Minden Road, Sutton, Surrey SM3 9PF
Tel: 020 8254 2620 Fax: 08701 696 736
Email: info@pslx.co.uk
Web Site: www.pslx.co.uk
Point Source Productions can organise, plan and supply technical services, including lighting, sound, AV and staging, for Corporate, Theatre and Live Events.

PRG UK
The Cofton Centre, Groveley Lane, Longbridge, B31 4PT
Tel: 0845 470 6400
Email: ukinfo@prg.com
Web Site: www.prg.com
Contact: Rich Rowley
With the largest inventory of rental lighting stock in Europe, PRG is the consummate supplier of lighting to the business of entertainment and in particular the theatre. Whether it's the lighting rig for a touring musical production, a West End show or opera at the Royal Albert Hall, we have the knowledge, the equipment and the expertise to ensure your success, every time.

PRISM LIGHTING
5A Hampton Industrial Estate, Malpas, Cheshire SY14 8JQ
Tel: 01948 820 201 Fax: 01948 820 480
Email: mail@prismlighting.co.uk
Web Site: www.prismlighting.co.uk
Business Co-Ordinator: Geraldine Flavel
Technician: Stephen Wright
Full range of lighting for all types of events. Large stock of moving lights, heavy duty truss, ground supports. Outdoor stage roof system.

PRO UV LAMPS LTD
Centauri House, Hillbottom Road, Sands Industrial Estate, High Wycombe, Buckinghamshire HP12 4HQ
Tel: 01494 838 389 Fax: 01494 461 093
Email: info@prouvlamps.com
Web Site: www.prouvlamps.com
Theatre and Studio lighting suppliers. Primarc have been established for 40 years and are one of the largest suppliers of stage and studio bulbs and filters in the country. We also offer same and next day delivery throughout London.

PULSAR LIGHT OF CAMBRIDGE LTD
3 Coldhams Business Park, Norman Way, Cambridge CB1 3LH
Tel: 01223 403 500 Fax: 01223 403 501
Email: sales@pulsarlight.com
Web Site: www.pulsarlight.com
Managing and Technical Director: Brian Pohl
Director of Sales and Marketing: Dave Cowan
We manufacture LED lighting and a broad range of lighting control desks, dimming/switching , effects control, datapaks etc which are suitable for theatre production.

R B LIGHTING LTD
PO Box 448, Teddington, Middlesex TW11 1AZ
Tel: 020 8977 9665 Fax: 020 8977 5687
Email: rb.lighting@tiscali.co.uk
Director: Richard Broadhurst

Wholesale suppliers of all theatre, studio and display lamps. Spare parts service for all current and obsolete lanterns. Colour supply and cutting service. CCT, Rosco & DHA main dealers. Immediate dispatch. Secondhand lighting equipment bought and sold.

RESOURCES CENTRE LTD
Cambridge House, 128 Park Road, Camberley, Surrey GU15 2LW
Tel: 01276 670 000 Fax: 01276 670 010
Hire and Supply of P.A. Systems. Supply of Operating Technicians.

ROBOLIGHTS LTD
5 G.D Units, Cofton Road, Marsh Barton, Exeter, Devon, EX2 8QW
Tel: 01392 823 040 Fax: 01392 824 062
Email: sales@robolights.com
Web Site: www.robolights.com
Contact: Julian Baycock
Robolights designs and manufactures innovative stage lighting products including the 'industry standard' Smart Socket used worldwide as a multi-purpose electrical outlet for internally wired lighting bars and lighting grids. As well as developing and marketing it's own products, Robolights also manufactures bespoke items for other companies and venues in the entertainment industry and has established a reputation for producing high quality production lighting panels, audio facility panels and power distribution units for fixed installations, along with replica items and custom metalwork of all descriptions. In 2005 the Company also launched its award winning, patented Smart Clamp; a product to supersede the humble hook clamp for attaching stage lighting equipment to lighting bars.

ROSCOLAB LTD
Blanchard Works, Kangley Bridge Road, Sydenham, London SE26 5AQ
Tel: 020 8659 2300 Fax: 020 8659 3153
Email: contact@rosco.com
Web Site: www.rosco.com
Shrink mirrors, breakaways. Rear & front projection screens, scenic materials, scenic paint systems. Lighting colour media including diffusion. Comprehensive range of gobos.
Director of Sales: Cristian Arroyo

THE SCAN WAREHOUSE
Kingfisher House, Hodgson Way, Wickford, Essex SS11 8YN
Tel: 08705 561 233 Fax: 08705 134 476
Email: info@scanwarehouse.com
Web Site: www.scanwarehouse.com
"The Professional Sound & Lighting Company"
The Scan Warehouse services offered are: Sound and Lighting Design, Supply, Installation, Programming and Maintenance.

SDD SOUND & LIGHT LTD
Temple Gardens, Staines, Middlesex TW18 3NQ
Tel: 01784 455 666 Fax: 01784 455 642
Email: info@sddsoundandlight.com
Web Site: www.sddsoundandlight.com
Rental, sales, repair and installation of all types and brands of equipment from multi channel radio microphone systems to intelligent lighting. Visit our website for our catalogue.

SGB WORLD SERVICE
Empire Buildings, 49 Church Street, Stoke, Stoke-on-Trent Staffordshire, ST4 1DQ
Tel: 01782 749 749
Email: sales@fireworkempire.co.uk
Web Site: www.fireworkempire.co.uk

SNP PRODUCTIONS LTD (UK)
53 Northfield Road London W13 9SY
Tel: 01908 410129 Mob: 07958 390034
Email: simon@snp-productions.co.uk
Web Site: www.snp-productions.co.uk
Contact: Simon Pugsley
Providing Lighting & Video Control Solutions.

SOUND AND LIGHT SOLUTIONS
Unit 2, Mossvale 9 Clark Street, Paisley, Renfrewshire PA3 1RX Scotland
Tel: 0141 887 7655 Mobile: 07876 682 267
Email: enquiries@slsscotland.net
Web Site: www.slsscotland.net
Contact: Mr Simon Bain

SPARKS THEATRICAL HIRE
Unit 4, Cannon Wharf Business Centre, 35 Evelyn Street, Surrey Quays, London SE8 5RT
Tel: 020 7237 2872 Fax: 020 7237 8572
Email: enquiries@sparkshire.co.uk
Web Site: www.sparkshire.co.uk
Director: Paul Anderson

SPECIALIST LAMP DISTRIBUTORS
Unit 31, Waybridge Industrial Estate, Daniel Adamson Road, Salford M50 1DS
Tel: 0161 873 7822 Fax: 0161 873 8089
Email: sales@sldlighting.co.uk
Contact: Andy North/ Oliver Janicki
Distributors of replacement lamps for stage, studio, concert and display purposes - nationwide overnight service.

SPECIALIST THEATRE SERVICES LTD
Unit 10, Parkway Court, Nottingham NG8 4GN
Tel/ Fax: 0115 985 4062
Email: hire@specialisttheatreservices.co.uk
Web: www.specialisttheatreservices.co.uk
ADMINISTRATION:
Company Directors: Richard Atkins and Chris Atkins
Sales and hire of Theatre and Studio lighting, lighting control and dimming, curtains & tracking and rigging equipment.
Sales counter open with stocks of scenery paints, lamps, filters, pyrotechnics, etc.

SPECIALZ
Unit 2, Kingston Industrial Estate, 81-86 Glover Street, Birmingham B9 4EN
Tel: 0121 766 7100 Fax: 0121 766 7113
Email: info@specialz.co.uk
Web Site: www.specialz.co.uk
Specialz offer a design and electro-mechanical manufacturing service for Lighting or Set designers with great ideas or concepts but lack technical resources or the time to realise them.

STAGE AUDIO SERVICES
Unit 2, Bridge Street Wordsley Stourbridge West Midlands DY8 5YU
Tel: 01384 263 629 Fax: 01384 263 6209
Email: kevinmobers@aol.com
Web Site: www.stageaudioservices.com
Contact: Kevin Mobers
Suppliers of Quality Sound, Lighting & Production Services.

STAGE CONTROL LTD
20 Station Parade, Whitchurch Lane, Edgware, Middlesex HA8 6RW
Tel: 020 8952 8982
Email: Admin@stagecontrol.com
Web Site: www.stagecontrol.com
Technical Contact: Mr I New
Contact: D Jenkins
Stockists of Colour Filters, Lanterns, Dimmers and Control desks. Main dealers of Le Maitre smoke machines and TP communications equipment. We provide design services for shows, refurbishments & new builds. We also have an extensive hire department.

STAGE ELECTRICS
Third Way, Avonmouth, Bristol, Avon BS11 9YL
Hire & Sales: 0117 938 4000 Accounts: 0117 937 9550 Admin: 0117 982 7282
Admin Fax: 0117 916 2825 Fax: 0117 916 2828
Email: bristol@stage-electrics.co.uk
Web Site: www.stage-electrics.co.uk
One of the UK's largest suppliers of technical equipment to the entertainment, leisure, conference and presentation industries.
Offering sales and hire of lighting, sound, rigging, staging and all related equipment.
Head of Marketing: Adam Blaxill
Managing Director: Dan Aldridge
London Branch:
175 Long Lane, London SE1 4PN
Tel: 020 7939 3000 Fax: 020 7939 3001
E-Mail: london@stage-electrics.co.uk
Exeter Branch:
1 Swan Units, Heron Road, Sowton Industrial Estate, Exeter EX2 7LL
Tel: 01392 824 100 Fax: 01392 891 116
E-Mail: exeter@stage-electrics.co.uk

STAGE TWO LIMITED
Unit J, Penfold Estate, Imperial Way, Watford, Hertfordshire WD24 4YY
Tel: 01923 230 789 Fax: 01923 255 048
Email: info@stage-two.co.uk
Web Site: www.stage-two.co.uk
Hire or Sale of sound, lighting and special effects for all applications. Special effects Flash Pots, Maroons, Bullet Hits. Supplier of special effects for stage, films and TV.

STAGECRAFT TECHNICAL SERVICES LTD
Unit E & F, Porton Business Centre, Porton, Salisbury SP4 0ND
Tel: 0845 838 2015
Email: office@stagecraft.co.uk
Web Site: www.stagecraft.co.uk
Managing Director: Lisa Tapper
Sales Director: Mike Naish
Marketing Assistant: Chris Robinson
We supply & install equipment from all leading lighting & sound sound manufacturers to the educational, amateur and professional entertainment sectors.

STARDREAM LTD
70 Mowbray Drive, Blackpool, Lancashire FY3 7UN
Tel: 01253 302 602
Email: sales@stardream.co.uk
Web Site: www.stardream.co.uk
Manager: Sam Barnet
Specialising in event management, planning and organising corporate events, private functions, product launches, weddings, conferences, exhibitons and more. Stardream also distributes and installs for major manufacturers of professional sound and lighting equipment and special effects.

STORM LIGHTING LTD
Warwick House, Monument Way West, Woking, Surrey GU21 5EN
Tel: 01483 757 211 Fax: 01483 757 710
Email: hire@stormlighting.co.uk
Web Site: www.stormlighting.co.uk
Managing Directors: Peter Kramer, David Knapp
Lighting design and production to theatre, conference and events. Comprehensive dry hire stock of latest lighting equipment from major manufacturers facilities available to cover major UK and US theatre tours, down to small local events. Moving light programming a speciality.

STRAND LIGHTING LTD
Unit 3 Hammersmith Studios Yeldham Road London, W6 8JF
Tel: 0208 735 9790 Fax: 0208 735 9799
Email: sales@stranduk.com
Web Site: www.strandlight.com

TMB
21 Armstrong Way, Southall, Middlesex UB2 4SD
Tel: 020 8574 9700 Fax: 020 8574 9701
Email: tmb-info@tmb.com
Web Site: www.tmb.com
Contact: Paul Hartley
Value added distributor of production lighting equipment, sound and lighting cabling and power distribution. TMB's product range includes all major US and European production lighting and hardware including all touring expendable supplies.

TERRALEC LTD
Osprey House, Featherby Way, Purdeys Industrial Estate, Rochford, Essex SS4 1LD
Tel: 01702 547 571 Fax: 01702 541 075
Email: sales@terralec.com
Web Site: www.terralec.co.uk
Suppliers of professional stage lighting, audio equipment, lighting control, microphones, staging, trussing, hardware, accessories & much more! For: Theatre, stage, commercial events and the entertainment industry.

RAY THOMPSON LTD
8 Lorne Street, Belfast, County Antrim BT9 7DU Northern Ireland
Tel: 028 9066 4411 Fax: 028 9066 4831
Email: keith.rolleston@raythompson.com / admin@raythompson.com
Web Site: www.raygroup.freeserve.co.uk
Manufacturers agents for Strand Lighting - AS Green lighting, portable stages.
Contact Sales Manager: Keith Rolleston

TORPEDO FACTORY LTD
The Old Torpedo Factory, St. Leonards Road, London NW10 6ST
Tel: 020 8537 1000 Fax: 020 8537 1001
Email: s.maskell@tfg.com
Web Site: www.tfg.com
Project Manager: Steve Maskell
Gordon Audio Visual provides leading edge technical services for events, meetings and related activities. Lighting, set design and construction, projection, audio systems, webcasting, streaming, pre- and post-production facilities and more.

TOTAL FABRICATIONS LIMITED
Units 3 - 4, Kingston Industrial Estate, 81 - 86 Glover Street, Birmingham B9 4EN
Tel: 0121 772 5234
Email: info@trussing.com
Web Site: www.trussing.com
Contact: Karen Cronin
Manufacturer of standard and custom aluminium trusses, roof structures, fixtures and associated equipment including motor controllers and full range of Verlinde products catering for broad spectrum of applications.

TRAFALGAR LIGHTING LTD
Also see sister company, 'Make Up Effects'
9 Northway, London N9 0AD
Tel: 020 8887 0082 Fax: 020 8887 0072
Email: hire@trafalgarlighting.co.uk
Web Site: www.trafalgarlighting.co.uk
Sales and hire of lighting, sound and power distribution equipment for all forms of entertainments. Free advice.

TREEBLE LIGHTING & CONFERENCES
55 High Street, Metheringham, Lincoln LN4 3DZ
Tel: 0800 026 0766 Fax: 01526 322 606
Mob: 07831 569 993
Email: mail@graham-mclusky.co.uk, graham@treeble.demon.co.uk
Web Site: www.treeble.demon.co.uk
Chief Executive: Graham McLusky

USED LIGHTING, LIGHTING PARTNERS LTD
Unit 22 The IO Centre, Croydon Road, Beddington, Croydon CR0 4WQ
Tel: 020 3637 0121 Fax: 0844 800 3413
Email: hello@usedlighting.co.uk
Web Site: www.usedlighting.co.uk, www.stagelighting.co.uk
Contact: David Morgan
The UK's premier source of used professional lighting equipment.

VIKING SOUND & LIGHT LTD
Unit 9 Woodstock Close Standard Way Ind. Park, Northallerton North Yorkshire DL6 2NB
Tel: 01609 780190 Mob Tel: 07980 023154
Email: steve@vikingsound.co.uk
Web Site: www.vikingsound.co.uk
Contact: Steve Williams
Viking Sound are suppliers of PA systems, lighting systems, stage hire, installations, artist bookings and event managment.

WHITE LIGHT LTD
Entertainment and Performance Lighting
20, Merton Industrial Park, Jubilee Way, London SW19 3WL
Tel: 020 8254 4800 Fax: 020 8254 4801
Email: Charlotte.Blackwell@WhiteLight.ltd.uk
Web Site: www.WhiteLight.ltd.uk
Managing Director: Bryan Raven
Hire & Technical Director: Dave Isherwood
Contact: Charlotte Blackwell

White Light offers an unparalleled lighting service from design, installation, hire, sales and service, across the theatrical, corporate and event industries. We are the exclusive UK distributors for Robert Juliat, LSC Lighting, Coemar, i-Pix, Look Solutions, RSC Lightlock, Wireless Solutions, Prism Lighting, Arkaos, JB Lighting, Rainbow colour scrollers, ELC DMX tools and Illieum. With over 40 years experience, White Light owns one of the UK's largest stocks of conventional and automated fixtures, an extensive workshop facilities in Wimbledon (London), and an online order facility (www.lxstore.com). White Light makes light work.

CHRISTOPHER WRAY'S LIGHTING
5 Southeron Place, London SW6 2EJ
Tel: 020 7751 8701 Fax: 020 7731 3507
Email: sales@christopherwray.com
Web Site: www.christopherwray.com
Contact: Chris Jordan
Over 6,000 light and lighting accessories in range of period styles to contemporary. Hire Service. Also offers a restoration and repair service and will consider commissions for special projects.

XTBA
Unit 2, The Old Curatage, The Street, Caston, Attlebrough, NR17 1DD
Tel: 0208 882 0100
Email: dmx@xtba.co.uk
Web Site: www.xtba.co.uk
Managing Director: Chris Cook

ZERO 88 (ZERO 88 LIGHTING LTD)
Usk House, Lakeside, Llantarnam Industrial Park, Cwmbran, Gwent NP44 3HD Wales
Tel: 01633 838 088 Fax: 01633 867 880
Email: enquiries@zero88.com
Web Site: www.zero88.com
Sales Manager (UK): Mark Morley
Specialists in lighting control for nearly 35 years, Zero 88 offer a complete range of desks, dimmers and controllers to suit most applications. From simple units to sophisticated memory desks, the Zero 88 range has been developed to serve the education, amateur/professional theatre, rental and architectural markets support an extensive distributor network both in the UK and all main overseas markets.
Multi language literature available.
Large, fully equipped demonstration studio and training centre also available.

Lighting Fibre Optics

EUROSOUND (UK) LTD
44 High Street, Clayton West, Huddersfield HD8 9NS
Tel: 01484 866 066 Fax: 01484 866 299
Email: eurosounduk@yahoo.co.uk
Web Site: www.eurosound.co.uk
Contact: Paul Martin

J & C JOEL LTD
Corporation Mill, Corporation Street, Sowerby Bridge, West Yorkshire HX6 2QQ
Tel: 01422 833835 Fax: 01422 835157
Email: sales@jcjoel.com
Web Site: www.jcjoel.com
Specialists in Flame Retardant Fabrics, manufacturers and installers of theatrical drapes and stage equipment. Probably the largest stock of flame retardant fabrics, tracks and all stage hardware, starcloths, dance flooring and portable staging.
Sales Manager: Oliver Marns

LASER CREATIONS INTERNATIONAL LTD (LCI)
55 Merthyr Terrace, Barnes, London SW13 8DL
Tel: 020 8741 5747 Fax: 020 8748 9879
Email: contact@lci-uk.com
Web Site: www.lci-uk.com
Managing Director: Marlyn Weeks
Originally famous for its laser spectaculars, LCI has extended its portfolio to include waterscreens, dancing waters, digital video projection, pyrotechnics and other special effects.

MARTIN PROFESSIONAL PLC
Cranborne House, Cranborune Industrial Estate, Cranbourne Road, Potters Bar, Hertfordshire, EN6 3JN
Tel: 0203 0021 170
Email: uksales@martin.dk
Web Site: www.martinpro.co.uk

MGC LAMPS LTD
1 Sovereign Centre, Farthing Road, Ipswich Suffolk IP1 5AP
Tel: 01473 466 300 Fax: 01473 240 081
Email: david@mgc-lamps.com / uksales@mgc-lamps.com
Web Site: www.mgc-lighting.com
Established for over 30 years as one of Europe's largest stage & studio lamp distributors, stocking over a million pounds worth of lighting consumables and LED products.

PAR OPTI PROJECTS LTD
67 Stirling Road, London W3 8DJ
Tel: 020 8896 2588 Fax: 020 8896 2599
Email: paropti@aol.com
Web Site: www.paropti.co.uk
Contact: Mary Conlon, Paul Raymond
Par Opti manufacture and distribute all fibre optic lighting materials: Parglas cables, harnesses and conduits, Parflex polymers, light sources, theatre curtain washers, spot ball and bullet lenses, side-emitting fractured fibres, ceiling fittings and large bore fibre optics.

UNIVERSAL FIBRE OPTICS
6 Home Place, Coldstream, Berwickshire TD12 4DT
Tel: 01890 883 416 Fax: 01890 883 062
Email: info@fibreopticlighting.com
Web Site: www.universal-fibre-optics.com / www.fibreopticlighting.com
Manufacturers of a complete range of quality fibre optic lighting and display systems for theatres. Light sources and harnesses manufactured to customers requirements. Also wide range of lenses and fittings.

Magical Equipment & Variety

INTERNATIONAL MAGIC
89 Clerkenwell Road, London EC1R 5BX
Tel: 020 7405 7324
Email: admin@internationalmagic.com
Web Site: www.internationalmagic.com
Contact: Martin MacMillan

PROFESSOR PATTEN'S PUNCH & JUDY
14 The Crest, Goffs Oak, Waltham Cross, Hertfordshire EN7 5NP
Tel/Fax: 01707 873 262
Email: d.patten998@btinternet.com, dennis@dennispatten.co.uk
Web Site: www.dennispatten.co.uk
Contact: Dennis Patten
Punch and Judy for Films, TV, Commercials, old time street scenes. Sales Promotion. Ventriloquist dummy hire and advice.

TREASURE TROVE PUPPET COMPANY
54 High Street, Caergwrle, Flintshire LL12 9LL Wales
Tel: 01978 761 053 Mob: 07802 800 817
Email: treasure.trove@virgin.net
Web: www.treasuretrovepuppets.co.uk
Directors: Stephen Sharples.
Operation includes: Puppets for all occasions, small/middle scale touring, workshops and demonstrations.
Makers of puppets. Extensive touring nationally and internationally.

VENTRILOQUIST'S DUMMIES
14 The Crest, Goffs Oak, Waltham Cross, Hertfordshire EN7 5NP
Tel/Fax: 01707 873 262
Email: dennis@dennispatten.co.uk
Web Site: www.dennispatten.co.uk
Hire and Advice.

Make-Up & Wigs

ANGELS WIGS
1 Garrick Road, London NW9 6AA
Tel: 020 8202 2244 Fax: 020 8202 1820
Email: info@angels.uk.com
Web Site: www.angels.uk.com
Contact: Ben Stanton

ARTISTES' THEATRE SHOP
23 City Road, Chester, Cheshire CH1 3AE
Tel: 01244 320 271 / 330 Fax: 01244 319 688
Email: carolsmith31@hotmail.com
Web Site: www.theatreshop.co.uk / www.dancewearuk.co.uk
Retail sale ballet shoes and requisites - Full range of theatrical make-up and costume hire. costumes also made to order both period and fancy dress for retail sales.

BANBURY POSTICHE LTD
Little Bourton House, Southam Road, Banbury, Oxfordshire OX16 1SR
Tel: 01295 757 402 Fax: 01295 757 401
Email: sales@banburypostiche.co.uk
Web Site: www.banburypostiche.co.uk
Contact: Nick Allen
The UK's leading supplier of wigmaking materials. Over 60 years of wigmaking expertise, specialising in custom made European hair wigs. Acrylic fashion wigs, and Mane Connection Human Hair system. We also supply hairdressing equipment.

BROMILEY LIMITED
The Wig & Fancy Dress Centre
166 Edleston Road, Crewe Cheshire CW2 7EZ
Tel: 01270 255 726 Fax: 01270 255 130
Email: bromileyltd@btconnect.com
Web Site: www.bromileyltd.co.uk
Directors: Margaret Taylor , Sheryl Haydock-Howorth
Stage wigs (hire and sale). Stage make-up. Costume accessories.

DAUPHINE'S OF BRISTOL
7 Cleeve Road, Downend, Bristol BS16 6AD
Tel/ Fax: 01179 560 805
Email: support@dauphines.co.uk
Web Site: www.dauphines.co.uk
Proprietor: Mrs M. Bills
Costumes, wigs for purchase or hire. Make-up supplies and make-up artists available for film, T.V and stage work.

DEREK EASTON WIGS
1 Dorothy Avenue, Peacehaven, East Sussex BN10 8LP
Tel/Fax: 01273 588 262 Mobile: 07768 166 733
Email: wigs@derekeastonwigs.co.uk
Web Site: www.derekeastonwigs.co.uk
Wigs for sale and hire in any style, any colour, for any show.

FANCY DRESS EXPERIENCE
88 Otley Road, Leeds LS6 4BA
Tel: 01132 304 700
Email: info@thefancydressexperience.co.uk
Web: www.thefancydressexperience.co.uk
Wigs and Fancy Dress, Shoes, Boas and Eyelashes.

TRACEY FLETCHER
32 Walnut Avenue, Tickhill, Doncaster, South Yorkshire DN11 9EJ
Mob: 07961 993584
Email: facecreations100@live.co.uk
Web Site: www.facecreations.co.uk

CHARLES H FOX LIMITED
Professional make-up centre for Film, Theatre, TV, and Fashion.
22 Tavistock Street, Covent Garden, London WC2E 7PY
Tel: 020 7240 3111 Fax: 020 7379 3410
Email: sales@charlesfox.co.uk
Web Site: www.charlesfox.co.uk
Manager: Ann Lee
Contact: Paul Merchant., Vicki Lee
Charles Fox Ltd supply a massive range of theatrical and television make-up and accessories.

FUN'N'FROLIC
16a Richfield Avenue, Reading RG1 8EQ
Tel: 0118 950 8597 Fax: 0118 959 9481
Email: jan@funnfrolic.co.uk
Web Site: www.funnfrolic.co.uk
Contacts: Jan Marketis, Dan Parsons
Suppliers of theatrical make-up, wigs and party goods, with a stock of over 7,500 costumes to hire.

HAIR DEVELOPMENT LTD
247 Mile End Road, London E1 4BJ
Tel: 020 7790 4567 Fax: 020 7790 3621
Email: hair@hair-development.com
Web Site: www.hair-development.com
Contact: Stan Levy
Supplying wigs for theatrical & everyday use. Also the worlds finest men's hair replacement systems & hairpieces.

HAIRAISERS LTD
9-11 Sunbeam Road, Park Royal, London NW10 6JP
Tel: 020 8965 2500 Fax: 020 8963 1600
Email: info@hairaisers.com
Web Site: www.hairaisersshop.com
Director: Mr Shahzad Anwar
Wigs available in 80 different styles, 38 colours. Also in carnival colours. Glitter wigs, beards and moustaches. Lace front stock wigs 300 different styles.

LANCELYN THEATRE SUPPLIES
Ferry Hinksey Road, Oxford OX2 0BY
Tel: 01865 722 468 Fax: 01865 728 791
Email: oxford@lancelynoxford.co.uk
Web Site: www.lancelyn.co.uk
Sales and Branch Manager: Reg Berry
Email: reg@lancelynoxford.co.uk
Marketing, Admin & Office Manager: Sara Ingham
Made to measure curtains, supply and fix, repair and cleaning.

MAKE UP EFFECTS
Also see sister company, 'Trafalgar Lighting Ltd'
9 North Way, Claverings Industrial Estate, London N9 0AD
Tel: 0208 887 0082 Fax: 0208 887 0072
Email: info@makeupeffects.co.uk
Web Site: www.makeupeffects.co.uk

MERCIA THEATRE SERVICES
2A Hotel Street, Coalville, Leicestershire LE67 3EP
Tel: 01530 263 454 Fax: 01530 260 206
Email: merciaarts@yahoo.co.uk
Contact: Simon Nickerson
Lighting: Sales of accessories and consumables including colour filter, cables, connectors, fixing hardware, adhesive tapes, lamps. Sales of lanterns and control systems. Installation service.
Sound: Sales of accessories and consumables including cables, connectors, batteries, sound effects CD's. Extensive range of hardware including microphones, mixing desks, amplifiers, speakers, CD, cassette and mini disc players, induction loop and Infra-red systems. Installation service. PA hire for indoor / outdoor meetings, conferences and events.
Effects:Sales of hardware and consumables for pyrotechnic and special effects.
Make-up: Sales of make-up by Ben Nye and Mehron. Also an extensive range of wigs, masks and costume accessories.
Mail order catalog available.

PIGS MIGHT FLY
The Barn Gawithfield, Arrad Foot, Ulverston, Cumbria LA12 7SL
Tel: 01229 861133 Fax: 01229 861144
Mob: 07894496217
Email: pigsmightfly@btconnect.com
Contact: Nick Dudman, Sue Dudman
Make-up Effects for Film, TV & Theatre.
Manufacturer and supplier of Nick Dudman washable "Blood".

PROPS4SHOWS
Osprey House, Featherby Way, Purdeys Industrial Estate, Rochford, Essex SS4 1LD
Tel: 03333 440 078 Fax: 03333 441 478
Email: sales@props4shows.com
Web Site: www.props4shows.co.uk
Contact: Lin Lorde
Suppliers of a wide range of props, display goods and fabrics, for stage, theatre, photography and marketing. The extensive range includes fake food, seasonal props, artificial trees, stage backdrops, scenery props, professional makeup, display accessories and much more.

ROSIE'S MAKE-UP BOX
Tel: 07976 965 520 Fax: 020 8390 7773
Email: rosiesmake-up@uwclub.net
Web Site: www.rosemarieswinfield.com
Contact: Rosemarie Swinfield
Make-up design, tuition, courses.
Rosemarie is head of make-up at LAMDA and author of "Stage Make-Up Step by Step", "Period Make-Up for the Stage" and "Hair & Wigs for the Stage".

SCREENFACE
48 Monmouth Street, Covent Garden, London WC2 9EP
Tel: 020 7836 3955 Fax: 020 7836 3944
Email: info@screenface.co.uk
Web Site: www.screenface.co.uk
Manager: Irene Christophis
Screenface has been supplying film, television and theatre companies for over 20 years and carries the largest range of professional make-up, make-up cases and location mirrors in the UK.

SANDRA SINGER ASSOCIATES
21 Cotswold Road, Westcliff-on-Sea, Essex SS0 8AA
Tel: 01702 331 616 Fax: 01702 339 393
Email: sandrasingeruk@aol.com
Web Site: www.sandrasinger.com
Senior Personnel: Sandra Singer
Film, TV, Musical Theatre Specialists, for adults and children. Specialist entertainment for Film & TV, Magic etc. Also represents composers and choreographers

WIG SPECIALITIES LIMITED
77 Ashmill Street, London NW1 6RA
Tel: 020 7724 0020
Email: wigspecialities@btconnect.com
Web Site: www.wigspecialities.com
Managing Director: Richard Mawbey
Hand made wigs & facial hair made for the Film, Theatre & Television industry.
Excellent Wig Hire Department.

WIG WORLD
39 Meadow Bank Court, Urmston Lane, Stretford, Manchester M32 9DY
Tel: 0161 865 0404
Contact: Rose Cartwright
Theatre Wigs and Hairpieces - all colours.
Stage Makeup, Hair and Beauty Books.
£30.00 the lot.

Management Consultants

AUDIENCES CENTRAL
601 The Big Peg, 120 Vyse Street, Hockley, Birmingham B18 6NF
Tel: 0121 685 2600 (Main Switchboard)
Email: info@audiencescentral.co.uk
Web Site: www.audiencescentral.co.uk, www.scenecentral.co.uk

Chief Executive: Nigel Singh
Senior Manager Audience Engagement: Jo Forrest
Finance Director: Ian Jarratt
Communications Manager: Dave Freak
Marketing Services Manager: Ali Finn
Audiences Central is the Audience Development Agency for the West Midlands, uniquely positioned to help arts and cultural organisations make a real difference to building and sustaining audiences for their work. We also offer a full range of consultancy and business services including: data cleaning; e-marketing; direct mail campaigns; research; press and media campaign planning and delivery; copywriting and publications; audience engagement; branding.

CHRIS BALDWIN
ACT Consultant Services, 2 The Old Wood Mill, Church Lane, Madingley, Cambridge CB23 8AF
Tel: 01954 210 766
Email: cbaldwin@actconsultantservices.co.uk
Web www.actconsultantservices.co.uk
Contact: Chris Baldwin
ACT Consultant Services is a multi-disciplinary practice covering arts strategies, business plans and market analysis through to feasibility studies and detailed design development of arts and entertainment buildings to include the visual and performing arts.

GARRY BROWN ASSOCIATES (INT) LTD
27 Downs Side, Cheam, Sutton, Surrey SM2 7EH
Tel: 020 8643 3991 Fax: 020 8770 7241
Email: gbaltd@btconnect.com
Senior Personnel: Garry Brown, Helen Machell, Brenda Capper, Denise Webb
Specialising in: Entertainment for Major Shipping Lines and Hotels Worldwide providing a range of artistes, particularly dance teams.

CARR & ANGIER
The Old Malthouse, Clarence Street, Bath, Somerset BA1 5NS
Tel: 01225 446 664 Fax: 01225 446 654
Email: info@carrandangier.co.uk
Web Site: www.carrandangier.co.uk
Principal & Theatre Consultant: Peter Angier
Consultancy services for the arts, entertainment and conference industries. Feasibility studies, planning and technical systems design for new and refurbishment projects.

DEP ARTS LTD
Yorkshire Dance Centre 3 St. Peters Buildings, Leeds West Yorkshire LS9 8AH
Tel: 0113 234 6911 Mob: 07970 718 785
Email: admin@departsltd.com
Web Site: www.departsltd.com
Independent Producer: David Edmunds

The company not ony specialises in producing Dance & Physical Theatre, but also provides consultancy services for arts based organisations or companies, including: Touring, Artist Development and Marketing.

MICHAEL HOLDEN
Octagon Business Park, Hospital RoadHospital Road, Little Plumstead, Norwich NR13 5FH
Tel: 01603 721 511 Fax: 01603 721 650
Email: michael@adrianjamesacoustics.co.uk
Web: www.adrienjamesacoustics.co.uk
Theatre Consultants, designers of new buildings or the adaption and refurbishment of existing buildings. Management Consultants experienced in the formation of Trusts and other management structures.

BERNARD MARTIN
39 Hughes Lane, Oxton, Wirral CH43 5TU
Tel: 0151 652 8085 Mob: 07980 846 750
Email: bernardrmartin@hotmail.com
Longest established Theatre Marketing specialist in the North.

TAYLOR PHILLIPS
The studio, High Green, Great Shelford, Cambridge CB22 5EG
Tel: 01223 550 808 Fax: 01223 550 806
Email: jobs@taylor-phillips.co.uk
Web Site: www.taylor-phillips.co.uk
Recruitment consultants for the entertainment industry.

THEATRE PROJECTS CONSULTANTS
4 Apollo Studios, Charlton Kings Road, London NW5 2SW
Tel: 020 7482 4224 Fax: 020 7284 0636
Email: uk@theatreprojects.com
Web Site: www.theatreprojects.com
Managing Director: Mark Stroomer
Accounts: Marion Daehms
Marketing: Ruth Smallshaw
Theatre and Leisure consulting service.

THEATREPLAN LLP
27 Colonnade London WC1N 1JA
Tel: 020 7841 0440 Fax: 020 7841 0450
Email: info@theatreplan.co.uk
Web Site: www.theatreplan.co.uk
Practice Manager: Paul Connolly
Auditorium design, theatre planning, technical equipment consultancy, feasibility studies and project development for theatres, conference venues and concert halls. Design of rigging, lighting, audio-visual and video systems and equipment specifications.

TOP DRAW ARTISTS
Cary Point, Babbacombe Downs Road, Torquay, Devon TQ1 3LU
Tel: 01803 322 233 Fax: 01803 322 244
Email: info@babbacombe-theatre.com
Web: www.babbacombe-theatre.com
Managing Director: Colin Matthews
Theatre consultants and artiste management.

Market Research

ARTSPROFESSIONAL
PO Box 1010, Histon, Cambridge CB4 9WH
01223 200200
Email: editors@artsprofessional.co.uk
Web Site: www.artsprofessional.co.uk
Editorial Co-Ordinator: Eleanor Turney
Arts Intelligence supplies professional business and marketing services to the arts and leisure industries; publishing ArtsProfessional magazine as well as developing major projects with key clients and serving the research needs of other consultants, agencies and freelances. Arts Intelligence specialises in quantitative and qualitative market research and data management and analysis.

BMG RESEARCH
7 Holt Court North, Heneage Street West, Birmingham B7 4AX
Tel: 0121 333 6006 Fax: 0121 333 6800
Email: info@bmgresearch.co.uk
Web Site: www.bmgresearch.co.uk
Managing Director: Dawn Hands

BUSINESS OF CULTURE LTD
6 Paddington Street, London W1U 5QG
Tel: 020 7224 5680
Email: info@businessofculture.com
Web Site: www.businessofculture.com
Founder Directors: William Tayleur, Graeme Jennings
Business of Culture Ltd is a dedicated arts and cultural consultancy offering a range of services to venues, local authorities, arts councils and other organisations. Services include strategic analysis and planning, market research, internal and external auditing, development strategies, consultation on staffing and practical freelance marketing.

MARKET & OPINION RESEARCH INTERNATIONAL
79-81 Borough Road, London SE1 1FY
Tel: 020 7347 3000 Fax: 020 7347 3800
Email: ukinfo@ipsos.com
Web Site: www.ipsos-mori.com
CEO: Ben Page

MARKETSCAN
8 Dukes Court, Bognor Road, Chichester, West Sussex PO19 8FX
Tel: 01243 786 711 Fax: 01243 779 671
Email: info@marketscan.co.uk
Web Site: www.marketscan.co.uk
Managing Director: Julie Knight

MPS & BBI INTERNATIONAL
Peerland House, 207 Desborough Road, High Wycombe, Buckinghamshire HP11 2QL
Tel: 01494 452 600 Fax: 01494 449 122
Email: bbi@bbi.co.uk
Web Site: www.bbi.co.uk
Managing Director: Andrew Libra

NOP WORLD
Ludgate House, 245 Blackfriars Road, London SE1 9UL
Tel: 020 7890 9000 Fax: 020 7890 9001
Email: info@nopworld.com
Web Site: www.gfknop.com

THE GALLUP ORGANIZATION LTD
The Adelphi 1-11 John Adam Street London WC2N 6HS
Tel: 020 7950 4400 Fax: 020 7950 4402
Email: kelly_carvalho@gallup.co.uk
Web Site: www.uk.gallup.com

Marketing & Media Services

AUDIENCES CENTRAL
601 The Big Peg, 120 Vyse Street, Hockley, Birmingham B18 6NF
Tel: 0121 685 2600 (Main Switchboard)
Email: info@audiencescentral.co.uk
Web Site: www.audiencescentral.co.uk, www.scenecentral.co.uk
Chief Executive: Nigel Singh
Senior Manager Audience Engagement: Jo Forrest
Finance Director: Ian Jarratt
Communications Manager: Dave Freak
Marketing Services Manager: Ali Finn
Audiences Central is the Audience Development Agency for the West Midlands, uniquely positioned to help arts and cultural organisations make a real difference to building and sustaining audiences for their work. We also offer a full range of consultancy and business services including: data cleaning; e-marketing; direct mail campaigns; research; press and media campaign planning and delivery; copywriting and publications; audience engagement; branding.

HAVARDS LIMITED
3rd floor, 33 Henrietta Street, Covent Garden, London WC2E 8NA
Tel: 020 7257 6395 Fax: 020 7257 6381
Mobile: +44 (0) 7802 218 266
Email: marketingsense@havards.com
Web Site: www.havards.com
Director: Michael Havard-Bilton
Creating powerful and imaginative solutions for the Arts through an innovative approach to the creation of integrated marketing, design and communication strategies.

MICHAEL MCCABE PRODUCTIONS
8th Floor, The Dutch House, 307-308 High Holborn, London WC1V 7LL
Tel: 020 7831 7077
Email: mailbox@michaelmccabe.net
Web Site: www.michaelmccabe.net
DIrector: Michael McCabe
Contact: Luke Shires, Sam Zdzieblo, David Bell
Strategic marketing advisor and consultant to the international live entertainment industry.

SPIN MARKETING & PR
15-17 Middle Street, Brighton BN1 1AL
Tel: 0845 257 1479 Fax: 0845 257 1463
Email: pr@spinpublicity.co.uk
Web Site: www.spinpublicity.co.uk
SPIN is renowned in the arts & entertainment industries for securing attention-grabbing media coverage on television, radio and within the press (nationally & regionally) working in the fields of stage, screen and celebrity.

UK FLYERS
Suite 210 Victory House, Somers Road North Portsmouth Hants PO1 1PJ
Tel: 023 9229 3050 Fax: 023 9229 5258
Email: sales@ukflyers.com
Web Site: www.ukflyers.com
Contact: Jim Cochrane

WORKHOUSE CREATIVE MARKETING
Workhouse Studios, Blackburn Road, Ribchester, Preston PR3 3ZQ
Tel: 01254 878 956 Fax: 01254 878 414
Email: mark@workhousemarketing.com
Web Site: www.workhousemarketing.com
Workhouse offers professional online and direct marketing, generating ideas for promotions, advertising, events & exhibitions, and photography. They also create quality designs for a range of products, making use of their newly fitted photography and video studio.

Marquee Hire & Outdoor Events

ABBAS MARQUEE HIRE
Wellhayes Farm, Lower Westholme, Pilton, Shepton Mallet, Somerset BA4 4HW
Tel: 01749 890 909
Email: enquiry@abbasmarquees.co.uk
Web Site: www.abbasmarquees.co.uk
Proprietor: James Dickson
Hirers of frame marquees, suitable for any surface, together with furniture, linings, etc.

ADVENTURE EVENTS
45 Greenvale Road, London SE9 1PB
Tel: 020 7476 1234 Fax: 020 8850 3499
Email: events@gokarting.co.uk
Web Site: www.gokarting.co.uk

AIR-SET LTD
3 Weston Colley, Micheldever, Winchester, Hampshire SO21 3AF
Tel: 01962 774 445 Fax: 01962 774 777
Email: david@air-set.co.uk
Web Site: www.air-set.co.uk
Proprietor: David Findley
Arched canopy and stages for outdoor or indoor music concerts. Visit our website for eye catching ideas to give your event a weatherproof inflatable shelter! Available for hire or sale.

ALBION WOODS SHOWTENTS
Albion Woods Show Tents, Cannards Farm, Shepton Mallet, Somerset BA4 4LY
Tel: 01749 346 002 Mob: 07815 871 132
Email: tents@albionwoods.co.uk
Web Site: www.albionwoods.co.uk
Contact: Hazel Hirst

ARENA STRUCTURES
Needingworth Road, St Ives, Cambridgeshire PE27 3ND
Tel: 01480 468 888 Fax: 01480 462 888
Email: info@arenastructures.com
Web Site: www.arenastructures.com
Hire of marquee and all temporary structures.

CLYDE CANVAS
4B East Mains, Ingliston Road, Edinburgh, Mid Lothain EH28 8NB Scotland
Tel: 0131 335 3685 Mob: 07810 123 360
Email: sales@purvis-marquees.co.uk
Web Site: www.purvis-marquees.co.uk
Contact: John Brown
Purvis Marquees is one of Britains leading companies for manufacture, hire and sale of quality marquees and fabric structures.

EVETRAKWAY
30-34 Weir Road, London SW19 8UG
Tel: 020 8879 8807 Fax: 020 8879 8808
Email: mail@evetrakway.co.uk
Web Site: www.evetrakway.co.uk
Hire of crowd control barriers.
Head Office Postal Address: Bramley Vale, Chesterfield, Derbyshire, S44 5GA.
Tel: 01246 858600

FIELD AND LAWN MARQUEES LTD
6/8 Clothier Road, Brislington Bristol BS4 5PS
Tel: 0117 9801 120
Email: bristol@fieldandlawn.com
Web Site: www.fieldandlawn.com
Director: Nick McLaren
Operations Manager: Gary Ferguson

Providing a high quality marquee hire service to customers across London, Bristol, Edinburgh, Glasgow, Leeds and Manchester.

FIELD & LAWN MARQUEES
Dunnet Way, East Mains Industrial Estate, Broxburn, West Lothian EH52 5NN
Tel: 01506 859 260 Fax: 01506 859 261
Web Site: www.fieldandlawn.com
Chief Executive: Cameron Stewart
Providing a high quality marquee hire service to customers across London, Bristol, Edinburgh, Glasgow, Leeds and Manchester.

GL EVENTS OWEN BROWN
Station Road, Castle Donington, Derby DE74 2NL
Tel: 01332 850 000 Fax: 01332 850 005
Email: info@owen-brown.co.uk
Web Site: www.owen-brown.co.uk
Contact: Katie Soutar

GO ENTERTAINMENTS
The Arts Exchange, Dane Mill Congleton, Cheshire CW12 1LA
Tel: 01260 276 627 Fax: 01260 270 777
Email: info@arts-exchange.com
Web Site: www.arts-exchange.com
Contact: Phillip or Carol Gandey
Big tops up to 5000 people worldwide supply.

HSL (HIRE) LTD
Unit E & F, Glenfield Park, Philips Road, Blackburn Lancashire BB1 5PF
Tel: 01254 698 808 Fax: 01254 698 835
Email: simon@hslgroup.com, contact@hslgroup.com
Web Site: www.hslgroup.com
Contact: Simon Stuart
Every client is special, each commission totally unique, our in house event management process ensuring that your project is carefully monitored, from the taking of your detailed instructions, through design and planning, and ultimately the installation and staging of the event itself.

KNIGHTLYS EUROPEAN LEISURE LTD
Knightlys Leisure Centre, Sandbank Road, Towyn, Abergele, Conwy LL22 9LD Wales
Tel: 07836 787 789 Fax: 01745 331 709
Email: luke@knightlysfunparks.com
Web Site: www.knightlysfunparks.com
Senior Personnel: Mr L Knightly
Knightlys can provide the following services; complete funfair hire to any destination, plus a resident amusement arcade and public house at Towyn.

THE MANCHESTER LIGHT AND STAGE LTD
76 - 78 North Western Street, Manchester M12 6DY
Tel: 0161 273 2662 Fax: 0161 273 2664
Office Address: 6 St Johns Road, Heaton Mersey, Stockport SK4
Email: info@manchesterlightandstage.com
Web Site: www.manchesterlightand-stage.com
Contact: Bruce Mitchell, Jim Gee
Lighting Hire and Sales "Steeldeck" Hire and Sales - Marquee Hire, Event Management - Site Electrics. Catwalks, outdoor roofs & stages.

MASTERS EXHIBITIONS & SHOWS
Units 3 -4 North Downs Business Park, Limepit Lane, Dunton Green, Sevenoaks, Kent TN13 2TL
Tel: 01732 740 370
Email: steve@mastersexhibitions.co.uk
Web Site: www.mastersexhibitions.co.uk
Mobile exhibition units and exhibition stands. Design and construction. Roadshows and product launches. Tented structures.

PURVIS MARQUEE HIRE
4b East Mains, Ingleston Road, Edinburgh, Mid Lothian EH28 8NB Scotland
Tel: 0131 335 3685 Fax: 0131 335 0294
Mob: 07810 123 360
Email: sales@purvis-marquees.co.uk
Web Site: www.purvis-marquees.co.uk
Contact: John Brown
Marquee and clearspan structure hire, furniture hire, textile repair (stage cloths etc).

Merchandising & Advertising Services

ADMIRAL SIGNS OF HULL LTD
Sainsbury Way, Hessle, North Humberside HU13 9NX
Tel: 01482 575 007 Fax: 01482 575 011
Email: info@admiral-signs-hull.co.uk
Web Site: www.admiral-signs-hull.co.uk
Production Manager: Mr D. Webster
Email: davew@admiral-signs-hull.co.uk
Every kind of sign internal and external. Including: neon & cold cathode signs and lighting, architectural signage, poster frames, internal signage, specialist lighting, vinyl graphics & front of house signs.

AKA
115 Shaftesbury Avenue, Cambridge Circus, London WC2H 8AF
Tel: 020 7836 4747
Email: reception@akauk.com
Web Site: www.akauk.com
Managing Director: Kate Turnball

ARTS CONTACT
Kenyon House, 104 Redbourne Road, Hibaldstow, Brigg, Lincolnshire DN20 9NP
Tel: 01652 656 775 Mob: 07831 166692 / 07860 374723
Email: sheila@artscontact.co.uk
Web Site: www.artscontact.co.uk
Directors: Sheila Thorpe, Tony Hyslop
A unique creative bulk distribution service for Arts publicity print, for any Arts event, anywhere in the U.K.

BRAVADO
Suite 1B-F, Chiswick Place, 272 Gunnersbury Avenue, London W4 5QB
Tel: 0330 587 1234
Email: david.boyne@bravado.com, rachel.redfearn@bravado.com
Web Site: www.bravado.com
Contact: David Boyne, Rachel Redfearn

CANTATE COMMUNICATIONS
1st Floor, 30 Cowcross Street, London EC1M 6DQ
Tel: 0203 651 1690
Email: info@cantatecommunications.com
Web: www.cantatecommunications.com
Business Development Manager: Simon Henry/ Till Siegers
Specialist theatre printers, e.g. programmes, souvenir brochures and publicity for the RNT, ENO, RSC, BBC, RPO etc. Comprehensive quality service. Our design subsidiary arc associates has worked for Bolshoi, ENO, BBC etc.

DANILO
Unit 3, The IO Centre, Lea Road, Waltham Abbey, Essex EN9 1AS
Tel: 01992 702 900 Fax: 01992 702 990
Email: vpatel@danilo.com
Web Site: www.danilo.com
Danilo is the leading publisher of official licensed calendars in Europe.

DESIGN IT
Mill House 3 Saddleworth Road, Elland, Halifax, West Yorkshire HX5 0RY
Tel: 01422 377761 Fax: 01422 371141
Email: studio@designit-uk.com
Web Site: www.designit-uk.com
Partner: Martin Pinder
Specialists in the design & production of promotional material for the arts & theatres. Design for print, branding, advertising, web site design, construction and print management.

DEWYNTERS PLC
Wellington House, 125 Strand, London WC2R 0AP
Tel: 020 7321 0488 Fax: 020 7321 0104
Email: info@dewynters.com

Web Site: www.dewynters.com
Client Management: Kirsty Doubleday
Dewynters is the UK entertainment industry's leading
full-service agency. We provide marketing, design, advertising, promotions, new media and merchandise skills across a broad spectrum. The agency's fields of expertise comprise theatre, opera, dance, music, galleries, museums, events, television and film. Our ground-breaking campaigns are synonymous with the energy and impact of modern entertainment - powerful, innovative and effective.

DISPLAY LED SCREENS LTD
The Pixel Depot, Copse Farm, Moorhurst Lane, Beare Green, Near Dorking, Surrey RH5 4LJ
Tel: +44 (0) 20 7381 7840
Email: guyh@displayLED.com, info@displayLED.com
Web Site: www.displayLED.com, www.digiLED.com
Contact: Guy Horrigan
Suppliers of Giant Video Screens, Electronic Displays and Scoreboards.

EMC ADVERTISING GIFTS
North London Business Park, Building 3, Oakleigh Road South, London N11 1GN
Tel: 0800 170 7570 Fax: 020 8445 9347
Email: sales@emcadgifts.co.uk
Web Site: www.emcadgifts.co.uk
Sales Director: Simon Kay
Advertising and Promotional gifts.

EVENT MERCHANDISING LTD
Unit 11, Edge Business Centre, Humber Road, London NW2 6EW
Tel: 020 8208 1166 Fax: 020 8208 4477
Email: event@eventmerch.com
Web Site: www.eventmerchandising.com
Contact: Jeremy Goldsmith
Promotional Merchandising Company. T/Shirts, Sweatshirts, Jackets, Tour Merchandise etc.
Film/ TV Office:
Event! Pinewood Office, Room 94, G Block, Pinewood Studios, Pinewood Road, Iver Heath, SL0 0NH

EXTERION MEDIA
28 Jamestown Road, Camden, London NW1 7BY
Tel: 020 7482 3000 Fax: 020 7267 2076
Email: sales@exterionmedia.co.uk
Web Site: www.exterionmedia.co.uk
Managing Director: Jason Cotterrell

THOMAS FATTORINI LTD
Regent Street Works, Birmingham B1 3HQ
Tel: 0121 236 1307 Fax: 0121 200 1568
Email: sales@fattorini.co.uk
Web Site: www.fattorini.co.uk
Conference and exhibition badge specialists.

A J GILBERT BIRMINGHAM LTD
66-77 Buckingham Street, Hockley, Birmingham B19 3HU
Tel: 0121 236 7774 / 0121 233 1394
Fax: 0121 236 6024
Email: lucysox@aol.com
Web Site: www.ajgilbert.co.uk
Sales Contacts: Lucy Cooper, Nathan Burns
Badges of all types and all promotional material.

GLOBAL MARKETING GROUP
Global House, Salisbury Road, Downton, Salisbury SP5 3JJ
Tel: 01725 511700 Fax: 01725 514985
Email: sales@globalmarketinggroup.co.uk
Web: www.globalmarketinggroup.co.uk
CEO: Carlos Candal
Design & Print: Andy Manning

CHESTER HOPKINS INTERNATIONAL
P.O. Box 536 Headington, Oxford OX3 7LR
Tel: 01865 766 766
Email: adrian@chesterhopkins.co.uk
Web Site: www.chesterhopkins.co.uk
Managing Director: Adrian Hopkins

ICON DISPLAY
Heather Court, 6 Maidstone Road, Sidcup, Kent DA14 5HS
Tel: 020 8302 4921 Fax: 020 8302 3971
Email: enquiries@icon-world.com
Web Site: www.icon-world.com
Contact: Andrew Hodson
Banners, flags, signs & display services.

KEENPAC LTD
Centurion Way, Meridian Business Park, Leicester LE19 1WH
Tel: 0116 289 0900 Fax: 0116 289 3757
Email: info@keenpac.co.uk
Web Site: www.keenpac.com
Leading the world in promotional carrier bags and retail packaging.

LEEP MARKETING & PR
5 Nassau House, 122 Shaftesbury Avenue, London W1D 5ER
Tel: 020 7439 9777 Fax: 020 7439 8833
Email: info@leep.biz
Web Site: www.leep.biz
Marketing, press and publicity for the Arts, with an emphasis on fresh ideas and innovative thinking, coupled with detailed and thorough execution of every campaign we work on.

LOGOMIKE
28 Victoria Avenue, Harrogate, North Yorkshire HG1 5PR
Tel: 01423 781 700
Web Site: www.logomike.com
We make LogoMike Microphone Flags and HiKoy Microphone Windshields. We sell them both plain from stock, or especially printed with customer's logos, and export to over 100 Countries worldwide.
Contact: John Smedley

LONDON EMBLEM PLC
4 Sherwood Road, Aston Fields Industrial Est, Bromsgrove Worcestershire, B60 3DR
Tel: 01329 822 900 Fax: 01329 829 000
Email: sales@londonemblem.com
Web Site: www.londonemblem.com, www.allaboutbadges.com
We offer an extensive range of promotional badges, from a straight forward button badge to a high quality stamped hard enamel brooch, packaged in a bespoke presentation box. We also stock reliable British made badgemaking machines suitable for commercial use.

THE RAYMOND MANDER & JOE MITCHENSON THEATRE COLLECTION
University of Bristol, Theatre Collection, Vandyck Building, Cantocks Close, Bristol, BS8 1UP
Tel: 0117 331 5086
Email: theatre-collection@bristol.ac.uk
Web Site: www.bristol.ac.uk/theatrecollection
Collection Manager: Jo Elsworth
The Theatre Collection is one of the world's largest and most significant collectionsrelating to the history of the British theatre. It is an accredited museum and research facility that is open to the public.Founded in 1951, its collections cover all aspects of theatre from seventeenth century up to the present day and include original documents, photographs, artwork, objects, costumes and an extensive library. Significant archive collections include London Old Vic, Bristol Old Vic and the world renowned Raymond Mander and Joe Mitchenson Collection. It is now used extensivley by authors, designers, publishers, BBC and television producers as well as local students and international academic scholars.
Commercial picture requests are handled through Arena Pal.

MARLER HALEY LTD
45 Booth Drive, Park Farm Industrial Estate, Wellingborough, Northamptonshire NN8 6GR
Tel: 01933 676 952 Fax: 01933 674 549
Email: info@marlerhaley.co.uk
Web Site: www.marlerhaley.co.uk
Sales and Marketing Director: Andrew Pocock
Comprehensive range of display and exhibition equipment; Roller banner stands, Pop Up displays and Panel displays.

METRO MERCHANDISING LTD
3 Prospect Court, Courteenhall Road,

Blisworth, Northants, NN7 3DG
Tel: 01536 415 005 Fax: 01536 415 006
Email: louise@metromerchandise.co.uk, sales@metromerchandise.co.uk
Web Site: www.metromerchandise.uk.clickpromo.com
Suppliers of promotional, safety wear and casual workwear.

PADBLOCKS LTD
Fishponds Road, Wokingham, Berkshire RG41 2QX
Tel: 0118 978 1499 Fax: 0118 977 1530
Email: info@padblocks.com
Web Site: www.padblocks.com
Contact: James and Paul Wight
Manufacturers of Notepads and Jigsaw puzzles for advertising and retail.

RANK RHINO
16 Commercial Road, Edmonton, London N18 1TP
Tel: 020 8803 2584 Fax: 020 8807 1139
Email: rankrhino@aol.com
Web Site: www.rankrhino.co.uk
UK promotional clothing printer. Services include; Printed T-shirts, sweatshirts and polo shirts, Silk screen printing, Baseball caps, Bags, Schoolwear, Embroidery, Workwear, Jackets and fleeces, Corporate wear.

STO-ROSE LIMITED
Trading as Fantasia Balloons
ITI (UK) Ltd, Unit A2, Commerce Way, Whitehall Industrial Estate, Colchester, CO2 8HH
Tel: 01206 790 300 Fax: 01206 790 200
Email: sales@fantasiaballoons.com
Web Site: www.fantasiaballoons.com
Supplier of printed latex balloons for promotional usage.

TAKEONE MEDIA
The Boulevard, Orbital Park, Ashford, Kent TN24 0GA
Tel: 01233 211 211
Email: sales@takeonemedia.co.uk
Web Site: www.takeonemedia.co.uk
Managing Director: Philippa Harris
Sales Director: David Johnston
Display and distribution of brochures for the entertainment and leisure industry. Targeted audiences and weekly merchandising to ensure cost effective control of advertising print.

THE AUDIENCE AGENCY
Unit 7G1, The Leather Market, Weston Street, London SE1 3ER
Tel: 0207 407 4625
Email: hello@theaudienceagency.org
Web Site: www.theaudienceagency.org
Head of Marketing: Howard Buckley
Audiences London offers advice and insight on audience development for arts, culture and heritage organisations.

THIRSTYS
Unit 11, William Street, Mounts Business Park, Northampton NN1 3EW
Tel: 01604 231 280
Email: sales@thirstys.co.uk
Web Site: www.thirstys.co.uk
Drip mat, coasters and beer mat printers and distributors throughout the UK.

TOP DRAW PUBLICITY
Cary Point, Babbacombe Downs Road, Torquay, Devon TQ1 3LU
Tel: 01803 322233 Fax: 01803 322244
Email: mail@matpro-show.biz
Marketing of shows and concerts.
Producers of theatre programmes.

TOTNOLL PROMOTIONS
17-20 Parr Street, London N1 7ET
Tel: 020 7253 4221 Fax: 020 7251 2984
Email: ca@sonata.co.uk
Web Site: www.sonata.co.uk
Paper promotional products, Promotional merchandise, Corporate Printing, and Print Management.

TOYE KENNING & SPENCER LTD
19 - 21 Great Queen Street, London WC2B 5BE
Tel: 020 7242 0471 Fax: 020 7405 3063
Email: sales@toye.com
Web Site: www.toye.com
Civil & Military regalia.
Additional offices:
77 Warstone Lane, Birmingham, B18 6NL, Tel: 0121 2622 950
Newton Road, Bedworth, CV12 8QR, Tel: 024 7684 8800

THE TRADEWINDS MERCHANDISING CO. LTD
The Courtyard, Lynton Road, London N8 8SL
Tel: 0845 230 9005 Fax: 0845 230 9006
Email: sales@tradewinds.eu.com
Web Site: www.tradewinds.eu.com
Printers and embroiderers of T-Shirts, S-Shirts, Polo Shirts, Baseball Caps, Jogging Suits, Corporate Clothing, Uniforms and all business gifts.

UK THEATRE WEB
37 Severn Avenue, Weston-super-Mare, Avon BS23 4DG
Tel: 01934 626 344
Email: info@uktw.co.uk
Web Site: www.uktw.co.uk
Contact: Robe Iles
The UK Theatre Web provides information about the UK theatre, opera and ballet scene to users all over the world via the Internet. UK Theatre Web is the premier index and information site for UK performing arts. In addition to promotional activities in UK Theatre Web provides free listings, tours and performances via "What`s On Stage".

Model Makers & Props

2D 3D
263 Abbeydale Road, Park Royal, Wembley, Middlesex HA0 1TW
Tel: 020 8998 3199 Fax: 020 8998 7767
Email: rob@2d3d.co.uk, Lynne@2d3d.co.uk
Web Site: www.2d3d.co.uk
Contact: Rob Edkins
We make models, props and sets for theatre, exhibitions, museums, display, commercials, television, film and events industries. Projects of every size.

ARTEM
Perivale Park, Horsenden Lane South, Perivale, Middlesex, UB6 7RH
Tel: 020 8997 7771 Fax: 020 8997 1503
Scotland Office: 64 - 68 Brand Street Pacific Quay Glasgow G51 1DG Tel: 0141 427 5775 Fax: 0141 427 1199
Email: sharon@artem.com
Web Site: www.artem.com
Operations Manager: Sharon Walter

CURLYWILLY PRODUCTIONS
Unit C4, Admiralty Park, Off Station Road, Holton Heath, Poole Dorset BH16 6HX
Mobile: 07970 956 621
Email: carol@curlywilly.co.uk
Web Site: www.curlywilly.co.uk
Proprietor: Carol Kerley
Creative Designers, Consultants, Bespoke Makers of Costumes, Character Heads, Animal Mascots, Props,Scenery, Large Board Games.
For use in Theatre, TV, Promotional Events, Public Relations etc
Whatever the size of your budget we will cater to your every requirement. All items sold are made by us in our own studios, therefore we have total control during every stage

FINAL CREATION
The Loft Studio 19 Hill Lane Industrial Estate, Markfield, Leicestershire LE67 9PN
Tel: 01530 249100 Fax: 01530 249400
Mobile. 07884 436885
Email: gemma@finalcreation.co.uk
Web Site: www.finalcreation.co.uk
Contact: Gemma Stenhouse

JUICY FRUITS
28 Mill Hill, Weston Colville, Cambridge CB21 5NY
Tel: 01223 290 396 Mobile: 07860 792 082 Fax: 01223 290 212
Email: enquiries@juicyfruitsuk.com
Web Site: www.juicyfruitsuk.com
Juicy Fruits make fine detail models for food advertising, photography and design. We are widely used by photogra-

phers, design agencies, production teams and stylists. We hold an extensive hire library and work to commission.

MODEL SOLUTIONS (2D3D) LTD
72x Clarence Road, London N22 8PW
Tel: 020 8881 2333 Fax: 020 8881 2233
Mob: 07921 436 061
Email: info@modelsolutions.co.uk
Web Site: www.modelsolutions.co.uk
Model Solutions' in-house modelmaking team comprises artists, craftsmen and designers each with a minimum of seven years industrial experience, working together under the same roof complimenting each others' skills and expertise.

PROPS4SHOWS
Osprey House, Featherby Way, Purdeys Industrial Estate, Rochford, Essex SS4 1LD
Tel: 03333 440 078 Fax: 03333 441 478
Email: sales@props4shows.com
Web Site: www.props4shows.co.uk
Contact: Lin Lorde
Suppliers of a wide range of props, display goods and fabrics, for stage, theatre, photography and marketing. The extensive range includes fake food, seasonal props, artificial trees, stage backdrops, scenery props, professional makeup, display accessories and much more.

Musical Equipment & Services

ARDIVAL HARPS
Orchard House, Castle Leod, Strathpeffer, Ross-Shire IV14 9AA Scotland
Tel: 01997 421 260
Email: info@ardival.com
Web Site: www.ardival.com
Contact: Zan or Alex Dann
Sale and hire of harps.

AUDIOHIRE
The Old Dairy, 133-137 Kilburn Lane, London W10 4AN
Tel: 020 8960 4466 Fax: 0845 860 1739
Email: admin@audiohire.co.uk
Web Site: www.audiohire.co.uk
Hire of Lights, Sound Equipment; Synthesizers, Samplers, Recording Equipment, Desks, Noise Reduction, Microphones, Backline, PA, Drum Machines, Fx, etc.

BARBER LUTHERIE
22 Radford Street, Stone, Staffordshire ST15 8DA
Tel/Fax: 01785 817 658
Email: phil@barberlutherie.co.uk
Web Site: www.barberlutherie.co.uk
Contact: Phil Barber
Suppliers and repairers of musical instruments and amplification. Guitar specialists.

BEAT ABOUT THE BUSH LTD
Unit 23, Enterprise Way, Salter Street, London NW10 6UG
Tel: 020 8960 2087 Fax: 020 8969 2281
Email: info@beataboutthebush.com
Web Site: www.beataboutthebush.com
Managing Director: Mr Purbrick

BLACK CAT MUSIC
Bankside House, Vale Road, Tunbridge Wells, Kent TN9 1SJ
Tel: 01732 371 555 Fax: 01732 371 556
Email: sales@blackcatmusic.com
Web Site: www.blackcatmusic.co.uk
Sales Manager: Teresa Rogers
Black Cat Music supplies an extensive range of hard-to-find, everyday, and total unique music equipment from music stands and chairs to sound-proofed rooms. Black Cat Acoustics offers a complete range of acoustic products and services.

BLOWOUT SAX
South Lodge, North Parade, Bath, B.A.N.E.S. BA2 4EU
Tel: 01225 339 007 Mobile: 07773 737 880
Email: markarcher@blowoutsax.com
Web Site: www.blowoutsax.com
School Director: Mark Archer
School, shop and musicians.

ENTERTAINMENT SOUND SPECIALISTS
2 Maun Close, Mansfield, Nottinghamshire NG18 5GY
Tel: 01623 647 291 Fax: 01623 622 500
Email: richardmjohn@me.com
Contacts: Phil McDaniel, Richard John
Committed to quality with care at sensible prices, giving you the best value for money.

ADAM HALL LTD
10 The Seedbed Business Centre, Vanguard Way, Shoeburyness, Essex SS3 9QY
Tel: 01702 613 922 Fax: 01702 617 168
Email: mail@adamhall.co.uk
Web Site: www.adamhall.com
Contact: Mark Stimpson
Distributor and supplier of fittings and hardware for flight cases and loudspeaker cabinets. Own brand stands for lighting, sound and musical instruments. Newly launched Adam Hall Cables. Sole distributor of Amphenol Audio Connectors, Palmer Professional Audio Tools and Power Amplifiers.

JOHN HENRY'S LTD
16-24 Brewery Road, London N7 9NH
Tel: 020 7609 9181 Fax: 020 7700 7040
Email: info@johnhenrys.com
Web Site: www.johnhenrys.com
Event Production: Pepin Clout
Rehearsal Studios: Andrea Westwood
Backline Production: Tark Bates

HINTON INSTRUMENTS
Whitechapel Lane, Oldford, Frome, Somerset BA11 2NN
Tel: 01373 451 927
Email: enquiries@hinton-instruments.co.uk
Web Site: www.hinton-instruments.co.uk
Contact: Graham Hinton

JOHN HORNBY SKEWES & CO
Salem House, Parkinson Approach, Garforth, Leeds, West Yorkshire LS25 2HR
Tel: 0113 286 5381 Fax: 0113 286 8515
Email: webinfo@jhs.co.uk
Web Site: www.jhs.co.uk
Proprietor: Mr John H Skewes
Publicity Manager: Simon Turnbull
Managing Director Designate: Dennis Drumm
The UK's No.1 independent trade distributor of musical equipment and pro-audio amplification.

HSL (HIRE) LTD
Unit E & F, Glenfield Park, Philips Road, Blackburn Lancashire BB1 5PF
Tel: 01254 698 808 Fax: 01254 698 835
Email: simon@hslgroup.com, contact@hslgroup.com
Web Site: www.hslgroup.com
Contact: Simon Stuart
Every client is special, each commission totally unique, our in house event management process ensuring that your project is carefully monitored, from the taking of your detailed instructions, through design and planning, and ultimately the installation and staging of the event itself.

HWL (UK) LTD
Cricket Street, Denton, Manchester M34 3DR
Tel: 0161 335 0220 Fax: 0161 320 3928
Email: guns@hwltd.co.uk
Web Site: www.hwltd.co.uk
Contact: Bob Howorth
Hirers of all types of furniture, set dressing, decorative lighting, pictures, hand props etc. Also specialist hirers of weapons and blank firing guns.

IMPACT PERCUSSION
7 Goose Green Trading Estate, 47 East Dulwich Road, London SE22 9BN
Tel: 020 8299 6700 Fax: 020 8299 6704
Email: sales@impactpercussion.com
Web Site: www.impactpercussion.com
Contact: Paul Hagen
Hire, retail and repair of percussion instruments and props.

JAQUES SAMUEL PIANOS LTD
142 Edgware Road, London W2 2DZ
Tel: 020 7723 8818 Fax: 020 7224 8692
Email: info@jspianos.com
Web Site: www.jspianos.com
Contact: Daniel Thomas (daniel@jspianos.com)
Piano Hire, Tuning Services and Refurbishment Services

MUSIC ROOM
The Old Library, 116-118 New Cross Road, London SE14 5BA
Tel: 020 7252 8271 Fax: 020 7252 8252
Email: sales@musicroomlondon.com
Web Site: www.musicroomlondon.com
Manager: Mr Garden Gapper
Sound and musical equipment, hire and sales, 7 days a week.

R.A.T. (MUSIC STANDS) LTD
16 Melville Road, Barnes, London SW13 9RJ
Tel: 020 8741 4804 Fax: 020 8741 8949
Email: sales@ratstands.com
Web Site: www.ratstands.com
Contact: Andrew Michell
Manufacturers of professional music stands for use in theatres, tv studios, concert halls and schools; and of versatile light-weight staging systems.

RITZ STUDIOS
The Courtyard, Esmond Street, Putney SW15 2LP
Tel: 020 8870 1335
Email: ben@ritzstudios.com
Web Site: www.ritzstudios.com
Contact: Ben Webber

STEINWAY & SONS
Steinway Hall, 44 Marylebone Lane, London W1U 2DB
Tel: 020 7487 3391
Email: ldelany@steinway.co.uk
Web Site: www.steinway.co.uk
Concert & Artists Manager: Wibke Grenius
Dealer & Institutional Sales Representative: Keith Glazebrook
Piano Retailer. Concert and tuning services.

STUDIOHIRE (LONDON) LTD
8 Daleham Mews, London NW3 5DB
Tel: 020 7431 0212 Fax: 020 7431 1134
Email: mail@studiohire.net
Web Site: www.studiohire.net
Contact: Paul Tattersall, Sam Thomas
Hire of musical and theatrical equipment. See our new website for details and prices.
You name it, we've got it!

SWANS MUSIC
The Belan, Moss Lane, Mobberley, Knutsford, Cheshire WA16 7BS
Tel/Fax: 01565 873 044 Mobile: 07710 341394

Email: info@swansmusic.co.uk
Web Site: www.swansmusic.co.uk
Contact Bill Swan.
Swans specialise in hiring and servicing all types of pianos. Other instruments also available. Recent credits include Ryan Adams, Procul Harem, Coldplay, Rat Pack, Ray Charles, Tony Bennett, Lesley Garrett, BBC Phil, Liverpool Phil, Stars in their Eyes etc.

Opera Glasses

THE LONDON OPERA GLASS COMPANY LTD
Unit 3, Crystal Business Centre, Sandwich Industrial Estate, Sandwich, Kent CT13 9QX
Tel: 01304 620 360
Email: admin@operaglasses.co.uk
Web Site: www.operaglasses.co.uk
Managing Director: Philip Main
Manufacturers and suppliers of opera glasses and opera glass vending equipment worldwide.

Passes & Security ID

3D-4D.COM
46 Calthorpe Street, London WC1X 0JZ
Tel: 0500 555 245
Email: enquiries@3d4d.com
Web Site: www.3D4D.com
Flexible holographic designs for posters, invitations and much more. Large-format Lenticulars for set design.

BAND PASS
First Floor, 20 Sunnydown, Witley, Godalming, Surrey GU8 5RP
Tel: 01428 684 926 Fax: 01428 683 501
Mob: 07939 409 450
Email: maxine@band-pass.co.uk
Web Site: www.band-pass.co.uk
Managing Director: Maxine
A UK Based company with over 26 years experience, offering wristbands, plasticards, laminated passes, cord, printed or plain lanyards, sticky passes and associated products.

COVENT GARDEN LAMINATES
13 Macklin Street, Covent Garden, London WC2B 5NH
Tel: 020 7242 1940 / 020 7242 1960
Fax: 020 7242 1001
Email: anthony@cgluk.net, info@cgluk.net
Web Site: www.cgluk.net
Director: Anthony Briggs

ID & C LTD
1 Decimus Park, Kingstanding Way, Tunbridge Wells, Kent TN2 3GP
Tel: 01892 548 364 Fax: 01892 519 048
Email: sales@idcband.co.uk
Web Site: www.idcband.co.uk
ID Wristbands a speciality. UVink, UVstamps and UVlamps. Products for ticketing and admission control.

LESAR UK LTD
Sentinal Court, Wilkinson Way, Blackburn BB1 2EH
Tel: 0800 622 6201 Fax: 0333 700 0124
Email: enquiries@lesar.co.uk
Web Site: www.lesar.co.uk

PUBLICITY & DISPLAY LTD
1 Corium House, Douglas Drive, Godalming, Surrey GU7 1HJ
Tel: 01483 428 326 Fax: 01483 424 566
Email: print@pubdis.com
Web Site: www.pubdis.com
Contact: Tim Cox
Design/print of posters, passes, leaflets, tickets and stickers for the entertainment industry. Mon-Thur: 9-5:30; Fri 9-5

SECURIT WORLD LTD
Spectrum House, Hillview Gardens, London, NW4 2JQ
Tel: 020 8266 3300 Fax: 020 8203 1027
Email: darrensnow@essentra.com
Web Site: www.securitworld.com
Director: Ed Heyden

Contact: Deborah Clapich
Photo ID systems and all ID accessories.
Visitor management systems.

Photography

DAVID BACHE PHOTOGRAPHY
10 Roehampton Vale, London SW15 3RY
Mobile: 07790 018315
Email: david@davidbache.co.uk
Web Site: www.davidbache.co.uk
Contact: David Bache

CLAIRE MCNAMEE PHOTOGRAPHY
1 Primrose Terrace, Hebden Bridge, West Yorkshire HX7 6HN
Tel: 01422 844 747
Email: claire@clairemcnamee.com
Web Site: www.clairemcnamee.com
Contact: Claire McNamee
Providing a fast reliable service in publicity photographs for actresses/actors, musicians and theatres.

DONALD COOPER
8 Drakes Mews, Crownhill, Milton Keynes MK8 0ER
Tel: 01908 262 324 Mobile: 07976 352438
Email: donald@photostage.co.uk
Web Site: www.photostage.co.uk

DENBRY REPROS LIMITED
57 High Street, Hemel Hempstead, Hertfordshire HP1 3AF
Tel : 01442 24 24 11
Email: info@denbryrepros.com
Web Site: www.denbryrepros.com
Photographer: Dan Harwood-Stamper
Top quality photographic reproductions and composites. Speedy service. Competitive prices. Mastercard, Switch and VISA accepted.

DOMINIC PHOTOGRAPHY
4b Moore Park Road, London SW6 2JT
Tel: 020 7381 0007 Fax: 020 7381 0008
Email: dominicphoto@catherineashmore.co.uk
Contacts: Zoe Dominic F.R.P.S., Catherine Ashmore Photography of Theatre, Opera, Dance and Musicals for publicity and FOH.

GETTY IMAGES
Formerly 'Redferns Music Picture Library'
101 Bayham Street, London NW1 0AG
Tel: 020 7579 5759 / 0800 376 7977
Fax: 020 7792 0921
Email: Jon.Wilton@gettyimages.com
Web Site: www.gettyimages.co.uk
Contact: John Wilton
Music and entertainment picture library with photographers specialising in performance photography.

GRESHPICS
Part of The Gresham Group
PO Box 3, Bradford, West Yorkshire BD1 4QN
Mob: 07932 750512 Fax: 01274 827 161
Email: gresh@carlgresham.co.uk
Web Site: www.carlgresham.co.uk
Senior Personnel: Carl Gresham
Suppliers of landscape and portrait photocards. Exclusive and unique services for celebrities and theatrical artistes.

JOHN HAYNES
32 Priory Terrace, London NW6 4DH
Tel/ Fax: 020 7624 2981
Email: info@johnhaynesphotography.com
Web: www.johnhaynesphotography.com

HOLLIS PHOTOGRAPHY.COM
Providing award-winning creative solutions. People and location digital specialists.
LCB Depot, 31 Rutland Street, Leicester LE1 1RE
Tel: 0116 210 6488 Mobile: 07971 442271
Email: info@hollisphotography.com
Web Site: www.hollisphotography.com
Leading Midlands photographers offering national and international service. Full photography and imaging service for artists and event organisers. Portfolios, portraits and events documented, performances captured. For design, marketing, PR and publicity. All formats including digital. Digital services with folio, prints and CDs.
Free client folder on our website provides you with access to your images at any time. Subjects include Elvis Costello, Craig David, Philharmonia, David Byrne, Muse, Courtney Pine and others.

IMAGE PHOTOGRAPHIC
82 Church View, Swanley, Kent BR8 8RF
Tel: 020 7602 1190 Fax: 020 7602 6219
Email: digital@imagephotographic.com
Web Site: www.imagephotographic.com
Contact: Steve Luck

JOE BANGAY PHOTOGRAPHY
River House, Riverwood Drive, Marlow, Buckinghamshire SL7 1QY
Tel: 01628 486 193 Fax: 01628 890 239
Email: william.b@btclick.com
Web Site: www.joebangay.com
Contacts: William and Joe Bangay
Casting, portrait and styling photography with established make up/hair team. Distribution of press material. Showbiz and Pop library from 1968 to the present. Theatre and Film Production Photography.
Stage, location, studio photography in the theatre, films and rock/pop music.

CAROLE LATIMER
113 Ledbury Road, London W11 2AQ
Tel: 020 7727 9371
Email: carole@carolelatimer.com
Web Site: www.carolelatimer.com

LEE FILTERS
Central Way, Walworth Ind. Estate, Andover, Hampshire SP10 5AN
Tel: 01264 366 245 Fax: 01264 355 058
Email: ecruffell@leefilters.com
Web Site: www.leefilters.com
Contact: Ralph Young, Paul Topliss
Manufacturers of light filter in both polyester and polycarbonate. Flame Retardant to BS5750 when stated. Also, manufacturers of Photographic Colour Correction and colour Printing Filters and optical Resin Camera Filters.

REAAZ PHOTO-GRAPHICS
56 Innes Street, Inverness IV1 1NS
Tel: 07776 422 462
Email: info@reaaz.com
Web Site: www.reaaz.com
Freelance Photographer: Reaaz Mohammad
Specialising in private commissions, art and commerical photography.

RICHARD CAMPBELL PHOTOGRAPHY LTD
Studio 114 111 West George Street, Glasgow G2 1QX
Tel: 0141 237 4066 Mob: 07721 325 326
Email: enquiries@richardcampbell.co.uk
Web Site: www.richardcampbell.co.uk
Contact: Richard Campbell
Award winning Photographer specialising in Theatre and Opera. Credits include: Blackbird for MJE Productions, Edinburgh International Festival, Scottish Opera, Citizens' Theatre, Traverse Theatre and Grin Iron Theatre Company.

ROBIN PHOTOGRAPHIC
Tel: 07747 618 264
Email: contact@robinstanley.com
Web Site: www.robinstanley.com
Robin Photographic offers photography for the corporate/PR market, event photography, portraitive, PR photography.

VISUALEYES PHOTOREPRO SERVICES
95 Mortimer Street, London W1W 7ST
Tel: 020 7323 7430 Fax: 020 7323 7438
Email: imaging@visualeyes.co.uk
Web Site: www.visualeyes.co.uk
Comprehensive photographic reproduction services, specialising in press, publicity, theatrical promotion, packshot and make-over studio picture printing.
Hi-end scanning and retouching services for digital repurpose.

ROBERT WORKMAN
32 West Kensington Mansions, Beaumont Crescent, London W14 9PF

Studio Tel: 020 7385 5442
Mob: 07814 126 260
Email: bob@robertworkman.demon.co.uk
Web: www.robertworkman.demon.co.uk
Contact: Robert Workman
Photography of Theatre, Opera and Ballet Productions. Photography for Theatre Posters and casting portraits of actors and singers.

Piano Hire

JAQUES SAMUEL PIANOS LTD
142 Edgware Road, London W2 2DZ
Tel: 020 7723 8818 Fax: 020 7224 8692
Email: info@jspianos.com
Web Site: www.jspianos.com
Contact: Daniel Thomas (daniel@jspianos.com)
Piano Hire, Tuning Services and Refurbishment Services

Picture Library

AQUARIUS LIBRARY
PO Box 5, Hastings, East Sussex TN34 1HR
Tel: 01424 721 196
Email: aquarius.lib@clara.net
Web Site: www.aquariuscollection.com
Managing Director: Gilbert Gibson
Literary division: David Corkill

Plastics Specialists

TALBOT DESIGNS LTD
223 - 225 Long Lane, Finchley, London N3 2RL
Tel: 020 8346 8515 Fax: 020 8349 0294
Email: sales@talbotdesigns.co.uk
Web Site: www.talbotdesigns.co.uk
Contact: Richard Woolff
Over the past 30 years have supplied most of the notable theatre productions with plastic flooring, plastic domes, scenery, special effects, hand held props and any plastic requirements.

Projection Equipment & Services

EMF TECHNOLOGY LTD
Unit 1A, Thurley Business Units, Pump Lane, Grazeley, Reading RG7 1LL
Tel: 0118 988 7647 Fax: 0118 988 7651
Email: info@emftechnology.co.uk
Web Site: www.emftechnology.co.uk
Contact: Stuart Roberts
EMF supply Large scale slide and video projection using 7KW Hardware, 12KW Pani, Christie & Barco for high power projections and 8KW high power searchlights for theatres and events.

ETC UK LTD T/A THE PROJECTION STUDIO
Unit 4a, 13 Tarves Way, London SE10 9JP
Tel: 0208 2934 270 Fax: 020 8594 1243
Email: info@theprojectionstudio.com
Web Site: www.theprojectionstudio.com
Contacts: Ross Ashton , Steve Larkins
If you need to fill any space with exciting images, then we can offer you the solution. The PIGI system is the world's most versatile and powerful image projection system.

PRG UK
The Cofton Centre, Groveley Lane, Longbridge, B31 4PT
Tel: 0845 470 6400
Email: ukinfo@prg.com
Web Site: www.prg.com
Contact: Rich Rowley
With the largest inventory of rental lighting stock in Europe, PRG is the consummate supplier of lighting to the business of entertainment and in particular the theatre. Whether it's the lighting rig for a touring musical production, a West End show or opera at the Royal Albert Hall, we have the knowledge, the equipment and the expertise to ensure your success, every time.

XL VIDEO
2 Eastman Way, Hemel Hempstead, Hertfordshire HP2 7DU
Tel: 01442 849 400 Fax: 01442 849 401
Email: theatre@xlvideo.tv
Web Site: www.xlvideo.tv
Contact: Malcolm Mellows
XL Video's specialist Theatre Department offers a wide range of video-visual equipment and services to Theatre and the Arts, including all types of Video Projections, Plasma, LCD and LED Displays.

Projection Screens

HARKNESS SCREENS
Unit A, Norton Road, Stevenage, Herts SG1 2BB
Tel: (+44) (0) 1438 725200
Fax: (+44) (0) 1438 344400
Email: sales@harkness-screens.com
Web Site: www.harkness-screens.com
Contact: Tony Dilley
Harkness Screens supply a range of front and rear projection surfaces for cinema, live theatre, opera, product launches, exhibitions and events.

Props (Hire & Sale)

3-D CREATIONS
Berth 33, 33 Malthouse Lane, Gorleston, Great Yarmouth, Norfolk NR31 0GW
Tel: 01493 652 055 (Workshop) Mob: 07860 707 287 Fax: 01493 443 124
Email: info@3dcreations.co.uk
Web Site: www.3dcreations.co.uk
Contact: Ian Westbrook
We can provide all your scenic needs for theatre, television and film. Scenery and prop design and construction specialists. Prop makers, set designers, sculptors, scenic artists we are always prepared to undertake work of the unusual. Location work undertaken.

A & M HIRE LTD
The Royals, Victoria Road, London NW10 6ND

Tel: 020 8233 1500 Fax: 020 8233 1550
Web Site: www.amhire.com
Managing Director: John Mantle
The distinguished supplier for period or modern furniture and dressings.

ADEN HYNES SCULPTURE STUDIOS
Unit 3F, Harvey Road, Nevendon Industrial Estate, Basildon, Essex SS13 1DA
Tel: 01268 726 470
Email: aden.hynes@hotmail.com
Web Site: www.sculpturestudios.co.uk
Specialising in polystyrene carving, scenic set building, from classical Greek figures to enchanted forests. Mould making, glass fibre production runs, scenic painting and installation.

CARDIFF THEATRICAL SERVICES LTD
Ellen Street, off Tyndall Street, Cardiff, South Glamorgan CF10 4TT
Tel: 029 2063 4680 Fax: 029 2048 1275
Email: cts@wno.org.uk, esther.morris@wno.org.uk
Web: www.cardifftheatricalservices.co.uk
Manager: Ed Wilson
Scenery builders, scenic artists and property makers.

CHASE 55
55 Chase Road, London NW10 6LU
Tel: 020 8453 3900 Fax: 020 8965 8107
Email: info@superhire.com
Web Site: www.superhire.com
Managing Directors: Mutch and Murli Mulchandi
Lighting and electrical, tableware and ornaments, office equipment, pictures, luggage and thousands of other set dressing props available for hire.

CINEBUILD LTD
Broadcast Engineering Centre, Eastbourne Road, Blindley Heath, R7 6JP
Tel: 020 7582 8750
Email: cinebuild@btclick.com
Web Site: www.cinebuild.co.uk
Directors: Tony Neale, Patrick Neale
We supply all types of breakaway glass for television and film, plus sales and hire of special effects and props - snow, mist, rain, cobwebs and dust.

CLAIRESOFTS
Soft Props & Upholstery
106 Westbourne Street, Hove, BN3 5FA
Mobile: 07970 032 919
Email: clairesofts@hotmail.com
Owner: Claire Sanderson
Props, soft props & upholstery for stage, TV and film. From furniture, to puppets & carnival costumes. No hiring.

THE COMPANY OF TEN
See also 'Abbey Theatre'
Abbey Theatre, Westminster Lodge, Holywell Hill, St Albans, Hertfordshire AL1 2DL
Tel: 01727 847 472 Fax: 01727 812 742
Email: manager@abbeytheatre.org.uk
Manager: Tina Swain
Property Mistress: Judith Goodban
Amateur Theatre Company

CREATIVE DRAPING
Unit 3, 29 Mount Avenue, Mount Farm, Milton Keynes MK1 1LS
Tel: 01908 368 141
Email: info@creativedraping.com
Web Site: www.creativedraping.com
Senior Personnel: Susie Carlino
Specialist in draping venues and stages for the nightclub and party events. We hire and make props and banners.

CUBIC DESIGN & CONSTRUCTION LTD
Ventureforth House, South Denes Road, Great Yarmouth, Norfolk NR30 3PT
Tel: 01493 332 031 Fax: 01493 745 120
Email: info@cubicdesign.biz
Web Site: www.cubicdesign.biz
Directors: Michael Hubbard, Stephanie Woolston

PETER EVANS STUDIOS LTD
12-14 Tavistock Street, Dunstable, Bedfordshire LU6 1NE
Tel: 01582 725 730 Fax: 01582 481 329
Email: sales@peterevansstudios.co.uk
Web Site: www.peterevansstudios.co.uk
Directors: P Evans, I Adams, R Evans
Makers of properties and scenic embellishments in rubber, GRP, polystyrene, etc. Supplier of a large range of columns, urns, cornices, friezes, balustrades, brickwork, etc. in vacuum formed PVC, ABS or GRP. Also vacuum forming done from your own patterns or patterns specially made. Catalogue available.

EVENT PROP HIRE
Unit 1, Green Park Business Centre, Eastmoor, Sutton-on-the-Forest, York YO61 1ET
Tel: 08450 940 816 Fax: 01347 812 019
Email: enquiries@eventprophire.com
Web Site: www.eventprophire.com

FARLEY
1- 17 Brunel Road, East Acton, London W3 7XR
Tel: 0208 749 9925 Fax: 0208 749 8372
Email: props@farley.co.uk
Web Site: www.farley.co.uk
Specialists in fine furniture.

CARL GRESHAM GROUP
PO Box 3, Bradford, West Yorkshire BD1 4QN
Mob: 07932 750512 Fax: 01274 827 161
Email: gresh@carlgresham.co.uk
Web Site: www.carlgresham.co.uk
Senior Personnel: Carl Gresham
Importers and suppliers of merchandise and memorabilia for theatrical and arena presentations and pantomimes.

HANGING GARDEN LTD
Wildmoor Lane, Sherfield-on-Loddon, Hook, Hampshire RG27 0HL
Tel: 01256 880 647 Fax: 01256 880 651
Email: nick@hanginggarden.co.uk
Web Site: www.hanginggarden.co.uk
Contact: Nick Kirby
We hire tropical and exterior plants, statues, balustrade columns and all types of props.

HWL (UK) LTD
Cricket Street, Denton, Manchester M34 3DR
Tel: 0161 335 0220 Fax: 0161 320 3928
Email: guns@hwltd.co.uk
Web Site: www.hwltd.co.uk
Contact: Bob Howorth
Hirers of all types of furniture, set dressing, decorative lighting, pictures, hand props etc. Also specialist hirers of weapons and blank firing guns.

IMPACT PERCUSSION
7 Goose Green Trading Estate, 47 East Dulwich Road, London SE22 9BN
Tel: 020 8299 6700 Fax: 020 8299 6704
Email: sales@impactpercussion.com
Web Site: www.impactpercussion.com
Contact: Paul Hagen
Hire, retail and repair of percussion instruments and props.

KEELEY HIRE LTD
Units 3-4a, Charlton Mead Lane South, Hoddesdon, Hertfordshire EN11 0DJ
Tel: 01992 464040 / 01992 444584 Fax: 01992 462239
Email: salesdesk@keeleyhire.co.uk
Web Site: www.keeleyhire.co.uk

JIM LAWS LIGHTING
Westend Lodge, West End Corner, Wrentham, Beccles, Suffolk NR34 7NH
Tel: 01502 675 264 Mob: 07776 238 249
Email: jimlawslighting@btconnect.com
Period Entertainment Lighting. Hire and Sales, lighting Design service.

LEWIS AND KAYE (HIRE) LTD
Subsidiary of the Farley Group
1 - 17 Brunel Road, London W3 7XR
Tel: 020 8749 2121 Fax: 020 8749 9455
Email: lewisandkaye@farley.co.uk
Web Site: www.lewisandkaye.co.uk
Managing Director: Mark Farely
Hire of props (silver, glass, china, objects d'art) to TV, films, theatres, photographers.

MIKE & ROSI COMPTON
11 Woodstock Road, Croydon, Surrey
CR0 1JS
Tel: 020 8680 4364 Mobile: 07900 258646 (Mike)
Email: mikeandrosicompton@btopenworld.com
We make props, mechanical visual effects, costumes and models, we specialise in the unusual, but can do almost anything! No hiring.

MOVETECH UK
Emblem Works, Emblem Street, Bolton, Lancashire BL3 5BW
Tel: 01204 525 626 London Depot: Tel: 01992 574 602 Fax: 01992 560 385
Email: info@turntable.co.uk
Web Site: www.british.turntable.co.uk, www.movetechuk.com
British Turntable Company, leaders in creating dramatic movement, offer a range of low profile, self-assembly revolving stages, in diameters ranging from 2m to 10m. Highly portable, these revolves can be assembled by two men in as little as half an hour*, can be supplied for manual or powered operation and include options such as variable speed, indexing and/or static centre.
This range is in addition to the extremely comprehensive range of revolves available for sale or hire up to 25 tonne capacity and which include units suitable for outdoor location applications.
Competitively priced, all units are available from depots throughout the UK and Europe.
*Assembly time based on a 6m standard revolve on sound, level surface.

NEWMAN HIRE COMPANY
16 The Vale, Acton, London W3 7SB
Tel: 020 8743 0741 Fax: 020 8749 3513
Email: sales@newmanhire.co.uk
Web Site: www.newmanprophire.co.uk
General Manager: Terry Poole
Hirers of properties to TV, film and stage.

PICTURES PROPS
Brunel House, 12-16 Brunel Road, London W3 7XR
Tel: 020 8749 2434 Fax: 020 8740 5846
Email: picturesprops@tiscali.co.uk
Paintings and works of art and small props and ceramics.
Contact: Jane Owen

PREWETT MILLER - FLOREAT (LONDON)
53 Connaught Street, London W2 2BB
Tel: 020 7723 4683 Fax: 020 7723 6998
Email: prewettmiller@hotmail.com
Director: J.W.M. Miller
Hire of plants, etc. and floral displays of every description.

PRODUCTS FROM SPAIN
Unit 17-18, Cumberland Business Park, 17 Cumberland Avenue, Park Royal, London NW10 7RT
Tel: 020 8965 7274 Fax: 020 8965 7235
Email: mail@productsfromspain.co.uk
Web Site: www.productsfromspain.co.uk
Contact: Beatrice Lopez
Importers of props - Spanish Lace Fans, Castanettes, Tambourines, Veils etc.

PROP SOLUTIONS
91 Acton Lane, London NW10 8UT
Tel: 020 8965 5152
Email: info@propsolutions.co.uk
Web Site: www.propsolutions.co.uk
Contact: Maya Crome

PROPS GALORE
Subsidiary of the Farley Group
1-17 Brunel Road, London W3 7XR
Tel: 020 8746 1222 Fax: 020 8354 1866
Email: propsgalore@farley.co.uk
Web Site: www.farley.co.uk
Specialists in the hire of period textiles, jewellery and accessories.

PROPS4SHOWS
Osprey House, Featherby Way, Purdeys Industrial Estate, Rochford, Essex SS4 1LD
Tel: 03333 440 078 Fax: 03333 441 478
Email: sales@props4shows.com
Web Site: www.props4shows.co.uk
Contact: Lin Lorde
Suppliers of a wide range of props, display goods and fabrics, for stage, theatre, photography and marketing. The extensive range includes fake food, seasonal props, artificial trees, stage backdrops, scenery props, professional makeup, display accessories and much more.

PROSCENEIUM LTD
Sladen Wood Mill, Todmorden Road, Littleborough, Lancashire OL15 9EW
Tel: 01706 377226 Fax: 01706 371953
Email: enquiries@prosceneium.co.uk
Web Site: www.prosceneium.co.uk
Set Hire: Robert Kershaw, Gary Hookham
Theatrical Scenery designed, built and painted for hire or for sale to Professional and Amateur groups. Full sets for most musicals and pantomimes available. Hirer of stage furniture and props, thousands of items in stock.

RITZ STUDIOS
The Courtyard, Esmond Street, Putney SW15 2LP
Tel: 020 8870 1335
Email: ben@ritzstudios.com
Web Site: www.ritzstudios.com
Contact: Ben Webber

S2 EVENTS LTD
3-5 Valentine Place, London SE1 8QH
Tel: 020 7928 5474 Fax: 020 7928 6082
Email: info@s2events.co.uk
Web Site: www.s2events.co.uk
Contact: Walter Dammers

SCREEN PRODUCTS LTD
Tel: 07926 196 471
Email: info@dirtydown.co.uk
Web Site: www.dirtydown.co.uk
Contact: Alan Taylor
Dirty Down sprays are "dirty" translucent dyes used extensively in film, theatre, and television on costumes, scenery and props. Make things look dirty/old. Rust, Mould, Frost/Snow and ice are Special Effects Sprays.

SEASONS TEXTILES LIMITED
9 Gorst Road, London NW10 6LA
Tel: 020 8965 6161 Fax: 020 8961 6433
Email: enquiries@seasonstextiles.net
Web Site: www.seasonstextiles.co.uk
Manager: Sue Toone
Hire and purchase of textiles for film, television, photography and interior design. To hire - large selection of tapestries, drapes and soft furnishings. To order - extensive range of fabrics, wallpapers and trimmings at competitive prices.

ADRIAN SNELL PRODUCTION SERVICES
Unit 12 Millbrook Ind Est. Millbrook, Torpoint, Cornwall PL11 3AX
Tel: 01752 829 393 Fax: 01752 829 394
Email: adriansnell@adriansnell.co.uk
Contact: Adrian Snell
Our large modern workshops offer a complete construction service, including engineering, steel fabrication and all other forms of construction.

SPILLER HIRE
Subsidiary of the Farley Group
1-17 Brunel Road, Acton, London W3 7XR
Tel: 020 8743 8747 Fax: 020 8354 1866
Email: spiller@farley.co.uk
Web Site: www.farley.co.uk
Picture and gilt frame hire.

STUDIO AND TV HIRE
See also 'Chase 55'
Chase55, 55 Chase Road, London NW10 6LU
Tel: 0871 231 0900 Fax: 020 8965 8107
Email: info@chase55.com
Web Site: www.stvhire.com
Contact: Andy Wills
Hire of general film and TV props, accessories and bric-a-brac for Production Designers, Set Designers and Art Directors working in the film and television industry.

TALBOT DESIGNS LTD
223 - 225 Long Lane, Finchley, London N3 2RL
Tel: 020 8346 8515 Fax: 020 8349 0294
Email: sales@talbotdesigns.co.uk
Web Site: www.talbotdesigns.co.uk
Contact: Richard Woolff
Over the past 30 years have supplied most of the notable theatre productions with plastic flooring, plastic domes, scenery, special effects, hand held props and any plastic requirements.

TRADING POST LTD
1-3 Beresford Avenue, Wembley, Middlesex HA0 1NU
Tel: 020 8903 3727 Fax: 020 8900 2565
Email: info@tradingposthire.co.uk
Web Site: www.tradingposthire.co.uk
Contact: Roy Langton
60 years supplying props to film, TV and the theatre industry.

TREASURE TROVE PUPPET COMPANY
54 High Street, Caergwrle, Flintshire LL12 9LL Wales
Tel: 01978 761 053 Mob: 07802 800 817
Email: treasure.trove@virgin.net
Web: www.treasuretrovepuppets.co.uk
Directors: Stephen Sharples.
Operation includes: Puppets for all occasions, small/middle scale touring, workshops and demonstrations.
Makers of puppets. Extensive touring nationally and internationally.

TURK FILM SERVICES LTD
Town End Pier, 68 High Street, Kingston-upon-Thames, Surrey KT1 1HN
Tel: 020 8546 2434
Email: operations@turks.co.uk
Web Site: www.turks.co.uk
Managing Director: Richard Turk
Hirers of: Marine and boat props, ships, locations and action sequences.

UBEEM (UNCLE BRIAN'S ENTERTAINMENT & EVENTS MANAGEMENT)
Burwell House, Folkton, Scarborough, North Yorkshire YO11 3UH
Tel: 01723 891 441 Mobile: 07801 969464
Email: s.reidfrow@btinternet.com
Web Site: www.ubeem.com
Senior Personnel: David Reid-Frow
Bands, catering, clown, car, disco, stilt-walkers, face painters, magicians, marquees and Punch & Judy.

Radio Microphones

HAND HELD AUDIO
Unit 8, Waterways Business Centre, Navigation Drive, South Ordnance Road, Enfield EN3 6JJ
Tel: 01992 719 078 Fax: 01992 763 860
Email: info@handheldaudio.co.uk
Web Site: www.handheldaudio.co.uk
Contact: Mick Shepherd
Wireless systems specialists. We hire, sell and service radio microphones and in ear systems.

MAC SOUND
1-2 Attenburys Park, Park Road, Altrincham, Cheshire WA14 5QE
Tel: 0161 969 8311 Fax: 0161 962 9423
Email: info@macsound.co.uk
Web Site: www.macsound.co.uk
Design: Clement Rawling
Sales: David Houghton
Hire: Andrew Simpson
Administration: Julie Murray
MAC Sound offers a complete sound design, equipment hire, engineering and personnel service for all types of theatre presentations and concerts. With over thirty years experience, we provide a free radio microphone planning and licensing service and offer quotations and site visits without obligation. Please visit our website or call for a current hire ratecard.

TERRALEC LTD
Osprey House, Featherby Way, Purdeys Industrial Estate, Rochford, Essex SS4 1LD
Tel: 01702 547 571 Fax: 01702 541 075
Email: sales@terralec.com
Web Site: www.terralec.co.uk
Suppliers of professional stage lighting, audio equipment, lighting control, microphones, staging, trussing, hardware, accessories & much more! For: Theatre, stage, commercial events and the entertainment industry.

Radios, Mobile Phones & Accessories

ADAM PHONES LTD
1-3 Dolphin Square, Edensor Road, London W4 2ST
Tel: 020 8742 0101
Email: moreinfo@adamphones.com
Web Site: www.adamphones.com
Chairman and Managing Director: Adam Toop

ASM COMMUNICATIONS
Ingoldfield Lane, Newtown, Fareham, Hampshire PO17 6LF
Tel: 01329 832 156 Mobile: 07753 799777
Email: aubrey.miles@fsmail.net
Contact General Manager: Aubrey Miles

AUDIOLINK RADIO COMMUNICATIONS
17 Iron Bridge Close, Great Central Way, Neasden London NW10 0UF
Tel: 020 8955 1100 Fax: 020 8955 1111
Email: info@audiolink.co.uk

Web Site: www.audiolink.co.uk
Senior Personnel: John Morgan

BETTER SOUND LTD
31 Cathcart Street, London NW5 3BJ
Tel: 020 7482 0177 Fax: 020 7482 2677
Email: admin@bettersound.co.uk
Web Site: www.bettersound.co.uk
General Manager: Christopher Column

COMMUNICATION & TECHNICAL SERVICES LTD
17 Pages Walk, London SE1 4SB
Tel: 020 7252 1849 Fax: 020 7252 3241
Email: hire@ctslimited.co.uk
Web Site: www.ctslimited.co.uk
Manager: Danny Parris
Whatever your mobile communication needs, CTS Hire can help. Our customers get the benefit of top quality equipment, first class service and real value for money. Why not join them?

COMMUNICATION SPECIALISTS
Unit 6, Murrell Green Business Park, London Road, Hook, Hampshire RG27 9GR
Tel: 01256 766 600 Fax: 01256 766 500
Email: kervin@comm-spec.co.uk / info@comm-spec.co.uk
Web Site: www.comm-spec.com
Contact: Kervin Labrosse
Specialising in the supply, servicing and hire of all aspects of two-way radios. We also carry a large stock of accessories.

DCRS LIMITED
Edison Road, St Ives, Cambridgeshire PE27 3LH
Tel: 01480 466 300 Fax: 01480 461 044
Email: sales@dcrs.co.uk
Web Site: www.dcrs.co.uk
Contact: Michelle Williamson
Hire, Sale and Service of two-way radio communications equipment. The complete service from start to finish. We are capable of supplying, servicing and maintaining all makes and models of equipment.

DIRECT TELECOM SERVICES
Generation Business Park, Barford Road, Little Barford, St. Neots, Cambridgeshire PE19 6YQ
Tel: 0800 542 7860
Email: sales@dts.solutions
Web Site: www.ukradios.com
Hire Manager: Amanda Pickering
Email: hire@dts.solutions
Suppliers of hand portable radios, covert radio systems and mobile phones. We offer short and long term hire, sales, service and maintenance all at very competitive prices. We are a professional organisation, being an authorised Motorola dealer together with other market leaders such as Maxon, Kenwood and Vodafone. We also offer a National and International delivery services.

GBS - GENERAL BATTERY SUPPLIES
Unit A 315 Collier Row Lane Collier Row Romford Essex RM5 3ND
Tel: 01708 769222 Fax: 01708 769282
Email: gbsbatteries@aol.com
Web Site: www.gbsbatteries.co.uk
Contact: Phillip Abbott or David Myers
Specialist Battery Suppliers to the sound, TV, film & theatre industry. Distributors for all main brands including: Duracell Procell, Energizer Industrial, Varta Industrial, Panasonic, Sanyo and many more.

MAC SOUND
1-2 Attenburys Park, Park Road, Altrincham, Cheshire WA14 5QE
Tel: 0161 969 8311 Fax: 0161 962 9423
Email: info@macsound.co.uk
Web Site: www.macsound.co.uk
Design: Clement Rawling
Sales: David Houghton
Hire: Andrew Simpson
Administration: Julie Murray
MAC Sound offers a complete sound design, equipment hire, engineering and personnel service for all types of theatre presentations and concerts. With over thirty years experience, we provide a free radio microphone planning and licensing service and offer quotations and site visits without obligation. Please visit our website or call for a current hire ratecard.

MOTOROLA LTD
Viables Industrial Estate, Jays Close, Basingstoke, Hampshire RG22 4PD
Tel: 01256 358 211
Email: garymarshall@motorolasolutions.com
Web Site: www.mot.com
Motorola Hire, offered through Customer Access, provides an efficient and reliable service including:-
Competitive rates, full equipment range, accessories (at no extra cost), delivery/collection service, licensing, free telephone service.
Chief Marketing Officer: Eduardo Conrado

MURPHY COMHIRE LTD
The Greyhound, 822 Attercliffe Road, Sheffield S9 3RS
Tel: 0114 243 4567 Fax: 0114 243 4127
Email: sales@murphy-com-hire.com
Web Site: www.murphy-com-hire.com
Managing Director: Karen Andrews

NATIONAL RADIO BANK
Pinfold Road, Bourne, Lincolnshire PE10 9HT
Tel: 01778 393 938 Fax: 01778 421 603
Email: sales@radiohire.com
Web Site: www.radiohire.com
Hire Manager: Jamis Lawrance
International two way radio hire specialists.

RADIO LINKS COMMUNICATIONS LTD (ORBITAL NET)
Lakehouse, 31 Miners Way, Lakesview International Busine Hersden, Canterbury, Kent CT3 4LQ
Tel: 01233 807 060
Email: info@radio-link.co.uk
Web Site: www.radio-link.co.uk
Specialist online store selling outdoor wireless equipment and accessories.

RADIOCOMS LTD
Unit 3 The Chase Centre, 8 Chase Road, Park Royal NW10 6QB
Tel: 020 8951 9820
Email: enquiries@radiocoms.co.uk
Web Site: www.radiocoms.co.uk

RELCOM COMMUNICATIONS
SandyHill Park, Middleton, Matlock, Derbyshire DE4 4LR
Tel: 020 8965 2333 Admin: 01629 823 427 Fax: 01629 820 800
Email: info@relcom.co.uk
Web Site: www.relcom.co.uk
Founded in 1983, Relcom Communication specialises in two-way radio hire, private mobile radio, digital radio and PMR446. Relcom became a division of Lowe Electronics in May 1999.

SDD SOUND & LIGHT LTD
Temple Gardens, Staines, Middlesex

TW18 3NQ
Tel: 01784 455 666 Fax: 01784 455 642
Email: info@sddsoundandlight.com
Web Site: www.sddsoundandlight.com
Rental, sales, repair and installation of all types and brands of equipment from multi channel radio microphone systems to intelligent lighting. Visit our website for our catalogue.

SHOW HIRE
Unit 4 Station Yard Ind Est, Station Lane, Milford, Godalming, Surrey GU8 5AD
Tel: 01483 414 337 Fax: 01483 426 926
Email: info@showhire.co.uk
Web Site: www.showhire.co.uk
Contact: Nick Chubb

SITELINK COMMUNICATIONS LTD
Unit 7, Loughton Business Centre, Langston Road, Loughton, Essex IG10 3FL
Tel: 020 8508 6688
Email: sales@sitelink.co.uk
Web Site: www.sitelink.co.uk
Contact: Ian Ross
Hire and sales of Motorola portable radios

SKARDA INTERNATIONAL COMMUNICATIONS
7 Portland Mews, London W1F 8JQ
Tel: 020 7734 7776 Fax: 020 7734 1360
Mobile: 07836 200700
Email: martin@skarda.net
Web Site: www.skarda.net
Contact: Martin Davidson

SOLENT SOUNDS SYSTEMS LTD
7 Mitchell Point, Ensign Park, Hamble, Southampton, Hampshire SO31 4RF
Tel: 023 8045 6700 Fax: 023 8045 6789
Email: sales@solentsound.com
Web Site: www.solentsound.com
Manager: Ray Gatehouse
Technical Manager: Adam Gatehouse

MIKE WEAVER COMMUNICATIONS LTD
Unit 10, Redland Close, Aldermans Green Ind Estate, Coventry, Warwickshire CV2 2NP
Tel: 024 76 602 605 Fax: 024 76 602 609
Email: mike@mwc.co.uk, sales@mwc.co.uk
Web Site: www.mwc.co.uk
Contacts: Anne and Mike Weaver

Ramps

RA'ALLOY RAMPS LTD
A1-A3 Stafford Park 15, Telford, Shropshire TF3 3BB
Tel: 01952 291 224 Fax: 01952 291 289
Email: enquiries@raalloy.co.uk
Web Site: www.raalloy.co.uk
Managing Director: Graham Corfield
Ra'Alloy manufacture a complete range of non-slip ramps in standard sizes or to customers own specifications.

Recording

BIG BEAR MUSIC
PO BOX 944, Edgbaston, Birmingham B16 8UT
Tel: 0121 454 7020
Email: admin@bigbearmusic.com/ tim@bigbearmusic.com
Web Site: www.bigbearmusic.com
Senior Personnel: Tim Jennings, Jim Simpson
Big Bear Music promote jazz, blues and swing through concert and club tours, UK and European festivals, the Starbucks Birmingham International Jazz Festival and Marbella Jazz Festival (Spain).

CANDLE
44 Southern Row, London W10 5AN
Tel: 020 8960 0111 Mobile: 07860 912192
Email: tony@candle.org.uk
Web Site: www.candle.org.uk
Managing Director: Tony Satchell
Creative Director: Charlie Spencer
Original composition for TV, Radio and Film.

OXRECS DIGITAL
Maytree Cottage, 51 Eaton Road, Appleton, Abingdon, Oxfordshire OX13 5JH
Tel: 01865 862310
Email: info@oxrecs.com
Web Site: www.oxrecs.com
Manager: Bernard Martin
Specialists in classicial location sound recording for choirs, chamber ensembles and orchestras. Typesetting and design service available for CD booklets and inlays.

REDBRIDGE RECORDING STUDIOS
Unit 2, Redbridge Industrial Estate, Breightmet Fold Lane, Breightmet, Bolton BL2 5PH
Tel: 01204 525579
Email: info@redbridgestudios.com
Web Site: www.redbridgestudios.com
Rehearsal and audio recording facilities.

SILVERWORD PRODUCTIONS
16 Lime Trees Avenue, Llangattock, Crickhowell, Powys NP8 1LD Wales
Tel: 01873 810 142
Email: silverwordgroup@aol.com
Web Site: www.silverwordgroup.com
Managing Director: Kevin King
Management company, record producers, marketing company and music publishers.

TABITHA MUSIC LTD
39 Cordery Road, Exeter, Devon EX2 9DJ
Tel: 01392 279 914
Email: graham@tabithamusic.com
Web Site: www.tabithamusic.com, www.grahamsclater.webs.com
Contact: Graham Sclater
Record Producer, music publisher, author, scriptwriter.

Rehearsal Rooms: London

ABACUS ARTS
Rehearsal space
2A Browning Street, London SE17 1LN
Tel: 020 7277 2880
Email: info@abacus-arts.org.uk
Web Site: www.abacus-arts.org.uk
Rehearsal space for hire in Zone 1 travel, and outside congestion area. Studio 12.2m x 9.5m, sprung floor. Breakout room 4.3m x 4m w. kitchen facilities & wifi. Exclusive 24/7 access available. Excellent transport, nearby parking & shops. A ground floor venue with easy street access and full height double doors.

THE ALBANY
Theatre and community centre.
Douglas Way, Deptford, London SE8 4AG
Admin: 020 8692 0231 BO: 020 8692 4446 Fax: 020 8469 2253
Email: senay.gaul@thealbany.org.uk
Web Site: www.thealbany.org.uk
ADMINISTRATION:
The Albany is a lively, intimate and friendly venue with an exciting programme of the very best in theatre, live music, cabaret, family shows, club nights and multimedia events in informal cabaret-style seating.
CEO/Artistic Director: Gavin Barlow
Operations & Administration: Senay Gaul
Room Bookings & Venue Hires: Lily Hannell
Production & Events: Ben Stephens
Head of Communications: Amber Massie-Bloomfield
Box Office: Vicky Harrison
Front of House: Kate Miners (reception@thealbany.org.uk)
Policy: Variety of events, including music, theatre, dance, spoken word, clubs and family events.
Capacity: Main Auditorium: 300 seated/ 500 standing. Studio/ Conference Rooms: 12 - 100.

ALL SAINTS ARTS CENTRE
122 Oakleigh Road North,
London N20 9EZ

Tel: 020 8445 8388
Email: arts@allsaints.uk.com
Web Site: www.allsaints.uk.com
Senior Personnel: Gregory Platten

AMADEUS CENTRE
50 Shirland Road, Little Venice, London W9 2JA
Tel: 020 7286 1686
Email: info@theamadeus.co.uk
Web Site: www.theamadeus.co.uk
A converted 19th Century Welsh Presbyterian chapel offering two halls for hire for receptions, seminars, and rehearsals.

ARCH 468
Unit 4, 209a Coldharbour Lane, London SW9 8RU
Mob: 07973 302908
Email: rebecca@arch468.com
Web Site: www.arch468.com
ADMINISTRATION:
Head Office (All post should be directed to this address):
Ground Floor, 106 Hinton Rd, London, SE24 0HU.

ARTSADMIN
Toynbee Studios, 28 Commercial Street, London E1 6AB
Tel: 020 7247 5102
Email: admin@artsadmin.co.uk
Web Site: www.artsadmin.co.uk
Managing Directors: Judith Knight and Gill Lloyd
Admin & Studios Manager: Jessica Denning
Marketing & development manager: Jennifer Tomkins
Studio Hire, Management Company.

BASEMENT STUDIOS
17-19 Greenhill Crescent, Watford, Hertfordshire WD1 8QU
Tel: 01923 220 169 Fax: 01923 250 341
Email: lalamanwo7@aol.com
Contact: Tony Smith

BATTERSEA ARTS CENTRE
Venue undergoing restoration, capacity unknown until 2016
Lavender Hill, London SW11 5TN
Mgt: 020 7223 6557 BO: 020 7223 2223
Fax: 020 7978 5207 Admin: 020 7326 8239
Email: boxoffice@bac.org.uk, mailbox@bac.org.uk
Web Site: www.bac.org.uk
ADMINISTRATION:
Artistic Director: David Jubb
Executive Manager: Rebecca Holt
Technical Manager: Kevin Miles
Theatre: Multi-purpose performance space. Capacity: 200 +
Lower Hall Capacity: 100 - 200
Recreation Room Capacity: 50 - 100
Policy: To work with artists and audiences towards the development of innovative forms of theatre.
For venue hire contact the theatre on: venues@bac.org.uk.

BBC TELEVISION REHEARSAL ROOMS
Victoria Road, North Acton, London W3 6UL
Tel: 020 7580 4468 ext 87377 (facilities MaGT)
Contact Events Co-ordinator: Corrina Wilkins

BEETHOVEN CENTRE
Third Avenue, London W10 4JL
Tel: 020 8969 5881 Fax: 020 8962 8648
Email: BeethovenCentre@a2dominion.co.uk
Web: www.a2dominion.co.uk/beethoven

BIG WHEEL THEATRE COMPANY (TIE)
Exmouth Market Centre, PO Box 18221, London EC1R 4WJ
Tel: 020 7689 8670
Email: info@bigwheel.org.uk
Web Site: www.bigwheel.org.uk
Contact: Roland Allen
Capacity: 80

CECIL SHARP HOUSE
2 Regents Park Road, Camden, London NW1 7AY
Tel: 020 7485 2206 Fax: 020 7284 0534
Email: info@efdss.org
Web Site: www.cecilsharophouse.org
Home of English Folk Dance and Song Society.
ADMINISTRATION:
Props: EFDSS
Chief Executive: Katy Spicer
Marketing and Communications Director: Tessa Norton
Capacity: Contains 6 spaces. Kennedy Hall; 500 standing / 420 seated (300 chairs, 120 on tiered seating). Trefusis Hall: 150 standing / 120 seated. Storrow Hall; 60.
Available for hire; ideal for rehearsals. Conact Hiring Administrator, Jessica Grimshaw, on 020 7485 2206 ext. 24 (Hirings Manager) or hire@efdss.org. Facilities include sprung floors, grand piano, bar, cafeteria and garden.

DANCE ATTIC
Old Fulham Baths 368 North End Road, Fulham, London SW6 1LY
Mgt/BO: 020 7610 2055
Email: danceattic@hotmail.com
Web Site: www.danceattic.com
ADMINISTRATION:
Props: Dance Attic Studios
Directors: Andrew Corbet Burcher
Perfs: Sat., Sun.
Seats: 100

DANCE WORKS
16 Balderton Street, London W1K 6TN
Tel: 020 7629 6183 Studio Hire Hotline: 020 7318 4100
Email: info@danceworks.net
Web Site: www.danceworks.net
We offer Europe's largest selection of dance classes, 7 large multi-purpose studios for hire, men's and women's changing facilities with showers, a lounge/ networking area which includes internet access and our first floor therapy centre, Natureworks.

EALING STUDIOS OPERATIONS LTD
Ealing Green, London W5 5EP
Tel: 020 8567 6655 Fax: 020 8758 8658
Web Site: www.ealingstudios.co.uk
Studio Managers: Gary Stone, Simon George
Facilities: Stage 5 22 x 44 ft, Stage 1 29 x 34 ft, Use of on site Cafe.

FACE FRONT INCLUSIVE THEATRE LTD
52 The Market Square, Edmonton Green Shopping Centre Edmonton, London N9 0TZ
Tel: 020 8350 3461
Email: info@facefront.org
Web Site: www.facefront.org
Artistic Director: Annie Smol
Administrator and Tour Booker: Tracey Viechweg
Face Front is a company of disabled and non-disabled artists who create multi-layered theatre which is accessible to all. The company works extensively in schools and other educational settings producing high quality Theatre In Education and participatory workshop programmes suitable for all ages over 5 years. Drama techniques include role-play, improvisation, storytelling, poetry and image work to raise issues relating to educational and home environments, including bullying, racism, disability and domestic violence.
Contact the company directly for more information on hiring the on-site studio; the high ceiling and sprung dance floor make it suitable for rehearsals, auditions, meetings and community events.

JOHN HENRY'S LTD
16-24 Brewery Road, London N7 9NH
Tel: 020 7609 9181 Fax: 020 7700 7040
Email: info@johnhenrys.com
Web Site: www.johnhenrys.com
Event Production: Pepin Clout
Rehearsal Studios: Andrea Westwood
Backline Production: Tark Bates

INSTITUTE OF INDIAN CULTURE
Bhavan Centre, 4a Castletown Road, West Kensington, London W14 9HQ

Tel: 020 7381 3086 / 4608 Fax: 020 7381 8758
Email: info@bhavan.net
Web Site: www.bhavan.net
Executive Director: Dr. M.N. Nandakumara
Theatre Capacity: 295 Seats
Rehearsal Rooms: Cap: Haithi Hall: 100. Dance Studio and Art Gallery also available.
Our auditorium is suitable for concerts, dances and dramas. It is fitted with light and sound. The other hall has a wooden floor and moveable chairs. Other rooms are suitable for meetings. All these spaces are for hire.

ITALIA CONTI ACADEMY OF THEATRE ARTS
Italia Conti House, 23 Goswell Road, London EC1M 7AJ
Tel: 020 7608 0044 Fax: 020 7253 1430
Acting School: 72 Landor Road, London SW9 9PH Tel: 020 7733 3210 Fax: 020 7737 2728
Email: baacting.italiaconti@btinternet.com, admin@italiaconti.co.uk
Web Site: www.italiaconti-acting.co.uk
Administration/Courses:
Principal: Ms Anne Sheward
GOSWELL ROAD SCHOOL:
Junior and student courses in performing arts, dance, drama and singing including GCSE.
Age 9+ full-time education. Weekend associate classes: Age 3 to adult in all. Student courses 16+ (1 and 3 year full-time). Diploma & B.A Hons Degree.
LANDOR ROAD SCHOOL:
Provides actor training for adult students. 3-year full-tim BA(Hons) Acting course for adult students. Accredited by the National Council for Drama Training, validated by South Bank University. Performing Arts and Singing courses also available for students 16+.

JACKSONS LANE COMMUNITY CENTRE
269a Archway Road, Highgate, London N6 5AA
Tel: 020 8340 5226 BO: 020 8341 4421
Fax: 020 8348 2424
Email: jenni@jacksonslane.org.uk
Web Site: www.jacksonslane.org.uk
Administrator: Jenni Archibald
Studio One: 8m x 37m (120 Capacity), Studio Two: 6.5m x 10m (80 Capacity).

LONDON WELSH TRUST LIMITED
157-163 Grays Inn Road, London WC1X 8UE
Tel: 020 7837 3722 Fax: 020 7837 6268
Email: administrator@lwcentre.demon.co.uk
Web Site: www.londonwelsh.org

MARYLEBONE DANCE STUDIOS
12 Lisson Grove, London NW1 6TS
Tel: 020 7258 0767
Email: producer@ukfd.co.uk
Web Site: www.m-dancestudio.co.uk
ADMINISTRATION:
Director: Tim Tubbs

MENIER CHOCOLATE FACTORY
53 Southwark Street, London SE1 1RU
Admin: 020 7378 1712
Email: office@menierchocolatefactory.com
Web Site: www.menierchocolatefactory.com
ADMINISTRATION:
Artistic Director: David Babani
General Manager: Thomas Siracusa
Associate Producer: Lucy McNally
The Menier Chocolate Factory has been a full time producing house since 2004, and comprises a theatre, restaurant, bar and large rehearsal space.
Capacity: 200

NATIONAL OPERA STUDIO
2 Chapel Yard, Wandsworth High Street London SW18 4HZ
Tel: 020 8874 8811
Email: k.jones@nationaloperastudio.org.uk
Web: www.nationaloperastudio.org.uk
Various rehearsal rooms for hire, including a large hall (10m x 13.00m) with prices starting from £12 per hour.
Nearest overground station Wandsworth Town.
To book a room, contact Katie Jones at k.jones@nationaloperastudio.org.uk or ring 020 8874 8811.
Facilities include a kitchen, disabled parking space and a lift.

OVAL HOUSE THEATRE
52-54 Kennington Oval, London SE11 5SW
Admin: 020 7582 0080 BO: 020 7582 7680 Fax: 020 7820 0990
Email: info@ovalhouse.com
Web Site: www.ovalhouse.com
ADMINISTRATION:
Props: Christ Church (Oxford) University Clubs
Lessees: C.C.O.U.C.
General Manager: Wendy Dempsey
Email: wendy.dempseyt@ovalhouse.com
Head of Press and Marketing: Debbie Vannozzi
Email: debbie.vannozzi@ovalhouse.com
Policy: New work, emerging companies, women's, lesbian & gay, black and Asian, work relevant to local audiences.
Performance and Rehearsal space.
Two performance spaces, upstairs and downstairs 50 and 100 capacity respectively.New cafe & cabaret space; extra dance studio and rehearsal space.

PINEAPPLE DANCE STUDIOS
7 Langley Street, London WC2H 9JA
Tel: 020 7836 4004 Fax: 020 7836 0803
Email: luke@pineapple.uk.com, caroline@pineapple.uk.com
Web Site: www.pineapple.uk.com
Manager: Caroline Granger

THE POOR SCHOOL
Reg.Charity No. 1084706
242 Pentonville Road, London N1 9JY
Tel: 020 7837 6030 Fax: 020 7837 5330
Email: acting@thepoorschool.com
Web Site: www.thepoorschool.com
Contact: Paul Caister
Full-time drama training scheduled in the evenings and at weekends and charged for at cost.

THE QUESTORS THEATRE
Mattock Lane, Ealing, London W5 5BQ
Mgt: 020 8567 0011 BO: 020 8567 5184
Fax: 020 8567 2275
Email: enquiries@questors.org.uk
Web Site: www.questors.org.uk
ADMINISTRATION:
Props: The Questors Ltd
Executive Director: Andrea Bath. Email: andrea@questors.org.uk
Theatre Administrator: Jane Mason. Email: jane@questors.org.uk
House and Technical Manager: Mike Hagan
Email: mike@questors.org.uk
Marketing Coordinator: Ian Briggs. Email: ian@questors.org.uk
Policy: Largest and best equipped Community Theatre in Europe. Regular visits from Professional Companies.
Venue comprises Playhouse, Studio, 3 large rehearsal rooms which are available for hire, Scenic Workshop, Large Wardrobe, various other meeting rooms and gallery space.
Perfs: Eves. 7.45 Mats. 2.30
Seats: Playhouse 320-400, Studio 80-100. Two bars, catering facilities available. Car Park. All FOH and Backstage facilities fully accessible.

RADA STUDIOS
16 Chenies Street, London WC1E 7EX
Admin/BO: 020 7307 5060 Fax: 020 7307 5062
Email: studiosboxoffice@rada.ac.uk
Web Site: www.radaenterprises.org
ADMINISTRATION:
General Manager: Stacie Novotny
Seats: 200 max.
Disabled access, licensed bar on ground floor.
The Drill Hall, just off Tottenham Court Road, in London's West End, has a 200 seat theatre,
Studio Theatre, a 50-seat cabaret-style. Club Theatre ,four rehearsal studios, four meeting rooms, a bar, an extensive programme of courses and classes (with changing rooms/ shower facilities) and is open seven days a week.

RAMBERT DANCE COMPANY
94 Chiswick High Road, London W4 1SH
Tel: 020 8630 0600 Fax: 020 8747 8323
Email: rdc@rambert.org.uk
Web Site: www.rambert.org.uk
ADMINISTRATION:
Artistic Director: Mark Baldwin
Music Director: Paul Hoskins
Rehearsal Directors: Mikaela Polley and Simon Cooper

RITZ STUDIOS
The Courtyard, Esmond Street, Putney SW15 2LP
Tel: 020 8870 1335
Email: ben@ritzstudios.com
Web Site: www.ritzstudios.com
Contact: Ben Webber

ROBIN HOWARD DANCE THEATRE
The Place, 17 Dukes Road London WC1H 9PY
Admin: 020 7121 1101 BO: 020 7121 1100
Email: info@theplace.org.uk, theatre@theplace.org.uk
Web Site: www.theplace.org.uk
ADMINISTRATION:
Props: Contemporary Dance Trust.
Theatre Director: Eddie Nixon
Director of Communications: Rosie Neave (Tel: 020 7121 1021)
Technical Manager: Graeme McGinty
Director of Administration & Finance: David Burnie
Policy: Independant Dance Companys. Presented for 30 weeks. Theatre available for hire in remaining 22 weeks.
Perfs: 8.00pm (or by arrangement).
Seats: 300. Bar and Café.

SADLER'S WELLS
Rosebery Avenue, Islington, London, EC1R 4TN
BO: 0844 412 4300 SD: 020 7863 8198
Events: 020 7863 8065 Fax: 020 7863 8199
Email: reception@sadlerswells.com
Web Site: www.sadlerswells.com
ADMINISTRATION:
Executive Director: Laura Stevenson
Head of Events and Catering: Zuzana Galikova
4 Rehearsal studios, 3 of which have sprung floors.
Capacity: 1,500

SHARED EXPERIENCE THEATRE COMPANY
27 - 29 Vauxhall Grove, London SW8 1SY
Tel: 020 7587 1596 Fax: 020 7735 0374
Email: admin@sharedexperience.org.uk
Web Site: www.sharedexperience.org.uk
Artistic Directors: Nancy Meckler, Polly Teale
Policy: To explore a physical way of working through a diverse range of theatrical forms.
Two centrally heated studios in the heart of London.
Studio 1: 62' x 28' - rest room
Studio 2: 30' x 21' - competitive rates.

SOHO THEATRE & WRITERS STUDIO
21 Dean Street, London W1D 3NE
BO: 020 7478 0100 Admin: 020 7287 5060
Email: hires@sohotheatre.com, amy-smith@sohotheatre.com
Web Site: www.sohotheatre.com
ADMINISTRATION:
Artistic Director: Steve Marmion
Executive Director: Mark Godfrey
Writers' Centre Director: Nina Steiger
General Manager: Catherine McKinney
Front of House and Events Manager: Amy Smith
Policy: New Writing. Hires suitable for; rehearsed readings, conferences, filming, press launches and lectures or meetings
Theatre available for hire, subject to availability.
Rehearsal rooms available for hire. (Contact Amy Smith)
Theatre Capacity: 144 Seats
Studio Capacity: 85 seats

ST. GABRIEL'S HALLS
Glasgow Terrace, Churchill Gardens, London SW1V 3AA
Tel: 020 7828 0185 Mob: 07967 655 515
Email: info@stgabrielshalls.org.uk
Web Site: www.stgabrielshalls.org.uk
ADMINISTRATION:
Props: St Gabriel's Parish House Trust (Charity No: 1114216)
General Manager: David King

ST. MARY'S CHURCH HALLS
York Street, London W1H 1PQ
Tel: 020 7258 5040
Email: contact@stmaryslondon.com
Web Site: www.stmaryslondon.com
ADMINISTRATION:
Rector/ General Manager: John Peters
Services & Events Administrator: Lisa Trundle
Tel: 020 7258 5040,
Policy: Not available for hire on Sundays. No events later than 10.30pm due to local restrictions.
Capacity: Main Auditorium; 500 Theatre Style, 300 Cabaret, 600+ Standing. Lower Floor; 250 Theatre Style, 400 Standing.

ST. MARY'S STOKE NEWINGTON COMMUNITY CENTRE
St. Mary's Church, Stoke Newington Church Street, London N16 9ES
Tel: 020 7254 6072
Email: stmarystokenewington@btinternet.com
Web Site: www.stmaryn16.org
Parish Administrator: Mark Perrett
ST MARY'S COMMUNITY CENTRE (Defoe Road, Stoke Newington): providing a large hall with adjoining kitchen, and a quieter upper room suitable for groups of 15 or less
THE NEW CHURCH ROOMS: providing a large room that would seat up to 50, a smaller conference type room for 10-15 people, and a kitchen is also available for hire.

THE ACTORS PROFESSIONAL CENTRE LTD
1a Tower Street, London WC2H 9NP
General Tel: 020 7240 3940 Admin: 020 7632 8013 Room Hire Tel: 020 7632 8012 Membership Enquiries: 020 7632 8003 Fax: 020 7240 3896
Email: admin@actorscentre.co.uk
Web Site: www.actorscentre.co.uk
Artistic Director: Matthew Lloyd
General Manager: Toma Dim
Theatre Producer: Laura Kriefman
Operations Manager: Richard Williams

THE CIRCUS SPACE
Coronet Street, London N1 6HD
Tel: 020 7729 9522 Fax: 020 7729 9422
Email: jane@thecircusspace.co.uk
Web Site: www.thecircusspace.co.uk
ADMINISTRATION:
Joint Chief Executives: Jane Rice-Bowen and Kate White
Operations Director: Jonathan Dix
Higher Education Courses Director: Tim Roberts
Participation and Outreach Director: Eira Gibson
Director of Circus Development: Daisy Drury
Finance and Administration Director: Edward Halshaw
Head of Marketing and Communication: Philip Nichols
Venue Hire: Alex Horder (alex@thecircusspace.co.uk)

THE COURTYARD THEATRE
Bowling Green Walk, 40 Pitfield Street, London N1 6EU
Tel: 020 7729 2202 BO: 0844 477 1000
Email: info@thecourtyard.org.uk
Web Site: www.thecourtyard.org.uk
ADMINISTRATION:
Co Artistic Directors: June Abbott and Tim Gill
Production Manager: John Bell
Theatres Manager: Rupert Holloway
Venue Manager: Mikel Krumins
Administrator: Joanna Kazmierska
The resident companies, the Court Theatre Company and the Court Theatre Training Company, together with visiting productions present both new and classical works.
Performances usually 8pm. Tuesdays to

Sundays.
Capacity: Main Theatre, 150 Seated.
Studio, 80 Seated.
Dressing room accommodates 15.

TRICYCLE THEATRE
269 Kilburn High Road, London NW6 7JR
Mgt: 020 7372 6611 BO: 020 7328 1000
Fax: 020 7328 0795
Email: info@tricycle.co.uk
Web Site: www.tricycle.co.uk
ADMINISTRATION:
Props: Tricycle Theatre Co. Ltd
Executive Director: Kate Devey
Artistic Director: Indhu Rubasingham
Company Secretary: Trish McElhill
Technical Manager: Shaz McGee
Policy: Presentation of new plays. Adult programme generally for 6-9 week runs. Childrens shows on Saturdays. Plays both by Tricycle Co. and by other production companies.
Seats: 235

WACARTS
Hampstead Town Hall Centre 213
Haverstock Hill, London NW3 4QP
Tel: 020 7692 5800 Events: 020 7692 5809
Email: events@wacarts.co.uk
Web Site: www.wacarts.co.uk
ADMINISTRATION:
Events Manager: Craig Huxley
Email: craig.huxley@wacarts.co.uk
Cap: Council Chamber Room 120, Main Hall 250, Smaller Hall 120 Standing.
Dance Studios and smaller rooms available to hire.

THE WAREHOUSE
13 Theed Street, South Bank, London SE1 8ST
Tel: 020 7928 9251 Fax: 020 7928 9252
Email: the.warehouse@lfo.co.uk
Web: www.thewarehouselondon.co.uk
ADMINISTRATION:
For further information on studio availability and hire charges, please contact Executive Director: Elizabeth Szücs
Email: easzucs@lfo.co.uk
Capacity: Standing Cap: Studio 1: 100, Studio 2: 50. Seated: Studio 1: 100, Studio 2: 40. Orchestral/Rehearsal Setup: 85 max.

WIMBLEDON SCHOOL OF ART
Merton Hall Road, Wimbledon, London SW19 3QA
Tel: 020 8408 5000 Fax: 020 8408 5050
Email: info@wimbledon.arts.ac.uk
Web Site: www.wimbledon.ac.uk
Administration/Courses:
Principal: George Blacklark
Courses: All Higher Education courses are validated by University of Surrey.
BA (Hons) Theatre with areas of specialisation including Design for Performance, Technical Arts and Special Effects, Set Design for Stage and Screen, Costume Interpretation and Costume Design. Plus, new foundation degree in Theatre Lighting Design and Practise, two years full time.
3 Years Full time MA Theatre:
Visual Language of Performance, 1 year Full Time.

Rehearsal Rooms: Regional

ANGEL LEISURE CENTRE
Angel Lane, Tonbridge, Kent TN9 1SF
Tel: 01732 359 966 Fax: 01732 363 677
Email: angel.leisurecentre@tmbc.gov.uk
Web Site: www.angelcentre.co.uk
Manager: Gary Littlejon
Policy: Multi-purpose Hall used for theatre, cinema, concerts, meetings, sports and social events, conferences, fairs and markets.
Seating/Capacity: 307 seated; 400 standing.

BINGLEY LITTLE THEATRE
Main Street, Bingley, West Yorkshire BD16 2LZ
Tel: 01274 564 049
Bkgs: 01274 432 000
Email: secretary@bingleylittletheatre.co.uk
Web Site: www.bingleylittletheatre.co.uk
Chairman: Jan Darnbrough
Vice Chair: Ian Wilkinson
Treasurer: Graeme Holbrough
Publicity Manager: David Helliwell
Secretary: Catherine Helliwell
Capacity: 300

BOLTON PHOENIX
Bark Street, Bolton BL1 2AZ
Tel: 01204 535 861
Email: info@boltonpheonix.co.uk
Web Site: www.boltonphoenix.co.uk
Artistic Director: Wendy Ellis
Arts Development Officer: Lee Brennan
Education Officer: Caroline Coates

The Phoenix aims to offer the highest quality performing arts workshops and facilities, at the lowest possible cost. The Phoenix encourages open access to the arts for all young people.

Inc: Theatre, Rehearsal Rooms, Dance Studio, Dark Room,
Recording Studio, Video editing Suite,
Costume & Theatrical Equipment Hire.

BREWERY ARTS CENTRE
122a Highgate, Kendal, Cumbria LA9 4HE
Admin: 01539 722 833 Fax: 01539 730 257 BO: 01539 725 133
Email: boxoffice@breweryarts.co.uk
Web Site: www.breweryarts.co.uk
ADMINISTRATION:
Director: Richard Foster
Technical Manager: Steve Parnaby
Marketing Officer: Debbie Bond
Cap: Theatre: 260 seated. Malt Room: 200 without catering (seating up to 120) or 175 with catering.
This multi-purpose arts centre also has a second music and theatre venue (known as the Malt Room), exhibition spaces, studio space, as well as two cinema auditoria.

THE CARRIAGEWORKS THEATRE
3 Millenium Square, Leeds LS2 3AD
Marketing: 0113 224 3139 BO: 0113 224 3801
Email: carriageworks@leeds.gov.uk
Web: www.carriageworkstheatre.org.uk
ADMINISTRATION:
Props: Leeds City Council
Press and Promotions Officer: Gwen Marie Ewing
Chief Technician: Peter Waddicor
Policy: Mixed programme professional and amateur productions of drama, dance concerts, opera, pantomime, children's shows, light entertainment, touring theatre companies, community arts.
The Carriageworks is a community theatre available for hire, housed in the electric press development in the heart of Leeds.
Separate additional rehearsal rooms available.
Main Capacity: 349
Studio Capacity: 55 (Maximum dependent on configuration)

LEEDS GRAND THEATRE AND OPERA HOUSE
46 New Briggate, Leeds, West Yorkshire LS1 6NZ
Mgt: 0113 2456014 BO: 0844 848 2700
Fax: 0113 2977049 Opera North (Switchboard) 0113 243 9999
Email: ian.sime@leedsgrandtheatre.com
Web Site: www.leedsgrandtheatre.com
ADMINISTRATION:
Props: Leeds Grand Theatre and Opera House Ltd
General Manager: Ian Sime
Head of Technical: Alan Dawson
Chief Electrician: Nick Stelmach
Stage Door: Steve Rushman
Policy: Touring plays, musicals, ballet, dance, concerts, home of Opera North, licensed catering centre. Facilities: Main theatre, 5 tier, seats 1400 + 84 stand. Conference, exhibition, concert reception, rehearsal rooms, 7 licensed Bars, 4 Coffee Lounges, 1 Sponsors Bar - Linacre Room.
Studios: Seats 192 stands 250.
Dimensions 10m x 14m x 5m _ two side Studios each 4.9m. x 12m x 2.43m.
Grand Hall: Seats 100 stands 160.
Dimensions 8.2m x 13.4m x 6.1m.
Assembly Rooms: Dimensions 13m x 22.75m x 2.95m minimum for rehearsals only.

Advanced Booking Office with ENTA computer ticket issuing system plus 120 booking agents.

LEIGHTON BUZZARD THEATRE

Lake Street, Leighton Buzzard, Bedfordshire LU7 1RX
Mgt: 0300 300 8130 BO: 0300 300 8125
Email: hazel.kerr@centralbedfordshire.gov.uk
Web: www.leightonbuzzardtheatre.co.uk
ADMINISTRATION:
Props: Central Bedfordshire Council
Theatre Manager: Hazel Kerr
Arts Development Officer: Victoria Abrahams
Centre Facilitator: Carole Perham
Technician: Phil Pattinson
Funded by Beds Central Bedfordshire
Policy: Mixed programme of film, professional small scale touring drama, music recitals, plus performance by local amateurs. Childrens films, drama shows and workshops. Exhibitions. Performing arts workshops. Perfs: Mon-Sat 8.00, mats. 1.30p.m
Hire, box office split, guarantee & split, guarantee by negotiation.
Seats: 170, raked.
Daytime coffee bar. Licensed bar on performance nights. Foyer coffee servery
Limited wheelchair space, lift-assistance available, contact Manager, level access.

LIVE THEATRE

Broad Chare, Quayside Newcastle upon Tyne NE1 3DQ
Admin: 0191 261 2694 BO: 0191 232 1232
Email: tickets@live.org.uk, wendy@live.org.uk
Web Site: www.live.org.uk
ADMINISTRATION:
Chief Executive: Jim Beirne
Artistic Director: Max Roberts
Operations Director: Wendy Barnfather
Marketing & Press Officer: Emma Hall
Technical Manager: Dave Flynn
Capacity: Main Theatre, 160. Studio Theatre, 60. Additional Rehearsal Room available.
Resident company Live Theatre Co.
For more information on hiring the venue, contact Events & Venue Hire Administrator, Chris Foley, on 0191 229 2376.

ST ANDREW'S & BLACKFRIARS HALLS

St Andrews Hall Plain, Norwich, Norfolk NR3 1AU
Tel: 01603 628 477 Fax: 01603 762 182
Email: thehalls@norwich.gov.uk
Web Site: www.thehallsnorwich.co.uk
Contact: Matthew White
Seating/Capacity: St. Andrews Hall: 900; Blackfriars Hall: 300
Hire only venue.

STANWIX ARTS THEATRE

Cumbria Institute Of The Arts Brampton Road, Carlisle, Cumbria CA3 9AY
Tel: 01228 400 331 Fax: 01228 514 491
Email: k.bassett@cumbria.ac.uk
Web Site: www.stanwixartstheatre.co.uk
ADMINISTRATION:
Recently Refurbished
Cap: Main Theatre 216 and Dance Studio 100
Manager & Senior Technician: Paul Edworthy
Manager & Administrator: Karen Basset

THE THIRD FLOOR ARTS CENTRE

Central Library, Guildhall Square, Portsmouth, Hampshire PO1 2DX
Tel: 01293 834 184 Fax: 023 9283 4904
Email: arts@portsmouthcc.gov.uk
Web Site: www.portsmouth.gov.uk
Arts Officer: Jane Leech
Capacity: 120
Our brand new 120 seat theatre plays host to visiting and local theatre companies, plus our ever popular children's shows, live music and dance productions. There are classes and workshops across various artforms and for varying age ranges and abilities, and we also have a new gallery space with ongoing exhibitions throughout the year. The Arts Centre is also available for hire. We have numerous function rooms available for rehearsals, meetings, classes and workshops.

THEATRE IN THE MILL

University of Bradford, Shearbridge Road, Bradford, West Yorkshire BD7 1DP
Tech: 01274 233 190 BO: 01274 233 200 General: 01274 233 185
Email: theatre@bradford.ac.uk
Web Site: www.bradford.ac.uk/theatre
ADMINISTRATION:
Props: University of Bradford
Artistic Director & Programming: Iain Bloomfield
Administrator: Ruth Prendergast
Email: r.prendergast@bradford.ac.uk
Technical Director: Ivan Mack (Tel: 01274 233 190)
Policy: Commissioning and support for the development of new work and practice. Hosts regular theatre workshop events. New Writing & Emerging Artists. Home to the University of Bradford Theatre Group.
Perfs: Variable. Three annual seasons.
Cap: Flexible Seating from 0-100. Theatre Bar.

TRESTLE THEATRE COMPANY

Trestle Arts Base, Russet Drive, St Albans, Hertfordshire AL4 0JQ
Tel: 01727 850 950
Email: admin@trestle.org.uk
Web Site: www.trestle.org.uk
ADMINISTRATION:
Artistic Director: Emily Gray
Buildings and Finance Manager: Clare Winter
Trestle Theatre Company was founded in 1981 and has enjoyed 30 successful years of touring mask and Physical led theatre. Trestle creates and tours theatrical productions and operates Trestle Arts Base as a performance venue. Trestle also produces international residencies and tours and delivers education programmes across the UK and abroad. The Company aims to engage audiences and participants in an interactive, inclusive and inventive experience of theatre.
Trestle Arts Base - Fully equipped studio theatre,rehearsal room and meeting room, all available for hire to professional and amateur companies for previews and runs
Capacity: 80 - 125

TRON THEATRE

63 Trongate, Glasgow, Strathclyde G1 5HB Scotland
Admin: 0141 552 3748 BO: 0141 552 4267 Bar: 0141 552 8587 Fax: 0141 552 6657 Delivery and Get-In Address: 38 Parnie Street, Glasgow, G1 5LS
Email: info@tron.co.uk
Web Site: www.tron.co.uk
ADMINISTRATION:
Props: Tron Theatre Ltd
Artistic Director: Andy Arnold
General Manager: Lesley Renton
Production Manager: Dave Shea
Policy: Theatre, Dance and Music from the UK and Abroad, plus 2/3 productions a year by Tron Theatre Co.
Perfs: 7.45 pm
Capacity: Theatre 230. Raked fixed seating. Wheelchair positions - front row and upper auditorium right. Changing house studio - 70. Two cafe/bar spaces. Bar open all day.

WEST YORKSHIRE PLAYHOUSE

Playhouse Square, Quarry Hill, Leeds LS2 7UP
Admin: 0113 213 7800 BO: 0113 213 7700 Press: 0113 213 7273 Minicom: 0113 213 7299
Email: info@wyp.org.uk
Web Site: www.wyp.org.uk
ADMINISTRATION:
Chief Executive: Sheena Wrigley
Artistic Director: James Brining
Producer: Mark Rosenblatt
Financal Director: Helen Makhwul
Director of Communications: Nick Hallam
Head of Arts Development: Sam Perkins
Technical Stage Manager: Mick Cassidy
Producing Theatre. Two auditoria seating 350 & 750.
Policy: Subsidised Repertory, year round programme; touring welcome National and Regional Drama and Dance. Young People's Theatre programme and black arts events: concerts, foyer events,

cabaret and late night shows, Schools Company. It also includes community work in its artistic policy. Restaurant, bar, shop, rehearsal room, function & entertainment facilities, full workshops.
Facilities for the disabled.
Seats: 750

Rigging

A.S.G. STAGE PRODUCTS LTD
Redgate Road, South Lancashire Ind. Estate, Ashton-in-Makerfield, Wigan, Lancashire WN4 8DT
Tel: 01942 718 347 Fax: 01942 718 219
Email: post@asgstage.co.uk
Web Site: www.asgstage.co.uk
Projects Manager: Paul McFerran
Since 1973 we have specialised in the supply and installation of performance facilities to professional, amateur and educational theatres - including tracks, curtains, rigging, lighting, sound, projection, seating and staging.

BLACKOUT LTD
280 Western Road, London SW19 2QA
Tel: 020 8687 8400 Fax: 020 8687 8500
Email: sales@blackout-ltd.com
Web Site: www.blackout-ltd.com
Managing Director: Martin Wood
Hire & Sales Co-Ordinator: Will Bryant
Blackout specialises in the manufacture for hire and sale of high quality flame retardant drapes and star cloths. We offer full consultancy, installation rigging and 24 hr backup service and can be relied upon to make any project happen. We also provide painted cloths to any size and artistic specification.

CENTRAL EVENTS UK LTD
The Barn Fifield Farm Marlston Road Marlston Nr Hermitage Berkshire RG18 9UN
Tel: 01235 760 342 Fax: 01635 202 088
Email: heidi.smith@s-l-v.co.uk
Web Site: www.central-production.co.uk
Senior Personnel: Jim Williams
Specialise in production of rigging, staging, lighting, PA, theming, power distribution, marquees and catering for corporate and private parties.
At Central Events UK, we pride ourselves in being a full service events management company whcih gives us the freedom to offer the very best in service, product and price to our customers.

CERTEX LIFTING PRODUCTS AND SERVICES
Unit C1, Harworth Industrial Estate, Bryans Close, Harworth, Doncaster, South Yorkshire DN11 8RY
Tel: 0845 230 7475 Fax: 0845 230 7476
Email: sales@certex.co.uk
Web Site: www.certex.co.uk
Regional Manager: Carly Noble
Supplier of rigging equipment as well as independent inspections and testing of riggings.

ENLIGHTENMENT
The Rubicon Centre, Broad Ground Road, Lakeside, Redditch, Worcestershire B98 8YP
Tel: 0845 257 1992
Email: info@enlightenment.co.uk
Web Site: www.enlightenment.co.uk
Contact: Paul Swansborough
Established since 1997 and trading on-line since 2006. Enlightenment is the UK on-line source for stage lighting, sound, audio visual and rigging equipment to the entertainment industry. Enlightenment is a main dealer for Showtec, DAP Audio and Dutch Media Tools.

FLINT HIRE & SUPPLY LTD
Theatrical Chandlers
Queens Row, London SE17 2PX
Tel: 020 7703 9786 Sales Fax: 020 7708 4189
Email: sales@flints.co.uk
Web Site: www.flints.co.uk
Contacts: Josefin Söderlund, Alasdair Flint, Richard Black
Flints are the major retailer of theatrical goods in the UK, established 25 years ago to provide a single source for specialist theatre hardware and materials.
Sales of wire rope, pulleys, yacht blocks, black polyester rope, slings, tested wire assemblies, Tirfor, rigging screws, shackles, Crosby products, drop blocks and divertors. Winches and Drop Blocks also available to hire. Scenery building hardware and scenic paints also supplied.

FUTURIST PROJECTS LTD
Unit 1, White Swan Yard, Otley, LS21 1AE
Tel: 0113 279 0033 Fax: 0113 301 0255
Email: info@futurist.co.uk
Web Site: www.futurist.co.uk
Managing Director: Jamie Hudson
Financial Director: Jamie Hudson
AV, Theatrical Productions, Lighting and Sound Specialists.

GLEISTEIN ROPES LTD
Unit G31, Atlas Industrial Park, Harbour Road, Rye, East Sussex TN31 7TE
Tel: 01797 222 005 Fax: 01797 222 755
Email: anderson@gleistein.com
Web Site: www.gleistein.com
Senior Personnel: Julian Anderson

HALL STAGE LIMITED
Unit 4, Cosgrove Way, Luton, Bedfordshire LU1 1XL
Tel: 0845 345 4255 Fax: 0845 345 4256
Email: sales@hallstage.com
Web Site: www.hallstage.com
Managing Director: Charles Haines
Technical Director: Phil Wells
Stage Sales Services Manager: Scott Oake
Sales Co-ordinator: Alison Price
Designs and manufactures standard and special products for the stage, screen, AV and industrial market.
Hall Stage and Theatre Supplies formed in 1895. Equipment ranges include T60 and T70 curtain track systems for all applications. Specialist products include rolloer or flying safety curtains, counterweight sets, hemp rope sets, the DynaGlide powered and manual hoists for powered fling and lighting bar operations, DynaLine pulleys, motor control systems, and a selection of theatrical and scenic hardware fittings.

J & C JOEL LTD
Corporation Mill, Corporation Street, Sowerby Bridge, West Yorkshire HX6 2QQ
Tel: 01422 833835 Fax: 01422 835157
Email: sales@jcjoel.com
Web Site: www.jcjoel.com
Specialists in Flame Retardant Fabrics, manufacturers and installers of theatrical drapes and stage equipment. Probably the largest stock of flame retardant fabrics, tracks and all stage hardware, starcloths, dance flooring and portable staging.
Sales Manager: Oliver Marns

LYON EQUIPMENT LTD
Rise Hill Mill Dent Sedbergh Cumbria LA10 5QL
Tel: 01539 626250 Mgmt: 015396 25493
Fax: 01539 625454
Email: info@lyon.co.uk, sales@lyon.co.uk
Web Site: www.lyon.co.uk, www.lyon-outdoor.co.uk
Joint Managing Directors: Carol Nicholls and Jonathan Capper
Senior Technical Sales: Dave Ellis
Technical Sales Representative: Scott Shaw
The experts in personal protective equipment and training for rigging and work at height: - Access and work positioning, fall prevention and fall arrest.

MARLOW ROPES
Ropemaker Park, Diplocks Way, Hailsham East Sussex BN27 3GU
Tel: 01323 444 444 Fax: 01323 444 455
Email: sales@marlowropes.com
Web Site: www.marlowropes.com
Contact: Richard Edge
Ropemakers

OUTBACK RIGGING LTD
Unit 5 Kendal Court, Western Ave. Trading Estate, Kendal Avenue, London W3 0RU
Tel: 020 8993 0066 Mob: 07710 975 678
Fax: 020 8752 1753
Email: enquiries@outbackrigging.com

Web Site: www.outbackholdings.co.uk
Operations Director: Stuart Cooper
Email: stuart@outbackrigging.com
Truss, hoists and sundry rigging equipment hire and installation.

OUTHWAITES LTD ROPEMAKERS

Town Foot, Burtersett Road, Hawes, North Yorkshire DL8 3NT
Tel: 01969 667 487 Fax: 01969 667 576
Email: sales@outhwaites.com
Web Site: www.ropemakers.com
Ropemaking and rope products. Tailor-made service for Barrier Ropes - quick delivery.

PCM / PFAFF-SILBERBLAU LTD

A division of Columbus McKinnon Corporation Ltd
Knutsford Way, Sealand Industrial Estate, Chester CH1 4NZ
Tel: 01244 375 375 Fax: 01244 377 403
Email: sales@pfaff-silberblau.co.uk
Web Site: www.pfaff-silberblau2.co.uk / www.cmworks.com
CMCO Managing Director: Steve Sherwin
Columbus McKinnon is a leading manufacturer of Material Handling Equipment with offices located all over the world.

RIGGING SERVICES

3 Mills Studios, Three Mill Lane, London E3 3DU
Tel: 020 8215 1240 Fax: 020 8215 1243
Email: london@riggingservices.co.uk
Web Site: www.riggingservices.co.uk
Managing Director: Paul Fulcher
National Sales Manager: Bob Dean
Locations in LONDON, BIRMINGHAM, & MANCHESTER. Specialising in HIRE, SALES, INSPECTION, TESTING, TRAINING, CONSULTATION, INSTALLATIONS & PROJECTS for the entertainment industry.
Sandstone Lane, ExCel, London E16 1BD. Tel: 0845 5 55 65 75 Email: excel-london@riggingservices.co.uk
Pinewood Studios, Pinewood Road, Iver Heath, Bucks SL0 0NH.
Tel: 01753 653 529 Email: pinewood@riggingservices.co.uk
Unit B3, Miller Street, Express Business Park, Birmingham, West Midlands B6 4NF
Tel: 0121 333 4409 Email: birmingham@riggingservices.co.uk
21 Rivington Court, Hardwick Grange, Warrington WA1 4RT
Tel: 01925 251 040 Email: manchester@riggingservices.co.uk

ROPE AND RIGGING LTD

Unit 6 Rossingtons Business Pa West Carr Road, Retford, Nottinghamshire DN22 7SW
Tel: 01777 948089 Fax: 01777 719327
Mob: 07886 584628
Email: info@ropeandrigging.co.uk
Web Site: ropeandrigging.co.uk

Contact: Jacqui Hilton
Specialists in the manufacture of Rigging Equipment for Theatre, Film & Entertainment industries.
Silver & Black Steels, Strops, Drifts & Safety Bonds. Suppliers of Shackles, Roundslings, Ratchet Straps.
Natural & Synthetic Fibre Rope lines, Bar Clamps, Hook Clamps etc., Safety Harnesses and attachments.
Renowned for our excellent customer service and fast delivery.

ROPE ASSEMBLIES LTD

Unit 6, Hallcroft Industrial Estate, Aurillac Way, Retford, Nottinghamshire DN22 7PX
Tel: 01777 700 714 Fax: 01777 860 719
Email: sales@ropeassemblies.co.uk
Web Site: www.ropeassemblies.co.uk
Contact: Siobhan Hitchen
Specialists in: Supply of Rigging equiptment inc. black wire ropes etc.

SLINGCO LTD

Station Road, Facit, Rochdale, Lancashire OL12 8LJ
Tel: 01706 855 558 Fax: 01706 855 559
Email: sales@thecablenet.net
Web Site: www.tensionwiregrid.com
Managing Directors: Chris and Nick Dykins
Slingco design and manufacture cablenet tension wire grids. These "virtual floors" supplied either in modular form or custom woven on site. Provide a safe and "transparent" architectural solution to high level access issues.

STAGE TECHNOLOGIES LTD

9 Falcon Park Industrial Estate, Neasden Lane, London NW10 1RZ
Tel: 020 8208 6000 Fax: 020 8208 6006
Email: automation@stagetech.com
Web Site: www.stagetech.com
Contacts: Ted Moore, Director of Rental Services; Nikki Scott, Commercial Director; John Hastie, Operations Director; Mark Ager, Managing Director.
Specialist design/manufacture of automation systems and stage engineering, including winch and track products; equipment hire, installation, maintenance and upgrades; mechanical consultancy, operator and vocational training; 24-hour global/online support.

STAGE TRACK LTD

Harbour Lane, Garboldisham, Diss, Norfolk IP22 2ST
Tel: 01953 688 188 Fax: 01953 688 144
Email: sales@stagetrack.co.uk
Web Site: www.stagetrack.co.uk
Contact: B. Skipp
Suppliers of various curtain systems, hoists, fire curtains and associated controls and equipment.

STAR EVENTS GROUP LTD

Milton Road, Thurleigh, Bedford MK44 2DF
Tel: 01234 772 233 Fax: 01234 772 272
Email: steve.shaw@stareventsgroup.com
Web Site: www.StarEventsGroup.com
Hire of technical services to the entertainment industry including stage constructions for both indoor and outdoor events.

TERRALEC LTD

Osprey House, Featherby Way, Purdeys Industrial Estate, Rochford, Essex SS4 1LD
Tel: 01702 547 571 Fax: 01702 541 075
Email: sales@terralec.com
Web Site: www.terralec.co.uk
Suppliers of professional stage lighting, audio equipment, lighting control, microphones, staging, trussing, hardware, accessories & much more! For: Theatre, stage, commercial events and the entertainment industry.

THE RIGGING PARTNERSHIP

Unit 7 Sugar House Business Centre, 24 Sugar House Lane, London E15 2QS
Tel: 0208 522 4347
Email: office@flywire.co.uk
Web Site: www.flywiretrp.co.uk
Suppliers of rigging for theatre, film, entertainment and conference events.
Services include: Design, Hire, Installation, engineering, project management, consultancy, risk assessment and health & safety management. Specialists in bespoke rigging solutions and automated flying systems/performer flying.

TOTAL FABRICATIONS LIMITED

Units 3 - 4, Kingston Industrial Estate, 81 - 86 Glover Street, Birmingham B9 4EN
Tel: 0121 772 5234
Email: info@trussing.com
Web Site: www.trussing.com
Contact: Karen Cronin
Manufacturer of standard and custom aluminium trusses, roof structures, fixtures and associated equipment including motor controllers and full range of Verlinde products catering for broad spectrum of applications.

UNUSUAL RIGGING LTD

The Wharf, Bugbrooke, Northampton NN7 3QB
Tel: 01604 830083 Fax: 01604 841144
Email: info@unusual.co.uk
Web Site: www.unusual.co.uk
Unusual brings the disciplines of design, rigging, fabrications and automation to provide an ideal installation service for the supply, renovation and renewal of stage engineering and flying systems.

Scenery (Builders, Painters & Hirers)

3-D CREATIONS
Berth 33, 33 Malthouse Lane, Gorleston, Great Yarmouth, Norfolk NR31 0GW
Tel: 01493 652 055 (Workshop) Mob: 07860 707 287 Fax: 01493 443 124
Email: info@3dcreations.co.uk
Web Site: www.3dcreations.co.uk
Contact: Ian Westbrook
We can provide all your scenic needs for theatre, television and film. Scenery and prop design and construction specialists. Prop makers, set designers, sculptors, scenic artists we are always prepared to undertake work of the unusual. Location work undertaken.

ADEN HYNES SCULPTURE STUDIOS
Unit 3F, Harvey Road, Nevendon Industrial Estate, Basildon, Essex SS13 1DA
Tel: 01268 726 470
Email: aden.hynes@hotmail.com
Web Site: www.sculpturestudios.co.uk
Specialising in polystyrene carving, scenic set building, from classical Greek figures to enchanted forests. Mould making, glass fibre production runs, scenic painting and installation.

ALBEMARLE
PO Box 240, Rotherfield, Crowborough, East Sussex TN6 3JU
Tel: 0845 6447 021 Fax: 01892 853 104
Email: kim.chritchley@albemarleproductions.co.uk
Web: www.albemarleproductions.com
ADMINISTRATION:
Production Management: Kim Chritchley
Pantomime Management: Basil Chritchley
General Manager (Scenic Studios): Philip Trickett
Scenic & costume departments, construction & hire.

ALBEMARLE SCENIC STUDIOS
Unit C1, Prees Industrial Estate, Shrewsbury Road, Prees, Whitchurch, Shropshire SY13 2DJ
Tel: 01948 840 930
Email: philip.trickett@albemarleproductions.co.uk
Web: www.albemarleproductions.com
General Manager: Philip Trickett
Scenery builders, scenic artists. Complete pantomimes for hire. Storage space for hire.

ALL SCENE, ALL PROPS
Units 2 & 3 Spelmonden Farm, Goudhurst, Cranbrook, Kent TN17 1HE
Tel: 01580 211 121 Fax: 01580 211 131
Email: info@allscene.net
Web Site: www.allscene.net
Contact: Piers Ross
We specialise in the construction of quality touring scenery and stage props. We also produce scenery for exhibition, installation, film, TV and other events.

ASETS UK LTD
Rear of 37 Westminster Road, Blackpool, Lancashire FY1 2QE
Tel: 01253 294 920 Fax: 01253 751 915
Email: info@asets.com
Web Site: www.asets.com
Contact: James Laughland
Scenery design, building and painting. Conference and exhibition producers, management & technical support.

BIRMINGHAM REP THEATRE WORKSHOP
Centenary Square 1 Albion Street Broad Street Birmingham B1 2EP
Tel: 0121 245 2000 BO: 0121 236 4455
Workshop: 0121 773 5591 Fax: 0121 245 2100
Email: stage.door@birmingham-rep.co.uk
Web Site: www.birmingham-rep.co.uk
General Manager: Trina Jones
Production Manager Milorad Zakula
Workshop Supervisor: Margaret Rees

BIRMINGHAM REPERTORY THEATRE
Centenary Square Broad Street Birmingham B1 2EP
Mgt: 0121 245 2000 BO: 0121 236 4455
SD: 0121 245 2000 Fax: 0121 245 2182
Email: ticketservices@birmingham-rep.co.uk
Web Site: www.birmingham-rep.co.uk

BOWER WOOD PRODUCTION SERVICES
Unit 5, The Billings, 3 Walnut Tree Close, Guildford, Surrey GU1 4UL
Tel: 01483 300 926 Fax: 01483 450 926
Email: enquiries@bowerwood.com
Web Site: www.bowerwood.com
Contact: Graham Bower Wood, Nigel Mathias
Scenery Construction & Metal Fabrication for the Theatre, Opera, Cruise Ships, Exhibitions & Special Events.

CAPITAL SCENERY LTD
Unit 3, Ellerslie Square, Lyham Road,

London SW2 5DZ
Tel: 020 7978 8822 Fax: 020 7978 8833
Email: frank@capitalscenery.co.uk
Web Site: www.capitalscenery.co.uk
Contact: Frank Maguire
Scenery - Builders, painters.
Theatrical scenery, painters and prop makers.

CARDIFF THEATRICAL SERVICES LTD
Ellen Street, off Tyndall Street, Cardiff, South Glamorgan CF10 4TT
Tel: 029 2063 4680 Fax: 029 2048 1275
Email: cts@wno.org.uk, esther.morris@wno.org.uk
Web www.cardifftheatricalservices.co.uk
Manager: Ed Wilson
Scenery builders, scenic artists and property makers.

CHRIS CLARK STUDIO
Liz and Chris Clark The Scenic Art Partnership
60 Chase Green Avenue, Enfield, Middlesex EN2 8EN
Tel: 020 8366 7335 Mobile: 07775 778 914 (Chris) Mobile: 07885 400 552 (Liz)
Email: chrisclark1@blueyonder.co.uk
Web Site: www.lizandchrisclark.net
Liz and Chris Clark, the scenic art partnership, for all scenic painting services. Any image or finish can be accomplished. Specialists in backcloths, gauzes, cycloramas, translights and built scenery painted to commission in our 330 square metre studio.

CLEARWATER SCENERY LIMITED
3 Laker Road, Rochester, Kent ME1 3QX
Tel: 01634 671 222 Fax: 01634 671 133
Email: sales@clearwater-scenery.co.uk
Web Site: www.clearwater-scenery.co.uk
Free brochure on request.

CREFFIELDS (TIMBER & BOARDS) LTD
Flameproof boards.
Unit 6, Marcus Close, Tilehurst, Reading, Berkshire RG30 4EA
Tel: 0118 945 3533 Fax: 0118 945 3633
Email: info@creffields.co.uk
Web Site: www.creffields.co.uk
Creffields is one of the UK's leading suppliers of
flame-proofed sheet materials and soft woods for the
exhibition and theatrical trades.
Large stocks are held allowing for urgent orders to be delivered promptly; together with Premierbond portable contact spray glue system.

DAP STUDIO
55 Longdown Lane North Epsom Surrey KT17 3JB
Studio Tel: 01892 730 897 Mob: 07973 406 830
Email: info@dapstudio.co.uk
Web Site: www.dapstudio.co.uk
Contact: James Rowse
We specialise in painting high quality scenery and backdrops, for theatre and the entertainment industry. We have a large well equipped studio and a team of experienced scenic artists.

THE EXPANDED METAL CO LTD
PO Box 14, Longhill Industrial Estate,
Hartlepool, Cleveland TS25 1PR
Tel: 01429 266 633 Fax: 01429 866 795
Email: sales@expamet.co.uk
Web: www.expandedmetalcompany.co.uk
Manufacturers of all types of expanded metal and Air Filters, Grease Filters, Walkway, Security Fencing, Enclosures and Gates, Mesh Cages & Lockers, Perforated Metals.

FAMEGLORE LTD
Westgate, Stansted Road, Eastbourne,
East Sussex BN22 8LG
Tel: 01323 739 478 Fax: 01323 736 127
Contact: Garth Harrison

FLINT HIRE & SUPPLY LTD
Theatrical Chandlers
Queens Row, London SE17 2PX
Tel: 020 7703 9786
Sales Fax: 020 7708 4189
Email: sales@flints.co.uk
Web Site: www.flints.co.uk
Contacts: George Ludgate, Richard Black, Alasdair Flint
Flints are the major retailer of theatrical goods in the UK. Established 25 years ago to provide a single source for specialist theatre hardware and materials.
Our Hire Department can provide: Rostra Units, Winches, Drop Blocks, Ladders & Access Towers, Stage Weights and Braces, Tab Tracks, Compressors & Spray Equipment, etc. Scenery building hardware and scenic paints also supplied.

HWL (UK) LTD
Cricket Street, Denton,
Manchester M34 3DR
Tel: 0161 335 0220 Fax: 0161 320 3928
Email: guns@hwltd.co.uk
Web Site: www.hwltd.co.uk
Contact: Bob Howorth
Hirers of all types of furniture, set dressing, decorative lighting, pictures, hand props etc. Also specialist hirers of weapons and blank firing guns.

ANDY LATHAM SCENERY
The Old Coldstore, Bilting Grange Farm,
Bilting, Canterbury Road, Ashford, Kent
TN25 4HA
Tel: 01233 812 971 Fax: 01233 812 552
Mobile: 07976 696012
Email: alscenery@aol.com
Proprietor: Andy Latham

NORWICH THEATRE ROYAL
Theatre Street, Norwich, Norfolk NR2 1RL
Tel: 01603 598 500 Fax: 01603 598 501
Email: technical@theatreroyalnorwich.co.uk
Web Site: www.theatreroyalnorwich.co.uk
General Manager: Jane Anthony
Technical Director: Will Hill
Pantomime Scenic Special Effects, Props and Costumes for hire.

PERRY SCENIC LTD
Unit D & E, 100 Dudley Road East,
Oldbury, West Midlands B69 3EB
Tel: 0121 552 9696 Fax: 0121 552 9697
Email: enquiries@perryscenic.com
Web Site: www.perryscenic.com
Contact: Michael Perry , Tony Guest, Jonathan Perry
Comprehensive service at competitive prices. Set Builders, Engineering, Scenic Artists, Sculptors, Prop Makers, Design, Drapes, Effects for Theatre, Film, TV, Exhibition and Pop Tours.

PROSCENEIUM LTD
Sladen Wood Mill, Todmorden Road,
Littleborough, Lancashire OL15 9EW
Tel: 01706 377226 Fax: 01706 371953
Email: enquiries@prosceneium.co.uk
Web Site: www.prosceneium.co.uk
Set Hire: Robert Kershaw, Gary Hookham
Theatrical Scenery designed, built and painted for hire or for sale to Professional and Amateur groups. Full sets for most musicals and pantomimes available. Hirer of stage furniture and props, thousands of items in stock.

RK RESOURCE
Unit 2, Wyvern Way, Henwood, Ashford,
Kent TN24 8DW
Tel: 01233 750 180 / 01233 664 126
Fax: 01233 750 133
Email: rkresource2007@aol.co.uk
Web Site: www.rk-resourcekent.com
Stage and television scenery contractors and engineers. Masking drapes, staging, revolves, sundry technical and rehearsal items for hire. Contact: Eric Parsons

RUTTERS
Bringing life to images and images to life
Unit 6, South Cambridgeshire Business Park, Babraham Road, Sawston, Cambs, CB2 4JH
Tel: 01223 833 522 Mobile: 07973 631 052 Fax: 01223 833 543
Email: info@ruttersuk.com
Web Site: www.ruttersuk.com
Contact: Paul Rutter, Lynn Rose
Producers of Translights, Photobackings and scenic cloths for Film, TV and all Theatrical productions with images printed onto a wide range of materials for both front and rear illumination, including gauzes, carpet and canvas. No size limitations.

S + H TECHNICAL SUPPORT LTD
Mullacott Cross Industrial Est Ilfracombe,
Devon EX34 8PL
Tel: 01271 866 832 Fax: 01271 865 423
Mobile: 07850 234151 London Address: Unit 3, Artesian Close Industrial Estate, off Brentfield Road, Harlesden, London, NW10 8RW Tel: 020 8451 5840
Email: shtsg@aol.com / enquiries@starcloth.co.uk
Web Site: www.starcloth.co.uk
Contract Sales: Terry Murtha, Billy Murtha
Marketing Officer: Dave Baxter
Technical Development Officer: Nigel Smith
Hire and sale of Starcloths/controllable LV, miniature lamp lighting designers.
Consultation and design of theatre/studio sets and backdrops.

S2 EVENTS LTD
3-5 Valentine Place, London SE1 8QH
Tel: 020 7928 5474 Fax: 020 7928 6082
Email: info@s2events.co.uk
Web Site: www.s2events.co.uk
Contact: Walter Dammers

SCENA PROJECTS LTD
240 Camberwell Road, Camberwell,
London SE5 0DP
Tel: 020 7703 4444 Fax: 020 7703 7012
Email: jessica@scenapro.com, info@scenapro.com
Web Site: www.scenapro.com
Directors: David Thompson, Paul Norman, Phil Winder, Mark Hubbard.

SCENETEC LTD
The Old Areodrome, Higher Woodsford,
Dorchester, Dorset DT2 8BL
Tel: 01305 854 400 Fax: 05601 261 530
Email: info@scenetec.co.uk
Web Site: www.scenetec.co.uk
Contact: Charles Camm
Complete scenic service for theatre, television, film, exhibitions and events. Set design, set construction, scenic art, prop making, set hire and scenic kits.

SCENIC PROJECTS LTD
The Studios, London Road, Brampton,
Beccles, Suffolk NR34 8DQ
Tel: 01502 575 000 Fax: 01502 575 840
Email: sales@scenicprojects.co.uk
Web Site: www.scenicprojects.co.uk
Technical Design: Nick Rowe

SMART LIVE
30 Maiden Lane, London WC2E 7JS
Tel: 0207 836 0562 Fax: 0207 836 1044
Email: smartlive@smartgroupltd.co.uk
Web Site: www.smartlive.co.uk
Creating events with edge.
Special event production company comprising set designers, choreographers, and artistic directors. Technically, we boast sound engineers, lighting technicians and stage managers. We combine our creative and technical talents to stage the most amazing themed events ever.

ADRIAN SNELL PRODUCTION SERVICES
Unit 12 Millbrook Ind Est. Millbrook,
Torpoint, Cornwall PL11 3AX
Tel: 01752 829 393 Fax: 01752 829 394
Email: adriansnell@adriansnell.co.uk
Contact: Adrian Snell

Our large modern workshops offer a complete construction service, including engineering, steel fabrication and all other forms of construction.

SOUVENIR SCENIC STUDIOS
Units 8, 12 Verney Road, London SE16 3DH
Tel: 020 7237 7557 Fax: 020 7237 7626
Email: info@souvenir.co.uk, jeannette@souvenir.co.uk
Web Site: www.souvenir.co.uk
Contact: Simon Kenny
Specialist scenery construction for theatre, opera and ballet. Large scale props, installations and scenic artists.

STAGE ELECTRICS
Third Way, Avonmouth, Bristol, Avon BS11 9YL
Sales and Hire: 0844 870 0077 Tel: 0117 982 1999
Email: sales@stage-electrics.co.uk
Web Site: www.stage-electrics.co.uk
Managing Director: David Whitehead
Head of Operations: Dan Aldridge
Set design and construction, scenic artists, stage engineering and complete set hire.

STEELDECK SALES LTD
Unit 58, T Marchant Estate 42-72 Verney Road London SE16 3DH
Tel: 020 8692 9721/020 7833 2031 Fax Rentals: 020 7232 1780 Fax Sales: 020 8691 4263
Email: info@steeldeck.co.uk / rentals@steeldeck.co.uk
Web Site: www.steeldeck.co.uk
Director: Richard Howey Nunn
Steeldeck specialise in staging, tiered seating and temporary structures. From finding creative structural solutions for the most challenging ideas to short-term stage hire, at Steeldeck we offer a complete staging service to a vast array of productions. Affordable, quick and versatile, we build our reputation on the safety of our certified staging structures.

SUFFOLK SCENERY
Pie Hatch Farm, Brettenham Road, Buxhall, Stowmarket, Suffolk IP14 3DZ
Tel: 01449 736 305 Mob: 07787 548744
Email: piehatch@aol.com
Web Site: www.suffolkscenery.info
Contact: Martin Dye
Scenery Manufacturers. UK distributors of Foyal and Atlas Silk Curtain tracks and accessories.

TESA UK
Tesa Division, Yeomans Drive, Blakelands, Milton Keynes, Buckinghamshire MK14 5LS
Tel: 01908 211 333 Fax: 01908 211 555
Email: steve.plastow@tesa.com
Web Site: www.tesa.co.uk
Director: Steve Plastow
Company PA: Shirley Peters
Suppliers of adhesive tapes.

THEATRE ROYAL (PLYMOUTH) LTD
TR2 - Theatre Royal Production
Cattedown Plymouth PL4 0SJ
Tel: 01752 230343 Fax: 01752 225985
Email: david.miller@theatreroyal.com
Web Site: www.theatreroyal.com
Contact: David Miller
Our comprehensively equipped workshop, paint and prop facilities offer the best innovative resources in theatre set construction.

TMS INTERNATIONAL LTD
306 St. James's Road, London SE1 5JX
Tel: 020 7394 9519 Fax: 020 7232 2347
Email: admin@tmsi.co.uk
Web Site: www.tmsinternational.co.uk
Managing Director: Duncan Barton
Production Manager: Gareth Edwards
Scenery constructed and painted to specification.

VISUAL BLISS
5 Memory Cross, Landscove, Ashburton, Newton Abbot, Devon TQ13 7NB
Tel: 01803 762 326
Email: office@visualbliss.co.uk
Web Site: www.visualbliss.co.uk
Proprietor: Colin Quinsey
Specialists in UV Backdrops. A huge range of backdrops, effects and modern designs. Available to rent or purchase, all made to respond to UV lighting. Also 3D props.

WELD-FAB STAGE ENGINEERING LTD
Harbour Lane Works, Garboldisham, Diss, Norfolk IP22 2ST
Tel: 01953 688 133 Fax: 01953 688 144
Email: weld-fab.stage@paston.co.uk
Web Site: www.weldfabstage.co.uk
Contact: Brian Skipp, Matthew Genner
Design and manufacturers of various stage, studio, television & exhibition equipment for sale or hire. Motorised and fixed scenery, revolving stages, scissor lifts, power flying & counterweight systems.

YVONNE ARNAUD THEATRE (SCENERY) LIMITED
Workshops, Unit 5 The Billings, 3 Walnut Tree Close, Guildford, Surrey GU1 4UL
Tel: 01483 300 926 Fax: 01483 450 926
Email: graham@bowerwood.com
Manager: Graham Bower Wood
Scenery Construction and Metal Fabrication for Theatre, Opera, Cruise Ships, Exhibitions and Special Events.

Scenery (Digital Prints Backdrops)

DAP STUDIO
55 Longdown Lane North Epsom Surrey KT17 3JB
Studio Tel: 01892 730 897
Mob: 07973 406 830
Email: info@dapstudio.co.uk
Web Site: www.dapstudio.co.uk
Contact: James Rowse
We specialise in painting high quality scenery and backdrops, for theatre and the entertainment industry. We have a large well equipped studio and a team of experienced scenic artists.

IMAGE FABRICATION
14 Mulberry Court, Bourne Road, Crayford DA1 4BF
Tel: 01322 554 455 Fax: 01322 529 282
Email: info@imagefabrication.co.uk
Web Site: www.imagefabrication.co.uk
Managing Director: Peter Baker

PERRY SCENIC LTD
Unit D & E, 100 Dudley Road East, Oldbury, West Midlands B69 3EB
Tel: 0121 552 9696 Fax: 0121 552 9697
Email: enquiries@perryscenic.com
Web Site: www.perryscenic.com
Contact: Michael Perry , Tony Guest, Jonathan Perry
Comprehensive service at competitive prices. Set Builders, Engineering, Scenic Artists, Sculptors, Prop Makers, Design, Drapes, Effects for Theatre, Film, TV, Exhibition and Pop Tours.

SUPER-WIDE DIGITAL LTD
Block E, TBA Industrial Estate, Spod Road, Rooley Moor Road, Rochdale, Lancashire OL12 7DQ
Tel: 0161 653 6500 Fax: 0161 654 9500
Email: paul@super-wide.com
Web Site: www.super-wide.com
Contact: Paul Carroll

Scenery Material & Equipment Suppliers

ARNOLD LAVER TIMBERWORLD
478 Basingstoke Road, Reading, Berkshire RG2 0QN
Tel: 0118 975 1100 Fax: 0118 975 1900
Email: sales@reading.timberworld.co.uk
Web Site: www.timberworld.co.uk
Director: Barry Stimpson
Specialist suppliers of Flame Retardent Plywood Chipboard, MDF, Hardboard & Softwood to Class '1' and Class '0'.

BJ HARDWARE LIMITED
Scenery House, 2 Hereward Road, London SW17 7EY
Tel: 020 8767 2887 Fax: 020 8767 0849
Email: sales@bjhardware.co.uk
Web Site: www.bjhardware.co.uk
Contact: Nancy Joseph
Suppliers of Hardware, Ironmongery, Scenic Artists' Materials, Make-Up and Special Effects to the Entertainments Industry, including: Stage, Theatre, Television, Film, Exhibitions, Clubs, Party/Event Organisers, Art Schools and Colleges.

DYLON INTERNATIONAL LTD
Spotless Punch Limited, Knowles House, Cromwell Road, Redhill RH1 1RT
Tel: 01737 742 020
Email: info@dylon.co.uk
Web Site: www.dylon.co.uk
Dylon supplies high quality fabric dyes and paints that are ideal for use in theatre and film productions where colour is absolutely crucial. Multi-Purpose Dyes are suitable for use on a range of fabrics including Nylon and Lycra. Cold Water Dyes can be used to dye wood.

PROPS4SHOWS
Osprey House, Featherby Way, Purdeys Industrial Estate, Rochford, Essex SS4 1LD
Tel: 03333 440 078 Fax: 03333 441 478
Email: sales@props4shows.com
Web Site: www.props4shows.co.uk
Contact: Lin Lorde
Suppliers of a wide range of props, display goods and fabrics, for stage, theatre, photography and marketing. The extensive range includes fake food, seasonal props, artificial trees, stage backdrops, scenery props, professional makeup, display accessories and much more.

Scenery Suppliers

3D-4D.COM
46 Calthorpe Street, London WC1X 0JZ
Tel: 0500 555 245
Email: enquiries@3d4d.com
Web Site: www.3D4D.com
Flexible holographic designs for posters, invitations and much more. Large-format Lenticulars for set design.

ADVANCED PROTECTIVE PACKAGING LTD
25 Towerfield Road, Shoeburyness, Southend-on-Sea, Essex SS3 9QT
Tel: 01702 293 312 Fax: 01702 298 556
Email: salesSouth@advanced-pp.co.uk
Web Site: www.advanced-pp.co.uk
Expanded polystyrene suppliers.
Manchester Offices: Unit 58, Pioneer Mill, Milltown St, Radcliffe, Manchester M26 1WN
Tel: 0161 724 8080, Fax: 0161 725 9074

ALEC TIRANTI LTD
3 Pipers Court, Berkshire Drive, Thatcham, Berkshire RG19 4ER
Tel: 0845 123 2100 Fax: 0845 123 2101
27 Warren Street, London W1T 5NB
Tel/Fax: 020 7380 0808
Email: enquiries@tiranti.co.uk
Web Site: www.tiranti.co.uk
Resins, glass fibre, plaster, clay, rubber moulding materials, white metal. Sculptors' Tools, Alginate, Plaster Bandage.

BJ HARDWARE LIMITED
Scenery House, 2 Hereward Road, London SW17 7EY
Tel: 020 8767 2887 Fax: 020 8767 0849
Email: sales@bjhardware.co.uk
Web Site: www.bjhardware.co.uk
Contact: Nancy Joseph
Suppliers of Hardware, Ironmongery, Scenic Artists' Materials, Make-Up and Special Effects to the Entertainments Industry, including: Stage, Theatre, Television, Film, Exhibitions, Clubs, Party/Event Organisers, Art Schools and Colleges.

BRISTOL (UK) LTD
1 Sutherland Court, Moor Park Industrial Centre, Tolpits Lane, Watford WD18 9SP
Tel: 01923 779 333 Fax: 01923 779 666
Email: tech.sales@bristolpaint.com
Web Site: www.bristolpaint.com
Managing Director: Mark Chapman
Manufactures of water-based paints and coatings for the Film, Television and Theatre sectors, and Exhibition & Visual

Merchandising Industries. Also available: Reversible, instant lay, flat PVC studio / dance flooring which can be decorated with exclusive water based PVC painting system; Special range of paints and matching fabric for visual effects backings; Anti-Graffiti coating; Range of Fire protection products. Newly available: Stardust range of Glitter paints.

BRODIE & MIDDLETON LTD

30-31 Store Street, London WC1E 7QE
Tel: 020 7836 3289 Fax: 020 7497 0554
Email: info@brodies.net
Web Site: www.brodies.net
Manager: Yanko Tihov
Established 1840. Located in the heart of theatreland. Supplier of Rosco and Bristol scenic colour, UV colour, dyes, glitters, metal leaf, gilding materials, brushes, pigments, fire proofing, scenic canvas, drapes, backcloths, gauzes and varnishes and artists materials.

L CORNELISSEN & SON LTD

105 Great Russell Street, London WC1B 3RY
Tel: 020 7636 1045 Fax: 020 7636 3655
Email: info@cornelissen.com
Web Site: www.cornelissen.com
General Manager: Yanko Tihiv
Established 1855. Supplier of gilding materials, dry pigment colour & brushes. Located near the British Museum. Nearest tube: Tottenham Court Road.

CREFFIELDS (TIMBER & BOARDS) LTD

Flameproof boards.
Unit 6, Marcus Close, Tilehurst, Reading, Berkshire RG30 4EA
Tel: 0118 945 3533 Fax: 0118 945 3633
Email: info@creffields.co.uk
Web Site: www.creffields.co.uk
Creffields is one of the UK's leading suppliers of
flame-proofed sheet materials and soft woods for the
exhibition and theatrical trades.
Large stocks are held allowing for urgent orders to be delivered promptly; together with Premierbond portable contact spray glue system.

CURLYWILLY PRODUCTIONS

Unit C4, Admiralty Park, Off Station Road, Holton Heath, Poole Dorset BH16 6HX
Mobile: 07970 956 621
Email: carol@curlywilly.co.uk
Web Site: www.curlywilly.co.uk
Proprietor: Carol Kerley
Creative Designers, Consultants, Bespoke Makers of Costumes, Character Heads, Animal Mascots, Props,Scenery, Large Board Games.
For use in Theatre, TV, Promotional Events, Public Relations etc
Whatever the size of your budget we will cater to your every requirement. All items sold are made by us in our own studios, therefore we have total control during every stage

DIRECTA (UK) LTD

Cold Norton, Chelmsford, Essex CM3 6UA
Tel: 01621 828 882 Fax: 01621 828 072
Email: head.office@directa.co.uk
Web Site: www.directa.co.uk
Five good reasons to buy from Directa:
1. Competitive Prices
2. Speedy Nationwide Delivery
3. Free Technical Advice
4. Strict Quality Control
5. BS EN ISO 9001:2000
For free catalogue phone: 01621 828882

DYLON INTERNATIONAL LTD

Spotless Punch Limited, Knowles House, Cromwell Road, Redhill RH1 1RT
Tel: 01737 742 020
Email: info@dylon.co.uk
Web Site: www.dylon.co.uk
Dylon supplies high quality fabric dyes and paints that are ideal for use in theatre and film productions where colour is absolutely crucial. Multi-Purpose Dyes are suitable for use on a range of fabrics including Nylon and Lycra. Cold Water Dyes can be used to dye wood.

PETER EVANS STUDIOS LTD

12-14 Tavistock Street, Dunstable, Bedfordshire LU6 1NE
Tel: 01582 725 730 Fax: 01582 481 329
Email: sales@peterevansstudios.co.uk
Web Site: www.peterevansstudios.co.uk
Directors: P Evans, I Adams, R Evans
Makers of properties and scenic embellishments in rubber, GRP, polystyrene, etc. Supplier of a large range of columns, urns, cornices, friezes, balustrades, brickwork, etc. in vacuum formed PVC, ABS or GRP. Also vacuum forming done from your own patterns or patterns specially made. Catalogue available.

FLINT HIRE & SUPPLY LTD

Theatrical Chandlers
Queens Row, London SE17 2PX
Tel: 020 7703 9786
Sales Fax: 020 7708 4189
Email: sales@flints.co.uk
Web Site: www.flints.co.uk
Contacts: Alasdair Flint, Richard Black
Flints are the major retailer of theatrical goods in the UK. Established 25 years ago to provide a single source for specialist theatre hardware and materials.
Suppliers of Scenic Paints (including Rosco, Bolloms, Bristol and Traditional Paints), Flame Retardants, Painters Equipment, Propmakers Materials & Effects, Adhesives, Scenic Fabrics, Scenery Fittings, Weights and Braces, Lifting Gear, Fibre Ropes, Wire Rope, Tab Tracks, Castors, Hinges, Fixings, Staples & Staplers, Adhesive Tapes, Tools, Podgers, Safety Equipment, Access Equipment, Staging, Truck Winches. Hire of Megadek Staging Units, Winches and Tab Tracks.

FORWARD GROUP

Forward House, 57 Buckland Road, Leyton, London E10 6QS
Tel: 020 8558 7110 Fax: 020 8558 5974
Email: sales@forward-group.co.uk
Web Site: www.forward-group.co.uk
Contact: Mr Davis
Suppliers of stage and marking tape - PVC Electrical tape, staples and staple tackers.
Double sided cloth tape.
Computer consumables and all types of printing.

GERRIETS OF GREAT BRITAIN LTD

18 Verney Road, London SE16 3DH
Tel: 020 7639 7704 Fax: 020 7732 5760
Email: info@gerriets.co.uk
Web Site: www.gerriets.com
Director Sales and Marketing: Stewart Crosbie
Suppliers and manufacturers of theatrical and display plastics, textiles and finished soft goods.

HALL STAGE LIMITED

Unit 4, Cosgrove Way, Luton, Bedfordshire LU1 1XL
Tel: 0845 345 4255 Fax: 0845 345 4256
Email: sales@hallstage.com
Web Site: www.hallstage.com
Managing Director: Charles Haines
Technical Director: Phil Wells
Stage Sales Services Manager: Scott Oake
Sales Co-ordinator: Alison Price
Designs and manufactures standard and special products for the stage, screen, AV and industrial market.
Hall Stage and Theatre Supplies formed in 1895. Equipment ranges include T60 and T70 curtain track systems for all applications. Specialist products include rolloer or flying safety curtains, counterweight sets, hemp rope sets, the DynaGlide powered and manual hoists for powered fling and lighting bar operations, DynaLine pulleys, motor control systems, and a selection of theatrical and scenic hardware fittings.

HWL (UK) LTD

Cricket Street, Denton, Manchester M34 3DR
Tel: 0161 335 0220 Fax: 0161 320 3928
Email: guns@hwltd.co.uk
Web Site: www.hwltd.co.uk
Contact: Bob Howorth
Hirers of all types of furniture, set dressing, decorative lighting, pictures, hand props etc. Also specialist hirers of weapons and blank firing guns.

I S & G STEEL STOCKHOLDERS LTD
Laker Estate, Kent House Lane,
Beckenham, Kent BR3 1JT
Tel: 020 8778 8881 Fax: 020 8659 1643
Email: info@isg-steel.co.uk
Web Site: www.isg-steel.co.uk
Suppliers of castors, wheels, bolts, screws, etc, aluminium sections, fixing and fasteners, steel sections, Commercial body fittings, turntables.

J & C JOEL LTD
Corporation Mill, Corporation Street,
Sowerby Bridge, West Yorkshire HX6 2QQ
Tel: 01422 833835 Fax: 01422 835157
Email: sales@jcjoel.com
Web Site: www.jcjoel.com
Specialists in Flame Retardant Fabrics, manufacturers and installers of theatrical drapes and stage equipment. Probably the largest stock of flame retardant fabrics, tracks and all stage hardware, starcloths, dance flooring and portable staging.
Sales Manager: Oliver Marns

LANCELYN LIGHTING (NORTHWEST)
Poulton Road, Bebington, Wirral CH63 9LN
Tel: 0151 334 8991 (24Hours) Fax: 0151 334 4047 Oxford Office: Ferry Hinksey Road, Oxford, England, OX2 0BY Tel: 01865 722 468 Fax: 01865 728 791
Email: northwest@lancelyn.co.uk
Web Site: www.lancelyn.co.uk
Sales and Branch Manager: Paul Cook (paul@lancelyn.co.uk)
Optical & special effects, Pyrotechnics supplied and delivered.

LANCELYN THEATRE SUPPLIES
Ferry Hinksey Road, Oxford OX2 0BY
Tel: 01865 722 468 Fax: 01865 728 791
Email: oxford@lancelynoxford.co.uk
Web Site: www.lancelyn.co.uk
Sales and Branch Manager: Reg Berry
Email: reg@lancelynoxford.co.uk
Marketing, Admin & Office Manager: Sara Ingham
Made to measure curtains, supply and fix, repair and cleaning.

JD MCDOUGALL LIMITED
4 McGrath Road, London E15 4JP
Tel: 020 8534 2921 Fax: 020 8519 8423
Email: mail@mcdougall.co.uk
Web Site: www.mcdougall.co.uk
Director: Mr I McDougall
Stage Drapes, Vision Gauzes, Backcloths, Cyclorama cloths, Flame-proof textile materials for Scenery Construction and Stage Effects.

MUDFORD LTD
400 Petre Street, Sheffield S4 8LU
Tel: 0114 243 3033 Fax: 0114 244 4536
Wakefield Office: Alverthorpe Road, Wakefield, West Yorkshire, WF2 9NT Tel: 01924 364 771 Fax: 01924 291 725
Email: sales@mudfords.co.uk
Web Site: www.mudfords.co.uk
Contacts (Sheffield): David Millington, Suzanne Jefford
Contacts (Wakefield): Simon Parker, Teresa Mann, Sarah Thompson
Ropemakers and all types of canvas goods.

JOHN MYLAND LTD
80 Norwood High Street, West Norwood, London SE27 9NW
Tel: 020 8670 9161 Fax: 020 8761 5700
Email: dominic@mylands.co.uk
Web Site: www.myland.co.uk
Emulsion and acrylic (metallic) paints and glazes.

NORRIS STEAM SERVICES (LONDON) LTD
6c Sheep Lane, Hackney, London E8 4QS
Tel: 020 7923 4345
Email: robert@norrissteam.co.uk
Web Site: www.norrissteam.com
Managing Director: Norris Shepherdson
Marketing Manager: Robert Shepherdson
Sales Manger: Josh Taylor
Complete range of portable steamers & light weight boiler & iron systems to suit all requirements & budgets. Sales & hire available.

OAKLEAF REPRODUCTIONS LTD
Unit A, Melbourne Mills, Chesham Street, Keighley, West Yorkshire BD21 4LG
Tel: 01535 663 274 Fax: 01535 661 951
Email: sales@oakleaf.co.uk
Web Site: www.oakleaf.co.uk
Manufacturers of polyurethane mouldings - ranging from simulated wood beams panelling, embellishments, pillasters, cornice to false book backs. Decorative mirrors, bed heads, four poster beds. Also able to prepare specials to individual requirements. All available to Class 1 BS. 476 Part 7 surface spread of flame to order.

PROPS4SHOWS
Osprey House, Featherby Way, Purdeys Industrial Estate, Rochford, Essex SS4 1LD
Tel: 03333 440 078 Fax: 03333 441 478
Email: sales@props4shows.com
Web Site: www.props4shows.co.uk
Contact: Lin Lorde
Suppliers of a wide range of props, display goods and fabrics, for stage, theatre, photography and marketing. The extensive range includes fake food, seasonal props, artificial trees, stage backdrops, scenery props, professional makeup, display accessories and much more.

QDOS ENTERTAINMENT
Qdos House, Queen Margarets Road, Scarborough, North Yorkshire YO11 2YH
Tel: 01723 500 038 Fax: 01723 361 958
Email: info@qdosentertainment.co.uk
Web Site: www.qdosentertainment.co.uk
Chairman: Nick Thomas
Producers, theatre operators, talent management, as well as suppliers of sets, scenery and costumes for hire.

REVVO CASTOR CO
Somerford Road, Christchurch, Dorset BH23 3PZ
Tel: 01202 484 211 Fax: 01202 477 896
Email: sales@revvo.co.uk
Web Site: www.revvo.co.uk
Managing Director: Andrew MacKenzie
Manufacturers of castor and wheels.
Manufacturers of castors and wheels including low profile and 'sceneshifter' castors.

C. ROBERSON & CO LTD
1a Hercules Street, London N7 6AT
Tel: 020 7272 0567 Fax: 020 7263 0212
Email: info@robco.co.uk
Web Site: www.robco.co.uk
Contact: Gary Bowles
Gilding materials manufacturer & supplier: leaf, gold size, bronze powders.

ROSCOLAB LTD
Kangley Bridge Road, Sydenham, London SE26 5AQ
Tel: 020 8659 2300 Fax: 020 8659 3153
Email: contact@rosco.com
Web Site: www.rosco.com
14 product groups with hundreds of permutations, Shrink Mirrors. Rear screen projection materials, scenic paints, brushes, matallized scenic design materials. Breakaways, bottles and glasses.
Suppliers of a wide range of products, including lighting filters, scenic paints, stage filters, stage flooring, screens and fog machines for special effects.

RUSSELL & CHAPPLE
30-31 Store Street, London WC1E 7QE
Tel: 020 7836 7521 Fax: 020 7497 0554
Email: info@randc.net
Web Site: www.randc.net
Contacts: Yanko Tihov
Supplying theatres for over 200 years.
Made to order drapes & backcloths and supplier of all basic materials: scenic canvas, calico, duck, hessian. Also supplying scenic & artists colours.

SCENIC PROJECTS LTD
The Studios, London Road, Brampton, Beccles, Suffolk NR34 8DQ

Tel: 01502 575 000 Fax: 01502 575 840
Email: sales@scenicprojects.co.uk
Web Site: www.scenicprojects.co.uk
Technical Design: Nick Rowe

SMART LIVE
30 Maiden Lane, London WC2E 7JS
Tel: 0207 836 0562 Fax: 0207 836 1044
Email: smartlive@smartgroupltd.co.uk
Web Site: www.smartlive.co.uk
Creating events with edge.
Special event production company comprising set designers, choreographers, and artistic directors. Technically, we boast sound engineers, lighting technicians and stage managers. We combine our creative and technical talents to stage the most amazing themed events ever.

ADRIAN SNELL PRODUCTION SERVICES
Unit 12 Millbrook Ind Est. Millbrook, Torpoint, Cornwall PL11 3AX
Tel: 01752 829 393 Fax: 01752 829 394
Email: adriansnell@adriansnell.co.uk
Contact: Adrian Snell
Our large modern workshops offer a complete construction service, including engineering, steel fabrication and all other forms of construction.

STAGE ELECTRICS
Third Way, Avonmouth, Bristol, Avon BS11 9YL
Sales and Hire: 0844 870 0077 Tel: 0117 982 1999
Email: sales@stage-electrics.co.uk
Web Site: www.stage-electrics.co.uk
Managing Director: David Whitehead
Head of Operations: Dan Aldridge
Set design and construction, scenic artists, stage engineering and complete set hire.

TALBOT DESIGNS LTD
223 - 225 Long Lane, Finchley, London N3 2RL
Tel: 020 8346 8515 Fax: 020 8349 0294
Email: sales@talbotdesigns.co.uk
Web Site: www.talbotdesigns.co.uk
Contact: Richard Woolff
Over the past 30 years have supplied most of the notable theatre productions with plastic flooring, plastic domes, scenery, special effects, hand held props and any plastic requirements.

TRAVIS PERKINS (SOUTHERN REGION)
Cobtree House, Forstal Road, Aylesford, Kent ME20 7AG
Tel: 01622 710 111 Fax: 01622 715 692
Email: alyesford2@travisperkins.co.uk
Web Site: www.travisperkins.co.uk
Contact: Vincent Murdoff
Suppliers of: Timber, Building Materials, Plumbing, Heating, Toolhire.

TRIMITE LTD
Arundel Road, Uxbridge, Middlesex UB8 2SD
Tel: 01895 251 234 Sales: 01895 201 444 Fax: 01895 256 789
Email: uxbridge.sales@trimite.com
Web Site: www.trimite.com
Paint manufacturers and suppliers.
Suppliers of fixative & bonding solution.
(Formerly Hamerfix bonding & texturising agent).

VISUAL BLISS
5 Memory Cross, Landscove, Ashburton, Newton Abbot, Devon TQ13 7NB
Tel: 01803 762 326
Email: office@visualbliss.co.uk
Web Site: www.visualbliss.co.uk
Proprietor: Colin Quinsey
Specialists in UV Backdrops. A huge range of backdrops, effects and modern designs. Available to rent or purchase, all made to respond to UV lighting. Also 3D props.

WHALEYS (BRADFORD) LTD
Harris Court, Great Horton, Bradford, West Yorkshire BD7 4EQ
Tel: 01274 576 718 Fax: 01274 521 309
Email: kevin.woodhead@whaleysltd.co.uk
Web Site: www.whaleys.co.uk/stage
General Manager: Mr Kevin Woodhead
Sales Manager: Barry Hardisty
Sales Office: David Carroll
Drapes/Backdrops/Borders/Legs etc. Full range of standard flameproof stage fabrics. Orders made up to customer specification. Also huge range of fabrics for costume (many ready for printing/dyeing).

WOLFIN TEXTILES LIMITED
Unit 4 Phoenix Works, Cornwall Road, Pinner Middlesex HA5 4UH
Tel: 020 8427 7429 Fax: 020 8428 4350
Email: cotton@wolfintextiles.co.uk
Web Site: www.wolfintextiles.co.uk
All basic materials for Stage, Screen and TV.
Costume interlinings, scenery canvas, calico, duck, blackout and hessian.

Scripts

READING AND RIGHTING
618b Finchley Road, London NW11 7RR
Tel/Fax: 020 8455 4564
Email: lambhorn@gmail.com
Web Site: http://readingandrighting.netfirms.com
Contact: Robert Lambolle
Script and manuscript evaluation/ editing/advice.

THE SCREENWRITERS WORKSHOP
Euroscript Ltd 64 Hemingford Road, London N1 1DB
Tel: 07958 244 656
Email: paul.bassettdavies@euroscript.co.uk
Web: www.screenwritersworkshop.co.uk
Forum for writers and novice aspiring writers for contact, information and tuition. Script reading service.

SILVERWORD PRODUCTIONS
16 Lime Trees Avenue, Llangattock, Crickhowell, Powys NP8 1LD Wales
Tel: 01873 810 142
Email: silverwordgroup@aol.com
Web Site: www.silverwordgroup.com
Managing Director: Kevin King
Management company, record producers, marketing company and music publishers.

Seating Refurbishment

EURO GROUP UK
7 Coopers Way, Temple Farm Industrial Estate, Southend-on-Sea SS2 5TE
Tel: +44 (0) 1702 614 444 Fax: +44 (0) 1702 616660
Email: enquires@euro-group-uk.com
Web Site: www.euro-group-uk.com
Managing Director: Grahame Jenkins
Bespoke upholsterers. Also available: cinema, theatre, lecture, conference, retractable and stadium seating.

Seats & Seating

ACANTHUS DESIGN
Highwood House, Hulland Ward, Ashbourne, Derbyshire DE6 3EG
Tel: 0781 584 8265
Email: acanthus1@btinternet.com
Contact: Ewen B McWilliam FRSA
Seating Solutions from Conception to Completion. Exclusively representing Jezet Seating LLC in the UK. Specialists in Curved & Traditional Retractable Seating Systems. Fixed Theatre Seating - Bespoke 'Period Seating' for Theatres of Architectural Heritage.

ARENA SEATING
Arena House, Membury, Lambourn Woodlands, Hungerford, Berkshire RG17 7TQ
Tel: 01488 674 800 Fax: 01488 674 822
Email: info@arenaseating.com
Web Site: www.arenaseating.com
Contact: Dave Withey
Arena Seating is the United Kingdom's principle supplier of demountable seating systems with over 30 years experience of designing, supplying and installing tiered seating equipment for all types of events, for hire or purchase.

We offer a complete service for all types of events, whether it is 23,000 tiered grandstand seats at Silverstone for the Formula 1 Grand Prix or 150 seats for BBC Question Time, Arena will help with your event management.

AUDIENCE SYSTEMS LTD
19b Washington Road, West Wilts Trading Estate, Westbury, Wiltshire BA13 4JP
Tel: 01373 865 050 Fax: 01373 827 545
Email: enquiries@audiencesystems.com
Web Site: www.audiencesystems.com
Contact: Mark Cowley or Nina Parmenter
Audience Systems design and manufacture auditorium seating for theatres and concert halls around the world and have worked with many prestigious venues including The Royal Albert Hall, Royal Court Theatre, Bridgewater Hall, Glyndebourne Opera House, Birmingham Repertory Theatre and Basel Music Theatre. We design and manage your seating solutions from concept to opening night.

AUDITORIA SERVICES LTD
Denby Way, Hellaby Industrial Estate, Rotherham, South Yorkshire S66 8HR
Tel: 01709 543 345 / 703 151 Fax: 01709 700 771
Email: patrick@auditoria-services.com
Web Site: www.auditoria-services.com
Sales Manager: Patrick Donoghue
Manufacturers of theatre and cinema seating, retractable seating, fixed and folding platforms.

BOURNEMOUTH UPHOLSTRY CENTRE
890 Wimborne Road, Bournemouth, Dorset BH9 2DR
Tel/ Fax: 01202 516 949
Email: enquiries@bourneupholstery.co.uk
Web Site: www.bourneupholstery.co.uk
Contact: Anthony Plascott
Suppliers of every upholstery requirement and fringes, braids and trimmings for curtains and furniture.

CPS SEATING & STAGING
Brunel House, Brunel Close, Harworth, Doncaster, South Yorkshire DN11 8QA
Tel: 01302 741 888 Fax: 01302 741 999
Email: sales@seatingandstaging.co.uk
Web Site: www.cpsmanufacturingco.com
Marketing Manager: John Hughes
Adaptable seating and staging systems. Including demountable staging for hire or sale.

EURO GROUP UK
7 Coopers Way, Temple Farm Industrial Estate, Southend-on-Sea SS2 5TE
Tel: +44 (0) 1702 614 444 Fax: +44 (0) 1702 616660
Email: enquires@euro-group-uk.com
Web Site: www.euro-group-uk.com
Managing Director: Grahame Jenkins
Bespoke upholsterers. Also available: cinema, theatre, lecture, conference, retractable and stadium seating.

EURO SEATING UK & ESSEX UPHOLSTERY LTD
Unit 7, Coopers Way, Temple Farm Industrial Estate, Southend-on-Sea SS2 5TE
Tel: 01702 614 444 Fax: 01702 616 660
Email: grahame@essexupholstery.com
Web Site: www.essexupholstery.com
Director: Grahame Jenkins
Suppliers of cinema seating, seating refurbishment and maintenance.

EVENT SERVICES LTD
The Old Foundry, Brow Mills, Brighouse Road, Hipperholme, Halifax, West Yorkshire HX3 8EF
Tel: 01422 204 114 Fax: 01422 204 431
Email: sales@event-services.co.uk
Web Site: www.event-services.co.uk
Stages, rostra, catwalks, tiered seating, front of stage barriers.

FIGUERAS INTERNATIONAL SEATING
International Seating.
15 Great Sutton Street, London EC1V 0BX
Mob: 07970810275
Email: bpanella@figuerasuk.com
Web Site: www.figueras.com
Director UK and Ireland: Barbara Panella

GLOBAL EXPERIENCE SPECIALISTS
Silverstone Drive, Gallagher Business Park, Coventry CV6 6PA
Tel: 02476 380 000 Fax: 02476 380 001
Email: enquiry@ges.com
Web Site: www.ges.com
Office Manager: Jo Mummery-Smith
Hire of furniture, floorcoverings and floral.

HUSSEY SEATWAY LTD
Roman Way, Crusader Park, Warminster, Wiltshire BA12 8SJ
Tel: 01985 847 200 Fax: 01985 847 300
Email: info@husseyseatway.com
Web Site: www.husseyseatway.com / www.husseyseating.com
Manufacturers of cinema, auditorium and conference hall seating, specialist design work undertaken to suit clients requirements.
Telescopic platforms with a comprehensive range of integral seating options. Full CAD design facilities - consultation without obligation.

JEZET SEATING
Siberiëstraat 10, B3900 Overpelt Belgium
Belgium Tel: 00 32 11 64 54 42 Jezet UK Tel: 0781 584 82 65
Email: info@jezet.com
Web Site: www.jezet.com
General Manager: Jimmy D'Joos
Commercial Agent UK: Ewen B McWilliam
Jezet Seating - your partner for innovative quality seating solutions. Jezet designs, manufactures and installs traditional and curved retractable seating systems and fixed seating solutions for arena venues, sporting complexes, lecture theatres, modern and traditional theatres. All projects are designed to meet the individual client's design criteria. Jezet Seating has valuable technical knowledge and experience of major international projects of immense complexity.

KIRWIN & SIMPSON
Unit 13 Globe Industrial Estate Rectory Road Grays Essex RM17 6ST
Tel: 01375 379 200
Email: sales@kirwin-simpson.co.uk
Web Site: www.kirwin-simpson.com
Enquiries: Andrew Simpson
Specialist manufacturers of new auditorium chairs, refurbishment and re-upholstery.

LANCELYN THEATRE SUPPLIES
Ferry Hinksey Road, Oxford OX2 0BY
Tel: 01865 722 468 Fax: 01865 728 791
Email: oxford@lancelynoxford.co.uk
Web Site: www.lancelyn.co.uk
Sales and Branch Manager: Reg Berry
Email: reg@lancelynoxford.co.uk
Marketing, Admin & Office Manager: Sara Ingham
Made to measure curtains, supply and fix, repair and cleaning.

PAUL OWEN SEATING
The Maltkiln Warehouse, Whitcliffe Road, Cleckheaton, West Yorkshire BD19 3DR
Tel: 01274 864 282 Mob: 07983 603 317
Email: paul@plowen.co.uk
Web Site: www.plowen.co.uk
Manager: Paul Owen
Seating Contractors. (Theatre and Auditorium)

SANDLER SEATING
58-64 Three Colts Lane, London E2 6JR
Tel: 020 7749 3000 Fax: 020 7729 2843
Email: sales@sandlerseating.com
Web Site: www.sandlerseating.com
CEO: Roy Sandler
Sales Manager (UK Office): Anita Haslett
Large range of portable folding seating for multi-purpose halls. Restaurant furniture.

SEATING SYSTEMS LTD
Assento House, Goodwood Close, White Horse Business Park, Trowbridge, Wiltshire BA14 0XE
Tel: 01225 776 873 Fax: 01225 774 423
Email: sales@seatingsystems.co.uk

Web Site: www.seatingsystems.co.uk
Contacts: Steve Dean, Helen Dale
The world's leading manufacture of theatre, cinema and auditorium seating with over 90 years of experience in satisfying customer requirements.

SOLVING LTD
Wessex House, Oxford Road, Newbury, Berkshire RG14 1PA
Tel: 01635 814 488 Fax: 01635 814 480
Email: sales@solving.co.uk
Web Site: www.solving.co.uk
Contact: John Cownley
We manufacture 'hover pads' and electrically-powered blowers for fixing to seating, staging and lighting towers.
Capacities range from 1 tonne to 20 tonnes or more.

STAGE SOLUTIONS
45 Chruch Road, Hove, East Sussex, BN3 2BE
Tel: 01273 783 710
Email: info@stagesolutions.uk.com
Web Site: www.stagesoltutions.uk.com
Warehouse: 10 Second Avenue, Chatham, Kent ME4 5AU
Maltbury designs, manufactures, delivers and installs staging for every kind of venue, both professional and amateur.
We have over 20 years' experience of the entertainment industry.
We also supply seating, truss and crowd control barriers.

STAR EVENTS GROUP LTD
Milton Road, Thurleigh, Bedford MK44 2DF
Tel: 01234 772 233 Fax: 01234 772 272
Email: steve.shaw@stareventsgroup.com
Web Site: www.StarEventsGroup.com
Hire of technical services to the entertainment industry including stage constructions for both indoor and outdoor events.

THE EVENT HIRE COMPANY
Subsidiary organisation of 'The Crown Group'
Crown House 855 London Road, Grays, RM20 3LG
Tel : 01708 335 184 Fax : 01708 341 909
Email: sales@eventhireonline.co.uk
Web Site: www.eventhireonline.co.uk
Full catering and event hire services, including a comprehensive range of high quality equipment and event furniture.

Security Services

AP SECURITY
33 The Metro Centre, Dwight Road, Watford WD18 9SB
Tel: 0870 412 2232 Fax: 0870 412 2231
Email: info@apsecurity.co.uk, kevin-lawrence@apsecurity.co.uk
Web Site: www.apsecurity.co.uk
Managing Director: Trevor Bence
Operations Directors: Kevin Lawrence, Martyn Webster

A specialist supplier of cost effective and professional security staff in security and stewarding services, V.I.P. protection services and sit guarding services.

BOSS SECURITY SERVICES LTD
Imperial House, 64 Willoughby Lane, London N17 0SP
Tel: 020 8493 8562 Fax: 020 8885 4930
Email: info@boss-security.co.uk
Web Site: www.boss-security.co.uk
Contact: Sonia Chowdhury

BUSINESS AND ENTERTAINMENT SECURITY LTD
38 Ashtree Road, Norwich, Norfolk NR5 0LS
Tel: 01603 441 806 Fax: 01603 441 807
Mobile: 07976 240878
Email: besecurity@boltblue.com
Web Site: www.besecurity.co.uk
Director: Sean Stone
Provision of high and low profile security, personal security, corporate hospitality security, conference and private function security, event and venue security.

EXECUTIVE GROUP HOLDINGS
Previously 'Bodyguard Protection'
Executive House, Wilderspool Causeway, Warrington WA4 6PU
Tel: 01925 652 652 Fax: 01925 652 525
Email: info@bodyguard-protection.com
Web: www.executivegroupholdings.co.uk
Contact: Damien Scott

EXODUS SECURITY SERVICES LTD
Channelsea Business Centre, Channelsea House, Canning Road, London E15 3ND
Tel: 020 8519 8989 Fax: 020 8519 5859
Email: enquiries@exodussecurity.com
Web Site: www.exodussecurity.com
Managing Director: Mr Frederick B Lee
24 Hour Service. Specialists in theatre security and all other events.

INITIAL SECURITY
2a King's Exchange, Tleyard Road, London N7 9AH
Tel: 020 7831 7551 Fax: 020 7697 2299
Email: derek.young@initial-security.co.uk
Web Site: www.initial-security.co.uk
Security guards, exhibition, attendants, mobile patrolmen & key holding services.
Contact Sales Manager: Derek Young

MC PRODUCTION GROUP
Unit SU4A, Lansbury Estate, 102 Lower Guildford Road, Woking, Surrey GU21 2EP
Tel: 01483 884488.
Web Site: www.mcpg.co.uk

PATHFINDER INTERNATIONAL ASSOCIATES
(formerly known as Suban Security Services)
40 Seely Road, Tooting London SW17 9QS
Tel: 07050 135 463 Fax: 020 8286 7203
Email: billyamarteifio990@hotmail.com
Prop: Bill Amarteifio

RELIANCE SECURITY GROUP LIMITED
Boundary House, Boundary House, Cricket Field Road, Uxbridge, Middlesex UB8 1QG
Tel: 01895 205 000 Fax: 01895 205 100
Email: info@reliancesecurity.co.uk
Web Site: www.reliancesecurity.co.uk
Sales and Marketing Director: Stephen Hollings
Providing electric and manned security.

RIGHT GUARD SECURITY
34 Simmonds Road, Wincheap Industrial Estate, Canterbury, Kent CT1 3RA
Tel: 01227 464588 Fax: 01227 464188
London Office: Office 23, 145 Seymore Place, Marylebone, London, W1H 4PA
Tel: 0207 241 5525
Email: info@rightguard.co.uk
Web Site: www.rightguard.co.uk

SPINDLEWOOD SECURITY
Spindlewood Limited, The Resource Centre, Regent Street, Featherstone, Pontefract, West Yorkshire WF7 5EW
Tel: 0845 230 0113
Email: sales@spindlewoodcctv.com
Web Site: www.spindlewoodcctv.com
No1 supplier of CCTV & event surveillance equipment to the event, exhibition & sporting industries. Fully installed CCTV systems for temporary hire.

STARGUARD SECURITY LTD
404 Bexhill Road, St. Leonards-on-Sea, East Sussex TN38 8AS
Tel: 0800 5300 293
Email: info@starguardsecurityltd.co.uk
Web Site: www.starguardsecurityltd.co.uk
Event security, Residential & Commercial Buildings, Private Funcations & Farties, Door Supervision, Reception Duties, CCTV Installation and Operation, Key Holding & Access Control, Retail Security, Industrial Parks, District Response Teams, Dog Units.

Self -Adhesive Tapes

COLOR PRODUCTS LTD
Unit 5, Tile House Farm, Birds Green Lane, Willingale, Ongar, Essex CM5 0PN
Tel: 08456 585212
Email: colorproducts@aol.com
Contact: Peter Randall
Manufacturers of flight case labels, equipment labels, touring labels, cable and cable coding labels, printed vinyl tapes and floor graphics.

FLASHLIGHT LTD
Unit A3, Axis Point, Hilltop Road, Heywood, Lancashire OL10 2RQ
Tel: 01706 625 866 Fax: 01706 620 756
Email: sales@flash-light.co.uk
Web Site: www.flash-light.co.uk
Contact: Rob Williamson
Flashlight are the ' one-stop shop' for entertainment lighting, accessories and consumables. We are main stockists for ETC, Lee Filters, Arri, Martin Professional, Zero 88, Pulsar, Doughty, Rosco, Philips, Le Maitre.

LE MARK GROUP
Houghton, Huntingdon, Cambridgeshire PE28 2DH
Tel: 01480 494 540
Email: linda@lemark.co.uk / info@lemark.co.uk
Web Site: www.lemark.co.uk
Sales Director: Linda Gibbons
Le Mark have serviced the theatre industry over the last 25 years with their range of self-adhesive products. We are well known for introducing new innovative products and winning awards for Blacktak & Slipway.

Shipping

ANGLO PACIFIC INTERNATIONAL PLC
5-9 Willen Field Road, London NW10 7BQ
Tel: 020 8965 1234 Fax: 020 8965 3988
Email: info@anglopacific.co.uk
Web Site: www.anglopacific.co.uk
Managing Director: Steve Perry
Ocean freight, air freight, trucking, full carnet services, forwarders to the performing arts.

BRUNELS REMOVAL SERVICES
20A Walnut Lane, Bristol BS15 4JG
Tel: 0117 907 7855 Mob: 07836 500 399
Email: enquires@brunelremovals.co.uk
Web Site: www.brunelremovals.co.uk
Contact: Simon Hippisley
A 24 hour professional service throughout the UK and Europe. We specialise in all forms of transport of scenery, props etc to film, TV and theatrical companies, including Storage. Competitive rates tailor-made to suit your needs. Our large fleet of vehicles ranges from transit vans to Supercube Airride step-framed trailers.

EXPRESS EXPORT SERVICES LTD
143 Wardour Street, London W1F 8WA
Tel: 020 7734 8356 Fax: 0800 034 1005
Email: john@express-exports.co.uk
Web Site: www.express-exports.co.uk
Shipper of costumes, props, stages and all other associated goods to the theatrical industry, by air, sea or overland truck to all parts of the world. Also specialise is offering discount airfare tickets worldwide.

ROCK-IT CARGO LTD
Delta Way, Egham, Surrey TW20 8RX
Tel: 01784 431 301 Fax: 01784 471 052
Email: info@rock-it.co.uk
Web Site: www.rock-itcargo.com
Contact: Matt Wright, Alan Durrant
Rock-It Cargo is the world's leading and most experienced freight and logistics specialist for the performing arts and touring productions. Air freight, ocean freight, charter, trucking, carnets & packing. Global door to door services.

TEAM RELOCATIONS
Drury Way London NW1 0JN
Tel: 020 8784 0100 Fax: 020 8451 0061
Email: reception@teamrelocations.com
Web Site: www.teamrelocations.com
As a quick reminder, our expertise lies in the planning and preparation of transport for UK, European and Worldwide Events, using our vehicle fleet and worldwide air and seas freight forwarding.

TNT FREIGHT MANAGEMENT
Units 5-6, Parkway Trading Estate, Cranford Lane, Hounslow, Middlesex TW5 9QA
Tel: 020 8814 7000 Fax: 020 8814 7080
Email: bill.billing@uk.tntfreight.com
A complete worldwide service for cargo. Embassy have over 30 years experience in the logistics of overseas touring and as part of Bilspedition Sweden are able to provide favourable rates to and from all parts of the world.
Contact Branch Manager (UK): Bill Billing

Sound & Sound Equipment Suppliers

ACCESS AUDIO LTD
Wintonfield House, New Winton, East Lothian, EH33 2NN
Tel: 0131 663 0777 Fax: 0131 660 9777
Email: info@accessaudio.co.uk
Web Site: www.accessaudio.co.uk
Managing Director: Douglas Telford
Radio and infrared communication system suppliers & installers. Audio description equipment specialists.

ACCUSOUND MICROPHONE SYSTEMS
172 Wadsley Lane, Sheffield, South Yorkshire S6 4EE
Tel: 0114 220 3517 Fax: 0870 094 0057
Email: info@accusound.com
Web Site: www.accusound.com
Accusound is a British Company producing instrument mounted microphone systems for all acoustic instruments, strings, woodwind and brass. Accusound is now a Trading name of Hebden Sound Ltd. The Accusound product range includes a variety of capsule (with different polar patterns) and contact (strip) microphones designed to retain the acoustic nature of the instrument whilst allowing adequate amplification. All systems are available as wired or wireless versions.

AIRO LIMITED
Duxons Turn, Maylands Avenue, Hemel Hempstead, Hertfordshire HP2 4SB
Tel: 01442 247 146 Fax: 01442 256 749
Email: airo@bcs.org.uk
Web Site: www.airo.co.uk
Acoustic consultants offering specialist sound system design service.

ALLEN & HEATH LIMITED
Kernick Industrial Estate, Penryn, Cornwall TR10 9LU
Tel: 01326 372 070 Fax: 01326 377 097
Email: sales@allen-heath.com
Web Site: www.allen-heath.com
Marketing Manager: David Kirk
Manufacturers of professional live sound mixing consoles for theatres, venues and studios.

ANDOLITE LTD
Unit A, Rennie Gate, West Port Industrial Estate, Andover, Hampshire SP10 3TU
Tel: 01264 356445 Fax: 01264 334 401
Email: sales@andolite.co.uk
Web Site: www.andolite.co.uk
Managing Director: Alan Good

APPLE SOUND LTD
6 Well House Barns, Chester Road, Bretton, Chester CH4 0DH
Tel: 01244 663 548 Tel (London Sales) : 0207 193 4610 Fax: 01244 66 14 64
Email: info@applesound.com
Web Site: www.applesound.co.uk
Managing Director: Tim Brown
Technical Director: Phil Brown

AUDIO & ACOUSTICS
United House, North Road, London N7 9DP
Tel: 020 7700 2900 Fax: 020 7700 6900
Email: aaaco@aol.com
Manager: Nick Kantoch
Sound system design and acoustic consultancy. Sound equipment installation and hire.

AUDIO FORUM LTD
PO Box 4359 Trowbridge, Wiltshire BA14 4DQ
Tel: 0870 240 6444
Email: hire@audioforum.co.uk
Web Site: www.audioforum.co.uk
Sales and Hire: Mike Reeves
Sales hire & service of audio products in the uk.

AUDIOHIRE
The Old Dairy, 133-137 Kilburn Lane, London W10 4AN
Tel: 020 8960 4466 Fax: 0845 860 1739
Email: admin@audiohire.co.uk
Web Site: www.audiohire.co.uk
Hire of Lights, Sound Equipment; Synthesizers, Samplers, Recording Equipment, Desks, Noise Reduction, Microphones, Backline, PA, Drum Machines, Fx, etc.

AUTOGRAPH SALES LTD
Unit 6, Bush Industrial Estate, Station Road, London N19 5UN
Tel: 020 7281 7574 Fax: 020 7281 3042
Email: sales@autograph.co.uk
Web Site: www.autograph.co.uk
Contact: Owen Ironside
For 25 years Autograph Sales has been recognised as one of the UK's most established professional audio distributors for sound and communications equipment. Autograph specialises in supplying the live, recording and broadcast marketplaces through a team of sales professionals with a wealth of knowledge, backed up by a specialist service department. Among products represented are Meyer Sound Labs loudspeakers, Clear-Com intercom systems, ATM Fly-Ware rigging equipment, Symphotec orchestral microphone systems, HAS fine wood furniture, and a range of microphones, radio microphones, mixing consoles, amplifiers and signal processing equipment.

BETTER SOUND LTD
31 Cathcart Street, London NW5 3BJ
Tel: 020 7482 0177 Fax: 020 7482 2677
Email: admin@bettersound.co.uk
Web Site: www.bettersound.co.uk
General Manager: Christopher Column

BLACKWING LTD
Barnes Farm, Battlesea Green, Stradbroke, Eye, Suffolk IP21 5NE
Tel: 01379 388519
Email: enquiries@blackwingltd.com
Web Site: www.blackwingltd.com
Managing Director: Torben Merriott
Company Secretary: Pamie Merriott
Lighting, Audio, and Special Effects, Steel Deck Staging - hire and sales.

BLITZ COMMUNICATIONS LTD
Unit B1, Junction 22 Business Park, Tweedale Way, Chadderton, Oldham OL9 8EH
Tel: 0161 688 1600 Fax: 0161 688 1633
Head Office: 100 Centennial Avenue, Elstee, Hertfordshire, WD6 3SA Tel: 0208 327 1000, Fax: 0208 327 1111
Email: cjordan@blitzcommunications.co.uk
Web: www.blitzcommunications.co.uk
Contacts: Chris Jordan

BRAHLER ICS UK LTD
Unit 2, The Business Centre, Church End, Cambridge CB1 3LB
Tel: 01223 411 601 Fax: 01223 411 602
Email: info@brahler.co.uk
Web Site: www.brahler-ics.co.uk
Managing Director: S.M. Sainsbury
Conference equipment. Simultaneous interpretation equipment.
Infra-red hearing assistance equipment.

BUBBLES LIGHTING LTD
Units 20 - 21, Black Moor Business Park, New Road, Maulden, Bedford MK45 2BG
Tel: 01525 402 400 Fax: 01525 404 399
Email: info@bubbleslighting.com
Web Site: www.bubbleslighting.com
Managing Director: P J Bottoms

CADAC HOLDINGS LTD
One New Street, Luton, Bedfordshire LU1 5DX
Tel: 01582 404 202 Fax: 01582 412 799
Email: info@cadac-sound.com
Web Site: www.cadac-sound.com

Designer and manufacturer of specialist theatre sound mixing consoles - used internationally on major musical and dramatic productions, in both permanent and touring installations

CANFORD AUDIO PLC
Crowther Road, Washington, Tyne and Wear NE38 0BW
Admin: 0191 418 1000 UK Sales: 0191 418 1122 International Sales: 0191 418 1133 Technical Support: 0191 418 1144
Hires: 0191 418 1166
Fax: 0191 418 1001
Email: info@canford.co.uk
Web Site: www.canford.co.uk
Sales & Operations Manager: Ian Elliott
Canford Audio was founded in 1976, and is unchallenged as the UK's largest pro-audio manufacturer and distributor.

CAPITAL SOUND
Abacus House, 60 Weir Road, London SW19 8UG
Tel: 020 8944 6777 Fax: 020 8944 9477
Email: info@capital-sound.co.uk
Web Site: www.capital-sound.co.uk
General Manager: Paul Timmins
Managing Director: Keith Davis
Our main business is the hire of sound equipment to the entertainment world, this may include the provision of freelance technical crew and transport.

C.A.V. (CONTRACT AUDIO VISUAL)
Unit 3, Venture Business Centre, Madleaze Road, Gloucester GL1 5SJ
Tel: 01452 505 500 Fax: 01452 502 600
Email: sales@cav.co.uk
Web Site: www.cav.co.uk
Proprietor: Hans Beier
LCAV (Contract Audio Visual) is a large production services company based in Gloucestershire. We provide solutions from basic unmanned hire of sound and lighting equipment through to total production services for large scale events, concerts, tour and conferences.

CENTRAL EVENTS UK LTD
The Barn Fifield Farm Marlston Road Marlston Nr Hermitage Berkshire RG18 9UN
Tel: 01235 760 342 Fax: 01635 202 088
Email: heidi.smith@s-l-v.co.uk
Web Site: www.central-production.co.uk
Senior Personnel: Jim Williams
Specialise in production of rigging, staging, lighting, PA, theming, power distribution, marquees and catering for corporate and private parties.
At Central Events UK, we pride ourselves in being a full service events management company whcih gives us the freedom to offer the very best in service, product and price to our customers.

CENTRAL THEATRE SUPPLIES
1186 Stratford Road, Hall Green, Birmingham West Midlands B28 8AB
Tel: 0121 778 6400
Email: enquiries@centraltheatresupplies.co.uk
Web: www.centraltheatresupplies.co.uk
Manager: David Harwood
Technical Manager: Ian Knight
Birmingham based Central Theatre Supplies have a large hire department supplying professional stage lighting, control systems and effects. We sell products from many leading manufacturers. Consumables are always in stock.

THE CLOUD ONE GROUP LTD
24 Proctor Street, Birmingham B7 4EE
Tel: 0845 269 7711 Fax: 0121 333 7799
Email: info@cloudone.net
Web Site: www.cloudone.net
Contact: Paul Stratford
Sound, lighting, staging, sales, hire, installation, consultancy.

CLYDE BROADCAST PRODUCTS LTD
Unit 2 Rutherford Court, 15 North Avenue, Clydebank Business Park, Clydebank, Dunbartonshire G81 2QP Scotland
Tel: 0141 952 7950 Fax: 0141 941 1224
Email: sales@clydebroadcast.com
Web Site: www.clydebroadcast.com
Clyde Broadcast Products are experts in the design, manufacture and installation of broadcast audio equipment and systems for radio stations of all sizes and complexity, in the UK and internationally.

CP SOUND LTD
Units 14 & 15, Penton Hook Marina, Staines Road, Chertsey, Surrey KT16 8PY
Tel: 01932 571 849 Fax: 01932 850 725
Email: info@cpsound.co.uk
Web Site: www.cpsound.co.uk
Manager: Colin Pattenden
CP Sound is a pro-active, creative and progressive thinking company that specifies, supplies and installs sound, lighting and audio visual systems for a diverse selection of venues and situations.

DENON
First Floor, Imperial House, 4 -11 Donegall Square East, Belfast BT1 5HD
Tel: 02890 279 830 Fax: 02890 312 643
Email: info@dm-uk.co.uk
Web Site: www.denon.co.uk
Marketing Manager: Marianne Mckay

DRAGON SERVICING
32 Woodstock Road, Carshalton, Surrey SM5 3DZ
Tel/Fax: 020 8395 6774
Email: dragonser@clara.net
Web Site: home.clara.net/dragonser
Contact: Peter Blackett
Servicing and repair of mixing desks and amplifiers, keyboards, tape machines, organs and electric pianos.

DRAX LIGHTING LTD
Unit 21B Icknield Way Farm, Tring Road, Dunstable, Bedfordshire LU6 2JX
Tel: 01582 475 614 Fax: 01582 475 669
Email: richard@draxlighting.com, info@draxlighting.com
Web Site: www.draxlighting.com
Contact: Richard Foster
Drax specialises in event lighting design and equipment supply for stage shows, outdoor productions and corporate events. Drax hire and sell quality lighting, sound and effects equipment for static, touring or short term use. Dry hire or hire with crew is available for both professional and amateur events, UK and worldwide. Hire equipment includes profiles, fresnels, PARs, floods, followspots, moving lights, rigging, special effects systems and dimmers. Control systems available include Avolites, Artistic Licence and Zero 88.

DRINKLE & MANN LTD
Unit 2, Peel Green Trading Estate, Green Street, Eccles, Manchester M30 7HF
Tel: 0161 707 7588 Fax: 0161 707 7599
Email: info@drinklemann.co.uk
Web Site: www.drinklemann.co.uk
Contact: C Hulme
Wet & dry hire specialists, operators & logistics, sales, installations & maintenance agents for all leading suppliers.

ELECTROSONIC LTD
Hawley Mill, Hawley Road, Dartford, Kent DA2 7SY
Tel: 01322 222 211 Fax: 01322 282 282
Email: info@electrosonic.co.uk
Web Site: www.electrosonic.co.uk
Manufacture and supply of audio visual and video control equipment from single screen up to multi-media spectaculars.

ENLIGHTENMENT
The Rubicon Centre, Broad Ground Road, Lakeside, Redditch, Worcestershire B98 8YP
Tel: 0845 257 1992
Email: info@enlightenment.co.uk
Web Site: www.enlightenment.co.uk
Contact: Paul Swansborough
Established since 1997 and trading online since 2006. Enlightenment is the UK on-line source for stage lighting, sound, audio visual and rigging equipment to the entertainment industry. Enlightenment is a main dealer for Showtec, DAP Audio and Dutch Media Tools.

ENTEC SOUND & LIGHT
517 Yeading Lane, Northolt, Middlesex UB5 6LN
Tel: 020 8842 4004 Fax: 020 8842 3310
Email: sales@entec-soundandlight.com

Web Site: www.entec-soundandlight.com
Entec is the UK's longest established lighting and sound company. Entec delivers quality audio and lighting, professional technicians, staging, sets and project management for any event. You name it - we can do it!

ENTERTAINMENT SOUND SPECIALISTS
2 Maun Close, Mansfield, Nottinghamshire NG18 5GY
Tel: 01623 647 291 Fax: 01623 622 500
Email: richardmjohn@me.com
Contacts: Phil McDaniel, Richard John
Committed to quality with care at sensible prices, giving you the best value for money.

EUROSOUND (UK) LTD
44 High Street, Clayton West, Huddersfield HD8 9NS
Tel: 01484 866 066 Fax: 01484 866 299
Email: eurosounduk@yahoo.co.uk
Web Site: www.eurosound.co.uk
Contact: Paul Martin

EVANS AUDIO LTD
Studio House, 5 Flowers Hill, Brislington Bristol BS4 5JJ
Tel: 0117 908 5558 Fax: 0117 908 5559
Email: paulg@evansaudio.com
Web Site: www.evansaudio.com
Contact: Paul Goold
Evans are sound equipment Hire, Sales, Design and installation specialists with over 20 years industrial experience. They provide support for theatre and corporate projects, and broadcast and live music throughout Europe and the UK.

FORMULA SOUND
Unit 23, Stadium Business Centre, North End Road, Wembley, Middlesex HA9 0AT
Tel: 0208 900 0947 Fax: 0208 903 8657
Email: info@formula-sound.com
Web Site: www.formula-sound.com
Contact: Sandra Cockell

FUTURE MEDIA
Unit 2, Grange Road Industrial Estate, Christchurch, Dorset BH23 4JD
Tel: 01425 270 511 Tel: 020 7100 0511 (London) Tel: 0121 314 0511 (Midlands)
Fax: 01425 278 615
Email: info@futuremediasystems.co.uk
Web: www.futuremediasystems.co.uk
Managing Director: Luke Siemaszko
Future Media specialise in Sound, Lighting and Video equipment. We are just as happy to provide a complete multimedia rig, or to sell just a single piece of equipment. We can supply only, hire, or install as required. Our emphasis is on providing a quality service, value for money, and excellent support. We can provide a full range of equipment from all manufacturers at competitive prices.

Theatre sound and communication systems, radio microphones, stage and effects lighting, video cameras and projection, show control, trussing, staging, infra - red and induction loop systems and consumables are all items we are keen to talk to you about!

FUTURIST PROJECTS LTD
Unit 1, White Swan Yard, Otley, LS21 1AE
Tel: 0113 279 0033 Fax: 0113 301 0255
Email: info@futurist.co.uk
Web Site: www.futurist.co.uk
Managing Director: Jamie Hudson
Financial Director: Jamie Hudson
AV, Theatrical Productions, Lighting and Sound Specialists.

FUZION PLC
Formerly Kelsey Acoustics Ltd
9 Lyon Road, Walton-on-Thames, Surrey KT12 3PU
Tel: 01932 882 222 Fax: 01932 882244
Email: sales@fuzion.co.uk
Web Site: www.fuzion.co.uk
Sales Director: Tony Torlini
Specialist audio/lighting connector and cable supplier

GB AUDIO
Unit D, 51 Brunswick Road, Edinburgh, Mid Lothian EH7 5PD Scotland
Tel/Fax: 0131 661 0022
Email: sales@gbaudio.co.uk
Web Site: www.gbaudio.co.uk
Hire, sale, installation and servicing of state-of-the-art sound equipment for concert, festival, theatre, conference and presentations.

GRADAV HIRE & SALES LTD
Elstree Light and Power, The Power House, Elstree Film Studios, Shenley Road, Borehamwood, Herts WD6 1JG
Tel: 020 8324 2100 Fax: 020 8324 2933
Email: office@gradav.co.uk
Web Site: www.gradav.co.uk
Sale & Dry Hire of technical equipment for theatre - including animation effects, moving head lanterns, radio mics & systems and Prolyte trussing. We also supply consummables.

ADAM HALL LTD
10 The Seedbed Business Centre, Vanguard Way, Shoeburyness, Essex SS3 9QY
Tel: 01702 613 922 Fax: 01702 617 168
Email: mail@adamhall.co.uk
Web Site: www.adamhall.com
Contact: Mark Stimpson
Distributor and supplier of fittings and hardware for flight cases and loudspeaker cabinets. Own brand stands for lighting, sound and musical instruments. Newly launched Adam Hall Cables. Sole distributor of Amphenol Audio Connectors,

Palmer Professional Audio Tools and Power Amplifiers.

HAND HELD AUDIO
Unit 8, Waterways Business Centre, Navigation Drive, South Ordnance Road, Enfield EN3 6JJ
Tel: 01992 719 078 Fax: 01992 763 860
Email: info@handheldaudio.co.uk
Web Site: www.handheldaudio.co.uk
Contact: Mick Shepherd
Wireless systems specialists. We hire, sell and service radio microphones and in ear systems.

HAWTHORN THEATRICAL LTD
Crown Business Park, Old Dalby, Leicestershire LE14 3NQ
Tel: 01664 821111 Fax: 01664 821119
Email: info@hawthorns.uk.com
Web Site: www.hawthorns.uk.com
Managing Director: Martin Hawthorn
Hire, Installation, design and sales of lighting, sound, staging, rigging, drapes, impact sales, starcloth and special effects.
Hire and sales open 7 days a week, main dealers for all leading brands.
London Office: Unit F, Western Trading Estate, London, NW10 7LU, Tel: 020 8955 6900

HD PRO AUDIO
6 Eversley Way, Thorpe Industrial Estate, Egham, Surrey TW20 8RG
Tel: 01784 433 687 Fax: 01784 479 910
Email: info@hdproaudio.co.uk
Web Site: www.hdproaudio.co.uk
Managing Director: Andy Huffer
HD Pro Audio are the UK's leading independent supplier and installer of professional audio visual systems.

JOHN HENRY'S LTD
16 - 24 Brewery Road, London N7 9NH
Tel: 020 7609 9181 Fax: 020 7700 7040
Email: info@johnhenrys.com
Web Site: www.johnhenrys.com
Contacts: Robert Harding, Pepin Clout
Suppliers of sound re-inforcement for Theatre, TV and Live Music.

JOHN HORNBY SKEWES & CO LTD
Salem House, Parkinson Approach, Garforth, Leeds, West Yorkshire LS25 2HR
Tel: 0113 286 5381 Fax: 0113 286 8515
Email: webinfo@jhs.co.uk
Web Site: www.jhs.co.uk
Proprietor: Mr John H Skewes
Publicity Manager: Simon Turnbull
Managing Director Designate: Dennis Drumm
The UK's No.1 independent trade distributor of musical equipment and pro-audio amplification.

HSL (HIRE) LTD
Unit E & F, Glenfield Park, Philips Road, Blackburn Lancashire BB1 5PF
Tel: 01254 698 808 Fax: 01254 698 835
Email: simon@hslgroup.com, contact@hslgroup.com
Web Site: www.hslgroup.com
Contact: Simon Stuart
Every client is special, each commission totally unique, our in house event management process ensuring that your project is carefully monitored, from the taking of your detailed instructions, through design and planning, and ultimately the installation and staging of the event itself.

RG JONES SOUND ENGINEERING
16 Endeavour Way, London SW19 8UH
Tel: 020 8971 3100 Fax: 020 8971 3101
Email: info@rgjones.co.uk
Web Site: www.rgjones.co.uk
Director: John Carroll
Design, hire and sales of professional sound equipment.

KAVE THEATRE SERVICES
Unit 1 and 2, 55 Victoria Road, Burgess Hill, West Sussex RH15 9LH
Tel: 01444 245 500 Fax: 01444 243 355
Email: sales@kave.co.uk
Web Site: www.kave.co.uk
Sales Manager: Michael Mackie Clarke

KEY AUDIO VISUAL
Black Tower Studios, 15 Bracondale, Norwich, Norfolk NR1 2AL
Tel: 01603 616 661 Fax: 01603 616 668
Email: daniel.forster@keyav.com
Web Site: www.keyav.com
Contact: Katrina Colgan

KICK AUDIO
Unit 4. The Box Works, Heysham Road, Bootle, Merseyside L30 6UR
Tel: 0151 430 7000 Fax: 0151 520 4020
Mob: 07798 566 390
Email: info@kickpa.co.uk
Web Site: www.kickpa.co.uk
Contact: Peter Jeffrey

KIRKPATRICK SOUND ENGINEERING
1 Clover Drive, The Paddocks, Pickmere, Knutsford, Cheshire WA16 0WF
Tel/Fax: 01565 733 200 Mobile: 07831 504 404
Email: roy@kirkpatrick4sound.co.uk
Web Site: www.kirkpatrick4sound.co.uk
Contact: Roy Kirkpatrick
Professional sound and communication systems and equipment. Sales, installation, hire and system design. Also Magnetic Induction Loop Systems.

KLARK TEKNIK
Klark Teknik Building, Walter Nash Road, Kidderminster, Worcestershire DY11 7HJ
Tel: 01562 741 515 Fax: 01562 745 371
Email: jason.kelly@midasklarkteknik.com
Web Site: www.klarkteknik.com / www.midasconsoles.com
Technical Sales Manager: Jason Kelly
Sales & Distribution of Klark Teknik , Midas, DDA concert sound products. Design and manufacture of Klark Teknik signal processing equipment and Midas audio mixing consoles.

LANCELYN THEATRE SUPPLIES
Ferry Hinksey Road, Oxford OX2 0BY
Tel: 01865 722 468 Fax: 01865 728 791
Email: oxford@lancelynoxford.co.uk
Web Site: www.lancelyn.co.uk
Sales and Branch Manager: Reg Berry
Email: reg@lancelynoxford.co.uk
Marketing, Admin & Office Manager: Sara Ingham
Made to measure curtains, supply and fix, repair and cleaning.

LINE-UP PMC
10 Matthew Close, Newcastle upon Tyne NE6 1XD
Tel / Fax: 0191 275 9745
Mob: 07808 300 906
Email: chrismurtagh@line-up.co.uk
Web Site: www.line-up.co.uk
Senior Personnel: Chris Murtagh

LINK COMMUNICATIONS
61 Ipswich Crescent, Great Barr, Birmingham B42 1LY
Tel: 0121 357 8261 Mob: 07929 42 75 91 / 07770 99 66 44
Email: info@linkcomms.co.uk
Web Site: www.linkcomms.co.uk
Contact: Paul Simms
Sound and Communication. Equipment Hire. Sound Reinforcement. PMR Radio and related products.

LIVE BUSINESS INTERNATIONAL
22 Prescott Place, London SW4 6BT
Tel: 0207 622 0751 Fax: 0207 801 8999
Email: info@livebusiness.co.uk
Web Site: www.livebusiness.co.uk
Contacts: Roland Hemming
Sound, lighting & video fit for any stage. Specialists in the design, installation & maintenance of sound, video & lighting systems.

LMC AUDIO SYSTEMS LTD
Unit 47, Phoenix Park, Avenue Road, Aston, Birmingham B7 4NU
Tel: 0121 359 4535 Fax: 0121 359 8789
London Office: LMC Audio Systems Ltd, Unit 10, Cowley Road, London W3 7XA
Tel: 020 8743 4680 Fax: 020 8749 9875
Email: sales@lmcaudio.co.uk
Web Site: www.lmcaudio.co.uk
Managing Director: Paul Hinkly
Sales Manager: Sean Hames
Specialising in all areas of live sound reinforcement, LMC has the biggest product portfolio in the business. Make LMC your "one stop shop" for all things pro audio.

LOCATION SOUND
82 Henbury Road, Henbury, Bristol BS10 7AA
Tel: 0119 950 8700 Mobile: 07971 154717
Email: sales@locationsound.co.uk
Web Site: www.locationsound.co.uk
Contact: Nick Langley
Suppliers and installers of Public Address Systems, Speech Paging, Background Music, Induction Loop, Infra Red Systems and Closed Circuit TV.

LOGIC SYSTEM PRO AUDIO LIMITED
Unit 5 and 6, Old Sandars Road, Heapham Road Industrial Estate Gainsborough, Lincolnshire DN21 1XT
Tel: 01427 611 791 Fax: 01427 677 008
Email: sales@logic-system.co.uk
Web Site: www.logic-system.co.uk
We make within the UK, high quality professional audio speakers using great quality components.
Sales Executive: Dave Crane

LOUD TECHNOLOGIES UL LTD
Century Point, Halifax Road, Cressex Business Park, High Wycombe, Buckinghamshire HP12 3SL
Tel: 01494 535 312 Fax: 01494 438 669
Email: james.blackwell@mackie.com
Web Site: www.mackie.com
Contact: James Blackwell
Mackie, Ampeg, Martin Audio, EAW Speaker System & Cinema Systems.

MAC SOUND
1-2 Attenburys Park, Park Road, Altrincham, Cheshire WA14 5QE
Tel: 0161 969 8311 Fax: 0161 962 9423
Email: info@macsound.co.uk
Web Site: www.macsound.co.uk
Design: Clement Rawling
Sales: David Houghton
Hire: Andrew Simpson
Administration: Julie Murray
MAC Sound offers a complete sound design, equipment hire, engineering and personnel service for all types of theatre presentations and concerts. With over thirty years experience, we provide a free radio microphone planning and licensing service and offer quotations and site visits without obligation. Please visit our website or call for a current hire ratecard.

MALDWYN BOWDEN INTERNATIONAL LTD
168 Edward Street, Brighton, East Sussex BN2 0JB

Tel: 01273 607 384 Fax: 01273 694 408
Email: mbi@mistral.co.uk
Web Site: www.mistral.co.uk/mbi
Maldwyn Bowden International design, supply and install sound and lighting systems for theatres and clubs and can also provide equipment on hire.

MARTIN PROFESSIONAL PLC
Cranborne House, Cranborune Industrial Estate, Cranbourne Road, Potters Bar, Hertfordshire, EN6 3JN
Tel: 0203 0021 170
Email: uksales@martin.dk
Web Site: www.martinpro.co.uk

MC PRODUCTION GROUP
Unit SU4A, Lansbury Estate, 102 Lower Guildford Road, Woking, Surrey GU21 2EP
Tel: 01483 884488.
Web Site: www.mcpg.co.uk

MCL
Catesby Park, Eckersall Road, Kings Norton, Birmingham B38 8SE
Tel: 0121 433 8899 Fax: 0121 433 8891
London Office: 14 Ockham Drive, Greenford Park, Greenford, London, UB6 0FD Tel: 0208 839 7010
Fax: 0208 839 7011
Email: info@mclcreate.com
Web Site: www.mclcreate.com
General Manager (Birmingham): Mark Simkin
Operations Manager (Birmingham): Paul Mandeville
Hire Manager (Birmingham): Chris Cheatle
Conference, exhibition and presentation equipment hire. Audio visual sound and lighting.

MERCIA THEATRE SERVICES
2A Hotel Street, Coalville, Leicestershire LE67 3EP
Tel: 01530 263 454 Fax: 01530 260 206
Email: merciaarts@yahoo.co.uk
Contact: Simon Nickerson
Lighting: Sales of accessories and consumables including colour filter, cables, connectors, fixing hardware, adhesive tapes, lamps. Sales of lanterns and control systems. Installation service.
Sound: Sales of accessories and consumables including cables, connectors, batteries, sound effects CD's. Extensive range of hardware including microphones, mixing desks, amplifiers, speakers, CD, cassette and mini disc players, induction loop and Infra-red systems. Installation service. PA hire for indoor / outdoor meetings, conferences and events.
Effects: Sales of hardware and consumables for pyrotechnic and special effects.
Make-up: Sales of make-up by Ben Nye and Mehron. Also an extensive range of wigs, masks and costume accessories.
Mail order catalog available.

MIDLAND SOUND HIRE
PA Systems, Lighting and Sound Reinforcement
53 Gorse Farm Road, Great Barr, Birmingham B43 5LS
Tel: 0778 792 2437 Tel: 07050 636 367 - Andrew Andley
Email: mshpasound@googlemail.com
2 kw to 10 kw PA sound systems for live bands, DJs, college and university events, festivals, tours and corporate events.
200 watt to 2 kw sound systems for vocalists, DJs and live bands.
2 kw/10 kw rigs: 12/16/24 channel mixers, 2/4 way aux foldback & full onstage mix, graphics, echo and reverb, fully experienced engineers.
Equipment Inc., AKG Altec, Allen & Heath, Audio Technica, Behringer, Beyer, Carlsboro, HH, JBL, Peavey, RCF, Shure & Studiomaster, EV, Crown, PSL.
Lighting rig: Par 56/64 spots (4/6 each side), 2 stands, strobe, rwisters, ultra violets, control desk and engineer.

ML SOUND ADVICE
Baileys Yard, Chatham Green, Little Waltham, Chelmsford, Essex CM3 3LE
Tel: 01322 625052 Fax: 01322 552929
Email: mail@mlsoundadvice.com
Web Site: www.mlsoundadvice.com
Contact: Gareth Jones

MM PRODUCTIONS
Unit 10 Smeaton Close, Severalls Industrial Park, Colchester CO4 9QY
Tel: 01206 845 947 Tech (Out of Hours): 07850 792 263
Web Site: www.mmproductions.co.uk
Email:
Sound Hire & Sales: inquiries@mmproductions.co.uk
Lighting Hire & Sales: lx@mmproductions.co.uk
Managing Director: Martyn Hunt

MUSIC ROOM
The Old Library, 116-118 New Cross Road, London SE14 5BA
Tel: 020 7252 8271 Fax: 020 7252 8252
Email: sales@musicroomlondon.com
Web Site: www.musicroomlondon.com
Manager: Mr Garden Gapper
Sound and musical equipment, hire and sales, 7 days a week.

MUSTANG COMMUNICATIONS LTD
Dunslow Road, Eastfield Industrial Estate, Scarborough, North Yorkshire YO11 3UT
Tel: 0845 652 4008 Fax: 0845 652 4009
Email: info@mustang.co.uk
Web Site: www.mustang.co.uk
Office Manager: Mrs Hardman
Manufacturer of amplification and loop induction
equipment.

NEWSTAGESOUND
Also see listing for UsedStageSound
Ivy Sound Ltd Ivy Cottage Middleton, Winterslow, Salisbury SP5 1QS
Tel: 01980 863733 Fax: 0870 248 6007
Mob: 07850 343 262
Email: mail@newstagesound.com
Web Site: www.newstagesound.com / www.usedstagesound.com
Director: Ian McDonald
*Suppliers of the highest quality Professional Sound Equipment for theatre, live music stage, Houses of Worship, Education and Professional Musicians.
*UK and Ireland Exclusive Distributors for the well known and respected Carver Professional range of Power Amplifiers.
*Approved Dealers for EM Acoustics, Matrix Amplification, Allen & Heath, Clockaudio, Shure, Adam Hall, LD Systems, Sennheiser and others, tending to promote the best UK manufacturers.
30 years experience in the Industry.
Technical Consultancy, System Design, Acoustics, Problem Solving and Engineering Services available. Designers and Constructors of bespoke equipment
Site visits arranged.

NORTHERN STAGE SERVICES
Trent Industrial Estate, Duchess Street, Shaw, Oldham, Lancashire OL2 7UT
Tel: 01706 849 469 Fax: 01706 840 138
Email: Info@nstage.co.uk, david.baxter@nstage.co.uk

Web Site: www.nstage.co.uk
Specialists in stage lighting, sound and curtain equipment.
Managing Director: Patrick Colin
Sales Manager: David Baxter
Business Administrator: Kelly Tracey

ON EVENT PRODUCTION COMPANY

Formerly Panda Hire Ltd.
Acton House, Acton Grove, Acton Road Industrial Estate, Long Eaton, Nottingham NG10 1FY
Tel: 01159 222 959 Fax: 01159 735 918
Email: sales@lovingitlive.co.uk
Web Site: www.lovingitlive.co.uk
MD: Guy Eaton
Operations Director: Paul White
Production Director: Chris Vernon-Smith
Hire Manger: James Pemblington
We hire PA / Staging / Lighting / Truss & Power distribution for either dry hire or as a complete package with engineers and/or event management.

ONE STAGE PRODUCTIONS LTD

11 Bramley Close, Cogenhoe, Northampton NN7 1LY
Tel: 0870 774 3522 Mobile: 07956 234192
Email: john@one-stage.com
Web Site: www.one-stage.com
Contacts: John Ryan, Jody Ryan
With a strong team of IT and Audio design staff we offer a friendly and professional service as suppliers of market leading equipment suitable for theatre, conferencing, exhibitions, broadcasting and touring. We also have an experienced team working in project and tour management.

ORBITAL SOUND

57 Acre Lane, Brixton, London SW2 5TN
Tel: 020 7501 6868 Fax: 020 7501 6869
Email: hire@orbitalsound.co.uk
Web Site: www.orbitalsound.co.uk
Managing Director: Chris Headlam
Event & Communications Director: Eric Simpson
A leading provider of sound systems and design services to touring and West End theatre.

OUT BOARD ELECTRONICS

(Sheriff Technology Ltd)
Unit 4 Church Meadows, Haslingfield Road, Barrington, Cambridge CB22 7RG
Tel: 01223 871015 Fax: 01223 871030
Email: info@outboard.co.uk
Web Site: www.outboard.co.uk
Contacts: Robin Whittaker, Dave Haydon
Manufacturers of automated sound control equipment for suround sound and level control, products include TiMax, QP4 quad panner, mains power distribution systems and hoist controllers.

OXRECS DIGITAL

Maytree Cottage, 51 Eaton Road, Appleton, Abingdon, Oxfordshire OX13 5JH
Tel: 01865 862310
Email: info@oxrecs.com
Web Site: www.oxrecs.com
Manager: Bernard Martin
Specialists in classicial location sound recording for choirs, chamber ensembles and orchestras. Typesetting and design service available for CD booklets and inlays.

THE P.A. COMPANY LIMITED

Unit 7, The Ashway Centre, Elm Crescent, Kingston-upon-Thames, Surrey KT2 6HH
Tel: 020 8546 6640 Fax: 020 8547 1469
Mob: 07836 600 081
Email: thepacompany@aol.com
Web Site: www.thepaco.com
Sound Engineer: Doug Beveridge
Hire/sale/installation of all sound equipment 'BOSE' main agents.

PAS SOUND ENGINEERING LTD

Senator Point, South Boundary Road, Knowsley Industrial Park, Liverpool L33 7RR
Tel: 0845 430 0546 / 0151 546 0546
Fax: 0151 546 2345
Email: sales@pas-sound.co.uk
Web Site: www.pas-sound.co.uk
Public Address, Audio, Communications, Security Systems.

PERFORMANCE LIGHT AND SOUND LTD

Unit 10, Cowley Road, London W3 7XA
Tel: 020 8743 4680
Email: sales@lmccaudio.co.uk
Web Site: www.lmcaudio.co.uk
Importers and distributers of chassis loudspeakers and lighting and cable.

PHONOPHOBIA

Unit 1B and 2B, Little Caring Farm, Caring Road, Leeds, Maidstone, Kent ME17 1TH
Tel (Hire): 01622 861626 Tel (Sales): 01622 863 344 Fax: 01622 863 150
Email: mail@phonophobia-online.co.uk
Web: www.phonophobia-online.co.uk
Director: Mark Chant
20 years supplying sound equipment and engineers for tours, theatres, festivals, etc

PHOSPHENE

Milton Road South, Stowmarket, Suffolk IP14 1EZ
Tel: 01449 770 011
Email: phosphene@btconnect.com
Web Site: www.phosphene.co.uk
Proprietor: Cliff Dix
Hire and sales of lamps, lanterns, radio mics and control equipment by all major manufacturers. Production design, rigging and operation for all styles. Specialise in "One nighters" in unusual venues; product launches, fashion shows, etc.

POINT SOURCE PRODUCTIONS LTD

Unit 5 Kimpton trade & Business Centre, Minden Road, Sutton, Surrey SM3 9PF
Tel: 020 8254 2620 Fax: 08701 696 736
Email: info@pslx.co.uk
Web Site: www.pslx.co.uk
Point Source Productions can organise, plan and supply technical services, including lighting, sound, AV and staging, for Corporate, Theatre and Live Events.

PRO AUDIO SYSTEMS LTD

153-155 Sunbridge Road, Bradford, West Yorkshire BD1 2NU
Tel: 01274 777 200 / 0845 166 7525
Fax: 01274 777 100
Email: sales@pasystems.co.uk
Web Site: www.proaudiosystems.co.uk
Managing Directors: Brian Lumb, Paul Siddall
We supply all types of audio equipment, including PA systems, multi-channel radio microphones & infra-red, all for hire or sale. Technicians are available as it is a system design service.

RAYCOM

Langton House, 19 Village Street, Harvington, Evesham, Worcestershire WR11 8NQ
Admin Tel: 01789 777 041 Admin Fax: 01789 881 330 Sales Tel: 01789 777 045
Email: info@raycom.co.uk, sales@raycom.co.uk
Web Site: www.raycom.co.uk
Supplying Radio systems to the Film, Broadcast and Entertainment industries since 1984.

ROBBOTRONIC CO

14 Blatchford Close, Industrial Estate, Horsham, West Sussex RH13 5RG
Tel: 01403 210 420
Email: bryan@robbotronic.plus.com
Manager: Mr. Bryan Robinson
Consult/design/supply and install sound re-inforcement and infra-red/audio frequency inductive loop systems.

THE SCAN WAREHOUSE

Kingfisher House, Hodgson Way, Wickford, Essex SS11 8YN
Tel: 08705 561 233 Fax: 08705 134 476
Email: info@scanwarehouse.com
Web Site: www.scanwarehouse.com
"The Professional Sound & Lighting Company"
The Scan Warehouse services offered are: Sound and Lighting Design, Supply, Installation, Programming and Maintenance.

SDD SOUND & LIGHT LTD
Temple Gardens, Staines, Middlesex TW18 3NQ
Tel: 01784 455 666 Fax: 01784 455 642
Email: info@sddsoundandlight.com
Web Site: www.sddsoundandlight.com
Rental, sales, repair and installation of all types and brands of equipment from multi channel radio microphone systems to intelligent lighting. Visit our website for our catalogue.

SENNHEISER UK LTD
3 Century Point, Halifax Road, High Wycombe, Buckinghamshire HP12 3SL
Tel: 01494 551 551 Fax: 01494 551 550
Email: info@sennheiser.co.uk
Web Site: www.sennheiser.co.uk
Contact: Dip Patel
Sound communications equipment. Specialists in headphones microphones, radio frequency and infra-red transmission systems, supplying all major national and local theatre productions. Clear technical advice and full service support.

SGB WORLD SERVICE
Empire Buildings, 49 Church Street, Stoke, Stoke-on-Trent Staffordshire, ST4 1DQ
Tel: 01782 749 749
Email: sales@fireworkempire.co.uk
Web Site: www.fireworkempire.co.uk

SHERMANN AUDIO
35 Vastre Enterprise Park, Newtown, Powys SY16 1DZ Wales
Tel: 01686 622 997
Email: sales@shermann.com, info@shermann.com
Web Site: www.shermannaudio.com
Contact: Ken Hughes
Professional loudspeaker systems with over 40 models in production. Shermann Systems are used worldwide yet designed and built in Britain. Distribution through selected dealers. Demo rigs available.

SOLENT SOUNDS SYSTEMS LTD
7 Mitchell Point, Ensign Park, Hamble, Southampton, Hampshire SO31 4RF
Tel: 023 8045 6700 Fax: 023 8045 6789
Email: sales@solentsound.com
Web Site: www.solentsound.com
Manager: Ray Gatehouse
Technical Manager: Adam Gatehouse

SONIFEX LIMITED
61 Station Road, Irthlingborough, Northamptonshire NN9 5QE
Tel: 01933 650 700 Fax: 01933 650 726
Email: sales@sonifex.co.uk
Web Site: www.sonifex.co.uk
Sales Dept: Eamonn Hefferman, Richard Butlin, Jill Brown
Manufacturing: Radio studio equipment: Audio loggers, digital and analogue telephone balance units, digital and analogue audio interfaces, radio broadcast mixers, studio equipment, bespoke audio equipment design and manufacture.

SOUND AND LIGHT SOLUTIONS
Unit 2, Mossvale 9 Clark Street, Paisley, Renfrewshire PA3 1RX Scotland
Tel: 0141 887 7655 Mobile: 07876 682 267
Email: enquiries@slsscotland.net
Web Site: www.slsscotland.net
Contact: Mr Simon Bain

SOUND BY DESIGN
Unit C, Imber Court Trading Estate, Orchard Lane, East Molesey, Surrey KT8 0BY
Tel: 020 8339 3888 Fax: 020 8339 3889
Email: chappie@soundbydesign.net
Web Site: www.soundbydesign.net
Managing Director: Andy Callin
General Manager: Emma Gallagher
Hire & Resources Manager: Phill Chapman (Chappie)

SSE HIRE LTD
Burnt Meadow House, Burnt Meadow Road, North Moons Moat, Redditch B98 9PA
Tel: 01527 528 822 Fax: 01527 528 840
Email: hire@sseaudio.com, spencer.beard@sseaudio.com
Web Site: www.sseaudiogroup.com
Managing Director: John Penn
Operations Director: Spencer Beard
Flightcase manufacture. Risers and set supply. PA systems sales and rental

STAGE ELECTRICS
Third Way, Avonmouth, Bristol, Avon BS11 9YL
Hire & Sales: 0117 938 4000 Accounts: 0117 937 9550 Admin: 0117 982 7282 Admin Fax: 0117 916 2825 Fax: 0117 916 2828
Email: bristol@stage-electrics.co.uk
Web Site: www.stage-electrics.co.uk
One of the UK's largest suppliers of technical equipment to the entertainment, leisure, conference and presentation industries.
Offering sales and hire of lighting, sound, rigging, staging and all related equipment.
Head of Marketing: Adam Blaxill
Managing Director: Dan Aldridge
London Branch:
175 Long Lane, London SE1 4PN
Tel: 020 7939 3000 Fax: 020 7939 3001
E-Mail: london@stage-electrics.co.uk
Exeter Branch:
1 Swan Units, Heron Road, Sowton Industrial Estate, Exeter EX2 7LL
Tel: 01392 824 100 Fax: 01392 891 116
E-Mail: exeter@stage-electrics.co.uk

STAGE TWO LIMITED
Unit J, Penfold Estate, Imperial Way, Watford, Hertfordshire WD24 4YY
Tel: 01923 230 789 Fax: 01923 255 048
Email: info@stage-two.co.uk
Web Site: www.stage-two.co.uk
Hire or Sale of sound, lighting and special effects for all applications. Special effects Flash Pots, Maroons, Bullet Hits. Supplier of special effects for stage, films and TV.

STAGECRAFT TECHNICAL SERVICES LTD
Unit E & F, Porton Business Centre, Porton, Salisbury SP4 0ND
Tel: 0845 838 2015
Email: office@stagecraft.co.uk
Web Site: www.stagecraft.co.uk
Managing Director: Lisa Tapper
Sales Director: Mike Naish
Marketing Assistant: Chris Robinson
We supply & install equipment from all leading lighting & sound sound manufacturers to the educational, amateur and professional entertainment sectors.

STARDREAM LTD
70 Mowbray Drive, Blackpool, Lancashire FY3 7UN
Tel: 01253 302 602
Email: sales@stardream.co.uk
Web Site: www.stardream.co.uk
Manager: Sam Barnet
Specialising in event management, planning and organising corporate events, private functions, product launches, weddings, conferences, exhibitons and more. Stardream also distributes and installs for major manufacturers of professional sound and lighting equipment and special effects.

STUDIOHIRE (LONDON) LTD
8 Daleham Mews, London NW3 5DB
Tel: 020 7431 0212 Fax: 020 7431 1134
Email: mail@studiohire.net
Web Site: www.studiohire.net
Contact: Paul Tattersall, Sam Thomas
Hire of musical and theatrical equipment. See our new website for details and prices.
You name it, we've got it!

TANNOY LTD
Professional Division, Rosehall Industrial Estate, Coatbridge, Lanarkshire ML5 4TF Scotland
Tel: 01236 420 199 Fax: 01236 428 230
Email: enquiries@tannoy.com
Web Site: www.tannoy.com
Managing Director: Andrzej Sosna
Tannoy's unique range of high performance point source systems are designed to offer the ultimate in sound reinforcement; compact, incredibly powerful, yet so natural they become invisible to the performance.

TERRALEC LTD
Osprey House, Featherby Way, Purdeys Industrial Estate, Rochford, Essex SS4 1LD
Tel: 01702 547 571 Fax: 01702 541 075
Email: sales@terralec.com
Web Site: www.terralec.co.uk
Suppliers of professional stage lighting, audio equipment, lighting control, microphones, staging, trussing, hardware, accessories & much more! For: Theatre, stage, commercial events and the entertainment industry.

THAMES AUDIO LTD
Building 11, Shepperton Film Studios, Studios Road, Shepperton, Middlesex TW17 0QD
Tel: 01932 567 681 Fax: 01932 569 758
Email: info@thamesaudio.co.uk
Web Site: www.thamesaudio.co.uk
Directors: Pete Cox, Graham Simpson
Project Manager: James Tebb
Specialists in Sound Design and Equipment Hire for Theatre, Concerts and Live Events.

TICKLE MUSIC HIRE LTD
133-137 Kilburn Lane, London W10 4AN
Tel: 020 8964 3399 Fax: 020 8964 0343
Email: tad@ticklemusichire.com, hire@ticklemusichire.com
Web Site: www.ticklemusichire.com
Contact: Tad Barker

TMC
Hillam Road, Bradford, West Yorkshire BD2 1QN
Tel: 01274 370 966 Fax: 01274 308 706
Email: sales@tmc.ltd.uk
Web Site: www.tmc.ltd.uk
Contact: Chris Smith
Highly specialised from the outset. TMC (The Music Company) is regarded as one of Britain's foremost centres of expertise in sound and vision technology, a position acknowledged by many industry awards and citations.
Product lines include radio mics, loudspeakers, amplifiers, mixing consoles, DVD players, video projectors, Plasma Screens and tour guide systems.
TMC are agents for d&b audiotechnik, Funktion 1, Turbosound, Allen & Heath, Crest Audio, Sennheiser, Trantec, Sony, Pioneer and Sanyo. To name but a few ...
Emergency call out service also available.

TORPEDO FACTORY LTD
The Old Torpedo Factory, St. Leonards Road, London NW10 6ST
Tel: 020 8537 1000 Fax: 020 8537 1001
Email: s.maskell@tfg.com
Web Site: www.tfg.com
Project Manager: Steve Maskell
Gordon Audio Visual provides leading edge technical services for events, meetings and related activities. Lighting, set design and construction, projection, audio systems, webcasting, streaming, pre- and post-production facilities and more.

TOUCHWOOD AUDIO PRODUCTIONS
6 Hyde Park Terrace, Leeds, West Yorkshire LS6 1BJ
Studio Tel: 0113 278 7180 Mob: 07745 377 772
Email: studio@touchwoodaudio.com
Web Site: www.touchwoodaudio.com
Specialists in production and recording of theatre backing tracks, voice-overs and special effects. Digital editing and large library of original and non-original source material available.

TRANTEC
TOA Corporation (UK) Ltd, HQ3 Unit 2, Hook Rise South, Surbiton, Surrey KT6 7LD
Tel: 0870 774 0987 Fax: 0870 777 0839
Email: info/sales@toa.co.uk
Web Site: www.trantec.co.uk
Head of Sales & Marketing: Brett Downing
Trantec offer a full range of both VHF and UHF radio microphones for all theatrical performances. All Trantec products are designed and manufactured in the UK and are fully DTI approved.

TRUE SOUND HIRE
Hillspur Close, Guildford, Surrey GU2 8HF
Tel: 01483 564438 Mob: 07908 732936
Email: info@truesoundhire.co.uk
Web Site: www.truesoundhire.co.uk

ROY TRUMAN SOUND SERVICES
Unit 2, Harp Business Centre, Apsley Way, London NW2 7LW
Tel: 020 8208 2468 Fax: 020 8208 3320
Email: rtss@london.com
Web Site: www.rtss.biz
Proprietor: Roy Truman
Contact Manager: Elizabeth Wirrer
Sound equipment hire, with engineers. Service aspect paramount... Because we care!

TURBOSOUND
Unit 1 - 6 Star Road, Partridge Green, Horsham, West Sussex RH13 8RY
Tel: 01403 711 447 Fax: 01403 710 155
Email: turbosales@turbosound.com
Web Site: www.turbosound.com
Sales Director: Dominic Harter
Contact: dominic.harter@turbosound.com or Tel: 01403 712741

TUSK SHOWHIRE
15 Manlake Avenue, Winterton, Scunthorpe, South Humberside DN15 9SD
Tel: 01724 271 527
Mobile: 07774 964 205

Email: trickolite@aol.com
Web Site: www.trickolite.co.uk
Contact: Phil Rose
Sound hire and installation. Live Sound engineering, Custom flight case manufacture.

VDC TRADING LTD
VDC House, 4 Brandon Road, London N7 9AA
Tel: 020 7700 2777 Fax: 020 7700 3888
Email: sales@vdctrading.com
Web Site: www.vdctrading.com
Contact: Niall Holden
Manufacturer and distributor of the VDM range of multi-channel audio connectors. The VDM range of connectors is available from 8 channels to 48 channels.
Manufacturer and distributor of audio & video cable and components. Also distribute the Van Damme range of cables. Specialise in producing bespoke assemblies for the recording, presentation and broadcast markets.

VIKING SOUND & LIGHT LTD
Unit 9 Woodstock Close Standard Way Ind. Park, Northallerton North Yorkshire DL6 2NB
Tel: 01609 780190 Mob Tel: 07980 023154
Email: steve@vikingsound.co.uk
Web Site: www.vikingsound.co.uk
Contact: Steve Williams
Viking Sound are suppliers of PA systems, lighting systems, stage hire, installations, artist bookings and event management.

WAAGNER BIRO UK LTD
The Street, Englefield, Reading RG7 5ES
Tel: 01189 640 033 Fax 01189 640 074
Email: alun.edwards@waagner-biro.com
Web Site: www.waagner-biro.com
Country Manager: Alun Edwards

THE WAREHOUSE SOUND SERVICES LTD
23 Water Street, Edinburgh, Mid Lothian EH6 6SU Scotland
Tel: 0131 555 6900 Fax: 0131 555 6901
40 Carmichael Street, Glasgow G51 6QU
Tel: 0141 445 4466 Fax: 0141 445 3636
Email: info@warehousesound.co.uk
Web Site: www.warehousesound.co.uk
Contact: Cameron Crosby
Hire and sales of professional audio equipment. All major makes of equipment including d & b audiotechnik. Next day delivery throughout the UK.

WHITWAM LTD
2 Moorside Business Park, Moorside Road, Winchester, Hampshire SO23 7RX
Tel: 01962 870 408 Fax: 01962 850 820
Email: service@whitwam.ltd.uk
Web Site: www.whitwam.ltd.uk
Professional Sound Sales: David Harding

(Director)
Technical Manager: Andy Pymm
Consultants, designers, equipment, supply and hire, installation and commissioning of sound, public address and communications systems for theatres, conference centres, local authorities, churches, arts centres, concerts halls, etc. Member Plasa.

WIGWAM ACOUSTICS LTD
Unit 101 Phoenix Park Industrial Estate
Phoenix Close, Heywood, Lancashire
OL10 2JG
Tel: 01706 363 400 Fax: 01706 363 410
Direct Hire: 01706 363 800
Email: sales@wigwam.co.uk
Web Site: www.wigwam.co.uk
Managing Director: Mick Spratt
Sales and Installations: David Orridge
Sound systems. Hiring everything from a microphone to a complete touring sound system. Sales and installation.

WILDING SOUND LTD
50 Beulah Road, London E17 9LQ
Tel: 020 8520 3401 Fax: 020 8520 1073
Email: info@wildingsound.co.uk
Web Site: www.wildingsound.co.uk

Sound Effects Libraries

DE WOLFE MUSIC
Shropshire House, 11-20 Capper Street, London WC1E 6JA
Tel: 020 7631 3600 Fax: 020 7631 3700
Email: info@dewolfemusic.co.uk
Web Site: www.dewolfe.co.uk
Senior Music Publisher: Warren De Wolfe
Whether you want to use the production music library, get help and advice on licensing music, commission some specially composed music, purchase some sound effects, or use our recording studios, our team of experienced consultants are here to help you.

THE SOUND EFFECTS LIBRARY
Roxburghe House, 273 Regent Street, London W1B 2HA
Tel: 020 7439 3325 Fax: 020 7734 9417
Email: matt@sound-effects-library.com
Web Site: www.sound-effects-library.com
Chairman: Matthew Mighell
Director: Christopher Coulcher

Sponsorship Consultants

BELL POTTINGER PUBLIC RELATIONS
5th Floor, Holborn Gate, 26 Southampton Buildings, London WC2A 1BP
Tel: 020 7861 2424 Fax: 020 7861 2474
Email: dwilson@bell-pottinger.co.uk
Web Site: www.bell-pottingerpr.co.uk
Chairman: David Wilson

KAREN EARL SPONSORSHIP
Gunpowder House, 66 Great Suffolk Street, London SE1 0BL
Tel: 020 7202 2800 Fax: 020 7702 2802
Email: info@karen-earl.co.uk
Web Site: www.karen-earl.co.uk
Office Manager: Rowena Kenyon
KES sponsorship consultancy offers the keys to answering the following questions:- What should you sponsor? How should you sponsor? And how do you make it work?
KES event management gives clients original, innovative, and overall clever event solutions.

KETCHUM
35-41 Folgate Street, London E1 6BX
Tel: 020 7611 3500 Fax: 020 7611 3501
Email: david.gallagher@ketchum.com
Web Site: www.ketchum.com
Contact Partner and CEO: David Gallagher

OCTAGON
81-83 Fulham High Street, London SW6 3JW
Tel: 020 7862 0000 Fax: 020 7862 0001
Email: kate.borthwick@octagon.com
Web Site: www.octagon.com
Consultant: Kate Borthwick

Stage & Scenic Engineering

AIR-SET LTD
3 Weston Colley, Micheldever, Winchester, Hampshire SO21 3AF
Tel: 01962 774 445 Fax: 01962 774 777
Email: david@air-set.co.uk
Web Site: www.air-set.co.uk
Proprietor: David Findley
Arched canopy and stages for outdoor or indoor music concerts. Visit our website for eye catching ideas to give your event a weatherproof inflatable shelter! Available for hire or sale.

ALISCAFF LTD
(Also Trading as Alistage)
Kenrich House, Elizabeth Way, Harlow, Essex CM19 5TL
Tel: 01279 406 270 Fax: 01279 406 292
Email: colin_w@alistage.co.uk
Web Site: www.alistage.co.uk
Managing Director: Colin Wright
Technical: Graham Hards
Stage systems, domed canopies, roof systems, raked seating, catwalks.

ALISTAGE
(also trading as Aliscaff Ltd)
Kenrich House, Elizabeth Way, Harlow, Essex CM19 5TL
Tel: 01279 406270 Fax: 01279 406292
Email: colin_w@alistage.co.uk
Web Site: www.alistage.co.uk
Managing Director: Colin Wright
Technical: Graham Hards
Modular stages for hire, sale and lease. Stage systems, domed canopies, roof systems, raked seating, catwalks.

A.S.G. STAGE PRODUCTS LTD
Redgate Road, South Lancashire Ind. Estate, Ashton-in-Makerfield, Wigan, Lancashire WN4 8DT
Tel: 01942 718 347 Fax: 01942 718 219
Email: post@asgstage.co.uk
Web Site: www.asgstage.co.uk
Projects Manager: Paul McFerran
Since 1973 we have specialised in the supply and installation of performance facilities to professional, amateur and educational theatres - including tracks, curtains, rigging, lighting, sound, projection, seating and staging.

AVW CONTROLS LTD
Unit 12, Willow Farm, Allwood Green, Rickinghall, Diss, Norfolk IP22 1LT
Tel: 01379 898 340 E-Fax: 08715 227 291
Email: sales@avw.co.uk
Web Site: www.avw.co.uk
Managing Director: Anton Woodward
Rigging and scenery motion control. Computerised automation.

BLACKWING LTD
Barnes Farm, Battlesea Green, Stradbroke, Eye, Suffolk IP21 5NE
Tel: 01379 388519
Email: enquiries@blackwingltd.com
Web Site: www.blackwingltd.com
Managing Director: Torben Merriott
Company Secretary: Pamie Merriott
Lighting, Audio, and Special Effects, Steel Deck Staging - hire and sales.

BOWER WOOD PRODUCTION SERVICES
Unit 5, The Billings, 3 Walnut Tree Close, Guildford, Surrey GU1 4UL
Tel: 01483 300 926 Fax: 01483 450 926
Email: enquiries@bowerwood.com
Web Site: www.bowerwood.com
Contact: Graham Bower Wood, Nigel

Mathias
Scenery Construction & Metal Fabrication for the Theatre, Opera, Cruise Ships, Exhibitions & Special Events.

BRILLIANT STAGES LIMITED
Unit 2, Hillgate, Hitchin,
Hertfordshire SG4 0RY
Tel: 01462 455 366 Fax: 01462 436 219
Email: tbowern@bstages.com
Web Site: www.brilliantstages.com

CENTRAL EVENTS UK LTD
The Barn Fifield Farm Marlston Road
Marlston Nr Hermitage Berkshire RG18 9UN
Tel: 01235 760 342 Fax: 01635 202 088
Email: heidi.smith@s-l-v.co.uk
Web Site: www.central-production.co.uk
Senior Personnel: Jim Williams
Specialise in production of rigging, staging, lighting, PA, theming, power distribution, marquees and catering for corporate and private parties.
At Central Events UK, we pride ourselves in being a full service events management company whcih gives us the freedom to offer the very best in service, product and price to our customers.

CENTRE STAGE ENGINEERING LTD
Unit 4, Highland Close, Fison Way
Industrial Estate, St. Helens Way,
Thetford, Norfolk IP24 1HG
Tel: 0844 499 6250 Fax: 0844 499 6252
Email: info@centre-stage.co.uk
Web Site: www.centre-stage.co.uk
Directors: John Deacon and Ian Napier
Centre Stage Engineering specialises in the design, manufacture and installation of stage engineering equipment. It also offers maintenance, trouble shooting and testing services.

CONCEPT STAGING
Wellington Mill, Ribble Street, Padiham,
Burnley, Lancashire BB12 8BQ
Tel: 01282 777600 Fax: 01282 777602
Mobile: 07976 733849
Email: enquiries@conceptstaging.co.uk
Web Site: www.conceptstaging.co.uk
Director: Gareth Hilton
Office Manager: Helen Pratt
Stage and set construction.
Concept Staging has developed an outstanding reputation on both large and small projects, nationwide and overseas. Our 'in house' manufacturing and installation teams have developed an outstanding rapport with all our clients.

DAVID BROWN GEAR SYSTEMS LTD
Park Works, Huddersfield,
West Yorkshire HD4 5DD
Tel: 01484 465 500 Tel: 01484 465 745
Fax: 01484 465 586
Email: sales@davidbrown.com
Web Site: www.davidbrown.com
Business Development & Marketing
Director: Peter Bulkley

DELSTAR ENGINEERING LTD
Homefield Road, Haverhill, Suffolk CB9 8QP
Tel: 01440 762518 Fax: 01440 703820
Email: general@delstar.co.uk
Web Site: www.delstar.co.uk
Contact: Ken Golding

DOUGHTY ENGINEERING LIMITED
Crow Arch Lane, Ringwood, Hampshire
BH24 1NZ
Tel: 01425 478961 Fax: 01425 474481
Email: sales@doughty-engineering.co.uk
Web: www.doughty-engineering.co.uk
Production Director: Stephen Wright
Marketing Director: Julian Chiverton
Doughty Engineering are often described as "Mind Over Metal" specialists. Among the areas we manufacture for are products for the Stage Lighting, Grip and Theatre markets.

EUROSOUND (UK) LTD
44 High Street, Clayton West,
Huddersfield HD8 9NS
Tel: 01484 866 066 Fax: 01484 866 299
Email: eurosounduk@yahoo.co.uk
Web Site: www.eurosound.co.uk
Contact: Paul Martin

EVENT SERVICES LTD
The Old Foundry, Brow Mills, Brighouse Road, Hipperholme, Halifax, West Yorkshire HX3 8EF
Tel: 01422 204 114 Fax: 01422 204 431
Email: sales@event-services.co.uk
Web Site: www.event-services.co.uk
Stages, rostra, catwalks, tiered seating, front of stage barriers.

FLINT HIRE & SUPPLY LTD
Theatrical Chandlers
Queens Row, London SE17 2PX
Tel: 020 7703 9786
Sales Fax: 020 7708 4189
Email: sales@flints.co.uk
Web Site: www.flints.co.uk
Contacts: Alasdair Flint, Richard Black
Flints are the major retailer of theatrical goods in the UK. Established 25 years ago to provide a single source for specialist theatre hardware and materials.
Suppliers of high tensile and BZP bolts, spanners, podgers, Podgalugs (tm), drills, angle grinders, drop blocks, winches, pulleys, Flints water based multi primer, wire rope, tested wire assemblies and all scenic hardware.

FUTURIST PROJECTS LTD
Unit 1, White Swan Yard,
Otley, LS21 1AE
Tel: 0113 279 0033 Fax: 0113 301 0255
Email: info@futurist.co.uk
Web Site: www.futurist.co.uk
Managing Director: Jamie Hudson
Financial Director: Jamie Hudson
AV, Theatrical Productions, Lighting and Sound Specialists.

HALL STAGE LIMITED
Unit 4, Cosgrove Way, Luton,
Bedfordshire LU1 1XL
Tel: 0845 345 4255 Fax: 0845 345 4256
Email: sales@hallstage.com
Web Site: www.hallstage.com
Managing Director: Charles Haines
Technical Director: Phil Wells
Stage Sales Services Manager: Scott Oake
Sales Co-ordinator: Alison Price
Designs and manufactures standard and special products for the stage, screen, AV and industrial market.
Hall Stage and Theatre Supplies formed in 1895. Equipment ranges include T60 and T70 curtain track systems for all applications. Specialist products include rolloer or flying safety curtains, counterweight sets, hemp rope sets, the DynaGlide powered and manual hoists for powered fling and lighting bar operations, DynaLine pulleys, motor control systems, and a selection of theatrical and scenic hardware fittings.

HANDS ON PRODUCTION SERVICES
79 Loanbank Quadrant, Glasgow G51 3HZ Scotland
Tel: 0141 440 2005
Email: info@hands-on-uk.com
Web Site: www.hands-on-uk.com
Hire of Weapons, Heraldic Shields, Armour and Allied Properties for Theatre, Film and Publicity Work.
We are the only BBC approved contractors in Scotland and have the authority of the Scottish executive to supply prohibited weapons under section 5 of the firearms act.

JOHN HENRY'S LTD
16-24 Brewery Road, London N7 9NH
Tel: 020 7609 9181 Fax: 020 7700 7040
Email: info@johnhenrys.com
Web Site: www.johnhenrys.com
Event Production: Pepin Clout
Rehearsal Studios: Andrea Westwood
Backline Production: Tark Bates

J & C JOEL LTD
Corporation Mill, Corporation Street,
Sowerby Bridge, West Yorkshire HX6 2QQ
Tel: 01422 833835 Fax: 01422 835157
Email: sales@jcjoel.com

Web Site: www.jcjoel.com
Specialists in Flame Retardant Fabrics, manufacturers and installers of theatrical drapes and stage equipment. Probably the largest stock of flame retardant fabrics, tracks and all stage hardware, starcloths, dance flooring and portable staging.
Sales Manager: Oliver Marns

LANCELYN THEATRE SUPPLIES
Ferry Hinksey Road, Oxford OX2 0BY
Tel: 01865 722 468 Fax: 01865 728 791
Email: oxford@lancelynoxford.co.uk
Web Site: www.lancelyn.co.uk
Sales and Branch Manager: Reg Berry
Email: reg@lancelynoxford.co.uk
Marketing, Admin & Office Manager: Sara Ingham
Made to measure curtains, supply and fix, repair and cleaning.

LEITNER GB LIMITED
4 Monks Pond Street, Northampton NN1 2LF
Tel: 01604 230 445 Fax: 01604 231389
Email: sales@leitner.co.uk
Web Site: www.leitner.co.uk
Contact: David Crockford
Builders and suppliers of exhibition systems.

LIFT TURN MOVE LTD
Argyle Industrial Estate, Unit 6, Appin Road, Birkenhead, Wirral CH41 9HH
Tel: 0151 649 0467 Fax: 0151 649 0099
Email: DavidKing@liftturnmove.co.uk
Web Site: www.liftturnmove.co.uk
Sales Contacts: John Jones, David King
Sales Administrator: Jenny Hobday
"The Lodestar People" suppliers of Entertainment
Lifting products & services

LS-LIVE LTD
See also, 'Prolyte Products UK Ltd'
Lidgate Crescent, Langthwaite Grange Ind Estate, South Kirkby, Pontefract, West Yorkshire WF9 3NR
Tel: 01977 659888
Email: sales@ls-live.com
Web Site: www.ls-live.com
General Manager: Ben Brooks
Project support co-ordinator: Adam "Bullet" Bettley
Hire Co-ordinator: Jess Woodward
LS Live Ltd, formally know as Litestructures offers a huge range of hire stock for the entertainment market. We have the largest stock of Litedeck in the UK, together with trussing, crowd barriers, rolling stages, scissor lifts, turntables, scissor lifts and outdoor stages. We are one of the UK's leaders in the design and manufacture of stage sets.
LS-Live rehearsal studio has been purpose built with large scale productions in mind. 1,641 square metes with a height of 16.5 metres, it has been the chosen rehearsal space for the likes of Robbie Williams, Coldplay and Cirque du Soleil.

THE MANCHESTER LIGHT AND STAGE LTD
76 - 78 North Western Street, Manchester M12 6DY
Tel: 0161 273 2662 Fax: 0161 273 2664
Office Address: 6 St Johns Road, Heaton Mersey, Stockport SK4
Email: info@manchesterlightandstage.com
Web Site: www.manchesterlightandstage.com
Contact: Bruce Mitchell, Jim Gee
Lighting Hire and Sales "Steeldeck" Hire and Sales - Marquee Hire, Event Management - Site Electrics. Catwalks, outdoor roofs & stages.

MOVETECH UK
Emblem Works, Emblem Street, Bolton, Lancashire BL3 5BW
Tel: 01204 525 626 London Depot: Tel: 01992 574 602 Fax: 01992 560 385
Email: info@turntable.co.uk
Web Site: www.british.turntable.co.uk, www.movetechuk.com
British Turntable Company, leaders in creating dramatic movement, offer a range of low profile, self-assembly revolving stages, in diameters ranging from 2m to 10m. Highly portable, these revolves can be assembled by two men in as little as half an hour*, can be supplied for manual or powered operation and include options such as variable speed, indexing and/or static centre.
This range is in addition to the extremely comprehensive range of revolves available for sale or hire up to 25 tonne capacity and which include units suitable for outdoor location applications.
Competitively priced, all units are available from depots throughout the UK and Europe.
*Assembly time based on a 6m standard revolve on sound, level surface.

ON EVENT PRODUCTION COMPANY
Formerly Panda Hire Ltd.
Acton House, Acton Grove, Acton Road Industrial Estate, Long Eaton, Nottingham NG10 1FY
Tel: 01159 222 959 Fax: 01159 735 918
Email: sales@lovingitlive.co.uk
Web Site: www.lovingitlive.co.uk
MD: Guy Eaton
Operations Director: Paul White
Production Director: Chris Vernon-Smith
Hire Manger: James Pemblington
We hire PA / Staging / Lighting / Truss & Power distribution for either dry hire or as a complete package with engineers and/or event management.

OPTIKINETICS (UK) LIMITED
38 Cromwell Road, Luton, Bedfordshire LU3 1DN
Tel: 01582 411 413 Fax: 01582 400 613
Email: ukadmin@optikinetics.com
Web Site: www.optikinetics.co.uk

OUTBACK RIGGING LTD
Unit 5 Kendal Court, Western Ave. Trading Estate, Kendal Avenue, London W3 0RU
Tel: 020 8993 0066 Mob: 07710 975 678
Fax: 020 8752 1753
Email: enquiries@outbackrigging.com
Web Site: www.outbackholdings.co.uk
Operations Director: Stuart Cooper
Email: stuart@outbackrigging.com
Truss, hoists and sundry rigging equipment hire and installation.

OWL VIDEO SYSTEMS LTD
GT 10 Waterside Centre, North Street, Lewes, East Sussex BN7 2PE
Tel: 01273 406 080
Email: sales@owlvisual.co.uk
Web Site: www.owlvisual.co.uk
Managing Director: Sean Marklew
Owl are sole UK distributors of the TetraDek Staging System. Truly lightweight, yet incredibly strong. Seeing is believing! The lightest, strongest demountable modular staging system available.

PERRY SCENIC LTD
Unit D & E, 100 Dudley Road East, Oldbury, West Midlands B69 3EB
Tel: 0121 552 9696 Fax: 0121 552 9697
Email: enquiries@perryscenic.com
Web Site: www.perryscenic.com
Contact: Michael Perry , Tony Guest, Jonathan Perry
Comprehensive service at competitive prices. Set Builders, Engineering, Scenic Artists, Sculptors, Prop Makers, Design, Drapes, Effects for Theatre, Film, TV, Exhibition and Pop Tours.

PROLYTE PRODUCTS UK LTD
See also, 'LS-Live Ltd'
Langthwaite Grange Ind Estate, South Kirkby, Wakefield, West Yorkshire WF9 3NR
Tel: 01977 659 800 Fax: 01977 659 801
Email: info@prolyte.co.uk
Web Site: www.prolyte.co.uk / www.litestructures.co.uk
Managing Director: Lee Brooks
Sales Contact: Kate Greenwood
The Prolyte Group designs and develops structural elements for the theatre, entertainment, exhibition, architectural and associated markets, including trussing, stages, barriers, roof systems, hoists and drive systems.
Based on extensive industry experience, Prolyte delivers high quality, innovative and efficient products with a strong emphasis on safety, underpinned by the

highest levels of service and technical support tailored to your needs.

RAT STANDS
16 Melville Road, London SW13 9RJ
Tel: 020 8741 4804 Fax: 020 8741 8949
Email: sales@ratstands.com
Web Site: www.ratstands.com
Supplying modern and traditional music stands, conductor stands, orchestra stands and lecterns since 1976. Other services include Portable Staging and Radio DMX systems.

THE REVOLVING STAGE COMPANY
Unit F5, Little Heath Industrial Estate, Old Church Road, Coventry Warwickshire CV6 7ND
Tel: 024 7668 7055 Fax: 024 7668 9355
Email: paul@therevolvingstagecompany.co.uk
Web: www.therevolvingstagecompany.co.uk
Contact: Paula Nodwell
The Revolving Stage Company carry a vast range of electronically controlled revolving stages, fully programmable and DMX compatible. To hire/purchase long and short term. Surround staging for all sized revolves and set building facility available.

RK RESOURCE
Unit 2, Wyvern Way, Henwood, Ashford, Kent TN24 8DW
Tel: 01233 750 180 / 01233 664 126
Fax: 01233 750 133
Email: rkresource2007@aol.co.uk
Web Site: www.rk-resourcekent.com
Stage and television scenery contractors and engineers. Masking drapes, staging, revolves, sundry technical and rehearsal items for hire. Contact: Eric Parsons

SICO EUROPE LIMITED
The Link Park, Lympne Industrial Estate, Lympne, Hythe, Kent CT21 4LR
Tel: 01303 234 000 Fax: 01303 234 001
Email: sales@sico-europe.com
Web Site: www.sico-europe.com
Sales Director: Steve Mason
Folding, mobile stage units, steps, guardrails, skirt curtains, backdrops, and mobile, folding choral risers.

SPECIALZ
Unit 2, Kingston Industrial Estate, 81-86 Glover Street, Birmingham B9 4EN
Tel: 0121 766 7100 Fax: 0121 766 7113
Email: info@specialz.co.uk
Web Site: www.specialz.co.uk
Specialz offer a design and electro-mechanical manufacturing service for Lighting or Set designers with great ideas or concepts but lack technical resources or the time to realise them.

SRC LTD
Secure House, 15A Plantagenet Road, Barnet, Hertfordshire EN5 5JG
Tel: 0870 240 4383 Fax: 0870 428 6542
Email: jon@srcuk.com
Web Site: www.srcuk.com
Manager: Jon Slater
Stage Barriers, Crowd Control Barriers, Mobile Stages and Platform Staging.

SSE HIRE LTD
Burnt Meadow House, Burnt Meadow Road, North Moons Moat, Redditch B98 9PA
Tel: 01527 528 822 Fax: 01527 528 840
Email: hire@sseaudio.com, spencer.beard@sseaudio.com
Web Site: www.sseaudiogroup.com
Managing Director: John Penn
Operations Director: Spencer Beard
Flightcase manufacture. Risers and set supply. PA systems sales and rental

STAGE ONE CREATIVE SERVICES LIMITED
Hanger 88 Marston Moor Business Park, Rudgate Lane, Tockwith, York YO26 7QF
Tel: 01423 358001 Fax: 01423 358016
Email: enquiries@stageone.co.uk
Web Site: www.stageone.co.uk
Managing Director: Mark Johnson
Director: Simon Wood
Technical Director: Jim Tinsley

STAGE SOLUTIONS
45 Chruch Road, Hove, East Sussex, BN3 2BE
Tel: 01273 783 710
Email: info@stagesolutions.uk.com
Web Site: www.stagesoltutions.uk.com
Warehouse: 10 Second Avenue, Chatham, Kent ME4 5AU
Maltbury designs, manufactures, delivers and installs staging for every kind of venue, both professional and amateur.
We have over 20 years' experience of the entertainment industry.
We also supply seating, truss and crowd control barriers.

STAGE SYSTEMS
Prince William Road, Loughborough, Leicestershire LE11 5GU
Tel: 01509 611 021 Fax: 01509 233 146
Email: info@stagesystems.co.uk
Web Site: www.stagesystems.co.uk
Team Leader: Damian Mawdsley
Demountable staging, tiering and seating systems.Systems are lightweight, easy to assemble and compact to store. Ideal as a semi-permanent fixture or stage extension. Also upholstered chairs that can be linked and stacked. Free design guidance available.

STAGE TECHNOLOGIES LTD
9 Falcon Park Industrial Estate, Neasden Lane, London NW10 1RZ
Tel: 020 8208 6000 Fax: 020 8208 6006
Email: automation@stagetech.com
Web Site: www.stagetech.com
Contacts: Ted Moore, Director of Rental Services; Nikki Scott, Commercial Director; John Hastie, Operations Director; Mark Ager, Managing Director.
Specialist design/manufacture of automation systems and stage engineering, including winch and track products; equipment hire, installation, maintenance and upgrades; mechanical consultancy, operator and vocational training; 24-hour global/online support.

STAGE TRACK LTD
Harbour Lane, Garboldisham, Diss, Norfolk IP22 2ST
Tel: 01953 688 188 Fax: 01953 688 144
Email: sales@stagetrack.co.uk
Web Site: www.stagetrack.co.uk
Contact: B. Skipp
Suppliers of various curtain systems, hoists, fire curtains and associated controls and equipment.

STAR EVENTS GROUP LTD
Milton Road, Thurleigh, Bedford MK44 2DF
Tel: 01234 772 233 Fax: 01234 772 272
Email: steve.shaw@stareventsgroup.com
Web Site: www.StarEventsGroup.com
Hire of technical services to the entertainment industry including stage constructions for both indoor and outdoor events.

STEELDECK SALES LTD
Unit 58, T Marchant Estate 42-72 Verney Road London SE16 3DH
Tel: 020 8692 9721/020 7833 2031 Fax Rentals: 020 7232 1780 Fax Sales: 020 8691 4263
Email: info@steeldeck.co.uk / rentals@steeldeck.co.uk
Web Site: www.steeldeck.co.uk
Director: Richard Howey Nunn
Steeldeck specialise in staging, tiered seating and temporary structures. From finding creative structural solutions for the most challenging ideas to short-term stage hire, at Steeldeck we offer a complete staging service to a vast array of productions. Affordable, quick and versatile, we build our reputation on the safety of our certified staging structures.

TOTAL FABRICATIONS LIMITED
Units 3 - 4, Kingston Industrial Estate, 81 - 86 Glover Street, Birmingham B9 4EN
Tel: 0121 772 5234
Email: info@trussing.com
Web Site: www.trussing.com
Contact: Karen Cronin
Manufacturer of standard and custom aluminium trusses, roof structures, fixtures and associated equipment including motor controllers and full range of Verlinde products catering for broad spectrum of applications.

TRIPLE E LTD
16 Airport Industrial Estate, Main Road, Biggin Hill, Kent TN16 3BW
Tel: 01959 570 333 Fax: 01959 570 888
Email: info@3-eee.com
Web Site: www.3-eee.com
Contact: David Edelstein

UNUSUAL RIGGING LTD
The Wharf, Bugbrooke, Northampton NN7 3QB
Tel: 01604 830083 Fax: 01604 841144
Email: info@unusual.co.uk
Web Site: www.unusual.co.uk
Unusual brings the disciplines of design, rigging, fabrications and automation to provide an ideal installation service for the supply, renovation and renewal of stage engineering and flying systems.

WAAGNER BIRO UK LTD
The Street, Englefield, Reading RG7 5ES
Tel: 01189 640 033 Fax 01189 640 074
Email: alun.edwards@waagner-biro.com
Web Site: www.waagner-biro.com
Country Manager: Alun Edwards

WELD-FAB STAGE ENGINEERING LTD
Harbour Lane Works, Garboldisham, Diss, Norfolk IP22 2ST
Tel: 01953 688 133 Fax: 01953 688 144
Email: weld-fab.stage@paston.co.uk
Web Site: www.weldfabstage.co.uk
Contact: Brian Skipp, Matthew Genner
Design and manufacturers of various stage, studio, television & exhibition equipment for sale or hire. Motorised and fixed scenery, revolving stages, scissor lifts, power flying & counterweight systems.

Storage

AIR-RIDER
18 Gisburn Mansions Tottenham Lane London N8 7EB
Tel: 020 8341 5871 Mobile: 07836 519902 Fax: 0208 361 9827
Email: air.rider@btinternet.com
Contact: Greg Haynes

CADOGAN TATE
Cadogan House, 239 Acton Lane, London NW10 7NP
Switchboard: 0800 988 6010 Storage
Tel: 0800 008 6040 Fax: 0800 587 4050
Email: storage@cadogantate.com
Web Site: www.cadogantate.com

LUCKINGS
Boston House, 69-75 Boston Manor Road, Brentford, Middlesex TW8 9JJ
Tel: 0845 603 8211 Fax: 0208 847 8677
Reading depot: 1 Viscount Way, Woodley, Reading RG5 4DZ Manchester depot:The Excel Centre, Preston Street, Gorton, Manchester M18 8BL
Email: info@luckings.co.uk
Web Site: www.luckings.co.uk
Contact: Merril Mathias

REDBURN TRANSFER LTD
Redburn House, Stockingswater Lane, Enfield, Middlesex EN3 7PH
Tel: 020 8804 0027 Fax: 020 8804 8021
Email: sales@redburn.co.uk
Web Site: www.redburn.co.uk
Contact: Chris Redburn
Offering full UK and International music transportation services to touring bands since 1870. Fleet of Volvo, DAF and Scania tractors and 45ft stepframe and Mega-cube trailers. 17 ton box trucks. Storage facilities available.

UPSTAGE THEATRICAL DRYCLEANERS
Unit 7- 8, Acorn Production Centre, 105 Blundell Street, London N7 9BN
Tel: 020 7609 9119
Email: upstage@lineone.net
Web Site: www.emily-may.co.uk
Managing Director: Peter Salmon
Storage available in secure, dry premises; 10 minutes from London's West End; Collection/delivery nationwide; East Access; Parking; Stage lit fitting room. Competitive long and short term rates.
Storage available in secure premises, 10 mins Londons W.E.
Collection/delivery nationwide easy access, parking, competitive long and short term rates.

Technical Staff

CREW CO
55 Main Street, Long Compton, Warwickshire CV36 5JS
Tel: 0845 458 9400 Fax: 0845 458 9411
Mob: 07970 986797 Mob: 07887 845994
Email: contactus@crewco.net
Web Site: www.crewco.net
CrewCo has access to a large number of casual local stage crew who work regularly on load ins and out, large and small, and can be supplied throughout London, the Home Counties and the Midlands at very reasonable rates.

ENLIGHTENMENT
The Rubicon Centre, Broad Ground Road, Lakeside, Redditch, Worcestershire B98 8YP
Tel: 0845 257 1992
Email: info@enlightenment.co.uk
Web Site: www.enlightenment.co.uk
Contact: Paul Swansborough
Established since 1997 and trading online since 2006. Enlightenment is the UK on-line source for stage lighting, sound, audio visual and rigging equipment to the entertainment industry. Enlightenment is a main dealer for Showtec, DAP Audio and Dutch Media Tools.

THE LUXFACTOR GROUP (UK)
Fleet Place, Nelson Drive, Petersfield, Hampshire GU31 4SJ
Tel: 0845 370 0589 Fax: 0845 370 0588
Email: info@luxfactor.co.uk
Web Site: www.luxfactor.co.uk
Managing Director & Agent: Michael D. Finch
Primarily representing Lighting, Sound, Video, Set, Costume and Scenic Designers, LUXFactor picks up where others are left bewildered. With clients on four continents we truly are an international agency. LUXFactor Client Management operates on a flexible international timeline status and during "theatre' hours too!

MATT-LX LTD
Unit 3,Vinehall Business Ctr Vinehall Road, Robertsbridge, East Sussex TN32 5JW
Tel: 0845 6808692
Email: matt.lx@mattlx.com
Web Site: www.mattlx.com
Project Manager: Rob Clutterham
MattLX is a specialist technical event production company, providing lighting and design, Audio Visual, equipment supply, programmers, operators, installation, training and Health & Safety services, for Theatre, Arts, Entertainment, Leisure, Marine, TV and Corporate Events.

MILLSEA PRODUCTION SERVICES
2a Rotherwood Mansions, 78 Madeira Road, Streatham, London SW16 2DE
Tel: 020 8677 2370 Mobile: 07770 428096
Email: millsea@mac.com
Contact: Caron Malcolm
Tour and production management, pre-production services, pass and itinerary making.

STAGE CREW
404 Russell Court, Claremont Street, Belfast BT9 6JW
Tel: 028 9032 9897 Mob: 077 1188 5164
Email: damian@stage-crew.co.uk
Web Site: www.stage-crew.co.uk
The longest established Stage Crew providers in Ireland, providing complete crews and production services to concert, conference and event organisers throughout Northern Ireland.

TORO EVENT CREWING SERVICES
24 Endeavour Way, London SW19 8UH Scotland
Tel: 020 8944 4970
Email: info@torocrew.co.uk
Web Site: www.torocrew.co.uk

Technical Training

LYON EQUIPMENT LTD
Rise Hill Mill Dent Sedbergh Cumbria LA10 5QL
Tel: 01539 626250 Mgmt: 015396 25493
Fax: 01539 625454
Email: info@lyon.co.uk, sales@lyon.co.uk
Web Site: www.lyon.co.uk, www.lyon-outdoor.co.uk
Joint Managing Directors: Carol Nicholls and Jonathan Capper
Senior Technical Sales: Dave Ellis
Technical Sales Representative: Scott Shaw
The experts in personal protective equipment and training for rigging and work at height: - Access and work positioning, fall prevention and fall arrest.

MATT-LX LTD
Unit 3,Vinehall Business Ctr Vinehall Road, Robertsbridge, East Sussex TN32 5JW
Tel: 0845 6808692
Email: matt.lx@mattlx.com
Web Site: www.mattlx.com
Project Manager: Rob Clutterham
MattLX is a specialist technical event production company, providing lighting and design, Audio Visual, equipment supply, programmers, operators, installation, training and Health & Safety services, fror Theatre, Arts, Entertainment, Leisure, Marine, TV and Corporate Events.

MERCIA ARTS
2A Hotel Street, Coalville, Leicestershire LE67 3EP
Tel: 01530 263 454 Fax: 01530 260 206
Email: merciaarts@yahoo.co.uk
Contact: Simon Nickerson
Specialists in the provision of one-day workshops and seminars in a range of technical theatre and arts management subjects, including lighting,sound, make-up, stage mangement, arts marketing , health & safety in the theatre.

STAGE TECHNOLOGIES LTD
9 Falcon Park Industrial Estate, Neasden Lane, London NW10 1RZ
Tel: 020 8208 6000 Fax: 020 8208 6006
Email: automation@stagetech.com
Web Site: www.stagetech.com
Contacts: Ted Moore, Director of Rental Services; Nikki Scott, Commercial Director; John Hastie, Operations Director; Mark Ager, Managing Director.
Specialist design/manufacture of automation systems and stage engineering, including winch and track products; equipment hire, installation, maintenance and upgrades; mechanical consultancy, operator and vocational training; 24-hour global/online support.

TOTAL FABRICATIONS LIMITED
Units 3 - 4, Kingston Industrial Estate, 81 - 86 Glover Street, Birmingham B9 4EN
Tel: 0121 772 5234
Email: info@trussing.com
Web Site: www.trussing.com
Contact: Karen Cronin
Manufacturer of standard and custom aluminium trusses, roof structures, fixtures and associated equipment including motor controllers and full range of Verlinde products catering for broad spectrum of applications.

Theatre Construction, Management & Renovation

BOVIS LEND LEASE
142 Northolt Road, Harrow, Middlesex HA2 0EE
Tel: 020 8271 8000 Fax: 020 8271 8188
Web Site: www.bovislendlease.com
Executive General Manager: Julian Daniel
Bovis is a market leader in the provision of consultancy, management and specialist contracting services services for theatre and leisure projects.
Our experience include Glyndebourne Opera House, The Savoy theatre, Sadlers Wells, Edinburgh Festival

STAGE ONE CREATIVE SERVICES LIMITED
Hanger 88 Marston Moor Business Park, Rudgate Lane, Tockwith, York YO26 7QF
Tel: 01423 358001 Fax: 01423 358016
Email: enquiries@stageone.co.uk
Web Site: www.stageone.co.uk
Managing Director: Mark Johnson
Director: Simon Wood
Technical Director: Jim Tinsley

THEATREPLAN LLP
27 Colonnade London WC1N 1JA
Tel: 020 7841 0440 Fax: 020 7841 0450
Email: info@theatreplan.co.uk
Web Site: www.theatreplan.co.uk
Practice Manager: Paul Connolly
Auditorium design, theatre planning, technical equipment consultancy, feasibility studies and project development for theatres, conference venues and concert halls. Design of rigging, lighting, audio-visual and video systems and equipment specifications.

THEATRESEARCH
Dacre Hall, Dacre, Harrogate, North Yorkshire HG3 4ET
Tel: 01423 780 497 Fax: 01423 781 957
Email: david@theatresearch.co.uk, info@theatresearch.co.uk
Web Site: www.theatresearch.co.uk
Contact: David Wilmore, Ric Green
Theatresearch specialises in the restoration of historic theatres, providing theatre consultancy services for planning, design, technical equipment, historic research/archives and project management. We also have significant experience with HLF funded restoration schemes and the preparation of conservation plans. Theatresearch also undertakes consultancy work for film and TV companies working on location in theatres, providing project management, script advice and historic information for period productions, and documentaries.

UNUSUAL RIGGING LTD
The Wharf, Bugbrooke, Northampton NN7 3QB
Tel: 01604 830083 Fax: 01604 841144
Email: info@unusual.co.uk
Web Site: www.unusual.co.uk
Unusual brings the disciplines of design, rigging, fabrications and automation to provide an ideal installation service for the supply, renovation and renewal of stage engineering and flying systems.

Translation & Interpretation Services

M & R COMMUNICATIONS
7 Bell Industrial Estate, 50 Cunnington Street, Chiswick, London W4 5HB
Tel: 020 8995 4714 Fax: 020 8995 5136
Email: office@m-rcom.com
Web Site: www.m-rcom.com
Technical Director: Jean Henriot
Office Manager: Ben Denness
Infra-red and radio systems for audio description and foreign language productions.

UPS TRANSLATIONS
111 Baker Street, London W1U 6RR
Tel: 020 7837 8300 / 020 7486 3454
Fax: 020 7486 3272
Email: info@upstranslations.com
Web Site: www.upstranslations.com
Managing Director: Justin Silver
The Language Division of United Publicity Services plc. Specialists in translation for the media, film, television and theatre. Script translation, voice overs, subtitling and interpreters, in all the languages of the world.

VOICE & SCRIPT INTERNATIONAL
128 - 134 Cleveland Street, London W1T 6AB
Tel: 020 7692 7700 Fax: 020 7692 7711
ISDN: 020 7692 7722
Email: info@vsi.tv
Web Site: www.vsi.tv

Managing Director: Norman Dawood
Office Manager: Krista Raag
Services include; Script translation, Foreign-language voices, Subtitling, Dubbing, Deaf & hard of hearing services, Audio suites, DVD & video services, Avid offline & online.

WESTMINSTER SONUS
800 Oxford Avenue, Slough SL1 4LN
Tel: 01753 578 822 Fax: 01753 553 867
Email: crn@westminstersonus.com
Web Site: www.westminstersonus.com
Senior Personnel: Julian Strawson

Transport & Travel

AIR-RIDER
18 Gisburn Mansions Tottenham Lane London N8 7EB
Tel: 020 8341 5871 Mobile: 07836 519902 Fax: 0208 361 9827
Email: air.rider@btinternet.com
Contact: Greg Haynes

ANGLO PACIFIC INTERNATIONAL PLC
5-9 Willen Field Road, London NW10 7BQ
Tel: 020 8965 1234 Fax: 020 8965 3988
Email: info@anglopacific.co.uk
Web Site: www.anglopacific.co.uk
Managing Director: Steve Perry

Ocean freight, air freight, trucking, full carnet services, forwarders to the performing arts.

BRITANNIA CHAPMANS
Units N & P, Block 9 Distribution Centre, Paddock Wood, Tonbridge, Kent TN12 6UU
Tel: 01892 833 313 Fax: 01892 834 714
Email: sales@britannia-movers.co.uk
Web Site: www.britannia-movers.co.uk
Furniture Removals and Storage. Theatrical Scenery and Works of Art Great Britain and T.I.R. Service to Europe - Worldwide Shipping.

BRUNELS REMOVAL SERVICES
20A Walnut Lane, Bristol BS15 4JG
Tel: 0117 907 7855 Mob: 07836 500 399
Email: enquires@brunelremovals.co.uk
Web Site: www.brunelremovals.co.uk
Contact: Simon Hippisley
A 24 hour professional service throughout the UK and Europe. We specialise in all forms of transport of scenery, props etc to film, TV and theatrical companies, including Storage. Competitive rates tailor-made to suit your needs. Our large fleet of vehicles ranges from transit vans to Supercube Airride step-framed trailers.

EST (EDWIN SHIRLEY TRUCKING LTD)
Bell Lane, North Woolwich Road, London E16 2AB
Tel: 020 7055 7200 Fax: 020 7055 7201
Email: delr@est-uk.com
Web Site: www.yourock-weroll.com
Contact: Del Roll
45' Air-ride trailors, 18 toppe & 7.5 toppe box vans. 31 Years National and International Experience.

EXPRESS EXPORT SERVICES LTD
143 Wardour Street, London W1F 8WA
Tel: 020 7734 8356 Fax: 0800 034 1005
Email: john@express-exports.co.uk
Web Site: www.express-exports.co.uk
Shipper of costumes, props, stages and all other associated goods to the theatrical industry, by air, sea or overland truck to all parts of the world. Also specialise is offering discount airfare tickets worldwide.

G & R REMOVALS
100 Bollo Lane, London W4 5LX
Tel: 020 8994 9733 Fax: 020 8995 0855
Email: info@gandrremovals.co.uk
Web Site: www.gandrremovals.co.uk
Contact: Lance or Vikki

INTERNATIONAL AIR CHARTER PLC
Gable House, 239 Regents Park Road, London N3 3LF
Tel: 020 8897 8979 Fax: 020 8897 8969
Email: sales@aircraftcharter.com
Web Site: www.aircraftcharter.com
Managing Director: Hugh Courtenay

Business Development Manager: Wendy Courtenay
Sales & Marketing Manager: Alison Russell
One of Europe's largest independent private aircraft charter specialists, providing a wide range of aircraft for the entertainment industry, corporate events, meetings, incentive travel, special events, groups and conferences, product launches, personal appearances and promotional trips. 24hr service - Free quotations.
Kent Office: Quayside House, Standard Quay, Faversham, Kent, ME13 7BS, United Kingdom, Tel: 01795 590888.

JET AIR LTD
3 City Place, Beehive Ring Road, London Gatwick Airport, Gatwick, West Sussex RH6 0PA
Tel: 01293 566 040 Fax: 01293 566 099
Email: aircraft@jetair.co.uk
Web Site: www.jetair.co.uk
Sales and Marketing: Nicola Rice
World Class Aviation. Experts in arranging all types of aircraft charter worldwide. From executive aircraft, helicopters and luxury jets to large commercial aircraft for conferences, incentives and events.

K W DEVEREUX & SONS
Daimler Drive, Cowpen Lane Industrial Estate, Billingham, Cleveland TS23 4JD Scotland
Tel: 01642 887700 Fax: 01642 565 562
Email: ken@devereuxtransport.com
Web Site: www.kwdevereux.co.uk
Contact: Anthony Devereux
Devereux's have been in the theatrical removal business for over 4 decades and being based in the centre of the UK are ideal for nationwide tours.

LOMAS HELICOPTERS
Lake Heliport, Abbotsham, Bideford, Devon EX39 5BQ
Tel: 01237 421 054 Fax: 01237 424 060
Email: lomashelos@aol.com
Web Site: www.lomashelicopters.com
Operations manager: Emma Lomas

LUCKINGS
Boston House, 69-75 Boston Manor Road, Brentford, Middlesex TW8 9JJ
Tel: 0845 603 8211 Fax: 0208 847 8677
Reading depot: 1 Viscount Way, Woodley, Reading RG5 4DZ Manchester depot:The Excel Centre, Preston Street, Gorton, Manchester M18 8BL
Email: info@luckings.co.uk
Web Site: www.luckings.co.uk
Contact: Merril Mathias

PAUL MATHEW TRANSPORT LTD
Unit 1, Littlehampton Marina, Ferry Road, Littlehampton, West Sussex BN17 5DS
Tel: 01903 730 930 Fax: 01903 730 630
Email: info@paulmathewtransport.com
Web: www.paulmathewtransport.com
Contact: Paul Mathew
International theatre scenery exhibition & concert movers.

MOTORVATION
Lenham Storage, Ham Lane, Lenham, Maidstone, Kent ME17 2LH
Tel: 01622 853 953 Fax: 01622 853 857
Email: steve@motorv.com, info@motorv.com
Web Site: www.motorv.com
Contact: Steve Marshall
Specialist transport for lighting, scenery and sound equipment for all types of Theatrical Tours.

P.S. COLLINGS
18 Billingshurst Road, Broadbridge Heath, Horsham, West Sussex RH12 3LW
Tel: 07785 717 179 Fax: 01403 266 059
Email: Philcollings60@hotmail.com
Contact: Philip Collings
A small van service for that urgent delivery such as a forgotten prop, wardrobe or LX.

PICKFORD REMOVALS LIMITED
Heritage House, 345 Southbury Road, Enfield, Middlesex EN1 1UP
Tel: 020 8219 8000 Fax: 020 8219 8201
Email: alan.nuwham@sirva.co.uk
Web Site: www.pickfords.co.uk
Haulage and transporting.

PICKFORDS BUSINESS MOVING
East Wing, The Granary, York Way, Kings Cross, London N1 0PS
Tel: 0208 219 8207 Fax: 020 7837 7783
Web Site: www.pickfords.co.uk
Marketing Director: Lindsey Daykin
Contact: Ms Elaine Draper-Ross
Branches covering UK and facilities in Europe. A comprehensive warehouse and transport service in the UK and on the continent for theatrical tours. Transport for scenery, props, electrics, orchestras etc.

REDBURN TRANSFER LTD
Redburn House, Stockingswater Lane, Enfield, Middlesex EN3 7PH
Tel: 020 8804 0027 Fax: 020 8804 8021
Email: sales@redburn.co.uk
Web Site: www.redburn.co.uk
Contact: Chris Redburn
Offering full UK and International music transportation services to touring bands since 1870. Fleet of Volvo, DAF and Scania tractors and 45ft stepframe and Mega-cube trailers. 17 ton box trucks. Storage facilities available.

RIMA TRAVEL MANAGEMENT
10 Angel Gate, London EC1V 2PT
Tel: 020 7833 5071 Fax: 020 7278 4700
Email: ernie.garcia@rima-travel.co.uk
Web Site: www.rima-travel.co.uk
Managing Director: Ernie Garcia-Sheriff
Music Touring: Dave Brock
Travel management for the corporate and entertainment industries.

SOUTHERN VAN LINES
River Wharf Business Park, Mulberry Way, Belvedere, Kent DA17 6AR
Tel: 020 8310 8512 Fax: 020 8312 0148
Email: david@southernvanlines.com
Web Site: www.southernvanlines.com
Contact: David Luckin

STAGE TRUCK
Speed House, Green Lane, Hounslow, Middlesex TW4 6BY
Tel: 020 8569 4444 Fax: 020 8569 4194
Email: info@stagetruck.com
Web Site: www.stagetruck.com
Directors: R.M. Hewett , J.A. Hewett
Contact: Adrienne Adkins

STAGEFREIGHT LTD
Evanston Avenue Leeds, West Yorkshire LS4 2HR
Tel: 0113 238 0805 Fax: 0113 238 0806
Email: showmover@aol.com
Web Site: www.stagefreight.com
Contact: Peter Cresswell
Transport specialists throughout Britain and Europe serving the needs of the Theatre, TV, Conference and Exhibition sectors. Above all reliable.

STARDES LTD
Ashes Buildings, Old Lane, Holbrook Industrial Estate, Halfway, Sheffield S20 3GZ
Tel: 0114 251 0051 Fax: 0114 251 0555
Email: dhs@stardes.co.uk
Web Site: www.stardes.co.uk
Contact: Sue or David Steinberg
Executive Car and Minibus, Truck and Van Rental, Concert Tour Transportation, Walk ramps. Transportation Consultants.

TEAM RELOCATIONS
Drury Way London NW1 0JN
Tel: 020 8784 0100 Fax: 020 8451 0061
Email: reception@teamrelocations.com
Web Site: www.teamrelocations.com
As a quick reminder, our expertise lies in the planning and preparation of transport for UK, European and Worldwide Events, using our vehicle fleet and worldwide air and seas freight forwarding.

UTS BOURNES
Unit C St. Michaels Close,, Aylesford, Kent ME20 7BU
Tel: 01622 791 013 Fax: 01622 710 237
Email: bournes@uts-bournes.co.uk
Web Site: www.bournes-uts.co.uk
Manager: Eric Bourne
Technical Manager: Charles Church
Van transport/removals and storage.

UK Sameday Delivery Services

P.S. COLLINGS
18 Billingshurst Road, Broadbridge Heath, Horsham, West Sussex RH12 3LW
Tel: 07785 717 179 Fax: 01403 266 059
Email: Philcollings60@hotmail.com
Contact: Philip Collings
A small van service for that urgent delivery such as a forgotten prop, wardrobe or LX.

Used Lighting & Lighting Equipment Suppliers

CONCERT-SYSTEMS.COM
Unit 8, Atlantic Business Centre, Atlantic Street, Altrincham, Cheshire WA14 5NQ
Tel: 0161 941 2707 Fax: 0161 332 8286
Email: sales@concert-systems.com
Web Site: www.concert-systems.com

CONCERTTRADE.COM
Unit 8, Atlantic Business Centre, Atlantic Street, Broadheath, Altrincham, Cheshire WA14 5NQ
Tel: 0161 941 2707 Fax: 0161 332 8286
Email: info@concerttrade.com
Web Site: www.concerttrade.com

LIGHTING PARTNERS LTD
Unit 22 The IO Centre, Croydon Road, Beddington, Croydon CR0 4WQ
Tel: 0844 800 3412 Fax: 0844 800 3413
Email: sales@usedlighting.co.uk
Web Site: www.usedlighting.co.uk / www.stagelighting.co.uk
Co-Managing Directors: Iain Dennis, David Morgan
Used Professional Equipment: Tested, Cleaned, Complete.

Used Sound & Sound Equipment Suppliers

CONCERT-SYSTEMS.COM
Unit 8, Atlantic Business Centre, Atlantic Street, Altrincham, Cheshire WA14 5NQ
Tel: 0161 941 2707 Fax: 0161 332 8286
Email: sales@concert-systems.com
Web Site: www.concert-systems.com

CONCERTTRADE.COM
Unit 8, Atlantic Business Centre, Atlantic Street, Broadheath, Altrincham, Cheshire WA14 5NQ
Tel: 0161 941 2707 Fax: 0161 332 8286
Email: info@concerttrade.com
Web Site: www.concerttrade.com

USEDSTAGESOUND.COM
Also see listing for Newstagesound
Ivy Sound Ltd, Ivy Cottage, Middleton, Winterslow, Salisbury SP5 1QS
Admin Tel: 01980 863733 Mobile: 07850 343 262 Fax: 0870 248 6007
Email: mail@newstagesound.com
Web Site: www.usedstagesound.com
Director: Ian McDonald
Usedstagesound specialises in sourcing and supplying the best available used professional sound equipment for the theatre, live music stage, houses of worship, schools, colleges, universities and hire firms.

Wardrobe

ARTISTES' THEATRE SHOP
23 City Road, Chester, Cheshire CH1 3AE
Tel: 01244 320 271 / 330 Fax: 01244 319 688
Email: carolsmith31@hotmail.com
Web Site: www.theatreshop.co.uk / www.dancewearuk.co.uk
Retail sale ballet shoes and requisites - Full range of theatrical make-up and costume hire. costumes also made to order both period and fancy dress for retail sales.

AURORA DANCEWEAR AND COSTUME
Unit 6, Rufus Business Centre, 22 Ravensbury Terrace, Earlsfield, London SW18 4RL
Tel: 020 8287 5092 Fax: 020 8287 1114
Email: auroracostume@aol.co.uk
Web Site: www.auroradancewear.co.uk

BABOUCHA SHOES
PO Box 405, Potters Bar, Hertfordshire EN6 9AB
Tel: 01707 859 502
Email: sales@baboucha.com
Web Site: www.baboucha.com
Theatrical and fashion shoe makers. Footwear for all occasions. Period, panto, Victorian etc. Also matching belts and bags, made in almost any leather or fabric.

BATH THEATRICAL COSTUME HIRE
Unit 8, Wallbridge Industrial Estate, Frome, Somerset BA11 5JZ
Tel/Fax: 01373 472 786
Email: baththeatrical@talktalk.net
Web Site: www.baththeatrical.com
Over 5,000 square feet of wardrode

space crammed with costume, hats, wigs, accessories and make-up. For productions set from Ancient Rome to 20th Century New York. Open Tuesday - Friday 10am-5pm, Saturday 10am-4pm or by appointment.

CELEBRITY CLEANERS
9 Greens Court, London W1F 0HJ
Tel: 020 7437 5324 (24 Hours)
Westminster Branch: Neville House, 27 Page Street, London, SW1P 4JS Tel: 020 7821 1777
Email: enquiries@celebritydrycleaners.co.uk
Web Site: www.celebritydrycleaners.co.uk
Contact: Robert Shooman or Sylvia Willingham
Specialist Dry Cleaners to the Theatre Profession and Theatrical Costumiers. Situated in the heart of Theatreland.

THE COMPANY OF TEN
See also 'Abbey Theatre'
Abbey Theatre, Westminster Lodge, Holywell Hill, St Albans, Hertfordshire AL1 2DL
Tel: 01727 847 472 Fax: 01727 812 742
Email: manager@abbeytheatre.org.uk
Manager: Tina Swain
Property Mistress: Judith Goodban
Amateur Theatre Company

CREATIVE BEADCRAFT LTD
Also Trading as Ells & Farrier
1 Marshall Street, London W1F 9BA
Tel: 01494 778818 Fax: 01494 776605
Email: beads@creativebeadcraft.co.uk
Web Site: www.creativebeadcraft.co.uk
Personal Callers Only: 20 Beak Street, London W1R 3HA
Importers and distributors of beads, imitation pearls, jewellery findings, diamante, imitation stones, trimmings, sequins, feathers.

EMPEE SILK FABRICS LTD
31 Commercial Road, Edmonton, London N18 1TP
Tel: 020 8887 6000 Fax: 020 8887 6000
Email: empee@wholesalefabrics.co.uk
Web Site: www.wholesalefabrics.co.uk
Wholesalers of a huge range of dress and theatrical fabrics including satins, nets, velvets, cottons, wools, corduroys and many more. We sell stocks and clearance lines off at very low prices.

A R FABB BROS LTD (EST. 1887)
The Barns, Longham Farm Close, Ringwood Road Ferndown, Dorset BH22 9DE
Tel: 01202 571600 Fax: 01202 571779
Email: fabb@fabb.co.uk
Web Site: www.fabb.co.uk
Contact: Mr A Quick
Costume gold wire embroiderers, manufacturers in metal of costume and wardrobe accessories, machine embroidery. Flags and banners etc.

FREED OF LONDON
94 St. Martin's Lane, London WC2N 4AT
Tel: 020 7240 0432
Email: freedshop@freed.co.uk
Web Site: www.freedshop.com
Ballroom, latin and social dance shoes for ladies, men and children.

GANDOLFI GROUP
150 Marylebone Road, London NW1 5PN
Tel: 020 7935 6049 Fax: 01933 227 009
Wellingborough Office: 190 Mill Road, Wellingborough, Northants NN8 1PR Tel: 01933 224007 (3 lines) Fax: 01933 227009
Email: gandolfisports@btconnect.com
Web Site: www.gandolfi.co.uk
Manufacturers, Suppliers and Importers of Dance and Ballet Footwear, Leotards, Tights etc. Distribution through Specialist Shops and Selected Retails. "Local Stockist List" provided against enquirer stating nearest centres.
Managing Directors: Mario Gandolfi (London), Derek Gandolfi (Wellingborough)

NEVTEX
PO Box 87, 29 Stoney Street, Nottingham NG1 1LP
Tel: 0115 959 8781 Fax: 0115 950 2687
Email: sales@nevtex.co.uk
Web Site: www.nevtex.co.uk
Contact: Robert Grummitt
Mail order merchants of bright fluorescent fabrics, feathers and trimmings.

NORRIS STEAM SERVICES (LONDON) LTD
6c Sheep Lane, Hackney, London E8 4QS
Tel: 020 7923 4345
Email: robert@norrissteam.co.uk
Web Site: www.norrissteam.com
Managing Director: Norris Shepherdson
Marketing Manager: Robert Shepherdson
Sales Manger: Josh Taylor
Complete range of portable steamers & light weight boiler & iron systems to suit all requirements & budgets. Sales & hire available.

PROPORTION LONDON LTD
Stockman House, 9 Dallington Street, London EC1V 0LN
Tel: 020 7251 6943 Fax: 020 7250 1798
Email: info@proportionlondon.com
Web Site: www.proportionlondon.com
Dressmakers and tailors dummies, workroom etc. millinery accessories. Mobile dress rails, hangers etc.

ROOTSTEIN DISPLAY MANNEQUINS
Adel Rootstein Ltd 9 Beaumont Avenue, London W14 9LP
Tel: 020 7381 1447 Fax: 0207 386 9594
Email: sales@adelrootstein.co.uk
Web Site: www.rootstein.com
Contact: Jo Olumide
Hire of Display mannequins.

WEST YORKSHIRE FABRICS LTD

Warehouse Address: Unit 5, Milestone Court, Stanningley, Leeds, West Yorkshire LS28 6HE
Tel: 0113 225 6550 Fax: 0870 443 9842
Email: njs@stroud-brothers.demon.co.uk
Contact: Neil Stroud
Administration Address: West Yorkshire House,
20 High Ash Drive, Alwoodley, Leeds, West Yorkshire LS17 8RA
Suppliers of wool suiting, Venetians, baratheas, melton, Linen and stretch fabrics to the theatre and opera industry for over 30 years. No minimum order. Credit cards accepted.

WOLFIN TEXTILES LIMITED

Unit 4 Phoenix Works, Cornwall Road, Pinner Middlesex HA5 4UH
Tel: 020 8427 7429 Fax: 020 8428 4350
Email: cotton@wolfintextiles.co.uk
Web Site: www.wolfintextiles.co.uk
All basic materials for Stage, Screen and TV.
Costume interlinings, scenery canvas, calico, duck, blackout and hessian.

Weapons & Armour

ENGLISH FIELD ARTILLERY COMPANY

The Old Forge Industrial Estat
Peterchurch, Hereford HR2 0SD
Mob: 07775643762
Email: john@artilleryhire.com
Web Site: www.artilleryhire.com
Contact: John Slough
For sale and hire, cannons, field artillery - blank firing from central control unit.
Open-air concerts - 1812 overture - our speciality. Antique and modern firearms and military props.
Special effects, controlled explosions.
Consultant on all things military and all aspects of firearms.

PETER EVANS STUDIOS LTD

12-14 Tavistock Street, Dunstable, Bedfordshire LU6 1NE
Tel: 01582 725 730 Fax: 01582 481 329
Email: sales@peterevansstudios.co.uk
Web Site: www.peterevansstudios.co.uk
Directors: P Evans, I Adams, R Evans
Makers of properties and scenic embellishments in rubber, GRP, polystyrene, etc. Supplier of a large range of columns, urns, cornices, friezes, balustrades, brickwork, etc. in vacuum formed PVC, ABS or GRP. Also vacuum forming done from your own patterns or patterns specially made. Catalogue available.

FIREBRAND

Leac Na Ban, Tayvallich, Lochgilphead, Argyll PA31 8PF Scotland
Tel: 01546 870 310
Email: firebrand@btinternet.com
Web Site: www.pollexpropsfirebrand.moonfruit.com
Contact: Alexander Hamilton
Flambeaux Torch - Supplies in association with "Pollex Props" - property makers.

HANDS ON PRODUCTION SERVICES

79 Loanbank Quadrant, Glasgow G51 3HZ Scotland
Tel: 0141 440 2005
Email: info@hands-on-uk.com
Web Site: www.hands-on-uk.com
Hire of Weapons, Heraldic Shields, Armour and Allied Properties for Theatre, Film and Publicity Work.
We are the only BBC approved contractors in Scotland and have the authority of the Scottish executive to supply prohibited weapons under section 5 of the firearms act.

HWL (UK) LTD

Cricket Street, Denton, Manchester M34 3DR
Tel: 0161 335 0220 Fax: 0161 320 3928
Email: guns@hwltd.co.uk
Web Site: www.hwltd.co.uk
Contact: Bob Howorth
Hirers of all types of furniture, set dressing, decorative lighting, pictures, hand props etc. Also specialist hirers of weapons and blank firing guns.